DISTANCE AND MIDPOINT FORMULAS

Distance between $P_1(x_1, y_1)$ and $P_2(x_2, y_2)$:

$$d = \sqrt{(x_2 - x_1)^2 + (y_2 - y_1)^2}$$

Midpoint of P_1P_2: $\left(\dfrac{x_1 + x_2}{2}, \dfrac{y_1 + y_2}{2}\right)$

LINES

Slope of line through $P_1(x_1, y_1)$ and $P_2(x_2, y_2)$

$$m = \frac{y_2 - y_1}{x_2 - x_1}$$

Point-slope equation of line through $P_1(x_1, y_1)$ with slope m

$$y - y_1 = m(x - x_1)$$

Slope-intercept equation of line with slope m and y-intercept b

$$y = mx + b$$

Two-intercept equation of line with x-intercept a and y-intercept b

$$\frac{x}{a} + \frac{y}{b} = 1$$

LOGARITHMS

$y = \log_a x$ means $a^y = x$

$\log_a a^x = x$ $\qquad$ $a^{\log_a x} = x$

$\log_a 1 = 0$ $\qquad$ $\log_a a = 1$

$\log x = \log_{10} x$ $\qquad$ $\ln x = \log_e x$

$\log_a xy = \log_a x + \log_a y$ $\qquad$ $\log_a\left(\dfrac{x}{y}\right) = \log_a x - \log_a y$

$\log_a x^b = b \log_a x$ $\qquad$ $\log_b x = \dfrac{\log_a x}{\log_a b}$

EXPONENTIAL AND LOGARITHMIC FUNCTIONS

$y = a^x$, $a > 1$

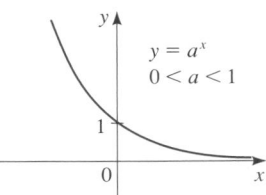
$y = a^x$, $0 < a < 1$

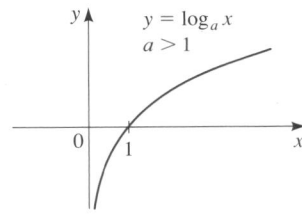
$y = \log_a x$, $a > 1$

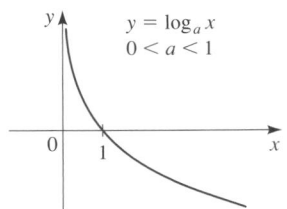
$y = \log_a x$, $0 < a < 1$

GRAPHS OF FUNCTIONS

Linear functions: $f(x) = mx + b$

$f(x) = b$ $\qquad$ $f(x) = mx + b$

Power functions: $f(x) = x^n$

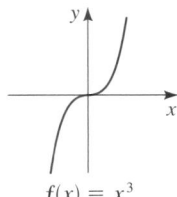

$f(x) = x^2$ $\qquad$ $f(x) = x^3$

Root functions: $f(x) = \sqrt[n]{x}$

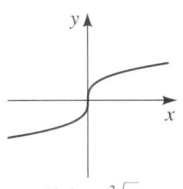

$f(x) = \sqrt{x}$ $\qquad$ $f(x) = \sqrt[3]{x}$

Reciprocal functions: $f(x) = 1/x^n$

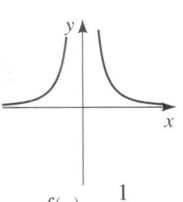

$f(x) = \dfrac{1}{x}$ $\qquad$ $f(x) = \dfrac{1}{x^2}$

Absolute value function $\qquad$ Greatest integer function

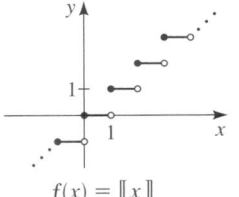

$f(x) = |x|$ $\qquad$ $f(x) = [\![x]\!]$

COMPLEX NUMBERS

For the complex number $z = a + bi$

the **conjugate** is $\bar{z} = a - bi$

the **modulus** is $|z| = \sqrt{a^2 + b^2}$

the **argument** is θ, where $\tan \theta = b/a$

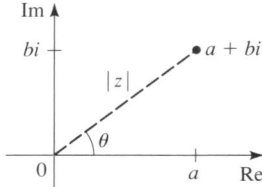

Polar form of a complex number

For $z = a + bi$, the **polar form** is

$$z = r(\cos \theta + i \sin \theta)$$

where $r = |z|$ is the modulus of z and θ is the argument of z

De Moivre's Theorem

$$z^n = [r(\cos \theta + i \sin \theta)]^n = r^n(\cos n\theta + i \sin n\theta)$$

$$\sqrt[n]{z} = [r(\cos \theta + i \sin \theta)]^{1/n}$$

$$= r^{1/n}\left(\cos \frac{\theta + 2k\pi}{n} + i \sin \frac{\theta + 2k\pi}{n}\right)$$

where $k = 0, 1, 2, \ldots, n - 1$

ROTATION OF AXES

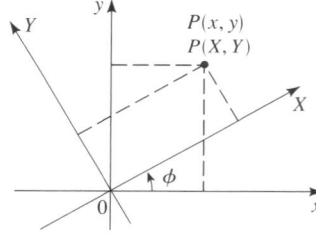

Rotation of axes formulas

$$x = X \cos \phi - Y \sin \phi$$

$$y = X \sin \phi + Y \cos \phi$$

Angle-of-rotation formula for conic sections

To eliminate the xy-term in the equation

$$Ax^2 + Bxy + Cy^2 + Dx + Ey + F = 0$$

rotate the axis by the angle ϕ that satisfies

$$\cot 2\phi = \frac{A - C}{B}$$

POLAR COORDINATES

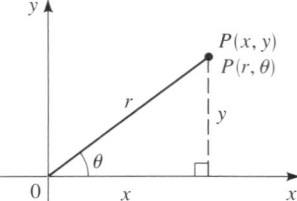

$$x = r \cos \theta$$

$$y = r \sin \theta$$

$$r^2 = x^2 + y^2$$

$$\tan \theta = \frac{y}{x}$$

SUMS OF POWERS OF INTEGERS

$$\sum_{k=1}^{n} 1 = n \qquad \sum_{k=1}^{n} k = \frac{n(n + 1)}{2}$$

$$\sum_{k=1}^{n} k^2 = \frac{n(n + 1)(2n + 1)}{6} \qquad \sum_{k=1}^{n} k^3 = \frac{n^2(n + 1)^2}{4}$$

THE DERIVATIVE

The **average rate of change** of f between a and b is

$$\frac{f(b) - f(a)}{b - a}$$

The **derivative** of f at a is

$$f'(a) = \lim_{x \to a} \frac{f(x) - f(a)}{x - a}$$

$$f'(a) = \lim_{h \to 0} \frac{f(a + h) - f(a)}{h}$$

AREA UNDER THE GRAPH OF f

The **area under the graph of f** on the interval $[a, b]$ is the limit of the sum of the areas of approximating rectangles

$$A = \lim_{n \to \infty} \sum_{k=1}^{n} f(x_k) \Delta x$$

where

$$\Delta x = \frac{b - a}{n}$$

$$x_k = a + k \Delta x$$

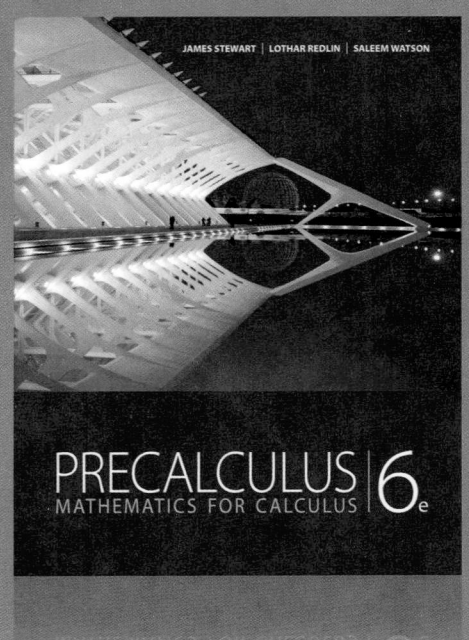

PRECALCULUS:
MATHEMATICS FOR CALCULUS, SIXTH EDITION

Discover a proven and accessible approach to the real-world importance of precalculus mathematics! With expert and patient guidance from best-selling authors James Stewart, Lothar Redlin, and Saleem Watson, *Precalculus: Mathematics for Calculus, Sixth Edition,* helps students develop not only technical skill but also conceptual understanding—essential for their success in subsequent mathematics and science courses. With a presentation that fits a wide range of instructional approaches, *Precalculus* leads students to a rich understanding of the practical power of mathematics.

Clear explanations instill confidence and provide encouragement—without ever glossing over difficult points. The authors' attention to detail and clarity, as in James Stewart's market-leading *Calculus* text, is what makes *Precalculus* the best-selling text for the course.

THE SKILLS AND THE CONCEPTS STUDENTS NEED FOR SUCCESS IN MATHEMATICS

Mathematics as a problem-solving endeavor

Problem solving and mathematical modeling are introduced early and reinforced throughout, so that when students finish the course, they have a solid foundation in the principles of mathematical thinking.

GEORGE POLYA (1887–1985) is famous among mathematicians for his ideas on problem solving. His lectures on problem solving at Stanford University attracted overflow crowds whom he held on the edges of their seats, leading them to discover solutions for themselves. He was able to do this because of his deep insight into the psychology of problem solving. His well-known book *How To Solve It* has been translated into 15 languages. He said that Euler (see page 266) was unique among great mathematicians because he explained how he found his results. Polya often said to his students and colleagues, "Yes, I see that your proof is correct, but how did you discover it?" In the preface to *How To Solve It,* Polya writes, "A great discovery solves a great problem but there is a grain of discov-

eral steps in the problem-solving process and we give principles that are useful in solving certain problems. These steps and principles are just common sense made explicit. They have been adapted from George Polya's insightful book *How To Solve It.*

1. Understand the Problem

The first step is to read the problem and make sure that you understand it. Ask yourself the following questions:

> *What is the unknown?*
> *What are the given quantities?*
> *What are the given conditions?*

For many problems it is useful to

> *draw a diagram*

and identify the given and required quantities on the diagram. Usually, it is necessary to

> *introduce suitable notation*

In choosing symbols for the unknown quantities, we often use letters such as a, b, c, m, n, x, and y, but in some cases it helps to use initials as suggestive symbols, for instance, V for volume or t for time.

2. Think of a Plan

Stewart, Redlin, and Watson focus on problem solving, with an emphasis on helping students develop mathematical thinking rather than rote memorization of "the rules." In this edition, the Prologue *Principles of Problem Solving* outlines the general steps in the problem-solving process and provides principles that are useful in solving certain problems.

◀ With this edition, more than 20% of the text's exercises are new, including new *Concept Exercises* and new *Cumulative Review* tests. A copious amount of carefully graded exercise sets will foster students' conceptual understanding and build their problem-solving skills. Key exercises are now linked to examples in the text.

3.1 EXERCISES

CONCEPTS

1. To put the quadratic function $f(x) = ax^2 + bx + c$ in standard form, we complete the _____ .

2. The quadratic function $f(x) = a(x - h)^2 + k$ is in standard form.
   (a) The graph of f is a parabola with vertex (____, ____).
   (b) If $a > 0$, the graph of f opens _____ . In this case
      $f(h) = k$ is the _____ value of f.
   (c) If $a < 0$, the graph of f opens _____ . In this case
      $f(h) = k$ is the _____ value of f.

3. The graph of $f(x) = 2(x - 3)^2 + 5$ is a parabola that opens
   _____ , with its vertex at (____, ____), and
   $f(3) =$ _____ is the (minimum/maximum) _____
   value of f.

4. The graph of $f(x) = -2(x - 3)^2 + 5$ is a parabola that
   opens _____ , with its vertex at (____, ____), and

$f(3) =$ _____ is the (minimum/maximum) _____
value of f.

SKILLS

5–8 ■ The graph of a quadratic function f is given. (a) Find the coordinates of the vertex. (b) Find the maximum or minimum value of f. (c) Find the domain and range of f.

5. $f(x) = -x^2 + 6x - 5$ 6. $f(x) = -\frac{1}{2}x^2 - 2x + 6$

 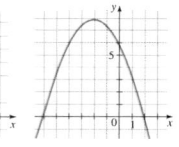

EXAMPLE 10 | An Equation Involving Fractional Expressions

Solve the equation $\dfrac{3}{x} + \dfrac{5}{x+2} = 2$.

SOLUTION We eliminate the denominators by multiplying each side by the lowest common denominator.

$$\left(\frac{3}{x} + \frac{5}{x+2}\right)x(x+2) = 2x(x+2) \qquad \text{Multiply by LCD } x(x+2)$$

$$3(x+2) + 5x = 2x^2 + 4x \qquad \text{Expand}$$

$$8x + 6 = 2x^2 + 4x \qquad \text{Expand LHS}$$

$$0 = 2x^2 - 4x - 6 \qquad \text{Subtract } 8x + 6$$

$$0 = x^2 - 2x - 3 \qquad \text{Divide both sides by 2}$$

$$0 = (x-3)(x+1) \qquad \text{Factor}$$

$$x - 3 = 0 \quad \text{or} \quad x + 1 = 0 \qquad \text{Zero-Product Property}$$

$$x = 3 \qquad\qquad x = -1 \qquad \text{Solve}$$

We must check our answers because multiplying by an expression that contains the variable can introduce extraneous solutions. From *Check Your Answers* we see that the solutions are $x = 3$ and -1.

CHECK YOUR ANSWERS

$x = 3$:

$$\text{LHS} = \frac{3}{3} + \frac{5}{3+2}$$

$$= 1 + 1 = 2$$

$$\text{RHS} = 2$$

$$\text{LHS} = \text{RHS} \quad \checkmark$$

$x = -1$:

$$\text{LHS} = \frac{3}{-1} + \frac{5}{-1+2}$$

$$= -3 + 5 = 2$$

$$\text{RHS} = 2$$

$$\text{LHS} = \text{RHS} \quad \checkmark$$

▲ | Many of the text's clarifying *Examples* include *Check Your Answers* to emphasize the importance of looking back to check whether an answer is reasonable. Plus, most *Examples* feature author notes, providing step-by-step guidance in working toward the solution.

"This textbook is mathematically sound and the authors present the material in a clear way that provides students opportunities to grasp the concepts behind the mathematics and see many applications for how that mathematics can be applied in 'real-life' problems."

– **Raji Baradwaj,** *University of Maryland*, Baltimore County

Mathematics for future success

Precalculus is a comprehensive, evenly paced book that provides in-depth exploration of concepts and integrates substantial graphing calculator materials to help students develop insight into mathematical ideas. The graphing calculator sections, subsections, examples, and exercises, all marked with the special symbol, are optional and may be omitted without loss of continuity.

GRAPHING CALCULATOR
SECTIONS' SPECIAL SYMBOL

DISCOVERY PROJECT

Relations and Functions

A function f can be represented as a set of ordered pairs (x, y) where x is the input and $y = f(x)$ is the output. For example, the function that squares each natural number can be represented by the ordered pairs $\{(1, 1), (2, 4), (3, 9), \dots\}$.

A **relation** is *any* collection of ordered pairs. If we denote the ordered pairs in a relation by (x, y) then the set of x-values (or inputs) is the **domain** and the set of y-values (or outputs) is the **range**. With this terminology a **function** is a relation where for each x-value there is *exactly one* y-value (or for each input there is *exactly one* output). The correspondences in the figure below are relations—the first is a function but the second is not because the input 7 in A corresponds to two different outputs, 15 and 17, in B.

Function   Not a function

We can describe a relation by listing all the ordered pairs in the relation or giving the rule of correspondence. Also, since a relation consists of ordered pairs we can sketch its graph. Let's consider the following relations and try to decide which are functions.

(a) The relation that consists of the ordered pairs $\{(1, 1), (2, 3), (3, 3), (4, 2)\}$.
(b) The relation that consists of the ordered pairs $\{(1, 2), (1, 3), (2, 4), (3, 2)\}$.

◀ Extended *Discovery Projects* help students become active learners by encouraging them to use their mathematics skills in a substantial way. A new website **www.stewartmath.com** contains *Discovery Projects* for each chapter and *Focus on Problem Solving* sections that highlight different problem-solving principles outlined in the Prologue.

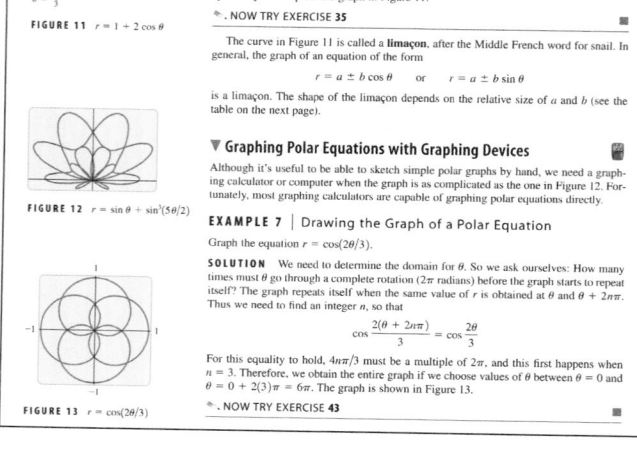

$\theta = \frac{4\pi}{3}$

FIGURE 11 $r = 1 + 2\cos\theta$

symmetry to complete the graph in Figure 11.

▲ NOW TRY EXERCISE **35**

The curve in Figure 11 is called a **limaçon**, after the Middle French word for snail. In general, the graph of an equation of the form

$$r = a \pm b\cos\theta \qquad \text{or} \qquad r = a \pm b\sin\theta$$

is a limaçon. The shape of the limaçon depends on the relative size of a and b (see the table on the next page).

FIGURE 12 $r = \sin\theta + \sin^3(5\theta/2)$

▼ Graphing Polar Equations with Graphing Devices

Although it's useful to be able to sketch simple polar graphs by hand, we need a graphing calculator or computer when the graph is as complicated as the one in Figure 12. Fortunately, most graphing calculators are capable of graphing polar equations directly.

EXAMPLE 7 | Drawing the Graph of a Polar Equation

Graph the equation $r = \cos(2\theta/3)$.

SOLUTION We need to determine the domain for θ. So we ask ourselves: How many times must θ go through a complete rotation (2π radians) before the graph starts to repeat itself? The graph repeats itself when the same value of r is obtained at θ and $\theta + 2n\pi$. Thus we need to find an integer n, so that

$$\cos\frac{2(\theta + 2n\pi)}{3} = \cos\frac{2\theta}{3}$$

For this equality to hold, $4n\pi/3$ must be a multiple of 2π, and this first happens when $n = 3$. Therefore, we obtain the entire graph if we choose values of θ between $\theta = 0$ and $\theta = 0 + 2(3)\pi = 6\pi$. The graph is shown in Figure 13.

FIGURE 13 $r = \cos(2\theta/3)$

▲ NOW TRY EXERCISE **43**

◀ As an option for problem solving, the authors introduce the graphing calculator early and view it as a powerful tool that extends students' ability to calculate and visualize mathematics. The authors integrate use of the graphing calculator throughout the text to graph functions, families of functions, and sequences; to calculate and graph regression curves; to perform matrix algebra; to graph linear inequalities; and more.

✎. NOW TRY EXERCISE **13**

Note that to find the 20th term of the sequence in Example 3, we must first find all 19 preceding terms. This is most easily done by using a graphing calculator. Figure 4(a) shows how to enter this sequence on the TI-83 calculator. From Figure 4(b) we see that the 20th term of the sequence is $a_{20} = 4{,}649{,}045{,}865$.

(a)   (b)

FIGURE 4 $u(n) = 3(u(n-1) + 2), u(1) = 1$

EXAMPLE 4 | The Fibonacci Sequence

Find the first 11 terms of the sequence defined recursively by $F_1 = 1$, $F_2 = 1$ and

$$F_n = F_{n-1} + F_{n-2}$$

FIBONACCI (1175–1250) was born in Pisa, Italy, and was educated in North Africa. He traveled widely in the Mediterranean area and learned the various methods then in use for writing numbers. On returning to Pisa in 1202, Fibonacci advocated the use of the Hindu-Arabic decimal system, the one we use today, over the Roman numeral system that was used in Europe in his time. His most famous book, *Liber Abaci*, expounds on the advantages of the Hindu-Arabic numerals. In fact, multiplication and division were so complicated using Roman numerals that a college degree was necessary to master these skills. Interestingly, in 1299 the city of Florence outlawed the use of the decimal system for merchants and businesses, requiring numbers to be written in Roman numerals or words. One can only speculate about the reasons for this law.

◀ The authors exploit the programming capabilities of a graphing calculator to simulate real-life situations, to sum series, or to compute the terms of a recursive sequence.

6.2 TRIGONOMETRY OF RIGHT TRIANGLES

Trigonometric Ratios ▶ Special Triangles ▶ Applications of Trigonometry of Right Triangles

In this section we study certain ratios of the sides of right triangles, called trigonometric ratios, and give several applications.

▼ Trigonometric Ratios

Consider a right triangle with θ as one of its acute angles. The trigonometric ratios are defined as follows (see Figure 1).

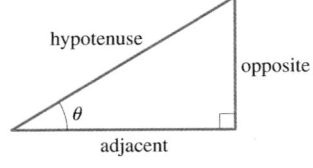

FIGURE 1

THE TRIGONOMETRIC RATIOS

$$\sin \theta = \frac{\text{opposite}}{\text{hypotenuse}} \qquad \cos \theta = \frac{\text{adjacent}}{\text{hypotenuse}} \qquad \tan \theta = \frac{\text{opposite}}{\text{adjacent}}$$

$$\csc \theta = \frac{\text{hypotenuse}}{\text{opposite}} \qquad \sec \theta = \frac{\text{hypotenuse}}{\text{adjacent}} \qquad \cot \theta = \frac{\text{adjacent}}{\text{opposite}}$$

The symbols we use for these ratios are abbreviations for their full names: **sine, cosine, tangent, cosecant, secant, cotangent.** Since any two right triangles with angle θ are

▲ Whether you're teaching trigonometry by beginning with the right-triangle approach (Chapter 6) or with the unit-circle approach (Chapter 5), **Precalculus** provides a flexible solution. The trigonometry chapters in the book were written so that either approach can be studied first. Each method is accompanied by appropriate applications, clarifying the reason for different approaches to trigonometry. For this Sixth Edition, Chapter 5 includes a new section on inverse trigonomic functions and their graphs.

Mathematics in everyday situations

Students will find a wealth of real-world applications and examples from engineering, physics, chemistry, business, biology, environmental studies, and other fields. Through this emphasis on modeling, the authors continually demonstrate relevance of mathematics to model real-life situations.

FOCUS ON MODELING
Fitting Exponential and Power Curves to Data

In a previous *Focus on Modeling* (page 296) we learned that the shape of a scatter plot helps us to choose the type of curve to use in modeling data. The first plot in Figure 1 fairly screams for a line to be fitted through it, and the second one points to a cubic polynomial. For the third plot it is tempting to fit a second-degree polynomial. But what if an exponential curve fits better? How do we decide this? In this section we learn how to fit exponential and power curves to data and how to decide which type of curve fits the data better. We also learn that for scatter plots like those in the last two plots in Figure 1, the data can be modeled by logarithmic or logistic functions.

▲ Each chapter concludes with a *Focus on Modeling* section that illustrates modeling techniques as well as how precalculus mathematics can be applied to model real-life situations. Six of this edition's *Focus on Modeling* sections are new, with high-interest applications ranging from surveying to agriculture. These sections are included in addition to many applied problems that give students a model to analyze, as well as problems in which students are required to construct models of real-life situations.

The next two examples illustrate how to model with systems of equations.

EXAMPLE 7 | A Distance-Speed-Time Problem

A woman rows a boat upstream from one point on a river to another point 4 mi away in $1\frac{1}{2}$ hours. The return trip, traveling with the current, takes only 45 min. How fast does she row relative to the water, and at what speed is the current flowing?

SOLUTION Identify the variables. We are asked to find the rowing speed and the speed of the current, so we let

$$x = \text{rowing speed (mi/h)}$$

$$y = \text{current speed (mi/h)}$$

current

4 mi

▲ The "modeling" theme has been used throughout to unify and clarify the many applications of precalculus. We have made a special effort to clarify the essential process of translating problems from English into the language of mathematics.

Coordinates as Addresses

The coordinates of a point in the *xy*-plane uniquely determine its location. We can think of the coordinates as the "address" of the point. In Salt Lake City, Utah, the addresses of most buildings are in fact expressed as coordinates. The city is divided into quadrants with Main Street as the vertical (North-South) axis and S. Temple Street as the horizontal (East-West) axis. An address such as

$$1760\,W \qquad 2100\,S$$

indicates a location 17.6 blocks west of Main Street and 21 blocks south of S. Temple Street. (This is the address of the main post office in Salt Lake City.) With this logical system it is possible for someone unfamiliar with the city to locate any address immediately, as easily as one locates a point in the coordinate plane.

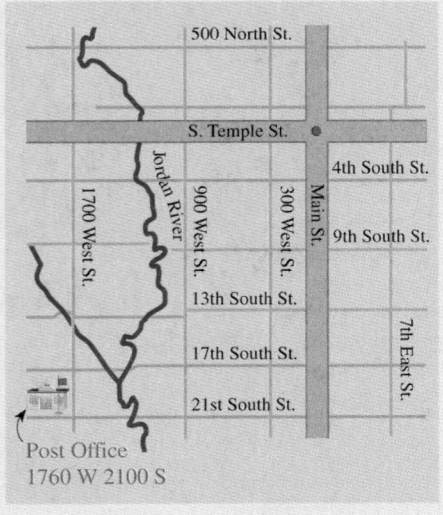

Mathematics in the Modern World vignettes further reveal the importance of mathematics as a living science, crucial to the scientific and technological progress of recent times—as well as to the social, behavioral, and life sciences. Students will also find biographical vignettes detailing various mathematicians' key insights relevant to precalculus.

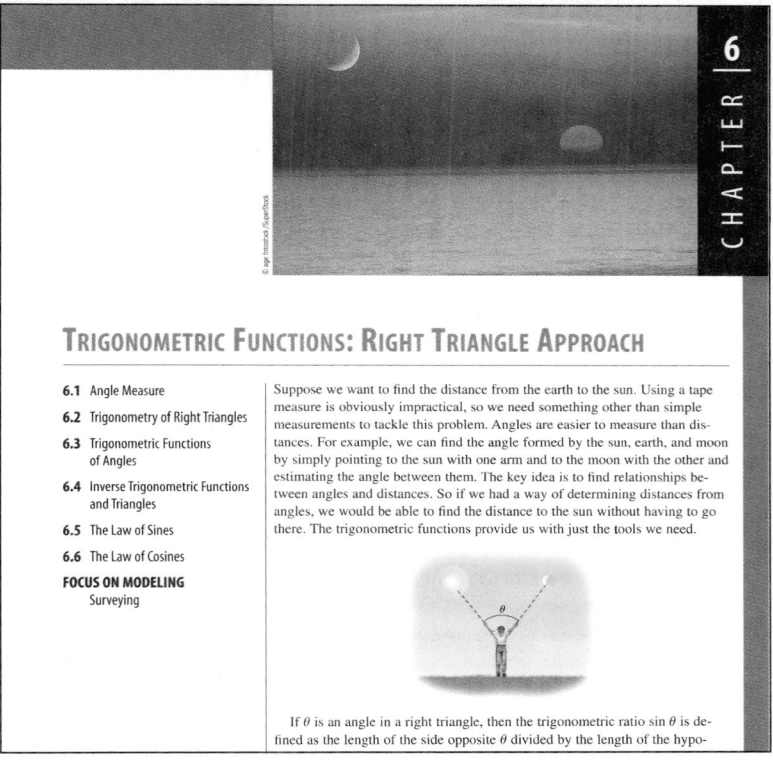

CHAPTER 6

TRIGONOMETRIC FUNCTIONS: RIGHT TRIANGLE APPROACH

Suppose we want to find the distance from the earth to the sun. Using a tape measure is obviously impractical, so we need something other than simple measurements to tackle this problem. Angles are easier to measure than distances. For example, we can find the angle formed by the sun, earth, and moon by simply pointing to the sun with one arm and to the moon with the other and estimating the angle between them. The key idea is to find relationships between angles and distances. So if we had a way of determining distances from angles, we would be able to find the distance to the sun without having to go there. The trigonometric functions provide us with just the tools we need.

If θ is an angle in a right triangle, then the trigonometric ratio $\sin \theta$ is defined as the length of the side opposite θ divided by the length of the hypo-

Each chapter begins with a new *Chapter Overview* that introduces the main ideas and indicates how they can be applied in true-to-life settings.

"At the present time, [***Precalculus***] is the best precalculus text in the market."

— **Irina Kloumova,** *Sacramento City College*

PRECALCULUS:
MATHEMATICS FOR CALCULUS, SIXTH EDITION

Additional resources to facilitate course preparation

Complete Solutions Manual for High School
The complete solutions manual provides worked-out solutions to all of the problems in the text.

Lesson Plans
Available in print and on the PowerLecture CD-ROM.

Instructor's Guide
Doug Shaw, author of the Instructor Guides for the widely used Stewart calculus texts, wrote this helpful teaching companion. It contains points to stress, suggested time to allot, text discussion topics, core materials for lectures, workshop/discussion suggestions, group work exercises in a form suitable for handout, solutions to group work exercises, and suggested homework problems.

Enhanced WebAssign

 Exclusively from Cengage Learning, Enhanced WebAssign® offers an extensive online program for Precalculus to encourage the practice that's so critical for concept mastery. The meticulously crafted pedagogy and exercises in this text become even more effective in Enhanced WebAssign, supplemented by multimedia tutorial support and immediate feedback as students complete their assignments.

ExamView Computerized Testing

 ExamView® testing software allows teachers to quickly create, deliver, and customize tests for class in print and online formats, and features automatic grading. Includes a test bank with hundreds of questions customized directly to the text. ExamView is available within the PowerLecture CD-ROM.

Solution Builder www.cengage.com/solutionbuilder
This online teachers database offers complete worked solutions to all exercises in the text, allowing you to create customized, secure solutions printouts (in PDF format) matched exactly to the problems you assign in class.

PowerLecture with ExamView for High Schools
 This CD-ROM provides the teacher with dynamic media tools for teaching. Create, deliver, and customize tests (both print and online) in minutes with ExamView® Computerized Testing Featuring Algorithmic Equations. Easily build solution sets for homework or exams using Solution Builder's online solutions manual. Microsoft® PowerPoint® lecture slides and figures from the book are also included on this CD-ROM.

Encourage student exploration with these learning tools

Student Solution Manual
Contains fully worked-out solutions to all of the odd-numbered exercises in the text, giving students a way to check their answers and ensure that they took the correct steps to arrive at an answer. Ask your sales representative about available discounts.

Study Guide
This carefully crafted learning resource helps students develop their problem-solving skills while reinforcing their understanding with detailed explanations, worked-out examples, and practice problems. Students will also find listings of key ideas to master. Each section of the main text has a corresponding section in the Study Guide. Ask your sales representative about available discounts.

Note Taking Guide
This innovative study aid helps students develop a section-by-section summary of key concepts. Ask your sales representative about available discounts.

Enhanced WebAssign

 Exclusively from Cengage Learning, Enhanced WebAssign® offers an extensive online program for Precalculus to encourage the practice that's so critical for concept mastery. You'll receive multimedia tutorial support as you complete your assignments. Ask your sales representative about available discounts.

Book Companion Website
A new website **www.stewartmath.com** contains *Discovery Projects* for each chapter and *Focus on Problem Solving* sections that highlight different problem-solving principles outlined in the Prologue.

Text-Specific DVDs
The Text-Specific DVDs include new learning objective based lecture videos. These DVDs provide comprehensive coverage of the course—along with additional explanations of concepts, sample problems, and applications—to help students review essential topics. Ask your sales representative about available discounts.

CengageBrain.com
CENGAGE**brain** Visit **www.cengagebrain.com** to access additional course materials and companion resources. At the CengageBrain.com home page, search for the ISBN of your title (from the back cover of your book) using the search box at the top of the page. This will take you to the product page where free companion resources can be found.

This Teacher's Edition is designed to save the teacher time by providing extra material and ideas that can be used in the classroom. For each section of *Precalculus: Mathematics for Calculus,* Sixth Edition, this Teacher's Edition provides the following:

- **Suggested Time and Emphasis** These suggestions assume that the class is thirty to fifty minutes long. They also advise whether or not the material is essential to the rest of the course.

- **Sample Questions** Some teachers have reported that they like to open or close class by handing out a single question, either as a quiz or to start a discussion. Two types are included:

  - *Text Question:* This question is designed for students who have done the reading, but haven't yet seen the material in class. These questions can be used to help ensure that the students are reading the textbook carefully.

  - *Drill Question:* These questions are designed to be straightforward "right down the middle" questions for students who have tried, but not necessarily mastered, the material.

- **In-Class Materials** These suggestions are meant to work along with the text to create a classroom atmosphere of experimentation and inquiry.

- **Alternate Examples** These are examples that correspond to examples provided in the text. All computations are worked out, designed to save a bit of time in class preparation.

- **Examples** These are routine examples with all the computations worked out, designed to save some time in class preparation.

ABOUT THE AUTHORS

JAMES STEWART received his MS from Stanford University and his PhD from the University of Toronto. He did research at the University of London and was influenced by the famous mathematician George Polya at Stanford University. Stewart is Professor Emeritus at McMaster University and is currently Professor of Mathematics at the University of Toronto. His research field is harmonic analysis and the connections between mathematics and music. James Stewart is the author of a bestselling calculus textbook series published by Brooks/Cole, Cengage Learning, including *Calculus, Calculus: Early Transcendentals*, and *Calculus: Concepts and Contexts*; a series of precalculus texts; and a series of high-school mathematics textbooks.

LOTHAR REDLIN grew up on Vancouver Island, received a Bachelor of Science degree from the University of Victoria, and received a PhD from McMaster University in 1978. He subsequently did research and taught at the University of Washington, the University of Waterloo, and California State University, Long Beach. He is currently Professor of Mathematics at The Pennsylvania State University, Abington Campus. His research field is topology.

SALEEM WATSON received his Bachelor of Science degree from Andrews University in Michigan. He did graduate studies at Dalhousie University and McMaster University, where he received his PhD in 1978. He subsequently did research at the Mathematics Institute of the University of Warsaw in Poland. He also taught at The Pennsylvania State University. He is currently Professor of Mathematics at California State University, Long Beach. His research field is functional analysis.

Stewart, Redlin, and Watson have also published *College Algebra, Trigonometry, Algebra and Trigonometry,* and (with Phyllis Panman) *College Algebra: Concepts and Contexts*.

Contributing annotations were pulled from *Stewart/Redlin/Watson Precalculus: Mathematics for Calculus 6/e Instructor's Guide* by Doug Shaw, University of Northern Iowa. Contributing reviewer for the text was Brian Shay, Department Chairperson, Canyon Crest Academy, San Diego, California.

ABOUT THE COVER

The cover photograph shows the Science Museum in the City of Arts and Sciences in Valencia, Spain, with a planetarium in the distance. Built from 1991 to 1996, it was designed by Santiago Calatrava, a Spanish architect. Calatrava has always been very interested in how mathematics can help him realize the buildings he imagines. As a young student, he taught himself descriptive geometry from books in order to represent three-dimensional objects in two dimensions. Trained as both an engineer and an architect, he wrote a doctoral thesis in 1981 entitled "On the Foldability of Space Frames," which is filled with mathematics, especially geometric transformations. His strength as an engineer enables him to be daring in his architecture.

PRECALCULUS
MATHEMATICS FOR CALCULUS

JAMES STEWART
MCMASTER UNIVERSITY AND UNIVERSITY OF TORONTO

LOTHAR REDLIN
THE PENNSYLVANIA STATE UNIVERSITY

SALEEM WATSON
CALIFORNIA STATE UNIVERSITY, LONG BEACH

BROOKS/COLE
CENGAGE Learning™

Australia • Brazil • Japan • Korea • Mexico • Singapore • Spain • United Kingdom • United States

BROOKS/COLE
CENGAGE Learning™

Precalculus: Mathematics for Calculus,
Sixth Edition
James Stewart, Lothar Redlin, Saleem Watson

Acquisitions Editor: Gary Whalen

Developmental Editor: Stacy Green

Assistant Editor: Cynthia Ashton

Editorial Assistant: Naomi Dreyer

Media Editor: Lynh Pham

Marketing Manager: Myriah Fitzgibbon

Marketing Assistant: Shannon Myers

Marketing Communications Manager:
   Darlene Macanan

Content Project Manager: Jennifer Risden

Design Director: Rob Hugel

Art Director: Vernon Boes

Print Buyer: Karen Hunt

Rights Acquisitions Specialist:
   Dean Dauphinais

Production Service: Martha Emry

Text Designer: Lisa Henry

Photo Researcher: Bill Smith Group

Copy Editor: Barbara Willette

Illustrators: Matrix Art Services,
   Precision Graphics

Cover Designer: Lisa Henry

Cover Image: © Jose Fuste Raga/CORBIS

Compositor: Graphic World, Inc.

VP, Director, Advanced and Elective Products
   Program: Alison Zetterquist

Editorial Coordinator, Advanced and Elective
   Products Program: Jean Woy

For product information and technology assistance, contact us at
Cengage Learning Customer & Sales Support, 1-800-354-9706.

For permission to use material from this text or product,
submit all requests online at **www.cengage.com/permissions**.
Further permissions questions can be e-mailed to
permissionrequest@cengage.com.

Library of Congress Control Number: 2010935410

ISBN-13: 978-0-8400-6887-3

ISBN-10: 0-8400-6887-5

Brooks/Cole
20 Davis Drive
Belmont, CA 94002-3098
USA

Cengage Learning is a leading provider of customized learning solutions with office locations around the globe, including Singapore, the United Kingdom, Australia, Mexico, Brazil, and Japan. Locate your local office at **www.cengage.com/global.**

Cengage Learning products are represented in Canada by Nelson Education, Ltd.

To learn more about Brooks/Cole, visit **www.cengage.com/brookscole.**
Purchase any of our products at our preferred online store
www.cengagebrain.com.

Printed in Canada
1 2 3 4 5 6 7 14 13 12 11

CONTENTS

PREFACE

What do students really need to know to be prepared for calculus? What tools do teachers really need to assist their students in preparing for calculus? These two questions have motivated the writing of this book.

To be prepared for calculus a student needs not only technical skill but also a clear understanding of concepts. Indeed, *conceptual understanding* and *technical skill* go hand in hand, each reinforcing the other. A student also needs to gain an appreciation for the power and utility of mathematics in *modeling* the real world. Every feature of this textbook is devoted to fostering these goals.

In writing this Sixth Edition our purpose is to further enhance the utility of the book as an instructional tool for teachers and as a learning tool for students. There are several major changes in this edition including a restructuring of each exercise set to better align the exercises with the examples of each section. In this edition each exercise set begins with *Concepts Exercises,* which encourage students to work with basic concepts and to use mathematical vocabulary appropriately. Several chapters have been reorganized and rewritten (as described below) to further focus the exposition on the main concepts; we have added a new chapter on vectors in two and three dimensions. In all these changes and numerous others (small and large) we have retained the main features that have contributed to the success of this book.

New to the Sixth Edition

- **Exercises** More than 20% of the exercises are new. This includes new *Concept* Exercises and new *Cumulative Review* tests. Key exercises are now linked to examples in the text.

- **Book Companion Website** A new website **www.stewartmath.com** contains *Discovery Projects* for each chapter and *Focus on Problem Solving* sections that highlight different problem-solving principles outlined in the Prologue.

- **CHAPTER 2 Functions** This chapter has been completely rewritten to focus more sharply on the fundamental and crucial concept of *function.* The material on quadratic functions, formerly in this chapter, is now part of the chapter on polynomial functions.

- **CHAPTER 3 Polynomial and Rational Functions** This chapter now begins with a section on quadratic functions, leading to higher degree polynomial functions.

- **CHAPTER 4 Exponential and Logarithmic Functions** The material on the natural exponential function is now in a separate section.

- **CHAPTER 5 Trigonometric Functions: Unit Circle Approach** This chapter includes a new section on inverse trigonometric functions and their graphs. Introducing this topic here reinforces the function concept in the context of trigonometry.

- **CHAPTER 6 Trigonometric Functions: Right Triangle Approach** This chapter includes a new section on inverse trigonometric functions and right triangles (Section 6.4) which is needed in applying the Laws of Sines and Cosines in the following section, as well as for solving trigonometric equations in Chapter 7.

- **CHAPTER 7 Analytic Trigonometry** This chapter has been completely revised. There are two new sections on trigonometric equations (Sections 7.4 and 7.5). The material on this topic (formerly in Section 7.5) has been expanded and revised.

- **CHAPTER 8 Polar Coordinates and Parametric Equations** This chapter is now more sharply focused on the concept of a coordinate system. The section on parametric equations is new to this chapter. The material on vectors is now in its own chapter.

- **CHAPTER 9 Vectors in Two and Three Dimensions** This is a new chapter with a new *Focus on Modeling* section.

- **CHAPTER 10 Systems of Equations and Inequalities** The material on systems of nonlinear equations is now in a separate section.

- **CHAPTER 11 Conic Sections** This chapter is now more closely devoted to the topic of analytic geometry, especially the conic sections; the section on parametric equations has been moved to Chapter 8.

- **CHAPTER 14 Probability and Statistics** This is a new chapter. The first four sections present the basic concepts of counting and probability, including binomial probability and expected value. The next two sections are about descriptive statistics, with an introduction to the normal distribution. Section 14.7 deals with practical issues in the selection of random samples, including the relationship between sample size and margin of error. Section 14.8 is an introduction to inferential statistics and shows how statistical conclusions can be made about populations from random samples. In this final section, *P*-values are calculated using the graphing calculator.

Teaching with the Help of This Book

We are keenly aware that good teaching comes in many forms, and that there are many different approaches to teaching the concepts and skills of precalculus. The organization of the topics in this book is designed to accommodate different teaching styles. For example, the trigonometry chapters have been organized so that either the unit circle approach or the right triangle approach can be taught first. Here are other special features that can be used to complement different teaching styles:

EXERCISE SETS The most important way to foster conceptual understanding and hone technical skill is through the problems that the teacher assigns. To that end we have provided a wide selection of exercises.

- **Concept Exercises** These exercises ask students to use mathematical language to state fundamental facts about the topics of each section.

- **Skills Exercises** Each exercise set is carefully graded, progressing from basic skill-development exercises to more challenging problems requiring synthesis of previously learned material with new concepts.

- **Applications Exercises** We have included substantial applied problems that we believe will capture the interest of students.

- **Discovery, Writing, and Group Learning** Each exercise set ends with a block of exercises labeled *Discovery* ▪ *Discussion* ▪ *Writing*. These exercises are designed to encourage students to experiment, preferably in groups, with the concepts developed in the section, and then to write about what they have learned, rather than simply look for the answer.

- **Now Try Exercise ...** At the end of each example in the text the student is directed to a similar exercise in the section that helps reinforce the concepts and skills developed in that example (see, for instance, page 4).

- **Check Your Answer** Students are encouraged to check whether an answer they obtained is reasonable. This is emphasized throughout the text in numerous *Check Your Answer* sidebars that accompany the examples. (See, for instance, page 52.)

A COMPLETE REVIEW CHAPTER We have included an extensive review chapter primarily as a handy reference for the basic concepts that are preliminary to this course.

- **Chapter 1** This is the review chapter; it contains the fundamental concepts from algebra and analytic geometry that a student needs in order to begin a precalculus course. As much or as little of this chapter can be covered in class as needed, depending on the background of the students.
- **Chapter 1 Test** The test at the end of Chapter 1 is designed as a diagnostic test for determining what parts of this review chapter need to be taught. It also serves to help students gauge exactly what topics they need to review.

FLEXIBLE APPROACH TO TRIGONOMETRY The trigonometry chapters of this text have been written so that either the right triangle approach or the unit circle approach may be taught first. Putting these two approaches in different chapters, each with its relevant applications, helps to clarify the purpose of each approach. The chapters introducing trigonometry are as follows:

- **Chapter 5 Trigonometric Functions: Unit Circle Approach** This chapter introduces trigonometry through the unit circle approach. This approach emphasizes that the trigonometric functions are functions of real numbers, just like the polynomial and exponential functions with which students are already familiar.
- **Chapter 6 Trigonometric Functions: Right Triangle Approach** This chapter introduces trigonometry through the right triangle approach. This approach builds on the foundation of a conventional high-school course in trigonometry.

Another way to teach trigonometry is to intertwine the two approaches. Some teachers teach this material in the following order: Sections 5.1, 5.2, 6.1, 6.2, 6.3, 5.3, 5.4, 5.5, 5.6, 6.4, 6.5, and 6.6. Our organization makes it easy to do this without obscuring the fact that the two approaches involve distinct representations of the same functions.

GRAPHING CALCULATORS AND COMPUTERS We make use of graphing calculators and computers in examples and exercises throughout the book. Our calculator-oriented examples are always preceded by examples in which students must graph or calculate by hand, so that they can understand precisely what the calculator is doing when they later use it to simplify the routine, mechanical part of their work. The graphing calculator sections, subsections, examples, and exercises, all marked with the special symbol 📱, are optional and may be omitted without loss of continuity. We use the following capabilities of the calculator.

- **Graphing, Regression, Matrix Algebra, Statistics** The capabilities of the graphing calculator are used throughout the text to graph and analyze functions, families of functions, and sequences; to calculate and graph regression curves; to perform matrix algebra; to graph systems of linear inequalities; to calculate one-variable statistics and perform statistical tests; and other powerful uses.
- **Simple Programs** We exploit the programming capabilities of a graphing calculator to simulate real-life situations, to sum series, or to compute the terms of a recursive sequence. (See, for instance, pages 787 and 791.)

FOCUS ON MODELING The "modeling" theme has been used throughout to unify and clarify the many applications of precalculus. We have made a special effort to clarify the essential process of translating problems from English into the language of mathematics (see pages 214 and 636).

- **Constructing Models** There are numerous applied problems throughout the book where students are given a model to analyze (see, for instance, page 228). But the material on modeling, in which students are required to *construct* mathematical models, has been organized into clearly defined sections and subsections (see for example, pages 213, 340, and 427).

- **Focus on Modeling** Each chapter concludes with a *Focus on Modeling* section. The first such section, after Chapter 1, introduces the basic idea of modeling a real-life situation by fitting lines to data (linear regression). Other sections present ways in which polynomial, exponential, logarithmic, and trigonometric functions, and systems of inequalities can all be used to model familiar phenomena from the sciences and from everyday life (see for example pages 296, 357, and 427).

BOOK COMPANION WEBSITE A website that accompanies this book is located at **www. stewartmath.com**. The site includes many useful resources for teaching precalculus, including the following:

- **Discovery Projects** *Discovery Projects* for each chapter are available on the website. Each project provides a challenging but accessible set of activities that enable students (perhaps working in groups) to explore in greater depth an interesting aspect of the topic they have just learned. (See for instance the Discovery Projects *Visualizing a Formula, Relations and Functions, Will the Species Survive?,* and *Computer Graphics I* and *II.*)

- **Focus on Problem Solving** Several *Focus on Problem Solving* sections are available on the website. Each such section highlights one of the problem-solving principles introduced in the Prologue and includes several challenging problems. (See for instance *Recognizing Patterns, Using Analogy, Introducing Something Extra, Taking Cases,* and *Working Backward.*)

MATHEMATICAL VIGNETTES Throughout the book we make use of the margins to provide historical notes, key insights, or applications of mathematics in the modern world. These serve to enliven the material and show that mathematics is an important, vital activity, and that even at this elementary level it is fundamental to everyday life.

- **Mathematical Vignettes** These vignettes include biographies of interesting mathematicians and often include a key insight that the mathematician discovered and which is relevant to precalculus. (See, for instance, the vignettes on Viète, page 49; Salt Lake City, page 84; and radiocarbon dating, page 333.)

- **Mathematics in the Modern World** This is a series of vignettes that emphasizes the central role of mathematics in current advances in technology and the sciences (see pages 283, 700, and 759, for example).

REVIEW SECTIONS AND CHAPTER TESTS Each chapter ends with an extensive review section including the following.

- **Concept Check** The *Concept Check* at the end of each chapter is designed to get the students to think about and explain in their own words the ideas presented in the chapter. These can be used as writing exercises, in a classroom discussion setting, or for personal study.

- **Review Exercises** The *Review Exercises* at the end of each chapter recapitulate the basic concepts and skills of the chapter and include exercises that combine the different ideas learned in the chapter.

- **Chapter Test** The review sections conclude with a *Chapter Test* designed to help students gauge their progress.

- **Cumulative Review Tests** The *Cumulative Review Tests* following Chapters 4, 7, 9, 11, and 13 combine skills and concepts from the preceding chapters and are designed to highlight the connections between the topics in these related chapters.

- **Answers** Brief answers to odd-numbered exercises in each section (including the review exercises), and to all questions in the Concepts Exercises and Chapter Tests, are given in the back of the book.

Acknowledgments

We thank the following reviewers for their thoughtful and constructive comments.

REVIEWERS FOR THE FIFTH EDITION Kenneth Berg, University of Maryland; Elizabeth Bowman, University of Alabama at Huntsville; William Cherry, University of North Texas; Barbara Cortzen, DePaul University; Gerry Fitch, Louisiana State University; Lana Grishchenko, Cal Poly State University, San Luis Obispo; Bryce Jenkins, Cal Poly State University, San Luis Obispo; Margaret Mary Jones, Rutgers University; Victoria Kauffman, University of New Mexico; Sharon Keener, Georgia Perimeter College; YongHee Kim-Park, California State University Long Beach; Mangala Kothari, Rutgers University; Andre Mathurin, Bellarmine College Prep; Donald Robertson, Olympic College; Jude Socrates, Pasadena City College; Enefiok Umana, Georgia Perimeter College; Michele Wallace, Washington State University; and Linda Waymire, Daytona Beach Community College.

REVIEWERS FOR THE SIXTH EDITION Raji Baradwaj, UMBC; Chris Herman, Lorain County Community College; Irina Kloumova, Sacramento City College; Jim McCleery, Skagit Valley College, Whidbey Island Campus; Sally S. Shao, Cleveland State University; David Slutzky, Gainesville State College; Edward Stumpf, Central Carolina Community College; Ricardo Teixeira, University of Texas at Austin; Taixi Xu, Southern Polytechnic State University; and Anna Wlodarczyk, Florida International University.

We are grateful to our colleagues who continually share with us their insights into teaching mathematics. We especially thank Andrew Bulman-Fleming for writing the Study Guide and the Solutions Manual and Doug Shaw at the University of Northern Iowa for writing the Instructor Guide.

We thank Martha Emry, our production service and art editor; her energy, devotion, experience, and intelligence were essential components in the creation of this book. We thank Barbara Willette, our copy editor, for her attention to every detail in the manuscript. We thank Jade Myers and his staff at Matrix Art Services for their attractive and accurate graphs and Precision Graphics for bringing many of our illustrations to life. We thank our designer Lisa Henry for the elegant and appropriate design for the interior of the book.

At Brooks/Cole we especially thank Stacy Green, developmental editor, for guiding and facilitating every aspect of the production of this book. Of the many Brooks/Cole staff involved in this project we particularly thank the following: Jennifer Risden, content project manager, Cynthia Ashton, assistant editor; Lynh Pham, media editor; Vernon Boes, art director; and Myriah Fitzgibbon, marketing manager. They have all done an outstanding job.

Numerous other people were involved in the production of this book—including permissions editors, photo researchers, text designers, typesetters, compositors, proof readers, printers, and many more. We thank them all.

Above all, we thank our editor Gary Whalen. His vast editorial experience, his extensive knowledge of current issues in the teaching of mathematics, and especially his deep interest in mathematics textbooks, have been invaluable resources in the writing of this book.

TEACHER RESOURCES

Printed

Complete Solutions Manual for High School
The complete solutions manual provides worked-out solutions to all of the problems in the text.

Lesson Plans
Available in print and on the PowerLecture CD-ROM.

Instructor's Guide
Doug Shaw, author of the Instructor Guides for the widely used Stewart calculus texts, wrote this helpful teaching companion. It contains points to stress, suggested time to allot, text discussion topics, core materials for lectures, workshop/discussion suggestions, group work exercises in a form suitable for handout, solutions to group work exercises, and suggested homework problems.

Media

Enhanced WebAssign
Exclusively from Cengage Learning, Enhanced WebAssign® offers an extensive online program for Precalculus to encourage the practice that's so critical for concept mastery. The meticulously crafted pedagogy and exercises in this text become even more effective in Enhanced WebAssign, supplemented by multimedia tutorial support and immediate feedback as students complete their assignments. Algorithmic problems allow you to assign unique versions to each student. The Practice Another Version feature (activated at your discretion) allows students to attempt the questions with new sets of values until they feel confident enough to work the original problem. Students benefit from a new Premium eBook with highlighting and search features; Personal Study Plans (based on diagnostic quizzing) that identify chapter topics they still need to master; and links to video solutions, interactive tutorials, and even live online help. Please contact your sales representative for available discounts.

ExamView Computerized Testing
ExamView® testing software allows teachers to quickly create, deliver, and customize tests for class in print and online formats, and features automatic grading. Includes a test bank with hundreds of questions customized directly to the text. ExamView is available within the PowerLecture CD-ROM.

Solution Builder   www.cengage.com/solutionbuilder

This online teachers database offers complete worked solutions to all exercises in the text, allowing you to create customized, secure solutions printouts (in PDF format) matched exactly to the problems you assign in class.

PowerLecture with ExamView for High Schools

This CD-ROM provides the teacher with dynamic media tools for teaching. Create, deliver, and customize tests (both print and online) in minutes with ExamView® Computerized Testing Featuring Algorithmic Equations. Easily build solution sets for homework or exams using Solution Builder's online solutions manual. Microsoft® PowerPoint® lecture slides and figures from the book are also included on this CD-ROM.

STUDENT RESOURCES

Printed

Student Solution Manual

Contains fully worked-out solutions to all of the odd-numbered exercises in the text, giving students a way to check their answers and ensure that they took the correct steps to arrive at an answer. Ask your sales representative about available discounts.

Study Guide

This carefully crafted learning resource helps students develop their problem-solving skills while reinforcing their understanding with detailed explanations, worked-out examples, and practice problems. Students will also find listings of key ideas to master. Each section of the main text has a corresponding section in the Study Guide. Ask your sales representative about available discounts.

Note Taking Guide

This innovative study aid helps students develop a section-by-section summary of key concepts. Ask your sales representative about available discounts.

Media

Enhanced WebAssign

Exclusively from Cengage Learning, Enhanced WebAssign® offers an extensive online program for Precalculus to encourage the practice that's so critical for concept mastery. You'll receive multimedia tutorial support as you complete your assignments. You'll also benefit from a new Premium eBook with highlighting and search features; Personal Study Plans (based on diagnostic quizzing) that identify chapter topics you still need to master; and links to video solutions, interactive tutorials, and even live online help. Please contact your sales representative for available discounts.

Book Companion Website

A new website **www.stewartmath.com** contains *Discovery Projects* for each chapter and *Focus on Problem Solving* sections that highlight different problem-solving principles outlined in the Prologue.

CengageBrain.com

Visit **www.cengagebrain.com** to access additional course materials and companion resources. At the CengageBrain.com home page, search for the ISBN of your title (from the back cover of your book) using the search box at the top of the page. This will take you to the product page where free companion resources can be found.

Text-Specific DVDs

The Text-Specific DVDs include new learning objective based lecture videos. These DVDs provide comprehensive coverage of the course—along with additional explanations of concepts, sample problems, and applications—to help students review essential topics. Ask your sales representative about available discounts.

This textbook was written for you to use as a guide to mastering precalculus mathematics. Here are some suggestions to help you get the most out of your course.

First of all, you should read the appropriate section of text *before* you attempt your homework problems. Reading a mathematics text is quite different from reading a novel, a newspaper, or even another textbook. You may find that you have to reread a passage several times before you understand it. Pay special attention to the examples, and work them out yourself with pencil and paper as you read. Then do the linked exercises referred to in *"Now Try Exercise . . ."* at the end of each example. With this kind of preparation you will be able to do your homework much more quickly and with more understanding.

Don't make the mistake of trying to memorize every single rule or fact you may come across. Mathematics doesn't consist simply of memorization. Mathematics is a *problem-solving art*, not just a collection of facts. To master the subject you must solve problems— lots of problems. Do as many of the exercises as you can. Be sure to write your solutions in a logical, step-by-step fashion. Don't give up on a problem if you can't solve it right away. Try to understand the problem more clearly—reread it thoughtfully and relate it to what you have learned from your teacher and from the examples in the text. Struggle with it until you solve it. Once you have done this a few times you will begin to understand what mathematics is really all about.

Answers to the odd-numbered exercises, as well as all the answers to the concepts exercises and to each chapter test, appear at the back of the book. If your answer differs from the one given, don't immediately assume that you are wrong. There may be a calculation that connects the two answers and makes both correct. For example, if you get $1/(\sqrt{2} - 1)$ but the answer given is $1 + \sqrt{2}$, your answer *is* correct, because you can multiply both numerator and denominator of your answer by $\sqrt{2} + 1$ to change it to the given answer. In rounding approximate answers, follow the guidelines in the Appendix: *Calculations and Significant Figures*.

The symbol ⊘ is used to warn against committing an error. We have placed this symbol in the margin to point out situations where we have found that many of our students make the same mistake.

ABBREVIATIONS

cm	centimeter		**mg**	milligram
dB	decibel		**MHz**	megahertz
F	farad		**mi**	mile
ft	foot		**min**	minute
g	gram		**mL**	milliliter
gal	gallon		**mm**	millimeter
h	hour		**N**	Newton
H	henry		**qt**	quart
Hz	Hertz		**oz**	ounce
in.	inch		**s**	second
J	Joule		**Ω**	ohm
kcal	kilocalorie		**V**	volt
kg	kilogram		**W**	watt
km	kilometer		**yd**	yard
kPa	kilopascal		**yr**	year
L	liter		**°C**	degree Celsius
lb	pound		**°F**	degree Fahrenheit
lm	lumen		**K**	Kelvin
M	mole of solute per liter of solution		$\Rightarrow$	implies
			$\Leftrightarrow$	is equivalent to
m	meter			

MATHEMATICS IN THE MODERN WORLD

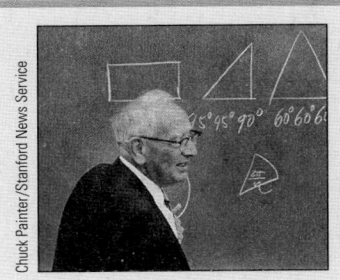

Chuck Painter/Stanford News Service

GEORGE POLYA (1887–1985) is famous among mathematicians for his ideas on problem solving. His lectures on problem solving at Stanford University attracted overflow crowds whom he held on the edges of their seats, leading them to discover solutions for themselves. He was able to do this because of his deep insight into the psychology of problem solving. His well-known book *How To Solve It* has been translated into 15 languages. He said that Euler (see page 266) was unique among great mathematicians because he explained how he found his results. Polya often said to his students and colleagues, "Yes, I see that your proof is correct, but how did you discover it?" In the preface to *How To Solve It,* Polya writes, "A great discovery solves a great problem but there is a grain of discovery in the solution of any problem. Your problem may be modest; but if it challenges your curiosity and brings into play your inventive faculties, and if you solve it by your own means, you may experience the tension and enjoy the triumph of discovery."

The ability to solve problems is a highly prized skill in many aspects of our lives; it is certainly an important part of any mathematics course. There are no hard and fast rules that will ensure success in solving problems. However, in this Prologue we outline some general steps in the problem-solving process and we give principles that are useful in solving certain problems. These steps and principles are just common sense made explicit. They have been adapted from George Polya's insightful book *How To Solve It*.

1. Understand the Problem

The first step is to read the problem and make sure that you understand it. Ask yourself the following questions:

> *What is the unknown?*
> *What are the given quantities?*
> *What are the given conditions?*

For many problems it is useful to

> *draw a diagram*

and identify the given and required quantities on the diagram. Usually, it is necessary to

> *introduce suitable notation*

In choosing symbols for the unknown quantities, we often use letters such as a, b, c, m, n, x, and y, but in some cases it helps to use initials as suggestive symbols, for instance, V for volume or t for time.

2. Think of a Plan

Find a connection between the given information and the unknown that enables you to calculate the unknown. It often helps to ask yourself explicitly: "How can I relate the given to the unknown?" If you don't see a connection immediately, the following ideas may be helpful in devising a plan.

▶ Try to Recognize Something Familiar

Relate the given situation to previous knowledge. Look at the unknown and try to recall a more familiar problem that has a similar unknown.

▶ **Try to Recognize Patterns**

Certain problems are solved by recognizing that some kind of pattern is occurring. The pattern could be geometric, numerical, or algebraic. If you can see regularity or repetition in a problem, then you might be able to guess what the pattern is and then prove it.

▶ **Use Analogy**

Try to think of an analogous problem, that is, a similar or related problem but one that is easier than the original. If you can solve the similar, simpler problem, then it might give you the clues you need to solve the original, more difficult one. For instance, if a problem involves very large numbers, you could first try a similar problem with smaller numbers. Or if the problem is in three-dimensional geometry, you could look for something similar in two-dimensional geometry. Or if the problem you start with is a general one, you could first try a special case.

▶ **Introduce Something Extra**

You might sometimes need to introduce something new—an auxiliary aid—to make the connection between the given and the unknown. For instance, in a problem for which a diagram is useful, the auxiliary aid could be a new line drawn in the diagram. In a more algebraic problem the aid could be a new unknown that relates to the original unknown.

▶ **Take Cases**

You might sometimes have to split a problem into several cases and give a different argument for each case. For instance, we often have to use this strategy in dealing with absolute value.

▶ **Work Backward**

Sometimes it is useful to imagine that your problem is solved and work backward, step by step, until you arrive at the given data. Then you might be able to reverse your steps and thereby construct a solution to the original problem. This procedure is commonly used in solving equations. For instance, in solving the equation $3x - 5 = 7$, we suppose that x is a number that satisfies $3x - 5 = 7$ and work backward. We add 5 to each side of the equation and then divide each side by 3 to get $x = 4$. Since each of these steps can be reversed, we have solved the problem.

▶ **Establish Subgoals**

In a complex problem it is often useful to set subgoals (in which the desired situation is only partially fulfilled). If you can attain or accomplish these subgoals, then you might be able to build on them to reach your final goal.

▶ **Indirect Reasoning**

Sometimes it is appropriate to attack a problem indirectly. In using **proof by contradiction** to prove that P implies Q, we assume that P is true and Q is false and try to see why this cannot happen. Somehow we have to use this information and arrive at a contradiction to what we absolutely know is true.

▶ **Mathematical Induction**

In proving statements that involve a positive integer n, it is frequently helpful to use the Principle of Mathematical Induction, which is discussed in Section 12.5.

3. Carry Out the Plan

In Step 2, a plan was devised. In carrying out that plan, you must check each stage of the plan and write the details that prove that each stage is correct.

4. Look Back

Having completed your solution, it is wise to look back over it, partly to see whether any errors have been made and partly to see whether you can discover an easier way to solve the problem. Looking back also familiarizes you with the method of solution, which may be useful for solving a future problem. Descartes said, "Every problem that I solved became a rule which served afterwards to solve other problems."

We illustrate some of these principles of problem solving with an example.

PROBLEM | Average Speed

A driver sets out on a journey. For the first half of the distance, she drives at the leisurely pace of 30 mi/h; during the second half she drives 60 mi/h. What is her average speed on this trip?

THINKING ABOUT THE PROBLEM

It is tempting to take the average of the speeds and say that the average speed for the entire trip is

$$\frac{30 + 60}{2} = 45 \text{ mi/h}$$

But is this simple-minded approach really correct?

Try a special case ▶   Let's look at an easily calculated special case. Suppose that the total distance traveled is 120 mi. Since the first 60 mi is traveled at 30 mi/h, it takes 2 h. The second 60 mi is traveled at 60 mi/h, so it takes one hour. Thus, the total time is $2 + 1 = 3$ hours and the average speed is

$$\frac{120}{3} = 40 \text{ mi/h}$$

So our guess of 45 mi/h was wrong.

SOLUTION

Understand the problem ▶   We need to look more carefully at the meaning of average speed. It is defined as

$$\text{average speed} = \frac{\text{distance traveled}}{\text{time elapsed}}$$

Introduce notation ▶   Let d be the distance traveled on each half of the trip. Let t_1 and t_2 be the times taken for the first and second halves of the trip. Now we can write down the information we have

State what is given ▶   been given. For the first half of the trip we have

$$30 = \frac{d}{t_1}$$

and for the second half we have

$$60 = \frac{d}{t_2}$$

Identify the unknown ▶   Now we identify the quantity that we are asked to find:

$$\text{average speed for entire trip} = \frac{\text{total distance}}{\text{total time}} = \frac{2d}{t_1 + t_2}$$

Connect the given
with the unknown ▶   To calculate this quantity, we need to know t_1 and t_2, so we solve the above equations for these times:

$$t_1 = \frac{d}{30} \qquad t_2 = \frac{d}{60}$$

Don't feel bad if you can't solve these problems right away. Problems 1 and 4 were sent to Albert Einstein by his friend Wertheimer. Einstein (and his friend Bucky) enjoyed the problems and wrote back to Wertheimer. Here is part of his reply:

Your letter gave us a lot of amusement. The first intelligence test fooled both of us (Bucky and me). Only on working it out did I notice that no time is available for the downhill run! Mr. Bucky was also taken in by the second example, but I was not. Such drolleries show us how stupid we are!

(See *Mathematical Intelligencer*, Spring 1990, page 41.)

Now we have the ingredients needed to calculate the desired quantity:

$$\text{average speed} = \frac{2d}{t_1 + t_1} = \frac{2d}{\dfrac{d}{30} + \dfrac{d}{60}}$$

$$= \frac{60(2d)}{60\left(\dfrac{d}{30} + \dfrac{d}{60}\right)} \qquad \text{Multiply numerator and denominator by 60}$$

$$= \frac{120d}{2d + d} = \frac{120d}{3d} = 40$$

So the average speed for the entire trip is 40 mi/h.

PROBLEMS

1. **Distance, Time, and Speed**   An old car has to travel a 2-mile route, uphill and down. Because it is so old, the car can climb the first mile—the ascent—no faster than an average speed of 15 mi/h. How fast does the car have to travel the second mile—on the descent it can go faster, of course—to achieve an average speed of 30 mi/h for the trip?

2. **Comparing Discounts**   Which price is better for the buyer, a 40% discount or two successive discounts of 20%?

3. **Cutting up a Wire**   A piece of wire is bent as shown in the figure. You can see that one cut through the wire produces four pieces and two parallel cuts produce seven pieces. How many pieces will be produced by 142 parallel cuts? Write a formula for the number of pieces produced by n parallel cuts.

4. **Amoeba Propagation**   An amoeba propagates by simple division; each split takes 3 minutes to complete. When such an amoeba is put into a glass container with a nutrient fluid, the container is full of amoebas in one hour. How long would it take for the container to be filled if we start with not one amoeba, but two?

5. **Batting Averages**   Player A has a higher batting average than player B for the first half of the baseball season. Player A also has a higher batting average than player B for the second half of the season. Is it necessarily true that player A has a higher batting average than player B for the entire season?

6. **Coffee and Cream**   A spoonful of cream is taken from a pitcher of cream and put into a cup of coffee. The coffee is stirred. Then a spoonful of this mixture is put into the pitcher of cream. Is there now more cream in the coffee cup or more coffee in the pitcher of cream?

7. **Wrapping the World**   A ribbon is tied tightly around the earth at the equator. How much more ribbon would you need if you raised the ribbon 1 ft above the equator everywhere? (You don't need to know the radius of the earth to solve this problem.)

8. **Ending Up Where You Started**   A woman starts at a point P on the earth's surface and walks 1 mi south, then 1 mi east, then 1 mi north, and finds herself back at P, the starting point. Describe all points P for which this is possible.   [*Hint:* There are infinitely many such points, all but one of which lie in Antarctica.]

Many more problems and examples that highlight different problem-solving principles are available at the book companion website: **www.stewartmath.com**. You can try them as you progress through the book.

Image copyright Monkey Business Images 2010.
Used under license from Shutterstock.com

FUNDAMENTALS

In this first chapter we review the real numbers, equations, and the coordinate plane. You are probably already familiar with these concepts, but it is helpful to get a fresh look at how these ideas work together to solve problems and model (or describe) real-world situations.

Let's see how all these ideas are used in a real-life situation: Suppose you get paid \$9 an hour at your part-time job. We can *model* your pay y for working x hours by the *equation* $y = 9x$. To find out how many hours you need to work to get paid 200 dollars, we solve the equation $200 = 9x$. Graphing the equation $y = 9x$ in a *coordinate plane* helps us "see" how pay increases with hours worked.

1

1.1 REAL NUMBERS

Properties of Real Numbers ▶ Addition and Subtraction ▶ Multiplication and Division ▶ The Real Line ▶ Sets and Intervals ▶ Absolute Value and Distance

Let's review the types of numbers that make up the real number system. We start with the **natural numbers**:

$$1, 2, 3, 4, \ldots$$

The **integers** consist of the natural numbers together with their negatives and 0:

$$\ldots, -3, -2, -1, 0, 1, 2, 3, 4, \ldots$$

The different types of real numbers were invented to meet specific needs. For example, natural numbers are needed for counting, negative numbers for describing debt or below-zero temperatures, rational numbers for concepts like "half a gallon of milk," and irrational numbers for measuring certain distances, like the diagonal of a square.

We construct the **rational numbers** by taking ratios of integers. Thus, any rational number r can be expressed as

$$r = \frac{m}{n}$$

where m and n are integers and $n \neq 0$. Examples are

$$\frac{1}{2} \qquad -\frac{3}{7} \qquad 46 = \frac{46}{1} \qquad 0.17 = \frac{17}{100}$$

(Recall that division by 0 is always ruled out, so expressions like $\frac{3}{0}$ and $\frac{0}{0}$ are undefined.) There are also real numbers, such as $\sqrt{2}$, that cannot be expressed as a ratio of integers and are therefore called **irrational numbers**. It can be shown, with varying degrees of difficulty, that these numbers are also irrational:

$$\sqrt{3} \qquad \sqrt{5} \qquad \sqrt[3]{2} \qquad \pi \qquad \frac{3}{\pi^2}$$

The set of all real numbers is usually denoted by the symbol $\mathbb{R}$. When we use the word *number* without qualification, we will mean "real number." Figure 1 is a diagram of the types of real numbers that we work with in this book.

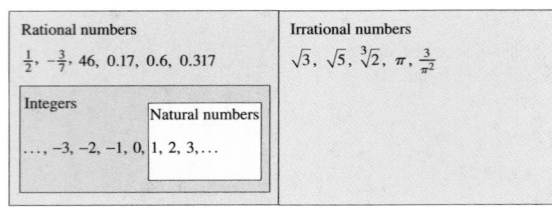

FIGURE 1 The real number system

A repeating decimal such as

$$x = 3.5474747\ldots$$

is a rational number. To convert it to a ratio of two integers, we write

$$1000x = 3547.47474747\ldots$$
$$10x = 35.47474747\ldots$$
$$\overline{990x = 3512.0}$$

Thus, $x = \frac{3512}{990}$. (The idea is to multiply x by appropriate powers of 10 and then subtract to eliminate the repeating part.)

Every real number has a decimal representation. If the number is rational, then its corresponding decimal is repeating. For example,

$$\frac{1}{2} = 0.5000\ldots = 0.5\overline{0} \qquad\qquad \frac{2}{3} = 0.66666\ldots = 0.\overline{6}$$

$$\frac{157}{495} = 0.3171717\ldots = 0.3\overline{17} \qquad \frac{9}{7} = 1.285714285714\ldots = 1.\overline{285714}$$

(The bar indicates that the sequence of digits repeats forever.) If the number is irrational, the decimal representation is nonrepeating:

$$\sqrt{2} = 1.414213562373095\ldots \qquad \pi = 3.141592653589793\ldots$$

TEXT QUESTIONS

Consider the numbers below from the text. Fill in each gray box with a label from the following list: integers, irrational numbers, natural numbers, and rational numbers.

1. $\dfrac{1}{2}, -\dfrac{3}{7}, 46, 0.17, 0.\overline{6}, 0.3\overline{17}, \ldots$

2. $\ldots, -3, -2, -1, 0, \ldots$

3. $1, 2, 3, \ldots$

4. $\sqrt{3}, \sqrt{5}, \sqrt[3]{2}, \pi, 3/\pi^2, \ldots$

Answers

1. Rational numbers
2. Integers
3. Natural numbers
4. Irrational numbers

If we stop the decimal expansion of any number at a certain place, we get an approximation to the number. For instance, we can write

$$\pi \approx 3.14159265$$

where the symbol $\approx$ is read "is approximately equal to." The more decimal places we retain, the better our approximation.

▼ Properties of Real Numbers

We all know that $2 + 3 = 3 + 2$, and $5 + 7 = 7 + 5$, and $513 + 87 = 87 + 513$, and so on. In algebra, we express all these (infinitely many) facts by writing

$$a + b = b + a$$

where a and b stand for any two numbers. In other words, "$a + b = b + a$" is a concise way of saying that "when we add two numbers, the order of addition doesn't matter." This fact is called the *Commutative Property* for addition. From our experience with numbers we know that the properties in the following box are also valid.

PROPERTIES OF REAL NUMBERS

Property	Example	Description
Commutative Properties		
$a + b = b + a$	$7 + 3 = 3 + 7$	When we add two numbers, order doesn't matter.
$ab = ba$	$3 \cdot 5 = 5 \cdot 3$	When we multiply two numbers, order doesn't matter.
Associative Properties		
$(a + b) + c = a + (b + c)$	$(2 + 4) + 7 = 2 + (4 + 7)$	When we add three numbers, it doesn't matter which two we add first.
$(ab)c = a(bc)$	$(3 \cdot 7) \cdot 5 = 3 \cdot (7 \cdot 5)$	When we multiply three numbers, it doesn't matter which two we multiply first.
Distributive Property		
$a(b + c) = ab + ac$	$2 \cdot (3 + 5) = 2 \cdot 3 + 2 \cdot 5$	When we multiply a number by a sum of two numbers, we get the same result as we would get if we multiply the number by each of the terms and then add the results.
$(b + c)a = ab + ac$	$(3 + 5) \cdot 2 = 2 \cdot 3 + 2 \cdot 5$	

The Distributive Property applies whenever we multiply a number by a sum. Figure 2 explains why this property works for the case in which all the numbers are positive integers, but the property is true for any real numbers a, b, and c.

The Distributive Property is crucial because it describes the way addition and multiplication interact with each other.

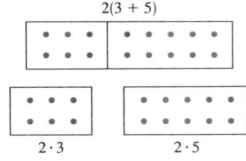

FIGURE 2 The Distributive Property

ALTERNATE EXAMPLE 1
Expand the expression
$(a + b)(c + d)$, using the
properties of the real numbers.

ANSWER
$a \cdot c + b \cdot c + a \cdot d + b \cdot d$

EXAMPLE 1 | Using the Distributive Property

(a) $2(x + 3) = 2 \cdot x + 2 \cdot 3$ Distributive Property

     $= 2x + 6$ Simplify

(b) $(a + b)(x + y) = (a + b)x + (a + b)y$ Distributive Property

     $= (ax + bx) + (ay + by)$ Distributive Property

     $= ax + bx + ay + by$ Associative Property of Addition

In the last step we removed the parentheses because, according to the Associative Property, the order of addition doesn't matter.

✎ NOW TRY EXERCISE 11   ■

▼ Addition and Subtraction

Don't assume that $-a$ is a negative number. Whether $-a$ is negative or positive depends on the value of a. For example, if $a = 5$, then $-a = -5$, a negative number, but if $a = -5$, then $-a = -(-5) = 5$ (Property 2), a positive number.

The number 0 is special for addition; it is called the **additive identity** because $a + 0 = a$ for any real number a. Every real number a has a **negative**, $-a$, that satisfies $a + (-a) = 0$. **Subtraction** is the operation that undoes addition; to subtract a number from another, we simply add the negative of that number. By definition

$$a - b = a + (-b)$$

To combine real numbers involving negatives, we use the following properties.

PROPERTIES OF NEGATIVES	
Property	**Example**
1. $(-1)a = -a$	$(-1)5 = -5$
2. $-(-a) = a$	$-(-5) = 5$
3. $(-a)b = a(-b) = -(ab)$	$(-5)7 = 5(-7) = -(5 \cdot 7)$
4. $(-a)(-b) = ab$	$(-4)(-3) = 4 \cdot 3$
5. $-(a + b) = -a - b$	$-(3 + 5) = -3 - 5$
6. $-(a - b) = b - a$	$-(5 - 8) = 8 - 5$

Property 6 states the intuitive fact that $a - b$ and $b - a$ are negatives of each other. Property 5 is often used with more than two terms:

$$-(a + b + c) = -a - b - c$$

EXAMPLE 2 | Using Properties of Negatives

Let x, y, and z be real numbers.

(a) $-(x + 2) = -x - 2$ Property 5: $-(a + b) = -a - b$

(b) $-(x + y - z) = -x - y - (-z)$ Property 5: $-(a + b) = -a - b$

     $= -x - y + z$ Property 2: $-(-a) = a$

✎ NOW TRY EXERCISE 23   ■

ALTERNATE EXAMPLE 2
Simplify the expression
$-(k + l - m)$.

ANSWER
$-k - l + m$

IN-CLASS MATERIALS

Students probably already know how to multiply binomial expressions together, some of them already are using the acronym FOIL to avoid thinking about the process altogether. Use the properties in this section to demonstrate why FOIL works.

$(a + b)(c + d) = a(c + d) + b(c + d)$ Distributive Property

     $= ac + ad + b(c + d)$ Distributive Property on the first term

     $= ac + ad + bc + bd$ Distributive Property on the second term

▼ Multiplication and Division

The number 1 is special for multiplication; it is called the **multiplicative identity** because $a \cdot 1 = a$ for any real number a. Every nonzero real number a has an **inverse**, $1/a$, that satisfies $a \cdot (1/a) = 1$. **Division** is the operation that undoes multiplication; to divide by a number, we multiply by the inverse of that number. If $b \neq 0$, then, by definition,

$$a \div b = a \cdot \frac{1}{b}$$

We write $a \cdot (1/b)$ as simply a/b. We refer to a/b as the **quotient** of a and b or as the **fraction** a over b; a is the **numerator** and b is the **denominator** (or **divisor**). To combine real numbers using the operation of division, we use the following properties.

PROPERTIES OF FRACTIONS

Property	Example	Description
1. $\frac{a}{b} \cdot \frac{c}{d} = \frac{ac}{bd}$	$\frac{2}{3} \cdot \frac{5}{7} = \frac{2 \cdot 5}{3 \cdot 7} = \frac{10}{21}$	When **multiplying fractions**, multiply numerators and denominators.
2. $\frac{a}{b} \div \frac{c}{d} = \frac{a}{b} \cdot \frac{d}{c}$	$\frac{2}{3} \div \frac{5}{7} = \frac{2}{3} \cdot \frac{7}{5} = \frac{14}{15}$	When **dividing fractions**, invert the divisor and multiply.
3. $\frac{a}{c} + \frac{b}{c} = \frac{a+b}{c}$	$\frac{2}{5} + \frac{7}{5} = \frac{2+7}{5} = \frac{9}{5}$	When **adding fractions** with the **same denominator**, add the numerators.
4. $\frac{a}{b} + \frac{c}{d} = \frac{ad+bc}{bd}$	$\frac{2}{5} + \frac{3}{7} = \frac{2 \cdot 7 + 3 \cdot 5}{35} = \frac{29}{35}$	When **adding fractions** with **different denominators**, find a common denominator. Then add the numerators.
5. $\frac{ac}{bc} = \frac{a}{b}$	$\frac{2 \cdot 5}{3 \cdot 5} = \frac{2}{3}$	**Cancel** numbers that are **common factors** in numerator and denominator.
6. If $\frac{a}{b} = \frac{c}{d}$, then $ad = bc$	$\frac{2}{3} = \frac{6}{9}$, so $2 \cdot 9 = 3 \cdot 6$	**Cross-multiply.**

When adding fractions with different denominators, we don't usually use Property 4. Instead we rewrite the fractions so that they have the smallest possible common denominator (often smaller than the product of the denominators), and then we use Property 3. This denominator is the **L**east **C**ommon **D**enominator (LCD) described in the next example.

EXAMPLE 3 | Using the LCD to Add Fractions

Evaluate: $\dfrac{5}{36} + \dfrac{7}{120}$

SOLUTION Factoring each denominator into prime factors gives

$$36 = 2^2 \cdot 3^2 \quad \text{and} \quad 120 = 2^3 \cdot 3 \cdot 5$$

We find the least common denominator (LCD) by forming the product of all the factors that occur in these factorizations, using the highest power of each factor.

ALTERNATE EXAMPLE 3

Evaluate: $\dfrac{11}{441} + \dfrac{41}{2079}$

ANSWER

$$\frac{650}{14,553}$$

IN-CLASS MATERIALS

Warn students that certain things cannot be rewritten. For example, an expression like $\dfrac{u}{u+1}$ cannot be simplified, while $\dfrac{u+1}{u}$ can be expressed as $1 + \dfrac{1}{u}$. Similarly, there is no way to simplify $a + bc$. Another common pitfall can be pointed out by asking the question "Is $-a$ a positive or negative number?"

Thus the LCD is $2^3 \cdot 3^2 \cdot 5 = 360$. So

$$\frac{5}{36} + \frac{7}{120} = \frac{5 \cdot 10}{36 \cdot 10} + \frac{7 \cdot 3}{120 \cdot 3} \qquad \text{Use common denominator}$$

$$= \frac{50}{360} + \frac{21}{360} = \frac{71}{360} \qquad \text{Property 3: Adding fractions with the same denominator}$$

✎ NOW TRY EXERCISE **25** ∎

▼ The Real Line

The real numbers can be represented by points on a line, as shown in Figure 3. The positive direction (toward the right) is indicated by an arrow. We choose an arbitrary reference point O, called the **origin**, which corresponds to the real number 0. Given any convenient unit of measurement, each positive number x is represented by the point on the line a distance of x units to the right of the origin, and each negative number $-x$ is represented by the point x units to the left of the origin. The number associated with the point P is called the coordinate of P, and the line is then called a **coordinate line**, or a **real number line**, or simply a **real line**. Often we identify the point with its coordinate and think of a number as being a point on the real line.

FIGURE 3 The real line

The real numbers are *ordered*. We say that **a is less than b** and write $a < b$ if $b - a$ is a positive number. Geometrically, this means that a lies to the left of b on the number line. Equivalently, we can say that **b is greater than a** and write $b > a$. The symbol $a \le b$ (or $b \ge a$) means that either $a < b$ or $a = b$ and is read "a is less than or equal to b." For instance, the following are true inequalities (see Figure 4):

$$7 < 7.4 < 7.5 \qquad -\pi < -3 \qquad \sqrt{2} < 2 \qquad 2 \le 2$$

FIGURE 4

▼ Sets and Intervals

A **set** is a collection of objects, and these objects are called the **elements** of the set. If S is a set, the notation $a \in S$ means that a is an element of S, and $b \notin S$ means that b is not an element of S. For example, if Z represents the set of integers, then $-3 \in Z$ but $\pi \notin Z$.

Some sets can be described by listing their elements within braces. For instance, the set A that consists of all positive integers less than 7 can be written as

$$A = \{1, 2, 3, 4, 5, 6\}$$

We could also write A in **set-builder notation** as

$$A = \{x \mid x \text{ is an integer and } 0 < x < 7\}$$

which is read "A is the set of all x such that x is an integer and $0 < x < 7$."

IN-CLASS MATERIALS

Ask the students why we never see intervals of the form $[3, \infty]$ or $(52, 3)$. Explain to them why these intervals are not well formed.

If S and T are sets, then their **union** $S \cup T$ is the set that consists of all elements that are in S *or* T (or in both). The **intersection** of S and T is the set $S \cap T$ consisting of all elements that are in both S *and* T. In other words, $S \cap T$ is the common part of S and T. The **empty set**, denoted by $\varnothing$, is the set that contains no element.

EXAMPLE 4 | Union and Intersection of Sets

If $S = \{1, 2, 3, 4, 5\}$, $T = \{4, 5, 6, 7\}$, and $V = \{6, 7, 8\}$, find the sets $S \cup T$, $S \cap T$, and $S \cap V$.

SOLUTION

$$S \cup T = \{1, 2, 3, 4, 5, 6, 7\} \qquad \text{All elements in } S \text{ or } T$$

$$S \cap T = \{4, 5\} \qquad \text{Elements common to both } S \text{ and } T$$

$$S \cap V = \varnothing \qquad S \text{ and } V \text{ have no element in common}$$

1, 2, 3, 4, 5, 6, 7, 8
T over 4, 5, 6, 7, 8 ; S under 1,2,3,4,5 ; V under 6,7,8

✎ **NOW TRY EXERCISE 39** ■

Certain sets of real numbers, called **intervals**, occur frequently in calculus and correspond geometrically to line segments. If $a < b$, then the **open interval** from a to b consists of all numbers between a and b and is denoted (a, b). The **closed interval** from a to b includes the endpoints and is denoted $[a, b]$. Using set-builder notation, we can write

$$(a, b) = \{x \mid a < x < b\} \qquad [a, b] = \{x \mid a \leq x \leq b\}$$

FIGURE 5 The open interval (a, b)

Note that parentheses ( ) in the interval notation and open circles on the graph in Figure 5 indicate that endpoints are *excluded* from the interval, whereas square brackets [ ] and solid circles in Figure 6 indicate that the endpoints are *included*. Intervals may also include one endpoint but not the other, or they may extend infinitely far in one direction or both. The following table lists the possible types of intervals.

FIGURE 6 The closed interval $[a, b]$

Notation	Set description	Graph
(a, b)	$\{x \mid a < x < b\}$	
$[a, b]$	$\{x \mid a \leq x \leq b\}$	
$[a, b)$	$\{x \mid a \leq x < b\}$	
$(a, b]$	$\{x \mid a < x \leq b\}$	
(a, ∞)	$\{x \mid a < x\}$	
$[a, \infty)$	$\{x \mid a \leq x\}$	
$(-\infty, b)$	$\{x \mid x < b\}$	
$(-\infty, b]$	$\{x \mid x \leq b\}$	
$(-\infty, \infty)$	$\mathbb{R}$ (set of all real numbers)	

The symbol ∞ ("infinity") does not stand for a number. The notation (a, ∞), for instance, simply indicates that the interval has no endpoint on the right but extends infinitely far in the positive direction.

EXAMPLE 5 | Graphing Intervals

Express each interval in terms of inequalities, and then graph the interval.

(a) $[-1, 2) = \{x \mid -1 \leq x < 2\}$

(b) $[1.5, 4] = \{x \mid 1.5 \leq x \leq 4\}$

(c) $(-3, \infty) = \{x \mid -3 < x\}$

✎ **NOW TRY EXERCISE 45** ■

ALTERNATE EXAMPLE 4
If $S = \{1, 3, 5, 6, 8\}$, $T = \{6, 8, 9, 10\}$, and $V = \{9, 10, 11\}$, find the sets $S \cup T$, $S \cap T$, and $S \cap V$.

ANSWER
$\{1, 3, 5, 6, 8, 9, 10\}, \{6, 8\}, \varnothing$

ALTERNATE EXAMPLE 5
Is the number 0 included in the interval $[-3, 6)$?

ANSWER
Yes

EXAMPLE

A nontrivial union of intervals: Let $S = \{x \mid x > 0, x \neq 1/n, \text{ where } n \text{ is a positive integer}\}$ (the set of all positive numbers, except those of the form $1/n$, where n, is a positive integer). This set is an infinite union of open intervals: $(1, \infty) \cup \left(\frac{1}{2}, 1\right) \cup \left(\frac{1}{3}, \frac{1}{2}\right) \cup \cdots$. Notice that each individual interval in the union is well behaved and easy to understand. Also notice that the intersection of S with any positive open interval such as $(0.1, 5)$ becomes a finite union.

ALTERNATE EXAMPLE 6

Find $S \cap T$, if $S = (2, 5)$ and $T = [4, 7]$.

ANSWER

$[4, 5)$

No Smallest or Largest Number in an Open Interval

Any interval contains infinitely many numbers—every point on the graph of an interval corresponds to a real number. In the closed interval $[0, 1]$, the smallest number is 0 and the largest is 1, but the open interval $(0, 1)$ contains no smallest or largest number. To see this, note that 0.01 is close to zero, but 0.001 is closer, 0.0001 is closer yet, and so on. We can always find a number in the interval $(0, 1)$ closer to zero than any given number. Since 0 itself is not in the interval, the interval contains no smallest number. Similarly, 0.99 is close to 1, but 0.999 is closer, 0.9999 closer yet, and so on. Since 1 itself is not in the interval, the interval has no largest number.

EXAMPLE 6 | Finding Unions and Intersections of Intervals

Graph each set.

(a) $(1, 3) \cap [2, 7]$ (b) $(1, 3) \cup [2, 7]$

SOLUTION

(a) The intersection of two intervals consists of the numbers that are in both intervals. Therefore

$$(1, 3) \cap [2, 7] = \{x \mid 1 < x < 3 \text{ and } 2 \le x \le 7\}$$
$$= \{x \mid 2 \le x < 3\} = [2, 3)$$

This set is illustrated in Figure 7.

(b) The union of two intervals consists of the numbers that are in either one interval or the other (or both). Therefore

$$(1, 3) \cup [2, 7] = \{x \mid 1 < x < 3 \text{ or } 2 \le x \le 7\}$$
$$= \{x \mid 1 < x \le 7\} = (1, 7]$$

This set is illustrated in Figure 8.

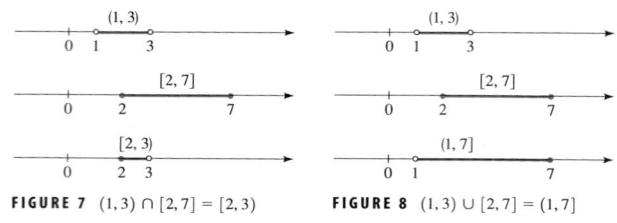

FIGURE 7 $(1, 3) \cap [2, 7] = [2, 3)$ **FIGURE 8** $(1, 3) \cup [2, 7] = (1, 7]$

✎ NOW TRY EXERCISE **59** ∎

$|-3| = 3$ $|5| = 5$

FIGURE 9

▼ **Absolute Value and Distance**

The **absolute value** of a number a, denoted by $|a|$, is the distance from a to 0 on the real number line (see Figure 9). Distance is always positive or zero, so we have $|a| \ge 0$ for every number a. Remembering that $-a$ is positive when a is negative, we have the following definition.

DEFINITION OF ABSOLUTE VALUE

If a is a real number, then the **absolute value** of a is

$$|a| = \begin{cases} a & \text{if } a \ge 0 \\ -a & \text{if } a < 0 \end{cases}$$

ALTERNATE EXAMPLE 7

(b) Evaluate the absolute value of the number $|-9|$.

(d) Evaluate the absolute value of the number $|\sqrt{2} - 1|$.

ANSWERS

(b) 9

(d) $\sqrt{2} - 1$

EXAMPLE 7 | Evaluating Absolute Values of Numbers

(a) $|3| = 3$

(b) $|-3| = -(-3) = 3$

(c) $|0| = 0$

(d) $|3 - \pi| = -(3 - \pi) = \pi - 3$ (since $3 < \pi \implies 3 - \pi < 0$)

✎ NOW TRY EXERCISE **65** ∎

IN-CLASS MATERIALS

Example 7(d) should be discussed: $|3 - \pi| = \pi - 3$. It touches on the ideas of distance, the absolute value of a negative number, and that we don't need to write out π to infinite precision to deduce that it is larger than 3.

When working with absolute values, we use the following properties.

PROPERTIES OF ABSOLUTE VALUE		
Property	**Example**	**Description**
1. $\lvert a\rvert \geq 0$	$\lvert -3\rvert = 3 \geq 0$	The absolute value of a number is always positive or zero.
2. $\lvert a\rvert = \lvert -a\rvert$	$\lvert 5\rvert = \lvert -5\rvert$	A number and its negative have the same absolute value.
3. $\lvert ab\rvert = \lvert a\rvert\lvert b\rvert$	$\lvert -2\cdot 5\rvert = \lvert -2\rvert\lvert 5\rvert$	The absolute value of a product is the product of the absolute values.
4. $\left\lvert \dfrac{a}{b}\right\rvert = \dfrac{\lvert a\rvert}{\lvert b\rvert}$	$\left\lvert \dfrac{12}{-3}\right\rvert = \dfrac{\lvert 12\rvert}{\lvert -3\rvert}$	The absolute value of a quotient is the quotient of the absolute values.

What is the distance on the real line between the numbers -2 and 11? From Figure 10 we see that the distance is 13. We arrive at this by finding either $\lvert 11 - (-2)\rvert = 13$ or $\lvert (-2) - 11\rvert = 13$. From this observation we make the following definition (see Figure 11).

FIGURE 10

FIGURE 11 Length of a line segment is $\lvert b - a\rvert$

DISTANCE BETWEEN POINTS ON THE REAL LINE
If a and b are real numbers, then the **distance** between the points a and b on the real line is $$d(a, b) = \lvert b - a\rvert$$

From Property 6 of negatives it follows that

$$\lvert b - a\rvert = \lvert a - b\rvert$$

This confirms that, as we would expect, the distance from a to b is the same as the distance from b to a.

EXAMPLE 8 | Distance Between Points on the Real Line

The distance between the numbers -8 and 2 is

$$d(a, b) = \lvert -8 - 2\rvert = \lvert -10\rvert = 10$$

We can check this calculation geometrically, as shown in Figure 12.

FIGURE 12

NOW TRY EXERCISE **73**

1.1 EXERCISES

CONCEPTS

1. Give an example of each of the following:

 (a) A natural number

 (b) An integer that is not a natural number

 (c) A rational number that is not an integer

 (d) An irrational number

2. Complete each statement and name the property of real numbers you have used.

 (a) $ab = $ _____; _____ Property

 (b) $a + (b + c) = $ _____; _____ Property

 (c) $a(b + c) = $ _____; _____ Property

3. The set of numbers between but not including 2 and 7 can be written as follows:

 _____ in set-builder notation and

 _____ in interval notation.

4. The symbol $|x|$ stands for the _____ of the number x. If x is not 0, then the sign of $|x|$ is always _____.

SKILLS

5–6 ■ List the elements of the given set that are

 (a) natural numbers

 (b) integers

 (c) rational numbers

 (d) irrational numbers

5. $\{0, -10, 50, \frac{22}{7}, 0.538, \sqrt{7}, 1.2\overline{3}, -\frac{1}{3}, \sqrt[3]{2}\}$

6. $\{1.001, 0.333\ldots, -\pi, -11, 11, \frac{13}{15}, \sqrt{16}, 3.14, \frac{15}{3}\}$

7–14 ■ State the property of real numbers being used.

7. $7 + 10 = 10 + 7$

8. $2(3 + 5) = (3 + 5)2$

9. $(x + 2y) + 3z = x + (2y + 3z)$

10. $2(A + B) = 2A + 2B$

11. $(5x + 1)3 = 15x + 3$

12. $(x + a)(x + b) = (x + a)x + (x + a)b$

13. $2x(3 + y) = (3 + y)2x$

14. $7(a + b + c) = 7(a + b) + 7c$

15–18 ■ Rewrite the expression using the given property of real numbers.

15. Commutative Property of addition, $x + 3 = $ ▨

16. Associative Property of multiplication, $7(3x) = $ ▨

17. Distributive Property, $4(A + B) = $ ▨

18. Distributive Property, $5x + 5y = $ ▨

19–24 ■ Use properties of real numbers to write the expression without parentheses.

19. $3(x + y)$

20. $(a - b)8$

21. $4(2m)$

22. $\frac{4}{3}(-6y)$

23. $-\frac{5}{2}(2x - 4y)$

24. $(3a)(b + c - 2d)$

25–30 ■ Perform the indicated operations.

25. (a) $\frac{3}{10} + \frac{4}{15}$ **(b)** $\frac{1}{4} + \frac{1}{5}$

26. (a) $\frac{2}{3} - \frac{3}{5}$ **(b)** $1 + \frac{5}{8} - \frac{1}{6}$

27. (a) $\frac{2}{3}(6 - \frac{3}{2})$ **(b)** $0.25(\frac{8}{9} + \frac{1}{2})$

28. (a) $(3 + \frac{1}{4})(1 - \frac{4}{5})$ **(b)** $(\frac{1}{2} - \frac{1}{3})(\frac{1}{2} + \frac{1}{3})$

29. (a) $\dfrac{\frac{2}{3} - \frac{2}{3}}{2}$ **(b)** $\dfrac{\frac{1}{12}}{\frac{1}{8} - \frac{1}{9}}$

30. (a) $\dfrac{2 - \frac{3}{4}}{\frac{1}{2} - \frac{1}{3}}$ **(b)** $\dfrac{\frac{2}{5} + \frac{1}{2}}{\frac{1}{10} + \frac{3}{15}}$

31–32 ■ Place the correct symbol ($<$, $>$, or $=$) in the space.

31. (a) 3 ▨ $\frac{7}{2}$ **(b)** -3 ▨ $-\frac{7}{2}$ **(c)** 3.5 ▨ $\frac{7}{2}$

32. (a) $\frac{2}{3}$ ▨ 0.67 **(b)** $\frac{2}{3}$ ▨ -0.67 **(c)** $|0.67|$ ▨ $|-0.67|$

33–36 ■ State whether each inequality is true or false.

33. (a) $-6 < -10$ **(b)** $\sqrt{2} > 1.41$

34. (a) $\dfrac{10}{11} < \dfrac{12}{13}$ **(b)** $-\dfrac{1}{2} < -1$

35. (a) $-\pi > -3$ **(b)** $8 \leq 9$

36. (a) $1.1 > 1.\overline{1}$ **(b)** $8 \leq 8$

37–38 ■ Write each statement in terms of inequalities.

37. (a) x is positive

 (b) t is less than 4

 (c) a is greater than or equal to π

 (d) x is less than $\frac{1}{3}$ and is greater than -5

 (e) The distance from p to 3 is at most 5

38. (a) y is negative

 (b) z is greater than 1

 (c) b is at most 8

 (d) w is positive and is less than or equal to 17

 (e) y is at least 2 units from π

39–42 ■ Find the indicated set if

$$A = \{1, 2, 3, 4, 5, 6, 7\} \qquad B = \{2, 4, 6, 8\}$$
$$C = \{7, 8, 9, 10\}$$

39. (a) $A \cup B$ **(b)** $A \cap B$

40. (a) $B \cup C$ **(b)** $B \cap C$

41. (a) $A \cup C$ **(b)** $A \cap C$

42. (a) $A \cup B \cup C$ **(b)** $A \cap B \cap C$

43–44 ■ Find the indicated set if

$$A = \{x \mid x \geq -2\} \qquad B = \{x \mid x < 4\}$$
$$C = \{x \mid -1 < x \leq 5\}$$

43. (a) $B \cup C$ **(b)** $B \cap C$

44. (a) $A \cap C$ **(b)** $A \cap B$

45–50 ■ Express the interval in terms of inequalities, and then graph the interval.

45. $(-3, 0)$ **46.** $(2, 8]$

47. $[2, 8)$ **48.** $\left[-6, -\frac{1}{2}\right]$

49. $[2, \infty)$ **50.** $(-\infty, 1)$

51–56 ■ Express the inequality in interval notation, and then graph the corresponding interval.

51. $x \leq 1$ **52.** $1 \leq x \leq 2$

53. $-2 < x \leq 1$ **54.** $x \geq -5$

55. $x > -1$ **56.** $-5 < x < 2$

57–58 ■ Express each set in interval notation.

57. (a)

     -3   0   5

     (b)

     -3   0   5

58. (a)

       0   2

     (b)

     -2   0

59–64 ■ Graph the set.

59. $(-2, 0) \cup (-1, 1)$ **60.** $(-2, 0) \cap (-1, 1)$

61. $[-4, 6] \cap [0, 8)$ **62.** $[-4, 6) \cup [0, 8)$

63. $(-\infty, -4) \cup (4, \infty)$ **64.** $(-\infty, 6] \cap (2, 10)$

65–70 ■ Evaluate each expression.

65. (a) $|100|$ **(b)** $|-73|$

66. (a) $|\sqrt{5} - 5|$ **(b)** $|10 - \pi|$

67. (a) $||-6| - |-4||$ **(b)** $\frac{-1}{|-1|}$

68. (a) $|2 - |-12||$ **(b)** $-1 - |1 - |-1||$

69. (a) $|(-2) \cdot 6|$ **(b)** $\left|\left(-\frac{1}{3}\right)(-15)\right|$

70. (a) $\left|\frac{-6}{24}\right|$ **(b)** $\left|\frac{7 - 12}{12 - 7}\right|$

71–74 ■ Find the distance between the given numbers.

71.

   -3   -2   -1   0   1   2   3

72.

   -3   -2   -1   0   1   2   3

73. (a) 2 and 17   **(b)** −3 and 21   **(c)** $\frac{11}{8}$ and $-\frac{3}{10}$

74. (a) $\frac{7}{15}$ and $-\frac{1}{21}$ **(b)** −38 and −57   **(c)** −2.6 and −1.8

75–76 ■ Express each repeating decimal as a fraction. (See the margin note on page 2.)

75. (a) $0.\overline{7}$ **(b)** $0.\overline{28}$ **(c)** $0.\overline{57}$

76. (a) $5.\overline{23}$ **(b)** $1.\overline{37}$ **(c)** $2.1\overline{35}$

APPLICATIONS

77. Area of a Garden Mary's backyard vegetable garden measures 20 ft by 30 ft, so its area is $20 \times 30 = 600$ ft². She decides to make it longer, as shown in the figure, so that the area increases to $A = 20(30 + x)$. Which property of real numbers tells us that the new area can also be written $A = 600 + 20x$?

30 ft x

20 ft

78. Temperature Variation The bar graph shows the daily high temperatures for Omak, Washington, and Geneseo, New York, during a certain week in June. Let T_O represent the temperature in Omak and T_G the temperature in Geneseo. Calculate $T_O - T_G$ and $|T_O - T_G|$ for each day shown. Which of these two values gives more information?

■ Omak, WA
■ Geneseo, NY

Daily high temperature (°F)

Sun Mon Tue Wed Thu Fri Sat
Day

79. Mailing a Package The post office will only accept packages for which the length plus the "girth" (distance around) is no more than 108 inches. Thus, for the package in the figure, we must have

$$L + 2(x + y) \leq 108$$

(a) Will the post office accept a package that is 6 in. wide, 8 in. deep, and 5 ft long? What about a package that measures 2 ft by 2 ft by 4 ft?

(b) What is the greatest acceptable length for a package that has a square base measuring 9 in. by 9 in.?

L

x
y

5 ft = 60 in.

6 in.

8 in.

DISCOVERY ▪ DISCUSSION ▪ WRITING

80. Signs of Numbers   Let a, b, and c be real numbers such that $a > 0$, $b < 0$, and $c < 0$. Find the sign of each expression.

(a) $-a$ (b) $-b$ (c) bc

(d) $a - b$ (e) $c - a$ (f) $a + bc$

(g) $ab + ac$ (h) $-abc$ (i) ab^2

81. Sums and Products of Rational and Irrational Numbers   Explain why the sum, the difference, and the product of two rational numbers are rational numbers. Is the product of two irrational numbers necessarily irrational? What about the sum?

82. Combining Rational Numbers with Irrational Numbers   Is $\frac{1}{2} + \sqrt{2}$ rational or irrational? Is $\frac{1}{2} \cdot \sqrt{2}$ rational or irrational? In general, what can you say about the sum of a rational and an irrational number? What about the product?

83. Limiting Behavior of Reciprocals   Complete the tables. What happens to the size of the fraction $1/x$ as x gets large? As x gets small?

x	$1/x$
1	
2	
10	
100	
1000	

x	$1/x$
1.0	
0.5	
0.1	
0.01	
0.001	

84. Irrational Numbers and Geometry   Using the following figure, explain how to locate the point $\sqrt{2}$ on a number line. Can you locate $\sqrt{5}$ by a similar method? What about $\sqrt{6}$? List some other irrational numbers that can be located this way.

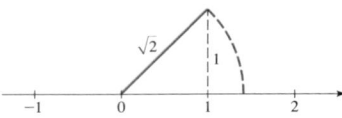

85. Commutative and Noncommutative Operations   We have seen that addition and multiplication are both commutative operations.

(a) Is subtraction commutative?

(b) Is division of nonzero real numbers commutative?

SUGGESTED TIME AND EMPHASIS

1–2 classes, essential material

1.2 EXPONENTS AND RADICALS

Integer Exponents ▶ Rules for Working with Exponents ▶ Scientific Notation ▶ Radicals ▶ Rational Exponents ▶ Rationalizing the Denominator

In this section we give meaning to expressions such as $a^{m/n}$ in which the exponent m/n is a rational number. To do this, we need to recall some facts about integer exponents, radicals, and nth roots.

▼ Integer Exponents

A product of identical numbers is usually written in exponential notation. For example, $5 \cdot 5 \cdot 5$ is written as 5^3. In general, we have the following definition.

EXPONENTIAL NOTATION

If a is any real number and n is a positive integer, then the **nth power** of a is

$$a^n = \underbrace{a \cdot a \cdots a}_{n \text{ factors}}$$

The number a is called the **base**, and n is called the **exponent**.

TEXT QUESTIONS

1. What is the definition of $a^{3/4}$?

2. Write 125,000,000 in scientific notation.

3. Why is scientific notation useful?

Answers

1. $a^{3/4} = \sqrt[4]{a^3}$

2. $125{,}000{,}000 = 1.25 \times 10^8$

3. It provides a compact way of writing very large numbers and very small numbers.

EXAMPLE 1 | Exponential Notation

Note the distinction between $(-3)^4$ and -3^4. In $(-3)^4$ the exponent applies to -3, but in -3^4 the exponent applies only to 3.

(a) $\left(\frac{1}{2}\right)^5 = \left(\frac{1}{2}\right)\left(\frac{1}{2}\right)\left(\frac{1}{2}\right)\left(\frac{1}{2}\right)\left(\frac{1}{2}\right) = \frac{1}{32}$

(b) $(-3)^4 = (-3)\cdot(-3)\cdot(-3)\cdot(-3) = 81$

(c) $-3^4 = -(3\cdot3\cdot3\cdot3) = -81$

✎. **NOW TRY EXERCISE 15**   ■

We can state several useful rules for working with exponential notation. To discover the rule for multiplication, we multiply 5^4 by 5^2:

$$5^4 \cdot 5^2 = \underbrace{(5\cdot5\cdot5\cdot5)}_{\text{4 factors}}\underbrace{(5\cdot5)}_{\text{2 factors}} = \underbrace{5\cdot5\cdot5\cdot5\cdot5\cdot5}_{\text{6 factors}} = 5^6 = 5^{4+2}$$

It appears that *to multiply two powers of the same base, we add their exponents*. In general, for any real number a and any positive integers m and n, we have

$$a^m a^n = \underbrace{(a\cdot a\cdots\cdot a)}_{m\text{ factors}}\underbrace{(a\cdot a\cdots\cdot a)}_{n\text{ factors}} = \underbrace{a\cdot a\cdot a\cdots\cdot a}_{m+n\text{ factors}} = a^{m+n}$$

Thus $a^m a^n = a^{m+n}$.

We would like this rule to be true even when m and n are 0 or negative integers. For instance, we must have

$$2^0 \cdot 2^3 = 2^{0+3} = 2^3$$

But this can happen only if $2^0 = 1$. Likewise, we want to have

$$5^4 \cdot 5^{-4} = 5^{4+(-4)} = 5^{4-4} = 5^0 = 1$$

and this will be true if $5^{-4} = 1/5^4$. These observations lead to the following definition.

ZERO AND NEGATIVE EXPONENTS

If $a \neq 0$ is any real number and n is a positive integer, then

$$a^0 = 1 \quad\text{and}\quad a^{-n} = \frac{1}{a^n}$$

EXAMPLE 2 | Zero and Negative Exponents

(a) $\left(\frac{4}{7}\right)^0 = 1$

(b) $x^{-1} = \frac{1}{x^1} = \frac{1}{x}$

(c) $(-2)^{-3} = \frac{1}{(-2)^3} = \frac{1}{-8} = -\frac{1}{8}$

✎. **NOW TRY EXERCISE 17**   ■

▼ Rules for Working with Exponents

Familiarity with the following rules is essential for our work with exponents and bases. In the table the bases a and b are real numbers, and the exponents m and n are integers.

ALTERNATE EXAMPLE 1
Evaluate $(-2)^6$ and -2^6.

ANSWER
$64, -64$

ALTERNATE EXAMPLE 2
Simplify:

(a) $\left(\frac{1}{3}\right)^{-1}$

(b) $(\sqrt{3} - \pi)^0$

ANSWERS
(a) 3
(b) 1

IN-CLASS MATERIALS
One nonrigorous way to justify the way negative exponents work is to start a table such as this:

2^5	32
2^4	16
2^3	8
2^2	4
2^1	2

Note that at every step we are dividing by 2, and continuing the pattern we get $2^0 = 1$ and $2^{-1} = \frac{1}{2}$. After explaining this concept, take a minute to do 2^{-2} and 2^{-3}.

LAWS OF EXPONENTS

Law	Example	Description
1. $a^m a^n = a^{m+n}$	$3^2 \cdot 3^5 = 3^{2+5} = 3^7$	To multiply two powers of the same number, add the exponents.
2. $\dfrac{a^m}{a^n} = a^{m-n}$	$\dfrac{3^5}{3^2} = 3^{5-2} = 3^3$	To divide two powers of the same number, subtract the exponents.
3. $(a^m)^n = a^{mn}$	$(3^2)^5 = 3^{2 \cdot 5} = 3^{10}$	To raise a power to a new power, multiply the exponents.
4. $(ab)^n = a^n b^n$	$(3 \cdot 4)^2 = 3^2 \cdot 4^2$	To raise a product to a power, raise each factor to the power.
5. $\left(\dfrac{a}{b}\right)^n = \dfrac{a^n}{b^n}$	$\left(\dfrac{3}{4}\right)^2 = \dfrac{3^2}{4^2}$	To raise a quotient to a power, raise both numerator and denominator to the power.

PROOF OF LAW 3   If m and n are positive integers, we have

$$(a^m)^n = \underbrace{(a \cdot a \cdots \cdots a)}_{m \text{ factors}}{}^n$$

$$= \underbrace{(a \cdot a \cdots \cdots a)}_{m \text{ factors}}\underbrace{(a \cdot a \cdots \cdots a)}_{m \text{ factors}} \cdots \underbrace{(a \cdot a \cdots \cdots a)}_{m \text{ factors}}$$

$$\underbrace{}_{n \text{ groups of factors}}$$

$$= \underbrace{a \cdot a \cdots \cdots a}_{mn \text{ factors}} = a^{mn}$$

The cases for which $m \leq 0$ or $n \leq 0$ can be proved using the definition of negative exponents. ∎

PROOF OF LAW 4   If n is a positive integer, we have

$$(ab)^n = \underbrace{(ab)(ab) \cdots (ab)}_{n \text{ factors}} = \underbrace{(a \cdot a \cdots \cdots a)}_{n \text{ factors}} \cdot \underbrace{(b \cdot b \cdots \cdots b)}_{n \text{ factors}} = a^n b^n$$

Here we have used the Commutative and Associative Properties repeatedly. If $n \leq 0$, Law 4 can be proved by using the definition of negative exponents. ∎

You are asked to prove Laws 2 and 5 in Exercise 94.

EXAMPLE 3 | Using Laws of Exponents

(a) $x^4 x^7 = x^{4+7} = x^{11}$ Law 1: $a^m a^n = a^{m+n}$

(b) $y^4 y^{-7} = y^{4-7} = y^{-3} = \dfrac{1}{y^3}$ Law 1: $a^m a^n = a^{m+n}$

(c) $\dfrac{c^9}{c^5} = c^{9-5} = c^4$ Law 2: $\dfrac{a^m}{a^n} = a^{m-n}$

(d) $(b^4)^5 = b^{4 \cdot 5} = b^{20}$ Law 3: $(a^m)^n = a^{mn}$

(e) $(3x)^3 = 3^3 x^3 = 27x^3$ Law 4: $(ab)^n = a^n b^n$

(f) $\left(\dfrac{x}{2}\right)^5 = \dfrac{x^5}{2^5} = \dfrac{x^5}{32}$ Law 5: $\left(\dfrac{a}{b}\right)^n = \dfrac{a^n}{b^n}$

✎ NOW TRY EXERCISES **35, 37, AND 39** ∎

ALTERNATE EXAMPLE 3
Simplify the expression using the laws of exponents: $x^3 x^5$.

ANSWER
x^8

IN-CLASS MATERIALS
Write $\sqrt{ab} = \sqrt{a}\sqrt{b}$ on the board, and ask the students if this statement is always true. Point out (or have them discover) that this is a false statement when a and b are negative. Also, write $\sqrt{a^2 + b^2}$ on the board, and point out that it cannot be simplified.

EXAMPLE 4 | Simplifying Expressions with Exponents

Simplify:

(a) $(2a^3b^2)(3ab^4)^3$ (b) $\left(\dfrac{x}{y}\right)^3\left(\dfrac{y^2x}{z}\right)^4$

SOLUTION

(a) $(2a^3b^2)(3ab^4)^3 = (2a^3b^2)[3^3a^3(b^4)^3]$ Law 4: $(ab)^n = a^nb^n$

$= (2a^3b^2)(27a^3b^{12})$ Law 3: $(a^m)^n = a^{mn}$

$= (2)(27)a^3a^3b^2b^{12}$ Group factors with the same base

$= 54a^6b^{14}$ Law 1: $a^ma^n = a^{m+n}$

(b) $\left(\dfrac{x}{y}\right)^3\left(\dfrac{y^2x}{z}\right)^4 = \dfrac{x^3}{y^3}\dfrac{(y^2)^4x^4}{z^4}$ Laws 5 and 4

$= \dfrac{x^3}{y^3}\dfrac{y^8x^4}{z^4}$ Law 3

$= (x^3x^4)\left(\dfrac{y^8}{y^3}\right)\dfrac{1}{z^4}$ Group factors with the same base

$= \dfrac{x^7y^5}{z^4}$ Laws 1 and 2

NOW TRY EXERCISES 43 AND 47

When simplifying an expression, you will find that many different methods will lead to the same result; you should feel free to use any of the rules of exponents to arrive at your own method. We now give two additional laws that are useful in simplifying expressions with negative exponents.

LAWS OF EXPONENTS

Law	Example	Description
6. $\left(\dfrac{a}{b}\right)^{-n} = \left(\dfrac{b}{a}\right)^n$	$\left(\dfrac{3}{4}\right)^{-2} = \left(\dfrac{4}{3}\right)^2$	To raise a fraction to a negative power, invert the fraction and change the sign of the exponent.
7. $\dfrac{a^{-n}}{b^{-m}} = \dfrac{b^m}{a^n}$	$\dfrac{3^{-2}}{4^{-5}} = \dfrac{4^5}{3^2}$	To move a number raised to a power from numerator to denominator or from denominator to numerator, change the sign of the exponent.

PROOF OF LAW 7 Using the definition of negative exponents and then Property 2 of fractions (page 5), we have

$$\frac{a^{-n}}{b^{-m}} = \frac{1/a^n}{1/b^m} = \frac{1}{a^n}\cdot\frac{b^m}{1} = \frac{b^m}{a^n}$$

You are asked to prove Law 6 in Exercise 94.

EXAMPLE 5 | Simplifying Expressions with Negative Exponents

Eliminate negative exponents and simplify each expression.

(a) $\dfrac{6st^{-4}}{2s^{-2}t^2}$ (b) $\left(\dfrac{y}{3z^3}\right)^{-2}$

IN-CLASS MATERIALS

When George Everest measured the mountain that bears his name (he never actually climbed it), he used techniques that were state-of-the-art at the time. According to his measurements, Mount Everest was exactly 29,000 ft tall (to the nearest foot). He was afraid that people would think it was an estimate—that he was merely saying that the mountain was between 28,500 ft and 29,500 ft tall. He was proud of his work. Discuss how he could have reported his results in such a way that people would know he was not estimating the height of the mountain. (Historically, he lied and said it was 29,002 ft tall, so people would know there were five significant figures. Since the 1950s the height has been listed at 29,028 ft, although as of 1999 some scientists want to add 7 ft to that number.)

Answer

He could have said it was 2.9000×10^4 ft tall—the extra zeros imply that the zeros are significant.

SOLUTION

(a) We use Law 7, which allows us to move a number raised to a power from the numerator to the denominator (or vice versa) by changing the sign of the exponent.

t^{-4} moves to denominator and becomes t^4

s^{-2} moves to numerator and becomes s^2

$$\frac{6st^{-4}}{2s^{-2}t^2} = \frac{6ss^2}{2t^2t^4} \qquad \text{Law 7}$$

$$= \frac{3s^3}{t^6} \qquad \text{Law 1}$$

(b) We use Law 6, which allows us to change the sign of the exponent of a fraction by inverting the fraction.

$$\left(\frac{y}{3z^3}\right)^{-2} = \left(\frac{3z^3}{y}\right)^2 \qquad \text{Law 6}$$

$$= \frac{9z^6}{y^2} \qquad \text{Laws 5 and 4}$$

✎ NOW TRY EXERCISE **49** ∎

▼ Scientific Notation

Scientists use exponential notation as a compact way of writing very large numbers and very small numbers. For example, the nearest star beyond the sun, Proxima Centauri, is approximately 40,000,000,000,000 km away. The mass of a hydrogen atom is about 0.00000000000000000000000166 g. Such numbers are difficult to read and to write, so scientists usually express them in *scientific notation*.

SCIENTIFIC NOTATION

A positive number x is said to be written in **scientific notation** if it is expressed as follows:

$$x = a \times 10^n \qquad \text{where } 1 \le a < 10 \text{ and } n \text{ is an integer}$$

For instance, when we state that the distance to the star Proxima Centauri is 4×10^{13} km, the positive exponent 13 indicates that the decimal point should be moved 13 places to the *right*:

$$4 \times 10^{13} = 40,000,000,000,000$$

Move decimal point 13 places to the right

When we state that the mass of a hydrogen atom is 1.66×10^{-24} g, the exponent -24 indicates that the decimal point should be moved 24 places to the *left*:

$$1.66 \times 10^{-24} = 0.00000000000000000000000166$$

Move decimal point 24 places to the left

IN-CLASS MATERIALS

When people talk about groups of objects, they often use the word *dozen* for convenience. It is easier to think about 3 dozen eggs than it is to think about 36 eggs. Chemists use a similar word for atoms: a *mole*. There is a mole of atoms in 22.4 L of gas (bring an empty 1-liter bottle to help the class picture it) and a mole of atoms in 18 mL of water (bring in a graduated cylinder to demonstrate). A mole of atoms is 6.02×10^{23} atoms. Ask the students which is bigger:

1. A mole or the number of inches along the Mississippi River
2. A mole or a trillion
3. A mole or the number of stars visible from Earth
4. A mole or the number of grains of sand on Earth
5. A mole or the number of sunlike stars in the universe

The answer for all five is a mole.

EXAMPLE 6 | Changing from Decimal to Scientific Notation

Write each number in scientific notation.

(a) 56,920   **(b)** 0.000093

SOLUTION

(a) $56{,}920 = 5.692 \times 10^4$
      4 places

(b) $0.000093 = 9.3 \times 10^{-5}$
      5 places

✎. NOW TRY EXERCISES **77** AND **79** ∎

To use scientific notation on a calculator, press the key labeled $\boxed{\text{EE}}$ *or* $\boxed{\text{EXP}}$ *or* $\boxed{\text{EEX}}$ *to enter the exponent. For example, to enter the number* 3.629×10^{15} *on a TI-83 calculator, we enter*

3.629 $\boxed{\text{2ND}}$ $\boxed{\text{EE}}$ 15

and the display reads

$3.629\text{E}15$

Scientific notation is often used on a calculator to display a very large or very small number. For instance, if we use a calculator to square the number 1,111,111, the display panel may show (depending on the calculator model) the approximation

$$\boxed{\texttt{1.234568 12}} \quad \text{or} \quad \boxed{\texttt{1.23468 E12}}$$

Here the final digits indicate the power of 10, and we interpret the result as

$$1.234568 \times 10^{12}$$

EXAMPLE 7 | Calculating with Scientific Notation

If $a \approx 0.00046$, $b \approx 1.697 \times 10^{22}$, and $c \approx 2.91 \times 10^{-18}$, use a calculator to approximate the quotient ab/c.

SOLUTION We could enter the data using scientific notation, or we could use laws of exponents as follows:

$$\frac{ab}{c} \approx \frac{(4.6 \times 10^{-4})(1.697 \times 10^{22})}{2.91 \times 10^{-18}}$$

$$= \frac{(4.6)(1.697)}{2.91} \times 10^{-4+22+18}$$

$$\approx 2.7 \times 10^{36}$$

For guidelines on working with significant figures, see the Appendix, Calculations and Significant Figures.

We state the answer rounded to two significant figures because the least accurate of the given numbers is stated to two significant figures.

✎. NOW TRY EXERCISES **83** AND **85** ∎

▼ Radicals

We know what 2^n means whenever n is an integer. To give meaning to a power, such as $2^{4/5}$, whose exponent is a rational number, we need to discuss radicals.

The symbol $\sqrt{\ }$ means "the positive square root of." Thus

It is true that the number 9 has two square roots, 3 and −3, but the notation $\sqrt{9}$ *is reserved for the* positive *square root of 9 (sometimes called the* principal square root *of 9). If we want the negative root, we must write* $-\sqrt{9}$, *which is −3.*

$$\boxed{\sqrt{a} = b \quad \text{means} \quad b^2 = a \quad \text{and} \quad b \geq 0}$$

Since $a = b^2 \geq 0$, the symbol $\sqrt{a}$ makes sense only when $a \geq 0$. For instance,

$$\sqrt{9} = 3 \quad \text{because} \quad 3^2 = 9 \quad \text{and} \quad 3 \geq 0$$

ALTERNATE EXAMPLE 6
Write each number in scientific notation:
(a) 8625.126
(b) 0.000331

ANSWERS
(a) 8.625126×10^3
(b) 3.31×10^{-4}

ALTERNATE EXAMPLE 7
If $a \approx 0.00084$, $b \approx 2.195 \times 10^{21}$, and $c \approx 6.81 \times 10^{-19}$, use a calculator to approximate the quotient $\dfrac{ab}{c}$.

ANSWER
2.71×10^{36}

IN-CLASS MATERIALS
There is a cube-root magic trick that illustrates an interesting property of the cube function. A student takes a two-digit integer, cubes it, and gives you the answer (for example, 274,625). You knit your brow, think, and give the cube root (65) using the power of your mind. If the students are not impressed, stop there. If they are, do the trick a second time, getting the answer wrong by 1. Try it a third time, and again get the correct answer. Have them try to figure the trick out, and promise to reveal the secret if they do well on a future quiz or test.

The trick is as follows. Memorize the first 10 cubes:

x	0	1	2	3	4	5	6	7	8	9
x^3	0	1	8	27	64	125	216	343	512	729

Notice that the last digit of each cube is unique and that they aren't very well scrambled (2's cube ends in 8 and vice versa; 3's ends in 7 and vice versa). So the last digit of the cube root is easily obtained (274,625 ends in 5, so the number you were given is of the form ?5). Now the first digit can be obtained by looking at the first three digits of the cube and seeing in which range they are. (274 is between 6^3 and 7^3, so the number you were given is 65.) Make sure to tell the students that if they do this trick for other people, they should not get the answer too fast, and they should get the last digit wrong occasionally. This will make it seem like they really can do cube roots in their heads.

Square roots are special cases of nth roots. The nth root of x is the number that, when raised to the nth power, gives x.

DEFINITION OF nth ROOT

If n is any positive integer, then the **principal nth root** of a is defined as follows:

$$\sqrt[n]{a} = b \quad \text{means} \quad b^n = a$$

If n is even, we must have $a \geq 0$ and $b \geq 0$.

Thus

$$\sqrt[4]{81} = 3 \qquad \text{because} \qquad 3^4 = 81 \qquad \text{and} \qquad 3 \geq 0$$

$$\sqrt[3]{-8} = -2 \qquad \text{because} \qquad (-2)^3 = -8$$

But $\sqrt{-8}$, $\sqrt[4]{-8}$, and $\sqrt[6]{-8}$ are not defined. (For instance, $\sqrt{-8}$ is not defined because the square of every real number is nonnegative.)

Notice that

$$\sqrt{4^2} = \sqrt{16} = 4 \qquad \text{but} \qquad \sqrt{(-4)^2} = \sqrt{16} = 4 = |-4|$$

So the equation $\sqrt{a^2} = a$ is not always true; it is true only when $a \geq 0$. However, we can always write $\sqrt{a^2} = |a|$. This last equation is true not only for square roots, but for any even root. This and other rules used in working with nth roots are listed in the following box. In each property we assume that all the given roots exist.

PROPERTIES OF nth ROOTS

Property	Example
1. $\sqrt[n]{ab} = \sqrt[n]{a}\sqrt[n]{b}$	$\sqrt[3]{-8 \cdot 27} = \sqrt[3]{-8}\sqrt[3]{27} = (-2)(3) = -6$
2. $\sqrt[n]{\dfrac{a}{b}} = \dfrac{\sqrt[n]{a}}{\sqrt[n]{b}}$	$\sqrt[4]{\dfrac{16}{81}} = \dfrac{\sqrt[4]{16}}{\sqrt[4]{81}} = \dfrac{2}{3}$
3. $\sqrt[m]{\sqrt[n]{a}} = \sqrt[mn]{a}$	$\sqrt{\sqrt[3]{729}} = \sqrt[6]{729} = 3$
4. $\sqrt[n]{a^n} = a$ if n is odd	$\sqrt[3]{(-5)^3} = -5, \quad \sqrt[5]{2^5} = 2$
5. $\sqrt[n]{a^n} = \|a\|$ if n is even	$\sqrt[4]{(-3)^4} = |-3| = 3$

ALTERNATE EXAMPLE 8

Simplify the radical expression $\sqrt[4]{625p^8q^4}$.

ANSWER

$5p^2|q|$

EXAMPLE 8 | Simplifying Expressions Involving nth Roots

(a) $\sqrt[3]{x^4} = \sqrt[3]{x^3 x}$ Factor out the largest cube

$\qquad = \sqrt[3]{x^3}\sqrt[3]{x}$ Property 1: $\sqrt[3]{ab} = \sqrt[3]{a}\sqrt[3]{b}$

$\qquad = x\sqrt[3]{x}$ Property 4: $\sqrt[3]{a^3} = a$

(b) $\sqrt[4]{81x^8y^4} = \sqrt[4]{81}\sqrt[4]{x^8}\sqrt[4]{y^4}$ Property 1: $\sqrt[4]{abc} = \sqrt[4]{a}\sqrt[4]{b}\sqrt[4]{c}$

$\qquad = 3\sqrt[4]{(x^2)^4}|y|$ Property 5: $\sqrt[4]{a^4} = |a|$

$\qquad = 3x^2|y|$ Property 5: $\sqrt[4]{a^4} = |a|, |x^2| = x^2$

✎ NOW TRY EXERCISES **55** AND **57** ∎

EXAMPLES

1. A product whose answer will be given by a calculator in scientific notation:

$$(4{,}678{,}200{,}000)(6{,}006{,}200{,}000) = 28{,}098{,}204{,}840{,}000{,}000{,}000$$

2. A product whose answer contains too many significant figures for many calculators to compute accurately:

$$(415{,}210{,}709)(519{,}080{,}123) = 215{,}527{,}625{,}898{,}637{,}207$$

3. A fractional exponent simplification that works out nicely:

$$\frac{\sqrt[3]{8^5}}{\sqrt[3]{8^4}} = \sqrt[3]{\frac{8^5}{8^4}} = \sqrt[3]{8} = 2$$

It is frequently useful to combine like radicals in an expression such as $2\sqrt{3} + 5\sqrt{3}$. This can be done by using the Distributive Property. Thus

$$2\sqrt{3} + 5\sqrt{3} = (2 + 5)\sqrt{3} = 7\sqrt{3}$$

The next example further illustrates this process.

EXAMPLE 9 | Combining Radicals

(a) $\sqrt{32} + \sqrt{200} = \sqrt{16 \cdot 2} + \sqrt{100 \cdot 2}$ Factor out the largest squares

$= \sqrt{16}\sqrt{2} + \sqrt{100}\sqrt{2}$ Property 1: $\sqrt{ab} = \sqrt{a}\sqrt{b}$

$= 4\sqrt{2} + 10\sqrt{2} = 14\sqrt{2}$ Distributive Property

(b) If $b > 0$, then

$\sqrt{25b} - \sqrt{b^3} = \sqrt{25}\sqrt{b} - \sqrt{b^2}\sqrt{b}$ Property 1: $\sqrt{ab} = \sqrt{a}\sqrt{b}$

$= 5\sqrt{b} - b\sqrt{b}$ Property 5, $b > 0$

$= (5 - b)\sqrt{b}$ Distributive Property

NOW TRY EXERCISES **29** AND **33**

Avoid making the following error:
$\sqrt{a + b} \ne \sqrt{a} + \sqrt{b}$
For instance, if we let $a = 9$ and $b = 16$, then we see the error:
$\sqrt{9 + 16} \stackrel{?}{=} \sqrt{9} + \sqrt{16}$
$\sqrt{25} \stackrel{?}{=} 3 + 4$
$5 \stackrel{?}{=} 7$ Wrong!

ALTERNATE EXAMPLE 9
Simplify the radical expression $\sqrt{125} + \sqrt{245}$.

ANSWER
$12\sqrt{5}$

▼ Rational Exponents

To define what is meant by a *rational exponent* or, equivalently, a *fractional exponent* such as $a^{1/3}$, we need to use radicals. To give meaning to the symbol $a^{1/n}$ in a way that is consistent with the Laws of Exponents, we would have to have

$$(a^{1/n})^n = a^{(1/n)n} = a^1 = a$$

So by the definition of nth root,

$$a^{1/n} = \sqrt[n]{a}$$

In general, we define rational exponents as follows.

DEFINITION OF RATIONAL EXPONENTS

For any rational exponent m/n in lowest terms, where m and n are integers and $n > 0$, we define

$$a^{m/n} = (\sqrt[n]{a})^m \quad \text{or equivalently} \quad a^{m/n} = \sqrt[n]{a^m}$$

If n is even, then we require that $a \ge 0$.

With this definition it can be proved that *the Laws of Exponents also hold for rational exponents*.

EXAMPLE 10 | Using the Definition of Rational Exponents

(a) $4^{1/2} = \sqrt{4} = 2$

(b) $8^{2/3} = (\sqrt[3]{8})^2 = 2^2 = 4$ Alternative solution: $8^{2/3} = \sqrt[3]{8^2} = \sqrt[3]{64} = 4$

(c) $125^{-1/3} = \dfrac{1}{125^{1/3}} = \dfrac{1}{\sqrt[3]{125}} = \dfrac{1}{5}$ **(d)** $\dfrac{1}{\sqrt[3]{x^4}} = \dfrac{1}{x^{4/3}} = x^{-4/3}$

NOW TRY EXERCISES **21** AND **23**

ALTERNATE EXAMPLE 10
Simplify $8^{1/3}$.

ANSWER
2

ALTERNATE EXAMPLE 11

Simplify $\dfrac{a^{1/3}b}{b^{1/5}a^{-2/3}b^{4/5}}$.

ANSWER

a

ALTERNATE EXAMPLE 12

Simplify the expression
$(4\sqrt{x})(9\sqrt[3]{x})$.

ANSWER

$36x^{5/6}$

ALTERNATE EXAMPLE 13

Rationalize the denominator

$\dfrac{1}{\sqrt[8]{x^7}}$.

ANSWER

$\dfrac{\sqrt[8]{x}}{x}$

DIOPHANTUS lived in Alexandria about 250 A.D. His book *Arithmetica* is considered the first book on algebra. In it he gives methods for finding integer solutions of algebraic equations. *Arithmetica* was read and studied for more than a thousand years. Fermat (see page 99) made some of his most important discoveries while studying this book. Diophantus' major contribution is the use of symbols to stand for the unknowns in a problem. Although his symbolism is not as simple as what we use today, it was a major advance over writing everything in words. In Diophantus' notation the equation

$$x^5 - 7x^2 + 8x - 5 = 24$$

is written

$$\Delta K^\gamma \alpha \varsigma \eta \ \phi \ \Delta^\gamma \zeta \mathring{M} \varepsilon \iota^{\prime\prime} \kappa \delta$$

Our modern algebraic notation did not come into common use until the 17th century.

EXAMPLE 11 | Using the Laws of Exponents with Rational Exponents

(a) $a^{1/3}a^{7/3} = a^{8/3}$ Law 1: $a^m a^n = a^{m+n}$

(b) $\dfrac{a^{2/5}a^{7/5}}{a^{3/5}} = a^{2/5+7/5-3/5} = a^{6/5}$ Law 1, Law 2: $\dfrac{a^m}{a^n} = a^{m-n}$

(c) $(2a^3b^4)^{3/2} = 2^{3/2}(a^3)^{3/2}(b^4)^{3/2}$ Law 4: $(abc)^n = a^n b^n c^n$

      $= (\sqrt{2})^3 a^{3(3/2)} b^{4(3/2)}$ Law 3: $(a^m)^n = a^{mn}$

      $= 2\sqrt{2}a^{9/2}b^6$

(d) $\left(\dfrac{2x^{3/4}}{y^{1/3}}\right)^3 \left(\dfrac{y^4}{x^{-1/2}}\right) = \dfrac{2^3(x^{3/4})^3}{(y^{1/3})^3} \cdot (y^4 x^{1/2})$ Laws 5, 4, and 7

      $= \dfrac{8x^{9/4}}{y} \cdot y^4 x^{1/2}$ Law 3

      $= 8x^{11/4}y^3$ Laws 1 and 2

 NOW TRY EXERCISES **61**, **63**, **67**, AND **69**   ■

EXAMPLE 12 | Simplifying by Writing Radicals as Rational Exponents

(a) $(2\sqrt{x})(3\sqrt[3]{x}) = (2x^{1/2})(3x^{1/3})$ Definition of rational exponents

      $= 6x^{1/2+1/3} = 6x^{5/6}$ Law 1

(b) $\sqrt{x\sqrt{x}} = (xx^{1/2})^{1/2}$ Definition of rational exponents

      $= (x^{3/2})^{1/2}$ Law 1

      $= x^{3/4}$ Law 3

 NOW TRY EXERCISES **71** AND **75**   ■

▼ Rationalizing the Denominator

It is often useful to eliminate the radical in a denominator by multiplying both numerator and denominator by an appropriate expression. This procedure is called **rationalizing the denominator**. If the denominator is of the form $\sqrt{a}$, we multiply numerator and denominator by $\sqrt{a}$. In doing this we multiply the given quantity by 1, so we do not change its value. For instance,

$$\frac{1}{\sqrt{a}} = \frac{1}{\sqrt{a}} \cdot 1 = \frac{1}{\sqrt{a}} \cdot \frac{\sqrt{a}}{\sqrt{a}} = \frac{\sqrt{a}}{a}$$

Note that the denominator in the last fraction contains no radical. In general, if the denominator is of the form $\sqrt[n]{a^m}$ with $m < n$, then multiplying the numerator and denominator by $\sqrt[n]{a^{n-m}}$ will rationalize the denominator, because (for $a > 0$)

$$\sqrt[n]{a^m}\sqrt[n]{a^{n-m}} = \sqrt[n]{a^{m+n-m}} = \sqrt[n]{a^n} = a$$

EXAMPLE 13 | Rationalizing Denominators

This equals 1

(a) $\dfrac{2}{\sqrt{3}} = \dfrac{2}{\sqrt{3}} \cdot \dfrac{\sqrt{3}}{\sqrt{3}} = \dfrac{2\sqrt{3}}{3}$

(b) $\dfrac{1}{\sqrt[3]{x^2}} = \dfrac{1}{\sqrt[3]{x^2}}\dfrac{\sqrt[3]{x}}{\sqrt[3]{x}} = \dfrac{\sqrt[3]{x}}{\sqrt[3]{x^3}} = \dfrac{\sqrt[3]{x}}{x}$

(c) $\sqrt[7]{\dfrac{1}{a^2}} = \dfrac{1}{\sqrt[7]{a^2}} = \dfrac{1}{\sqrt[7]{a^2}}\dfrac{\sqrt[7]{a^5}}{\sqrt[7]{a^5}} = \dfrac{\sqrt[7]{a^5}}{\sqrt[7]{a^7}} = \dfrac{\sqrt[7]{a^5}}{a}$

✎ NOW TRY EXERCISES **89** AND **91**   ■

1.2 EXERCISES

CONCEPTS

1. (a) Using exponential notation, we can write the product $5 \cdot 5 \cdot 5 \cdot 5 \cdot 5 \cdot 5$ as _____.

   (b) In the expression 3^4, the number 3 is called the _____, and the number 4 is called the _____.

2. (a) When we multiply two powers with the same base, we _____ the exponents. So $3^4 \cdot 3^5 =$ _____.

   (b) When we divide two powers with the same base, we _____ the exponents. So $\dfrac{3^5}{3^2} =$ _____.

3. (a) Using exponential notation, we can write $\sqrt[3]{5}$ as _____.

   (b) Using radicals, we can write $5^{1/2}$ as _____.

   (c) Is there a difference between $\sqrt{5^2}$ and $(\sqrt{5})^2$? Explain.

4. Explain what $4^{3/2}$ means, then calculate $4^{3/2}$ in two different ways:
   $(4^{1/2})^{\square} =$ _____   or $(4^3)^{\square} =$ _____

5. Explain how we rationalize a denominator, then complete the following steps to rationalize $\dfrac{1}{\sqrt{3}}$:
   $\dfrac{1}{\sqrt{3}} = \dfrac{1}{\sqrt{3}} \cdot \dfrac{\square}{\square} = \square$

6. Find the missing power in the following calculation:
   $5^{1/3} \cdot 5^{\square} = 5$.

SKILLS

7–14 ■ Write each radical expression using exponents, and each exponential expression using radicals.

Radical expression	Exponential expression
7. $\dfrac{1}{\sqrt{5}}$	
8. $\sqrt[3]{7^2}$	
9.	$4^{2/3}$
10.	$11^{-3/2}$
11. $\sqrt[5]{5^3}$	
12.	$2^{-1.5}$

Radical expression	Exponential expression
13.	$a^{2/5}$
14. $\dfrac{1}{\sqrt{x^5}}$	

15–24 ■ Evaluate each expression.

15. (a) -3^2 (b) $(-3)^2$ (c) $\left(\tfrac{1}{3}\right)^4(-3)^2$

16. (a) $5^4 \cdot 5^{-2}$ (b) $\dfrac{10^7}{10^4}$ (c) $\dfrac{3}{3^{-2}}$

17. (a) $\left(\tfrac{5}{3}\right)^0 2^{-1}$ (b) $\dfrac{2^{-3}}{3^0}$ (c) $\left(\tfrac{1}{4}\right)^{-2}$

18. (a) $\left(-\tfrac{2}{3}\right)^{-3}$ (b) $\left(\tfrac{3}{2}\right)^{-2} \cdot \tfrac{9}{16}$ (c) $\left(\tfrac{1}{2}\right)^4 \cdot \left(\tfrac{5}{2}\right)^{-2}$

19. (a) $\sqrt{16}$ (b) $\sqrt[4]{16}$ (c) $\sqrt[4]{\tfrac{1}{16}}$

20. (a) $\sqrt{64}$ (b) $\sqrt[3]{-64}$ (c) $\sqrt[5]{-32}$

21. (a) $\sqrt{\tfrac{4}{9}}$ (b) $\sqrt[4]{256}$ (c) $\sqrt[6]{\tfrac{1}{64}}$

22. (a) $\sqrt{7}\sqrt{28}$ (b) $\dfrac{\sqrt{48}}{\sqrt{3}}$ (c) $\sqrt[3]{24}\sqrt[3]{54}$

23. (a) $\left(\tfrac{4}{9}\right)^{-1/2}$ (b) $(-32)^{2/5}$ (c) $-32^{2/5}$

24. (a) $1024^{-0.1}$ (b) $\left(-\tfrac{27}{8}\right)^{2/3}$ (c) $\left(\tfrac{25}{64}\right)^{-3/2}$

25–28 ■ Evaluate the expression using $x = 3$, $y = 4$, and $z = -1$.

25. $\sqrt{x^2 + y^2}$ 26. $\sqrt[4]{x^3 + 14y + 2z}$

27. $(9x)^{2/3} + (2y)^{2/3} + z^{2/3}$ 28. $(xy)^{2z}$

29–34 ■ Simplify the expression.

29. $\sqrt{32} + \sqrt{18}$ 30. $\sqrt{75} + \sqrt{48}$

31. $\sqrt[5]{96} + \sqrt[5]{3}$ 32. $\sqrt[4]{48} - \sqrt[4]{3}$

33. $\sqrt{16x} + \sqrt{x^5}$ 34. $\sqrt[3]{2y^4} - \sqrt[3]{y}$

35–40 ■ Simplify each expression.

35. (a) $x^8 x^2$ (b) $(3y^2)(4y^5)$ (c) $x^2 x^{-6}$

36. (a) $x^{-5}x^3$ (b) $w^{-2}w^{-4}w^6$ (c) $z^5 z^{-3} z^{-4}$

37. (a) $\dfrac{y^{10}y^0}{y^7}$ (b) $\dfrac{x^6}{x^{10}}$ (c) $\dfrac{a^9 a^{-2}}{a}$

38. (a) $\dfrac{z^2 z^4}{z^3 z^{-1}}$ (b) $(2y^2)^3$ (c) $(8x)^2$

39. (a) $(a^2a^4)^3$ **(b)** $\left(\dfrac{a^2}{4}\right)^3$ **(c)** $(3z)^2(6z^2)^{-3}$

40. (a) $(2z^2)^{-5}z^{10}$ **(b)** $(2a^3a^2)^4$ **(c)** $\left(\dfrac{3x^4}{4x^2}\right)^2$

41–52 ■ Simplify the expression and eliminate any negative exponents(s).

41. (a) $(4x^2y^4)(2x^5y)$ **(b)** $(8a^2z)(\tfrac{1}{2}a^3z^4)$

42. (a) $b^4(3ab^3)(2a^2b^{-5})$ **(b)** $(2s^3t^{-2})(\tfrac{1}{4}s^7t)(16t^4)$

43. (a) $(5x^2y^3)(3x^2y^5)^4$ **(b)** $(2a^3b^2)^2(5a^2b^5)^3$

44. (a) $(s^{-2}t^2)^2(s^2t)^3$ **(b)** $(2u^2v^3)^3(3u^{-3}v)^2$

45. (a) $\dfrac{6y^3z}{2yz^2}$ **(b)** $\dfrac{(xy^2z^3)^4}{(x^2y^2z)^3}$

46. (a) $\dfrac{2x^3y^4}{x^5y^3}$ **(b)** $\dfrac{(2v^3w)^2}{v^3w^2}$

47. (a) $\left(\dfrac{a^2}{b}\right)^5\left(\dfrac{a^3b^2}{c^3}\right)^3$ **(b)** $\dfrac{(u^{-1}v^2)^2}{(u^3v^{-2})^3}$

48. (a) $\left(\dfrac{x^4z}{4y^5}\right)\left(\dfrac{2x^3y^2}{z^3}\right)^2$ **(b)** $\dfrac{(rs^2)^3}{(r^{-3}s^2)^2}$

49. (a) $\dfrac{8a^3b^{-4}}{2a^{-5}b^5}$ **(b)** $\left(\dfrac{y}{5x^{-2}}\right)^{-3}$

50. (a) $\dfrac{5xy^{-2}}{x^{-1}y^{-3}}$ **(b)** $\left(\dfrac{2a^{-1}b}{a^2b^{-3}}\right)^{-3}$

51. (a) $\left(\dfrac{3a}{b^3}\right)^{-1}$ **(b)** $\left(\dfrac{q^{-1}r^{-1}s^{-2}}{r^{-5}sq^{-8}}\right)^{-1}$

52. (a) $\left(\dfrac{s^2t^{-4}}{5s^{-1}t}\right)^{-2}$ **(b)** $\left(\dfrac{xy^{-2}z^{-3}}{x^2y^3z^{-4}}\right)^{-3}$

53–60 ■ Simplify the expression. Assume that the letters denote any real numbers.

53. $\sqrt[4]{x^4}$ **54.** $\sqrt[5]{x^{10}}$

55. $\sqrt[4]{16x^8}$ **56.** $\sqrt[3]{x^3y^6}$

57. $\sqrt[6]{64a^6b^7}$ **58.** $\sqrt[3]{a^2b}\sqrt[3]{64a^4b}$

59. $\sqrt[3]{\sqrt{64x^6}}$ **60.** $\sqrt[4]{x^4y^2z^2}$

61–70 ■ Simplify the expression and eliminate any negative exponent(s). Assume that all letters denote positive numbers.

61. (a) $x^{3/4}x^{5/4}$ **(b)** $y^{2/3}y^{4/3}$

62. (a) $(4b)^{1/2}(8b^{1/4})$ **(b)** $(3a^{3/4})^2(5a^{1/2})$

63. (a) $\dfrac{w^{4/3}w^{2/3}}{w^{1/3}}$ **(b)** $\dfrac{s^{5/2}(2s^{5/4})^2}{s^{1/2}}$

64. (a) $(8y^3)^{-2/3}$ **(b)** $(u^4v^6)^{-1/3}$

65. (a) $(8a^6b^{3/2})^{2/3}$ **(b)** $(4a^6b^8)^{3/2}$

66. (a) $(x^{-5}y^{1/3})^{-3/5}$ **(b)** $(2x^3y^{-1/4})^2(8y^{-3/2})^{-1/3}$

67. (a) $\dfrac{(8s^3t^3)^{2/3}}{(s^4t^{-8})^{1/4}}$ **(b)** $\dfrac{(32y^{-5}z^{10})^{1/5}}{(64y^6z^{-12})^{-1/6}}$

68. (a) $\left(\dfrac{x^8y^{-4}}{16y^{4/3}}\right)^{-1/4}$ **(b)** $\left(\dfrac{-8y^{3/4}}{y^3z^6}\right)^{-1/3}$

69. (a) $\left(\dfrac{x^{-2/3}}{y^{1/2}}\right)\left(\dfrac{x^{-2}}{y^{-3}}\right)^{1/6}$ **(b)** $\left(\dfrac{4y^3z^{2/3}}{x^{1/2}}\right)^2\left(\dfrac{x^{-3}y^6}{8z^4}\right)^{1/3}$

70. (a) $\left(\dfrac{a^{1/6}b^{-3}}{x^{-1}y}\right)^3\left(\dfrac{x^{-2}b^{-1}}{a^{3/2}y^{1/3}}\right)$ **(b)** $\dfrac{(9st)^{3/2}}{(27s^3t^{-4})^{2/3}}\left(\dfrac{3s^{-2}}{4t^{1/3}}\right)^{-1}$

71–76 ■ Simplify the expression and eliminate any negative exponents(s). Assume that all letters denote positive numbers.

71. (a) $\sqrt[6]{y^5}\sqrt[3]{y^2}$ **(b)** $(5\sqrt[3]{x})(2\sqrt[4]{x})$

72. (a) $\sqrt[4]{b^3}\sqrt{b}$ **(b)** $(2\sqrt{a})(\sqrt[3]{a^2})$

73. (a) $\sqrt{4st^3}\sqrt[6]{s^3t^2}$ **(b)** $\dfrac{\sqrt[4]{x^7}}{\sqrt[3]{x^3}}$

74. (a) $\sqrt[5]{x^3y^2}\sqrt[10]{x^4y^{16}}$ **(b)** $\dfrac{\sqrt[3]{8x^2}}{\sqrt{x}}$

75. (a) $\sqrt[3]{y\sqrt{y}}$ **(b)** $\sqrt{\dfrac{16u^3v}{uv^5}}$

76. (a) $\sqrt{s\sqrt{s^3}}$ **(b)** $\sqrt[3]{\dfrac{54x^2y^4}{2x^5y}}$

77–78 ■ Write each number in scientific notation.

77. (a) 69,300,000 **(b)** 7,200,000,000,000
  (c) 0.000028536 **(d)** 0.0001213

78. (a) 129,540,000 **(b)** 7,259,000,000
  (c) 0.0000000014 **(d)** 0.0007029

79–80 ■ Write each number in decimal notation.

79. (a) 3.19×10^5 **(b)** 2.721×10^8
  (c) 2.670×10^{-8} **(d)** 9.999×10^{-9}

80. (a) 7.1×10^{14} **(b)** 6×10^{12}
  (c) 8.55×10^{-3} **(d)** 6.257×10^{-10}

81–82 ■ Write the number indicated in each statement in scientific notation.

81. (a) A light-year, the distance that light travels in one year, is about 5,900,000,000,000 mi.
  (b) The diameter of an electron is about 0.0000000000004 cm.
  (c) A drop of water contains more than 33 billion billion molecules.

82. (a) The distance from the earth to the sun is about 93 million miles.
  (b) The mass of an oxygen molecule is about 0.000000000000000000000053 g.
  (c) The mass of the earth is about 5,970,000,000,000,000,000,000,000 kg.

83–88 ■ Use scientific notation, the Laws of Exponents, and a calculator to perform the indicated operations. State your answer rounded to the number of significant digits indicated by the given data.

83. $(7.2 \times 10^{-9})(1.806 \times 10^{-12})$

84. $(1.062 \times 10^{24})(8.61 \times 10^{19})$

85. $\dfrac{1.295643 \times 10^9}{(3.610 \times 10^{-17})(2.511 \times 10^6)}$

86. $\dfrac{(73.1)(1.6341 \times 10^{28})}{0.0000000019}$

87. $\dfrac{(0.0000162)(0.01582)}{(594,621,000)(0.0058)}$

88. $\dfrac{(3.542 \times 10^{-6})^9}{(5.05 \times 10^4)^{12}}$

89–92 ■ Rationalize the denominator.

89. (a) $\dfrac{1}{\sqrt{10}}$ (b) $\sqrt{\dfrac{2}{x}}$ (c) $\sqrt{\dfrac{x}{3}}$

90. (a) $\sqrt{\dfrac{5}{12}}$ (b) $\sqrt{\dfrac{x}{6}}$ (c) $\sqrt{\dfrac{y}{2z}}$

91. (a) $\dfrac{2}{\sqrt[3]{x}}$ (b) $\dfrac{1}{\sqrt[4]{y^3}}$ (c) $\dfrac{x}{y^{2/5}}$

92. (a) $\dfrac{1}{\sqrt[4]{a}}$ (b) $\dfrac{a}{\sqrt[3]{b^2}}$ (c) $\dfrac{1}{c^{3/7}}$

93. Let a, b, and c be real numbers with $a > 0$, $b < 0$, and $c < 0$. Determine the sign of each expression.

(a) b^5 (b) b^{10} (c) ab^2c^3

(d) $(b - a)^3$ (e) $(b - a)^4$ (f) $\dfrac{a^3c^3}{b^6c^6}$

94. Prove the given Laws of Exponents for the case in which m and n are positive integers and $m > n$.

(a) Law 2   (b) Law 5   (c) Law 6

APPLICATIONS

95. Distance to the Nearest Star   Proxima Centauri, the star nearest to our solar system, is 4.3 light-years away. Use the information in Exercise 81(a) to express this distance in miles.

96. Speed of Light   The speed of light is about 186,000 mi/s. Use the information in Exercise 82(a) to find how long it takes for a light ray from the sun to reach the earth.

97. Volume of the Oceans   The average ocean depth is 3.7×10^3 m, and the area of the oceans is 3.6×10^{14} m². What is the total volume of the ocean in liters? (One cubic meter contains 1000 liters.)

98. National Debt   As of July 2010, the population of the United States was 3.070×10^8, and the national debt was 1.320×10^{13} dollars. How much was each person's share of the debt?

99. Number of Molecules   A sealed room in a hospital, measuring 5 m wide, 10 m long, and 3 m high, is filled with pure oxygen. One cubic meter contains 1000 L, and 22.4 L of any gas contains 6.02×10^{23} molecules (Avogadro's number). How many molecules of oxygen are there in the room?

100. How Far Can You See?   Because of the curvature of the earth, the maximum distance D that you can see from the top of a tall building of height h is estimated by the formula

$$D = \sqrt{2rh + h^2}$$

where $r = 3960$ mi is the radius of the earth and D and h are also measured in miles. How far can you see from the observation deck of the Toronto CN Tower, 1135 ft above the ground?

CN Tower

101. Speed of a Skidding Car   Police use the formula $s = \sqrt{30fd}$ to estimate the speed s (in mi/h) at which a car is traveling if it skids d feet after the brakes are applied suddenly. The number f is the coefficient of friction of the road, which is a measure of the "slipperiness" of the road. The table gives some typical estimates for f.

	Tar	Concrete	Gravel
Dry	1.0	0.8	0.2
Wet	0.5	0.4	0.1

(a) If a car skids 65 ft on wet concrete, how fast was it moving when the brakes were applied?

(b) If a car is traveling at 50 mi/h, how far will it skid on wet tar?

102. Distance from the Earth to the Sun   It follows from **Kepler's Third Law** of planetary motion that the average distance from a planet to the sun (in meters) is

$$d = \left(\frac{GM}{4\pi^2}\right)^{1/3} T^{2/3}$$

where $M = 1.99 \times 10^{30}$ kg is the mass of the sun, $G = 6.67 \times 10^{-11}$ N·m²/kg² is the gravitational constant, and T is the period of the planet's orbit (in seconds). Use the fact that the period of the earth's orbit is about 365.25 days to find the distance from the earth to the sun.

DISCOVERY ▪ DISCUSSION ▪ WRITING

103. How Big Is a Billion?   If you had a million (10^6) dollars in a suitcase, and you spent a thousand (10^3) dollars each day, how many years would it take you to use all the money? Spending at the same rate, how many years would it take you to empty a suitcase filled with a *billion* (10^9) dollars?

104. Easy Powers That Look Hard   Calculate these expressions in your head. Use the Laws of Exponents to help you.

(a) $\dfrac{18^5}{9^5}$　　　　(b) $20^6 \cdot (0.5)^6$

105. Limiting Behavior of Powers   Complete the following tables. What happens to the nth root of 2 as n gets large? What about the nth root of $\frac{1}{2}$?

n	$2^{1/n}$
1	
2	
5	
10	
100	

n	$\left(\frac{1}{2}\right)^{1/n}$
1	
2	
5	
10	
100	

Construct a similar table for $n^{1/n}$. What happens to the nth root of n as n gets large?

106. Comparing Roots   Without using a calculator, determine which number is larger in each pair.

(a) $2^{1/2}$ or $2^{1/3}$　　(b) $\left(\frac{1}{2}\right)^{1/2}$ or $\left(\frac{1}{2}\right)^{1/3}$
(c) $7^{1/4}$ or $4^{1/3}$　　(d) $\sqrt[3]{5}$ or $\sqrt{3}$

SUGGESTED TIME AND EMPHASIS
1–2 classes, essential material

1.3 ALGEBRAIC EXPRESSIONS

Adding and Subtracting Polynomials ▶ Multiplying Algebraic Expressions ▶ Special Product Formulas ▶ Factoring Common Factors ▶ Factoring Trinomials ▶ Special Factoring Formulas ▶ Factoring by Grouping Terms

A **variable** is a letter that can represent any number from a given set of numbers. If we start with variables, such as x, y, and z and some real numbers, and combine them using addition, subtraction, multiplication, division, powers, and roots, we obtain an **algebraic expression**. Here are some examples:

$$2x^2 - 3x + 4 \qquad \sqrt{x} + 10 \qquad \frac{y - 2z}{y^2 + 4}$$

A **monomial** is an expression of the form ax^k, where a is a real number and k is a nonnegative integer. A **binomial** is a sum of two monomials and a **trinomial** is a sum of three monomials. In general, a sum of monomials is called a *polynomial*. For example, the first expression listed above is a polynomial, but the other two are not.

POLYNOMIALS

A **polynomial** in the variable x is an expression of the form

$$a_n x^n + a_{n-1}x^{n-1} + \cdots + a_1 x + a_0$$

where $a_0, a_1, \ldots, a_n$ are real numbers, and n is a nonnegative integer. If $a_n \neq 0$, then the polynomial has **degree n**. The monomials $a_k x^k$ that make up the polynomial are called the **terms** of the polynomial.

Note that the degree of a polynomial is the highest power of the variable that appears in the polynomial.

TEXT QUESTIONS
(a) Give an example of an expression that is a polynomial.
(b) Give an example of an expression that is not a polynomial.

Polynomial	Type	Terms	Degree
$2x^2 - 3x + 4$	trinomial	$2x^2, -3x, 4$	2
$x^8 + 5x$	binomial	$x^8, 5x$	8
$3 - x + x^2 - \frac{1}{2}x^3$	four terms	$-\frac{1}{2}x^3, x^2, -x, 3$	3
$5x + 1$	binomial	$5x, 1$	1
$9x^5$	monomial	$9x^5$	5
6	monomial	6	0

▼ Adding and Subtracting Polynomials

Distributive Property

$ac + bc = (a + b)c$

We **add** and **subtract** polynomials using the properties of real numbers that were discussed in Section 1.1. The idea is to combine **like terms** (that is, terms with the same variables raised to the same powers) using the Distributive Property. For instance,

$$5x^7 + 3x^7 = (5 + 3)x^7 = 8x^7$$

 In subtracting polynomials, we have to remember that if a minus sign precedes an expression in parentheses, then the sign of every term within the parentheses is changed when we remove the parentheses:

$$-(b + c) = -b - c$$

[This is simply a case of the Distributive Property, $a(b + c) = ab + ac$, with $a = -1$.]

EXAMPLE 1 | Adding and Subtracting Polynomials

(a) Find the sum $(x^3 - 6x^2 + 2x + 4) + (x^3 + 5x^2 - 7x)$.
(b) Find the difference $(x^3 - 6x^2 + 2x + 4) - (x^3 + 5x^2 - 7x)$.

SOLUTION

(a) $(x^3 - 6x^2 + 2x + 4) + (x^3 + 5x^2 - 7x)$

$= (x^3 + x^3) + (-6x^2 + 5x^2) + (2x - 7x) + 4$ Group like terms

$= 2x^3 - x^2 - 5x + 4$ Combine like terms

(b) $(x^3 - 6x^2 + 2x + 4) - (x^3 + 5x^2 - 7x)$

$= x^3 - 6x^2 + 2x + 4 - x^3 - 5x^2 + 7x$ Distributive Property

$= (x^3 - x^3) + (-6x^2 - 5x^2) + (2x + 7x) + 4$ Group like terms

$= -11x^2 + 9x + 4$ Combine like terms

✎. NOW TRY EXERCISES **15** AND **17**   ■

▼ Multiplying Algebraic Expressions

To find the **product** of polynomials or other algebraic expressions, we need to use the Distributive Property repeatedly. In particular, using it three times on the product of two binomials, we get

$$(a + b)(c + d) = a(c + d) + b(c + d) = ac + ad + bc + bd$$

This says that we multiply the two factors by multiplying each term in one factor by each term in the other factor and adding these products. Schematically, we have

The acronym **FOIL** helps us remember that the product of two binomials is the sum of the products of the First terms, the Outer terms, the Inner terms, and the Last terms.

$$(a + b)(c + d) = ac + ad + bc + bd$$
$$\qquad\quad \uparrow \quad \uparrow \quad \uparrow \quad \uparrow$$
$$\qquad\quad F \quad O \quad I \quad L$$

IN-CLASS MATERIALS

Remind students of the standard multiplication algorithm (some people don't learn it) by multiplying 352 by 65. Then multiply $3x^2 + 5x + 2$ by $6x + 5$ using the algorithm in the text. If your students are used to "lattice multiplication," this can also be done. One doesn't really need the lattice, but the process can be put into the same form they are used to.

$$3x^2 + 5x + 2$$
$$\underline{\times \qquad\qquad 6x + 5}$$
$$15x^2 + 25x + 10$$
$$\underline{18x^3 + 30x^2 + 12x}$$
$$18x^3 + 45x^2 + 37x + 10$$

$18x^3$

$45x^2$

ALTERNATE EXAMPLE 2
Find the product:
$(4x + 1)(5x - 4)$

ANSWER
$20x^2 - 11x - 4$

ALTERNATE EXAMPLE 3
Find the product:
$(5x - 3)(x^2 + 2x - 2)$

ANSWER
$5x^3 + 7x^2 - 16x + 6$

In general, we can multiply two algebraic expressions by using the Distributive Property and the Laws of Exponents.

EXAMPLE 2 | Multiplying Binomials Using FOIL

$$(2x + 1)(3x - 5) = 6x^2 - 10x + 3x - 5 \qquad \text{Distributive Property}$$
$$\qquad\qquad\qquad\quad\;\; \text{F} \quad \text{O} \quad \text{I} \quad \text{L}$$
$$\qquad\qquad\qquad = 6x^2 - 7x - 5 \qquad\qquad \text{Combine like terms}$$

✎ **NOW TRY EXERCISE 23**

When we multiply trinomials or other polynomials with more terms, we use the Distributive Property. It is also helpful to arrange our work in table form. The next example illustrates both methods.

EXAMPLE 3 | Multiplying Polynomials

Find the product: $(2x + 3)(x^2 - 5x + 4)$

SOLUTION 1: Using the Distributive Property

$$(2x + 3)(x^2 - 5x + 4) = 2x(x^2 - 5x + 4) + 3(x^2 - 5x + 4) \qquad \text{Distributive Property}$$
$$= (2x \cdot x^2 - 2x \cdot 5x + 2x \cdot 4) + (3 \cdot x^2 - 3 \cdot 5x + 3 \cdot 4) \qquad \text{Distributive Property}$$
$$= (2x^3 - 10x^2 + 8x) + (3x^2 - 15x + 12) \qquad \text{Laws of Exponents}$$
$$= 2x^3 - 7x^2 - 7x + 12 \qquad \text{Combine like terms}$$

SOLUTION 2: Using Table Form

$$
\begin{array}{r}
x^2 - 5x + 4 \\
2x + 3 \\
\hline
3x^2 - 15x + 12 \\
2x^3 - 10x^2 + 8x \\
\hline
2x^3 - 7x^2 - 7x + 12
\end{array}
$$

Multiply $x^2 - 5x + 4$ by 3
Multiply $x^2 - 5x + 4$ by $2x$
Add like terms

✎ **NOW TRY EXERCISE 45**

▼ **Special Product Formulas**

Certain types of products occur so frequently that you should memorize them. You can verify the following formulas by performing the multiplications.

See the *Discovery Project* referenced on page 34 for a geometric interpretation of some of these formulas.

SPECIAL PRODUCT FORMULAS

If A and B are any real numbers or algebraic expressions, then

1. $(A + B)(A - B) = A^2 - B^2$ — Sum and product of same terms

2. $(A + B)^2 = A^2 + 2AB + B^2$ — Square of a sum

3. $(A - B)^2 = A^2 - 2AB + B^2$ — Square of a difference

4. $(A + B)^3 = A^3 + 3A^2B + 3AB^2 + B^3$ — Cube of a sum

5. $(A - B)^3 = A^3 - 3A^2B + 3AB^2 - B^3$ — Cube of a difference

---

IN-CLASS MATERIALS

This is an interesting product to look at with students:

$$(x - 1)(1 + x + x^2 + x^3 + x^4 + \cdots + x^n) = x^{n+1} - 1$$

Have them work it out for $n = 2, 3, 4$ and see the pattern. Once they see how it goes, you can derive

$$(1 + x + x^2 + x^3 + x^4 + \cdots + x^n) = \frac{x^{n+1} - 1}{x - 1}$$

and use it to estimate such things as $1 + \dfrac{1}{2} + \dfrac{1}{4} + \dfrac{1}{8} + \cdots$ or the sum of any geometric series.

The key idea in using these formulas (or any other formula in algebra) is the **Principle of Substitution**: We may substitute any algebraic expression for any letter in a formula. For example, to find $(x^2 + y^3)^2$ we use Product Formula 2, substituting x^2 for A and y^3 for B, to get

$$(x^2 + y^3)^2 = (x^2)^2 + 2(x^2)(y^3) + (y^3)^2$$

$$(A + B)^2 \quad = \quad A^2 \quad + \quad 2AB \quad + \quad B^2$$

EXAMPLE 4 | Using the Special Product Formulas

Use the Special Product Formulas to find each product.

(a) $(3x + 5)^2$ **(b)** $(x^2 - 2)^3$

SOLUTION

(a) Substituting $A = 3x$ and $B = 5$ in Product Formula 2, we get

$$(3x + 5)^2 = (3x)^2 + 2(3x)(5) + 5^2 = 9x^2 + 30x + 25$$

(b) Substituting $A = x^2$ and $B = 2$ in Product Formula 5, we get

$$(x^2 - 2)^3 = (x^2)^3 - 3(x^2)^2(2) + 3(x^2)(2)^2 - 2^3$$
$$= x^6 - 6x^4 + 12x^2 - 8$$

✎ NOW TRY EXERCISES **29** AND **41**   ■

EXAMPLE 5 | Using the Special Product Formulas

Find each product.

(a) $(2x - \sqrt{y})(2x + \sqrt{y})$ **(b)** $(x + y - 1)(x + y + 1)$

SOLUTION

(a) Substituting $A = 2x$ and $B = \sqrt{y}$ in Product Formula 1, we get

$$(2x - \sqrt{y})(2x + \sqrt{y}) = (2x)^2 - (\sqrt{y})^2 = 4x^2 - y$$

(b) If we group $x + y$ together and think of this as one algebraic expression, we can use Product Formula 1 with $A = x + y$ and $B = 1$.

$$(x + y - 1)(x + y + 1) = [(x + y) - 1][(x + y) + 1]$$
$$= (x + y)^2 - 1^2 \qquad \text{Product Formula 1}$$
$$= x^2 + 2xy + y^2 - 1 \qquad \text{Product Formula 2}$$

✎ NOW TRY EXERCISES **55** AND **59**   ■

▼ Factoring Common Factors

We use the Distributive Property to expand algebraic expressions. We sometimes need to reverse this process (again using the Distributive Property) by **factoring** an expression as a product of simpler ones. For example, we can write

◼◼◼◼ FACTORING ➡

$$x^2 - 4 = (x - 2)(x + 2)$$

⬅ EXPANDING ◼◼◼◼

We say that $x - 2$ and $x + 2$ are **factors** of $x^2 - 4$.

IN-CLASS MATERIALS

After doing some routine examples, show your students that grouping is not always obvious, as in examples like

$$2xa + 4y + ay + 8x = (2xa + ay) + (4y + 8x) = a(2x + y) + 4(y + 2x) = (2x + y)(a + 4)$$

Some of the standard formulas can also be awkward. For example, $x^2 - 2$ can be factored, even though we don't often refer to the number 2 as a "square."

The easiest type of factoring occurs when the terms have a common factor.

ALTERNATE EXAMPLE 6

Factor the expression
$3x^2 - 21x$.

ANSWER

$3x(x - 7)$

EXAMPLE 6 | Factoring Out Common Factors

Factor each expression.

(a) $3x^2 - 6x$ (b) $8x^4y^2 + 6x^3y^3 - 2xy^4$
(c) $(2x + 4)(x - 3) - 5(x - 3)$

SOLUTION

(a) The greatest common factor of the terms $3x^2$ and $-6x$ is $3x$, so we have

$$3x^2 - 6x = 3x(x - 2)$$

(b) We note that

8, 6, and -2 have the greatest common factor 2

x^4, x^3, and x have the greatest common factor x

y^2, y^3, and y^4 have the greatest common factor y^2

So the greatest common factor of the three terms in the polynomial is $2xy^2$, and we have

$$8x^4y^2 + 6x^3y^3 - 2xy^4 = (2xy^2)(4x^3) + (2xy^2)(3x^2y) + (2xy^2)(-y^2)$$
$$= 2xy^2(4x^3 + 3x^2y - y^2)$$

(c) The two terms have the common factor $x - 3$.

$$(2x + 4)(x - 3) - 5(x - 3) = [(2x + 4) - 5](x - 3) \quad \text{Distributive Property}$$
$$= (2x - 1)(x - 3) \quad \text{Simplify}$$

✎. NOW TRY EXERCISES **61, 63,** AND **65** ◼

CHECK YOUR ANSWER

Multiplying gives

$$3x(x - 2) = 3x^2 - 6x \quad ✔$$

CHECK YOUR ANSWER

Multiplying gives

$$2xy^2(4x^3 + 3x^2y - y^2)$$
$$= 8x^4y^2 + 6x^3y^3 - 2xy^4 \quad ✔$$

▼ **Factoring Trinomials**

To factor a trinomial of the form $x^2 + bx + c$, we note that

$$(x + r)(x + s) = x^2 + (r + s)x + rs$$

so we need to choose numbers r and s so that $r + s = b$ and $rs = c$.

ALTERNATE EXAMPLE 7

Factor:
$x^2 + x - 6$

ANSWER

$(x - 2)(x + 3)$

EXAMPLE 7 | Factoring $x^2 + bx + c$ by Trial and Error

Factor: $x^2 + 7x + 12$

SOLUTION We need to find two integers whose product is 12 and whose sum is 7. By trial and error we find that the two integers are 3 and 4. Thus, the factorization is

$$x^2 + 7x + 12 = (x + 3)(x + 4)$$
$$\underset{\text{factors of 12}}{\underbrace{\qquad\qquad}}$$

✎. NOW TRY EXERCISE **67** ◼

CHECK YOUR ANSWER

Multiplying gives

$$(x + 3)(x + 4) = x^2 + 7x + 12 \quad ✔$$

To factor a trinomial of the form $ax^2 + bx + c$ with $a \neq 1$, we look for factors of the form $px + r$ and $qx + s$:

$$\overset{\text{factors of } a}{ax^2 + bx + c = (px + r)(qx + s)} = pqx^2 + (ps + qr)x + rs$$
$$\underset{\text{factors of } c}{\qquad\qquad}$$

Therefore, we try to find numbers p, q, r, and s such that $pq = a$, $rs = c$, $ps + qr = b$. If these numbers are all integers, then we will have a limited number of possibilities to try for p, q, r, and s.

IN-CLASS MATERIALS

Most people would look at $x^4 + 324$ and think it cannot be factored. (Point out that we could use the difference of two squares formula if it were $x^4 - 324$.) It can be factored, although the factorization is not obvious:

$$x^4 + 324 = x^4 + 36x^2 - 36x^2 + 324$$
$$= (x^2 + 18)^2 - 36x^2$$
$$= (x^2 + 18)^2 - (6x)^2$$
$$= (x^2 + 6x + 18)(x^2 - 6x + 18)$$

EXAMPLE 8 | Factoring $ax^2 + bx + c$ by Trial and Error

Factor: $6x^2 + 7x - 5$

SOLUTION   We can factor 6 as $6 \cdot 1$ or $3 \cdot 2$, and -5 as $-5 \cdot 1$ or $5 \cdot (-1)$. By trying these possibilities, we arrive at the factorization

factors of 6

$$6x^2 + 7x - 5 = (3x + 5)(2x - 1)$$

factors of -5

CHECK YOUR ANSWER

Multiplying gives

$(3x + 5)(2x - 1) = 6x^2 + 7x - 5$ ✔

✎. NOW TRY EXERCISE **69**

EXAMPLE 9 | Recognizing the Form of an Expression

Factor each expression.

(a) $x^2 - 2x - 3$ **(b)** $(5a + 1)^2 - 2(5a + 1) - 3$

SOLUTION

(a) $x^2 - 2x - 3 = (x - 3)(x + 1)$ Trial and error

(b) This expression is of the form

$$\blacksquare^2 - 2\,\blacksquare - 3$$

where $\blacksquare$ represents $5a + 1$. This is the same form as the expression in part (a), so it will factor as $(\blacksquare - 3)(\blacksquare + 1)$.

$$(\boxed{5a + 1})^2 - 2(\boxed{5a + 1}) - 3 = [(\boxed{5a + 1}) - 3][(\boxed{5a + 1}) + 1]$$

$$= (5a - 2)(5a + 2)$$

✎. NOW TRY EXERCISE **71**

▼ Special Factoring Formulas

Some special algebraic expressions can be factored using the following formulas. The first three are simply Special Product Formulas written backward.

SPECIAL FACTORING FORMULAS	
Formula	**Name**
1. $A^2 - B^2 = (A - B)(A + B)$	Difference of squares
2. $A^2 + 2AB + B^2 = (A + B)^2$	Perfect square
3. $A^2 - 2AB + B^2 = (A - B)^2$	Perfect square
4. $A^3 - B^3 = (A - B)(A^2 + AB + B^2)$	Difference of cubes
5. $A^3 + B^3 = (A + B)(A^2 - AB + B^2)$	Sum of cubes

EXAMPLE 10 | Factoring Differences of Squares

Factor each expression.

(a) $4x^2 - 25$ **(b)** $(x + y)^2 - z^2$

ALTERNATE EXAMPLE 8

Factor:

$6x^2 - x - 2$

ANSWER

$(2x + 1)(3x - 2)$

ALTERNATE EXAMPLE 9

Factor each expression:

(a) $x^2 + 5x + 6$

(b) $(2a - 1)^2 + 5(2a - 1) + 6$

ANSWERS

(a) $(x + 2)(x + 3)$

(b) $(2a + 1)(2a + 2)$

ALTERNATE EXAMPLE 10

(a) Factor the polynomial $4x^2 - 49$.

(b) Factor the polynomial $x^6 + 125$.

ANSWERS

(a) $(2x - 7)(2x + 7)$

(b) $(x^2 + 5)(x^4 - 5x^2 + 25)$

SOLUTION

(a) Using the Difference of Squares Formula with $A = 2x$ and $B = 5$, we have
$$4x^2 - 25 = (2x)^2 - 5^2 = (2x - 5)(2x + 5)$$
$$A^2 - B^2 = (A - B)(A + B)$$

(b) We use the Difference of Squares Formula with $A = x + y$ and $B = z$.
$$(x + y)^2 - z^2 = (x + y - z)(x + y + z)$$

✎. NOW TRY EXERCISES **75** AND **109** ∎

EXAMPLE 11 | Factoring Differences and Sums of Cubes

Factor each polynomial.
(a) $27x^3 - 1$ (b) $x^6 + 8$

SOLUTION

(a) Using the Difference of Cubes Formula with $A = 3x$ and $B = 1$, we get
$$27x^3 - 1 = (3x)^3 - 1^3 = (3x - 1)[(3x)^2 + (3x)(1) + 1^2]$$
$$= (3x - 1)(9x^2 + 3x + 1)$$

(b) Using the Sum of Cubes Formula with $A = x^2$ and $B = 2$, we have
$$x^6 + 8 = (x^2)^3 + 2^3 = (x^2 + 2)(x^4 - 2x^2 + 4)$$

✎. NOW TRY EXERCISES **77** AND **79** ∎

A trinomial is a perfect square if it is of the form
$$A^2 + 2AB + B^2 \quad \text{or} \quad A^2 - 2AB + B^2$$
So we **recognize a perfect square** if the middle term ($2AB$ or $-2AB$) is plus or minus twice the product of the square roots of the outer two terms.

EXAMPLE 12 | Recognizing Perfect Squares

Factor each trinomial.
(a) $x^2 + 6x + 9$ (b) $4x^2 - 4xy + y^2$

SOLUTION

(a) Here $A = x$ and $B = 3$, so $2AB = 2 \cdot x \cdot 3 = 6x$. Since the middle term is $6x$, the trinomial is a perfect square. By the Perfect Square Formula we have
$$x^2 + 6x + 9 = (x + 3)^2$$

(b) Here $A = 2x$ and $B = y$, so $2AB = 2 \cdot 2x \cdot y = 4xy$. Since the middle term is $-4xy$, the trinomial is a perfect square. By the Perfect Square Formula we have
$$4x^2 - 4xy + y^2 = (2x - y)^2$$

✎. NOW TRY EXERCISES **105** AND **107** ∎

When we factor an expression, the result can sometimes be factored further. In general, *we first factor out common factors*, then inspect the result to see whether it can be factored by any of the other methods of this section. We repeat this process until we have factored the expression completely.

ALTERNATE EXAMPLE 11
Factor the expression completely:
$2x^4 - 8x^2$

ANSWER
$2x^2(x - 2)(x + 2)$

ALTERNATE EXAMPLE 12
Factor the trinomial
$25x^2 - 10xy + y^2$.

ANSWER
$(5x - y)^2$

IN-CLASS MATERIALS
This is a good opportunity to foreshadow polynomial division, which is covered in Section 3.2. Have students try to factor an expression such as $x^3 + 2x^2 - 21x + 18$. Now assume you have the hint that $x - 1$ is a factor. Show them how you can use the hint by dividing the polynomial by $x - 1$ to get a remaining quadratic, which is easy to break down.

Answer
$(x - 3)(x + 6)(x - 1)$

EXAMPLE 13 | Factoring an Expression Completely

Factor each expression completely.

(a) $2x^4 - 8x^2$ (b) $x^5y^2 - xy^6$

SOLUTION

(a) We first factor out the power of x with the smallest exponent.

$$2x^4 - 8x^2 = 2x^2(x^2 - 4) \qquad \text{Common factor is } 2x^2$$
$$= 2x^2(x - 2)(x + 2) \qquad \text{Factor } x^2 - 4 \text{ as a difference of squares}$$

(b) We first factor out the powers of x and y with the smallest exponents.

$$x^5y^2 - xy^6 = xy^2(x^4 - y^4) \qquad \text{Common factor is } xy^2$$
$$= xy^2(x^2 + y^2)(x^2 - y^2) \qquad \text{Factor } x^4 - y^4 \text{ as a difference of squares}$$
$$= xy^2(x^2 + y^2)(x + y)(x - y) \qquad \text{Factor } x^2 - y^2 \text{ as a difference of squares}$$

✎. NOW TRY EXERCISES **115** AND **117**   ■

In the next example we factor out variables with fractional exponents. This type of factoring occurs in calculus.

EXAMPLE 14 | Factoring Expressions with Fractional Exponents

Factor each expression.

(a) $3x^{3/2} - 9x^{1/2} + 6x^{-1/2}$ (b) $(2 + x)^{-2/3}x + (2 + x)^{1/3}$

SOLUTION

(a) Factor out the power of x with the *smallest exponent*, that is, $x^{-1/2}$.

$$3x^{3/2} - 9x^{1/2} + 6x^{-1/2} = 3x^{-1/2}(x^2 - 3x + 2) \qquad \text{Factor out } 3x^{-1/2}$$
$$= 3x^{-1/2}(x - 1)(x - 2) \qquad \begin{array}{l}\text{Factor the quadratic}\\ x^2 - 3x + 2\end{array}$$

(b) Factor out the power of $2 + x$ with the *smallest exponent*, that is, $(2 + x)^{-2/3}$.

$$(2 + x)^{-2/3}x + (2 + x)^{1/3} = (2 + x)^{-2/3}[x + (2 + x)] \qquad \text{Factor out } (2 + x)^{-2/3}$$
$$= (2 + x)^{-2/3}(2 + 2x) \qquad \text{Simplify}$$
$$= 2(2 + x)^{-2/3}(1 + x) \qquad \text{Factor out } 2$$

To factor out $x^{-1/2}$ from $x^{3/2}$, we *subtract* exponents:

$$x^{3/2} = x^{-1/2}(x^{3/2 - (-1/2)})$$
$$= x^{-1/2}(x^{3/2 + 1/2})$$
$$= x^{-1/2}(x^2)$$

CHECK YOUR ANSWERS

To see that you have factored correctly, multiply using the Laws of Exponents.

(a) $3x^{-1/2}(x^2 - 3x + 2)$
$$= 3x^{3/2} - 9x^{1/2} + 6x^{-1/2} \quad ✔$$

(b) $(2 + x)^{-2/3}[x + (2 + x)]$
$$= (2 + x)^{-2/3}x + (2 + x)^{1/3} \quad ✔$$

✎. NOW TRY EXERCISES **91** AND **93**   ■

▼ Factoring by Grouping Terms

Polynomials with at least four terms can sometimes be factored by grouping terms. The following example illustrates the idea.

EXAMPLE 15 | Factoring by Grouping

Factor each polynomial.

(a) $x^3 + x^2 + 4x + 4$ (b) $x^3 - 2x^2 - 3x + 6$

ALTERNATE EXAMPLE 13

Factor:

$12x^3y^2 - 3xy^4$

ANSWER

$3xy^2(2x + y)(2x - y)$

ALTERNATE EXAMPLE 14

Factor the expression:

$3x^{3/2} - 15x^{1/2} + 18x^{-1/2}$

ANSWER

$3x^{-1/2}(x - 2)(x - 3)$

ALTERNATE EXAMPLE 15

Factor the polynomial:

$x^3 - 5x^2 - 2x + 10$

ANSWER

$(x^2 - 2)(x - 5)$

EXAMPLES

1. A cubic product: $(3x^3 - 2x^2 + 4x - 5)(x^3 - 2x^2 - 4x + 1) = 3x^6 - 8x^5 - 4x^4 - 2x^3 - 8x^2 + 24x - 5$

2. A fourth-degree polynomial with integer factors: $(x - 1)(x - 1)(x + 2)(x - 3) = x^4 - 3x^3 - 3x^2 + 11x - 6$

3. A polynomial that can be factored nicely using the method of "In-Class Material" on page 28:

$x^4 + 64 = (x^2 - 4x + 8)(x^2 + 4x + 8)$

SOLUTION

(a) $x^3 + x^2 + 4x + 4 = (x^3 + x^2) + (4x + 4)$ Group terms

$\qquad\qquad\qquad\qquad = x^2(x + 1) + 4(x + 1)$ Factor out common factors

$\qquad\qquad\qquad\qquad = (x^2 + 4)(x + 1)$ Factor out $x + 1$ from each term

(b) $x^3 - 2x^2 - 3x + 6 = (x^3 - 2x^2) - (3x - 6)$ Group terms

$\qquad\qquad\qquad\qquad = x^2(x - 2) - 3(x - 2)$ Factor out common factors

$\qquad\qquad\qquad\qquad = (x^2 - 3)(x - 2)$ Factor out $x - 2$ from each term

✎. NOW TRY EXERCISE **83**

1.3 EXERCISES

CONCEPTS

1. Consider the polynomial $2x^5 + 6x^4 + 4x^3$.

   How many terms does this polynomial have? _____

       List the terms: _____

   What factor is common to each term? _____

       Factor the polynomial: $2x^5 + 6x^4 + 4x^3 =$ _____.

2. To factor the trinomial $x^2 + 7x + 10$, we look for two integers

   whose product is _____ and whose sum is _____.

   These integers are _____ and _____, so the trinomial

   factors as _____.

3. The Special Product Formula for the "square of a sum" is

   $(A + B)^2 =$ _____.

   So $(2x + 3)^2 =$ _____.

4. The Special Product Formula for the "sum and difference

   of the same terms" is $(A + B)(A - B) =$ _____.

   So $(5 + x)(5 - x) =$ _____.

5. The Special Factoring Formula for the "difference of squares"

   is $A^2 - B^2 =$ _____. So $4x^2 - 25$ factors as _____.

6. The Special Factoring Formula for a "perfect square" is

   $A^2 + 2AB + B^2 =$ _____. So $x^2 + 10x + 25$ factors as

   _____.

SKILLS

7–12 ■ Complete the following table by stating whether the polynomial is a monomial, binomial, or trinomial; then list its terms and state its degree.

Polynomial	Type	Terms	Degree
7. $x^2 - 3x + 7$			
8. $2x^5 + 4x^2$			

Polynomial	Type	Terms	Degree
9. -8			
10. $\frac{1}{2}x^7$			
11. $x - x^2 + x^3 - x^4$			
12. $\sqrt{2}x - \sqrt{3}$			

13–22 ■ Find the sum, difference, or product.

13. $(12x - 7) - (5x - 12)$ 14. $(5 - 3x) + (2x - 8)$

15. $(3x^2 + x + 1) + (2x^2 - 3x - 5)$

16. $(3x^2 + x + 1) - (2x^2 - 3x - 5)$

17. $(x^3 + 6x^2 - 4x + 7) - (3x^2 + 2x - 4)$

18. $3(x - 1) + 4(x + 2)$

19. $8(2x + 5) - 7(x - 9)$

20. $4(x^2 - 3x + 5) - 3(x^2 - 2x + 1)$

21. $2(2 - 5t) + t^2(t - 1) - (t^4 - 1)$

22. $5(3t - 4) - (t^2 + 2) - 2t(t - 3)$

23–28 ■ Multiply the algebraic expressions using the FOIL method and simplify.

23. $(3t - 2)(7t - 4)$ 24. $(4s - 1)(2s + 5)$

25. $(3x + 5)(2x - 1)$ 26. $(7y - 3)(2y - 1)$

27. $(x + 3y)(2x - y)$ 28. $(4x - 5y)(3x - y)$

29–44 ■ Multiply the algebraic expressions using a Special Product Formula and simplify.

29. $(3x + 4)^2$ 30. $(1 - 2y)^2$

31. $(2u + v)^2$ 32. $(x - 3y)^2$

33. $(2x + 3y)^2$ 34. $(r - 2s)^2$

35. $(x + 5)(x - 5)$ 36. $(y - 3)(y + 3)$

37. $(3x - 4)(3x + 4)$ 38. $(2y + 5)(2y - 5)$

39. $(\sqrt{x} + 2)(\sqrt{x} - 2)$ 40. $(\sqrt{y} + \sqrt{2})(\sqrt{y} - \sqrt{2})$

41. $(y + 2)^3$ **42.** $(x - 3)^3$

43. $(1 - 2r)^3$ **44.** $(3 + 2y)^3$

45–60 ■ Perform the indicated operations and simplify.

45. $(x + 2)(x^2 + 2x + 3)$ **46.** $(x + 1)(2x^2 - x + 1)$

47. $(2x - 5)(x^2 - x + 1)$ **48.** $(1 + 2x)(x^2 - 3x + 1)$

49. $\sqrt{x}(x - \sqrt{x})$ **50.** $x^{3/2}(\sqrt{x} - 1/\sqrt{x})$

51. $y^{1/3}(y^{2/3} + y^{5/3})$ **52.** $x^{1/4}(2x^{3/4} - x^{1/4})$

53. $(x^2 - a^2)(x^2 + a^2)$ **54.** $(x^{1/2} + y^{1/2})(x^{1/2} - y^{1/2})$

55. $(\sqrt{a} - b)(\sqrt{a} + b)$

56. $(\sqrt{h^2 + 1} + 1)(\sqrt{h^2 + 1} - 1)$

57. $((x - 1) + x^2)((x - 1) - x^2)$

58. $(x + (2 + x^2))(x - (2 + x^2))$

59. $(2x + y - 3)(2x + y + 3)$ **60.** $(x + y + z)(x - y - z)$

61–66 ■ Factor out the common factor.

61. $-2x^3 + 16x$ **62.** $2x^4 + 4x^3 - 14x^2$

63. $y(y - 6) + 9(y - 6)$ **64.** $(z + 2)^2 - 5(z + 2)$

65. $2x^2y - 6xy^2 + 3xy$ **66.** $-7x^4y^2 + 14xy^3 + 21xy^4$

67–74 ■ Factor the trinomial.

67. $x^2 + 2x - 3$ **68.** $x^2 - 6x + 5$

69. $8x^2 - 14x - 15$ **70.** $6y^2 + 11y - 21$

71. $3x^2 - 16x + 5$ **72.** $5x^2 - 7x - 6$

73. $(3x + 2)^2 + 8(3x + 2) + 12$

74. $2(a + b)^2 + 5(a + b) - 3$

75–82 ■ Use a Special Factoring Formula to factor the expression.

75. $9a^2 - 16$ **76.** $(x + 3)^2 - 4$

77. $27x^3 + y^3$ **78.** $a^3 - b^6$

79. $8s^3 - 125t^3$ **80.** $1 + 1000y^3$

81. $x^2 + 12x + 36$ **82.** $16z^2 - 24z + 9$

83–88 ■ Factor the expression by grouping terms.

83. $x^3 + 4x^2 + x + 4$ **84.** $3x^3 - x^2 + 6x - 2$

85. $2x^3 + x^2 - 6x - 3$ **86.** $-9x^3 - 3x^2 + 3x + 1$

87. $x^3 + x^2 + x + 1$ **88.** $x^5 + x^4 + x + 1$

89–94 ■ Factor the expression completely. Begin by factoring out the lowest power of each common factor.

89. $x^{5/2} - x^{1/2}$ **90.** $3x^{-1/2} + 4x^{1/2} + x^{3/2}$

91. $x^{-3/2} + 2x^{-1/2} + x^{1/2}$ **92.** $(x - 1)^{7/2} - (x - 1)^{3/2}$

93. $(x^2 + 1)^{1/2} + 2(x^2 + 1)^{-1/2}$

94. $x^{-1/2}(x + 1)^{1/2} + x^{1/2}(x + 1)^{-1/2}$

95–124 ■ Factor the expression completely.

95. $12x^3 + 18x$ **96.** $30x^3 + 15x^4$

97. $x^2 - 2x - 8$ **98.** $x^2 - 14x + 48$

99. $2x^2 + 5x + 3$ **100.** $2x^2 + 7x - 4$

101. $9x^2 - 36x - 45$ **102.** $8x^2 + 10x + 3$

103. $49 - 4y^2$ **104.** $4t^2 - 9s^2$

105. $t^2 - 6t + 9$ **106.** $x^2 + 10x + 25$

107. $4x^2 + 4xy + y^2$ **108.** $r^2 - 6rs + 9s^2$

109. $(a + b)^2 - (a - b)^2$ **110.** $\left(1 + \dfrac{1}{x}\right)^2 - \left(1 - \dfrac{1}{x}\right)^2$

111. $x^2(x^2 - 1) - 9(x^2 - 1)$ **112.** $(a^2 - 1)b^2 - 4(a^2 - 1)$

113. $8x^3 - 125$ **114.** $x^6 + 64$

115. $x^3 + 2x^2 + x$ **116.** $3x^3 - 27x$

117. $x^4y^3 - x^2y^5$ **118.** $18y^3x^2 - 2xy^4$

119. $2x^3 + 4x^2 + x + 2$ **120.** $3x^3 + 5x^2 - 6x - 10$

121. $(x - 1)(x + 2)^2 - (x - 1)^2(x + 2)$

122. $y^4(y + 2)^3 + y^5(y + 2)^4$

123. $(a^2 + 1)^2 - 7(a^2 + 1) + 10$

124. $(a^2 + 2a)^2 - 2(a^2 + 2a) - 3$

125–128 ■ Factor the expression completely. (This type of expression arises in calculus when using the "Product Rule.")

125. $5(x^2 + 4)^4(2x)(x - 2)^4 + (x^2 + 4)^5(4)(x - 2)^3$

126. $3(2x - 1)^2(2)(x + 3)^{1/2} + (2x - 1)^3(\frac{1}{2})(x + 3)^{-1/2}$

127. $(x^2 + 3)^{-1/3} - \frac{2}{3}x^2(x^2 + 3)^{-4/3}$

128. $\frac{1}{2}x^{-1/2}(3x + 4)^{1/2} - \frac{3}{2}x^{1/2}(3x + 4)^{-1/2}$

129. (a) Show that $ab = \frac{1}{2}[(a + b)^2 - (a^2 + b^2)]$.

   (b) Show that $(a^2 + b^2)^2 - (a^2 - b^2)^2 = 4a^2b^2$.

   (c) Show that
   $$(a^2 + b^2)(c^2 + d^2) = (ac + bd)^2 + (ad - bc)^2$$

   (d) Factor completely: $4a^2c^2 - (a^2 - b^2 + c^2)^2$.

130. Verify Special Factoring Formulas 4 and 5 by expanding their right-hand sides.

APPLICATIONS

131. Volume of Concrete A culvert is constructed out of large cylindrical shells cast in concrete, as shown in the figure. Using the formula for the volume of a cylinder given on the inside front cover of this book, explain why the volume of the cylindrical shell is

$$V = \pi R^2 h - \pi r^2 h$$

Factor to show that

$$V = 2\pi \cdot \text{average radius} \cdot \text{height} \cdot \text{thickness}$$

Use the "unrolled" diagram to explain why this makes sense geometrically.

132. Mowing a Field A square field in a certain state park is mowed around the edges every week. The rest of the field is kept unmowed to serve as a habitat for birds and small animals (see the figure). The field measures b feet by b feet, and the mowed strip is x feet wide.

(a) Explain why the area of the mowed portion is $b^2 - (b - 2x)^2$.

(b) Factor the expression in part (a) to show that the area of the mowed portion is also $4x(b - x)$.

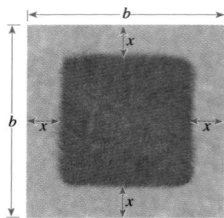

DISCOVERY ■ DISCUSSION ■ WRITING

133. Degrees of Sums and Products of Polynomials Make up several pairs of polynomials, then calculate the sum and product of each pair. On the basis of your experiments and observations, answer the following questions.

(a) How is the degree of the product related to the degrees of the original polynomials?

(b) How is the degree of the sum related to the degrees of the original polynomials?

134. The Power of Algebraic Formulas Use the Difference of Squares Formula to factor $17^2 - 16^2$. Notice that it is easy to calculate the factored form in your head but not so easy to calculate the original form in this way. Evaluate each expression in your head:

(a) $528^2 - 527^2$

(b) $122^2 - 120^2$

(c) $1020^2 - 1010^2$

Now use the Special Product Formula

$$(A + B)(A - B) = A^2 - B^2$$

to evaluate these products in your head:

(d) $79 \cdot 51$

(e) $998 \cdot 1002$

135. Differences of Even Powers

(a) Factor the expressions completely: $A^4 - B^4$ and $A^6 - B^6$.

(b) Verify that $18{,}335 = 12^4 - 7^4$ and that $2{,}868{,}335 = 12^6 - 7^6$.

(c) Use the results of parts (a) and (b) to factor the integers $18{,}335$ and $2{,}868{,}335$. Then show that in both of these factorizations, all the factors are prime numbers.

136. Factoring $A^n - 1$ Verify these formulas by expanding and simplifying the right-hand side.

$$A^2 - 1 = (A - 1)(A + 1)$$

$$A^3 - 1 = (A - 1)(A^2 + A + 1)$$

$$A^4 - 1 = (A - 1)(A^3 + A^2 + A + 1)$$

On the basis of the pattern displayed in this list, how do you think $A^5 - 1$ would factor? Verify your conjecture. Now generalize the pattern you have observed to obtain a factoring formula for $A^n - 1$, where n is a positive integer.

137. Factoring $x^4 + ax^2 + b$ A trinomial of the form $x^4 + ax^2 + b$ can sometimes be factored easily. For example,

$$x^4 + 3x^2 - 4 = (x^2 + 4)(x^2 - 1)$$

But $x^4 + 3x^2 + 4$ cannot be factored in this way. Instead, we can use the following method.

$$x^4 + 3x^2 + 4 = (x^4 + 4x^2 + 4) - x^2 \qquad \text{Add and subtract } x^2$$

$$= (x^2 + 2)^2 - x^2 \qquad \text{Factor perfect square}$$

$$= [(x^2 + 2) - x][(x^2 + 2) + x] \qquad \text{Difference of squares}$$

$$= (x^2 - x + 2)(x^2 + x + 2)$$

Factor the following, using whichever method is appropriate.

(a) $x^4 + x^2 - 2$

(b) $x^4 + 2x^2 + 9$

(c) $x^4 + 4x^2 + 16$

(d) $x^4 + 2x^2 + 1$

DISCOVERY PROJECT Visualizing a Formula

In this project we discover geometric interpretations of some of the Special Product Formulas. You can find the project at the book companion website: **www.stewartmath.com**

1.4 RATIONAL EXPRESSIONS

The Domain of an Algebraic Expression ▶ Simplifying Rational Expressions ▶ Multiplying and Dividing Rational Expressions ▶ Adding and Subtracting Rational Expressions ▶ Compound Fractions ▶ Rationalizing the Denominator or the Numerator ▶ Avoiding Common Errors

SUGGESTED TIME
AND EMPHASIS
$\frac{1}{2}$–1 class, essential material

A quotient of two algebraic expressions is called a **fractional expression**. Here are some examples:

$$\frac{2x}{x-1} \qquad \frac{\sqrt{x}+3}{x+1} \qquad \frac{y-2}{y^2+4}$$

A **rational expression** is a fractional expression where both the numerator and denominator are polynomials. For example, the following are rational expressions:

$$\frac{2x}{x-1} \qquad \frac{x}{x^2+1} \qquad \frac{x^3-x}{x^2-5x+6}$$

In this section we learn how to perform algebraic operations on rational expressions.

▼ The Domain of an Algebraic Expression

Expression	Domain
$\dfrac{1}{x}$	$\{x \mid x \neq 0\}$
$\sqrt{x}$	$\{x \mid x \geq 0\}$
$\dfrac{1}{\sqrt{x}}$	$\{x \mid x > 0\}$

In general, an algebraic expression may not be defined for all values of the variable. The **domain** of an algebraic expression is the set of real numbers that the variable is permitted to have. The table in the margin gives some basic expressions and their domains.

EXAMPLE 1 | Finding the Domain of an Expression

Find the domains of the following expressions.

(a) $2x^2 + 3x - 1$ 　　　**(b)** $\dfrac{x}{x^2-5x+6}$ 　　　**(c)** $\dfrac{\sqrt{x}}{x-5}$

SOLUTION

(a) This polynomial is defined for every x. Thus, the domain is the set $\mathbb{R}$ of real numbers.

(b) We first factor the denominator.

$$\frac{x}{x^2-5x+6} = \frac{x}{(x-2)(x-3)}$$

Denominator would be 0 if $x=2$ or $x=3$

Since the denominator is zero when $x = 2$ or 3, the expression is not defined for these numbers. The domain is $\{x \mid x \neq 2 \text{ and } x \neq 3\}$.

(c) For the numerator to be defined, we must have $x \geq 0$. Also, we cannot divide by zero, so $x \neq 5$.

Must have $x \geq 0$ to take square root 　　$\dfrac{\sqrt{x}}{x-5}$　　 Denominator would be 0 if $x = 5$

Thus, the domain is $\{x \mid x \geq 0 \text{ and } x \neq 5\}$.

↖. NOW TRY EXERCISE **11**　　　　■

ALTERNATE EXAMPLE 1
Find the domain of
$$\sqrt{x^2 + 3x + 2}.$$

ANSWER
$\{x \mid x \leq -2 \text{ or } x \geq -1\}$

TEXT QUESTION
What is a rational expression?

Answer
A rational expression is a fractional expression where both the numerator and the denominator are polynomials.

▼ Simplifying Rational Expressions

To **simplify rational expressions**, we factor both numerator and denominator and use the following property of fractions:

$$\frac{AC}{BC} = \frac{A}{B}$$

This allows us to **cancel** common factors from the numerator and denominator.

EXAMPLE 2 | Simplifying Rational Expressions by Cancellation

Simplify: $\dfrac{x^2 - 1}{x^2 + x - 2}$

SOLUTION

⊘ We can't cancel the x^2's in $\dfrac{x^2 - 1}{x^2 + x - 2}$ because x^2 is not a factor.

$$\frac{x^2 - 1}{x^2 + x - 2} = \frac{(x - 1)(x + 1)}{(x - 1)(x + 2)} \qquad \text{Factor}$$

$$= \frac{x + 1}{x + 2} \qquad \text{Cancel common factors}$$

✎. NOW TRY EXERCISE **17**   ∎

▼ Multiplying and Dividing Rational Expressions

To **multiply rational expressions**, we use the following property of fractions:

$$\frac{A}{B} \cdot \frac{C}{D} = \frac{AC}{BD}$$

This says that to multiply two fractions we multiply their numerators and multiply their denominators.

EXAMPLE 3 | Multiplying Rational Expressions

Perform the indicated multiplication and simplify: $\dfrac{x^2 + 2x - 3}{x^2 + 8x + 16} \cdot \dfrac{3x + 12}{x - 1}$

SOLUTION   We first factor.

$$\frac{x^2 + 2x - 3}{x^2 + 8x + 16} \cdot \frac{3x + 12}{x - 1} = \frac{(x - 1)(x + 3)}{(x + 4)^2} \cdot \frac{3(x + 4)}{x - 1} \qquad \text{Factor}$$

$$= \frac{3(x - 1)(x + 3)(x + 4)}{(x - 1)(x + 4)^2} \qquad \text{Property of fractions}$$

$$= \frac{3(x + 3)}{x + 4} \qquad \text{Cancel common factors}$$

✎. NOW TRY EXERCISE **25**   ∎

To **divide rational expressions**, we use the following property of fractions:

$$\frac{A}{B} \div \frac{C}{D} = \frac{A}{B} \cdot \frac{D}{C}$$

ALTERNATE EXAMPLE 2

Simplify the fractional expression

$$\frac{x^2 - 64}{x^2 + x - 72}.$$

ANSWER

$$\frac{x + 8}{x + 9}$$

ALTERNATE EXAMPLE 3

Perform the indicated multiplication and simplify:

$$\frac{x^2 + 4x - 12}{x^2 + 8x + 16} \cdot \frac{2x + 8}{x - 2}$$

ANSWER

$$\frac{2(x + 6)}{x + 4}$$

IN-CLASS MATERIALS

One of the most persistent mistakes students make is confusing the following two expressions:

$$\frac{a + b}{c} = \frac{a}{c} + \frac{b}{c} \qquad \frac{a}{b + c} = \frac{a}{b} + \frac{a}{c} \leftarrow \text{Wrong!}$$

Make sure students understand the difference between these two cases. Perhaps give them the following expressions to simplify:

$$\frac{2 + 3}{5} = \frac{2}{5} + \frac{3}{5} \qquad \frac{u + 1}{u} = 1 + \frac{1}{u} \qquad \frac{x^3 + x + \sqrt[3]{x}}{x} = x^2 + 1 + x^{-2/3}$$

$$\frac{5}{2 + 3} = \frac{5}{2 + 3} \qquad \frac{u}{u + 1} = \frac{u}{u + 1} \qquad \frac{x}{x^3 + x + \sqrt[3]{x}} = \frac{x}{x^3 + x + \sqrt[3]{x}}$$

This says that to divide a fraction by another fraction, we invert the divisor and multiply.

EXAMPLE 4 | Dividing Rational Expressions

Perform the indicated division and simplify:

$$\frac{x-4}{x^2-4} \div \frac{x^2-3x-4}{x^2+5x+6}$$

SOLUTION

$$\frac{x-4}{x^2-4} \div \frac{x^2-3x-4}{x^2+5x+6} = \frac{x-4}{x^2-4} \cdot \frac{x^2+5x+6}{x^2-3x-4}$$ Invert and multiply

$$= \frac{(x-4)(x+2)(x+3)}{(x-2)(x+2)(x-4)(x+1)}$$ Factor

$$= \frac{x+3}{(x-2)(x+1)}$$ Cancel common factors

NOW TRY EXERCISE 31

▼ Adding and Subtracting Rational Expressions

Avoid making the following error:

$$\frac{A}{B+C} \neq \frac{A}{B} + \frac{A}{C}$$

For instance, if we let $A=2$, $B=1$, and $C=1$, then we see the error:

$$\frac{2}{1+1} \stackrel{?}{=} \frac{2}{1} + \frac{2}{1}$$
$$\frac{2}{2} \stackrel{?}{=} 2+2$$
$$1 \stackrel{?}{=} 4 \quad \text{Wrong!}$$

To **add or subtract rational expressions**, we first find a common denominator and then use the following property of fractions:

$$\frac{A}{C} + \frac{B}{C} = \frac{A+B}{C}$$

Although any common denominator will work, it is best to use the **least common denominator** (LCD) as explained in Section 1.1. The LCD is found by factoring each denominator and taking the product of the distinct factors, using the highest power that appears in any of the factors.

EXAMPLE 5 | Adding and Subtracting Rational Expressions

Perform the indicated operations and simplify:

(a) $\dfrac{3}{x-1} + \dfrac{x}{x+2}$ **(b)** $\dfrac{1}{x^2-1} - \dfrac{2}{(x+1)^2}$

SOLUTION

(a) Here the LCD is simply the product $(x-1)(x+2)$.

$$\frac{3}{x-1} + \frac{x}{x+2} = \frac{3(x+2)}{(x-1)(x+2)} + \frac{x(x-1)}{(x-1)(x+2)}$$ Write fractions using LCD

$$= \frac{3x+6+x^2-x}{(x-1)(x+2)}$$ Add fractions

$$= \frac{x^2+2x+6}{(x-1)(x+2)}$$ Combine terms in numerator

ALTERNATE EXAMPLE 4
Perform the indicated division and simplify:
$$\frac{x-5}{x^2-16} \div \frac{x^2-2x-15}{x^2+11x+28}$$

ANSWER
$$\frac{x+7}{(x-4)(x+3)}$$

ALTERNATE EXAMPLE 5
Perform the addition and simplify:
$$\frac{5}{x-1} + \frac{x}{x+3}$$

ANSWER
$$\frac{x^2+4x+15}{(x-1)(x+3)}$$

IN-CLASS MATERIALS
Ask your students why we like to rationalize the denominator. Note that it is often a matter of context, or even a matter of taste! There is nothing inherently "simpler" about $\dfrac{\sqrt{2}}{2}$ as opposed to $\dfrac{1}{\sqrt{2}}$ if they are just sitting there as numbers. However, we prefer to add $\dfrac{\sqrt{2}}{2} + \dfrac{\sqrt{3}}{3} + \dfrac{1}{6}$ than to add $\dfrac{1}{\sqrt{2}} + \dfrac{1}{\sqrt{3}} + \dfrac{1}{6}$. See if students can come up with other reasons or instances of when it is convenient to rationalize a denominator.

(b) The LCD of $x^2 - 1 = (x - 1)(x + 1)$ and $(x + 1)^2$ is $(x - 1)(x + 1)^2$.

$$\frac{1}{x^2 - 1} - \frac{2}{(x + 1)^2} = \frac{1}{(x - 1)(x + 1)} - \frac{2}{(x + 1)^2} \qquad \text{Factor}$$

$$= \frac{(x + 1) - 2(x - 1)}{(x - 1)(x + 1)^2} \qquad \text{Combine fractions using LCD}$$

$$= \frac{x + 1 - 2x + 2}{(x - 1)(x + 1)^2} \qquad \text{Distributive Property}$$

$$= \frac{3 - x}{(x - 1)(x + 1)^2} \qquad \text{Combine terms in numerator}$$

✎ NOW TRY EXERCISES **43** AND **45** ■

▼ Compound Fractions

A **compound fraction** is a fraction in which the numerator, the denominator, or both, are themselves fractional expressions.

EXAMPLE 6 │ Simplifying a Compound Fraction

Simplify: $\dfrac{\dfrac{x}{y} + 1}{1 - \dfrac{y}{x}}$

SOLUTION 1 We combine the terms in the numerator into a single fraction. We do the same in the denominator. Then we invert and multiply.

$$\frac{\dfrac{x}{y} + 1}{1 - \dfrac{y}{x}} = \frac{\dfrac{x + y}{y}}{\dfrac{x - y}{x}} = \frac{x + y}{y} \cdot \frac{x}{x - y}$$

$$= \frac{x(x + y)}{y(x - y)}$$

ALTERNATE EXAMPLE 6
Simplify the fraction:
$$\frac{\dfrac{u}{v} + 1}{\dfrac{v}{u} - 1}$$

ANSWER
$$\frac{u(u + v)}{v(v - u)}$$

IN-CLASS MATERIALS

This is a good time to start talking about magnitudes. For example, look at $\dfrac{x + 6}{x^2 + 4}$ and ask the questions, "What happens to this fraction when x gets large?" "What happens when x gets close to zero?" and "What happens when x is large and negative, such as $-1{,}000{,}000$?" The idea is not yet to be rigorous, but to give students a feel for the idea that a large denominator yields a small fraction, and vice versa. You can pursue this idea with fractions like $\dfrac{x^2 + 4}{x}$ and $\dfrac{6}{x + (3/x)}$.

SOLUTION 2 We find the LCD of all the fractions in the expression, then multiply numerator and denominator by it. In this example the LCD of all the fractions is xy. Thus

$$\frac{\frac{x}{y}+1}{1-\frac{y}{x}}=\frac{\frac{x}{y}+1}{1-\frac{y}{x}}\cdot\frac{xy}{xy} \qquad \text{Multiply numerator and denominator by } xy$$

$$=\frac{x^2+xy}{xy-y^2} \qquad \text{Simplify}$$

$$=\frac{x(x+y)}{y(x-y)} \qquad \text{Factor}$$

✏. NOW TRY EXERCISES **59** AND **61** ■

The next two examples show situations in calculus that require the ability to work with fractional expressions.

EXAMPLE 7 | Simplifying a Compound Fraction

Simplify: $\dfrac{\dfrac{1}{a+h}-\dfrac{1}{a}}{h}$

SOLUTION We begin by combining the fractions in the numerator using a common denominator.

$$\frac{\frac{1}{a+h}-\frac{1}{a}}{h}=\frac{\frac{a-(a+h)}{a(a+h)}}{h} \qquad \text{Combine fractions in the numerator}$$

$$=\frac{a-(a+h)}{a(a+h)}\cdot\frac{1}{h} \qquad \text{Property 2 of fractions (invert divisor and multiply)}$$

$$=\frac{a-a-h}{a(a+h)}\cdot\frac{1}{h} \qquad \text{Distributive Property}$$

$$=\frac{-h}{a(a+h)}\cdot\frac{1}{h} \qquad \text{Simplify}$$

$$=\frac{-1}{a(a+h)} \qquad \text{Property 5 of fractions (cancel common factors)}$$

✏. NOW TRY EXERCISE **69** ■

EXAMPLE 8 | Simplifying a Compound Fraction

Simplify: $\dfrac{(1+x^2)^{1/2}-x^2(1+x^2)^{-1/2}}{1+x^2}$

SOLUTION 1 Factor $(1+x^2)^{-1/2}$ from the numerator.

$$\frac{(1+x^2)^{1/2}-x^2(1+x^2)^{-1/2}}{1+x^2}=\frac{(1+x^2)^{-1/2}[(1+x^2)-x^2]}{1+x^2}$$

$$=\frac{(1+x^2)^{-1/2}}{1+x^2}=\frac{1}{(1+x^2)^{3/2}}$$

Factor out the power of $1+x^2$ with the *smallest* exponent, in this case $(1+x^2)^{-1/2}$.

ALTERNATE EXAMPLE 7
Simplify the compound fraction:
$$\frac{\dfrac{1}{(b+h)^2}-\dfrac{1}{b^2}}{h}$$

ANSWER
$$-\frac{2b+h}{(b+h)^2b^2}$$

ALTERNATE EXAMPLE 8
Simplify the compound fraction:
$$\frac{(2+x^2)^{1/2}-x^2(2+x^2)^{-1/2}}{2+x^2}$$

ANSWER
$$\frac{2}{(2+x^2)^{3/2}}$$

SOLUTION 2 Since $(1 + x^2)^{-1/2} = 1/(1 + x^2)^{1/2}$ is a fraction, we can clear all fractions by multiplying numerator and denominator by $(1 + x^2)^{1/2}$.

$$\frac{(1 + x^2)^{1/2} - x^2(1 + x^2)^{-1/2}}{1 + x^2} = \frac{(1 + x^2)^{1/2} - x^2(1 + x^2)^{-1/2}}{1 + x^2} \cdot \frac{(1 + x^2)^{1/2}}{(1 + x^2)^{1/2}}$$

$$= \frac{(1 + x^2) - x^2}{(1 + x^2)^{3/2}} = \frac{1}{(1 + x^2)^{3/2}}$$

✎. NOW TRY EXERCISE **77** ∎

▼ Rationalizing the Denominator or the Numerator

If a fraction has a denominator of the form $A + B\sqrt{C}$, we may rationalize the denominator by multiplying numerator and denominator by the **conjugate radical** $A - B\sqrt{C}$. This works because, by Special Product Formula 1 in Section 1.3, the product of the denominator and its conjugate radical does not contain a radical:

$$(A + B\sqrt{C})(A - B\sqrt{C}) = A^2 - B^2C$$

EXAMPLE 9 | Rationalizing the Denominator

Rationalize the denominator: $\dfrac{1}{1 + \sqrt{2}}$

SOLUTION We multiply both the numerator and the denominator by the conjugate radical of $1 + \sqrt{2}$, which is $1 - \sqrt{2}$.

> Special Product Formula 1
> $(A + B)(A - B) = A^2 - B^2$

$$\frac{1}{1 + \sqrt{2}} = \frac{1}{1 + \sqrt{2}} \cdot \frac{1 - \sqrt{2}}{1 - \sqrt{2}} \quad \begin{array}{l}\text{Multiply numerator and}\\ \text{denominator by the}\\ \text{conjugate radical}\end{array}$$

$$= \frac{1 - \sqrt{2}}{1^2 - (\sqrt{2})^2} \quad \text{Special Product Formula 1}$$

$$= \frac{1 - \sqrt{2}}{1 - 2} = \frac{1 - \sqrt{2}}{-1} = \sqrt{2} - 1$$

✎. NOW TRY EXERCISE **81** ∎

EXAMPLE 10 | Rationalizing the Numerator

Rationalize the numerator: $\dfrac{\sqrt{4 + h} - 2}{h}$

SOLUTION We multiply numerator and denominator by the conjugate radical $\sqrt{4 + h} + 2$.

> Special Product Formula 1
> $(A + B)(A - B) = A^2 - B^2$

$$\frac{\sqrt{4 + h} - 2}{h} = \frac{\sqrt{4 + h} - 2}{h} \cdot \frac{\sqrt{4 + h} + 2}{\sqrt{4 + h} + 2} \quad \begin{array}{l}\text{Multiply numerator and}\\ \text{denominator by the}\\ \text{conjugate radical}\end{array}$$

$$= \frac{(\sqrt{4 + h})^2 - 2^2}{h(\sqrt{4 + h} + 2)} \quad \text{Special Product Formula 1}$$

$$= \frac{4 + h - 4}{h(\sqrt{4 + h} + 2)}$$

$$= \frac{h}{h(\sqrt{4 + h} + 2)} = \frac{1}{\sqrt{4 + h} + 2} \quad \begin{array}{l}\text{Property 5 of fractions}\\ \text{(cancel common factors)}\end{array}$$

✎. NOW TRY EXERCISE **87** ∎

ALTERNATE EXAMPLE 9

Rationalize the denominator:

$$\frac{12}{1 - \sqrt{7}}$$

ANSWER

$$-2 - 2\sqrt{7}$$

ALTERNATE EXAMPLE 10

Rationalize the numerator:

$$\frac{\sqrt{1 + h} - 1}{h}$$

ANSWER

$$\frac{1}{\sqrt{1 + h} + 1}$$

EXAMPLES

1. A compound fraction to simplify: $\dfrac{x + (3/b)}{b + (2x/6)} = 3\dfrac{xb + 3}{b(3b + x)}$

2. A denominator to rationalize: $\dfrac{x}{\sqrt{x} + \sqrt{3}} = \dfrac{x(\sqrt{x} - \sqrt{3})}{x - 3}$

▼ Avoiding Common Errors

 Don't make the mistake of applying properties of multiplication to the operation of addition. Many of the common errors in algebra involve doing just that. The following table states several properties of multiplication and illustrates the error in applying them to addition.

Correct multiplication property	Common error with addition
$(a \cdot b)^2 = a^2 \cdot b^2$	$(a + b)^2 \ne a^2 + b^2$
$\sqrt{a \cdot b} = \sqrt{a}\sqrt{b}$ $(a, b \ge 0)$	$\sqrt{a + b} \ne \sqrt{a} + \sqrt{b}$
$\sqrt{a^2 \cdot b^2} = a \cdot b$ $(a, b \ge 0)$	$\sqrt{a^2 + b^2} \ne a + b$
$\dfrac{1}{a} \cdot \dfrac{1}{b} = \dfrac{1}{a \cdot b}$	$\dfrac{1}{a} + \dfrac{1}{b} \ne \dfrac{1}{a + b}$
$\dfrac{ab}{a} = b$	$\dfrac{a + b}{a} \ne b$
$a^{-1} \cdot b^{-1} = (a \cdot b)^{-1}$	$a^{-1} + b^{-1} \ne (a + b)^{-1}$

To verify that the equations in the right-hand column are wrong, simply substitute numbers for a and b and calculate each side. For example, if we take $a = 2$ and $b = 2$ in the fourth error, we find that the left-hand side is

$$\frac{1}{a} + \frac{1}{b} = \frac{1}{2} + \frac{1}{2} = 1$$

whereas the right-hand side is

$$\frac{1}{a + b} = \frac{1}{2 + 2} = \frac{1}{4}$$

Since $1 \ne \frac{1}{4}$, the stated equation is wrong. You should similarly convince yourself of the error in each of the other equations. (See Exercise 105.)

1.4 EXERCISES

CONCEPTS

1. Which of the following are rational expressions?

(a) $\dfrac{3x}{x^2 - 1}$ (b) $\dfrac{\sqrt{x + 1}}{2x + 3}$ (c) $\dfrac{x(x^2 - 1)}{x + 3}$

2. To simplify a rational expression, we cancel *factors* that are common to the _____ and _____. So the expression

$$\frac{(x + 1)(x + 2)}{(x + 3)(x + 2)}$$

simplifies to _____.

3. To multiply two rational expressions, we multiply their _____ together and multiply their _____ together.

So $\dfrac{2}{x + 1} \cdot \dfrac{x}{x + 3}$ is the same as _____.

4. Consider the expression $\dfrac{1}{x} - \dfrac{2}{x + 1} - \dfrac{x}{(x + 1)^2}$.

(a) How many terms does this expression have?

(b) Find the least common denominator of all the terms.

(c) Perform the addition and simplify.

SKILLS

5–12 ■ Find the domain of the expression.

5. $4x^2 - 10x + 3$

6. $-x^4 + x^3 + 9x$

7. $\dfrac{2x + 1}{x - 4}$

8. $\dfrac{2t^2 - 5}{3t + 6}$

9. $\sqrt{x + 3}$

10. $\dfrac{1}{\sqrt{x - 1}}$

11. $\dfrac{x^2 + 1}{x^2 - x - 2}$

12. $\dfrac{\sqrt{2x}}{x + 1}$

13–22 ■ Simplify the rational expression.

13. $\dfrac{3(x + 2)(x - 1)}{6(x - 1)^2}$

14. $\dfrac{4(x^2 - 1)}{12(x + 2)(x - 1)}$

15. $\dfrac{x - 2}{x^2 - 4}$

16. $\dfrac{x^2 - x - 2}{x^2 - 1}$

17. $\dfrac{x^2 + 6x + 8}{x^2 + 5x + 4}$

18. $\dfrac{x^2 - x - 12}{x^2 + 5x + 6}$

19. $\dfrac{y^2 + y}{y^2 - 1}$

20. $\dfrac{y^2 - 3y - 18}{2y^2 + 5y + 3}$

21. $\dfrac{2x^3 - x^2 - 6x}{2x^2 - 7x + 6}$

22. $\dfrac{1 - x^2}{x^3 - 1}$

23–38 ■ Perform the multiplication or division and simplify.

23. $\dfrac{4x}{x^2 - 4} \cdot \dfrac{x + 2}{16x}$

24. $\dfrac{x^2 - 25}{x^2 - 16} \cdot \dfrac{x + 4}{x + 5}$

25. $\dfrac{x^2 - 2x - 15}{x^2 - 9} \cdot \dfrac{x + 3}{x - 5}$

26. $\dfrac{x^2 + 2x - 3}{x^2 - 2x - 3} \cdot \dfrac{3 - x}{3 + x}$

27. $\dfrac{t - 3}{t^2 + 9} \cdot \dfrac{t + 3}{t^2 - 9}$

28. $\dfrac{x^2 - x - 6}{x^2 + 2x} \cdot \dfrac{x^3 + x^2}{x^2 - 2x - 3}$

29. $\dfrac{x^2 + 7x + 12}{x^2 + 3x + 2} \cdot \dfrac{x^2 + 5x + 6}{x^2 + 6x + 9}$

30. $\dfrac{x^2 + 2xy + y^2}{x^2 - y^2} \cdot \dfrac{2x^2 - xy - y^2}{x^2 - xy - 2y^2}$

31. $\dfrac{x + 3}{4x^2 - 9} \div \dfrac{x^2 + 7x + 12}{2x^2 + 7x - 15}$

32. $\dfrac{2x + 1}{2x^2 + x - 15} \div \dfrac{6x^2 - x - 2}{x + 3}$

33. $\dfrac{2x^2 + 3x + 1}{x^2 + 2x - 15} \div \dfrac{x^2 + 6x + 5}{2x^2 - 7x + 3}$

34. $\dfrac{4y^2 - 9}{2y^2 + 9y - 18} \div \dfrac{2y^2 + y - 3}{y^2 + 5y - 6}$

35. $\dfrac{\dfrac{x^3}{x + 1}}{\dfrac{x}{x^2 + 2x + 1}}$

36. $\dfrac{\dfrac{2x^2 - 3x - 2}{x^2 - 1}}{\dfrac{2x^2 + 5x + 2}{x^2 + x - 2}}$

37. $\dfrac{x/y}{z}$

38. $\dfrac{x}{y/z}$

39–58 ■ Perform the addition or subtraction and simplify.

39. $2 + \dfrac{x}{x + 3}$

40. $\dfrac{2x - 1}{x + 4} - 1$

41. $\dfrac{1}{x + 5} + \dfrac{2}{x - 3}$

42. $\dfrac{1}{x + 1} + \dfrac{1}{x - 1}$

43. $\dfrac{1}{x + 1} - \dfrac{1}{x + 2}$

44. $\dfrac{x}{x - 4} - \dfrac{3}{x + 6}$

45. $\dfrac{x}{(x + 1)^2} + \dfrac{2}{x + 1}$

46. $\dfrac{5}{2x - 3} - \dfrac{3}{(2x - 3)^2}$

47. $u + 1 + \dfrac{u}{u + 1}$

48. $\dfrac{2}{a^2} - \dfrac{3}{ab} + \dfrac{4}{b^2}$

49. $\dfrac{1}{x^2} + \dfrac{1}{x^2 + x}$

50. $\dfrac{1}{x} + \dfrac{1}{x^2} + \dfrac{1}{x^3}$

51. $\dfrac{2}{x + 3} - \dfrac{1}{x^2 + 7x + 12}$

52. $\dfrac{x}{x^2 - 4} + \dfrac{1}{x - 2}$

53. $\dfrac{1}{x + 3} + \dfrac{1}{x^2 - 9}$

54. $\dfrac{x}{x^2 + x - 2} - \dfrac{2}{x^2 - 5x + 4}$

55. $\dfrac{2}{x} + \dfrac{3}{x - 1} - \dfrac{4}{x^2 - x}$

56. $\dfrac{x}{x^2 - x - 6} - \dfrac{1}{x + 2} - \dfrac{2}{x - 3}$

57. $\dfrac{1}{x^2 + 3x + 2} - \dfrac{1}{x^2 - 2x - 3}$

58. $\dfrac{1}{x + 1} - \dfrac{2}{(x + 1)^2} + \dfrac{3}{x^2 - 1}$

59–68 ■ Simplify the compound fractional expression.

59. $\dfrac{x + \dfrac{1}{x + 2}}{x - \dfrac{1}{x + 2}}$

60. $\dfrac{1 + \dfrac{1}{c - 1}}{1 - \dfrac{1}{c - 1}}$

61. $\dfrac{\dfrac{x + 2}{x - 1} - \dfrac{x - 3}{x - 2}}{x + 2}$

62. $\dfrac{\dfrac{x - 3}{x - 4} - \dfrac{x + 2}{x + 1}}{x + 3}$

63. $\dfrac{\dfrac{x}{y} - \dfrac{y}{x}}{\dfrac{1}{x^2} - \dfrac{1}{y^2}}$

64. $x - \dfrac{y}{\dfrac{x}{y} + \dfrac{y}{x}}$

65. $\dfrac{x^{-2} - y^{-2}}{x^{-1} + y^{-1}}$

66. $\dfrac{x^{-1} + y^{-1}}{(x + y)^{-1}}$

67. $1 - \dfrac{1}{1 - \dfrac{1}{x}}$

68. $1 + \dfrac{1}{1 + \dfrac{1}{1 + x}}$

69–74 ■ Simplify the fractional expression. (Expressions like these arise in calculus.)

69. $\dfrac{\dfrac{1}{1 + x + h} - \dfrac{1}{1 + x}}{h}$

70. $\dfrac{\dfrac{1}{\sqrt{x + h}} - \dfrac{1}{\sqrt{x}}}{h}$

71. $\dfrac{\dfrac{1}{(x + h)^2} - \dfrac{1}{x^2}}{h}$

72. $\dfrac{(x + h)^3 - 7(x + h) - (x^3 - 7x)}{h}$

73. $\sqrt{1 + \left(\dfrac{x}{\sqrt{1 - x^2}}\right)^2}$

74. $\sqrt{1 + \left(x^3 - \dfrac{1}{4x^3}\right)^2}$

75–80 ■ Simplify the expression. (This type of expression arises in calculus when using the "quotient rule.")

75. $\dfrac{3(x + 2)^2(x - 3)^2 - (x + 2)^3(2)(x - 3)}{(x - 3)^4}$

76. $\dfrac{2x(x + 6)^4 - x^2(4)(x + 6)^3}{(x + 6)^8}$

77. $\dfrac{2(1 + x)^{1/2} - x(1 + x)^{-1/2}}{x + 1}$

78. $\dfrac{(1 - x^2)^{1/2} + x^2(1 - x^2)^{-1/2}}{1 - x^2}$

79. $\dfrac{3(1 + x)^{1/3} - x(1 + x)^{-2/3}}{(1 + x)^{2/3}}$

80. $\dfrac{(7 - 3x)^{1/2} + \frac{3}{2}x(7 - 3x)^{-1/2}}{7 - 3x}$

81–86 ■ Rationalize the denominator.

81. $\dfrac{1}{2 - \sqrt{3}}$ **82.** $\dfrac{2}{3 - \sqrt{5}}$

83. $\dfrac{2}{\sqrt{2} + \sqrt{7}}$ **84.** $\dfrac{1}{\sqrt{x} + 1}$

85. $\dfrac{y}{\sqrt{3} + \sqrt{y}}$ **86.** $\dfrac{2(x - y)}{\sqrt{x} - \sqrt{y}}$

87–92 ■ Rationalize the numerator.

87. $\dfrac{1 - \sqrt{5}}{3}$ **88.** $\dfrac{\sqrt{3} + \sqrt{5}}{2}$

89. $\dfrac{\sqrt{r} + \sqrt{2}}{5}$ **90.** $\dfrac{\sqrt{x} - \sqrt{x + h}}{h\sqrt{x}\sqrt{x + h}}$

91. $\sqrt{x^2 + 1} - x$ **92.** $\sqrt{x + 1} - \sqrt{x}$

93–100 ■ State whether the given equation is true for all values of the variables. (Disregard any value that makes a denominator zero.)

93. $\dfrac{16 + a}{16} = 1 + \dfrac{a}{16}$ **94.** $\dfrac{b}{b - c} = 1 - \dfrac{b}{c}$

95. $\dfrac{2}{4 + x} = \dfrac{1}{2} + \dfrac{2}{x}$ **96.** $\dfrac{x + 1}{y + 1} = \dfrac{x}{y}$

97. $\dfrac{x}{x + y} = \dfrac{1}{1 + y}$ **98.** $2\left(\dfrac{a}{b}\right) = \dfrac{2a}{2b}$

99. $\dfrac{-a}{b} = -\dfrac{a}{b}$ **100.** $\dfrac{1 + x + x^2}{x} = \dfrac{1}{x} + 1 + x$

APPLICATIONS

101. Electrical Resistance   If two electrical resistors with resistances R_1 and R_2 are connected in parallel (see the figure), then the total resistance R is given by

$$R = \dfrac{1}{\dfrac{1}{R_1} + \dfrac{1}{R_2}}$$

(a) Simplify the expression for R.

(b) If $R_1 = 10$ ohms and $R_2 = 20$ ohms, what is the total resistance R?

102. Average Cost   A clothing manufacturer finds that the cost of producing x shirts is $500 + 6x + 0.01x^2$ dollars.

(a) Explain why the average cost per shirt is given by the rational expression

$$A = \dfrac{500 + 6x + 0.01x^2}{x}$$

(b) Complete the table by calculating the average cost per shirt for the given values of x.

x	Average cost
10	
20	
50	
100	
200	
500	
1000	

DISCOVERY ■ DISCUSSION ■ WRITING

103. Limiting Behavior of a Rational Expression   The rational expression

$$\dfrac{x^2 - 9}{x - 3}$$

is not defined for $x = 3$. Complete the tables and determine what value the expression approaches as x gets closer and closer to 3. Why is this reasonable? Factor the numerator of the expression and simplify to see why.

x	$\dfrac{x^2 - 9}{x - 3}$
2.80	
2.90	
2.95	
2.99	
2.999	

x	$\dfrac{x^2 - 9}{x - 3}$
3.20	
3.10	
3.05	
3.01	
3.001	

104. Is This Rationalization?   In the expression $2/\sqrt{x}$ we would eliminate the radical if we were to square both numerator and denominator. Is this the same thing as rationalizing the denominator?

105. Algebraic Errors   The left-hand column in the table on the following page lists some common algebraic errors. In each case, give an example using numbers that show that the formula is not valid. An example of this type, which shows that a statement is false, is called a *counterexample*.

Algebraic error	Counterexample
$\dfrac{1}{a} + \dfrac{1}{b} \;\cancel{=}\; \dfrac{1}{a+b}$	$\dfrac{1}{2} + \dfrac{1}{2} \neq \dfrac{1}{2+2}$
$(a+b)^2 \;\cancel{=}\; a^2 + b^2$	
$\sqrt{a^2 + b^2} \;\cancel{=}\; a + b$	
$\dfrac{a+b}{a} \;\cancel{=}\; b$	
$(a^3 + b^3)^{1/3} \;\cancel{=}\; a + b$	
$a^m / a^n \;\cancel{=}\; a^{m/n}$	
$a^{-1/n} \;\cancel{=}\; \dfrac{1}{a^n}$	

106. The Form of an Algebraic Expression An algebraic expression may look complicated, but its "form" is always simple; it must be a sum, a product, a quotient, or a power. For example, consider the following expressions:

$$(1 + x^2)^2 + \left(\frac{x+2}{x+1}\right)^3 \qquad (1+x)\left(1 + \frac{x+5}{1+x^4}\right)$$

$$\frac{5 - x^3}{1 + \sqrt{1 + x^2}} \qquad \sqrt{\frac{1+x}{1-x}}$$

With appropriate choices for A and B, the first has the form $A + B$, the second AB, the third A/B, and the fourth $A^{1/2}$. Recognizing the form of an expression helps us expand, simplify, or factor it correctly. Find the form of the following algebraic expressions.

(a) $x + \sqrt{1 + \dfrac{1}{x}}$ (b) $(1 + x^2)(1 + x)^3$

(c) $\sqrt[3]{x^4(4x^2 + 1)}$ (d) $\dfrac{1 - 2\sqrt{1+x}}{1 + \sqrt{1 + x^2}}$

1.5 EQUATIONS

SUGGESTED TIME
AND EMPHASIS
2 classes, essential material

Solving Linear Equations ▶ Solving Quadratic Equations ▶ Other Types of Equations

An equation is a statement that two mathematical expressions are equal. For example,

$$3 + 5 = 8$$

is an equation. Most equations that we study in algebra contain variables, which are symbols (usually letters) that stand for numbers. In the equation

$$4x + 7 = 19$$

the letter x is the variable. We think of x as the "unknown" in the equation, and our goal is to find the value of x that makes the equation true. The values of the unknown that make the equation true are called the **solutions** or **roots** of the equation, and the process of finding the solutions is called **solving the equation**.

Two equations with exactly the same solutions are called **equivalent equations**. To solve an equation, we try to find a simpler, equivalent equation in which the variable stands alone on one side of the "equal" sign. Here are the properties that we use to solve an equation. (In these properties, A, B, and C stand for any algebraic expressions, and the symbol $\Leftrightarrow$ means "is equivalent to.")

$x = 3$ is a solution of the equation $4x + 7 = 19$, because substituting $x = 3$ makes the equation true:

$$x = 3$$

$$4(3) + 7 = 19 \quad ✔$$

PROPERTIES OF EQUALITY

Property	Description
1. $A = B \quad \Leftrightarrow \quad A + C = B + C$	Adding the same quantity to both sides of an equation gives an equivalent equation.
2. $A = B \quad \Leftrightarrow \quad CA = CB \quad (C \neq 0)$	Multiplying both sides of an equation by the same nonzero quantity gives an equivalent equation.

TEXT QUESTIONS

1. Give two reasons why it is important to check your answer after you have solved an equation such as $2 + \dfrac{5}{x - 4} = \dfrac{x + 1}{x - 4}$.

2. Solve: $\dfrac{1}{x + 4} = \dfrac{1}{2x}$

Answers

1. First, we must make sure that our answer is not extraneous. Second, we should check that we have not made an error in calculation.

2. $x = 4$

These properties require that you *perform the same operation on both sides of an equation* when solving it. Thus, if we say "*add* −7" when solving an equation, that is just a short way of saying "*add* −7 to each side of the equation."

▼ Solving Linear Equations

The simplest type of equation is a *linear equation*, or first-degree equation, which is an equation in which each term is either a constant or a nonzero multiple of the variable.

LINEAR EQUATIONS

A **linear equation** in one variable is an equation equivalent to one of the form

$$ax + b = 0$$

where a and b are real numbers and x is the variable.

Here are some examples that illustrate the difference between linear and nonlinear equations.

Linear equations	Nonlinear equations	
$4x - 5 = 3$	$x^2 + 2x = 8$	Not linear; contains the square of the variable
$2x = \frac{1}{2}x - 7$	$\sqrt{x} - 6x = 0$	Not linear; contains the square root of the variable
$x - 6 = \dfrac{x}{3}$	$\dfrac{3}{x} - 2x = 1$	Not linear; contains the reciprocal of the variable

EXAMPLE 1 | Solving a Linear Equation

Solve the equation $7x - 4 = 3x + 8$.

SOLUTION We solve this by changing it to an equivalent equation with all terms that have the variable x on one side and all constant terms on the other.

$7x - 4 = 3x + 8$	Given equation
$(7x - 4) + 4 = (3x + 8) + 4$	Add 4
$7x = 3x + 12$	Simplify
$7x - 3x = (3x + 12) - 3x$	Subtract $3x$
$4x = 12$	Simplify
$\frac{1}{4} \cdot 4x = \frac{1}{4} \cdot 12$	Multiply by $\frac{1}{4}$
$x = 3$	Simplify

Because it is important to CHECK YOUR ANSWER, we do this in many of our examples. In these checks, LHS stands for "left-hand side" and RHS stands for "right-hand side" of the original equation.

CHECK YOUR ANSWER

$x = 3$:

$x = 3$ LHS = $7(3) - 4$ RHS = $3(3) + 8$
          = 17   = 17

LHS = RHS   ✔

✎ NOW TRY EXERCISE **15**

Many formulas in the sciences involve several variables, and it is often necessary to express one of the variables in terms of the others. In the next example we solve for a variable in Newton's Law of Gravity.

ALTERNATE EXAMPLE 1
Solve the equation
$6x - 5 = 2x + 11$.

ANSWER
$x = 4$

46 CHAPTER 1 **Fundamentals**

ALTERNATE EXAMPLE 2

Solve for the variable R in the equation $V = IR$.

ANSWER

$R = V/I$

ALTERNATE EXAMPLE 3

The surface area A of the closed rectangular box can be calculated from the length l, the width w, and the height h according to the formula

$$A = 2lw + 2wh + 2lh$$

Solve for l in terms of the other variables in this equation.

ANSWER

$$\frac{(A - 2wh)}{(2w + 2h)} = l$$

This is Newton's Law of Gravity. It gives the gravitational force F between two masses m and M that are a distance r apart. The constant G is the universal gravitational constant.

EXAMPLE 2 | Solving for One Variable in Terms of Others

Solve for the variable M in the equation

$$F = G\frac{mM}{r^2}$$

SOLUTION Although this equation involves more than one variable, we solve it as usual by isolating M on one side and treating the other variables as we would numbers.

$$F = \left(\frac{Gm}{r^2}\right)M \qquad \text{Factor } M \text{ from RHS}$$

$$\left(\frac{r^2}{Gm}\right)F = \left(\frac{r^2}{Gm}\right)\left(\frac{Gm}{r^2}\right)M \qquad \text{Multiply by reciprocal of } \frac{Gm}{r^2}$$

$$\frac{r^2 F}{Gm} = M \qquad \text{Simplify}$$

The solution is $M = \dfrac{r^2 F}{Gm}$.

✎. NOW TRY EXERCISE **29** ∎

EXAMPLE 3 | Solving for One Variable in Terms of Others

The surface area A of the closed rectangular box shown in Figure 1 can be calculated from the length l, the width w, and the height h according to the formula

$$A = 2lw + 2wh + 2lh$$

Solve for w in terms of the other variables in this equation.

SOLUTION Although this equation involves more than one variable, we solve it as usual by isolating w on one side, treating the other variables as we would numbers.

$$A = (2lw + 2wh) + 2lh \qquad \text{Collect terms involving } w$$

$$A - 2lh = 2lw + 2wh \qquad \text{Subtract } 2lh$$

$$A - 2lh = (2l + 2h)w \qquad \text{Factor } w \text{ from RHS}$$

$$\frac{A - 2lh}{2l + 2h} = w \qquad \text{Divide by } 2l + 2h$$

The solution is $w = \dfrac{A - 2lh}{2l + 2h}$.

✎. NOW TRY EXERCISE **31** ∎

FIGURE 1 A closed rectangular box

▼ Solving Quadratic Equations

Linear equations are first-degree equations like $2x + 1 = 5$ or $4 - 3x = 2$. Quadratic equations are second-degree equations like $x^2 + 2x - 3 = 0$ or $2x^2 + 3 = 5x$.

Quadratic Equations

$$x^2 - 2x - 8 = 0$$
$$3x + 10 = 4x^2$$
$$\tfrac{1}{2}x^2 + \tfrac{1}{3}x - \tfrac{1}{6} = 0$$

QUADRATIC EQUATIONS

A **quadratic equation** is an equation of the form

$$ax^2 + bx + c = 0$$

where a, b, and c are real numbers with $a \neq 0$.

Some quadratic equations can be solved by factoring and using the following basic property of real numbers.

ZERO-PRODUCT PROPERTY

$$AB = 0 \quad \text{if and only if} \quad A = 0 \quad \text{or} \quad B = 0$$

 This means that if we can factor the left-hand side of a quadratic (or other) equation, then we can solve it by setting each factor equal to 0 in turn. This method works only when the right-hand side of the equation is 0.

EXAMPLE 4 | Solving a Quadratic Equation by Factoring

Solve the equation $x^2 + 5x = 24$.

SOLUTION   We must first rewrite the equation so that the right-hand side is 0.

$$
\begin{array}{lll}
x^2 + 5x = 24 & & \\
x^2 + 5x - 24 = 0 & & \text{Subtract 24} \\
(x - 3)(x + 8) = 0 & & \text{Factor} \\
x - 3 = 0 \quad \text{or} \quad x + 8 = 0 & & \text{Zero-Product Property} \\
x = 3 \qquad\qquad x = -8 & & \text{Solve}
\end{array}
$$

The solutions are $x = 3$ and $x = -8$.

✎ NOW TRY EXERCISE **43**   ■

CHECK YOUR ANSWERS

$x = 3$:

$(3)^2 + 5(3) = 9 + 15 = 24$ ✔

$x = -8$:

$(-8)^2 + 5(-8) = 64 - 40 = 24$ ✔

Do you see why one side of the equation must be 0 in Example 4? Factoring the equation as $x(x + 5) = 24$ does not help us find the solutions, since 24 can be factored in infinitely many ways, such as $6 \cdot 4$, $\frac{1}{2} \cdot 48$, $\left(-\frac{2}{5}\right) \cdot (-60)$, and so on.

A quadratic equation of the form $x^2 - c = 0$, where c is a positive constant, factors as $(x - \sqrt{c})(x + \sqrt{c}) = 0$, so the solutions are $x = \sqrt{c}$ and $x = -\sqrt{c}$. We often abbreviate this as $x = \pm\sqrt{c}$.

SOLVING A SIMPLE QUADRATIC EQUATION

The solutions of the equation $x^2 = c$ are $x = \sqrt{c}$ and $x = -\sqrt{c}$.

EXAMPLE 5 | Solving Simple Quadratics

Solve each equation.

(a) $x^2 = 5$ **(b)** $(x - 4)^2 = 5$

SOLUTION

(a) From the principle in the preceding box, we get $x = \pm\sqrt{5}$.

(b) We can take the square root of each side of this equation as well.

$$
\begin{array}{ll}
(x - 4)^2 = 5 & \\
x - 4 = \pm\sqrt{5} & \text{Take the square root} \\
x = 4 \pm\sqrt{5} & \text{Add 4}
\end{array}
$$

The solutions are $x = 4 + \sqrt{5}$ and $x = 4 - \sqrt{5}$.

✎ NOW TRY EXERCISES **51** AND **53**   ■

IN-CLASS MATERIALS

There are two main anomalies that students may encounter when solving linear equations: $0 = 0$ and $1 = 0$. Although it is not a good idea to dwell on the anomalies, as opposed to focusing on the cases where the students will spend a majority of their time, it is good to address them, because they do come up in math class and in real life. Have the students attempt to solve the following equations, and check their work:

$$
\begin{array}{l}
3x + 4 = x + 6 \\
3x + 4 = x + 6 + 2x - 2 \\
3x + 4 = x + 6 + 2x + 2
\end{array}
$$

By the time this example is presented, most students should be able to obtain $x = 1$ for the first equation and to check this answer. The second one gives $0 = 0$. Point out that $0 = 0$ is always a true statement. (If you like, introduce the term *tautology*.) It is a true statement if $x = 1$, it is a true statement if $x = 2$, it is a true statement if the author Lemony Snicket writes another book, it is a true statement if he does not write another book. Therefore, students can test $x = 1$, $x = 2$, and $x = -\sqrt{2}$ in the second equation, and all of them will yield truth. The third statement gives $1 = 0$ (actually, it gives $0 = 4$, but we can multiply both sides of the equation by $\frac{1}{4}$). This is a false statement, no matter what value we assign to x.

See page 30 for how to recognize when a quadratic expression is a perfect square.

Completing the Square
The area of the blue region is

$$x^2 + 2\left(\frac{b}{2}\right)x = x^2 + bx$$

Add a small square of area $(b/2)^2$ to "complete" the square.

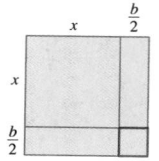

As we saw in Example 5, if a quadratic equation is of the form $(x \pm a)^2 = c$, then we can solve it by taking the square root of each side. In an equation of this form the left-hand side is a *perfect square*: the square of a linear expression in x. So if a quadratic equation does not factor readily, then we can solve it using the technique of **completing the square**. This means that we add a constant to an expression to make it a perfect square. For example, to make $x^2 - 6x$ a perfect square, we must add 9, since $x^2 - 6x + 9 = (x - 3)^2$.

COMPLETING THE SQUARE

To make $x^2 + bx$ a perfect square, add $\left(\dfrac{b}{2}\right)^2$, the square of half the coefficient of x. This gives the perfect square

$$x^2 + bx + \left(\frac{b}{2}\right)^2 = \left(x + \frac{b}{2}\right)^2$$

ALTERNATE EXAMPLE 6
Solve the equation
$5x^2 - 20x + 10 = 0$.

ANSWER
$x = 2 + \sqrt{2}, x = 2 - \sqrt{2}$

EXAMPLE 6 | Solving Quadratic Equations by Completing the Square

Solve each equation.

(a) $x^2 - 8x + 13 = 0$ **(b)** $3x^2 - 12x + 6 = 0$

SOLUTION

⊘ When completing the square, make sure the coefficient of x^2 is 1. If it isn't, you must factor this coefficient from both terms that contain x:

$$ax^2 + bx = a\left(x^2 + \frac{b}{a}x\right)$$

Then complete the square inside the parentheses. Remember that the term added inside the parentheses is multiplied by a.

(a)

$x^2 - 8x + 13 = 0$	Given equation
$x^2 - 8x = -13$	Subtract 13
$x^2 - 8x + 16 = -13 + 16$	Complete the square: add $\left(\dfrac{-8}{2}\right)^2 = 16$
$(x - 4)^2 = 3$	Perfect square
$x - 4 = \pm\sqrt{3}$	Take square root
$x = 4 \pm \sqrt{3}$	Add 4

(b) After subtracting 6 from each side of the equation, we must factor the coefficient of x^2 (the 3) from the left side to put the equation in the correct form for completing the square.

$3x^2 - 12x + 6 = 0$	Given equation
$3x^2 - 12x = -6$	Subtract 6
$3(x^2 - 4x) = -6$	Factor 3 from LHS

Now we complete the square by adding $(-2)^2 = 4$ *inside* the parentheses. Since everything inside the parentheses is multiplied by 3, this means that we are actually adding $3 \cdot 4 = 12$ to the left side of the equation. Thus, we must add 12 to the right side as well.

$3(x^2 - 4x + 4) = -6 + 3 \cdot 4$	Complete the square: add 4
$3(x - 2)^2 = 6$	Perfect square
$(x - 2)^2 = 2$	Divide by 3
$x - 2 = \pm\sqrt{2}$	Take square root
$x = 2 \pm \sqrt{2}$	Add 2

✎ NOW TRY EXERCISES **55** AND **59** ∎

IN-CLASS MATERIALS

The Zero-Product Property is the basis of various methods of solving quadratic equations. Many errors students make in solving these equations stem from misunderstanding the Zero-Product Property. Students should see the difference between these two equations:

$$(x - 2)(x - 3)(x - 4) = 0$$
$$(x - 2)(x - 3)(x - 4) = -24$$

Note how the solution to the first is immediate, whereas the solution to the second requires some work. ($x = 0$ is the only real solution to the second.)

We can use the technique of completing the square to derive a formula for the roots of the general quadratic equation $ax^2 + bx + c = 0$.

THE QUADRATIC FORMULA

The roots of the quadratic equation $ax^2 + bx + c = 0$, where $a \neq 0$, are

$$x = \frac{-b \pm \sqrt{b^2 - 4ac}}{2a}$$

PROOF   First, we divide each side of the equation by a and move the constant to the right side, giving

$$x^2 + \frac{b}{a}x = -\frac{c}{a} \qquad \text{Divide by } a$$

We now complete the square by adding $(b/2a)^2$ to each side of the equation:

$$x^2 + \frac{b}{a}x + \left(\frac{b}{2a}\right)^2 = -\frac{c}{a} + \left(\frac{b}{2a}\right)^2 \qquad \text{Complete the square: Add } \left(\frac{b}{2a}\right)^2$$

$$\left(x + \frac{b}{2a}\right)^2 = \frac{-4ac + b^2}{4a^2} \qquad \text{Perfect square}$$

$$x + \frac{b}{2a} = \pm\frac{\sqrt{b^2 - 4ac}}{2a} \qquad \text{Take square root}$$

$$x = \frac{-b \pm \sqrt{b^2 - 4ac}}{2a} \qquad \text{Subtract } \frac{b}{2a} \qquad \blacksquare$$

The Quadratic Formula could be used to solve the equations in Examples 4 and 6. You should carry out the details of these calculations.

EXAMPLE 7 | Using the Quadratic Formula

Find all solutions of each equation.

(a) $3x^2 - 5x - 1 = 0$ **(b)** $4x^2 + 12x + 9 = 0$ **(c)** $x^2 + 2x + 2 = 0$

SOLUTION

(a) In this quadratic equation $a = 3$, $b = -5$, and $c = -1$.

$$\overset{b = -5}{\underset{a = 3 \qquad c = -1}{3x^2 - 5x - 1 = 0}}$$

By the Quadratic Formula,

$$x = \frac{-(-5) \pm \sqrt{(-5)^2 - 4(3)(-1)}}{2(3)} = \frac{5 \pm \sqrt{37}}{6}$$

If approximations are desired, we can use a calculator to obtain

$$x = \frac{5 + \sqrt{37}}{6} \approx 1.8471 \qquad \text{and} \qquad x = \frac{5 - \sqrt{37}}{6} \approx -0.1805$$

(b) Using the Quadratic Formula with $a = 4$, $b = 12$, and $c = 9$ gives

$$x = \frac{-12 \pm \sqrt{(12)^2 - 4 \cdot 4 \cdot 9}}{2 \cdot 4} = \frac{-12 \pm 0}{8} = -\frac{3}{2}$$

This equation has only one solution, $x = -\frac{3}{2}$.

*Sidebar:*

FRANÇOIS VIÈTE (1540–1603) had a successful political career before taking up mathematics late in life. He became one of the most famous French mathematicians of the 16th century. Viète introduced a new level of abstraction in algebra by using letters to stand for *known* quantities in an equation. Before Viète's time, each equation had to be solved on its own. For instance, the quadratic equations

$$3x^2 + 2x + 8 = 0$$
$$5x^2 - 6x + 4 = 0$$

had to be solved separately by completing the square. Viète's idea was to consider all quadratic equations at once by writing

$$ax^2 + bx + c = 0$$

where a, b, and c are known quantities. Thus, he made it possible to write a *formula* (in this case, the quadratic formula) involving a, b, and c that can be used to solve all such equations in one fell swoop.

Viète's mathematical genius proved quite valuable during a war between France and Spain. To communicate with their troops, the Spaniards used a complicated code that Viète managed to decipher. Unaware of Viète's accomplishment, the Spanish king, Philip II, protested to the Pope, claiming that the French were using witchcraft to read his messages.

Another Method
$$4x^2 + 12x + 9 = 0$$
$$(2x + 3)^2 = 0$$
$$2x + 3 = 0$$
$$x = -\tfrac{3}{2}$$

*Margin (right):*

ALTERNATE EXAMPLE 7

Find all solutions of the equation $2x^2 - 3x - 1 = 0$.

ANSWER

$$x = \frac{3 \pm \sqrt{17}}{4}$$

IN-CLASS MATERIALS

Go through an example where the appearance of a quadratic equation may be unexpected. For example, assume that if we charge $200 for a pair of handmade shoes, we can sell 100 pairs. For every $5 we raise the price, we will sell one less pair. (Conversely, for every $5 we lower the price, we can sell one more pair.) At what prices will our revenue be $23,520? (Answer: $280, $420.) Point out that this is somewhat artificial—in practice we would be more interested in finding a maximum revenue or (ideally) maximum profit. Later (in Chapter 3) students will be able to solve such problems.

(c) Using the Quadratic Formula with $a = 1$, $b = 2$, and $c = 2$ gives

$$x = \frac{-2 \pm \sqrt{2^2 - 4 \cdot 2}}{2} = \frac{-2 \pm \sqrt{-4}}{2} = \frac{-2 \pm 2\sqrt{-1}}{2} = -1 \pm \sqrt{-1}$$

Since the square of any real number is nonnegative, $\sqrt{-1}$ is undefined in the real number system. The equation has no real solution.

◆. NOW TRY EXERCISES **65**, **69**, AND **75**   ■

In Section 3.5 we study the complex number system, in which the square roots of negative numbers do exist. The equation in Example 7(c) does have solutions in the complex number system.

The quantity $b^2 - 4ac$ that appears under the square root sign in the quadratic formula is called the *discriminant* of the equation $ax^2 + bx + c = 0$ and is given the symbol D. If $D < 0$, then $\sqrt{b^2 - 4ac}$ is undefined, and the quadratic equation has no real solution, as in Example 7(c). If $D = 0$, then the equation has only one real solution, as in Example 7(b). Finally, if $D > 0$, then the equation has two distinct real solutions, as in Example 7(a). The following box summarizes these observations.

> **THE DISCRIMINANT**
>
> The **discriminant** of the general quadratic $ax^2 + bx + c = 0$ $(a \neq 0)$ is $D = b^2 - 4ac$.
>
> **1.** If $D > 0$, then the equation has two distinct real solutions.
>
> **2.** If $D = 0$, then the equation has exactly one real solution.
>
> **3.** If $D < 0$, then the equation has no real solution.

EXAMPLE 8 | Using the Discriminant

Use the discriminant to determine how many real solutions each equation has.

(a) $x^2 + 4x - 1 = 0$ **(b)** $4x^2 - 12x + 9 = 0$ **(c)** $\frac{1}{3}x^2 - 2x + 4 = 0$

SOLUTION

(a) The discriminant is $D = 4^2 - 4(1)(-1) = 20 > 0$, so the equation has two distinct real solutions.

(b) The discriminant is $D = (-12)^2 - 4 \cdot 4 \cdot 9 = 0$, so the equation has exactly one real solution.

(c) The discriminant is $D = (-2)^2 - 4(\frac{1}{3})4 = -\frac{4}{3} < 0$, so the equation has no real solution.

◆. NOW TRY EXERCISES **79**, **81**, AND **83**   ■

Now let's consider a real-life situation that can be modeled by a quadratic equation.

EXAMPLE 9 | The Path of a Projectile

An object thrown or fired straight upward at an initial speed of v_0 ft/s will reach a height of h feet after t seconds, where h and t are related by the formula

$$h = -16t^2 + v_0 t$$

Suppose that a bullet is shot straight upward with an initial speed of 800 ft/s. Its path is shown in Figure 2.

(a) When does the bullet fall back to ground level?

(b) When does it reach a height of 6400 ft?

This formula depends on the fact that acceleration due to gravity is constant near the earth's surface. Here we neglect the effect of air resistance.

Resistors in series   Resistors in parallel

FIGURE 2

6400 ft

2 mi

10,000 ft

(c) When does it reach a height of 2 mi?

(d) How high is the highest point the bullet reaches?

SOLUTION Since the initial speed in this case is $v_0 = 800$ ft/s, the formula is

$$h = -16t^2 + 800t$$

(a) Ground level corresponds to $h = 0$, so we must solve the equation

$$0 = -16t^2 + 800t \qquad \text{Set } h = 0$$

$$0 = -16t(t - 50) \qquad \text{Factor}$$

Thus, $t = 0$ or $t = 50$. This means the bullet starts ($t = 0$) at ground level and returns to ground level after 50 s.

(b) Setting $h = 6400$ gives the equation

$$6400 = -16t^2 + 800t \qquad \text{Set } h = 6400$$

$$16t^2 - 800t + 6400 = 0 \qquad \text{All terms to LHS}$$

$$t^2 - 50t + 400 = 0 \qquad \text{Divide by 16}$$

$$(t - 10)(t - 40) = 0 \qquad \text{Factor}$$

$$t = 10 \quad \text{or} \quad t = 40 \qquad \text{Solve}$$

The bullet reaches 6400 ft after 10 s (on its ascent) and again after 40 s (on its descent to earth).

(c) Two miles is $2 \times 5280 = 10{,}560$ ft.

$$10{,}560 = -16t^2 + 800t \qquad \text{Set } h = 10{,}560$$

$$16t^2 - 800t + 10{,}560 = 0 \qquad \text{All terms to LHS}$$

$$t^2 - 50t + 660 = 0 \qquad \text{Divide by 16}$$

The discriminant of this equation is $D = (-50)^2 - 4(660) = -140$, which is negative. Thus, the equation has no real solution. The bullet never reaches a height of 2 mi.

(d) Each height the bullet reaches is attained twice, once on its ascent and once on its descent. The only exception is the highest point of its path, which is reached only once. This means that for the highest value of h, the following equation has only one solution for t:

$$h = -16t^2 + 800t$$

$$16t^2 - 800t + h = 0 \qquad \text{All terms to LHS}$$

This in turn means that the discriminant D of the equation is 0, so

$$D = (-800)^2 - 4(16)h = 0$$

$$640{,}000 - 64h = 0$$

$$h = 10{,}000$$

The maximum height reached is 10,000 ft.

✎ NOW TRY EXERCISE **111** ∎

▼ Other Types of Equations

So far we have learned how to solve linear and quadratic equations. Now we study other types of equations, including those that involve higher powers, fractional expressions, and radicals.

IN-CLASS MATERIALS

One can demonstrate an equation involving two square roots. For example: The square root of a number, plus one more than that number, is exactly 5. Find the number.

Answer

$$\sqrt{x} + (x + 1) = 5 \quad \Leftrightarrow \quad \sqrt{x} = 4 - x \quad \Leftrightarrow \quad x = (4 - x)^2 \quad \Leftrightarrow \quad x^2 - 9x + 16 = 0$$

The solutions to the quadratic are approximately 2.438 and 6.562. The latter proves to be extraneous, leaving 2.438 as the answer.

ALTERNATE EXAMPLE 10
Solve the equation
$$\frac{10}{x} + \frac{98}{x + 9} = 9.$$

ANSWER
$5, -2$

EXAMPLE 10 | An Equation Involving Fractional Expressions

Solve the equation $\dfrac{3}{x} + \dfrac{5}{x + 2} = 2$.

SOLUTION We eliminate the denominators by multiplying each side by the lowest common denominator.

$$\left(\frac{3}{x} + \frac{5}{x + 2}\right)x(x + 2) = 2x(x + 2) \qquad \text{Multiply by LCD } x(x + 2)$$

$$3(x + 2) + 5x = 2x^2 + 4x \qquad \text{Expand}$$

$$8x + 6 = 2x^2 + 4x \qquad \text{Expand LHS}$$

$$0 = 2x^2 - 4x - 6 \qquad \text{Subtract } 8x + 6$$

$$0 = x^2 - 2x - 3 \qquad \text{Divide both sides by 2}$$

$$0 = (x - 3)(x + 1) \qquad \text{Factor}$$

$$x - 3 = 0 \quad \text{or} \quad x + 1 = 0 \qquad \text{Zero-Product Property}$$

$$x = 3 \qquad\qquad x = -1 \qquad \text{Solve}$$

We must check our answers because multiplying by an expression that contains the variable can introduce extraneous solutions. From *Check Your Answers* we see that the solutions are $x = 3$ and -1.

✎. **NOW TRY EXERCISE 85** ■

CHECK YOUR ANSWERS

$x = 3$:

$$\text{LHS} = \frac{3}{3} + \frac{5}{3 + 2}$$
$$= 1 + 1 = 2$$
$$\text{RHS} = 2$$
$$\text{LHS} = \text{RHS} \quad ✔$$

$x = -1$:

$$\text{LHS} = \frac{3}{-1} + \frac{5}{-1 + 2}$$
$$= -3 + 5 = 2$$
$$\text{RHS} = 2$$
$$\text{LHS} = \text{RHS} \quad ✔$$

When you solve an equation that involves radicals, you must be especially careful to check your final answers. The next example demonstrates why.

EXAMPLE 11 | An Equation Involving a Radical

Solve the equation $2x = 1 - \sqrt{2 - x}$.

SOLUTION To eliminate the square root, we first isolate it on one side of the equal sign, then square:

$$2x - 1 = -\sqrt{2 - x} \qquad \text{Subtract 1}$$

$$(2x - 1)^2 = 2 - x \qquad \text{Square each side}$$

$$4x^2 - 4x + 1 = 2 - x \qquad \text{Expand LHS}$$

$$4x^2 - 3x - 1 = 0 \qquad \text{Add } -2 + x$$

$$(4x + 1)(x - 1) = 0 \qquad \text{Factor}$$

$$4x + 1 = 0 \quad \text{or} \quad x - 1 = 0 \qquad \text{Zero-Product Property}$$

$$x = -\tfrac{1}{4} \qquad\qquad x = 1 \qquad \text{Solve}$$

The values $x = -\frac{1}{4}$ and $x = 1$ are only potential solutions. We must check them to see if they satisfy the original equation. From *Check Your Answers* we see that $x = -\frac{1}{4}$ is a solution but $x = 1$ is not. The only solution is $x = -\frac{1}{4}$.

✎. **NOW TRY EXERCISE 91** ■

ALTERNATE EXAMPLE 11
Solve the equation
$$2x = 2 - \sqrt{6 - x}.$$

ANSWER
$x = -\dfrac{1}{4}$

CHECK YOUR ANSWERS

$x = -\frac{1}{4}$:

$$\text{LHS} = 2\left(-\tfrac{1}{4}\right) = -\tfrac{1}{2}$$
$$\text{RHS} = 1 - \sqrt{2 - \left(-\tfrac{1}{4}\right)}$$
$$= 1 - \sqrt{\tfrac{9}{4}}$$
$$= 1 - \tfrac{3}{2} = -\tfrac{1}{2}$$
$$\text{LHS} = \text{RHS} \quad ✔$$

$x = 1$:

$$\text{LHS} = 2(1) = 2$$
$$\text{RHS} = 1 - \sqrt{2 - 1}$$
$$= 1 - 1 = 0$$
$$\text{LHS} \neq \text{RHS} \quad ✗$$

When we solve an equation, we may end up with one or more **extraneous solutions**, that is, potential solutions that do not satisfy the original equation. In Example 11 the value $x = 1$ is an extraneous solution. Extraneous solutions may be introduced when we square each side of an equation because the operation of squaring can turn a false equation into a true one. For example, $-1 \neq 1$, but $(-1)^2 = 1^2$. Thus, the squared equation

IN-CLASS MATERIALS

It has been proved mathematically that any polynomial can be factored into the products of linear factors and irreducible quadratic factors. It has also been proved that if the degree of the polynomial is greater than four, there is no formula (analogous to the quadratic formula) that will allow us to find those factors in general.

may be true for more values of the variable than the original equation. That is why you must always check your answers to make sure that each satisfies the original equation.

An equation of the form $aW^2 + bW + c = 0$, where W is an algebraic expression, is an equation of **quadratic type**. We solve equations of quadratic type by substituting for the algebraic expression, as we see in the next two examples.

EXAMPLE 12 | A Fourth-Degree Equation of Quadratic Type

Find all solutions of the equation $x^4 - 8x^2 + 8 = 0$.

SOLUTION If we set $W = x^2$, then we get a quadratic equation in the new variable W:

$$(x^2)^2 - 8x^2 + 8 = 0 \qquad \text{Write } x^4 \text{ as } (x^2)^2$$
$$W^2 - 8W + 8 = 0 \qquad \text{Let } W = x^2$$
$$W = \frac{-(-8) \pm \sqrt{(-8)^2 - 4\cdot 8}}{2} = 4 \pm 2\sqrt{2} \qquad \text{Quadratic Formula}$$
$$x^2 = 4 \pm 2\sqrt{2} \qquad W = x^2$$
$$x = \pm\sqrt{4 \pm 2\sqrt{2}} \qquad \text{Take square roots}$$

So, there are four solutions:

$$\sqrt{4 + 2\sqrt{2}}, \qquad \sqrt{4 - 2\sqrt{2}}, \qquad -\sqrt{4 + 2\sqrt{2}}, \qquad -\sqrt{4 - 2\sqrt{2}}$$

Using a calculator, we obtain the approximations $x \approx 2.61, 1.08, -2.61, -1.08$.

✎. NOW TRY EXERCISE **95**

EXAMPLE 13 | An Equation Involving Fractional Powers

Find all solutions of the equation $x^{1/3} + x^{1/6} - 2 = 0$.

SOLUTION This equation is of quadratic type because if we let $W = x^{1/6}$, then $W^2 = (x^{1/6})^2 = x^{1/3}$.

$$x^{1/3} + x^{1/6} - 2 = 0$$
$$W^2 + W - 2 = 0 \qquad \text{Let } W = x^{1/6}$$
$$(W - 1)(W + 2) = 0 \qquad \text{Factor}$$
$$W - 1 = 0 \quad \text{or} \quad W + 2 = 0 \qquad \text{Zero-Product Property}$$
$$W = 1 \qquad\qquad W = -2 \qquad \text{Solve}$$
$$x^{1/6} = 1 \qquad\qquad x^{1/6} = -2 \qquad W = x^{1/6}$$
$$x = 1^6 = 1 \qquad x = (-2)^6 = 64 \qquad \text{Take the 6th power}$$

From *Check Your Answers* we see that $x = 1$ is a solution but $x = 64$ is not. The only solution is $x = 1$.

CHECK YOUR ANSWERS

$x = 1$:

LHS $= 1^{1/3} + 1^{1/6} - 2 = 0$

RHS $= 0$

LHS = RHS ✔

$x = 64$:

LHS $= 64^{1/3} + 64^{1/6} - 2$
$= 4 + 2 - 2 = 4$

RHS $= 0$

LHS ≠ RHS ✗

✎. NOW TRY EXERCISE **99**

ALTERNATE EXAMPLE 12
Find all solutions of the equation $x^4 - 8x^2 + 13 = 0$.

ANSWER
$x = \pm\sqrt{4 \pm \sqrt{3}}$

ALTERNATE EXAMPLE 13
Find all the solutions of the equation $x^{1/3} + x^{1/6} - 6 = 0$.

ANSWER
64

EXAMPLES

1. An equation with an extraneous solution: $\dfrac{x^2}{x+1} = \dfrac{x+2}{x+1}$

This simplifies to $x^2 - x - 2 = 0$, either by multiplying by $x + 1$ directly or by first subtracting the RHS from the LHS and simplifying. The students can verify that $x = -2$ and $x = 2$ are solutions and that $x = -1$ is an extraneous solution.

2. Quadratic equations with zero, one, and two solutions:
$$x^2 - 6x + 11 = 3 \text{ has two solutions, } x = 2 \text{ and } x = 4.$$
$$x^2 - 6x + 12 = 3 \text{ has one solution, } x = 3.$$
$$x^2 - 5x + 13 = 3 \text{ has no real solution.}$$

3. An equation in quadratic form:
$$(x^2 + 4x + 5)^2 - 3(x^2 + 4x + 5) + 2 = 0 \Rightarrow x = -3, x = -2, \text{ or } x = -1.$$

When solving equations that involve absolute values, we usually take cases.

EXAMPLE 14 | An Absolute Value Equation

Solve the equation $|2x - 5| = 3$.

SOLUTION   By the definition of absolute value, $|2x - 5| = 3$ is equivalent to

$$2x - 5 = 3 \qquad \text{or} \qquad 2x - 5 = -3$$
$$2x = 8 \qquad\qquad\qquad 2x = 2$$
$$x = 4 \qquad\qquad\qquad x = 1$$

The solutions are $x = 1$, $x = 4$.

✎. **NOW TRY EXERCISE 105**

1.5 EXERCISES

CONCEPTS

1. *True or false*?
   (a) Adding the same number to each side of an equation always gives an equivalent equation.
   (b) Multiplying each side of an equation by the same number always gives an equivalent equation.
   (c) Squaring each side of an equation always gives an equivalent equation.

2. Explain how you would use each method to solve the equation $x^2 - 4x - 5 = 0$.
   (a) By factoring: _____
   (b) By completing the square: _____
   (c) By using the Quadratic Formula: _____

3. (a) The solutions of the equation $x^2(x - 4) = 0$ are _____.
   (b) To solve the equation $x^3 - 4x^2 = 0$, we _____ the left-hand side.

4. Solve the equation $\sqrt{2x} + x = 0$ by doing the following steps.
   (a) Isolate the radical: _____.
   (b) Square both sides: _____.
   (c) The solutions of the resulting quadratic equation are _____.
   (d) The solution(s) that satisfy the original equation are _____.

5. The equation $(x + 1)^2 - 5(x + 1) + 6 = 0$ is of _____ type. To solve the equation, we set $W = $ _____. The resulting quadratic equation is _____.

6. The equation $x^6 + 7x^3 - 8 = 0$ is of _____ type. To solve the equation, we set $W = $ _____. The resulting quadratic equation is _____.

SKILLS

7–10 ■ Determine whether the given value is a solution of the equation.

7. $4x + 7 = 9x - 3$
   (a) $x = -2$ (b) $x = 2$

8. $1 - [2 - (3 - x)] = 4x - (6 + x)$
   (a) $x = 2$ (b) $x = 4$

9. $\dfrac{1}{x} - \dfrac{1}{x - 4} = 1$
   (a) $x = 2$ (b) $x = 4$

10. $\dfrac{x^{3/2}}{x - 6} = x - 8$
   (a) $x = 4$ (b) $x = 8$

11–28 ■ The given equation is either linear or equivalent to a linear equation. Solve the equation.

11. $2x + 7 = 31$

12. $5x - 3 = 4$

13. $\frac{1}{2}x - 8 = 1$

14. $3 + \frac{1}{3}x = 5$

15. $-7w = 15 - 2w$

16. $5t - 13 = 12 - 5t$

17. $\frac{1}{2}y - 2 = \frac{1}{3}y$

18. $\dfrac{z}{5} = \dfrac{3}{10}z + 7$

19. $2(1 - x) = 3(1 + 2x) + 5$

20. $\dfrac{2}{3}y + \dfrac{1}{2}(y - 3) = \dfrac{y + 1}{4}$

21. $x - \frac{1}{3}x - \frac{1}{2}x - 5 = 0$

22. $2x - \dfrac{x}{2} + \dfrac{x + 1}{4} = 6x$

23. $\dfrac{1}{x} = \dfrac{4}{3x} + 1$

24. $\dfrac{2x - 1}{x + 2} = \dfrac{4}{5}$

25. $\dfrac{3}{x + 1} - \dfrac{1}{2} = \dfrac{1}{3x + 3}$

26. $\dfrac{4}{x - 1} + \dfrac{2}{x + 1} = \dfrac{35}{x^2 - 1}$

27. $(t - 4)^2 = (t + 4)^2 + 32$

28. $\sqrt{3}x + \sqrt{12} = \dfrac{x + 5}{\sqrt{3}}$

29–42 ■ Solve the equation for the indicated variable.

29. $PV = nRT$; for R

30. $F = G\dfrac{mM}{r^2}$; for m

31. $P = 2l + 2w$; for w **32.** $\dfrac{1}{R} = \dfrac{1}{R_1} + \dfrac{1}{R_2}$; for R_1

33. $\dfrac{ax + b}{cx + d} = 2$; for x

34. $a - 2[b - 3(c - x)] = 6$; for x

35. $a^2x + (a - 1) = (a + 1)x$; for x

36. $\dfrac{a + 1}{b} = \dfrac{a - 1}{b} + \dfrac{b + 1}{a}$; for a

37. $V = \frac{1}{3}\pi r^2 h$; for r **38.** $F = G\dfrac{mM}{r^2}$; for r

39. $a^2 + b^2 = c^2$; for b

40. $A = P\left(1 + \dfrac{i}{100}\right)^2$; for i

41. $h = \frac{1}{2}gt^2 + v_0 t$; for t **42.** $S = \dfrac{n(n + 1)}{2}$; for n

43–54 ■ Solve the equation by factoring.

43. $x^2 + x - 12 = 0$ **44.** $x^2 + 3x - 4 = 0$

45. $x^2 - 7x + 12 = 0$ **46.** $x^2 + 8x + 12 = 0$

47. $4x^2 - 4x - 15 = 0$ **48.** $2y^2 + 7y + 3 = 0$

49. $3x^2 + 5x = 2$ **50.** $6x(x - 1) = 21 - x$

51. $2x^2 = 8$ **52.** $3x^2 - 27 = 0$

53. $(3x + 2)^2 = 10$ **54.** $(2x - 1)^2 = 8$

55–62 ■ Solve the equation by completing the square.

55. $x^2 + 2x - 5 = 0$ **56.** $x^2 - 4x + 2 = 0$

57. $x^2 - 6x - 11 = 0$ **58.** $x^2 + 3x - \frac{7}{4} = 0$

59. $2x^2 + 8x + 1 = 0$ **60.** $3x^2 - 6x - 1 = 0$

61. $4x^2 - x = 0$ **62.** $x^2 = \frac{3}{4}x - \frac{1}{8}$

63–78 ■ Find all real solutions of the quadratic equation.

63. $x^2 - 2x - 15 = 0$ **64.** $x^2 + 5x - 6 = 0$

65. $x^2 - 7x + 10 = 0$ **66.** $x^2 + 30x + 200 = 0$

67. $2x^2 + x - 3 = 0$ **68.** $3x^2 + 7x + 4 = 0$

69. $3x^2 + 6x - 5 = 0$ **70.** $x^2 - 6x + 1 = 0$

71. $z^2 - \frac{3}{2}z + \frac{9}{16} = 0$ **72.** $2y^2 - y - \frac{1}{2} = 0$

73. $4x^2 + 16x - 9 = 0$ **74.** $0 = x^2 - 4x + 1$

75. $w^2 = 3(w - 1)$ **76.** $3 + 5z + z^2 = 0$

77. $10y^2 - 16y + 5 = 0$ **78.** $25x^2 + 70x + 49 = 0$

79–84 ■ Use the discriminant to determine the number of real solutions of the equation. Do not solve the equation.

79. $x^2 - 6x + 1 = 0$ **80.** $3x^2 = 6x - 9$

81. $x^2 + 2.20x + 1.21 = 0$ **82.** $x^2 + 2.21x + 1.21 = 0$

83. $4x^2 + 5x + \frac{13}{8} = 0$ **84.** $x^2 + rx - s = 0$ $(s > 0)$

85–108 ■ Find all real solutions of the equation.

85. $\dfrac{1}{x - 1} + \dfrac{1}{x + 2} = \dfrac{5}{4}$ **86.** $\dfrac{10}{x} - \dfrac{12}{x - 3} + 4 = 0$

87. $\dfrac{x^2}{x + 100} = 50$ **88.** $\dfrac{1}{x - 1} - \dfrac{2}{x^2} = 0$

89. $\dfrac{x + 5}{x - 2} = \dfrac{5}{x + 2} + \dfrac{28}{x^2 - 4}$ **90.** $\dfrac{x}{2x + 7} - \dfrac{x + 1}{x + 3} = 1$

91. $\sqrt{2x + 1} + 1 = x$ **92.** $\sqrt{5 - x} + 1 = x - 2$

93. $2x + \sqrt{x + 1} = 8$ **94.** $\sqrt{\sqrt{x - 5} + x} = 5$

95. $x^4 - 13x^2 + 40 = 0$ **96.** $x^4 - 5x^2 + 4 = 0$

97. $2x^4 + 4x^2 + 1 = 0$ **98.** $x^6 - 2x^3 - 3 = 0$

99. $x^{4/3} - 5x^{2/3} + 6 = 0$ **100.** $\sqrt{x} - 3\sqrt[4]{x} - 4 = 0$

101. $4(x + 1)^{1/2} - 5(x + 1)^{3/2} + (x + 1)^{5/2} = 0$

102. $x^{1/2} + 3x^{-1/2} = 10x^{-3/2}$

103. $x^{1/2} - 3x^{1/3} = 3x^{1/6} - 9$ **104.** $x - 5\sqrt{x} + 6 = 0$

105. $|3x + 5| = 1$ **106.** $|2x| = 3$

107. $|x - 4| = 0.01$ **108.** $|x - 6| = -1$

APPLICATIONS

109–110 ■ **Falling-Body Problems** Suppose an object is dropped from a height h_0 above the ground. Then its height after t seconds is given by $h = -16t^2 + h_0$, where h is measured in feet. Use this information to solve the problem.

109. If a ball is dropped from 288 ft above the ground, how long does it take to reach ground level?

110. A ball is dropped from the top of a building 96 ft tall.
    (a) How long will it take to fall half the distance to ground level?
    (b) How long will it take to fall to ground level?

111–112 ■ **Falling-Body Problems** Use the formula $h = -16t^2 + v_0 t$ discussed in Example 9.

111. A ball is thrown straight upward at an initial speed of $v_0 = 40$ ft/s.
    (a) When does the ball reach a height of 24 ft?
    (b) When does it reach a height of 48 ft?
    (c) What is the greatest height reached by the ball?
    (d) When does the ball reach the highest point of its path?
    (e) When does the ball hit the ground?

112. How fast would a ball have to be thrown upward to reach a maximum height of 100 ft?   [*Hint:* Use the discriminant of the equation $16t^2 - v_0 t + h = 0$.]

113. **Shrinkage in Concrete Beams** As concrete dries, it shrinks—the higher the water content, the greater the shrinkage. If a concrete beam has a water content of w kg/m³, then it will shrink by a factor

$$S = \dfrac{0.032w - 2.5}{10,000}$$

where S is the fraction of the original beam length that disappears due to shrinkage.
    (a) A beam 12.025 m long is cast in concrete that contains 250 kg/m³ water. What is the shrinkage factor S? How long will the beam be when it has dried?

(b) A beam is 10.014 m long when wet. We want it to shrink to 10.009 m, so the shrinkage factor should be $S = 0.00050$. What water content will provide this amount of shrinkage?

114. The Lens Equation If F is the focal length of a convex lens and an object is placed at a distance x from the lens, then its image will be at a distance y from the lens, where F, x, and y are related by the *lens equation*

$$\frac{1}{F} = \frac{1}{x} + \frac{1}{y}$$

Suppose that a lens has a focal length of 4.8 cm and that the image of an object is 4 cm closer to the lens than the object itself. How far from the lens is the object?

115. Fish Population The fish population in a certain lake rises and falls according to the formula

$$F = 1000(30 + 17t - t^2)$$

Here F is the number of fish at time t, where t is measured in years since January 1, 2002, when the fish population was first estimated.

(a) On what date will the fish population again be the same as it was on January 1, 2002?

(b) By what date will all the fish in the lake have died?

116. Fish Population A large pond is stocked with fish. The fish population P is modeled by the formula $P = 3t + 10\sqrt{t} + 140$, where t is the number of days since the fish were first introduced into the pond. How many days will it take for the fish population to reach 500?

117. Profit A small-appliance manufacturer finds that the profit P (in dollars) generated by producing x microwave ovens per week is given by the formula $P = \frac{1}{10}x(300 - x)$ provided that $0 \le x \le 200$. How many ovens must be manufactured in a given week to generate a profit of $1250?

118. Gravity If an imaginary line segment is drawn between the centers of the earth and the moon, then the net gravitational force F acting on an object situated on this line segment is

$$F = \frac{-K}{x^2} + \frac{0.012K}{(239 - x)^2}$$

where $K > 0$ is a constant and x is the distance of the object from the center of the earth, measured in thousands of miles. How far from the center of the earth is the "dead spot" where no net gravitational force acts upon the object? (Express your answer to the nearest thousand miles.)

119. Depth of a Well One method for determining the depth of a well is to drop a stone into it and then measure the time it takes until the splash is heard. If d is the depth of the well (in feet) and t_1 the time (in seconds) it takes for the stone to fall, then $d = 16t_1^2$, so $t_1 = \sqrt{d}/4$. Now if t_2 is the time it takes for the sound to travel back up, then $d = 1090t_2$ because the speed of sound is 1090 ft/s. So $t_2 = d/1090$. Thus, the total time elapsed between dropping the stone and hearing the splash is

$$t_1 + t_2 = \frac{\sqrt{d}}{4} + \frac{d}{1090}$$

How deep is the well if this total time is 3 s?

Time stone falls: $t_1 = \frac{\sqrt{d}}{4}$

Time sound rises: $t_2 = \frac{d}{1090}$

DISCOVERY ▪ DISCUSSION ▪ WRITING

120. A Family of Equations The equation

$$3x + k - 5 = kx - k + 1$$

is really a **family of equations**, because for each value of k, we get a different equation with the unknown x. The letter k is called a **parameter** for this family. What value should we pick for k to make the given value of x a solution of the resulting equation?

(a) $x = 0$ **(b)** $x = 1$ **(c)** $x = 2$

121. Proof That 0 = 1? The following steps appear to give equivalent equations, which seem to prove that $1 = 0$. Find the error.

$x = 1$	Given
$x^2 = x$	Multiply by x
$x^2 - x = 0$	Subtract x
$x(x - 1) = 0$	Factor
$\dfrac{x(x - 1)}{x - 1} = \dfrac{0}{x - 1}$	Divide by $x - 1$
$x = 0$	Simplify
$1 = 0$	Given $x = 1$

122. Volumes of Solids The sphere, cylinder, and cone shown here all have the same radius r and the same volume V.

(a) Use the volume formulas given on the inside front cover of this book, to show that

$$\tfrac{4}{3}\pi r^3 = \pi r^2 h_1 \qquad \text{and} \qquad \tfrac{4}{3}\pi r^3 = \tfrac{1}{3}\pi r^2 h_2$$

(b) Solve these equations for h_1 and h_2.

123. Relationship Between Roots and Coefficients
The Quadratic Formula gives us the roots of a quadratic equation from its coefficients. We can also obtain the coefficients from the roots. For example, find the roots of the equation $x^2 - 9x + 20 = 0$ and show that the product of the roots is the constant term 20 and the sum of the roots is 9, the negative of the coefficient of x. Show that the same relationship between roots and coefficients holds for the following equations:

$$x^2 - 2x - 8 = 0$$
$$x^2 + 4x + 2 = 0$$

Use the Quadratic Formula to prove that in general, if the equation $x^2 + bx + c = 0$ has roots r_1 and r_2, then $c = r_1 r_2$ and $b = -(r_1 + r_2)$.

124. Solving an Equation in Different Ways We have learned several different ways to solve an equation in this section. Some equations can be tackled by more than one method. For example, the equation $x - \sqrt{x} - 2 = 0$ is of quadratic type. We can solve it by letting $\sqrt{x} = u$ and $x = u^2$, and factoring. Or we could solve for $\sqrt{x}$, square each side, and then solve the resulting quadratic equation. Solve the following equations using both methods indicated, and show that you get the same final answers.

(a) $x - \sqrt{x} - 2 = 0$ quadratic type; solve for the radical, and square

(b) $\dfrac{12}{(x-3)^2} + \dfrac{10}{x-3} + 1 = 0$ quadratic type; multiply by LCD

1.6 MODELING WITH EQUATIONS

Making and Using Models ▶ Problems About Interest ▶ Problems About Area or Length ▶ Problems About Mixtures ▶ Problems About the Time Needed to Do a Job ▶ Problems About Distance, Rate, and Time

Many problems in the sciences, economics, finance, medicine, and numerous other fields can be translated into algebra problems; this is one reason that algebra is so useful. In this section we use equations as mathematical models to solve real-life problems.

▼ Making and Using Models

We will use the following guidelines to help us set up equations that model situations described in words. To show how the guidelines can help you to set up equations, we note them as we work each example in this section.

GUIDELINES FOR MODELING WITH EQUATIONS

1. **Identify the Variable.** Identify the quantity that the problem asks you to find. This quantity can usually be determined by a careful reading of the question that is posed at the end of the problem. Then **introduce notation** for the variable (call it x or some other letter).

2. **Translate from Words to Algebra.** Read each sentence in the problem again, and express all the quantities mentioned in the problem in terms of the variable you defined in Step 1. To organize this information, it is sometimes helpful to **draw a diagram** or **make a table**.

3. **Set Up the Model.** Find the crucial fact in the problem that gives a relationship between the expressions you listed in Step 2. **Set up an equation** (or **model**) that expresses this relationship.

4. **Solve the Equation and Check Your Answer.** Solve the equation, check your answer, and express it as a sentence that answers the question posed in the problem.

SUGGESTED TIME AND EMPHASIS
1 class, essential material

TEXT QUESTION
Discuss one of the problems presented in this section. You don't have to use any specific numbers, but describe the problem and the method of solution.

The following example illustrates how these guidelines are used to translate a "word problem" into the language of algebra.

EXAMPLE 1 | Renting a Car

A car rental company charges $30 a day and 15¢ a mile for renting a car. Helen rents a car for two days, and her bill comes to $108. How many miles did she drive?

SOLUTION

Identify the variable.   We are asked to find the number of miles Helen has driven. So we let

$$x = \text{number of miles driven}$$

Translate from words to algebra.   Now we translate all the information given in the problem into the language of algebra.

In Words	In Algebra
Number of miles driven	x
Mileage cost (at $0.15 per mile)	$0.15x$
Daily cost (at $30 per day)	$2(30)$

Set up the model.   Now we set up the model.

$$\boxed{\text{mileage cost}} \; + \; \boxed{\text{daily cost}} \; = \; \boxed{\text{total cost}}$$

$$0.15x + 2(30) = 108$$

Solve.   Now we solve for x.

$$0.15x = 48 \qquad \text{Subtract 60}$$

$$x = \frac{48}{0.15} \qquad \text{Divide by 0.15}$$

$$x = 320 \qquad \text{Calculator}$$

Helen drove her rental car 320 miles.

NOW TRY EXERCISE 19 ■

CHECK YOUR ANSWER

total cost = mileage cost + daily cost

$$= 0.15(320) + 2(30)$$

$$= 108 \;\checkmark$$

In the examples and exercises that follow, we construct equations that model problems in many different real-life situations.

▼ Problems About Interest

When you borrow money from a bank or when a bank "borrows" your money by keeping it for you in a savings account, the borrower in each case must pay for the privilege of using the money. The fee that is paid is called **interest**. The most basic type of interest is **simple interest**, which is just an annual percentage of the total amount borrowed or deposited. The amount of a loan or deposit is called the **principal** P. The annual percentage paid for the use of this money is the **interest rate** r. We will use the variable t to stand for the number of years that the money is on deposit and the variable I to stand for the total interest earned. The following **simple interest formula** gives the amount of interest I earned when a principal P is deposited for t years at an interest rate r.

$$\boxed{I = Prt}$$

When using this formula, remember to convert r from a percentage to a decimal. For example, in decimal form, 5% is 0.05. So at an interest rate of 5%, the interest paid on a $1000 deposit over a 3-year period is $I = Prt = 1000(0.05)(3) = \$150$.

EXAMPLE 2 | Interest on an Investment

Mary inherits $100,000 and invests it in two certificates of deposit. One certificate pays 6% and the other pays $4\frac{1}{2}$% simple interest annually. If Mary's total interest is $5025 per year, how much money is invested at each rate?

SOLUTION

Identify the variable.   The problem asks for the amount she has invested at each rate. So we let

$$x = \text{the amount invested at 6\%}$$

Translate from words to algebra.   Since Mary's total inheritance is $100,000, it follows that she invested $100,000 - x$ at $4\frac{1}{2}$%. We translate all the information given into the language of algebra.

In Words	In Algebra
Amount invested at 6%	x
Amount invested at $4\frac{1}{2}$%	$100,000 - x$
Interest earned at 6%	$0.06x$
Interest earned at $4\frac{1}{2}$%	$0.045(100,000 - x)$

Set up the model.   We use the fact that Mary's total interest is $5025 to set up the model.

$$\boxed{\text{interest at 6\%}} + \boxed{\text{interest at }4\tfrac{1}{2}\%} = \boxed{\text{total interest}}$$

$$0.06x + 0.045(100,000 - x) = 5025$$

Solve.   Now we solve for x.

$$0.06x + 4500 - 0.045x = 5025 \qquad \text{Distributive Property}$$
$$0.015x + 4500 = 5025 \qquad \text{Combine the } x\text{-terms}$$
$$0.015x = 525 \qquad \text{Subtract 4500}$$
$$x = \frac{525}{0.015} = 35,000 \qquad \text{Divide by 0.015}$$

So Mary has invested $35,000 at 6% and the remaining $65,000 at $4\frac{1}{2}$%.

CHECK YOUR ANSWER

$$\text{total interest} = 6\% \text{ of } \$35,000 + 4\tfrac{1}{2}\% \text{ of } \$65,000$$
$$= \$2100 + \$2925 = \$5025 \quad \checkmark$$

NOW TRY EXERCISE 21 ∎

▼ Problems About Area or Length

When we use algebra to model a physical situation, we must sometimes use basic formulas from geometry. For example, we may need a formula for an area or a perimeter, or the formula that relates the sides of similar triangles, or the Pythagorean Theorem. Most of these formulas are listed in the front endpapers of this book. The next two examples use these geometric formulas to solve some real-world problems.

ALTERNATE EXAMPLE 2
Mary inherits $100,000 and invests it in two certificates of deposit. One certificate pays 6% and the other pays $4\frac{1}{2}$% simple interest annually.

If Mary's total interest is $5775 per year, how much money is invested at each rate?

ANSWER
$85,000; $15,000

ALTERNATE EXAMPLE 3

A poster has a rectangular printed area 140 cm by 180 cm and a blank strip of uniform width around the four edges. The perimeter of the poster is $1\frac{1}{2}$ times the perimeter of the printed area.

Find the width of the blank strip and the dimensions of the poster.

ANSWER

40 cm, 260 cm × 220 cm

ALTERNATE EXAMPLE 4

A rectangular building lot is 6 ft longer than it is wide and has an area of 3960 ft². Find the dimensions of the lot.

ANSWER

(60, 66)

EXAMPLE 3 | Dimensions of a Garden

A square garden has a walkway 3 ft wide around its outer edge, as shown in Figure 1. If the area of the entire garden, including the walkway, is 18,000 ft², what are the dimensions of the planted area?

SOLUTION

Identify the variable. We are asked to find the length and width of the planted area. So we let

$$x = \text{the length of the planted area}$$

Translate from words to algebra. Next, translate the information from Figure 1 into the language of algebra.

In Words	In Algebra
Length of planted area	x
Length of entire garden	$x + 6$
Area of entire garden	$(x + 6)^2$

Set up the model. We now set up the model.

$$\boxed{\text{area of entire garden}} = \boxed{18{,}000 \text{ ft}^2}$$

$$(x + 6)^2 = 18{,}000$$

Solve. Now we solve for x.

$$x + 6 = \sqrt{18{,}000} \qquad \text{Take square roots}$$

$$x = \sqrt{18{,}000} - 6 \qquad \text{Subtract 6}$$

$$x \approx 128$$

The planted area of the garden is about 128 ft by 128 ft.

✎ NOW TRY EXERCISE **47** ∎

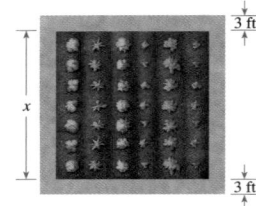

FIGURE 1

EXAMPLE 4 | Dimensions of a Building Lot

A rectangular building lot is 8 ft longer than it is wide and has an area of 2900 ft². Find the dimensions of the lot.

SOLUTION

Identify the variable. We are asked to find the width and length of the lot. So let

$$w = \text{width of lot}$$

Translate from words to algebra. Then we translate the information given in the problem into the language of algebra (see Figure 2).

In Words	In Algebra
Width of lot	w
Length of Lot	$w + 8$

Set up the model. Now we set up the model.

$$\boxed{\text{width of lot}} \cdot \boxed{\text{length of lot}} = \boxed{\text{area of lot}}$$

$$w(w + 8) = 2900$$

Solve.   Now we solve for w.

$$w^2 + 8w = 2900 \qquad \text{Expand}$$

$$w^2 + 8w - 2900 = 0 \qquad \text{Subtract 2900}$$

$$(w - 50)(w + 58) = 0 \qquad \text{Factor}$$

$$w = 50 \quad \text{or} \quad w = -58 \qquad \text{Zero-Product Property}$$

Since the width of the lot must be a positive number, we conclude that $w = 50$ ft. The length of the lot is $w + 8 = 50 + 8 = 58$ ft.

FIGURE 2

w

$w + 8$

◥ NOW TRY EXERCISE **39**

EXAMPLE 5 | Determining the Height of a Building Using Similar Triangles

A man who is 6 ft tall wishes to find the height of a certain four-story building. He measures its shadow and finds it to be 28 ft long, while his own shadow is $3\frac{1}{2}$ ft long. How tall is the building?

SOLUTION

Identify the variable.   The problem asks for the height of the building. So let

$$h = \text{the height of the building}$$

Translate from words to algebra.   We use the fact that the triangles in Figure 3 are similar. Recall that for any pair of similar triangles the ratios of corresponding sides are equal. Now we translate these observations into the language of algebra.

In Words	In Algebra
Height of building	h
Ratio of height to base in large triangle	$\frac{h}{28}$
Ratio of height to base in small triangle	$\frac{6}{3.5}$

FIGURE 3

h

6 ft

28 ft

$3\frac{1}{2}$ ft

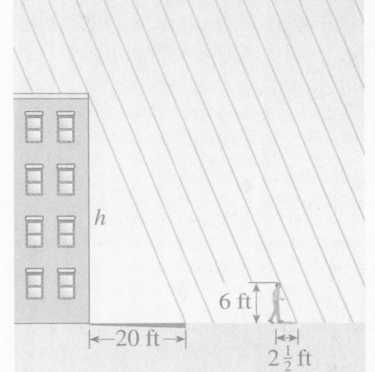
IN-CLASS MATERIALS

Here is a simple-sounding problem: A person is currently making $25,000 a year (after taxes) working at a large company and has an opportunity to quit the job and make $35,000 independently. Is this a good deal financially? Elicit other considerations. For example: insurance tends to cost $400 per month for an individual—the company is no longer paying for that. Taxes will be roughly 30%. The large company probably pays some percentage (say 2%) toward a retirement account. Based on the discussion of your particular class, come up with a linear equation that converts an annual gross income for an independent contractor to a net income, and then figure out how much the independent contractor would have to charge to net $25,000. Other hard-to-quantify considerations may come up, such as paid vacations, sick leave, "being one's own boss," the tax benefits of having a home office, quality of life, and so forth. Acknowledge these considerations, and perhaps (for purposes of comparison) try to quantify them. Perhaps assume that the tax benefits for the home office add 5% to the gross income. Ask the class if the pleasure of not having a boss is worth, say, $2000 a year. (On the other hand, would they get any work done at all without a boss standing over them?) This is a real-life modeling situation that, every year, more and more people find themselves thinking about.

Set up the model.   Since the large and small triangles are similar, we get the equation

ratio of height to base in large triangle	=	ratio of height to base in small triangle

$$\frac{h}{28} = \frac{6}{3.5}$$

Solve.   Now we solve for h.

$$h = \frac{6 \cdot 28}{3.5} = 48 \qquad \text{Multiply by 28}$$

So the building is 48 ft tall.

✎ **NOW TRY EXERCISE 51** ∎

▼ Problems About Mixtures

Many real-world problems involve mixing different types of substances. For example, construction workers may mix cement, gravel, and sand; fruit juice from concentrate may involve mixing different types of juices. Problems involving mixtures and concentrations make use of the fact that if an amount x of a substance is dissolved in a solution with volume V, then the concentration C of the substance is given by

$$C = \frac{x}{V}$$

So if 10 g of sugar is dissolved in 5 L of water, then the sugar concentration is $C = 10/5 = 2$ g/L. Solving a mixture problem usually requires us to analyze the amount x of the substance that is in the solution. When we solve for x in this equation, we see that $x = CV$. Note that in many mixture problems the concentration C is expressed as a percentage, as in the next example.

EXAMPLE 6 | Mixtures and Concentration

A manufacturer of soft drinks advertises their orange soda as "naturally flavored," although it contains only 5% orange juice. A new federal regulation stipulates that to be called "natural," a drink must contain at least 10% fruit juice. How much pure orange juice must this manufacturer add to 900 gal of orange soda to conform to the new regulation?

SOLUTION

Identify the variable.   The problem asks for the amount of pure orange juice to be added. So let

$$x = \text{the amount (in gallons) of pure orange juice to be added}$$

Translate from words to algebra.   In any problem of this type—in which two different substances are to be mixed—drawing a diagram helps us to organize the given information (see Figure 4).

The information in the figure can be translated into the language of algebra, as follows:

In Words	In Algebra
Amount of orange juice to be added	x
Amount of the mixture	$900 + x$
Amount of orange juice in the first vat	$0.05(900) = 45$
Amount of orange juice in the second vat	$1 \cdot x = x$
Amount of orange juice in the mixture	$0.10(900 + x)$

IN-CLASS MATERIALS

This section is particularly suited to having students come up with their own problems to solve or have others solve. Once they understand the concept, with a little (or a lot of) thought, they should be able to come up with practical, relevant problems. If students need a little prompting (try to get away without such prompting), you can wonder how many recordable CDs one would have to buy to store a hard drive full of music, how many people one could invite to a party that has a firm budget of $200 (have them list fixed costs and per-person costs), how many miles one could drive a car (paying all expenses) for $2000/year, etc.

FIGURE 4

Volume	900 gallons	x gallons	$900 + x$ gallons
Amount of orange juice	5% of 900 gallons = 45 gallons	100% of x gallons = x gallons	10% of $900 + x$ gallons = $0.1(900 + x)$ gallons

Set up the model. To set up the model, we use the fact that the total amount of orange juice in the mixture is equal to the orange juice in the first two vats.

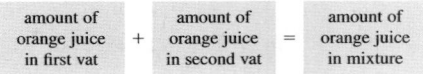

$$45 + x = 0.1(900 + x) \qquad \text{From Figure 4}$$

Solve. Now we solve for x.

$$45 + x = 90 + 0.1x \qquad \text{Distributive Property}$$
$$0.9x = 45 \qquad \text{Subtract } 0.1x \text{ and } 45$$
$$x = \frac{45}{0.9} = 50 \qquad \text{Divide by } 0.9$$

The manufacturer should add 50 gal of pure orange juice to the soda.

CHECK YOUR ANSWER

amount of juice before mixing = 5% of 900 gal + 50 gal pure juice

= 45 gal + 50 gal = 95 gal

amount of juice after mixing = 10% of 950 gal = 95 gal

Amounts are equal.   ✔

◥. **NOW TRY EXERCISE 53**

▼ Problems About the Time Needed to Do a Job

When solving a problem that involves determining how long it takes several workers to complete a job, we use the fact that if a person or machine takes H time units to complete the task, then in one time unit the fraction of the task that has been completed is $1/H$. For example, if a worker takes 5 hours to mow a lawn, then in 1 hour the worker will mow 1/5 of the lawn.

EXAMPLE 7 | Time Needed to Do a Job

Because of an anticipated heavy rainstorm, the water level in a reservoir must be lowered by 1 ft. Opening spillway A lowers the level by this amount in 4 hours, whereas opening the smaller spillway B does the job in 6 hours. How long will it take to lower the water level by 1 ft if both spillways are opened?

ALTERNATE EXAMPLE 7

It takes 8 hours for a cheap pump to clear out a flooded basement. It takes only 5 hours for an expensive pump to do so. How long would it take if we owned one of each?

ANSWER

$\dfrac{40}{13}$ or approximately 3 hours and 5 minutes.

EXAMPLES

1. A straightforward mixture problem: A child makes 2 quarts of chocolate milk consisting of 30% syrup and 70% milk. It is far too sweet. How much milk would you have to add to get a mixture that is 5% syrup?

2. A straightforward job-sharing problem: If it takes Mike 2 hours to mow the lawn and Al 3 hours to mow the lawn, how long does it take the two of them, working together?

ANSWERS

1. 10 quarts
2. 1.2 hours

SOLUTION **Identify the variable.** We are asked to find the time needed to lower the level by 1 ft if both spillways are open. So let

$$x = \text{the time (in hours) it takes to lower the water level}$$
$$\text{by 1 ft if both spillways are open}$$

Translate from words to algebra. Finding an equation relating x to the other quantities in this problem is not easy. Certainly x is not simply $4 + 6$, because that would mean that together the two spillways require longer to lower the water level than either spillway alone. Instead, *we look at the fraction of the job that can be done in 1 hour by each spillway.*

In Words	In Algebra
Time it takes to lower level 1 ft with A and B together	x h
Distance A lowers level in 1 h	$\frac{1}{4}$ ft
Distance B lowers level in 1 h	$\frac{1}{6}$ ft
Distance A and B together lower levels in 1 h	$\frac{1}{x}$ ft

Set up the model. Now we set up the model.

$$\boxed{\text{fraction done by A}} \;+\; \boxed{\text{fraction done by B}} \;=\; \boxed{\text{fraction done by both}}$$

$$\frac{1}{4} + \frac{1}{6} = \frac{1}{x}$$

Solve. Now we solve for x.

$$3x + 2x = 12 \qquad \text{Multiply by the LCD, } 12x$$
$$5x = 12 \qquad \text{Add}$$
$$x = \frac{12}{5} \qquad \text{Divide by 5}$$

It will take $2\frac{2}{5}$ hours, or 2 h 24 min, to lower the water level by 1 ft if both spillways are open.

✎. NOW TRY EXERCISE **61** ∎

▼ Problems About Distance, Rate, and Time

The next example deals with distance, rate (speed), and time. The formula to keep in mind here is

$$\boxed{\text{distance} = \text{rate} \times \text{time}}$$

where the rate is either the constant speed or average speed of a moving object. For example, driving at 60 mi/h for 4 hours takes you a distance of $60 \cdot 4 = 240$ mi.

EXAMPLE 8 | A Distance-Speed-Time Problem

A jet flew from New York to Los Angeles, a distance of 4200 km. The speed for the return trip was 100 km/h faster than the outbound speed. If the total trip took 13 hours, what was the jet's speed from New York to Los Angeles?

SOLUTION **Identify the variable.** We are asked for the speed of the jet from New York to Los Angeles. So let

$$s = \text{speed from New York to Los Angeles}$$

Then

$$s + 100 = \text{speed from Los Angeles to New York}$$

ALTERNATE EXAMPLE 8

A jet flew from New York to Los Angeles, a distance of approximately 4000 km. The speed for the return trip was 50 km/h faster than the outbound speed. If the total trip took 10 hours, 20 minutes, what was the speed from New York to Los Angeles?

ANSWER

750 km/h

Translate from words to algebra.   Now we organize the information in a table. We fill in the "Distance" column first, since we know that the cities are 4200 km apart. Then we fill in the "Speed" column, since we have expressed both speeds (rates) in terms of the variable s. Finally, we calculate the entries for the "Time" column, using

$$\text{time} = \frac{\text{distance}}{\text{rate}}$$

	Distance (km)	Speed (km/h)	Time (h)
N.Y. to L.A.	4200	s	$\frac{4200}{s}$
L.A. to N.Y.	4200	$s + 100$	$\frac{4200}{s + 100}$

Set up the model.   The total trip took 13 hours, so we have the model

$$\boxed{\begin{array}{c}\text{time from}\\ \text{N.Y. to L.A.}\end{array}} + \boxed{\begin{array}{c}\text{time from}\\ \text{L.A. to N.Y.}\end{array}} = \boxed{\begin{array}{c}\text{total}\\ \text{time}\end{array}}$$

$$\frac{4200}{s} + \frac{4200}{s + 100} = 13$$

Solve.   Multiplying by the common denominator, $s(s + 100)$, we get

$$4200(s + 100) + 4200s = 13s(s + 100)$$
$$8400s + 420{,}000 = 13s^2 + 1300s$$
$$0 = 13s^2 - 7100s - 420{,}000$$

Although this equation does factor, with numbers this large it is probably quicker to use the Quadratic Formula and a calculator.

$$s = \frac{7100 \pm \sqrt{(-7100)^2 - 4(13)(-420{,}000)}}{2(13)}$$

$$= \frac{7100 \pm 8500}{26}$$

$$s = 600 \quad \text{or} \quad s = \frac{-1400}{26} \approx -53.8$$

Since s represents speed, we reject the negative answer and conclude that the jet's speed from New York to Los Angeles was 600 km/h.

✏. **NOW TRY EXERCISE 67**   ■

island

A

5 mi

B   C   D

x

nesting area

12 mi

FIGURE 5

EXAMPLE 9 | Energy Expended in Bird Flight

Ornithologists have determined that some species of birds tend to avoid flights over large bodies of water during daylight hours, because air generally rises over land and falls over water in the daytime, so flying over water requires more energy. A bird is released from point A on an island, 5 mi from B, the nearest point on a straight shoreline. The bird flies to a point C on the shoreline and then flies along the shoreline to its nesting area D, as shown in Figure 5. Suppose the bird has 170 kcal of energy reserves. It uses 10 kcal/mi flying over land and 14 kcal/mi flying over water.

(a) Where should the point C be located so that the bird uses exactly 170 kcal of energy during its flight?

(b) Does the bird have enough energy reserves to fly directly from A to D?

ALTERNATE EXAMPLE 9
Ornithologists have determined that some species of birds tend to avoid flights over large bodies of water during daylight hours, because air generally rises over land and falls over water in the daytime, so flying over water requires more energy. A bird is released from point A on an island, 7 mi from B, the nearest point on a straight shoreline. The bird flies to a point C on the shoreline and then flies along the shoreline to its

nesting area D. Suppose the bird has 170 kcal of energy reserves. It uses 10 kcal/mi flying over land and 14 kcal/mi flying over water. Where should the point C be located so that the bird uses exactly 170 kcal of energy during its flight, if the distance between B and D is 10 mi?

ANSWER

$x = 5\frac{1}{4}, x = 9\frac{1}{3}$

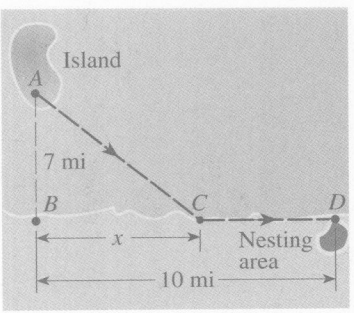

Island

A

7 mi

B   C   D

x

Nesting area

10 mi

SOLUTION

(a) Identify the variable. We are asked to find the location of C. So let

$$x = \text{distance from } B \text{ to } C$$

Translate from words to algebra. From the figure, and from the fact that

$$\text{energy used} = \text{energy per mile} \times \text{miles flown}$$

we determine the following:

In Words	In Algebra	
Distance from B to C	x	
Distance flown over water (from A to C)	$\sqrt{x^2 + 25}$	Pythagorean Theorem
Distance flown over land (from C to D)	$12 - x$	
Energy used over water	$14\sqrt{x^2 + 25}$	
Energy used over land	$10(12 - x)$	

Set up the model. Now we set up the model.

$$\text{total energy used} = \text{energy used over water} + \text{energy used over land}$$

$$170 = 14\sqrt{x^2 + 25} + 10(12 - x)$$

Solve. To solve this equation, we eliminate the square root by first bringing all other terms to the left of the equal sign and then squaring each side.

$$170 - 10(12 - x) = 14\sqrt{x^2 + 25} \qquad \text{Isolate square-root term on RHS}$$
$$50 + 10x = 14\sqrt{x^2 + 25} \qquad \text{Simplify LHS}$$
$$(50 + 10x)^2 = (14)^2(x^2 + 25) \qquad \text{Square each side}$$
$$2500 + 1000x + 100x^2 = 196x^2 + 4900 \qquad \text{Expand}$$
$$0 = 96x^2 - 1000x + 2400 \qquad \text{All terms to RHS}$$

This equation could be factored, but because the numbers are so large it is easier to use the Quadratic Formula and a calculator:

$$x = \frac{1000 \pm \sqrt{(-1000)^2 - 4(96)(2400)}}{2(96)}$$
$$= \frac{1000 \pm 280}{192} = 6\frac{2}{3} \quad \text{or} \quad 3\frac{3}{4}$$

Point C should be either $6\frac{2}{3}$ mi or $3\frac{3}{4}$ mi from B so that the bird uses exactly 170 kcal of energy during its flight.

(b) By the Pythagorean Theorem (see page 219), the length of the route directly from A to D is $\sqrt{5^2 + 12^2} = 13$ mi, so the energy the bird requires for that route is $14 \times 13 = 182$ kcal. This is more energy than the bird has available, so it can't use this route.

NOW TRY EXERCISE 83

DRILL QUESTION

A car rental company charges $20 a day and 30 cents per mile for renting a car. Janice rents a car for three days and her bill comes to $72. How many miles did she drive?

ANSWER

The total cost is $C = 20d + 0.30m$, where d is the number of days and m is the mileage. In this case we have $72 = 20(3) + 0.30m \Rightarrow m = 40$, so Janice drove 40 miles.

1.6 EXERCISES

CONCEPTS

1. Explain in your own words what it means for an equation to model a real-world situation, and give an example.

2. In the formula $I = Prt$ for simple interest, P stands for _____, r for _____, and t for _____.

3. Give a formula for the area of the geometric figure.

   (a) A square of side x: $A =$ _____.

   (b) A rectangle of length l and width w: $A =$ _____.

   (c) A circle of radius r: $A =$ _____.

4. Balsamic vinegar contains 5% acetic acid, so a 32-oz bottle of balsamic vinegar contains _____ ounces of acetic acid.

5. A painter paints a wall in x hours, so the fraction of the wall that she paints in 1 hour is _____.

6. The formula $d = rt$ models the distance d traveled by an object moving at the constant rate r in time t. Find formulas for the following quantities.

$$r = \underline{\hspace{1cm}} \qquad t = \underline{\hspace{1cm}}.$$

SKILLS

7–18 ■ Express the given quantity in terms of the indicated variable.

7. The sum of three consecutive integers; $n =$ first integer of the three

8. The sum of three consecutive integers; $n =$ middle integer of the three

9. The average of three test scores if the first two scores are 78 and 82; $s =$ third test score

10. The average of four quiz scores if each of the first three scores is 8; $q =$ fourth quiz score

11. The interest obtained after one year on an investment at $2\frac{1}{2}\%$ simple interest per year; $x =$ number of dollars invested

12. The total rent paid for an apartment if the rent is $795 a month; $n =$ number of months

13. The area (in ft^2) of a rectangle that is three times as long as it is wide; $w =$ width of the rectangle (in ft)

14. The perimeter (in cm) of a rectangle that is 5 cm longer than it is wide; $w =$ width of the rectangle (in cm)

15. The distance (in mi) that a car travels in 45 min; $s =$ speed of the car (in mi/h)

16. The time (in hours) it takes to travel a given distance at 55 mi/h; $d =$ given distance (in mi)

17. The concentration (in oz/gal) of salt in a mixture of 3 gal of brine containing 25 oz of salt to which some pure water has been added; $x =$ volume of pure water added (in gal)

18. The value (in cents) of the change in a purse that contains twice as many nickels as pennies, four more dimes than nickels, and as many quarters as dimes and nickels combined; $p =$ number of pennies

APPLICATIONS

19. Renting a Truck   A rental company charges $65 a day and 20 cents a mile for renting a truck. Michael rented a truck for 3 days, and his bill came to $275. How many miles did he drive?

20. Cell Phone Costs   A cell phone company charges a monthly fee of $10 for the first 1000 text messages and 10 cents for each additional text message. Miriam's bill for text messages for the month of June is $38.50. How many text messages did she send that month?

21. Investments   Phyllis invested $12,000, a portion earning a simple interest rate of $4\frac{1}{2}\%$ per year and the rest earning a rate of 4% per year. After 1 year the total interest earned on these investments was $525. How much money did she invest at each rate?

22. Investments   If Ben invests $4000 at 4% interest per year, how much additional money must he invest at $5\frac{1}{2}\%$ annual interest to ensure that the interest he receives each year is $4\frac{1}{2}\%$ of the total amount invested?

23. Investments   What annual rate of interest would you have to earn on an investment of $3500 to ensure receiving $262.50 interest after 1 year?

24. Investments   Jack invests $1000 at a certain annual interest rate, and he invests another $2000 at an annual rate that is one-half percent higher. If he receives a total of $190 interest in 1 year, at what rate is the $1000 invested?

25. Salaries   An executive in an engineering firm earns a monthly salary plus a Christmas bonus of $8500. If she earns a total of $97,300 per year, what is her monthly salary?

26. Salaries   A woman earns 15% more than her husband. Together they make $69,875 per year. What is the husband's annual salary?

27. Inheritance   Craig is saving to buy a vacation home. He inherits some money from a wealthy uncle, then combines this with the $22,000 he has already saved and doubles the total in a lucky investment. He ends up with $134,000—just enough to buy a cabin on the lake. How much did he inherit?

28. Overtime Pay   Helen earns $7.50 an hour at her job, but if she works more than 35 hours in a week, she is paid $1\frac{1}{2}$ times her regular salary for the overtime hours worked. One week her gross pay was $352.50. How many overtime hours did she work that week?

29. Labor Costs   A plumber and his assistant work together to replace the pipes in an old house. The plumber charges $45 an hour for his own labor and $25 an hour for his assistant's labor. The plumber works twice as long as his assistant on this job, and the labor charge on the final bill is $4025. How long did the plumber and his assistant work on this job?

30. A Riddle A father is four times as old as his daughter. In 6 years, he will be three times as old as she is. How old is the daughter now?

31. A Riddle A movie star, unwilling to give his age, posed the following riddle to a gossip columnist: "Seven years ago, I was eleven times as old as my daughter. Now I am four times as old as she is." How old is the movie star?

32. Career Home Runs During his major league career, Hank Aaron hit 41 more home runs than Babe Ruth hit during his career. Together they hit 1469 home runs. How many home runs did Babe Ruth hit?

33. Value of Coins A change purse contains an equal number of pennies, nickels, and dimes. The total value of the coins is $1.44. How many coins of each type does the purse contain?

34. Value of Coins Mary has $3.00 in nickels, dimes, and quarters. If she has twice as many dimes as quarters and five more nickels than dimes, how many coins of each type does she have?

35. Length of a Garden A rectangular garden is 25 ft wide. If its area is 1125 ft², what is the length of the garden?

25 ft   x ft

36. Width of a Pasture A pasture is twice as long as it is wide. Its area is 115,200 ft². How wide is the pasture?

37. Dimensions of a Lot A square plot of land has a building 60 ft long and 40 ft wide at one corner. The rest of the land outside the building forms a parking lot. If the parking lot has area 12,000 ft², what are the dimensions of the entire plot of land?

38. Dimensions of a Lot A half-acre building lot is five times as long as it is wide. What are its dimensions? [*Note:* 1 acre = 43,560 ft².]

39. Dimensions of a Garden A rectangular garden is 10 ft longer than it is wide. Its area is 875 ft². What are its dimensions?

40. Dimensions of a Room A rectangular bedroom is 7 ft longer than it is wide. Its area is 228 ft². What is the width of the room?

41. Dimensions of a Garden A farmer has a rectangular garden plot surrounded by 200 ft of fence. Find the length and width of the garden if its area is 2400 ft².

perimeter = 200 ft

42. Dimensions of a Lot A parcel of land is 6 ft longer than it is wide. Each diagonal from one corner to the opposite corner is 174 ft long. What are the dimensions of the parcel?

43. Dimensions of a Lot A rectangular parcel of land is 50 ft wide. The length of a diagonal between opposite corners is 10 ft more than the length of the parcel. What is the length of the parcel?

44. Dimensions of a Track A running track has the shape shown in the figure, with straight sides and semicircular ends. If the length of the track is 440 yd and the two straight parts are each 110 yd long, what is the radius of the semicircular parts (to the nearest yard)?

|———— 110 yd ————|

r

45. Length and Area Find the length x in the figure. The area of the shaded region is given.

(a)   x   (b)   x

10 cm   6 cm   14 in.
                                  13 in.
              x   x

area = 144 cm²   area = 160 in²

46. Length and Area Find the length y in the figure. The area of the shaded region is given.

(a)   (b)

              y
   y   y   y

area = 120 in²   y →| |←
                                 1 cm
                           area = 1200 cm²

47. Framing a Painting Ali paints with watercolors on a sheet of paper 20 in. wide by 15 in. high. He then places this sheet on a mat so that a uniformly wide strip of the mat shows all around the picture. The perimeter of the mat is 102 in. How wide is the strip of the mat showing around the picture?

←x→   15 in.

|←———— 20 in. ————→|

48. Dimensions of a Poster   A poster has a rectangular printed area 100 cm by 140 cm and a blank strip of uniform width around the edges. The perimeter of the poster is $1\frac{1}{2}$ times the perimeter of the printed area. What is the width of the blank strip?

49. Reach of a Ladder   A $19\frac{1}{2}$-foot ladder leans against a building. The base of the ladder is $7\frac{1}{2}$ ft from the building. How high up the building does the ladder reach?

50. Height of a Flagpole   A flagpole is secured on opposite sides by two guy wires, each of which is 5 ft longer than the pole. The distance between the points where the wires are fixed to the ground is equal to the length of one guy wire. How tall is the flagpole (to the nearest inch)?

51. Length of a Shadow   A man is walking away from a lamppost with a light source 6 m above the ground. The man is 2 m tall. How long is the man's shadow when he is 10 m from the lamppost?   [*Hint:* Use similar triangles.]

52. Height of a Tree   A woodcutter determines the height of a tall tree by first measuring a smaller one 125 ft away, then moving so that his eyes are in the line of sight along the tops of the trees and measuring how far he is standing from the small tree (see the figure). Suppose the small tree is 20 ft tall, the man is 25 ft from the small tree, and his eye level is 5 ft above the ground. How tall is the taller tree?

53. Mixture Problem   What quantity of a 60% acid solution must be mixed with a 30% solution to produce 300 mL of a 50% solution?

54. Mixture Problem   What quantity of pure acid must be added to 300 mL of a 50% acid solution to produce a 60% acid solution?

55. Mixture Problem   A jeweler has five rings, each weighing 18 g, made of an alloy of 10% silver and 90% gold. She decides to melt down the rings and add enough silver to reduce the gold content to 75%. How much silver should she add?

56. Mixture Problem   A pot contains 6 L of brine at a concentration of 120 g/L. How much of the water should be boiled off to increase the concentration to 200 g/L?

57. Mixture Problem   The radiator in a car is filled with a solution of 60% antifreeze and 40% water. The manufacturer of the antifreeze suggests that for summer driving, optimal cooling of the engine is obtained with only 50% antifreeze. If the capacity of the radiator is 3.6 L, how much coolant should be drained and replaced with water to reduce the antifreeze concentration to the recommended level?

58. Mixture Problem   A health clinic uses a solution of bleach to sterilize petri dishes in which cultures are grown. The sterilization tank contains 100 gal of a solution of 2% ordinary household bleach mixed with pure distilled water. New research indicates that the concentration of bleach should be 5% for complete sterilization. How much of the solution should be drained and replaced with bleach to increase the bleach content to the recommended level?

59. Mixture Problem   A bottle contains 750 mL of fruit punch with a concentration of 50% pure fruit juice. Jill drinks 100 mL of the punch and then refills the bottle with an equal amount of a cheaper brand of punch. If the concentration of juice in the bottle is now reduced to 48%, what was the concentration in the punch that Jill added?

60. Mixture Problem   A merchant blends tea that sells for $3.00 a pound with tea that sells for $2.75 a pound to produce 80 lb of a mixture that sells for $2.90 a pound. How many pounds of each type of tea does the merchant use in the blend?

61. Sharing a Job   Candy and Tim share a paper route. It takes Candy 70 min to deliver all the papers, and it takes Tim 80 min. How long does it take the two when they work together?

62. Sharing a Job   Stan and Hilda can mow the lawn in 40 min if they work together. If Hilda works twice as fast as Stan, how long does it take Stan to mow the lawn alone?

63. Sharing a Job   Betty and Karen have been hired to paint the houses in a new development. Working together, the women can paint a house in two-thirds the time that it takes Karen working alone. Betty takes 6 h to paint a house alone. How long does it take Karen to paint a house working alone?

64. Sharing a Job   Next-door neighbors Bob and Jim use hoses from both houses to fill Bob's swimming pool. They know that it takes 18 h using both hoses. They also know that Bob's hose, used alone, takes 20% less time than Jim's hose alone. How much time is required to fill the pool by each hose alone?

65. Sharing a Job   Henry and Irene working together can wash all the windows of their house in 1 h 48 min. Working alone, it takes Henry $1\frac{1}{2}$ h more than Irene to do the job. How long does it take each person working alone to wash all the windows?

66. Sharing a Job   Jack, Kay, and Lynn deliver advertising flyers in a small town. If each person works alone, it takes Jack 4 h to deliver all the flyers, and it takes Lynn 1 h longer than it takes Kay. Working together, they can deliver all the flyers in 40% of the time it takes Kay working alone. How long does it take Kay to deliver all the flyers alone?

67. Distance, Speed, and Time   Wendy took a trip from Davenport to Omaha, a distance of 300 mi. She traveled part of the way by bus, which arrived at the train station just in time for Wendy to complete her journey by train. The bus averaged 40 mi/h, and the train averaged 60 mi/h. The entire trip took $5\frac{1}{2}$ h. How long did Wendy spend on the train?

68. Distance, Speed, and Time   Two cyclists, 90 mi apart, start riding toward each other at the same time. One cycles twice as fast as the other. If they meet 2 h later, at what average speed is each cyclist traveling?

69. Distance, Speed, and Time   A pilot flew a jet from Montreal to Los Angeles, a distance of 2500 mi. On the return trip, the average speed was 20% faster than the outbound speed. The round-trip took 9 h 10 min. What was the speed from Montreal to Los Angeles?

70. Distance, Speed, and Time   A woman driving a car 14 ft long is passing a truck 30 ft long. The truck is traveling at 50 mi/h. How fast must the woman drive her car so that she can pass the truck completely in 6 s, from the position shown in figure (a) to the position shown in figure (b)?   [*Hint:* Use feet and seconds instead of miles and hours.]

(a)

(b)

71. Distance, Speed, and Time   A salesman drives from Ajax to Barrington, a distance of 120 mi, at a steady speed. He then increases his speed by 10 mi/h to drive the 150 mi from Barrington to Collins. If the second leg of his trip took 6 min more time than the first leg, how fast was he driving between Ajax and Barrington?

72. Distance, Speed, and Time   Kiran drove from Tortula to Cactus, a distance of 250 mi. She increased her speed by 10 mi/h for the 360-mi trip from Cactus to Dry Junction. If the total trip took 11 h, what was her speed from Tortula to Cactus?

73. Distance, Speed, and Time   It took a crew 2 h 40 min to row 6 km upstream and back again. If the rate of flow of the stream was 3 km/h, what was the rowing speed of the crew in still water?

74. Speed of a Boat   Two fishing boats depart a harbor at the same time, one traveling east, the other south. The eastbound boat travels at a speed 3 mi/h faster than the southbound boat. After two hours the boats are 30 mi apart. Find the speed of the southbound boat.

75. Law of the Lever   The figure shows a lever system, similar to a seesaw that you might find in a children's playground. For the system to balance, the product of the weight and its distance from the fulcrum must be the same on each side; that is,

$$w_1x_1 = w_2x_2$$

This equation is called the **law of the lever** and was first discovered by Archimedes (see page 729).

A woman and her son are playing on a seesaw. The boy is at one end, 8 ft from the fulcrum. If the son weighs 100 lb and the mother weighs 125 lb, where should the woman sit so that the seesaw is balanced?

76. Law of the Lever A plank 30 ft long rests on top of a flat-roofed building, with 5 of the plank projecting over the edge, as shown in the figure. A worker weighing 240 lb sits on one end of the plank. What is the largest weight that can be hung on the projecting end of the plank if it is to remain in balance? (Use the law of the lever stated in Exercise 75.)

77. Dimensions of a Box A large plywood box has a volume of 180 ft³. Its length is 9 ft greater than its height, and its width is 4 ft less than its height. What are the dimensions of the box?

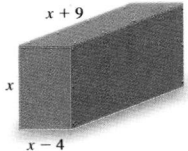

78. Radius of a Sphere A jeweler has three small solid spheres made of gold, of radius 2 mm, 3 mm, and 4 mm. He decides to melt these down and make just one sphere out of them. What will the radius of this larger sphere be?

79. Dimensions of a Box A box with a square base and no top is to be made from a square piece of cardboard by cutting 4-in. squares from each corner and folding up the sides, as shown in the figure. The box is to hold 100 in³. How big a piece of cardboard is needed?

80. Dimensions of a Can A cylindrical can has a volume of 40π cm³ and is 10 cm tall. What is its diameter? [*Hint:* Use the volume formula listed on the inside front cover of this book.]

81. Radius of a Tank A spherical tank has a capacity of 750 gallons. Using the fact that one gallon is about 0.1337 ft³, find the radius of the tank (to the nearest hundredth of a foot).

82. Dimensions of a Lot A city lot has the shape of a right triangle whose hypotenuse is 7 ft longer than one of the other sides. The perimeter of the lot is 392 ft. How long is each side of the lot?

83. Construction Costs The town of Foxton lies 10 mi north of an abandoned east-west road that runs through Grimley, as shown in the figure. The point on the abandoned road closest to Foxton is 40 mi from Grimley. County officials are about to build a new road connecting the two towns. They have determined that restoring the old road would cost $100,000 per mile, whereas building a new road would cost $200,000 per mile. How much of the abandoned road should be used (as indicated in the figure) if the officials intend to spend exactly $6.8 million? Would it cost less than this amount to build a new road connecting the towns directly?

84. Distance, Speed, and Time A boardwalk is parallel to and 210 ft inland from a straight shoreline. A sandy beach lies between the boardwalk and the shoreline. A man is standing on the boardwalk, exactly 750 ft across the sand from his beach umbrella, which is right at the shoreline. The man walks 4 ft/s on the boardwalk and 2 ft/s on the sand. How far should he walk on the boardwalk before veering off onto the sand if he wishes to reach his umbrella in exactly 4 min 45 s?

boardwalk

85. Volume of Grain   Grain is falling from a chute onto the ground, forming a conical pile whose diameter is always three times its height. How high is the pile (to the nearest hundredth of a foot) when it contains 1000 ft³ of grain?

86. TV Monitors   Two television monitors sitting side by side on a shelf in an appliance store have the same screen height. One has a conventional screen, which is 5 in. wider than it is high. The other has a wider, high-definition screen, which is 1.8 times as wide as it is high. The diagonal measure of the wider screen is 14 in. more than the diagonal measure of the smaller screen. What is the height of the screens, correct to the nearest 0.1 in.?

87. Dimensions of a Structure   A storage bin for corn consists of a cylindrical section made of wire mesh, surmounted by a conical tin roof, as shown in the figure. The height of the roof is one-third the height of the entire structure. If the total volume of the structure is 1400π ft³ and its radius is 10 ft, what is its height?   [*Hint:* Use the volume formulas listed on the inside front cover of this book.]

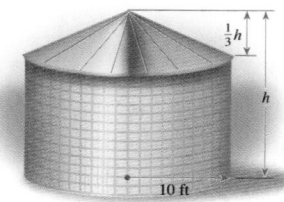

88. Comparing Areas   A wire 360 in. long is cut into two pieces. One piece is formed into a square, and the other is formed into a circle. If the two figures have the same area, what are the lengths of the two pieces of wire (to the nearest tenth of an inch)?

89. An Ancient Chinese Problem   This problem is taken from a Chinese mathematics textbook called *Chui-chang suan-shu*, or *Nine Chapters on the Mathematical Art*, which was written about 250 B.C.

A 10-ft-long stem of bamboo is broken in such a way that its tip touches the ground 3 ft from the base of the stem, as shown in the figure. What is the height of the break?

[*Hint:* Use the Pythagorean Theorem.]

3 ft

DISCOVERY ■ DISCUSSION ■ WRITING

90. Historical Research   Read the biographical notes on Pythagoras (page 219), Euclid (page 497), and Archimedes (page 729). Choose one of these mathematicians and find out more about him from the library or on the Internet. Write a short essay on your findings. Include both biographical information and a description of the mathematics for which he is famous.

91. A Babylonian Quadratic Equation   The ancient Babylonians knew how to solve quadratic equations. Here is a problem from a cuneiform tablet found in a Babylonian school dating back to about 2000 B.C.

I have a reed, I know not its length. I broke from it one cubit, and it fit 60 times along the length of my field. I restored to the reed what I had broken off, and it fit 30 times along the width of my field. The area of my field is 375 square nindas. What was the original length of the reed?

Solve this problem. Use the fact that 1 ninda = 12 cubits.

○ **DISCOVERY PROJECT**   **Equations Through the Ages**

In this project we study equations that were created and solved by the ancient peoples of Egypt, Babylon, India, and China. You can find the project at the book companion website: **www.stewartmath.com**

1.7 INEQUALITIES

Solving Linear Inequalities ▶ Solving Nonlinear Inequalities ▶ Absolute Value Inequalities ▶ Modeling with Inequalities

SUGGESTED TIME AND EMPHASIS

1 class, essential material

Some problems in algebra lead to **inequalities** instead of equations. An inequality looks just like an equation, except that in the place of the equal sign is one of the symbols, $<$, $>$, $\leq$, or $\geq$. Here is an example of an inequality:

$$4x + 7 \leq 19$$

x	$4x + 7 \leq 19$	
1	$11 \leq 19$	✔
2	$15 \leq 19$	✔
3	$19 \leq 19$	✔
4	$23 \leq 19$	✗
5	$27 \leq 19$	✗

The table in the margin shows that some numbers satisfy the inequality and some numbers don't.

To **solve** an inequality that contains a variable means to find all values of the variable that make the inequality true. Unlike an equation, an inequality generally has infinitely many solutions, which form an interval or a union of intervals on the real line. The following illustration shows how an inequality differs from its corresponding equation:

		Solution	Graph
Equation:	$4x + 7 = 19$	$x = 3$	
Inequality:	$4x + 7 \leq 19$	$x \leq 3$	

To solve inequalities, we use the following rules to isolate the variable on one side of the inequality sign. These rules tell us when two inequalities are *equivalent* (the symbol $\Leftrightarrow$ means "is equivalent to"). In these rules the symbols A, B, and C stand for real numbers or algebraic expressions. Here we state the rules for inequalities involving the symbol $\leq$, but they apply to all four inequality symbols.

RULES FOR INEQUALITIES

Rule	**Description**
1. $A \leq B \quad \Leftrightarrow \quad A + C \leq B + C$	**Adding** the same quantity to each side of an inequality gives an equivalent inequality.
2. $A \leq B \quad \Leftrightarrow \quad A - C \leq B - C$	**Subtracting** the same quantity from each side of an inequality gives an equivalent inequality.
3. If $C > 0$, then $A \leq B \quad \Leftrightarrow \quad CA \leq CB$	**Multiplying** each side of an inequality by the same *positive* quantity gives an equivalent inequality.
4. If $C < 0$, then $A \leq B \quad \Leftrightarrow \quad CA \geq CB$	**Multiplying** each side of an inequality by the same *negative* quantity *reverses the direction* of the inequality.
5. If $A > 0$ and $B > 0$, then $A \leq B \quad \Leftrightarrow \quad \dfrac{1}{A} \geq \dfrac{1}{B}$	**Taking reciprocals** of each side of an inequality involving *positive* quantities *reverses the direction* of the inequality.
6. If $A \leq B$ and $C \leq D$, then $A + C \leq B + D$	Inequalities can be added.

 Pay special attention to Rules 3 and 4. Rule 3 says that we can multiply (or divide) each side of an inequality by a *positive* number, but Rule 4 says that if we multiply each side of an inequality by a *negative* number, then we reverse the direction of the inequality. For example, if we start with the inequality

$$3 < 5$$

TEXT QUESTION

Solve the inequality $(x - 1)(x - 3) < 0$.

Answer

$1 < x < 3$

and multiply by 2, we get

$$6 < 10$$

but if we multiply by -2, we get

$$-6 > -10$$

▼ Solving Linear Inequalities

An inequality is **linear** if each term is constant or a multiple of the variable. To solve a linear inequality, we isolate the variable on one side of the inequality sign.

EXAMPLE 1 | Solving a Linear Inequality

Solve the inequality $3x < 9x + 4$ and sketch the solution set.

SOLUTION

$3x < 9x + 4$	Given inequality
$3x - 9x < 9x + 4 - 9x$	Subtract $9x$
$-6x < 4$	Simplify
$\left(-\frac{1}{6}\right)(-6x) > \left(-\frac{1}{6}\right)(4)$	Multiply by $-\frac{1}{6}$ and reverse inequality
$x > -\frac{2}{3}$	Simplify

The solution set consists of all numbers greater than $-\frac{2}{3}$. In other words the solution of the inequality is the interval $\left(-\frac{2}{3}, \infty\right)$. It is graphed in Figure 1.

✎. NOW TRY EXERCISE **21**

Multiplying by the negative number $-\frac{1}{6}$ *reverses* the direction of the inequality.

FIGURE 1

EXAMPLE 2 | Solving a Pair of Simultaneous Inequalities

Solve the inequalities $4 \le 3x - 2 < 13$.

SOLUTION   The solution set consists of all values of x that satisfy both of the inequalities $4 \le 3x - 2$ and $3x - 2 < 13$. Using Rules 1 and 3, we see that the following inequalities are equivalent:

$4 \le 3x - 2 < 13$	Given inequality
$6 \le 3x < 15$	Add 2
$2 \le x < 5$	Divide by 3

Therefore, the solution set is $[2, 5)$, as shown in Figure 2.

✎. NOW TRY EXERCISE **31**

FIGURE 2

▼ Solving Nonlinear Inequalities

To solve inequalities involving squares and other powers of the variable, we use factoring, together with the following principle.

THE SIGN OF A PRODUCT OR QUOTIENT

If a product or a quotient has an *even* number of *negative* factors, then its value is *positive*.

If a product or a quotient has an *odd* number of *negative* factors, then its value is *negative*.

IN-CLASS MATERIALS

Just as a quadratic equation can have zero, one, or two solutions, quadratic inequalities can have zero, one, or infinitely many solutions. A good way to clarify this point is to solve the following with your students:

$$x^2 + 2x \le 0$$
$$x^2 + 2x + 1 \le 0$$
$$x^2 + 2x + 1 < 0$$
$$x^2 + 2x + 2 \le 0$$

For example, to solve the inequality $x^2 - 5x \le -6$, we first move all terms to the left-hand side and factor to get

$$(x - 2)(x - 3) \le 0$$

This form of the inequality says that the product $(x - 2)(x - 3)$ must be negative or zero, so to solve the inequality, we must determine where each factor is negative or positive (because the sign of a product depends on the sign of the factors). The details are explained in Example 3, in which we use the following guidelines.

GUIDELINES FOR SOLVING NONLINEAR INEQUALITIES

1. **Move All Terms to One Side.** If necessary, rewrite the inequality so that all nonzero terms appear on one side of the inequality sign. If the nonzero side of the inequality involves quotients, bring them to a common denominator.

2. **Factor.** Factor the nonzero side of the inequality.

3. **Find the Intervals.** Determine the values for which each factor is zero. These numbers will divide the real line into intervals. List the intervals that are determined by these numbers.

4. **Make a Table or Diagram.** Use test values to make a table or diagram of the signs of each factor on each interval. In the last row of the table determine the sign of the product (or quotient) of these factors.

5. **Solve.** Determine the solution of the inequality from the last row of the sign table. Be sure to check whether the inequality is satisfied by some or all of the endpoints of the intervals. (This may happen if the inequality involves $\le$ or $\ge$.)

 The factoring technique that is described in these guidelines works only if all nonzero terms appear on one side of the inequality symbol. **If the inequality is not written in this form, first rewrite it, as indicated in Step 1.**

EXAMPLE 3 | Solving a Quadratic Inequality

Solve the inequality $x^2 \le 5x - 6$.

SOLUTION We will follow the guidelines given above.

Move all terms to one side. We move all the terms to the left-hand side.

$$
\begin{aligned}
x^2 &\le 5x - 6 &&\text{Given inequality} \\
x^2 - 5x + 6 &\le 0 &&\text{Subtract } 5x, \text{ add } 6
\end{aligned}
$$

Factor. Factoring the left-hand side of the inequality, we get

$$(x - 2)(x - 3) \le 0 \qquad \text{Factor}$$

Find the intervals. The factors of the left-hand side are $x - 2$ and $x - 3$. These factors are zero when x is 2 and 3, respectively. As shown in Figure 3, the numbers 2 and 3 divide the real line into the three intervals

$$(-\infty, 2), (2, 3), (3, \infty)$$

The factors $x - 2$ and $x - 3$ change sign only at 2 and 3, respectively. So these factors maintain their sign on each of these three intervals.

FIGURE 3

FIGURE 4

Make a table or diagram. To determine the sign of each factor on each of the intervals that we found, we use **test values**. We choose a number inside each interval and check the sign of the factors $x - 2$ and $x - 3$ at the number we chose. For the interval $(-\infty, 2)$, let's choose the test value 1 (see Figure 4). Substituting 1 for x in the factors $x - 2$ and $x - 3$, we get

$$
\begin{aligned}
x - 2 &= 1 - 2 = -1 < 0 \\
x - 3 &= 1 - 3 = -2 < 0
\end{aligned}
$$

ALTERNATE EXAMPLE 3
Solve the inequality
$x^2 - x - 2 < 0$.

ANSWER
$\{x \mid -1 < x < 2\} = (-1, 2)$

IN-CLASS MATERIALS

A nice comparison is the difference between these two inequalities:

$$\frac{x}{x^2 + 4} < 0 \text{ and } \frac{x}{x^2 - 4} < 0$$

So both factors are negative on this interval. Notice that we need to check only one test value for each interval because the factors $x - 2$ and $x - 3$ do not change sign on any of the three intervals we found.

Using the test values $x = 2\frac{1}{2}$ and $x = 4$ for the intervals $(2, 3)$ and $(3, \infty)$ (see Figure 4), respectively, we construct the following sign table. The final row of the table is obtained from the fact that the expression in the last row is the product of the two factors.

Interval	$(-\infty, 2)$	$(2, 3)$	$(3, \infty)$
Sign of $x - 2$	−	+	+
Sign of $x - 3$	−	−	+
Sign of $(x - 2)(x - 3)$	+	−	+

If you prefer, you can represent this information on a real line, as in the following sign diagram. The vertical lines indicate the points at which the real line is divided into intervals:

	2	3	
Sign of $x - 2$	−	+	+
Sign of $x - 3$	−	−	+
Sign of $(x - 2)(x - 3)$	+	−	+

Solve. We read from the table or the diagram that $(x - 2)(x - 3)$ is negative on the interval $(2, 3)$. Thus, the solution of the inequality $(x - 2)(x - 3) \le 0$ is

$$\{x \mid 2 \le x \le 3\} = [2, 3]$$

We have included the endpoints 2 and 3 because we seek values of x such that the product is either less than *or equal to* zero. The solution is illustrated in Figure 5.

FIGURE 5

NOW TRY EXERCISE **41**

EXAMPLE 4 | Solving an Inequality with Repeated Factors

Solve the inequality $x(x - 1)^2(x - 3) < 0$.

SOLUTION All nonzero terms are already on one side of the inequality, and the nonzero side of the inequality is already factored. So we begin by finding the intervals for this inequality.

Find the intervals. The factors of the left-hand side are x, $(x - 1)^2$, and $x - 3$. These are zero when $x = 0, 1, 3$. These numbers divide the real line into the intervals

$$(-\infty, 0), (0, 1), (1, 3), (3, \infty)$$

Make a diagram. We make the following diagram, using test points to determine the sign of each factor in each interval.

	0	1	3	
Sign of x	−	+	+	+
Sign of $(x - 1)^2$	+	+	+	+
Sign of $(x - 3)$	−	−	−	+
Sign of $x(x - 1)^2(x - 3)$	+	−	−	+

ALTERNATE EXAMPLE 4

Solve the inequality
$x^3 - 8x^2 \ge = -15x$.

ANSWER

$[0, 3] \cup [5, \text{infinity})$

IN-CLASS MATERIALS

Ask students if there is an inequality that is true for every value of x *except* a single number, say 22. See if they can come up with something like $(x - 22)^2 > 0$.

Solve.   From the diagram we see that $x(x - 1)^2(x - 3) < 0$ for x in the interval $(0, 1)$ or for x in $(1, 3)$. So the solution set is the union of these two intervals:

$$(0, 1) \cup (1, 3)$$

The solution set is graphed in Figure 6.

FIGURE 6

✎. **NOW TRY EXERCISE 53**   ■

EXAMPLE 5 | Solving an Inequality Involving a Quotient

Solve the inequality $\dfrac{1 + x}{1 - x} \geq 1$.

SOLUTION

Move all terms to one side.   We move the terms to the left-hand side and simplify using a common denominator.

 It is tempting to simply multiply both sides of the inequality by $1 - x$ (as you would if this were an *equation*). But this doesn't work because we don't know whether $1 - x$ is positive or negative, so we can't tell whether the inequality needs to be reversed. (See Exercise 123.)

$$\frac{1 + x}{1 - x} \geq 1 \qquad \text{Given inequality}$$

$$\frac{1 + x}{1 - x} - 1 \geq 0 \qquad \text{Subtract 1}$$

$$\frac{1 + x}{1 - x} - \frac{1 - x}{1 - x} \geq 0 \qquad \text{Common denominator } 1 - x$$

$$\frac{1 + x - 1 + x}{1 - x} \geq 0 \qquad \text{Combine the fractions}$$

$$\frac{2x}{1 - x} \geq 0 \qquad \text{Simplify}$$

Find the intervals.   The factors of the left-hand side are $2x$ and $1 - x$. These are zero when x is 0 and 1. These numbers divide the real line into the intervals

$$(-\infty, 0), (0, 1), (1, \infty)$$

Make a diagram.   We make the following diagram using test points to determine the sign of each factor in each interval.

	0	1	
Sign of $2x$	−	+	+
Sign of $1 - x$	+	+	−
Sign of $\dfrac{2x}{1 - x}$	−	+	−

Solve.   From the diagram we see that $\dfrac{2x}{1 - x} \geq 0$ for x in the interval $[0, 1)$. We include the endpoint 0 because the original inequality requires that the quotient be greater than *or equal to* 1. However, we do not include the other endpoint 1 because the quotient in the inequality is not defined at 1. So the solution set is the interval

$$[0, 1)$$

The solution set is graphed in Figure 7.

FIGURE 7

✎. **NOW TRY EXERCISE 59**   ■

   Example 5 shows that we should always check the endpoints of the solution set to see whether they satisfy the original inequality.

IN-CLASS MATERIALS

One of the themes of this chapter is taking verbal descriptions and translating them into algebraic equations. Assume we know that a length of tubing (to three significant figures) is 11.6 cm. Because of significant figures, there is a range of possible exact lengths of tubing. For example, if the actual length is 11.6000323 cm, we would report the length as 11.6 cm. Have students try to express the range of values as an absolute value inequality: $|x - 11.6| \leq 0.05$.

▼ Absolute Value Inequalities

We use the following properties to solve inequalities that involve absolute value.

These properties hold when x is replaced by any algebraic expression. (In the figures we assume that $c > 0$.)

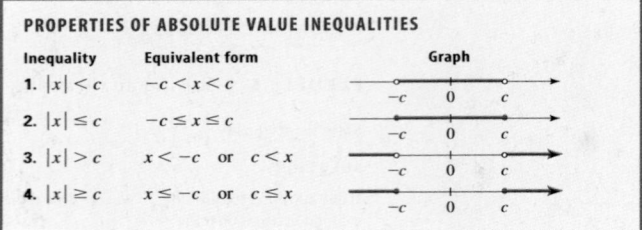

These properties can be proved using the definition of absolute value. To prove Property 1, for example, note that the inequality $|x| < c$ says that the distance from x to 0 is less than c, and from Figure 8 you can see that this is true if and only if x is between $-c$ and c.

FIGURE 8

EXAMPLE 6 | Solving an Absolute Value Inequality

Solve the inequality $|x - 5| < 2$.

SOLUTION 1   The inequality $|x - 5| < 2$ is equivalent to

$$-2 < x - 5 < 2 \qquad \text{Property 1}$$
$$3 < x < 7 \qquad \text{Add 5}$$

The solution set is the open interval $(3, 7)$.

SOLUTION 2   Geometrically, the solution set consists of all numbers x whose distance from 5 is less than 2. From Figure 9 we see that this is the interval $(3, 7)$.

FIGURE 9

✎. NOW TRY EXERCISE **79**   ■

EXAMPLE 7 | Solving an Absolute Value Inequality

Solve the inequality $|3x + 2| \geq 4$.

SOLUTION   By Property 4 the inequality $|3x + 2| \geq 4$ is equivalent to

$$3x + 2 \geq 4 \qquad \text{or} \qquad 3x + 2 \leq -4$$
$$3x \geq 2 \qquad\qquad\qquad 3x \leq -6 \qquad \text{Subtract 2}$$
$$x \geq \tfrac{2}{3} \qquad\qquad\qquad x \leq -2 \qquad \text{Divide by 3}$$

So the solution set is

$$\left\{ x \mid x \leq -2 \quad \text{or} \quad x \geq \tfrac{2}{3} \right\} = (-\infty, -2] \cup [\tfrac{2}{3}, \infty)$$

The set is graphed in Figure 10.

FIGURE 10

✎. NOW TRY EXERCISE **83**   ■

▼ Modeling with Inequalities

Modeling real-life problems frequently leads to inequalities because we are often interested in determining when one quantity is more (or less) than another.

IN-CLASS MATERIALS

There is a particular type of inequality that shows up often in higher mathematics: $0 < |x - a| < \delta$. Ask students to graph $0 < |x - 3| < \frac{1}{10}$ and similar inequalities, emphasizing the idea that x is close to 3, but not equal to 3. For fun, you can now write the definition of "limit" on the blackboard, and see what you and the students can do with it at this stage. Note that $\dfrac{x^2 - 9}{x - 3}$ is not defined at $x = 3$, but is close to 6 when x is close to 3. Then write the formal definition:

$$\text{We say } \lim_{x \to 3} \frac{x^2 - 9}{x - 3} = 6 \text{ because for every } \varepsilon > 0, \text{ there is a } \delta$$

$$\text{such that } \left| \frac{x^2 - 9}{x - 3} - 6 \right| < \varepsilon \text{ whenever } 0 < |x - 3| < \delta.$$

Remember, putting this on the board at this point in the game is for fun only.

EXAMPLE 8 | Carnival Tickets

A carnival has two plans for tickets.

Plan A: $5 entrance fee and 25¢ each ride

Plan B: $2 entrance fee and 50¢ each ride

How many rides would you have to take for Plan A to be less expensive than Plan B?

SOLUTION Identify the variable.   We are asked for the number of rides for which Plan A is less expensive than Plan B. So let

$$x = \text{number of rides}$$

Translate from words to algebra.   The information in the problem may be organized as follows.

In Words	In Algebra
Number of rides	x
Cost with Plan A	$5 + 0.25x$
Cost with Plan B	$2 + 0.50x$

Set up the model.   Now we set up the model.

$$\boxed{\begin{array}{c}\text{cost with}\\\text{Plan A}\end{array}} < \boxed{\begin{array}{c}\text{cost with}\\\text{Plan B}\end{array}}$$

$$5 + 0.25x < 2 + 0.50x$$

Solve.   Now we solve for x.

$$3 + 0.25x < 0.50x \qquad \text{Subtract 2}$$
$$3 < 0.25x \qquad \text{Subtract } 0.25x$$
$$12 < x \qquad \text{Divide by } 0.25$$

So if you plan to take *more than* 12 rides, Plan A is less expensive.

✎. NOW TRY EXERCISE **107** ■

EXAMPLE 9 | Relationship Between Fahrenheit and Celsius Scales

The instructions on a bottle of medicine indicate that the bottle should be stored at a temperature between 5°C and 30°C. What range of temperatures does this correspond to on the Fahrenheit scale?

SOLUTION   The relationship between degrees Celsius (C) and degrees Fahrenheit (F) is given by the equation $C = \frac{5}{9}(F - 32)$. Expressing the statement on the bottle in terms of inequalities, we have

$$5 < C < 30$$

So the corresponding Fahrenheit temperatures satisfy the inequalities

$$5 < \tfrac{5}{9}(F - 32) < 30 \qquad \text{Substitute } C = \tfrac{5}{9}(F - 32)$$
$$\tfrac{9}{5} \cdot 5 < F - 32 < \tfrac{9}{5} \cdot 30 \qquad \text{Multiply by } \tfrac{9}{5}$$
$$9 < F - 32 < 54 \qquad \text{Simplify}$$
$$9 + 32 < F < 54 + 32 \qquad \text{Add 32}$$
$$41 < F < 86 \qquad \text{Simplify}$$

The medicine should be stored at a temperature between 41°F and 86°F.

✎. NOW TRY EXERCISE **105** ■

ALTERNATE EXAMPLE 8
A carnival has two plans for tickets.

Plan A: $7 entrance fee and 50¢ each ride
Plan B: $3 entrance fee and 75¢ each ride

How many rides would you have to take for plan A to be less expensive than plan B?

ANSWER
$16 < x$

ALTERNATE EXAMPLE 9
On an extremely hot summer day, the temperature peaks at 40° C during the afternoon, but cools down to 5° C at night. To what range of temperatures does this correspond on the Fahrenheit scale?

ANSWER
$41 < F < 104$

EXAMPLES

1. Solve $-5 < x^2 + 3x + 2 < 10$.

2. Quadratic inequalities involving absolute values:
$$|x^2 - 8x + 6| < 6 \Rightarrow x \in (0, 2) \cup (6, 8)$$
$$|x^2 - 8x + 6| \geq 6 \Rightarrow x \in (-\infty, 0] \cup [2, 6] \cup [8, \infty)$$

ANSWER

1. $-\frac{3}{2} - \frac{1}{2}\sqrt{41} < x < -\frac{3}{2} + \frac{1}{2}\sqrt{41}$

DRILL QUESTION

Solve $|3x + 5| = 14$.

Answer

$x = -\dfrac{19}{3}$ or $x = 3$

1.7 EXERCISES

CONCEPTS

1. Fill in the blank with an appropriate inequality sign.

    (a) If $x < 5$, then $x - 3$ _____ 2.

    (b) If $x \leq 5$, then $3x$ _____ 15.

    (c) If $x \geq 2$, then $-3x$ _____ -6.

    (d) If $x < -2$, then $-x$ _____ 2.

2. *True or false?*

    (a) If $x(x + 1) > 0$, then x and $x + 1$ are either both positive or both negative.

    (b) If $x(x + 1) > 5$, then x and $x + 1$ are each greater than 5.

3. **(a)** The solution of the inequality $|x| \leq 3$ is the interval

    _____.

    (b) The solution of the inequality $|x| \geq 3$ is a union of two

    intervals _____ $\cup$ _____.

4. **(a)** The set of all points on the real line whose distance from zero is less than 3 can be described by the absolute value

    inequality $|x|$_____.

    (b) The set of all points on the real line whose distance from zero is greater than 3 can be described by the absolute

    value inequality $|x|$ _____.

SKILLS

5–10 ■ Let $S = \{-2, -1, 0, \frac{1}{2}, 1, \sqrt{2}, 2, 4\}$. Determine which elements of S satisfy the inequality.

5. $3 - 2x \leq \frac{1}{2}$ **6.** $2x - 1 \geq x$

7. $1 < 2x - 4 \leq 7$ **8.** $-2 \leq 3 - x < 2$

9. $\dfrac{1}{x} \leq \dfrac{1}{2}$ **10.** $x^2 + 2 < 4$

11–34 ■ Solve the linear inequality. Express the solution using interval notation and graph the solution set.

11. $2x \leq 7$ **12.** $-4x \geq 10$

13. $2x - 5 > 3$ **14.** $3x + 11 < 5$

15. $7 - x \geq 5$ **16.** $5 - 3x \leq -16$

17. $2x + 1 < 0$ **18.** $0 < 5 - 2x$

19. $3x + 11 \leq 6x + 8$ **20.** $6 - x \geq 2x + 9$

21. $\frac{1}{2}x - \frac{2}{3} > 2$ **22.** $\frac{2}{5}x + 1 < \frac{1}{5} - 2x$

23. $\frac{1}{3}x + 2 < \frac{1}{6}x - 1$ **24.** $\frac{2}{3} - \frac{1}{2}x \geq \frac{1}{6} + x$

25. $4 - 3x \leq -(1 + 8x)$ **26.** $2(7x - 3) \leq 12x + 16$

27. $2 \leq x + 5 < 4$ **28.** $5 \leq 3x - 4 \leq 14$

29. $-1 < 2x - 5 < 7$ **30.** $1 < 3x + 4 \leq 16$

31. $-2 < 8 - 2x \leq -1$ **32.** $-3 \leq 3x + 7 \leq \frac{1}{2}$

33. $\dfrac{1}{6} < \dfrac{2x - 13}{12} \leq \dfrac{2}{3}$ **34.** $-\dfrac{1}{2} \leq \dfrac{4 - 3x}{5} \leq \dfrac{1}{4}$

35–72 ■ Solve the nonlinear inequality. Express the solution using interval notation and graph the solution set.

35. $(x + 2)(x - 3) < 0$ **36.** $(x - 5)(x + 4) \geq 0$

37. $x(2x + 7) \geq 0$ **38.** $x(2 - 3x) \leq 0$

39. $x^2 - 3x - 18 \leq 0$ **40.** $x^2 + 5x + 6 > 0$

41. $2x^2 + x \geq 1$ **42.** $x^2 < x + 2$

43. $3x^2 - 3x < 2x^2 + 4$ **44.** $5x^2 + 3x \geq 3x^2 + 2$

45. $x^2 > 3(x + 6)$ **46.** $x^2 + 2x > 3$

47. $x^2 < 4$ **48.** $x^2 \geq 9$

49. $(x + 2)(x - 1)(x - 3) \leq 0$

50. $(x - 5)(x - 2)(x + 1) > 0$

51. $(x - 4)(x + 2)^2 < 0$ **52.** $(x + 3)^2(x + 1) > 0$

53. $(x - 2)^2(x - 3)(x + 1) \leq 0$

54. $x^2(x^2 - 1) \geq 0$

55. $x^3 - 4x > 0$ **56.** $16x \leq x^3$

57. $\dfrac{x - 3}{x + 1} \geq 0$ **58.** $\dfrac{2x + 6}{x - 2} < 0$

59. $\dfrac{4x}{2x + 3} > 2$ **60.** $-2 < \dfrac{x + 1}{x - 3}$

61. $\dfrac{2x + 1}{x - 5} \leq 3$ **62.** $\dfrac{3 + x}{3 - x} \geq 1$

63. $\dfrac{4}{x} < x$ **64.** $\dfrac{x}{x + 1} > 3x$

65. $1 + \dfrac{2}{x + 1} \leq \dfrac{2}{x}$ **66.** $\dfrac{3}{x - 1} - \dfrac{4}{x} \geq 1$

67. $\dfrac{6}{x - 1} - \dfrac{6}{x} \geq 1$ **68.** $\dfrac{x}{2} \geq \dfrac{5}{x + 1} + 4$

69. $\dfrac{x + 2}{x + 3} < \dfrac{x - 1}{x - 2}$ **70.** $\dfrac{1}{x + 1} + \dfrac{1}{x + 2} \leq 0$

71. $x^4 > x^2$ **72.** $x^5 > x^2$

73–88 ■ Solve the absolute value inequality. Express the answer using interval notation and graph the solution set.

73. $|x| \leq 4$ **74.** $|3x| < 15$

75. $|2x| > 7$ **76.** $\frac{1}{2}|x| \geq 1$

77. $|x - 5| \leq 3$ **78.** $|x + 1| \geq 1$

79. $|2x - 3| \leq 0.4$ **80.** $|5x - 2| < 6$

81. $|3x - 2| \geq 5$ **82.** $|8x + 3| > 12$

83. $\left|\dfrac{x - 2}{3}\right| < 2$ **84.** $\left|\dfrac{x + 1}{2}\right| \geq 4$

85. $|x + 6| < 0.001$ **86.** $3 - |2x + 4| \leq 1$

87. $8 - |2x - 1| \geq 6$ **88.** $7|x + 2| + 5 > 4$

89–92 ■ A phrase describing a set of real numbers is given. Express the phrase as an inequality involving an absolute value.

89. All real numbers x less than 3 units from 0

90. All real numbers x more than 2 units from 0

91. All real numbers x at least 5 units from 7

92. All real numbers x at most 4 units from 2

93–98 ■ A set of real numbers is graphed. Find an inequality involving an absolute value that describes the set.

93.
```
 -5 -4 -3 -2 -1  0  1  2  3  4  5
```

94.
```
 -5 -4 -3 -2 -1  0  1  2  3  4  5
```

95.
```
 -5 -4 -3 -2 -1  0  1  2  3  4  5
```

96.
```
 -5 -4 -3 -2 -1  0  1  2  3  4  5
```

97.
```
 -5 -4 -3 -2 -1  0  1  2  3  4  5
```

98.
```
 -5 -4 -3 -2 -1  0  1  2  3  4  5
```

99–102 ■ Determine the values of the variable for which the expression is defined as a real number.

99. $\sqrt{16 - 9x^2}$ **100.** $\sqrt{3x^2 - 5x + 2}$

101. $\left(\dfrac{1}{x^2 - 5x - 14} \right)^{1/2}$ **102.** $\sqrt[4]{\dfrac{1 - x}{2 + x}}$

103. Solve the inequality for x, assuming that a, b, and c are positive constants.

   (a) $a(bx - c) \geq bc$ **(b)** $a \leq bx + c < 2a$

104. Suppose that a, b, c, and d are positive numbers such that

$$\frac{a}{b} < \frac{c}{d}$$

Show that $\dfrac{a}{b} < \dfrac{a + c}{b + d} < \dfrac{c}{d}$.

APPLICATIONS

105. Temperature Scales Use the relationship between C and F given in Example 9 to find the interval on the Fahrenheit scale corresponding to the temperature range $20 \leq C \leq 30$.

106. Temperature Scales What interval on the Celsius scale corresponds to the temperature range $50 \leq F \leq 95$?

107. Car Rental Cost A car rental company offers two plans for renting a car.

   Plan A: $30 per day and 10¢ per mile

   Plan B: $50 per day with free unlimited mileage

   For what range of miles will Plan B save you money?

108. Long-Distance Cost A telephone company offers two long-distance plans.

   Plan A: $25 per month and 5¢ per minute

   Plan B: $5 per month and 12¢ per minute

   For how many minutes of long-distance calls would Plan B be financially advantageous?

109. Driving Cost It is estimated that the annual cost of driving a certain new car is given by the formula

$$C = 0.35m + 2200$$

where m represents the number of miles driven per year and C is the cost in dollars. Jane has purchased such a car and decides to budget between $6400 and $7100 for next year's driving costs. What is the corresponding range of miles that she can drive her new car?

110. Air Temperature As dry air moves upward, it expands and, in so doing, cools at a rate of about 1°C for each 100-meter rise, up to about 12 km.
   (a) If the ground temperature is 20°C, write a formula for the temperature at height h.
   (b) What range of temperatures can be expected if a plane takes off and reaches a maximum height of 5 km?

111. Airline Ticket Price A charter airline finds that on its Saturday flights from Philadelphia to London all 120 seats will be sold if the ticket price is $200. However, for each $3 increase in ticket price, the number of seats sold decreases by one.
   (a) Find a formula for the number of seats sold if the ticket price is P dollars.
   (b) Over a certain period the number of seats sold for this flight ranged between 90 and 115. What was the corresponding range of ticket prices?

112. Accuracy of a Scale A coffee merchant sells a customer 3 lb of Hawaiian Kona at $6.50 per pound. The merchant's scale is accurate to within ± 0.03 lb. By how much could the customer have been overcharged or undercharged because of possible inaccuracy in the scale?

113. Gravity The gravitational force F exerted by the earth on an object having a mass of 100 kg is given by the equation

$$F = \frac{4{,}000{,}000}{d^2}$$

where d is the distance (in km) of the object from the center of the earth, and the force F is measured in newtons (N). For what distances will the gravitational force exerted by the earth on this object be between 0.0004 N and 0.01 N?

114. Bonfire Temperature In the vicinity of a bonfire the temperature T in °C at a distance of x meters from the center of the fire was given by

$$T = \frac{600{,}000}{x^2 + 300}$$

At what range of distances from the fire's center was the temperature less than 500 °C?

115. Falling Ball   Using calculus, it can be shown that if a ball is thrown upward with an initial velocity of 16 ft/s from the top of a building 128 ft high, then its height h above the ground t seconds later will be

$$h = 128 + 16t - 16t^2$$

During what time interval will the ball be at least 32 ft above the ground?

116. Gas Mileage   The gas mileage g (measured in mi/gal) for a particular vehicle, driven at v mi/h, is given by the formula $g = 10 + 0.9v - 0.01v^2$, as long as v is between 10 mi/h and 75 mi/h. For what range of speeds is the vehicle's mileage 30 mi/gal or better?

117. Stopping Distance   For a certain model of car the distance d required to stop the vehicle if it is traveling at v mi/h is given by the formula

$$d = v + \frac{v^2}{20}$$

where d is measured in feet. Kerry wants her stopping distance not to exceed 240 ft. At what range of speeds can she travel?

240 ft

118. Manufacturer's Profit   If a manufacturer sells x units of a certain product, revenue R and cost C (in dollars) are given by

$$R = 20x$$

$$C = 2000 + 8x + 0.0025x^2$$

Use the fact that

$$\text{profit} = \text{revenue} - \text{cost}$$

to determine how many units the manufacturer should sell to enjoy a profit of at least $2400.

119. Fencing a Garden   A determined gardener has 120 ft of deer-resistant fence. She wants to enclose a rectangular vegetable garden in her backyard, and she wants the area that is enclosed to be at least 800 ft^2. What range of values is possible for the length of her garden?

120. Thickness of a Laminate   A company manufactures industrial laminates (thin nylon-based sheets) of thickness 0.020 in, with a tolerance of 0.003 in.

   (a) Find an inequality involving absolute values that describes the range of possible thickness for the laminate.

   (b) Solve the inequality you found in part (a).

0.020 in.

121. Range of Height   The average height of adult males is 68.2 in, and 95% of adult males have height h that satisfies the inequality

$$\left| \frac{h - 68.2}{2.9} \right| \le 2$$

Solve the inequality to find the range of heights.

DISCOVERY ▪ DISCUSSION ▪ WRITING

122. Do Powers Preserve Order?   If $a < b$, is $a^2 < b^2$? (Check both positive and negative values for a and b.) If $a < b$, is $a^3 < b^3$? On the basis of your observations, state a general rule about the relationship between a^n and b^n when $a < b$ and n is a positive integer.

123. What's Wrong Here?   It is tempting to try to solve an inequality like an equation. For instance, we might try to solve $1 < 3/x$ by multiplying both sides by x, to get $x < 3$, so the solution would be $(-\infty, 3)$. But that's wrong; for example, $x = -1$ lies in this interval but does not satisfy the original inequality. Explain why this method doesn't work (think about the *sign* of x). Then solve the inequality correctly.

124. Using Distances to Solve Absolute Value Inequalities   Recall that $|a - b|$ is the distance between a and b on the number line. For any number x, what do $|x - 1|$ and $|x - 3|$ represent? Use this interpretation to solve the inequality $|x - 1| < |x - 3|$ geometrically. In general, if $a < b$, what is the solution of the inequality $|x - a| < |x - b|$?

1.8 COORDINATE GEOMETRY

| The Coordinate Plane ▶ The Distance and Midpoint Formulas ▶ Graphs of
| Equations in Two Variables ▶ Intercepts ▶ Circles ▶ Symmetry

The *coordinate plane* is the link between algebra and geometry. In the coordinate plane we can draw graphs of algebraic equations. The graphs, in turn, allow us to "see" the relationship between the variables in the equation. In this section we study the coordinate plane.

▼ The Coordinate Plane

The Cartesian plane is named in honor of the French mathematician René Descartes (1596–1650), although another Frenchman, Pierre Fermat (1601–1665), also invented the principles of coordinate geometry at the same time. (See their biographies on pages 181 and 99.)

Just as points on a line can be identified with real numbers to form the coordinate line, points in a plane can be identified with ordered pairs of numbers to form the **coordinate plane** or **Cartesian plane**. To do this, we draw two perpendicular real lines that intersect at 0 on each line. Usually, one line is horizontal with positive direction to the right and is called the **x-axis**; the other line is vertical with positive direction upward and is called the **y-axis**. The point of intersection of the x-axis and the y-axis is the **origin O**, and the two axes divide the plane into four **quadrants**, labeled I, II, III, and IV in Figure 1. (The points *on* the coordinate axes are not assigned to any quadrant.)

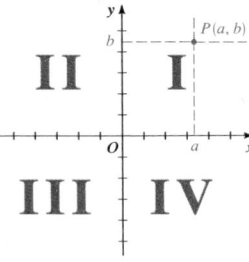

FIGURE 1

FIGURE 2

Any point P in the coordinate plane can be located by a unique **ordered pair** of numbers (a, b), as shown in Figure 1. The first number a is called the **x-coordinate** of P; the second number b is called the **y-coordinate** of P. We can think of the coordinates of P as its "address," because they specify its location in the plane. Several points are labeled with their coordinates in Figure 2.

Although the notation for a point (a, b) is the same as the notation for an open interval (a, b), the context should make clear which meaning is intended.

EXAMPLE 1 | Graphing Regions in the Coordinate Plane

Describe and sketch the regions given by each set.

(a) $\{(x, y) \mid x \geq 0\}$ (b) $\{(x, y) \mid y = 1\}$ (c) $\{(x, y) \mid |y| < 1\}$

SOLUTION

(a) The points whose x-coordinates are 0 or positive lie on the y-axis or to the right of it, as shown in Figure 3(a).

(b) The set of all points with y-coordinate 1 is a horizontal line one unit above the x-axis, as in Figure 3(b).

ALTERNATE EXAMPLE 1
Does the point $(1, -2)$ belong to the region given by the set $\{(x, y) \mid -3 < y < 4\}$?

ANSWER
Yes

Coordinates as Addresses

The coordinates of a point in the *xy*-plane uniquely determine its location. We can think of the coordinates as the "address" of the point. In Salt Lake City, Utah, the addresses of most buildings are in fact expressed as coordinates. The city is divided into quadrants with Main Street as the vertical (North-South) axis and S. Temple Street as the horizontal (East-West) axis. An address such as

1760 W 2100 S

indicates a location 17.6 blocks west of Main Street and 21 blocks south of S. Temple Street. (This is the address of the main post office in Salt Lake City.) With this logical system it is possible for someone unfamiliar with the city to locate any address immediately, as easily as one locates a point in the coordinate plane.

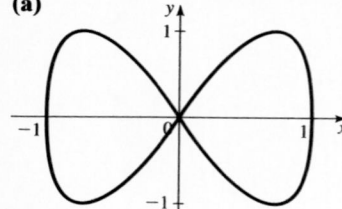

(c) Recall from Section 1.7 that

$$|y| < 1 \quad \text{if and only if} \quad -1 < y < 1$$

So the given region consists of those points in the plane whose *y*-coordinates lie between -1 and 1. Thus, the region consists of all points that lie between (but not on) the horizontal lines $y = 1$ and $y = -1$. These lines are shown as broken lines in Figure 3(c) to indicate that the points on these lines do not lie in the set.

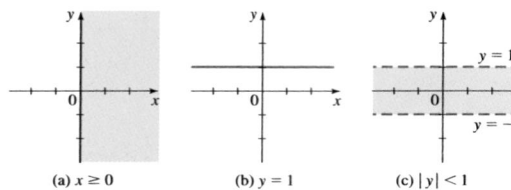

(a) $x \geq 0$ (b) $y = 1$ (c) $|y| < 1$

FIGURE 3

✎ NOW TRY EXERCISES **23, 25,** AND **29** ∎

▼ The Distance and Midpoint Formulas

We now find a formula for the distance $d(A, B)$ between two points $A(x_1, y_1)$ and $B(x_2, y_2)$ in the plane. Recall from Section 1.1 that the distance between points a and b on a number line is $d(a, b) = |b - a|$. So from Figure 4 we see that the distance between the points $A(x_1, y_1)$ and $C(x_2, y_1)$ on a horizontal line must be $|x_2 - x_1|$, and the distance between $B(x_2, y_2)$ and $C(x_2, y_1)$ on a vertical line must be $|y_2 - y_1|$.

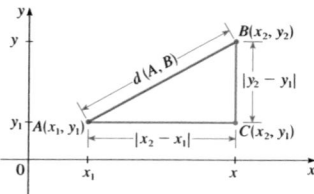

FIGURE 4

Since triangle ABC is a right triangle, the Pythagorean Theorem gives

$$d(A, B) = \sqrt{|x_2 - x_1|^2 + |y_2 - y_1|^2} = \sqrt{(x_2 - x_1)^2 + (y_2 - y_1)^2}$$

DISTANCE FORMULA

The distance between the points $A(x_1, y_1)$ and $B(x_2, y_2)$ in the plane is

$$d(A, B) = \sqrt{(x_2 - x_1)^2 + (y_2 - y_1)^2}$$

EXAMPLE 2 | Applying the Distance Formula

Which of the points $P(1, -2)$ or $Q(8, 9)$ is closer to the point $A(5, 3)$?

TEXT QUESTIONS

Circle the types of symmetry exhibited by each of the following figures.

(a)

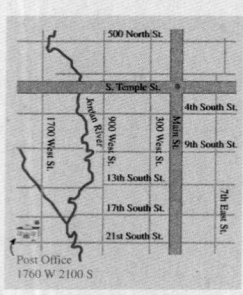

(i) About the *x*-axis
(ii) About the *y*-axis
(iii) About the origin

(b)

(i) About the *x*-axis
(ii) About the *y*-axis
(iii) About the origin

Answers
(a) (i), (ii), and (iii)
(b) (ii)

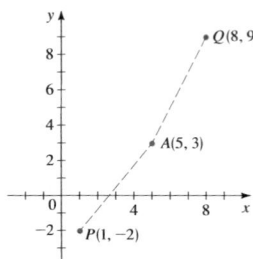

FIGURE 5

SOLUTION   By the Distance Formula we have

$$d(P, A) = \sqrt{(5-1)^2 + [3-(-2)]^2} = \sqrt{4^2 + 5^2} = \sqrt{41}$$

$$d(Q, A) = \sqrt{(5-8)^2 + (3-9)^2} = \sqrt{(-3)^2 + (-6)^2} = \sqrt{45}$$

This shows that $d(P, A) < d(Q, A)$, so P is closer to A (see Figure 5).

✎. NOW TRY EXERCISE **33**

Now let's find the coordinates (x, y) of the midpoint M of the line segment that joins the point $A(x_1, y_1)$ to the point $B(x_2, y_2)$. In Figure 6 notice that triangles APM and MQB are congruent because $d(A, M) = d(M, B)$ and the corresponding angles are equal.

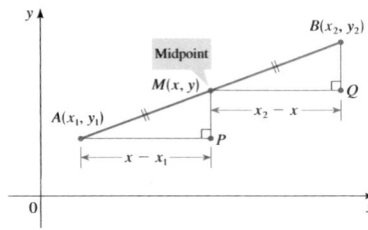

FIGURE 6

It follows that $d(A, P) = d(M, Q)$, so

$$x - x_1 = x_2 - x$$

Solving this equation for x, we get $2x = x_1 + x_2$, so $x = \dfrac{x_1 + x_2}{2}$. Similarly, $y = \dfrac{y_1 + y_2}{2}$.

MIDPOINT FORMULA

The midpoint of the line segment from $A(x_1, y_1)$ to $B(x_2, y_2)$ is

$$\left(\frac{x_1 + x_2}{2}, \frac{y_1 + y_2}{2} \right)$$

EXAMPLE 3 | Applying the Midpoint Formula

Show that the quadrilateral with vertices $P(1, 2)$, $Q(4, 4)$, $R(5, 9)$, and $S(2, 7)$ is a parallelogram by proving that its two diagonals bisect each other.

SOLUTION   If the two diagonals have the same midpoint, then they must bisect each other. The midpoint of the diagonal PR is

$$\left(\frac{1+5}{2}, \frac{2+9}{2} \right) = \left(3, \frac{11}{2} \right)$$

and the midpoint of the diagonal QS is

$$\left(\frac{4+2}{2}, \frac{4+7}{2} \right) = \left(3, \frac{11}{2} \right)$$

so each diagonal bisects the other, as shown in Figure 7. (A theorem from elementary geometry states that the quadrilateral is therefore a parallelogram.)

✎. NOW TRY EXERCISE **37**

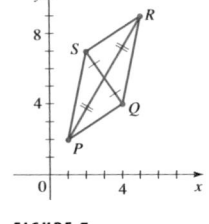

FIGURE 7

ALTERNATE EXAMPLE 2
Which of the points, $P(2, -3)$ or $Q(8, 8)$, is closer to the point $A(3, 4)$?

ANSWER
Q

ALTERNATE EXAMPLE 3
Is the quadrilateral with vertices $P(1, 0)$, $Q(5, -1)$, $R(5, 5)$, and $S(1, 6)$ a parallelogram?

ANSWER
Yes

▼ Graphs of Equations in Two Variables

Fundamental Principle of Analytic Geometry

A point (x, y) lies on the graph of an equation if and only if its coordinates satisfy the equation.

An **equation in two variables**, such as $y = x^2 + 1$, expresses a relationship between two quantities. A point (x, y) **satisfies** the equation if it makes the equation true when the values for x and y are substituted into the equation. For example, the point $(3, 10)$ satisfies the equation $y = x^2 + 1$ because $10 = 3^2 + 1$, but the point $(1, 3)$ does not, because $3 \neq 1^2 + 1$.

THE GRAPH OF AN EQUATION

The **graph** of an equation in x and y is the set of all points (x, y) in the coordinate plane that satisfy the equation.

The graph of an equation is a curve, so to graph an equation, we plot as many points as we can, then connect them by a smooth curve.

EXAMPLE 4 | Sketching a Graph by Plotting Points

Sketch the graph of the equation $2x - y = 3$.

SOLUTION   We first solve the given equation for y to get

$$y = 2x - 3$$

This helps us calculate the y-coordinates in the following table.

x	$y = 2x - 3$	(x, y)
-1	-5	$(-1, -5)$
0	-3	$(0, -3)$
1	-1	$(1, -1)$
2	1	$(2, 1)$
3	3	$(3, 3)$
4	5	$(4, 5)$

Of course, there are infinitely many points on the graph, and it is impossible to plot all of them. But the more points we plot, the better we can imagine what the graph represented by the equation looks like. We plot the points we found in Figure 8; they appear to lie on a line. So we complete the graph by joining the points by a line. (In Section 1.10 we verify that the graph of this equation is indeed a line.)

✎. NOW TRY EXERCISE 59   ■

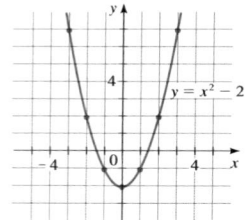

FIGURE 8

$y = 2x - 3$

A detailed discussion of parabolas and their geometric properties is presented in Chapter 10.

EXAMPLE 5 | Sketching a Graph by Plotting Points

Sketch the graph of the equation $y = x^2 - 2$.

SOLUTION   We find some of the points that satisfy the equation in the following table. In Figure 9 we plot these points and then connect them by a smooth curve. A curve with this shape is called a *parabola*.

x	$y = x^2 - 2$	(x, y)
-3	7	$(-3, 7)$
-2	2	$(-2, 2)$
-1	-1	$(-1, -1)$
0	-2	$(0, -2)$
1	-1	$(1, -1)$
2	2	$(2, 2)$
3	7	$(3, 7)$

FIGURE 9

$y = x^2 - 2$

✎. NOW TRY EXERCISE 63   ■

ALTERNATE EXAMPLE 4

For the graph of the equation $3x - y = 5$, find the coordinates of the points with $x = -1, 0, 1, 2,$ and 4.

ANSWER

$(-1, -8), (0, -5), (1, 2), (2, 1),$ $(4, 7)$

ALTERNATE EXAMPLE 5

For the graph of the equation $y = x^2 - 3$, find the coordinates of the points with $x = -3, -1, 0, 1,$ and 3.

ANSWER

$(-3, 6), (-1, -2), (0, -3), (1, -2),$ $(3, 6)$

IN-CLASS MATERIALS

Obtain a transparency of a local map, and overlay it with an appropriately sized grid. Try to estimate the walking distance between the classroom and various points of interest. Then use the distance formula to find the distance "as the crow flies."

EXAMPLE 6 | Graphing an Absolute Value Equation

Sketch the graph of the equation $y = |x|$.

SOLUTION We make a table of values:

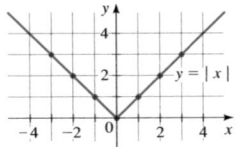

FIGURE 10

x	$y = |x|$	(x, y)
-3	3	$(-3, 3)$
-2	2	$(-2, 2)$
-1	1	$(-1, 1)$
0	0	$(0, 0)$
1	1	$(1, 1)$
2	2	$(2, 2)$
3	3	$(3, 3)$

In Figure 10 we plot these points and use them to sketch the graph of the equation.

NOW TRY EXERCISE **75**

▼ Intercepts

The x-coordinates of the points where a graph intersects the x-axis are called the **x-intercepts** of the graph and are obtained by setting $y = 0$ in the equation of the graph. The y-coordinates of the points where a graph intersects the y-axis are called the **y-intercepts** of the graph and are obtained by setting $x = 0$ in the equation of the graph.

DEFINITION OF INTERCEPTS

Intercepts	How to find them	Where they are on the graph
x-intercepts: The x-coordinates of points where the graph of an equation intersects the x-axis	Set $y = 0$ and solve for x	
y-intercepts: The y-coordinates of points where the graph of an equation intersects the y-axis	Set $x = 0$ and solve for y	

EXAMPLE 7 | Finding Intercepts

Find the x- and y-intercepts of the graph of the equation $y = x^2 - 2$.

SOLUTION To find the x-intercepts, we set $y = 0$ and solve for x. Thus

$$0 = x^2 - 2 \quad \text{Set } y = 0$$
$$x^2 = 2 \quad \text{Add 2 to each side}$$
$$x = \pm\sqrt{2} \quad \text{Take the square root}$$

The x-intercepts are $\sqrt{2}$ and $-\sqrt{2}$.

ALTERNATE EXAMPLE 6
For the graph of the equation $y = |-x|$, find the coordinates of the points with $x = -2, -1, 0, 1,$ and 2.

ANSWER
$(-2, 2), (-1, 1), (0, 0), (1, 1), (2, 2)$

ALTERNATE EXAMPLE 7
Find the x- and y-intercepts of the graph of the equation $y = x^2 - 3x + 2$.

ANSWER
The x-intercepts are 1 and 2. The y-intercept is 2.

IN-CLASS MATERIALS
Assume that a meter stick is situated as in the diagram here. Ask the students to find the 50-cm mark and then the 25-cm mark.

To find the *y*-intercepts, we set $x = 0$ and solve for *y*. Thus

$$y = 0^2 - 2 \qquad \text{Set } x = 0$$

$$y = -2$$

The *y*-intercept is -2.

The graph of this equation was sketched in Example 5. It is repeated in Figure 11 with the *x*- and *y*-intercepts labeled.

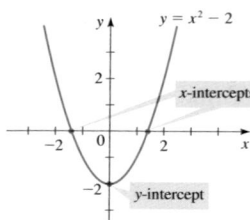

FIGURE 11

⬆. NOW TRY EXERCISE **65**

▼ Circles

So far, we have discussed how to find the graph of an equation in *x* and *y*. The converse problem is to find an equation of a graph, that is, an equation that represents a given curve in the *xy*-plane. Such an equation is satisfied by the coordinates of the points on the curve and by no other point. This is the other half of the fundamental principle of analytic geometry as formulated by Descartes and Fermat. The idea is that if a geometric curve can be represented by an algebraic equation, then the rules of algebra can be used to analyze the curve.

As an example of this type of problem, let's find the equation of a circle with radius *r* and center (h, k). By definition the circle is the set of all points $P(x, y)$ whose distance from the center $C(h, k)$ is *r* (see Figure 12). Thus *P* is on the circle if and only if $d(P, C) = r$. From the distance formula we have

$$\sqrt{(x - h)^2 + (y - k)^2} = r$$

$$(x - h)^2 + (y - k)^2 = r^2 \qquad \text{Square each side}$$

This is the desired equation.

FIGURE 12

EQUATION OF A CIRCLE

An equation of the circle with center (h, k) and radius *r* is

$$(x - h)^2 + (y - k)^2 = r^2$$

This is called the **standard form** for the equation of the circle. If the center of the circle is the origin $(0, 0)$, then the equation is

$$x^2 + y^2 = r^2$$

EXAMPLE 8 | Graphing a Circle

Graph each equation.

(a) $x^2 + y^2 = 25$ **(b)** $(x - 2)^2 + (y + 1)^2 = 25$

ALTERNATE EXAMPLE 8

For the graph of the equation $(x - 2)^2 + (y + 4)^2 = 36$, find its center and radius.

ANSWER

Center: $(2, -4)$

Radius: 6

SOLUTION

(a) Rewriting the equation as $x^2 + y^2 = 5^2$, we see that this is an equation of the circle of radius 5 centered at the origin. Its graph is shown in Figure 13.

(b) Rewriting the equation as $(x - 2)^2 + (y + 1)^2 = 5^2$, we see that this is an equation of the circle of radius 5 centered at $(2, -1)$. Its graph is shown in Figure 14.

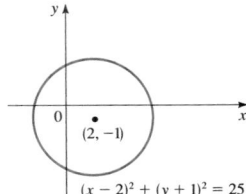

FIGURE 13

FIGURE 14

✎. NOW TRY EXERCISES **87** AND **89**

EXAMPLE 9 | Finding an Equation of a Circle

(a) Find an equation of the circle with radius 3 and center $(2, -5)$.

(b) Find an equation of the circle that has the points $P(1, 8)$ and $Q(5, -6)$ as the endpoints of a diameter.

SOLUTION

(a) Using the equation of a circle with $r = 3$, $h = 2$, and $k = -5$, we obtain

$$(x - 2)^2 + (y + 5)^2 = 9$$

The graph is shown in Figure 15.

(b) We first observe that the center is the midpoint of the diameter PQ, so by the Midpoint Formula the center is

$$\left(\frac{1 + 5}{2}, \frac{8 - 6}{2}\right) = (3, 1)$$

The radius r is the distance from P to the center, so by the Distance Formula

$$r^2 = (3 - 1)^2 + (1 - 8)^2 = 2^2 + (-7)^2 = 53$$

Therefore, the equation of the circle is

$$(x - 3)^2 + (y - 1)^2 = 53$$

The graph is shown in Figure 16.

✎. NOW TRY EXERCISES **93** AND **97**

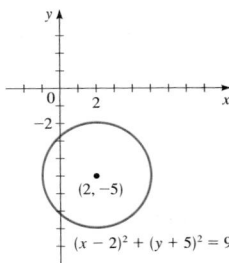

$(x - 2)^2 + (y + 5)^2 = 9$

FIGURE 15

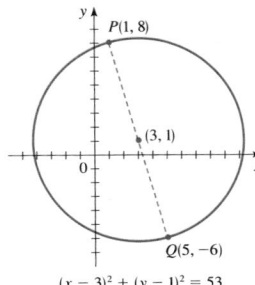

$(x - 3)^2 + (y - 1)^2 = 53$

FIGURE 16

Let's expand the equation of the circle in the preceding example.

$$(x - 3)^2 + (y - 1)^2 = 53 \qquad \text{Standard form}$$
$$x^2 - 6x + 9 + y^2 - 2y + 1 = 53 \qquad \text{Expand the squares}$$
$$x^2 - 6x + y^2 - 2y = 43 \qquad \text{Subtract 10 to get expanded form}$$

Suppose we are given the equation of a circle in expanded form. Then to find its center and radius, we must put the equation back in standard form. That means that we must reverse the steps in the preceding calculation, and to do that we need to know what to add to an expression like $x^2 - 6x$ to make it a perfect square—that is, we need to complete the square, as in the next example.

Completing the square is used in many contexts in algebra. In Section 1.5 we used completing the square to solve quadratic equations.

ALTERNATE EXAMPLE 9

Find an equation of the circle that has the points $P(1, 8)$ and $Q(3, -6)$ as the endpoints of a diameter.

ANSWER

$(x - 2)^2 + (y - 1)^2 = 50$

IN-CLASS MATERIALS

Graph $y = \||x| - 1| - 2$ by plotting points. This is a nice curve because it is easy to get points, but students will not immediately see what the curve should look like. Have different students obtain different points, and plot them on a common graph on the board.

Answer

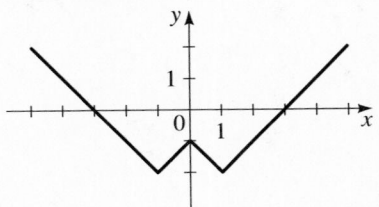

ALTERNATE EXAMPLE 10
For the graph of the circle
$x^2 + y^2 + 4x - 10y + 6 = 0$, find
its center and radius.

ANSWER
$(-2, 5)$, $\sqrt{23}$

EXAMPLE 10 | Identifying an Equation of a Circle

Show that the equation $x^2 + y^2 + 2x - 6y + 7 = 0$ represents a circle, and find the center and radius of the circle.

SOLUTION   We first group the x-terms and y-terms. Then we complete the square within each grouping. That is, we complete the square for $x^2 + 2x$ by adding $\left(\frac{1}{2} \cdot 2\right)^2 = 1$, and we complete the square for $y^2 - 6y$ by adding $\left[\frac{1}{2} \cdot (-6)\right]^2 = 9$.

$$(x^2 + 2x \quad) + (y^2 - 6y \quad) = -7 \qquad \text{Group terms}$$

$$(x^2 + 2x + 1) + (y^2 - 6y + 9) = -7 + 1 + 9 \qquad \begin{array}{l}\text{Complete the square by}\\\text{adding 1 and 9 to each side}\end{array}$$

$$(x + 1)^2 + (y - 3)^2 = 3 \qquad \text{Factor and simplify}$$

Comparing this equation with the standard equation of a circle, we see that $h = -1$, $k = 3$, and $r = \sqrt{3}$, so the given equation represents a circle with center $(-1, 3)$ and radius $\sqrt{3}$.

. NOW TRY EXERCISE **103**   ■

⊘ We must add the same numbers to *each side* to maintain equality.

▼ **Symmetry**

Figure 17 shows the graph of $y = x^2$. Notice that the part of the graph to the left of the y-axis is the mirror image of the part to the right of the y-axis. The reason is that if the point (x, y) is on the graph, then so is $(-x, y)$, and these points are reflections of each other about the y-axis. In this situation we say that the graph is **symmetric with respect to the y-axis**. Similarly, we say that a graph is **symmetric with respect to the x-axis** if whenever the point (x, y) is on the graph, then so is $(x, -y)$. A graph is **symmetric with respect to the origin** if whenever (x, y) is on the graph, so is $(-x, -y)$.

FIGURE 17

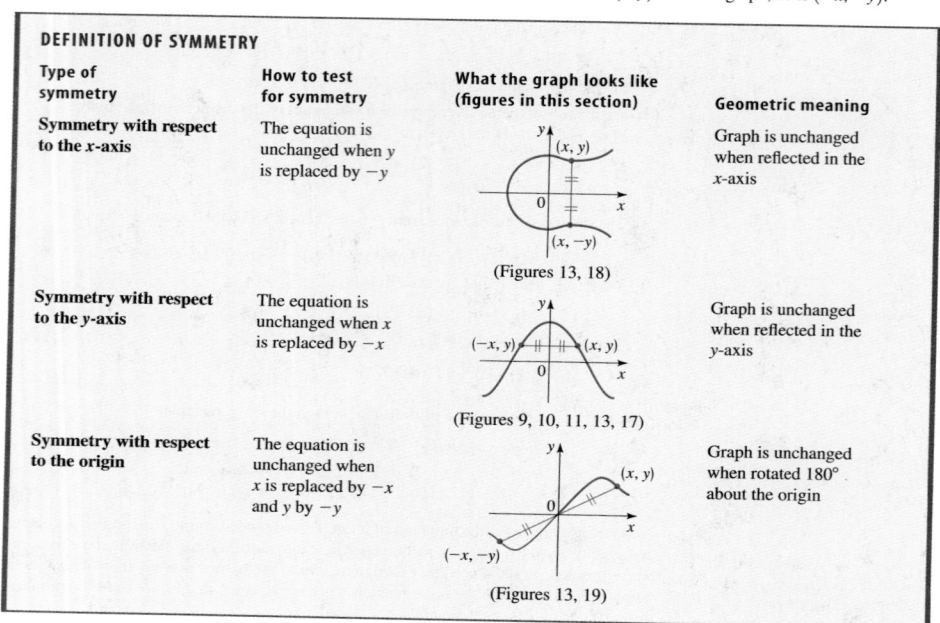

DEFINITION OF SYMMETRY			
Type of symmetry	**How to test for symmetry**	**What the graph looks like** (figures in this section)	**Geometric meaning**
Symmetry with respect to the x-axis	The equation is unchanged when y is replaced by $-y$	(Figures 13, 18)	Graph is unchanged when reflected in the x-axis
Symmetry with respect to the y-axis	The equation is unchanged when x is replaced by $-x$	(Figures 9, 10, 11, 13, 17)	Graph is unchanged when reflected in the y-axis
Symmetry with respect to the origin	The equation is unchanged when x is replaced by $-x$ and y by $-y$	(Figures 13, 19)	Graph is unchanged when rotated 180° about the origin

IN-CLASS MATERIALS

Emphasize that the equation $(x - 2)^2 + (y + 3)^2 = 100$ and the equation $x^2 - 4x + y^2 + 6y = -3$ have the same graph—the same points satisfy both equations. Perhaps test $(2, 7)$ and $(1, 1)$ in both equations and notice that $(2, 7)$ satisfies both and $(1, 1)$ fails to satisfy either. The only difference between the two equations is the form: It is easier to work with the first than the second.

The remaining examples in this section show how symmetry helps us sketch the graphs of equations.

EXAMPLE 11 | Using Symmetry to Sketch a Graph

Test the equation $x = y^2$ for symmetry and sketch the graph.

SOLUTION   If y is replaced by $-y$ in the equation $x = y^2$, we get

$$x = (-y)^2 \qquad \text{Replace } y \text{ by } -y$$
$$x = y^2 \qquad \text{Simplify}$$

and so the equation is unchanged. Therefore, the graph is symmetric about the x-axis. But changing x to $-x$ gives the equation $-x = y^2$, which is not the same as the original equation, so the graph is not symmetric about the y-axis.

We use the symmetry about the x-axis to sketch the graph by first plotting points just for $y > 0$ and then reflecting the graph in the x-axis, as shown in Figure 18.

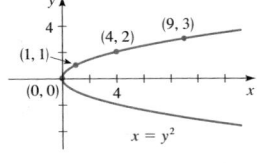

FIGURE 18

y	$x = y^2$	(x, y)
0	0	$(0, 0)$
1	1	$(1, 1)$
2	4	$(4, 2)$
3	9	$(9, 3)$

 NOW TRY EXERCISE **77**

EXAMPLE 12 | Using Symmetry to Sketch a Graph

Test the equation $y = x^3 - 9x$ for symmetry and sketch its graph.

SOLUTION   If we replace x by $-x$ and y by $-y$ in the equation, we get

$$-y = (-x)^3 - 9(-x) \qquad \text{Replace } x \text{ by } -x \text{ and } y \text{ by } -y$$
$$-y = -x^3 + 9x \qquad \text{Simplify}$$
$$y = x^3 - 9x \qquad \text{Multiply by } -1$$

and so the equation is unchanged. This means that the graph is symmetric with respect to the origin. We sketch it by first plotting points for $x > 0$ and then using symmetry about the origin (see Figure 19).

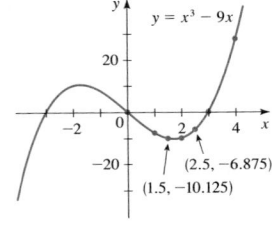

FIGURE 19

x	$y = x^3 - 9x$	(x, y)
0	0	$(0, 0)$
1	-8	$(1, -8)$
1.5	-10.125	$(1.5, -10.125)$
2	-10	$(2, -10)$
2.5	-6.875	$(2.5, -6.875)$
3	0	$(3, 0)$
4	28	$(4, 28)$

 NOW TRY EXERCISE **79**

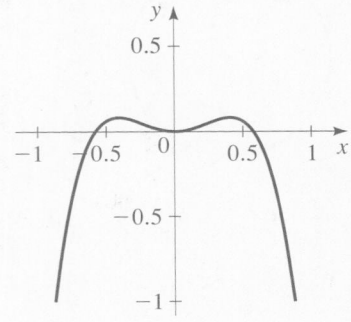
EXAMPLES

1. Investigate the trapezoidal region given by the inequalities $x > 2$, $y > \frac{3}{2}x - 3$, $y > -x + 7$, and $y < -x + 12$.

2. A curve with a lot of intercepts: $y = x^5 - 15x^4 + 85x^3 - 225x^2 + 274x - 120$ looks frightening until students are given the factored form: $y = (x - 1)(x - 2)(x - 3)(x - 4)(x - 5)$.

DRILL QUESTION

Graph the circle with equation $x^2 + 2x + y^2 - 4y = 20$.

Answer

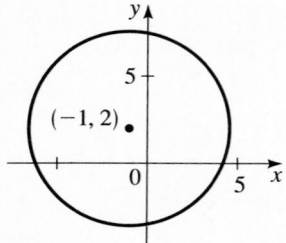

1.8 EXERCISES

CONCEPTS

1. The point that is 3 units to the right of the y-axis and 5 units below the x-axis has coordinates (_____, _____).

2. The distance between the points (a, b) and (c, d) is _____. So the distance between $(1, 2)$ and $(7, 10)$ is _____.

3. The point midway between (a, b) and (c, d) is _____. So the point midway between $(1, 2)$ and $(7, 10)$ is _____.

4. If the point $(2, 3)$ is on the graph of an equation in x and y, then the equation is satisfied when we replace x by _____ and y by _____. Is the point $(2, 3)$ on the graph of the equation $2y = x + 1$?

5. (a) To find the x-intercept(s) of the graph of an equation, we set _____ equal to 0 and solve for _____. So the x-intercept of $2y = x + 1$ is _____.

   (b) To find the y-intercept(s) of the graph of an equation, we set _____ equal to 0 and solve for _____. So the y-intercept of $2y = x + 1$ is _____.

6. The graph of the equation $(x - 1)^2 + (y - 2)^2 = 9$ is a circle with center (_____, _____) and radius _____.

SKILLS

7. Plot the given points in a coordinate plane.
$$(2, 3), (-2, 3), (4, 5), (4, -5), (-4, 5), (-4, -5)$$

8. Find the coordinates of the points shown in the figure.

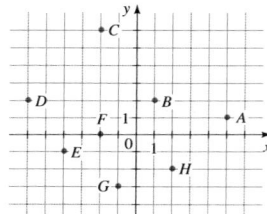

9–12 ■ A pair of points is graphed.
   (a) Find the distance between them.
   (b) Find the midpoint of the segment that joins them.

9.

10.

11.

12.

13–18 ■ A pair of points is graphed.
   (a) Plot the points in a coordinate plane.
   (b) Find the distance between them.
   (c) Find the midpoint of the segment that joins them.

13. $(0, 8), (6, 16)$ 14. $(-2, 5), (10, 0)$

15. $(-3, -6), (4, 18)$ 16. $(-1, -1), (9, 9)$

17. $(6, -2), (-6, 2)$ 18. $(0, -6), (5, 0)$

19. Draw the rectangle with vertices $A(1, 3), B(5, 3), C(1, -3)$, and $D(5, -3)$ on a coordinate plane. Find the area of the rectangle.

20. Draw the parallelogram with vertices $A(1, 2), B(5, 2), C(3, 6)$, and $D(7, 6)$ on a coordinate plane. Find the area of the parallelogram.

21. Plot the points $A(1, 0), B(5, 0), C(4, 3)$, and $D(2, 3)$ on a coordinate plane. Draw the segments AB, BC, CD, and DA. What kind of quadrilateral is $ABCD$, and what is its area?

22. Plot the points $P(5, 1), Q(0, 6)$, and $R(-5, 1)$ on a coordinate plane. Where must the point S be located so that the quadrilateral $PQRS$ is a square? Find the area of this square.

23–32 ■ Sketch the region given by the set.

23. $\{(x, y) \mid x \geq 3\}$ 24. $\{(x, y) \mid y < 3\}$

25. $\{(x, y) \mid y = 2\}$ 26. $\{(x, y) \mid x = -1\}$

27. $\{(x, y) \mid 1 < x < 2\}$ 28. $\{(x, y) \mid 0 \leq y \leq 4\}$

29. $\{(x, y) \mid |x| > 4\}$ 30. $\{(x, y) \mid |y| \leq 2\}$

31. $\{(x, y) \mid x \geq 1 \text{ and } y < 3\}$

32. $\{(x, y) \mid |x| \leq 2 \text{ and } |y| \leq 3\}$

33. Which of the points $A(6, 7)$ or $B(-5, 8)$ is closer to the origin?

34. Which of the points $C(-6, 3)$ or $D(3, 0)$ is closer to the point $E(-2, 1)$?

35. Which of the points $P(3, 1)$ or $Q(-1, 3)$ is closer to the point $R(-1, -1)$?

36. (a) Show that the points $(7, 3)$ and $(3, 7)$ are the same distance from the origin.

(b) Show that the points (a, b) and (b, a) are the same distance from the origin.

37. Show that the triangle with vertices $A(0, 2)$, $B(-3, -1)$, and $C(-4, 3)$ is isosceles.

38. Find the area of the triangle shown in the figure.

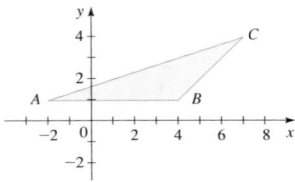

39. Refer to triangle ABC in the figure below.

(a) Show that triangle ABC is a right triangle by using the converse of the Pythagorean Theorem (see page 219).

(b) Find the area of triangle ABC.

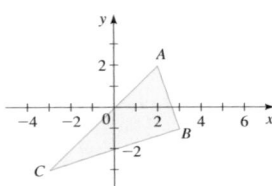

40. Show that the triangle with vertices $A(6, -7)$, $B(11, -3)$, and $C(2, -2)$ is a right triangle by using the converse of the Pythagorean Theorem. Find the area of the triangle.

41. Show that the points $A(-2, 9)$, $B(4, 6)$, $C(1, 0)$, and $D(-5, 3)$ are the vertices of a square.

42. Show that the points $A(-1, 3)$, $B(3, 11)$, and $C(5, 15)$ are collinear by showing that $d(A, B) + d(B, C) = d(A, C)$.

43. Find a point on the y-axis that is equidistant from the points $(5, -5)$ and $(1, 1)$.

44. Find the lengths of the medians of the triangle with vertices $A(1, 0)$, $B(3, 6)$, and $C(8, 2)$. (A *median* is a line segment from a vertex to the midpoint of the opposite side.)

45. Plot the points $P(-1, -4)$, $Q(1, 1)$, and $R(4, 2)$ on a coordinate plane. Where should the point S be located so that the figure $PQRS$ is a parallelogram?

46. If $M(6, 8)$ is the midpoint of the line segment AB and if A has coordinates $(2, 3)$, find the coordinates of B.

47. (a) Sketch the parallelogram with vertices $A(-2, -1)$, $B(4, 2)$, $C(7, 7)$, and $D(1, 4)$.

(b) Find the midpoints of the diagonals of this parallelogram.

(c) From part (b) show that the diagonals bisect each other.

48. The point M in the figure is the midpoint of the line segment AB. Show that M is equidistant from the vertices of triangle ABC.

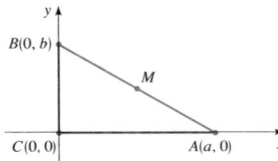

49–52 ■ Determine whether the given points are on the graph of the equation.

49. $x - 2y - 1 = 0$; $(0, 0), (1, 0), (-1, -1)$

50. $y(x^2 + 1) = 1$; $(1, 1), \left(1, \frac{1}{2}\right), \left(-1, \frac{1}{2}\right)$

51. $x^2 + xy + y^2 = 4$; $(0, -2), (1, -2), (2, -2)$

52. $x^2 + y^2 = 1$; $(0, 1), \left(\frac{1}{\sqrt{2}}, \frac{1}{\sqrt{2}}\right), \left(\frac{\sqrt{3}}{2}, \frac{1}{2}\right)$

53–56 ■ An equation and its graph are given. Find the x- and y-intercepts.

53. $y = 4x - x^2$

54. $\dfrac{x^2}{9} + \dfrac{y^2}{4} = 1$

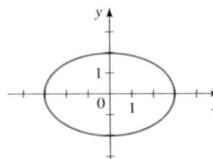

55. $x^4 + y^2 - xy = 16$

56. $x^2 + y^3 - x^2y^2 = 64$

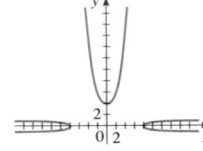

57–76 ■ Make a table of values and sketch the graph of the equation. Find the x- and y-intercepts and test for symmetry.

57. $y = -x + 4$ **58.** $y = 3x + 3$

59. $2x - y = 6$ **60.** $x + y = 3$

61. $y = 1 - x^2$ **62.** $y = x^2 + 2$

63. $4y = x^2$ **64.** $8y = x^3$

65. $y = x^2 - 9$ **66.** $y = 9 - x^2$

67. $xy = 2$ **68.** $y = \sqrt{x + 4}$

69. $y = \sqrt{4 - x^2}$ **70.** $y = -\sqrt{4 - x^2}$

71. $x + y^2 = 4$ **72.** $x = y^3$

73. $y = 16 - x^4$ **74.** $x = |y|$

75. $y = 4 - |x|$ **76.** $y = |4 - x|$

77–82 ■ Test the equation for symmetry.

77. $y = x^4 + x^2$ **78.** $x = y^4 - y^2$

79. $x^2 y^2 + xy = 1$ **80.** $x^4 y^4 + x^2 y^2 = 1$

81. $y = x^3 + 10x$ **82.** $y = x^2 + |x|$

83–86 ■ Complete the graph using the given symmetry property.

83. Symmetric with respect to the y-axis

84. Symmetric with respect to the x-axis

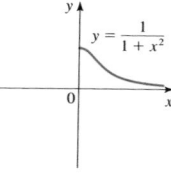

$y = \dfrac{1}{1 + x^2}$

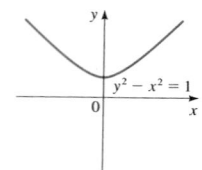

$y^2 - x^2 = 1$

85. Symmetric with respect to the origin

86. Symmetric with respect to the origin

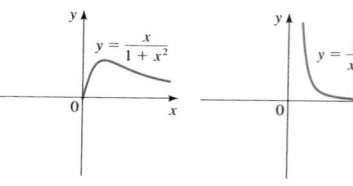

$y = \dfrac{x}{1 + x^2}$

$y = \dfrac{1}{x^3}$

87–92 ■ Find the center and radius of the circle and sketch its graph

87. $x^2 + y^2 = 9$ **88.** $x^2 + y^2 = 5$

89. $(x - 3)^2 + y^2 = 16$ **90.** $x^2 + (y - 2)^2 = 4$

91. $(x + 3)^2 + (y - 4)^2 = 25$ **92.** $(x + 1)^2 + (y + 2)^2 = 36$

93–100 ■ Find an equation of the circle that satisfies the given conditions.

93. Center $(2, -1)$;   radius 3

94. Center $(-1, -4)$;   radius 8

95. Center at the origin;   passes through $(4, 7)$

96. Center $(-1, 5)$;   passes through $(-4, -6)$

97. Endpoints of a diameter are $P(-1, 1)$ and $Q(5, 9)$

98. Endpoints of a diameter are $P(-1, 3)$ and $Q(7, -5)$

99. Center $(7, -3)$;   tangent to the x-axis

100. Circle lies in the first quadrant, tangent to both x-and y-axes; radius 5

101–102 ■ Find the equation of the circle shown in the figure.

101.   **102.**

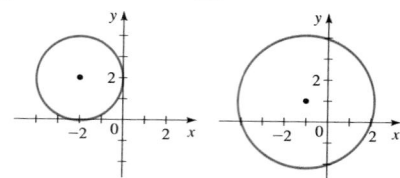

103–108 ■ Show that the equation represents a circle, and find the center and radius of the circle.

103. $x^2 + y^2 - 4x + 10y + 13 = 0$

104. $x^2 + y^2 + 6y + 2 = 0$

105. $x^2 + y^2 - \frac{1}{2}x + \frac{1}{2}y = \frac{1}{8}$

106. $x^2 + y^2 + \frac{1}{2}x + 2y + \frac{1}{16} = 0$

107. $2x^2 + 2y^2 - 3x = 0$

108. $3x^2 + 3y^2 + 6x - y = 0$

109–110 ■ Sketch the region given by the set.

109. $\{(x, y) \mid x^2 + y^2 \leq 1\}$

110. $\{(x, y) \mid x^2 + y^2 > 4\}$

111. Find the area of the region that lies outside the circle $x^2 + y^2 = 4$ but inside the circle

$$x^2 + y^2 - 4y - 12 = 0$$

112. Sketch the region in the coordinate plane that satisfies both the inequalities $x^2 + y^2 \leq 9$ and $y \geq |x|$. What is the area of this region?

APPLICATIONS

113. Distances in a City A city has streets that run north and south and avenues that run east and west, all equally spaced. Streets and avenues are numbered sequentially, as shown in the figure. The *walking* distance between points A and B is 7 blocks—that is, 3 blocks east and 4 blocks north. To find the *straight-line* distance d, we must use the Distance Formula.

(a) Find the straight-line distance (in blocks) between A and B.

(b) Find the walking distance and the straight-line distance between the corner of 4th St. and 2nd Ave. and the corner of 11th St. and 26th Ave.

(c) What must be true about the points P and Q if the walking distance between P and Q equals the straight-line distance between P and Q?

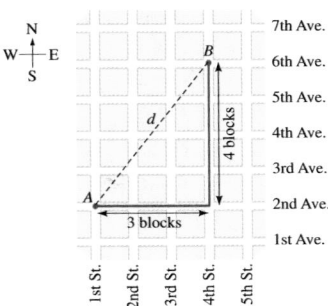

114. Halfway Point Two friends live in the city described in Exercise 113, one at the corner of 3rd St. and 7th Ave., the other at the corner of 27th St. and 17th Ave. They frequently meet at a coffee shop halfway between their homes.

(a) At what intersection is the coffee shop located?

(b) How far must each of them walk to get to the coffee shop?

115. Orbit of a Satellite A satellite is in orbit around the moon. A coordinate plane containing the orbit is set up with the center of the moon at the origin, as shown in the graph, with distances measured in megameters (Mm). The equation of the satellite's orbit is

$$\frac{(x-3)^2}{25} + \frac{y^2}{16} = 1$$

(a) From the graph, determine the closest and the farthest that the satellite gets to the center of the moon.

(b) There are two points in the orbit with y-coordinates 2. Find the x-coordinates of these points, and determine their distances to the center of the moon.

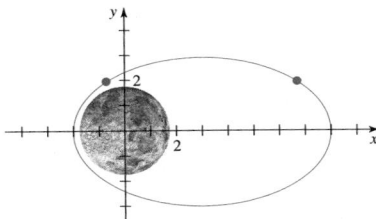

DISCOVERY ▪ DISCUSSION ▪ WRITING

116. Shifting the Coordinate Plane Suppose that each point in the coordinate plane is shifted 3 units to the right and 2 units upward.

(a) The point $(5, 3)$ is shifted to what new point?

(b) The point (a, b) is shifted to what new point?

(c) What point is shifted to $(3, 4)$?

(d) Triangle ABC in the figure has been shifted to triangle $A'B'C'$. Find the coordinates of the points A', B', and C'.

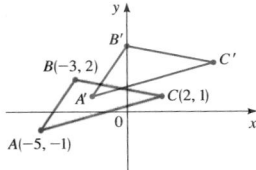

117. Reflecting in the Coordinate Plane Suppose that the y-axis acts as a mirror that reflects each point to the right of it into a point to the left of it.

(a) The point $(3, 7)$ is reflected to what point?

(b) The point (a, b) is reflected to what point?

(c) What point is reflected to $(-4, -1)$?

(d) Triangle ABC in the figure is reflected to triangle $A'B'C'$. Find the coordinates of the points A', B', and C'.

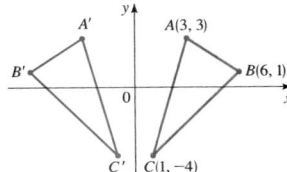

118. Completing a Line Segment Plot the points $M(6, 8)$ and $A(2, 3)$ on a coordinate plane. If M is the midpoint of the line segment AB, find the coordinates of B. Write a brief description of the steps you took to find B, and your reasons for taking them.

119. Completing a Parallelogram Plot the points $P(0, 3)$, $Q(2, 2)$, and $R(5, 3)$ on a coordinate plane. Where should the point S be located so that the figure $PQRS$ is a parallelogram? Write a brief description of the steps you took and your reasons for taking them.

120. Circle, Point, or Empty Set? Complete the squares in the general equation $x^2 + ax + y^2 + by + c = 0$ and simplify the result as much as possible. Under what conditions on the coefficients a, b, and c does this equation represent a circle? A single point? The empty set? In the case that the equation does represent a circle, find its center and radius.

121. Do the Circles Intersect?

(a) Find the radius of each circle in the pair and the distance between their centers; then use this information to determine whether the circles intersect.

   (i) $(x - 2)^2 + (y - 1)^2 = 9$;
      $(x - 6)^2 + (y - 4)^2 = 16$

   (ii) $x^2 + (y - 2)^2 = 4$;
      $(x - 5)^2 + (y - 14)^2 = 9$

   (iii) $(x - 3)^2 + (y + 1)^2 = 1$;
      $(x - 2)^2 + (y - 2)^2 = 25$

(b) How can you tell, just by knowing the radii of two circles and the distance between their centers, whether the circles intersect? Write a short paragraph describing how you would decide this and draw graphs to illustrate your answer.

122. Making a Graph Symmetric The graph shown in the figure is not symmetric about the x-axis, the y-axis, or the origin. Add more line segments to the graph so that it exhibits the indicated symmetry. In each case, add as little as possible.

(a) Symmetry about the x-axis

(b) Symmetry about the y-axis

(c) Symmetry about the origin

SUGGESTED TIME
AND EMPHASIS
1 class, essential material

1.9 GRAPHING CALCULATORS; SOLVING EQUATIONS AND INEQUALITIES GRAPHICALLY

Using a Graphing Calculator ▶ Solving Equations Graphically ▶ Solving Inequalities Graphically

In Sections 1.5 and 1.7 we solved equations and inequalities algebraically. In Section 1.8 we learned how to sketch the graph of an equation in a coordinate plane. In this section we use graphs to solve equations and inequalities. To do this, we must first draw a graph using a graphing device. So we begin by giving a few guidelines to help us use graphing devices effectively.

▼ Using a Graphing Calculator

A graphing calculator or computer displays a rectangular portion of the graph of an equation in a display window or viewing screen, which we call a **viewing rectangle**. The default screen often gives an incomplete or misleading picture, so it is important to choose the viewing rectangle with care. If we choose the x-values to range from a minimum value of $\text{Xmin} = a$ to a maximum value of $\text{Xmax} = b$ and the y-values to range from a minimum value of $\text{Ymin} = c$ to a maximum value of $\text{Ymax} = d$, then the displayed portion of the graph lies in the rectangle

$$[a, b] \times [c, d] = \{(x, y) \mid a \le x \le b, c \le y \le d\}$$

as shown in Figure 1. We refer to this as the $[a, b]$ by $[c, d]$ viewing rectangle.

FIGURE 1 The viewing rectangle $[a, b]$ by $[c, d]$

The graphing device draws the graph of an equation much as you would. It plots points of the form (x, y) for a certain number of values of x, equally spaced between a and b. If the equation is not defined for an x-value or if the corresponding y-value lies outside the viewing rectangle, the device ignores this value and moves on to the next x-value. The machine connects each point to the preceding plotted point to form a representation of the graph of the equation.

EXAMPLE 1 | Choosing an Appropriate Viewing Rectangle

Graph the equation $y = x^2 + 3$ in an appropriate viewing rectangle.

TEXT QUESTION

Give an advantage of solving an equation graphically and an advantage of solving an equation algebraically.

SOLUTION   Let's experiment with different viewing rectangles. We start with the viewing rectangle $[-2, 2]$ by $[-2, 2]$, so we set

$$\text{Xmin} = -2 \qquad \text{Ymin} = -2$$
$$\text{Xmax} = 2 \qquad \text{Ymax} = 2$$

The resulting graph in Figure 2(a) is blank! This is because $x^2 \geq 0$, so $x^2 + 3 \geq 3$ for all x. Thus, the graph lies entirely above the viewing rectangle, so this viewing rectangle is not appropriate. If we enlarge the viewing rectangle to $[-4, 4]$ by $[-4, 4]$, as in Figure 2(b), we begin to see a portion of the graph.

Now let's try the viewing rectangle $[-10, 10]$ by $[-5, 30]$. The graph in Figure 2(c) seems to give a more complete view of the graph. If we enlarge the viewing rectangle even further, as in Figure 2(d), the graph doesn't show clearly that the y-intercept is 3.

So the viewing rectangle $[-10, 10]$ by $[-5, 30]$ gives an appropriate representation of the graph.

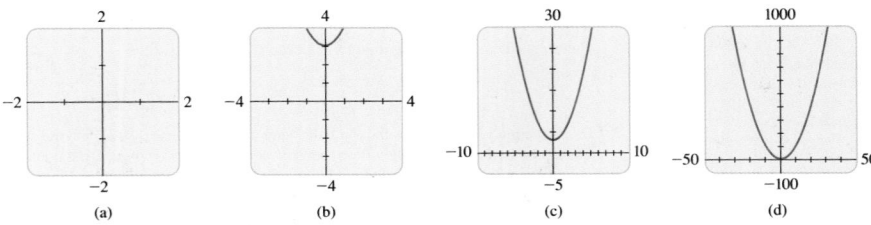

(a)   (b)   (c)   (d)

FIGURE 2   Graphs of $y = x^2 + 3$

✎. NOW TRY EXERCISE **5**

EXAMPLE 2 | Two Graphs on the Same Screen

Graph the equations $y = 3x^2 - 6x + 1$ and $y = 0.23x - 2.25$ together in the viewing rectangle $[-1, 3]$ by $[-2.5, 1.5]$. Do the graphs intersect in this viewing rectangle?

SOLUTION   Figure 3(a) shows the essential features of both graphs. One is a parabola, and the other is a line. It looks as if the graphs intersect near the point $(1, -2)$. However, if we zoom in on the area around this point as shown in Figure 3(b), we see that although the graphs almost touch, they do not actually intersect.

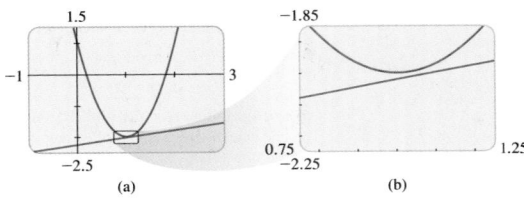

(a)   (b)

FIGURE 3

✎. NOW TRY EXERCISE **23**

ALTERNATE EXAMPLE 1
Graph the equation in an appropriate viewing rectangle:
$x^3 - 6x^2 + 11x - 5$

ANSWER
Answers can vary.

$[0, 4]$ by $[-4, 6]$ is an example of a good viewing rectangle for this function.

ALTERNATE EXAMPLE 2
Graph the equations
$y = 2x^2 - 4x + 1$ and
$y = 0.15x - 1.15$ using the graphing calculator together on the same screen in the viewing rectangle $[-1, 3]$ by $[-1.5, 3.5]$. Do the graphs intersect in this viewing rectangle?

ANSWER
Yes

You can see from Examples 1 and 2 that the choice of a viewing rectangle makes a big difference in the appearance of a graph. If you want an overview of the essential features of a graph, you must choose a relatively large viewing rectangle to obtain a global view of the graph. If you want to investigate the details of a graph, you must zoom in to a small viewing rectangle that shows just the feature of interest.

Most graphing calculators can only graph equations in which y is isolated on one side of the equal sign. The next example shows how to graph equations that don't have this property.

EXAMPLE 3 | Graphing a Circle

Graph the circle $x^2 + y^2 = 1$.

SOLUTION   We first solve for y, to isolate it on one side of the equal sign.

$$y^2 = 1 - x^2 \qquad \text{Subtract } x^2$$

$$y = \pm\sqrt{1 - x^2} \qquad \text{Take square roots}$$

Therefore, the circle is described by the graphs of *two* equations:

$$y = \sqrt{1 - x^2} \quad \text{and} \quad y = -\sqrt{1 - x^2}$$

The first equation represents the top half of the circle (because $y \geq 0$), and the second represents the bottom half of the circle (because $y \leq 0$). If we graph the first equation in the viewing rectangle $[-2, 2]$ by $[-2, 2]$, we get the semicircle shown in Figure 4(a). The graph of the second equation is the semicircle in Figure 4(b). Graphing these semicircles together on the same viewing screen, we get the full circle in Figure 4(c).

The graph in Figure 4(c) looks somewhat flattened. Most graphing calculators allow you to set the scales on the axes so that circles really look like circles. On the TI-82 and TI-83, from the ZOOM menu, choose ZSquare to set the scales appropriately. (On the TI-86 the command is Zsq.)

  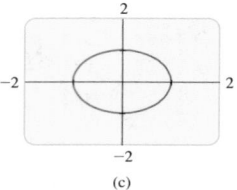

(a)   (b)   (c)

FIGURE 4   Graphing the equation $x^2 + y^2 = 1$

✎. NOW TRY EXERCISE **27**   ■

▼ Solving Equations Graphically

In Section 1.5 we learned how to solve equations. To solve an equation such as

$$3x - 5 = 0$$

we used the **algebraic method**. This means that we used the rules of algebra to isolate x on one side of the equation. We view x as an *unknown*, and we use the rules of algebra to hunt it down. Here are the steps in the solution:

$$3x - 5 = 0$$
$$3x = 5 \qquad \text{Add 5}$$
$$x = \tfrac{5}{3} \qquad \text{Divide by 3}$$

So the solution is $x = \tfrac{5}{3}$.

IN-CLASS MATERIALS

Have students find a viewing rectangle for $y = 3x + 1$, $y = -x^2 + 2$, and $y = x^6 - 100x^4 + 50$. Specify that this figure is for the third equation.

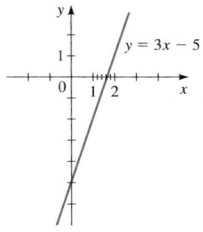

FIGURE 5

We can also solve this equation by the **graphical method**. In this method we view x as a *variable* and sketch the graph of the equation

$$y = 3x - 5$$

Different values for x give different values for y. Our goal is to find the value of x for which $y = 0$. From the graph in Figure 5 we see that $y = 0$ when $x \approx 1.7$. Thus, the solution is $x \approx 1.7$. Note that from the graph we obtain an approximate solution. We summarize these methods in the box below.

SOLVING AN EQUATION

Algebraic Method

Use the rules of algebra to isolate the unknown x on one side of the equation.

Example: $2x = 6 - x$

$\quad\quad 3x = 6 \quad\quad$ Add x

$\quad\quad\ x = 2 \quad\quad$ Divide by 3

The solution is $x = 2$.

Graphical Method

Move all terms to one side and set equal to y. Sketch the graph to find the value of x where $y = 0$.

Example: $2x = 6 - x$

$\quad\quad\quad\ 0 = 6 - 3x$

Set $y = 6 - 3x$ and graph.

From the graph, the solution is $x \approx 2$.

The advantage of the algebraic method is that it gives exact answers. Also, the process of unraveling the equation to arrive at the answer helps us to understand the algebraic structure of the equation. On the other hand, for many equations it is difficult or impossible to isolate x.

The graphical method gives a numerical approximation to the answer. This is an advantage when a numerical answer is desired. (For example, an engineer might find an answer expressed as $x \approx 2.6$ more immediately useful than $x = \sqrt{7}$.) Also, graphing an equation helps us to visualize how the solution is related to other values of the variable.

The *Discovery Project* referenced on page 263 describes a numerical method for solving equations.

PIERRE DE FERMAT (1601–1665) was a French lawyer who became interested in mathematics at the age of 30. Because of his job as a magistrate, Fermat had little time to write complete proofs of his discoveries and often wrote them in the margin of whatever book he was reading at the time. After his death, his copy of Diophantus' *Arithmetica* (see page 20) was found to contain a particularly tantalizing comment. Where Diophantus discusses the solutions of $x^2 + y^2 = z^2$ (for example, $x = 3, y = 4,$ and $z = 5$), Fermat states in the margin that for $n \geq 3$ there are no natural number solutions to the equation $x^n + y^n = z^n$. In other words, it's impossible for a cube to equal the sum of two cubes, a fourth power to equal the sum of two fourth powers, and so on. Fermat writes, "I have discovered a truly wonderful proof for this but the margin is too small to contain it." All the other margin comments in Fermat's copy of *Arithmetica* have been proved. This one, however, remained unproved, and it came to be known as "Fermat's Last Theorem."

In 1994, Andrew Wiles of Princeton University announced a proof of Fermat's Last Theorem, an astounding 350 years after it was conjectured. His proof is one of the most widely reported mathematical results in the popular press.

IN-CLASS MATERIALS

If graphing calculators are going to be an important part of the course, do not hurry the concept of finding appropriate windows. Let the students play with functions such as $\sin x$, $\ln x$, $\cos^{-1} x$, and so forth. At this stage, don't ask students to worry too much about what they mean; let them play. Let them develop the idea of the variety of functions their calculators contain and the idea that each function gives rise to its own special curve. In the unfortunate event that your students can't "play," perhaps ask them which functions are bounded or unbounded, which are symmetric about the y-axis, which are symmetric about the origin, and so on.

ALTERNATE EXAMPLE 4

Solve the equation

$x^2 - 14x + 49 = 0$.

ANSWER

7

EXAMPLE 4 | Solving a Quadratic Equation Algebraically and Graphically

Solve the quadratic equations algebraically and graphically.

(a) $x^2 - 4x + 2 = 0$ **(b)** $x^2 - 4x + 4 = 0$ **(c)** $x^2 - 4x + 6 = 0$

SOLUTION 1: Algebraic

We use the Quadratic Formula to solve each equation.

The Quadratic Formula is discussed on page 49.

(a) $x = \dfrac{-(-4) \pm \sqrt{(-4)^2 - 4 \cdot 1 \cdot 2}}{2} = \dfrac{4 \pm \sqrt{8}}{2} = 2 \pm \sqrt{2}$

There are two solutions, $x = 2 + \sqrt{2}$ and $x = 2 - \sqrt{2}$.

(b) $x = \dfrac{-(-4) \pm \sqrt{(-4)^2 - 4 \cdot 1 \cdot 4}}{2} = \dfrac{4 \pm \sqrt{0}}{2} = 2$

There is just one solution, $x = 2$.

(c) $x = \dfrac{-(-4) \pm \sqrt{(-4)^2 - 4 \cdot 1 \cdot 6}}{2} = \dfrac{4 \pm \sqrt{-8}}{2}$

There is no real solution.

SOLUTION 2: Graphical

We graph the equations $y = x^2 - 4x + 2$, $y = x^2 - 4x + 4$, and $y = x^2 - 4x + 6$ in Figure 6. By determining the x-intercepts of the graphs, we find the following solutions.

(a) $x \approx 0.6$ and $x \approx 3.4$

(b) $x = 2$

(c) There is no x-intercept, so the equation has no solution.

(a) $y = x^2 - 4x + 2$ (b) $y = x^2 - 4x + 4$ (c) $y = x^2 - 4x + 6$

FIGURE 6

✎. **NOW TRY EXERCISE 35** ◼

ALAN TURING (1912–1954) was at the center of two pivotal events of the 20th century: World War II and the invention of computers. At the age of 23 Turing made his mark on mathematics by solving an important problem in the foundations of mathematics that had been posed by David Hilbert at the 1928 International Congress of Mathematicians (see page 683). In this research he invented a theoretical machine, now called a Turing machine, which was the inspiration for modern digital computers. During World War II Turing was in charge of the British effort to decipher secret German codes. His complete success in this endeavor played a decisive role in the Allies' victory. To carry out the numerous logical steps that are required to break a coded message, Turing developed decision procedures similar to modern computer programs. After the war he helped to develop the first electronic computers in Britain. He also did pioneering work on artificial intelligence and computer models of biological processes. At the age of 42 Turing died of poisoning after eating an apple that had mysteriously been laced with cyanide.

IN-CLASS MATERIALS

Have students determine the intersection points of $y = x^2 - 2$ and $y = -x^2 + 5x + 1$ both graphically and algebraically.

Answers

$x = -\frac{1}{2}, x = 3$

The graphs in Figure 6 show visually why a quadratic equation may have two solutions, one solution, or no real solution. We proved this fact algebraically in Section 1.5 when we studied the discriminant.

EXAMPLE 5 | Another Graphical Method

Solve the equation algebraically and graphically: $5 - 3x = 8x - 20$

SOLUTION 1: Algebraic

$$5 - 3x = 8x - 20$$
$$-3x = 8x - 25 \qquad \text{Subtract 5}$$
$$-11x = -25 \qquad \text{Subtract } 8x$$
$$x = \frac{-25}{-11} = 2\tfrac{3}{11} \qquad \text{Divide by } -11 \text{ and simplify}$$

FIGURE 7

SOLUTION 2: Graphical

We could move all terms to one side of the equal sign, set the result equal to y, and graph the resulting equation. But to avoid all this algebra, we graph two equations instead:

$$y_1 = 5 - 3x \qquad \text{and} \qquad y_2 = 8x - 20$$

The solution of the original equation will be the value of x that makes y_1 equal to y_2; that is, the solution is the x-coordinate of the intersection point of the two graphs. Using the $\boxed{\text{TRACE}}$ feature or the `intersect` command on a graphing calculator, we see from Figure 7 that the solution is $x \approx 2.27$.

✎. NOW TRY EXERCISE **31**   ∎

In the next example we use the graphical method to solve an equation that is extremely difficult to solve algebraically.

EXAMPLE 6 | Solving an Equation in an Interval

Solve the equation

$$x^3 - 6x^2 + 9x = \sqrt{x}$$

in the interval $[1, 6]$.

SOLUTION   We are asked to find all solutions x that satisfy $1 \le x \le 6$, so we will graph the equation in a viewing rectangle for which the x-values are restricted to this interval.

$$x^3 - 6x^2 + 9x = \sqrt{x}$$
$$x^3 - 6x^2 + 9x - \sqrt{x} = 0 \qquad \text{Subtract } \sqrt{x}$$

We can also use the `zero` command to find the solutions, as shown in Figures 8(a) and 8(b).

Figure 8 shows the graph of the equation $y = x^3 - 6x^2 + 9x - \sqrt{x}$ in the viewing rectangle $[1, 6]$ by $[-5, 5]$. There are two x-intercepts in this viewing rectangle; zooming in, we see that the solutions are $x \approx 2.18$ and $x \approx 3.72$.

(a)   (b)

FIGURE 8

✎. NOW TRY EXERCISE **43**   ∎

ALTERNATE EXAMPLE 5
Solve the equation algebraically
and graphically:
$5 - 4x = 7x - 7$

ANSWER
1.1

ALTERNATE EXAMPLE 6
Solve the equation in the interval
$[6, 9]$:
$x^3 - 14x^2 + 49x = \sqrt{x}$

ANSWER
6.4, 7.6

IN-CLASS MATERIALS
Have students compare the values of $100x^2$ and $x^4 + 1$ for $x = 0$, $x = \frac{1}{2}$, $x = 1$, and $x = 2$. Then ask the question: For what values of x is $100x^2 > x^4 + 1$? See if they can use their calculators to approximate the answer.

Answer
$100x^2 > x^4 + 1$ for $x \in [-10, -0.1] \cup [0.1, 10]$, approximately. Notice that it is possible to find the right windows by trial and error, but sometimes plugging a number or two into the functions can give a clue as to the best y-range.

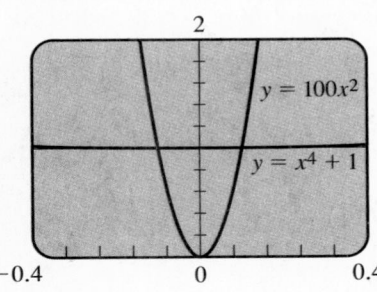

CHAPTER 1 | Fundamentals

The equation in Example 6 actually has four solutions. You are asked to find the other two in Exercise 71.

EXAMPLE 7 | Intensity of Light

Two light sources are 10 m apart. One is three times as intense as the other. The light intensity L (in lux) at a point x meters from the weaker source is given by

$$L = \frac{10}{x^2} + \frac{30}{(10-x)^2}$$

(See Figure 9.) Find the points at which the light intensity is 4 lux.

FIGURE 9

SOLUTION We need to solve the equation

$$4 = \frac{10}{x^2} + \frac{30}{(10-x)^2}$$

The graphs of

$$y_1 = 4 \quad \text{and} \quad y_2 = \frac{10}{x^2} + \frac{30}{(10-x)^2}$$

are shown in Figure 10. Zooming in (or using the `intersect` command), we find two solutions, $x \approx 1.67431$ and $x \approx 7.1927193$. So the light intensity is 4 lux at the points that are 1.67 m and 7.19 m from the weaker source.

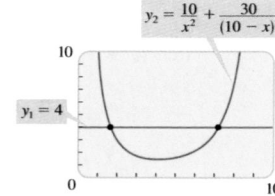

FIGURE 10

↖ NOW TRY EXERCISE **73**   ∎

▼ Solving Inequalities Graphically

Inequalities can be solved graphically. To describe the method, we solve

$$x^2 - 5x + 6 \le 0$$

This inequality was solved algebraically in Example 3 of Section 1.7. To solve the inequality graphically, we draw the graph of

$$y = x^2 - 5x + 6$$

Our goal is to find those values of x for which $y \le 0$. These are simply the x-values for which the graph lies below the x-axis. From Figure 11 we see that the solution of the inequality is the interval $[2, 3]$.

FIGURE 11 $x^2 - 5x + 6 \le 0$

Two light sources are 25 m apart. One is twice as intense as the other. The light intensity L at a point x meters from the weaker source is given by

$$L = \frac{10}{x^2} + \frac{20}{(25-x)^2}$$

Find the points between the two lights at which the light intensity is 4 lux.

ANSWER

1.59, 22.76 m from the weaker source

EXAMPLES

Graphs that some calculators get wrong:

1. $y = \sqrt{x} - 2\sqrt{x-4}$:   Some calculators do not give a graph with the correct domain.

2. $y = \sin x + \frac{1}{100}\cos 100x$:   The "standard" viewing rectangle misses the bumps that a rectangle of $[-0.1, 0.1] \times [-0.1, 0.1]$ will catch.

3. $y = x^{1/3}$:   Some calculators dislike taking negative numbers to rational powers, even when it is possible.

4. $y = \frac{\sin(x - \sqrt{2})}{x - \sqrt{2}}$:   Calculators are not good at graphing functions with holes.

EXAMPLE 8 | Solving an Inequality Graphically

Solve the inequality $3.7x^2 + 1.3x - 1.9 \le 2.0 - 1.4x$.

SOLUTION   We graph the equations

$$y_1 = 3.7x^2 + 1.3x - 1.9 \qquad \text{and} \qquad y_2 = 2.0 - 1.4x$$

in the same viewing rectangle in Figure 12. We are interested in those values of x for which $y_1 \le y_2$; these are points for which the graph of y_2 lies on or above the graph of y_1. To determine the appropriate interval, we look for the x-coordinates of points where the graphs intersect. We conclude that the solution is (approximately) the interval $[-1.45, 0.72]$.

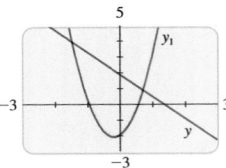

FIGURE 12
$y_1 = 3.7x^2 + 1.3x - 1.9$
$y_2 = 2.0 - 1.4x$

✎. NOW TRY EXERCISE **59**   ∎

EXAMPLE 9 | Solving an Inequality Graphically

Solve the inequality $x^3 - 5x^2 \ge -8$.

SOLUTION   We write the inequality as

$$x^3 - 5x^2 + 8 \ge 0$$

and then graph the equation

$$y = x^3 - 5x^2 + 8$$

in the viewing rectangle $[-6, 6]$ by $[-15, 15]$, as shown in Figure 13. The solution of the inequality consists of those intervals on which the graph lies on or above the x-axis. By moving the cursor to the x-intercepts, we find that, rounded to one decimal place, the solution is $[-1.1, 1.5] \cup [4.6, \infty)$.

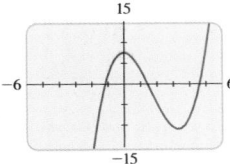

FIGURE 13 $x^3 - 5x^2 + 8 \ge 0$

✎. NOW TRY EXERCISE **61**   ∎

ALTERNATE EXAMPLE 8
Solve the inequality
$x^4 - 2x^2 \le x + 10$.

ANSWER
$[-2, 2.15]$

ALTERNATE EXAMPLE 9
Solve the inequality
$x^3 - 12x^2 \ge -122$ to the nearest integer.

ANSWER
$[-3, 4] \cup [11, \infty)$

DRILL QUESTION
Solve the equation
$x^3 - \sqrt{x} = 2x - 1$ to the nearest thousandth.

Answer
$x = 0.2556$ or $x = 1.464$

1.9 EXERCISES

CONCEPTS

1. The solutions of the equation $x^2 - 2x - 3 = 0$ are the _____-intercepts of the graph of $y = x^2 - 2x - 3$.

2. The solutions of the inequality $x^2 - 2x - 3 > 0$ are the x-coordinates of the points on the graph of $y = x^2 - 2x - 3$ that lie _____ the x-axis.

3. The figure shows a graph of $y = x^4 - 3x^3 - x^2 + 3x$. Use the graph to do the following.
   (a) Find the solutions of the equation $x^4 - 3x^3 - x^2 + 3x = 0$.
   (b) Find the solutions of the inequality $x^4 - 3x^3 - x^2 + 3x \le 0$.

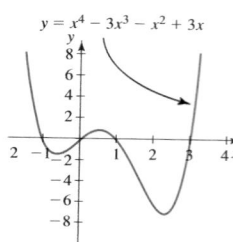

$y = x^4 - 3x^3 - x^2 + 3x$

4. The figure shows the graphs of $y = 5x - x^2$ and $y = 4$. Use the graphs to do the following.
   (a) Find the solutions of the equation $5x - x^2 = 4$.
   (b) Find the solutions of the inequality $5x - x^2 > 4$.

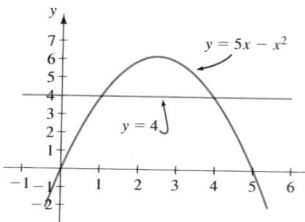

$y = 5x - x^2$

$y = 4$

SKILLS

5–10 ■ Use a graphing calculator or computer to decide which viewing rectangle (a)–(d) produces the most appropriate graph of the equation.

5. $y = x^4 + 2$
   (a) $[-2, 2]$ by $[-2, 2]$
   (b) $[0, 4]$ by $[0, 4]$
   (c) $[-8, 8]$ by $[-4, 40]$
   (d) $[-40, 40]$ by $[-80, 800]$

6. $y = x^2 + 7x + 6$
   (a) $[-5, 5]$ by $[-5, 5]$
   (b) $[0, 10]$ by $[-20, 100]$
   (c) $[-15, 8]$ by $[-20, 100]$
   (d) $[-10, 3]$ by $[-100, 20]$

7. $y = 100 - x^2$
   (a) $[-4, 4]$ by $[-4, 4]$
   (b) $[-10, 10]$ by $[-10, 10]$
   (c) $[-15, 15]$ by $[-30, 110]$
   (d) $[-4, 4]$ by $[-30, 110]$

8. $y = 2x^2 - 1000$
   (a) $[-10, 10]$ by $[-10, 10]$
   (b) $[-10, 10]$ by $[-100, 100]$
   (c) $[-10, 10]$ by $[-1000, 1000]$
   (d) $[-25, 25]$ by $[-1200, 200]$

9. $y = 10 + 25x - x^3$
   (a) $[-4, 4]$ by $[-4, 4]$
   (b) $[-10, 10]$ by $[-10, 10]$
   (c) $[-20, 20]$ by $[-100, 100]$
   (d) $[-100, 100]$ by $[-200, 200]$

10. $y = \sqrt{8x - x^2}$
   (a) $[-4, 4]$ by $[-4, 4]$
   (b) $[-5, 5]$ by $[0, 100]$
   (c) $[-10, 10]$ by $[-10, 40]$
   (d) $[-2, 10]$ by $[-2, 6]$

11–22 ■ Determine an appropriate viewing rectangle for the equation, and use it to draw the graph.

11. $y = 100x^2$

12. $y = -100x^2$

13. $y = 4 + 6x - x^2$

14. $y = 0.3x^2 + 1.7x - 3$

15. $y = \sqrt[4]{256 - x^2}$

16. $y = \sqrt{12x - 17}$

17. $y = 0.01x^3 - x^2 + 5$

18. $y = x(x + 6)(x - 9)$

19. $y = x^4 - 4x^3$

20. $y = \dfrac{x}{x^2 + 25}$

21. $y = 1 + |x - 1|$

22. $y = 2x - |x^2 - 5|$

23–26 ■ Do the graphs intersect in the given viewing rectangle? If they do, how many points of intersection are there?

23. $y = -3x^2 + 6x - \frac{1}{2}$, $y = \sqrt{7 - \frac{7}{12}x^2}$; $[-4, 4]$ by $[-1, 3]$

24. $y = \sqrt{49 - x^2}$, $y = \frac{1}{5}(41 - 3x)$; $[-8, 8]$ by $[-1, 8]$

25. $y = 6 - 4x - x^2$, $y = 3x + 18$; $[-6, 2]$ by $[-5, 20]$

26. $y = x^3 - 4x$, $y = x + 5$; $[-4, 4]$ by $[-15, 15]$

27. Graph the circle $x^2 + y^2 = 9$ by solving for y and graphing two equations as in Example 3.

28. Graph the circle $(y - 1)^2 + x^2 = 1$ by solving for y and graphing two equations as in Example 3.

29. Graph the equation $4x^2 + 2y^2 = 1$ by solving for y and graphing two equations corresponding to the negative and positive square roots. (This graph is called an *ellipse*.)

30. Graph the equation $y^2 - 9x^2 = 1$ by solving for y and graphing the two equations corresponding to the positive and negative square roots. (This graph is called a *hyperbola*.)

31–42 ■ Solve the equation both algebraically and graphically.

31. $x - 4 = 5x + 12$

32. $\frac{1}{2}x - 3 = 6 + 2x$

33. $\frac{2}{x} + \frac{1}{2x} = 7$

34. $\frac{4}{x + 2} - \frac{6}{2x} = \frac{5}{2x + 4}$

35. $x^2 - 32 = 0$

36. $x^3 + 16 = 0$

37. $x^2 + 9 = 0$

38. $x^2 + 3 = 2x$

39. $16x^4 = 625$

40. $2x^5 - 243 = 0$

41. $(x - 5)^4 - 80 = 0$

42. $6(x + 2)^5 = 64$

43–50 ■ Solve the equation graphically in the given interval. State each answer rounded to two decimals.

43. $x^2 - 7x + 12 = 0; \quad [0, 6]$

44. $x^2 - 0.75x + 0.125 = 0; \quad [-2, 2]$

45. $x^3 - 6x^2 + 11x - 6 = 0; \quad [-1, 4]$

46. $16x^3 + 16x^2 = x + 1; \quad [-2, 2]$

47. $x - \sqrt{x + 1} = 0; \quad [-1, 5]$

48. $1 + \sqrt{x} = \sqrt{1 + x^2}; \quad [-1, 5]$

49. $x^{1/3} - x = 0; \quad [-3, 3]$

50. $x^{1/2} + x^{1/3} - x = 0; \quad [-1, 5]$

51–54 ■ Use the graphical method to solve the equation in the indicated exercise from Section 1.5.

51. Exercise 91

52. Exercise 92

53. Exercise 97

54. Exercise 98

55–58 ■ Find all real solutions of the equation, rounded to two decimals.

55. $x^3 - 2x^2 - x - 1 = 0$

56. $x^4 - 8x^2 + 2 = 0$

57. $x(x - 1)(x + 2) = \frac{1}{6}x$

58. $x^4 = 16 - x^3$

59–66 ■ Find the solutions of the inequality by drawing appropriate graphs. State each answer rounded to two decimals.

59. $x^2 \le 3x + 10$

60. $0.5x^2 + 0.875x \le 0.25$

61. $x^3 + 11x \le 6x^2 + 6$

62. $16x^3 + 24x^2 > -9x - 1$

63. $x^{1/3} < x$

64. $\sqrt{0.5x^2 + 1} \le 2|x|$

65. $(x + 1)^2 < (x - 1)^2$

66. $(x + 1)^2 \le x^3$

67–70 ■ Use the graphical method to solve the inequality in the indicated exercise from Section 1.7.

67. Exercise 43

68. Exercise 44

69. Exercise 53

70. Exercise 54

71. In Example 6 we found two solutions of the equation $x^3 - 6x^2 + 9x = \sqrt{x}$, the solutions that lie between 1 and 6. Find two more solutions, correct to two decimals.

APPLICATIONS

72. Estimating Profit An appliance manufacturer estimates that the profit y (in dollars) generated by producing x cooktops per month is given by the equation

$$y = 10x + 0.5x^2 - 0.001x^3 - 5000$$

where $0 \le x \le 450$.

(a) Graph the equation.

(b) How many cooktops must be produced to begin generating a profit?

(c) For what range of values of x is the company's profit greater than $15,000?

73. How Far Can You See? If you stand on a ship in a calm sea, then your height x (in ft) above sea level is related to the farthest distance y (in mi) that you can see by the equation

$$y = \sqrt{1.5x + \left(\frac{x}{5280}\right)^2}$$

(a) Graph the equation for $0 \le x \le 100$.

(b) How high up do you have to be to be able to see 10 mi?

DISCOVERY ■ DISCUSSION ■ WRITING

74. Misleading Graphs Write a short essay describing different ways in which a graphing calculator might give a misleading graph of an equation.

75. Algebraic and Graphical Solution Methods Write a short essay comparing the algebraic and graphical methods for solving equations. Make up your own examples to illustrate the advantages and disadvantages of each method.

76. Equation Notation on Graphing Calculators When you enter the following equations into your calculator, how does what you see on the screen differ from the usual way of writing the equations? (Check your user's manual if you're not sure.)

(a) $y = |x|$

(b) $y = \sqrt[5]{x}$

(c) $y = \dfrac{x}{x - 1}$

(d) $y = x^3 + \sqrt[3]{x + 2}$

77. Enter Equations Carefully A student wishes to graph the equations

$$y = x^{1/3} \quad \text{and} \quad y = \frac{x}{x + 4}$$

on the same screen, so he enters the following information into his calculator:

$$\text{Y}_1 = \text{X}\wedge 1/3 \qquad \text{Y}_2 = \text{X}/\text{X} + 4$$

The calculator graphs two lines instead of the equations he wanted. What went wrong?

**SUGGESTED TIME
AND EMPHASIS**

1 class, essential material

1.10 LINES

The Slope of a Line ▶ Point-Slope Form of the Equation of a Line ▶ Slope-Intercept Form of the Equation of a Line ▶ Vertical and Horizontal Lines ▶ General Equation of a Line ▶ Parallel and Perpendicular Lines ▶ Modeling with Linear Equations: Slope as Rate of Change

In this section we find equations for straight lines lying in a coordinate plane. The equations will depend on how the line is inclined, so we begin by discussing the concept of slope.

▼ The Slope of a Line

We first need a way to measure the "steepness" of a line, or how quickly it rises (or falls) as we move from left to right. We define *run* to be the distance we move to the right and *rise* to be the corresponding distance that the line rises (or falls). The *slope* of a line is the ratio of rise to run:

$$\text{slope} = \frac{\text{rise}}{\text{run}}$$

Figure 1 shows situations in which slope is important. Carpenters use the term *pitch* for the slope of a roof or a staircase; the term *grade* is used for the slope of a road.

Slope of a ramp
Slope $= \frac{1}{12}$

Pitch of a roof
Slope $= \frac{1}{3}$

Grade of a road
Slope $= \frac{8}{100}$

FIGURE 1

If a line lies in a coordinate plane, then the **run** is the change in the x-coordinate and the **rise** is the corresponding change in the y-coordinate between any two points on the line (see Figure 2). This gives us the following definition of slope.

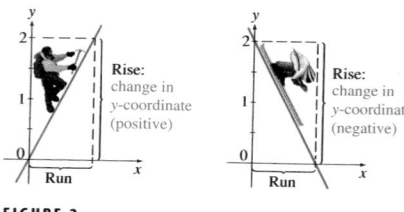

FIGURE 2

TEXT QUESTION

Which of the three lines graphed here has the largest slope?

Answer

The dotted line that goes through $(0, -2)$

SLOPE OF A LINE

The **slope** m of a nonvertical line that passes through the points $A(x_1, y_1)$ and $B(x_2, y_2)$ is

$$m = \frac{\text{rise}}{\text{run}} = \frac{y_2 - y_1}{x_2 - x_1}$$

The slope of a vertical line is not defined.

The slope is independent of which two points are chosen on the line. We can see that this is true from the similar triangles in Figure 3:

$$\frac{y_2 - y_1}{x_2 - x_1} = \frac{y_2' - y_1'}{x_2' - x_1'}$$

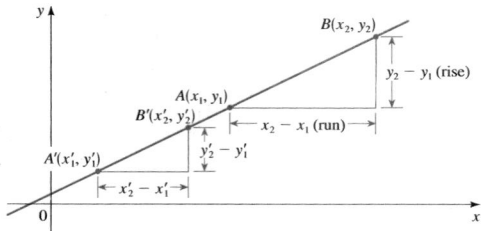

FIGURE 3

Figure 4 shows several lines labeled with their slopes. Notice that lines with positive slope slant upward to the right, whereas lines with negative slope slant downward to the right. The steepest lines are those for which the absolute value of the slope is the largest; a horizontal line has slope zero.

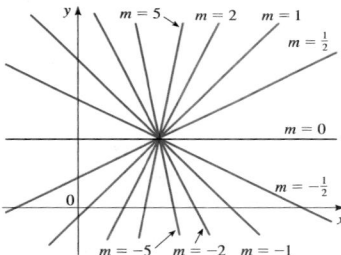

FIGURE 4 Lines with various slopes

EXAMPLE 1 | Finding the Slope of a Line Through Two Points

Find the slope of the line that passes through the points $P(2, 1)$ and $Q(8, 5)$.

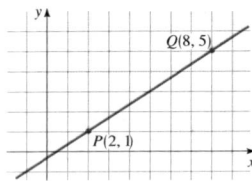

FIGURE 5

SOLUTION Since any two different points determine a line, only one line passes through these two points. From the definition the slope is

$$m = \frac{y_2 - y_1}{x_2 - x_1} = \frac{5 - 1}{8 - 2} = \frac{4}{6} = \frac{2}{3}$$

This says that for every 3 units we move to the right, the line rises 2 units. The line is drawn in Figure 5.

✎ NOW TRY EXERCISE **5** ◼

▼ Point-Slope Form of the Equation of a Line

Now let's find the equation of the line that passes through a given point $P(x_1, y_1)$ and has slope m. A point $P(x, y)$ with $x \neq x_1$ lies on this line if and only if the slope of the line through P_1 and P is equal to m (see Figure 6), that is,

$$\frac{y - y_1}{x - x_1} = m$$

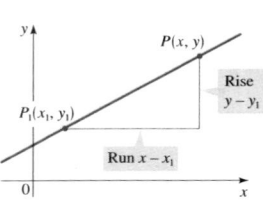

FIGURE 6

This equation can be rewritten in the form $y - y_1 = m(x - x_1)$; note that the equation is also satisfied when $x = x_1$ and $y = y_1$. Therefore, it is an equation of the given line.

POINT-SLOPE FORM OF THE EQUATION OF A LINE

An equation of the line that passes through the point (x_1, y_1) and has slope m is

$$y - y_1 = m(x - x_1)$$

EXAMPLE 2 | Finding the Equation of a Line with Given Point and Slope

(a) Find an equation of the line through $(1, -3)$ with slope $-\frac{1}{2}$.

(b) Sketch the line.

SOLUTION

(a) Using the point-slope form with $m = -\frac{1}{2}$, $x_1 = 1$, and $y_1 = -3$, we obtain an equation of the line as

$$y + 3 = -\tfrac{1}{2}(x - 1) \qquad \text{Slope } m = -\tfrac{1}{2}, \text{ point } (1, -3)$$
$$2y + 6 = -x + 1 \qquad \text{Multiply by 2}$$
$$x + 2y + 5 = 0 \qquad \text{Rearrange}$$

(b) The fact that the slope is $-\frac{1}{2}$ tells us that when we move to the right 2 units, the line drops 1 unit. This enables us to sketch the line in Figure 7.

✎ NOW TRY EXERCISE **19** ◼

FIGURE 7

EXAMPLE 3 | Finding the Equation of a Line Through Two Given Points

Find an equation of the line through the points $(-1, 2)$ and $(3, -4)$.

SOLUTION The slope of the line is

$$m = \frac{-4 - 2}{3 - (-1)} = -\frac{6}{4} = -\frac{3}{2}$$

ALTERNATE EXAMPLE 2

Find an equation of the line through $(1, -3)$ with slope $-\frac{3}{4}$.

ANSWER

$3x + 4y + 9 = 0$

ALTERNATE EXAMPLE 3

Find an equation of the line through the points $(-4, 3)$ and $(4, -3)$.

ANSWER

$3x + 4y + 0 = 0$

We can use *either* point, $(-1, 2)$ *or* $(3, -4)$, in the point-slope equation. We will end up with the same final answer.

Using the point-slope form with $x_1 = -1$ and $y_1 = 2$, we obtain

$$y - 2 = -\tfrac{3}{2}(x + 1) \qquad \text{Slope } m = -\tfrac{3}{2}, \text{ point } (-1, 2)$$

$$2y - 4 = -3x - 3 \qquad \text{Multiply by 2}$$

$$3x + 2y - 1 = 0 \qquad \text{Rearrange}$$

✎. NOW TRY EXERCISE **23**

▼ Slope-Intercept Form of the Equation of a Line

Suppose a nonvertical line has slope m and y-intercept b (see Figure 8). This means that the line intersects the y-axis at the point $(0, b)$, so the point-slope form of the equation of the line, with $x = 0$ and $y = b$, becomes

$$y - b = m(x - 0)$$

This simplifies to $y = mx + b$, which is called the **slope-intercept form** of the equation of a line.

FIGURE 8

> **SLOPE-INTERCEPT FORM OF THE EQUATION OF A LINE**
>
> An equation of the line that has slope m and y-intercept b is
>
> $$y = mx + b$$

EXAMPLE 4 | Lines in Slope-Intercept Form

(a) Find the equation of the line with slope 3 and y-intercept -2.

(b) Find the slope and y-intercept of the line $3y - 2x = 1$.

SOLUTION

(a) Since $m = 3$ and $b = -2$, from the slope-intercept form of the equation of a line we get

$$y = 3x - 2$$

(b) We first write the equation in the form $y = mx + b$:

$$3y - 2x = 1$$
$$3y = 2x + 1 \qquad \text{Add } 2x$$
$$y = \tfrac{2}{3}x + \tfrac{1}{3} \qquad \text{Divide by 3}$$

From the slope-intercept form of the equation of a line, we see that the slope is $m = \tfrac{2}{3}$ and the y-intercept is $b = \tfrac{1}{3}$.

✎. NOW TRY EXERCISES **25** AND **47**

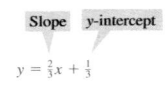

$y = \tfrac{2}{3}x + \tfrac{1}{3}$

▼ Vertical and Horizontal Lines

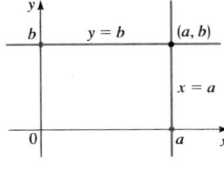

If a line is horizontal, its slope is $m = 0$, so its equation is $y = b$, where b is the y-intercept (see Figure 9). A vertical line does not have a slope, but we can write its equation as $x = a$, where a is the x-intercept, because the x-coordinate of every point on the line is a.

FIGURE 9

IN-CLASS MATERIALS

One good way to get students used to slope is to have them do quick estimates. Stand in front of the class, raise your arm at various angles, and have them write down (or call out) estimates. Students should be able to tell a positive from a negative slope and whether a slope is closer to $\tfrac{1}{3}$ than it is to 3. Also note that if the x- and y-scales on a graph are different, the appearance of the slope can be misleading.

ALTERNATE EXAMPLE 5

Describe the graphs of the following equations:

(a) $x = -2$

(b) $y = 3$

(c) $y = 0$

(d) $x = 0$

ANSWERS

(a) A vertical line with x-intercept -2

(b) A horizontal line with y-intercept 3

(c) The x-axis

(d) The y-axis

VERTICAL AND HORIZONTAL LINES

An equation of the vertical line through (a, b) is $x = a$.

An equation of the horizontal line through (a, b) is $y = b$.

FIGURE 10

EXAMPLE 5 | Vertical and Horizontal Lines

(a) An equation for the vertical line through $(3, 5)$ is $x = 3$.

(b) The graph of the equation $x = 3$ is a vertical line with x-intercept 3.

(c) An equation for the horizontal line through $(8, -2)$ is $y = -2$.

(d) The graph of the equation $y = -2$ is a horizontal line with y-intercept -2.

The lines are graphed in Figure 10.

➤ NOW TRY EXERCISES **29** AND **33** ∎

▼ General Equation of a Line

A **linear equation** is an equation of the form

$$Ax + By + C = 0$$

where A, B, and C are constants and A and B are not both 0. The equation of a line is a linear equation:

- A nonvertical line has the equation $y = mx + b$ or $-mx + y - b = 0$, which is a linear equation with $A = -m$, $B = 1$, and $C = -b$.
- A vertical line has the equation $x = a$ or $x - a = 0$, which is a linear equation with $A = 1$, $B = 0$, and $C = -a$.

  Conversely, the graph of a linear equation is a line.

- If $B \neq 0$, the equation becomes

$$y = -\frac{A}{B}x - \frac{C}{B} \qquad \text{Divide by } B$$

  and this is the slope-intercept form of the equation of a line (with $m = -A/B$ and $b = -C/B$).

- If $B = 0$, the equation becomes

$$Ax + C = 0 \qquad \text{Set } B = 0$$

  or $x = -C/A$, which represents a vertical line.

We have proved the following.

GENERAL EQUATION OF A LINE

The graph of every **linear equation**

$$Ax + By + C = 0 \qquad (A, B \text{ not both zero})$$

is a line. Conversely, every line is the graph of a linear equation.

IN-CLASS MATERIALS

A classic example is to have students come up with conversion formulas from Fahrenheit to centigrade and vice versa, using the fact that in centigrade measurement, water freezes at 0° and boils at 100° (32°F and 212°F, respectively). Other conversion formulas can be found, using facts such as the following: 3 ft ≈ 0.914 m, 1 L ≈ 0.264 gal (US), a 250-calorie snack is equivalent to 0.991 BTU.

EXAMPLE 6 | **Graphing a Linear Equation**

Sketch the graph of the equation $2x - 3y - 12 = 0$.

SOLUTION 1 Since the equation is linear, its graph is a line. To draw the graph, it is enough to find any two points on the line. The intercepts are the easiest points to find.

x-intercept: Substitute $y = 0$, to get $2x - 12 = 0$, so $x = 6$

y-intercept: Substitute $x = 0$, to get $-3y - 12 = 0$, so $y = -4$

With these points we can sketch the graph in Figure 11.

SOLUTION 2 We write the equation in slope-intercept form:

$$2x - 3y - 12 = 0$$

$$2x - 3y = 12 \qquad \text{Add 12}$$

$$-3y = -2x + 12 \qquad \text{Subtract } 2x$$

$$y = \tfrac{2}{3}x - 4 \qquad \text{Divide by } -3$$

This equation is in the form $y = mx + b$, so the slope is $m = \tfrac{2}{3}$ and the y-intercept is $b = -4$. To sketch the graph, we plot the y-intercept and then move 3 units to the right and 2 units up as shown in Figure 12.

FIGURE 11

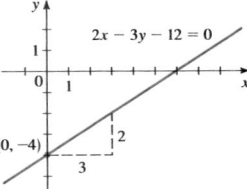

FIGURE 12

✎ NOW TRY EXERCISE **53**

▼ **Parallel and Perpendicular Lines**

Since slope measures the steepness of a line, it seems reasonable that parallel lines should have the same slope. In fact, we can prove this.

> **PARALLEL LINES**
>
> Two nonvertical lines are parallel if and only if they have the same slope.

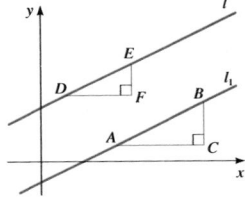

FIGURE 13

PROOF Let the lines l_1 and l_2 in Figure 13 have slopes m_1 and m_2. If the lines are parallel, then the right triangles ABC and DEF are similar, so

$$m_1 = \frac{d(B, C)}{d(A, C)} = \frac{d(E, F)}{d(D, F)} = m_2$$

Conversely, if the slopes are equal, then the triangles will be similar, so $\angle BAC = \angle EDF$ and the lines are parallel. ■

IN-CLASS MATERIALS

Ask students to figure out if three given points are vertices of a right triangle. They can go ahead and plot them to get a guess going. Ask them to come up with a strategy, and reveal (or ideally elicit) the idea of writing equations of lines between each pair of points and checking for perpendicular lines. $(3, 4)$, $(3, 12)$, and $(6, 5)$ do not form a right triangle; $(-2, -1)$, $(-2, 8)$, and $(8, -1)$ form a right triangle.

EXAMPLE 7 | Finding the Equation of a Line Parallel
to a Given Line

Find an equation of the line through the point $(5, 2)$ that is parallel to the line
$4x + 6y + 5 = 0$.

SOLUTION   First we write the equation of the given line in slope-intercept form.

$$4x + 6y + 5 = 0$$

$$6y = -4x - 5 \qquad \text{Subtract } 4x + 5$$

$$y = -\tfrac{2}{3}x - \tfrac{5}{6} \qquad \text{Divide by 6}$$

So the line has slope $m = -\tfrac{2}{3}$. Since the required line is parallel to the given line, it
also has slope $m = -\tfrac{2}{3}$. From the point-slope form of the equation of a line, we get

$$y - 2 = -\tfrac{2}{3}(x - 5) \qquad \text{Slope } m = -\tfrac{2}{3}, \text{ point } (5, 2)$$

$$3y - 6 = -2x + 10 \qquad \text{Multiply by 3}$$

$$2x + 3y - 16 = 0 \qquad \text{Rearrange}$$

Thus, the equation of the required line is $2x + 3y - 16 = 0$.

✎. **NOW TRY EXERCISE 31**   ■

The condition for perpendicular lines is not as obvious as that for parallel lines.

PERPENDICULAR LINES

Two lines with slopes m_1 and m_2 are perpendicular if and only if $m_1 m_2 = -1$,
that is, their slopes are negative reciprocals:

$$m_2 = -\frac{1}{m_1}$$

Also, a horizontal line (slope 0) is perpendicular to a vertical line (no slope).

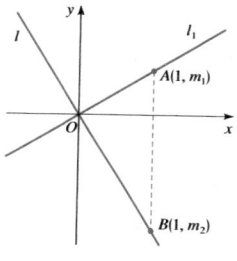

FIGURE 14

PROOF   In Figure 14 we show two lines intersecting at the origin. (If the lines intersect
at some other point, we consider lines parallel to these that intersect at the origin. These
lines have the same slopes as the original lines.)

If the lines l_1 and l_2 have slopes m_1 and m_2, then their equations are $y = m_1 x$ and
$y = m_2 x$. Notice that $A(1, m_1)$ lies on l_1 and $B(1, m_2)$ lies on l_2. By the Pythagorean Theorem and its converse (see page 219), $OA \perp OB$ if and only if

$$[d(O, A)]^2 + [d(O, B)]^2 = [d(A, B)]^2$$

By the Distance Formula this becomes

$$(1^2 + m_1^2) + (1^2 + m_2^2) = (1 - 1)^2 + (m_2 - m_1)^2$$

$$2 + m_1^2 + m_2^2 = m_2^2 - 2m_1 m_2 + m_1^2$$

$$2 = -2m_1 m_2$$

$$m_1 m_2 = -1 \qquad\qquad ■$$

EXAMPLE 8 | Perpendicular Lines

Show that the points $P(3, 3)$, $Q(8, 17)$, and $R(11, 5)$ are the vertices of a right triangle.

IN-CLASS MATERIALS
Don't neglect to give students horizontal and vertical lines to explore—they often find equations of vertical
lines challenging.

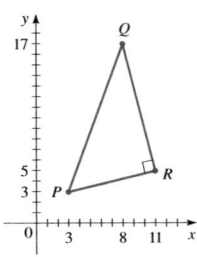

FIGURE 15

SOLUTION The slopes of the lines containing PR and QR are, respectively,

$$m_1 = \frac{5-3}{11-3} = \frac{1}{4} \quad \text{and} \quad m_2 = \frac{5-17}{11-8} = -4$$

Since $m_1 m_2 = -1$, these lines are perpendicular, so PQR is a right triangle. It is sketched in Figure 15.

✎. NOW TRY EXERCISE **57** ■

EXAMPLE 9 | Finding an Equation of a Line Perpendicular to a Given Line

Find an equation of the line that is perpendicular to the line $4x + 6y + 5 = 0$ and passes through the origin.

SOLUTION In Example 7 we found that the slope of the line $4x + 6y + 5 = 0$ is $-\frac{2}{3}$. Thus, the slope of a perpendicular line is the negative reciprocal, that is, $\frac{3}{2}$. Since the required line passes through $(0, 0)$, the point-slope form gives

$$y - 0 = \tfrac{3}{2}(x - 0) \qquad \text{Slope } m = \tfrac{3}{2}, \text{ point } (0,0)$$
$$y = \tfrac{3}{2}x \qquad\qquad \text{Simplify}$$

✎. NOW TRY EXERCISE **35** ■

EXAMPLE 10 | Graphing a Family of Lines

Use a graphing calculator to graph the family of lines

$$y = 0.5x + b$$

for $b = -2, -1, 0, 1, 2$. What property do the lines share?

SOLUTION The lines are graphed in Figure 16 in the viewing rectangle $[-6, 6]$ by $[-6, 6]$. The lines all have the same slope, so they are parallel.

FIGURE 16 $y = 0.5x + b$

✎. NOW TRY EXERCISE **41** ■

▼ Modeling with Linear Equations: Slope as Rate of Change

When a line is used to model the relationship between two quantities, the slope of the line is the **rate of change** of one quantity with respect to the other. For example, the graph in Figure 17(a) on the next page gives the amount of gas in a tank that is being filled. The slope between the indicated points is

$$m = \frac{6 \text{ gallons}}{3 \text{ minutes}} = 2 \text{ gal/min}$$

EXAMPLES
Equations of some standard lines:

1. Through $(3, 5)$ and $(-1, 13)$: $y = -2x + 11$
2. Through $(6, -5)$ with a slope of $\frac{1}{3}$: $y = \frac{1}{3}x - 7$

The slope is the *rate* at which the tank is being filled, 2 gallons per minute. In Figure 17(b) the tank is being drained at the *rate* of 0.03 gallon per minute, and the slope is −0.03.

(a) Tank filled at 2 gal/min
Slope of line is 2

(b) Tank drained at 0.03 gal/min
Slope of line is −0.03

FIGURE 17

The next two examples give other situations in which the slope of a line is a rate of change.

EXAMPLE 11 | Slope as Rate of Change

A dam is built on a river to create a reservoir. The water level w in the reservoir is given by the equation

$$w = 4.5t + 28$$

where t is the number of years since the dam was constructed and w is measured in feet.

(a) Sketch a graph of this equation.

(b) What do the slope and w-intercept of this graph represent?

SOLUTION

(a) This equation is linear, so its graph is a line. Since two points determine a line, we plot two points that lie on the graph and draw a line through them.

When $t = 0$, then $w = 4.5(0) + 28 = 28$, so $(0, 28)$ is on the line.

When $t = 2$, then $w = 4.5(2) + 28 = 37$, so $(2, 37)$ is on the line.

The line that is determined by these points is shown in Figure 18.

(b) The slope is $m = 4.5$; it represents the rate of change of water level with respect to time. This means that the water level *increases* 4.5 ft per year. The w-intercept is 28 and occurs when $t = 0$, so it represents the water level when the dam was constructed.

➤. NOW TRY EXERCISE **69**   ■

EXAMPLE 12 | Linear Relationship Between Temperature and Elevation

(a) As dry air moves upward, it expands and cools. If the ground temperature is 20°C and the temperature at a height of 1 km is 10°C, express the temperature T (in °C) in terms of the height h (in km). (Assume that the relationship between T and h is linear.)

$w = 4.5t + 28$

FIGURE 18

ALTERNATE EXAMPLE 11

The cost of a cup of coffee at Jag's Java is given by $c = 0.25t + 1$, where t is in years since 2005 and c is in dollars. What do the slope and c-intercept of this graph represent?

ANSWER

The slope, $m = 0.25$, means that the cost is going up by a quarter every year. The c-intercept, 1, means that in 2005, a cup of coffee cost $1.00.

ALTERNATE EXAMPLE 12

As dry air moves upward, it expands and cools. If the ground temperature is 22 °C and the temperature at a height of 1 km is 10°C, express the temperature T (in °C) in terms of the height h (in kilometers). (Assume that the relationship between T and h is linear.) Also, find the temperature at a height of 1.5 km.

ANSWER

$T = -12h + 22, 4$

Temperature decreases with elevation

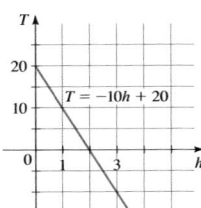

$T = -10h + 20$

FIGURE 19

(b) Draw the graph of the linear equation. What does its slope represent?

(c) What is the temperature at a height of 2.5 km?

SOLUTION

(a) Because we are assuming a linear relationship between T and h, the equation must be of the form

$$T = mh + b$$

where m and b are constants. When $h = 0$, we are given that $T = 20$, so

$$20 = m(0) + b$$
$$b = 20$$

Thus, we have

$$T = mh + 20$$

When $h = 1$, we have $T = 10$, so

$$10 = m(1) + 20$$
$$m = 10 - 20 = -10$$

The required expression is

$$T = -10h + 20$$

(b) The graph is sketched in Figure 19. The slope is $m = -10°C/km$, and this represents the rate of change of temperature with respect to distance above the ground. So the temperature *decreases* $10°C$ per kilometer of height.

(c) At a height of $h = 2.5$ km the temperature is

$$T = -10(2.5) + 20 = -25 + 20 = -5°C$$

✎ NOW TRY EXERCISE **73**

DRILL QUESTION
Find an equation of the line through the points (2, 4) and (3, −1).

Answer
$y = -5x + 14$

1.10 EXERCISES

CONCEPTS

1. We find the "steepness," or slope, of a line passing through two points by dividing the difference in the _____-coordinates of these points by the difference in the _____-coordinates. So the line passing through the points $(0, 1)$ and $(2, 5)$ has slope _____.

2. A line has the equation $y = 3x + 2$.

   (a) This line has slope _____.

   (b) Any line parallel to this line has slope _____.

   (c) Any line perpendicular to this line has slope _____.

3. The point-slope form of the equation of the line with slope 3 passing through the point $(1, 2)$ is _____.

4. (a) The slope of a horizontal line is _____. The equation of the horizontal line passing through $(2, 3)$ is _____.

   (b) The slope of a vertical line is _____. The equation of the vertical line passing through $(2, 3)$ is _____.

SKILLS

5–12 ■ Find the slope of the line through P and Q.

  ✎ **5.** $P(0, 0), Q(4, 2)$ **6.** $P(0, 0), Q(2, -6)$

    7. $P(2, 2), Q(-10, 0)$ **8.** $P(1, 2), Q(3, 3)$

    9. $P(2, 4), Q(4, 3)$ **10.** $P(2, -5), Q(-4, 3)$

   11. $P(1, -3), Q(-1, 6)$ **12.** $P(-1, -4), Q(6, 0)$

13. Find the slopes of the lines l_1, l_2, l_3, and l_4 in the figure below.

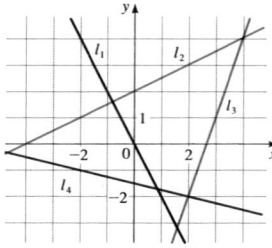

14. (a) Sketch lines through $(0, 0)$ with slopes 1, 0, $\frac{1}{2}$, 2, and -1.

(b) Sketch lines through $(0, 0)$ with slopes $\frac{1}{3}$, $\frac{1}{2}$, $-\frac{1}{3}$, and 3.

15–18 ■ Find an equation for the line whose graph is sketched.

15.

16.

17.

18.

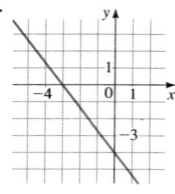

19–38 ■ Find an equation of the line that satisfies the given conditions.

19. Through $(2, 3)$; slope 5

20. Through $(-2, 4)$; slope -1

21. Through $(1, 7)$; slope $\frac{2}{3}$

22. Through $(-3, -5)$; slope $-\frac{7}{2}$

23. Through $(2, 1)$ and $(1, 6)$

24. Through $(-1, -2)$ and $(4, 3)$

25. Slope 3; y-intercept -2

26. Slope $\frac{2}{3}$; y-intercept 4

27. x-intercept 1; y-intercept -3

28. x-intercept -8; y-intercept 6

29. Through $(4, 5)$; parallel to the x-axis

30. Through $(4, 5)$; parallel to the y-axis

31. Through $(1, -6)$; parallel to the line $x + 2y = 6$

32. y-intercept 6; parallel to the line $2x + 3y + 4 = 0$

33. Through $(-1, 2)$; parallel to the line $x = 5$

34. Through $(2, 6)$; perpendicular to the line $y = 1$

35. Through $(-1, -2)$; perpendicular to the line $2x + 5y + 8 = 0$

36. Through $\left(\frac{1}{2}, -\frac{2}{3}\right)$; perpendicular to the line $4x - 8y = 1$

37. Through $(1, 7)$; parallel to the line passing through $(2, 5)$ and $(-2, 1)$

38. Through $(-2, -11)$; perpendicular to the line passing through $(1, 1)$ and $(5, -1)$

39. (a) Sketch the line with slope $\frac{3}{2}$ that passes through the point $(-2, 1)$.

(b) Find an equation for this line.

40. (a) Sketch the line with slope -2 that passes through the point $(4, -1)$.

(b) Find an equation for this line.

41–44 ■ Use a graphing device to graph the given family of lines in the same viewing rectangle. What do the lines have in common?

41. $y = -2x + b$ for $b = 0$, ± 1, ± 3, ± 6

42. $y = mx - 3$ for $m = 0$, ± 0.25, ± 0.75, ± 1.5

43. $y = m(x - 3)$ for $m = 0$, ± 0.25, ± 0.75, ± 1.5

44. $y = 2 + m(x + 3)$ for $m = 0$, ± 0.5, ± 1, ± 2, ± 6

45–56 ■ Find the slope and y-intercept of the line and draw its graph.

45. $x + y = 3$ ⎮ **46.** $3x - 2y = 12$

47. $x + 3y = 0$ ⎮ **48.** $2x - 5y = 0$

49. $\frac{1}{2}x - \frac{1}{3}y + 1 = 0$ ⎮ **50.** $-3x - 5y + 30 = 0$

51. $y = 4$ ⎮ **52.** $x = -5$

53. $3x - 4y = 12$ ⎮ **54.** $4y + 8 = 0$

55. $3x + 4y - 1 = 0$ ⎮ **56.** $4x + 5y = 10$

57. Use slopes to show that $A(1, 1)$, $B(7, 4)$, $C(5, 10)$, and $D(-1, 7)$ are vertices of a parallelogram.

58. Use slopes to show that $A(-3, -1)$, $B(3, 3)$, and $C(-9, 8)$ are vertices of a right triangle.

59. Use slopes to show that $A(1, 1)$, $B(11, 3)$, $C(10, 8)$, and $D(0, 6)$ are vertices of a rectangle.

60. Use slopes to determine whether the given points are collinear (lie on a line).

(a) $(1, 1)$, $(3, 9)$, $(6, 21)$

(b) $(-1, 3)$, $(1, 7)$, $(4, 15)$

61. Find an equation of the perpendicular bisector of the line segment joining the points $A(1, 4)$ and $B(7, -2)$.

62. Find the area of the triangle formed by the coordinate axes and the line

$$2y + 3x - 6 = 0$$

63. (a) Show that if the x- and y-intercepts of a line are nonzero numbers a and b, then the equation of the line can be written in the form

$$\frac{x}{a} + \frac{y}{b} = 1$$

This is called the **two-intercept form** of the equation of a line.

(b) Use part (a) to find an equation of the line whose x-intercept is 6 and whose y-intercept is −8.

64. (a) Find an equation for the line tangent to the circle $x^2 + y^2 = 25$ at the point $(3, -4)$. (See the figure.)

(b) At what other point on the circle will a tangent line be parallel to the tangent line in part (a)?

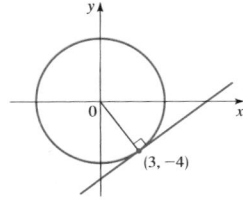

APPLICATIONS

65. Grade of a Road   West of Albuquerque, New Mexico, Route 40 eastbound is straight and makes a steep descent toward the city. The highway has a 6% grade, which means that its slope is $-\frac{6}{100}$. Driving on this road, you notice from elevation signs that you have descended a distance of 1000 ft. What is the change in your horizontal distance?

6% grade

1000 ft

66. Global Warming   Some scientists believe that the average surface temperature of the world has been rising steadily. The average surface temperature can be modeled by

$$T = 0.02t + 15.0$$

where T is temperature in °C and t is years since 1950.

(a) What do the slope and T-intercept represent?

(b) Use the equation to predict the average global surface temperature in 2050.

67. Drug Dosages   If the recommended adult dosage for a drug is D (in mg), then to determine the appropriate dosage c for a child of age a, pharmacists use the equation

$$c = 0.0417D(a + 1)$$

Suppose the dosage for an adult is 200 mg.

(a) Find the slope. What does it represent?

(b) What is the dosage for a newborn?

68. Flea Market   The manager of a weekend flea market knows from past experience that if she charges x dollars for a rental space at the flea market, then the number y of spaces she can rent is given by the equation $y = 200 - 4x$.

(a) Sketch a graph of this linear equation. (Remember that the rental charge per space and the number of spaces rented must both be nonnegative quantities.)

(b) What do the slope, the y-intercept, and the x-intercept of the graph represent?

69. Production Cost   A small-appliance manufacturer finds that if he produces x toaster ovens in a month, his production cost is given by the equation

$$y = 6x + 3000$$

(where y is measured in dollars).

(a) Sketch a graph of this linear equation.

(b) What do the slope and y-intercept of the graph represent?

70. Temperature Scales   The relationship between the Fahrenheit (F) and Celsius (C) temperature scales is given by the equation $F = \frac{9}{5}C + 32$.

(a) Complete the table to compare the two scales at the given values.

(b) Find the temperature at which the scales agree. [*Hint:* Suppose that a is the temperature at which the scales agree. Set $F = a$ and $C = a$. Then solve for a.]

C	F
−30°	
−20°	
−10°	
0°	
	50°
	68°
	86°

71. Crickets and Temperature   Biologists have observed that the chirping rate of crickets of a certain species is related to temperature, and the relationship appears to be very nearly linear. A cricket produces 120 chirps per minute at 70°F and 168 chirps per minute at 80°F.

(a) Find the linear equation that relates the temperature t and the number of chirps per minute n.

(b) If the crickets are chirping at 150 chirps per minute, estimate the temperature.

72. Depreciation   A small business buys a computer for $4000. After 4 years the value of the computer is expected to be $200. For accounting purposes the business uses *linear depreciation* to assess the value of the computer at a given time.

This means that if V is the value of the computer at time t, then a linear equation is used to relate V and t.

(a) Find a linear equation that relates V and t.

(b) Sketch a graph of this linear equation.

(c) What do the slope and V-intercept of the graph represent?

(d) Find the depreciated value of the computer 3 years from the date of purchase.

73. Pressure and Depth At the surface of the ocean the water pressure is the same as the air pressure above the water, 15 lb/in². Below the surface the water pressure increases by 4.34 lb/in² for every 10 ft of descent.

(a) Find an equation for the relationship between pressure and depth below the ocean surface.

(b) Sketch a graph of this linear equation.

(c) What do the slope and y-intercept of the graph represent?

(d) At what depth is the pressure 100 lb/in²?

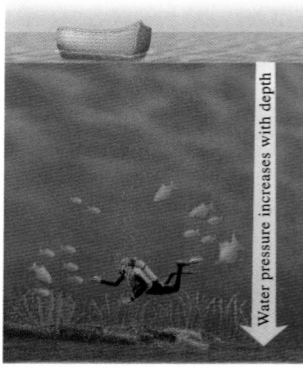

Water pressure increases with depth

74. Distance, Speed, and Time Jason and Debbie leave Detroit at 2:00 P.M. and drive at a constant speed, traveling west on I-90. They pass Ann Arbor, 40 mi from Detroit, at 2:50 P.M.

(a) Express the distance traveled in terms of the time elapsed.

(b) Draw the graph of the equation in part (a).

(c) What is the slope of this line? What does it represent?

75. Cost of Driving The monthly cost of driving a car depends on the number of miles driven. Lynn found that in May her driving cost was $380 for 480 mi and in June her cost was $460 for 800 mi. Assume that there is a linear relationship between the monthly cost C of driving a car and the distance driven d.

(a) Find a linear equation that relates C and d.

(b) Use part (a) to predict the cost of driving 1500 mi per month.

(c) Draw the graph of the linear equation. What does the slope of the line represent?

(d) What does the y-intercept of the graph represent?

(e) Why is a linear relationship a suitable model for this situation?

76. Manufacturing Cost The manager of a furniture factory finds that it costs $2200 to manufacture 100 chairs in one day and $4800 to produce 300 chairs in one day.

(a) Assuming that the relationship between cost and the number of chairs produced is linear, find an equation that expresses this relationship. Then graph the equation.

(b) What is the slope of the line in part (a), and what does it represent?

(c) What is the y-intercept of this line, and what does it represent?

DISCOVERY ■ DISCUSSION ■ WRITING

77. What Does the Slope Mean? Suppose that the graph of the outdoor temperature over a certain period of time is a line. How is the weather changing if the slope of the line is positive? If it is negative? If it is zero?

78. Collinear Points Suppose that you are given the coordinates of three points in the plane and you want to see whether they lie on the same line. How can you do this using slopes? Using the Distance Formula? Can you think of another method?

1.11 MAKING MODELS USING VARIATION

| Direct Variation ▶ Inverse Variation ▶ Joint Variation

When scientists talk about a mathematical model for a real-world phenomenon, they often mean an equation that describes the relationship between two quantities. For instance, the model might describe how the population of an animal species varies with time or how the pressure of a gas varies as its temperature changes. In this section we study a kind of modeling called *variation*.

TEXT QUESTIONS

(a) If y is proportional to x, must there be a linear equation relating y and x?

(b) If there is a linear equation relating y and x, must y be proportional to x?

Answers

(a) Yes

(b) No

▼ Direct Variation

Two types of mathematical models occur so often that they are given special names. The first is called *direct variation* and occurs when one quantity is a constant multiple of the other, so we use an equation of the form $y = kx$ to model this dependence.

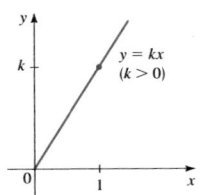

FIGURE 1

> **DIRECT VARIATION**
>
> If the quantities x and y are related by an equation
>
> $$y = kx$$
>
> for some constant $k \neq 0$, we say that y **varies directly as** x, or y is **directly proportional to** x, or simply y **is proportional to** x. The constant k is called the **constant of proportionality**.

Recall that the graph of an equation of the form $y = mx + b$ is a line with slope m and y-intercept b. So the graph of an equation $y = kx$ that describes direct variation is a line with slope k and y-intercept 0 (see Figure 1).

EXAMPLE 1 | Direct Variation

During a thunderstorm you see the lightning before you hear the thunder because light travels much faster than sound. The distance between you and the storm varies directly as the time interval between the lightning and the thunder.

(a) Suppose that the thunder from a storm 5400 ft away takes 5 s to reach you. Determine the constant of proportionality, and write the equation for the variation.

(b) Sketch the graph of this equation. What does the constant of proportionality represent?

(c) If the time interval between the lightning and thunder is now 8 s, how far away is the storm?

SOLUTION

(a) Let d be the distance from you to the storm, and let t be the length of the time interval. We are given that d varies directly as t, so

$$d = kt$$

where k is a constant. To find k, we use the fact that $t = 5$ when $d = 5400$. Substituting these values in the equation, we get

$$5400 = k(5) \qquad \text{Substitute}$$

$$k = \frac{5400}{5} = 1080 \qquad \text{Solve for } k$$

Substituting this value of k in the equation for d, we obtain

$$d = 1080t$$

as the equation for d as a function of t.

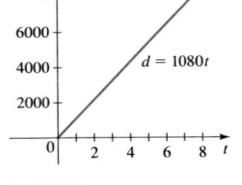

FIGURE 2

(b) The graph of the equation $d = 1080t$ is a line through the origin with slope 1080 and is shown in Figure 2. The constant $k = 1080$ is the approximate speed of sound (in ft/s).

(c) When $t = 8$, we have

$$d = 1080 \cdot 8 = 8640$$

So the storm is 8640 ft ≈ 1.6 mi away.

✎ NOW TRY EXERCISES **17** AND **29**

IN-CLASS MATERIALS

Have students come up with as many examples of proportionality as they can. One quick, effective way would be to give them a minute to write down as many as they can think of, then another couple of minutes to discuss their list with a neighbor, generating more. Finally, have them write down their answers on the board. With luck, some will accidentally give examples that are not proportional or that are inversely proportional. If these don't come up, you can ask, "What about the height of a person and that person's average rent?" or "What about the cost of a computer and its weight, all other things being equal?"

▼ Inverse Variation

Another equation that is frequently used in mathematical modeling is $y = k/x$, where k is a constant.

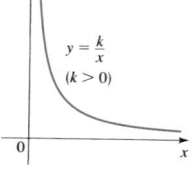

FIGURE 3   Inverse variation

> **INVERSE VARIATION**
>
> If the quantities x and y are related by the equation
>
> $$y = \frac{k}{x}$$
>
> for some constant $k \neq 0$, we say that y **is inversely proportional to** x or y **varies inversely as** x. The constant k is called the **constant of proportionality**.

The graph of $y = k/x$ for $x > 0$ is shown in Figure 3 for the case $k > 0$. It gives a picture of what happens when y is inversely proportional to x.

EXAMPLE 2 | Inverse Variation

Boyle's Law states that when a sample of gas is compressed at a constant temperature, the pressure of the gas is inversely proportional to the volume of the gas.

(a) Suppose the pressure of a sample of air that occupies 0.106 m³ at 25°C is 50 kPa. Find the constant of proportionality, and write the equation that expresses the inverse proportionality.

(b) If the sample expands to a volume of 0.3 m³, find the new pressure.

SOLUTION

(a) Let P be the pressure of the sample of gas, and let V be its volume. Then, by the definition of inverse proportionality, we have

$$P = \frac{k}{V}$$

where k is a constant. To find k, we use the fact that $P = 50$ when $V = 0.106$. Substituting these values in the equation, we get

$$50 = \frac{k}{0.106} \qquad \text{Substitute}$$

$$k = (50)(0.106) = 5.3 \qquad \text{Solve for } k$$

Putting this value of k in the equation for P, we have

$$P = \frac{5.3}{V}$$

(b) When $V = 0.3$, we have

$$P = \frac{5.3}{0.3} \approx 17.7$$

So the new pressure is about 17.7 kPa.

✎. NOW TRY EXERCISES **19** AND **35**   ■

▼ Joint Variation

A physical quantity often depends on more than one other quantity. If one quantity is proportional to two or more other quantities, we call this relationship *joint variation*.

IN-CLASS MATERIALS

Point out that proportionality is a model, just like a linear model or any other kind of model. For example, show students an example of a scatter plot such as the one here.

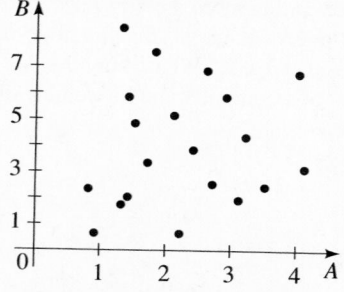

Clearly there is no straight line that will go through the points, but we can model the relationship by a straight line to try to make predictions. In this case, the straight-line model would not be very good.

JOINT VARIATION

If the quantities x, y, and z are related by the equation

$$z = kxy$$

where k is a nonzero constant, we say that z **varies jointly as** x and y or z **is jointly proportional to** x and y.

In the sciences, relationships between three or more variables are common, and any combination of the different types of proportionality that we have discussed is possible. For example, if

$$z = k\frac{x}{y}$$

we say that z **is proportional to** x and **inversely proportional to** y.

EXAMPLE 3 | Newton's Law of Gravitation

Newton's Law of Gravitation says that two objects with masses m_1 and m_2 attract each other with a force F that is jointly proportional to their masses and inversely proportional to the square of the distance r between the objects. Express Newton's Law of Gravitation as an equation.

SOLUTION   Using the definitions of joint and inverse variation and the traditional notation G for the gravitational constant of proportionality, we have

$$F = G\frac{m_1 m_2}{r^2}$$

◥. NOW TRY EXERCISES **21** AND **41** ∎

FIGURE 4   Graph of $F = \dfrac{1}{r^2}$

If m_1 and m_2 are fixed masses, then the gravitational force between them is $F = C/r^2$ (where $C = Gm_1 m_2$ is a constant). Figure 4 shows the graph of this equation for $r > 0$ with $C = 1$. Observe how the gravitational attraction decreases with increasing distance.

1.11 EXERCISES

CONCEPTS

1. If the quantities x and y are related by the equation $y = 3x$, then we say that y is _____ _____ to x and the constant of _____ is 3.

2. If the quantities x and y are related by the equation $y = \dfrac{3}{x}$, then we say that y is _____ _____ to x and the constant of _____ is 3.

3. If the quantities x, y, and z are related by the equation $z = 3\dfrac{x}{y}$, then we say that z is _____ _____ to x and _____ _____ to y.

4. If z is jointly proportional to x and y and if z is 10 when x is 4 and y is 5, then x, y, and z are related by the equation

$$z = \text{_____}.$$

SKILLS

5–16 ■ Write an equation that expresses the statement.

5. T varies directly as x.

6. P is directly proportional to w.

7. v is inversely proportional to z.

8. w is jointly proportional to m and n.

9. y is proportional to s and inversely proportional to t.

IN-CLASS MATERIALS

Discuss the difference between a general linear relationship and direct variation: In a directly proportional relationship, the origin is a data point. For example, the number of cans of beans you buy and the price you pay are in direct proportion—zero cans cost zero dollars. If you have to pay a fee to get into the store (as in some discount stores), the two quantities are no longer in direct proportion.

10. P varies inversely as T.

11. z is proportional to the square root of y.

12. A is proportional to the square of t and inversely proportional to the cube of x.

13. V is jointly proportional to l, w, and h.

14. S is jointly proportional to the squares of r and θ.

15. R is proportional to i and inversely proportional to P and t.

16. A is jointly proportional to the square roots of x and y.

17–28 ■ Express the statement as an equation. Use the given information to find the constant of proportionality.

17. y is directly proportional to x. If $x = 6$, then $y = 42$.

18. z varies inversely as t. If $t = 3$, then $z = 5$.

19. R is inversely proportional to s. If $s = 4$, then $R = 3$.

20. P is directly proportional to T. If $T = 300$, then $P = 20$.

21. M varies directly as x and inversely as y. If $x = 2$ and $y = 6$, then $M = 5$.

22. S varies jointly as p and q. If $p = 4$ and $q = 5$, then $S = 180$.

23. W is inversely proportional to the square of r. If $r = 6$, then $W = 10$.

24. t is jointly proportional to x and y, and inversely proportional to r. If $x = 2$, $y = 3$, and $r = 12$, then $t = 25$.

25. C is jointly proportional to l, w, and h. If $l = w = h = 2$, then $C = 128$.

26. H is jointly proportional to the squares of l and w. If $l = 2$ and $w = \frac{1}{3}$, then $H = 36$.

27. s is inversely proportional to the square root of t. If $s = 100$, then $t = 25$.

28. M is jointly proportional to a, b, and c and inversely proportional to d. If a and d have the same value and if b and c are both 2, then $M = 128$.

APPLICATIONS

29. **Hooke's Law** Hooke's Law states that the force needed to keep a spring stretched x units beyond its natural length is directly proportional to x. Here the constant of proportionality is called the **spring constant**.

    (a) Write Hooke's Law as an equation.

    (b) If a spring has a natural length of 10 cm and a force of 40 N is required to maintain the spring stretched to a length of 15 cm, find the spring constant.

    (c) What force is needed to keep the spring stretched to a length of 14 cm?

5 cm

30. **Law of the Pendulum** The period of a pendulum (the time elapsed during one complete swing of the pendulum) varies directly with the square root of the length of the pendulum.

    (a) Express this relationship by writing an equation.

    (b) To double the period, how would we have to change the length l?

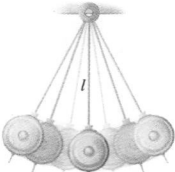

31. **Printing Costs** The cost C of printing a magazine is jointly proportional to the number of pages p in the magazine and the number of magazines printed m.

    (a) Write an equation that expresses this joint variation.

    (b) Find the constant of proportionality if the printing cost is $60,000 for 4000 copies of a 120-page magazine.

    (c) How much would the printing cost be for 5000 copies of a 92-page magazine?

32. **Boyle's Law** The pressure P of a sample of gas is directly proportional to the temperature T and inversely proportional to the volume V.

    (a) Write an equation that expresses this variation.

    (b) Find the constant of proportionality if 100 L of gas exerts a pressure of 33.2 kPa at a temperature of 400 K (absolute temperature measured on the Kelvin scale).

    (c) If the temperature is increased to 500 K and the volume is decreased to 80 L, what is the pressure of the gas?

33. **Power from a Windmill** The power P that can be obtained from a windmill is directly proportional to the cube of the wind speed s.

    (a) Write an equation that expresses this variation.

    (b) Find the constant of proportionality for a windmill that produces 96 watts of power when the wind is blowing at 20 mi/h.

    (c) How much power will this windmill produce if the wind speed increases to 30 mi/h?

34. **Power Needed to Propel a Boat** The power P (measured in horse power, hp) needed to propel a boat is directly proportional to the cube of the speed s. An 80-hp engine is needed to propel a certain boat at 10 knots. Find the power needed to drive the boat at 15 knots.

IN-CLASS MATERIALS

There are many proportional and inversely proportional relationships that students already understand, but students may not have thought about using that vocabulary. For example, the area of a circle is directly proportional to the square of its radius. The area of a rectangle is jointly proportional to its length and width. The time it takes to make a trip (of fixed distance) is inversely proportional to the average speed.

35. Loudness of Sound The loudness L of a sound (measured in decibels, dB) is inversely proportional to the square of the distance d from the source of the sound. A person who is 10 ft from a lawn mower experiences a sound level of 70 dB. How loud is the lawn mower when the person is 100 ft away?

36. Stopping Distance The stopping distance D of a car after the brakes have been applied varies directly as the square of the speed s. A certain car traveling at 50 mi/h can stop in 240 ft. What is the maximum speed it can be traveling if it needs to stop in 160 ft?

37. A Jet of Water The power P of a jet of water is jointly proportional to the cross-sectional area A of the jet and to the cube of the velocity v. If the velocity is doubled and the cross-sectional area is halved, by what factor will the power increase?

38. Aerodynamic Lift The lift L on an airplane wing at take-off varies jointly as the square of the speed s of the plane and the area A of its wings. A plane with a wing area of 500 ft^2 traveling at 50 mi/h experiences a lift of 1700 lb. How much lift would a plane with a wing area of 600 ft^2 traveling at 40 mi/h experience?

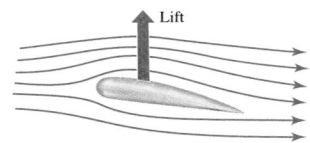

39. Drag Force on a Boat The drag force F on a boat is jointly proportional to the wetted surface area A on the hull and the square of the speed s of the boat. A boat experiences a drag force of 220 lb when traveling at 5 mi/h with a wetted surface area of 40 ft^2. How fast must a boat be traveling if it has 28 ft^2 of wetted surface area and is experiencing a drag force of 175 lb?

40. Skidding in a Curve A car is traveling on a curve that forms a circular arc. The force F needed to keep the car from skidding is jointly proportional to the weight w of the car and the square of its speed s, and is inversely proportional to the radius r of the curve.

(a) Write an equation that expresses this variation.

(b) A car weighing 1600 lb travels around a curve at 60 mi/h. The next car to round this curve weighs 2500 lb and requires the same force as the first car to keep from skidding. How fast is the second car traveling?

41. Electrical Resistance The resistance R of a wire varies directly as its length L and inversely as the square of its diameter d.

(a) Write an equation that expresses this joint variation.

(b) Find the constant of proportionality if a wire 1.2 m long and 0.005 m in diameter has a resistance of 140 ohms.

(c) Find the resistance of a wire made of the same material that is 3 m long and has a diameter of 0.008 m.

42. Kepler's Third Law Kepler's Third Law of planetary motion states that the square of the period T of a planet (the time it takes for the planet to make a complete revolution about the sun) is directly proportional to the cube of its average distance d from the sun.

(a) Express Kepler's Third Law as an equation.

(b) Find the constant of proportionality by using the fact that for our planet the period is about 365 days and the average distance is about 93 million miles.

(c) The planet Neptune is about 2.79×10^9 mi from the sun. Find the period of Neptune.

43. Radiation Energy The total radiation energy E emitted by a heated surface per unit area varies as the fourth power of its absolute temperature T. The temperature is 6000 K at the surface of the sun and 300 K at the surface of the earth.

(a) How many times more radiation energy per unit area is produced by the sun than by the earth?

(b) The radius of the earth is 3960 mi and the radius of the sun is 435,000 mi. How many times more total radiation does the sun emit than the earth?

44. Value of a Lot The value of a building lot on Galiano Island is jointly proportional to its area and the quantity of water produced by a well on the property. A 200 ft by 300 ft lot has a well producing 10 gallons of water per minute, and is valued at $48,000. What is the value of a 400 ft by 400 ft lot if the well on the lot produces 4 gallons of water per minute?

45. Growing Cabbages In the short growing season of the Canadian arctic territory of Nunavut, some gardeners find it possible to grow gigantic cabbages in the midnight sun.

EXAMPLES

1. Newton's Law: The rate of change of temperature of an object is proportional to the difference between the current temperature of the object and the temperature of its surroundings.

2. Torricelli's Law: The velocity at which liquid pours out of a cylindrical container (like orange juice out of a can with a hole at the bottom) is proportional to the square root of its height in the container.

3. Einstein's Law: The energy of a photon is directly proportional to its frequency.

4. Einstein's Theory of Relativity: The energy of a particle is proportional to its mass. (The constant of proportionality is the speed of light, squared.)

Assume that the final size of a cabbage is proportional to the amount of nutrients it receives and inversely proportional to the number of other cabbages surrounding it. A cabbage that received 20 oz of nutrients and had 12 other cabbages around it grew to 30 lb. What size would it grow to if it received 10 oz of nutrients and had only 5 cabbage "neighbors"?

46. Heat of a Campfire The heat experienced by a hiker at a campfire is proportional to the amount of wood on the fire and inversely proportional to the cube of his distance from the fire. If the hiker is 20 ft from the fire and someone doubles the amount of wood burning, how far from the fire would he have to be so that he feels the same heat as before?

47. Frequency of Vibration The frequency f of vibration of a violin string is inversely proportional to its length L. The constant of proportionality k is positive and depends on the tension and density of the string.

   (a) Write an equation that represents this variation.

   (b) What effect does doubling the length of the string have on the frequency of its vibration?

48. Spread of a Disease The rate r at which a disease spreads in a population of size P is jointly proportional to the number x of infected people and the number $P - x$ who are not infected. An infection erupts in a small town that has population $P = 5000$.

   (a) Write an equation that expresses r as a function of x.

   (b) Compare the rate of spread of this infection when 10 people are infected to the rate of spread when 1000 people are infected. Which rate is larger? By what factor?

   (c) Calculate the rate of spread when the entire population is infected. Why does this answer make intuitive sense?

DISCOVERY ▪ DISCUSSION ▪ WRITING

49. Is Proportionality Everything? A great many laws of physics and chemistry are expressible as proportionalities. Give at least one example of a function that occurs in the sciences that is *not* a proportionality.

CHAPTER 1 | REVIEW

■ CONCEPT CHECK

1. Define each term in your own words. (Check by referring to the definition in the text.)

   (a) An integer   (b) A rational number

   (c) An irrational number (d) A real number

2. State each of these properties of real numbers.

   (a) Commutative Property

   (b) Associative Property

   (c) Distributive Property

3. What is an open interval? What is a closed interval? What notation is used for these intervals?

4. What is the absolute value of a number?

5. (a) In the expression a^x, which is the base and which is the exponent?

   (b) What does a^x mean if $x = n$, a positive integer?

   (c) What if $x = 0$?

   (d) What if x is a negative integer: $x = -n$, where n is a positive integer?

   (e) What if $x = m/n$, a rational number?

   (f) State the Laws of Exponents.

6. (a) What does $\sqrt[n]{a} = b$ mean?

   (b) Why is $\sqrt{a^2} = |a|$?

   (c) How many real nth roots does a positive real number have if n is odd? If n is even?

7. Explain how the procedure of rationalizing the denominator works.

8. State the Special Product Formulas for $(a + b)^2$, $(a - b)^2$, $(a + b)^3$, and $(a - b)^3$.

9. State each Special Factoring Formula.

   (a) Difference of squares (b) Difference of cubes

   (c) Sum of cubes

10. What is a solution of an equation?

11. How do you solve an equation involving radicals? Why is it important to check your answers when solving equations of this type?

12. How do you solve an equation

   (a) algebraically?   (b) graphically?

13. Write the general form of each type of equation.

   (a) A linear equation   (b) A quadratic equation

14. What are the three ways to solve a quadratic equation?

15. State the Zero-Product Property.

16. Describe the process of completing the square.

17. State the quadratic formula.

18. What is the discriminant of a quadratic equation?

19. State the rules for working with inequalities.

20. How do you solve
   (a) a linear inequality?
   (b) a nonlinear inequality?

21. (a) How do you solve an equation involving an absolute value?
   (b) How do you solve an inequality involving an absolute value?

22. (a) Describe the coordinate plane.
   (b) How do you locate points in the coordinate plane?

23. State each formula.
   (a) The Distance Formula
   (b) The Midpoint Formula

24. Given an equation, what is its graph?

25. How do you find the x-intercepts and y-intercepts of a graph?

26. Write an equation of the circle with center (h, k) and radius r.

27. Explain the meaning of each type of symmetry. How do you test for it?
   (a) Symmetry with respect to the x-axis

(b) Symmetry with respect to the y-axis
(c) Symmetry with respect to the origin

28. Define the slope of a line.

29. Write each form of the equation of a line.
   (a) The point-slope form
   (b) The slope-intercept form

30. (a) What is the equation of a vertical line?
   (b) What is the equation of a horizontal line?

31. What is the general equation of a line?

32. Given lines with slopes m_1 and m_2, explain how you can tell if the lines are
   (a) parallel   **(b)** perpendicular

33. Write an equation that expresses each relationship.
   (a) y is directly proportional to x.
   (b) y is inversely proportional to x.
   (c) z is jointly proportional to x and y.

■ EXERCISES

1–4 ■ State the property of real numbers being used.

1. $3x + 2y = 2y + 3x$

2. $(a + b)(a - b) = (a - b)(a + b)$

3. $4(a + b) = 4a + 4b$

4. $(A + 1)(x + y) = (A + 1)x + (A + 1)y$

5–6 ■ Express the interval in terms of inequalities, and then graph the interval.

5. $[-2, 6)$ **6.** $(-\infty, 4]$

7–8 ■ Express the inequality in interval notation, and then graph the corresponding interval.

7. $x \geq 5$ **8.** $-1 < x \leq 5$

9–18 ■ Evaluate the expression.

9. $|3 - |-9||$ **10.** $1 - |1 - |-1||$

11. $2^{-3} - 3^{-2}$ **12.** $\sqrt[3]{-125}$

13. $216^{-1/3}$ **14.** $64^{2/3}$

15. $\dfrac{\sqrt{242}}{\sqrt{2}}$ **16.** $\sqrt[4]{4}\,\sqrt[4]{324}$

17. $2^{1/2}8^{1/2}$ **18.** $\sqrt{2}\,\sqrt{50}$

19–28 ■ Simplify the expression.

19. $\dfrac{x^2(2x)^4}{x^3}$ **20.** $(a^2)^{-3}(a^3b)^2(b^3)^4$

21. $(3xy^2)^3(\tfrac{2}{3}x^{-1}y)^2$ **22.** $\left(\dfrac{r^2s^{4/3}}{r^{1/3}s}\right)^6$

23. $\sqrt[3]{(x^3y)^2y^4}$ **24.** $\sqrt{x^2y^4}$

25. $\left(\dfrac{9x^3y}{y^{-3}}\right)^{1/2}$ **26.** $\left(\dfrac{x^{-2}y^3}{x^2y}\right)^{-1/2}\left(\dfrac{x^3y}{y^{1/2}}\right)^2$

27. $\dfrac{8r^{1/2}s^{-3}}{2r^{-2}s^4}$ **28.** $\left(\dfrac{ab^2c^{-3}}{2a^3b^{-4}}\right)^{-2}$

29. Write the number 78,250,000,000 in scientific notation.

30. Write the number 2.08×10^{-8} in ordinary decimal notation.

31. If $a \approx 0.00000293$, $b \approx 1.582 \times 10^{-14}$, and $c \approx 2.8064 \times 10^{12}$, use a calculator to approximate the number ab/c.

32. If your heart beats 80 times per minute and you live to be 90 years old, estimate the number of times your heart beats during your lifetime. State your answer in scientific notation.

33–48 ■ Factor the expression completely.

33. $12x^2y^4 - 3xy^5 + 9x^3y^2$ **34.** $x^2 - 9x + 18$

35. $x^2 + 3x - 10$ **36.** $6x^2 + x - 12$

37. $4t^2 - 13t - 12$ **38.** $x^4 - 2x^2 + 1$

39. $25 - 16t^2$ **40.** $2y^6 - 32y^2$

41. $x^6 - 1$ **42.** $y^3 - 2y^2 - y + 2$

43. $x^{-1/2} - 2x^{1/2} + x^{3/2}$ **44.** $a^4b^2 + ab^5$

45. $4x^3 - 8x^2 + 3x - 6$ **46.** $8x^3 + y^6$

47. $(x^2 + 2)^{5/2} + 2x(x^2 + 2)^{3/2} + x^2\sqrt{x^2 + 2}$

48. $3x^3 - 2x^2 + 18x - 12$

49–64 ■ Perform the indicated operations and simplify.

49. $(2x + 1)(3x - 2) - 5(4x - 1)$

50. $(2y - 7)(2y + 7)$

51. $(1 + x)(2 - x) - (3 - x)(3 + x)$

52. $\sqrt{x}(\sqrt{x} + 1)(2\sqrt{x} - 1)$

53. $x^2(x - 2) + x(x - 2)^2$ **54.** $\dfrac{x^2 - 2x - 3}{2x^2 + 5x + 3}$

55. $\dfrac{x^2 + 2x - 3}{x^2 + 8x + 16} \cdot \dfrac{3x + 12}{x - 1}$ **56.** $\dfrac{t^3 - 1}{t^2 - 1}$

57. $\dfrac{x^2 - 2x - 15}{x^2 - 6x + 5} \div \dfrac{x^2 - x - 12}{x^2 - 1}$

58. $\dfrac{2}{x} + \dfrac{1}{x - 2} + \dfrac{3}{(x - 2)^2}$ **59.** $\dfrac{1}{x - 1} - \dfrac{2}{x^2 - 1}$

60. $\dfrac{1}{x + 2} + \dfrac{1}{x^2 - 4} - \dfrac{2}{x^2 - x - 2}$

61. $\dfrac{\dfrac{1}{x} - \dfrac{1}{2}}{x - 2}$ **62.** $\dfrac{\dfrac{1}{x} - \dfrac{1}{x + 1}}{\dfrac{1}{x} + \dfrac{1}{x + 1}}$

63. $\dfrac{\sqrt{6}}{\sqrt{3} + \sqrt{2}}$ (rationalize the denominator)

64. $\dfrac{\sqrt{x + h} - \sqrt{x}}{h}$ (rationalize the numerator)

65–80 ■ Find all real solutions of the equation.

65. $7x - 6 = 4x + 9$ **66.** $8 - 2x = 14 + x$

67. $\dfrac{x + 1}{x - 1} = \dfrac{3x}{3x - 6}$ **68.** $(x + 2)^2 = (x - 4)^2$

69. $x^2 - 9x + 14 = 0$ **70.** $x^2 + 24x + 144 = 0$

71. $2x^2 + x = 1$ **72.** $3x^2 + 5x - 2 = 0$

73. $4x^3 - 25x = 0$ **74.** $x^3 - 2x^2 - 5x + 10 = 0$

75. $3x^2 + 4x - 1 = 0$ **76.** $\dfrac{1}{x} + \dfrac{2}{x - 1} = 3$

77. $\dfrac{x}{x - 2} + \dfrac{1}{x + 2} = \dfrac{8}{x^2 - 4}$

78. $x^4 - 8x^2 - 9 = 0$

79. $|x - 7| = 4$ **80.** $|2x - 5| = 9$

81. The owner of a store sells raisins for $3.20 per pound and nuts for $2.40 per pound. He decides to mix the raisins and nuts and sell 50 lb of the mixture for $2.72 per pound. What quantities of raisins and nuts should he use?

82. Anthony leaves Kingstown at 2:00 P.M. and drives to Queensville, 160 mi distant, at 45 mi/h. At 2:15 P.M. Helen leaves Queensville and drives to Kingstown at 40 mi/h. At what time do they pass each other on the road?

83. A woman cycles 8 mi/h faster than she runs. Every morning she cycles 4 mi and runs $2\frac{1}{2}$ mi, for a total of one hour of exercise. How fast does she run?

84. The hypotenuse of a right triangle has length 20 cm. The sum of the lengths of its other two sides is 28 cm. Find the lengths of the other two sides of the triangle.

85. Abbie paints twice as fast as Beth and three times as fast as Cathie. If it takes them 60 min to paint a living room with all three working together, how long would it take Abbie if she works alone?

86. A homeowner wishes to fence in three adjoining garden plots, one for each of her children, as shown in the figure. If each

plot is to be 80 ft² in area and she has 88 ft of fencing material at hand, what dimensions should each plot have?

87–94 ■ Solve the inequality. Express the solution using interval notation and graph the solution set on the real number line.

87. $3x - 2 > -11$ **88.** $-1 < 2x + 5 \le 3$

89. $x^2 + 4x - 12 > 0$ **90.** $x^2 \le 1$

91. $\dfrac{x - 4}{x^2 - 4} \le 0$ **92.** $\dfrac{5}{x^3 - x^2 - 4x + 4} < 0$

93. $|x - 5| \le 3$ **94.** $|x - 4| < 0.02$

95–98 ■ Solve the equation or inequality graphically.

95. $x^2 - 4x = 2x + 7$ **96.** $\sqrt{x + 4} = x^2 - 5$

97. $4x - 3 \ge x^2$ **98.** $x^3 - 4x^2 - 5x > 2$

99–100 ■ Two points P and Q are given.

   (a) Plot P and Q on a coordinate plane.

   (b) Find the distance from P to Q.

   (c) Find the midpoint of the segment PQ.

   (d) Sketch the line determined by P and Q, and find its equation in slope-intercept form.

   (e) Sketch the circle that passes through Q and has center P, and find the equation of this circle.

99. $P(2, 0)$, $Q(-5, 12)$ **100.** $P(7, -1)$, $Q(2, -11)$

101–102 ■ Sketch the region given by the set.

101. $\{(x, y) \mid -4 < x < 4 \text{ and } -2 < y < 2\}$

102. $\{(x, y) \mid x \ge 4 \text{ or } y \ge 2\}$

103. Which of the points $A(4, 4)$ or $B(5, 3)$ is closer to the point $C(-1, -3)$?

104. Find an equation of the circle that has center $(2, -5)$ and radius $\sqrt{2}$.

105. Find an equation of the circle that has center $(-5, -1)$ and passes through the origin.

106. Find an equation of the circle that contains the points $P(2, 3)$ and $Q(-1, 8)$ and has the midpoint of the segment PQ as its center.

107–110 ■ Determine whether the equation represents a circle, represents a point, or has no graph. If the equation is that of a circle, find its center and radius.

107. $x^2 + y^2 + 2x - 6y + 9 = 0$

108. $2x^2 + 2y^2 - 2x + 8y = \frac{1}{2}$

109. $x^2 + y^2 + 72 = 12x$

110. $x^2 + y^2 - 6x - 10y + 34 = 0$

111–118 ■ Test the equation for symmetry, and sketch its graph.

111. $y = 2 - 3x$ **112.** $2x - y + 1 = 0$

113. $x + 3y = 21$ **114.** $x = 2y + 12$

115. $y = 16 - x^2$ **116.** $8x + y^2 = 0$

117. $x = \sqrt{y}$ **118.** $y = -\sqrt{1 - x^2}$

 119–122 ■ Use a graphing device to graph the equation in an appropriate viewing rectangle.

119. $y = x^2 - 6x$ **120.** $y = \sqrt{5 - x}$

121. $y = x^3 - 4x^2 - 5x$ **122.** $\dfrac{x^2}{4} + y^2 = 1$

123. Find an equation for the line that passes through the points $(-1, -6)$ and $(2, -4)$.

124. Find an equation for the line that passes through the point $(6, -3)$ and has slope $-\frac{1}{2}$.

125. Find an equation for the line that has x-intercept 4 and y-intercept 12.

126. Find an equation for the line that passes through the point $(1, 7)$ and is perpendicular to the line $x - 3y + 16 = 0$.

127. Find an equation for the line that passes through the origin and is parallel to the line $3x + 15y = 22$.

128. Find an equation for the line that passes through the point $(5, 2)$ and is parallel to the line passing through $(-1, -3)$ and $(3, 2)$.

129–130 ■ Find equations for the circle and the line in the figure.

129.

130.

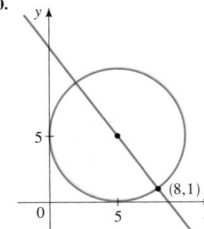

131. Hooke's Law states that if a weight w is attached to a hanging spring, then the stretched length s of the spring is linearly related to w. For a particular spring we have

$$s = 0.3w + 2.5$$

where s is measured in inches and w in pounds.

(a) What do the slope and s-intercept in this equation represent?

(b) How long is the spring when a 5-lb weight is attached?

132. Margarita is hired by an accounting firm at a salary of $60,000 per year. Three years later her annual salary has increased to $70,500. Assume that her salary increases linearly.

(a) Find an equation that relates her annual salary S and the number of years t that she has worked for the firm.

(b) What do the slope and S-intercept of her salary equation represent?

(c) What will her salary be after 12 years with the firm?

133. Suppose that M varies directly as z, and $M = 120$ when $z = 15$. Write an equation that expresses this variation.

134. Suppose that z is inversely proportional to y, and that $z = 12$ when $y = 16$. Write an equation that expresses z in terms of y.

135. The intensity of illumination I from a light varies inversely as the square of the distance d from the light.

(a) Write this statement as an equation.

(b) Determine the constant of proportionality if it is known that a lamp has an intensity of 1000 candles at a distance of 8 m.

(c) What is the intensity of this lamp at a distance of 20 m?

136. The frequency of a vibrating string under constant tension is inversely proportional to its length. If a violin string 12 inches long vibrates 440 times per second, to what length must it be shortened to vibrate 660 times per second?

137. The terminal velocity of a parachutist is directly proportional to the square root of his weight. A 160-lb parachutist attains a terminal velocity of 9 mi/h. What is the terminal velocity for a parachutist weighing 240 lb?

138. The maximum range of a projectile is directly proportional to the square of its velocity. A baseball pitcher throws a ball at 60 mi/h, with a maximum range of 242 ft. What is his maximum range if he throws the ball at 70 mi/h?

1. **(a)** Graph the intervals $(-5, 3]$ and $(2, \infty)$ on the real number line.
   (b) Express the inequalities $x \le 3$ and $-1 \le x < 4$ in interval notation.
   (c) Find the distance between -7 and 9 on the real number line.

2. Evaluate each expression.
   (a) $(-3)^4$ **(b)** -3^4 **(c)** 3^{-4} **(d)** $\dfrac{5^{23}}{5^{21}}$ **(e)** $\left(\dfrac{2}{3}\right)^{-2}$ **(f)** $16^{-3/4}$

3. Write each number in scientific notation.
   (a) 186,000,000,000   **(b)** 0.0000003965

4. Simplify each expression. Write your final answer without negative exponents.
   (a) $\sqrt{200} - \sqrt{32}$ **(b)** $(3a^3b^3)(4ab^2)^2$ **(c)** $\left(\dfrac{3x^{3/2}y^3}{x^2y^{-1/2}}\right)^{-2}$

   (d) $\dfrac{x^2 + 3x + 2}{x^2 - x - 2}$ **(e)** $\dfrac{x^2}{x^2 - 4} - \dfrac{x+1}{x+2}$ **(f)** $\dfrac{\dfrac{y}{x} - \dfrac{x}{y}}{\dfrac{1}{y} - \dfrac{1}{x}}$

5. Rationalize the denominator and simplify: $\dfrac{\sqrt{10}}{\sqrt{5} - 2}$

6. Perform the indicated operations and simplify.
   (a) $3(x + 6) + 4(2x - 5)$ **(b)** $(x + 3)(4x - 5)$ **(c)** $(\sqrt{a} + \sqrt{b})(\sqrt{a} - \sqrt{b})$
   (d) $(2x + 3)^2$ **(e)** $(x + 2)^3$

7. Factor each expression completely.
   (a) $4x^2 - 25$ **(b)** $2x^2 + 5x - 12$ **(c)** $x^3 - 3x^2 - 4x + 12$
   (d) $x^4 + 27x$ **(e)** $3x^{3/2} - 9x^{1/2} + 6x^{-1/2}$ **(f)** $x^3y - 4xy$

8. Find all real solutions.
   (a) $x + 5 = 14 - \frac{1}{2}x$ **(b)** $\dfrac{2x}{x+1} = \dfrac{2x-1}{x}$ **(c)** $x^2 - x - 12 = 0$

   (d) $2x^2 + 4x + 1 = 0$ **(e)** $\sqrt{3} - \sqrt{x + 5} = 2$ **(f)** $x^4 - 3x^2 + 2 = 0$
   (g) $3|x - 4| = 10$

9. Mary drove from Amity to Belleville at a speed of 50 mi/h. On the way back, she drove at 60 mi/h. The total trip took $4\frac{2}{5}$ h of driving time. Find the distance between these two cities.

10. A rectangular parcel of land is 70 ft longer than it is wide. Each diagonal between opposite corners is 130 ft. What are the dimensions of the parcel?

11. Solve each inequality. Write the answer using interval notation, and sketch the solution on the real number line.
    (a) $-4 < 5 - 3x \le 17$ **(b)** $x(x - 1)(x + 2) > 0$

    (c) $|x - 4| < 3$ **(d)** $\dfrac{2x - 3}{x + 1} \le 1$

12. A bottle of medicine is to be stored at a temperature between 5°C and 10°C. What range does this correspond to on the Fahrenheit scale? [*Note:* Fahrenheit (F) and Celsius (C) temperatures satisfy the relation $C = \frac{5}{9}(F - 32)$.]

13. For what values of x is the expression $\sqrt{6x - x^2}$ defined as a real number?

14. Solve the equation and the inequality graphically.
    (a) $x^3 - 9x - 1 = 0$ **(b)** $x^2 - 1 \le |x + 1|$

15. **(a)** Plot the points $P(0, 3)$, $Q(3, 0)$, and $R(6, 3)$ in the coordinate plane. Where must the point S be located so that $PQRS$ is a square?
    (b) Find the area of $PQRS$.

16. **(a)** Sketch the graph of $y = x^2 - 4$.
    (b) Find the x- and y-intercepts of the graph.
    (c) Is the graph symmetric about the x-axis, the y-axis, or the origin?

17. Let $P(-3,1)$ and $Q(5,6)$ be two points in the coordinate plane.

    (a) Plot P and Q in the coordinate plane.

    (b) Find the distance between P and Q.

    (c) Find the midpoint of the segment PQ.

    (d) Find the slope of the line that contains P and Q.

    (e) Find the perpendicular bisector of the line that contains P and Q.

    (f) Find an equation for the circle for which the segment PQ is a diameter.

18. Find the center and radius of each circle and sketch its graph.

    (a) $x^2 + y^2 = 25$ **(b)** $(x - 2)^2 + (y + 1)^2 = 9$ **(c)** $x^2 + 6x + y^2 - 2y + 6 = 0$

19. Write the linear equation $2x - 3y = 15$ in slope-intercept form, and sketch its graph. What are the slope and y-intercept?

20. Find an equation for the line with the given property.

    (a) It passes through the point $(3, -6)$ and is parallel to the line $3x + y - 10 = 0$.

    (b) It has x-intercept 6 and y-intercept 4.

21. A geologist uses a probe to measure the temperature T (in °C) of the soil at various depths below the surface, and finds that at a depth of x cm, the temperature is given by the linear equation $T = 0.08x - 4$.

    (a) What is the temperature at a depth of one meter (100 cm)?

    (b) Sketch a graph of the linear equation.

    (c) What do the slope, the x-intercept, and T-intercept of the graph of this equation represent?

22. The maximum weight M that can be supported by a beam is jointly proportional to its width w and the square of its height h, and inversely proportional to its length L.

    (a) Write an equation that expresses this proportionality.

    (b) Determine the constant of proportionality if a beam 4 in. wide, 6 in. high, and 12 ft long can support a weight of 4800 lb.

    (c) If a 10-ft beam made of the same material is 3 in. wide and 10 in. high, what is the maximum weight it can support?

If you had difficulty with any of these problems, you may wish to review the section of this chapter indicated below.

If you had trouble with this test problem	Review this section
1	Section 1.1
2, 3, 4(a), 4(b), 4(c)	Section 1.2
4(d), 4(e), 4(f), 5	Section 1.4
6, 7	Section 1.3
8	Section 1.5
9, 10	Section 1.6
11, 12, 13	Section 1.7
14	Section 1.9
15, 16, 17(a), 17(b)	Section 1.8
17(c), 17(d)	Section 1.10
17(e), 17(f), 18	Section 1.8
19, 20, 21	Section 1.10
22	Section 1.11

Fitting Lines to Data

A model is a representation of an object or process. For example, a toy Ferrari is a model of the actual car; a road map is a model of the streets in a city. A **mathematical model** is a mathematical representation (usually an equation) of an object or process. Once a mathematical model is made it can be used to obtain useful information or make predictions about the thing being modeled. In these *Focus on Modeling* sections we explore different ways in which mathematics is used to model real-world phenomena.

▼ The Line That Best Fits the Data

In Section 1.10 we used linear equations to model relationships between varying quantities. In practice, such relationships are discovered by collecting data. But real-world data seldom fall into a precise line. The **scatter plot** in Figure 1(a) shows the result of a study on childhood obesity. The graph plots the body mass index (BMI) versus the number of hours of television watched per day for 25 adolescent subjects. Of course, we would not expect the data to be exactly linear as in Figure 1(b). But there is a linear *trend* indicated by the blue line in Figure 1(a): The more hours a subject watches TV the higher the BMI. In this section we learn how to find the line that best fits the data.

(a) Line of best fit (b) Line fits data exactly

FIGURE 1

Table 1 gives the nationwide infant mortality rate for the period from 1950 to 2000. The *rate* is the number of infants who die before reaching their first birthday, out of every 1000 live births.

TABLE 1
U.S. Infant Mortality

Year	Rate
1950	29.2
1960	26.0
1970	20.0
1980	12.6
1990	9.2
2000	6.9

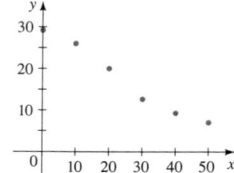

FIGURE 2 U.S. infant mortality rate

The scatter plot in Figure 2 shows that the data lie roughly on a straight line. We can try to fit a line visually to approximate the data points, but since the data aren't *exactly*

130

linear, there are many lines that might seem to work. Figure 3 shows two attempts at "eye-balling" a line to fit the data.

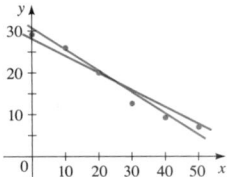

FIGURE 3 Visual attempts to fit line to data

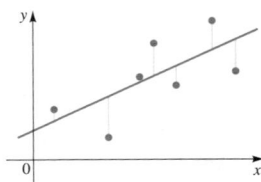

FIGURE 4 Distance from the data points to the line

Of all the lines that run through these data points, there is one that "best" fits the data, in the sense that it provides the most accurate linear model for the data. We now describe how to find this line.

It seems reasonable that the line of best fit is the line that is as close as possible to all the data points. This is the line for which the sum of the vertical distances from the data points to the line is as small as possible (see Figure 4). For technical reasons it is better to use the line where the sum of the squares of these distances is smallest. This is called the **regression line**. The formula for the regression line is found by using calculus, but fortunately, the formula is programmed into most graphing calculators. In Example 1 we see how to use a TI-83 calculator to find the regression line for the infant mortality data described above. (The process for other calculators is similar.)

EXAMPLE 1 | Regression Line for U.S. Infant Mortality Rates

(a) Find the regression line for the infant mortality data in Table 1.

(b) Graph the regression line on a scatter plot of the data.

(c) Use the regression line to estimate the infant mortality rates in 1995 and 2006.

SOLUTION

(a) To find the regression line using a TI-83 calculator, we must first enter the data into the lists L_1 and L_2, which are accessed by pressing the [STAT] key and selecting Edit. Figure 5 shows the calculator screen after the data have been entered. (Note that we are letting $x = 0$ correspond to the year 1950, so that $x = 50$ corresponds to 2000. This makes the equations easier to work with.) We then press the [STAT] key again and select Calc, then 4:LinReg(ax+b), which provides the output shown in Figure 6(a). This tells us that the regression line is

$$y = -0.48x + 29.4$$

Here x represents the number of years since 1950, and y represents the corresponding infant mortality rate.

(b) The scatter plot and the regression line have been plotted on a graphing calculator screen in Figure 6(b).

L1	L2	L3	1
0	29.2	-------	
10	26		
20	20		
30	12.6		
40	9.2		
50	6.9		

L2(7)=

FIGURE 5 Entering the data

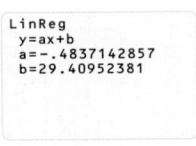

(a) Output of the LinReg command

(b) Scatter plot and regression line

FIGURE 6

(c) The year 1995 is 45 years after 1950, so substituting 45 for x, we find that
$y = -0.48(45) + 29.4 = 7.8$. So the infant mortality rate in 1995 was about 7.8.
Similarly, substituting 56 for x, we find that the infant mortality rate predicted for
2006 was about $-0.48(56) + 29.4 \approx 2.5$. ■

An Internet search shows that the actual infant mortality rate was 7.6 in 1995 and 6.4
in 2006. So the regression line is fairly accurate for 1995 (the actual rate was slightly
lower than the predicted rate), but it is considerably off for 2006 (the actual rate was more
than twice the predicted rate). The reason is that infant mortality in the United States
stopped declining and actually started rising in 2002, for the first time in more than a century. This shows that we have to be very careful about extrapolating linear models outside
the domain over which the data are spread.

▼ Examples of Regression Analysis

Since the modern Olympic Games began in 1896, achievements in track and field events
have been improving steadily. One example in which the winning records have shown an
upward linear trend is the pole vault. Pole vaulting began in the northern Netherlands as
a practical activity: When traveling from village to village, people would vault across the
many canals that crisscrossed the area to avoid having to go out of their way to find a
bridge. Households maintained a supply of wooden poles of lengths appropriate for each
member of the family. Pole vaulting for height rather than distance became a collegiate
track and field event in the mid-1800s and was one of the events in the first modern
Olympics. In the next example we find a linear model for the gold-medal-winning records
in the men's Olympic pole vault.

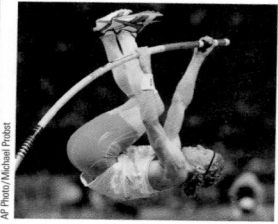

Steven Hooker, 2008 Olympic gold
medal winner, men's pole vault

EXAMPLE 2 | Regression Line for Olympic Pole Vault Records

Table 2 gives the men's Olympic pole vault records up to 2004.

(a) Find the regression line for the data.

(b) Make a scatter plot of the data, and graph the regression line. Does the regression
line appear to be a suitable model for the data?

(c) What does the slope of the regression line represent?

(d) Use the model to predict the winning pole vault height for the 2008 Olympics.

TABLE 2
Men's Olympic Pole Vault Records

Year	x	Gold medalist	Height (m)	Year	x	Gold medalist	Height (m)
1896	−4	William Hoyt, USA	3.30	1956	56	Robert Richards, USA	4.56
1900	0	Irving Baxter, USA	3.30	1960	60	Don Bragg, USA	4.70
1904	4	Charles Dvorak, USA	3.50	1964	64	Fred Hansen, USA	5.10
1906	6	Fernand Gonder, France	3.50	1968	68	Bob Seagren, USA	5.40
1908	8	A. Gilbert, E. Cook, USA	3.71	1972	72	W. Nordwig, E. Germany	5.64
1912	12	Harry Babcock, USA	3.95	1976	76	Tadeusz Slusarski, Poland	5.64
1920	20	Frank Foss, USA	4.09	1980	80	W. Kozakiewicz, Poland	5.78
1924	24	Lee Barnes, USA	3.95	1984	84	Pierre Quinon, France	5.75
1928	28	Sabin Can, USA	4.20	1988	88	Sergei Bubka, USSR	5.90
1932	32	William Miller, USA	4.31	1992	92	M. Tarassob, Unified Team	5.87
1936	36	Earle Meadows, USA	4.35	1996	96	Jean Jaffione, France	5.92
1948	48	Guinn Smith, USA	4.30	2000	100	Nick Hysong, USA	5.90
1952	52	Robert Richards, USA	4.55	2004	104	Timothy Mack, USA	5.95

```
LinReg
 y=ax+b
  a=.0265652857
  b=3.400989881
```

Output of the `LinReg`
function on the TI-83

SOLUTION

(a) Let x = year − 1900, so 1896 corresponds to $x = -4$, 1900 to $x = 0$, and so on. Using a calculator, we find the following regression line:

$$y = 0.0266x + 3.40$$

(b) The scatter plot and the regression line are shown in Figure 7. The regression line appears to be a good model for the data.

(c) The slope is the average rate of increase in the pole vault record per year. So on average, the pole vault record increased by 0.0266 m/yr.

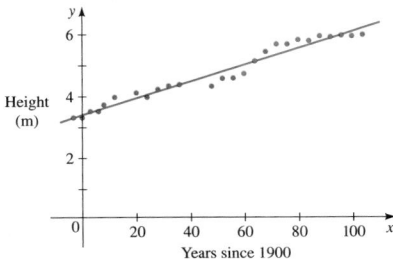

FIGURE 7 Scatter plot and regression line for pole vault data

(d) The year 2008 corresponds to $x = 108$ in our model. The model gives

$$y = 0.0266(108) + 3.40$$

$$\approx 6.27$$

So the model predicts that in 2008 the winning pole vault will be 6.27 m. ∎

At the 2008 Olympics in Beijing, China, the men's Olympic gold medal in the pole vault was won by Steven Hooker of Australia, with a vault of 5.96 m. Although this height set an Olympic record, it was considerably lower than the 6.27 m predicted by the model of Example 2. In Problem 10 we find a regression line for the pole vault data from 1972 to 2004. Do the problem to see whether this restricted set of more recent data provides a better predictor for the 2008 record.

Is a linear model really appropriate for the data of Example 2? In subsequent *Focus on Modeling* sections, we study regression models that use other types of functions, and we learn how to choose the best model for a given set of data.

In the next example we see how linear regression is used in medical research to investigate potential causes of diseases such as cancer.

EXAMPLE 3 | Regression Line for Links Between Asbestos and Cancer

When laboratory rats are exposed to asbestos fibers, some of the rats develop lung tumors. Table 3 lists the results of several experiments by different scientists.

(a) Find the regression line for the data.

(b) Make a scatter plot and graph the regression line. Does the regression line appear to be a suitable model for the data?

(c) What does the y-intercept of the regression line represent?

TABLE 3
Asbestos–Tumor Data

Asbestos exposure (fibers/mL)	Percent that develop lung tumors
50	2
400	6
500	5
900	10
1100	26
1600	42
1800	37
2000	28
3000	50

SOLUTION

(a) Using a calculator, we find the following regression line (see Figure 8(a)):

$$y = 0.0177x + 0.5405$$

(b) The scatter plot and regression line are graphed in Figure 8(b). The regression line appears to be a reasonable model for the data.

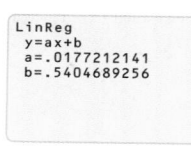

(a) Output of the `LinReg` command

(b) Scatter plot and regression line

FIGURE 8 Linear regression for the asbestos–tumor data

(c) The y-intercept is the percentage of rats that develop tumors when no asbestos fibers are present. In other words, this is the percentage that normally develop lung tumors (for reasons other than asbestos). ∎

▼ How Good Is the Fit? The Correlation Coefficient

For any given set of two-variable data it is always possible to find a regression line, even if the data points do not tend to lie on a line and even if the variables don't seem to be related at all. Look at the three scatter plots in Figure 9. In the first scatter plot, the data points lie close to a line. In the second plot, there is still a linear trend but the points are more scattered. In the third plot there doesn't seem to be any trend at all, linear or otherwise.

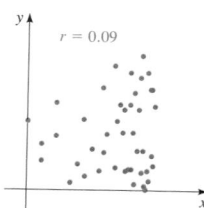

FIGURE 9

A graphing calculator can give us a regression line for each of these scatter plots. But how well do these lines represent or "fit" the data? To answer this question, statisticians have invented the **correlation coefficient**, usually denoted r. The correlation coefficient is a number between -1 and 1 that measures how closely the data follow the regression line—or, in other words, how strongly the variables are **correlated**. Many graphing calculators give the value of r when they compute a regression line. If r is close to -1

or 1, then the variables are strongly correlated—that is, the scatter plot follows the regression line closely. If r is close to 0, then the variables are weakly correlated or not correlated at all. (The sign of r depends on the slope of the regression line.) The correlation coefficients of the scatter plots in Figure 9 are indicated on the graphs. For the first plot, r is close to 1 because the data are very close to linear. The second plot also has a relatively large r, but it is not as large as the first, because the data, while fairly linear, are more diffuse. The third plot has an r close to 0, since there is virtually no linear trend in the data.

There are no hard and fast rules for deciding what values of r are sufficient for deciding that a linear correlation is "significant." The correlation coefficient is only a rough guide in helping us decide how much faith to put into a given regression line. In Example 1 the correlation coefficient is -0.99, indicating a very high level of correlation, so we can safely say that the drop in infant mortality rates from 1950 to 2000 was strongly linear. (The value of r is negative, since infant mortality trended *down* over this period.) In Example 3 the correlation coefficient is 0.92, which also indicates a strong correlation between the variables. So exposure to asbestos is clearly associated with the growth of lung tumors in rats. Does this mean that asbestos *causes* lung cancer?

If two variables are correlated, it does not necessarily mean that a change in one variable *causes* a change in the other. For example, the mathematician John Allen Paulos points out that shoe size is strongly correlated to mathematics scores among schoolchildren. Does this mean that big feet cause high math scores? Certainly not—both shoe size and math skills increase independently as children get older. So it is important not to jump to conclusions: Correlation and causation are not the same thing. Correlation is a useful tool in bringing important cause-and-effect relationships to light; but to prove causation, we must explain the mechanism by which one variable affects the other. For example, the link between smoking and lung cancer was observed as a correlation long before science found the mechanism through which smoking causes lung cancer.

PROBLEMS

1. **Femur Length and Height**   Anthropologists use a linear model that relates femur length to height. The model allows an anthropologist to determine the height of an individual when only a partial skeleton (including the femur) is found. In this problem we find the model by analyzing the data on femur length and height for the eight males given in the table.

   (a) Make a scatter plot of the data.

   (b) Find and graph a linear function that models the data.

   (c) An anthropologist finds a femur of length 58 cm. How tall was the person?

Femur →

Femur length (cm)	Height (cm)
50.1	178.5
48.3	173.6
45.2	164.8
44.7	163.7
44.5	168.3
42.7	165.0
39.5	155.4
38.0	155.8

2. **Demand for Soft Drinks**   A convenience store manager notices that sales of soft drinks are higher on hotter days, so he assembles the data in the table.

   (a) Make a scatter plot of the data.

   (b) Find and graph a linear function that models the data.

(c) Use the model to predict soft drink sales if the temperature is 95°F.

High temperature (°F)	Number of cans sold
55	340
58	335
64	410
68	460
70	450
75	610
80	735
84	780

3. **Tree Diameter and Age**   To estimate ages of trees, forest rangers use a linear model that relates tree diameter to age. The model is useful because tree diameter is much easier to measure than tree age (which requires special tools for extracting a representative cross section of the tree and counting the rings). To find the model, use the data in the table, which were collected for a certain variety of oaks.

(a) Make a scatter plot of the data.

(b) Find and graph a linear function that models the data.

(c) Use the model to estimate the age of an oak whose diameter is 18 in.

Diameter (in.)	Age (years)
2.5	15
4.0	24
6.0	32
8.0	56
9.0	49
9.5	76
12.5	90
15.5	89

4. **Carbon Dioxide Levels**   The Mauna Loa Observatory, located on the island of Hawaii, has been monitoring carbon dioxide (CO_2) levels in the atmosphere since 1958. The table lists the average annual CO_2 levels measured in parts per million (ppm) from 1984 to 2006.

(a) Make a scatter plot of the data.

(b) Find and graph the regression line.

(c) Use the linear model in part (b) to estimate the CO_2 level in the atmosphere in 2005. Compare your answer with the actual CO_2 level of 379.7 that was measured in 2005.

Year	CO_2 level (ppm)
1984	344.3
1986	347.0
1988	351.3
1990	354.0
1992	356.3
1994	358.9
1996	362.7
1998	366.5
2000	369.4
2002	372.0
2004	377.5
2006	380.9

Temperature (°F)	Chirping rate (chirps/min)
50	20
55	46
60	79
65	91
70	113
75	140
80	173
85	198
90	211

5. Temperature and Chirping Crickets   Biologists have observed that the chirping rate of crickets of a certain species appears to be related to temperature. The table shows the chirping rates for various temperatures.

(a) Make a scatter plot of the data.

(b) Find and graph the regression line.

(c) Use the linear model in part (b) to estimate the chirping rate at 100°F.

6. Extent of Arctic Sea Ice   The National Snow and Ice Data Center monitors the amount of ice in the Arctic year round. The table gives approximate values for the sea ice extent in millions of square kilometers from 1980 to 2006, in two-year intervals.

(a) Make a scatter plot of the data.

(b) Find and graph the regression line.

(c) Use the linear model in part (b) to estimate the ice extent in the year 2010.

Year	Ice extent (million km²)	Year	Ice extent (million km²)
1980	7.9	1994	7.1
1982	7.4	1996	7.9
1984	7.2	1998	6.6
1986	7.6	2000	6.3
1988	7.5	2002	6.0
1990	6.2	2004	6.1
1992	7.6	2006	5.7

Flow rate (%)	Mosquito positive rate (%)
0	22
10	16
40	12
60	11
90	6
100	2

7. Mosquito Prevalence   The table lists the relative abundance of mosquitoes (as measured by the mosquito positive rate) versus the flow rate (measured as a percentage of maximum flow) of canal networks in Saga City, Japan.

(a) Make a scatter plot of the data.

(b) Find and graph the regression line.

(c) Use the linear model in part (b) to estimate the mosquito positive rate if the canal flow is 70% of maximum.

8. Noise and Intelligibility   Audiologists study the intelligibility of spoken sentences under different noise levels. Intelligibility, the MRT score, is measured as the percent of a spoken sentence that the listener can decipher at a certain noise level in decibels (dB). The table shows the results of one such test.

(a) Make a scatter plot of the data.

(b) Find and graph the regression line.

(c) Find the correlation coefficient. Is a linear model appropriate?

(d) Use the linear model in part (b) to estimate the intelligibility of a sentence at a 94-dB noise level.

Noise level (dB)	MRT score (%)
80	99
84	91
88	84
92	70
96	47
100	23
104	11

9. Life Expectancy   The average life expectancy in the United States has been rising steadily over the past few decades, as shown in the table.

(a) Make a scatter plot of the data.

(b) Find and graph the regression line.

(c) Use the linear model you found in part (b) to predict the life expectancy in the year 2006.

(d) Search the Internet or your campus library to find the actual 2006 average life expectancy. Compare to your answer in part (c).

Year	Life expectancy
1920	54.1
1930	59.7
1940	62.9
1950	68.2
1960	69.7
1970	70.8
1980	73.7
1990	75.4
2000	76.9

10. Olympic Pole Vault   The graph in Figure 7 indicates that in recent years the winning Olympic men's pole vault height has fallen below the value predicted by the regression line in Example 2. This might have occurred because when the pole vault was a new event, there was much room for improvement in vaulters' performances, whereas now even the best training can produce only incremental advances. Let's see whether concentrating on more recent results gives a better predictor of future records.

(a) Use the data in Table 2 to complete the table of winning pole vault heights. (Note that we are using $x = 0$ to correspond to the year 1972, where this restricted data set begins.)

(b) Find the regression line for the data in part (a).

(c) Plot the data and the regression line on the same axes. Does the regression line seem to provide a good model for the data?

(d) What does the regression line predict as the winning pole vault height for the 2008 Olympics? Compare this predicted value to the actual 2008 winning height of 5.96 m, as described on page 133. Has this new regression line provided a better prediction than the line in Example 2?

Year	x	Height (m)
1972	0	5.64
1976	4	
1980	8	
1984		
1988		
1992		
1996		
2000		
2004		

11. **Olympic Swimming Records**   The tables give the gold medal times in the men's and women's 100-m freestyle Olympic swimming event.

   (a) Find the regression lines for the men's data and the women's data.

   (b) Sketch both regression lines on the same graph. When do these lines predict that the women will overtake the men in the event? Does this conclusion seem reasonable?

MEN

Year	Gold medalist	Time (s)
1908	C. Daniels, USA	65.6
1912	D. Kahanamoku, USA	63.4
1920	D. Kahanamoku, USA	61.4
1924	J. Weissmuller, USA	59.0
1928	J. Weissmuller, USA	58.6
1932	Y. Miyazaki, Japan	58.2
1936	F. Csik, Hungary	57.6
1948	W. Ris, USA	57.3
1952	C. Scholes, USA	57.4
1956	J. Henricks, Australia	55.4
1960	J. Devitt, Australia	55.2
1964	D. Schollander, USA	53.4
1968	M. Wenden, Australia	52.2
1972	M. Spitz, USA	51.22
1976	J. Montgomery, USA	49.99
1980	J. Woithe, E. Germany	50.40
1984	R. Gaines, USA	49.80
1988	M. Biondi, USA	48.63
1992	A. Popov, Russia	49.02
1996	A. Popov, Russia	48.74
2000	P. van den Hoogenband, Netherlands	48.30
2004	P. van den Hoogenband, Netherlands	48.17
2008	A. Bernard, France	47.21

WOMEN

Year	Gold medalist	Time (s)
1912	F. Durack, Australia	82.2
1920	E. Bleibtrey, USA	73.6
1924	E. Lackie, USA	72.4
1928	A. Osipowich, USA	71.0
1932	H. Madison, USA	66.8
1936	H. Mastenbroek, Holland	65.9
1948	G. Andersen, Denmark	66.3
1952	K. Szoke, Hungary	66.8
1956	D. Fraser, Australia	62.0
1960	D. Fraser, Australia	61.2
1964	D. Fraser, Australia	59.5
1968	J. Henne, USA	60.0
1972	S. Nielson, USA	58.59
1976	K. Ender, E. Germany	55.65
1980	B. Krause, E. Germany	54.79
1984	(Tie) C. Steinseifer, USA	55.92
	N. Hogshead, USA	55.92
1988	K. Otto, E. Germany	54.93
1992	Z. Yong, China	54.64
1996	L. Jingyi, China	54.50
2000	I. DeBruijn, Netherlands	53.83
2004	J. Henry, Australia	53.84
2008	B. Steffen, Germany	53.12

12. **Shoe Size and Height**   Do you think that shoe size and height are correlated? Find out by surveying the shoe sizes and heights of people in your class. (Of course, the data for men and women should be separate.) Find the correlation coefficient.

13. **Demand for Candy Bars**   In this problem you will determine a linear demand equation that describes the demand for candy bars in your class. Survey your classmates to determine what price they would be willing to pay for a candy bar. Your survey form might look like the sample to the left.

   (a) Make a table of the number of respondents who answered "yes" at each price level.

   (b) Make a scatter plot of your data.

   (c) Find and graph the regression line $y = mp + b$, which gives the number of responents y who would buy a candy bar if the price were p cents. This is the *demand equation*. Why is the slope m negative?

   (d) What is the p-intercept of the demand equation? What does this intercept tell you about pricing candy bars?

Would you buy a candy bar from the vending machine in the hallway if the price is as indicated?

Price	Yes or No
30¢	
40¢	
50¢	
60¢	
70¢	
80¢	
90¢	
$1.00	
$1.10	
$1.20	

Image copyright ArmannWitte 2010.
Used under license from Shutterstock.com

FUNCTIONS

Perhaps the most useful idea for modeling the real world is the concept of *function*. Let's look at an example. If a rock climber drops a stone from a high cliff, we know that the stone will fall. But this general description doesn't help us figure out when the stone will hit the ground. To find out, we need a *rule* that relates the distance d the stone falls to the time it has been falling. Galileo was the first to discover the rule: In t seconds the stone falls $16t^2$ feet. This "rule" is called a *function;* we write this function as $d(t) = 16t^2$. Using this function model, we can *predict* when the stone will hit the ground. In this chapter we study properties of functions and how function models can help us to get precise information about the thing or process being modeled.

$$d(t) = 16t^2$$

General description: The stone falls.   **Function:** In t seconds the stone falls $16t^2$ ft.

141

SUGGESTED TIME AND EMPHASIS

$\frac{1}{2}$–1 class, essential material

2.1 WHAT IS A FUNCTION?

| Functions All Around Us ▶ Definition of Function ▶ Evaluating a Function
| ▶ Domain of a Function ▶ Four Ways to Represent a Function

In this section we explore the idea of a function and then give the mathematical definition of function.

▼ Functions All Around Us

In nearly every physical phenomenon we observe that one quantity depends on another. For example, your height depends on your age, the temperature depends on the date, the cost of mailing a package depends on its weight (see Figure 1). We use the term *function* to describe this dependence of one quantity on another. That is, we say the following:

- Height is a function of age.
- Temperature is a function of date.
- Cost of mailing a package is a function of weight.

The U.S. Post Office uses a simple rule to determine the cost of mailing a first-class parcel on the basis of its weight. But it's not so easy to describe the rule that relates height to age or the rule that relates temperature to date.

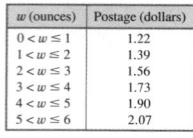

w (ounces)	Postage (dollars)
$0 < w \le 1$	1.22
$1 < w \le 2$	1.39
$2 < w \le 3$	1.56
$3 < w \le 4$	1.73
$4 < w \le 5$	1.90
$5 < w \le 6$	2.07

FIGURE 1   Height is a function of age.   Temperature is a function of date.   Postage is a function of weight.

Can you think of other functions? Here are some more examples:

- The area of a circle is a function of its radius.
- The number of bacteria in a culture is a function of time.
- The weight of an astronaut is a function of her elevation.
- The price of a commodity is a function of the demand for that commodity.

The rule that describes how the area A of a circle depends on its radius r is given by the formula $A = \pi r^2$. Even when a precise rule or formula describing a function is not available, we can still describe the function by a graph. For example, when you turn on a hot water faucet, the temperature of the water depends on how long the water has been running. So we can say:

- The temperature of water from the faucet is a function of time.

Figure 2 shows a rough graph of the temperature T of the water as a function of the time t that has elapsed since the faucet was turned on. The graph shows that the initial temperature of the water is close to room temperature. When the water from the hot water tank reaches the faucet, the water's temperature T increases quickly. In the next phase, T is constant at the temperature of the water in the tank. When the tank is drained, T decreases to the temperature of the cold water supply.

TEXT QUESTION
What is a function?

Answer
Answers will vary. Anything that gets at the idea of assigning an element in one set to an element in another set should be given full credit.

FIGURE 2 Graph of water temperature T as a function of time t

▼ Definition of Function

We have previously used letters to stand for numbers. Here we do something quite different: We use letters to represent *rules*.

A function is a rule. To talk about a function, we need to give it a name. We will use letters such as $f, g, h, \ldots$ to represent functions. For example, we can use the letter f to represent a rule as follows:

"f" is the rule "square the number"

When we write $f(2)$, we mean "apply the rule f to the number 2." Applying the rule gives $f(2) = 2^2 = 4$. Similarly, $f(3) = 3^2 = 9$, $f(4) = 4^2 = 16$, and in general $f(x) = x^2$.

DEFINITION OF A FUNCTION

A **function** f is a rule that assigns to each element x in a set A exactly one element, called $f(x)$, in a set B.

The $\boxed{\sqrt{}}$ key on your calculator is a good example of a function as a machine. First you input x into the display. Then you press the key labeled $\boxed{\sqrt{}}$. (On most *graphing* calculators the order of these operations is reversed.) If $x < 0$, then x is not in the domain of this function; that is, x is not an acceptable input, and the calculator will indicate an error. If $x \geq 0$, then an approximation to $\sqrt{x}$ appears in the display, correct to a certain number of decimal places. (Thus, the $\boxed{\sqrt{}}$ key on your calculator is not quite the same as the exact mathematical function f defined by $f(x) = \sqrt{x}$.)

We usually consider functions for which the sets A and B are sets of real numbers. The symbol $f(x)$ is read "f of x" or "f at x" and is called the **value of f at x**, or the **image of x under f**. The set A is called the **domain** of the function. The **range** of f is the set of all possible values of $f(x)$ as x varies throughout the domain, that is,

$$\text{range of } f = \{f(x) \mid x \in A\}$$

The symbol that represents an arbitrary number in the domain of a function f is called an **independent variable**. The symbol that represents a number in the range of f is called a **dependent variable**. So if we write $y = f(x)$, then x is the independent variable and y is the dependent variable.

It is helpful to think of a function as a **machine** (see Figure 3). If x is in the domain of the function f, then when x enters the machine, it is accepted as an **input** and the machine produces an **output** $f(x)$ according to the rule of the function. Thus, we can think of the domain as the set of all possible inputs and the range as the set of all possible outputs.

FIGURE 3 Machine diagram of f

Another way to picture a function is by an **arrow diagram** as in Figure 4. Each arrow connects an element of A to an element of B. The arrow indicates that $f(x)$ is associated with x, $f(a)$ is associated with a, and so on.

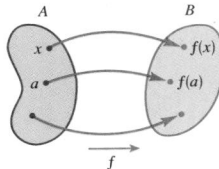

FIGURE 4 Arrow diagram of f

IN-CLASS MATERIALS

If students are using calculators, discuss the ties between the idea of a function and a calculator key. The keys such as sin, cos, tan, and $\sqrt{}$ represent functions. It is easy to compute and graph functions on a calculator. Contrast this with equations such as $y^3 - x^3 = 2xy$, which have graphs but are not easy to work with, even with a calculator. (Even symbolic algebra calculators such as the *TI*–89 do not do well with all general relations.) Point out that the calculator often gives approximations to function values—applying the square root function key to the number 2 gives 1.4142136, which is close, but not equal, to $\sqrt{2}$.

ALTERNATE EXAMPLE 1

A function f is defined by the formula $f(x) = 3x^4 - 2$.

(a) Express in words how f acts on the input x to produce the output $f(x)$.

(b) Evaluate $f(2), f(-1)$, and $f(\pi)$.

(c) Find the domain and range of f.

ANSWERS

(a) Raise to the fourth power, multiply by 3, and then subtract 2.

(b) $46, 1, 3\pi^4 - 2$

(c) Domain: the set of all real numbers, Range: $[-2, \infty)$

ALTERNATE EXAMPLE 2

(a) Let $f(x) = 5x^2 + x - 6$.
Evaluate the function value $f(-5)$.

(b) Let $f(x) = 3x^2 + x - 6$.
Evaluate the function value $f(5)$.

(c) Let $f(x) = 3x^2 + x - 7$.
Evaluate the function value $f\left(\dfrac{1}{6}\right)$.

ANSWERS

(a) $f(-5) = 114$

(b) $f(5) = 74$

(c) $f\left(\dfrac{1}{6}\right) = -\dfrac{27}{4}$

EXAMPLE 1 | Analyzing a Function

A function f is defined by the formula

$$f(x) = x^2 + 4$$

(a) Express in words how f acts on the input x to produce the output $f(x)$.

(b) Evaluate $f(3), f(-2)$, and $f(\sqrt{5})$.

(c) Find the domain and range of f.

(d) Draw a machine diagram for f.

SOLUTION

(a) The formula tells us that f first squares the input x and then adds 4 to the result. So f is the function

"square, then add 4"

(b) The values of f are found by substituting for x in the formula $f(x) = x^2 + 4$.

$$f(3) = 3^2 + 4 = 13 \qquad \text{Replace } x \text{ by } 3$$
$$f(-2) = (-2)^2 + 4 = 8 \qquad \text{Replace } x \text{ by } {-2}$$
$$f(\sqrt{5}) = (\sqrt{5})^2 + 4 = 9 \qquad \text{Replace } x \text{ by } \sqrt{5}$$

(c) The domain of f consists of all possible inputs for f. Since we can evaluate the formula $f(x) = x^2 + 4$ for every real number x, the domain of f is the set $\mathbb{R}$ of all real numbers.

The range of f consists of all possible outputs of f. Because $x^2 \geq 0$ for all real numbers x, we have $x^2 + 4 \geq 4$, so for every output of f we have $f(x) \geq 4$. Thus, the range of f is $\{y \mid y \geq 4\} = [4, \infty)$.

(d) A machine diagram for f is shown in Figure 5.

FIGURE 5 Machine diagram

✎. NOW TRY EXERCISES **9, 13, 17**, AND **43** ∎

▼ Evaluating a Function

In the definition of a function the independent variable x plays the role of a placeholder. For example, the function $f(x) = 3x^2 + x - 5$ can be thought of as

$$f(\;\blacksquare\;) = 3 \cdot \blacksquare^2 + \blacksquare - 5$$

To evaluate f at a number, we substitute the number for the placeholder.

EXAMPLE 2 | Evaluating a Function

Let $f(x) = 3x^2 + x - 5$. Evaluate each function value.

(a) $f(-2)$ (b) $f(0)$ (c) $f(4)$ (d) $f\left(\frac{1}{2}\right)$

SOLUTION To evaluate f at a number, we substitute the number for x in the definition of f.

(a) $f(-2) = 3 \cdot (-2)^2 + (-2) - 5 = 5$

(b) $f(0) = 3 \cdot 0^2 + 0 - 5 = -5$

(c) $f(4) = 3 \cdot (4)^2 + 4 - 5 = 47$

(d) $f\left(\frac{1}{2}\right) = 3 \cdot \left(\frac{1}{2}\right)^2 + \frac{1}{2} - 5 = -\frac{15}{4}$

✎. NOW TRY EXERCISE **19** ∎

IN-CLASS MATERIALS

This course emphasizes functions where both the domain and range sets are numeric. One could give a more abstract definition of function, where D and R can be any set. For example, there is a function mapping each student in the class to his or her birthplace. A nice thing about this point of view is that it can be pointed out that the map from each student to his or her telephone number may *not* be a function, because a student may have more than one telephone number, or none at all.

EXAMPLE 3 | A Piecewise Defined Function

A cell phone plan costs $39 a month. The plan includes 400 free minutes and charges 20¢ for each additional minute of usage. The monthly charges are a function of the number of minutes used, given by

$$C(x) = \begin{cases} 39 & \text{if } 0 \le x \le 400 \\ 39 + 0.20(x - 400) & \text{if } x > 400 \end{cases}$$

Find $C(100)$, $C(400)$, and $C(480)$.

SOLUTION Remember that a function is a rule. Here is how we apply the rule for this function. First we look at the value of the input x. If $0 \le x \le 400$, then the value of $C(x)$ is 39. On the other hand, if $x > 400$, then the value of $C(x)$ is $39 + 0.20(x - 400)$.

Since $100 \le 400$, we have $C(100) = 39$.
Since $400 \le 400$, we have $C(400) = 39$.
Since $480 > 400$, we have $C(480) = 39 + 0.20(480 - 400) = 55$.

Thus, the plan charges $39 for 100 minutes, $39 for 400 minutes, and $55 for 480 minutes.

A **piecewise defined function** is defined by different formulas on different parts of its domain. The function C of Example 3 is piecewise defined.

🖎 NOW TRY EXERCISE **27** ■

EXAMPLE 4 | Evaluating a Function

If $f(x) = 2x^2 + 3x - 1$, evaluate the following.

(a) $f(a)$ **(b)** $f(-a)$

(c) $f(a + h)$ **(d)** $\dfrac{f(a + h) - f(a)}{h}$, $h \ne 0$

Expressions like the one in part (d) of Example 4 occur frequently in calculus; they are called *difference quotients*, and they represent the average change in the value of f between $x = a$ and $x = a + h$.

SOLUTION

(a) $f(a) = 2a^2 + 3a - 1$

(b) $f(-a) = 2(-a)^2 + 3(-a) - 1 = 2a^2 - 3a - 1$

(c) $f(a + h) = 2(a + h)^2 + 3(a + h) - 1$

$$= 2(a^2 + 2ah + h^2) + 3(a + h) - 1$$

$$= 2a^2 + 4ah + 2h^2 + 3a + 3h - 1$$

(d) Using the results from parts (c) and (a), we have

$$\frac{f(a + h) - f(a)}{h} = \frac{(2a^2 + 4ah + 2h^2 + 3a + 3h - 1) - (2a^2 + 3a - 1)}{h}$$

$$= \frac{4ah + 2h^2 + 3h}{h} = 4a + 2h + 3$$

🖎 NOW TRY EXERCISE **35** ■

EXAMPLE 5 | The Weight of an Astronaut

If an astronaut weighs 130 pounds on the surface of the earth, then her weight when she is h miles above the earth is given by the function

$$w(h) = 130\left(\frac{3960}{3960 + h}\right)^2$$

(a) What is her weight when she is 100 mi above the earth?

ALTERNATE EXAMPLE 3
Evaluate the following function at $x = 1$, $x = 3$, and $x = 5$.

$$f(x) = \begin{cases} 3 - x & \text{if } x \le 3 \\ x^2 & \text{if } x > 3 \end{cases}$$

ANSWER
$f(1) = 2$, $f(3) = 0$, and $f(5) = 25$

ALTERNATE EXAMPLE 4
(a) If $f(x) = 3x^2 + 4x - 1$, evaluate $f(a + h)$.
(b) If $f(x) = 2x^2 + 4x - 1$, evaluate

$$\frac{f(a + h) - f(a)}{h}, h \ne 0.$$

ANSWERS
(a)
$3a^2 + 6a \cdot h + 3h^2 + 4a + 4h - 1$
(b) $4a + 2h + 4$

IN-CLASS MATERIALS

Function notation can trip students up. Start with a function such as $f(x) = x^2 - x$ and have your students find $f(0)$, $f(1)$, $f(\sqrt{3})$, and $f(-1)$. Then have them find $f(\pi)$, $f(y)$, and (of course) $f(x + h)$. Some students will invariably, some day, assume that $f(a + b) = f(a) + f(b)$ for all functions, but this can be minimized if plenty of examples such as $f(2 + 3)$ are done at the outset.

ALTERNATE EXAMPLE 5

If the speed limit on a 100-mile stretch of road is 75 miles per hour, then the amount of time it takes a car going x miles per hour over the limit to traverse the stretch is given by $t(x) = \dfrac{100}{75 + x}$.

(a) How long does it take the car to travel the stretch if the car is going 10 miles per hour over the limit?

(b) How long does it take the car to travel the stretch if the car is not speeding at all?

(c) Construct a table of values giving the travel time for x values from 0 to 40 miles per hour. What do you conclude from the table?

ANSWERS

(a) We want the value of the function t when $x = 10$.
$$t(10) = \frac{100}{75 + 10}$$
$$\approx 1.18 \text{ hours}$$

(b) We want the value of the function t when $x = 0$.
$$t(10) = \frac{100}{75 + 0}$$
$$\approx 1.33 \text{ hours}$$

(c) The table gives the travel time, rounded to two decimal places, in 5-mile increments. The values of the table are calculated as in parts (a) and (b).

x	$t(x)$
0	1.33
5	1.25
10	1.18
15	1.11
20	1.05
25	1.00
30	0.95
35	0.90
40	0.87

We can conclude that the more the car speeds, the less time it takes to make the trip, but after a certain point, the time saved isn't all that much.

The weight of an object on or near the earth is the gravitational force that the earth exerts on it. When in orbit around the earth, an astronaut experiences the sensation of "weightlessness" because the centripetal force that keeps her in orbit is exactly the same as the gravitational pull of the earth.

Domains of algebraic expressions are discussed on page 35.

(b) Construct a table of values for the function w that gives her weight at heights from 0 to 500 mi. What do you conclude from the table?

SOLUTION

(a) We want the value of the function w when $h = 100$; that is, we must calculate $w(100)$.

$$w(100) = 130\left(\frac{3960}{3960 + 100}\right)^2 \approx 123.67$$

So at a height of 100 mi she weighs about 124 lb.

(b) The table gives the astronaut's weight, rounded to the nearest pound, at 100-mile increments. The values in the table are calculated as in part (a).

h	$w(h)$
0	130
100	124
200	118
300	112
400	107
500	102

The table indicates that the higher the astronaut travels, the less she weighs.

✎ NOW TRY EXERCISE **71**

▼ The Domain of a Function

Recall that the *domain* of a function is the set of all inputs for the function. The domain of a function may be stated explicitly. For example, if we write

$$f(x) = x^2 \qquad 0 \le x \le 5$$

then the domain is the set of all real numbers x for which $0 \le x \le 5$. If the function is given by an algebraic expression and the domain is not stated explicitly, then by convention *the domain of the function is the domain of the algebraic expression—that is, the set of all real numbers for which the expression is defined as a real number*. For example, consider the functions

$$f(x) = \frac{1}{x - 4} \qquad g(x) = \sqrt{x}$$

The function f is not defined at $x = 4$, so its domain is $\{x \mid x \ne 4\}$. The function g is not defined for negative x, so its domain is $\{x \mid x \ge 0\}$.

EXAMPLE 6 | Finding Domains of Functions

Find the domain of each function.

(a) $f(x) = \dfrac{1}{x^2 - x}$ **(b)** $g(x) = \sqrt{9 - x^2}$ **(c)** $h(t) = \dfrac{t}{\sqrt{t + 1}}$

IN-CLASS MATERIALS

Discuss the straightforward things to look for when trying to find the domain of a function: zero denominators and negative even roots. Discuss the domain and range of a function such as

$$f(x) = \begin{cases} x^2 & \text{if } x \text{ is an integer} \\ 0 & \text{if } x \text{ is not an integer} \end{cases}$$

If the class seems interested, perhaps let them think about

$$f(x) = \begin{cases} x^2 & \text{if } x \text{ is rational} \\ 0 & \text{if } x \text{ is irrational} \end{cases}$$

Let $f(x) = \dfrac{x(x - 2)}{(x - 2)}$ and $g(x) = x$. Ask students if the functions are the same function. If they say "yes," ask them to compare the domains or to compute $g(2)$ and $f(2)$. If they say "no," ask them to find a value such that $f(x) \ne g(x)$.

ALTERNATE EXAMPLE 6
(a) Find the domain of the
    function $f(x) = \dfrac{4}{x^2 + x}$.
(b) Find the domain of the
    function $g(x) = \sqrt{16 - x^2}$.

ANSWERS
(a)
$(-\infty, -1) \cup (-1, 0) \cup (0, \infty)$
(b) $[-4, 4]$

SOLUTION

(a) A rational expression is not defined when the denominator is 0. Since

$$f(x) = \frac{1}{x^2 - x} = \frac{1}{x(x - 1)}$$

we see that $f(x)$ is not defined when $x = 0$ or $x = 1$. Thus, the domain of f is

$$\{x \mid x \neq 0, x \neq 1\}$$

The domain may also be written in interval notation as

$$(\infty, 0) \cup (0, 1) \cup (1, \infty)$$

(b) We can't take the square root of a negative number, so we must have $9 - x^2 \geq 0$. Using the methods of Section 1.7, we can solve this inequality to find that $-3 \leq x \leq 3$. Thus, the domain of g is

$$\{x \mid -3 \leq x \leq 3\} = [-3, 3]$$

(c) We can't take the square root of a negative number, and we can't divide by 0, so we must have $t + 1 > 0$, that is, $t > -1$. So the domain of h is

$$\{t \mid t > -1\} = (-1, \infty)$$

✎ NOW TRY EXERCISES **47** AND **51**   ■

▼ Four Ways to Represent a Function

To help us understand what a function is, we have used machine and arrow diagrams. We can describe a specific function in the following four ways:

- verbally (by a description in words)
- algebraically (by an explicit formula)
- visually (by a graph)
- numerically (by a table of values)

A single function may be represented in all four ways, and it is often useful to go from one representation to another to gain insight into the function. However, certain functions are described more naturally by one method than by the others. An example of a verbal description is the following rule for converting between temperature scales:

"To find the Fahrenheit equivalent of a Celsius temperature, multiply the Celsius temperature by $\frac{9}{5}$, then add 32."

In Example 7 we see how to describe this verbal rule or function algebraically, graphically, and numerically. A useful representation of the area of a circle as a function of its radius is the algebraic formula

$$A(r) = \pi r^2$$

The graph produced by a seismograph (see the box on the next page) is a visual representation of the vertical acceleration function $a(t)$ of the ground during an earthquake. As a final example, consider the function $C(w)$, which is described verbally as "the cost of mailing a first-class letter with weight w." The most convenient way of describing this function is numerically—that is, using a table of values.

We will be using all four representations of functions throughout this book. We summarize them in the following box.

IN-CLASS MATERIALS

Real-world piecewise functions:

1. The cost of mailing a letter that weighs x ounces (see Exercise 83 in Section 2.2)
2. The cost of making x photocopies (given that there is usually a bulk discount)
3. The cost of printing x pages from a computer (at some point the toner cartridge must be replaced)

ALTERNATE EXAMPLE 7

To find the volume of a cone of height 5, square the radius, and multiply by $\frac{5}{3}\pi$. Let f be the function that converts a radius r into the volume of a cone of height 5 with radius r.

Find ways to represent this function:

(a) Algebraically (using formula)
(b) Numerically (using a table of values)
(c) Visually (using a graph)

ANSWERS

(a) $f(r) = \frac{5}{3}\pi r^2$

(b)

r	$f(r)$
1	$\frac{5}{3}\pi \approx 5.236$
2	$\frac{20}{3}\pi \approx 20.944$
3	$\frac{45}{3}\pi \approx 47.124$
4	$\frac{80}{3}\pi \approx 83.776$
5	$\frac{125}{3}\pi \approx 130.900$

(c)

FOUR WAYS TO REPRESENT A FUNCTION

Verbal

Using words:

"To convert from Celsius to Fahrenheit, multiply the Celsius temperature by $\frac{9}{5}$, then add 32."

Relation between Celsius and Fahrenheit temperature scales

Algebraic

Using a formula:

$$A(r) = \pi r^2$$

Area of a circle

Visual

Using a graph:

Vertical acceleration during an earthquake

Source: California Department of Mines and Geology

Numerical

Using a table of values:

w (ounces)	$C(w)$ (dollars)
$0 < w \le 1$	1.22
$1 < w \le 2$	1.39
$2 < w \le 3$	1.56
$3 < w \le 4$	1.73
$4 < w \le 5$	1.90
⋮	⋮

Cost of mailing a first-class parcel

EXAMPLE 7 | Representing a Function Verbally, Algebraically, Numerically, and Graphically

Let $F(C)$ be the Fahrenheit temperature corresponding to the Celsius temperature C. (Thus, F is the function that converts Celsius inputs to Fahrenheit outputs.) The box above gives a verbal description of this function. Find ways to represent this function

(a) Algebraically (using a formula)
(b) Numerically (using a table of values)
(c) Visually (using a graph)

SOLUTION

(a) The verbal description tells us that we should first multiply the input C by $\frac{9}{5}$ and then add 32 to the result. So we get

$$F(C) = \tfrac{9}{5}C + 32$$

(b) We use the algebraic formula for F that we found in part (a) to construct a table of values:

C (Celsius)	F (Fahrenheit)
-10	14
0	32
10	50
20	68
30	86
40	104

EXAMPLE

A function with a nontrivial domain $\dfrac{\sqrt{x^2 - 5x + 6}}{x^2 - 2x + 1}$ has domain $(-\infty, 1) \cup (1, 2] \cup [3, \infty)$.

DRILL QUESTION

Let $f(x) = x + \sqrt{x}$. Find $f(0)$ and $f(4)$.

Answer

$f(0) = 0, f(4) = 6$

(c) We use the points tabulated in part (b) to help us draw the graph of this function in Figure 6.

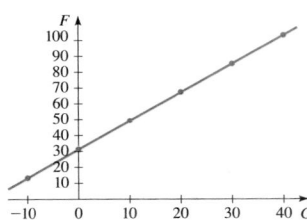

FIGURE 6 Celsius and Fahrenheit

.- NOW TRY EXERCISE **65**

2.1 EXERCISES

CONCEPTS

1. If a function f is given by the formula $y = f(x)$, then $f(a)$ is the

_____ of f at $x = a$.

2. For a function f, the set of all possible inputs is called the

_____ of f, and the set of all possible outputs is called the

_____ of f.

3. (a) Which of the following functions have 5 in their domain?

$$f(x) = x^2 - 3x \qquad g(x) = \frac{x-5}{x} \qquad h(x) = \sqrt{x-10}$$

(b) For the functions from part (a) that *do* have 5 in their domain, find the value of the function at 5.

4. A function is given algebraically by the formula $f(x) = (x-4)^2 + 3$. Complete these other ways to represent f:

(a) *Verbal:* "Subtract 4, then _____ and _____.

(b) *Numerical:*

x	$f(x)$
0	19
2	
4	
6	

SKILLS

5–8 ■ Express the rule in function notation. (For example, the rule "square, then subtract 5" is expressed as the function $f(x) = x^2 - 5$.)

5. Add 3, then multiply by 2   **6.** Divide by 7, then subtract 4

7. Subtract 5, then square

8. Take the square root, add 8, then multiply by $\frac{1}{3}$

9–12 ■ Express the function (or rule) in words.

9. $h(x) = x^2 + 2$ **10.** $k(x) = \sqrt{x+2}$

11. $f(x) = \dfrac{x-4}{3}$ **12.** $g(x) = \dfrac{x}{3} - 4$

13–14 ■ Draw a machine diagram for the function.

13. $f(x) = \sqrt{x-1}$ **14.** $f(x) = \dfrac{3}{x-2}$

15–16 ■ Complete the table.

15. $f(x) = 2(x-1)^2$ **16.** $g(x) = |2x+3|$

x	$f(x)$
−1	
0	
1	
2	
3	

x	$g(x)$
−3	
−2	
0	
1	
3	

17–26 ■ Evaluate the function at the indicated values.

17. $f(x) = x^2 - 6$; $f(-3), f(3), f(0), f(\frac{1}{2}), f(10)$

18. $f(x) = x^3 + 2x$; $f(-2), f(1), f(0), f(\frac{1}{3}), f(0.2)$

19. $f(x) = 2x + 1$;

$f(1), f(-2), f(\frac{1}{2}), f(a), f(-a), f(a+b)$

20. $f(x) = x^2 + 2x$;

$f(0), f(3), f(-3), f(a), f(-x), f\left(\dfrac{1}{a}\right)$

21. $g(x) = \dfrac{1-x}{1+x}$;

$g(2), g(-2), g(\frac{1}{2}), g(a), g(a-1), g(-1)$

22. $h(t) = t + \dfrac{1}{t}$;

$h(1), h(-1), h(2), h\left(\dfrac{1}{2}\right), h(x), h\left(\dfrac{1}{x}\right)$

23. $f(x) = 2x^2 + 3x - 4$;

$f(0), f(2), f(-2), f(\sqrt{2}), f(x + 1), f(-x)$

24. $f(x) = x^3 - 4x^2$;

$f(0), f(1), f(-1), f\left(\dfrac{3}{2}\right), f\left(\dfrac{x}{2}\right), f(x^2)$

25. $f(x) = 2|x - 1|$;

$f(-2), f(0), f\left(\dfrac{1}{2}\right), f(2), f(x + 1), f(x^2 + 2)$

26. $f(x) = \dfrac{|x|}{x}$;

$f(-2), f(-1), f(0), f(5), f(x^2), f\left(\dfrac{1}{x}\right)$

27–30 ■ Evaluate the piecewise defined function at the indicated values.

27. $f(x) = \begin{cases} x^2 & \text{if } x < 0 \\ x + 1 & \text{if } x \ge 0 \end{cases}$

$f(-2), f(-1), f(0), f(1), f(2)$

28. $f(x) = \begin{cases} 5 & \text{if } x \le 2 \\ 2x - 3 & \text{if } x > 2 \end{cases}$

$f(-3), f(0), f(2), f(3), f(5)$

29. $f(x) = \begin{cases} x^2 + 2x & \text{if } x \le -1 \\ x & \text{if } -1 < x \le 1 \\ -1 & \text{if } x > 1 \end{cases}$

$f(-4), f\left(-\dfrac{3}{2}\right), f(-1), f(0), f(25)$

30. $f(x) = \begin{cases} 3x & \text{if } x < 0 \\ x + 1 & \text{if } 0 \le x \le 2 \\ (x - 2)^2 & \text{if } x > 2 \end{cases}$

$f(-5), f(0), f(1), f(2), f(5)$

31–34 ■ Use the function to evaluate the indicated expressions and simplify.

31. $f(x) = x^2 + 1$; $f(x + 2), f(x) + f(2)$

32. $f(x) = 3x - 1$; $f(2x), 2f(x)$

33. $f(x) = x + 4$; $f(x^2), (f(x))^2$

34. $f(x) = 6x - 18$; $f\left(\dfrac{x}{3}\right), \dfrac{f(x)}{3}$

35–42 ■ Find $f(a)$, $f(a + h)$, and the difference quotient $\dfrac{f(a + h) - f(a)}{h}$, where $h \ne 0$.

35. $f(x) = 3x + 2$

36. $f(x) = x^2 + 1$

37. $f(x) = 5$

38. $f(x) = \dfrac{1}{x + 1}$

39. $f(x) = \dfrac{x}{x + 1}$

40. $f(x) = \dfrac{2x}{x - 1}$

41. $f(x) = 3 - 5x + 4x^2$

42. $f(x) = x^3$

43–64 ■ Find the domain of the function.

43. $f(x) = 2x$

44. $f(x) = x^2 + 1$

45. $f(x) = 2x, \quad -1 \le x \le 5$

46. $f(x) = x^2 + 1, \quad 0 \le x \le 5$

47. $f(x) = \dfrac{1}{x - 3}$

48. $f(x) = \dfrac{1}{3x - 6}$

49. $f(x) = \dfrac{x + 2}{x^2 - 1}$

50. $f(x) = \dfrac{x^4}{x^2 + x - 6}$

51. $f(x) = \sqrt{x - 5}$

52. $f(x) = \sqrt[4]{x + 9}$

53. $f(t) = \sqrt[3]{t - 1}$

54. $g(x) = \sqrt{7 - 3x}$

55. $h(x) = \sqrt{2x - 5}$

56. $G(x) = \sqrt{x^2 - 9}$

57. $g(x) = \dfrac{\sqrt{2 + x}}{3 - x}$

58. $g(x) = \dfrac{\sqrt{x}}{2x^2 + x - 1}$

59. $g(x) = \sqrt[4]{x^2 - 6x}$

60. $g(x) = \sqrt{x^2 - 2x - 8}$

61. $f(x) = \dfrac{3}{\sqrt{x - 4}}$

62. $f(x) = \dfrac{x^2}{\sqrt{6 - x}}$

63. $f(x) = \dfrac{(x + 1)^2}{\sqrt{2x - 1}}$

64. $f(x) = \dfrac{x}{\sqrt[4]{9 - x^2}}$

65–68 ■ A verbal description of a function is given. Find **(a)** algebraic, **(b)** numerical, and **(c)** graphical representations for the function.

65. To evaluate $f(x)$, divide the input by 3 and add $\dfrac{2}{3}$ to the result.

66. To evaluate $g(x)$, subtract 4 from the input and multiply the result by $\dfrac{3}{4}$.

67. Let $T(x)$ be the amount of sales tax charged in Lemon County on a purchase of x dollars. To find the tax, take 8% of the purchase price.

68. Let $V(d)$ be the volume of a sphere of diameter d. To find the volume, take the cube of the diameter, then multiply by π and divide by 6.

APPLICATIONS

69. Production Cost   The cost C in dollars of producing x yards of a certain fabric is given by the function

$$C(x) = 1500 + 3x + 0.02x^2 + 0.0001x^3$$

(a) Find $C(10)$ and $C(100)$.

(b) What do your answers in part (a) represent?

(c) Find $C(0)$. (This number represents the *fixed costs*.)

70. Area of a Sphere The surface area S of a sphere is a function of its radius r given by

$$S(r) = 4\pi r^2$$

(a) Find $S(2)$ and $S(3)$.
(b) What do your answers in part (a) represent?

71. Torricelli's Law A tank holds 50 gallons of water, which drains from a leak at the bottom, causing the tank to empty in 20 minutes. The tank drains faster when it is nearly full because the pressure on the leak is greater. **Torricelli's Law** gives the volume of water remaining in the tank after t minutes as

$$V(t) = 50\left(1 - \frac{t}{20}\right)^2 \qquad 0 \le t \le 20$$

(a) Find $V(0)$ and $V(20)$.
(b) What do your answers to part (a) represent?
(c) Make a table of values of $V(t)$ for $t = 0, 5, 10, 15, 20$.

72. How Far Can You See? Because of the curvature of the earth, the maximum distance D that you can see from the top of a tall building or from an airplane at height h is given by the function

$$D(h) = \sqrt{2rh + h^2}$$

where $r = 3960$ mi is the radius of the earth and D and h are measured in miles.
(a) Find $D(0.1)$ and $D(0.2)$.
(b) How far can you see from the observation deck of Toronto's CN Tower, 1135 ft above the ground?
(c) Commercial aircraft fly at an altitude of about 7 mi. How far can the pilot see?

73. Blood Flow As blood moves through a vein or an artery, its velocity v is greatest along the central axis and decreases as the distance r from the central axis increases (see the figure). The formula that gives v as a function of r is called the **law of laminar flow**. For an artery with radius 0.5 cm, the relationship between v (in cm/s) and r (in cm) is given by the function

$$v(r) = 18,500(0.25 - r^2) \qquad 0 \le r \le 0.5$$

(a) Find $v(0.1)$ and $v(0.4)$.
(b) What do your answers to part (a) tell you about the flow of blood in this artery?
(c) Make a table of values of $v(r)$ for $r = 0, 0.1, 0.2, 0.3, 0.4, 0.5$.

74. Pupil Size When the brightness x of a light source is increased, the eye reacts by decreasing the radius R of the pupil. The dependence of R on x is given by the function

$$R(x) = \sqrt{\frac{13 + 7x^{0.4}}{1 + 4x^{0.4}}}$$

where R is measured in millimeters and x is measured in appropriate units of brightness.
(a) Find $R(1)$, $R(10)$, and $R(100)$.
(b) Make a table of values of $R(x)$.

75. Relativity According to the Theory of Relativity, the length L of an object is a function of its velocity v with respect to an observer. For an object whose length at rest is 10 m, the function is given by

$$L(v) = 10\sqrt{1 - \frac{v^2}{c^2}}$$

where c is the speed of light (300,000 km/s).
(a) Find $L(0.5c)$, $L(0.75c)$, and $L(0.9c)$.
(b) How does the length of an object change as its velocity increases?

76. Income Tax In a certain country, income tax T is assessed according to the following function of income x:

$$T(x) = \begin{cases} 0 & \text{if } 0 \le x \le 10{,}000 \\ 0.08x & \text{if } 10{,}000 < x \le 20{,}000 \\ 1600 + 0.15x & \text{if } 20{,}000 < x \end{cases}$$

(a) Find $T(5{,}000)$, $T(12{,}000)$, and $T(25{,}000)$.
(b) What do your answers in part (a) represent?

77. Internet Purchases An Internet bookstore charges $15 shipping for orders under $100 but provides free shipping for orders of $100 or more. The cost C of an order is a function of the total price x of the books purchased, given by

$$C(x) = \begin{cases} x + 15 & \text{if } x < 100 \\ x & \text{if } x \ge 100 \end{cases}$$

(a) Find $C(75)$, $C(90)$, $C(100)$, and $C(105)$.
(b) What do your answers in part (a) represent?

78. Cost of a Hotel Stay A hotel chain charges $75 each night for the first two nights and $50 for each additional night's stay. The total cost T is a function of the number of nights x that a guest stays.

(a) Complete the expressions in the following piecewise defined function.

$$T(x) = \begin{cases} \rule{1cm}{0.3cm} & \text{if } 0 \leq x \leq 2 \\ \rule{1cm}{0.3cm} & \text{if } x > 2 \end{cases}$$

(b) Find $T(2)$, $T(3)$, and $T(5)$.

(c) What do your answers in part (b) represent?

79. Speeding Tickets   In a certain state the maximum speed permitted on freeways is 65 mi/h, and the minimum is 40. The fine F for violating these limits is $15 for every mile above the maximum or below the minimum.

(a) Complete the expressions in the following piecewise defined function, where x is the speed at which you are driving.

$$F(x) = \begin{cases} \rule{1cm}{0.3cm} & \text{if } 0 < x < 40 \\ \rule{1cm}{0.3cm} & \text{if } 40 \leq x \leq 65 \\ \rule{1cm}{0.3cm} & \text{if } x > 65 \end{cases}$$

(b) Find $F(30)$, $F(50)$, and $F(75)$.

(c) What do your answers in part (b) represent?

80. Height of Grass   A home owner mows the lawn every Wednesday afternoon. Sketch a rough graph of the height of the grass as a function of time over the course of a four-week period beginning on a Sunday.

81. Temperature Change   You place a frozen pie in an oven and bake it for an hour. Then you take the pie out and let it cool before eating it. Sketch a rough graph of the temperature of the pie as a function of time.

82. Daily Temperature Change   Temperature readings T (in °F) were recorded every 2 hours from midnight to noon in Atlanta, Georgia, on March 18, 1996. The time t was measured in hours from midnight. Sketch a rough graph of T as a function of t.

t	0	2	4	6	8	10	12
T	58	57	53	50	51	57	61

83. Population Growth   The population P (in thousands) of San Jose, California, from 1988 to 2000 is shown in the table. (Midyear estimates are given.) Draw a rough graph of P as a function of time t.

t	1988	1990	1992	1994	1996	1998	2000
P	733	782	800	817	838	861	895

DISCOVERY ▪ DISCUSSION ▪ WRITING

84. Examples of Functions   At the beginning of this section we discussed three examples of everyday, ordinary functions: Height is a function of age, temperature is a function of date, and postage cost is a function of weight. Give three other examples of functions from everyday life.

85. Four Ways to Represent a Function   In the box on page 148 we represented four different functions verbally, algebraically, visually, and numerically. Think of a function that can be represented in all four ways, and write the four representations.

SUGGESTED TIME AND EMPHASIS

1 class, essential material

2.2   GRAPHS OF FUNCTIONS

Graphing Functions by Plotting Points ▶ Graphing Functions with a Graphing Calculator ▶ Graphing Piecewise Defined Functions ▶ The Vertical Line Test ▶ Equations That Define Functions

The most important way to visualize a function is through its graph. In this section we investigate in more detail the concept of graphing functions.

▼ Graphing Functions by Plotting Points

To graph a function f, we plot the points $(x, f(x))$ in a coordinate plane. In other words, we plot the points (x, y) whose x-coordinate is an input and whose y-coordinate is the corresponding output of the function.

TEXT QUESTION

Your text discusses the greatest integer function $[\![x]\!]$. Compute $[\![2.6]\!]$, $[\![2]\!]$, $[\![-2.6]\!]$, and $[\![-2]\!]$.

Answer

$[\![2.6]\!] = 2$, $[\![2]\!] = 2$, $[\![-2.6]\!] = -3$, $[\![-2]\!] = -2$

THE GRAPH OF A FUNCTION

If f is a function with domain A, then the **graph** of f is the set of ordered pairs

$$\{(x, f(x)) \mid x \in A\}$$

plotted in a coordinate plane. In other words, the graph of f is the set of all points (x, y) such that $y = f(x)$; that is, the graph of f is the graph of the equation $y = f(x)$.

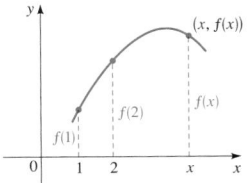

FIGURE 1 The height of the graph above the point x is the value of $f(x)$.

The graph of a function f gives a picture of the behavior or "life history" of the function. We can read the value of $f(x)$ from the graph as being the height of the graph above the point x (see Figure 1).

A function f of the form $f(x) = mx + b$ is called a **linear function** because its graph is the graph of the equation $y = mx + b$, which represents a line with slope m and y-intercept b. A special case of a linear function occurs when the slope is $m = 0$. The function $f(x) = b$, where b is a given number, is called a **constant function** because all its values are the same number, namely, b. Its graph is the horizontal line $y = b$. Figure 2 shows the graphs of the constant function $f(x) = 3$ and the linear function $f(x) = 2x + 1$.

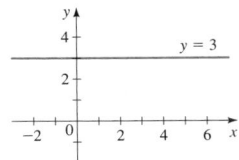

The constant function $f(x) = 3$

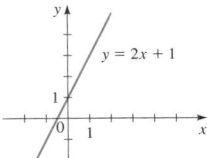

The linear function $f(x) = 2x + 1$

FIGURE 2

EXAMPLE 1 | Graphing Functions by Plotting Points

Sketch graphs of the following functions.

(a) $f(x) = x^2$ **(b)** $g(x) = x^3$ **(c)** $h(x) = \sqrt{x}$

SOLUTION We first make a table of values. Then we plot the points given by the table and join them by a smooth curve to obtain the graph. The graphs are sketched in Figure 3 on the next page.

x	$f(x) = x^2$
0	0
$\pm\frac{1}{2}$	$\frac{1}{4}$
± 1	1
± 2	4
± 3	9

x	$g(x) = x^3$
0	0
$\frac{1}{2}$	$\frac{1}{8}$
1	1
2	8
$-\frac{1}{2}$	$-\frac{1}{8}$
-1	-1
-2	-8

x	$h(x) = \sqrt{x}$
0	0
1	1
2	$\sqrt{2}$
3	$\sqrt{3}$
4	2
5	$\sqrt{5}$

ALTERNATE EXAMPLE 1

(a) For the graph of the function $f(x) = 3x^2$, find the coordinates of the points with $x = 0$, $x = \pm\frac{1}{2}$, $x = \pm 1$, $x = \pm 2$, $x = \pm 3$.

(b) For the graph of the function $f(x) = 4x^3$, find the coordinates of the points with $x = 0$, $x = \pm\frac{1}{2}$, $x = \pm 1$, $x = \pm 2$.

ANSWERS

(a) $(0, 0)$, $\left(\frac{1}{2}, \frac{3}{4}\right)$, $\left(-\frac{1}{2}, \frac{3}{4}\right)$, $(1, 3)$, $(-1, 3)$, $(2, 12)$, $(-2, 12)$, $(3, 27)$, $(-3, 27)$

(b) $(0, 0)$, $\left(\frac{1}{2}, \frac{1}{2}\right)$, $\left(-\frac{1}{2}, -\frac{1}{2}\right)$, $(1, 4)$, $(-1, -4)$, $(2, 32)$, $(-2, -32)$

IN-CLASS MATERIALS

Draw a graph of fuel efficiency versus time on a trip, such as the one here. Lead a discussion of what could have happened on the trip.

ALTERNATE EXAMPLE 2
Use a graphing calculator to graph the function $f(x) = x^4 - 2x^2 + 20$ in an appropriate viewing rectangle.

ANSWER
One good rectangle is $-2 \le x \le 2$, $18 \le y \le 28$.

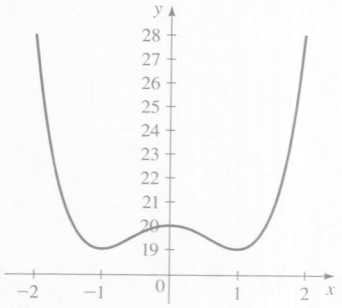

ALTERNATE EXAMPLE 3
(a) Graph the functions $f(x) = x^n$ for $n = 1, 2, 3, 4, 5, 6$ in the viewing rectangle [0, 1.1] by [0, 1.1].
(b) Graph the functions $f(x) = x^n$ for $n = 1, 2, 3, 4, 5, 6$ in the viewing rectangle [0, 2.6] by [0, 300].
(c) What conclusions can you draw?

ANSWERS
(a)

(b)

(c) For values of x between 0 and 1, as n increases, the curve grows more slowly. All the curves go through the points (0, 0) and (1, 1). For values of x larger than 1, the curves grow more quickly as n increases, dramatically so.

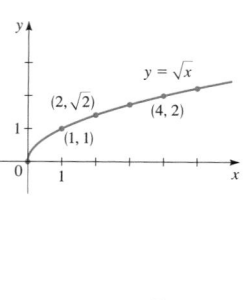

FIGURE 3   (a) $f(x) = x^2$ (b) $g(x) = x^3$ (c) $h(x) = \sqrt{x}$

✎ NOW TRY EXERCISES **11, 15,** AND **19**

▼ Graphing Functions with a Graphing Calculator

A convenient way to graph a function is to use a graphing calculator. Because the graph of a function f is the graph of the equation $y = f(x)$, we can use the methods of Section 1.9 to graph functions on a graphing calculator.

EXAMPLE 2 | Graphing a Function with a Graphing Calculator

Use a graphing calculator to graph the function $f(x) = x^3 - 8x^2$ in an appropriate viewing rectangle.

SOLUTION To graph the function $f(x) = x^3 - 8x^2$, we must graph the equation $y = x^3 - 8x^2$. On the TI-83 graphing calculator the default viewing rectangle gives the graph in Figure 4(a). But this graph appears to spill over the top and bottom of the screen. We need to expand the vertical axis to get a better representation of the graph. The viewing rectangle $[-4, 10]$ by $[-100, 100]$ gives a more complete picture of the graph, as shown in Figure 4(b).

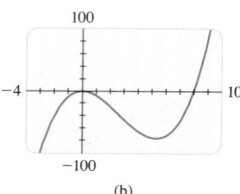

FIGURE 4 Graphing the function $f(x) = x^3 - 8x^2$

(a)   (b)

✎ NOW TRY EXERCISE **29**

EXAMPLE 3 | A Family of Power Functions

(a) Graph the functions $f(x) = x^n$ for $n = 2, 4,$ and 6 in the viewing rectangle $[-2, 2]$ by $[-1, 3]$.
(b) Graph the functions $f(x) = x^n$ for $n = 1, 3,$ and 5 in the viewing rectangle $[-2, 2]$ by $[-2, 2]$.
(c) What conclusions can you draw from these graphs?

IN-CLASS MATERIALS
In 1984, U.S. President Ronald Reagan proposed a plan to change the U.S. personal income tax system. According to his plan, the income tax would be 15% on the first $19,300 earned, 25% on the next $18,800, and 35% on all income above and beyond that. Describe this situation to the class, and have them graph (marginal) tax rate and tax owed versus income for incomes ranging from $0 to $80,000. Then have them try to come up with equations describing this situation.

SOLUTION To graph the function $f(x) = x^n$, we graph the equation $y = x^n$. The graphs for parts (a) and (b) are shown in Figure 5.

FIGURE 5 A family of power functions $f(x) = x^n$

(a) Even powers of x (b) Odd powers of x

(c) We see that the general shape of the graph of $f(x) = x^n$ depends on whether n is even or odd.

If n is even, the graph of $f(x) = x^n$ is similar to the parabola $y = x^2$.

If n is odd, the graph of $f(x) = x^n$ is similar to that of $y = x^3$.

✎ NOW TRY EXERCISE **69**

Notice from Figure 5 that as n increases, the graph of $y = x^n$ becomes flatter near 0 and steeper when $x > 1$. When $0 < x < 1$, the lower powers of x are the "bigger" functions. But when $x > 1$, the higher powers of x are the dominant functions.

▼ Graphing Piecewise Defined Functions

A piecewise defined function is defined by different formulas on different parts of its domain. As you might expect, the graph of such a function consists of separate pieces.

EXAMPLE 4 | Graph of a Piecewise Defined Function

Sketch the graph of the function.

$$f(x) = \begin{cases} x^2 & \text{if } x \le 1 \\ 2x + 1 & \text{if } x > 1 \end{cases}$$

On many graphing calculators the graph in Figure 6 can be produced by using the logical functions in the calculator. For example, on the TI-83 the following equation gives the required graph:

$$Y_1 = (X \le 1)X^2 + (X > 1)(2X + 1)$$

(To avoid the extraneous vertical line between the two parts of the graph, put the calculator in D o t mode.)

SOLUTION If $x \le 1$, then $f(x) = x^2$, so the part of the graph to the left of $x = 1$ coincides with the graph of $y = x^2$, which we sketched in Figure 3. If $x > 1$, then $f(x) = 2x + 1$, so the part of the graph to the right of $x = 1$ coincides with the line $y = 2x + 1$, which we graphed in Figure 2. This enables us to sketch the graph in Figure 6.

The solid dot at $(1, 1)$ indicates that this point is included in the graph; the open dot at $(1, 3)$ indicates that this point is excluded from the graph.

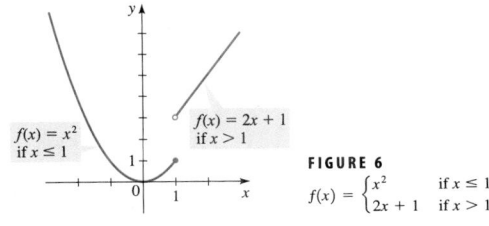

FIGURE 6

$$f(x) = \begin{cases} x^2 & \text{if } x \le 1 \\ 2x + 1 & \text{if } x > 1 \end{cases}$$

✎ NOW TRY EXERCISE **35**

IN-CLASS MATERIALS

In the year 2000, presidential candidate Steve Forbes proposed a "flat tax" model: 0% on the first $36,000 and 17% on the rest. Have your students do the same analysis and compare the two models. As an extension, consider having them look at a current tax table and draw similar graphs.

ALTERNATE EXAMPLE 5

Write a piecewise defined function whose combined graph is identical to the one defined by $f(x) = 6|x|$.

ANSWER

$$f(x) = \begin{cases} 6x & \text{if } x \geq 0 \\ -6x & \text{if } x < 0 \end{cases}$$

ALTERNATE EXAMPLE 6

Write two functions whose combined graphs are identical to the one defined by

$$f(x) = \begin{cases} x^2 & \text{if } x \leq 1 \\ 2x + 3 & \text{if } x > 1 x \leq 2 \end{cases}$$

for the interval $(-\infty, 1]$ and for the interval $(1, \infty)$.

ANSWER

$f(x) = x^2$, $f(x) = 2x + 3$

ALTERNATE EXAMPLE 7

The cost of a long-distance daytime phone call from Toronto to New York City is 20 cents for the first minute and 15 cents for each additional minute (or part of a minute). For the graph of the function C (in dollars) of the phone call as a function of time t (in minutes), find $C(t)$ for $0 < t \leq 1, 1 < t \leq 2, 2 < t \leq 3, 3 < t \leq 4$.

ANSWER

0.71, 1.37, 2.03, 2.69

EXAMPLE 5 | Graph of the Absolute Value Function

Sketch a graph of the absolute value function $f(x) = |x|$.

SOLUTION   Recall that

$$|x| = \begin{cases} x & \text{if } x \geq 0 \\ -x & \text{if } x < 0 \end{cases}$$

Using the same method as in Example 4, we note that the graph of f coincides with the line $y = x$ to the right of the y-axis and coincides with the line $y = -x$ to the left of the y-axis (see Figure 7).

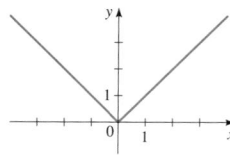

FIGURE 7 Graph of $f(x) = |x|$

➴. NOW TRY EXERCISE **23**

The **greatest integer function** is defined by

$$[\![x]\!] = \text{greatest integer less than or equal to } x$$

For example, $[\![2]\!] = 2$, $[\![2.3]\!] = 2$, $[\![1.999]\!] = 1$, $[\![0.002]\!] = 0$, $[\![-3.5]\!] = -4$, and $[\![-0.5]\!] = -1$.

EXAMPLE 6 | Graph of the Greatest Integer Function

Sketch a graph of $f(x) = [\![x]\!]$.

SOLUTION   The table shows the values of f for some values of x. Note that $f(x)$ is constant between consecutive integers, so the graph between integers is a horizontal line segment, as shown in Figure 8.

x	$[\![x]\!]$
$\vdots$	$\vdots$
$-2 \leq x < -1$	-2
$-1 \leq x < 0$	-1
$0 \leq x < 1$	0
$1 \leq x < 2$	1
$2 \leq x < 3$	2
$\vdots$	$\vdots$

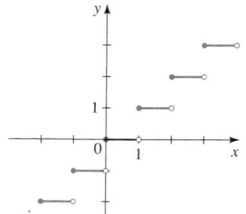

FIGURE 8 The greatest integer function, $y = [\![x]\!]$

The greatest integer function is an example of a **step function**. The next example gives a real-world example of a step function.

EXAMPLE 7 | The Cost Function for Long-Distance Phone Calls

The cost of a long-distance daytime phone call from Toronto, Canada, to Mumbai, India, is 69 cents for the first minute and 58 cents for each additional minute (or part of a minute). Draw the graph of the cost C (in dollars) of the phone call as a function of time t (in minutes).

IN-CLASS MATERIALS

Discuss the shape, symmetries, and general "flatness" near 0 of the power functions x^n for various values of n. Similarly, discuss $\sqrt[n]{x}$ for n even and n odd.

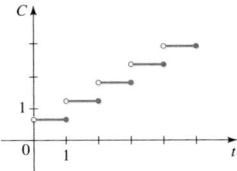

FIGURE 9 Cost of a long-distance call

Continuous functions are defined more precisely in Section 13.2, on page 851.

SOLUTION   Let $C(t)$ be the cost for t minutes. Since $t > 0$, the domain of the function is $(0, \infty)$. From the given information we have

$$C(t) = 0.69 \qquad\qquad\qquad \text{if } 0 < t \le 1$$
$$C(t) = 0.69 + 0.58 = 1.27 \qquad \text{if } 1 < t \le 2$$
$$C(t) = 0.69 + 2(0.58) = 1.85 \quad \text{if } 2 < t \le 3$$
$$C(t) = 0.69 + 3(0.58) = 2.43 \quad \text{if } 3 < t \le 4$$

and so on. The graph is shown in Figure 9.

◥. NOW TRY EXERCISE **81**   ■

A function is called **continuous** if its graph has no "breaks" or "holes." The functions in Examples 1, 2, 3, and 5 are continuous; the functions in Examples 4, 6, and 7 are not continuous.

▼ The Vertical Line Test

The graph of a function is a curve in the xy-plane. But the question arises: Which curves in the xy-plane are graphs of functions? This is answered by the following test.

> **THE VERTICAL LINE TEST**
>
> A curve in the coordinate plane is the graph of a function if and only if no vertical line intersects the curve more than once.

We can see from Figure 10 why the Vertical Line Test is true. If each vertical line $x = a$ intersects a curve only once at (a, b), then exactly one functional value is defined by $f(a) = b$. But if a line $x = a$ intersects the curve twice, at (a, b) and at (a, c), then the curve cannot represent a function because a function cannot assign two different values to a.

  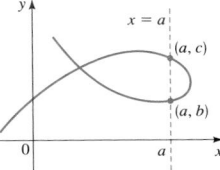

Graph of a function   Not a graph of a function

FIGURE 10 Vertical Line Test

EXAMPLE 8 | Using the Vertical Line Test

Using the Vertical Line Test, we see that the curves in parts (b) and (c) of Figure 11 represent functions, whereas those in parts (a) and (d) do not.

    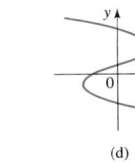

FIGURE 11   (a)   (b)   (c)   (d)

◥. NOW TRY EXERCISE **51**   ■

▼ Equations That Define Functions

Any equation in the variables x and y defines a relationship between these variables. For example, the equation

$$y - x^2 = 0$$

defines a relationship between y and x. Does this equation define y as a *function* of x? To find out, we solve for y and get

$$y = x^2$$

We see that the equation defines a rule, or function, that gives one value of y for each value of x. We can express this rule in function notation as

$$f(x) = x^2$$

But not every equation defines y as a function of x, as the following example shows.

EXAMPLE 9 | Equations That Define Functions

Does the equation define y as a function of x?

(a) $y - x^2 = 2$ **(b)** $x^2 + y^2 = 4$

SOLUTION

(a) Solving for y in terms of x gives

$$y - x^2 = 2$$
$$y = x^2 + 2 \qquad \text{Add } x^2$$

The last equation is a rule that gives one value of y for each value of x, so it defines y as a function of x. We can write the function as $f(x) = x^2 + 2$.

(b) We try to solve for y in terms of x:

$$x^2 + y^2 = 4$$
$$y^2 = 4 - x^2 \qquad \text{Subtract } x^2$$
$$y = \pm\sqrt{4 - x^2} \qquad \text{Take square roots}$$

The last equation gives two values of y for a given value of x. Thus, the equation does not define y as a function of x.

✎. NOW TRY EXERCISES **57** AND **61**

The graphs of the equations in Example 9 are shown in Figure 12. The Vertical Line Test shows graphically that the equation in Example 9(a) defines a function but the equation in Example 9(b) does not.

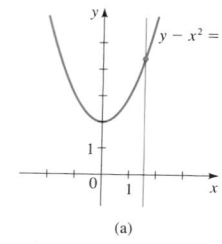

(a)   (b)

FIGURE 12

EXAMPLE

A continuous piecewise-defined function

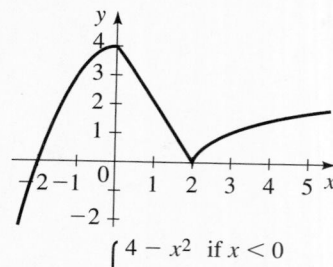

$$f(x) = \begin{cases} 4 - x^2 & \text{if } x < 0 \\ 4 - 2x & \text{if } 0 \le x \le 2 \\ \sqrt{x - 2} & \text{if } x > 2 \end{cases}$$

A discontinuous piecewise-defined function

$$f(x) = \begin{cases} 4 - x^2 & \text{if } x < 0 \\ x + 2 & \text{if } 0 \le x \le 2 \\ \sqrt[3]{x} & \text{if } x > 2 \end{cases}$$

Classic rational functions with interesting graphs

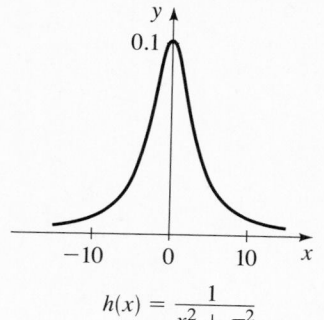

$$h(x) = \frac{1}{x^2 + \pi^2}$$

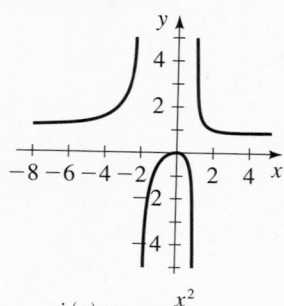

$$i(x) = \frac{x^2}{x^2 + x - 2}$$

The following table shows the graphs of some functions that you will see frequently in this book.

SOME FUNCTIONS AND THEIR GRAPHS

Linear functions
$f(x) = mx + b$

Power functions
$f(x) = x^n$

$f(x) = x^2$ $f(x) = x^3$ $f(x) = x^4$ $f(x) = x^5$

Root functions
$f(x) = \sqrt[n]{x}$

$f(x) = \sqrt{x}$ $f(x) = \sqrt[3]{x}$ $f(x) = \sqrt[4]{x}$ $f(x) = \sqrt[5]{x}$

Reciprocal functions
$f(x) = \dfrac{1}{x^n}$

$f(x) = \dfrac{1}{x}$ $f(x) = \dfrac{1}{x^2}$

Absolute value function
$f(x) = |x|$

Greatest integer function
$f(x) = [\![x]\!]$

$f(x) = |x|$ $f(x) = [\![x]\!]$

2.2 EXERCISES

CONCEPTS

1. To graph the function f, we plot the points $(x, \underline{\qquad})$ in a coordinate plane. To graph $f(x) = x^3 + 2$, we plot the points $(x, \underline{\qquad})$. So the point $(2, \underline{\qquad})$ is on the graph of f.

The height of the graph of f above the x-axis when $x = 2$ is $\underline{\qquad}$.

2. If $f(2) = 3$, then the point $(2, \underline{\qquad})$ is on the graph of f.

DRILL QUESTION

Let $f(x) = x^2 + |x|$. Which of the following is the graph of f? How do you know?

(a)

(b)

(c)

(d)

Answer

(b) is the graph of f, because $f(x) \geq 0$ for all x.

3. If the point $(2, 3)$ is on the graph of f, then $f(2) = $ _____.

4. Match the function with its graph.

    (a) $f(x) = x^2$ **(b)** $f(x) = x^3$

    (c) $f(x) = \sqrt{x}$ **(d)** $f(x) = |x|$

I   II

III   IV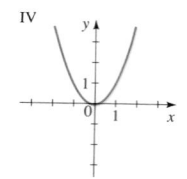

SKILLS

5–28 ■ Sketch the graph of the function by first making a table of values.

5. $f(x) = 2$ **6.** $f(x) = -3$

7. $f(x) = 2x - 4$ **8.** $f(x) = 6 - 3x$

9. $f(x) = -x + 3, \quad -3 \le x \le 3$

10. $f(x) = \dfrac{x - 3}{2}, \quad 0 \le x \le 5$

11. $f(x) = -x^2$ **12.** $f(x) = x^2 - 4$

13. $h(x) = 16 - x^2$ **14.** $g(x) = (x - 3)^2$

15. $g(x) = x^3 - 8$ **16.** $g(x) = (x + 2)^3$

17. $g(x) = x^2 - 2x$ **18.** $h(x) = 4x^2 - x^4$

19. $f(x) = 1 + \sqrt{x}$ **20.** $f(x) = \sqrt{x + 4}$

21. $g(x) = -\sqrt{x}$ **22.** $g(x) = \sqrt{-x}$

23. $H(x) = |2x|$ **24.** $H(x) = |x + 1|$

25. $G(x) = |x| + x$ **26.** $G(x) = |x| - x$

27. $f(x) = |2x - 2|$ **28.** $f(x) = \dfrac{x}{|x|}$

29–32 ■ Graph the function in each of the given viewing rectangles, and select the one that produces the most appropriate graph of the function.

29. $f(x) = 8x - x^2$

    (a) $[-5, 5]$ by $[-5, 5]$

    (b) $[-10, 10]$ by $[-10, 10]$

    (c) $[-2, 10]$ by $[-5, 20]$

    (d) $[-10, 10]$ by $[-100, 100]$

30. $g(x) = x^2 - x - 20$

    (a) $[-2, 2]$ by $[-5, 5]$

    (b) $[-10, 10]$ by $[-10, 10]$

    (c) $[-7, 7]$ by $[-25, 20]$

    (d) $[-10, 10]$ by $[-100, 100]$

31. $h(x) = x^3 - 5x - 4$

    (a) $[-2, 2]$ by $[-2, 2]$

    (b) $[-3, 3]$ by $[-10, 10]$

    (c) $[-3, 3]$ by $[-10, 5]$

    (d) $[-10, 10]$ by $[-10, 10]$

32. $k(x) = \frac{1}{32}x^4 - x^2 + 2$

    (a) $[-1, 1]$ by $[-1, 1]$

    (b) $[-2, 2]$ by $[-2, 2]$

    (c) $[-5, 5]$ by $[-5, 5]$

    (d) $[-10, 10]$ by $[-10, 10]$

33–46 ■ Sketch the graph of the piecewise defined function.

33. $f(x) = \begin{cases} 0 & \text{if } x < 2 \\ 1 & \text{if } x \ge 2 \end{cases}$

34. $f(x) = \begin{cases} 1 & \text{if } x \le 1 \\ x + 1 & \text{if } x > 1 \end{cases}$

35. $f(x) = \begin{cases} 3 & \text{if } x < 2 \\ x - 1 & \text{if } x \ge 2 \end{cases}$

36. $f(x) = \begin{cases} 1 - x & \text{if } x < -2 \\ 5 & \text{if } x \ge -2 \end{cases}$

37. $f(x) = \begin{cases} x & \text{if } x \le 0 \\ x + 1 & \text{if } x > 0 \end{cases}$

38. $f(x) = \begin{cases} 2x + 3 & \text{if } x < -1 \\ 3 - x & \text{if } x \ge -1 \end{cases}$

39. $f(x) = \begin{cases} -1 & \text{if } x < -1 \\ 1 & \text{if } -1 \le x \le 1 \\ -1 & \text{if } x > 1 \end{cases}$

40. $f(x) = \begin{cases} -1 & \text{if } x < -1 \\ x & \text{if } -1 \le x \le 1 \\ 1 & \text{if } x > 1 \end{cases}$

41. $f(x) = \begin{cases} 2 & \text{if } x \le -1 \\ x^2 & \text{if } x > -1 \end{cases}$

42. $f(x) = \begin{cases} 1 - x^2 & \text{if } x \le 2 \\ x & \text{if } x > 2 \end{cases}$

43. $f(x) = \begin{cases} 0 & \text{if } |x| \le 2 \\ 3 & \text{if } |x| > 2 \end{cases}$

44. $f(x) = \begin{cases} x^2 & \text{if } |x| \le 1 \\ 1 & \text{if } |x| > 1 \end{cases}$

45. $f(x) = \begin{cases} 4 & \text{if } x < -2 \\ x^2 & \text{if } -2 \le x \le 2 \\ -x + 6 & \text{if } x > 2 \end{cases}$

46. $f(x) = \begin{cases} -x & \text{if } x \le 0 \\ 9 - x^2 & \text{if } 0 < x \le 3 \\ x - 3 & \text{if } x > 3 \end{cases}$

47–48 ■ Use a graphing device to draw the graph of the piecewise defined function. (See the margin note on page 155.)

47. $f(x) = \begin{cases} x + 2 & \text{if } x \le -1 \\ x^2 & \text{if } x > -1 \end{cases}$

48. $f(x) = \begin{cases} 2x - x^2 & \text{if } x > 1 \\ (x - 1)^3 & \text{if } x \le 1 \end{cases}$

49–50 ■ The graph of a piecewise defined function is given. Find a formula for the function in the indicated form.

49.

$f(x) = \begin{cases} \rule{1.5em}{0.6em} & \text{if } x < -2 \\ \rule{1.5em}{0.6em} & \text{if } -2 \le x \le 2 \\ \rule{1.5em}{0.6em} & \text{if } x > 2 \end{cases}$

50.
$f(x) = \begin{cases} \rule{1.5em}{0.6em} & \text{if } x \le -1 \\ \rule{1.5em}{0.6em} & \text{if } -1 < x \le 2 \\ \rule{1.5em}{0.6em} & \text{if } x > 2 \end{cases}$

51–52 ■ Use the Vertical Line Test to determine whether the curve is the graph of a function of x.

51. (a)

(b)

(c)

(d)

52. (a)

(b)

(c)

(d)
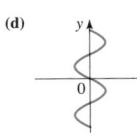

53–56 ■ Use the Vertical Line Test to determine whether the curve is the graph of a function of x. If it is, state the domain and range of the function.

53.

54.

55.
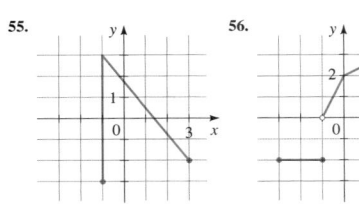
56.

57–68 ■ Determine whether the equation defines y as a function of x. (See Example 9.)

57. $x^2 + 2y = 4$ **58.** $3x + 7y = 21$

59. $x = y^2$ **60.** $x^2 + (y - 1)^2 = 4$

61. $x + y^2 = 9$ **62.** $x^2 + y = 9$

63. $x^2 y + y = 1$ **64.** $\sqrt{x} + y = 12$

65. $2|x| + y = 0$ **66.** $2x + |y| = 0$

67. $x = y^3$ **68.** $x = y^4$

69–74 ■ A family of functions is given. In parts (a) and (b) graph all the given members of the family in the viewing rectangle indicated. In part (c) state the conclusions that you can make from your graphs.

69. $f(x) = x^2 + c$
  (a) $c = 0, 2, 4, 6$; $[-5, 5]$ by $[-10, 10]$
  (b) $c = 0, -2, -4, -6$; $[-5, 5]$ by $[-10, 10]$
  (c) How does the value of c affect the graph?

70. $f(x) = (x - c)^2$
  (a) $c = 0, 1, 2, 3$; $[-5, 5]$ by $[-10, 10]$
  (b) $c = 0, -1, -2, -3$; $[-5, 5]$ by $[-10, 10]$
  (c) How does the value of c affect the graph?

71. $f(x) = (x - c)^3$
  (a) $c = 0, 2, 4, 6$; $[-10, 10]$ by $[-10, 10]$
  (b) $c = 0, -2, -4, -6$; $[-10, 10]$ by $[-10, 10]$
  (c) How does the value of c affect the graph?

72. $f(x) = cx^2$
  (a) $c = 1, \frac{1}{2}, 2, 4$; $[-5, 5]$ by $[-10, 10]$
  (b) $c = 1, -1, -\frac{1}{2}, -2$; $[-5, 5]$ by $[-10, 10]$
  (c) How does the value of c affect the graph?

73. $f(x) = x^c$
  (a) $c = \frac{1}{2}, \frac{1}{4}, \frac{1}{6}$; $[-1, 4]$ by $[-1, 3]$
  (b) $c = 1, \frac{1}{3}, \frac{1}{5}$; $[-3, 3]$ by $[-2, 2]$
  (c) How does the value of c affect the graph?

74. $f(x) = \dfrac{1}{x^n}$

   (a) $n = 1, 3$; $[-3, 3]$ by $[-3, 3]$

   (b) $n = 2, 4$; $[-3, 3]$ by $[-3, 3]$

   (c) How does the value of n affect the graph?

75–78 ■ Find a function whose graph is the given curve.

75. The line segment joining the points $(-2, 1)$ and $(4, -6)$

76. The line segment joining the points $(-3, -2)$ and $(6, 3)$

77. The top half of the circle $x^2 + y^2 = 9$

78. The bottom half of the circle $x^2 + y^2 = 9$

APPLICATIONS

79. Weather Balloon As a weather balloon is inflated, the thickness T of its rubber skin is related to the radius of the balloon by

$$T(r) = \frac{0.5}{r^2}$$

where T and r are measured in centimeters. Graph the function T for values of r between 10 and 100.

80. Power from a Wind Turbine The power produced by a wind turbine depends on the speed of the wind. If a windmill has blades 3 meters long, then the power P produced by the turbine is modeled by

$$P(v) = 14.1v^3$$

where P is measured in watts (W) and v is measured in meters per second (m/s). Graph the function P for wind speeds between 1 m/s and 10 m/s.

81. Utility Rates Westside Energy charges its electric customers a base rate of $6.00 per month, plus 10¢ per kilowatt-hour (kWh) for the first 300 kWh used and 6¢ per kWh for all usage over 300 kWh. Suppose a customer uses x kWh of electricity in one month.

   (a) Express the monthly cost E as a piecewise-defined function of x.

   (b) Graph the function E for $0 \le x \le 600$.

82. Taxicab Function A taxi company charges $2.00 for the first mile (or part of a mile) and 20 cents for each succeeding tenth of a mile (or part). Express the cost C (in dollars) of a ride as a piecewise-defined function of the distance x traveled (in miles) for $0 < x < 2$, and sketch the graph of this function.

83. Postage Rates The domestic postage rate for first-class letters weighing 3.5 oz or less is 44 cents for the first ounce (or less), plus 17 cents for each additional ounce (or part of an ounce). Express the postage P as a piecewise-defined function of the weight x of a letter, with $0 < x \le 3.5$, and sketch the graph of this function.

DISCOVERY ■ DISCUSSION ■ WRITING

84. When Does a Graph Represent a Function? For every integer n, the graph of the equation $y = x^n$ is the graph of a function, namely $f(x) = x^n$. Explain why the graph of $x = y^2$ is *not* the graph of a function of x. Is the graph of $x = y^3$ the graph of a function of x? If so, of what function of x is it the graph? Determine for what integers n the graph of $x = y^n$ is the graph of a function of x.

85. Step Functions In Example 7 and Exercises 82 and 83 we are given functions whose graphs consist of horizontal line segments. Such functions are often called *step functions*, because their graphs look like stairs. Give some other examples of step functions that arise in everyday life.

86. Stretched Step Functions Sketch graphs of the functions $f(x) = [\![x]\!]$, $g(x) = [\![2x]\!]$, and $h(x) = [\![3x]\!]$ on separate graphs. How are the graphs related? If n is a positive integer, what does the graph of $k(x) = [\![nx]\!]$ look like?

87. Graph of the Absolute Value of a Function

   (a) Draw the graphs of the functions

$$f(x) = x^2 + x - 6$$

   and $$g(x) = |x^2 + x - 6|$$

   How are the graphs of f and g related?

   (b) Draw the graphs of the functions $f(x) = x^4 - 6x^2$ and $g(x) = |x^4 - 6x^2|$. How are the graphs of f and g related?

   (c) In general, if $g(x) = |f(x)|$, how are the graphs of f and g related? Draw graphs to illustrate your answer.

◯ DISCOVERY PROJECT **Relations and Functions**

In this project we explore the concept of function by comparing it with the concept of a *relation*. You can find the project at the book companion website:
www.stewartmath.com

2.3 GETTING INFORMATION FROM THE GRAPH OF A FUNCTION

| Values of a Function; Domain and Range ▶ Increasing and Decreasing
| Functions ▶ Local Maximum and Minimum Values of a Function

Many properties of a function are more easily obtained from a graph than from the rule that describes the function. We will see in this section how a graph tells us whether the values of a function are increasing or decreasing and also where the maximum and minimum values of a function are.

▼ Values of a Function; Domain and Range

A complete graph of a function contains all the information about a function, because the graph tells us which input values correspond to which output values. To analyze the graph of a function, we must keep in mind that *the height of the graph is the value of the function*. So we can read off the values of a function from its graph.

EXAMPLE 1 | Finding the Values of a Function from a Graph

The function T graphed in Figure 1 gives the temperature between noon and 6:00 P.M. at a certain weather station.

(a) Find $T(1)$, $T(3)$, and $T(5)$.

(b) Which is larger, $T(2)$ or $T(4)$?

(c) Find the value(s) of x for which $T(x) = 25$.

(d) Find the value(s) of x for which $T(x) \geq 25$.

SOLUTION

(a) $T(1)$ is the temperature at 1:00 P.M. It is represented by the height of the graph above the x-axis at $x = 1$. Thus, $T(1) = 25$. Similarly, $T(3) = 30$ and $T(5) = 20$.

(b) Since the graph is higher at $x = 2$ than at $x = 4$, it follows that $T(2)$ is larger than $T(4)$.

(c) The height of the graph is 25 when x is 1 and when x is 4. In other words, the temperature is 25 at 1:00 P.M. and 4:00 P.M.

(d) The graph is higher than 25 for x between 1 and 4. In other words, the temperature was 25 or greater between 1:00 P.M. and 4:00 P.M.

◥ **NOW TRY EXERCISE 5**

The graph of a function helps us to picture the domain and range of the function on the x-axis and y-axis, as shown in Figure 2.

FIGURE 1 Temperature function

FIGURE 2 Domain and range of f

SUGGESTED TIME AND EMPHASIS

$\frac{1}{2}$–1 class, essential material

ALTERNATE EXAMPLE 1

The function P graphed in the accompanying figure gives the % charge of my laptop battery over a 24-hour period, where 0 represents midnight and 12 represents noon.

(a) Find $P(0)$, $P(9)$, $P(12)$, $P(17)$.

(b) Which is larger, $P(14)$ or $P(18)$?

(c) Find the value(s) of x for which $P(x) = 80$.

(d) Find the value(s) of x for which $P(x) \leq 70$.

ANSWERS

(a) $P(0) = 80$, $P(9) \approx 95$, $P(12) \approx 75$, $P(18) \approx 95$

(b) $P(18)$

(c) $P(x) = 80$ for $x \approx 0,11,17$

(d) $P(x) \leq 70$ for $13 < x < 16.5$ (approximately)

TEXT QUESTION

Over what interval is the function $x^3 + x$ increasing?

Answer

$(-\infty, \infty)$

ALTERNATE EXAMPLE 2

Use a graphing calculator to draw the graph of $f(x) = \dfrac{1}{1 + x^2}$, and use your graph to find the domain and range of f.

ANSWER

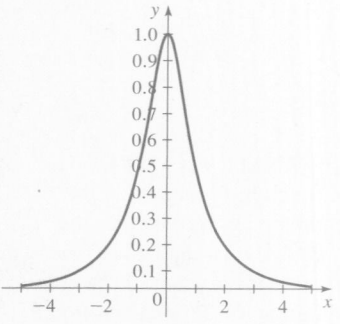

Domain: all real numbers
Range: (0, 1]

EXAMPLE 2 | Finding the Domain and Range from a Graph

(a) Use a graphing calculator to draw the graph of $f(x) = \sqrt{4 - x^2}$.

(b) Find the domain and range of f.

SOLUTION

(a) The graph is shown in Figure 3.

Range = [0, 2]

Domain = [−2, 2]

FIGURE 3 Graph of $f(x) = \sqrt{4 - x^2}$

(b) From the graph in Figure 3 we see that the domain is $[-2, 2]$ and the range is $[0, 2]$.

✎. NOW TRY EXERCISE **15**

▼ **Increasing and Decreasing Functions**

It is very useful to know where the graph of a function rises and where it falls. The graph shown in Figure 4 rises, falls, then rises again as we move from left to right: It rises from A to B, falls from B to C, and rises again from C to D. The function f is said to be *increasing* when its graph rises and *decreasing* when its graph falls.

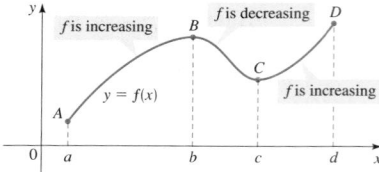

FIGURE 4 f is increasing on $[a, b]$ and $[c, d]$. f is decreasing on $[b, c]$.

We have the following definition.

DEFINITION OF INCREASING AND DECREASING FUNCTIONS

f is **increasing** on an interval I if $f(x_1) < f(x_2)$ whenever $x_1 < x_2$ in I.

f is **decreasing** on an interval I if $f(x_1) > f(x_2)$ whenever $x_1 < x_2$ in I.

f is increasing

f is decreasing

IN-CLASS MATERIALS

Explore domain and range with some graphs that have holes.

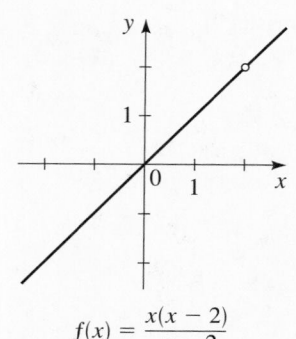

$$f(x) = \frac{x(x - 2)}{x - 2}$$

$$g(x) = \sqrt{\frac{x^2 - 5x + 6}{x^2 - 2x + 1}}$$

EXAMPLE 3 | Intervals on Which a Function Increases and Decreases

The graph in Figure 5 gives the weight W of a person at age x. Determine the intervals on which the function W is increasing and on which it is decreasing.

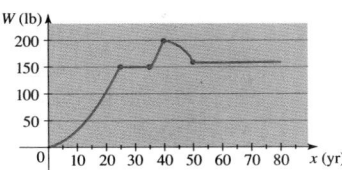

FIGURE 5   Weight as a function of age

SOLUTION   The function W is increasing on $[0, 25]$ and $[35, 40]$. It is decreasing on $[40, 50]$. The function W is constant (neither increasing nor decreasing) on $[25, 30]$ and $[50, 80]$. This means that the person gained weight until age 25, then gained weight again between ages 35 and 40. He lost weight between ages 40 and 50.

✎. NOW TRY EXERCISE **45**   ■

EXAMPLE 4 | Finding Intervals Where a Function Increases and Decreases

(a) Sketch a graph of the function $f(x) = 12x^2 + 4x^3 - 3x^4$.

(b) Find the domain and range of f.

(c) Find the intervals on which f increases and decreases.

SOLUTION

(a) We use a graphing calculator to sketch the graph in Figure 6.

(b) The domain of f is $\mathbb{R}$ because f is defined for all real numbers. Using the TRACE feature on the calculator, we find that the highest value is $f(2) = 32$. So the range of f is $(-\infty, 32]$.

(c) From the graph we see that f is increasing on the intervals $(-\infty, -1]$ and $[0, 2]$ and is decreasing on $[-1, 0]$ and $[2, \infty)$.

FIGURE 6   Graph of
$f(x) = 12x^2 + 4x^3 - 3x^4$

✎. NOW TRY EXERCISE **23**   ■

IN-CLASS MATERIALS

Draw a graph of electrical power consumption in the classroom versus time on a typical weekday, pointing out important features throughout and using the vocabulary of this section as much as possible.

ALTERNATE EXAMPLE 5

(a) Sketch a graph of the function
$$f(x) = \frac{1}{x^2}.$$

(b) Find the domain and range of f.

(c) Find the intervals on which f increases and decreases.

ANSWERS

(a)

(b) Domain: all real numbers except $x = 0$
Range: $(0, \infty)$

(c) Increasing on $(-\infty, 0)$
Decreasing on $(0, \infty)$

EXAMPLE 5 | Finding Intervals Where a Function Increases and Decreases

(a) Sketch the graph of the function $f(x) = x^{2/3}$.

(b) Find the domain and range of the function.

(c) Find the intervals on which f increases and decreases.

SOLUTION

(a) We use a graphing calculator to sketch the graph in Figure 7.

(b) From the graph we observe that the domain of f is $\mathbb{R}$ and the range is $[0, \infty)$.

(c) From the graph we see that f is decreasing on $(-\infty, 0]$ and increasing on $[0, \infty)$.

FIGURE 7 Graph of $f(x) = x^{2/3}$

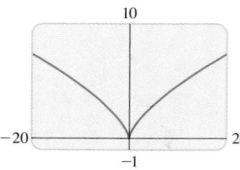

✎ NOW TRY EXERCISE **29** ∎

▼ Local Maximum and Minimum Values of a Function

Finding the largest or smallest values of a function is important in many applications. For example, if a function represents revenue or profit, then we are interested in its maximum value. For a function that represents cost, we would want to find its minimum value. (See *Focus on Modeling: Modeling with Functions* on pages 213–222 for many such examples.) We can easily find these values from the graph of a function. We first define what we mean by a local maximum or minimum.

LOCAL MAXIMA AND MINIMA OF A FUNCTION

1. The function value $f(a)$ is a **local maximum value** of f if

$$f(a) \geq f(x) \quad \text{when } x \text{ is near } a$$

(This means that $f(a) \geq f(x)$ for all x in some open interval containing a.) In this case we say that f has a **local maximum** at $x = a$.

2. The function value $f(a)$ is a **local minimum** of f if

$$f(a) \leq f(x) \quad \text{when } x \text{ is near } a$$

(This means that $f(a) \leq f(x)$ for all x in some open interval containing a.) In this case we say that f has a **local minimum** at $x = a$.

IN-CLASS MATERIALS

Notice that it is fairly easy to tell where some functions are increasing and decreasing by looking at their graphs. For example, the graph of $f(x) = x^4 - 8x^2$ makes things very clear. Note that in this case, the intervals are not immediately apparent from looking at the formula. However, for many functions such as $g(x) = x^3 - 3x^2 + x + 1$, it is very difficult to find the exact intervals where the function is increasing/decreasing. In this example, the endpoints of the intervals will occur at precisely $x = 1 \pm \frac{1}{3}\sqrt{6}$.

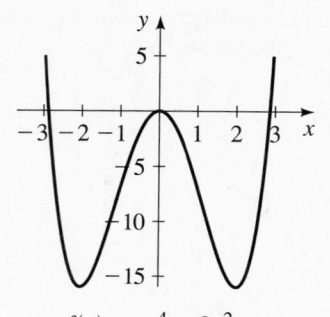

$$f(x) = x^4 - 8x^2$$

$$g(x) = x^3 - 3x^2 + x + 1$$

We can find the local maximum and minimum values of a function using a graphing calculator.

If there is a viewing rectangle such that the point $(a, f(a))$ is the highest point on the graph of f *within* the viewing rectangle (not on the edge), then the number $f(a)$ is a local maximum value of f (see Figure 8). Notice that $f(a) \geq f(x)$ for all numbers x that are close to a.

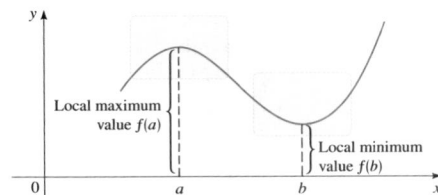

FIGURE 8

Similarly, if there is a viewing rectangle such that the point $(b, f(b))$ is the lowest point on the graph of f within the viewing rectangle, then the number $f(b)$ is a local minimum value of f. In this case, $f(b) \leq f(x)$ for all numbers x that are close to b.

EXAMPLE 6 | Finding Local Maxima and Minima from a Graph

Find the local maximum and minimum values of the function $f(x) = x^3 - 8x + 1$, correct to three decimal places.

SOLUTION The graph of f is shown in Figure 9. There appears to be one local maximum between $x = -2$ and $x = -1$, and one local minimum between $x = 1$ and $x = 2$.

Let's find the coordinates of the local maximum point first. We zoom in to enlarge the area near this point, as shown in Figure 10. Using the TRACE feature on the graphing device, we move the cursor along the curve and observe how the y-coordinates change. The local maximum value of y is 9.709, and this value occurs when x is -1.633, correct to three decimal places.

We locate the minimum value in a similar fashion. By zooming in to the viewing rectangle shown in Figure 11, we find that the local minimum value is about -7.709, and this value occurs when $x \approx 1.633$.

FIGURE 9 Graph of
$f(x) = x^3 - 8x + 1$

FIGURE 10

FIGURE 11

⬩ NOW TRY EXERCISE 35

The `maximum` and `minimum` commands on a TI-83 or TI-84 calculator provide another method for finding extreme values of functions. We use this method in the next example.

IN-CLASS MATERIALS

Examine $f(x) = \begin{cases} x^2 & \text{if } x \text{ is rational} \\ 0 & \text{if } x \text{ is irrational} \end{cases}$, pointing out that it is neither increasing nor decreasing near $x = 0$.

Stress that when dealing with new sorts of functions, it becomes important to know the precise mathematical definitions of such terms.

ALTERNATE EXAMPLE 7

The profit, in millions of dollars, a factory makes by producing x thousand items is approximated by the function

$$f(x) = -\frac{x^6}{10000} + x^2$$

when x is between 0 and 10,000. Estimate the amount of items that the factory should make to maximize its profit.

ANSWER

The graph of f as a function of x is shown here. There appears to be a maximum between $x = 7$ and $x = 9$. Using the *maximum* command, we see that the maximum value of f is 38.49, or $38,490,000. It occurs when the factory produces 7598 items.

DRILL QUESTION

What are the domain and range of this function?

Answer

Domain: $0 \le x \le 7$ or $x \le 7$
Range: $0 \le y \le 6$

EXAMPLE 7 | A Model for the Food Price Index

A model for the food price index (the price of a representative "basket" of foods) between 1990 and 2000 is given by the function

$$I(t) = -0.0113t^3 + 0.0681t^2 + 0.198t + 99.1$$

where t is measured in years since midyear 1990, so $0 \le t \le 10$, and $I(t)$ is scaled so that $I(3) = 100$. Estimate the time when food was most expensive during the period 1990–2000.

SOLUTION   The graph of I as a function of t is shown in Figure 12(a). There appears to be a maximum between $t = 4$ and $t = 7$. Using the *maximum* command, as shown in Figure 12(b), we see that the maximum value of I is about 100.38, and it occurs when $t \approx 5.15$, which corresponds to August 1995.

FIGURE 12   (a)   (b)

▶. NOW TRY EXERCISE **53**

2.3 EXERCISES

CONCEPTS

1–4 ■ These exercises refer to the graph of the function f shown below.

1. To find a function value $f(a)$ from the graph of f, we find the height of the graph above the x-axis at $x =$_____. From the graph of f we see that $f(3) =$ _____.

2. The domain of the function f is all the _____-values of the points on the graph, and the range is all the corresponding _____-values. From the graph of f we see that the domain of f is the interval _____ and the range of f is the interval _____.

3. (a) If f is increasing on an interval, then the y-values of the points on the graph _____ as the x-values increase. From the graph of f we see that f is increasing on the intervals _____ and _____.

(b) If f is decreasing on an interval, then y-values of the points on the graph _____ as the x-values increase. From the graph of f we see that f is decreasing on the intervals _____ and _____.

4. (a) A function value $f(a)$ is a local maximum value of f if $f(a)$ is the _____ value of f on some interval containing a. From the graph of f we see that one local maximum value of f is _____ and that this value occurs when x is _____.

(b) The function value $f(a)$ is a local minimum value of f if $f(a)$ is the _____ value of f on some interval containing a. From the graph of f we see that one local minimum value of f is _____ and that this value occurs when x is _____.

EXAMPLE

A function with two integer turning points and a flat spot:

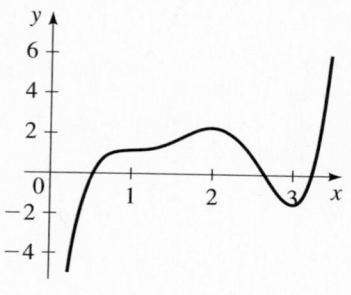

$$\frac{1}{6}(12x^5 - 105x^4 + 340x^3 - 510x^2 + 360x - 90)$$

SKILLS

5. The graph of a function h is given.
  (a) Find $h(-2)$, $h(0)$, $h(2)$, and $h(3)$.
  (b) Find the domain and range of h.
  (c) Find the values of x for which $h(x) = 3$.
  (d) Find the values of x for which $h(x) \leq 3$.

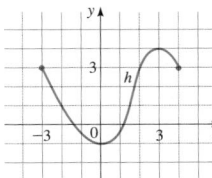

6. The graph of a function g is given.
  (a) Find $g(-2)$, $g(0)$, and $g(7)$.
  (b) Find the domain and range of g.
  (c) Find the values of x for which $g(x) = 4$.
  (d) Find the values of x for which $g(x) > 4$.

7. The graph of a function g is given.
  (a) Find $g(-4)$, $g(-2)$, $g(0)$, $g(2)$, and $g(4)$.
  (b) Find the domain and range of g.

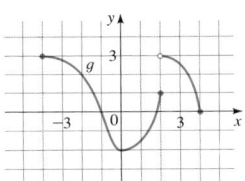

8. Graphs of the functions f and g are given.
  (a) Which is larger, $f(0)$ or $g(0)$?
  (b) Which is larger, $f(-3)$ or $g(-3)$?
  (c) For which values of x is $f(x) = g(x)$?

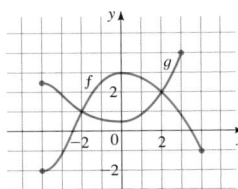

9–18 ■ A function f is given. **(a)** Use a graphing calculator to draw the graph of f. **(b)** Find the domain and range of f from the graph.

9. $f(x) = x - 1$ **10.** $f(x) = 2(x + 1)$

11. $f(x) = 4, \quad 1 \leq x \leq 3$ **12.** $f(x) = x^2, \quad -2 \leq x \leq 5$

13. $f(x) = 4 - x^2$ **14.** $f(x) = x^2 + 4$

15. $f(x) = \sqrt{16 - x^2}$ **16.** $f(x) = -\sqrt{25 - x^2}$

17. $f(x) = \sqrt{x - 1}$ **18.** $f(x) = \sqrt{x + 2}$

19–22 ■ The graph of a function is given. Determine the intervals on which the function is **(a)** increasing and **(b)** decreasing.

19.   **20.**

21.   **22.**

23–30 ■ A function f is given. **(a)** Use a graphing device to draw the graph of f. **(b)** State approximately the intervals on which f is increasing and on which f is decreasing.

23. $f(x) = x^2 - 5x$ **24.** $f(x) = x^3 - 4x$

25. $f(x) = 2x^3 - 3x^2 - 12x$ **26.** $f(x) = x^4 - 16x^2$

27. $f(x) = x^3 + 2x^2 - x - 2$

28. $f(x) = x^4 - 4x^3 + 2x^2 + 4x - 3$

29. $f(x) = x^{2/5}$ **30.** $f(x) = 4 - x^{2/3}$

31–34 ■ The graph of a function is given. **(a)** Find all the local maximum and minimum values of the function and the value of x at which each occurs. **(b)** Find the intervals on which the function is increasing and on which the function is decreasing.

31.   **32.**

33.

34.

Source: California Department of
Mines and Geology

35–42 ■ A function is given. **(a)** Find all the local maximum and minimum values of the function and the value of x at which each occurs. State each answer correct to two decimal places. **(b)** Find the intervals on which the function is increasing and on which the function is decreasing. State each answer correct to two decimal places.

35. $f(x) = x^3 - x$

36. $f(x) = 3 + x + x^2 - x^3$

37. $g(x) = x^4 - 2x^3 - 11x^2$

38. $g(x) = x^5 - 8x^3 + 20x$

39. $U(x) = x\sqrt{6 - x}$

40. $U(x) = x\sqrt{x - x^2}$

41. $V(x) = \dfrac{1 - x^2}{x^3}$

42. $V(x) = \dfrac{1}{x^2 + x + 1}$

APPLICATIONS

43. Power Consumption The figure shows the power consumption in San Francisco for September 19, 1996 (P is measured in megawatts; t is measured in hours starting at midnight).

(a) What was the power consumption at 6:00 A.M.? At 6:00 P.M.?

(b) When was the power consumption the lowest?

(c) When was the power consumption the highest?

Source: Pacific Gas & Electric

44. Earthquake The graph shows the vertical acceleration of the ground from the 1994 Northridge earthquake in Los Angeles, as measured by a seismograph. (Here t represents the time in seconds.)

(a) At what time t did the earthquake first make noticeable movements of the earth?

(b) At what time t did the earthquake seem to end?

(c) At what time t was the maximum intensity of the earthquake reached?

45. Weight Function The graph gives the weight W of a person at age x.

(a) Determine the intervals on which the function W is increasing and those on which it is decreasing.

(b) What do you think happened when this person was 30 years old?

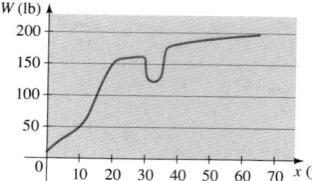

46. Distance Function The graph gives a sales representative's distance from his home as a function of time on a certain day.

(a) Determine the time intervals on which his distance from home was increasing and those on which it was decreasing.

(b) Describe in words what the graph indicates about his travels on this day.

47. Changing Water Levels The graph shows the depth of water W in a reservoir over a one-year period as a function of the number of days x since the beginning of the year.

(a) Determine the intervals on which the function W is increasing and on which it is decreasing.

(b) At what value of x does W achieve a local maximum? A local minimum?

48. Population Growth and Decline The graph shows the population P in a small industrial city from 1950 to 2000. The variable x represents the number of years since 1950.
(a) Determine the intervals on which the function P is increasing and on which it is decreasing.
(b) What was the maximum population, and in what year was it attained?

49. Hurdle Race Three runners compete in a 100-meter hurdle race. The graph depicts the distance run as a function of time for each runner. Describe in words what the graph tells you about this race. Who won the race? Did each runner finish the race? What do you think happened to runner B?

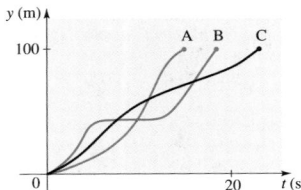

50. Gravity Near the Moon We can use Newton's Law of Gravity to measure the gravitational attraction between the moon and an algebra student in a space ship located a distance x above the moon's surface:

$$F(x) = \frac{350}{x^2}$$

Here F is measured in newtons (N), and x is measured in millions of meters.
(a) Graph the function F for values of x between 0 and 10.
(b) Use the graph to describe the behavior of the gravitational attraction F as the distance x increases.

51. Radii of Stars Astronomers infer the radii of stars using the Stefan Boltzmann Law:

$$E(T) = (5.67 \times 10^{-8})T^4$$

where E is the energy radiated per unit of surface area

measured in watts (W) and T is the absolute temperature measured in kelvins (K).
(a) Graph the function E for temperatures T between 100 K and 300 K.
(b) Use the graph to describe the change in energy E as the temperature T increases.

52. Migrating Fish A fish swims at a speed v relative to the water, against a current of 5 mi/h. Using a mathematical model of energy expenditure, it can be shown that the total energy E required to swim a distance of 10 mi is given by

$$E(v) = 2.73v^3\frac{10}{v - 5}$$

Biologists believe that migrating fish try to minimize the total energy required to swim a fixed distance. Find the value of v that minimizes energy required.

NOTE: This result has been verified; migrating fish swim against a current at a speed 50% greater than the speed of the current.

53. Highway Engineering A highway engineer wants to estimate the maximum number of cars that can safely travel a particular highway at a given speed. She assumes that each car is 17 ft long, travels at a speed s, and follows the car in front of it at the "safe following distance" for that speed. She finds that the number N of cars that can pass a given point per minute is modeled by the function

$$N(s) = \frac{88s}{17 + 17\left(\dfrac{s}{20}\right)^2}$$

At what speed can the greatest number of cars travel the highway safely?

54. Volume of Water Between 0°C and 30°C, the volume V (in cubic centimeters) of 1 kg of water at a temperature T is given by the formula

$$V = 999.87 - 0.06426T + 0.0085043T^2 - 0.0000679T^3$$

Find the temperature at which the volume of 1 kg of water is a minimum.

55. Coughing When a foreign object that is lodged in the trachea (windpipe) forces a person to cough, the diaphragm thrusts upward, causing an increase in pressure in the lungs. At the same time, the trachea contracts, causing the expelled air to move faster and increasing the pressure on the foreign object. According to a mathematical model of coughing, the velocity v of the airstream through an average-sized person's trachea is related to the radius r of the trachea (in centimeters) by the function

$$v(r) = 3.2(1 - r)r^2 \qquad \tfrac{1}{2} \le r \le 1$$

Determine the value of r for which v is a maximum.

DISCOVERY ▪ DISCUSSION ▪ WRITING

56. Functions That Are Always Increasing or Decreasing   Sketch rough graphs of functions that are defined for all real numbers and that exhibit the indicated behavior (or explain why the behavior is impossible).
(a) f is always increasing, and $f(x) > 0$ for all x
(b) f is always decreasing, and $f(x) > 0$ for all x
(c) f is always increasing, and $f(x) < 0$ for all x
(d) f is always decreasing, and $f(x) < 0$ for all x

57. Maxima and Minima   In Example 7 we saw a real-world situation in which the maximum value of a function is important. Name several other everyday situations in which a maximum or minimum value is important.

58. Minimizing a Distance   When we seek a minimum or maximum value of a function, it is sometimes easier to work with a simpler function instead.
(a) Suppose
$$g(x) = \sqrt{f(x)}$$
where $f(x) \geq 0$ for all x. Explain why the local minima and maxima of f and g occur at the same values of x.
(b) Let $g(x)$ be the distance between the point $(3, 0)$ and the point (x, x^2) on the graph of the parabola $y = x^2$. Express g as a function of x.
(c) Find the minimum value of the function g that you found in part (b). Use the principle described in part (a) to simplify your work.

SUGGESTED TIME AND EMPHASIS
$\frac{1}{2}$–1 class, essential material

2.4 AVERAGE RATE OF CHANGE OF A FUNCTION

| Average Rate of Change ▶ Linear Functions Have Constant Rate of Change

Functions are often used to model changing quantities. In this section we learn how to find the rate at which the values of a function change as the input variable changes.

▼ Average Rate of Change

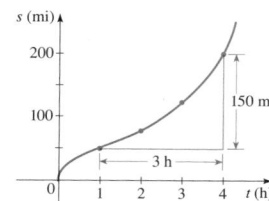

We are all familiar with the concept of speed: If you drive a distance of 120 miles in 2 hours, then your average speed, or rate of travel, is $\frac{120 \text{ mi}}{2 \text{ h}} = 60$ mi/h. Now suppose you take a car trip and record the distance that you travel every few minutes. The distance s you have traveled is a function of the time t:

$$s(t) = \text{total distance traveled at time } t$$

We graph the function s as shown in Figure 1. The graph shows that you have traveled a total of 50 miles after 1 hour, 75 miles after 2 hours, 140 miles after 3 hours, and so on. To find your *average* speed between any two points on the trip, we divide the distance traveled by the time elapsed.

FIGURE 1
Average speed

Let's calculate your average speed between 1:00 P.M. and 4:00 P.M. The time elapsed is $4 - 1 = 3$ hours. To find the distance you traveled, we subtract the distance at 1:00 P.M. from the distance at 4:00 P.M., that is, $200 - 50 = 150$ mi. Thus, your average speed is

$$\text{average speed} = \frac{\text{distance traveled}}{\text{time elapsed}} = \frac{150 \text{ mi}}{3 \text{ h}} = 50 \text{ mi/h}$$

TEXT QUESTIONS
Let $f(t) = 3t + 2$.

(a) What is the average rate of change of f from $t = 1$ to $t = 3$?
(b) What is the average rate of change of f from $t = 1$ to $t = \pi$?

Answers
(a) 3
(b) 3

The average speed that we have just calculated can be expressed by using function notation:

$$\text{average speed} = \frac{s(4) - s(1)}{4 - 1} = \frac{200 - 50}{3} = 50 \text{ mi/h}$$

Note that the average speed is different over different time intervals. For example, between 2:00 P.M. and 3:00 P.M. we find that

$$\text{average speed} = \frac{s(3) - s(2)}{3 - 2} = \frac{140 - 75}{1} = 65 \text{ mi/h}$$

Finding average rates of change is important in many contexts. For instance, we might be interested in knowing how quickly the air temperature is dropping as a storm approaches or how fast revenues are increasing from the sale of a new product. So we need to know how to determine the average rate of change of the functions that model these quantities. In fact, the concept of average rate of change can be defined for any function.

AVERAGE RATE OF CHANGE

The **average rate of change** of the function $y = f(x)$ between $x = a$ and $x = b$ is

$$\text{average rate of change} = \frac{\text{change in } y}{\text{change in } x} = \frac{f(b) - f(a)}{b - a}$$

The average rate of change is the slope of the **secant line** between $x = a$ and $x = b$ on the graph of f, that is, the line that passes through $(a, f(a))$ and $(b, f(b))$.

EXAMPLE 1 | Calculating the Average Rate of Change

For the function $f(x) = (x - 3)^2$, whose graph is shown in Figure 2, find the average rate of change between the following points:

(a) $x = 1$ and $x = 3$ **(b)** $x = 4$ and $x = 7$

SOLUTION

(a) Average rate of change $= \dfrac{f(3) - f(1)}{3 - 1}$ Definition

$$= \frac{(3 - 3)^2 - (1 - 3)^2}{3 - 1} \quad \text{Use } f(x) = (x - 3)^2$$

$$= \frac{0 - 4}{2} = -2$$

FIGURE 2 $f(x) = (x - 3)^2$

ALTERNATE EXAMPLE 1

(a) For the function $f(x) = x^2 + 7$, find the average rate of change between $x = 2$ and $x = 7$.

(b) For the function $f(x) = x^2 + 6$, find the average rate of change of the function between the points $x = y$ and $x = y + d$ $(d \neq 0)$.

ANSWERS
(a) 9
(b) $2y + d$

IN-CLASS MATERIALS

Students should see the geometry of the average rate of change—that the average rate of change from $x = a$ to $x = b$ is the slope of the line from $(a, f(a))$ to $(b, f(b))$. Armed with this knowledge, students now have a way of estimating average rate of change: graph the function (making sure that the x- and y-scales are the same), plot the relevant points, and then estimate the slope of the line between them.

(b) Average rate of change $= \dfrac{f(7) - f(4)}{7 - 4}$ Definition

$= \dfrac{(7 - 3)^2 - (4 - 3)^2}{7 - 4}$ Use $f(x) = (x - 3)^2$

$= \dfrac{16 - 1}{3} = 5$

✎ **NOW TRY EXERCISE 11** ∎

ALTERNATE EXAMPLE 2

Find the direction and the value when vertically shifting the graph of the function $f(x) = x^3 - 3x$ to obtain the graph of the function $g(x) = x^3 - 3x - 25$.

ANSWER

Downward, 25

EXAMPLE 2 | Average Speed of a Falling Object

If an object is dropped from a high cliff or a tall building, then the distance it has fallen after t seconds is given by the function $d(t) = 16t^2$. Find its average speed (average rate of change) over the following intervals:

(a) Between 1 s and 5 s   **(b)** Between $t = a$ and $t = a + h$

SOLUTION

Function: In t seconds the stone falls $16t^2$ ft.

(a) Average rate of change $= \dfrac{d(5) - d(1)}{5 - 1}$ Definition

$= \dfrac{16(5)^2 - 16(1)^2}{5 - 1}$ Use $d(t) = 16t^2$

$= \dfrac{400 - 16}{4}$

$= 96$ ft/s

(b) Average rate of change $= \dfrac{d(a + h) - d(a)}{(a + h) - a}$ Definition

$= \dfrac{16(a + h)^2 - 16(a)^2}{(a + h) - a}$ Use $d(t) = 16t^2$

$= \dfrac{16(a^2 + 2ah + h^2 - a^2)}{h}$ Expand and factor 16

$= \dfrac{16(2ah + h^2)}{h}$ Simplify numerator

$= \dfrac{16h(2a + h)}{h}$ Factor h

$= 16(2a + h)$ Simplify

✎ **NOW TRY EXERCISE 15** ∎

The average rate of change calculated in Example 2(b) is known as a *difference quotient*. In calculus we use difference quotients to calculate *instantaneous* rates of change. An example of an instantaneous rate of change is the speed shown on the speedometer of your car. This changes from one instant to the next as your car's speed changes.

The graphs in Figure 3 show that if a function is increasing on an interval, then the average rate of change between any two points is positive, whereas if a function is decreasing on an interval, then the average rate of change between any two points is negative.

IN-CLASS MATERIALS

It is possible, at this point, to foreshadow calculus nicely. Take a simple function such as $l(t) = t^2$ and look at the average rate of change from $t = 1$ to $t = 2$. Then look at the average rate of change from $t = 1$ to $t = \frac{3}{2}$. If students work in parallel, they should be able to fill in the following table:

From	To	Average Rate of Change
$t = 1$	2	2
$t = 1$	1.5	2.5
$t = 1$	1.25	2.25
$t = 1$	1.1	2.1
$t = 1$	1.01	2.01
$t = 1$	1.001	2.001

Note that these numbers seem to be approaching 2.

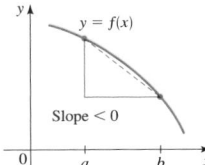

f increasing
Average rate of change positive

f decreasing
Average rate of change negative

FIGURE 3

EXAMPLE 3 | Average Rate of Temperature Change

The table gives the outdoor temperatures observed by a science student on a spring day. Draw a graph of the data, and find the average rate of change of temperature between the following times:

(a) 8:00 A.M. and 9:00 A.M.

(b) 1:00 P.M. and 3:00 P.M.

(c) 4:00 P.M. and 7:00 P.M.

Time	Temperature (°F)
8:00 A.M.	38
9:00 A.M.	40
10:00 A.M.	44
11:00 A.M.	50
12:00 NOON	56
1:00 P.M.	62
2:00 P.M.	66
3:00 P.M.	67
4:00 P.M.	64
5:00 P.M.	58
6:00 P.M.	55
7:00 P.M.	51

SOLUTION   A graph of the temperature data is shown in Figure 4. Let t represent time, measured in hours since midnight (so, for example, 2:00 P.M. corresponds to $t = 14$). Define the function F by

$$F(t) = \text{temperature at time } t$$

(a) Average rate of change $= \dfrac{\text{temperature at 9 A.M.} - \text{temperature at 8 A.M.}}{9 - 8}$

$$= \frac{F(9) - F(8)}{9 - 8} = \frac{40 - 38}{9 - 8} = 2$$

The average rate of change was 2°F per hour.

FIGURE 4

ALTERNATE EXAMPLE 3
The table gives the outdoor temperatures observed by a science student on a spring day. Find the average rate of change of temperature between the following times:

(a) 10:00 A.M. and 11:00 A.M.

(b) 11:00 A.M. and 2:00 P.M.

Time	Temperature (°F)
8:00 A.M.	35
9:00 A.M.	38
10:00 A.M.	40
11:00 A.M.	45
12:00 NOON	50
1:00 P.M.	53
2:00 P.M.	55
3:00 P.M.	56
4:00 P.M.	54
5:00 P.M.	51
6:00 P.M.	47
7:00 P.M.	45

ANSWER

(a) 5

(b) 10/3

EXAMPLE

Let $f(x) = x^2 - x + 1$. Find the average rate of change between $x = 1$ and $x = 5$.

Answer

5

(b) Average rate of change $= \dfrac{\text{temperature at 3 P.M.} - \text{temperature at 1 P.M.}}{15 - 13}$

$$= \dfrac{F(15) - F(13)}{15 - 13} = \dfrac{67 - 62}{2} = 2.5$$

The average rate of change was 2.5°F per hour.

(c) Average rate of change $= \dfrac{\text{temperature at 7 P.M.} - \text{temperature at 4 P.M.}}{19 - 16}$

$$= \dfrac{F(19) - F(16)}{19 - 16} = \dfrac{51 - 64}{3} \approx -4.3$$

The average rate of change was about −4.3°F per hour during this time interval. The negative sign indicates that the temperature was dropping.

✎. NOW TRY EXERCISE **25**

▼ Linear Functions Have Constant Rate of Change

For a linear function $f(x) = mx + b$ the average rate of change between any two points is the same constant m. This agrees with what we learned in Section 1.10: that the slope of a line $y = mx + b$ is the average rate of change of y with respect to x. On the other hand, if a function f has constant average rate of change, then it must be a linear function. You are asked to prove this fact in Exercise 33. In the next example we find the average rate of change for a particular linear function.

EXAMPLE 4 | Linear Functions Have Constant Rate of Change

Let $f(x) = 3x - 5$. Find the average rate of change of f between the following points.

(a) $x = 0$ and $x = 1$

(b) $x = 3$ and $x = 7$

(c) $x = a$ and $x = a + h$

What conclusion can you draw from your answers?

SOLUTION

(a) Average rate of change $= \dfrac{f(1) - f(0)}{1 - 0} = \dfrac{(3 \cdot 1 - 5) - (3 \cdot 0 - 5)}{1}$

$$= \dfrac{(-2) - (-5)}{1} = 3$$

(b) Average rate of change $= \dfrac{f(7) - f(3)}{7 - 3} = \dfrac{(3 \cdot 7 - 5) - (3 \cdot 3 - 5)}{4}$

$$= \dfrac{16 - 4}{4} = 3$$

(c) Average rate of change $= \dfrac{f(a + h) - f(a)}{(a + h) - a} = \dfrac{[3(a + h) - 5] - [3a - 5]}{h}$

$$= \dfrac{3a + 3h - 5 - 3a + 5}{h} = \dfrac{3h}{h} = 3$$

It appears that the average rate of change is always 3 for this function. In fact, part (c) proves that the rate of change between any two arbitrary points $x = a$ and $x = a + h$ is 3.

✎. NOW TRY EXERCISE **21**

ALTERNATE EXAMPLE 4

(a) Let $f(x) = 5x - 10$. Find the average rate of change between $x = 4$ and $x = 8$.

(b) Let $f(x) = 3x - 4$. Find the average rate of change of f between the points $x = b$ and $x = b + d$.

ANSWERS

(a) 5

(b) 3

2.4 EXERCISES

CONCEPTS

1. If you travel 100 miles in two hours, then your average speed for the trip is

average speed = ──── = ────

2. The average rate of change of a function f between $x = a$ and $x = b$ is

average rate of change = ────

3. The average rate of change of the function $f(x) = x^2$ between $x = 1$ and $x = 5$ is

average rate of change = ──── = ────

4. (a) The average rate of change of a function f between $x = a$ and $x = b$ is the slope of the _____ line between $(a, f(a))$ and $(b, f(b))$.

(b) The average rate of change of the linear function

$f(x) = 3x + 5$ between any two points is _____.

SKILLS

5–8 ■ The graph of a function is given. Determine the average rate of change of the function between the indicated points on the graph.

5.   **6.**

7.   **8.**

9–20 ■ A function is given. Determine the average rate of change of the function between the given values of the variable.

9. $f(x) = 3x - 2$; $x = 2, x = 3$

10. $g(x) = 5 + \frac{1}{2}x$; $x = 1, x = 5$

11. $h(t) = t^2 + 2t$; $t = -1, t = 4$

12. $f(z) = 1 - 3z^2$; $z = -2, z = 0$

13. $f(x) = x^3 - 4x^2$; $x = 0, x = 10$

14. $f(x) = x + x^4$; $x = -1, x = 3$

15. $f(x) = 3x^2$; $x = 2, x = 2 + h$

16. $f(x) = 4 - x^2$; $x = 1, x = 1 + h$

17. $g(x) = \frac{1}{x}$; $x = 1, x = a$

18. $g(x) = \frac{2}{x + 1}$; $x = 0, x = h$

19. $f(t) = \frac{2}{t}$; $t = a, t = a + h$

20. $f(t) = \sqrt{t}$; $t = a, t = a + h$

21–22 ■ A linear function is given. **(a)** Find the average rate of change of the function between $x = a$ and $x = a + h$. **(b)** Show that the average rate of change is the same as the slope of the line.

21. $f(x) = \frac{1}{2}x + 3$ **22.** $g(x) = -4x + 2$

APPLICATIONS

23. Changing Water Levels   The graph shows the depth of water W in a reservoir over a one-year period as a function of the number of days x since the beginning of the year. What was the average rate of change of W between $x = 100$ and $x = 200$?

24. Population Growth and Decline   The graph shows the population P in a small industrial city from 1950 to 2000. The variable x represents the number of years since 1950.
(a) What was the average rate of change of P between $x = 20$ and $x = 40$?
(b) Interpret the value of the average rate of change that you found in part (a).

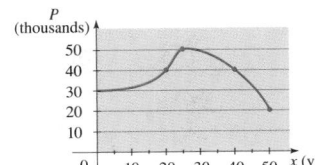

DRILL QUESTION
If $f(t) = t^2 - |3t|$, what is the average rate of change between $t = -3$ and $t = -1$?

Answer
-1

25. Population Growth and Decline The table gives the population in a small coastal community for the period 1997–2006. Figures shown are for January 1 in each year.
- (a) What was the average rate of change of population between 1998 and 2001?
- (b) What was the average rate of change of population between 2002 and 2004?
- (c) For what period of time was the population increasing?
- (d) For what period of time was the population decreasing?

Year	Population
1997	624
1998	856
1999	1,336
2000	1,578
2001	1,591
2002	1,483
2003	994
2004	826
2005	801
2006	745

26. Running Speed A man is running around a circular track that is 200 m in circumference. An observer uses a stopwatch to record the runner's time at the end of each lap, obtaining the data in the following table.
- (a) What was the man's average speed (rate) between 68 s and 152 s?
- (b) What was the man's average speed between 263 s and 412 s?
- (c) Calculate the man's speed for each lap. Is he slowing down, speeding up, or neither?

Time (s)	Distance (m)
32	200
68	400
108	600
152	800
203	1000
263	1200
335	1400
412	1600

27. CD Player Sales The table shows the number of CD players sold in a small electronics store in the years 1993–2003.
- (a) What was the average rate of change of sales between 1993 and 2003?
- (b) What was the average rate of change of sales between 1993 and 1994?
- (c) What was the average rate of change of sales between 1994 and 1996?

(d) Between which two successive years did CD player sales *increase* most quickly? *Decrease* most quickly?

Year	CD players sold
1993	512
1994	520
1995	413
1996	410
1997	468
1998	510
1999	590
2000	607
2001	732
2002	612
2003	584

28. Book Collection Between 1980 and 2000, a rare book collector purchased books for his collection at the rate of 40 books per year. Use this information to complete the following table. (Note that not every year is given in the table.)

Year	Number of books
1980	420
1981	460
1982	
1985	
1990	
1992	
1995	
1997	
1998	
1999	
2000	1220

29. Cooling Soup When a bowl of hot soup is left in a room, the soup eventually cools down to room temperature. The temperature T of the soup is a function of time t. The table below gives the temperature (in °F) of a bowl of soup t minutes after it was set on the table. Find the average rate of change of the temperature of the soup over the first 20 minutes and over the next 20 minutes. During which interval did the soup cool off more quickly?

t (min)	T (°F)	t (min)	T (°F)
0	200	35	94
5	172	40	89
10	150	50	81
15	133	60	77
20	119	90	72
25	108	120	70
30	100	150	70

30. Farms in the United States The graph gives the number of farms in the United States from 1850 to 2000.

(a) Estimate the average rate of change in the number of farms between (i) 1860 and 1890 and (ii) 1950 and 1970.

(b) In which decade did the number of farms experience the greatest average rate of decline?

DISCOVERY ▪ DISCUSSION ▪ WRITING

31. 100-Meter Race A 100-m race ends in a three-way tie for first place. The graph at the top of the next column shows distance as a function of time for each of the three winners.

(a) Find the average speed for each winner.

(b) Describe the differences between the ways in which the three runners ran the race.

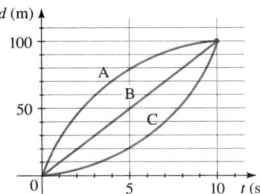

32. Linear Functions Have Constant Rate of Change
If $f(x) = mx + b$ is a linear function, then the average rate of change of f between any two real numbers x_1 and x_2 is

$$\text{average rate of change} = \frac{f(x_2) - f(x_1)}{x_2 - x_1}$$

Calculate this average rate of change to show that it is the same as the slope m.

33. Functions with Constant Rate of Change Are Linear
If the function f has the same average rate of change c between any two points, then for the points a and x we have

$$c = \frac{f(x) - f(a)}{x - a}$$

Rearrange this expression to show that

$$f(x) = cx + (f(a) - ca)$$

and conclude that f is a linear function.

2.5 TRANSFORMATIONS OF FUNCTIONS

> Vertical Shifting ▶ Horizontal Shifting ▶ Reflecting Graphs ▶ Vertical Stretching and Shrinking ▶ Horizontal Stretching and Shrinking ▶ Even and Odd Functions

In this section we study how certain transformations of a function affect its graph. This will give us a better understanding of how to graph functions. The transformations that we study are shifting, reflecting, and stretching.

▼ Vertical Shifting

Adding a constant to a function shifts its graph vertically: upward if the constant is positive and downward if it is negative.

In general, suppose we know the graph of $y = f(x)$. How do we obtain from it the graphs of

$$y = f(x) + c \qquad \text{and} \qquad y = f(x) - c \qquad (c > 0)$$

Recall that the graph of the function f is the same as the graph of the equation $y = f(x)$.

The y-coordinate of each point on the graph of $y = f(x) + c$ is c units above the y-coordinate of the corresponding point on the graph of $y = f(x)$. So we obtain the graph of $y = f(x) + c$ simply by shifting the graph of $y = f(x)$ upward c units. Similarly, we obtain the graph of $y = f(x) - c$ by shifting the graph of $y = f(x)$ downward c units.

SUGGESTED TIME AND EMPHASIS

1 class, essential material

TEXT QUESTION

What is the difference between a vertical stretch and a vertical shift?

Answer

A vertical stretch extends the graph in the vertical direction, changing its shape. A vertical shift simply moves the graph in the vertical direction, preserving its shape.

VERTICAL SHIFTS OF GRAPHS

Suppose $c > 0$.

To graph $y = f(x) + c$, shift the graph of $y = f(x)$ upward c units.

To graph $y = f(x) - c$, shift the graph of $y = f(x)$ downward c units.

ALTERNATE EXAMPLE 1

How is the graph of

$f(x) = x^4 - 2x$ related to the

graph of $g(x) = x^4 - 2x + 3$?

ANSWER

g is obtained by vertically shifting the graph f by 3 units upward.

EXAMPLE 1 | Vertical Shifts of Graphs

Use the graph of $f(x) = x^2$ to sketch the graph of each function.

(a) $g(x) = x^2 + 3$ **(b)** $h(x) = x^2 - 2$

SOLUTION The function $f(x) = x^2$ was graphed in Example 1(a), Section 2.2. It is sketched again in Figure 1.

(a) Observe that

$$g(x) = x^2 + 3 = f(x) + 3$$

So the y-coordinate of each point on the graph of g is 3 units above the corresponding point on the graph of f. This means that to graph g, we shift the graph of f upward 3 units, as in Figure 1.

(b) Similarly, to graph h, we shift the graph of f downward 2 units, as shown in Figure 1.

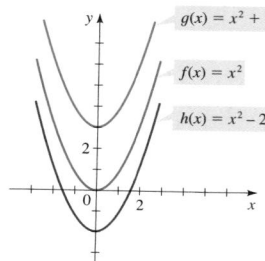

FIGURE 1

✎. NOW TRY EXERCISES **21** AND **23** ■

▼ **Horizontal Shifting**

Suppose that we know the graph of $y = f(x)$. How do we use it to obtain the graphs of

$$y = f(x + c) \quad \text{and} \quad y = f(x - c) \quad (c > 0)$$

The value of $f(x - c)$ at x is the same as the value of $f(x)$ at $x - c$. Since $x - c$ is c units to the left of x, it follows that the graph of $y = f(x - c)$ is just the graph of $y = f(x)$

IN-CLASS MATERIALS

Students will often view this section as a process of memorizing eight similar formulas. Although it doesn't hurt to memorize how to shift, reflect, or stretch a graph, emphasize to students the importance of understanding what they are doing when they transform a graph.

shifted to the right c units. Similar reasoning shows that the graph of $y = f(x + c)$ is the graph of $y = f(x)$ shifted to the left c units. The following box summarizes these facts.

HORIZONTAL SHIFTS OF GRAPHS

Suppose $c > 0$.

To graph $y = f(x - c)$, shift the graph of $y = f(x)$ to the right c units.

To graph $y = f(x + c)$, shift the graph of $y = f(x)$ to the left c units.

EXAMPLE 2 | Horizontal Shifts of Graphs

Use the graph of $f(x) = x^2$ to sketch the graph of each function.

(a) $g(x) = (x + 4)^2$ (b) $h(x) = (x - 2)^2$

SOLUTION

(a) To graph g, we shift the graph of f to the left 4 units.

(b) To graph h, we shift the graph of f to the right 2 units.

The graphs of g and h are sketched in Figure 2.

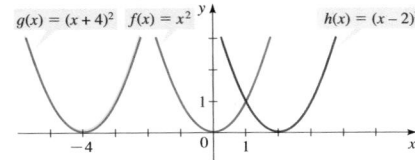

FIGURE 2

✎. NOW TRY EXERCISE **25** AND **27**

RENÉ DESCARTES (1596–1650) was born in the town of La Haye in southern France. From an early age Descartes liked mathematics because of "the certainty of its results and the clarity of its reasoning." He believed that to arrive at truth, one must begin by doubting everything, including one's own existence; this led him to formulate perhaps the best-known sentence in all of philosophy: "I think, therefore I am." In his book *Discourse on Method* he described what is now called the Cartesian plane. This idea of combining algebra and geometry enabled mathematicians for the first time to graph functions and thus "see" the equations they were studying. The philosopher John Stuart Mill called this invention "the greatest single step ever made in the progress of the exact sciences." Descartes liked to get up late and spend the morning in bed thinking and writing. He invented the coordinate plane while lying in bed watching a fly crawl on the ceiling, reasoning that he could describe the exact location of the fly by knowing its distance from two perpendicular walls. In 1649 Descartes became the tutor of Queen Christina of Sweden. She liked her lessons at 5 o'clock in the morning, when, she said, her mind was sharpest. However, the change from his usual habits and the ice-cold library where they studied proved too much for Descartes. In February 1650, after just two months of this, he caught pneumonia and died.

ALTERNATE EXAMPLE 2

How is the graph of $f(x) = x^4 - 2x$ related to the graph of $g(x) = (x - 6)^4 - 2(x - 6)$?

ANSWER

g is obtained by horizontally shifting the graph f by 6 units to the right.

IN-CLASS MATERIALS

Show the class a function they have not learned about yet, such as $f(x) = \sin x$. (If students know about sin, then show them arctan or e^{-x^2}—any function with which they are unfamiliar.) Point out that even though they don't know a lot about $\sin x$, once they've seen the graph, they can graph $\sin x + 3$, $\sin (x - 1)$, $2 \sin x$, $-\sin x$, etc.

MATHEMATICS IN THE MODERN WORLD

Computers

For centuries machines have been designed to perform specific tasks. For example, a washing machine washes clothes, a weaving machine weaves cloth, an adding machine adds numbers, and so on. The computer has changed all that.

The computer is a machine that does nothing—until it is given instructions on what to do. So your computer can play games, draw pictures, or calculate π to a million decimal places; it all depends on what program (or instructions) you give the computer. The computer can do all this because it is able to accept instructions and logically change those instructions based on incoming data. This versatility makes computers useful in nearly every aspect of human endeavor.

The idea of a computer was described theoretically in the 1940s by the mathematician Allan Turing (see page 100) in what he called a *universal machine.* In 1945 the mathematician John Von Neumann, extending Turing's ideas, built one of the first electronic computers.

Mathematicians continue to develop new theoretical bases for the design of computers. The heart of the computer is the "chip," which is capable of processing logical instructions. To get an idea of the chip's complexity, consider that the Pentium chip has over 3.5 million logic circuits!

EXAMPLE 3 | Combining Horizontal and Vertical Shifts

Sketch the graph of $f(x) = \sqrt{x - 3} + 4$.

SOLUTION We start with the graph of $y = \sqrt{x}$ (Example 1(c), Section 2.2) and shift it to the right 3 units to obtain the graph of $y = \sqrt{x - 3}$. Then we shift the resulting graph upward 4 units to obtain the graph of $f(x) = \sqrt{x - 3} + 4$ shown in Figure 3.

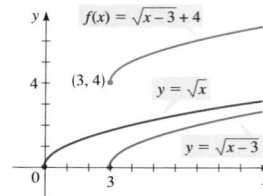

FIGURE 3

NOW TRY EXERCISE **37**

▼ **Reflecting Graphs**

Suppose we know the graph of $y = f(x)$. How do we use it to obtain the graphs of $y = -f(x)$ and $y = f(-x)$? The y-coordinate of each point on the graph of $y = -f(x)$ is simply the negative of the y-coordinate of the corresponding point on the graph of $y = f(x)$. So the desired graph is the reflection of the graph of $y = f(x)$ in the x-axis. On the other hand, the value of $y = f(-x)$ at x is the same as the value of $y = f(x)$ at $-x$, so the desired graph here is the reflection of the graph of $y = f(x)$ in the y-axis. The following box summarizes these observations.

REFLECTING GRAPHS

To graph $y = -f(x)$, reflect the graph of $y = f(x)$ in the x-axis.

To graph $y = f(-x)$, reflect the graph of $y = f(x)$ in the y-axis.

EXAMPLE 4 | Reflecting Graphs

Sketch the graph of each function.

(a) $f(x) = -x^2$ (b) $g(x) = \sqrt{-x}$

SOLUTION

(a) We start with the graph of $y = x^2$. The graph of $f(x) = -x^2$ is the graph of $y = x^2$ reflected in the x-axis (see Figure 4).

IN-CLASS MATERIALS

This is a good time in the course to start seriously discussing parameters. Ask your students to imagine a scientist who knows that a given function will be shaped like a stretched parabola but has to do some more measurements to find out exactly what the stretching factor is. In other words, she can write $f(x) = -ax^2$, noting that she will have to figure out the a experimentally. The a is not a variable, it is a parameter. Similarly, if we are going to do a bunch of calculations with the function $f(x) = \sqrt[3]{x} + 2$, and then do the same calculations with $\sqrt[3]{x} + 3$, $\sqrt[3]{x} - \pi$, and $\sqrt[3]{x} - \frac{2}{3}$, it is faster and easier to do the set of calculations just once, with the function $g(x) = \sqrt[3]{x} + h$, and then fill in the different values for h at the end. Again, this letter h is called a parameter. Ask the class how, in the expression $f(t) = t + 3s$, they can tell which is the variable and which is the parameter—the answer may encourage them to use careful notation.

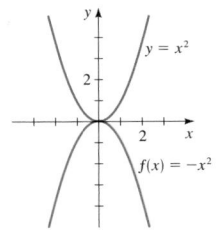

FIGURE 4

(b) We start with the graph of $y = \sqrt{x}$ (Example 1(c) in Section 2.2). The graph of $g(x) = \sqrt{-x}$ is the graph of $y = \sqrt{x}$ reflected in the y-axis (see Figure 5). Note that the domain of the function $g(x) = \sqrt{-x}$ is $\{x \mid x \le 0\}$.

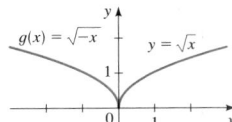

FIGURE 5

✎ NOW TRY EXERCISES **29** AND **31** ■

▼ Vertical Stretching and Shrinking

Suppose we know the graph of $y = f(x)$. How do we use it to obtain the graph of $y = cf(x)$? The y-coordinate of $y = cf(x)$ at x is the same as the corresponding y-coordinate of $y = f(x)$ multiplied by c. Multiplying the y-coordinates by c has the effect of vertically stretching or shrinking the graph by a factor of c.

VERTICAL STRETCHING AND SHRINKING OF GRAPHS

To graph $y = cf(x)$:

If $c > 1$, stretch the graph of $y = f(x)$ vertically by a factor of c.

If $0 < c < 1$, shrink the graph of $y = f(x)$ vertically by a factor of c.

$y = cf(x)$ / $y = f(x)$	$y = f(x)$ / $y = cf(x)$
$c > 1$	$0 < c < 1$

EXAMPLE 5 | Vertical Stretching and Shrinking of Graphs

Use the graph of $f(x) = x^2$ to sketch the graph of each function.

(a) $g(x) = 3x^2$ **(b)** $h(x) = \frac{1}{3}x^2$

SOLUTION

(a) The graph of g is obtained by multiplying the y-coordinate of each point on the graph of f by 3. That is, to obtain the graph of g, we stretch the graph of f vertically by a factor of 3. The result is the narrower parabola in Figure 6.

(b) The graph of h is obtained by multiplying the y-coordinate of each point on the graph of f by $\frac{1}{3}$. That is, to obtain the graph of h, we shrink the graph of f vertically by a factor of $\frac{1}{3}$. The result is the wider parabola in Figure 6.

✎ NOW TRY EXERCISES **33** AND **35** ■

We illustrate the effect of combining shifts, reflections, and stretching in the following example.

FIGURE 6

ALTERNATE EXAMPLE 5

Find what is needed to perform (stretching or shrinking) with the graph of the function $y = x^2$ to obtain the graph of the function $f(x) = 2x^2$. Find the corresponding factor of that stretching or shrinking.

ANSWER
Stretching, 2

EXAMPLE
A distinctive-looking, asymmetric curve that can be stretched, shifted, and reflected:

$$f(x) = |x^2 - 5x + \sqrt{x}|$$

ALTERNATE EXAMPLE 6

Sketch the graph of the function

$f(x) = 3\sqrt{x + 2} + 4.$

ANSWER

Starting with the graph of $y = \sqrt{x}$, we first shift to the left 2 units to get the graph of $y = \sqrt{x + 2}$. Then we stretch by a factor of 3 to get the graph of $y = 3\sqrt{x + 2}$. Finally, we shift upward 4 units to get the graph of $f(x) = 3\sqrt{x + 2} + 4$, as shown here:

EXAMPLE 6 | Combining Shifting, Stretching, and Reflecting

Sketch the graph of the function $f(x) = 1 - 2(x - 3)^2$.

SOLUTION Starting with the graph of $y = x^2$, we first shift to the right 3 units to get the graph of $y = (x - 3)^2$. Then we reflect in the x-axis and stretch by a factor of 2 to get the graph of $y = -2(x - 3)^2$. Finally, we shift upward 1 unit to get the graph of $f(x) = 1 - 2(x - 3)^2$ shown in Figure 7.

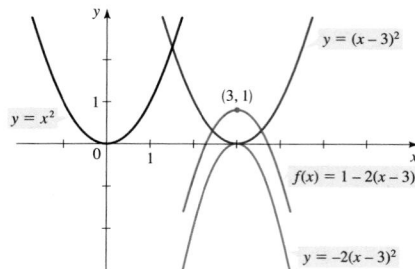

FIGURE 7

✎. NOW TRY EXERCISE **39** ∎

▼ Horizontal Stretching and Shrinking

Now we consider horizontal shrinking and stretching of graphs. If we know the graph of $y = f(x)$, then how is the graph of $y = f(cx)$ related to it? The y-coordinate of $y = f(cx)$ at x is the same as the y-coordinate of $y = f(x)$ at cx. Thus, the x-coordinates in the graph of $y = f(x)$ correspond to the x-coordinates in the graph of $y = f(cx)$ multiplied by c. Looking at this the other way around, we see that the x-coordinates in the graph of $y = f(cx)$ are the x-coordinates in the graph of $y = f(x)$ multiplied by $1/c$. In other words, to change the graph of $y = f(x)$ to the graph of $y = f(cx)$, we must shrink (or stretch) the graph horizontally by a factor of $1/c$, as summarized in the following box.

HORIZONTAL SHRINKING AND STRETCHING OF GRAPHS

To graph $y = f(cx)$:

If $c > 1$, shrink the graph of $y = f(x)$ horizontally by a factor of $1/c$.

If $0 < c < 1$, stretch the graph of $y = f(x)$ horizontally by a factor of $1/c$.

EXAMPLE 7 | Horizontal Stretching and Shrinking of Graphs

The graph of $y = f(x)$ is shown in Figure 8 on the next page. Sketch the graph of each function.

(a) $y = f(2x)$ **(b)** $y = f(\tfrac{1}{2}x)$

SONYA KOVALEVSKY (1850–1891) is considered the most important woman mathematician of the 19th century. She was born in Moscow to an aristocratic family. While a child, she was exposed to the principles of calculus in a very unusual fashion: Her bedroom was temporarily wallpapered with the pages of a calculus book. She later wrote that she "spent many hours in front of that wall, trying to understand it." Since Russian law forbade women from studying in universities, she entered a marriage of convenience, which allowed her to travel to Germany and obtain a doctorate in mathematics from the University of Göttingen. She eventually was awarded a full professorship at the University of Stockholm, where she taught for eight years before dying in an influenza epidemic at the age of 41. Her research was instrumental in helping to put the ideas and applications of functions and calculus on a sound and logical foundation. She received many accolades and prizes for her research work.

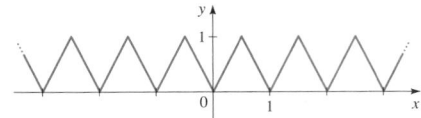

FIGURE 8 $y = f(x)$

SOLUTION   Using the principles described in the preceding box, we obtain the graphs shown in Figures 9 and 10.

FIGURE 9 $y = f(2x)$

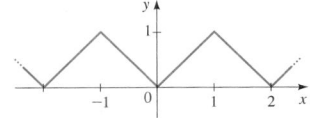

FIGURE 10 $y = f(\frac{1}{2}x)$

↖ NOW TRY EXERCISE **63**   ∎

▼ Even and Odd Functions

If a function f satisfies $f(-x) = f(x)$ for every number x in its domain, then f is called an **even function**. For instance, the function $f(x) = x^2$ is even because

$$f(-x) = (-x)^2 = (-1)^2 x^2 = x^2 = f(x)$$

The graph of an even function is symmetric with respect to the y-axis (see Figure 11). This means that if we have plotted the graph of f for $x \geq 0$, then we can obtain the entire graph simply by reflecting this portion in the y-axis.

If f satisfies $f(-x) = -f(x)$ for every number x in its domain, then f is called an **odd function**. For example, the function $f(x) = x^3$ is odd because

$$f(-x) = (-x)^3 = (-1)^3 x^3 = -x^3 = -f(x)$$

The graph of an odd function is symmetric about the origin (see Figure 12). If we have plotted the graph of f for $x \geq 0$, then we can obtain the entire graph by rotating this portion through 180° about the origin. (This is equivalent to reflecting first in the x-axis and then in the y-axis.)

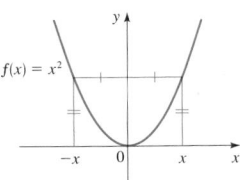

FIGURE 11 $f(x) = x^2$ is an even function.

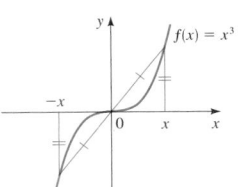

FIGURE 12 $f(x) = x^3$ is an odd function.

EVEN AND ODD FUNCTIONS

Let f be a function.

f is **even** if $f(-x) = f(x)$ for all x in the domain of f.

f is **odd** if $f(-x) = -f(x)$ for all x in the domain of f.

The graph of an even function is symmetric with respect to the y-axis.

The graph of an odd function is symmetric with respect to the origin.

ALTERNATE EXAMPLE 8

Determine whether the following functions are even, odd, or neither:

(a) $f(x) = x^3 + x$
(b) $f(x) = 7 - x^6$
(c) $f(x) = 3x - x^3$

ANSWERS

(a) Odd
(b) Even
(c) Odd

EXAMPLE 8 | Even and Odd Functions

Determine whether the functions are even, odd, or neither even nor odd.

(a) $f(x) = x^5 + x$
(b) $g(x) = 1 - x^4$
(c) $h(x) = 2x - x^2$

SOLUTION

(a) $f(-x) = (-x)^5 + (-x)$
$$= -x^5 - x = -(x^5 + x)$$
$$= -f(x)$$

Therefore, f is an odd function.

(b) $g(-x) = 1 - (-x)^4 = 1 - x^4 = g(x)$

So g is even.

(c) $h(-x) = 2(-x) - (-x)^2 = -2x - x^2$

Since $h(-x) \neq h(x)$ and $h(-x) \neq -h(x)$, we conclude that h is neither even nor odd.

✎. NOW TRY EXERCISES **75, 77,** AND **79**

The graphs of the functions in Example 8 are shown in Figure 13. The graph of f is symmetric about the origin, and the graph of g is symmetric about the y-axis. The graph of h is not symmetric either about the y-axis or the origin.

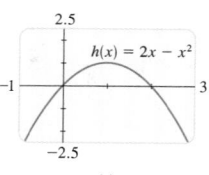

FIGURE 13

(a)   (b)   (c)

2.5 EXERCISES

CONCEPTS

1–2 ■ Fill in the blank with the appropriate direction (left, right, up, or down).

1. (a) The graph of $y = f(x) + 3$ is obtained from the graph of

$y = f(x)$ by shifting _____ 3 units.

(b) The graph of $y = f(x + 3)$ is obtained from the graph of

$y = f(x)$ by shifting _____ 3 units.

2. (a) The graph of $y = f(x) - 3$ is obtained from the graph of

$y = f(x)$ by shifting _____ 3 units.

(b) The graph of $y = f(x - 3)$ is obtained from the graph of

$y = f(x)$ by shifting _____ 3 units.

3. Fill in the blank with the appropriate axis (x-axis or y-axis).

(a) The graph of $y = -f(x)$ is obtained from the graph of

$y = f(x)$ by reflecting in the _____.

(b) The graph of $y = f(-x)$ is obtained from the graph of

$y = f(x)$ by reflecting in the _____.

4. Match the graph with the function.

(a) $y = |x + 1|$ **(b)** $y = |x - 1|$

(c) $y = |x| - 1$ **(d)** $y = -|x|$

I

II

III

IV
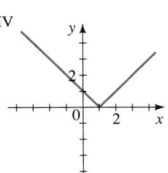

SKILLS

5–14 ■ Suppose the graph of f is given. Describe how the graph of each function can be obtained from the graph of f.

5. (a) $y = f(x) - 5$ **(b)** $y = f(x - 5)$

6. (a) $y = f(x + 7)$ **(b)** $y = f(x) + 7$

7. (a) $y = -f(x)$ **(b)** $y = f(-x)$

8. (a) $y = -2f(x)$ **(b)** $y = -\frac{1}{2}f(x)$

9. (a) $y = -f(x) + 5$ **(b)** $y = 3f(x) - 5$

10. (a) $y = f(x - 4) + \frac{3}{4}$ **(b)** $y = f(x + 4) - \frac{3}{4}$

11. (a) $y = 2f(x + 1) - 3$ **(b)** $y = 2f(x - 1) + 3$

12. (a) $y = 3 - 2f(x)$ **(b)** $y = 2 - f(-x)$

13. (a) $y = f(4x)$ **(b)** $y = f(\frac{1}{4}x)$

14. (a) $y = f(2x) - 1$ **(b)** $y = 2f(\frac{1}{2}x)$

15–18 ■ Explain how the graph of g is obtained from the graph of f.

15. (a) $f(x) = x^2$, $g(x) = (x + 2)^2$
   (b) $f(x) = x^2$, $g(x) = x^2 + 2$

16. (a) $f(x) = x^3$, $g(x) = (x - 4)^3$
   (b) $f(x) = x^3$, $g(x) = x^3 - 4$

17. (a) $f(x) = |x|$, $g(x) = |x + 2| - 2$
   (b) $f(x) = |x|$, $g(x) = |x - 2| + 2$

18. (a) $f(x) = \sqrt{x}$, $g(x) = -\sqrt{x} + 1$
   (b) $f(x) = \sqrt{x}$, $g(x) = \sqrt{-x} + 1$

19. Use the graph of $y = x^2$ in Figure 4 to graph the following.
   (a) $g(x) = x^2 + 1$
   (b) $g(x) = (x - 1)^2$
   (c) $g(x) = -x^2$
   (d) $g(x) = (x - 1)^2 + 3$

20. Use the graph of $y = \sqrt{x}$ in Figure 5 to graph the following.
   (a) $g(x) = \sqrt{x - 2}$
   (b) $g(x) = \sqrt{x} + 1$
   (c) $g(x) = \sqrt{x + 2} + 2$
   (d) $g(x) = -\sqrt{x} + 1$

21–44 ■ Sketch the graph of the function, not by plotting points, but by starting with the graph of a standard function and applying transformations.

21. $f(x) = x^2 - 1$

22. $f(x) = x^2 + 5$

23. $f(x) = \sqrt{x} + 1$

24. $f(x) = |x| - 1$

25. $f(x) = (x - 5)^2$

26. $f(x) = (x + 1)^2$

27. $f(x) = \sqrt{x + 4}$

28. $f(x) = |x - 3|$

29. $f(x) = -x^3$

30. $f(x) = -|x|$

31. $y = \sqrt[4]{-x}$

32. $y = \sqrt[3]{-x}$

33. $y = \frac{1}{4}x^2$

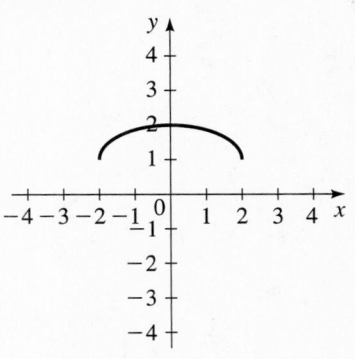

34. $y = -5\sqrt{x}$

35. $y = 3|x|$

36. $y = \frac{1}{2}|x|$

37. $y = (x - 3)^2 + 5$

38. $y = \sqrt{x + 4} - 3$

39. $y = 3 - \frac{1}{2}(x - 1)^2$

40. $y = 2 - \sqrt{x + 1}$

41. $y = |x + 2| + 2$

42. $y = 2 - |x|$

43. $y = \frac{1}{2}\sqrt{x + 4} - 3$

44. $y = 3 - 2(x - 1)^2$

45–54 ■ A function f is given, and the indicated transformations are applied to its graph (in the given order). Write the equation for the final transformed graph.

45. $f(x) = x^2$; shift upward 3 units

46. $f(x) = x^3$; shift downward 1 unit

47. $f(x) = \sqrt{x}$; shift 2 units to the left

48. $f(x) = \sqrt[3]{x}$; shift 1 unit to the right

49. $f(x) = |x|$; shift 3 units to the right and shift upward 1 unit

50. $f(x) = |x|$; shift 4 units to the left and shift downward 2 units

51. $f(x) = \sqrt[4]{x}$; reflect in the y-axis and shift upward 1 unit

52. $f(x) = x^2$; shift 2 units to the left and reflect in the x-axis

53. $f(x) = x^2$; stretch vertically by a factor of 2, shift downward 2 units, and shift 3 units to the right

54. $f(x) = |x|$; shrink vertically by a factor of $\frac{1}{2}$, shift to the left 1 unit, and shift upward 3 units

55–60 ■ The graphs of f and g are given. Find a formula for the function g.

55.

56.

57.

58.

59.

60.

61–62 ■ The graph of $y = f(x)$ is given. Match each equation with its graph.

61. **(a)** $y = f(x - 4)$ **(b)** $y = f(x) + 3$
     (c) $y = 2f(x + 6)$ **(d)** $y = -f(2x)$

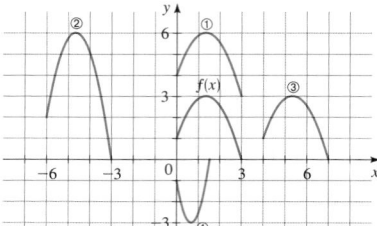

62. **(a)** $y = \frac{1}{3}f(x)$ **(b)** $y = -f(x + 4)$
     (c) $y = f(x - 4) + 3$ **(d)** $y = f(-x)$

63. The graph of f is given. Sketch the graphs of the following functions.
    (a) $y = f(x - 2)$ **(b)** $y = f(x) - 2$
    (c) $y = 2f(x)$ **(d)** $y = -f(x) + 3$
    (e) $y = f(-x)$ **(f)** $y = \frac{1}{2}f(x - 1)$

64. The graph of g is given. Sketch the graphs of the following functions.
 (a) $y = g(x + 1)$ (b) $y = g(-x)$
 (c) $y = g(x - 2)$ (d) $y = g(x) - 2$
 (e) $y = -g(x)$ (f) $y = 2g(x)$

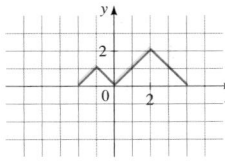

65. The graph of g is given. Use it to graph each of the following functions.
 (a) $y = g(2x)$ (b) $y = g\left(\frac{1}{2}x\right)$

66. The graph of h is given. Use it to graph each of the following functions.
 (a) $y = h(3x)$ (b) $y = h\left(\frac{1}{3}x\right)$

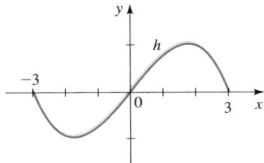

67–68 ■ Use the graph of $f(x) = [\![x]\!]$ described on page 156 to graph the indicated function.

67. $y = [\![2x]\!]$ **68.** $y = \left[\!\left[\frac{1}{4}x\right]\!\right]$

 69–72 ■ Graph the functions on the same screen using the given viewing rectangle. How is each graph related to the graph in part (a)?

69. Viewing rectangle $[-8, 8]$ by $[-2, 8]$
 (a) $y = \sqrt[4]{x}$ (b) $y = \sqrt[4]{x + 5}$
 (c) $y = 2\sqrt[4]{x + 5}$ (d) $y = 4 + 2\sqrt[4]{x + 5}$

70. Viewing rectangle $[-8, 8]$ by $[-6, 6]$
 (a) $y = |x|$ (b) $y = -|x|$
 (c) $y = -3|x|$ (d) $y = -3|x - 5|$

71. Viewing rectangle $[-4, 6]$ by $[-4, 4]$
 (a) $y = x^6$ (b) $y = \frac{1}{3}x^6$
 (c) $y = -\frac{1}{3}x^6$ (d) $y = -\frac{1}{3}(x - 4)^6$

72. Viewing rectangle $[-6, 6]$ by $[-4, 4]$
 (a) $y = \frac{1}{\sqrt{x}}$ (b) $y = \frac{1}{\sqrt{x + 3}}$
 (c) $y = \frac{1}{2\sqrt{x + 3}}$ (d) $y = \frac{1}{2\sqrt{x + 3}} - 3$

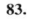 **73.** If $f(x) = \sqrt{2x - x^2}$, graph the following functions in the viewing rectangle $[-5, 5]$ by $[-4, 4]$. How is each graph related to the graph in part (a)?
 (a) $y = f(x)$ (b) $y = f(2x)$ (c) $y = f\left(\frac{1}{2}x\right)$

74. If $f(x) = \sqrt{2x - x^2}$, graph the following functions in the viewing rectangle $[-5, 5]$ by $[-4, 4]$. How is each graph related to the graph in part (a)?
 (a) $y = f(x)$ (b) $y = f(-x)$
 (c) $y = -f(-x)$ (d) $y = f(-2x)$
 (e) $y = f\left(-\frac{1}{2}x\right)$

75–82 ■ Determine whether the function f is even, odd, or neither. If f is even or odd, use symmetry to sketch its graph.

75. $f(x) = x^4$ **76.** $f(x) = x^3$
77. $f(x) = x^2 + x$ **78.** $f(x) = x^4 - 4x^2$
79. $f(x) = x^3 - x$ **80.** $f(x) = 3x^3 + 2x^2 + 1$
81. $f(x) = 1 - \sqrt[3]{x}$ **82.** $f(x) = x + \frac{1}{x}$

83–84 ■ The graph of a function defined for $x \geq 0$ is given. Complete the graph for $x < 0$ to make (a) an even function and (b) an odd function.

83.   **84.**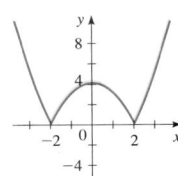

85–86 ■ These exercises show how the graph of $y = |f(x)|$ is obtained from the graph of $y = f(x)$.

85. The graphs of $f(x) = x^2 - 4$ and $g(x) = |x^2 - 4|$ are shown. Explain how the graph of g is obtained from the graph of f.

$f(x) = x^2 - 4$ $g(x) = |x^2 - 4|$

86. The graph of $f(x) = x^4 - 4x^2$ is shown. Use this graph to sketch the graph of $g(x) = |x^4 - 4x^2|$.

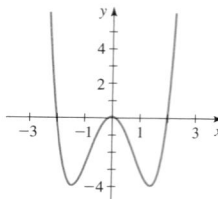

87–88 ■ Sketch the graph of each function.

87. (a) $f(x) = 4x - x^2$ **(b)** $g(x) = |4x - x^2|$

88. (a) $f(x) = x^3$ **(b)** $g(x) = |x^3|$

APPLICATIONS

89. Sales Growth The annual sales of a certain company can be modeled by the function $f(t) = 4 + 0.01t^2$, where t represents years since 1990 and $f(t)$ is measured in millions of dollars.
  (a) What shifting and shrinking operations must be performed on the function $y = t^2$ to obtain the function $y = f(t)$?
  (b) Suppose you want t to represent years since 2000 instead of 1990. What transformation would you have to apply to the function $y = f(t)$ to accomplish this? Write the new function $y = g(t)$ that results from this transformation.

90. Changing Temperature Scales The temperature on a certain afternoon is modeled by the function

$$C(t) = \tfrac{1}{2}t^2 + 2$$

where t represents hours after 12 noon ($0 \le t \le 6$) and C is measured in °C.
  (a) What shifting and shrinking operations must be performed on the function $y = t^2$ to obtain the function $y = C(t)$?
  (b) Suppose you want to measure the temperature in °F instead. What transformation would you have to apply to the function $y = C(t)$ to accomplish this? (Use the fact that the relationship between Celsius and Fahrenheit degrees is given by $F = \tfrac{9}{5}C + 32$.) Write the new function $y = F(t)$ that results from this transformation.

DISCOVERY ▪ DISCUSSION ▪ WRITING

91. Sums of Even and Odd Functions If f and g are both even functions, is $f + g$ necessarily even? If both are odd, is their sum necessarily odd? What can you say about the sum if one is odd and one is even? In each case, prove your answer.

92. Products of Even and Odd Functions Answer the same questions as in Exercise 91, except this time consider the product of f and g instead of the sum.

93. Even and Odd Power Functions What must be true about the integer n if the function

$$f(x) = x^n$$

is an even function? If it is an odd function? Why do you think the names "even" and "odd" were chosen for these function properties?

SUGGESTED TIME AND EMPHASIS

$\tfrac{1}{2}$–1 class, essential material

2.6 COMBINING FUNCTIONS

| Sums, Differences, Products, and Quotients ▶ Composition of Functions

In this section we study different ways to combine functions to make new functions.

▼ Sums, Differences, Products, and Quotients

The sum of f and g is defined by

$$(f + g)(x) = f(x) + g(x)$$

The name of the new function is "$f + g$." So this $+$ sign stands for the operation of addition of *functions*. The $+$ sign on the right side, however, stands for addition of the *numbers* $f(x)$ and $g(x)$.

Two functions f and g can be combined to form new functions $f + g$, $f - g$, fg, and f/g in a manner similar to the way we add, subtract, multiply, and divide real numbers. For example, we define the function $f + g$ by

$$(f + g)(x) = f(x) + g(x)$$

The new function $f + g$ is called the **sum** of the functions f and g; its value at x is $f(x) + g(x)$. Of course, the sum on the right-hand side makes sense only if both $f(x)$ and $g(x)$ are defined, that is, if x belongs to the domain of f and also to the domain of g. So if the domain of f is A and the domain of g is B, then the domain of $f + g$ is the intersection of these domains, that is, $A \cap B$. Similarly, we can define the **difference** $f - g$, the **product** fg, and the **quotient** f/g of the functions f and g. Their domains are $A \cap B$, but in the case of the quotient we must remember not to divide by 0.

TEXT QUESTION

The text describes addition, multiplication, division, and composition of functions. Which of these operations is represented by the following diagram?

Answer

Composition

ALGEBRA OF FUNCTIONS

Let f and g be functions with domains A and B. Then the functions $f + g$, $f - g$, fg, and f/g are defined as follows.

$$(f + g)(x) = f(x) + g(x) \qquad \text{Domain } A \cap B$$

$$(f - g)(x) = f(x) - g(x) \qquad \text{Domain } A \cap B$$

$$(fg)(x) = f(x)g(x) \qquad \text{Domain } A \cap B$$

$$\left(\frac{f}{g}\right)(x) = \frac{f(x)}{g(x)} \qquad \text{Domain } \{x \in A \cap B \mid g(x) \neq 0\}$$

EXAMPLE 1 | Combinations of Functions and Their Domains

Let $f(x) = \dfrac{1}{x - 2}$ and $g(x) = \sqrt{x}$.

(a) Find the functions $f + g$, $f - g$, fg, and f/g and their domains.

(b) Find $(f + g)(4)$, $(f - g)(4)$, $(fg)(4)$, and $(f/g)(4)$.

SOLUTION

(a) The domain of f is $\{x \mid x \neq 2\}$, and the domain of g is $\{x \mid x \geq 0\}$. The intersection of the domains of f and g is

$$\{x \mid x \geq 0 \text{ and } x \neq 2\} = [0, 2) \cup (2, \infty)$$

Thus, we have

$$(f + g)(x) = f(x) + g(x) = \frac{1}{x - 2} + \sqrt{x} \qquad \text{Domain } \{x \mid x \geq 0 \text{ and } x \neq 2\}$$

$$(f - g)(x) = f(x) - g(x) = \frac{1}{x - 2} - \sqrt{x} \qquad \text{Domain } \{x \mid x \geq 0 \text{ and } x \neq 2\}$$

$$(fg)(x) = f(x)g(x) = \frac{\sqrt{x}}{x - 2} \qquad \text{Domain } \{x \mid x \geq 0 \text{ and } x \neq 2\}$$

$$\left(\frac{f}{g}\right)(x) = \frac{f(x)}{g(x)} = \frac{1}{(x - 2)\sqrt{x}} \qquad \text{Domain } \{x \mid x > 0 \text{ and } x \neq 2\}$$

> To divide fractions, invert the denominator and multiply:
>
> $$\frac{1/(x - 2)}{\sqrt{x}} = \frac{1/(x - 2)}{\sqrt{x}/1}$$
> $$= \frac{1}{x - 2} \cdot \frac{1}{\sqrt{x}}$$
> $$= \frac{1}{(x - 2)\sqrt{x}}$$

Note that in the domain of f/g we exclude 0 because $g(0) = 0$.

(b) Each of these values exist because $x = 4$ is in the domain of each function.

$$(f + g)(4) = f(4) + g(4) = \frac{1}{4 - 2} + \sqrt{4} = \frac{5}{2}$$

$$(f - g)(4) = f(4) - g(4) = \frac{1}{4 - 2} - \sqrt{4} = -\frac{3}{2}$$

$$(fg)(4) = f(4)g(4) = \left(\frac{1}{4 - 2}\right)\sqrt{4} = 1$$

$$\left(\frac{f}{g}\right)(4) = \frac{f(4)}{g(4)} = \frac{1}{(4 - 2)\sqrt{4}} = \frac{1}{4}$$

✎ NOW TRY EXERCISE **5** ∎

ALTERNATE EXAMPLE 1

Let $f(x) = x^2$ and $g(x) = \sqrt{3x}$.

(a) Find the function $f + g$ and its domain.

(b) Find $(f + g)(3)$.

ANSWERS

(a) $x^2 + \sqrt{3x}$

(b) 12

IN-CLASS MATERIALS

Do the following problem with the class:

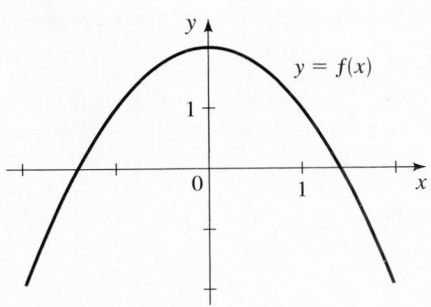

From the graph of $y = f(x) = -x^2 + 2$ shown, compute $f \circ f$ at $x = -1, 0$, and 1.
First do it graphically, then algebraically.

The graph of the function $f + g$ can be obtained from the graphs of f and g by **graphical addition**. This means that we add corresponding y-coordinates, as illustrated in the next example.

EXAMPLE 2 | Using Graphical Addition

The graphs of f and g are shown in Figure 1. Use graphical addition to graph the function $f + g$.

SOLUTION   We obtain the graph of $f + g$ by "graphically adding" the value of $f(x)$ to $g(x)$ as shown in Figure 2. This is implemented by copying the line segment PQ on top of PR to obtain the point S on the graph of $f + g$.

FIGURE 1

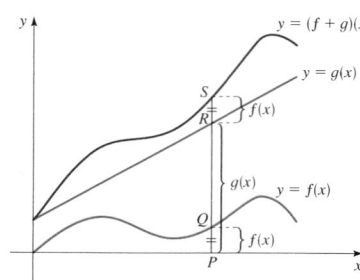

FIGURE 2   Graphical addition

◆. NOW TRY EXERCISE **15**

▼ Composition of Functions

Now let's consider a very important way of combining two functions to get a new function. Suppose $f(x) = \sqrt{x}$ and $g(x) = x^2 + 1$. We may define a new function h as

$$h(x) = f(g(x)) = f(x^2 + 1) = \sqrt{x^2 + 1}$$

The function h is made up of the functions f and g in an interesting way: Given a number x, we first apply the function g to it, then apply f to the result. In this case, f is the rule "take the square root," g is the rule "square, then add 1," and h is the rule "square, then add 1, then take the square root." In other words, we get the rule h by applying the rule g and then the rule f. Figure 3 shows a machine diagram for h.

FIGURE 3   The h machine is composed of the g machine (first) and then the f machine.

In general, given any two functions f and g, we start with a number x in the domain of g and find its image $g(x)$. If this number $g(x)$ is in the domain of f, we can then calculate the value of $f(g(x))$. The result is a new function $h(x) = f(g(x))$ that is obtained by substituting g into f. It is called the *composition* (or *composite*) of f and g and is denoted by $f \circ g$ ("f composed with g").

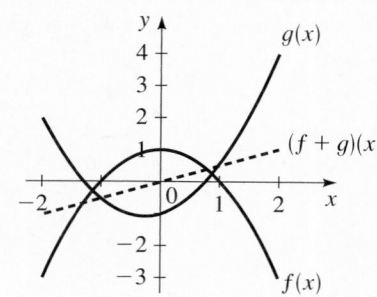

COMPOSITION OF FUNCTIONS

Given two functions f and g, the **composite function** $f \circ g$ (also called the **composition** of f and g) is defined by

$$(f \circ g)(x) = f(g(x))$$

The domain of $f \circ g$ is the set of all x in the domain of g such that $g(x)$ is in the domain of f. In other words, $(f \circ g)(x)$ is defined whenever both $g(x)$ and $f(g(x))$ are defined. We can picture $f \circ g$ using an arrow diagram (Figure 4).

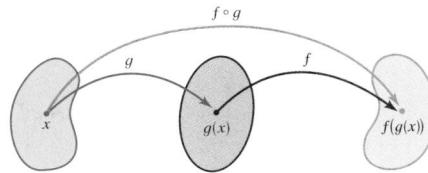

FIGURE 4 Arrow diagram for $f \circ g$

EXAMPLE 3 | Finding the Composition of Functions

Let $f(x) = x^2$ and $g(x) = x - 3$.
(a) Find the functions $f \circ g$ and $g \circ f$ and their domains.
(b) Find $(f \circ g)(5)$ and $(g \circ f)(7)$.

SOLUTION

In Example 3, f is the rule "square" and g is the rule "subtract 3." The function $f \circ g$ *first* subtracts 3 and *then* squares; the function $g \circ f$ *first* squares and *then* subtracts 3.

(a) We have

$$(f \circ g)(x) = f(g(x)) \qquad \text{Definition of } f \circ g$$
$$= f(x - 3) \qquad \text{Definition of } g$$
$$= (x - 3)^2 \qquad \text{Definition of } f$$

and

$$(g \circ f)(x) = g(f(x)) \qquad \text{Definition of } g \circ f$$
$$= g(x^2) \qquad \text{Definition of } f$$
$$= x^2 - 3 \qquad \text{Definition of } g$$

The domains of both $f \circ g$ and $g \circ f$ are $\mathbb{R}$.

(b) We have

$$(f \circ g)(5) = f(g(5)) = f(2) = 2^2 = 4$$
$$(g \circ f)(7) = g(f(7)) = g(49) = 49 - 3 = 46$$

✎ NOW TRY EXERCISES **21** AND **35**   ∎

You can see from Example 3 that, in general, $f \circ g \neq g \circ f$. Remember that the notation $f \circ g$ means that the function g is applied first and then f is applied second.

ALTERNATE EXAMPLE 3
(a) Find the function $f \circ g$ and its domain.
(b) Let $f(x) = x^2$ and $g(x) = x - 4$. Find $(g \circ f)(3)$.

ANSWERS
(a) $(x - 4)^2$, $\mathbb{R}$
(b) 5

EXAMPLE
Given $F(x) = (3x + 1)^{10}$, find functions f and g such that $F = f \circ g$.

ANSWER
We let $g(x) = 3x + 1$ and $f(x) = x^{10}$.

IN-CLASS MATERIALS

After doing a few basic examples of composition, it is possible to foreshadow the idea of inverses, which will be covered in the next section. Let $f(x) = 2x^3 + 3$ and $g(x) = x^2 - x$. Compute $f \circ g$ and $g \circ f$ for your students. Then ask them to come up with a function $h(x)$ with the property that $(f \circ h)(x) = x$.

They may not be used to the idea of coming up with examples for themselves, so the main hints they will need might be "Don't give up," "When in doubt, just try something and see what happens," and "I'm not expecting you to get it in 15 seconds." If the class is really stuck, have them try $f(x) = 2x^3$ to get a feel for

how the game is played. Once they have determined that $h(x) = \sqrt[3]{\dfrac{x - 3}{2}}$, have them compute $(h \circ f)(x)$

and have them conjecture whether, in general, if $(f \circ g)(x) = x$, then $(g \circ f)(x)$ must also equal x.

ALTERNATE EXAMPLE 4

(a) If $f(x) = \sqrt{x}$ and
$g(x) = \sqrt{4 - x}$, find the
function $f \circ g$ and its domain.

(d) If $f(x) = \sqrt{x}$ and
$g(x) = \sqrt{4 - x}$, find the
function $g \circ g$ and its
domain.

ANSWERS

(a) $\sqrt[4]{4 - x}, (-\infty, 4]$

(d) $\sqrt{4 - \sqrt{4 - x}}, [-12, 4]$

ALTERNATE EXAMPLE 5

If $f(x) = 1/x$ and $g(x) = \sqrt[4]{x - 1}$,
find the following functions and
their domains.

(a) $f \circ g$ (b) $g \circ f$

(c) $f \circ f$ (d) $g \circ g$

ANSWERS

(a) $f(g(x)) = f\left(\sqrt[4]{x - 1}\right)$

$= \dfrac{1}{\sqrt[4]{x - 1}}.$

The domain of $f \circ g$ is
$\{x \mid x > 1\}$.

(b) $g(f(x)) = g(1/x) = \sqrt[4]{\dfrac{1}{x} - 1}$

The domain of $g \circ f$ is
$\{x \mid 0 < x \le 1\}$.

(c) $f(f(x)) = x$

The domain of $f \circ f$ is
$\{x \mid x \ne 0\}$.

(d) $g(g(x)) = \sqrt[4]{\sqrt[4]{x - 1} - 1}$

The domain of $g \circ g$ is
$\{x \mid x \ge 2\}$.

The graphs of f and g of Example 4, as well as those of $f \circ g, g \circ f, f \circ f$, and $g \circ g$, are shown below. These graphs indicate that the operation of composition can produce functions that are quite different from the original functions.

$f \circ g$

$g \circ f$

$f \circ f$

$g \circ g$

EXAMPLE 4 | Finding the Composition of Functions

If $f(x) = \sqrt{x}$ and $g(x) = \sqrt{2 - x}$, find the following functions and their domains.

(a) $f \circ g$ (b) $g \circ f$ (c) $f \circ f$ (d) $g \circ g$

SOLUTION

(a) $(f \circ g)(x) = f(g(x))$ Definition of $f \circ g$

$= f(\sqrt{2 - x})$ Definition of g

$= \sqrt{\sqrt{2 - x}}$ Definition of f

$= \sqrt[4]{2 - x}$

The domain of $f \circ g$ is $\{x \mid 2 - x \ge 0\} = \{x \mid x \le 2\} = (-\infty, 2]$.

(b) $(g \circ f)(x) = g(f(x))$ Definition of $g \circ f$

$= g(\sqrt{x})$ Definition of f

$= \sqrt{2 - \sqrt{x}}$ Definition of g

For $\sqrt{x}$ to be defined, we must have $x \ge 0$. For $\sqrt{2 - \sqrt{x}}$ to be defined, we must have $2 - \sqrt{x} \ge 0$, that is, $\sqrt{x} \le 2$, or $x \le 4$. Thus, we have $0 \le x \le 4$, so the domain of $g \circ f$ is the closed interval $[0, 4]$.

(c) $(f \circ f)(x) = f(f(x))$ Definition of $f \circ f$

$= f(\sqrt{x})$ Definition of f

$= \sqrt{\sqrt{x}}$ Definition of f

$= \sqrt[4]{x}$

The domain of $f \circ f$ is $[0, \infty)$.

(d) $(g \circ g)(x) = g(g(x))$ Definition of $g \circ g$

$= g(\sqrt{2 - x})$ Definition of g

$= \sqrt{2 - \sqrt{2 - x}}$ Definition of g

This expression is defined when both $2 - x \ge 0$ and $2 - \sqrt{2 - x} \ge 0$. The first inequality means $x \le 2$, and the second is equivalent to $\sqrt{2 - x} \le 2$, or $2 - x \le 4$, or $x \ge -2$. Thus, $-2 \le x \le 2$, so the domain of $g \circ g$ is $[-2, 2]$.

🖉 **NOW TRY EXERCISE 41** ∎

It is possible to take the composition of three or more functions. For instance, the composite function $f \circ g \circ h$ is found by first applying h, then g, and then f as follows:

$$(f \circ g \circ h)(x) = f(g(h(x)))$$

EXAMPLE 5 | A Composition of Three Functions

Find $f \circ g \circ h$ if $f(x) = x/(x + 1), g(x) = x^{10}$, and $h(x) = x + 3$.

SOLUTION

$(f \circ g \circ h)(x) = f(g(h(x)))$ Definition of $f \circ g \circ h$

$= f(g(x + 3))$ Definition of h

$= f((x + 3)^{10})$ Definition of g

$= \dfrac{(x + 3)^{10}}{(x + 3)^{10} + 1}$ Definition of f

🖉 **NOW TRY EXERCISE 45** ∎

IN-CLASS MATERIALS

Point out that it is important to keep track of domains, especially when doing algebraic simplification. For example, if $f(x) = x + \sqrt{x}$ and $g(x) = 3x^2 + \sqrt{x}$, even though $(f - g)(x) = x - 3x^2$, its domain is not the real numbers, but $\{x \mid x \ge 0\}$.

So far, we have used composition to build complicated functions from simpler ones. But in calculus it is useful to be able to "decompose" a complicated function into simpler ones, as shown in the following example.

EXAMPLE 6 | Recognizing a Composition of Functions

Given $F(x) = \sqrt[4]{x + 9}$, find functions f and g such that $F = f \circ g$.

SOLUTION   Since the formula for F says to first add 9 and then take the fourth root, we let

$$g(x) = x + 9 \quad \text{and} \quad f(x) = \sqrt[4]{x}$$

Then

$$
\begin{aligned}
(f \circ g)(x) &= f(g(x)) && \text{Definition of } f \circ g \\
&= f(x + 9) && \text{Definition of } g \\
&= \sqrt[4]{x + 9} && \text{Definition of } f \\
&= F(x)
\end{aligned}
$$

✏. NOW TRY EXERCISE **49**

EXAMPLE 7 | An Application of Composition of Functions

A ship is traveling at 20 mi/h parallel to a straight shoreline. The ship is 5 mi from shore. It passes a lighthouse at noon.

(a) Express the distance s between the lighthouse and the ship as a function of d, the distance the ship has traveled since noon; that is, find f so that $s = f(d)$.

(b) Express d as a function of t, the time elapsed since noon; that is, find g so that $d = g(t)$.

(c) Find $f \circ g$. What does this function represent?

SOLUTION   We first draw a diagram as in Figure 5.

(a) We can relate the distances s and d by the Pythagorean Theorem. Thus, s can be expressed as a function of d by

$$s = f(d) = \sqrt{25 + d^2}$$

(b) Since the ship is traveling at 20 mi/h, the distance d it has traveled is a function of t as follows:

$$d = g(t) = 20t$$

(c) We have

$$
\begin{aligned}
(f \circ g)(t) &= f(g(t)) && \text{Definition of } f \circ g \\
&= f(20t) && \text{Definition of } g \\
&= \sqrt{25 + (20t)^2} && \text{Definition of } f
\end{aligned}
$$

The function $f \circ g$ gives the distance of the ship from the lighthouse as a function of time.

✏. NOW TRY EXERCISE **63**

FIGURE 5

distance = rate $\times$ time

ALTERNATE EXAMPLE 6

Find $f \circ g \circ h$ if $f(x) = \dfrac{x + 1}{x - 1}$, $g(x) = 2x + 1$, and $h(x) = x^2$.

ANSWER

$$
\begin{aligned}
f(g(h(x))) &= f(g(x^2)) \\
&= f(2x^2 + 1) \\
&= \frac{2x^2 + 2}{2x^2}
\end{aligned}
$$

ALTERNATE EXAMPLE 7

A circle has radius 2. It starts to grow. The radius is growing at 3 inches per hour.

(a) Express the area A of the circle as a function of its radius r. In other words, find f such that $A = f(r)$.

(b) Express the radius as a function of the number of hours t since the circle started to grow. That is, find g such that $r = g(t)$.

(c) Find $f \circ g$. What does this function represent?

ANSWERS

(a) $f(r) = \pi r^2$

(b) $g(t) = 2 + 3t$

(c) $(f \circ g)(t) = \pi(2 + 3t)^2$. The composite function represents the area of the circle t hours after it started to grow.

DRILL QUESTION

Let $f(x) = 4x$ and $g(x) = x^3 + x$.

(a) Compute $(f \circ g)(x)$.

(b) Compute $(g \circ f)(x)$.

Answers

(a) $4(x^3 + x) = 4x^3 + 4x$

(b) $(4x)^3 + 4x = 64x^3 + 4x$

EXAMPLE

Combined functions with graphs:

Let $f(x) = x^2 - 3x + 2$ and

$g(x) = -\sqrt{x}$.

2.6 EXERCISES

CONCEPTS

1. From the graphs of f and g in the figure, we find

$(f + g)(2) =$ _____ $(f - g)(2) =$ _____

$(fg)(2) =$ _____ $\left(\dfrac{f}{g}\right)(2) =$ _____

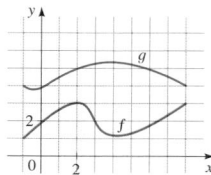

2. By definition, $f \circ g(x) =$ _____. So if $g(2) = 5$ and

$f(5) = 12$, then $f \circ g(2) =$ _____.

3. If the rule of the function f is "add one" and the rule of the function g is "multiply by 2," then the rule of $f \circ g$ is

"_____,"

and the rule of $g \circ f$ is

"_____."

4. We can express the functions in Exercise 3 algebraically as

$f(x) =$ _____ $g(x) =$ _____

$f \circ g(x) =$ _____ $g \circ f(x) =$ _____

SKILLS

5–10 ■ Find $f + g$, $f - g$, fg, and f/g and their domains.

5. $f(x) = x - 3$, $g(x) = x^2$

6. $f(x) = x^2 + 2x$, $g(x) = 3x^2 - 1$

7. $f(x) = \sqrt{4 - x^2}$, $g(x) = \sqrt{1 + x}$

8. $f(x) = \sqrt{9 - x^2}$, $g(x) = \sqrt{x^2 - 4}$

9. $f(x) = \dfrac{2}{x}$, $g(x) = \dfrac{4}{x + 4}$

10. $f(x) = \dfrac{2}{x + 1}$, $g(x) = \dfrac{x}{x + 1}$

11–14 ■ Find the domain of the function.

11. $f(x) = \sqrt{x} + \sqrt{1 - x}$ **12.** $g(x) = \sqrt{x + 1} - \dfrac{1}{x}$

13. $h(x) = (x - 3)^{-1/4}$ **14.** $k(x) = \dfrac{\sqrt{x + 3}}{x - 1}$

15–16 ■ Use graphical addition to sketch the graph of $f + g$.

15.

16.

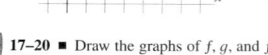

17–20 ■ Draw the graphs of f, g, and $f + g$ on a common screen to illustrate graphical addition.

17. $f(x) = \sqrt{1 + x}$, $g(x) = \sqrt{1 - x}$

18. $f(x) = x^2$, $g(x) = \sqrt{x}$

19. $f(x) = x^2$, $g(x) = \frac{1}{3}x^3$

20. $f(x) = \sqrt[4]{1 - x}$, $g(x) = \sqrt{1 - \dfrac{x^2}{9}}$

21–26 ■ Use $f(x) = 3x - 5$ and $g(x) = 2 - x^2$ to evaluate the expression.

21. (a) $f(g(0))$ **(b)** $g(f(0))$

22. (a) $f(f(4))$ **(b)** $g(g(3))$

23. (a) $(f \circ g)(-2)$ **(b)** $(g \circ f)(-2)$

24. (a) $(f \circ f)(-1)$ **(b)** $(g \circ g)(2)$

25. (a) $(f \circ g)(x)$ **(b)** $(g \circ f)(x)$

26. (a) $(f \circ f)(x)$ **(b)** $(g \circ g)(x)$

27–32 ■ Use the given graphs of f and g to evaluate the expression.

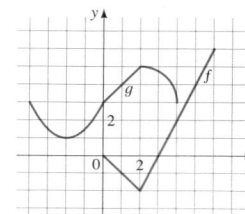

27. $f(g(2))$

28. $g(f(0))$

29. $(g \circ f)(4)$

30. $(f \circ g)(0)$

31. $(g \circ g)(-2)$

32. $(f \circ f)(4)$

33–44 ■ Find the functions $f \circ g$, $g \circ f$, $f \circ f$, and $g \circ g$ and their domains.

33. $f(x) = 2x + 3$, $g(x) = 4x - 1$

34. $f(x) = 6x - 5$, $g(x) = \dfrac{x}{2}$

35. $f(x) = x^2$, $g(x) = x + 1$

36. $f(x) = x^3 + 2$, $g(x) = \sqrt[3]{x}$

37. $f(x) = \dfrac{1}{x}$, $g(x) = 2x + 4$

38. $f(x) = x^2$, $g(x) = \sqrt{x - 3}$

39. $f(x) = |x|$, $g(x) = 2x + 3$

40. $f(x) = x - 4$, $g(x) = |x + 4|$

41. $f(x) = \dfrac{x}{x + 1}$, $g(x) = 2x - 1$

42. $f(x) = \dfrac{1}{\sqrt{x}}$, $g(x) = x^2 - 4x$

43. $f(x) = \dfrac{x}{x + 1}$, $g(x) = \dfrac{1}{x}$

44. $f(x) = \dfrac{2}{x}$, $g(x) = \dfrac{x}{x + 2}$

45–48 ■ Find $f \circ g \circ h$.

45. $f(x) = x - 1$, $g(x) = \sqrt{x}$, $h(x) = x - 1$

46. $f(x) = \dfrac{1}{x}$, $g(x) = x^3$, $h(x) = x^2 + 2$

47. $f(x) = x^4 + 1$, $g(x) = x - 5$, $h(x) = \sqrt{x}$

48. $f(x) = \sqrt{x}$, $g(x) = \dfrac{x}{x - 1}$, $h(x) = \sqrt[3]{x}$

49–54 ■ Express the function in the form $f \circ g$.

49. $F(x) = (x - 9)^5$

50. $F(x) = \sqrt{x} + 1$

51. $G(x) = \dfrac{x^2}{x^2 + 4}$

52. $G(x) = \dfrac{1}{x + 3}$

53. $H(x) = |1 - x^3|$

54. $H(x) = \sqrt{1 + \sqrt{x}}$

55–58 ■ Express the function in the form $f \circ g \circ h$.

55. $F(x) = \dfrac{1}{x^2 + 1}$

56. $F(x) = \sqrt[3]{\sqrt{x} - 1}$

57. $G(x) = (4 + \sqrt[3]{x})^9$

58. $G(x) = \dfrac{2}{(3 + \sqrt{x})^2}$

APPLICATIONS

59–60 ■ **Revenue, Cost, and Profit**   A print shop makes bumper stickers for election campaigns. If x stickers are ordered (where $x < 10{,}000$), then the price per bumper sticker is $0.15 - 0.000002x$ dollars, and the total cost of producing the order is $0.095x - 0.0000005x^2$ dollars.

59. Use the fact that

| revenue | = | price per item | × | number of items sold |

to express $R(x)$, the revenue from an order of x stickers, as a product of two functions of x.

60. Use the fact that

| profit | = | revenue | − | cost |

to express $P(x)$, the profit on an order of x stickers, as a difference of two functions of x.

61. **Area of a Ripple**   A stone is dropped in a lake, creating a circular ripple that travels outward at a speed of 60 cm/s.
 (a) Find a function g that models the radius as a function of time.
 (b) Find a function f that models the area of the circle as a function of the radius.
 (c) Find $f \circ g$. What does this function represent?

62. **Inflating a Balloon**   A spherical balloon is being inflated. The radius of the balloon is increasing at the rate of 1 cm/s.
 (a) Find a function f that models the radius as a function of time.
 (b) Find a function g that models the volume as a function of the radius.
 (c) Find $g \circ f$. What does this function represent?

63. **Area of a Balloon**   A spherical weather balloon is being inflated. The radius of the balloon is increasing at the rate of 2 cm/s. Express the surface area of the balloon as a function of time t (in seconds).

64. **Multiple Discounts**   You have a $50 coupon from the manufacturer good for the purchase of a cell phone. The store where you are purchasing your cell phone is offering a 20% discount on all cell phones. Let x represent the regular price of the cell phone.
 (a) Suppose only the 20% discount applies. Find a function f that models the purchase price of the cell phone as a function of the regular price x.

(b) Suppose only the $50 coupon applies. Find a function g that models the purchase price of the cell phone as a function of the sticker price x.

(c) If you can use the coupon and the discount, then the purchase price is either $f \circ g(x)$ or $g \circ f(x)$, depending on the order in which they are applied to the price. Find both $f \circ g(x)$ and $g \circ f(x)$. Which composition gives the lower price?

65. Multiple Discounts An appliance dealer advertises a 10% discount on all his washing machines. In addition, the manufacturer offers a $100 rebate on the purchase of a washing machine. Let x represent the sticker price of the washing machine.

(a) Suppose only the 10% discount applies. Find a function f that models the purchase price of the washer as a function of the sticker price x.

(b) Suppose only the $100 rebate applies. Find a function g that models the purchase price of the washer as a function of the sticker price x.

(c) Find $f \circ g$ and $g \circ f$. What do these functions represent? Which is the better deal?

66. Airplane Trajectory An airplane is flying at a speed of 350 mi/h at an altitude of one mile. The plane passes directly above a radar station at time $t = 0$.

(a) Express the distance s (in miles) between the plane and the radar station as a function of the horizontal distance d (in miles) that the plane has flown.

(b) Express d as a function of the time t (in hours) that the plane has flown.

(c) Use composition to express s as a function of t.

DISCOVERY ■ DISCUSSION ■ WRITING

67. Compound Interest A savings account earns 5% interest compounded annually. If you invest x dollars in such an account, then the amount $A(x)$ of the investment after one year is the initial investment plus 5%; that is,

$$A(x) = x + 0.05x = 1.05x$$

Find

$$A \circ A$$

$$A \circ A \circ A$$

$$A \circ A \circ A \circ A$$

What do these compositions represent? Find a formula for what you get when you compose n copies of A.

68. Composing Linear Functions The graphs of the functions

$$f(x) = m_1 x + b_1$$

$$g(x) = m_2 x + b_2$$

are lines with slopes m_1 and m_2, respectively. Is the graph of $f \circ g$ a line? If so, what is its slope?

69. Solving an Equation for an Unknown Function Suppose that

$$g(x) = 2x + 1$$

$$h(x) = 4x^2 + 4x + 7$$

Find a function f such that $f \circ g = h$. (Think about what operations you would have to perform on the formula for g to end up with the formula for h.) Now suppose that

$$f(x) = 3x + 5$$

$$h(x) = 3x^2 + 3x + 2$$

Use the same sort of reasoning to find a function g such that $f \circ g = h$.

70. Compositions of Odd and Even Functions Suppose that

$$h = f \circ g$$

If g is an even function, is h necessarily even? If g is odd, is h odd? What if g is odd and f is odd? What if g is odd and f is even?

2.7 ONE-TO-ONE FUNCTIONS AND THEIR INVERSES

| One-to-One Functions ▶ The Inverse of a Function ▶ Graphing the Inverse of a Function

The *inverse* of a function is a rule that acts on the output of the function and produces the corresponding input. So the inverse "undoes" or reverses what the function has done. Not all functions have inverses; those that do are called *one-to-one*.

▼ One-to-One Functions

Let's compare the functions f and g whose arrow diagrams are shown in Figure 1. Note that f never takes on the same value twice (any two numbers in A have different images), whereas g does take on the same value twice (both 2 and 3 have the same image, 4). In symbols, $g(2) = g(3)$ but $f(x_1) \neq f(x_2)$ whenever $x_1 \neq x_2$. Functions that have this latter property are called *one-to-one*.

f is one-to-one

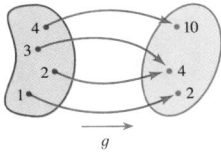
g is not one-to-one

FIGURE 1

DEFINITION OF A ONE-TO-ONE FUNCTION

A function with domain A is called a **one-to-one function** if no two elements of A have the same image, that is,

$$f(x_1) \neq f(x_2) \quad \text{whenever } x_1 \neq x_2$$

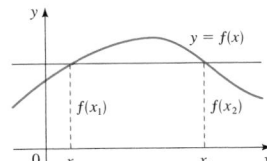

FIGURE 2 This function is not one-to-one because $f(x_1) = f(x_2)$.

An equivalent way of writing the condition for a one-to-one function is this:

$$\text{If } f(x_1) = f(x_2), \text{ then } x_1 = x_2.$$

If a horizontal line intersects the graph of f at more than one point, then we see from Figure 2 that there are numbers $x_1 \neq x_2$ such that $f(x_1) = f(x_2)$. This means that f is not one-to-one. Therefore, we have the following geometric method for determining whether a function is one-to-one.

HORIZONTAL LINE TEST

A function is one-to-one if and only if no horizontal line intersects its graph more than once.

SUGGESTED TIME AND EMPHASIS

1–2 classes, essential material

TEXT QUESTION

The function f is graphed below. Sketch the inverse function of f.

Answer

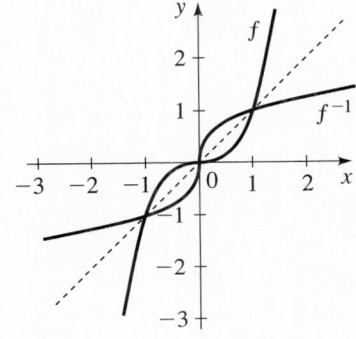

ALTERNATE EXAMPLE 1

Is the function $f(x) = 2x^3$ one-to-one?

ANSWER

Yes

ALTERNATE EXAMPLE 2

Is the function $f(x) = x^2 - 3x + 2$ one-to-one?

ANSWER

Solution 1: The function is not one-to-one because, for instance, $f(1) = 0 = f(2)$, so 1 and 2 have the same image.

Solution 2: When we graph $f(x)$, we see that it fails the horizontal line test.

ALTERNATE EXAMPLE 3

Show that $f(x) = 3x^3 - 1$ is one-to-one.

ANSWER

Suppose there are numbers x_1 and x_2 such that $f(x_1) = f(x_2)$. Then

$$3x_1^3 - 1 = 3x_2^3 - 1$$
$$3x_1^3 = 3x_2^3$$
$$x_1^3 = x_2^3$$
$$x_1 = x_2$$

Therefore, f is one-to-one.

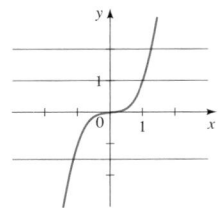

FIGURE 3 $f(x) = x^3$ is one-to-one.

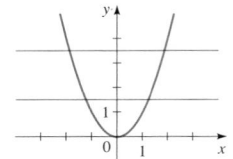

FIGURE 4 $f(x) = x^2$ is not one-to-one.

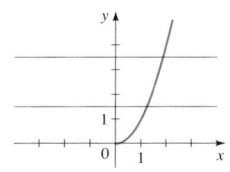

FIGURE 5 $f(x) = x^2$ ($x \geq 0$) is one-to-one.

EXAMPLE 1 | Deciding Whether a Function Is One-to-One

Is the function $f(x) = x^3$ one-to-one?

SOLUTION 1 If $x_1 \neq x_2$, then $x_1^3 \neq x_2^3$ (two different numbers cannot have the same cube). Therefore, $f(x) = x^3$ is one-to-one.

SOLUTION 2 From Figure 3 we see that no horizontal line intersects the graph of $f(x) = x^3$ more than once. Therefore, by the Horizontal Line Test, f is one-to-one.

✎. NOW TRY EXERCISE **13** ■

Notice that the function f of Example 1 is increasing and is also one-to-one. In fact, it can be proved that *every increasing function and every decreasing function is one-to-one.*

EXAMPLE 2 | Deciding Whether a Function Is One-to-One

Is the function $g(x) = x^2$ one-to-one?

SOLUTION 1 This function is not one-to-one because, for instance,

$$g(1) = 1 \quad \text{and} \quad g(-1) = 1$$

so 1 and -1 have the same image.

SOLUTION 2 From Figure 4 we see that there are horizontal lines that intersect the graph of g more than once. Therefore, by the Horizontal Line Test, g is not one-to-one.

✎. NOW TRY EXERCISE **15** ■

Although the function g in Example 2 is not one-to-one, it is possible to restrict its domain so that the resulting function is one-to-one. In fact, if we define

$$h(x) = x^2 \quad x \geq 0$$

then h is one-to-one, as you can see from Figure 5 and the Horizontal Line Test.

EXAMPLE 3 | Showing That a Function Is One-to-One

Show that the function $f(x) = 3x + 4$ is one-to-one.

SOLUTION Suppose there are numbers x_1 and x_2 such that $f(x_1) = f(x_2)$. Then

$$3x_1 + 4 = 3x_2 + 4 \qquad \text{Suppose } f(x_1) = f(x_2)$$
$$3x_1 = 3x_2 \qquad \text{Subtract 4}$$
$$x_1 = x_2 \qquad \text{Divide by 3}$$

Therefore, f is one-to-one.

✎. NOW TRY EXERCISE **11** ■

▼ The Inverse of a Function

One-to-one functions are important because they are precisely the functions that possess inverse functions according to the following definition.

IN-CLASS MATERIALS

Make sure students understand the notation f^{-1} is not the same thing as $\dfrac{1}{f}$.

DEFINITION OF THE INVERSE OF A FUNCTION

Let f be a one-to-one function with domain A and range B. Then its **inverse function** f^{-1} has domain B and range A and is defined by

$$f^{-1}(y) = x \quad \Leftrightarrow \quad f(x) = y$$

for any y in B.

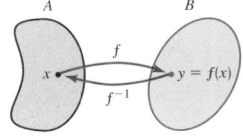

FIGURE 6

This definition says that if f takes x to y, then f^{-1} takes y back to x. (If f were not one-to-one, then f^{-1} would not be defined uniquely.) The arrow diagram in Figure 6 indicates that f^{-1} reverses the effect of f. From the definition we have

$$\text{domain of } f^{-1} = \text{range of } f$$
$$\text{range of } f^{-1} = \text{domain of } f$$

EXAMPLE 4 | Finding f^{-1} for Specific Values

⊘ Don't mistake the -1 in f^{-1} for an exponent.

$$f^{-1}(x) \quad \textit{does not mean} \quad \frac{1}{f(x)}$$

The reciprocal $1/f(x)$ is written as $(f(x))^{-1}$.

If $f(1) = 5$, $f(3) = 7$, and $f(8) = -10$, find $f^{-1}(5)$, $f^{-1}(7)$, and $f^{-1}(-10)$.

SOLUTION From the definition of f^{-1} we have

$$f^{-1}(5) = 1 \quad \text{because} \quad f(1) = 5$$
$$f^{-1}(7) = 3 \quad \text{because} \quad f(3) = 7$$
$$f^{-1}(-10) = 8 \quad \text{because} \quad f(8) = -10$$

Figure 7 shows how f^{-1} reverses the effect of f in this case.

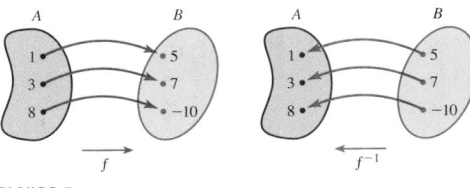

FIGURE 7

✎ NOW TRY EXERCISE **21**

By definition the inverse function f^{-1} undoes what f does: If we start with x, apply f, and then apply f^{-1}, we arrive back at x, where we started. Similarly, f undoes what f^{-1} does. In general, any function that reverses the effect of f in this way must be the inverse of f. These observations are expressed precisely as follows.

INVERSE FUNCTION PROPERTY

Let f be a one-to-one function with domain A and range B. The inverse function f^{-1} satisfies the following cancellation properties:

$$f^{-1}(f(x)) = x \quad \text{for every } x \text{ in } A$$
$$f(f^{-1}(x)) = x \quad \text{for every } x \text{ in } B$$

Conversely, any function f^{-1} satisfying these equations is the inverse of f.

ALTERNATE EXAMPLE 4

If $f(3) = 1$, $f(4) = 5$, and $f(9) = -8$, find $f^{-1}(1)$, $f^{-1}(5)$, and $f^{-1}(-8)$.

ANSWER

3, 4, 9

EXAMPLE

The graph of a complicated function and its inverse:

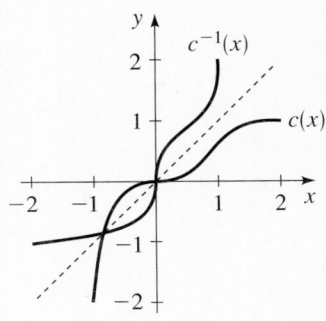

IN-CLASS MATERIALS

Starting with $f(x) = \sqrt[3]{x - 4}$, compute $f^{-1}(-2)$ and $f^{-1}(0)$. Then use algebra to find a formula for $f^{-1}(x)$. Have the class try to repeat the process with $g(x) = x^3 + x - 2$. Note that facts such as $g^{-1}(-2) = 0$, $g^{-1}(0) = 1$, and $g^{-1}(8) = 2$ can be found by looking at a table of values for $g(x)$ but that the algebraic approach fails to give us a general formula for $g^{-1}(x)$. Finally, draw graphs of f, f^{-1}, g, and g^{-1}.

These properties indicate that f is the inverse function of f^{-1}, so we say that f and f^{-1} are *inverses of each other*.

EXAMPLE 5 | Verifying That Two Functions Are Inverses

Show that $f(x) = x^3$ and $g(x) = x^{1/3}$ are inverses of each other.

SOLUTION   Note that the domain and range of both f and g is $\mathbb{R}$. We have

$$g(f(x)) = g(x^3) = (x^3)^{1/3} = x$$
$$f(g(x)) = f(x^{1/3}) = (x^{1/3})^3 = x$$

So by the Property of Inverse Functions, f and g are inverses of each other. These equations simply say that the cube function and the cube root function, when composed, cancel each other.

✎. NOW TRY EXERCISE **27**   ∎

Now let's examine how we compute inverse functions. We first observe from the definition of f^{-1} that

$$y = f(x) \quad \Leftrightarrow \quad f^{-1}(y) = x$$

So if $y = f(x)$ and if we are able to solve this equation for x in terms of y, then we must have $x = f^{-1}(y)$. If we then interchange x and y, we have $y = f^{-1}(x)$, which is the desired equation.

HOW TO FIND THE INVERSE OF A ONE-TO-ONE FUNCTION

1. Write $y = f(x)$.
2. Solve this equation for x in terms of y (if possible).
3. Interchange x and y. The resulting equation is $y = f^{-1}(x)$.

Note that Steps 2 and 3 can be reversed. In other words, we can interchange x and y first and then solve for y in terms of x.

EXAMPLE 6 | Finding the Inverse of a Function

Find the inverse of the function $f(x) = 3x - 2$.

SOLUTION   First we write $y = f(x)$.

$$y = 3x - 2$$

Then we solve this equation for x.

$$3x = y + 2 \qquad \text{Add 2}$$
$$x = \frac{y + 2}{3} \qquad \text{Divide by 3}$$

Finally, we interchange x and y.

$$y = \frac{x + 2}{3}$$

Therefore, the inverse function is $f^{-1}(x) = \dfrac{x + 2}{3}$.

✎. NOW TRY EXERCISE **37**   ∎

In Example 6 note how f^{-1} reverses the effect of f. The function f is the rule "Multiply by 3, then subtract 2," whereas f^{-1} is the rule "Add 2, then divide by 3."

CHECK YOUR ANSWER

We use the Inverse Function Property.

$$f^{-1}(f(x)) = f^{-1}(3x - 2)$$
$$= \frac{(3x - 2) + 2}{3}$$
$$= \frac{3x}{3} = x$$

$$f(f^{-1}(x)) = f\left(\frac{x + 2}{3}\right)$$
$$= 3\left(\frac{x + 2}{3}\right) - 2$$
$$= x + 2 - 2 = x \quad ✔$$

ALTERNATE EXAMPLE 5

Are the functions $f(x) = x^5$ and $g(x) = x^{1/5}$ inverses of each other?

ANSWER

Yes

ALTERNATE EXAMPLE 6

Find the inverse of the function $f(x) = 6x - 8$.

ANSWER

$f(x) = (x + 8)/6$

IN-CLASS MATERIALS

Pose the question: If f is always increasing, is f^{-1} always increasing? Give students time to try to prove their answer.

Answer

This is true. Proofs may involve diagrams and reflections about $y = x$, or you may try to get them to be more rigorous. This is an excellent opportunity to discuss concavity, noting that if f is concave up and increasing, then f^{-1} is concave down and increasing.

EXAMPLE 7 | Finding the Inverse of a Function

In Example 7 note how f^{-1} reverses the effect of f. The function f is the rule "Take the fifth power, subtract 3, then divide by 2," whereas f^{-1} is the rule "Multiply by 2, add 3, then take the fifth root."

Find the inverse of the function $f(x) = \dfrac{x^5 - 3}{2}$.

SOLUTION   We first write $y = (x^5 - 3)/2$ and solve for x.

$$y = \frac{x^5 - 3}{2} \qquad \text{Equation defining function}$$

$$2y = x^5 - 3 \qquad \text{Multiply by 2}$$

$$x^5 = 2y + 3 \qquad \text{Add 3 (and switch sides)}$$

$$x = (2y + 3)^{1/5} \qquad \text{Take fifth root of each side}$$

Then we interchange x and y to get $y = (2x + 3)^{1/5}$. Therefore, the inverse function is $f^{-1}(x) = (2x + 3)^{1/5}$.

✎. **NOW TRY EXERCISE 53**   ■

CHECK YOUR ANSWER

We use the Inverse Function Property.

$$f^{-1}(f(x)) = f^{-1}\left(\frac{x^5 - 3}{2}\right)$$

$$= \left[2\left(\frac{x^5 - 3}{2}\right) + 3\right]^{1/5}$$

$$= (x^5 - 3 + 3)^{1/5}$$

$$= (x^5)^{1/5} = x$$

$$f(f^{-1}(x)) = f((2x + 3)^{1/5})$$

$$= \frac{[(2x + 3)^{1/5}]^5 - 3}{2}$$

$$= \frac{2x + 3 - 3}{2}$$

$$= \frac{2x}{2} = x \quad ✔$$

A **rational function** is a function defined by a rational expression. In the next example we find the inverse of a rational function.

Rational functions are studied in Section 3.7.

EXAMPLE 8 | Finding the Inverse of a Rational Function

Find the inverse of the function $f(x) = \dfrac{2x + 3}{x - 1}$.

SOLUTION   We first write $y = (2x + 3)/(x - 1)$ and solve for x.

$$y = \frac{2x + 3}{x - 1} \qquad \text{Equation defining function}$$

$$y(x - 1) = 2x + 3 \qquad \text{Multiply by } x - 1$$

$$yx - y = 2x + 3 \qquad \text{Expand}$$

$$yx - 2x = y + 3 \qquad \text{Bring } x\text{-terms to LHS}$$

$$x(y - 2) = y + 3 \qquad \text{Factor } x$$

$$x = \frac{y + 3}{y - 2} \qquad \text{Divide by } y - 2$$

Therefore the inverse function is $f^{-1}(x) = \dfrac{x + 3}{x - 2}$.

✎. **NOW TRY EXERCISE 45**   ■

▼ Graphing the Inverse of a Function

The principle of interchanging x and y to find the inverse function also gives us a method for obtaining the graph of f^{-1} from the graph of f. If $f(a) = b$, then $f^{-1}(b) = a$. Thus, the point (a, b) is on the graph of f if and only if the point (b, a) is on the graph of f^{-1}. But we get the point (b, a) from the point (a, b) by reflecting in the line $y = x$ (see Figure 8 on the next page). Therefore, as Figure 9 on the next page illustrates, the following is true.

> The graph of f^{-1} is obtained by reflecting the graph of f in the line $y = x$.

IN-CLASS MATERIALS

Make sure to discuss units carefully: When comparing $y = f(x)$ to $y = f^{-1}(x)$, the units of y and x trade places.

FIGURE 8

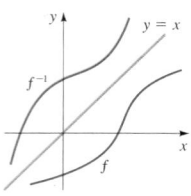

FIGURE 9

EXAMPLE 9 | Graphing the Inverse of a Function

(a) Sketch the graph of $f(x) = \sqrt{x - 2}$.

(b) Use the graph of f to sketch the graph of f^{-1}.

(c) Find an equation for f^{-1}.

SOLUTION

(a) Using the transformations from Section 2.5, we sketch the graph of $y = \sqrt{x - 2}$ by plotting the graph of the function $y = \sqrt{x}$ (Example 1(c) in Section 2.2) and moving it to the right 2 units.

(b) The graph of f^{-1} is obtained from the graph of f in part (a) by reflecting it in the line $y = x$, as shown in Figure 10.

(c) Solve $y = \sqrt{x - 2}$ for x, noting that $y \geq 0$.

$$\sqrt{x - 2} = y$$
$$x - 2 = y^2 \qquad \text{Square each side}$$
$$x = y^2 + 2 \qquad y \geq 0 \qquad \text{Add 2}$$

Interchange x and y:

$$y = x^2 + 2 \qquad x \geq 0$$

Thus $\qquad f^{-1}(x) = x^2 + 2 \qquad x \geq 0$

This expression shows that the graph of f^{-1} is the right half of the parabola $y = x^2 + 2$, and from the graph shown in Figure 10, this seems reasonable.

✎ NOW TRY EXERCISE **63**

FIGURE 10

In Example 9 note how f^{-1} reverses the effect of f. The function f is the rule "Subtract 2, then take the square root," whereas f^{-1} is the rule "Square, then add 2."

2.7 EXERCISES

CONCEPTS

1. A function f is one-to-one if different inputs produce

_____ outputs. You can tell from the graph that a function

is one-to-one by using the _____ Test.

2. (a) For a function to have an inverse, it must be _____.
So which one of the following functions has an inverse?

$$f(x) = x^2 \qquad g(x) = x^3$$

(b) What is the inverse of the function that you chose in part (a)?

3. A function f has the following verbal description: "Multiply by 3, add 5, and then take the third power of the result."
(a) Write a verbal description for f^{-1}.
(b) Find algebraic formulas that express f and f^{-1} in terms of the input x.

4. *True or false?*

(a) If f has an inverse, then $f^{-1}(x)$ is the same as $\dfrac{1}{f(x)}$.

(b) If f has an inverse, then $f^{-1}(f(x)) = x$.

IN-CLASS MATERIALS

Point out that the idea of "reversing input and output" permeates the idea of inverse functions in all four representations of "function." When finding inverse functions algebraically, we explicitly reverse x and y. When drawing the inverse function of a graph, by reflecting across the line $y = x$ we are reversing the y- and x-axes. If $c(x)$ is the cost (in dollars) to make x fruit roll-ups, then $c^{-1}(x)$ is the number of fruit roll-ups that could be made for x dollars—again reversing the input and the output. Finally, show the class how to find the inverse of a function given a numeric data table, and note that again the inputs and outputs are reversed.

x	$f(x)$		x	$f^{-1}(x)$
1	3		3	1
2	4.2		4.2	2
3	5.7		5.7	3
4	8		8	4

SKILLS

5–10 ■ The graph of a function f is given. Determine whether f is one-to-one.

5.

6.

7.

8.

9.

10.

11–20 ■ Determine whether the function is one-to-one.

11. $f(x) = -2x + 4$ **12.** $f(x) = 3x - 2$

13. $g(x) = \sqrt{x}$ **14.** $g(x) = |x|$

15. $h(x) = x^2 - 2x$ **16.** $h(x) = x^3 + 8$

17. $f(x) = x^4 + 5$

18. $f(x) = x^4 + 5, \quad 0 \le x \le 2$

19. $f(x) = \dfrac{1}{x^2}$ **20.** $f(x) = \dfrac{1}{x}$

21–22 ■ Assume that f is a one-to-one function.

21. (a) If $f(2) = 7$, find $f^{-1}(7)$.
  (b) If $f^{-1}(3) = -1$, find $f(-1)$.

22. (a) If $f(5) = 18$, find $f^{-1}(18)$.
  (b) If $f^{-1}(4) = 2$, find $f(2)$.

23. If $f(x) = 5 - 2x$, find $f^{-1}(3)$.

24. If $g(x) = x^2 + 4x$ with $x \ge -2$, find $g^{-1}(5)$.

25–36 ■ Use the Inverse Function Property to show that f and g are inverses of each other.

25. $f(x) = x - 6; \quad g(x) = x + 6$

26. $f(x) = 3x; \quad g(x) = \dfrac{x}{3}$

27. $f(x) = 2x - 5; \quad g(x) = \dfrac{x + 5}{2}$

28. $f(x) = \dfrac{3 - x}{4}; \quad g(x) = 3 - 4x$

29. $f(x) = \dfrac{1}{x}; \quad g(x) = \dfrac{1}{x}$

30. $f(x) = x^5; \quad g(x) = \sqrt[5]{x}$

31. $f(x) = x^2 - 4, \quad x \ge 0;$
  $g(x) = \sqrt{x + 4}, \quad x \ge -4$

32. $f(x) = x^3 + 1; \quad g(x) = (x - 1)^{1/3}$

33. $f(x) = \dfrac{1}{x - 1}, \quad x \ne 1; \quad g(x) = \dfrac{1}{x} + 1, \quad x \ne 0$

34. $f(x) = \sqrt{4 - x^2}, \quad 0 \le x \le 2;$
  $g(x) = \sqrt{4 - x^2}, \quad 0 \le x \le 2$

35. $f(x) = \dfrac{x + 2}{x - 2}; \quad g(x) = \dfrac{2x + 2}{x - 1}$

36. $f(x) = \dfrac{x - 5}{3x + 4}; \quad g(x) = \dfrac{5 + 4x}{1 - 3x}$

37–60 ■ Find the inverse function of f.

37. $f(x) = 2x + 1$ **38.** $f(x) = 6 - x$

39. $f(x) = 4x + 7$ **40.** $f(x) = 3 - 5x$

41. $f(x) = 5 - 4x^3$ **42.** $f(x) = \dfrac{1}{x^2}, \quad x > 0$

43. $f(x) = \dfrac{1}{x + 2}$ **44.** $f(x) = \dfrac{x - 2}{x + 2}$

45. $f(x) = \dfrac{x}{x + 4}$ **46.** $f(x) = \dfrac{3x}{x - 2}$

47. $f(x) = \dfrac{2x + 5}{x - 7}$ **48.** $f(x) = \dfrac{4x - 2}{3x + 1}$

49. $f(x) = \dfrac{1 + 3x}{5 - 2x}$ **50.** $f(x) = \dfrac{2x - 1}{x - 3}$

51. $f(x) = \sqrt{2 + 5x}$ **52.** $f(x) = x^2 + x, \quad x \ge -\tfrac{1}{2}$

53. $f(x) = 4 - x^2, \quad x \ge 0$ **54.** $f(x) = \sqrt{2x - 1}$

55. $f(x) = 4 + \sqrt[3]{x}$ **56.** $f(x) = (2 - x^3)^5$

57. $f(x) = 1 + \sqrt{1 + x}$

58. $f(x) = \sqrt{9 - x^2}, \quad 0 \le x \le 3$

59. $f(x) = x^4, \quad x \ge 0$ **60.** $f(x) = 1 - x^3$

61–64 ■ A function f is given. (a) Sketch the graph of f. (b) Use the graph of f to sketch the graph of f^{-1}. (c) Find f^{-1}.

61. $f(x) = 3x - 6$ **62.** $f(x) = 16 - x^2, \quad x \ge 0$

63. $f(x) = \sqrt{x + 1}$ **64.** $f(x) = x^3 - 1$

 65–70 ■ Draw the graph of f and use it to determine whether the function is one-to-one.

65. $f(x) = x^3 - x$ **66.** $f(x) = x^3 + x$

67. $f(x) = \dfrac{x + 12}{x - 6}$ **68.** $f(x) = \sqrt{x^3 - 4x + 1}$

69. $f(x) = |x| - |x - 6|$ **70.** $f(x) = x \cdot |x|$

71–74 ■ A one-to-one function is given. **(a)** Find the inverse of the function. **(b)** Graph both the function and its inverse on the same screen to verify that the graphs are reflections of each other in the line $y = x$.

71. $f(x) = 2 + x$

72. $f(x) = 2 - \frac{1}{2}x$

73. $g(x) = \sqrt{x + 3}$

74. $g(x) = x^2 + 1, \quad x \geq 0$

75–78 ■ The given function is not one-to-one. Restrict its domain so that the resulting function *is* one-to-one. Find the inverse of the function with the restricted domain. (There is more than one correct answer.)

75. $f(x) = 4 - x^2$

76. $g(x) = (x - 1)^2$

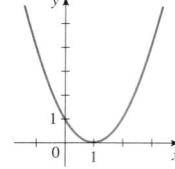

77. $h(x) = (x + 2)^2$

78. $k(x) = |x - 3|$

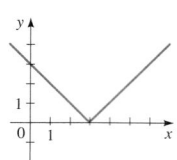

79–80 ■ Use the graph of f to sketch the graph of f^{-1}.

79.

80.

APPLICATIONS

81. Fee for Service For his services, a private investigator requires a $500 retention fee plus $80 per hour. Let x represent the number of hours the investigator spends working on a case.
(a) Find a function f that models the investigator's fee as a function of x.
(b) Find f^{-1}. What does f^{-1} represent?
(c) Find $f^{-1}(1220)$. What does your answer represent?

82. Toricelli's Law A tank holds 100 gallons of water, which drains from a leak at the bottom, causing the tank to empty in 40 minutes. Toricelli's Law gives the volume of water remaining in the tank after t minutes as

$$V(t) = 100\left(1 - \frac{t}{40}\right)^2$$

(a) Find V^{-1}. What does V^{-1} represent?
(b) Find $V^{-1}(15)$. What does your answer represent?

83. Blood Flow As blood moves through a vein or artery, its velocity v is greatest along the central axis and decreases as the distance r from the central axis increases (see the figure below). For an artery with radius 0.5 cm, v (in cm/s) is given as a function of r (in cm) by

$$v(r) = 18{,}500(0.25 - r^2)$$

(a) Find v^{-1}. What does v^{-1} represent?
(b) Find $v^{-1}(30)$. What does your answer represent?

84. Demand Function The amount of a commodity that is sold is called the *demand* for the commodity. The demand D for a certain commodity is a function of the price given by

$$D(p) = -3p + 150$$

(a) Find D^{-1}. What does D^{-1} represent?
(b) Find $D^{-1}(30)$. What does your answer represent?

85. Temperature Scales The relationship between the Fahrenheit (F) and Celsius (C) scales is given by

$$F(C) = \frac{9}{5}C + 32$$

(a) Find F^{-1}. What does F^{-1} represent?
(b) Find $F^{-1}(86)$. What does your answer represent?

86. Exchange Rates The relative value of currencies fluctuates every day. When this problem was written, one Canadian dollar was worth 1.0573 U.S. dollar.
(a) Find a function f that gives the U.S. dollar value $f(x)$ of x Canadian dollars.
(b) Find f^{-1}. What does f^{-1} represent?
(c) How much Canadian money would $12,250 in U.S. currency be worth?

87. Income Tax In a certain country, the tax on incomes less than or equal to €20,000 is 10%. For incomes that are more than €20,000, the tax is €2000 plus 20% of the amount over €20,000.
(a) Find a function f that gives the income tax on an income x. Express f as a piecewise defined function.
(b) Find f^{-1}. What does f^{-1} represent?
(c) How much income would require paying a tax of €10,000?

88. Multiple Discounts A car dealership advertises a 15% discount on all its new cars. In addition, the manufacturer offers a $1000 rebate on the purchase of a new car. Let x represent the sticker price of the car.
(a) Suppose only the 15% discount applies. Find a function f that models the purchase price of the car as a function of the sticker price x.

(b) Suppose only the $1000 rebate applies. Find a function g that models the purchase price of the car as a function of the sticker price x.

(c) Find a formula for $H = f \circ g$.

(d) Find H^{-1}. What does H^{-1} represent?

(e) Find $H^{-1}(13,000)$. What does your answer represent?

89. Pizza Cost   Marcello's Pizza charges a base price of $7 for a large pizza plus $2 for each topping. Thus, if you order a large pizza with x toppings, the price of your pizza is given by the function $f(x) = 7 + 2x$. Find f^{-1}. What does the function f^{-1} represent?

DISCOVERY ▪ DISCUSSION ▪ WRITING

90. Determining When a Linear Function Has an Inverse   For the linear function $f(x) = mx + b$ to be one-to-one, what must be true about its slope? If it is one-to-one, find its inverse. Is the inverse linear? If so, what is its slope?

91. Finding an Inverse "in Your Head"   In the margin notes in this section we pointed out that the inverse of a function can be found by simply reversing the operations that make up the function. For instance, in Example 6 we saw that the inverse of

$$f(x) = 3x - 2 \quad \text{is} \quad f^{-1}(x) = \frac{x + 2}{3}$$

because the "reverse" of "Multiply by 3 and subtract 2" is "Add 2 and divide by 3." Use the same procedure to find the inverse of the following functions.

(a) $f(x) = \dfrac{2x + 1}{5}$ **(b)** $f(x) = 3 - \dfrac{1}{x}$

(c) $f(x) = \sqrt{x^3 + 2}$ **(d)** $f(x) = (2x - 5)^3$

Now consider another function:

$$f(x) = x^3 + 2x + 6$$

Is it possible to use the same sort of simple reversal of operations to find the inverse of this function? If so, do it. If not, explain what is different about this function that makes this task difficult.

92. The Identity Function   The function $I(x) = x$ is called the **identity function**. Show that for any function f we have $f \circ I = f, I \circ f = f$, and $f \circ f^{-1} = f^{-1} \circ f = I$. (This means that the identity function I behaves for functions and composition just the way the number 1 behaves for real numbers and multiplication.)

93. Solving an Equation for an Unknown Function   In Exercise 69 of Section 2.6 you were asked to solve equations in which the unknowns were functions. Now that we know about inverses and the identity function (see Exercise 92), we can use algebra to solve such equations. For instance, to solve $f \circ g = h$ for the unknown function f, we perform the following steps:

$$
\begin{array}{ll}
f \circ g = h & \text{Problem: Solve for } f \\
f \circ g \circ g^{-1} = h \circ g^{-1} & \text{Compose with } g^{-1} \text{ on the right} \\
f \circ I = h \circ g^{-1} & \text{Because } g \circ g^{-1} = I \\
f = h \circ g^{-1} & \text{Because } f \circ I = f
\end{array}
$$

So the solution is $f = h \circ g^{-1}$. Use this technique to solve the equation $f \circ g = h$ for the indicated unknown function.

(a) Solve for f, where $g(x) = 2x + 1$ and $h(x) = 4x^2 + 4x + 7$.

(b) Solve for g, where $f(x) = 3x + 5$ and $h(x) = 3x^2 + 3x + 2$.

CHAPTER 2 | REVIEW

■ CONCEPT CHECK

1. Define each concept in your own words. (Check by referring to the definition in the text.)
   (a) Function
   (b) Domain and range of a function
   (c) Graph of a function
   (d) Independent and dependent variables

2. Sketch by hand, on the same axes, the graphs of the following functions.
   (a) $f(x) = x$ **(b)** $g(x) = x^2$
   (c) $h(x) = x^3$ **(d)** $j(x) = x^4$

3. (a) State the Vertical Line Test.
   (b) State the Horizontal Line Test.

4. How is the average rate of change of the function f between two points defined?

5. What can you say about the average rate of change of a linear function?

6. Define each concept in your own words.
   (a) Increasing function
   (b) Decreasing function
   (c) Constant function

7. Suppose the graph of f is given. Write an equation for each graph that is obtained from the graph of f as follows.
   (a) Shift 3 units upward.
   (b) Shift 3 units downward.
   (c) Shift 3 units to the right.
   (d) Shift 3 units to the left.
   (e) Reflect in the x-axis.
   (f) Reflect in the y-axis.
   (g) Stretch vertically by a factor of 3.
   (h) Shrink vertically by a factor of $\frac{1}{3}$.
   (i) Stretch horizontally by a factor of 2.
   (j) Shrink horizontally by a factor of $\frac{1}{2}$.

8. (a) What is an even function? What symmetry does its graph possess? Give an example of an even function.

(b) What is an odd function? What symmetry does its graph possess? Give an example of an odd function.

9. What does it mean to say that $f(3)$ is a local maximum value of f?

10. Suppose that f has domain A and g has domain B.
(a) What is the domain of $f + g$?
(b) What is the domain of fg?
(c) What is the domain of f/g?

11. How is the composite function $f \circ g$ defined?

12. (a) What is a one-to-one function?
(b) How can you tell from the graph of a function whether it is one-to-one?
(c) Suppose f is a one-to-one function with domain A and range B. How is the inverse function f^{-1} defined? What is the domain of f^{-1}? What is the range of f^{-1}?
(d) If you are given a formula for f, how do you find a formula for f^{-1}?
(e) If you are given the graph of f, how do you find the graph of f^{-1}?

■ **EXERCISES**

1–2 ■ A verbal description of a function f is given. Find a formula that expresses f in function notation.

1. "Square, then subtract 5."

2. "Divide by 2, then add 9."

3–4 ■ A formula for a function f is given. Give a verbal description of the function.

3. $f(x) = 3(x + 10)$

4. $f(x) = \sqrt{6x - 10}$

5–6 ■ Complete the table of values for the given function.

5. $g(x) = x^2 - 4x$

x	$g(x)$
-1	
0	
1	
2	
3	

6. $h(x) = 3x^2 + 2x - 5$

x	$h(x)$
-2	
-1	
0	
1	
2	

7. A publisher estimates that the cost $C(x)$ of printing a run of x copies of a certain mathematics textbook is given by the function $C(x) = 5000 + 30x - 0.001x^2$.
(a) Find $C(1000)$ and $C(10,000)$.
(b) What do your answers in part (a) represent?
(c) Find $C(0)$. What does this number represent?

8. Reynalda works as a salesperson in the electronics division of a department store. She earns a base weekly salary plus a commission based on the retail price of the goods she has sold. If she sells x dollars worth of goods in a week, her earnings for that week are given by the function $E(x) = 400 + 0.03x$.
(a) Find $E(2000)$ and $E(15,000)$.
(b) What do your answers in part (a) represent?
(c) Find $E(0)$. What does this number represent?
(d) From the formula for E, determine what percentage Reynalda earns on the goods that she sells.

9. If $f(x) = x^2 - 4x + 6$, find $f(0)$, $f(2)$, $f(-2)$, $f(a)$, $f(-a)$, $f(x + 1)$, $f(2x)$, and $2f(x) - 2$.

10. If $f(x) = 4 - \sqrt{3x - 6}$, find $f(5)$, $f(9)$, $f(a + 2)$, $f(-x)$, $f(x^2)$, and $[f(x)]^2$.

11. Which of the following figures are graphs of functions? Which of the functions are one-to-one?

(a)
(b)
(c)
(d)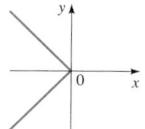

12. The graph of a function f is given.
(a) Find $f(-2)$ and $f(2)$.
(b) Find the domain of f.
(c) Find the range of f.
(d) On what intervals is f increasing? On what intervals is f decreasing?
(e) What are the local maximum values of f?
(f) Is f one-to-one?

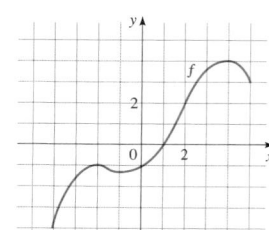

13–14 ■ Find the domain and range of the function.

13. $f(x) = \sqrt{x + 3}$

14. $F(t) = t^2 + 2t + 5$

15–22 ■ Find the domain of the function.

15. $f(x) = 7x + 15$

16. $f(x) = \dfrac{2x + 1}{2x - 1}$

17. $f(x) = \sqrt{x + 4}$

18. $f(x) = 3x - \dfrac{2}{\sqrt{x + 1}}$

19. $f(x) = \dfrac{1}{x} + \dfrac{1}{x + 1} + \dfrac{1}{x + 2}$

20. $g(x) = \dfrac{2x^2 + 5x + 3}{2x^2 - 5x - 3}$

21. $h(x) = \sqrt{4 - x} + \sqrt{x^2 - 1}$

22. $f(x) = \dfrac{\sqrt[3]{2x + 1}}{\sqrt[3]{2x + 2}}$

23–40 ■ Sketch the graph of the function.

23. $f(x) = 1 - 2x$

24. $f(x) = \frac{1}{3}(x - 5), \ 2 \le x \le 8$

25. $f(t) = 1 - \frac{1}{2}t^2$

26. $g(t) = t^2 - 2t$

27. $f(x) = x^2 - 6x + 6$

28. $f(x) = 3 - 8x - 2x^2$

29. $g(x) = 1 - \sqrt{x}$

30. $g(x) = -|x|$

31. $h(x) = \frac{1}{2}x^3$

32. $h(x) = \sqrt{x + 3}$

33. $h(x) = \sqrt[3]{x}$

34. $H(x) = x^3 - 3x^2$

35. $g(x) = \dfrac{1}{x^2}$

36. $G(x) = \dfrac{1}{(x - 3)^2}$

37. $f(x) = \begin{cases} 1 - x & \text{if } x < 0 \\ 1 & \text{if } x \ge 0 \end{cases}$

38. $f(x) = \begin{cases} 1 - 2x & \text{if } x \le 0 \\ 2x - 1 & \text{if } x > 0 \end{cases}$

39. $f(x) = \begin{cases} x + 6 & \text{if } x < -2 \\ x^2 & \text{if } x \ge -2 \end{cases}$

40. $f(x) = \begin{cases} -x & \text{if } x < 0 \\ x^2 & \text{if } 0 \le x < 2 \\ 1 & \text{if } x \ge 2 \end{cases}$

41–44 ■ Determine whether the equation defines y as a function of x.

41. $x + y^2 = 14$

42. $3x - \sqrt{y} = 8$

43. $x^3 - y^3 = 27$

44. $2x = y^4 - 16$

45. Determine which viewing rectangle produces the most appropriate graph of the function

$$f(x) = 6x^3 - 15x^2 + 4x - 1$$

  (i) $[-2, 2]$ by $[-2, 2]$ (ii) $[-8, 8]$ by $[-8, 8]$
  (iii) $[-4, 4]$ by $[-12, 12]$ (iv) $[-100, 100]$ by $[-100, 100]$

46. Determine which viewing rectangle produces the most appropriate graph of the function $f(x) = \sqrt{100 - x^3}$.
  (i) $[-4, 4]$ by $[-4, 4]$
  (ii) $[-10, 10]$ by $[-10, 10]$
  (iii) $[-10, 10]$ by $[-10, 40]$
  (iv) $[-100, 100]$ by $[-100, 100]$

47–50 ■ Draw the graph of the function in an appropriate viewing rectangle.

47. $f(x) = x^2 + 25x + 173$

48. $f(x) = 1.1x^3 - 9.6x^2 - 1.4x + 3.2$

49. $f(x) = \dfrac{x}{\sqrt{x^2 + 16}}$

50. $f(x) = |x(x + 2)(x + 4)|$

51. Find, approximately, the domain of the function

$$f(x) = \sqrt{x^3 - 4x + 1}$$

52. Find, approximately, the range of the function

$$f(x) = x^4 - x^3 + x^2 + 3x - 6$$

53–54 ■ Draw a graph of the function f, and determine the intervals on which f is increasing and on which f is decreasing.

53. $f(x) = x^3 - 4x^2$

54. $f(x) = |x^4 - 16|$

55–58 ■ Find the average rate of change of the function between the given points.

55. $f(x) = x^2 + 3x; \quad x = 0, x = 2$

56. $f(x) = \dfrac{1}{x - 2}; \quad x = 4, x = 8$

57. $f(x) = \dfrac{1}{x}; \quad x = 3, x = 3 + h$

58. $f(x) = (x + 1)^2; \quad x = a, x = a + h$

59. The population of a planned seaside community in Florida is given by the function $P(t) = 3000 + 200t + 0.1t^2$, where t represents the number of years since the community was incorporated in 1985.
  (a) Find $P(10)$ and $P(20)$. What do these values represent?
  (b) Find the average rate of change of P between $t = 10$ and $t = 20$. What does this number represent?

60. Ella is saving for her retirement by making regular deposits into a 401(k) plan. As her salary rises, she finds that she can deposit increasing amounts each year. Between 1995 and 2008, the annual amount (in dollars) that she deposited was given by the function $D(t) = 3500 + 15t^2$, where t represents the year of the deposit measured from the start of the plan (so 1995 corresponds to $t = 0$ and 1996 corresponds to $t = 1$, and so on).
  (a) Find $D(0)$ and $D(15)$. What do these values represent?
  (b) Assuming that her deposits continue to be modeled by the function D, in what year will she deposit $17,000?
  (c) Find the average rate of change of D between $t = 0$ and $t = 15$. What does this number represent?

61–62 ■ A function f is given. **(a)** Find the average rate of change of f between $x = 0$ and $x = 2$, and the average rate of change of f between $x = 15$ and $x = 50$. **(b)** Were the two average rates of change that you found in part (a) the same? Explain why or why not.

61. $f(x) = \frac{1}{2}x - 6$

62. $f(x) = 8 - 3x$

63. Suppose the graph of f is given. Describe how the graphs of the following functions can be obtained from the graph of f.
  (a) $y = f(x) + 8$ **(b)** $y = f(x + 8)$
  (c) $y = 1 + 2f(x)$ **(d)** $y = f(x - 2) - 2$
  (e) $y = f(-x)$ **(f)** $y = -f(-x)$
  (g) $y = -f(x)$ **(h)** $y = f^{-1}(x)$

64. The graph of f is given. Draw the graphs of the following functions.

(a) $y = f(x - 2)$ (b) $y = -f(x)$

(c) $y = 3 - f(x)$ (d) $y = \frac{1}{2}f(x) - 1$

(e) $y = f^{-1}(x)$ (f) $y = f(-x)$

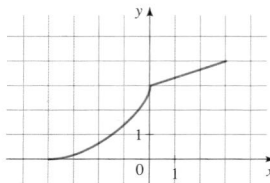

65. Determine whether f is even, odd, or neither.

(a) $f(x) = 2x^5 - 3x^2 + 2$ (b) $f(x) = x^3 - x^7$

(c) $f(x) = \dfrac{1 - x^2}{1 + x^2}$ (d) $f(x) = \dfrac{1}{x + 2}$

66. Determine whether the function in the figure is even, odd, or neither.

(a)   (b)

(c)   (d)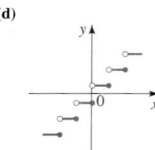

67. Find the minimum value of the function $g(x) = 2x^2 + 4x - 5$.

68. Find the maximum value of the function $f(x) = 1 - x - x^2$.

69. A stone is thrown upward from the top of a building. Its height (in feet) above the ground after t seconds is given by

$$h(t) = -16t^2 + 48t + 32$$

What maximum height does it reach?

70. The profit P (in dollars) generated by selling x units of a certain commodity is given by

$$P(x) = -1500 + 12x - 0.0004x^2$$

What is the maximum profit, and how many units must be sold to generate it?

71–72 ■ Find the local maximum and minimum values of the function and the values of x at which they occur. State each answer correct to two decimal places.

71. $f(x) = 3.3 + 1.6x - 2.5x^3$ **72.** $f(x) = x^{2/3}(6 - x)^{1/3}$

73–74 ■ Two functions, f and g, are given. Draw graphs of f, g, and $f + g$ on the same graphing calculator screen to illustrate the concept of graphical addition.

73. $f(x) = x + 2$, $g(x) = x^2$

74. $f(x) = x^2 + 1$, $g(x) = 3 - x^2$

75. If $f(x) = x^2 - 3x + 2$ and $g(x) = 4 - 3x$, find the following functions.

(a) $f + g$ (b) $f - g$ (c) fg

(d) f/g (e) $f \circ g$ (f) $g \circ f$

76. If $f(x) = 1 + x^2$ and $g(x) = \sqrt{x - 1}$, find the following.

(a) $f \circ g$ (b) $g \circ f$ (c) $(f \circ g)(2)$

(d) $(f \circ f)(2)$ (e) $f \circ g \circ f$ (f) $g \circ f \circ g$

77–78 ■ Find the functions $f \circ g$, $g \circ f$, $f \circ f$, and $g \circ g$ and their domains.

77. $f(x) = 3x - 1$, $g(x) = 2x - x^2$

78. $f(x) = \sqrt{x}$, $g(x) = \dfrac{2}{x - 4}$

79. Find $f \circ g \circ h$, where $f(x) = \sqrt{1 - x}$, $g(x) = 1 - x^2$, and $h(x) = 1 + \sqrt{x}$.

80. If $T(x) = \dfrac{1}{\sqrt{1 + \sqrt{x}}}$, find functions f, g, and h such that

$$f \circ g \circ h = T$$

81–86 ■ Determine whether the function is one-to-one.

81. $f(x) = 3 + x^3$

82. $g(x) = 2 - 2x + x^2$

83. $h(x) = \dfrac{1}{x^4}$

84. $r(x) = 2 + \sqrt{x + 3}$

85. $p(x) = 3.3 + 1.6x - 2.5x^3$

86. $q(x) = 3.3 + 1.6x + 2.5x^3$

87–90 ■ Find the inverse of the function.

87. $f(x) = 3x - 2$ **88.** $f(x) = \dfrac{2x + 1}{3}$

89. $f(x) = (x + 1)^3$ **90.** $f(x) = 1 + \sqrt[5]{x - 2}$

91. (a) Sketch the graph of the function

$$f(x) = x^2 - 4 \qquad x \ge 0$$

(b) Use part (a) to sketch the graph of f^{-1}.

(c) Find an equation for f^{-1}.

92. (a) Show that the function $f(x) = 1 + \sqrt[4]{x}$ is one-to-one.

(b) Sketch the graph of f.

(c) Use part (b) to sketch the graph of f^{-1}.

(d) Find an equation for f^{-1}.

1. Which of the following are graphs of functions? If the graph is that of a function, is it one-to-one?

(a)

(b)

(c)
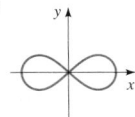

(d)

2. Let $f(x) = \dfrac{\sqrt{x+1}}{x}$.

   (a) Evaluate $f(3)$, $f(5)$, and $f(a-1)$.

   (b) Find the domain of f.

3. A function f has the following verbal description: "Subtract 2, then cube the result."

   (a) Find a formula that expresses f algebraically.

   (b) Make a table of values of f, for the inputs $-1, 0, 1, 2, 3$, and 4.

   (c) Sketch a graph of f, using the table of values from part (b) to help you.

   (d) How do we know that f has an inverse? Give a verbal description for f^{-1}.

   (e) Find a formula that expresses f^{-1} algebraically.

 4. A school fund-raising group sells chocolate bars to help finance a swimming pool for their physical education program. The group finds that when they set their price at x dollars per bar (where $0 < x \le 5$), their total sales revenue (in dollars) is given by the function $R(x) = -500x^2 + 3000x$.

   (a) Evaluate $R(2)$ and $R(4)$. What do these values represent?

   (b) Use a graphing calculator to draw a graph of R. What does the graph tell us about what happens to revenue as the price increases from 0 to 5 dollars?

   (c) What is the maximum revenue, and at what price is it achieved?

5. Determine the average rate of change for the function $f(t) = t^2 - 2t$ between $t = 2$ and $t = 5$.

6. (a) Sketch the graph of the function $f(x) = x^3$.

   (b) Use part (a) to graph the function $g(x) = (x-1)^3 - 2$.

7. (a) How is the graph of $y = f(x-3) + 2$ obtained from the graph of f?

   (b) How is the graph of $y = f(-x)$ obtained from the graph of f?

8. Let $f(x) = \begin{cases} 1-x & \text{if } x \le 1 \\ 2x+1 & \text{if } x > 1 \end{cases}$

   (a) Evaluate $f(-2)$ and $f(1)$.

   (b) Sketch the graph of f.

9. If $f(x) = x^2 + 1$ and $g(x) = x - 3$, find the following.

   (a) $f \circ g$ (b) $g \circ f$

   (c) $f(g(2))$ (d) $g(f(2))$

   (e) $g \circ g \circ g$

211

10. **(a)** If $f(x) = \sqrt{3 - x}$, find the inverse function f^{-1}.

    (b) Sketch the graphs of f and f^{-1} on the same coordinate axes.

11. The graph of a function f is given.

    (a) Find the domain and range of f.

    (b) Sketch the graph of f^{-1}.

    (c) Find the average rate of change of f between $x = 2$ and $x = 6$.

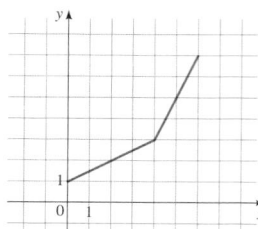

12. Let $f(x) = 3x^4 - 14x^2 + 5x - 3$.

    (a) Draw the graph of f in an appropriate viewing rectangle.

    (b) Is f one-to-one?

    (c) Find the local maximum and minimum values of f and the values of x at which they occur. State each answer correct to two decimal places.

    (d) Use the graph to determine the range of f.

    (e) Find the intervals on which f is increasing and on which f is decreasing.

Modeling with Functions

Many of the processes that are studied in the physical and social sciences involve understanding how one quantity varies with respect to another. Finding a function that describes the dependence of one quantity on another is called *modeling*. For example, a biologist observes that the number of bacteria in a certain culture increases with time. He tries to model this phenomenon by finding the precise function (or rule) that relates the bacteria population to the elapsed time.

In this *Focus* we will learn how to find models that can be constructed using geometric or algebraic properties of the object under study. Once the model is found, we use it to analyze and predict properties of the object or process being studied.

▼ Modeling with Functions

We begin with a simple real-life situation that illustrates the modeling process.

EXAMPLE 1 | Modeling the Volume of a Box

A breakfast cereal company manufactures boxes to package their product. For aesthetic reasons, the box must have the following proportions: Its width is 3 times its depth, and its height is 5 times its depth.

(a) Find a function that models the volume of the box in terms of its depth.

(b) Find the volume of the box if the depth is 1.5 in.

(c) For what depth is the volume 90 in^3?

(d) For what depth is the volume greater than 60 in^3?

THINKING ABOUT THE PROBLEM

Let's experiment with the problem. If the depth is 1 in., then the width is 3 in. and the height is 5 in. So in this case, the volume is $V = 1 \times 3 \times 5 = 15$ in^3. The table gives other values. Notice that all the boxes have the same shape, and the greater the depth, the greater the volume.

Depth	Volume
1	$1 \times 3 \times 5 = 15$
2	$2 \times 6 \times 10 = 120$
3	$3 \times 9 \times 15 = 405$
4	$4 \times 12 \times 20 = 96$

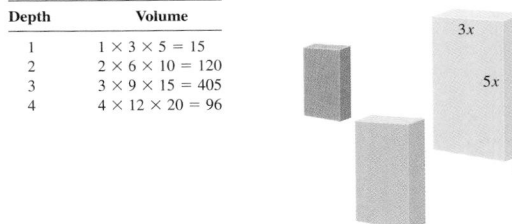

SOLUTION

(a) To find the function that models the volume of the box, we use the following steps.

213

► **Express the Model in Words**

We know that the volume of a rectangular box is

$$\boxed{\text{volume}} \; = \; \boxed{\text{depth}} \; \times \; \boxed{\text{width}} \; \times \; \boxed{\text{height}}$$

► **Choose the Variable**

There are three varying quantities: width, depth, and height. Because the function we want depends on the depth, we let

$$x = \text{depth of the box}$$

Then we express the other dimensions of the box in terms of x.

In Words	In Algebra
Depth	x
Width	$3x$
Height	$5x$

FIGURE 1

► **Set Up the Model**

The model is the function V that gives the volume of the box in terms of the depth x.

$$\boxed{\text{volume}} \; = \; \boxed{\text{depth}} \; \times \; \boxed{\text{width}} \; \times \; \boxed{\text{height}}$$

$$V(x) = x \cdot 3x \cdot 5x$$

$$V(x) = 15x^3$$

The volume of the box is modeled by the function $V(x) = 15x^3$. The function V is graphed in Figure 1.

$$15x^3 = 90$$

FIGURE 2

► **Use the Model**

We use the model to answer the questions in parts (b), (c), and (d).

(b) If the depth is 1.5 in., the volume is $V(1.5) = 15(1.5)^3 = 50.625 \text{ in}^3$.

(c) We need to solve the equation $V(x) = 90$ or

$$15x^3 = 90$$

$$x^3 = 6$$

$$x = \sqrt[3]{6} \approx 1.82 \text{ in.}$$

The volume is 90 in³ when the depth is about 1.82 in. (We can also solve this equation graphically, as shown in Figure 2.)

(d) We need to solve the inequality $V(x) \geq 60$ or

$$15x^3 \geq 60$$

$$x^3 \geq 4$$

$$x \geq \sqrt[3]{4} \approx 1.59$$

$$15x^3 \geq 60$$

FIGURE 3

The volume will be greater than 60 in³ if the depth is greater than 1.59 in. (We can also solve this inequality graphically, as shown in Figure 3.) ■

The steps in Example 1 are typical of how we model with functions. They are summarized in the following box.

GUIDELINES FOR MODELING WITH FUNCTIONS

1. **Express the Model in Words.**   Identify the quantity you want to model, and express it, in words, as a function of the other quantities in the problem.

2. **Choose the Variable.**   Identify all the variables that are used to express the function in Step 1. Assign a symbol, such as x, to one variable, and express the other variables in terms of this symbol.

3. **Set up the Model.**   Express the function in the language of algebra by writing it as a function of the single variable chosen in Step 2.

4. **Use the Model.**   Use the function to answer the questions posed in the problem. (To find a maximum or a minimum, use the methods described in Section 2.3.)

EXAMPLE 2 | Fencing a Garden

A gardener has 140 feet of fencing to fence in a rectangular vegetable garden.

(a) Find a function that models the area of the garden she can fence.

(b) For what range of widths is the area greater than 825 ft^2?

(c) Can she fence a garden with area 1250 ft^2?

(d) Find the dimensions of the largest area she can fence.

THINKING ABOUT THE PROBLEM

If the gardener fences a plot with width 10 ft, then the length must be 60 ft, because $10 + 10 + 60 + 60 = 140$. So the area is

$$A = \text{width} \times \text{length} = 10 \cdot 60 = 600 \text{ ft}^2$$

The table shows various choices for fencing the garden. We see that as the width increases, the fenced area increases, then decreases.

Width	Length	Area
10	60	600
20	50	1000
30	40	1200
40	30	1200
50	20	1000
60	10	600

SOLUTION

(a) The model that we want is a function that gives the area she can fence.

▶ **Express the Model in Words**

We know that the area of a rectangular garden is

$$\text{area} = \text{width} \times \text{length}$$

▶ **Choose the Variable**

There are two varying quantities: width and length. Because the function we want depends on only one variable, we let

$$x = \text{width of the garden}$$

Then we must express the length in terms of x. The perimeter is fixed at 140 ft, so the length is determined once we choose the width. If we let the length be l, as in Figure 4, then $2x + 2l = 140$, so $l = 70 - x$. We summarize these facts.

FIGURE 4

In Words	In Algebra
Width	x
Length	$70 - x$

▶ **Set Up the Model**

The model is the function A that gives the area of the garden for any width x.

$$\boxed{\text{area}} = \boxed{\text{width}} \times \boxed{\text{length}}$$

$$A(x) = x(70 - x)$$
$$A(x) = 70x - x^2$$

The area that she can fence is modeled by the function $A(x) = 70x - x^2$.

▶ **Use the Model**

We use the model to answer the questions in parts (b)–(d).

(b) We need to solve the inequality $A(x) \geq 825$. To solve graphically, we graph $y = 70x - x^2$ and $y = 825$ in the same viewing rectangle (see Figure 5). We see that $15 \leq x \leq 55$.

(c) From Figure 6 we see that the graph of $A(x)$ always lies below the line $y = 1250$, so an area of 1250 ft^2 is never attained.

Maximum values of functions are discussed on page 166.

(d) We need to find where the maximum value of the function $A(x) = 70x - x^2$ occurs. The function is graphed in Figure 7. Using the [TRACE] feature on a graphing calculator, we find that the function achieves its maximum value at $x = 35$. So the maximum area that she can fence is that when the garden's width is 35 ft and its length is $70 - 35 = 35$ ft. The maximum area then is $35 \times 35 = 1225$ ft^2.

FIGURE 5

FIGURE 6

FIGURE 7

EXAMPLE 3 | Minimizing the Metal in a Can

A manufacturer makes a metal can that holds 1 L (liter) of oil. What radius minimizes the amount of metal in the can?

THINKING ABOUT THE PROBLEM

To use the least amount of metal, we must minimize the surface area of the can, that is, the area of the top, bottom, and the sides. The area of the top and bottom is $2\pi r^2$ and the area of the sides is $2\pi rh$ (see Figure 8), so the surface area of the can is

$$S = 2\pi r^2 + 2\pi rh$$

The radius and height of the can must be chosen so that the volume is exactly 1 L, or 1000 cm^3. If we want a small radius, say $r = 3$, then the height must be just tall enough to make the total volume 1000 cm^3. In other words, we must have

$$\pi(3)^2 h = 1000 \qquad \text{Volume of the can is } \pi r^2 h$$

$$h = \frac{1000}{9\pi} \approx 35.4 \text{ cm} \qquad \text{Solve for } h$$

Now that we know the radius and height, we can find the surface area of the can:

$$\text{surface area} = 2\pi(3)^2 + 2\pi(3)(35.4) \approx 723.8 \text{ cm}^3$$

If we want a different radius, we can find the corresponding height and surface area in a similar fashion.

FIGURE 8

SOLUTION   The model that we want is a function that gives the surface area of the can.

▶ **Express the Model in Words**

We know that for a cylindrical can

surface area	=	area of top and bottom	+	area of sides

▶ **Choose the Variable**

There are two varying quantities: radius and height. Because the function we want depends on the radius, we let

$$r = \text{radius of can}$$

Next, we must express the height in terms of the radius r. Because the volume of a cylindrical can is $V = \pi r^2 h$ and the volume must be 1000 cm^3, we have

$$\pi r^2 h = 1000 \qquad \text{Volume of can is 1000 cm}^3$$

$$h = \frac{1000}{\pi r^2} \qquad \text{Solve for } h$$

We can now express the areas of the top, bottom, and sides in terms of r only.

In Words	In Algebra
Radius of can	r
Height of can	$\dfrac{1000}{\pi r^2}$
Area of top and bottom	$2\pi r^2$
Area of sides ($2\pi rh$)	$2\pi r\left(\dfrac{1000}{\pi r^2}\right)$

▶ **Set Up the Model**

The model is the function S that gives the surface area of the can as a function of the radius r.

$$\boxed{\text{surface area}} \;=\; \boxed{\text{area of top and bottom}} \;+\; \boxed{\text{area of sides}}$$

$$S(r) = 2\pi r^2 + 2\pi r\left(\frac{1000}{\pi r^2}\right)$$

$$S(r) = 2\pi r^2 + \frac{2000}{r}$$

▶ **Use the Model**

We use the model to find the minimum surface area of the can. We graph S in Figure 9 and zoom in on the minimum point to find that the minimum value of S is about 554 cm^2 and occurs when the radius is about 5.4 cm.

FIGURE 9 $S(r) = 2\pi r^2 + \dfrac{2000}{r}$

PROBLEMS

1–18 ◼ In these problems you are asked to find a function that models a real-life situation. Use the principles of modeling described in this *Focus* to help you.

1. **Area** A rectangular building lot is three times as long as it is wide. Find a function that models its area A in terms of its width w.

2. **Area** A poster is 10 inches longer than it is wide. Find a function that models its area A in terms of its width w.

3. **Volume** A rectangular box has a square base. Its height is half the width of the base. Find a function that models its volume V in terms of its width w.

4. **Volume** The height of a cylinder is four times its radius. Find a function that models the volume V of the cylinder in terms of its radius r.

5. **Area** A rectangle has a perimeter of 20 ft. Find a function that models its area A in terms of the length x of one of its sides.

6. **Perimeter** A rectangle has an area of 16 m^2. Find a function that models its perimeter P in terms of the length x of one of its sides.

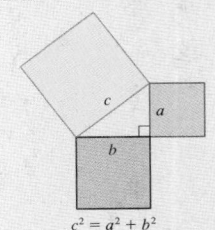

$$c^2 = a^2 + b^2$$

7. Area   Find a function that models the area A of an equilateral triangle in terms of the length x of one of its sides.

8. Area   Find a function that models the surface area S of a cube in terms of its volume V.

9. Radius   Find a function that models the radius r of a circle in terms of its area A.

10. Area   Find a function that models the area A of a circle in terms of its circumference C.

11. Area   A rectangular box with a volume of 60 ft³ has a square base. Find a function that models its surface area S in terms of the length x of one side of its base.

12. Length   A woman 5 ft tall is standing near a street lamp that is 12 ft tall, as shown in the figure. Find a function that models the length L of her shadow in terms of her distance d from the base of the lamp.

13. Distance   Two ships leave port at the same time. One sails south at 15 mi/h, and the other sails east at 20 mi/h. Find a function that models the distance D between the ships in terms of the time t (in hours) elapsed since their departure.

14. Product   The sum of two positive numbers is 60. Find a function that models their product P in terms of x, one of the numbers.

15. Area   An isosceles triangle has a perimeter of 8 cm. Find a function that models its area A in terms of the length of its base b.

16. Perimeter   A right triangle has one leg twice as long as the other. Find a function that models its perimeter P in terms of the length x of the shorter leg.

17. Area   A rectangle is inscribed in a semicircle of radius 10, as shown in the figure. Find a function that models the area A of the rectangle in terms of its height h.

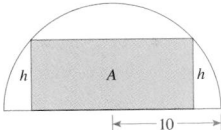

18. Height   The volume of a cone is 100 in³. Find a function that models the height h of the cone in terms of its radius r.

19–32 ■ In these problems you are asked to find a function that models a real-life situation, and then use the model to answer questions about the situation. Use the guidelines on page 215 to help you.

19. Maximizing a Product Consider the following problem: Find two numbers whose sum is 19 and whose product is as large as possible.

(a) Experiment with the problem by making a table like the one following, showing the product of different pairs of numbers that add up to 19. On the basis of the evidence in your table, estimate the answer to the problem.

(b) Find a function that models the product in terms of one of the two numbers.

(c) Use your model to solve the problem, and compare with your answer to part (a).

20. Minimizing a Sum Find two positive numbers whose sum is 100 and the sum of whose squares is a minimum.

21. Fencing a Field Consider the following problem: A farmer has 2400 ft of fencing and wants to fence off a rectangular field that borders a straight river. He does not need a fence along the river (see the figure). What are the dimensions of the field of largest area that he can fence?

(a) Experiment with the problem by drawing several diagrams illustrating the situation. Calculate the area of each configuration, and use your results to estimate the dimensions of the largest possible field.

First number	Second number	Product
1	18	18
2	17	34
3	16	48
⋮	⋮	⋮

(b) Find a function that models the area of the field in terms of one of its sides.

(c) Use your model to solve the problem, and compare with your answer to part (a).

22. Dividing a Pen A rancher with 750 ft of fencing wants to enclose a rectangular area and then divide it into four pens with fencing parallel to one side of the rectangle (see the figure).

(a) Find a function that models the total area of the four pens.

(b) Find the largest possible total area of the four pens.

23. Fencing a Garden Plot A property owner wants to fence a garden plot adjacent to a road, as shown in the figure. The fencing next to the road must be sturdier and costs $5 per foot, but the other fencing costs just $3 per foot. The garden is to have an area of 1200 ft².

(a) Find a function that models the cost of fencing the garden.

(b) Find the garden dimensions that minimize the cost of fencing.

(c) If the owner has at most $600 to spend on fencing, find the range of lengths he can fence along the road.

24. Maximizing Area   A wire 10 cm long is cut into two pieces, one of length x and the other of length $10 - x$, as shown in the figure. Each piece is bent into the shape of a square.

(a) Find a function that models the total area enclosed by the two squares.

(b) Find the value of x that minimizes the total area of the two squares.

25. Light from a Window   A Norman window has the shape of a rectangle surmounted by a semicircle, as shown in the figure to the left. A Norman window with perimeter 30 ft is to be constructed.

(a) Find a function that models the area of the window.

(b) Find the dimensions of the window that admits the greatest amount of light.

26. Volume of a Box   A box with an open top is to be constructed from a rectangular piece of cardboard with dimensions 12 in. by 20 in. by cutting out equal squares of side x at each corner and then folding up the sides (see the figure).

(a) Find a function that models the volume of the box.

(b) Find the values of x for which the volume is greater than 200 in^3.

(c) Find the largest volume that such a box can have.

27. Area of a Box   An open box with a square base is to have a volume of 12 ft^3.

(a) Find a function that models the surface area of the box.

(b) Find the box dimensions that minimize the amount of material used.

28. Inscribed Rectangle   Find the dimensions that give the largest area for the rectangle shown in the figure. Its base is on the x-axis and its other two vertices are above the x-axis, lying on the parabola $y = 8 - x^2$.

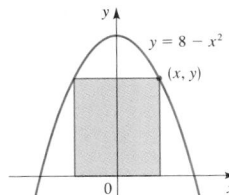

29. Minimizing Costs   A rancher wants to build a rectangular pen with an area of 100 m^2.

(a) Find a function that models the length of fencing required.

(b) Find the pen dimensions that require the minimum amount of fencing.

30. Minimizing Time   A man stands at a point A on the bank of a straight river, 2 mi wide. To reach point B, 7 mi downstream on the opposite bank, he first rows his boat to point P on the opposite bank and then walks the remaining distance x to B, as shown in the figure. He can row at a speed of 2 mi/h and walk at a speed of 5 mi/h.

(a) Find a function that models the time needed for the trip.

(b) Where should he land so that he reaches B as soon as possible?

31. Bird Flight   A bird is released from point A on an island, 5 mi from the nearest point B on a straight shoreline. The bird flies to a point C on the shoreline and then flies along the shoreline to its nesting area D (see the figure). Suppose the bird requires 10 kcal/mi of energy to fly over land and 14 kcal/mi to fly over water.

(a) Use the fact that

$$\text{energy used} = \text{energy per mile} \times \text{miles flown}$$

to show that the total energy used by the bird is modeled by the function

$$E(x) = 14\sqrt{x^2 + 25} + 10(12 - x)$$

(b) If the bird instinctively chooses a path that minimizes its energy expenditure, to what point does it fly?

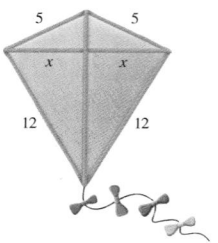

32. Area of a Kite   A kite frame is to be made from six pieces of wood. The four pieces that form its border have been cut to the lengths indicated in the figure. Let x be as shown in the figure.

(a) Show that the area of the kite is given by the function

$$A(x) = x\left(\sqrt{25 - x^2} + \sqrt{144 - x^2}\right)$$

(b) How long should each of the two crosspieces be to maximize the area of the kite?

Image 100/Corbis

CHAPTER

POLYNOMIAL AND RATIONAL FUNCTIONS

Functions defined by polynomial expressions are called polynomial functions. The graphs of polynomial functions can have many peaks and valleys; this makes them suitable models for many real-world situations. For example, a factory owner notices that if she increases the number of workers, productivity increases, but if there are too many workers, productivity begins to decrease. This situation is modeled by a polynomial function of degree 2 (a quadratic function). As another example, when a volleyball is hit, it goes up and then down, following a path that is also modeled by a quadratic function. The graphs of polynomial functions are smooth curves that are used in designing many things. For example, sailboat designers put together portions of the graphs of different cubic functions (called cubic splines) to make the curves of the hull of a sailboat.

**SUGGESTED TIME
AND EMPHASIS**

1 class, essential material

3.1 QUADRATIC FUNCTIONS AND MODELS

Graphing Quadratic Functions Using the Standard Form ▶ Maximum and Minimum Values of Quadratic Functions ▶ Modeling with Quadratic Functions

A polynomial function is a function that is defined by a polynomial expression. So a **polynomial function of degree n** is a function of the form

$$P(x) = a_n x^n + a_{n-1} x^{n-1} + \cdots + a_1 x + a_0$$

Polynomial expressions are defined in Section 1.3.

We have already studied polynomial functions of degree 0 and 1. These are functions of the form $P(x) = a_0$ and $P(x) = a_1 x + a_0$, respectively, whose graphs are lines. In this section we study polynomial functions of degree 2. These are called quadratic functions.

QUADRATIC FUNCTIONS

A **quadratic function** is a polynomial function of degree 2. So a quadratic function is a function of the form

$$f(x) = ax^2 + bx + c, \qquad a \neq 0$$

We see in this section how quadratic functions model many real-world phenomena. We begin by analyzing the graphs of quadratic functions.

▼ Graphing Quadratic Functions Using the Standard Form

For a geometric definition of parabolas, see Section 11.1.

If we take $a = 1$ and $b = c = 0$ in the quadratic function $f(x) = ax^2 + bx + c$, we get the quadratic function $f(x) = x^2$, whose graph is the parabola graphed in Example 1 of Section 2.2. In fact, the graph of any quadratic function is a **parabola**; it can be obtained from the graph of $f(x) = x^2$ by the transformations given in Section 2.5.

STANDARD FORM OF A QUADRATIC FUNCTION

A quadratic function $f(x) = ax^2 + bx + c$ can be expressed in the **standard form**

$$f(x) = a(x - h)^2 + k$$

by completing the square. The graph of f is a parabola with **vertex** (h, k); the parabola opens upward if $a > 0$ or downward if $a < 0$.

$$f(x) = a(x - h)^2 + k, \ a > 0 \qquad\qquad f(x) = a(x - h)^2 + k, \ a < 0$$

EXAMPLE 1 | Standard Form of a Quadratic Function

Let $f(x) = 2x^2 - 12x + 23$.

(a) Express f in standard form.   **(b)** Sketch the graph of f.

TEXT QUESTION

How does expressing a quadratic function in standard form make it easier to find its maximum or minimum value?

Answer

Once a quadratic function is expressed in standard form, the y-coordinate of the vertex can be read right off the function's expression.

Completing the square is discussed in Section 1.5.

$$f(x) = 2(x - 3)^2 + 5$$

Vertex is $(3, 5)$

SOLUTION

(a) Since the coefficient of x^2 is not 1, we must factor this coefficient from the terms involving x before we complete the square.

$$f(x) = 2x^2 - 12x + 23$$
$$= 2(x^2 - 6x) + 23 \qquad \text{Factor 2 from the } x\text{-terms}$$
$$= 2(x^2 - 6x + 9) + 23 - 2 \cdot 9 \qquad \text{Complete the square: Add 9 inside parentheses, subtract } 2 \cdot 9 \text{ outside}$$
$$= 2(x - 3)^2 + 5 \qquad \text{Factor and simplify}$$

The standard form is $f(x) = 2(x - 3)^2 + 5$.

(b) The standard form tells us that we get the graph of f by taking the parabola $y = x^2$, shifting it to the right 3 units, stretching it by a factor of 2, and moving it upward 5 units. The vertex of the parabola is at $(3, 5)$, and the parabola opens upward. We sketch the graph in Figure 1 after noting that the y-intercept is $f(0) = 23$.

$f(x) = 2(x - 3)^2 + 5$

Vertex $(3, 5)$

FIGURE 1

✎. NOW TRY EXERCISE **13**

▼ Maximum and Minimum Values of Quadratic Functions

If a quadratic function has vertex (h, k), then the function has a minimum value at the vertex if its graph opens upward and a maximum value at the vertex if its graph opens downward. For example, the function graphed in Figure 1 has minimum value 5 when $x = 3$, since the vertex $(3, 5)$ is the lowest point on the graph.

MAXIMUM OR MINIMUM VALUE OF A QUADRATIC FUNCTION

Let f be a quadratic function with standard form $f(x) = a(x - h)^2 + k$. The maximum or minimum value of f occurs at $x = h$.

If $a > 0$, then the **minimum value** of f is $f(h) = k$.

If $a < 0$, then the **maximum value** of f is $f(h) = k$.

$f(x) = a(x - h)^2 + k, a > 0$

$f(x) = a(x - h)^2 + k, a < 0$

IN-CLASS MATERIALS

A straightforward way to demonstrate the utility of quadratic functions is to demonstrate how thrown objects follow parabolic paths. Toss a ball (perhaps trying to get it into the wastebasket) and have the class observe the shape of its path. Note that not only can thrown objects' paths be modeled by parabolas, their height as a function of time can (on Earth) be modeled by quadratic functions of the form $f(x) = -16t^2 + v_0 t + s_0$, where t is in seconds, f is in feet, v_0 is initial velocity, and s_0 is initial height (see Exercise 63).

ALTERNATE EXAMPLE 2

Consider the quadratic function $x^2 + 2x - 2$.

(a) Express f in standard form.
(b) Sketch the graph of f.
(c) Find the minimum value of f.

ANSWERS

(a) $f(x) = (x + 1)^2 - 3$
(b)

(c) The minimum value is $f(-1) = -3$.

ALTERNATE EXAMPLE 3

Consider the quadratic function $-3x^2 + 2x + 1$.

(a) Express f in standard form.
(b) Sketch the graph of f.
(c) Find the maximum value of f.

ANSWERS

(a) $f(x) = -3\left(x - \dfrac{1}{3}\right)^2 + \dfrac{4}{3}$
(b)

(c) The minimum value is $f(1/3) = 4/3$.

EXAMPLE 2 | Minimum Value of a Quadratic Function

Consider the quadratic function $f(x) = 5x^2 - 30x + 49$.

(a) Express f in standard form.
(b) Sketch the graph of f.
(c) Find the minimum value of f.

SOLUTION

(a) To express this quadratic function in standard form, we complete the square.

$$f(x) = 5x^2 - 30x + 49$$

$$= 5(x^2 - 6x) + 49 \qquad \text{Factor 5 from the } x\text{-terms}$$

$$= 5(x^2 - 6x + 9) + 49 - 5 \cdot 9 \qquad \text{Complete the square: Add 9 inside parentheses, subtract } 5 \cdot 9 \text{ outside}$$

$$= 5(x - 3)^2 + 4 \qquad \text{Factor and simplify}$$

(b) The graph is a parabola that has its vertex at $(3, 4)$ and opens upward, as sketched in Figure 2.

(c) Since the coefficient of x^2 is positive, f has a minimum value. The minimum value is $f(3) = 4$.

↖. NOW TRY EXERCISE **25**

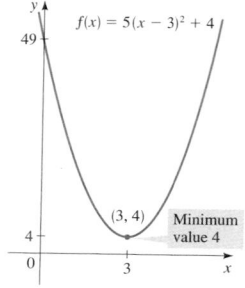

FIGURE 2

EXAMPLE 3 | Maximum Value of a Quadratic Function

Consider the quadratic function $f(x) = -x^2 + x + 2$.

(a) Express f in standard form.
(b) Sketch the graph of f.
(c) Find the maximum value of f.

SOLUTION

(a) To express this quadratic function in standard form, we complete the square.

$$y = -x^2 + x + 2$$

$$= -(x^2 - x) + 2 \qquad \text{Factor } -1 \text{ from the } x\text{-terms}$$

$$= -\left(x^2 - x + \tfrac{1}{4}\right) + 2 - (-1)\tfrac{1}{4} \qquad \text{Complete the square: Add } \tfrac{1}{4} \text{ inside parentheses, subtract } (-1)\tfrac{1}{4} \text{ outside}$$

$$= -\left(x - \tfrac{1}{2}\right)^2 + \tfrac{9}{4} \qquad \text{Factor and simplify}$$

(b) From the standard form we see that the graph is a parabola that opens downward and has vertex $\left(\tfrac{1}{2}, \tfrac{9}{4}\right)$. As an aid to sketching the graph, we find the intercepts. The y-intercept is $f(0) = 2$. To find the x-intercepts, we set $f(x) = 0$ and factor the resulting equation.

$$-x^2 + x + 2 = 0 \qquad \text{Set } y = 0$$

$$x^2 - x - 2 = 0 \qquad \text{Multiply by } -1$$

$$(x - 2)(x + 1) = 0 \qquad \text{Factor}$$

Thus the x-intercepts are $x = 2$ and $x = -1$. The graph of f is sketched in Figure 3.

(c) Since the coefficient of x^2 is negative, f has a maximum value, which is $f\left(\tfrac{1}{2}\right) = \tfrac{9}{4}$.

↖. NOW TRY EXERCISE **27**

Expressing a quadratic function in standard form helps us to sketch its graph as well as to find its maximum or minimum value. If we are interested only in finding the maxi-

FIGURE 3 Graph of $f(x) = -x^2 + x + 2$

IN-CLASS MATERIALS

Note that we can consider the minimum or maximum value of a quadratic function as the place where the graph goes from decreasing to increasing or vice versa. We will see in the next section that a cubic has at most two such points and that an nth-degree polynomial function has at most $n - 1$ such points.

mum or minimum value, then a formula is available for doing so. This formula is obtained by completing the square for the general quadratic function as follows:

$$f(x) = ax^2 + bx + c$$

$$= a\left(x^2 + \frac{b}{a}x\right) + c \qquad \text{Factor } a \text{ from the } x\text{-terms}$$

$$= a\left(x^2 + \frac{b}{a}x + \frac{b^2}{4a^2}\right) + c - a\left(\frac{b^2}{4a^2}\right) \qquad \begin{array}{l}\text{Complete the square: Add } \frac{b^2}{4a^2} \\ \text{inside parentheses, subtract} \\ a\left(\frac{b^2}{4a^2}\right) \text{ outside}\end{array}$$

$$= a\left(x + \frac{b}{2a}\right)^2 + c - \frac{b^2}{4a} \qquad \text{Factor}$$

This equation is in standard form with $h = -b/(2a)$ and $k = c - b^2/(4a)$. Since the maximum or minimum value occurs at $x = h$, we have the following result.

MAXIMUM OR MINIMUM VALUE OF A QUADRATIC FUNCTION

The maximum or minimum value of a quadratic function $f(x) = ax^2 + bx + c$ occurs at

$$x = -\frac{b}{2a}$$

If $a > 0$, then the **minimum value** is $f\left(-\frac{b}{2a}\right)$.

If $a < 0$, then the **maximum value** is $f\left(-\frac{b}{2a}\right)$.

EXAMPLE 4 | Finding Maximum and Minimum Values of Quadratic Functions

Find the maximum or minimum value of each quadratic function.

(a) $f(x) = x^2 + 4x$ (b) $g(x) = -2x^2 + 4x - 5$

SOLUTION

(a) This is a quadratic function with $a = 1$ and $b = 4$. Thus, the maximum or minimum value occurs at

$$x = -\frac{b}{2a} = -\frac{4}{2 \cdot 1} = -2$$

Since $a > 0$, the function has the *minimum* value

$$f(-2) = (-2)^2 + 4(-2) = -4$$

(b) This is a quadratic function with $a = -2$ and $b = 4$. Thus, the maximum or minimum value occurs at

$$x = -\frac{b}{2a} = -\frac{4}{2 \cdot (-2)} = 1$$

Since $a < 0$, the function has the *maximum* value

$$f(1) = -2(1)^2 + 4(1) - 5 = -3$$

NOW TRY EXERCISES 33 AND 35

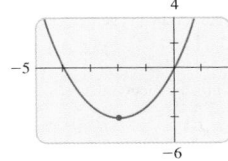

The minimum value occurs at $x = -2$.

The maximum value occurs at $x = 1$.

▼ Modeling with Quadratic Functions

We study some examples of real-world phenomena that are modeled by quadratic functions. These examples and the *Application* exercises for this section show some of the variety of situations that are naturally modeled by quadratic functions.

EXAMPLE 5 | Maximum Gas Mileage for a Car

Most cars get their best gas mileage when traveling at a relatively modest speed. The gas mileage M for a certain new car is modeled by the function

$$M(s) = -\frac{1}{28}s^2 + 3s - 31, \qquad 15 \le s \le 70$$

where s is the speed in mi/h and M is measured in mi/gal. What is the car's best gas mileage, and at what speed is it attained?

SOLUTION   The function M is a quadratic function with $a = -\frac{1}{28}$ and $b = 3$. Thus, its maximum value occurs when

$$s = -\frac{b}{2a} = -\frac{3}{2\left(-\frac{1}{28}\right)} = 42$$

The maximum is $M(42) = -\frac{1}{28}(42)^2 + 3(42) - 31 = 32$. So the car's best gas mileage is 32 mi/gal, when it is traveling at 42 mi/h.

✎. NOW TRY EXERCISE **67**   ∎

EXAMPLE 6 | Maximizing Revenue from Ticket Sales

A hockey team plays in an arena that has a seating capacity of 15,000 spectators. With the ticket price set at $14, average attendance at recent games has been 9500. A market survey indicates that for each dollar the ticket price is lowered, the average attendance increases by 1000.

(a) Find a function that models the revenue in terms of ticket price.

(b) Find the price that maximizes revenue from ticket sales.

(c) What ticket price is so high that no one attends and so no revenue is generated?

SOLUTION

(a) **Express the model in words.**   The model that we want is a function that gives the revenue for any ticket price.

$$\boxed{\text{revenue}} = \boxed{\text{ticket price}} \times \boxed{\text{attendance}}$$

Choose the variable.   There are two varying quantities: ticket price and attendance. Since the function we want depends on price, we let

$$x = \text{ticket price}$$

Next, we express attendance in terms of x.

In Words	In Algebra
Ticket price	x
Amount ticket price is lowered	$14 - x$
Increase in attendance	$1000(14 - x)$
Attendance	$9500 + 1000(14 - x)$

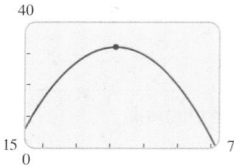

The maximum gas mileage occurs at 42 mi/h.

Set up the model.   The model that we want is the function R that gives the revenue for a given ticket price x.

$$\boxed{\text{revenue}} = \boxed{\text{ticket price}} \times \boxed{\text{attendance}}$$

$$R(x) = x \times [9500 + 1000(14 - x)]$$
$$R(x) = x(23{,}500 - 1000x)$$
$$R(x) = 23{,}500x - 1000x^2$$

(b) Use the model.   Since R is a quadratic function with $a = -1000$ and $b = 23{,}500$, the maximum occurs at

$$x = -\frac{b}{2a} = -\frac{23{,}500}{2(-1000)} = 11.75$$

So a ticket price of $11.75 gives the maximum revenue.

(c) Use the model.   We want to find the ticket price for which $R(x) = 0$.

$$\begin{aligned}
23{,}500x - 1000x^2 &= 0 && \text{Set } R(x) = 0 \\
23.5x - x^2 &= 0 && \text{Divide by 1000} \\
x(23.5 - x) &= 0 && \text{Factor} \\
x = 0 \quad \text{or} \quad x &= 23.5 && \text{Solve for } x
\end{aligned}$$

So according to this model, a ticket price of $23.50 is just too high; at that price, no one attends to watch this team play. (Of course, revenue is also zero if the ticket price is zero.)

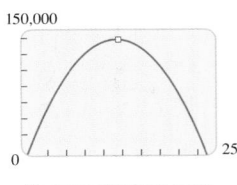

150,000

0   25

Maximum attendance occurs
when ticket price is $11.75.

◤. NOW TRY EXERCISE **77**

3.1 EXERCISES

CONCEPTS

1. To put the quadratic function $f(x) = ax^2 + bx + c$ in standard

form, we complete the _____ .

2. The quadratic function $f(x) = a(x - h)^2 + k$ is in standard
form.
   (a) The graph of f is a parabola with vertex (____, ____).

   (b) If $a > 0$, the graph of f opens _____ . In this case

   $f(h) = k$ is the _____ value of f.

   (c) If $a < 0$, the graph of f opens _____ . In this case

   $f(h) = k$ is the _____ value of f.

3. The graph of $f(x) = 2(x - 3)^2 + 5$ is a parabola that opens

_____ , with its vertex at (____, ____), and

$f(3) =$ _____ is the (minimum/maximum) _____
value of f.

4. The graph of $f(x) = -2(x - 3)^2 + 5$ is a parabola that

opens _____ , with its vertex at (____, ____), and

$f(3) =$ _____ is the (minimum/maximum) _____
value of f.

SKILLS

5–8 ■ The graph of a quadratic function f is given. **(a)** Find the
coordinates of the vertex. **(b)** Find the maximum or minimum
value of f. **(c)** Find the domain and range of f.

5. $f(x) = -x^2 + 6x - 5$

6. $f(x) = -\frac{1}{2}x^2 - 2x + 6$

7. $f(x) = 2x^2 - 4x - 1$ **8.** $f(x) = 3x^2 + 6x - 1$

9–22 ■ A quadratic function is given. **(a)** Express the quadratic function in standard form. **(b)** Find its vertex and its x- and y-intercept(s). **(c)** Sketch its graph.

9. $f(x) = x^2 - 6x$ **10.** $f(x) = x^2 + 8x$

11. $f(x) = 2x^2 + 6x$ **12.** $f(x) = -x^2 + 10x$

13. $f(x) = x^2 + 4x + 3$ **14.** $f(x) = x^2 - 2x + 2$

15. $f(x) = -x^2 + 6x + 4$ **16.** $f(x) = -x^2 - 4x + 4$

17. $f(x) = 2x^2 + 4x + 3$ **18.** $f(x) = -3x^2 + 6x - 2$

19. $f(x) = 2x^2 - 20x + 57$ **20.** $f(x) = 2x^2 + x - 6$

21. $f(x) = -4x^2 - 16x + 3$ **22.** $f(x) = 6x^2 + 12x - 5$

23–32 ■ A quadratic function is given. **(a)** Express the quadratic function in standard form. **(b)** Sketch its graph. **(c)** Find its maximum or minimum value.

23. $f(x) = x^2 + 2x - 1$ **24.** $f(x) = x^2 - 8x + 8$

25. $f(x) = 3x^2 - 6x + 1$ **26.** $f(x) = 5x^2 + 30x + 4$

27. $f(x) = -x^2 - 3x + 3$ **28.** $f(x) = 1 - 6x - x^2$

29. $g(x) = 3x^2 - 12x + 13$ **30.** $g(x) = 2x^2 + 8x + 11$

31. $h(x) = 1 - x - x^2$ **32.** $h(x) = 3 - 4x - 4x^2$

33–42 ■ Find the maximum or minimum value of the function.

33. $f(x) = x^2 + x + 1$ **34.** $f(x) = 1 + 3x - x^2$

35. $f(t) = 100 - 49t - 7t^2$ **36.** $f(t) = 10t^2 + 40t + 113$

37. $f(s) = s^2 - 1.2s + 16$ **38.** $g(x) = 100x^2 - 1500x$

39. $h(x) = \frac{1}{2}x^2 + 2x - 6$ **40.** $f(x) = -\frac{x^2}{3} + 2x + 7$

41. $f(x) = 3 - x - \frac{1}{2}x^2$ **42.** $g(x) = 2x(x - 4) + 7$

43. Find a function whose graph is a parabola with vertex $(1, -2)$ and that passes through the point $(4, 16)$.

44. Find a function whose graph is a parabola with vertex $(3, 4)$ and that passes through the point $(1, -8)$.

45–48 ■ Find the domain and range of the function.

45. $f(x) = -x^2 + 4x - 3$ **46.** $f(x) = x^2 - 2x - 3$

47. $f(x) = 2x^2 + 6x - 7$ **48.** $f(x) = -3x^2 + 6x + 4$

49–50 ■ A quadratic function is given. **(a)** Use a graphing device to find the maximum or minimum value of the quadratic function f, correct to two decimal places. **(b)** Find the exact maximum or minimum value of f, and compare it with your answer to part (a).

49. $f(x) = x^2 + 1.79x - 3.21$

50. $f(x) = 1 + x - \sqrt{2}x^2$

51–54 ■ Find all local maximum and minimum values of the function whose graph is shown.

51.   **52.**

53.   **54.**

 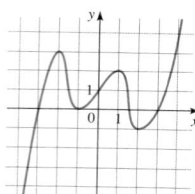

55–62 ■ Find the local maximum and minimum values of the function and the value of x at which each occurs. State each answer correct to two decimal places.

55. $f(x) = x^3 - x$

56. $f(x) = 3 + x + x^2 - x^3$

57. $g(x) = x^4 - 2x^3 - 11x^2$

58. $g(x) = x^5 - 8x^3 + 20x$

59. $U(x) = x\sqrt{6 - x}$

60. $U(x) = x\sqrt{x - x^2}$

61. $V(x) = \frac{1 - x^2}{x^3}$

62. $V(x) = \frac{1}{x^2 + x + 1}$

APPLICATIONS

63. Height of a Ball   If a ball is thrown directly upward with a velocity of 40 ft/s, its height (in feet) after t seconds is given by $y = 40t - 16t^2$. What is the maximum height attained by the ball?

64. Path of a Ball   A ball is thrown across a playing field from a height of 5 ft above the ground at an angle of 45° to the horizontal at a speed of 20 ft/s. It can be deduced from physical principles that the path of the ball is modeled by the function

$$y = -\frac{32}{(20)^2}x^2 + x + 5$$

where x is the distance in feet that the ball has traveled horizontally.

(a) Find the maximum height attained by the ball.

(b) Find the horizontal distance the ball has traveled when it hits the ground.

65. Revenue   A manufacturer finds that the revenue generated by selling x units of a certain commodity is given by the function $R(x) = 80x - 0.4x^2$, where the revenue $R(x)$ is measured in dollars. What is the maximum revenue, and how many units should be manufactured to obtain this maximum?

66. Sales   A soft-drink vendor at a popular beach analyzes his sales records and finds that if he sells x cans of soda pop in one day, his profit (in dollars) is given by

$$P(x) = -0.001x^2 + 3x - 1800$$

What is his maximum profit per day, and how many cans must he sell for maximum profit?

67. Advertising   The effectiveness of a television commercial depends on how many times a viewer watches it. After some experiments an advertising agency found that if the effectiveness E is measured on a scale of 0 to 10, then

$$E(n) = \tfrac{2}{3}n - \tfrac{1}{90}n^2$$

where n is the number of times a viewer watches a given commercial. For a commercial to have maximum effectiveness, how many times should a viewer watch it?

68. Pharmaceuticals   When a certain drug is taken orally, the concentration of the drug in the patient's bloodstream after t minutes is given by $C(t) = 0.06t - 0.0002t^2$, where $0 \le t \le 240$ and the concentration is measured in mg/L. When is the maximum serum concentration reached, and what is that maximum concentration?

69. Agriculture   The number of apples produced by each tree in an apple orchard depends on how densely the trees are planted. If n trees are planted on an acre of land, then each tree produces $900 - 9n$ apples. So the number of apples produced per acre is

$$A(n) = n(900 - 9n)$$

How many trees should be planted per acre to obtain the maximum yield of apples?

70. Agriculture   At a certain vineyard it is found that each grape vine produces about 10 pounds of grapes in a season when about 700 vines are planted per acre. For each additional vine that is planted, the production of each vine decreases by about 1 percent. So the number of pounds of grapes produced per acre is modeled by

$$A(n) = (700 + n)(10 - 0.01n)$$

where n is the number of additional vines planted. Find the number of vines that should be planted to maximize grape production.

71–74 ■ Use the formulas of this section to give an alternative solution to the indicated problem in *Focus on Modeling: Modeling with Functions* on pages 220–221.

71. Problem 21   **72.** Problem 22

73. Problem 25   **74.** Problem 24

75. Fencing a Horse Corral   Carol has 2400 ft of fencing to fence in a rectangular horse corral.

(a) Find a function that models the area of the corral in terms of the width x of the corral.

(b) Find the dimensions of the rectangle that maximize the area of the corral.

76. Making a Rain Gutter   A rain gutter is formed by bending up the sides of a 30-inch-wide rectangular metal sheet as shown in the figure.

(a) Find a function that models the cross-sectional area of the gutter in terms of x.

(b) Find the value of x that maximizes the cross-sectional area of the gutter.

(c) What is the maximum cross-sectional area for the gutter?

77. Stadium Revenue A baseball team plays in a stadium that holds 55,000 spectators. With the ticket price at $10, the average attendance at recent games has been 27,000. A market survey indicates that for every dollar the ticket price is lowered, attendance increases by 3000.

(a) Find a function that models the revenue in terms of ticket price.

(b) Find the price that maximizes revenue from ticket sales.

(c) What ticket price is so high that no revenue is generated?

78. Maximizing Profit A community bird-watching society makes and sells simple bird feeders to raise money for its conservation activities. The materials for each feeder cost $6, and the society sells an average of 20 per week at a price of $10 each. The society has been considering raising the price, so it conducts a survey and finds that for every dollar increase, it loses 2 sales per week.

(a) Find a function that models weekly profit in terms of price per feeder.

(b) What price should the society charge for each feeder to maximize profits? What is the maximum weekly profit?

DISCOVERY ▪ DISCUSSION ▪ WRITING

79. Vertex and x-Intercepts We know that the graph of the quadratic function $f(x) = (x - m)(x - n)$ is a parabola. Sketch a rough graph of what such a parabola would look like. What are the x-intercepts of the graph of f? Can you tell from your graph the x-coordinate of the vertex in terms of m and n? (Use the symmetry of the parabola.) Confirm your answer by expanding and using the formulas of this section.

80. Maximum of a Fourth-Degree Polynomial Find the maximum value of the function

$$f(x) = 3 + 4x^2 - x^4$$

[*Hint:* Let $t = x^2$.]

SUGGESTED TIME AND EMPHASIS

1 class, essential material

3.2 POLYNOMIAL FUNCTIONS AND THEIR GRAPHS

Graphing Basic Polynomial Functions ▶ End Behavior and the Leading Term ▶ Using Zeros to Graph Polynomials ▶ Shape of the Graph Near a Zero ▶ Local Maxima and Minima of Polynomials

In this section we study polynomial functions of any degree. But before we work with polynomial functions, we must agree on some terminology.

POLYNOMIAL FUNCTIONS

A **polynomial function of degree n** is a function of the form

$$P(x) = a_n x^n + a_{n-1} x^{n-1} + \cdots + a_1 x + a_0$$

where n is a nonnegative integer and $a_n \neq 0$.

The numbers $a_0, a_1, a_2, \ldots, a_n$ are called the **coefficients** of the polynomial.

The number a_0 is the **constant coefficient** or **constant term**.

The number a_n, the coefficient of the highest power, is the **leading coefficient**, and the term $a_n x^n$ is the **leading term**.

We often refer to polynomial functions simply as *polynomials*. The following polynomial has degree 5, leading coefficient 3, and constant term -6.

Leading coefficient 3   Degree 5   Constant term -6

$$3x^5 + 6x^4 - 2x^3 + x^2 + 7x - 6$$

Leading term $3x^5$

Coefficients 3, 6, -2, 1, 7, and -6

TEXT QUESTIONS

Which of the following are polynomial functions?

(a) $f(x) = -x^3 + 2x + 4$

(b) $f(x) = \left(\sqrt{x}\right)^3 - 2\left(\sqrt{x}\right)^2 + 5\left(\sqrt{x}\right) - 1$

(c) $f(x) = (x - 2)(x - 1)(x + 4)^2$

(d) $f(x) = \dfrac{x^2 + 2}{x^2 - 2}$

Answers

(a) and **(c)**

Here are some more examples of polynomials.

$$P(x) = 3 \qquad\qquad \text{Degree 0}$$
$$Q(x) = 4x - 7 \qquad \text{Degree 1}$$
$$R(x) = x^2 + x \qquad \text{Degree 2}$$
$$S(x) = 2x^3 - 6x^2 - 10 \qquad \text{Degree 3}$$

If a polynomial consists of just a single term, then it is called a **monomial**. For example, $P(x) = x^3$ and $Q(x) = -6x^5$ are monomials.

▼ Graphing Basic Polynomial Functions

The graphs of polynomials of degree 0 or 1 are lines (Section 1.10), and the graphs of polynomials of degree 2 are parabolas (Section 3.1). The greater the degree of a polynomial, the more complicated its graph can be. However, the graph of a polynomial function is **continuous**. This means that the graph has no breaks or holes (see Figure 1). Moreover, the graph of a polynomial function is a smooth curve; that is, it has no corners or sharp points (cusps) as shown in Figure 1.

Continuous functions are studied in Section 13.2, page 851.

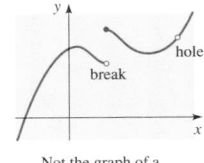

Not the graph of a
polynomial function

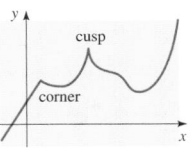

Not the graph of a
polynomial function

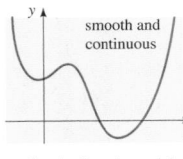

Graph of a polynomial
function

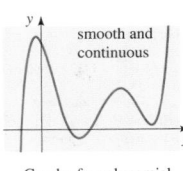

Graph of a polynomial
function

FIGURE 1

The simplest polynomial functions are the monomials $P(x) = x^n$, whose graphs are shown in Figure 2. As the figure suggests, the graph of $P(x) = x^n$ has the same general shape as the graph of $y = x^2$ when n is even and the same general shape as the graph of $y = x^3$ when n is odd. However, as the degree n becomes larger, the graphs become flatter around the origin and steeper elsewhere.

(a) $y = x$

(b) $y = x^2$

(c) $y = x^3$

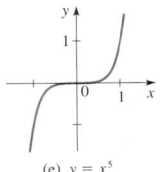

(d) $y = x^4$

(e) $y = x^5$

FIGURE 2 Graphs of monomials

EXAMPLE 1 | Transformations of Monomials

Sketch the graphs of the following functions.

(a) $P(x) = -x^3$ **(b)** $Q(x) = (x - 2)^4$
(c) $R(x) = -2x^5 + 4$

IN-CLASS MATERIALS

Point out that while the students can, by the end of this section, sketch the graph of a polynomial function like $f(x) = (x - 1)(x - 2)^2(x - 3)$ relatively quickly, they still cannot find the precise coordinates of the two local minima, nor could they tell how fast the function is increasing as x gets large. Point out that they now have a good method for getting a general idea of the shape of a polynomial, and more precision will come with calculus.

ALTERNATE EXAMPLE 1

Sketch the graphs of the following functions:

(a) $P(x) = -x^2$
(b) $Q(x) = (x + 1)^5$
(c) $R(x) = -3x^2 + 3$

ANSWERS

(a)

(b)

(c)

SOLUTION We use the graphs in Figure 2 and transform them using the techniques of Section 2.5.

(a) The graph of $P(x) = -x^3$ is the reflection of the graph of $y = x^3$ in the x-axis, as shown in Figure 3(a) below.

(b) The graph of $Q(x) = (x - 2)^4$ is the graph of $y = x^4$ shifted to the right 2 units, as shown in Figure 3(b).

(c) We begin with the graph of $y = x^5$. The graph of $y = -2x^5$ is obtained by stretching the graph vertically and reflecting it in the x-axis (see the dashed blue graph in Figure 3(c)). Finally, the graph of $R(x) = -2x^5 + 4$ is obtained by shifting upward 4 units (see the red graph in Figure 3(c)).

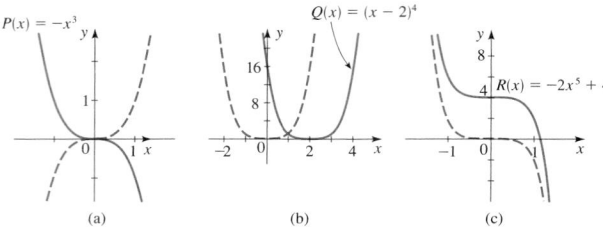

(a)   (b)   (c)

FIGURE 3

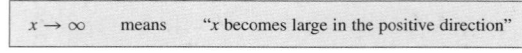

✎. NOW TRY EXERCISE **5**

▼ End Behavior and the Leading Term

The **end behavior** of a polynomial is a description of what happens as x becomes large in the positive or negative direction. To describe end behavior, we use the following notation:

$$x \to \infty \qquad \text{means} \qquad \text{"}x \text{ becomes large in the positive direction"}$$

$$x \to -\infty \qquad \text{means} \qquad \text{"}x \text{ becomes large in the negative direction"}$$

For example, the monomial $y = x^2$ in Figure 2(b) has the following end behavior:

$$y \to \infty \quad \text{as} \quad x \to \infty \qquad \text{and} \qquad y \to \infty \quad \text{as} \quad x \to -\infty$$

The monomial $y = x^3$ in Figure 2(c) has the following end behavior:

$$y \to \infty \quad \text{as} \quad x \to \infty \qquad \text{and} \qquad y \to -\infty \quad \text{as} \quad x \to -\infty$$

For any polynomial *the end behavior is determined by the term that contains the highest power of x*, because when x is large, the other terms are relatively insignificant in size. The following box shows the four possible types of end behavior, based on the highest power and the sign of its coefficient.

END BEHAVIOR OF POLYNOMIALS

The end behavior of the polynomial $P(x) = a_n x^n + a_{n-1}x^{n-1} + \cdots + a_1 x + a_0$ is determined by the degree n and the sign of the leading coefficient a_n, as indicated in the following graphs.

P has odd degree

P has even degree

Leading coefficient positive   Leading coefficient negative   Leading coefficient positive   Leading coefficient negative

EXAMPLE 2 | End Behavior of a Polynomial

Determine the end behavior of the polynomial

$$P(x) = -2x^4 + 5x^3 + 4x - 7$$

SOLUTION   The polynomial P has degree 4 and leading coefficient -2. Thus, P has *even* degree and *negative* leading coefficient, so it has the following end behavior:

$$y \to -\infty \quad \text{as} \quad x \to \infty \qquad \text{and} \qquad y \to -\infty \quad \text{as} \quad x \to -\infty$$

The graph in Figure 4 illustrates the end behavior of P.

FIGURE 4
$P(x) = -2x^4 + 5x^3 + 4x - 7$

✎. **NOW TRY EXERCISE 11**

EXAMPLE 3 | End Behavior of a Polynomial

(a) Determine the end behavior of the polynomial $P(x) = 3x^5 - 5x^3 + 2x$.

(b) Confirm that P and its leading term $Q(x) = 3x^5$ have the same end behavior by graphing them together.

SOLUTION

(a) Since P has odd degree and positive leading coefficient, it has the following end behavior:

$$y \to \infty \quad \text{as} \quad x \to \infty \qquad \text{and} \qquad y \to -\infty \quad \text{as} \quad x \to -\infty$$

ALTERNATE EXAMPLE 2
Determine the end behavior of the polynomial
$f(x) = -3x^3 + 20x^2 + 60x + 2.$

ANSWER
$y \to -\infty$ as $x \to \infty, y \to \infty$ as $x \to -\infty$

ALTERNATE EXAMPLE 3
Determine the end behavior of the graph of the function
$y = 8x^3 - 7x^2 + 3x + 7.$

ANSWER
$y \to -\infty$ as $x \to -\infty$ and $y \to \infty$ as $x \to \infty$

IN-CLASS MATERIALS

When discussing local extrema, make sure students understand that just because a fifth-degree polynomial (for example) *can* have four local extrema doesn't mean it *must* have four local extrema. Have students graph $f(x) = x^5$ as a quick example, and then $f(x) = x^5 - x^3$ as an example of a fifth-degree polynomial with two local extrema. Have students try to come up with a proof that there can't be a fifth-degree polynomial with exactly one or three local extrema.

(b) Figure 5 shows the graphs of P and Q in progressively larger viewing rectangles. The larger the viewing rectangle, the more the graphs look alike. This confirms that they have the same end behavior.

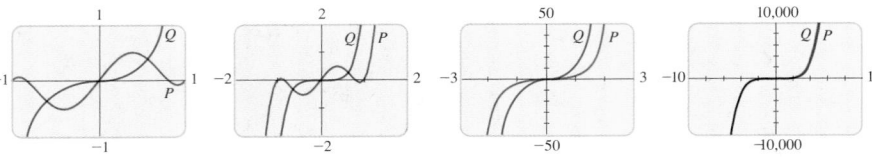

FIGURE 5
$P(x) = 3x^5 - 5x^3 + 2x$
$Q(x) = 3x^5$

✎. **NOW TRY EXERCISE 41**

To see algebraically why P and Q in Example 3 have the same end behavior, factor P as follows and compare with Q.

$$P(x) = 3x^5\left(1 - \frac{5}{3x^2} + \frac{2}{3x^4}\right) \qquad Q(x) = 3x^5$$

When x is large, the terms $5/3x^2$ and $2/3x^4$ are close to 0 (see Exercise 83 on page 12). So for large x, we have

$$P(x) \approx 3x^5(1 - 0 - 0) = 3x^5 = Q(x)$$

So when x is large, P and Q have approximately the same values. We can also see this numerically by making a table like the one shown below.

x	$P(x)$	$Q(x)$
15	2,261,280	2,278,125
30	72,765,060	72,900,000
50	936,875,100	937,500,000

By the same reasoning we can show that the end behavior of *any* polynomial is determined by its leading term.

▼ Using Zeros to Graph Polynomials

If P is a polynomial function, then c is called a **zero** of P if $P(c) = 0$. In other words, the zeros of P are the solutions of the polynomial equation $P(x) = 0$. Note that if $P(c) = 0$, then the graph of P has an x-intercept at $x = c$, so the x-intercepts of the graph are the zeros of the function.

REAL ZEROS OF POLYNOMIALS

If P is a polynomial and c is a real number, then the following are equivalent:

1. c is a zero of P.
2. $x = c$ is a solution of the equation $P(x) = 0$.
3. $x - c$ is a factor of $P(x)$.
4. c is an x-intercept of the graph of P.

To find the zeros of a polynomial P, we factor and then use the Zero-Product Property (see page 47). For example, to find the zeros of $P(x) = x^2 + x - 6$, we factor P to get

$$P(x) = (x - 2)(x + 3)$$

EXAMPLE

A polynomial function with zeros of various multiplicities:

$$f(x) = x^6 + x^5 - x^4 - x^3 = (x - 1)x^3(x + 1)^2$$

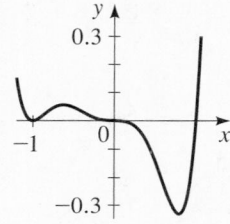

From this factored form we easily see that

1. 2 is a zero of P.
2. $x = 2$ is a solution of the equation $x^2 + x - 6 = 0$.
3. $x - 2$ is a factor of $x^2 + x - 6$.
4. 2 is an x-intercept of the graph of P.

The same facts are true for the other zero, -3.

The following theorem has many important consequences. (See, for instance, the *Discovery Project* referenced on page 263.) Here we use it to help us graph polynomial functions.

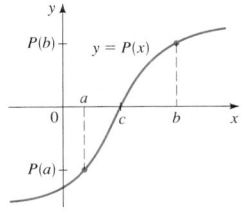

FIGURE 6

INTERMEDIATE VALUE THEOREM FOR POLYNOMIALS

If P is a polynomial function and $P(a)$ and $P(b)$ have opposite signs, then there exists at least one value c between a and b for which $P(c) = 0$.

We will not prove this theorem, but Figure 6 shows why it is intuitively plausible.

One important consequence of this theorem is that between any two successive zeros the values of a polynomial are either all positive or all negative. That is, between two successive zeros the graph of a polynomial lies *entirely above* or *entirely below* the x-axis. To see why, suppose c_1 and c_2 are successive zeros of P. If P has both positive and negative values between c_1 and c_2, then by the Intermediate Value Theorem P must have another zero between c_1 and c_2. But that's not possible because c_1 and c_2 are successive zeros. This observation allows us to use the following guidelines to graph polynomial functions.

GUIDELINES FOR GRAPHING POLYNOMIAL FUNCTIONS

1. Zeros. Factor the polynomial to find all its real zeros; these are the x-intercepts of the graph.

2. Test Points. Make a table of values for the polynomial. Include test points to determine whether the graph of the polynomial lies above or below the x-axis on the intervals determined by the zeros. Include the y-intercept in the table.

3. End Behavior. Determine the end behavior of the polynomial.

4. Graph. Plot the intercepts and other points you found in the table. Sketch a smooth curve that passes through these points and exhibits the required end behavior.

EXAMPLE 4 | Using Zeros to Graph a Polynomial Function

Sketch the graph of the polynomial function $P(x) = (x + 2)(x - 1)(x - 3)$.

SOLUTION   The zeros are $x = -2$, 1, and 3. These determine the intervals $(-\infty, -2)$, $(-2, 1)$, $(1, 3)$, and $(3, \infty)$. Using test points in these intervals, we get the information in the following sign diagram (see Section 1.7).

IN-CLASS MATERIALS

This is one application of the Intermediate Value Theorem for Polynomials: Consider $f(x) = 90x^3 + 100x^2 + 10x + 1$ and $g(x) = 91x^3 - 60x^2$. Have students graph each on their calculators, if they can find a good window. It will be tough. After giving them some time, put some graphs on the board.

It certainly looks like these two curves never cross. One way to prove that they do would be to actually find the crossing point—to solve $f(x) - g(x) = 0$. But a much quicker way is to use the Intermediate Value Theorem for Polynomials. Let $h(x) = f(x) - g(x)$. We know $g(x)$ will cross $f(x)$ when $h(x) = 0$. Now $h(0)$ is positive and $h(1000)$ is negative. We don't *need* to go hunting for the value of x that makes $h(x) = 0$; we can simply invoke the intermediate value property to prove that such an x does exist.

Plotting a few additional points and connecting them with a smooth curve helps us to complete the graph in Figure 7.

x	P(x)
Test point → -3	-24
-2	0
Test point → -1	8
0	6
1	0
Test point → 2	-4
3	0
Test point → 4	18

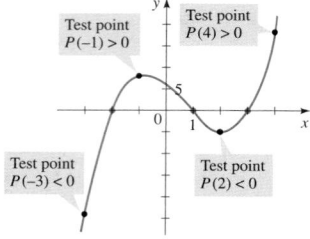

Test point
$P(-1) > 0$

Test point
$P(4) > 0$

Test point
$P(-3) < 0$

Test point
$P(2) < 0$

FIGURE 7 $P(x) = (x + 2)(x - 1)(x - 3)$

✎. NOW TRY EXERCISE **17**

ALTERNATE EXAMPLE 5

Let $P(x) = x^3 - 9x^2 + 20x$.

(a) Find the zeros of P.

(b) Sketch the graph of P.

ANSWERS

(a) $P(x) = x(x - 4)(x - 5)$, so the zeros are $x = 0$, $x = 4$, $x = 5$.

(b) End term behavior: $y \to \infty$ as $x \to \infty$, $y \to -\infty$ as $x \to -\infty$

We use test points -1, 3, 4.5, and 6 to obtain the graph:

EXAMPLE 5 | Finding Zeros and Graphing a Polynomial Function

Let $P(x) = x^3 - 2x^2 - 3x$.

(a) Find the zeros of P.

(b) Sketch a graph of P.

SOLUTION

(a) To find the zeros, we factor completely.

$$P(x) = x^3 - 2x^2 - 3x$$
$$= x(x^2 - 2x - 3) \qquad \text{Factor } x$$
$$= x(x - 3)(x + 1) \qquad \text{Factor quadratic}$$

Thus, the zeros are $x = 0$, $x = 3$, and $x = -1$.

(b) The x-intercepts are $x = 0$, $x = 3$, and $x = -1$. The y-intercept is $P(0) = 0$. We make a table of values of $P(x)$, making sure that we choose test points between (and to the right and left of) successive zeros.

Since P is of odd degree and its leading coefficient is positive, it has the following end behavior:

$$y \to \infty \quad \text{as} \quad x \to \infty \qquad \text{and} \qquad y \to -\infty \quad \text{as} \quad x \to -\infty$$

We plot the points in the table and connect them by a smooth curve to complete the graph, as shown in Figure 8.

x	P(x)
Test point → -2	-10
-1	0
Test point → $-\frac{1}{2}$	$\frac{7}{8}$
0	0
Test point → 1	-4
2	-6
3	0
Test point → 4	20

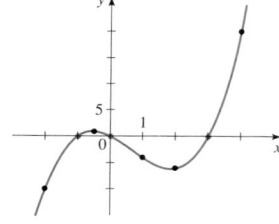

FIGURE 8 $P(x) = x^3 - 2x^2 - 3x$

✎. NOW TRY EXERCISE **27**

EXAMPLE 6 | Finding Zeros and Graphing a Polynomial Function

Let $P(x) = -2x^4 - x^3 + 3x^2$.

(a) Find the zeros of P.　　　**(b)** Sketch a graph of P.

SOLUTION

(a) To find the zeros, we factor completely.

$$
\begin{aligned}
P(x) &= -2x^4 - x^3 + 3x^2 \\
&= -x^2(2x^2 + x - 3) &&\text{Factor } -x^2 \\
&= -x^2(2x + 3)(x - 1) &&\text{Factor quadratic}
\end{aligned}
$$

Thus, the zeros are $x = 0$, $x = -\frac{3}{2}$, and $x = 1$.

(b) The x-intercepts are $x = 0$, $x = -\frac{3}{2}$, and $x = 1$. The y-intercept is $P(0) = 0$. We make a table of values of $P(x)$, making sure that we choose test points between (and to the right and left of) successive zeros.

Since P is of even degree and its leading coefficient is negative, it has the following end behavior:

$$y \to -\infty \quad \text{as} \quad x \to \infty \qquad \text{and} \qquad y \to -\infty \quad \text{as} \quad x \to -\infty$$

We plot the points from the table and connect the points by a smooth curve to complete the graph in Figure 9.

A table of values is most easily calculated by using a programmable calculator or a graphing calculator.

x	$P(x)$
-2	-12
-1.5	0
-1	2
-0.5	0.75
0	0
0.5	0.5
1	0
1.5	-6.75

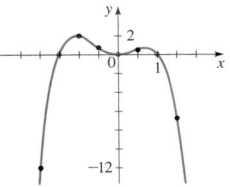

FIGURE 9　$P(x) = -2x^4 - x^3 + 3x^2$

✎. NOW TRY EXERCISE **31**

EXAMPLE 7 | Finding Zeros and Graphing a Polynomial Function

Let $P(x) = x^3 - 2x^2 - 4x + 8$.

(a) Find the zeros of P.　　　**(b)** Sketch a graph of P.

SOLUTION

(a) To find the zeros, we factor completely.

$$
\begin{aligned}
P(x) &= x^3 - 2x^2 - 4x + 8 \\
&= x^2(x - 2) - 4(x - 2) &&\text{Group and factor} \\
&= (x^2 - 4)(x - 2) &&\text{Factor } x - 2 \\
&= (x + 2)(x - 2)(x - 2) &&\text{Difference of squares} \\
&= (x + 2)(x - 2)^2 &&\text{Simplify}
\end{aligned}
$$

Thus the zeros are $x = -2$ and $x = 2$.

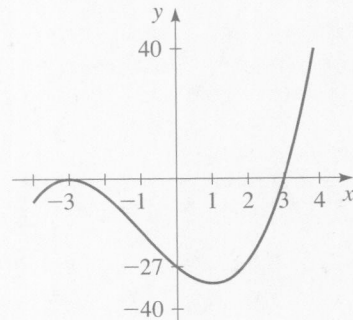

(b) The x-intercepts are $x = -2$ and $x = 2$. The y-intercept is $P(0) = 8$. The table gives additional values of $P(x)$.

Since P is of odd degree and its leading coefficient is positive, it has the following end behavior:

$$y \to \infty \quad \text{as} \quad x \to \infty \qquad \text{and} \qquad y \to -\infty \quad \text{as} \quad x \to -\infty$$

We connect the points by a smooth curve to complete the graph in Figure 10.

x	$P(x)$
-3	-25
-2	0
-1	9
0	8
1	3
2	0
3	5

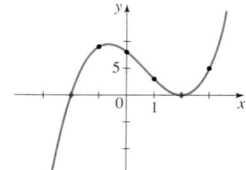

FIGURE 10 $P(x) = x^3 - 2x^2 - 4x + 8$

NOW TRY EXERCISE **33**

▼ Shape of the Graph Near a Zero

Although $x = 2$ is a zero of the polynomial in Example 7, the graph does not cross the x-axis at the x-intercept 2. This is because the factor $(x - 2)^2$ corresponding to that zero is raised to an even power, so it doesn't change sign as we test points on either side of 2. In the same way the graph does not cross the x-axis at $x = 0$ in Example 6.

In general, if c is a zero of P, and the corresponding factor $x - c$ occurs exactly m times in the factorization of P, then we say that c is a **zero of multiplicity m**. By considering test points on either side of the x-intercept c, we conclude that the graph crosses the x-axis at c if the multiplicity m is odd and does not cross the x-axis if m is even. Moreover, it can be shown by using calculus that near $x = c$ the graph has the same general shape as the graph of $y = A(x - c)^m$.

SHAPE OF THE GRAPH NEAR A ZERO OF MULTIPLICITY m

If c is a zero of P of multiplicity m, then the shape of the graph of P near c is as follows.

Multiplicity of c	Shape of the graph of P near the x-intercept c
m odd, $m > 1$	OR
m even, $m > 1$	OR

EXAMPLE 8 | Graphing a Polynomial Function Using Its Zeros

Graph the polynomial $P(x) = x^4(x - 2)^3(x + 1)^2$.

SOLUTION   The zeros of P are -1, 0, and 2 with multiplicities 2, 4, and 3, respectively.

| 0 is a zero of multiplicity 4 | 2 is a zero of multiplicity 3 | -1 is a zero of multiplicity 2 |

$$P(x) = x^4(x-2)^3(x+1)^2$$

The zero 2 has *odd* multiplicity, so the graph crosses the x-axis at the x-intercept 2. But the zeros 0 and -1 have *even* multiplicity, so the graph does not cross the x-axis at the x-intercepts 0 and -1.

Since P is a polynomial of degree 9 and has positive leading coefficient, it has the following end behavior:

$$y \to \infty \quad \text{as} \quad x \to \infty \qquad \text{and} \qquad y \to -\infty \quad \text{as} \quad x \to -\infty$$

With this information and a table of values we sketch the graph in Figure 11.

x	$P(x)$
-1.3	-9.2
-1	0
-0.5	-3.9
0	0
1	-4
2	0
2.3	8.2

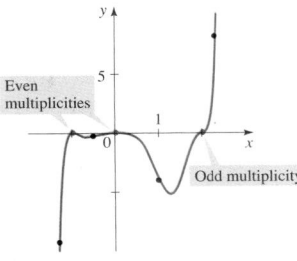

FIGURE 11 $P(x) = x^4(x-2)^3(x+1)^2$

✎. NOW TRY EXERCISE **25**

▼ Local Maxima and Minima of Polynomials

Recall from Section 2.3 that if the point $(a, f(a))$ is the highest point on the graph of f within some viewing rectangle, then $f(a)$ is a local maximum value of f, and if $(b, f(b))$ is the lowest point on the graph of f within a viewing rectangle, then $f(b)$ is a local minimum value (see Figure 12). We say that such a point $(a, f(a))$ is a **local maximum point** on the graph and that $(b, f(b))$ is a **local minimum point**. The local maximum and minimum points on the graph of a function are called its **local extrema**.

FIGURE 12

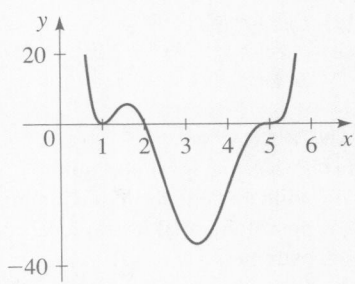
EXAMPLES

Two sixth-degree polynomial functions that look very similar but have different numbers of extrema: $f(x) = x^6 - 3x^3$ has one local minimum and a flat spot at $x = 0$; $f(x) = x^6 - 3.0x^3 - 0.015x^4 + 0.09x$ has two local minima and one local maximum—an obvious local minimum at $x \approx 1.145$ and two very subtle extrema at $x \approx \pm 0.1$.

For a polynomial function the number of local extrema must be less than the degree, as the following principle indicates. (A proof of this principle requires calculus.)

LOCAL EXTREMA OF POLYNOMIALS

If $P(x) = a_n x^n + a_{n-1}x^{n-1} + \cdots + a_1 x + a_0$ is a polynomial of degree n, then the graph of P has at most $n - 1$ local extrema.

A polynomial of degree n may in fact have less than $n - 1$ local extrema. For example, $P(x) = x^5$ (graphed in Figure 2) has *no* local extrema, even though it is of degree 5. The preceding principle tells us only that a polynomial of degree n can have no more than $n - 1$ local extrema.

EXAMPLE 9 | The Number of Local Extrema

Determine how many local extrema each polynomial has.
(a) $P_1(x) = x^4 + x^3 - 16x^2 - 4x + 48$
(b) $P_2(x) = x^5 + 3x^4 - 5x^3 - 15x^2 + 4x - 15$
(c) $P_3(x) = 7x^4 + 3x^2 - 10x$

SOLUTION   The graphs are shown in Figure 13.

(a) P_1 has two local minimum points and one local maximum point, for a total of three local extrema.

(b) P_2 has two local minimum points and two local maximum points, for a total of four local extrema.

(c) P_3 has just one local extremum, a local minimum.

 (a) $P_1(x) = x^4 + x^3 - 16x^2 - 4x + 48$
 (b) $P_2(x) = x^5 + 3x^4 - 5x^3 - 15x^2 + 4x - 15$
(c) $P_3(x) = 7x^4 + 3x^2 - 10x$

FIGURE 13

NOW TRY EXERCISES 61 AND 63

With a graphing calculator we can quickly draw the graphs of many functions at once, on the same viewing screen. This allows us to see how changing a value in the definition of the functions affects the shape of its graph. In the next example we apply this principle to a family of third-degree polynomials.

EXAMPLE 10 | A Family of Polynomials

Sketch the family of polynomials $P(x) = x^3 - cx^2$ for $c = 0, 1, 2,$ and 3. How does changing the value of c affect the graph?

ALTERNATE EXAMPLE 9

Determine how many local extrema each polynomial has.
(a) $P_1(x) = x^3 - x$
(b) $P_2(x) = x^4 - 8x^3 + 22x^2 - 24x + 5$

ANSWERS

(a) P_1 has one local minimum point and one local maximum point for a total of two local extrema.

(b) P_2 has two local minimum points and one local maximum point for a total of three local extrema.

SOLUTION The polynomials

$$P_0(x) = x^3 \qquad\qquad P_1(x) = x^3 - x^2$$
$$P_2(x) = x^3 - 2x^2 \qquad P_3(x) = x^3 - 3x^2$$

are graphed in Figure 14. We see that increasing the value of c causes the graph to develop an increasingly deep "valley" to the right of the y-axis, creating a local maximum at the origin and a local minimum at a point in Quadrant IV. This local minimum moves lower and farther to the right as c increases. To see why this happens, factor $P(x) = x^2(x - c)$. The polynomial P has zeros at 0 and c, and the larger c gets, the farther to the right the minimum between 0 and c will be.

FIGURE 14 A family of polynomials
$P(x) = x^3 - cx^2$

✎. NOW TRY EXERCISE **71**

3.2 EXERCISES

CONCEPTS

1. Only one of the following graphs could be the graph of a polynomial function. Which one? Why are the others not graphs of polynomials?

I

II

III
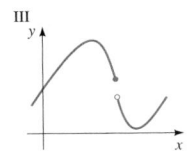

2. Every polynomial has one of the following behaviors:
 (i) $y \to \infty$ as $x \to \infty$ and $y \to \infty$ as $x \to -\infty$
 (ii) $y \to \infty$ as $x \to \infty$ and $y \to -\infty$ as $x \to -\infty$
 (iii) $y \to -\infty$ as $x \to \infty$ and $y \to \infty$ as $x \to -\infty$
 (iv) $y \to -\infty$ as $x \to \infty$ and $y \to -\infty$ as $x \to -\infty$

For each polynomial, choose the appropriate description of its end behavior from the list above.

 (a) $y = x^3 - 8x^2 + 2x - 15$: end behavior _____.

 (b) $y = -2x^4 + 12x + 100$: end behavior _____.

3. If c is a zero of the polynomial P, which of the following statements must be true?
 (a) $P(c) = 0$.   (b) $P(0) = c$.
 (c) $x - c$ is a factor of $P(x)$.
 (d) c is the y-intercept of the graph of P.

4. Which of the following statements couldn't possibly be true about the polynomial function P?
 (a) P has degree 3, two local maxima, and two local minima.
 (b) P has degree 3 and no local maxima or minima.
 (c) P has degree 4, one local maximum, and no local minima.

SKILLS

5–8 ■ Sketch the graph of each function by transforming the graph of an appropriate function of the form $y = x^n$ from Figure 2. Indicate all x- and y-intercepts on each graph.

✎. **5.** (a) $P(x) = x^2 - 4$ (b) $Q(x) = (x - 4)^2$
  (c) $R(x) = 2x^2 - 2$ (d) $S(x) = 2(x - 2)^2$

6. (a) $P(x) = x^4 - 16$ (b) $Q(x) = (x + 2)^4$
  (c) $R(x) = (x + 2)^4 - 16$ (d) $S(x) = -2(x + 2)^4$

7. (a) $P(x) = x^3 - 8$ (b) $Q(x) = -x^3 + 27$
  (c) $R(x) = -(x + 2)^3$ (d) $S(x) = \frac{1}{2}(x - 1)^3 + 4$

8. (a) $P(x) = (x + 3)^5$ (b) $Q(x) = 2(x + 3)^5 - 64$
  (c) $R(x) = -\frac{1}{2}(x - 2)^5$ (d) $S(x) = -\frac{1}{2}(x - 2)^5 + 16$

9–14 ■ Match the polynomial function with one of the graphs I–VI on the next page. Give reasons for your choice.

9. $P(x) = x(x^2 - 4)$ **10.** $Q(x) = -x^2(x^2 - 4)$

✎. **11.** $R(x) = -x^5 + 5x^3 - 4x$ **12.** $S(x) = \frac{1}{2}x^6 - 2x^4$

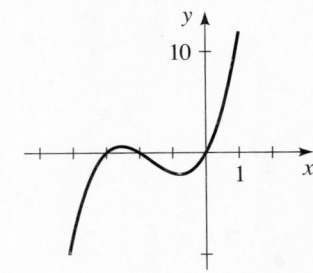

13. $T(x) = x^4 + 2x^3$

14. $U(x) = -x^3 + 2x^2$

I

II

III

IV

V

VI
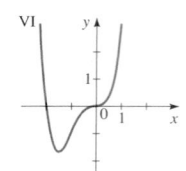

15–26 ■ Sketch the graph of the polynomial function. Make sure your graph shows all intercepts and exhibits the proper end behavior.

15. $P(x) = (x - 1)(x + 2)$

16. $P(x) = (x - 1)(x + 1)(x - 2)$

17. $P(x) = x(x - 3)(x + 2)$

18. $P(x) = (2x - 1)(x + 1)(x + 3)$

19. $P(x) = (x - 3)(x + 2)(3x - 2)$

20. $P(x) = \frac{1}{5}x(x - 5)^2$

21. $P(x) = (x - 1)^2(x - 3)$ **22.** $P(x) = \frac{1}{4}(x + 1)^3(x - 3)$

23. $P(x) = \frac{1}{12}(x + 2)^2(x - 3)^2$ **24.** $P(x) = (x - 1)^2(x + 2)^3$

25. $P(x) = x^3(x + 2)(x - 3)^2$ **26.** $P(x) = (x - 3)^2(x + 1)^2$

27–40 ■ Factor the polynomial and use the factored form to find the zeros. Then sketch the graph.

27. $P(x) = x^3 - x^2 - 6x$ **28.** $P(x) = x^3 + 2x^2 - 8x$

29. $P(x) = -x^3 + x^2 + 12x$ **30.** $P(x) = -2x^3 - x^2 + x$

31. $P(x) = x^4 - 3x^3 + 2x^2$ **32.** $P(x) = x^5 - 9x^3$

33. $P(x) = x^3 + x^2 - x - 1$ **34.** $P(x) = x^3 + 3x^2 - 4x - 12$

35. $P(x) = 2x^3 - x^2 - 18x + 9$

36. $P(x) = \frac{1}{8}(2x^4 + 3x^3 - 16x - 24)^2$

37. $P(x) = x^4 - 2x^3 - 8x + 16$

38. $P(x) = x^4 - 2x^3 + 8x - 16$

39. $P(x) = x^4 - 3x^2 - 4$ **40.** $P(x) = x^6 - 2x^3 + 1$

41–46 ■ Determine the end behavior of P. Compare the graphs of P and Q in large and small viewing rectangles, as in Example 3(b).

41. $P(x) = 3x^3 - x^2 + 5x + 1$; $Q(x) = 3x^3$

42. $P(x) = -\frac{1}{8}x^3 + \frac{1}{4}x^2 + 12x$; $Q(x) = -\frac{1}{8}x^3$

43. $P(x) = x^4 - 7x^2 + 5x + 5$; $Q(x) = x^4$

44. $P(x) = -x^5 + 2x^2 + x$; $Q(x) = -x^5$

45. $P(x) = x^{11} - 9x^9$; $Q(x) = x^{11}$

46. $P(x) = 2x^2 - x^{12}$; $Q(x) = -x^{12}$

47–50 ■ The graph of a polynomial function is given. From the graph, find **(a)** the x- and y-intercepts, and **(b)** the coordinates of all local extrema.

47. $P(x) = -x^2 + 4x$ **48.** $P(x) = \frac{2}{9}x^3 - x^2$

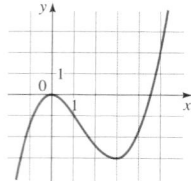

49. $P(x) = -\frac{1}{2}x^3 + \frac{3}{2}x - 1$ **50.** $P(x) = \frac{1}{9}x^4 - \frac{4}{9}x^3$

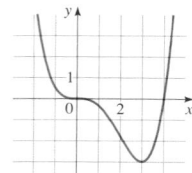

51–58 ■ Graph the polynomial in the given viewing rectangle. Find the coordinates of all local extrema. State each answer rounded to two decimal places.

51. $y = -x^2 + 8x$, $[-4, 12]$ by $[-50, 30]$

52. $y = x^3 - 3x^2$, $[-2, 5]$ by $[-10, 10]$

53. $y = x^3 - 12x + 9$, $[-5, 5]$ by $[-30, 30]$

54. $y = 2x^3 - 3x^2 - 12x - 32$, $[-5, 5]$ by $[-60, 30]$

55. $y = x^4 + 4x^3$, $[-5, 5]$ by $[-30, 30]$

56. $y = x^4 - 18x^2 + 32$, $[-5, 5]$ by $[-100, 100]$

57. $y = 3x^5 - 5x^3 + 3$, $[-3, 3]$ by $[-5, 10]$

58. $y = x^5 - 5x^2 + 6$, $[-3, 3]$ by $[-5, 10]$

59–68 ■ Graph the polynomial and determine how many local maxima and minima it has.

59. $y = -2x^2 + 3x + 5$ **60.** $y = x^3 + 12x$

61. $y = x^3 - x^2 - x$ **62.** $y = 6x^3 + 3x + 1$

63. $y = x^4 - 5x^2 + 4$

64. $y = 1.2x^5 + 3.75x^4 - 7x^3 - 15x^2 + 18x$

65. $y = (x - 2)^5 + 32$ **66.** $y = (x^2 - 2)^3$

67. $y = x^8 - 3x^4 + x$ **68.** $y = \frac{1}{3}x^7 - 17x^2 + 7$

69–74 ■ Graph the family of polynomials in the same viewing rectangle, using the given values of c. Explain how changing the value of c affects the graph.

69. $P(x) = cx^3$; $c = 1, 2, 5, \frac{1}{2}$

70. $P(x) = (x - c)^4$; $c = -1, 0, 1, 2$

71. $P(x) = x^4 + c$; $c = -1, 0, 1, 2$

72. $P(x) = x^3 + cx$; $c = 2, 0, -2, -4$

73. $P(x) = x^4 - cx$; $c = 0, 1, 8, 27$

74. $P(x) = x^c$; $c = 1, 3, 5, 7$

75. (a) On the same coordinate axes, sketch graphs (as accurately as possible) of the functions

$$y = x^3 - 2x^2 - x + 2 \quad \text{and} \quad y = -x^2 + 5x + 2$$

(b) On the basis of your sketch in part (a), at how many points do the two graphs appear to intersect?

(c) Find the coordinates of all intersection points.

76. Portions of the graphs of $y = x^2$, $y = x^3$, $y = x^4$, $y = x^5$, and $y = x^6$ are plotted in the figures. Determine which function belongs to each graph.

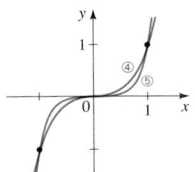

77. Recall that a function f is *odd* if $f(-x) = -f(x)$ or *even* if $f(-x) = f(x)$ for all real x.

(a) Show that a polynomial $P(x)$ that contains only odd powers of x is an odd function.

(b) Show that a polynomial $P(x)$ that contains only even powers of x is an even function.

(c) Show that if a polynomial $P(x)$ contains both odd and even powers of x, then it is neither an odd nor an even function.

(d) Express the function

$$P(x) = x^5 + 6x^3 - x^2 - 2x + 5$$

as the sum of an odd function and an even function.

78. (a) Graph the function $P(x) = (x - 1)(x - 3)(x - 4)$ and find all local extrema, correct to the nearest tenth.

(b) Graph the function

$$Q(x) = (x - 1)(x - 3)(x - 4) + 5$$

and use your answers to part (a) to find all local extrema, correct to the nearest tenth.

79. (a) Graph the function $P(x) = (x - 2)(x - 4)(x - 5)$ and determine how many local extrema it has.

(b) If $a < b < c$, explain why the function

$$P(x) = (x - a)(x - b)(x - c)$$

must have two local extrema.

80. (a) How many x-intercepts and how many local extrema does the polynomial $P(x) = x^3 - 4x$ have?

(b) How many x-intercepts and how many local extrema does the polynomial $Q(x) = x^3 + 4x$ have?

(c) If $a > 0$, how many x-intercepts and how many local extrema does each of the polynomials $P(x) = x^3 - ax$ and $Q(x) = x^3 + ax$ have? Explain your answer.

APPLICATIONS

81. Market Research   A market analyst working for a small-appliance manufacturer finds that if the firm produces and sells x blenders annually, the total profit (in dollars) is

$$P(x) = 8x + 0.3x^2 - 0.0013x^3 - 372$$

Graph the function P in an appropriate viewing rectangle and use the graph to answer the following questions.

(a) When just a few blenders are manufactured, the firm loses money (profit is negative). (For example, $P(10) = -263.3$, so the firm loses \$263.30 if it produces and sells only 10 blenders.) How many blenders must the firm produce to break even?

(b) Does profit increase indefinitely as more blenders are produced and sold? If not, what is the largest possible profit the firm could have?

82. Population Change   The rabbit population on a small island is observed to be given by the function

$$P(t) = 120t - 0.4t^4 + 1000$$

where t is the time (in months) since observations of the island began.

(a) When is the maximum population attained, and what is that maximum population?

(b) When does the rabbit population disappear from the island?

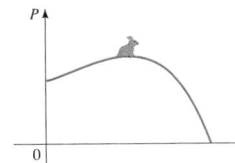

83. Volume of a Box   An open box is to be constructed from
a piece of cardboard 20 cm by 40 cm by cutting squares of
side length x from each corner and folding up the sides, as
shown in the figure.
(a) Express the volume V of the box as a function of x.
(b) What is the domain of V? (Use the fact that length and
volume must be positive.)
(c) Draw a graph of the function V, and use it to estimate the
maximum volume for such a box.

84. Volume of a Box   A cardboard box has a square base,
with each edge of the base having length x inches, as shown in
the figure. The total length of all 12 edges of the box is 144 in.
(a) Show that the volume of the box is given by the function
$V(x) = 2x^2(18 - x)$.
(b) What is the domain of V? (Use the fact that length and
volume must be positive.)
(c) Draw a graph of the function V and use it to estimate the
maximum volume for such a box.

DISCOVERY ■ DISCUSSION ■ WRITING

85. Graphs of Large Powers   Graph the functions $y = x^2$,
$y = x^3$, $y = x^4$, and $y = x^5$, for $-1 \le x \le 1$, on the same
coordinate axes. What do you think the graph of $y = x^{100}$
would look like on this same interval? What about $y = x^{101}$?
Make a table of values to confirm your answers.

86. Maximum Number of Local Extrema   What is the
smallest possible degree that the polynomial whose graph is
shown can have? Explain.

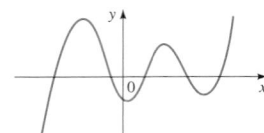

87. Possible Number of Local Extrema   Is it possible for
a third-degree polynomial to have exactly one local extremum? Can a fourth-degree polynomial have exactly two local
extrema? How many local extrema can polynomials of third,
fourth, fifth, and sixth degree have? (Think about the end
behavior of such polynomials.) Now give an example of a
polynomial that has six local extrema.

88. Impossible Situation?   Is it possible for a polynomial to
have two local maxima and no local minimum? Explain.

**SUGGESTED TIME
AND EMPHASIS**

$\frac{1}{2}$–1 class (may be combined with
Section 3.4)

3.3   DIVIDING POLYNOMIALS

| Long Division of Polynomials ▶ Synthetic Division ▶ The Remainder
and Factor Theorems

So far in this chapter we have been studying polynomial functions *graphically*. In this section we begin to study polynomials *algebraically*. Most of our work will be concerned
with factoring polynomials, and to factor, we need to know how to divide polynomials.

▼ Long Division of Polynomials

Dividing polynomials is much like the familiar process of dividing numbers. When we divide 38 by 7, the quotient is 5 and the remainder is 3. We write

TEXT QUESTION
It is a fact that $x^3 + 2x^2 - 3x + 1 = (x + 2)(x^2 + 1) + (-4x - 1)$. Fill in the blanks:

Remainder:

$$x^2 + 1 \overline{\smash{\big)}\, x^3 + 2x^2 - 3x + 1}$$

Answer
$x + 2$, $-4x - 1$

To divide polynomials, we use long division, as follows.

> **DIVISION ALGORITHM**
>
> If $P(x)$ and $D(x)$ are polynomials, with $D(x) \neq 0$, then there exist unique polynomials $Q(x)$ and $R(x)$, where $R(x)$ is either 0 or of degree less than the degree of $D(x)$, such that
>
> $$P(x) = D(x) \cdot Q(x) + R(x)$$
>
> Dividend   Divisor   Quotient   Remainder
>
> The polynomials $P(x)$ and $D(x)$ are called the **dividend** and **divisor**, respectively, $Q(x)$ is the **quotient**, and $R(x)$ is the **remainder**.

To write the division algorithm another way, divide through by $D(x)$:

$$\frac{P(x)}{D(x)} = Q(x) + \frac{R(x)}{D(x)}$$

EXAMPLE 1 | Long Division of Polynomials

Divide $6x^2 - 26x + 12$ by $x - 4$.

SOLUTION The *dividend* is $6x^2 - 26x + 12$ and the *divisor* is $x - 4$. We begin by arranging them as follows:

$$x - 4 \overline{)6x^2 - 26x + 12}$$

Next we divide the leading term in the dividend by the leading term in the divisor to get the first term of the quotient: $6x^2/x = 6x$. Then we multiply the divisor by $6x$ and subtract the result from the dividend.

$$
\begin{array}{r}
6x \\
x - 4 \overline{)6x^2 - 26x + 12} \\
6x^2 - 24x \\
\hline
-2x + 12
\end{array}
$$

Divide leading terms: $\frac{6x^2}{x} = 6x$

Multiply: $6x(x-4) = 6x^2 - 24x$

Subtract and "bring down" 12

We repeat the process using the last line $-2x + 12$ as the dividend.

$$
\begin{array}{r}
6x^2 - 2 \\
x - 4 \overline{)6x^2 - 26x + 12} \\
6x^2 - 24x \\
\hline
-2x + 12 \\
-2x + 8 \\
\hline
4
\end{array}
$$

Divide leading terms: $\frac{-2x}{x} = -2$

Multiply: $-2(x-4) = -2x + 8$

Subtract

The division process ends when the last line is of lesser degree than the divisor. The last line then contains the *remainder*, and the top line contains the *quotient*. The result of the division can be interpreted in either of two ways.

$$\frac{6x^2 - 26x + 12}{x - 4} = 6x - 2 + \frac{4}{x - 4}$$

Dividend / Divisor = Quotient + Remainder

or

$$6x^2 - 26x + 12 = (x - 4)(6x - 2) + 4$$

Dividend = Divisor · Quotient + Remainder

NOW TRY EXERCISE **3**

ALTERNATE EXAMPLE 1
Divide $8x^3 - 3x^2 + 2x - 1$ by $x + 2$.

ANSWER
Dividend $= 8x^3 - 3x^2 + 2x - 1$
Divisor $= x + 2$
Quotient $= 8x^2 - 19x + 40$
Remainder $= -81$

IN-CLASS MATERIALS
At this time, the teaching of long division in elementary schools is inconsistent. It will save time, in the long run, to do an integer long division problem for students, cautioning them to pay attention to every step in the process, because you are going to be extending it to polynomials. For example, divide 31,673 by 5 using the long division algorithm.

Then show how the answer can be written as $\frac{31,673}{5} = 6334 + \frac{3}{5}$ or 6334 R 3.

They will not be used to writing the result this way: $31,673 = 5(6334) + 3$.
It is important that they understand the form dividend = divisor · quotient + remainder, because that is the form in which the division algorithm is presented, both in this course and any future math courses involving generalized division. If students don't seem to understand (or start moving their lips as if beginning the process of rote memorization) it may even be worth the time to write out a very simple example, such as

$35 = 3(11) + 2$, just so students are very clear how this is a trivial restatement of $\frac{35}{3} = 11$ R 2.

ALTERNATE EXAMPLE 2
Let $P(x) = 6x^4 + 2x^3 - x + 2$.
Let $D(x) = x^2 - 2x + 2$. Find
polynomials $Q(x)$ and $R(x)$ such
that $P(x) = D(x) \cdot Q(x) + R(x)$.

ANSWER
$Q(x) = 6x^2 + 14x + 16$,
$R(x) = 3x - 30$

EXAMPLE 2 | Long Division of Polynomials

Let $P(x) = 8x^4 + 6x^2 - 3x + 1$ and $D(x) = 2x^2 - x + 2$. Find polynomials $Q(x)$ and $R(x)$ such that $P(x) = D(x) \cdot Q(x) + R(x)$.

SOLUTION We use long division after first inserting the term $0x^3$ into the dividend to ensure that the columns line up correctly.

$$
\begin{array}{r}
4x^2 + 2x \\
2x^2 - x + 2 \overline{)8x^4 + 0x^3 + 6x^2 - 3x + 1} \\
\underline{8x^4 - 4x^3 + 8x^2} \\
4x^3 - 2x^2 - 3x \\
\underline{4x^3 - 2x^2 + 4x} \\
-7x + 1
\end{array}
$$

Multiply divisor by $4x^2$
Subtract
Multiply divisor by $2x$
Subtract

The process is complete at this point because $-7x + 1$ is of lesser degree than the divisor $2x^2 - x + 2$. From the above long division we see that $Q(x) = 4x^2 + 2x$ and $R(x) = -7x + 1$, so

$$8x^4 + 6x^2 - 3x + 1 = (2x^2 - x + 2)(4x^2 + 2x) + (-7x + 1)$$

✎. NOW TRY EXERCISE **19** ■

▼ **Synthetic Division**

Synthetic division is a quick method of dividing polynomials; it can be used when the divisor is of the form $x - c$. In synthetic division we write only the essential parts of the long division. Compare the following long and synthetic divisions, in which we divide $2x^3 - 7x^2 + 5$ by $x - 3$. (We'll explain how to perform the synthetic division in Example 3.)

Long Division

$$
\begin{array}{r}
2x^2 - x - 3 \\
x - 3 \overline{)2x^3 - 7x^2 + 0x + 5} \\
\underline{2x^3 - 6x^2} \\
-x^2 + 0x \\
\underline{-x^2 + 3x} \\
-3x + 5 \\
\underline{-3x + 9} \\
-4
\end{array}
$$

Quotient

Remainder

Synthetic Division

$$
\begin{array}{c|cccc}
3 & 2 & -7 & 0 & 5 \\
& & 6 & -3 & -9 \\
\hline
& 2 & -1 & -3 & -4
\end{array}
$$

Quotient   Remainder

Note that in synthetic division we abbreviate $2x^3 - 7x^2 + 5$ by writing only the coefficients: $2 \ -7 \ 0 \ 5$, and instead of $x - 3$, we simply write 3. (Writing 3 instead of -3 allows us to add instead of subtract, but this changes the sign of all the numbers that appear in the gold boxes.)

The next example shows how synthetic division is performed.

ALTERNATE EXAMPLE 3
Use synthetic division to divide
$5x^3 - 2x^2 + x - 10$ by $x - 3$.

ANSWER
Quotient: $5x^2 + 13x + 40$
Remainder: 110

EXAMPLE 3 | Synthetic Division

Use synthetic division to divide $2x^3 - 7x^2 + 5$ by $x - 3$.

SOLUTION We begin by writing the appropriate coefficients to represent the divisor and the dividend.

$$
\text{Divisor } x - 3 \qquad 3 \ \begin{array}{|cccc} 2 & -7 & 0 & 5 \end{array} \qquad \begin{array}{l} \text{Dividend} \\ 2x^3 - 7x^2 + 0x + 5 \end{array}
$$

IN-CLASS MATERIALS

After doing a routine example, such as $\dfrac{x^4 + 3x^3 - x^2 - x + 3}{x^2 + 2x - 1} = x^2 + x - 2 + \dfrac{1 + 4x}{x^2 + 2x - 1}$, verify the answer by having students go through the multiplication. In other words, write $(x^2 + 2x - 1)(x^2 + x - 2) + (4x + 1)$ and multiply it out to verify that the result is $x^4 + 3x^3 - x^2 - x + 3$.

We bring down the 2, multiply $3 \cdot 2 = 6$, and write the result in the middle row. Then we add.

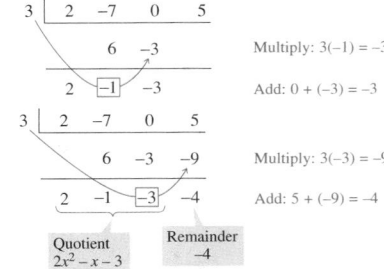

We repeat this process of multiplying and then adding until the table is complete.

From the last line of the synthetic division we see that the quotient is $2x^2 - x - 3$ and the remainder is -4. Thus

$$2x^3 - 7x^2 + 5 = (x - 3)(2x^2 - x - 3) - 4$$

✎ NOW TRY EXERCISE **31**   ■

▼ The Remainder and Factor Theorems

The next theorem shows how synthetic division can be used to evaluate polynomials easily.

> **REMAINDER THEOREM**
>
> If the polynomial $P(x)$ is divided by $x - c$, then the remainder is the value $P(c)$.

PROOF   If the divisor in the Division Algorithm is of the form $x - c$ for some real number c, then the remainder must be a constant (since the degree of the remainder is less than the degree of the divisor). If we call this constant r, then

$$P(x) = (x - c) \cdot Q(x) + r$$

Replacing x by c in this equation, we get $P(c) = (c - c) \cdot Q(x) + r = 0 + r = r$, that is, $P(c)$ is the remainder r.   ■

EXAMPLE 4 | Using the Remainder Theorem to Find the Value of a Polynomial

Let $P(x) = 3x^5 + 5x^4 - 4x^3 + 7x + 3$.

(a) Find the quotient and remainder when $P(x)$ is divided by $x + 2$.

(b) Use the Remainder Theorem to find $P(-2)$.

ALTERNATE EXAMPLE 4
Let $P(x) = 8x^5 - 2x^4 + 10x^3 + x^2 - 20x + 10$.
(a) Find the quotient and remainder when $P(x)$ is divided by $x + 2$.
(b) Use the Remainder Theorem to find $P(-2)$.

ANSWERS
(a) Quotient: $8x^4 - 18x^3 + 46x^2 - 91x + 162$
Remainder: -314
(b) $P(-2) = -314$

IN-CLASS MATERIALS

Students often miss the crucial idea that synthetic division is a technique that works only for divisors of the form $x - c$. They also tend to believe that synthetic division is a magical process that has nothing to do with the long division they have just learned. Divide the polynomial $x^3 - x^2 + x - 1$ by $x - 2$ using both methods, showing all work, and then have students point out the similarities between the two computations. They should see that both processes are essentially the same, the only difference being that synthetic division minimizes the amount of writing.

EXAMPLE

An example to use in demonstrating the remainder and factor theorems: $f(x) = x^3 - x^2 - 14x + 24$ has zeros $x = -4$, 2, and 3; $f(0) = 24$, $f(1) = 10$, and $f(-1) = 36$.

SOLUTION

(a) Since $x + 2 = x - (-2)$, the synthetic division for this problem takes the following form.

$$
\begin{array}{r|rrrrrr}
-2 & 3 & 5 & -4 & 0 & 7 & 3 \\
   &   & -6 & 2 & 4 & -8 & 2 \\
\hline
   & 3 & -1 & -2 & 4 & -1 & 5
\end{array}
$$

Remainder is 5, so $P(-2) = 5$

The quotient is $3x^4 - x^3 - 2x^2 + 4x - 1$, and the remainder is 5.

(b) By the Remainder Theorem, $P(-2)$ is the remainder when $P(x)$ is divided by $x - (-2) = x + 2$. From part (a) the remainder is 5, so $P(-2) = 5$.

▸ NOW TRY EXERCISE **39**

The next theorem says that *zeros* of polynomials correspond to *factors*; we used this fact in Section 3.2 to graph polynomials.

FACTOR THEOREM

c is a zero of P if and only if $x - c$ is a factor of $P(x)$.

PROOF   If $P(x)$ factors as $P(x) = (x - c) \cdot Q(x)$, then

$$P(c) = (c - c) \cdot Q(c) = 0 \cdot Q(c) = 0$$

Conversely, if $P(c) = 0$, then by the Remainder Theorem

$$P(x) = (x - c) \cdot Q(x) + 0 = (x - c) \cdot Q(x)$$

so $x - c$ is a factor of $P(x)$. ∎

EXAMPLE 5 | Factoring a Polynomial Using the Factor Theorem

Let $P(x) = x^3 - 7x + 6$. Show that $P(1) = 0$, and use this fact to factor $P(x)$ completely.

SOLUTION   Substituting, we see that $P(1) = 1^3 - 7 \cdot 1 + 6 = 0$. By the Factor Theorem this means that $x - 1$ is a factor of $P(x)$. Using synthetic or long division (shown in the margin), we see that

$$
\begin{array}{r|rrrr}
1 & 1 & 0 & -7 & 6 \\
  &   & 1 & 1 & -6 \\
\hline
  & 1 & 1 & -6 & 0
\end{array}
$$

$$
\begin{array}{r}
x^2 + x - 6 \\
x - 1 \overline{)\, x^3 + 0x^2 - 7x + 6} \\
\underline{x^3 - x^2} \\
x^2 - 7x \\
\underline{x^2 - x} \\
-6x + 6 \\
\underline{-6x + 6} \\
0
\end{array}
$$

$$
\begin{aligned}
P(x) &= x^3 - 7x + 6 && \text{Given polynomial} \\
&= (x - 1)(x^2 + x - 6) && \text{See margin} \\
&= (x - 1)(x - 2)(x + 3) && \text{Factor quadratic } x^2 + x - 6
\end{aligned}
$$

▸ NOW TRY EXERCISES **53** AND **57**

EXAMPLE 6 | Finding a Polynomial with Specified Zeros

Find a polynomial of degree 4 that has zeros -3, 0, 1, and 5.

SOLUTION   By the Factor Theorem $x - (-3)$, $x - 0$, $x - 1$, and $x - 5$ must all be factors of the desired polynomial.

ALTERNATE EXAMPLE 5

Let $P(x) = x^3 + 21x^2 - 157x + 135$. Use the fact that $P(1) = 0$ to factor $P(x)$ completely.

ANSWER

$P(1) = 0$ implies that $x - 1$ is a factor of $P(x)$. We divide by $x - 1$ to get a quotient of $x^2 + 22x - 135$ (and a remainder of zero). Now the quadratic formula, or factoring, gives the other factors of $(x - 5)$ and $(x + 27)$.

IN-CLASS MATERIALS

One important application of polynomial division is finding asymptotes for rational functions. This is a good time to introduce the concept of a horizontal asymptote. A good example to discuss with students is $f(x) = \dfrac{2x^2 + 3x + 5}{x^2 - 4x + 2}$. Use long division to write this as $f(x) = 2 + \dfrac{11x + 1}{x^2 - 4x + 2}$. Now note what happens to the second term for large values of x. If students have calculators, they can go ahead and try $x = 100$, $x = 100{,}000$, and $x = 1{,}000{,}000{,}000$. Show how, graphically, this corresponds to a horizontal asymptote. Now point out that the 2 came from only the highest-degree term in the numerator and the highest-degree term in the denominator. Now discuss the possibilities for horizontal asymptotes in the rational functions $\dfrac{x^2 + 2x + 2}{3x^2 + 2x + 2}$, $\dfrac{x^2 + 2x + 2}{x - 7}$, and $\dfrac{x^2 + 2x + 2}{x^5 - x + 4}$. In all cases, go ahead and do the long division, so the students see the possibilities. (The second one has no horizontal asymptote.)

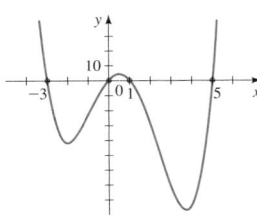

FIGURE 1
$P(x) = (x + 3)x(x - 1)(x - 5)$ has zeros $-3, 0, 1,$ and $5.$

Let

$$P(x) = (x + 3)(x - 0)(x - 1)(x - 5)$$
$$= x^4 - 3x^3 - 13x^2 + 15x$$

Since $P(x)$ is of degree 4, it is a solution of the problem. Any other solution of the problem must be a constant multiple of $P(x)$, since only multiplication by a constant does not change the degree.

✎. NOW TRY EXERCISE **59**

The polynomial P of Example 6 is graphed in Figure 1. Note that the zeros of P correspond to the x-intercepts of the graph.

3.3 EXERCISES

CONCEPTS

1. If we divide the polynomial P by the factor $x - c$ and we obtain the equation $P(x) = (x - c)Q(x) + R(x)$, then we say that $x - c$ is the divisor, $Q(x)$ is the _____, and $R(x)$ is the

_____.

2. (a) If we divide the polynomial $P(x)$ by the factor $x - c$ and we obtain a remainder of 0, then we know that c is a

_____ of P.

   (b) If we divide the polynomial $P(x)$ by the factor $x - c$ and we obtain a remainder of k, then we know that

   $P(c) = $ _____.

SKILLS

3–8 ■ Two polynomials P and D are given. Use either synthetic or long division to divide $P(x)$ by $D(x)$, and express P in the form $P(x) = D(x) \cdot Q(x) + R(x)$.

✎. 3. $P(x) = 3x^2 + 5x - 4, \quad D(x) = x + 3$

4. $P(x) = x^3 + 4x^2 - 6x + 1, \quad D(x) = x - 1$

5. $P(x) = 2x^3 - 3x^2 - 2x, \quad D(x) = 2x - 3$

6. $P(x) = 4x^3 + 7x + 9, \quad D(x) = 2x + 1$

7. $P(x) = x^4 - x^3 + 4x + 2, \quad D(x) = x^2 + 3$

8. $P(x) = 2x^5 + 4x^4 - 4x^3 - x - 3, \quad D(x) = x^2 - 2$

9–14 ■ Two polynomials P and D are given. Use either synthetic or long division to divide $P(x)$ by $D(x)$, and express the quotient $P(x)/D(x)$ in the form

$$\frac{P(x)}{D(x)} = Q(x) + \frac{R(x)}{D(x)}$$

9. $P(x) = x^2 + 4x - 8, \quad D(x) = x + 3$

10. $P(x) = x^3 + 6x + 5, \quad D(x) = x - 4$

11. $P(x) = 4x^2 - 3x - 7, \quad D(x) = 2x - 1$

12. $P(x) = 6x^3 + x^2 - 12x + 5, \quad D(x) = 3x - 4$

13. $P(x) = 2x^4 - x^3 + 9x^2, \quad D(x) = x^2 + 4$

14. $P(x) = x^5 + x^4 - 2x^3 + x + 1, \quad D(x) = x^2 + x - 1$

15–24 ■ Find the quotient and remainder using long division.

15. $\dfrac{x^2 - 6x - 8}{x - 4}$

16. $\dfrac{x^3 - x^2 - 2x + 6}{x - 2}$

17. $\dfrac{4x^3 + 2x^2 - 2x - 3}{2x + 1}$

18. $\dfrac{x^3 + 3x^2 + 4x + 3}{3x + 6}$

✎. 19. $\dfrac{x^3 + 6x + 3}{x^2 - 2x + 2}$

20. $\dfrac{3x^4 - 5x^3 - 20x - 5}{x^2 + x + 3}$

21. $\dfrac{6x^3 + 2x^2 + 22x}{2x^2 + 5}$

22. $\dfrac{9x^2 - x + 5}{3x^2 - 7x}$

23. $\dfrac{x^6 + x^4 + x^2 + 1}{x^2 + 1}$

24. $\dfrac{2x^5 - 7x^4 - 13}{4x^2 - 6x + 8}$

25–38 ■ Find the quotient and remainder using synthetic division.

25. $\dfrac{x^2 - 5x + 4}{x - 3}$

26. $\dfrac{x^2 - 5x + 4}{x - 1}$

27. $\dfrac{3x^2 + 5x}{x - 6}$

28. $\dfrac{4x^2 - 3}{x + 5}$

29. $\dfrac{x^3 + 2x^2 + 2x + 1}{x + 2}$

30. $\dfrac{3x^3 - 12x^2 - 9x + 1}{x - 5}$

✎. 31. $\dfrac{x^3 - 8x + 2}{x + 3}$

32. $\dfrac{x^4 - x^3 + x^2 - x + 2}{x - 2}$

33. $\dfrac{x^5 + 3x^3 - 6}{x - 1}$

34. $\dfrac{x^3 - 9x^2 + 27x - 27}{x - 3}$

---

35. $\dfrac{2x^3 + 3x^2 - 2x + 1}{x - \frac{1}{2}}$

36. $\dfrac{6x^4 + 10x^3 + 5x^2 + x + 1}{x + \frac{2}{3}}$

37. $\dfrac{x^3 - 27}{x - 3}$

38. $\dfrac{x^4 - 16}{x + 2}$

39–51 ■ Use synthetic division and the Remainder Theorem to evaluate $P(c)$.

39. $P(x) = 4x^2 + 12x + 5, \quad c = -1$

40. $P(x) = 2x^2 + 9x + 1, \quad c = \frac{1}{2}$

41. $P(x) = x^3 + 3x^2 - 7x + 6, \quad c = 2$

42. $P(x) = x^3 - x^2 + x + 5, \quad c = -1$

43. $P(x) = x^3 + 2x^2 - 7, \quad c = -2$

44. $P(x) = 2x^3 - 21x^2 + 9x - 200, \quad c = 11$

45. $P(x) = 5x^4 + 30x^3 - 40x^2 + 36x + 14, \quad c = -7$

46. $P(x) = 6x^5 + 10x^3 + x + 1, \quad c = -2$

47. $P(x) = x^7 - 3x^2 - 1, \quad c = 3$

48. $P(x) = -2x^6 + 7x^5 + 40x^4 - 7x^2 + 10x + 112, \quad c = -3$

49. $P(x) = 3x^3 + 4x^2 - 2x + 1, \quad c = \frac{2}{3}$

50. $P(x) = x^3 - x + 1, \quad c = \frac{1}{4}$

51. $P(x) = x^3 + 2x^2 - 3x - 8, \quad c = 0.1$

52. Let

$$P(x) = 6x^7 - 40x^6 + 16x^5 - 200x^4$$
$$- 60x^3 - 69x^2 + 13x - 139$$

Calculate $P(7)$ by **(a)** using synthetic division and **(b)** substituting $x = 7$ into the polynomial and evaluating directly.

53–56 ■ Use the Factor Theorem to show that $x - c$ is a factor of $P(x)$ for the given value(s) of c.

53. $P(x) = x^3 - 3x^2 + 3x - 1, \quad c = 1$

54. $P(x) = x^3 + 2x^2 - 3x - 10, \quad c = 2$

55. $P(x) = 2x^3 + 7x^2 + 6x - 5, \quad c = \frac{1}{2}$

56. $P(x) = x^4 + 3x^3 - 16x^2 - 27x + 63, \quad c = 3, -3$

57–58 ■ Show that the given value(s) of c are zeros of $P(x)$, and find all other zeros of $P(x)$.

57. $P(x) = x^3 - x^2 - 11x + 15, \quad c = 3$

58. $P(x) = 3x^4 - x^3 - 21x^2 - 11x + 6, \quad c = \frac{1}{3}, -2$

59–62 ■ Find a polynomial of the specified degree that has the given zeros.

59. Degree 3;   zeros $-1, 1, 3$

60. Degree 4;   zeros $-2, 0, 2, 4$

61. Degree 4;   zeros $-1, 1, 3, 5$

62. Degree 5;   zeros $-2, -1, 0, 1, 2$

63. Find a polynomial of degree 3 that has zeros $1, -2$, and 3 and in which the coefficient of x^2 is 3.

64. Find a polynomial of degree 4 that has integer coefficients and zeros $1, -1, 2$, and $\frac{1}{2}$.

65–68 ■ Find the polynomial of the specified degree whose graph is shown.

65. Degree 3

66. Degree 3

67. Degree 4

68. Degree 4

DISCOVERY ■ DISCUSSION ■ WRITING

69. Impossible Division?   Suppose you were asked to solve the following two problems on a test:
  A. Find the remainder when $6x^{1000} - 17x^{562} + 12x + 26$ is divided by $x + 1$.
  B. Is $x - 1$ a factor of $x^{567} - 3x^{400} + x^9 + 2$?

Obviously, it's impossible to solve these problems by dividing, because the polynomials are of such large degree. Use one or more of the theorems in this section to solve these problems *without* actually dividing.

70. Nested Form of a Polynomial   Expand Q to prove that the polynomials P and Q are the same.

$$P(x) = 3x^4 - 5x^3 + x^2 - 3x + 5$$

$$Q(x) = (((3x - 5)x + 1)x - 3)x + 5$$

Try to evaluate $P(2)$ and $Q(2)$ in your head, using the forms given. Which is easier? Now write the polynomial $R(x) = x^5 - 2x^4 + 3x^3 - 2x^2 + 3x + 4$ in "nested" form, like the polynomial Q. Use the nested form to find $R(3)$ in your head.

Do you see how calculating with the nested form follows the same arithmetic steps as calculating the value of a polynomial using synthetic division?

3.4 REAL ZEROS OF POLYNOMIALS

Rational Zeros of Polynomials ▶ Descartes' Rule of Signs and Upper and Lower Bounds for Roots ▶ Using Algebra and Graphing Devices to Solve Polynomial Equations

The Factor Theorem tells us that finding the zeros of a polynomial is really the same thing as factoring it into linear factors. In this section we study some algebraic methods that help us to find the real zeros of a polynomial and thereby factor the polynomial. We begin with the *rational* zeros of a polynomial.

▼ Rational Zeros of Polynomials

To help us understand the next theorem, let's consider the polynomial

$$P(x) = (x - 2)(x - 3)(x + 4) \qquad \text{Factored form}$$
$$= x^3 - x^2 - 14x + 24 \qquad \text{Expanded form}$$

From the factored form we see that the zeros of P are 2, 3, and -4. When the polynomial is expanded, the constant 24 is obtained by multiplying $(-2) \times (-3) \times 4$. This means that the zeros of the polynomial are all factors of the constant term. The following generalizes this observation.

RATIONAL ZEROS THEOREM

If the polynomial $P(x) = a_n x^n + a_{n-1}x^{n-1} + \cdots + a_1 x + a_0$ has integer coefficients, then every rational zero of P is of the form

$$\frac{p}{q}$$

where p is a factor of the constant coefficient a_0
and q is a factor of the leading coefficient a_n.

PROOF If p/q is a rational zero, in lowest terms, of the polynomial P, then we have

$$a_n\left(\frac{p}{q}\right)^n + a_{n-1}\left(\frac{p}{q}\right)^{n-1} + \cdots + a_1\left(\frac{p}{q}\right) + a_0 = 0$$

$$a_n p^n + a_{n-1}p^{n-1}q + \cdots + a_1 pq^{n-1} + a_0 q^n = 0 \qquad \text{Multiply by } q^n$$

$$p(a_n p^{n-1} + a_{n-1}p^{n-2}q + \cdots + a_1 q^{n-1}) = -a_0 q^n \qquad \begin{array}{l}\text{Subtract } a_0 q^n \\ \text{and factor LHS}\end{array}$$

Now p is a factor of the left side, so it must be a factor of the right side as well. Since p/q is in lowest terms, p and q have no factor in common, so p must be a factor of a_0. A similar proof shows that q is a factor of a_n. ■

We see from the Rational Zeros Theorem that if the leading coefficient is 1 or -1, then the rational zeros must be factors of the constant term.

EXAMPLE 1 | Using the Rational Zeros Theorem

Find the rational zeros of $P(x) = x^3 - 3x + 2$.

TEXT QUESTIONS
Consider $f(x) = x^6 - 2x^5 - x^4 + 4x^3 - x^2 - 2x + 1$.

(a) According to the Rational Zeros Theorem, how many possible rational zeros can this polynomial have?
(b) List all the rational zeros of $f(x)$. Ignore multiplicities and show your work.

Answers
(a) 2
(b) Both 1 and -1 are zeros of f. This can be shown by manually calculating $f(1)$ and $f(-1)$.

SOLUTION Since the leading coefficient is 1, any rational zero must be a divisor of the constant term 2. So the possible rational zeros are ± 1 and ± 2. We test each of these possibilities.

$$P(1) = (1)^3 - 3(1) + 2 = 0$$
$$P(-1) = (-1)^3 - 3(-1) + 2 = 4$$
$$P(2) = (2)^3 - 3(2) + 2 = 4$$
$$P(-2) = (-2)^3 - 3(-2) + 2 = 0$$

The rational zeros of P are 1 and -2.

◆ **NOW TRY EXERCISE 15**

EVARISTE GALOIS (1811–1832) is one of the very few mathematicians to have an entire theory named in his honor. Not yet 21 when he died, he completely settled the central problem in the theory of equations by describing a criterion that reveals whether a polynomial equation can be solved by algebraic operations. Galois was one of the greatest mathematicians in the world at that time, although no one knew it but him. He repeatedly sent his work to the eminent mathematicians Cauchy and Poisson, who either lost his letters or did not understand his ideas. Galois wrote in a terse style and included few details, which probably played a role in his failure to pass the entrance exams at the Ecole Polytechnique in Paris. A political radical, Galois spent several months in prison for his revolutionary activities. His brief life came to a tragic end when he was killed in a duel over a love affair. The night before his duel, fearing that he would die, Galois wrote down the essence of his ideas and entrusted them to his friend Auguste Chevalier. He concluded by writing "there will, I hope, be people who will find it to their advantage to decipher all this mess." The mathematician Camille Jordan did just that, 14 years later.

The following box explains how we use the Rational Zeros Theorem with synthetic division to factor a polynomial.

FINDING THE RATIONAL ZEROS OF A POLYNOMIAL

1. **List Possible Zeros.** List all possible rational zeros, using the Rational Zeros Theorem.

2. **Divide.** Use synthetic division to evaluate the polynomial at each of the candidates for the rational zeros that you found in Step 1. When the remainder is 0, note the quotient you have obtained.

3. **Repeat.** Repeat Steps 1 and 2 for the quotient. Stop when you reach a quotient that is quadratic or factors easily, and use the quadratic formula or factor to find the remaining zeros.

EXAMPLE 2 | Finding Rational Zeros

Factor the polynomial $P(x) = 2x^3 + x^2 - 13x + 6$, and find all its zeros.

SOLUTION By the Rational Zeros Theorem the rational zeros of P are of the form

$$\text{possible rational zero of } P = \frac{\text{factor of constant term}}{\text{factor of leading coefficient}}$$

The constant term is 6 and the leading coefficient is 2, so

$$\text{possible rational zero of } P = \frac{\text{factor of 6}}{\text{factor of 2}}$$

The factors of 6 are ± 1, ± 2, ± 3, ± 6, and the factors of 2 are ± 1, ± 2. Thus, the possible rational zeros of P are

$$\pm\frac{1}{1}, \quad \pm\frac{2}{1}, \quad \pm\frac{3}{1}, \quad \pm\frac{6}{1}, \quad \pm\frac{1}{2}, \quad \pm\frac{2}{2}, \quad \pm\frac{3}{2}, \quad \pm\frac{6}{2}$$

Simplifying the fractions and eliminating duplicates, we get the following list of possible rational zeros:

$$\pm 1, \quad \pm 2, \quad \pm 3, \quad \pm 6, \quad \pm\frac{1}{2}, \quad \pm\frac{3}{2}$$

ALTERNATE EXAMPLE 2
Factor the polynomial
$P(x) = 3x^3 - 4x^2 - 13x - 6$.

ANSWER
$P(x) = (x + 1)(x - 3)(3x + 2)$

IN-CLASS MATERIALS

Students often misinterpret the Rational Zeros Theorem in two ways. Some believe that it classifies *all* the real zeros of a polynomial function, not just the rational ones. Others believe that it applies to *all* polynomial functions, not just the ones with integer coefficients.

Start with the simple quadratic $p(x) = x^2 - 2$, pointing out that the candidates for rational zeros are ± 1 and ± 2. None of these candidates are zeros of $p(x)$, but it is simple to find that there are two real zeros: $x = \pm\sqrt{2}$. Then move to a polynomial with one real zero and two irrational ones, such as $p(x) = x^3 - 6x + 4$. Ask students if they can come up with a polynomial with three real, irrational zeros. One example is $p(x) = x^3 - 3x - \sqrt{2}$ (the zeros are $-\sqrt{2}$ and $\frac{1}{2}\sqrt{2} \pm \frac{1}{2}\sqrt{6}$). This might be perceived as a bit of a cheat, so follow up by asking them if they can come up with a polynomial with integer coefficients and three real, irrational zeros. ($x^3 - 5x + 1$ works. The fact that there are three real roots can be determined from a graph; the fact that none are rational can be determined using the Rational Zeros Theorem.)

To check which of these *possible* zeros actually *are* zeros, we need to evaluate P at each of these numbers. An efficient way to do this is to use synthetic division.

Test whether 1 is a zero

$$
\begin{array}{r|rrrr}
1 & 2 & 1 & -13 & 6 \\
  &   & 2 & 3 & -10 \\
\hline
  & 2 & 3 & -10 & -4
\end{array}
$$

Remainder is *not* 0, so 1 is *not* a zero

Test whether 2 is a zero

$$
\begin{array}{r|rrrr}
2 & 2 & 1 & -13 & 6 \\
  &   & 4 & 10 & -6 \\
\hline
  & 2 & 5 & -3 & 0
\end{array}
$$

Remainder *is* 0, so 2 *is* a zero

From the last synthetic division we see that 2 is a zero of P and that P factors as

$$
\begin{aligned}
P(x) &= 2x^3 + x^2 - 13x + 6 && \text{Given polynomial} \\
&= (x - 2)(2x^2 + 5x - 3) && \text{From synthetic division} \\
&= (x - 2)(2x - 1)(x + 3) && \text{Factor } 2x^2 + 5x - 3
\end{aligned}
$$

From the factored form we see that the zeros of P are 2, $\frac{1}{2}$, and –3.

✎. **NOW TRY EXERCISE 27** ▪

EXAMPLE 3 | Using the Rational Zeros Theorem and the Quadratic Formula

Let $P(x) = x^4 - 5x^3 - 5x^2 + 23x + 10$.

(a) Find the zeros of P.   **(b)** Sketch the graph of P.

SOLUTION

$$
\begin{array}{r|rrrrr}
1 & 1 & -5 & -5 & 23 & 10 \\
  &   & 1 & -4 & -9 & 14 \\
\hline
  & 1 & -4 & -9 & 14 & \boxed{24}
\end{array}
$$

$$
\begin{array}{r|rrrrr}
2 & 1 & -5 & -5 & 23 & 10 \\
  &   & 2 & -6 & -22 & 2 \\
\hline
  & 1 & -3 & -11 & 1 & \boxed{12}
\end{array}
$$

$$
\begin{array}{r|rrrrr}
5 & 1 & -5 & -5 & 23 & 10 \\
  &   & 5 & 0 & -25 & -10 \\
\hline
  & 1 & 0 & -5 & -2 & \boxed{0}
\end{array}
$$

$$
\begin{array}{r|rrrr}
-2 & 1 & 0 & -5 & -2 \\
   &   & -2 & 4 & 2 \\
\hline
   & 1 & -2 & -1 & \boxed{0}
\end{array}
$$

(a) The leading coefficient of P is 1, so all the rational zeros are integers: They are divisors of the constant term 10. Thus, the possible candidates are

$$\pm 1, \quad \pm 2, \quad \pm 5, \quad \pm 10$$

Using synthetic division (see the margin), we find that 1 and 2 are not zeros but that 5 is a zero and that P factors as

$$x^4 - 5x^3 - 5x^2 + 23x + 10 = (x - 5)(x^3 - 5x - 2)$$

We now try to factor the quotient $x^3 - 5x - 2$. Its possible zeros are the divisors of -2, namely,

$$\pm 1, \quad \pm 2$$

Since we already know that 1 and 2 are not zeros of the original polynomial P, we don't need to try them again. Checking the remaining candidates, -1 and -2, we see that -2 is a zero (see the margin), and P factors as

$$
\begin{aligned}
x^4 - 5x^3 - 5x^2 + 23x + 10 &= (x - 5)(x^3 - 5x - 2) \\
&= (x - 5)(x + 2)(x^2 - 2x - 1)
\end{aligned}
$$

Now we use the quadratic formula to obtain the two remaining zeros of P:

$$x = \frac{2 \pm \sqrt{(-2)^2 - 4(1)(-1)}}{2} = 1 \pm \sqrt{2}$$

The zeros of P are 5, -2, $1 + \sqrt{2}$, and $1 - \sqrt{2}$.

ALTERNATE EXAMPLE 3

Let

$$P(x) = -x^3 - 3x^2 + 13x + 15.$$

Find all the real zeros of P and sketch its graph.

ANSWER

Zeros: $3, -1, -5$

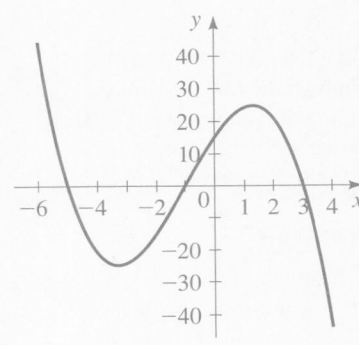

IN-CLASS MATERIALS

Ask students why we do not advocate using synthetic division to find the roots of a polynomial such as $p(x) = x^2 + 9x + 20, p(x) = x^2 + 9x - 7$, or even $p(x) = x^2 + \pi x - \sqrt[5]{2}$. Hopefully, they will arrive at the conclusion that the quadratic formula is easier to use and will find all the zeros, not just the rational ones. Point out that there is a formula, analogous to the quadratic formula, for third-degree polynomials, but it is much harder to use. (For those interested, refer to Exercises 107 and 108.) There is one for fourth-degree polynomials as well. It has been proved that there is no such formula for arbitrary fifth-degree polynomials. In other words, we can find the exact roots for any polynomial up through a fourth-degree polynomial, but there are some polynomials, fifth-degree and higher, whose roots we can only approximate.

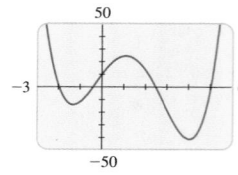

FIGURE 1
$P(x) = x^4 - 5x^3 - 5x^2 + 23x + 10$

(b) Now that we know the zeros of P, we can use the methods of Section 3.2 to sketch the graph. If we want to use a graphing calculator instead, knowing the zeros allows us to choose an appropriate viewing rectangle—one that is wide enough to contain all the x-intercepts of P. Numerical approximations to the zeros of P are

$$5, \quad -2, \quad 2.4, \quad \text{and} \quad -0.4$$

So in this case we choose the rectangle $[-3, 6]$ by $[-50, 50]$ and draw the graph shown in Figure 1.

✎. NOW TRY EXERCISES **47** AND **57** ∎

▼ Descartes' Rule of Signs and Upper and Lower Bounds for Roots

In some cases, the following rule—discovered by the French philosopher and mathematician René Descartes around 1637 (see page 181)—is helpful in eliminating candidates from lengthy lists of possible rational roots. To describe this rule, we need the concept of *variation in sign*. If $P(x)$ is a polynomial with real coefficients, written with descending powers of x (and omitting powers with coefficient 0), then a **variation in sign** occurs whenever adjacent coefficients have opposite signs. For example,

$$P(x) = 5x^7 - 3x^5 - x^4 + 2x^2 + x - 3$$

has three variations in sign.

Polynomial	Variations in sign
$x^2 + 4x + 1$	0
$2x^3 + x - 6$	1
$x^4 - 3x^2 - x + 4$	2

DESCARTES' RULE OF SIGNS

Let P be a polynomial with real coefficients.

1. The number of positive real zeros of $P(x)$ either is equal to the number of variations in sign in $P(x)$ or is less than that by an even whole number.

2. The number of negative real zeros of $P(x)$ either is equal to the number of variations in sign in $P(-x)$ or is less than that by an even whole number.

EXAMPLE 4 | Using Descartes' Rule

Use Descartes' Rule of Signs to determine the possible number of positive and negative real zeros of the polynomial

$$P(x) = 3x^6 + 4x^5 + 3x^3 - x - 3$$

SOLUTION   The polynomial has one variation in sign, so it has one positive zero. Now

$$P(-x) = 3(-x)^6 + 4(-x)^5 + 3(-x)^3 - (-x) - 3$$
$$= 3x^6 - 4x^5 - 3x^3 + x - 3$$

So $P(-x)$ has three variations in sign. Thus, $P(x)$ has either three or one negative zero(s), making a total of either two or four real zeros.

✎. NOW TRY EXERCISE **67** ∎

We say that a is a **lower bound** and b is an **upper bound** for the zeros of a polynomial if every real zero c of the polynomial satisfies $a \le c \le b$. The next theorem helps us to find such bounds for the zeros of a polynomial.

IN-CLASS MATERIALS

Point out that being able to find the zeros of a polynomial allows us to solve many types of problems. The text gives several examples of applied problems (and there are many more, of course). For example, we can now find the intersection points between two polynomial curves [if $f(x) = g(x)$, then $f(x) - g(x) = 0$]. If $p(x)$ is a polynomial with an inverse, we can find $p^{-1}(k)$ for a specific k by solving $p(x) - k = 0$. In addition, being able to factor polynomials is very important. For example, the graph of $f(x) = \dfrac{x^3 - 4x}{x^3 + 6x^2 + 11x + 6}$ has a hole at $x = -2$, vertical asymptotes at $x = -1$ and $x = -3$, and x-intercepts at $(2, 0)$ and $(0, 0)$. This information is easily obtained if we write $f(x)$ as $\dfrac{(x + 2)(x - 2)x}{(x + 1)(x + 2)(x + 3)}$.

THE UPPER AND LOWER BOUNDS THEOREM

Let P be a polynomial with real coefficients.

1. If we divide $P(x)$ by $x - b$ (with $b > 0$) using synthetic division and if the row that contains the quotient and remainder has no negative entry, then b is an upper bound for the real zeros of P.

2. If we divide $P(x)$ by $x - a$ (with $a < 0$) using synthetic division and if the row that contains the quotient and remainder has entries that are alternately nonpositive and nonnegative, then a is a lower bound for the real zeros of P.

A proof of this theorem is suggested in Exercise 97. The phrase "alternately nonpositive and nonnegative" simply means that the signs of the numbers alternate, with 0 considered to be positive or negative as required.

EXAMPLE 5 | Upper and Lower Bounds for Zeros of a Polynomial

Show that all the real zeros of the polynomial $P(x) = x^4 - 3x^2 + 2x - 5$ lie between -3 and 2.

SOLUTION   We divide $P(x)$ by $x - 2$ and $x + 3$ using synthetic division.

```
2 | 1   0  -3   2  -5              -3 | 1   0   -3    2   -5
  |     2   4   2   8                 |    -3    9  -18   48
  ------------------------           -----------------------------
    1   2   1   4   3                   1  -3    6  -16   43
```
All entries positive   Entries alternate in sign

By the Upper and Lower Bounds Theorem, -3 is a lower bound and 2 is an upper bound for the zeros. Since neither -3 nor 2 is a zero (the remainders are not 0 in the division table), all the real zeros lie between these numbers.

✎ NOW TRY EXERCISE 71 ■

EXAMPLE 6 | Factoring a Fifth-Degree Polynomial

Factor completely the polynomial

$$P(x) = 2x^5 + 5x^4 - 8x^3 - 14x^2 + 6x + 9$$

SOLUTION   The possible rational zeros of P are $\pm\frac{1}{2}$, ± 1, $\pm\frac{3}{2}$, ± 3, $\pm\frac{9}{2}$, and ± 9. We check the positive candidates first, beginning with the smallest.

```
1/2 | 2   5   -8     -14     6     9          1 | 2   5   -8  -14    6    9
    |     1    3    -5/2  -33/4  -9/8           |     2    7   -1  -15   -9
    -------------------------------------      ----------------------------------
      2   6   -5   -33/2   -9/4   63/8           2   7   -1  -15   -9    0
```
$\frac{1}{2}$ is not a zero $P(1) = 0$

So 1 is a zero, and $P(x) = (x - 1)(2x^4 + 7x^3 - x^2 - 15x - 9)$. We continue by factoring the quotient. We still have the same list of possible zeros except that $\frac{1}{2}$ has been eliminated.

```
1 | 2   7   -1  -15   -9          3/2 | 2   7    -1  -15   -9
  |     2    9    8   -7              |     3    15   21    9
  ------------------------           ------------------------------
    2   9    8   -7  -16               2  10    14    6    0
```
1 is not a zero $P(\frac{3}{2}) = 0$, all entries nonnegative

EXAMPLE

A polynomial with many rational zeros: $f(x) = 6x^5 + 17x^4 - 40x^3 - 45x^2 + 14x + 8$

Factored form: $(2x - 1)(3x + 1)(x + 4)(x + 1)(x - 2)$

Zeros: $x = \dfrac{1}{2}, \dfrac{1}{3}, -4, -1,$ and 2

We see that $\frac{3}{2}$ is both a zero and an upper bound for the zeros of $P(x)$, so we do not need to check any further for positive zeros, because all the remaining candidates are greater than $\frac{3}{2}$.

$$P(x) = (x - 1)(x - \tfrac{3}{2})(2x^3 + 10x^2 + 14x + 6) \qquad \text{From synthetic division}$$

$$= (x - 1)(2x - 3)(x^3 + 5x^2 + 7x + 3) \qquad \text{Factor 2 from last factor, multiply into second factor}$$

By Descartes' Rule of Signs, $x^3 + 5x^2 + 7x + 3$ has no positive zero, so its only possible rational zeros are -1 and -3.

Therefore,

$$P(x) = (x - 1)(2x - 3)(x + 1)(x^2 + 4x + 3) \qquad \text{From synthetic division}$$

$$= (x - 1)(2x - 3)(x + 1)^2(x + 3) \qquad \text{Factor quadratic}$$

This means that the zeros of P are $1, \frac{3}{2}, -1$, and -3. The graph of the polynomial is shown in Figure 2.

✎ NOW TRY EXERCISE **79**

FIGURE 2
$P(x) = 2x^5 + 5x^4 - 8x^3 - 14x^2 + 6x + 9$
$= (x - 1)(2x - 3)(x + 1)^2(x + 3)$

▼ Using Algebra and Graphing Devices to Solve Polynomial Equations

In Section 1.9 we used graphing devices to solve equations graphically. We can now use the algebraic techniques that we've learned to select an appropriate viewing rectangle when solving a polynomial equation graphically.

EXAMPLE 7 | Solving a Fourth-Degree Equation Graphically

Find all real solutions of the following equation, rounded to the nearest tenth.

$$3x^4 + 4x^3 - 7x^2 - 2x - 3 = 0$$

SOLUTION   To solve the equation graphically, we graph

$$P(x) = 3x^4 + 4x^3 - 7x^2 - 2x - 3$$

We use the Upper and Lower Bounds Theorem to see where the solutions can be found.

First we use the Upper and Lower Bounds Theorem to find two numbers between which all the solutions must lie. This allows us to choose a viewing rectangle that is certain to contain all the x-intercepts of P. We use synthetic division and proceed by trial and error.

To find an upper bound, we try the whole numbers, $1, 2, 3, \ldots,$ as potential candidates. We see that 2 is an upper bound for the solutions.

$$
\begin{array}{r|rrrrr}
2 & 3 & 4 & -7 & -2 & -3 \\
  &   & 6 & 20 & 26 & 48 \\
\hline
  & 3 & 10 & 13 & 24 & 45
\end{array}
$$

All positive

ALTERNATE EXAMPLE 7

Find all real solutions of the following equation, correct to the nearest hundredth:
$10x^4 - x^2 + 4x - 6$

ANSWER

Roots to the nearest hundredth:
$-1.03, 0.77$

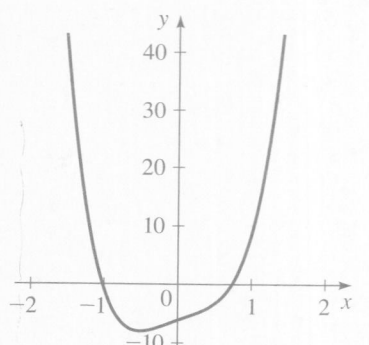

EXAMPLE

A polynomial with one rational zero and four irrational zeros that can be found by elementary methods:

$$f(x) = 2x^5 - 10x^3 + 12x - x^4 + 5x^2 - 6 = (2x - 1)(x^2 - 2)(x^2 - 3)$$

Zeros: $x = \frac{1}{2}, \pm\sqrt{2},$ and $\pm\sqrt{3}$

FIGURE 3
$y = 3x^4 + 4x^3 - 7x^2 - 2x - 3$

Now we look for a lower bound, trying the numbers -1, -2, and -3 as potential candidates. We see that -3 is a lower bound for the solutions.

$$
\begin{array}{r|rrrrr}
-3 & 3 & 4 & -7 & -2 & -3 \\
 & & -9 & 15 & -24 & 78 \\
\hline
 & 3 & -5 & 8 & -26 & 75
\end{array}
$$

Entries
alternate
in sign

Thus, all the solutions lie between -3 and 2. So the viewing rectangle $[-3, 2]$ by $[-20, 20]$ contains all the x-intercepts of P. The graph in Figure 3 has two x-intercepts, one between -3 and -2 and the other between 1 and 2. Zooming in, we find that the solutions of the equation, to the nearest tenth, are -2.3 and 1.3.

✎. NOW TRY EXERCISE **93**   ■

EXAMPLE 8 | Determining the Size of a Fuel Tank

A fuel tank consists of a cylindrical center section that is 4 ft long and two hemispherical end sections, as shown in Figure 4. If the tank has a volume of 100 ft³, what is the radius r shown in the figure, rounded to the nearest hundredth of a foot?

|← 4 ft →|

FIGURE 4

SOLUTION   Using the volume formula listed on the inside front cover of this book, we see that the volume of the cylindrical section of the tank is

$$\pi \cdot r^2 \cdot 4$$

The two hemispherical parts together form a complete sphere whose volume is

$$\tfrac{4}{3}\pi r^3$$

Because the total volume of the tank is 100 ft³, we get the following equation:

$$\tfrac{4}{3}\pi r^3 + 4\pi r^2 = 100$$

A negative solution for r would be meaningless in this physical situation, and by substitution we can verify that $r = 3$ leads to a tank that is over 226 ft³ in volume, much larger than the required 100 ft³. Thus, we know the correct radius lies somewhere between 0 and 3 ft, so we use a viewing rectangle of $[0, 3]$ by $[50, 150]$ to graph the function $y = \tfrac{4}{3}\pi x^3 + 4\pi x^2$, as shown in Figure 5. Since we want the value of this function to be 100, we also graph the horizontal line $y = 100$ in the same viewing rectangle. The correct radius will be the x-coordinate of the point of intersection of the curve and the line. Using the cursor and zooming in, we see that at the point of intersection $x \approx 2.15$, rounded to two decimal places. Thus the tank has a radius of about 2.15 ft.

✎. NOW TRY EXERCISE **99**   ■

Note that we also could have solved the equation in Example 8 by first writing it as

$$\tfrac{4}{3}\pi r^3 + 4\pi r^2 - 100 = 0$$

and then finding the x-intercept of the function $y = \tfrac{4}{3}\pi x^3 + 4\pi x^2 - 100$.

Volume of a cylinder: $V = \pi r^2 h$

Volume of a sphere: $V = \tfrac{4}{3}\pi r^3$

150

0
50
3

FIGURE 5
$y = \tfrac{4}{3}\pi x^3 + 4\pi x^2$ and $y = 100$

ALTERNATE EXAMPLE 8
A fuel tank consists of a cylindrical center section 10 ft long and two hemispherical end sections, as shown in Figure 4. If the tank has a volume of 400 ft³, what is the radius r shown in the figure, correct to the nearest hundredth of a foot?

ANSWER
As in the text, we get the equation $\tfrac{4}{3}\pi r^3 + 10\pi r^2 - 400$. We graph to find its x-intercept to the nearest hundredth, $r = 3.01$ ft.

DRILL QUESTION
Factor $f(x) = x^3 - 6x + 4$.

Answer
$f(x) = (x - 2)(x + 1 + \sqrt{3}) \times (x + 1 - \sqrt{3})$

3.4 EXERCISES

CONCEPTS

1. If the polynomial function

$$P(x) = a_n x^n + a_{n-1} x^{n-1} + \cdots + a_1 x + a_0$$

has integer coefficients, then the only numbers that could possibly be rational zeros of P are all of the form $\frac{p}{q}$, where p is a factor of _____ and q is a factor of _____. The possible rational zeros of $P(x) = 6x^3 + 5x^2 - 19x - 10$ are

_____.

2. Using Descartes' Rule of Signs, we can tell that the polynomial $P(x) = x^5 - 3x^4 + 2x^3 - x^2 + 8x - 8$ has

_____, _____, or _____ positive real zeros and

_____ negative real zeros.

3. *True or false?* If c is a real zero of the polynomial P, then all the other zeros of P are zeros of $P(x)/(x - c)$.

4. *True or false?* If a is an upper bound for the real zeros of the polynomial P, then $-a$ is necessarily a lower bound for the real zeros of P.

SKILLS

5–10 ■ List all possible rational zeros given by the Rational Zeros Theorem (but don't check to see which actually are zeros).

5. $P(x) = x^3 - 4x^2 + 3$

6. $Q(x) = x^4 - 3x^3 - 6x + 8$

7. $R(x) = 2x^5 + 3x^3 + 4x^2 - 8$

8. $S(x) = 6x^4 - x^2 + 2x + 12$

9. $T(x) = 4x^4 - 2x^2 - 7$

10. $U(x) = 12x^5 + 6x^3 - 2x - 8$

11–14 ■ A polynomial function P and its graph are given. **(a)** List all possible rational zeros of P given by the Rational Zeros Theorem. **(b)** From the graph, determine which of the possible rational zeros actually turn out to be zeros.

11. $P(x) = 5x^3 - x^2 - 5x + 1$

12. $P(x) = 3x^3 + 4x^2 - x - 2$

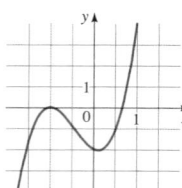

13. $P(x) = 2x^4 - 9x^3 + 9x^2 + x - 3$

14. $P(x) = 4x^4 - x^3 - 4x + 1$

15–46 ■ Find all rational zeros of the polynomial, and write the polynomial in factored form.

15. $P(x) = x^3 + 3x^2 - 4$

16. $P(x) = x^3 - 7x^2 + 14x - 8$

17. $P(x) = x^3 - 3x - 2$

18. $P(x) = x^3 + 4x^2 - 3x - 18$

19. $P(x) = x^3 - 6x^2 + 12x - 8$

20. $P(x) = x^3 - x^2 - 8x + 12$

21. $P(x) = x^3 - 4x^2 + x + 6$

22. $P(x) = x^3 - 4x^2 - 7x + 10$

23. $P(x) = x^3 + 3x^2 - x - 3$

24. $P(x) = x^3 - 4x^2 - 11x + 30$

25. $P(x) = x^4 - 5x^2 + 4$

26. $P(x) = x^4 - 2x^3 - 3x^2 + 8x - 4$

27. $P(x) = x^4 + 6x^3 + 7x^2 - 6x - 8$

28. $P(x) = x^4 - x^3 - 23x^2 - 3x + 90$

29. $P(x) = 4x^4 - 25x^2 + 36$

30. $P(x) = 2x^4 - x^3 - 19x^2 + 9x + 9$

31. $P(x) = 3x^4 - 10x^3 - 9x^2 + 40x - 12$

32. $P(x) = 2x^3 + 7x^2 + 4x - 4$

33. $P(x) = 4x^3 + 4x^2 - x - 1$

34. $P(x) = 2x^3 - 3x^2 - 2x + 3$

35. $P(x) = 4x^3 - 7x + 3$

36. $P(x) = 8x^3 + 10x^2 - x - 3$

37. $P(x) = 4x^3 + 8x^2 - 11x - 15$

38. $P(x) = 6x^3 + 11x^2 - 3x - 2$

39. $P(x) = 20x^3 - 8x^2 - 5x + 2$

40. $P(x) = 12x^3 - 20x^2 + x + 3$

41. $P(x) = 2x^4 - 7x^3 + 3x^2 + 8x - 4$

42. $P(x) = 6x^4 - 7x^3 - 12x^2 + 3x + 2$

43. $P(x) = x^5 + 3x^4 - 9x^3 - 31x^2 + 36$

44. $P(x) = x^5 - 4x^4 - 3x^3 + 22x^2 - 4x - 24$

45. $P(x) = 3x^5 - 14x^4 - 14x^3 + 36x^2 + 43x + 10$

46. $P(x) = 2x^6 - 3x^5 - 13x^4 + 29x^3 - 27x^2 + 32x - 12$

47–56 ■ Find all the real zeros of the polynomial. Use the quadratic formula if necessary, as in Example 3(a).

47. $P(x) = x^3 + 4x^2 + 3x - 2$

48. $P(x) = x^3 - 5x^2 + 2x + 12$

49. $P(x) = x^4 - 6x^3 + 4x^2 + 15x + 4$

50. $P(x) = x^4 + 2x^3 - 2x^2 - 3x + 2$

51. $P(x) = x^4 - 7x^3 + 14x^2 - 3x - 9$

52. $P(x) = x^5 - 4x^4 - x^3 + 10x^2 + 2x - 4$

53. $P(x) = 4x^3 - 6x^2 + 1$

54. $P(x) = 3x^3 - 5x^2 - 8x - 2$

55. $P(x) = 2x^4 + 15x^3 + 17x^2 + 3x - 1$

56. $P(x) = 4x^5 - 18x^4 - 6x^3 + 91x^2 - 60x + 9$

57–64 ■ A polynomial P is given. **(a)** Find all the real zeros of P. **(b)** Sketch the graph of P.

57. $P(x) = x^3 - 3x^2 - 4x + 12$

58. $P(x) = -x^3 - 2x^2 + 5x + 6$

59. $P(x) = 2x^3 - 7x^2 + 4x + 4$

60. $P(x) = 3x^3 + 17x^2 + 21x - 9$

61. $P(x) = x^4 - 5x^3 + 6x^2 + 4x - 8$

62. $P(x) = -x^4 + 10x^2 + 8x - 8$

63. $P(x) = x^5 - x^4 - 5x^3 + x^2 + 8x + 4$

64. $P(x) = x^5 - x^4 - 6x^3 + 14x^2 - 11x + 3$

65–70 ■ Use Descartes' Rule of Signs to determine how many positive and how many negative real zeros the polynomial can have. Then determine the possible total number of real zeros.

65. $P(x) = x^3 - x^2 - x - 3$

66. $P(x) = 2x^3 - x^2 + 4x - 7$

67. $P(x) = 2x^6 + 5x^4 - x^3 - 5x - 1$

68. $P(x) = x^4 + x^3 + x^2 + x + 12$

69. $P(x) = x^5 + 4x^3 - x^2 + 6x$

70. $P(x) = x^8 - x^5 + x^4 - x^3 + x^2 - x + 1$

71–74 ■ Show that the given values for a and b are lower and upper bounds for the real zeros of the polynomial.

71. $P(x) = 2x^3 + 5x^2 + x - 2$; $a = -3, b = 1$

72. $P(x) = x^4 - 2x^3 - 9x^2 + 2x + 8$; $a = -3, b = 5$

73. $P(x) = 8x^3 + 10x^2 - 39x + 9$; $a = -3, b = 2$

74. $P(x) = 3x^4 - 17x^3 + 24x^2 - 9x + 1$; $a = 0, b = 6$

75–78 ■ Find integers that are upper and lower bounds for the real zeros of the polynomial.

75. $P(x) = x^3 - 3x^2 + 4$

76. $P(x) = 2x^3 - 3x^2 - 8x + 12$

77. $P(x) = x^4 - 2x^3 + x^2 - 9x + 2$

78. $P(x) = x^5 - x^4 + 1$

79–84 ■ Find all rational zeros of the polynomial, and then find the irrational zeros, if any. Whenever appropriate, use the Rational Zeros Theorem, the Upper and Lower Bounds Theorem, Descartes' Rule of Signs, the quadratic formula, or other factoring techniques.

79. $P(x) = 2x^4 + 3x^3 - 4x^2 - 3x + 2$

80. $P(x) = 2x^4 + 15x^3 + 31x^2 + 20x + 4$

81. $P(x) = 4x^4 - 21x^2 + 5$

82. $P(x) = 6x^4 - 7x^3 - 8x^2 + 5x$

83. $P(x) = x^5 - 7x^4 + 9x^3 + 23x^2 - 50x + 24$

84. $P(x) = 8x^5 - 14x^4 - 22x^3 + 57x^2 - 35x + 6$

85–88 ■ Show that the polynomial does not have any rational zeros.

85. $P(x) = x^3 - x - 2$

86. $P(x) = 2x^4 - x^3 + x + 2$

87. $P(x) = 3x^3 - x^2 - 6x + 12$

88. $P(x) = x^{50} - 5x^{25} + x^2 - 1$

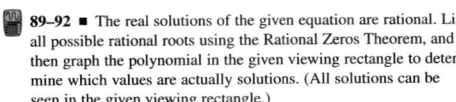 **89–92** ■ The real solutions of the given equation are rational. List all possible rational roots using the Rational Zeros Theorem, and then graph the polynomial in the given viewing rectangle to determine which values are actually solutions. (All solutions can be seen in the given viewing rectangle.)

89. $x^3 - 3x^2 - 4x + 12 = 0$; $[-4, 4]$ by $[-15, 15]$

90. $x^4 - 5x^2 + 4 = 0$; $[-4, 4]$ by $[-30, 30]$

91. $2x^4 - 5x^3 - 14x^2 + 5x + 12 = 0$; $[-2, 5]$ by $[-40, 40]$

92. $3x^3 + 8x^2 + 5x + 2 = 0$; $[-3, 3]$ by $[-10, 10]$

93–96 ■ Use a graphing device to find all real solutions of the equation, rounded to two decimal places.

93. $x^4 - x - 4 = 0$

94. $2x^3 - 8x^2 + 9x - 9 = 0$

95. $4.00x^4 + 4.00x^3 - 10.96x^2 - 5.88x + 9.09 = 0$

96. $x^5 + 2.00x^4 + 0.96x^3 + 5.00x^2 + 10.00x + 4.80 = 0$

97. Let $P(x)$ be a polynomial with real coefficients and let $b > 0$. Use the Division Algorithm to write

$$P(x) = (x - b) \cdot Q(x) + r$$

Suppose that $r \geq 0$ and that all the coefficients in $Q(x)$ are nonnegative. Let $z > b$.

(a) Show that $P(z) > 0$.

(b) Prove the first part of the Upper and Lower Bounds Theorem.

(c) Use the first part of the Upper and Lower Bounds Theorem to prove the second part.   [*Hint:* Show that if $P(x)$ satisfies the second part of the theorem, then $P(-x)$ satisfies the first part.]

98. Show that the equation

$$x^5 - x^4 - x^3 - 5x^2 - 12x - 6 = 0$$

has exactly one rational root, and then prove that it must have either two or four irrational roots.

APPLICATIONS

99. Volume of a Silo   A grain silo consists of a cylindrical main section and a hemispherical roof. If the total volume of the silo (including the part inside the roof section) is 15,000 ft^3 and the cylindrical part is 30 ft tall, what is the radius of the silo, rounded to the nearest tenth of a foot?

30 ft

100. Dimensions of a Lot   A rectangular parcel of land has an area of 5000 ft^2. A diagonal between opposite corners is measured to be 10 ft longer than one side of the parcel. What are the dimensions of the land, rounded to the nearest foot?

x

x + 10

101. Depth of Snowfall   Snow began falling at noon on Sunday. The amount of snow on the ground at a certain location at time t was given by the function

$$h(t) = 11.60t - 12.41t^2 + 6.20t^3$$
$$- 1.58t^4 + 0.20t^5 - 0.01t^6$$

where t is measured in days from the start of the snowfall and $h(t)$ is the depth of snow in inches. Draw a graph of this function, and use your graph to answer the following questions.

(a) What happened shortly after noon on Tuesday?

(b) Was there ever more than 5 in. of snow on the ground? If so, on what day(s)?

(c) On what day and at what time (to the nearest hour) did the snow disappear completely?

102. Volume of a Box   An open box with a volume of 1500 cm^3 is to be constructed by taking a piece of cardboard 20 cm by 40 cm, cutting squares of side length x cm from each corner, and folding up the sides. Show that this can be done in two different ways, and find the exact dimensions of the box in each case.

40 cm

20 cm

x

x

103. Volume of a Rocket   A rocket consists of a right circular cylinder of height 20 m surmounted by a cone whose height and diameter are equal and whose radius is the same as that of the cylindrical section. What should this radius be (rounded to two decimal places) if the total volume is to be 500π/3 m^3?

20 m

104. Volume of a Box A rectangular box with a volume of $2\sqrt{2}$ ft^3 has a square base as shown below. The diagonal of the box (between a pair of opposite corners) is 1 ft longer than each side of the base.

(a) If the base has sides of length x feet, show that

$$x^6 - 2x^5 - x^4 + 8 = 0$$

(b) Show that two different boxes satisfy the given conditions. Find the dimensions in each case, rounded to the nearest hundredth of a foot.

105. Girth of a Box A box with a square base has length plus girth of 108 in. (Girth is the distance "around" the box.) What is the length of the box if its volume is 2200 in^3?

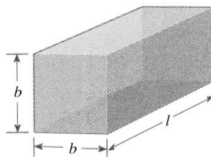

DISCOVERY ▪ DISCUSSION ▪ WRITING

106. How Many Real Zeros Can a Polynomial Have? Give examples of polynomials that have the following properties, or explain why it is impossible to find such a polynomial.

(a) A polynomial of degree 3 that has no real zeros
(b) A polynomial of degree 4 that has no real zeros
(c) A polynomial of degree 3 that has three real zeros, only one of which is rational
(d) A polynomial of degree 4 that has four real zeros, none of which is rational

What must be true about the degree of a polynomial with integer coefficients if it has no real zeros?

107. The Depressed Cubic The most general cubic (third-degree) equation with rational coefficients can be written as

$$x^3 + ax^2 + bx + c = 0$$

(a) Show that if we replace x by $X - a/3$ and simplify, we end up with an equation that doesn't have an X^2 term, that is, an equation of the form

$$X^3 + pX + q = 0$$

This is called a *depressed cubic*, because we have "depressed" the quadratic term.

(b) Use the procedure described in part (a) to depress the equation $x^3 + 6x^2 + 9x + 4 = 0$.

108. The Cubic Formula The quadratic formula can be used to solve any quadratic (or second-degree) equation. You might have wondered whether similar formulas exist for cubic (third-degree), quartic (fourth-degree), and higher-degree equations. For the depressed cubic $x^3 + px + q = 0$, Cardano (page 274) found the following formula for one solution:

$$x = \sqrt[3]{-\frac{q}{2} + \sqrt{\frac{q^2}{4} + \frac{p^3}{27}}} + \sqrt[3]{-\frac{q}{2} - \sqrt{\frac{q^2}{4} + \frac{p^3}{27}}}$$

A formula for quartic equations was discovered by the Italian mathematician Ferrari in 1540. In 1824 the Norwegian mathematician Niels Henrik Abel proved that it is impossible to write a quintic formula, that is, a formula for fifth-degree equations. Finally, Galois (page 254) gave a criterion for determining which equations can be solved by a formula involving radicals.

Use the cubic formula to find a solution for the following equations. Then solve the equations using the methods you learned in this section. Which method is easier?

(a) $x^3 - 3x + 2 = 0$
(b) $x^3 - 27x - 54 = 0$
(c) $x^3 + 3x + 4 = 0$

DISCOVERY PROJECT   **Zeroing in on a Zero**

In this project we explore a numerical method for approximating the zeros of a polynomial function. You can find the project at the book companion website: **www.stewartmath.com**

**SUGGESTED TIME
AND EMPHASIS**
$\frac{1}{2}$–1 class, essential material

3.5 COMPLEX NUMBERS

| Arithmetic Operations on Complex Numbers ▶ Square Roots of Negative
| Numbers ▶ Complex Solutions of Quadratic Equations

In Section 1.5 we saw that if the discriminant of a quadratic equation is negative, the equation has no real solution. For example, the equation

$$x^2 + 4 = 0$$

has no real solution. If we try to solve this equation, we get $x^2 = -4$, so

$$x = \pm\sqrt{-4}$$

But this is impossible, since the square of any real number is positive. [For example, $(-2)^2 = 4$, a positive number.] Thus, negative numbers don't have real square roots.

See the note on Cardano (page 274) for an example of how complex numbers are used to find real solutions of polynomial equations.

To make it possible to solve *all* quadratic equations, mathematicians invented an expanded number system, called the *complex number system*. First they defined the new number

$$i = \sqrt{-1}$$

This means that $i^2 = -1$. A complex number is then a number of the form $a + bi$, where a and b are real numbers.

DEFINITION OF COMPLEX NUMBERS

A **complex number** is an expression of the form

$$a + bi$$

where a and b are real numbers and $i^2 = -1$. The **real part** of this complex number is a and the **imaginary part** is b. Two complex numbers are **equal** if and only if their real parts are equal and their imaginary parts are equal.

Note that both the real and imaginary parts of a complex number are real numbers.

EXAMPLE 1 | Complex Numbers

The following are examples of complex numbers.

$3 + 4i$	Real part 3, imaginary part 4
$\frac{1}{2} - \frac{2}{3}i$	Real part $\frac{1}{2}$, imaginary part $-\frac{2}{3}$
$6i$	Real part 0, imaginary part 6
-7	Real part -7, imaginary part 0

✎ NOW TRY EXERCISES **5** AND **9** ∎

A number such as $6i$, which has real part 0, is called a **pure imaginary number**. A real number such as -7 can be thought of as a complex number with imaginary part 0.

In the complex number system every quadratic equation has solutions. The numbers $2i$ and $-2i$ are solutions of $x^2 = -4$ because

$$(2i)^2 = 2^2i^2 = 4(-1) = -4 \quad \text{and} \quad (-2i)^2 = (-2)^2i^2 = 4(-1) = -4$$

Although we use the term *imaginary* in this context, imaginary numbers should not be thought of as any less "real" (in the ordinary rather than the mathematical sense of that word) than negative numbers or irrational numbers. All numbers (except possibly the positive integers) are creations of the human mind—the numbers -1 and $\sqrt{2}$ as well as the number i. We study complex numbers because they complete, in a useful and elegant fashion, our study

TEXT QUESTION
Write out all solutions (real and complex) to the equation $z^2 = -9$.

Answer
$z = \pm3i$

ALTERNATE EXAMPLE 1
Write the real and imaginary parts of the complex number $4 + 9i$.

ANSWER
4, 9

IN-CLASS MATERIALS
Students often believe that the relationship between real and complex numbers is similar to the relationship between rational and irrational numbers—they don't see that the number 5 can be thought of as complex $(5 + 0i)$ as well as real. Perhaps show them this figure:

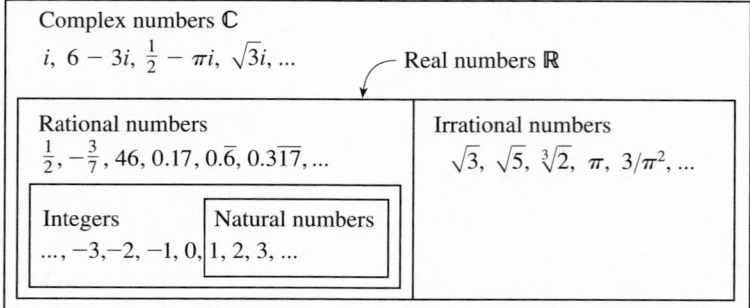

of the solutions of equations. In fact, imaginary numbers are useful not only in algebra and mathematics, but in the other sciences as well. To give just one example, in electrical theory the *reactance* of a circuit is a quantity whose measure is an imaginary number.

▼ Arithmetic Operations on Complex Numbers

Complex numbers are added, subtracted, multiplied, and divided just as we would any number of the form $a + b\sqrt{c}$. The only difference that we need to keep in mind is that $i^2 = -1$. Thus, the following calculations are valid.

$$(a + bi)(c + di) = ac + (ad + bc)i + bdi^2 \qquad \text{Multiply and collect like terms}$$
$$= ac + (ad + bc)i + bd(-1) \qquad i^2 = -1$$
$$= (ac - bd) + (ad + bc)i \qquad \text{Combine real and imaginary parts}$$

We therefore define the sum, difference, and product of complex numbers as follows.

ADDING, SUBTRACTING, AND MULTIPLYING COMPLEX NUMBERS

Definition	Description
Addition	
$(a + bi) + (c + di) = (a + c) + (b + d)i$	To add complex numbers, add the real parts and the imaginary parts.
Subtraction	
$(a + bi) - (c + di) = (a - c) + (b - d)i$	To subtract complex numbers, subtract the real parts and the imaginary parts.
Multiplication	
$(a + bi) \cdot (c + di) = (ac - bd) + (ad + bc)i$	Multiply complex numbers like binomials, using $i^2 = -1$.

Graphing calculators can perform arithmetic operations on complex numbers.

```
(3+5i)+(4-2i)
            7+3i
(3+5i)*(4-2i)
          22+14i
```

EXAMPLE 2 | Adding, Subtracting, and Multiplying Complex Numbers

Express the following in the form $a + bi$.

(a) $(3 + 5i) + (4 - 2i)$ (b) $(3 + 5i) - (4 - 2i)$
(c) $(3 + 5i)(4 - 2i)$ (d) i^{23}

SOLUTION

(a) According to the definition, we add the real parts and we add the imaginary parts.

$$(3 + 5i) + (4 - 2i) = (3 + 4) + (5 - 2)i = 7 + 3i$$

(b) $(3 + 5i) - (4 - 2i) = (3 - 4) + [5 - (-2)]i = -1 + 7i$
(c) $(3 + 5i)(4 - 2i) = [3 \cdot 4 - 5(-2)] + [3(-2) + 5 \cdot 4]i = 22 + 14i$
(d) $i^{23} = i^{22+1} = (i^2)^{11}i = (-1)^{11}i = (-1)i = -i$

✎ NOW TRY EXERCISES **15, 19, 25,** AND **33**

Complex Conjugates

Number	Conjugate
$3 + 2i$	$3 - 2i$
$1 - i$	$1 + i$
$4i$	$-4i$
5	5

Division of complex numbers is much like rationalizing the denominator of a radical expression, which we considered in Section 1.4. For the complex number $z = a + bi$ we define its **complex conjugate** to be $\bar{z} = a - bi$. Note that

$$z \cdot \bar{z} = (a + bi)(a - bi) = a^2 + b^2$$

IN-CLASS MATERIALS

One doesn't have to think of complex numbers as a philosophical abstraction. Many applied fields use complex numbers, because the result of complex arithmetic leads to real-world understanding. One can think of complex numbers as points in the plane with the real and imaginary axes replacing the x- and y-axes. (In that sense, the complex numbers become a geometric extension of a number line.) Now we can model walking 2 ft north and 1 ft east as $1 + 2i$, and 1 ft north and 3 ft east as $3 + i$. Adding the numbers now has a physical significance: They reveal the final location. Multiplication has a meaning too: When we multiply two complex numbers (thinking of them as points on the plane), we are multiplying their distances from the origin and adding their vector angles. So when we say $i^2 = -1$, we are really just saying that a 90° angle plus a 90° angle is a 180° angle. The statement $i = \sqrt{-1}$ is then a notational aid. Engineers represent waves of a fixed frequency as a magnitude and a phase angle. This interpretation of a complex number is well suited to that model.

LEONHARD EULER (1707–1783) was born in Basel, Switzerland, the son of a pastor. When Euler was 13, his father sent him to the University at Basel to study theology, but Euler soon decided to devote himself to the sciences. Besides theology he studied mathematics, medicine, astronomy, physics, and Asian languages. It is said that Euler could calculate as effortlessly as "men breathe or as eagles fly." One hundred years before Euler, Fermat (see page 99) had conjectured that $2^{2^x} + 1$ is a prime number for all n. The first five of these numbers are 5, 17, 257, 65537, and 4,294,967,297. It is easy to show that the first four are prime. The fifth was also thought to be prime until Euler, with his phenomenal calculating ability, showed that it is the product 641 × 6,700,417 and so is not prime. Euler published more than any other mathematician in history. His collected works comprise 75 large volumes. Although he was blind for the last 17 years of his life, he continued to work and publish. In his writings he popularized the use of the symbols π, e, and i, which you will find in this textbook. One of Euler's most lasting contributions is his development of complex numbers.

So the product of a complex number and its conjugate is always a nonnegative real number. We use this property to divide complex numbers.

DIVIDING COMPLEX NUMBERS

To simplify the quotient $\dfrac{a + bi}{c + di}$, multiply the numerator and the denominator by the complex conjugate of the denominator:

$$\frac{a + bi}{c + di} = \left(\frac{a + bi}{c + di}\right)\left(\frac{c - di}{c - di}\right) = \frac{(ac + bd) + (bc - ad)i}{c^2 + d^2}$$

Rather than memorizing this entire formula, it is easier to just remember the first step and then multiply out the numerator and the denominator as usual.

EXAMPLE 3 | Dividing Complex Numbers

Express the following in the form $a + bi$.

(a) $\dfrac{3 + 5i}{1 - 2i}$ (b) $\dfrac{7 + 3i}{4i}$

SOLUTION   We multiply both the numerator and denominator by the complex conjugate of the denominator to make the new denominator a real number.

(a) The complex conjugate of $1 - 2i$ is $\overline{1 - 2i} = 1 + 2i$.

$$\frac{3 + 5i}{1 - 2i} = \left(\frac{3 + 5i}{1 - 2i}\right)\left(\frac{1 + 2i}{1 + 2i}\right) = \frac{-7 + 11i}{5} = -\frac{7}{5} + \frac{11}{5}i$$

(b) The complex conjugate of $4i$ is $-4i$. Therefore,

$$\frac{7 + 3i}{4i} = \left(\frac{7 + 3i}{4i}\right)\left(\frac{-4i}{-4i}\right) = \frac{12 - 28i}{16} = \frac{3}{4} - \frac{7}{4}i$$

✎ NOW TRY EXERCISES **37** AND **43**   ■

▼ Square Roots of Negative Numbers

Just as every positive real number r has two square roots ($\sqrt{r}$ and $-\sqrt{r}$), every negative number has two square roots as well. If $-r$ is a negative number, then its square roots are $\pm i\sqrt{r}$, because $(i\sqrt{r})^2 = i^2r = -r$ and $(-i\sqrt{r})^2 = (-1)^2i^2r = -r$.

SQUARE ROOTS OF NEGATIVE NUMBERS

If $-r$ is negative, then the **principal square root** of $-r$ is

$$\sqrt{-r} = i\sqrt{r}$$

The two square roots of $-r$ are $i\sqrt{r}$ and $-i\sqrt{r}$.

We usually write $i\sqrt{b}$ instead of $\sqrt{b}i$ to avoid confusion with $\sqrt{bi}$.

EXAMPLE 4 | Square Roots of Negative Numbers

(a) $\sqrt{-1} = i\sqrt{1} = i$ (b) $\sqrt{-16} = i\sqrt{16} = 4i$ (c) $\sqrt{-3} = i\sqrt{3}$

✎ NOW TRY EXERCISES **47** AND **49**   ■

ALTERNATE EXAMPLE 3

Express the following in the form $a + bi$.

(a) $\dfrac{5 + 6i}{1 - 3i}$

(b) $\dfrac{13 + 11i}{4i}$

ANSWERS

(a) $-\dfrac{13}{10} + \dfrac{21}{10}i$

(b) $\dfrac{11}{4} - \dfrac{13}{4}i$

ALTERNATE EXAMPLE 4

Simplify the following:

(a) $\sqrt{-16}$

(b) $-\sqrt{-25}$

(c) $\sqrt{-12}$

ANSWERS

(a) $4i$

(b) $-5i$

(c) $2i\sqrt{3}$

IN-CLASS MATERIALS

The text states an important truth: Every quadratic equation has two solutions (allowing for multiplicities) if complex numbers are considered. Equivalently, we can say that every quadratic expression $ax^2 + bx + c$ can be factored into two linear factors $(x - z_1)(x - z_2)$, where z_1 and z_2 are complex numbers (and possibly real). An important, easy-to-understand generalization is the Fundamental Theorem of Algebra: Every nth-degree polynomial can be factored into n linear factors, if we allow complex numbers. (If we do not, it can be shown that every nth-degree polynomial can be factored into linear factors and irreducible quadratic factors.) The Fundamental Theorem will be covered explicitly in Section 3.6.

Special care must be taken in performing calculations that involve square roots of negative numbers. Although $\sqrt{a} \cdot \sqrt{b} = \sqrt{ab}$ when a and b are positive, this is *not* true when both are negative. For example,

$$\sqrt{-2} \cdot \sqrt{-3} = i\sqrt{2} \cdot i\sqrt{3} = i^2\sqrt{6} = -\sqrt{6}$$

but

$$\sqrt{(-2)(-3)} = \sqrt{6}$$

so

$$\sqrt{-2} \cdot \sqrt{-3} \neq \sqrt{(-2)(-3)}$$

 When multiplying radicals of negative numbers, express them first in the form $i\sqrt{r}$ (where $r > 0$) to avoid possible errors of this type.

EXAMPLE 5 | Using Square Roots of Negative Numbers

Evaluate $(\sqrt{12} - \sqrt{-3})(3 + \sqrt{-4})$ and express in the form $a + bi$.

SOLUTION

$$\begin{aligned}(\sqrt{12} - \sqrt{-3})(3 + \sqrt{-4}) &= (\sqrt{12} - i\sqrt{3})(3 + i\sqrt{4}) \\ &= (2\sqrt{3} - i\sqrt{3})(3 + 2i) \\ &= (6\sqrt{3} + 2\sqrt{3}) + i(2 \cdot 2\sqrt{3} - 3\sqrt{3}) \\ &= 8\sqrt{3} + i\sqrt{3}\end{aligned}$$

✎ NOW TRY EXERCISE **51** ∎

▼ Complex Solutions of Quadratic Equations

We have already seen that if $a \neq 0$, then the solutions of the quadratic equation $ax^2 + bx + c = 0$ are

$$x = \frac{-b \pm \sqrt{b^2 - 4ac}}{2a}$$

If $b^2 - 4ac < 0$, then the equation has no real solution. But in the complex number system, this equation will always have solutions, because negative numbers have square roots in this expanded setting.

EXAMPLE 6 | Quadratic Equations with Complex Solutions

Solve each equation.

(a) $x^2 + 9 = 0$ **(b)** $x^2 + 4x + 5 = 0$

SOLUTION

(a) The equation $x^2 + 9 = 0$ means $x^2 = -9$, so

$$x = \pm\sqrt{-9} = \pm i\sqrt{9} = \pm 3i$$

The solutions are therefore $3i$ and $-3i$.

(b) By the Quadratic Formula we have

$$\begin{aligned}x &= \frac{-4 \pm \sqrt{4^2 - 4 \cdot 5}}{2} \\ &= \frac{-4 \pm \sqrt{-4}}{2} \\ &= \frac{-4 \pm 2i}{2} = \frac{2(-2 \pm i)}{2} = -2 \pm i\end{aligned}$$

So the solutions are $-2 + i$ and $-2 - i$.

✎ NOW TRY EXERCISES **57** AND **59** ∎

ALTERNATE EXAMPLE 5

Evaluate $(\sqrt{63} - \sqrt{-7}) \times (7 + \sqrt{-9})$ and express your answer in the form $a + bi$.

ANSWER

$24\sqrt{7} + i \cdot 2\sqrt{7}$

ALTERNATE EXAMPLE 6

Solve each equation.

(a) $x^2 + 16 = 0$

(b) $x^2 - 4x + 6.25 = 0$

ANSWERS

(a) $4i$ and $-4i$

(b) $2 + 1.5i$, $2 - 1.5i$

IN-CLASS MATERIALS

There is a certain similarity to dividing complex numbers and rationalizing denominators. Make this similarity explicit by having the students do these two problems:

1. Rationalize the denominator of $\dfrac{8}{3 + \sqrt{2}i}$.

2. Simplify $\dfrac{8}{3 + 2i}$.

Answers

1. $\dfrac{24}{7} - \dfrac{8}{7}\sqrt{2}$

2. $\dfrac{24}{13} - \dfrac{16}{13}i$

We see from Example 6 that if a quadratic equation with real coefficients has complex solutions, then these solutions are complex conjugates of each other. So if $a + bi$ is a solution, then $a - bi$ is also a solution.

EXAMPLE 7 | Complex Conjugates as Solutions of a Quadratic

Show that the solutions of the equation

$$4x^2 - 24x + 37 = 0$$

are complex conjugates of each other.

SOLUTION   We use the Quadratic Formula to get

$$x = \frac{24 \pm \sqrt{(24)^2 - 4(4)(37)}}{2(4)}$$

$$= \frac{24 \pm \sqrt{-16}}{8} = \frac{24 \pm 4i}{8} = 3 \pm \frac{1}{2}i$$

So the solutions are $3 + \frac{1}{2}i$ and $3 - \frac{1}{2}i$, and these are complex conjugates.

NOW TRY EXERCISE 65

ALTERNATE EXAMPLE 7
Show that the solutions of the equation $2x^2 + 5x + 10 = 0$ are complex conjugates of each other.

ANSWER
The quadratic formula gives the solutions $\frac{1}{4}(-5 + \sqrt{55})$ and $\frac{1}{4}(-5 - \sqrt{55})$. These two solutions are complex conjugates.

EXAMPLE
Simplify $\dfrac{3i + 2}{3 + 4i}$.

Answer
$\dfrac{18}{25} + \dfrac{1}{25}i$

3.5 EXERCISES

CONCEPTS

1. The imaginary number i has the property that $i^2 = $ _____.

2. For the complex number $3 + 4i$ the real part is _____ and the imaginary part is _____.

3. (a) The complex conjugate of $3 + 4i$ is $\overline{3 + 4i} = $ _____.

   (b) $(3 + 4i)(\overline{3 + 4i}) = $ _____.

4. If $3 + 4i$ is a solution of a quadratic equation with real coefficients, then _____ is also a solution of the equation.

SKILLS

5–14 ■ Find the real and imaginary parts of the complex number.

5. $5 - 7i$

6. $-6 + 4i$

7. $\dfrac{-2 - 5i}{3}$

8. $\dfrac{4 + 7i}{2}$

9. 3

10. $-\frac{1}{2}$

11. $-\frac{2}{3}i$

12. $i\sqrt{3}$

13. $\sqrt{3} + \sqrt{-4}$

14. $2 - \sqrt{-5}$

15–46 ■ Evaluate the expression and write the result in the form $a + bi$.

15. $(2 - 5i) + (3 + 4i)$

16. $(2 + 5i) + (4 - 6i)$

17. $(-6 + 6i) + (9 - i)$

18. $(3 - 2i) + (-5 - \frac{1}{3}i)$

19. $(7 - \frac{1}{2}i) - (5 + \frac{3}{2}i)$

20. $(-4 + i) - (2 - 5i)$

21. $(-12 + 8i) - (7 + 4i)$

22. $6i - (4 - i)$

23. $4(-1 + 2i)$

24. $2i(\frac{1}{2} - i)$

25. $(7 - i)(4 + 2i)$

26. $(5 - 3i)(1 + i)$

27. $(3 - 4i)(5 - 12i)$

28. $(\frac{2}{3} + 12i)(\frac{1}{6} + 24i)$

29. $(6 + 5i)(2 - 3i)$

30. $(-2 + i)(3 - 7i)$

31. i^3

32. $(2i)^4$

33. i^{100}

34. i^{1002}

35. $\dfrac{1}{i}$

36. $\dfrac{1}{1 + i}$

37. $\dfrac{2 - 3i}{1 - 2i}$

38. $\dfrac{5 - i}{3 + 4i}$

39. $\dfrac{26 + 39i}{2 - 3i}$

40. $\dfrac{25}{4 - 3i}$

41. $\dfrac{10i}{1 - 2i}$

42. $(2 - 3i)^{-1}$

43. $\dfrac{4 + 6i}{3i}$

44. $\dfrac{-3 + 5i}{15i}$

45. $\dfrac{1}{1 + i} - \dfrac{1}{1 - i}$

46. $\dfrac{(1 + 2i)(3 - i)}{2 + i}$

47–56 ■ Evaluate the radical expression and express the result in the form $a + bi$.

47. $\sqrt{-25}$

48. $\sqrt{\dfrac{-9}{4}}$

49. $\sqrt{-3}\sqrt{-12}$

50. $\sqrt{\frac{1}{3}}\sqrt{-27}$

EXAMPLE
Sample operations with complex numbers: Let $a = 3 + 2i$ and $b = 7 - 2i$. Then

$$a + b = 10$$
$$a - b = -4 + 4i$$
$$ab = 25 + 8i$$
$$\frac{a}{b} = \frac{17}{53} + \frac{20}{53}i$$

51. $(3 - \sqrt{-5})(1 + \sqrt{-1})$

52. $(\sqrt{3} - \sqrt{-4})(\sqrt{6} - \sqrt{-8})$

53. $\dfrac{2 + \sqrt{-8}}{1 + \sqrt{-2}}$ **54.** $\dfrac{1 - \sqrt{-1}}{1 + \sqrt{-1}}$

55. $\dfrac{\sqrt{-36}}{\sqrt{-2}\sqrt{-9}}$ **56.** $\dfrac{\sqrt{-7}\sqrt{-49}}{\sqrt{28}}$

57–72 ■ Find all solutions of the equation and express them in the form $a + bi$.

57. $x^2 + 49 = 0$ **58.** $9x^2 + 4 = 0$

59. $x^2 - 4x + 5 = 0$ **60.** $x^2 + 2x + 2 = 0$

61. $x^2 + 2x + 5 = 0$ **62.** $x^2 - 6x + 10 = 0$

63. $x^2 + x + 1 = 0$ **64.** $x^2 - 3x + 3 = 0$

65. $2x^2 - 2x + 1 = 0$ **66.** $2x^2 + 3 = 2x$

67. $t + 3 + \dfrac{3}{t} = 0$ **68.** $z + 4 + \dfrac{12}{z} = 0$

69. $6x^2 + 12x + 7 = 0$ **70.** $4x^2 - 16x + 19 = 0$

71. $\frac{1}{2}x^2 - x + 5 = 0$ **72.** $x^2 + \frac{1}{2}x + 1 = 0$

73–80 ■ Recall that the symbol $\bar{z}$ represents the complex conjugate of z. If $z = a + bi$ and $w = c + di$, prove each statement.

73. $\bar{z} + \bar{w} = \overline{z + w}$ **74.** $\overline{zw} = \bar{z} \cdot \bar{w}$

75. $(\bar{z})^2 = \overline{z^2}$ **76.** $\bar{\bar{z}} = z$

77. $z + \bar{z}$ is a real number.

78. $z - \bar{z}$ is a pure imaginary number.

79. $z \cdot \bar{z}$ is a real number.

80. $z = \bar{z}$ if and only if z is real.

DISCOVERY ■ DISCUSSION ■ WRITING

81. Complex Conjugate Roots   Suppose that the equation $ax^2 + bx + c = 0$ has real coefficients and complex roots. Why must the roots be complex conjugates of each other? (Think about how you would find the roots using the Quadratic Formula.)

82. Powers of i   Calculate the first 12 powers of i, that is, $i, i^2, i^3, \ldots, i^{12}$. Do you notice a pattern? Explain how you would calculate any whole number power of i, using the pattern that you have discovered. Use this procedure to calculate i^{4446}.

3.6 COMPLEX ZEROS AND THE FUNDAMENTAL THEOREM OF ALGEBRA

The Fundamental Theorem of Algebra and Complete Factorization ▶ Zeros and Their Multiplicities ▶ Complex Zeros Come in Conjugate Pairs ▶ Linear and Quadratic Factors

We have already seen that an nth-degree polynomial can have at most n real zeros. In the complex number system an nth-degree polynomial has exactly n zeros and so can be factored into exactly n linear factors. This fact is a consequence of the Fundamental Theorem of Algebra, which was proved by the German mathematician C. F. Gauss in 1799 (see page 272).

▼ The Fundamental Theorem of Algebra and Complete Factorization

The following theorem is the basis for much of our work in factoring polynomials and solving polynomial equations.

FUNDAMENTAL THEOREM OF ALGEBRA

Every polynomial

$$P(x) = a_n x^n + a_{n-1} x^{n-1} + \cdots + a_1 x + a_0 \quad (n \geq 1, a_n \neq 0)$$

with complex coefficients has at least one complex zero.

Because any real number is also a complex number, the theorem applies to polynomials with real coefficients as well.

SUGGESTED TIME AND EMPHASIS

1 class, essential material

TEXT QUESTIONS

Let $f(x) = x^3 + ax^2 + bx + c$.

(a) What is the maximum number of zeros this polynomial function can have?

(b) What is the minimum number of real zeros this polynomial function can have?

Answers

(a) 3

(b) 1

The Fundamental Theorem of Algebra and the Factor Theorem together show that a polynomial can be factored completely into linear factors, as we now prove.

> **COMPLETE FACTORIZATION THEOREM**
>
> If $P(x)$ is a polynomial of degree $n \geq 1$, then there exist complex numbers $a, c_1, c_2, \ldots, c_n$ (with $a \neq 0$) such that
> $$P(x) = a(x - c_1)(x - c_2) \cdots (x - c_n)$$

PROOF   By the Fundamental Theorem of Algebra, P has at least one zero. Let's call it c_1. By the Factor Theorem (see page 250), $P(x)$ can be factored as

$$P(x) = (x - c_1) \cdot Q_1(x)$$

where $Q_1(x)$ is of degree $n - 1$. Applying the Fundamental Theorem to the quotient $Q_1(x)$ gives us the factorization

$$P(x) = (x - c_1) \cdot (x - c_2) \cdot Q_2(x)$$

where $Q_2(x)$ is of degree $n - 2$ and c_2 is a zero of $Q_1(x)$. Continuing this process for n steps, we get a final quotient $Q_n(x)$ of degree 0, a nonzero constant that we will call a. This means that P has been factored as

$$P(x) = a(x - c_1)(x - c_2) \cdots (x - c_n)$$ ∎

To actually find the complex zeros of an nth-degree polynomial, we usually first factor as much as possible, then use the quadratic formula on parts that we can't factor further.

EXAMPLE 1 | Factoring a Polynomial Completely

Let $P(x) = x^3 - 3x^2 + x - 3$.

(a) Find all the zeros of P.

(b) Find the complete factorization of P.

SOLUTION

(a) We first factor P as follows.

$$\begin{aligned} P(x) &= x^3 - 3x^2 + x - 3 & \text{Given} \\ &= x^2(x - 3) + (x - 3) & \text{Group terms} \\ &= (x - 3)(x^2 + 1) & \text{Factor } x - 3 \end{aligned}$$

We find the zeros of P by setting each factor equal to 0:

$$P(x) = (x - 3)(x^2 + 1)$$

This factor is 0 when $x = 3$ This factor is 0 when $x = i$ or $-i$

Setting $x - 3 = 0$, we see that $x = 3$ is a zero. Setting $x^2 + 1 = 0$, we get $x^2 = -1$, so $x = \pm i$. So the zeros of P are 3, i, and $-i$.

(b) Since the zeros are 3, i, and $-i$, by the Complete Factorization Theorem P factors as

$$\begin{aligned} P(x) &= (x - 3)(x - i)[x - (-i)] \\ &= (x - 3)(x - i)(x + i) \end{aligned}$$

NOW TRY EXERCISE **5**   ∎

IN-CLASS MATERIALS

It is possible to use the techniques of the previous sections to solve polynomials with nonreal coefficients. If you want to demonstrate this fact, consider the polynomial $f(z) = z^3 + (2 - 3i)z^2 + (-3 - 6i) + 9i$ and use synthetic division to obtain $f(z) = (z - 1)(z + 3)(z - 3i)$.

EXAMPLE 2 | Factoring a Polynomial Completely

Let $P(x) = x^3 - 2x + 4$.

(a) Find all the zeros of P.

(b) Find the complete factorization of P.

SOLUTION

$$\begin{array}{r|rrrr} -2 & 1 & -0 & -2 & -4 \\ & & -2 & 4 & -4 \\ \hline & 1 & -2 & -2 & 0 \end{array}$$

(a) The possible rational zeros are the factors of 4, which are ± 1, ± 2, ± 4. Using synthetic division (see the margin), we find that -2 is a zero, and the polynomial factors as

$$P(x) = (x + 2)(x^2 - 2x + 2)$$

This factor is 0 when $x = -2$	Use the Quadratic Formula to find when this factor is 0

To find the zeros, we set each factor equal to 0. Of course, $x + 2 = 0$ means that $x = -2$. We use the quadratic formula to find when the other factor is 0.

$$x^2 - 2x + 2 = 0 \qquad \text{Set factor equal to 0}$$

$$x = \frac{2 \pm \sqrt{4 - 8}}{2} \qquad \text{Quadratic Formula}$$

$$x = \frac{2 \pm 2i}{2} \qquad \text{Take square root}$$

$$x = 1 \pm i \qquad \text{Simplify}$$

So the zeros of P are -2, $1 + i$, and $1 - i$.

(b) Since the zeros are -2, $1 + i$, and $1 - i$, by the Complete Factorization Theorem, P factors as

$$P(x) = [x - (-2)][x - (1 + i)][x - (1 - i)]$$

$$= (x + 2)(x - 1 - i)(x - 1 + i)$$

✎ NOW TRY EXERCISE **19**   ■

▼ Zeros and Their Multiplicities

In the Complete Factorization Theorem the numbers $c_1, c_2, \ldots, c_n$ are the zeros of P. These zeros need not all be different. If the factor $x - c$ appears k times in the complete factorization of $P(x)$, then we say that c is a zero of **multiplicity k** (see page 240). For example, the polynomial

$$P(x) = (x - 1)^3(x + 2)^2(x + 3)^5$$

has the following zeros:

$$1 \text{ (multiplicity 3)}, \qquad -2 \text{ (multiplicity 2)}, \qquad -3 \text{ (multiplicity 5)}$$

The polynomial P has the same number of zeros as its degree: It has degree 10 and has 10 zeros, provided that we count multiplicities. This is true for all polynomials, as we prove in the following theorem.

ZEROS THEOREM

Every polynomial of degree $n \geq 1$ has exactly n zeros, provided that a zero of multiplicity k is counted k times.

ALTERNATE EXAMPLE 2

Let $P(x) = x^4 - 3x^3 + 7x^2 + 21x - 26$.

(a) Find all the zeros of P.

(b) Find the complete factorization of P.

ANSWERS

(a) $1, -2, 2 + 3i, 2 - 3i$

(b) $P(x) = (x - 1)(x + 2)$
$(x - 2 - 3i)(x - 2 + 3i)$

IN-CLASS MATERIALS

Stress the power of the Complete Factorization Theorem and how it dovetails with the Linear and Quadratic Factors Theorem. Once we allow complex numbers, we can view *all* polynomial functions as functions of the form $f(x) = a(x - c_1)(x - c_2) \cdots (x - c_n)$; simple products of linear factors. If we don't want to allow complex numbers (the preference of many students), we still can write all polynomials almost as simply, as the product of linear and (irreducible) quadratic factors.

ALTERNATE EXAMPLE 3

Find the complete factorization of the polynomial
$P(x) = 3x^5 + 54x^3 + 243x$.

ANSWER

$P(x) = 3x((x - 3i)(x + 3i))^2$

CARL FRIEDRICH GAUSS
(1777–1855) is considered the greatest mathematician of modern times. His contemporaries called him the "Prince of Mathematics." He was born into a poor family; his father made a living as a mason. As a very small child, Gauss found a calculation error in his father's accounts, the first of many incidents that gave evidence of his mathematical precocity. (See also page 796.) At 19, Gauss demonstrated that the regular 17-sided polygon can be constructed with straight-edge and compass alone. This was remarkable because, since the time of Euclid, it had been thought that the only regular polygons constructible in this way were the triangle and pentagon. Because of this discovery Gauss decided to pursue a career in mathematics instead of languages, his other passion. In his doctoral dissertation, written at the age of 22, Gauss proved the Fundamental Theorem of Algebra: A polynomial of degree n with complex coefficients has n roots. His other accomplishments range over every branch of mathematics, as well as physics and astronomy.

PROOF Let P be a polynomial of degree n. By the Complete Factorization Theorem

$$P(x) = a(x - c_1)(x - c_2) \cdots (x - c_n)$$

Now suppose that c is a zero of P other than $c_1, c_2, \ldots, c_n$. Then

$$P(c) = a(c - c_1)(c - c_2) \cdots (c - c_n) = 0$$

Thus, by the Zero-Product Property, one of the factors $c - c_i$ must be 0, so $c = c_i$ for some i. It follows that P has exactly the n zeros $c_1, c_2, \ldots, c_n$. ∎

EXAMPLE 3 | Factoring a Polynomial with Complex Zeros

Find the complete factorization and all five zeros of the polynomial

$$P(x) = 3x^5 + 24x^3 + 48x$$

SOLUTION Since $3x$ is a common factor, we have

$$P(x) = 3x(x^4 + 8x^2 + 16)$$
$$= 3x(x^2 + 4)^2$$

This factor is 0 when $x = 0$	This factor is 0 when $x = 2i$ or $x = -2i$

To factor $x^2 + 4$, note that $2i$ and $-2i$ are zeros of this polynomial. Thus, $x^2 + 4 = (x - 2i)(x + 2i)$, so

$$P(x) = 3x[(x - 2i)(x + 2i)]^2$$
$$= 3x(x - 2i)^2(x + 2i)^2$$

0 is a zero of multiplicity 1	$2i$ is a zero of multiplicity 2	$-2i$ is a zero of multiplicity 2

The zeros of P are 0, $2i$, and $-2i$. Since the factors $x - 2i$ and $x + 2i$ each occur twice in the complete factorization of P, the zeros $2i$ and $-2i$ are of multiplicity 2 (or *double* zeros). Thus, we have found all five zeros.

NOW TRY EXERCISE 29 ∎

The following table gives further examples of polynomials with their complete factorizations and zeros.

Degree	Polynomial	Zero(s)	Number of zeros
1	$P(x) = x - 4$	4	1
2	$P(x) = x^2 - 10x + 25$ $= (x - 5)(x - 5)$	5 (multiplicity 2)	2
3	$P(x) = x^3 + x$ $= x(x - i)(x + i)$	0, i, $-i$	3
4	$P(x) = x^4 + 18x^2 + 81$ $= (x - 3i)^2(x + 3i)^2$	$3i$ (multiplicity 2), $-3i$ (multiplicity 2)	4
5	$P(x) = x^5 - 2x^4 + x^3$ $= x^3(x - 1)^2$	0 (multiplicity 3), 1 (multiplicity 2)	5

IN-CLASS MATERIALS

Point out that when graphing $y = f(x)$, the real zeros appear as x-intercepts, as expected. Remind students how the multiplicities of the real zeros can be seen. A multiplicity of 1 crosses the x-axis, an even multiplicity touches the x-axis, and an odd multiplicity greater than 1 crosses the x-axis and is flat there. (See Section 3.1.) Note that the complex zeros don't appear on the real plane.

EXAMPLE 4 | Finding Polynomials with Specified Zeros

(a) Find a polynomial $P(x)$ of degree 4, with zeros i, $-i$, 2, and -2, and with $P(3) = 25$.

(b) Find a polynomial $Q(x)$ of degree 4, with zeros -2 and 0, where -2 is a zero of multiplicity 3.

SOLUTION

(a) The required polynomial has the form

$$P(x) = a(x - i)(x - (-i))(x - 2)(x - (-2))$$

$$= a(x^2 + 1)(x^2 - 4) \qquad \text{Difference of squares}$$

$$= a(x^4 - 3x^2 - 4) \qquad \text{Multiply}$$

We know that $P(3) = a(3^4 - 3 \cdot 3^2 - 4) = 50a = 25$, so $a = \frac{1}{2}$. Thus,

$$P(x) = \tfrac{1}{2}x^4 - \tfrac{3}{2}x^2 - 2$$

(b) We require

$$Q(x) = a[x - (-2)]^3(x - 0)$$

$$= a(x + 2)^3 x$$

$$= a(x^3 + 6x^2 + 12x + 8)x \qquad \text{Special Product Formula 4 (Section 1.3)}$$

$$= a(x^4 + 6x^3 + 12x^2 + 8x)$$

Since we are given no information about Q other than its zeros and their multiplicity, we can choose any number for a. If we use $a = 1$, we get

$$Q(x) = x^4 + 6x^3 + 12x^2 + 8x$$

✎ NOW TRY EXERCISE **35**   ∎

EXAMPLE 5 | Finding All the Zeros of a Polynomial

Find all four zeros of $P(x) = 3x^4 - 2x^3 - x^2 - 12x - 4$.

SOLUTION Using the Rational Zeros Theorem from Section 3.4, we obtain the following list of possible rational zeros: ± 1, ± 2, ± 4, $\pm \frac{1}{3}$, $\pm \frac{2}{3}$, $\pm \frac{4}{3}$. Checking these using synthetic division, we find that 2 and $-\frac{1}{3}$ are zeros, and we get the following factorization:

$$P(x) = 3x^4 - 2x^3 - x^2 - 12x - 4$$

$$= (x - 2)(3x^3 + 4x^2 + 7x + 2) \qquad \text{Factor } x - 2$$

$$= (x - 2)\left(x + \tfrac{1}{3}\right)(3x^2 + 3x + 6) \qquad \text{Factor } x + \tfrac{1}{3}$$

$$= 3(x - 2)\left(x + \tfrac{1}{3}\right)(x^2 + x + 2) \qquad \text{Factor 3}$$

The zeros of the quadratic factor are

$$x = \frac{-1 \pm \sqrt{1 - 8}}{2} = -\frac{1}{2} \pm i\frac{\sqrt{7}}{2} \qquad \text{Quadratic Formula}$$

so the zeros of $P(x)$ are

$$2, \quad -\frac{1}{3}, \quad -\frac{1}{2} + i\frac{\sqrt{7}}{2}, \quad \text{and} \quad -\frac{1}{2} - i\frac{\sqrt{7}}{2}$$

✎ NOW TRY EXERCISE **45**   ∎

FIGURE 1
$P(x) = 3x^4 - 2x^3 - x^2 - 12x - 4$

Figure 1 shows the graph of the polynomial P in Example 5. The x-intercepts correspond to the real zeros of P. The imaginary zeros cannot be determined from the graph.

ALTERNATE EXAMPLE 4
Find the polynomial of degree 4, with zeros i, $-i$, 2, and -2 and with $P(5) = 273$.

ANSWER
$P(x) = \frac{1}{2}x^4 - \frac{3}{2}x^2 - 2$

ALTERNATE EXAMPLE 5
Find all four zeros of $P(x) = 2x^4 - 7x^3 - 4x^2 - 50x - 25$.

ANSWER
$5, -\dfrac{1}{2}, \dfrac{-1 + i\sqrt{19}}{2}, \dfrac{-1 - i\sqrt{19}}{2}$

IN-CLASS MATERIALS
Exercise 74 discusses roots of unity—the zeros of polynomials of the form $f(x) = x^n - 1$ or, equivalently, the solutions of $x^n = 1$. It is easy to find the real solutions, 1 if n is odd and ± 1 if n is even. Exercise 74 prompts students to solve $x^n = 1$ for $n = 2$, 3, and 4. If your students have been exposed to trigonometric functions, then you can show them the general formula:

$$x^n = 1 \Leftrightarrow x = \cos\left(\frac{2\pi k}{n}\right)$$
$$+ i \sin\left(\frac{2\pi k}{n}\right)$$
for $k = 0, \ldots, n$.

Interestingly enough, if you plot the solutions in the complex plane, there is a wonderful amount of symmetry. Even if you don't want to discuss the general formula, you can show your students where the roots of unity live. The complex roots of unity can be thought of as points that are evenly distributed around the unit circle.

$n = 2$

$n = 3$

$n = 4$

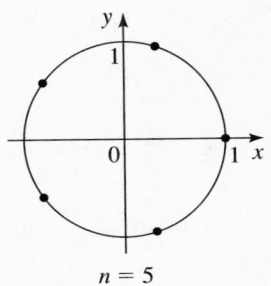

$n = 5$

GEROLAMO CARDANO
(1501–1576) is certainly one of the most colorful figures in the history of mathematics. He was the best-known physician in Europe in his day, yet throughout his life he was plagued by numerous maladies, including ruptures, hemorrhoids, and an irrational fear of encountering rabid dogs. He was a doting father, but his beloved sons broke his heart—his favorite was eventually beheaded for murdering his own wife. Cardano was also a compulsive gambler; indeed, this vice might have driven him to write the *Book on Games of Chance*, the first study of probability from a mathematical point of view.

In Cardano's major mathematical work, the *Ars Magna*, he detailed the solution of the general third- and fourth-degree polynomial equations. At the time of its publication, mathematicians were uncomfortable even with negative numbers, but Cardano's formulas paved the way for the acceptance not just of negative numbers, but also of imaginary numbers, because they occurred naturally in solving polynomial equations. For example, for the cubic equation

$$x^3 - 15x - 4 = 0$$

one of his formulas gives the solution

$$x = \sqrt[3]{2 + \sqrt{-121}} + \sqrt[3]{2 - \sqrt{-121}}$$

(See page 263, Exercise 108). This value for x actually turns out to be the *integer* 4, yet to find it, Cardano had to use the imaginary number $\sqrt{-121} = 11i$.

▼ Complex Zeros Come in Conjugate Pairs

As you might have noticed from the examples so far, the complex zeros of polynomials with real coefficients come in pairs. Whenever $a + bi$ is a zero, its complex conjugate $a - bi$ is also a zero.

> **CONJUGATE ZEROS THEOREM**
>
> If the polynomial P has real coefficients and if the complex number z is a zero of P, then its complex conjugate $\bar{z}$ is also a zero of P.

PROOF Let

$$P(x) = a_n x^n + a_{n-1}x^{n-1} + \cdots + a_1 x + a_0$$

where each coefficient is real. Suppose that $P(z) = 0$. We must prove that $P(\bar{z}) = 0$. We use the facts that the complex conjugate of a sum of two complex numbers is the sum of the conjugates and that the conjugate of a product is the product of the conjugates.

$$
\begin{aligned}
P(\bar{z}) &= a_n(\bar{z})^n + a_{n-1}(\bar{z})^{n-1} + \cdots + a_1\bar{z} + a_0 \\
&= \overline{a_n}\,\overline{z^n} + \overline{a_{n-1}}\,\overline{z^{n-1}} + \cdots + \overline{a_1}\,\bar{z} + \overline{a_0} \qquad \text{Because the coefficients are real} \\
&= \overline{a_n z^n} + \overline{a_{n-1}z^{n-1}} + \cdots + \overline{a_1 z} + \overline{a_0} \\
&= \overline{a_n z^n + a_{n-1}z^{n-1} + \cdots + a_1 z + a_0} \\
&= \overline{P(z)} = \overline{0} = 0
\end{aligned}
$$

This shows that $\bar{z}$ is also a zero of $P(x)$, which proves the theorem. ∎

EXAMPLE 6 | A Polynomial with a Specified Complex Zero

Find a polynomial $P(x)$ of degree 3 that has integer coefficients and zeros $\frac{1}{2}$ and $3 - i$.

SOLUTION Since $3 - i$ is a zero, then so is $3 + i$ by the Conjugate Zeros Theorem. This means that $P(x)$ must have the following form.

$$
\begin{aligned}
P(x) &= a\left(x - \tfrac{1}{2}\right)[x - (3 - i)][x - (3 + i)] \\
&= a\left(x - \tfrac{1}{2}\right)[(x - 3) + i][(x - 3) - i] \qquad \text{Regroup} \\
&= a\left(x - \tfrac{1}{2}\right)[(x - 3)^2 - i^2] \qquad \text{Difference of Squares Formula} \\
&= a\left(x - \tfrac{1}{2}\right)(x^2 - 6x + 10) \qquad \text{Expand} \\
&= a\left(x^3 - \tfrac{13}{2}x^2 + 13x - 5\right) \qquad \text{Expand}
\end{aligned}
$$

To make all coefficients integers, we set $a = 2$ and get

$$P(x) = 2x^3 - 13x^2 + 26x - 10$$

Any other polynomial that satisfies the given requirements must be an integer multiple of this one.

✎ NOW TRY EXERCISE **39** ∎

ALTERNATE EXAMPLE 6

Find a polynomial $P(x)$ of degree 3 that has integer coefficients and zeros $\frac{1}{3}$ and $5 - 2i$.

ANSWER

$P(x) = 3\left(x - \frac{1}{3}\right)(x - 5 - 2i) \times$
$(x - 5 + 2i) = 3x^3 - 31x^2$
$+ 97x - 29$

▼ Linear and Quadratic Factors

We have seen that a polynomial factors completely into linear factors if we use complex numbers. If we don't use complex numbers, then a polynomial with real coefficients can always be factored into linear and quadratic factors. We use this property in Section 10.7 when we study partial fractions. A quadratic polynomial with no real zeros is called **irreducible** over the real numbers. Such a polynomial cannot be factored without using complex numbers.

LINEAR AND QUADRATIC FACTORS THEOREM

Every polynomial with real coefficients can be factored into a product of linear and irreducible quadratic factors with real coefficients.

PROOF   We first observe that if $c = a + bi$ is a complex number, then

$$(x - c)(x - \bar{c}) = [x - (a + bi)][x - (a - bi)]$$
$$= [(x - a) - bi][(x - a) + bi]$$
$$= (x - a)^2 - (bi)^2$$
$$= x^2 - 2ax + (a^2 + b^2)$$

The last expression is a quadratic with *real* coefficients.

Now, if P is a polynomial with real coefficients, then by the Complete Factorization Theorem

$$P(x) = a(x - c_1)(x - c_2) \cdots (x - c_n)$$

Since the complex roots occur in conjugate pairs, we can multiply the factors corresponding to each such pair to get a quadratic factor with real coefficients. This results in P being factored into linear and irreducible quadratic factors.   ■

EXAMPLE 7 | Factoring a Polynomial into Linear and Quadratic Factors

Let $P(x) = x^4 + 2x^2 - 8$.

(a) Factor P into linear and irreducible quadratic factors with real coefficients.

(b) Factor P completely into linear factors with complex coefficients.

SOLUTION

(a)
$$P(x) = x^4 + 2x^2 - 8$$
$$= (x^2 - 2)(x^2 + 4)$$
$$= (x - \sqrt{2})(x + \sqrt{2})(x^2 + 4)$$

The factor $x^2 + 4$ is irreducible, since it has no real zeros.

(b) To get the complete factorization, we factor the remaining quadratic factor.
$$P(x) = (x - \sqrt{2})(x + \sqrt{2})(x^2 + 4)$$
$$= (x - \sqrt{2})(x + \sqrt{2})(x - 2i)(x + 2i)$$

✎ NOW TRY EXERCISE **65**   ■

EXAMPLES

1. A polynomial that is the product of two irreducible quadratic terms:

$$f(x) = x^4 + 2x^3 + 9x^2 + 2x + 8$$
$$= (x^2 + 1)(x^2 + 2x + 8)$$

This can be factored by noting that $x = i$ is a zero, and therefore $x = -i$ is a zero, and then dividing by $(x^2 + 1)$.

2. A polynomial that is the product of two linear terms and an irreducible quadratic term:

$$f(x) = x^4 + 5x^3 + 10x^2 + 16x - 32 = (x^2 + 2x + 8)(x - 1)(x + 4)$$

ALTERNATE EXAMPLE 7
Factor the polynomial $P(x)$ completely into linear factors with complex coefficients:
$P(x) = x^4 + 9x^2 - 112$

ANSWER
$P(x) = (x - \sqrt{7})(x + \sqrt{7}) \times (x + 4i)(x - 4i)$

DRILL QUESTION

Consider the polynomial $f(x) = x^5 - 2x^4 + 16x^3 + 8x^2 + 20x + 200$. It is a fact that -2 is a zero of this polynomial and that $(x - 1 - 3i)^2$ is a factor of this polynomial. Using this information, factor the polynomial completely.

Answer

$f(x) = (x - 1 - 3i)^2(x - 1 + 3i)^2(x + 2)$

3.6 EXERCISES

CONCEPTS

1. The polynomial $P(x) = 3(x - 5)^3(x - 3)(x + 2)$ has degree _____. It has zeros 5, 3, and _____. The zero 5 has multiplicity _____, and the zero 3 has multiplicity

_____.

2. (a) If a is a zero of the polynomial P, then _____ must be a factor of $P(x)$.
   (b) If a is a zero of multiplicity m of the polynomial P, then

   _____ must be a factor of $P(x)$ when we factor P completely.

3. A polynomial of degree $n \geq 1$ has exactly _____ zeros if a zero of multiplicity m is counted m times.

4. If the polynomial function P has real coefficients and if $a + bi$ is a zero of P, then _____ is also a zero of P.

SKILLS

5–16 ■ A polynomial P is given. **(a)** Find all zeros of P, real and complex. **(b)** Factor P completely.

5. $P(x) = x^4 + 4x^2$ **6.** $P(x) = x^5 + 9x^3$

7. $P(x) = x^3 - 2x^2 + 2x$ **8.** $P(x) = x^3 + x^2 + x$

9. $P(x) = x^4 + 2x^2 + 1$ **10.** $P(x) = x^4 - x^2 - 2$

11. $P(x) = x^4 - 16$ **12.** $P(x) = x^4 + 6x^2 + 9$

13. $P(x) = x^3 + 8$ **14.** $P(x) = x^3 - 8$

15. $P(x) = x^6 - 1$ **16.** $P(x) = x^6 - 7x^3 - 8$

17–34 ■ Factor the polynomial completely, and find all its zeros. State the multiplicity of each zero.

17. $P(x) = x^2 + 25$ **18.** $P(x) = 4x^2 + 9$

19. $Q(x) = x^2 + 2x + 2$ **20.** $Q(x) = x^2 - 8x + 17$

21. $P(x) = x^3 + 4x$ **22.** $P(x) = x^3 - x^2 + x$

23. $Q(x) = x^4 - 1$ **24.** $Q(x) = x^4 - 625$

25. $P(x) = 16x^4 - 81$ **26.** $P(x) = x^3 - 64$

27. $P(x) = x^3 + x^2 + 9x + 9$ **28.** $P(x) = x^6 - 729$

29. $Q(x) = x^4 + 2x^2 + 1$ **30.** $Q(x) = x^4 + 10x^2 + 25$

31. $P(x) = x^4 + 3x^2 - 4$ **32.** $P(x) = x^5 + 7x^3$

33. $P(x) = x^5 + 6x^3 + 9x$ **34.** $P(x) = x^6 + 16x^3 + 64$

35–44 ■ Find a polynomial with integer coefficients that satisfies the given conditions.

35. P has degree 2 and zeros $1 + i$ and $1 - i$.

36. P has degree 2 and zeros $1 + i\sqrt{2}$ and $1 - i\sqrt{2}$.

37. Q has degree 3 and zeros 3, $2i$, and $-2i$.

38. Q has degree 3 and zeros 0 and i.

39. P has degree 3 and zeros 2 and i.

40. Q has degree 3 and zeros -3 and $1 + i$.

41. R has degree 4 and zeros $1 - 2i$ and 1, with 1 a zero of multiplicity 2.

42. S has degree 4 and zeros $2i$ and $3i$.

43. T has degree 4, zeros i and $1 + i$, and constant term 12.

44. U has degree 5, zeros $\frac{1}{2}$, -1, and $-i$, and leading coefficient 4; the zero -1 has multiplicity 2.

45–62 ■ Find all zeros of the polynomial.

45. $P(x) = x^3 + 2x^2 + 4x + 8$

46. $P(x) = x^3 - 7x^2 + 17x - 15$

47. $P(x) = x^3 - 2x^2 + 2x - 1$

48. $P(x) = x^3 + 7x^2 + 18x + 18$

49. $P(x) = x^3 - 3x^2 + 3x - 2$

50. $P(x) = x^3 - x - 6$

51. $P(x) = 2x^3 + 7x^2 + 12x + 9$

52. $P(x) = 2x^3 - 8x^2 + 9x - 9$

53. $P(x) = x^4 + x^3 + 7x^2 + 9x - 18$

54. $P(x) = x^4 - 2x^3 - 2x^2 - 2x - 3$

55. $P(x) = x^5 - x^4 + 7x^3 - 7x^2 + 12x - 12$

56. $P(x) = x^5 + x^3 + 8x^2 + 8$ [*Hint:* Factor by grouping.]

57. $P(x) = x^4 - 6x^3 + 13x^2 - 24x + 36$

58. $P(x) = x^4 - x^2 + 2x + 2$

59. $P(x) = 4x^4 + 4x^3 + 5x^2 + 4x + 1$

60. $P(x) = 4x^4 + 2x^3 - 2x^2 - 3x - 1$

61. $P(x) = x^5 - 3x^4 + 12x^3 - 28x^2 + 27x - 9$

62. $P(x) = x^5 - 2x^4 + 2x^3 - 4x^2 + x - 2$

63–68 ■ A polynomial P is given. **(a)** Factor P into linear and irreducible quadratic factors with real coefficients. **(b)** Factor P completely into linear factors with complex coefficients.

63. $P(x) = x^3 - 5x^2 + 4x - 20$

64. $P(x) = x^3 - 2x - 4$

65. $P(x) = x^4 + 8x^2 - 9$ **66.** $P(x) = x^4 + 8x^2 + 16$

67. $P(x) = x^6 - 64$ **68.** $P(x) = x^5 - 16x$

69. By the Zeros Theorem, every nth-degree polynomial equation has exactly n solutions (including possibly some that are repeated). Some of these may be real, and some may be imaginary. Use a graphing device to determine how many real and imaginary solutions each equation has.
   (a) $x^4 - 2x^3 - 11x^2 + 12x = 0$
   (b) $x^4 - 2x^3 - 11x^2 + 12x - 5 = 0$
   (c) $x^4 - 2x^3 - 11x^2 + 12x + 40 = 0$

70–72 ■ So far, we have worked only with polynomials that have real coefficients. These exercises involve polynomials with real and imaginary coefficients.

70. Find all solutions of the equation.
   (a) $2x + 4i = 1$ **(b)** $x^2 - ix = 0$
   (c) $x^2 + 2ix - 1 = 0$ **(d)** $ix^2 - 2x + i = 0$

71. (a) Show that $2i$ and $1 - i$ are both solutions of the equation

$$x^2 - (1 + i)x + (2 + 2i) = 0$$

but that their complex conjugates $-2i$ and $1 + i$ are not.
   (b) Explain why the result of part (a) does not violate the Conjugate Zeros Theorem.

72. (a) Find the polynomial with *real* coefficients of the smallest possible degree for which i and $1 + i$ are zeros and in which the coefficient of the highest power is 1.
   (b) Find the polynomial with *complex* coefficients of the smallest possible degree for which i and $1 + i$ are zeros and in which the coefficient of the highest power is 1.

DISCOVERY ▪ DISCUSSION ▪ WRITING

73. Polynomials of Odd Degree   The Conjugate Zeros Theorem says that the complex zeros of a polynomial with real coefficients occur in complex conjugate pairs. Explain how this fact proves that a polynomial with real coefficients and odd degree has at least one real zero.

74. Roots of Unity   There are two square roots of 1, namely, 1 and -1. These are the solutions of $x^2 = 1$. The fourth roots of 1 are the solutions of the equation $x^4 = 1$ or $x^4 - 1 = 0$. How many fourth roots of 1 are there? Find them. The cube roots of 1 are the solutions of the equation $x^3 = 1$ or $x^3 - 1 = 0$. How many cube roots of 1 are there? Find them. How would you find the sixth roots of 1? How many are there? Make a conjecture about the number of nth roots of 1.

3.7 RATIONAL FUNCTIONS

Rational Functions and Asymptotes ▶ Transformations of $y = 1/x$ ▶
Asymptotes of Rational Functions ▶ Graphing Rational Functions ▶ Slant
Asymptotes and End Behavior ▶ Applications

A rational function is a function of the form

$$r(x) = \frac{P(x)}{Q(x)}$$

where P and Q are polynomials. We assume that $P(x)$ and $Q(x)$ have no factor in common. Even though rational functions are constructed from polynomials, their graphs look quite different from the graphs of polynomial functions.

▼ Rational Functions and Asymptotes

Domains of rational expressions are discussed in Section 1.4.

The *domain* of a rational function consists of all real numbers x except those for which the denominator is zero. When graphing a rational function, we must pay special attention to the behavior of the graph near those x-values. We begin by graphing a very simple rational function.

EXAMPLE 1 | A Simple Rational Function

Graph the rational function $f(x) = \frac{1}{x}$, and state the domain and range.

SOLUTION   The function f is not defined for $x = 0$. The following tables show that when x is close to zero, the value of $|f(x)|$ is large, and the closer x gets to zero, the larger $|f(x)|$ gets.

For positive real numbers,

$$\frac{1}{\text{BIG NUMBER}} = \text{small number}$$

$$\frac{1}{\text{small number}} = \text{BIG NUMBER}$$

x	$f(x)$
-0.1	-10
-0.01	-100
-0.00001	$-100,000$

Approaching 0^- Approaching $-\infty$

x	$f(x)$
0.1	10
0.01	100
0.00001	100,000

Approaching 0^+ Approaching ∞

SUGGESTED TIME AND EMPHASIS

2 classes, essential material

ALTERNATE EXAMPLE 1

For the graph of the rational function $r(x) = \frac{3}{x}$, evaluate the values of $r(x)$ as x approaches $-\infty, 0^-, 0^+, +\infty$.

ANSWER

$0, -\infty, \infty, 0$

TEXT QUESTION

What is a slant asymptote?

Answer

Answers will vary.

We describe this behavior in words and in symbols as follows. The first table shows that as x approaches 0 from the left, the values of $y = f(x)$ decrease without bound. In symbols,

$$f(x) \to -\infty \quad \text{as} \quad x \to 0^- \qquad \text{``}y \text{ approaches negative infinity as } x \text{ approaches 0 from the left''}$$

The second table shows that as x approaches 0 from the right, the values of $f(x)$ increase without bound. In symbols,

$$f(x) \to \infty \quad \text{as} \quad x \to 0^+ \qquad \text{``}y \text{ approaches infinity as } x \text{ approaches 0 from the right''}$$

The next two tables show how $f(x)$ changes as $|x|$ becomes large.

x	$f(x)$
-10	-0.1
-100	-0.01
$-100{,}000$	-0.00001

x	$f(x)$
10	0.1
100	0.01
$100{,}000$	0.00001

Approaching $-\infty$ Approaching 0   Approaching ∞ Approaching 0

These tables show that as $|x|$ becomes large, the value of $f(x)$ gets closer and closer to zero. We describe this situation in symbols by writing

$$f(x) \to 0 \quad \text{as} \quad x \to -\infty \qquad \text{and} \qquad f(x) \to 0 \quad \text{as} \quad x \to \infty$$

Using the information in these tables and plotting a few additional points, we obtain the graph shown in Figure 1.

x	$f(x) = \frac{1}{x}$
-2	$-\frac{1}{2}$
-1	-1
$-\frac{1}{2}$	-2
$\frac{1}{2}$	2
1	1
2	$\frac{1}{2}$

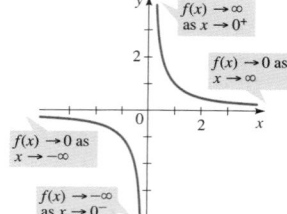

FIGURE 1
$f(x) = \frac{1}{x}$

The function f is defined for all values of x other than 0, so the domain is $\{x \mid x \neq 0\}$. From the graph we see that the range is $\{y \mid y \neq 0\}$.

▸. NOW TRY EXERCISE **7**

In Example 1 we used the following arrow notation.

Symbol	Meaning
$x \to a^-$	x approaches a from the left
$x \to a^+$	x approaches a from the right
$x \to -\infty$	x goes to negative infinity; that is, x decreases without bound
$x \to \infty$	x goes to infinity; that is, x increases without bound

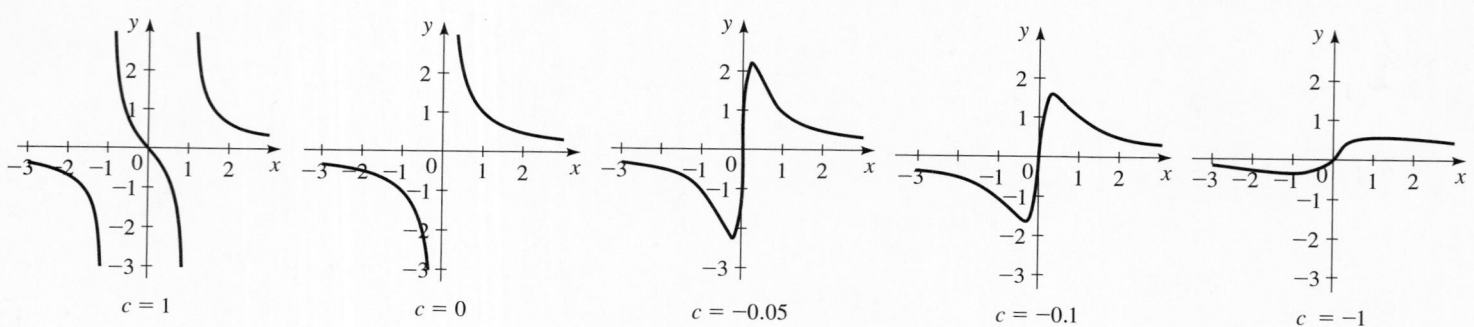

The line $x = 0$ is called a *vertical asymptote* of the graph in Figure 1, and the line $y = 0$ is a *horizontal asymptote*. Informally speaking, an asymptote of a function is a line to which the graph of the function gets closer and closer as one travels along that line.

DEFINITION OF VERTICAL AND HORIZONTAL ASYMPTOTES

1. The line $x = a$ is a **vertical asymptote** of the function $y = f(x)$ if y approaches $\pm\infty$ as x approaches a from the right or left.

$y \to \infty$ as $x \to a^+$ $y \to \infty$ as $x \to a^-$ $y \to -\infty$ as $x \to a^+$ $y \to -\infty$ as $x \to a^-$

2. The line $y = b$ is a **horizontal asymptote** of the function $y = f(x)$ if y approaches b as x approaches $\pm\infty$.

$y \to b$ as $x \to \infty$ $y \to b$ as $x \to -\infty$

A rational function has vertical asymptotes where the function is undefined, that is, where the denominator is zero.

▼ Transformations of $y = 1/x$

A rational function of the form

$$r(x) = \frac{ax + b}{cx + d}$$

can be graphed by shifting, stretching, and/or reflecting the graph of $f(x) = \frac{1}{x}$ shown in Figure 1, using the transformations studied in Section 2.5. (Such functions are called *linear fractional transformations*.)

EXAMPLE 2 | Using Transformations to Graph Rational Functions

Graph each rational function, and state the domain and range.

(a) $r(x) = \dfrac{2}{x - 3}$ **(b)** $s(x) = \dfrac{3x + 5}{x + 2}$

SOLUTION

(a) Let $f(x) = \frac{1}{x}$. Then we can express r in terms of f as follows:

$$r(x) = \frac{2}{x - 3}$$

$$= 2\left(\frac{1}{x - 3}\right) \qquad \text{Factor 2}$$

$$= 2(f(x - 3)) \qquad \text{Since } f(x) = \frac{1}{x}$$

From this form we see that the graph of r is obtained from the graph of f by shifting 3 units to the right and stretching vertically by a factor of 2. Thus, r has vertical asymptote $x = 3$ and horizontal asymptote $y = 0$. The graph of r is shown in Figure 2.

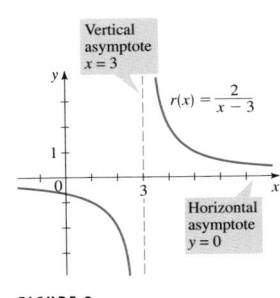

Vertical asymptote $x = 3$

$r(x) = \dfrac{2}{x - 3}$

Horizontal asymptote $y = 0$

FIGURE 2

IN-CLASS MATERIALS

A bit of care should be exercised when checking vertical asymptotes. For example, have students examine $f(x) = \dfrac{x^2 + 3x + 2}{x^2 - 1}$. If they are alert, they will notice an apparent x-intercept at $x = -1$, making it impossible to follow the text's dictum: "When choosing test values, we must make sure that there is no x-intercept between the test point and the vertical asymptote." The reason there is not a vertical asymptote at $x = -1$ is that there is a hole there, as seen when f is factored: $f(x) = \dfrac{(x + 1)(x + 2)}{(x + 1)(x - 1)}$. See Exercise 91 in the text.

The function r is defined for all x other than 3, so the domain is $\{x \mid x \neq 3\}$. From the graph we see that the range is $\{y \mid y \neq 0\}$.

(b) Using long division (see the margin), we get $s(x) = 3 - \frac{1}{x+2}$. Thus, we can express s in terms of f as follows:

$$\begin{array}{r} 3 \\ x+2 \overline{)3x+5} \\ \underline{3x+6} \\ -1 \end{array}$$

$$s(x) = 3 - \frac{1}{x+2}$$

$$= -\frac{1}{x+2} + 3 \qquad \text{Rearrange terms}$$

$$= -f(x+2) + 3 \qquad \text{Since } f(x) = \frac{1}{x}$$

From this form we see that the graph of s is obtained from the graph of f by shifting 2 units to the left, reflecting in the x-axis, and shifting upward 3 units. Thus, s has vertical asymptote $x = -2$ and horizontal asymptote $y = 3$. The graph of s is shown in Figure 3.

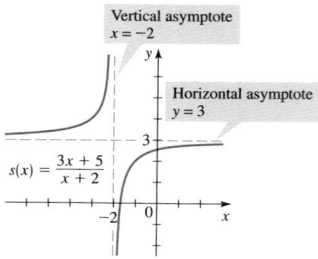

FIGURE 3

The function s is defined for all x other than -2, so the domain is $\{x \mid x \neq -2\}$. From the graph we see that the range is $\{y \mid y \neq 3\}$.

✎. NOW TRY EXERCISES **35** AND **37**   ■

▼ Asymptotes of Rational Functions

The methods of Example 2 work only for simple rational functions. To graph more complicated ones, we need to take a closer look at the behavior of a rational function near its vertical and horizontal asymptotes.

EXAMPLE 3 | Asymptotes of a Rational Function

Graph $r(x) = \dfrac{2x^2 - 4x + 5}{x^2 - 2x + 1}$, and state the domain and range.

SOLUTION

Vertical asymptote: We first factor the denominator

$$r(x) = \frac{2x^2 - 4x + 5}{(x-1)^2}$$

The line $x = 1$ is a vertical asymptote because the denominator of r is zero when $x = 1$.

IN-CLASS MATERIALS

A good example to do with students is $f(x) = \dfrac{1}{x^2 + 1}$. A curve of this type is called a *Witch of Agnesi*.

Its history may amuse your students. Italian mathematician Maria Agnesi (1718–1799) was a scholar whose first paper was published when she was nine years old. She called a particular curve *versiera* or "turning curve." John Colson from Cambridge confused the word with *avversiera* or "wife of the devil," and translated it "witch."

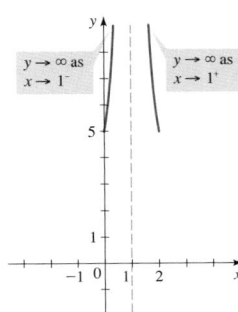

$y \to \infty$ as $x \to 1^{-}$

$y \to \infty$ as $x \to 1^{+}$

FIGURE 4

To see what the graph of r looks like near the vertical asymptote, we make tables of values for x-values to the left and to the right of 1. From the tables shown below we see that

$$y \to \infty \quad \text{as} \quad x \to 1^{-} \qquad \text{and} \qquad y \to \infty \quad \text{as} \quad x \to 1^{+}$$

$x \to 1^{-}$

x	y
0	5
0.5	14
0.9	302
0.99	30,002

$x \to 1^{+}$

x	y
2	5
1.5	14
1.1	302
1.01	30,002

Approaching 1^{-} Approaching ∞

Approaching 1^{+} Approaching ∞

Thus, near the vertical asymptote $x = 1$, the graph of r has the shape shown in Figure 4.

Horizontal asymptote: The horizontal asymptote is the value that y approaches as $x \to \pm\infty$. To help us find this value, we divide both numerator and denominator by x^2, the highest power of x that appears in the expression:

$$y = \frac{2x^2 - 4x + 5}{x^2 - 2x + 1} \cdot \frac{\dfrac{1}{x^2}}{\dfrac{1}{x^2}} = \frac{2 - \dfrac{4}{x} + \dfrac{5}{x^2}}{1 - \dfrac{2}{x} + \dfrac{1}{x^2}}$$

The fractional expressions $\frac{4}{x}$, $\frac{5}{x^2}$, $\frac{2}{x}$, and $\frac{1}{x^2}$ all approach 0 as $x \to \pm\infty$ (see Exercise 83, page 12). So as $x \to \pm\infty$, we have

These terms approach 0

$$y = \frac{2 - \dfrac{4}{x} + \dfrac{5}{x^2}}{1 - \dfrac{2}{x} + \dfrac{1}{x^2}} \longrightarrow \frac{2 - 0 + 0}{1 - 0 + 0} = 2$$

These terms approach 0

Thus, the horizontal asymptote is the line $y = 2$.

Since the graph must approach the horizontal asymptote, we can complete it as in Figure 5.

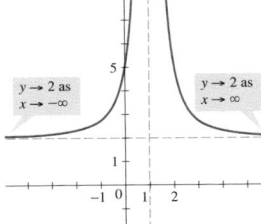

$y \to 2$ as $x \to -\infty$

$y \to 2$ as $x \to \infty$

FIGURE 5

$r(x) = \dfrac{2x^2 - 4x + 5}{x^2 - 2x + 1}$

Domain and range: The function r is defined for all values of x other than 1, so the domain is $\{x \mid x \neq 1\}$. From the graph we see that the range is $\{y \mid y > 2\}$.

✎ **NOW TRY EXERCISE 45** ■

From Example 3 we see that the horizontal asymptote is determined by the leading coefficients of the numerator and denominator, since after dividing through by x^2 (the highest power of x), all other terms approach zero. In general, if $r(x) = P(x)/Q(x)$ and the degrees of P and Q are the same (both n, say), then dividing both numerator and denominator by x^n shows that the horizontal asymptote is

$$y = \frac{\text{leading coefficient of } P}{\text{leading coefficient of } Q}$$

The following box summarizes the procedure for finding asymptotes.

> **FINDING ASYMPTOTES OF RATIONAL FUNCTIONS**
>
> Let r be the rational function
>
> $$r(x) = \frac{a_n x^n + a_{n-1}x^{n-1} + \cdots + a_1 x + a_0}{b_m x^m + b_{m-1}x^{m-1} + \cdots + b_1 x + b_0}$$
>
> **1.** The vertical asymptotes of r are the lines $x = a$, where a is a zero of the denominator.
>
> **2.** (a) If $n < m$, then r has horizontal asymptote $y = 0$.
>
>   (b) If $n = m$, then r has horizontal asymptote $y = \dfrac{a_n}{b_m}$.
>
>   (c) If $n > m$, then r has no horizontal asymptote.

EXAMPLE 4 | Asymptotes of a Rational Function

Find the vertical and horizontal asymptotes of $r(x) = \dfrac{3x^2 - 2x - 1}{2x^2 + 3x - 2}$.

SOLUTION

Vertical asymptotes: We first factor

$$r(x) = \frac{3x^2 - 2x - 1}{(2x - 1)(x + 2)}$$

This factor is 0 when $x = \frac{1}{2}$ This factor is 0 when $x = -2$

The vertical asymptotes are the lines $x = \frac{1}{2}$ and $x = -2$.

Horizontal asymptote: The degrees of the numerator and denominator are the same, and

$$\frac{\text{leading coefficient of numerator}}{\text{leading coefficient of denominator}} = \frac{3}{2}$$

Thus, the horizontal asymptote is the line $y = \frac{3}{2}$.

To confirm our results, we graph r using a graphing calculator (see Figure 6).

FIGURE 6
$$r(x) = \frac{3x^2 - 2x - 1}{2x^2 + 3x - 2}$$
Graph is drawn using dot mode to avoid extraneous lines.

✎. NOW TRY EXERCISES **23** AND **25**   ∎

▼ Graphing Rational Functions

We have seen that asymptotes are important when graphing rational functions. In general, we use the following guidelines to graph rational functions.

ALTERNATE EXAMPLE 4

Find the vertical and horizontal asymptotes of

$$r(x) = \frac{x^2 - 4x + 4}{9x^2 - 9x + 2}.$$

ANSWER

The vertical asymptotes are at $x = \frac{1}{3}$ and $x = \frac{2}{3}$. There is a horizontal asymptote at $y = \frac{1}{9}$. If students want to see these asymptotes, they should choose their graphing window carefully.

EXAMPLE

A rational function with many asymptotes and intercepts that are hard to find by inspecting a single viewing rectangle:

$$f(x) = \frac{3x^3 + 6x^2 - 3x - 6}{x^3 - 5x^2 + 6x}$$

$$= \frac{3(x + 1)(x - 1)(x + 2)}{x(x - 2)(x - 3)}$$

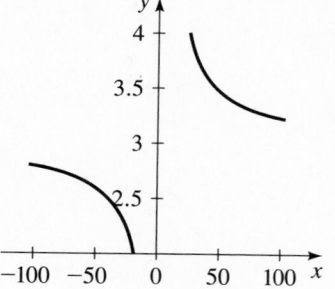

Intercepts: $(1, 0)$, $(-1, 0)$, $(-2, 0)$
Asymptotes: $x = 0$, $x = 2$, $x = 3$, $y = 3$

SKETCHING GRAPHS OF RATIONAL FUNCTIONS

1. **Factor.** Factor the numerator and denominator.

2. **Intercepts.** Find the x-intercepts by determining the zeros of the numerator and the y-intercept from the value of the function at $x = 0$.

3. **Vertical Asymptotes.** Find the vertical asymptotes by determining the zeros of the denominator, and then see whether $y \to \infty$ or $y \to -\infty$ on each side of each vertical asymptote by using test values.

4. **Horizontal Asymptote.** Find the horizontal asymptote (if any), using the procedure described in the box on page 282.

5. **Sketch the Graph.** Graph the information provided by the first four steps. Then plot as many additional points as needed to fill in the rest of the graph of the function.

A fraction is 0 if and only if its numerator is 0.

EXAMPLE 5 | Graphing a Rational Function

Graph $r(x) = \dfrac{2x^2 + 7x - 4}{x^2 + x - 2}$, and state the domain and range.

SOLUTION We factor the numerator and denominator, find the intercepts and asymptotes, and sketch the graph.

Factor: $\quad y = \dfrac{(2x - 1)(x + 4)}{(x - 1)(x + 2)}$

x-Intercepts: The x-intercepts are the zeros of the numerator, $x = \frac{1}{2}$ and $x = -4$.

y-Intercept: To find the y-intercept, we substitute $x = 0$ into the original form of the function.

$$r(0) = \frac{2(0)^2 + 7(0) - 4}{(0)2 + (0) - 2} = \frac{-4}{-2} = 2$$

The y-intercept is 2.

Vertical asymptotes: The vertical asymptotes occur where the denominator is 0, that is, where the function is undefined. From the factored form we see that the vertical asymptotes are the lines $x = 1$ and $x = -2$.

When choosing test values, we must make sure that there is no x-intercept between the test point and the vertical asymptote.

Behavior near vertical asymptotes: We need to know whether $y \to \infty$ or $y \to -\infty$ on each side of each vertical asymptote. To determine the sign of y for x-values near the vertical asymptotes, we use test values. For instance, as $x \to 1^-$, we use a test value close to and to the left of 1 ($x = 0.9$, say) to check whether y is positive or negative to the left of $x = 1$.

$$y = \frac{(2(0.9) - 1)((0.9) + 4)}{((0.9) - 1)((0.9) + 2)} \quad \text{whose sign is} \quad \frac{(+)(+)}{(-)(+)} \quad \text{(negative)}$$

So $y \to -\infty$ as $x \to 1^-$. On the other hand, as $x \to 1^+$, we use a test value close to and to the right of 1 ($x = 1.1$, say), to get

$$y = \frac{(2(1.1) - 1)((1.1) + 4)}{((1.1) - 1)((1.1) + 2)} \quad \text{whose sign is} \quad \frac{(+)(+)}{(+)(+)} \quad \text{(positive)}$$

So $y \to \infty$ as $x \to 1^+$. The other entries in the following table are calculated similarly.

As $x \to$	-2^-	-2^+	1^-	1^+
the sign of $y = \dfrac{(2x - 1)(x + 4)}{(x - 1)(x + 2)}$ is	$\dfrac{(-)(+)}{(-)(-)}$	$\dfrac{(-)(+)}{(-)(+)}$	$\dfrac{(+)(+)}{(-)(+)}$	$\dfrac{(+)(+)}{(+)(+)}$
so $y \to$	$-\infty$	∞	$-\infty$	∞

ALTERNATE EXAMPLE 5

Graph the rational function

$$r(x) = \frac{4x^2 - 16x + 16}{x^3 - 6x^2 - 9x + 54}.$$

ANSWER

We factor to obtain

$$r(x) = \frac{4(x - 2)^2}{(x + 3)(x - 3)(x - 6)}.$$

The x-intercept is at $x = 2$. The y-intercept is at $y = \frac{8}{27}$. The vertical asymptotes are at $x = -3$, $x = 3$, and $x = 6$. The horizontal asymptote is at $y = 0$. We plot a few additional points to obtain the graph:

EXAMPLE

A rational function with no asymptote:

$$f(x) = \frac{x^4 + 3x^2 + 2}{x^2 - 4x + 5} = \frac{(x^2 + 1)(x^2 + 2)}{x^2 - 4x + 5}$$

Note that the end behavior of this function is similar to that of $y = x^2 + 4x + 14$.

Horizontal asymptote: The degrees of the numerator and denominator are the same, and

$$\frac{\text{leading coefficient of numerator}}{\text{leading coefficient of denominator}} = \frac{2}{1} = 2$$

Thus, the horizontal asymptote is the line $y = 2$.

Graph: We use the information we have found, together with some additional values, to sketch the graph in Figure 7.

x	y
-6	0.93
-3	-1.75
-1	4.50
1.5	6.29
2	4.50
3	3.50

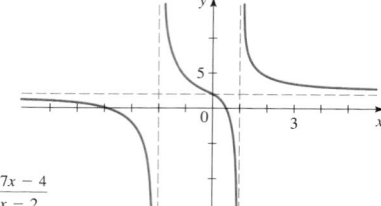

FIGURE 7
$$r(x) = \frac{2x^2 + 7x - 4}{x^2 + x - 2}$$

Domain and range: The domain is $\{x \mid x \neq 1, x \neq -2\}$. From the graph we see that the range is all real numbers.

✎. NOW TRY EXERCISE **53** ∎

EXAMPLE 6 | Graphing a Rational Function

Graph $r(x) = \dfrac{5x + 21}{x^2 + 10x + 25}$, and state the domain and range.

SOLUTION

Factor: $\quad y = \dfrac{5x + 21}{(x + 5)^2}$

x-Intercept: $\quad -\dfrac{21}{5}$, from $5x + 21 = 0$

y-Intercept: $\quad \dfrac{21}{25}$, because $r(0) = \dfrac{5 \cdot 0 + 21}{0^2 + 10 \cdot 0 + 25}$

$$= \dfrac{21}{25}$$

Vertical asymptote: $\quad x = -5$, from the zeros of the denominator

Behavior near vertical asymptote:

As $x \to$	-5^-	-5^+
the sign of $y = \dfrac{5x + 21}{(x + 5)^2}$ is	$\dfrac{(-)}{(-)(-)}$	$\dfrac{(-)}{(+)(+)}$
so $y \to$	$-\infty$	$-\infty$

Horizontal asymptote: $\quad y = 0$, because the degree of the numerator is less than the degree of the denominator

---

ALTERNATE EXAMPLE 6

Graph the rational function

$$r(x) = \frac{3x + 2}{x^2 - 4x + 4}.$$

ANSWER

Factor: $r(x) = \dfrac{3x + 6}{(x - 2)^2}$

x-intercept: -2

y-intercept: $\dfrac{3}{2}$

Vertical asymptote: $x = 2$

Behavior near vertical asymptote:

$y \to +\infty$ as $x \to 2^-$,

$y \to +\infty$ as $x \to 2^+$

Horizontal asymptote: $y = 0$

Graph: We use the information we have found, together with some additional values, to sketch the graph in Figure 8.

x	y
-15	-0.5
-10	-1.2
-3	1.5
-1	1.0
3	0.6
5	0.5
10	0.3

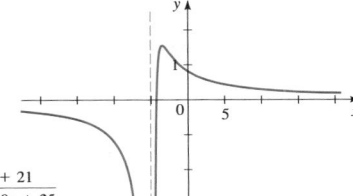

FIGURE 8

$$r(x) = \frac{5x + 21}{x^2 + 10x + 25}$$

Domain and range: The domain is $\{x \mid x \neq -5\}$. From the graph we see that the range is approximately the interval $(-\infty, 1.5]$.

◥. **NOW TRY EXERCISE 55**

⊘ From the graph in Figure 8 we see that, contrary to common misconception, a graph may cross a horizontal asymptote. The graph in Figure 8 crosses the x-axis (the horizontal asymptote) from below, reaches a maximum value near $x = -3$, and then approaches the x-axis from above as $x \to \infty$.

EXAMPLE 7 | Graphing a Rational Function

Graph the rational function $r(x) = \dfrac{x^2 - 3x - 4}{2x^2 + 4x}$.

SOLUTION

Factor: $y = \dfrac{(x + 1)(x - 4)}{2x(x + 2)}$

x-Intercepts: -1 and 4, from $x + 1 = 0$ and $x - 4 = 0$

y-Intercept: None, because $r(0)$ is undefined

Vertical asymptotes: $x = 0$ and $x = -2$, from the zeros of the denominator

Behavior near vertical asymptotes:

As $x \to$	-2^-	-2^+	0^-	0^+
the sign of $y = \dfrac{(x+1)(x-4)}{2x(x+2)}$ is	$\dfrac{(-)(-)}{(-)(-)}$	$\dfrac{(-)(-)}{(-)(+)}$	$\dfrac{(+)(-)}{(-)(+)}$	$\dfrac{(+)(-)}{(+)(+)}$
so $y \to$	∞	$-\infty$	∞	$-\infty$

Horizontal asymptote: $y = \frac{1}{2}$, because the degree of the numerator and the degree of the denominator are the same and

$$\frac{\text{leading coefficient of numerator}}{\text{leading coefficient of denominator}} = \frac{1}{2}$$

Graph: We use the information we have found, together with some additional values, to sketch the graph in Figure 9.

x	y
-3	2.33
-2.5	3.90
-0.5	1.50
1	-1.00
3	-0.13
5	0.09

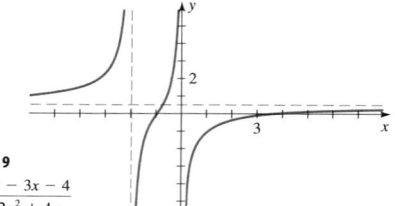

FIGURE 9

$$r(x) = \frac{x^2 - 3x - 4}{2x^2 + 4x}$$

Domain and range: The domain is $\{x \mid x \neq 0, x \neq -2\}$. From the graph we see that the range is all real numbers.

✎. NOW TRY EXERCISE **57**   ∎

▼ Slant Asymptotes and End Behavior

If $r(x) = P(x)/Q(x)$ is a rational function in which the degree of the numerator is one more than the degree of the denominator, we can use the Division Algorithm to express the function in the form

$$r(x) = ax + b + \frac{R(x)}{Q(x)}$$

where the degree of R is less than the degree of Q and $a \neq 0$. This means that as $x \to \pm\infty$, $R(x)/Q(x) \to 0$, so for large values of $|x|$ the graph of $y = r(x)$ approaches the graph of the line $y = ax + b$. In this situation we say that $y = ax + b$ is a **slant asymptote**, or an **oblique asymptote**.

EXAMPLE 8 | A Rational Function with a Slant Asymptote

Graph the rational function $r(x) = \dfrac{x^2 - 4x - 5}{x - 3}$.

SOLUTION

Factor: $y = \dfrac{(x + 1)(x - 5)}{x - 3}$

x-Intercepts: -1 and 5, from $x + 1 = 0$ and $x - 5 = 0$

y-Intercepts: $\dfrac{5}{3}$, because $r(0) = \dfrac{0^2 - 4 \cdot 0 - 5}{0 - 3} = \dfrac{5}{3}$

Horizontal asymptote: None, because the degree of the numerator is greater than the degree of the denominator

Vertical asymptote: $x = 3$, from the zero of the denominator

Behavior near vertical asymptote: $y \to \infty$ as $x \to 3^-$ and $y \to -\infty$ as $x \to 3^+$

ALTERNATE EXAMPLE 8

Graph the rational function

$$r(x) = \frac{x^2 - 3x - 1}{1 - x}.$$

ANSWER

Factor: $r(x) =$

$$\frac{\left(x - \dfrac{3 + \sqrt{13}}{2}\right)\left(x - \dfrac{3 - \sqrt{13}}{2}\right)}{-(x - 1)}$$

x-intercepts: $\dfrac{3 \pm \sqrt{13}}{2}$

y-intercept: -1

Vertical asymptote: $x = 1$

Behavior near vertical asymptote:

$y \to -\infty$ as $x \to 1^-$,

$y \to +\infty$ as $x \to 1^+$

Slant asymptote: $r(x) =$

$-x + 2 + 3/(x - 1)$

Slant asymptote at $y = -x + 2$

EXAMPLE

A rational function with a slant asymptote:

$$f(x) = \frac{x^2 + x - 2}{x - 2} = \frac{(x - 1)(x + 2)}{x - 2}$$

Intercepts: $(1, 0), (-2, 0), (0, 1)$

Asymptotes: $x = 2$, $y = x + \dfrac{3}{2}$

$$x - 3 \overline{\smash{\big)}\ x^2 - 4x - 5}$$ with quotient $x - 1$ shown and remainder -8:

$$\begin{array}{r} x - 1 \\ x - 3 \overline{\smash{\big)}\ x^2 - 4x - 5} \\ \underline{x^2 - 3x} \\ -x - 5 \\ \underline{-x + 3} \\ -8 \end{array}$$

Slant asymptote: Since the degree of the numerator is one more than the degree of the denominator, the function has a slant asymptote. Dividing (see the margin), we obtain

$$r(x) = x - 1 - \frac{8}{x - 3}$$

Thus, $y = x - 1$ is the slant asymptote.

Graph: We use the information we have found, together with some additional values, to sketch the graph in Figure 10.

x	y
-2	-1.4
1	4
2	9
4	-5
6	2.33

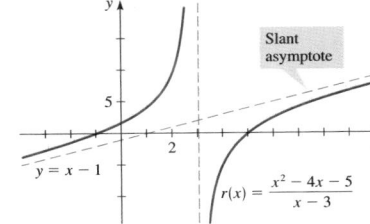

FIGURE 10

✎. **NOW TRY EXERCISE 65** ■

So far, we have considered only horizontal and slant asymptotes as end behaviors for rational functions. In the next example we graph a function whose end behavior is like that of a parabola.

EXAMPLE 9 | End Behavior of a Rational Function

Graph the rational function

$$r(x) = \frac{x^3 - 2x^2 + 3}{x - 2}$$

and describe its end behavior.

SOLUTION

Factor: $y = \dfrac{(x + 1)(x^2 - 3x + 3)}{x - 2}$

x-Intercepts: -1, from $x + 1 = 0$ (The other factor in the numerator has no real zeros.)

y-Intercepts: $-\dfrac{3}{2}$, because $r(0) = \dfrac{0^3 - 2 \cdot 0^2 + 3}{0 - 2} = -\dfrac{3}{2}$

Vertical asymptote: $x = 2$, from the zero of the denominator

Behavior near vertical asymptote: $y \to -\infty$ as $x \to 2^-$ and $y \to \infty$ as $x \to 2^+$

Horizontal asymptote: None, because the degree of the numerator is greater than the degree of the denominator

$$\begin{array}{r} x^2 \\ x - 2 \overline{\smash{\big)}\ x^3 - 2x^2 + 0x + 3} \\ \underline{x^3 - 2x^2} \\ 3 \end{array}$$

End behavior: Dividing (see the margin), we get

$$r(x) = x^2 + \frac{3}{x - 2}$$

This shows that the end behavior of r is like that of the parabola $y = x^2$ because $3/(x - 2)$ is small when $|x|$ is large. That is, $3/(x - 2) \to 0$ as $x \to \pm\infty$. This means that the graph of r will be close to the graph of $y = x^2$ for large $|x|$.

ALTERNATE EXAMPLE 9

Graph the rational function

$$r(x) = \frac{x^4 - x^3 + 1}{x - 1}.$$

ANSWER

Factor: Examining the graph of $x^4 - x^3 + 1$ shows us that the numerator has no real factors.

x-intercepts: none

y-intercept: -1

Vertical asymptote: $x = 1$

Behavior near vertical asymptote:
$y \to -\infty$ as $x \to 1^-$,
$y \to +\infty$ as $x \to 1^+$

Horizontal asymptote: none

End behavior:

$$r(x) = x^3 + \frac{1}{x - 1}$$

The end behavior is like the power function $y = x^3$.

Graph: In Figure 11(a) we graph r in a small viewing rectangle; we can see the intercepts, the vertical asymptotes, and the local minimum. In Figure 11(b) we graph r in a larger viewing rectangle; here the graph looks almost like the graph of a parabola. In Figure 11(c) we graph both $y = r(x)$ and $y = x^2$; these graphs are very close to each other except near the vertical asymptote.

(a)

(b)

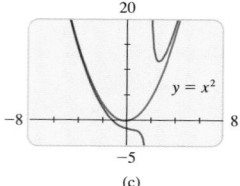
(c)

FIGURE 11
$r(x) = \dfrac{x^3 - 2x^2 + 3}{x - 2}$

NOW TRY EXERCISE 73

▼ Applications

Rational functions occur frequently in scientific applications of algebra. In the next example we analyze the graph of a function from the theory of electricity.

EXAMPLE 10 | Electrical Resistance

When two resistors with resistances R_1 and R_2 are connected in parallel, their combined resistance R is given by the formula

$$R = \frac{R_1 R_2}{R_1 + R_2}$$

Suppose that a fixed 8-ohm resistor is connected in parallel with a variable resistor, as shown in Figure 12. If the resistance of the variable resistor is denoted by x, then the combined resistance R is a function of x. Graph R, and give a physical interpretation of the graph.

SOLUTION Substituting $R_1 = 8$ and $R_2 = x$ into the formula gives the function

$$R(x) = \frac{8x}{8 + x}$$

Since resistance cannot be negative, this function has physical meaning only when $x > 0$. The function is graphed in Figure 13(a) using the viewing rectangle $[0, 20]$ by $[0, 10]$. The function has no vertical asymptote when x is restricted to positive values. The combined resistance R increases as the variable resistance x increases. If we widen the viewing rectangle to $[0, 100]$ by $[0, 10]$, we obtain the graph in Figure 13(b). For large x the combined resistance R levels off, getting closer and closer to the horizontal asymptote $R = 8$. No matter how large the variable resistance x, the combined resistance is never greater than 8 ohms.

FIGURE 12

(a)

(b)

FIGURE 13
$R(x) = \dfrac{8x}{8 + x}$

NOW TRY EXERCISE 83

DRILL QUESTION

Find all the asymptotes of the rational function $f(x) = \dfrac{x^2 + 1}{2x^2 - 5x - 3}$.

Answer

Horizontal asymptote at $y = \frac{1}{2}$, vertical asymptotes at $x = -\frac{1}{2}$ and $x = 3$

3.7 EXERCISES

CONCEPTS

1. If the rational function $y = r(x)$ has the vertical asymptote

$x = 2$, then as $x \to 2^+$, either $y \to$ _____ or $y \to$ _____.

2. If the rational function $y = r(x)$ has the horizontal asymptote

$y = 2$, then $y \to$ _____ as $x \to \pm\infty$.

3–6 ■ The following questions are about the rational function

$$r(x) = \frac{(x + 1)(x - 2)}{(x + 2)(x - 3)}$$

3. The function r has x-intercepts _____ and _____.

4. The function r has y-intercept _____.

5. The function r has vertical asymptotes $x =$ _____ and

$x =$ _____.

6. The function r has horizontal asymptote $y =$ _____.

SKILLS

7–10 ■ A rational function is given. **(a)** Complete each table for the function. **(b)** Describe the behavior of the function near its vertical asymptote, based on Tables 1 and 2. **(c)** Determine the horizontal asymptote, based on Tables 3 and 4.

TABLE 1

x	$r(x)$
1.5	
1.9	
1.99	
1.999	

TABLE 2

x	$r(x)$
2.5	
2.1	
2.01	
2.001	

TABLE 3

x	$r(x)$
10	
50	
100	
1000	

TABLE 4

x	$r(x)$
-10	
-50	
-100	
-1000	

7. $r(x) = \dfrac{x}{x - 2}$

8. $r(x) = \dfrac{4x + 1}{x - 2}$

9. $r(x) = \dfrac{3x - 10}{(x - 2)^2}$

10. $r(x) = \dfrac{3x^2 + 1}{(x - 2)^2}$

11–16 ■ Find the x- and y-intercepts of the rational function.

11. $r(x) = \dfrac{x - 1}{x + 4}$

12. $s(x) = \dfrac{3x}{x - 5}$

13. $t(x) = \dfrac{x^2 - x - 2}{x - 6}$

14. $r(x) = \dfrac{2}{x^2 + 3x - 4}$

15. $r(x) = \dfrac{x^2 - 9}{x^2}$

16. $r(x) = \dfrac{x^3 + 8}{x^2 + 4}$

17–20 ■ From the graph, determine the x- and y-intercepts and the vertical and horizontal asymptotes.

17.

18.

19.

20.

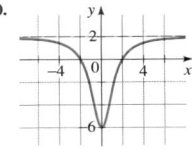

21–32 ■ Find all horizontal and vertical asymptotes (if any).

21. $r(x) = \dfrac{5}{x - 2}$

22. $r(x) = \dfrac{2x - 3}{x^2 - 1}$

23. $r(x) = \dfrac{6x}{x^2 + 2}$

24. $r(x) = \dfrac{2x - 4}{x^2 + x + 1}$

25. $s(x) = \dfrac{6x^2 + 1}{2x^2 + x - 1}$

26. $s(x) = \dfrac{8x^2 + 1}{4x^2 + 2x - 6}$

27. $s(x) = \dfrac{(5x - 1)(x + 1)}{(3x - 1)(x + 2)}$

28. $s(x) = \dfrac{(2x - 1)(x + 3)}{(3x - 1)(x - 4)}$

29. $r(x) = \dfrac{6x^3 - 2}{2x^3 + 5x^2 + 6x}$

30. $r(x) = \dfrac{5x^3}{x^3 + 2x^2 + 5x}$

31. $t(x) = \dfrac{x^2 + 2}{x - 1}$

32. $r(x) = \dfrac{x^3 + 3x^2}{x^2 - 4}$

33–40 ■ Use transformations of the graph of $y = \frac{1}{x}$ to graph the rational function, as in Example 2.

33. $r(x) = \dfrac{1}{x - 1}$

34. $r(x) = \dfrac{1}{x + 4}$

35. $s(x) = \dfrac{3}{x + 1}$

36. $s(x) = \dfrac{-2}{x - 2}$

37. $t(x) = \dfrac{2x - 3}{x - 2}$

38. $t(x) = \dfrac{3x - 3}{x + 2}$

39. $r(x) = \dfrac{x + 2}{x + 3}$

40. $r(x) = \dfrac{2x - 9}{x - 4}$

41–64 ■ Find the intercepts and asymptotes, and then sketch a graph of the rational function and state the domain and range. Use a graphing device to confirm your answer.

41. $r(x) = \dfrac{4x - 4}{x + 2}$

42. $r(x) = \dfrac{2x + 6}{-6x + 3}$

43. $s(x) = \dfrac{4 - 3x}{x + 7}$

44. $s(x) = \dfrac{1 - 2x}{2x + 3}$

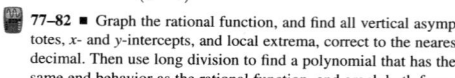 **45.** $r(x) = \dfrac{18}{(x - 3)^2}$

46. $r(x) = \dfrac{x - 2}{(x + 1)^2}$

47. $s(x) = \dfrac{4x - 8}{(x - 4)(x + 1)}$

48. $s(x) = \dfrac{x + 2}{(x + 3)(x - 1)}$

49. $s(x) = \dfrac{6}{x^2 - 5x - 6}$

50. $s(x) = \dfrac{2x - 4}{x^2 + x - 2}$

51. $t(x) = \dfrac{3x + 6}{x^2 + 2x - 8}$

52. $t(x) = \dfrac{x - 2}{x^2 - 4x}$

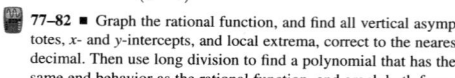 **53.** $r(x) = \dfrac{(x - 1)(x + 2)}{(x + 1)(x - 3)}$

54. $r(x) = \dfrac{2x(x + 2)}{(x - 1)(x - 4)}$

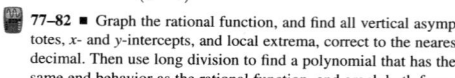 **55.** $r(x) = \dfrac{x^2 - 2x + 1}{x^2 + 2x + 1}$

56. $r(x) = \dfrac{4x^2}{x^2 - 2x - 3}$

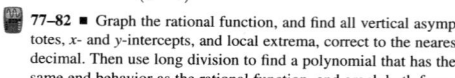 **57.** $r(x) = \dfrac{2x^2 + 10x - 12}{x^2 + x - 6}$

58. $r(x) = \dfrac{2x^2 + 2x - 4}{x^2 + x}$

59. $r(x) = \dfrac{x^2 - x - 6}{x^2 + 3x}$

60. $r(x) = \dfrac{x^2 + 3x}{x^2 - x - 6}$

61. $r(x) = \dfrac{3x^2 + 6}{x^2 - 2x - 3}$

62. $r(x) = \dfrac{5x^2 + 5}{x^2 + 4x + 4}$

63. $s(x) = \dfrac{x^2 - 2x + 1}{x^3 - 3x^2}$

64. $t(x) = \dfrac{x^3 - x^2}{x^3 - 3x - 2}$

65–72 ■ Find the slant asymptote, the vertical asymptotes, and sketch a graph of the function.

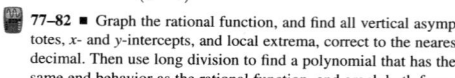 **65.** $r(x) = \dfrac{x^2}{x - 2}$

66. $r(x) = \dfrac{x^2 + 2x}{x - 1}$

67. $r(x) = \dfrac{x^2 - 2x - 8}{x}$

68. $r(x) = \dfrac{3x - x^2}{2x - 2}$

69. $r(x) = \dfrac{x^2 + 5x + 4}{x - 3}$

70. $r(x) = \dfrac{x^3 + 4}{2x^2 + x - 1}$

71. $r(x) = \dfrac{x^3 + x^2}{x^2 - 4}$

72. $r(x) = \dfrac{2x^3 + 2x}{x^2 - 1}$

 73–76 ■ Graph the rational function f, and determine all vertical asymptotes from your graph. Then graph f and g in a sufficiently large viewing rectangle to show that they have the same end behavior.

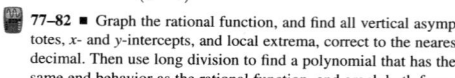 **73.** $f(x) = \dfrac{2x^2 + 6x + 6}{x + 3}$, $\quad g(x) = 2x$

74. $f(x) = \dfrac{-x^3 + 6x^2 - 5}{x^2 - 2x}$, $\quad g(x) = -x + 4$

75. $f(x) = \dfrac{x^3 - 2x^2 + 16}{x - 2}$, $\quad g(x) = x^2$

76. $f(x) = \dfrac{-x^4 + 2x^3 - 2x}{(x - 1)^2}$, $\quad g(x) = 1 - x^2$

77–82 ■ Graph the rational function, and find all vertical asymptotes, x- and y-intercepts, and local extrema, correct to the nearest decimal. Then use long division to find a polynomial that has the same end behavior as the rational function, and graph both func-

tions in a sufficiently large viewing rectangle to verify that the end behaviors of the polynomial and the rational function are the same.

77. $y = \dfrac{2x^2 - 5x}{2x + 3}$

78. $y = \dfrac{x^4 - 3x^3 + x^2 - 3x + 3}{x^2 - 3x}$

79. $y = \dfrac{x^5}{x^3 - 1}$

80. $y = \dfrac{x^4}{x^2 - 2}$

81. $r(x) = \dfrac{x^4 - 3x^3 + 6}{x - 3}$

82. $r(x) = \dfrac{4 + x^2 - x^4}{x^2 - 1}$

APPLICATIONS

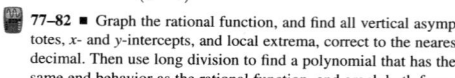 **83. Population Growth** Suppose that the rabbit population on Mr. Jenkins' farm follows the formula

$$p(t) = \dfrac{3000t}{t + 1}$$

where $t \geq 0$ is the time (in months) since the beginning of the year.

(a) Draw a graph of the rabbit population.

(b) What eventually happens to the rabbit population?

84. Drug Concentration After a certain drug is injected into a patient, the concentration c of the drug in the bloodstream is monitored. At time $t \geq 0$ (in minutes since the injection), the concentration (in mg/L) is given by

$$c(t) = \dfrac{30t}{t^2 + 2}$$

(a) Draw a graph of the drug concentration.

(b) What eventually happens to the concentration of drug in the bloodstream?

85. Drug Concentration A drug is administered to a patient, and the concentration of the drug in the bloodstream is monitored. At time $t \geq 0$ (in hours since giving the drug), the concentration (in mg/L) is given by

$$c(t) = \dfrac{5t}{t^2 + 1}$$

Graph the function c with a graphing device.

(a) What is the highest concentration of drug that is reached in the patient's bloodstream?

(b) What happens to the drug concentration after a long period of time?

(c) How long does it take for the concentration to drop below 0.3 mg/L?

86. Flight of a Rocket Suppose a rocket is fired upward from the surface of the earth with an initial velocity v (measured in meters per second). Then the maximum height h (in meters) reached by the rocket is given by the function

$$h(v) = \frac{Rv^2}{2gR - v^2}$$

where $R = 6.4 \times 10^6$ m is the radius of the earth and $g = 9.8$ m/s^2 is the acceleration due to gravity. Use a graphing device to draw a graph of the function h. (Note that h and v must both be positive, so the viewing rectangle need not contain negative values.) What does the vertical asymptote represent physically?

 87. The Doppler Effect As a train moves toward an observer (see the figure), the pitch of its whistle sounds higher to the observer than it would if the train were at rest, because the crests of the sound waves are compressed closer together. This phenomenon is called the *Doppler effect*. The observed pitch P is a function of the speed v of the train and is given by

$$P(v) = P_0\left(\frac{s_0}{s_0 - v}\right)$$

where P_0 is the actual pitch of the whistle at the source and $s_0 = 332$ m/s is the speed of sound in air. Suppose that a train has a whistle pitched at $P_0 = 440$ Hz. Graph the function $y = P(v)$ using a graphing device. How can the vertical asymptote of this function be interpreted physically?

88. Focusing Distance For a camera with a lens of fixed focal length F to focus on an object located a distance x from the lens, the film must be placed a distance y behind the lens, where F, x, and y are related by

$$\frac{1}{x} + \frac{1}{y} = \frac{1}{F}$$

(See the figure.) Suppose the camera has a 55-mm lens ($F = 55$).
(a) Express y as a function of x and graph the function.
(b) What happens to the focusing distance y as the object moves far away from the lens?
(c) What happens to the focusing distance y as the object moves close to the lens?

DISCOVERY ■ DISCUSSION ■ WRITING

89. Constructing a Rational Function from Its Asymptotes Give an example of a rational function that has vertical asymptote $x = 3$. Now give an example of one that has vertical asymptote $x = 3$ *and* horizontal asymptote $y = 2$. Now give an example of a rational function with vertical asymptotes $x = 1$ and $x = -1$, horizontal asymptote $y = 0$, and x-intercept 4.

90. A Rational Function with No Asymptote Explain how you can tell (without graphing it) that the function

$$r(x) = \frac{x^6 + 10}{x^4 + 8x^2 + 15}$$

has no x-intercept and no horizontal, vertical, or slant asymptote. What is its end behavior?'

91. Graphs with Holes In this chapter we adopted the convention that in rational functions, the numerator and denominator don't share a common factor. In this exercise we consider the graph of a rational function that does not satisfy this rule.
(a) Show that the graph of

$$r(x) = \frac{3x^2 - 3x - 6}{x - 2}$$

is the line $y = 3x + 3$ with the point $(2, 9)$ removed. [*Hint:* Factor. What is the domain of r?]
(b) Graph the rational functions:

$$s(x) = \frac{x^2 + x - 20}{x + 5}$$

$$t(x) = \frac{2x^2 - x - 1}{x - 1}$$

$$u(x) = \frac{x - 2}{x^2 - 2x}$$

92. Transformations of $y = 1/x^2$ In Example 2 we saw that some simple rational functions can be graphed by shifting, stretching, or reflecting the graph of $y = 1/x$. In this exercise we consider rational functions that can be graphed by transforming the graph of $y = 1/x^2$, shown on the following page.
(a) Graph the function

$$r(x) = \frac{1}{(x - 2)^2}$$

by transforming the graph of $y = 1/x^2$.
(b) Use long division and factoring to show that the function

$$s(x) = \frac{2x^2 + 4x + 5}{x^2 + 2x + 1}$$

can be written as

$$s(x) = 2 + \frac{3}{(x + 1)^2}$$

Then graph s by transforming the graph of $y = 1/x^2$.

(c) One of the following functions can be graphed by transforming the graph of $y = 1/x^2$; the other cannot. Use transformations to graph the one that can be, and explain why this method doesn't work for the other one.

$$p(x) = \frac{2 - 3x^2}{x^2 - 4x + 4} \qquad q(x) = \frac{12x - 3x^2}{x^2 - 4x + 4}$$

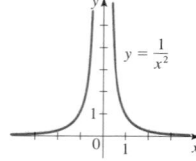

CHAPTER 3 | REVIEW

■ CONCEPT CHECK

1. (a) Write the defining equation for a polynomial P of degree n.
   (b) What does it mean to say that c is a zero of P?

2. Sketch graphs showing the possible end behaviors of polynomials of odd degree and of even degree.

3. What steps would you follow to graph a polynomial by hand?

4. (a) What is meant by a local maximum point or local minimum point of a polynomial?
   (b) How many local extrema can a polynomial of degree n have?

5. State the Division Algorithm and identify the dividend, divisor, quotient, and remainder.

6. How does synthetic division work?

7. (a) State the Remainder Theorem.
   (b) State the Factor Theorem.

8. (a) State the Rational Zeros Theorem.
   (b) What steps would you take to find the rational zeros of a polynomial?

9. State Descartes' Rule of Signs.

10. (a) What does it mean to say that a is a lower bound and b is an upper bound for the zeros of a polynomial?
    (b) State the Upper and Lower Bounds Theorem.

11. (a) What is a complex number?
    (b) What are the real and imaginary parts of a complex number?
    (c) What is the complex conjugate of a complex number?
    (d) How do you add, subtract, multiply, and divide complex numbers?

12. (a) State the Fundamental Theorem of Algebra.
    (b) State the Complete Factorization Theorem.
    (c) What does it mean to say that c is a zero of multiplicity k of a polynomial P?
    (d) State the Zeros Theorem.
    (e) State the Conjugate Zeros Theorem.

13. (a) What is a rational function?
    (b) What does it mean to say that $x = a$ is a vertical asymptote of $y = f(x)$?
    (c) How do you locate a vertical asymptote?
    (d) What does it mean to say that $y = b$ is a horizontal asymptote of $y = f(x)$?
    (e) How do you locate a horizontal asymptote?
    (f) What steps do you follow to sketch the graph of a rational function by hand?
    (g) Under what circumstances does a rational function have a slant asymptote? If one exists, how do you find it?
    (h) How do you determine the end behavior of a rational function?

■ EXERCISES

1–4 ■ A quadratic function is given. (a) Express the function in standard form. (b) Graph the function.

1. $f(x) = x^2 + 4x + 1$
2. $f(x) = -2x^2 + 12x + 12$
3. $g(x) = 1 + 8x - x^2$
4. $g(x) = 6x - 3x^2$

5–6 ■ Find the maximum or minimum value of the quadratic function.

5. $f(x) = 2x^2 + 4x - 5$
6. $g(x) = 1 - x - x^2$

7. A stone is thrown upward from the top of a building. Its height (in feet) above the ground after t seconds is given by the function $h(t) = -16t^2 + 48t + 32$. What maximum height does the stone reach?

8. The profit P (in dollars) generated by selling x units of a certain commodity is given by the function

$$P(x) = -1500 + 12x - 0.004x^2$$

What is the maximum profit, and how many units must be sold to generate it?

9–14 ■ Graph the polynomial by transforming an appropriate graph of the form $y = x^n$. Show clearly all x- and y-intercepts.

9. $P(x) = -x^3 + 64$
10. $P(x) = 2x^3 - 16$
11. $P(x) = 2(x + 1)^4 - 32$
12. $P(x) = 81 - (x - 3)^4$
13. $P(x) = 32 + (x - 1)^5$
14. $P(x) = -3(x + 2)^5 + 96$

15–16 ■ A polynomial function P is given. **(a)** Determine the multiplicity of each zero of P. **(b)** Sketch a graph of P.

15. $P(x) = x^3(x - 2)^2$ **16.** $P(x) = x(x + 1)^3(x - 1)^2$

 17–20 ■ Use a graphing device to graph the polynomial. Find the x- and y-intercepts and the coordinates of all local extrema, correct to the nearest decimal. Describe the end behavior of the polynomial.

17. $P(x) = x^3 - 4x + 1$ **18.** $P(x) = -2x^3 + 6x^2 - 2$

19. $P(x) = 3x^4 - 4x^3 - 10x - 1$

20. $P(x) = x^5 + x^4 - 7x^3 - x^2 + 6x + 3$

21. The strength S of a wooden beam of width x and depth y is given by the formula $S = 13.8xy^2$. A beam is to be cut from a log of diameter 10 in., as shown in the figure.

    (a) Express the strength S of this beam as a function of x only.

    (b) What is the domain of the function S?

    (c) Draw a graph of S.

    (d) What width will make the beam the strongest?

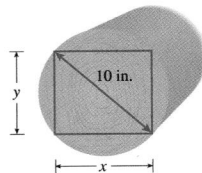

22. A small shelter for delicate plants is to be constructed of thin plastic material. It will have square ends and a rectangular top and back, with an open bottom and front, as shown in the figure. The total area of the four plastic sides is to be 1200 in^2.

    (a) Express the volume V of the shelter as a function of the depth x.

    (b) Draw a graph of V.

    (c) What dimensions will maximize the volume of the shelter?

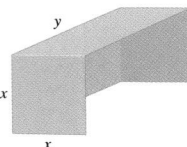

23–30 ■ Find the quotient and remainder.

23. $\dfrac{x^2 - 3x + 5}{x - 2}$ **24.** $\dfrac{x^2 + x - 12}{x - 3}$

25. $\dfrac{x^3 - x^2 + 11x + 2}{x - 4}$ **26.** $\dfrac{x^3 + 2x^2 - 10}{x + 3}$

27. $\dfrac{x^4 - 8x^2 + 2x + 7}{x + 5}$ **28.** $\dfrac{2x^4 + 3x^3 - 12}{x + 4}$

29. $\dfrac{2x^3 + x^2 - 8x + 15}{x^2 + 2x - 1}$ **30.** $\dfrac{x^4 - 2x^2 + 7x}{x^2 - x + 3}$

31–32 ■ Find the indicated value of the polynomial using the Remainder Theorem.

31. $P(x) = 2x^3 - 9x^2 - 7x + 13$;   find $P(5)$

32. $Q(x) = x^4 + 4x^3 + 7x^2 + 10x + 15$;   find $Q(-3)$

33. Show that $\frac{1}{2}$ is a zero of the polynomial

$$P(x) = 2x^4 + x^3 - 5x^2 + 10x - 4$$

34. Use the Factor Theorem to show that $x + 4$ is a factor of the polynomial

$$P(x) = x^5 + 4x^4 - 7x^3 - 23x^2 + 23x + 12$$

35. What is the remainder when the polynomial

$$P(x) = x^{500} + 6x^{201} - x^2 - 2x + 4$$

    is divided by $x - 1$?

36. What is the remainder when $x^{101} - x^4 + 2$ is divided by $x + 1$?

37–38 ■ A polynomial P is given. **(a)** List all possible rational zeros (without testing to see whether they actually are zeros). **(b)** Determine the possible number of positive and negative real zeros using Descartes' Rule of Signs.

37. $P(x) = x^5 - 6x^3 - x^2 + 2x + 18$

38. $P(x) = 6x^4 + 3x^3 + x^2 + 3x + 4$

39–46 ■ A polynomial P is given. **(a)** Find all real zeros of P, and state their multiplicities. **(b)** Sketch the graph of P.

39. $P(x) = x^3 - 16x$

40. $P(x) = x^3 - 3x^2 - 4x$

41. $P(x) = x^4 + x^3 - 2x^2$

42. $P(x) = x^4 - 5x^2 + 4$

43. $P(x) = x^4 - 2x^3 - 7x^2 + 8x + 12$

44. $P(x) = x^4 - 2x^3 - 2x^2 + 8x - 8$

45. $P(x) = 2x^4 + x^3 + 2x^2 - 3x - 2$

46. $P(x) = 9x^5 - 21x^4 + 10x^3 + 6x^2 - 3x - 1$

47–56 ■ Evaluate the expression and write in the form $a + bi$.

47. $(2 - 3i) + (1 + 4i)$ **48.** $(3 - 6i) - (6 - 4i)$

49. $(2 + i)(3 - 2i)$ **50.** $4i(2 - \frac{1}{2}i)$

51. $\dfrac{4 + 2i}{2 - i}$ **52.** $\dfrac{8 + 3i}{4 + 3i}$

53. i^{25} **54.** $(1 + i)^3$

55. $(1 - \sqrt{-1})(1 + \sqrt{-1})$ **56.** $\sqrt{-10} \cdot \sqrt{-40}$

57. Find a polynomial of degree 3 with constant coefficient 12 and zeros $-\frac{1}{2}$, 2, and 3.

58. Find a polynomial of degree 4 that has integer coefficients and zeros $3i$ and 4, with 4 a double zero.

59. Does there exist a polynomial of degree 4 with integer coefficients that has zeros i, $2i$, $3i$, and $4i$? If so, find it. If not, explain why.

60. Prove that the equation $3x^4 + 5x^2 + 2 = 0$ has no real root.

61–70 ■ Find all rational, irrational, and complex zeros (and state their multiplicities). Use Descartes' Rule of Signs, the Upper and Lower Bounds Theorem, the Quadratic Formula, or other factoring techniques to help you whenever possible.

61. $P(x) = x^3 - 3x^2 - 13x + 15$

62. $P(x) = 2x^3 + 5x^2 - 6x - 9$

63. $P(x) = x^4 + 6x^3 + 17x^2 + 28x + 20$

64. $P(x) = x^4 + 7x^3 + 9x^2 - 17x - 20$

65. $P(x) = x^5 - 3x^4 - x^3 + 11x^2 - 12x + 4$

66. $P(x) = x^4 - 81$

67. $P(x) = x^6 - 64$

68. $P(x) = 18x^3 + 3x^2 - 4x - 1$

69. $P(x) = 6x^4 - 18x^3 + 6x^2 - 30x + 36$

70. $P(x) = x^4 + 15x^2 + 54$

71–74 ■ Use a graphing device to find all real solutions of the equation.

71. $2x^2 = 5x + 3$

72. $x^3 + x^2 - 14x - 24 = 0$

73. $x^4 - 3x^3 - 3x^2 - 9x - 2 = 0$

74. $x^5 = x + 3$

75–76 ■ A polynomial function P is given. Find all the real zeros of P, and factor P completely into linear and irreducible quadratic factors with real coefficients.

75. $P(x) = x^3 - 2x - 4$ **76.** $P(x) = x^4 + 3x^2 - 4$

77–82 ■ Graph the rational function. Show clearly all x- and y-intercepts and asymptotes.

77. $r(x) = \dfrac{3x - 12}{x + 1}$ **78.** $r(x) = \dfrac{1}{(x + 2)^2}$

79. $r(x) = \dfrac{x - 2}{x^2 - 2x - 8}$ **80.** $r(x) = \dfrac{2x^2 - 6x - 7}{x - 4}$

81. $r(x) = \dfrac{x^2 - 9}{2x^2 + 1}$ **82.** $r(x) = \dfrac{x^3 + 27}{x + 4}$

83–86 ■ Use a graphing device to analyze the graph of the rational function. Find all x- and y-intercepts and all vertical, horizontal, and slant asymptotes. If the function has no horizontal or slant asymptote, find a polynomial that has the same end behavior as the rational function.

83. $r(x) = \dfrac{x - 3}{2x + 6}$ **84.** $r(x) = \dfrac{2x - 7}{x^2 + 9}$

85. $r(x) = \dfrac{x^3 + 8}{x^2 - x - 2}$ **86.** $r(x) = \dfrac{2x^3 - x^2}{x + 1}$

87. Find the coordinates of all points of intersection of the graphs of

$$y = x^4 + x^2 + 24x \qquad \text{and} \qquad y = 6x^3 + 20$$

1. Express the quadratic function $f(x) = x^2 - x - 6$ in standard form, and sketch its graph.

2. Find the maximum or minimum value of the quadratic function $g(x) = 2x^2 + 6x + 3$.

3. A cannonball fired out to sea from a shore battery follows a parabolic trajectory given by the graph of the equation
$$h(x) = 10x - 0.01x^2$$
where $h(x)$ is the height of the cannonball above the water when it has traveled a horizontal distance of x feet.

   (a) What is the maximum height that the cannonball reaches?

   (b) How far does the cannonball travel horizontally before splashing into the water?

4. Graph the polynomial $P(x) = -(x + 2)^3 + 27$, showing clearly all x- and y-intercepts.

5. (a) Use synthetic division to find the quotient and remainder when $x^4 - 4x^2 + 2x + 5$ is divided by $x - 2$.

   (b) Use long division to find the quotient and remainder when $2x^5 + 4x^4 - x^3 - x^2 + 7$ is divided by $2x^2 - 1$.

6. Let $P(x) = 2x^3 - 5x^2 - 4x + 3$.

   (a) List all possible rational zeros of P.

   (b) Find the complete factorization of P.

   (c) Find the zeros of P.

   (d) Sketch the graph of P.

7. Perform the indicated operation and write the result in the form $a + bi$.

   (a) $(3 - 2i) + (4 + 3i)$ (b) $(3 - 2i) - (4 + 3i)$

   (c) $(3 - 2i)(4 + 3i)$ (d) $\dfrac{3 - 2i}{4 + 3i}$

   (e) i^{48} (f) $(\sqrt{2} - \sqrt{-2})(\sqrt{8} + \sqrt{-2})$

8. Find all real and complex zeros of $P(x) = x^3 - x^2 - 4x - 6$.

9. Find the complete factorization of $P(x) = x^4 - 2x^3 + 5x^2 - 8x + 4$.

10. Find a fourth-degree polynomial with integer coefficients that has zeros $3i$ and -1, with -1 a zero of multiplicity 2.

11. Let $P(x) = 2x^4 - 7x^3 + x^2 - 18x + 3$.

    (a) Use Descartes' Rule of Signs to determine how many positive and how many negative real zeros P can have.

    (b) Show that 4 is an upper bound and -1 is a lower bound for the real zeros of P.

     (c) Draw a graph of P, and use it to estimate the real zeros of P, correct to two decimal places.

    (d) Find the coordinates of all local extrema of P, correct to two decimals.

12. Consider the following rational functions:
$$r(x) = \frac{2x - 1}{x^2 - x - 2} \qquad s(x) = \frac{x^3 + 27}{x^2 + 4} \qquad t(x) = \frac{x^3 - 9x}{x + 2} \qquad u(x) = \frac{x^2 + x - 6}{x^2 - 25}$$

    (a) Which of these rational functions has a horizontal asymptote?

    (b) Which of these functions has a slant asymptote?

    (c) Which of these functions has no vertical asymptote?

    (d) Graph $y = u(x)$, showing clearly any asymptotes and x- and y-intercepts the function may have.

    (e) Use long division to find a polynomial P that has the same end behavior as t. Graph both P and t on the same screen to verify that they have the same end behavior.

We have learned how to fit a line to data (see *Focus on Modeling*, page 130). The line models the increasing or decreasing trend in the data. If the data exhibit more variability, such as an increase followed by a decrease, then to model the data, we need to use a curve rather than a line. Figure 1 shows a scatter plot with three possible models that appear to fit the data. Which model fits the data best?

| Linear model | Quadratic model | Cubic model |

FIGURE 1

▼ Polynomial Functions as Models

Polynomial functions are ideal for modeling data for which the scatter plot has peaks or valleys (that is, local maxima or minima). For example, if the data have a single peak as in Figure 2(a), then it may be appropriate to use a quadratic polynomial to model the data. The more peaks or valleys the data exhibit, the higher the degree of the polynomial needed to model the data (see Figure 2).

(a)   (b)   (c)

FIGURE 2

Graphing calculators are programmed to find the **polynomial of best fit** of a specified degree. As is the case for lines (see page 131), a polynomial of a given degree fits the data *best* if the sum of the squares of the distances between the graph of the polynomial and the data points is minimized.

EXAMPLE 1 | Rainfall and Crop Yield

Rain is essential for crops to grow, but too much rain can diminish crop yields. The data give rainfall and cotton yield per acre for several seasons in a certain county.

(a) Make a scatter plot of the data. What degree polynomial seems appropriate for modeling the data?

(b) Use a graphing calculator to find the polynomial of best fit. Graph the polynomial on the scatter plot.

(c) Use the model that you found to estimate the yield if there are 25 in. of rainfall.

296

Season	Rainfall (in.)	Yield (kg/acre)
1	23.3	5311
2	20.1	4382
3	18.1	3950
4	12.5	3137
5	30.9	5113
6	33.6	4814
7	35.8	3540
8	15.5	3850
9	27.6	5071
10	34.5	3881

SOLUTION

(a) The scatter plot is shown in Figure 3. The data appear to have a peak, so it is appropriate to model the data by a quadratic polynomial (degree 2).

FIGURE 3 Scatter plot of yield vs. rainfall data

(b) Using a graphing calculator, we find that the quadratic polynomial of best fit is

$$y = -12.6x^2 + 651.5x - 3283.2$$

The calculator output and the scatter plot, together with the graph of the quadratic model, are shown in Figure 4.

(a)

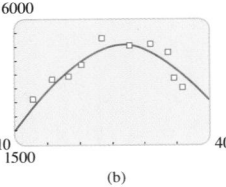

(b)

FIGURE 4

(c) Using the model with $x = 25$, we get

$$y = -12.6(25)^2 + 651.5(25) - 3283.2 \approx 5129.3$$

We estimate the yield to be about 5130 kg/acre. ∎

Cod   Redfish   Hake

Otoliths for several fish species

EXAMPLE 2 | Length-at-Age Data for Fish

Otoliths ("earstones") are tiny structures that are found in the heads of fish. Microscopic growth rings on the otoliths, not unlike growth rings on a tree, record the age of a fish. The table gives the lengths of rock bass caught at different ages, as determined by the otoliths. Scientists have proposed a cubic polynomial to model this data.

(a) Use a graphing calculator to find the cubic polynomial of best fit for the data.

(b) Make a scatter plot of the data and graph the polynomial from part (a).

(c) A fisherman catches a rock bass 20 in. long. Use the model to estimate its age.

Age (yr)	Length (in.)	Age (yr)	Length (in.)
1	4.8	9	18.2
2	8.8	9	17.1
2	8.0	10	18.8
3	7.9	10	19.5
4	11.9	11	18.9
5	14.4	12	21.7
6	14.1	12	21.9
6	15.8	13	23.8
7	15.6	14	26.9
8	17.8	14	25.1

SOLUTION

(a) Using a graphing calculator (see Figure 5(a)), we find the cubic polynomial of best fit:

$$y = 0.0155x^3 - 0.372x^2 + 3.95x + 1.21$$

(b) The scatter plot of the data and the cubic polynomial are graphed in Figure 5(b).

(a)   (b)

FIGURE 5

(c) Moving the cursor along the graph of the polynomial, we find that $y = 20$ when $x \approx 10.8$. Thus, the fish is about 11 years old. ∎

PROBLEMS

1. **Tire Inflation and Treadwear**   Car tires need to be inflated properly. Overinflation or underinflation can cause premature treadwear. The data and scatter plot on the next page show tire life for different inflation values for a certain type of tire.

(a) Find the quadratic polynomial that best fits the data.

(b) Draw a graph of the polynomial from part (a) together with a scatter plot of the data.

(c) Use your result from part (b) to estimate the pressure that gives the longest tire life.

Pressure (lb/in²)	Tire life (mi)
26	50,000
28	66,000
31	78,000
35	81,000
38	74,000
42	70,000
45	59,000

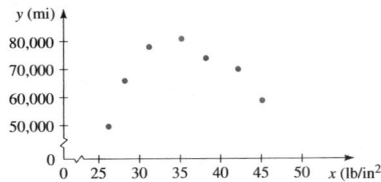

2. Too Many Corn Plants per Acre? The more corn a farmer plants per acre, the greater is the yield the farmer can expect, but only up to a point. Too many plants per acre can cause overcrowding and decrease yields. The data give crop yields per acre for various densities of corn plantings, as found by researchers at a university test farm.

(a) Find the quadratic polynomial that best fits the data.

(b) Draw a graph of the polynomial from part (a) together with a scatter plot of the data.

(c) Use your result from part (b) to estimate the yield for 37,000 plants per acre.

Density (plants/acre)	Crop yield (bushels/acre)
15,000	43
20,000	98
25,000	118
30,000	140
35,000	142
40,000	122
45,000	93
50,000	67

3. How Fast Can You List Your Favorite Things? If you are asked to make a list of objects in a certain category, how fast you can list them follows a predictable pattern. For example, if you try to name as many vegetables as you can, you'll probably think of several right away—for example, carrots, peas, beans, corn, and so on. Then after a pause you might think of ones you eat less frequently—perhaps zucchini, eggplant, and asparagus. Finally, a few more exotic vegetables might come to mind—artichokes, jicama, bok choy, and the like. A psychologist performs this experiment on a number of subjects. The table below gives the average number of vegetables that the subjects named by a given number of seconds.

(a) Find the cubic polynomial that best fits the data.

(b) Draw a graph of the polynomial from part (a) together with a scatter plot of the data.

(c) Use your result from part (b) to estimate the number of vegetables that subjects would be able to name in 40 seconds.

(d) According to the model, how long (to the nearest 0.1 second) would it take a person to name five vegetables?

Seconds	Number of vegetables
1	2
2	6
5	10
10	12
15	14
20	15
25	18
30	21

4. Clothing Sales Are Seasonal Clothing sales tend to vary by season, with more clothes sold in spring and fall. The table gives sales figures for each month at a certain clothing store.

(a) Find the quartic (fourth-degree) polynomial that best fits the data.

(b) Draw a graph of the polynomial from part (a) together with a scatter plot of the data.

(c) Do you think that a quartic polynomial is a good model for these data? Explain.

Month	Sales ($)
January	8,000
February	18,000
March	22,000
April	31,000
May	29,000
June	21,000
July	22,000
August	26,000
September	38,000
October	40,000
November	27,000
December	15,000

5. Height of a Baseball A baseball is thrown upward, and its height measured at 0.5-second intervals using a strobe light. The resulting data are given in the table.

(a) Draw a scatter plot of the data. What degree polynomial is appropriate for modeling the data?

(b) Find a polynomial model that best fits the data, and graph it on the scatter plot.

(c) Find the times when the ball is 20 ft above the ground.

(d) What is the maximum height attained by the ball?

Time (s)	Height (ft)
0	4.2
0.5	26.1
1.0	40.1
1.5	46.0
2.0	43.9
2.5	33.7
3.0	15.8

6. Torricelli's Law Water in a tank will flow out of a small hole in the bottom faster when the tank is nearly full than when it is nearly empty. According to Torricelli's Law, the height $h(t)$ of water remaining at time t is a quadratic function of t.

A certain tank is filled with water and allowed to drain. The height of the water is measured at different times as shown in the table.

(a) Find the quadratic polynomial that best fits the data.

(b) Draw a graph of the polynomial from part (a) together with a scatter plot of the data.

(c) Use your graph from part (b) to estimate how long it takes for the tank to drain completely.

Time (min)	Height (ft)
0	5.0
4	3.1
8	1.9
12	0.8
16	0.2

George Marks/Retrofile/Getty Images

EXPONENTIAL AND LOGARITHMIC FUNCTIONS

In this chapter we study a class of functions called *exponential functions*. These are functions, like $f(x) = 2^x$, where the independent variable is in the exponent. Exponential functions are used in modeling many real-world phenomena, such as the growth of a population or the growth of an investment that earns compound interest. Once an exponential model is obtained, we can use the model to predict population size or calculate the amount of an investment for any future date. To find out *when* a population will reach a certain level, we use the inverse functions of exponential functions, called *logarithmic functions*. So if we have an exponential model for population growth, we can answer questions like: When will my city be as crowded as the New York City street pictured above?

301

**SUGGESTED TIME
AND EMPHASIS**

$1-1\frac{1}{2}$ classes, essential material

4.1 EXPONENTIAL FUNCTIONS

Exponential Functions ▶ Graphs of Exponential Functions ▶ Compound Interest

In this chapter we study a new class of functions called *exponential functions*. For example,

$$f(x) = 2^x$$

is an exponential function (with base 2). Notice how quickly the values of this function increase:

$$f(3) = 2^3 = 8$$

$$f(10) = 2^{10} = 1024$$

$$f(30) = 2^{30} = 1,073,741,824$$

Compare this with the function $g(x) = x^2$, where $g(30) = 30^2 = 900$. The point is that when the variable is in the exponent, even a small change in the variable can cause a dramatic change in the value of the function.

▼ Exponential Functions

To study exponential functions, we must first define what we mean by the exponential expression a^x when x is any real number. In Section 1.2 we defined a^x for $a > 0$ and x a rational number, but we have not yet defined irrational powers. So what is meant by $5^{\sqrt{3}}$ or 2^π? To define a^x when x is irrational, we approximate x by rational numbers.

For example, since

$$\sqrt{3} \approx 1.73205\ldots$$

is an irrational number, we successively approximate $a^{\sqrt{3}}$ by the following rational powers:

$$a^{1.7}, a^{1.73}, a^{1.732}, a^{1.7320}, a^{1.73205}, \ldots$$

Intuitively, we can see that these rational powers of a are getting closer and closer to $a^{\sqrt{3}}$. It can be shown by using advanced mathematics that there is exactly one number that these powers approach. We define $a^{\sqrt{3}}$ to be this number.

For example, using a calculator, we find

$$5^{\sqrt{3}} \approx 5^{1.732}$$

$$\approx 16.2411\ldots$$

The more decimal places of $\sqrt{3}$ we use in our calculation, the better our approximation of $5^{\sqrt{3}}$.

The Laws of Exponents are listed on page 14.

It can be proved that the *Laws of Exponents are still true when the exponents are real numbers*.

EXPONENTIAL FUNCTIONS

The **exponential function with base a** is defined for all real numbers x by

$$f(x) = a^x$$

where $a > 0$ and $a \neq 1$.

We assume that $a \neq 1$ because the function $f(x) = 1^x = 1$ is just a constant function. Here are some examples of exponential functions:

$$f(x) = 2^x \qquad g(x) = 3^x \qquad h(x) = 10^x$$

Base 2   Base 3   Base 10

EXAMPLE 1 | Evaluating Exponential Functions

Let $f(x) = 3^x$, and evaluate the following:

(a) $f(2)$ (b) $f(-\frac{2}{3})$

(c) $f(\pi)$ (d) $f(\sqrt{2})$

SOLUTION We use a calculator to obtain the values of f.

		Calculator keystrokes	Output
(a) $f(2) = 3^2 = 9$		`3` `^` `2` `ENTER`	`9`
(b) $f(-\frac{2}{3}) = 3^{-2/3} \approx 0.4807$		`3` `^` `(` `(−)` `2` `÷` `3` `)` `ENTER`	`0.4807498`
(c) $f(\pi) = 3^\pi \approx 31.544$		`3` `^` `π` `ENTER`	`31.5442807`
(d) $f(\sqrt{2}) = 3^{\sqrt{2}} \approx 4.7288$		`3` `^` `√` `2` `ENTER`	`4.7288043`

✎ NOW TRY EXERCISE 5 ■

▼ Graphs of Exponential Functions

We first graph exponential functions by plotting points. We will see that the graphs of such functions have an easily recognizable shape.

EXAMPLE 2 | Graphing Exponential Functions by Plotting Points

Draw the graph of each function.

(a) $f(x) = 3^x$ (b) $g(x) = \left(\dfrac{1}{3}\right)^x$

SOLUTION We calculate values of $f(x)$ and $g(x)$ and plot points to sketch the graphs in Figure 1.

x	$f(x) = 3^x$	$g(x) = \left(\frac{1}{3}\right)^x$
−3	$\frac{1}{27}$	27
−2	$\frac{1}{9}$	9
−1	$\frac{1}{3}$	3
0	1	1
1	3	$\frac{1}{3}$
2	9	$\frac{1}{9}$
3	27	$\frac{1}{27}$

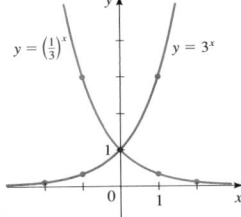

FIGURE 1

Notice that

$$g(x) = \left(\frac{1}{3}\right)^x = \frac{1}{3^x} = 3^{-x} = f(-x)$$

Reflecting graphs is explained in Section 2.5.

so we could have obtained the graph of g from the graph of f by reflecting in the y-axis.

✎ NOW TRY EXERCISE 15 ■

Figure 2 shows the graphs of the family of exponential functions $f(x) = a^x$ for various values of the base a. All of these graphs pass through the point $(0, 1)$ because $a^0 = 1$ for $a \neq 0$. You can see from Figure 2 that there are two kinds of exponential functions: If $0 < a < 1$, the exponential function decreases rapidly. If $a > 1$, the function increases rapidly (see the margin note).

To see just how quickly $f(x) = 2^x$ increases, let's perform the following thought experiment. Suppose we start with a piece of paper that is a thousandth of an inch thick, and we fold it in half 50 times. Each time we fold the paper, the thickness of the paper stack doubles, so the thickness of the resulting stack would be $2^{50}/1000$ inches. How thick do you think that is? It works out to be more than 17 million miles!

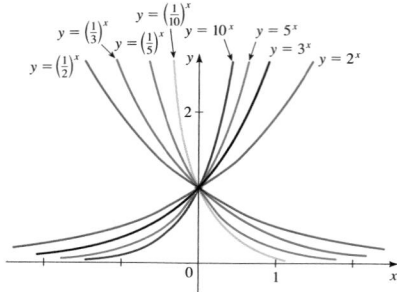

FIGURE 2 A family of exponential functions

See Section 3.7, page 278, where the "arrow notation" used here is explained.

The x-axis is a horizontal asymptote for the exponential function $f(x) = a^x$. This is because when $a > 1$, we have $a^x \to 0$ as $x \to -\infty$, and when $0 < a < 1$, we have $a^x \to 0$ as $x \to \infty$ (see Figure 2). Also, $a^x > 0$ for all $x \in \mathbb{R}$, so the function $f(x) = a^x$ has domain $\mathbb{R}$ and range $(0, \infty)$. These observations are summarized in the following box.

GRAPHS OF EXPONENTIAL FUNCTIONS

The exponential function

$$f(x) = a^x \quad (a > 0, a \neq 1)$$

has domain $\mathbb{R}$ and range $(0, \infty)$. The line $y = 0$ (the x-axis) is a horizontal asymptote of f. The graph of f has one of the following shapes.

EXAMPLE 3 | Identifying Graphs of Exponential Functions

Find the exponential function $f(x) = a^x$ whose graph is given.

(a)

(b)

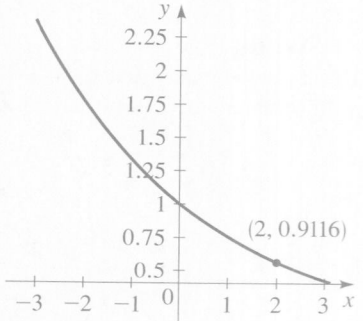
IN-CLASS MATERIALS

Point out this contrast between exponential and linear functions: For equally spaced x-values, linear functions have constant *differences* in y-values, whereas pure exponential functions have constant *ratios* in y-values. Use this fact to show that the following table describes an exponential function, not a linear one.

x	y
-6.2	0.62000
-2.4	0.65100
1.4	0.68355
5.2	0.71773
9.0	0.75361
12.8	0.79129

SOLUTION

(a) Since $f(2) = a^2 = 25$, we see that the base is $a = 5$. So $f(x) = 5^x$.

(b) Since $f(3) = a^3 = \frac{1}{8}$, we see that the base is $a = \frac{1}{2}$. So $f(x) = \left(\frac{1}{2}\right)^x$.

✎. **NOW TRY EXERCISE 19**   ■

In the next example we see how to graph certain functions, not by plotting points, but by taking the basic graphs of the exponential functions in Figure 2 and applying the shifting and reflecting transformations of Section 2.5.

EXAMPLE 4 | Transformations of Exponential Functions

Use the graph of $f(x) = 2^x$ to sketch the graph of each function.

(a) $g(x) = 1 + 2^x$ (b) $h(x) = -2^x$ (c) $k(x) = 2^{x-1}$

SOLUTION

(a) To obtain the graph of $g(x) = 1 + 2^x$, we start with the graph of $f(x) = 2^x$ and shift it upward 1 unit. Notice from Figure 3(a) that the line $y = 1$ is now a horizontal asymptote.

Shifting and reflecting of graphs is explained in Section 2.5.

(b) Again we start with the graph of $f(x) = 2^x$, but here we reflect in the x-axis to get the graph of $h(x) = -2^x$ shown in Figure 3(b).

(c) This time we start with the graph of $f(x) = 2^x$ and shift it to the right by 1 unit to get the graph of $k(x) = 2^{x-1}$ shown in Figure 3(c).

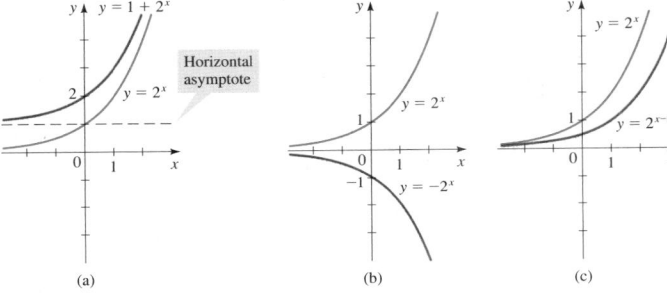

FIGURE 3

(a)   (b)   (c)

✎. **NOW TRY EXERCISES 25, 27, AND 31**   ■

EXAMPLE 5 | Comparing Exponential and Power Functions

Compare the rates of growth of the exponential function $f(x) = 2^x$ and the power function $g(x) = x^2$ by drawing the graphs of both functions in the following viewing rectangles.

(a) $[0, 3]$ by $[0, 8]$

(b) $[0, 6]$ by $[0, 25]$

(c) $[0, 20]$ by $[0, 1000]$

IN-CLASS MATERIALS

Estimate where $3^x > x^3$ and where $2^x > x^8$ using technology. Notice that exponential functions start by growing much more *slowly* than polynomial functions, and then wind up growing much *faster*. For example, if one were to graph x^2 versus x using 1 inch per unit, then when $x = 60$, y would be only 100 yards, as opposed to a light-year for $y = 2^x$. (The sun is only 8 light minutes from the earth.)

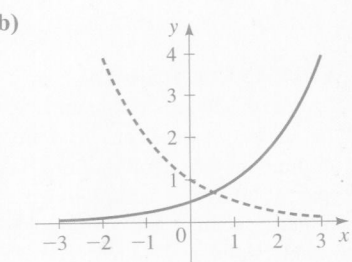

EXAMPLE

A shifted exponential curve:

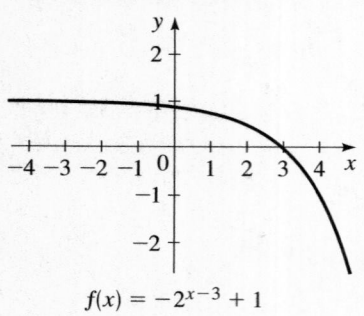

$$f(x) = -2^{x-3} + 1$$

ALTERNATE EXAMPLE 6

A sum of $2000 is put in an IRA that earns 7% per year. Find the amounts in the account after 10 years if interest is compounded annually, semiannually, monthly, weekly, daily, and hourly.

ANSWERS

Compounded annually	$3934.30
Compounded semiannually	$3979.58
Compounded monthly	$4019.32
Compounded weekly	$4025.61
Compounded daily	$4027.24
Compounded hourly	$4027.50

SOLUTION

(a) Figure 4(a) shows that the graph of $g(x) = x^2$ catches up with, and becomes higher than, the graph of $f(x) = 2^x$ at $x = 2$.

(b) The larger viewing rectangle in Figure 4(b) shows that the graph of $f(x) = 2^x$ overtakes that of $g(x) = x^2$ when $x = 4$.

(c) Figure 4(c) gives a more global view and shows that when x is large, $f(x) = 2^x$ is much larger than $g(x) = x^2$.

  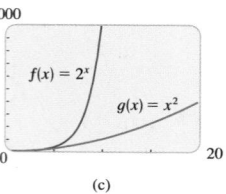

FIGURE 4   (a)   (b)   (c)

✎. NOW TRY EXERCISE **41**   ■

▼ Compound Interest

Exponential functions occur in calculating compound interest. If an amount of money P, called the **principal**, is invested at an interest rate i per time period, then after one time period the interest is Pi, and the amount A of money is

$$A = P + Pi = P(1 + i)$$

If the interest is reinvested, then the new principal is $P(1 + i)$, and the amount after another time period is $A = P(1 + i)(1 + i) = P(1 + i)^2$. Similarly, after a third time period the amount is $A = P(1 + i)^3$. In general, after k periods the amount is

$$A = P(1 + i)^k$$

Notice that this is an exponential function with base $1 + i$.

If the annual interest rate is r and if interest is compounded n times per year, then in each time period the interest rate is $i = r/n$, and there are nt time periods in t years. This leads to the following formula for the amount after t years.

> **COMPOUND INTEREST**
>
> **Compound interest** is calculated by the formula
>
> $$A(t) = P\left(1 + \frac{r}{n}\right)^{nt}$$
>
> where
> $A(t)$ = amount after t years
> P = principal
> r = interest rate per year
> n = number of times interest is compounded per year
> t = number of years

r is often referred to as the nominal annual interest rate.

EXAMPLE 6 | Calculating Compound Interest

A sum of $1000 is invested at an interest rate of 12% per year. Find the amounts in the account after 3 years if interest is compounded annually, semiannually, quarterly, monthly, and daily.

SOLUTION   We use the compound interest formula with $P = \$1000$, $r = 0.12$, and $t = 3$.

Compounding	n	Amount after 3 years	
Annual	1	$1000\left(1 + \dfrac{0.12}{1}\right)^{1(3)}$	$= \$1404.93$
Semiannual	2	$1000\left(1 + \dfrac{0.12}{2}\right)^{2(3)}$	$= \$1418.52$
Quarterly	4	$1000\left(1 + \dfrac{0.12}{4}\right)^{4(3)}$	$= \$1425.76$
Monthly	12	$1000\left(1 + \dfrac{0.12}{12}\right)^{12(3)}$	$= \$1430.77$
Daily	365	$1000\left(1 + \dfrac{0.12}{365}\right)^{365(3)}$	$= \$1433.24$

✎ NOW TRY EXERCISE **51**   ◼

If an investment earns compound interest, then the **annual percentage yield** (APY) is the *simple* interest rate that yields the same amount at the end of one year.

EXAMPLE 7 | Calculating the Annual Percentage Yield

Find the annual percentage yield for an investment that earns interest at a rate of 6% per year, compounded daily.

SOLUTION   After one year, a principal P will grow to the amount

$$A = P\left(1 + \frac{0.06}{365}\right)^{365} = P(1.06183)$$

Simple interest is studied in Section 1.6.

The formula for simple interest is

$$A = P(1 + r)$$

Comparing, we see that $1 + r = 1.06183$, so $r = 0.06183$. Thus, the annual percentage yield is 6.183%.

✎ NOW TRY EXERCISE **57**   ◼

ALTERNATE EXAMPLE 7
Find the annual percentage yield for an investment that earns interest at a rate of 4% per year, compounded quarterly.

ANSWER
4.06%

4.1 EXERCISES

CONCEPTS

1. The function $f(x) = 5^x$ is an exponential function with base

_____; $f(-2) = $ _____, $f(0) = $ _____,

$f(2) = $ _____, and $f(6) = $ _____.

2. Match the exponential function with its graph.

   (a) $f(x) = 2^x$

   (b) $f(x) = 2^{-x}$

   (c) $f(x) = -2^x$

   (d) $f(x) = -2^{-x}$

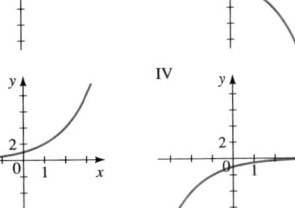

3. (a) To obtain the graph of $g(x) = 2^x - 1$, we start with the graph of $f(x) = 2^x$ and shift it _____ (upward/downward) 1 unit.

(b) To obtain the graph of $h(x) = 2^{x-1}$, we start with the graph of $f(x) = 2^x$ and shift it to the _____ (left/right) 1 unit.

4. In the formula $A(t) = P\left(1 + \frac{r}{n}\right)^{nt}$ for compound interest the letters P, r, n, and t stand for _____, _____, _____, and _____, respectively, and $A(t)$ stands for _____. So if \$100 is invested at an interest rate of 6% compounded quarterly, then the amount after 2 years is _____.

SKILLS

5–10 ■ Use a calculator to evaluate the function at the indicated values. Round your answers to three decimals.

5. $f(x) = 4^x$; $f(0.5), f(\sqrt{2}), f(-\pi), f\left(\frac{1}{3}\right)$

6. $f(x) = 3^{x+1}$; $f(-1.5), f(\sqrt{3}), f(e), f\left(-\frac{5}{4}\right)$

7. $g(x) = \left(\frac{2}{3}\right)^{x-1}$; $g(1.3), g(\sqrt{5}), g(2\pi), g\left(-\frac{1}{2}\right)$

8. $g(x) = \left(\frac{3}{4}\right)^{2x}$; $g(0.7), g(\sqrt{7}/2), g(1/\pi), g\left(\frac{2}{3}\right)$

9–14 ■ Sketch the graph of the function by making a table of values. Use a calculator if necessary.

9. $f(x) = 2^x$

10. $g(x) = 8^x$

11. $f(x) = \left(\frac{1}{3}\right)^x$

12. $h(x) = (1.1)^x$

13. $g(x) = 3(1.3)^x$

14. $h(x) = 2\left(\frac{1}{4}\right)^x$

15–18 ■ Graph both functions on one set of axes.

15. $f(x) = 2^x$ and $g(x) = 2^{-x}$

16. $f(x) = 3^{-x}$ and $g(x) = \left(\frac{1}{3}\right)^x$

17. $f(x) = 4^x$ and $g(x) = 7^x$

18. $f(x) = \left(\frac{2}{3}\right)^x$ and $g(x) = \left(\frac{4}{3}\right)^x$

19–22 ■ Find the exponential function $f(x) = a^x$ whose graph is given.

19.

20.

21.

22.

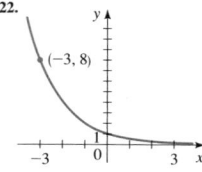

23–24 ■ Match the exponential function with one of the graphs labeled I or II.

23. $f(x) = 5^{x+1}$

24. $f(x) = 5^x + 1$

I

II

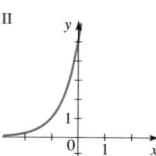

25–36 ■ Graph the function, not by plotting points, but by starting from the graphs in Figure 2. State the domain, range, and asymptote.

25. $f(x) = -3^x$

26. $f(x) = 10^{-x}$

27. $g(x) = 2^x - 3$

28. $g(x) = 2^{x-3}$

29. $h(x) = 4 + \left(\frac{1}{2}\right)^x$

30. $h(x) = 6 - 3^x$

31. $f(x) = 10^{x+3}$

32. $f(x) = -\left(\frac{1}{5}\right)^x$

33. $y = 5^{-x} + 1$

34. $g(x) = 1 - 3^{-x}$

35. $y = 3 - 10^{x-1}$

36. $h(x) = 2^{x-4} + 1$

37. (a) Sketch the graphs of $f(x) = 2^x$ and $g(x) = 3(2^x)$.
(b) How are the graphs related?

38. (a) Sketch the graphs of $f(x) = 9^{x/2}$ and $g(x) = 3^x$.
(b) Use the Laws of Exponents to explain the relationship between these graphs.

39. Compare the functions $f(x) = x^3$ and $g(x) = 3^x$ by evaluating both of them for $x = 0, 1, 2, 3, 4, 5, 6, 7, 8, 9, 10, 15,$ and 20. Then draw the graphs of f and g on the same set of axes.

40. If $f(x) = 10^x$, show that $\dfrac{f(x + h) - f(x)}{h} = 10^x\left(\dfrac{10^h - 1}{h}\right)$.

41. (a) Compare the rates of growth of the functions $f(x) = 2^x$ and $g(x) = x^5$ by drawing the graphs of both functions in the following viewing rectangles.
  (i) $[0, 5]$ by $[0, 20]$
  (ii) $[0, 25]$ by $[0, 10^7]$
  (iii) $[0, 50]$ by $[0, 10^8]$

(b) Find the solutions of the equation $2^x = x^5$, rounded to one decimal place.

42. (a) Compare the rates of growth of the functions $f(x) = 3^x$ and $g(x) = x^4$ by drawing the graphs of both functions in the following viewing rectangles:

    (i) $[-4, 4]$ by $[0, 20]$
    (ii) $[0, 10]$ by $[0, 5000]$
    (iii) $[0, 20]$ by $[0, 10^5]$

    (b) Find the solutions of the equation $3^x = x^4$, rounded to two decimal places.

 43–44 ■ Draw graphs of the given family of functions for $c = 0.25, 0.5, 1, 2, 4$. How are the graphs related?

43. $f(x) = c2^x$ **44.** $f(x) = 2^{cx}$

 45–46 ■ Find, rounded to two decimal places, **(a)** the intervals on which the function is increasing or decreasing and **(b)** the range of the function.

45. $y = 10^{x-x^2}$ **46.** $y = x2^x$

APPLICATIONS

47. Bacteria Growth A bacteria culture contains 1500 bacteria initially and doubles every hour.
    (a) Find a function that models the number of bacteria after t hours.
    (b) Find the number of bacteria after 24 hours.

48. Mouse Population A certain breed of mouse was introduced onto a small island with an initial population of 320 mice, and scientists estimate that the mouse population is doubling every year.
    (a) Find a function that models the number of mice after t years.
    (b) Estimate the mouse population after 8 years.

49–50 ■ **Compound Interest** An investment of $5000 is deposited into an account in which interest is compounded monthly. Complete the table by filling in the amounts to which the investment grows at the indicated times or interest rates.

49. $r = 4\%$ **50.** $t = 5$ years

Time (years)	Amount
1	
2	
3	
4	
5	
6	

Rate per year	Amount
1%	
2%	
3%	
4%	
5%	
6%	

 51. Compound Interest If $10,000 is invested at an interest rate of 3% per year, compounded semiannually, find the value of the investment after the given number of years.

    (a) 5 years   **(b)** 10 years   **(c)** 15 years

52. Compound Interest If $2500 is invested at an interest rate of 2.5% per year, compounded daily, find the value of the investment after the given number of years.
    (a) 2 years   **(b)** 3 years   **(c)** 6 years

53. Compound Interest If $500 is invested at an interest rate of 3.75% per year, compounded quarterly, find the value of the investment after the given number of years.
    (a) 1 year   **(b)** 2 years   **(c)** 10 years

54. Compound Interest If $4000 is borrowed at a rate of 5.75% interest per year, compounded quarterly, find the amount due at the end of the given number of years.
    (a) 4 years   **(b)** 6 years   **(c)** 8 years

55–56 ■ **Present Value** The **present value** of a sum of money is the amount that must be invested now, at a given rate of interest, to produce the desired sum at a later date.

55. Find the present value of $10,000 if interest is paid at a rate of 9% per year, compounded semiannually, for 3 years.

56. Find the present value of $100,000 if interest is paid at a rate of 8% per year, compounded monthly, for 5 years.

57. Annual Percentage Yield Find the annual percentage yield for an investment that earns 8% per year, compounded monthly.

58. Annual Percentage Yield Find the annual percentage yield for an investment that earns $5\frac{1}{2}\%$ per year, compounded quarterly.

DISCOVERY ■ DISCUSSION ■ WRITING

59. Growth of an Exponential Function Suppose you are offered a job that lasts one month, and you are to be very well paid. Which of the following methods of payment is more profitable for you?
    (a) One million dollars at the end of the month
    (b) Two cents on the first day of the month, 4 cents on the second day, 8 cents on the third day, and, in general, 2^n cents on the nth day

60. The Height of the Graph of an Exponential Function Your mathematics instructor asks you to sketch a graph of the exponential function

$$f(x) = 2^x$$

for x between 0 and 40, using a scale of 10 units to one inch. What are the dimensions of the sheet of paper you will need to sketch this graph?

○ DISCOVERY PROJECT   **Exponential Explosion**

In this project we explore an example about collecting pennies that helps us experience how exponential growth works. You can find the project at the book companion website: **www.stewartmath.com**

**SUGGESTED TIME
AND EMPHASIS**
$\frac{1}{2}$ class, essential material

4.2 THE NATURAL EXPONENTIAL FUNCTION

> The Number e ▶ The Natural Exponential Function ▶ Continuously Compounded Interest

Any positive number can be used as a base for an exponential function. In this section we study the special base e, which is convenient for applications involving calculus.

▼ The Number e

The number e is defined as the value that $(1 + 1/n)^n$ approaches as n becomes large. (In calculus this idea is made more precise through the concept of a limit. See Chapter 13.) The table shows the values of the expression $(1 + 1/n)^n$ for increasingly large values of n.

The **Gateway Arch** in St. Louis, Missouri, is shaped in the form of the graph of a combination of exponential functions (*not* a parabola, as it might first appear). Specifically, it is a **catenary**, which is the graph of an equation of the form

$$y = a(e^{bx} + e^{-bx})$$

(see Exercise 17). This shape was chosen because it is optimal for distributing the internal structural forces of the arch. Chains and cables suspended between two points (for example, the stretches of cable between pairs of telephone poles) hang in the shape of a catenary.

n	$\left(1 + \dfrac{1}{n}\right)^n$
1	2.00000
5	2.48832
10	2.59374
100	2.70481
1000	2.71692
10,000	2.71815
100,000	2.71827
1,000,000	2.71828

It appears that, correct to five decimal places, $e \approx 2.71828$; in fact, the approximate value to 20 decimal places is

$$e \approx 2.71828182845904523536$$

It can be shown that e is an irrational number, so we cannot write its exact value in decimal form.

▼ The Natural Exponential Function

The notation e was chosen by Leonhard Euler (see page 266), probably because it is the first letter of the word *exponential*.

The number e is the base for the natural exponential function. Why use such a strange base for an exponential function? It might seem at first that a base such as 10 is easier to work with. We will see, however, that in certain applications the number e is the best possible base. In this section we study how e occurs in the description of compound interest.

> **THE NATURAL EXPONENTIAL FUNCTION**
>
> The **natural exponential function** is the exponential function
>
> $$f(x) = e^x$$
>
> with base e. It is often referred to as *the* exponential function.

Since $2 < e < 3$, the graph of the natural exponential function lies between the graphs of $y = 2^x$ and $y = 3^x$, as shown in Figure 1.

Scientific calculators have a special key for the function $f(x) = e^x$. We use this key in the next example.

FIGURE 1 Graph of the natural exponential function

TEXT QUESTION

In Example 3, we model the number of people infected by a virus after t days by the function $v(t) = \dfrac{10{,}000}{5 + 1245e^{-0.97t}}$. Why is it true to say that the number of infected people levels off at about 2000 people?

Answer
Answers will vary. The idea is that, for large t, $v(t)$ approaches 2000.

EXAMPLE 1 | Evaluating the Exponential Function

Evaluate each expression rounded to five decimal places.

(a) e^3 (b) $2e^{-0.53}$ (c) $e^{4.8}$

SOLUTION   We use the $\boxed{e^x}$ key on a calculator to evaluate the exponential function.

(a) $e^3 \approx 20.08554$ (b) $2e^{-0.53} \approx 1.17721$ (c) $e^{4.8} \approx 121.51042$

✎. **NOW TRY EXERCISE 3**   ▪

EXAMPLE 2 | Transformations of the Exponential Function

Sketch the graph of each function.

(a) $f(x) = e^{-x}$ (b) $g(x) = 3e^{0.5x}$

SOLUTION

(a) We start with the graph of $y = e^x$ and reflect in the y-axis to obtain the graph of $y = e^{-x}$ as in Figure 2.

(b) We calculate several values, plot the resulting points, then connect the points with a smooth curve. The graph is shown in Figure 3.

$y = e^{-x}$ $y = e^x$

FIGURE 2

x	$f(x) = 3e^{0.5x}$
-3	0.67
-2	1.10
-1	1.82
0	3.00
1	4.95
2	8.15
3	13.45

$y = 3e^{0.5x}$

FIGURE 3

✎. **NOW TRY EXERCISES 5 AND 7**   ▪

EXAMPLE 3 | An Exponential Model for the Spread of a Virus

An infectious disease begins to spread in a small city of population 10,000. After t days, the number of people who have succumbed to the virus is modeled by the function

$$v(t) = \frac{10,000}{5 + 1245e^{-0.97t}}$$

(a) How many infected people are there initially (at time $t = 0$)?

(b) Find the number of infected people after one day, two days, and five days.

📱 (c) Graph the function v, and describe its behavior.

SOLUTION

(a) Since $v(0) = 10{,}000/(5 + 1245e^0) = 10{,}000/1250 = 8$, we conclude that 8 people initially have the disease.

(b) Using a calculator, we evaluate $v(1), v(2)$, and $v(5)$ and then round off to obtain the following values.

Days	Infected people
1	21
2	54
5	678

IN-CLASS MATERIALS
Have your students fill out the following table, using their calculators, to give them a feel for $y = e^x$.

x	2^x	3^x	e^x
-2	$\frac{1}{4} = 0.25$	$\frac{1}{9} \approx 0.111$	≈ 0.135
-1	$\frac{1}{2} = 0.5$	$\frac{1}{3} \approx 0.333$	≈ 0.368
0	1	1	1
1	2	3	≈ 2.718
2	4	9	≈ 7.389
3	8	27	≈ 20.086

FIGURE 4

$$v(t) = \frac{10,000}{5 + 1245e^{-0.97t}}$$

(c) From the graph in Figure 4 we see that the number of infected people first rises slowly, then rises quickly between day 3 and day 8, and then levels off when about 2000 people are infected.

✎ NOW TRY EXERCISE **25** ◼

The graph in Figure 4 is called a *logistic curve* or a *logistic growth model*. Curves like it occur frequently in the study of population growth. (See Exercises 25–28.)

▼ Continuously Compounded Interest

In Example 6 of Section 4.1 we saw that the interest paid increases as the number of compounding periods n increases. Let's see what happens as n increases indefinitely. If we let $m = n/r$, then

$$A(t) = P\left(1 + \frac{r}{n}\right)^{nt} = P\left[\left(1 + \frac{r}{n}\right)^{n/r}\right]^{rt} = P\left[\left(1 + \frac{1}{m}\right)^{m}\right]^{rt}$$

Recall that as m becomes large, the quantity $(1 + 1/m)^m$ approaches the number e. Thus, the amount approaches $A = Pe^{rt}$. This expression gives the amount when the interest is compounded at "every instant."

CONTINUOUSLY COMPOUNDED INTEREST

Continuously compounded interest is calculated by the formula

$$A(t) = Pe^{rt}$$

where $A(t)$ = amount after t years

  P = principal

  r = interest rate per year

  t = number of years

EXAMPLE 4 | Calculating Continuously Compounded Interest

Find the amount after 3 years if $1000 is invested at an interest rate of 12% per year, compounded continuously.

SOLUTION We use the formula for continuously compounded interest with P = $1000, $r = 0.12$, and $t = 3$ to get

$$A(3) = 1000e^{(0.12)3} = 1000e^{0.36} = \$1433.33$$

Compare this amount with the amounts in Example 6 of Section 4.1.

✎ NOW TRY EXERCISE **31** ◼

4.2 EXERCISES

CONCEPTS

1. The function $f(x) = e^x$ is called the _____ exponential function. The number e is approximately equal to _____.

2. In the formula $A(t) = Pe^{rt}$ for continuously compound interest, the letters P, r, and t stand for _____, _____, and _____, respectively, and $A(t)$ stands for _____. So if $100 is invested at an interest rate of 6% compounded continuously, then the amount after 2 years is _____.

SKILLS

3–4 ■ Use a calculator to evaluate the function at the indicated values. Round your answers to three decimals.

 3. $h(x) = e^x$; $h(3), h(0.23), h(1), h(-2)$

4. $h(x) = e^{-2x}$; $h(1), h(\sqrt{2}), h(-3), h(\frac{1}{2})$

5–6 ■ Complete the table of values, rounded to two decimal places, and sketch a graph of the function.

 5.

x	$f(x) = 3e^x$
-2	
-1	
-0.5	
0	
0.5	
1	
2	

6.

x	$f(x) = 2e^{-0.5x}$
-3	
-2	
-1	
0	
1	
2	
3	

7–14 ■ Graph the function, not by plotting points, but by starting from the graph of $y = e^x$ in Figure 1. State the domain, range, and asymptote.

7. $f(x) = -e^x$ **8.** $y = 1 - e^x$

9. $y = e^{-x} - 1$ **10.** $f(x) = -e^{-x}$

11. $f(x) = e^{x-2}$ **12.** $y = e^{x-3} + 4$

13. $h(x) = e^{x+1} - 3$ **14.** $g(x) = -e^{x-1} - 2$

15. The *hyperbolic cosine function* is defined by

$$\cosh(x) = \frac{e^x + e^{-x}}{2}$$

(a) Sketch the graphs of the functions $y = \frac{1}{2}e^x$ and $y = \frac{1}{2}e^{-x}$ on the same axes, and use graphical addition (see Section 2.6) to sketch the graph of $y = \cosh(x)$.

(b) Use the definition to show that $\cosh(-x) = \cosh(x)$.

16. The *hyperbolic sine function* is defined by

$$\sinh(x) = \frac{e^x - e^{-x}}{2}$$

(a) Sketch the graph of this function using graphical addition as in Exercise 15.

(b) Use the definition to show that $\sinh(-x) = -\sinh(x)$.

17. (a) Draw the graphs of the family of functions

$$f(x) = \frac{a}{2}(e^{x/a} + e^{-x/a})$$

for $a = 0.5, 1, 1.5,$ and 2.

(b) How does a larger value of a affect the graph?

18–19 ■ Find the local maximum and minimum values of the function and the value of x at which each occurs. State each answer correct to two decimal places.

18. $g(x) = x^x$ $(x > 0)$ **19.** $g(x) = e^x + e^{-3x}$

APPLICATIONS

20. Medical Drugs   When a certain medical drug is administered to a patient, the number of milligrams remaining in the patient's bloodstream after t hours is modeled by

$$D(t) = 50e^{-0.2t}$$

How many milligrams of the drug remain in the patient's bloodstream after 3 hours?

21. Radioactive Decay   A radioactive substance decays in such a way that the amount of mass remaining after t days is given by the function

$$m(t) = 13e^{-0.015t}$$

where $m(t)$ is measured in kilograms.
(a) Find the mass at time $t = 0$.
(b) How much of the mass remains after 45 days?

22. Radioactive Decay   Doctors use radioactive iodine as a tracer in diagnosing certain thyroid gland disorders. This type of iodine decays in such a way that the mass remaining after t days is given by the function

$$m(t) = 6e^{-0.087t}$$

where $m(t)$ is measured in grams.
(a) Find the mass at time $t = 0$.
(b) How much of the mass remains after 20 days?

23. Sky Diving   A sky diver jumps from a reasonable height above the ground. The air resistance she experiences is proportional to her velocity, and the constant of proportionality is 0.2. It can be shown that the downward velocity of the sky diver at time t is given by

$$v(t) = 80(1 - e^{-0.2t})$$

where t is measured in seconds and $v(t)$ is measured in feet per second (ft/s).
(a) Find the initial velocity of the sky diver.
(b) Find the velocity after 5 s and after 10 s.
(c) Draw a graph of the velocity function $v(t)$.
(d) The maximum velocity of a falling object with wind resistance is called its *terminal velocity*. From the graph in part (c) find the terminal velocity of this sky diver.

$v(t) = 80(1 - e^{-0.2t})$

24. Mixtures and Concentrations   A 50-gallon barrel is filled completely with pure water. Salt water with a concentration of 0.3 lb/gal is then pumped into the barrel, and the resulting mixture overflows at the same rate. The amount of salt in the barrel at time t is given by

$$Q(t) = 15(1 - e^{-0.04t})$$

where t is measured in minutes and $Q(t)$ is measured in pounds.
(a) How much salt is in the barrel after 5 min?
(b) How much salt is in the barrel after 10 min?
 (c) Draw a graph of the function $Q(t)$.

(d) Use the graph in part (c) to determine the value that the amount of salt in the barrel approaches as t becomes large. Is this what you would expect?

$$Q(t) = 15(1 - e^{-0.04t})$$

25. Logistic Growth Animal populations are not capable of unrestricted growth because of limited habitat and food supplies. Under such conditions the population follows a *logistic growth model*:

$$P(t) = \frac{d}{1 + ke^{-ct}}$$

where c, d, and k are positive constants. For a certain fish population in a small pond $d = 1200$, $k = 11$, $c = 0.2$, and t is measured in years. The fish were introduced into the pond at time $t = 0$.

(a) How many fish were originally put in the pond?
(b) Find the population after 10, 20, and 30 years.
(c) Evaluate $P(t)$ for large values of t. What value does the population approach as $t \to \infty$? Does the graph shown confirm your calculations?

26. Bird Population The population of a certain species of bird is limited by the type of habitat required for nesting. The population behaves according to the logistic growth model

$$n(t) = \frac{5600}{0.5 + 27.5e^{-0.044t}}$$

where t is measured in years.

(a) Find the initial bird population.
(b) Draw a graph of the function $n(t)$.
(c) What size does the population approach as time goes on?

27. World Population The relative growth rate of world population has been decreasing steadily in recent years. On the basis of this, some population models predict that world population will eventually stabilize at a level that the planet can support. One such logistic model is

$$P(t) = \frac{73.2}{6.1 + 5.9e^{-0.02t}}$$

where $t = 0$ is the year 2000 and population is measured in billions.

(a) What world population does this model predict for the year 2200? For 2300?
(b) Sketch a graph of the function P for the years 2000 to 2500.
(c) According to this model, what size does the world population seem to approach as time goes on?

28. Tree Diameter For a certain type of tree the diameter D (in feet) depends on the tree's age t (in years) according to the logistic growth model

$$D(t) = \frac{5.4}{1 + 2.9e^{-0.01t}}$$

Find the diameter of a 20-year-old tree.

29–30 ■ Compound Interest An investment of $7,000 is deposited into an account in which interest is compounded continuously. Complete the table by filling in the amounts to which the investment grows at the indicated times or interest rates.

29. $r = 3\%$

Time (years)	Amount
1	
2	
3	
4	
5	
6	

30. $t = 10$ years

Rate per year	Amount
1%	
2%	
3%	
4%	
5%	
6%	

31. Compound Interest If $2000 is invested at an interest rate of 3.5% per year, compounded continuously, find the value of the investment after the given number of years.
(a) 2 years   **(b)** 4 years   **(c)** 12 years

32. Compound Interest If $3500 is invested at an interest rate of 6.25% per year, compounded continuously, find the value of the investment after the given number of years.
(a) 3 years   **(b)** 6 years   **(c)** 9 years

33. Compound Interest If $600 is invested at an interest rate of 2.5% per year, find the amount of the investment at the end of 10 years for the following compounding methods.
(a) Annually   **(b)** Semiannually
(c) Quarterly   **(d)** Continuously

34. Compound Interest If $8000 is invested in an account for which interest is compounded continuously, find the amount of the investment at the end of 12 years for the following interest rates.
(a) 2%   **(b)** 3%   **(c)** 4.5%   **(d)** 7%

35. Compound Interest Which of the given interest rates and compounding periods would provide the best investment?
(a) $2\frac{1}{2}\%$ per year, compounded semiannually
(b) $2\frac{1}{4}\%$ per year, compounded monthly
(c) 2% per year, compounded continuously

36. Compound Interest Which of the given interest rates and compounding periods would provide the better investment?
(a) $5\frac{1}{8}\%$ per year, compounded semiannually
(b) 5% per year, compounded continuously

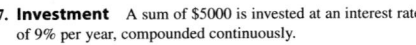 **37. Investment** A sum of $5000 is invested at an interest rate of 9% per year, compounded continuously.
(a) Find the value $A(t)$ of the investment after t years.

(b) Draw a graph of $A(t)$.
(c) Use the graph of $A(t)$ to determine when this investment will amount to $25,000.

DISCOVERY ▪ DISCUSSION ▪ WRITING

38. The Definition of e Illustrate the definition of the number e by graphing the curve $y = (1 + 1/x)^x$ and the line $y = e$ on the same screen, using the viewing rectangle $[0, 40]$ by $[0, 4]$.

4.3 LOGARITHMIC FUNCTIONS

SUGGESTED TIME AND EMPHASIS
1 class, essential material

> Logarithmic Functions ▶ Graphs of Logarithmic Functions ▶ Common Logarithms ▶ Natural Logarithms

In this section we study the inverses of exponential functions.

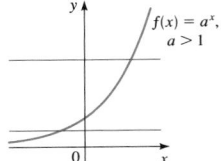

FIGURE 1 $f(x) = a^x$ is one-to-one.

▼ Logarithmic Functions

Every exponential function $f(x) = a^x$, with $a > 0$ and $a \neq 1$, is a one-to-one function by the Horizontal Line Test (see Figure 1 for the case $a > 1$) and therefore has an inverse function. The inverse function f^{-1} is called the *logarithmic function with base a* and is denoted by $\log_a$. Recall from Section 2.6 that f^{-1} is defined by

$$f^{-1}(x) = y \quad \Leftrightarrow \quad f(y) = x$$

This leads to the following definition of the logarithmic function.

We read $\log_a x = y$ as "log base a of x is y."

DEFINITION OF THE LOGARITHMIC FUNCTION

Let a be a positive number with $a \neq 1$. The **logarithmic function with base a**, denoted by $\log_a$, is defined by

$$\log_a x = y \quad \Leftrightarrow \quad a^y = x$$

So $\log_a x$ is the *exponent* to which the base a must be raised to give x.

By tradition the name of the logarithmic function is $\log_a$, not just a single letter. Also, we usually omit the parentheses in the function notation and write

$$\log_a(x) = \log_a x$$

When we use the definition of logarithms to switch back and forth between the **logarithmic form** $\log_a x = y$ and the **exponential form** $a^y = x$, it is helpful to notice that, in both forms, the base is the same:

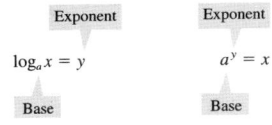

TEXT QUESTION

It is a fact that $10^\pi \approx 1385.46$. Is it possible to approximate $\log_{10} 1385.46$ without the use of a calculator? If so, then approximate this number. If not, why not?

Answer

$\log_{10} 1385.46 \approx \pi$

EXAMPLE 1 | Logarithmic and Exponential Forms

The logarithmic and exponential forms are equivalent equations: If one is true, then so is the other. So we can switch from one form to the other as in the following illustrations.

Logarithmic form	Exponential form
$\log_{10} 100{,}000 = 5$	$10^5 = 100{,}000$
$\log_2 8 = 3$	$2^3 = 8$
$\log_2\left(\frac{1}{8}\right) = -3$	$2^{-3} = \frac{1}{8}$
$\log_5 s = r$	$5^r = s$

✎ NOW TRY EXERCISE **5** ■

It is important to understand that $\log_a x$ is an *exponent*. For example, the numbers in the right column of the table in the margin are the logarithms (base 10) of the numbers in the left column. This is the case for all bases, as the following example illustrates.

x	$\log_{10} x$
10^4	4
10^3	3
10^2	2
10	1
1	0
10^{-1}	-1
10^{-2}	-2
10^{-3}	-3
10^{-4}	-4

EXAMPLE 2 | Evaluating Logarithms

(a) $\log_{10} 1000 = 3$ because $10^3 = 1000$

(b) $\log_2 32 = 5$ because $2^5 = 32$

(c) $\log_{10} 0.1 = -1$ because $10^{-1} = 0.1$

(d) $\log_{16} 4 = \frac{1}{2}$ because $16^{1/2} = 4$

✎ NOW TRY EXERCISES **7** AND **9** ■

Inverse Function Property:

$$f^{-1}(f(x)) = x$$

$$f(f^{-1}(x)) = x$$

When we apply the Inverse Function Property described on page 201 to $f(x) = a^x$ and $f^{-1}(x) = \log_a x$, we get

$$\log_a(a^x) = x, \qquad x \in \mathbb{R}$$

$$a^{\log_a x} = x, \qquad x > 0$$

We list these and other properties of logarithms discussed in this section.

PROPERTIES OF LOGARITHMS

Property	Reason
1. $\log_a 1 = 0$	We must raise a to the power 0 to get 1.
2. $\log_a a = 1$	We must raise a to the power 1 to get a.
3. $\log_a a^x = x$	We must raise a to the power x to get a^x.
4. $a^{\log_a x} = x$	$\log_a x$ is the power to which a must be raised to get x.

EXAMPLE 3 | Applying Properties of Logarithms

We illustrate the properties of logarithms when the base is 5.

$\log_5 1 = 0$ Property 1 $\log_5 5 = 1$ Property 2

$\log_5 5^8 = 8$ Property 3 $5^{\log_5 12} = 12$ Property 4

✎ NOW TRY EXERCISES **19** AND **25** ■

IN-CLASS MATERIALS

Sketch a graph of $f(x) = 2\log_2(x + 3)$. Sketch the inverse function, then find an algebraic formula for the inverse. Foreshadow the next section by showing that the graph of $f(x)$ is the same as that of $g(x) = \log_2[(x + 3)^2]$.

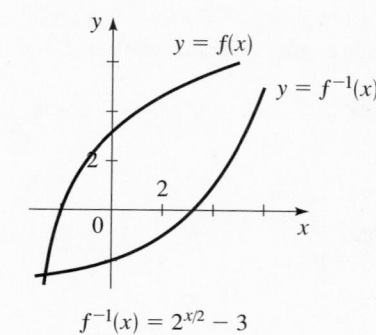

$$f^{-1}(x) = 2^{x/2} - 3$$

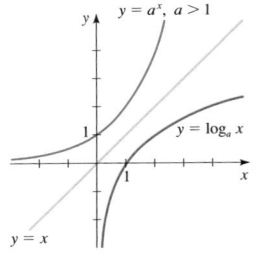

FIGURE 2 Graph of the logarithmic function $f(x) = \log_a x$

▼ Graphs of Logarithmic Functions

Recall that if a one-to-one function f has domain A and range B, then its inverse function f^{-1} has domain B and range A. Since the exponential function $f(x) = a^x$ with $a \neq 1$ has domain $\mathbb{R}$ and range $(0, \infty)$, we conclude that its inverse function, $f^{-1}(x) = \log_a x$, has domain $(0, \infty)$ and range $\mathbb{R}$.

The graph of $f^{-1}(x) = \log_a x$ is obtained by reflecting the graph of $f(x) = a^x$ in the line $y = x$. Figure 2 shows the case $a > 1$. The fact that $y = a^x$ (for $a > 1$) is a very rapidly increasing function for $x > 0$ implies that $y = \log_a x$ is a very slowly increasing function for $x > 1$ (see Exercise 92).

Since $\log_a 1 = 0$, the x-intercept of the function $y = \log_a x$ is 1. The y-axis is a vertical asymptote of $y = \log_a x$ because $\log_a x \rightarrow -\infty$ as $x \rightarrow 0^+$.

EXAMPLE 4 | Graphing a Logarithmic Function by Plotting Points

Sketch the graph of $f(x) = \log_2 x$.

SOLUTION   To make a table of values, we choose the x-values to be powers of 2 so that we can easily find their logarithms. We plot these points and connect them with a smooth curve as in Figure 3.

x	$\log_2 x$
2^3	3
2^2	2
2	1
1	0
2^{-1}	-1
2^{-2}	-2
2^{-3}	-3
2^{-4}	-4

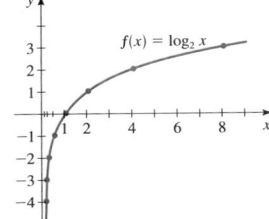

FIGURE 3

✎ NOW TRY EXERCISE 41

Figure 4 shows the graphs of the family of logarithmic functions with bases 2, 3, 5, and 10. These graphs are drawn by reflecting the graphs of $y = 2^x$, $y = 3^x$, $y = 5^x$, and $y = 10^x$ (see Figure 2 in Section 4.1) in the line $y = x$. We can also plot points as an aid to sketching these graphs, as illustrated in Example 4.

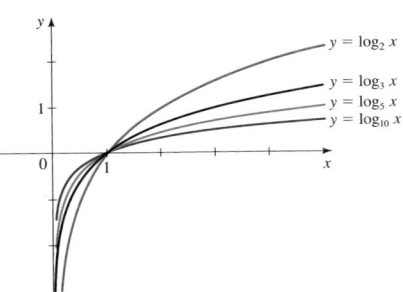

FIGURE 4 A family of logarithmic functions

x	0.1	1	2	3	4	5	6	7	8	9	10
$\log_{10} x$	-1	0	0.30	0.47	0.60	0.70	0.78	0.85	0.90	0.95	1

ALTERNATE EXAMPLE 5

Sketch the graph of each function.
(a) $g(x) = -\log_3 x$
(b) $h(x) = \log_3(-x)$

ANSWERS:

(a)

(b)

ALTERNATE EXAMPLE 6

Sketch the graph of the following function:

$$g(x) = \log_2(x-2) - 3$$

ANSWER

© Bettmann /CORBIS   © Hulton-Deutsch Collection /CORBIS

Law Enforcement
Mathematics aids law enforcement in numerous and surprising ways, from the reconstruction of bullet trajectories to determining the time of death to calculating the probability that a DNA sample is from a particular person. One interesting use is in the search for missing persons. A person who has been missing for several years might look quite different from his or her most recent available photograph. This is particularly true if the missing person is a child. Have you ever wondered what you will look like 5, 10, or 15 years from now?

Researchers have found that different parts of the body grow at different rates. For example, you have no doubt noticed that a baby's head is much larger relative to its body than an adult's. As another example, the ratio of arm length to height is $\frac{1}{3}$ in a child but about $\frac{2}{5}$ in an adult. By collecting data and analyzing the graphs, researchers are able to determine the functions that model growth. As in all growth phenomena, exponential and logarithmic functions play a crucial role. For instance, the formula that relates arm length l to height h is $l = ae^{kh}$ where a and k are constants. By studying various physical characteristics of a person, mathematical biologists model each characteristic by a function that describes how it changes over time. Models of facial characteristics can be programmed into a computer to give a picture of how a person's appearance changes over time. These pictures aid law enforcement agencies in locating missing persons.

In the next two examples we graph logarithmic functions by starting with the basic graphs in Figure 4 and using the transformations of Section 2.5.

EXAMPLE 5 | Reflecting Graphs of Logarithmic Functions

Sketch the graph of each function.
(a) $g(x) = -\log_2 x$
(b) $h(x) = \log_2(-x)$

SOLUTION

(a) We start with the graph of $f(x) = \log_2 x$ and reflect in the x-axis to get the graph of $g(x) = -\log_2 x$ in Figure 5(a).

(b) We start with the graph of $f(x) = \log_2 x$ and reflect in the y-axis to get the graph of $h(x) = \log_2(-x)$ in Figure 5(b).

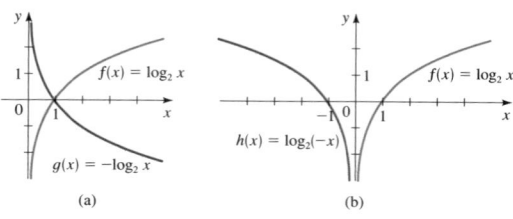

(a)   (b)

FIGURE 5

NOW TRY EXERCISE 55

EXAMPLE 6 | Shifting Graphs of Logarithmic Functions

Find the domain of each function, and sketch the graph.
(a) $g(x) = 2 + \log_5 x$
(b) $h(x) = \log_{10}(x - 3)$

SOLUTION

(a) The graph of g is obtained from the graph of $f(x) = \log_5 x$ (Figure 4) by shifting upward 2 units (see Figure 6). The domain of f is $(0, \infty)$.

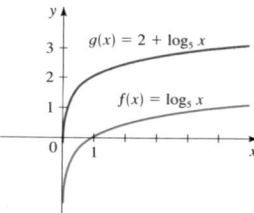

FIGURE 6

(b) The graph of h is obtained from the graph of $f(x) = \log_{10} x$ (Figure 4) by shifting to the right 3 units (see Figure 7). The line $x = 3$ is a vertical asymptote. Since $\log_{10} x$ is defined only when $x > 0$, the domain of $h(x) = \log_{10}(x - 3)$ is

$$\{x \mid x - 3 > 0\} = \{x \mid x > 3\} = (3, \infty)$$

IN-CLASS MATERIALS

Ask your students if they have ever had to deal with recharging a battery, for example, the battery to a music device or a laptop. Assume that the battery is dead and it takes an hour to charge it up halfway. Ask them how much it will be charged in 2 hours. (The answer is 75% charged.) They may have noticed that, when charging older laptop batteries, the power meter rarely says "100% charged." It turns out that the time it takes to charge the battery to $n\%$ is given by $t = -k \ln\left(1 - \frac{n}{100}\right)$; in our example, $k = 1.4427$. Have students compute how long it would take the battery to get a 97% charge, a 98% charge, and a 99% charge. (Remind them that it took only an hour to go from 0% to 50%.) Graph t versus n to demonstrate that the battery will never be fully charged.

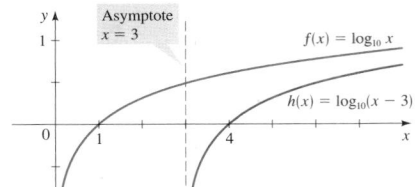

FIGURE 7

↖. NOW TRY EXERCISES **53** AND **57**

JOHN NAPIER (1550–1617) was a Scottish landowner for whom mathematics was a hobby. We know him today because of his key invention: logarithms, which he published in 1614 under the title *A Description of the Marvelous Rule of Logarithms*. In Napier's time, logarithms were used exclusively for simplifying complicated calculations. For example, to multiply two large numbers, we would write them as powers of 10. The exponents are simply the logarithms of the numbers. For instance,

4532 × 57783

$\approx 10^{3.65629} \times 10^{4.76180}$

$= 10^{8.41809}$

$\approx 261{,}872{,}564$

The idea is that multiplying powers of 10 is easy (we simply add their exponents). Napier produced extensive tables giving the logarithms (or exponents) of numbers. Since the advent of calculators and computers, logarithms are no longer used for this purpose. The logarithmic functions, however, have found many applications, some of which are described in this chapter.

Napier wrote on many topics. One of his most colorful works is a book entitled *A Plaine Discovery of the Whole Revelation of Saint John*, in which he predicted that the world would end in the year 1700.

▼ **Common Logarithms**

We now study logarithms with base 10.

COMMON LOGARITHM

The logarithm with base 10 is called the **common logarithm** and is denoted by omitting the base:

$$\log x = \log_{10} x$$

From the definition of logarithms we can easily find that

$$\log 10 = 1 \quad \text{and} \quad \log 100 = 2$$

But how do we find log 50? We need to find the exponent y such that $10^y = 50$. Clearly, 1 is too small and 2 is too large. So

$$1 < \log 50 < 2$$

To get a better approximation, we can experiment to find a power of 10 closer to 50. Fortunately, scientific calculators are equipped with a ⎡LOG⎤ key that directly gives values of common logarithms.

EXAMPLE 7 | Evaluating Common Logarithms

Use a calculator to find appropriate values of $f(x) = \log x$ and use the values to sketch the graph.

SOLUTION   We make a table of values, using a calculator to evaluate the function at those values of x that are not powers of 10. We plot those points and connect them by a smooth curve as in Figure 8.

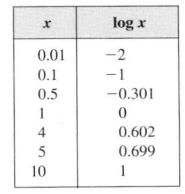

x	$\log x$
0.01	−2
0.1	−1
0.5	−0.301
1	0
4	0.602
5	0.699
10	1

FIGURE 8

↖. NOW TRY EXERCISE **43**

IN-CLASS MATERIALS

Show students semilog graph paper (available from the web, university bookstores, or your friendly neighborhood physics teacher). Point out how the distance between the y-axis lines is based on the logarithm of the y-coordinate, not on the y-coordinate itself. Have them graph $y = 2^x$ on semilog graph paper.

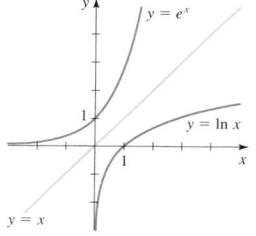

Human response to sound and light intensity is logarithmic.

We study the decibel scale in more detail in Section 4.6.

Scientists model human response to stimuli (such as sound, light, or pressure) using logarithmic functions. For example, the intensity of a sound must be increased manyfold before we "feel" that the loudness has simply doubled. The psychologist Gustav Fechner formulated the law as

$$S = k \log\left(\frac{I}{I_0}\right)$$

where S is the subjective intensity of the stimulus, I is the physical intensity of the stimulus, I_0 stands for the threshold physical intensity, and k is a constant that is different for each sensory stimulus.

EXAMPLE 8 | Common Logarithms and Sound

The perception of the loudness B (in decibels, dB) of a sound with physical intensity I (in W/m^2) is given by

$$B = 10 \log\left(\frac{I}{I_0}\right)$$

where I_0 is the physical intensity of a barely audible sound. Find the decibel level (loudness) of a sound whose physical intensity I is 100 times that of I_0.

SOLUTION   We find the decibel level B by using the fact that $I = 100I_0$.

$$B = 10 \log\left(\frac{I}{I_0}\right) \qquad \text{Definition of } B$$

$$= 10 \log\left(\frac{100I_0}{I_0}\right) \qquad I = 100I_0$$

$$= 10 \log 100 \qquad \text{Cancel } I_0$$

$$= 10 \cdot 2 = 20 \qquad \text{Definition of log}$$

The loudness of the sound is 20 dB.

✎ NOW TRY EXERCISE **87**   ■

▼ Natural Logarithms

The notation ln is an abbreviation for the Latin name *logarithmus naturalis*.

Of all possible bases a for logarithms, it turns out that the most convenient choice for the purposes of calculus is the number e, which we defined in Section 4.2.

NATURAL LOGARITHM

The logarithm with base e is called the **natural logarithm** and is denoted by **ln**:

$$\ln x = \log_e x$$

The natural logarithmic function $y = \ln x$ is the inverse function of the natural exponential function $y = e^x$. Both functions are graphed in Figure 9. By the definition of inverse functions we have

$$\ln x = y \quad \Leftrightarrow \quad e^y = x$$

FIGURE 9   Graph of the natural logarithmic function

If we substitute $a = e$ and write "ln" for "$\log_e$" in the properties of logarithms mentioned earlier, we obtain the following properties of natural logarithms.

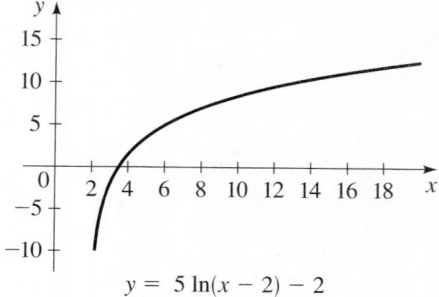

PROPERTIES OF NATURAL LOGARITHMS	
Property	**Reason**
1. $\ln 1 = 0$	We must raise e to the power 0 to get 1.
2. $\ln e = 1$	We must raise e to the power 1 to get e.
3. $\ln e^x = x$	We must raise e to the power x to get e^x.
4. $e^{\ln x} = x$	$\ln x$ is the power to which e must be raised to get x.

Calculators are equipped with an $\boxed{\text{LN}}$ key that directly gives the values of natural logarithms.

EXAMPLE 9 | Evaluating the Natural Logarithm Function

(a) $\ln e^8 = 8$ Definition of natural logarithm

(b) $\ln\left(\dfrac{1}{e^2}\right) = \ln e^{-2} = -2$ Definition of natural logarithm

(c) $\ln 5 \approx 1.609$ Use $\boxed{\text{LN}}$ key on calculator

✎. NOW TRY EXERCISE **39**

EXAMPLE 10 | Finding the Domain of a Logarithmic Function

Find the domain of the function $f(x) = \ln(4 - x^2)$.

SOLUTION   As with any logarithmic function, $\ln x$ is defined when $x > 0$. Thus, the domain of f is

$$\{x \mid 4 - x^2 > 0\} = \{x \mid x^2 < 4\} = \{x \mid |x| < 2\}$$
$$= \{x \mid -2 < x < 2\} = (-2, 2)$$

✎. NOW TRY EXERCISE **63**

EXAMPLE 11 | Drawing the Graph of a Logarithmic Function

Draw the graph of the function $y = x \ln(4 - x^2)$, and use it to find the asymptotes and local maximum and minimum values.

SOLUTION   As in Example 10 the domain of this function is the interval $(-2, 2)$, so we choose the viewing rectangle $[-3, 3]$ by $[-3, 3]$. The graph is shown in Figure 10, and from it we see that the lines $x = -2$ and $x = 2$ are vertical asymptotes.

The function has a local maximum point to the right of $x = 1$ and a local minimum point to the left of $x = -1$. By zooming in and tracing along the graph with the cursor, we find that the local maximum value is approximately 1.13 and this occurs when $x \approx 1.15$. Similarly (or by noticing that the function is odd), we find that the local minimum value is about -1.13, and it occurs when $x \approx -1.15$.

✎. NOW TRY EXERCISE **69**

FIGURE 10
$y = x \ln(4 - x^2)$

4.3 EXERCISES

CONCEPTS

1. $\log x$ is the exponent to which the base 10 must be raised to get

_____. So we can complete the following table for $\log x$.

x	10^3	10^2	10^1	10^0	10^{-1}	10^{-2}	10^{-3}	$10^{1/2}$
$\log x$								

2. The function $f(x) = \log_9 x$ is the logarithm function with

base _____. So $f(9) = $ _____, $f(1) = $ _____,

$f(\frac{1}{9}) = $ _____, $f(81) = $ _____, and $f(3) = $ _____.

3. (a) $5^3 = 125$, so $\log$ ▦ ▦ = ▦

(b) $\log_5 25 = 2$, so ▦ ▦ = ▦

4. Match the logarithmic function with its graph.
(a) $f(x) = \log_2 x$ (b) $f(x) = \log_2(-x)$
(c) $f(x) = -\log_2 x$ (d) $f(x) = -\log_2(-x)$

I

II

III

IV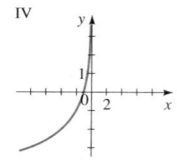

SKILLS

5–6 ■ Complete the table by finding the appropriate logarithmic or exponential form of the equation, as in Example 1.

5.

Logarithmic form	Exponential form
$\log_8 8 = 1$	
$\log_8 64 = 2$	
	$8^{2/3} = 4$
	$8^3 = 512$
$\log_8 \left(\frac{1}{8}\right) = -1$	
	$8^{-2} = \frac{1}{64}$

6.

Logarithmic form	Exponential form
	$4^3 = 64$
$\log_4 2 = \frac{1}{2}$	
	$4^{3/2} = 8$
$\log_4\left(\frac{1}{16}\right) = -2$	
$\log_4\left(\frac{1}{2}\right) = -\frac{1}{2}$	
	$4^{-5/2} = \frac{1}{32}$

7–12 ■ Express the equation in exponential form.

7. (a) $\log_5 25 = 2$ (b) $\log_5 1 = 0$

8. (a) $\log_{10} 0.1 = -1$ (b) $\log_8 512 = 3$

9. (a) $\log_8 2 = \frac{1}{3}$ (b) $\log_2\left(\frac{1}{8}\right) = -3$

10. (a) $\log_3 81 = 4$ (b) $\log_8 4 = \frac{2}{3}$

11. (a) $\ln 5 = x$ (b) $\ln y = 5$

12. (a) $\ln(x + 1) = 2$ (b) $\ln(x - 1) = 4$

13–18 ■ Express the equation in logarithmic form.

13. (a) $5^3 = 125$ (b) $10^{-4} = 0.0001$

14. (a) $10^3 = 1000$ (b) $81^{1/2} = 9$

15. (a) $8^{-1} = \frac{1}{8}$ (b) $2^{-3} = \frac{1}{8}$

16. (a) $4^{-3/2} = 0.125$ (b) $7^3 = 343$

17. (a) $e^x = 2$ (b) $e^3 = y$

18. (a) $e^{x+1} = 0.5$ (b) $e^{0.5x} = t$

19–28 ■ Evaluate the expression.

19. (a) $\log_3 3$ (b) $\log_3 1$ (c) $\log_3 3^2$

20. (a) $\log_5 5^4$ (b) $\log_4 64$ (c) $\log_3 9$

21. (a) $\log_6 36$ (b) $\log_9 81$ (c) $\log_7 7^{10}$

22. (a) $\log_2 32$ (b) $\log_8 8^{17}$ (c) $\log_6 1$

23. (a) $\log_3\left(\frac{1}{27}\right)$ (b) $\log_{10} \sqrt{10}$ (c) $\log_5 0.2$

24. (a) $\log_5 125$ (b) $\log_{49} 7$ (c) $\log_9 \sqrt{3}$

25. (a) $2^{\log_2 37}$ (b) $3^{\log_3 8}$ (c) $e^{\ln\sqrt{5}}$

26. (a) $e^{\ln \pi}$ (b) $10^{\log 5}$ (c) $10^{\log 87}$

27. (a) $\log_8 0.25$ (b) $\ln e^4$ (c) $\ln(1/e)$

28. (a) $\log_4 \sqrt{2}$ (b) $\log_4\left(\frac{1}{2}\right)$ (c) $\log_4 8$

29–36 ■ Use the definition of the logarithmic function to find x.

29. (a) $\log_2 x = 5$ (b) $\log_2 16 = x$

30. (a) $\log_5 x = 4$ (b) $\log_{10} 0.1 = x$

31. (a) $\log_3 243 = x$ (b) $\log_3 x = 3$

32. (a) $\log_4 2 = x$ (b) $\log_4 x = 2$

33. (a) $\log_{10} x = 2$ (b) $\log_5 x = 2$

34. (a) $\log_x 1000 = 3$ (b) $\log_x 25 = 2$

35. (a) $\log_x 16 = 4$ (b) $\log_x 8 = \frac{3}{2}$

36. (a) $\log_x 6 = \frac{1}{2}$ (b) $\log_x 3 = \frac{1}{3}$

37–40 ■ Use a calculator to evaluate the expression, correct to four decimal places.

37. (a) $\log 2$ (b) $\log 35.2$ (c) $\log\left(\frac{2}{3}\right)$

38. (a) $\log 50$ (b) $\log \sqrt{2}$ (c) $\log(3\sqrt{2})$

39. (a) $\ln 5$ (b) $\ln 25.3$ (c) $\ln(1 + \sqrt{3})$

40. (a) $\ln 27$ (b) $\ln 7.39$ (c) $\ln 54.6$

41–44 ■ Sketch the graph of the function by plotting points.

41. $f(x) = \log_3 x$ **42.** $g(x) = \log_4 x$

43. $f(x) = 2 \log x$ **44.** $g(x) = 1 + \log x$

45–48 ■ Find the function of the form $y = \log_a x$ whose graph is given.

45.

(5, 1)

46.

$\left(\frac{1}{2}, -1\right)$

47.

$\left(3, \frac{1}{2}\right)$

48.

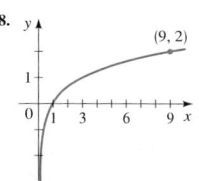

(9, 2)

49–50 ■ Match the logarithmic function with one of the graphs labeled I or II.

49. $f(x) = 2 + \ln x$ **50.** $f(x) = \ln(x - 2)$

I

(1, 2)

II

$x = 2$

(3, 0)

51. Draw the graph of $y = 4^x$, then use it to draw the graph of $y = \log_4 x$.

52. Draw the graph of $y = 3^x$, then use it to draw the graph of $y = \log_3 x$.

53–62 ■ Graph the function, not by plotting points, but by starting from the graphs in Figures 4 and 9. State the domain, range, and asymptote.

53. $f(x) = \log_2(x - 4)$ **54.** $f(x) = -\log_{10} x$

55. $g(x) = \log_5(-x)$ **56.** $g(x) = \ln(x + 2)$

57. $y = 2 + \log_3 x$ **58.** $y = \log_3(x - 1) - 2$

59. $y = 1 - \log_{10} x$ **60.** $y = 1 + \ln(-x)$

61. $y = |\ln x|$ **62.** $y = \ln|x|$

63–68 ■ Find the domain of the function.

63. $f(x) = \log_{10}(x + 3)$ **64.** $f(x) = \log_5(8 - 2x)$

65. $g(x) = \log_3(x^2 - 1)$ **66.** $g(x) = \ln(x - x^2)$

67. $h(x) = \ln x + \ln(2 - x)$

68. $h(x) = \sqrt{x - 2} - \log_5(10 - x)$

69–74 ■ Draw the graph of the function in a suitable viewing rectangle, and use it to find the domain, the asymptotes, and the local maximum and minimum values.

69. $y = \log_{10}(1 - x^2)$ **70.** $y = \ln(x^2 - x)$

71. $y = x + \ln x$ **72.** $y = x(\ln x)^2$

73. $y = \dfrac{\ln x}{x}$ **74.** $y = x \log_{10}(x + 10)$

75-78 ■ Find the functions $f \circ g$ and $g \circ f$ and their domains.

75. $f(x) = 2^x$, $g(x) = x + 1$

76. $f(x) = 3^x$, $g(x) = x^2 + 1$

77. $f(x) = \log_2 x$, $g(x) = x - 2$

78. $f(x) = \log x$, $g(x) = x^2$

79. Compare the rates of growth of the functions $f(x) = \ln x$ and $g(x) = \sqrt{x}$ by drawing their graphs on a common screen using the viewing rectangle $[-1, 30]$ by $[-1, 6]$.

80. (a) By drawing the graphs of the functions

$$f(x) = 1 + \ln(1 + x) \quad \text{and} \quad g(x) = \sqrt{x}$$

in a suitable viewing rectangle, show that even when a logarithmic function starts out higher than a root function, it is ultimately overtaken by the root function.

(b) Find, correct to two decimal places, the solutions of the equation $\sqrt{x} = 1 + \ln(1 + x)$.

81–82 ■ A family of functions is given. (a) Draw graphs of the family for $c = 1, 2, 3,$ and 4. (b) How are the graphs in part (a) related?

81. $f(x) = \log(cx)$ **82.** $f(x) = c \log x$

83–84 ■ A function $f(x)$ is given. (a) Find the domain of the function f. (b) Find the inverse function of f.

83. $f(x) = \log_2(\log_{10} x)$ **84.** $f(x) = \ln(\ln(\ln x))$

85. (a) Find the inverse of the function $f(x) = \dfrac{2^x}{1 + 2^x}$.

(b) What is the domain of the inverse function?

APPLICATIONS

86. Absorption of Light A spectrophotometer measures the concentration of a sample dissolved in water by shining a light through it and recording the amount of light that emerges. In other words, if we know the amount of light that is absorbed, we can calculate the concentration of the sample. For a certain substance the concentration (in moles per liter) is found by using the formula

$$C = -2500 \ln\left(\frac{I}{I_0}\right)$$

where I_0 is the intensity of the incident light and I is the intensity of light that emerges. Find the concentration of the substance if the intensity I is 70% of I_0.

87. Carbon Dating The age of an ancient artifact can be determined by the amount of radioactive carbon-14 remaining in it. If D_0 is the original amount of carbon-14 and D is the amount remaining, then the artifact's age A (in years) is given by

$$A = -8267 \ln\left(\frac{D}{D_0}\right)$$

Find the age of an object if the amount D of carbon-14 that remains in the object is 73% of the original amount D_0.

88. Bacteria Colony A certain strain of bacteria divides every three hours. If a colony is started with 50 bacteria, then the time t (in hours) required for the colony to grow to N bacteria is given by

$$t = 3\frac{\log(N/50)}{\log 2}$$

Find the time required for the colony to grow to a million bacteria.

89. Investment The time required to double the amount of an investment at an interest rate r compounded continuously is given by

$$t = \frac{\ln 2}{r}$$

Find the time required to double an investment at 6%, 7%, and 8%.

90. Charging a Battery The rate at which a battery charges is slower the closer the battery is to its maximum charge C_0. The time (in hours) required to charge a fully discharged battery to a charge C is given by

$$t = -k \ln\left(1 - \frac{C}{C_0}\right)$$

where k is a positive constant that depends on the battery. For a certain battery, $k = 0.25$. If this battery is fully discharged, how long will it take to charge to 90% of its maximum charge C_0?

91. Difficulty of a Task The difficulty in "acquiring a target" (such as using your mouse to click on an icon on your computer screen) depends on the distance to the target and the size of the target. According to Fitts's Law, the index of difficulty (ID) is given by

$$ID = \frac{\log(2A/W)}{\log 2}$$

where W is the width of the target and A is the distance to the center of the target. Compare the difficulty of clicking on an icon that is 5 mm wide to clicking on one that is 10 mm wide. In each case, assume that the mouse is 100 mm from the icon.

DISCOVERY ▪ DISCUSSION ▪ WRITING

92. The Height of the Graph of a Logarithmic Function Suppose that the graph of $y = 2^x$ is drawn on a coordinate plane where the unit of measurement is an inch.
(a) Show that at a distance 2 ft to the right of the origin the height of the graph is about 265 mi.
(b) If the graph of $y = \log_2 x$ is drawn on the same set of axes, how far to the right of the origin do we have to go before the height of the curve reaches 2 ft?

93. The Googolplex A **googol** is 10^{100}, and a **googolplex** is 10^{googol}. Find

$$\log(\log(\text{googol})) \qquad \text{and} \qquad \log(\log(\log(\text{googolplex})))$$

94. Comparing Logarithms Which is larger, $\log_4 17$ or $\log_5 24$? Explain your reasoning.

95. The Number of Digits in an Integer Compare $\log 1000$ to the number of digits in 1000. Do the same for 10,000. How many digits does any number between 1000 and 10,000 have? Between what two values must the common logarithm of such a number lie? Use your observations to explain why the number of digits in any positive integer x is $\llbracket \log x \rrbracket + 1$. (The symbol $\llbracket n \rrbracket$ is the greatest integer function defined in Section 2.2.) How many digits does the number 2^{100} have?

4.4 LAWS OF LOGARITHMS

Laws of Logarithms ▶ Expanding and Combining Logarithmic Expressions ▶ Change of Base Formula

In this section we study properties of logarithms. These properties give logarithmic functions a wide range of applications, as we will see in Section 4.6.

▼ Laws of Logarithms

Since logarithms are exponents, the Laws of Exponents give rise to the Laws of Logarithms.

LAWS OF LOGARITHMS

Let a be a positive number, with $a \neq 1$. Let A, B, and C be any real numbers with $A > 0$ and $B > 0$.

Law	Description
1. $\log_a(AB) = \log_a A + \log_a B$	The logarithm of a product of numbers is the sum of the logarithms of the numbers.
2. $\log_a\left(\dfrac{A}{B}\right) = \log_a A - \log_a B$	The logarithm of a quotient of numbers is the difference of the logarithms of the numbers.
3. $\log_a(A^C) = C \log_a A$	The logarithm of a power of a number is the exponent times the logarithm of the number.

PROOF   We make use of the property $\log_a a^x = x$ from Section 4.3.

Law 1   Let $\log_a A = u$ and $\log_a B = v$. When written in exponential form, these equations become

$$a^u = A \qquad \text{and} \qquad a^v = B \ .$$

Thus
$$\log_a(AB) = \log_a(a^u a^v) = \log_a(a^{u+v})$$
$$= u + v = \log_a A + \log_a B$$

Law 2   Using Law 1, we have
$$\log_a A = \log_a\left[\left(\frac{A}{B}\right)B\right] = \log_a\left(\frac{A}{B}\right) + \log_a B$$

so
$$\log_a\left(\frac{A}{B}\right) = \log_a A - \log_a B$$

Law 3   Let $\log_a A = u$. Then $a^u = A$, so
$$\log_a(A^C) = \log_a(a^u)^C = \log_a(a^{uC}) = uC = C \log_a A \qquad \blacksquare$$

EXAMPLE 1 | Using the Laws of Logarithms to Evaluate Expressions

Evaluate each expression.
(a) $\log_4 2 + \log_4 32$
(b) $\log_2 80 - \log_2 5$
(c) $-\frac{1}{3} \log 8$

SUGGESTED TIME AND EMPHASIS

1 class, essential material

ALTERNATE EXAMPLE 1
Evaluate each expression.
(a) $\log_6 8 + \log_6 27$
(b) $\log 8000 - \log 8$
(c) $\frac{1}{2}\log_3 25$

ANSWERS
(a)
$\log_6 8 + \log_6 27 = \log_6 216 = 3$
(b)
$\log 8000 - \log 8 = \log(1000) = 3$
(c) $\frac{1}{2}\log_3 25 = \log_3 5 \approx 1.465$

TEXT QUESTION
Given that $\log_2 3 \approx 1.58496$, what is the approximate value of $\log_2 9$?

Answer
$\log_2 9 \approx 3.16992$

SOLUTION

(a) $\log_4 2 + \log_4 32 = \log_4(2 \cdot 32)$ Law 1

                  $= \log_4 64 = 3$ Because $64 = 4^3$

(b) $\log_2 80 - \log_2 5 = \log_2\left(\frac{80}{5}\right)$ Law 2

                  $= \log_2 16 = 4$ Because $16 = 2^4$

(c) $-\frac{1}{3}\log 8 = \log 8^{-1/3}$ Law 3

             $= \log\left(\frac{1}{2}\right)$ Property of negative exponents

             ≈ -0.301 Calculator

✎ **NOW TRY EXERCISES 7, 9, AND 11** ◼

▼ Expanding and Combining Logarithmic Expressions

The Laws of Logarithms allow us to write the logarithm of a product or a quotient as the sum or difference of logarithms. This process, called *expanding* a logarithmic expression, is illustrated in the next example.

EXAMPLE 2 | Expanding Logarithmic Expressions

Use the Laws of Logarithms to expand each expression.

(a) $\log_2(6x)$ (b) $\log_5(x^3 y^6)$ (c) $\ln\left(\dfrac{ab}{\sqrt[3]{c}}\right)$

SOLUTION

(a) $\log_2(6x) = \log_2 6 + \log_2 x$ Law 1

(b) $\log_5(x^3 y^6) = \log_5 x^3 + \log_5 y^6$ Law 1

               $= 3\log_5 x + 6\log_5 y$ Law 3

(c) $\ln\left(\dfrac{ab}{\sqrt[3]{c}}\right) = \ln(ab) - \ln\sqrt[3]{c}$ Law 2

              $= \ln a + \ln b - \ln c^{1/3}$ Law 1

              $= \ln a + \ln b - \frac{1}{3}\ln c$ Law 3

✎ **NOW TRY EXERCISES 19, 21, AND 33** ◼

The Laws of Logarithms also allow us to reverse the process of expanding that was done in Example 2. That is, we can write sums and differences of logarithms as a single logarithm. This process, called *combining* logarithmic expressions, is illustrated in the next example.

EXAMPLE 3 | Combining Logarithmic Expressions

Combine $3 \log x + \frac{1}{2}\log(x + 1)$ into a single logarithm.

SOLUTION

     $3\log x + \frac{1}{2}\log(x+1) = \log x^3 + \log(x+1)^{1/2}$ Law 3

                           $= \log(x^3(x+1)^{1/2})$ Law 1

✎ **NOW TRY EXERCISE 47** ◼

EXAMPLE 4 | Combining Logarithmic Expressions

Combine $3 \ln s + \frac{1}{2}\ln t - 4\ln(t^2 + 1)$ into a single logarithm.

ALTERNATE EXAMPLE 2

Use the laws of logarithms to expand each expression:

(a) $\log_3(9x)$

(b) $\log_{10}(x^3 y^4)$

(c) $\ln\left(\dfrac{a\sqrt{b}}{c^8}\right)$

ANSWERS

(a) $\log_3 9 + \log_3 x = 2 + \log_3 x$

(b) $3\log_{10} x + 4\log_{10} y$

(c) $\ln a + \dfrac{1}{2}\ln b - 8\ln c$

ALTERNATE EXAMPLE 3

Combine $3\ln(x) + \frac{3}{2}\ln(x + 3)$ into a single logarithm.

ANSWER

$\ln\left(x^3\sqrt{(x+3)^3}\right)$

EXAMPLE

A set of logarithms that can be combined:

$a\ln(b + c) + \dfrac{3}{4}(\ln a - \ln b) =$

$\ln\left[(b + c)^a \sqrt[4]{\left(\dfrac{a}{b}\right)^3}\right]$

IN-CLASS MATERIALS

Make sure your students do not neglect the warning after Example 4. Perhaps have them write out all the rules of logarithms they have learned so far, organized as shown in the chart at right. Perhaps if your students memorize the non-rules, they will be less likely to indulge in algebraic mischief under exam pressure.

The Equivalence Definition	$y = \log_m x$ is equivalent to $x = m^y$
The Conversion Rule	$\log_m(\text{expression}) = \dfrac{\log_n(\text{expression})}{\log_n(m)}$
The Combining Rules	$\log_m(m^{\text{expression}}) = \text{expression}$ $m^{\log_m(\text{expression})} = \text{expression}$
The Arithmetic Rules	$\log_m 1 = 0$ $\log_m(ab) = \log_m a + \log_m b$ $\log_m\left(\dfrac{a}{b}\right) = \log_m a - \log_m b$ $\log_m(a^b) = b\log_m a$
The Non-Rules	$\log_m(a + b) = \log_m(a + b)$ $\dfrac{\log_m a}{\log_m b} = \dfrac{\log_m a}{\log_m b}$ $(\log_m a)^b = (\log_m a)^b$

SOLUTION

$$3 \ln s + \tfrac{1}{2} \ln t - 4 \ln(t^2 + 1) = \ln s^3 + \ln t^{1/2} - \ln(t^2 + 1)^4 \qquad \text{Law 3}$$

$$= \ln(s^3 t^{1/2}) - \ln(t^2 + 1)^4 \qquad \text{Law 1}$$

$$= \ln\!\left(\frac{s^3 \sqrt{t}}{(t^2 + 1)^4}\right) \qquad \text{Law 2}$$

✎. NOW TRY EXERCISE **49**   ■

Warning   Although the Laws of Logarithms tell us how to compute the logarithm of a product or a quotient, *there is no corresponding rule for the logarithm of a sum or a difference.* For instance,

⊘
$$\log_a(x + y) \neq \log_a x + \log_a y$$

In fact, we know that the right side is equal to $\log_a(xy)$. Also, don't improperly simplify quotients or powers of logarithms. For instance,

⊘
$$\frac{\log 6}{\log 2} \neq \log\!\left(\frac{6}{2}\right) \qquad \text{and} \qquad (\log_2 x)^3 \neq 3 \log_2 x$$

Logarithmic functions are used to model a variety of situations involving human behavior. One such behavior is how quickly we forget things we have learned. For example, if you learn algebra at a certain performance level (say, 90% on a test) and then don't use algebra for a while, how much will you retain after a week, a month, or a year? Hermann Ebbinghaus (1850–1909) studied this phenomenon and formulated the law described in the next example.

EXAMPLE 5 | The Law of Forgetting

If a task is learned at a performance level P_0, then after a time interval t the performance level P satisfies

$$\log P = \log P_0 - c \log(t + 1)$$

where c is a constant that depends on the type of task and t is measured in months.

(a) Solve for P.

(b) If your score on a history test is 90, what score would you expect to get on a similar test after two months? After a year? (Assume that $c = 0.2$.)

SOLUTION

(a) We first combine the right-hand side.

$$\log P = \log P_0 - c \log(t + 1) \qquad \text{Given equation}$$

$$\log P = \log P_0 - \log(t + 1)^c \qquad \text{Law 3}$$

$$\log P = \log \frac{P_0}{(t + 1)^c} \qquad \text{Law 2}$$

$$P = \frac{P_0}{(t + 1)^c} \qquad \text{Because log is one-to-one}$$

(b) Here $P_0 = 90$, $c = 0.2$, and t is measured in months.

In two months: $t = 2$ and $P = \dfrac{90}{(2 + 1)^{0.2}} \approx 72$

In one year: $t = 12$ and $P = \dfrac{90}{(12 + 1)^{0.2}} \approx 54$

Your expected scores after two months and one year are 72 and 54, respectively.

✎. NOW TRY EXERCISE **69**   ■

Forgetting what we've learned depends on how long ago we learned it.

IN-CLASS MATERIALS

Note that the log rules assume that all numbers lie within the proper domains. For example, $\ln\!\left(\dfrac{-5}{-6}\right)$ is not equal to $\ln(-5) - \ln(-6)$. The first expression is defined, and the second expression is not.

ALTERNATE EXAMPLE 4
Combine $\log(x) - 3 \log(y) + \log(x + y)$ into a single logarithm.

ANSWER
$$\log\!\left[\frac{x(x + y)}{y^3}\right]$$

ALTERNATE EXAMPLE 5
A ninth-grade student memorizes the Latin terms for 50 animals. One year later, she still knows 40 of them. According to Ebbinghaus' Law of Forgetting, how many will she know 2 years after that—when she is in 12th grade?

ANSWER
First we need to find c:
$\log 40 = \log 50 - c \log(13)$
So $c \approx 0.087$.

Next, we use our value of c in the Ebbinghaus' equation:
$\log P = \log 50 - 0.087 \log(37)$
So P is between 36 and 37 Latin terms.

EXAMPLE
A set of logarithms that can be expanded:
Given $\ln 2 \approx 0.693$ and $\ln 3 \approx 1.099$, compute $\ln \dfrac{8}{9}\sqrt[5]{6}$.

ANSWER
$$\frac{8}{9}\sqrt[5]{6} = \frac{2^3}{3^2} = (2 \cdot 3)^{1/5}$$
$$\ln\!\left(\frac{8}{9}\sqrt[5]{6}\right) = 3 \ln 2 -$$
$$2 \ln 3 + \frac{1}{5}(\ln 2 + \ln 3)$$
$$\approx 0.240569$$

▼ Change of Base Formula

For some purposes we find it useful to change from logarithms in one base to logarithms in another base. Suppose we are given $\log_a x$ and want to find $\log_b x$. Let

$$y = \log_b x$$

We write this in exponential form and take the logarithm, with base a, of each side.

$$b^y = x \qquad \text{Exponential form}$$
$$\log_a(b^y) = \log_a x \qquad \text{Take } \log_a \text{ of each side}$$
$$y \log_a b = \log_a x \qquad \text{Law 3}$$
$$y = \frac{\log_a x}{\log_a b} \qquad \text{Divide by } \log_a b$$

This proves the following formula.

> We may write the Change of Base Formula as
>
> $$\log_b x = \left(\frac{1}{\log_a b}\right)\log_a x$$
>
> So $\log_b x$ is just a constant multiple of $\log_a x$; the constant is $\dfrac{1}{\log_a b}$.

CHANGE OF BASE FORMULA

$$\log_b x = \frac{\log_a x}{\log_a b}$$

In particular, if we put $x = a$, then $\log_a a = 1$, and this formula becomes

$$\log_b a = \frac{1}{\log_a b}$$

We can now evaluate a logarithm to *any* base by using the Change of Base Formula to express the logarithm in terms of common logarithms or natural logarithms and then using a calculator.

EXAMPLE 6 | Evaluating Logarithms with the Change of Base Formula

Use the Change of Base Formula and common or natural logarithms to evaluate each logarithm, correct to five decimal places.

(a) $\log_8 5$ **(b)** $\log_9 20$

SOLUTION

(a) We use the Change of Base Formula with $b = 8$ and $a = 10$:

$$\log_8 5 = \frac{\log_{10} 5}{\log_{10} 8} \approx 0.77398$$

(b) We use the Change of Base Formula with $b = 9$ and $a = e$:

$$\log_9 20 = \frac{\ln 20}{\ln 9} \approx 1.36342$$

✎. NOW TRY EXERCISES **55** AND **57**

EXAMPLE 7 | Using the Change of Base Formula to Graph a Logarithmic Function

Use a graphing calculator to graph $f(x) = \log_6 x$.

SOLUTION Calculators don't have a key for $\log_6$, so we use the Change of Base Formula to write

$$f(x) = \log_6 x = \frac{\ln x}{\ln 6}$$

Since calculators do have an $\boxed{\text{LN}}$ key, we can enter this new form of the function and graph it. The graph is shown in Figure 1.

✎ **NOW TRY EXERCISE 63**

FIGURE 1 $f(x) = \log_6 x = \dfrac{\ln x}{\ln 6}$

4.4 EXERCISES

CONCEPTS

1. The logarithm of a product of two numbers is the same as the _____ of the logarithms of these numbers. So $\log_5(25 \cdot 125) =$ _____ + _____ .

2. The logarithm of a quotient of two numbers is the same as the _____ of the logarithms of these numbers. So $\log_5\left(\frac{25}{125}\right) =$ _____ − _____ .

3. The logarithm of a number raised to a power is the same as the power _____ the logarithm of the number. So $\log_5(25^{10}) =$ _____ · _____ .

4. **(a)** We can expand $\log\left(\dfrac{x^2 y}{z}\right)$ to get _____ .
   (b) We can combine $2 \log x + \log y - \log z$ to get _____ .

5. Most calculators can find logarithms with base _____ and base _____ . To find logarithms with different bases, we use the _____ Formula. To find $\log_7 12$, we write
$$\log_7 12 = \frac{\log \square}{\log \square} = \text{\_\_\_\_\_}$$

6. *True or false?* We get the same answer if we do the calculation in Exercise 5 using ln in place of log.

SKILLS

7–18 ■ Evaluate the expression.

✎ **7.** $\log_3 \sqrt{27}$ **8.** $\log_2 160 - \log_2 5$

✎ **9.** $\log 4 + \log 25$ **10.** $\log \dfrac{1}{\sqrt{1000}}$

✎ **11.** $\log_4 192 - \log_4 3$ **12.** $\log_{12} 9 + \log_{12} 16$

13. $\log_2 6 - \log_2 15 + \log_2 20$

14. $\log_3 100 - \log_3 18 - \log_3 50$

15. $\log_4 16^{100}$ **16.** $\log_2 8^{33}$

17. $\log(\log 10^{10,000})$ **18.** $\ln(\ln e^{e^{200}})$

19–44 ■ Use the Laws of Logarithms to expand the expression.

✎ **19.** $\log_2(2x)$ **20.** $\log_3(5y)$

✎ **21.** $\log_2(x(x-1))$ **22.** $\log_5 \dfrac{x}{2}$

23. $\log 6^{10}$ **24.** $\ln \sqrt{z}$

25. $\log_2(AB^2)$ **26.** $\log_6 \sqrt[4]{17}$

27. $\log_3(x\sqrt{y})$ **28.** $\log_2(xy)^{10}$

29. $\log_5 \sqrt[3]{x^2+1}$ **30.** $\log_a\left(\dfrac{x^2}{yz^3}\right)$

31. $\ln\sqrt{ab}$ **32.** $\ln\sqrt[3]{3r^2 s}$

✎ **33.** $\log\left(\dfrac{x^3 y^4}{z^6}\right)$ **34.** $\log\left(\dfrac{a^2}{b^4\sqrt{c}}\right)$

35. $\log_2\left(\dfrac{x(x^2+1)}{\sqrt{x^2-1}}\right)$ **36.** $\log_5\sqrt{\dfrac{x-1}{x+1}}$

37. $\ln\left(x\sqrt{\dfrac{y}{z}}\right)$ **38.** $\ln\dfrac{3x^2}{(x+1)^{10}}$

39. $\log\sqrt[4]{x^2+y^2}$ **40.** $\log\left(\dfrac{x}{\sqrt[3]{1-x}}\right)$

41. $\log\sqrt{\dfrac{x^2+4}{(x^2+1)(x^3-7)^2}}$ **42.** $\log\sqrt{x\sqrt{y\sqrt{z}}}$

43. $\ln\left(\dfrac{x^3\sqrt{x-1}}{3x+4}\right)$ **44.** $\log\left(\dfrac{10^x}{x(x^2+1)(x^4+2)}\right)$

45–54 ■ Use the Laws of Logarithms to combine the expression.

45. $\log_3 5 + 5 \log_3 2$

46. $\log 12 + \frac{1}{2}\log 7 - \log 2$

✎ **47.** $\log_2 A + \log_2 B - 2\log_2 C$

48. $\log_5(x^2-1) - \log_5(x-1)$

✎ **49.** $4\log x - \frac{1}{3}\log(x^2+1) + 2\log(x-1)$

50. $\ln(a+b) + \ln(a-b) - 2\ln c$

51. $\ln 5 + 2\ln x + 3\ln(x^2+5)$

52. $2(\log_5 x + 2\log_5 y - 3\log_5 z)$

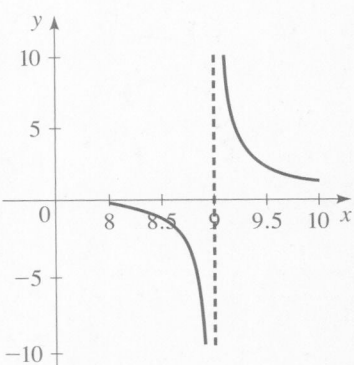

DRILL QUESTION

Express $5\log(x+2) - \dfrac{1}{3}\log x$ as a single logarithm.

Answer

$$\log\left[\frac{(x+2)^5}{\sqrt[3]{x}}\right]$$

53. $\frac{1}{3}\log(x + 2)^3 + \frac{1}{2}[\log x^4 - \log(x^2 - x - 6)^2]$

54. $\log_a b + c \log_a d - r \log_a s$

55–62 ■ Use the Change of Base Formula and a calculator to evaluate the logarithm, rounded to six decimal places. Use either natural or common logarithms.

55. $\log_2 5$

56. $\log_5 2$

57. $\log_3 16$

58. $\log_6 92$

59. $\log_7 2.61$

60. $\log_6 532$

61. $\log_4 125$

62. $\log_{12} 2.5$

63. Use the Change of Base Formula to show that

$$\log_3 x = \frac{\ln x}{\ln 3}$$

Then use this fact to draw the graph of the function $f(x) = \log_3 x$.

64. Draw graphs of the family of functions $y = \log_a x$ for $a = 2, e,$ 5, and 10 on the same screen, using the viewing rectangle $[0, 5]$ by $[-3, 3]$. How are these graphs related?

65. Use the Change of Base Formula to show that

$$\log e = \frac{1}{\ln 10}$$

66. Simplify: $(\log_2 5)(\log_5 7)$

67. Show that $-\ln(x - \sqrt{x^2 - 1}) = \ln(x + \sqrt{x^2 - 1})$.

APPLICATIONS

68. **Forgetting** Use the Law of Forgetting (Example 5) to estimate a student's score on a biology test two years after he got a score of 80 on a test covering the same material. Assume that $c = 0.3$ and t is measured in months.

69. **Wealth Distribution** Vilfredo Pareto (1848–1923) observed that most of the wealth of a country is owned by a few members of the population. **Pareto's Principle** is

$$\log P = \log c - k \log W$$

where W is the wealth level (how much money a person has) and P is the number of people in the population having that much money.
(a) Solve the equation for P.
(b) Assume that $k = 2.1$, $c = 8000$, and W is measured in millions of dollars. Use part (a) to find the number of people who have \$2 million or more. How many people have \$10 million or more?

70. **Biodiversity** Some biologists model the number of species S in a fixed area A (such as an island) by the species-area relationship

$$\log S = \log c + k \log A$$

where c and k are positive constants that depend on the type of species and habitat.
(a) Solve the equation for S.

(b) Use part (a) to show that if $k = 3$, then doubling the area increases the number of species eightfold.

71. **Magnitude of Stars** The magnitude M of a star is a measure of how bright a star appears to the human eye. It is defined by

$$M = -2.5 \log\left(\frac{B}{B_0}\right)$$

where B is the actual brightness of the star and B_0 is a constant.
(a) Expand the right-hand side of the equation.
(b) Use part (a) to show that the brighter a star, the less its magnitude.
(c) Betelgeuse is about 100 times brighter than Albiero. Use part (a) to show that Betelgeuse is 5 magnitudes less bright than Albiero.

DISCOVERY ■ DISCUSSION ■ WRITING

72. **True or False?** Discuss each equation and determine whether it is true for all possible values of the variables. (Ignore values of the variables for which any term is undefined.)

(a) $\log\left(\dfrac{x}{y}\right) = \dfrac{\log x}{\log y}$

(b) $\log_2(x - y) = \log_2 x - \log_2 y$

(c) $\log_5\left(\dfrac{a}{b^2}\right) = \log_5 a - 2 \log_5 b$

(d) $\log 2^z = z \log 2$

(e) $(\log P)(\log Q) = \log P + \log Q$

(f) $\dfrac{\log a}{\log b} = \log a - \log b$

(g) $(\log_2 7)^x = x \log_2 7$

(h) $\log_a a^a = a$

(i) $\log(x - y) = \dfrac{\log x}{\log y}$

(j) $-\ln\left(\dfrac{1}{A}\right) = \ln A$

73. Find the Error What is wrong with the following argument?

$$\log 0.1 < 2 \log 0.1$$
$$= \log(0.1)^2$$
$$= \log 0.01$$
$$\log 0.1 < \log 0.01$$
$$0.1 < 0.01$$

74. Shifting, Shrinking, and Stretching Graphs of Functions Let $f(x) = x^2$. Show that $f(2x) = 4f(x)$, and explain how this shows that shrinking the graph of f horizontally has the same effect as stretching it vertically. Then use the identities $e^{2+x} = e^2 e^x$ and $\ln(2x) = \ln 2 + \ln x$ to show that for $g(x) = e^x$ a horizontal shift is the same as a vertical stretch and for $h(x) = \ln x$ a horizontal shrinking is the same as a vertical shift.

4.5 EXPONENTIAL AND LOGARITHMIC EQUATIONS

| Exponential Equations ▶ Logarithmic Equations ▶ Compound Interest

In this section we solve equations that involve exponential or logarithmic functions. The techniques that we develop here will be used in the next section for solving applied problems.

▼ Exponential Equations

An *exponential equation* is one in which the variable occurs in the exponent. For example,

$$2^x = 7$$

The variable x presents a difficulty because it is in the exponent. To deal with this difficulty, we take the logarithm of each side and then use the Laws of Logarithms to "bring down x" from the exponent.

$$2^x = 7 \qquad \text{Given equation}$$
$$\ln 2^x = \ln 7 \qquad \text{Take ln of each side}$$
$$x \ln 2 = \ln 7 \qquad \text{Law 3 (bring down exponent)}$$
$$x = \frac{\ln 7}{\ln 2} \qquad \text{Solve for } x$$
$$\approx 2.807 \qquad \text{Calculator}$$

Recall that Law 3 of the Laws of Logarithms says that $\log_a A^C = C \log_a A$.

The method that we used to solve $2^x = 7$ is typical of how we solve exponential equations in general.

GUIDELINES FOR SOLVING EXPONENTIAL EQUATIONS

1. Isolate the exponential expression on one side of the equation.

2. Take the logarithm of each side, then use the Laws of Logarithms to "bring down the exponent."

3. Solve for the variable.

EXAMPLE 1 | Solving an Exponential Equation

Find the solution of the equation $3^{x+2} = 7$, rounded to six decimal places.

SUGGESTED TIME AND EMPHASIS

1 class, essential and optional material (may be combined with Section 4.6)

ALTERNATE EXAMPLE 1

Find the solution of the equation $3^{x+3} = 5$. If necessary, correct the result to six decimal places.

ANSWER

-1.535026

TEXT QUESTION

Solve the equation $4 + 3 \log(2x) = 16$.

Answer

$x = 5000$

SOLUTION   We take the common logarithm of each side and use Law 3.

$$3^{x+2} = 7 \qquad \text{Given equation}$$

$$\log(3^{x+2}) = \log 7 \qquad \text{Take log of each side}$$

$$(x + 2)\log 3 = \log 7 \qquad \text{Law 3 (bring down exponent)}$$

$$x + 2 = \frac{\log 7}{\log 3} \qquad \text{Divide by log 3}$$

$$x = \frac{\log 7}{\log 3} - 2 \qquad \text{Subtract 2}$$

$$\approx -0.228756 \qquad \text{Calculator}$$

We could have used natural logarithms instead of common logarithms. In fact, using the same steps, we get

$$x = \frac{\ln 7}{\ln 3} - 2 \approx -0.228756$$

CHECK YOUR ANSWER

Substituting $x = -0.228756$ into the original equation and using a calculator, we get

$$3^{(-0.228756)+2} \approx 7 \qquad \checkmark$$

✎. NOW TRY EXERCISE **7**   ∎

EXAMPLE 2 | Solving an Exponential Equation

Solve the equation $8e^{2x} = 20$.

SOLUTION   We first divide by 8 to isolate the exponential term on one side of the equation.

$$8e^{2x} = 20 \qquad \text{Given equation}$$

$$e^{2x} = \tfrac{20}{8} \qquad \text{Divide by 8}$$

$$\ln e^{2x} = \ln 2.5 \qquad \text{Take ln of each side}$$

$$2x = \ln 2.5 \qquad \text{Property of ln}$$

$$x = \frac{\ln 2.5}{2} \qquad \text{Divide by 2}$$

$$\approx 0.458 \qquad \text{Calculator}$$

CHECK YOUR ANSWER

Substituting $x = 0.458$ into the original equation and using a calculator, we get

$$8e^{2(0.458)} \approx 20 \qquad \checkmark$$

✎. NOW TRY EXERCISE **9**   ∎

EXAMPLE 3 | Solving an Exponential Equation Algebraically and Graphically

Solve the equation $e^{3-2x} = 4$ algebraically and graphically.

SOLUTION 1: Algebraic

Since the base of the exponential term is e, we use natural logarithms to solve this equation.

$$e^{3-2x} = 4 \qquad \text{Given equation}$$

$$\ln(e^{3-2x}) = \ln 4 \qquad \text{Take ln of each side}$$

$$3 - 2x = \ln 4 \qquad \text{Property of ln}$$

$$-2x = -3 + \ln 4 \qquad \text{Subtract 3}$$

$$x = \tfrac{1}{2}(3 - \ln 4) \approx 0.807 \qquad \text{Multiply by } -\tfrac{1}{2}$$

You should check that this answer satisfies the original equation.

ALTERNATE EXAMPLE 2
Solve the equation $8\, e^{2x} = 24$. Round the answer to the nearest thousandth.

ANSWER
0.549

ALTERNATE EXAMPLE 3
Solve the equation $e^{5-2x} = 3$. Round the answer to the nearest thousandth.

ANSWER
1.951

IN-CLASS MATERIALS

Review the concept of inverse functions. Have students find the inverse of functions such as $f(x) = 2^{x^3+1}$ and $f(x) = \ln(x - 5) + e^3$.

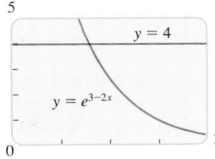

FIGURE 1

If we let $w = e^x$, we get the quadratic equation

$$w^2 - w - 6 = 0$$

which factors as

$$(w - 3)(w + 2) = 0$$

SOLUTION 2: Graphical

We graph the equations $y = e^{3-2x}$ and $y = 4$ in the same viewing rectangle as in Figure 1. The solutions occur where the graphs intersect. Zooming in on the point of intersection of the two graphs, we see that $x \approx 0.81$.

✎ NOW TRY EXERCISE 11

EXAMPLE 4 | An Exponential Equation of Quadratic Type

Solve the equation $e^{2x} - e^x - 6 = 0$.

SOLUTION   To isolate the exponential term, we factor.

$$
\begin{array}{lll}
e^{2x} - e^x - 6 = 0 & & \text{Given equation} \\
(e^x)^2 - e^x - 6 = 0 & & \text{Law of Exponents} \\
(e^x - 3)(e^x + 2) = 0 & & \text{Factor (a quadratic in } e^x\text{)} \\
e^x - 3 = 0 \quad \text{or} \quad e^x + 2 = 0 & & \text{Zero-Product Property} \\
e^x = 3 \qquad\qquad e^x = -2 & &
\end{array}
$$

The equation $e^x = 3$ leads to $x = \ln 3$. But the equation $e^x = -2$ has no solution because $e^x > 0$ for all x. Thus, $x = \ln 3 \approx 1.0986$ is the only solution. You should check that this answer satisfies the original equation.

✎ NOW TRY EXERCISE 29

EXAMPLE 5 | Solving an Exponential Equation

Solve the equation $3xe^x + x^2e^x = 0$.

SOLUTION   First we factor the left side of the equation.

$$
\begin{array}{lll}
3xe^x + x^2e^x = 0 & & \text{Given equation} \\
x(3 + x)e^x = 0 & & \text{Factor out common factors} \\
x(3 + x) = 0 & & \text{Divide by } e^x \text{ (because } e^x \neq 0\text{)} \\
x = 0 \quad \text{or} \quad 3 + x = 0 & & \text{Zero-Product Property}
\end{array}
$$

Thus the solutions are $x = 0$ and $x = -3$.

✎ NOW TRY EXERCISE 33

CHECK YOUR ANSWER

$x = 0$:

$$3(0)e^0 + 0^2e^0 = 0 \quad ✔$$

$x = -3$:

$$3(-3)e^{-3} + (-3)^2e^{-3}$$
$$= -9e^{-3} + 9e^{-3} = 0 \quad ✔$$

ALTERNATE EXAMPLE 4

Solve the equation $e^{2x} - e^x - 2 = 0$. Round the answer to four decimal places.

ANSWER

0.6931

ALTERNATE EXAMPLE 5

Solve the equation $5x^4 e^x - x^5 e^x = 0$.

ANSWER

$x = 0$, $x = 5$

Radiocarbon Dating is a method archeologists use to determine the age of ancient objects. The carbon dioxide in the atmosphere always contains a fixed fraction of radioactive carbon, carbon-14 (^{14}C), with a half-life of about 5730 years. Plants absorb carbon dioxide from the atmosphere, which then makes its way to animals through the food chain. Thus, all living creatures contain the same fixed proportions of ^{14}C to nonradioactive ^{12}C as the atmosphere.

After an organism dies, it stops assimilating ^{14}C, and the amount of ^{14}C in it begins to decay exponentially. We can then determine the time elapsed since the death of the organism by measuring the amount of ^{14}C left in it.

For example, if a donkey bone contains 73% as much ^{14}C as a living donkey and it died t years ago, then by the formula for radioactive decay (Section 4.6),

$$0.73 = (1.00)e^{-(t\ln 2)/5730}$$

We solve this exponential equation to find $t \approx 2600$, so the bone is about 2600 years old.

IN-CLASS MATERIALS

At this point students know the algebraic rules for working with exponential and logarithmic functions. Stress that if these rules do not suffice to solve an equation, there is a good chance they cannot find an exact solution. Give students an equation such as $x^2 = 2 \ln(x + 2)$ (Example 9) and have them try to solve it algebraically. The correct answer is that students cannot do so, but you will find that many make up rules and somehow wind up with a solution.

▼ Logarithmic Equations

A *logarithmic equation* is one in which a logarithm of the variable occurs. For example,

$$\log_2(x + 2) = 5$$

To solve for x, we write the equation in exponential form.

$$x + 2 = 2^5 \qquad \text{Exponential form}$$

$$x = 32 - 2 = 30 \qquad \text{Solve for } x$$

Another way of looking at the first step is to raise the base, 2, to each side of the equation.

$$2^{\log_2(x+2)} = 2^5 \qquad \text{Raise 2 to each side}$$

$$x + 2 = 2^5 \qquad \text{Property of logarithms}$$

$$x = 32 - 2 = 30 \qquad \text{Solve for } x$$

The method used to solve this simple problem is typical. We summarize the steps as follows.

GUIDELINES FOR SOLVING LOGARITHMIC EQUATIONS

1. Isolate the logarithmic term on one side of the equation; you might first need to combine the logarithmic terms.

2. Write the equation in exponential form (or raise the base to each side of the equation).

3. Solve for the variable.

ALTERNATE EXAMPLE 6

(a) Solve the equation $\ln x = 3$. Round the answer to the nearest integer.

(b) Solve the equation $\log_2(22 - x) = 3$.

ANSWERS

(a) 20

(b) $x = 14$

EXAMPLE 6 | Solving Logarithmic Equations

Solve each equation for x.

(a) $\ln x = 8$ **(b)** $\log_2(25 - x) = 3$

SOLUTION

(a)

$$\ln x = 8 \qquad \text{Given equation}$$

$$x = e^8 \qquad \text{Exponential form}$$

Therefore, $x = e^8 \approx 2981$.

We can also solve this problem another way:

$$\ln x = 8 \qquad \text{Given equation}$$

$$e^{\ln x} = e^8 \qquad \text{Raise } e \text{ to each side}$$

$$x = e^8 \qquad \text{Property of ln}$$

(b) The first step is to rewrite the equation in exponential form.

$$\log_2(25 - x) = 3 \qquad \text{Given equation}$$

$$25 - x = 2^3 \qquad \text{Exponential form (or raise 2 to each side)}$$

$$25 - x = 8$$

$$x = 25 - 8 = 17$$

CHECK YOUR ANSWER

If $x = 17$, we get

$\log_2(25 - 17) = \log_2 8 = 3$ ✔

✎. NOW TRY EXERCISES **37** AND **41** ■

IN-CLASS MATERIALS

Build up some tough problems from simple ones. For example, first have students solve $x^2 + 2x - 15 = 0$. Then have them solve $(e^x - 1)^2 + 2(e^x - 1) - 15 = 0$. One can go even further with $\ln[(e^x - 1)^2 + 2(e^x - 1) - 14] = 0$.

EXAMPLE 7 | Solving a Logarithmic Equation

Solve the equation $4 + 3 \log(2x) = 16$.

SOLUTION We first isolate the logarithmic term. This allows us to write the equation in exponential form.

$$4 + 3 \log(2x) = 16 \qquad \text{Given equation}$$
$$3 \log(2x) = 12 \qquad \text{Subtract 4}$$
$$\log(2x) = 4 \qquad \text{Divide by 3}$$
$$2x = 10^4 \qquad \text{Exponential form (or raise 10 to each side)}$$
$$x = 5000 \qquad \text{Divide by 2}$$

CHECK YOUR ANSWER

If $x = 5000$, we get

$$4 + 3 \log 2(5000) = 4 + 3 \log 10{,}000$$
$$= 4 + 3(4)$$
$$= 16 \quad ✔$$

👉. NOW TRY EXERCISE **43**

EXAMPLE 8 | Solving a Logarithmic Equation Algebraically and Graphically

Solve the equation $\log(x + 2) + \log(x - 1) = 1$ algebraically and graphically.

SOLUTION 1: Algebraic

We first combine the logarithmic terms, using the Laws of Logarithms.

$$\log[(x + 2)(x - 1)] = 1 \qquad \text{Law 1}$$
$$(x + 2)(x - 1) = 10 \qquad \text{Exponential form (or raise 10 to each side)}$$
$$x^2 + x - 2 = 10 \qquad \text{Expand left side}$$
$$x^2 + x - 12 = 0 \qquad \text{Subtract 10}$$
$$(x + 4)(x - 3) = 0 \qquad \text{Factor}$$
$$x = -4 \quad \text{or} \quad x = 3$$

We check these potential solutions in the original equation and find that $x = -4$ is not a solution (because logarithms of negative numbers are undefined), but $x = 3$ is a solution. (See *Check Your Answers*.)

CHECK YOUR ANSWER

$x = -4$:

$\log(-4 + 2) + \log(-4 - 1)$

$= \log(-2) + \log(-5)$

$\qquad\qquad\qquad$ undefined ✗

$x = 3$:

$\log(3 + 2) + \log(3 - 1)$

$= \log 5 + \log 2 = \log(5 \cdot 2)$

$= \log 10 = 1 \quad ✔$

SOLUTION 2: Graphical

We first move all terms to one side of the equation:

$$\log(x + 2) + \log(x - 1) - 1 = 0$$

Then we graph

$$y = \log(x + 2) + \log(x - 1) - 1$$

as in Figure 2. The solutions are the x-intercepts of the graph. Thus, the only solution is $x \approx 3$.

FIGURE 2

👉. NOW TRY EXERCISE **49**

ALTERNATE EXAMPLE 7

Solve the equation $5 + 4 \log(6x) = 25$. Round noninteger answers to the nearest hundredth.

ANSWER

$x = 16666.67$

ALTERNATE EXAMPLE 8

Solve the equation $\log(x + 8) + \log(x - 1) = 1$.

ANSWER

$x = 2$

EXAMPLE

Solve $(\ln x - 2)^3 - 4(\ln x - 2) = 0$.

ANSWER

$x = 1, e^2, e^4$

ALTERNATE EXAMPLE 9

Solve the equation $x^2 = 15 \ln(x + 5)$ to the nearest integer.

ANSWER

$-3, 6$

In Example 9 it's not possible to isolate x algebraically, so we must solve the equation graphically.

FIGURE 3

EXAMPLE 9 | Solving a Logarithmic Equation Graphically

Solve the equation $x^2 = 2 \ln(x + 2)$.

SOLUTION   We first move all terms to one side of the equation

$$x^2 - 2 \ln(x + 2) = 0$$

Then we graph

$$y = x^2 - 2 \ln(x + 2)$$

as in Figure 3. The solutions are the x-intercepts of the graph. Zooming in on the x-intercepts, we see that there are two solutions:

$$x \approx -0.71 \qquad \text{and} \qquad x \approx 1.60$$

✎. NOW TRY EXERCISE **59**   ∎

Logarithmic equations are used in determining the amount of light that reaches various depths in a lake. (This information helps biologists to determine the types of life a lake can support.) As light passes through water (or other transparent materials such as glass or plastic), some of the light is absorbed. It's easy to see that the murkier the water, the more light is absorbed. The exact relationship between light absorption and the distance light travels in a material is described in the next example.

ALTERNATE EXAMPLE 10

For a certain lake, the light intensity goes from 20 lumens at the surface to 18 lumens at a depth of 5 ft.

(a) Find the value of k.
(b) What will the intensity be at a depth of 40 ft?

ANSWERS

(a) $-\dfrac{1}{k} \ln\left(\dfrac{18}{20}\right) = 5$. Therefore $k \approx 0.0211$.

(b) $-\dfrac{1}{0.0211} \ln\left(\dfrac{I}{20}\right) = 40$.
Solving for I gives $I \approx 8.5997426$ lumens.

The intensity of light in a lake diminishes with depth.

EXAMPLE 10 | Transparency of a Lake

If I_0 and I denote the intensity of light before and after going through a material and x is the distance (in feet) the light travels in the material, then according to the **Beer-Lambert Law**,

$$-\frac{1}{k} \ln\left(\frac{I}{I_0}\right) = x$$

where k is a constant depending on the type of material.

(a) Solve the equation for I.
(b) For a certain lake $k = 0.025$, and the light intensity is $I_0 = 14$ lumens (lm). Find the light intensity at a depth of 20 ft.

SOLUTION

(a) We first isolate the logarithmic term.

$$-\frac{1}{k} \ln\left(\frac{I}{I_0}\right) = x \qquad \text{Given equation}$$

$$\ln\left(\frac{I}{I_0}\right) = -kx \qquad \text{Multiply by } -k$$

$$\frac{I}{I_0} = e^{-kx} \qquad \text{Exponential form}$$

$$I = I_0 e^{-kx} \qquad \text{Multiply by } I_0$$

(b) We find I using the formula from part (a).

$$I = I_0 e^{-kx} \qquad \text{From part (a)}$$

$$= 14 e^{(-0.025)(20)} \qquad I_0 = 14, k = 0.025, x = 20$$

$$\approx 8.49 \qquad \text{Calculator}$$

The light intensity at a depth of 20 ft is about 8.5 lm.

✎. NOW TRY EXERCISE **85**   ∎

EXAMPLE

Solve $\log(x^2 - 1) - \log(x + 1) = 3$.

ANSWER

$x = 1001$

▼ Compound Interest

Recall the formulas for interest that we found in Section 4.1. If a principal P is invested at an interest rate r for a period of t years, then the amount A of the investment is given by

$$A = P(1 + r) \qquad \text{Simple interest (for one year)}$$

$$A(t) = P\left(1 + \frac{r}{n}\right)^{nt} \qquad \text{Interest compounded } n \text{ times per year}$$

$$A(t) = Pe^{rt} \qquad \text{Interest compounded continuously}$$

We can use logarithms to determine the time it takes for the principal to increase to a given amount.

EXAMPLE 11 | Finding the Term for an Investment to Double

A sum of $5000 is invested at an interest rate of 5% per year. Find the time required for the money to double if the interest is compounded according to the following method.

(a) Semiannually   (b) Continuously

SOLUTION

(a) We use the formula for compound interest with $P = \$5000$, $A(t) = \$10,000$, $r = 0.05$, and $n = 2$ and solve the resulting exponential equation for t.

$$5000\left(1 + \frac{0.05}{2}\right)^{2t} = 10,000 \qquad P\left(1 + \frac{r}{n}\right)^{nt} = A$$

$$(1.025)^{2t} = 2 \qquad \text{Divide by 5000}$$

$$\log 1.025^{2t} = \log 2 \qquad \text{Take log of each side}$$

$$2t \log 1.025 = \log 2 \qquad \text{Law 3 (bring down the exponent)}$$

$$t = \frac{\log 2}{2 \log 1.025} \qquad \text{Divide by 2 log 1.025}$$

$$t \approx 14.04 \qquad \text{Calculator}$$

The money will double in 14.04 years.

(b) We use the formula for continuously compounded interest with $P = \$5000$, $A(t) = \$10,000$, and $r = 0.05$ and solve the resulting exponential equation for t.

$$5000e^{0.05t} = 10,000 \qquad Pe^{rt} = A$$

$$e^{0.05t} = 2 \qquad \text{Divide by 5000}$$

$$\ln e^{0.05t} = \ln 2 \qquad \text{Take ln of each side}$$

$$0.05t = \ln 2 \qquad \text{Property of ln}$$

$$t = \frac{\ln 2}{0.05} \qquad \text{Divide by 0.05}$$

$$t \approx 13.86 \qquad \text{Calculator}$$

The money will double in 13.86 years.

✎ NOW TRY EXERCISE **75** ■

EXAMPLE 12 | Time Required to Grow an Investment

A sum of $1000 is invested at an interest rate of 4% per year. Find the time required for the amount to grow to $4000 if interest is compounded continuously.

ALTERNATE EXAMPLE 11

A sum of $2000 is invested at an interest rate of 3.25% per year. Find the time for the money to double if the interest is compounded according to the following methods:

(a) Semiannually
(b) Monthly
(c) Continuously

ANSWERS

(a) Approximately 21.500 years
(b) Approximately 21.356 years
(c) Approximately 21.328 years

ALTERNATE EXAMPLE 12

A sum of $4000 is invested at an interest rate of 9% per year. Find the time required for the money to double if the interest is compounded continuously.

ANSWER

7.7

SOLUTION We use the formula for continuously compounded interest with $P = \$1000$, $A(t) = \$4000$, and $r = 0.04$ and solve the resulting exponential equation for t.

$$1000e^{0.04t} = 4000 \qquad Pe^{rt} = A$$

$$e^{0.04t} = 4 \qquad \text{Divide by 1000}$$

$$0.04t = \ln 4 \qquad \text{Take ln of each side}$$

$$t = \frac{\ln 4}{0.04} \qquad \text{Divide by 0.04}$$

$$t \approx 34.66 \qquad \text{Calculator}$$

The amount will be \$4000 in about 34 years and 8 months.

✎. NOW TRY EXERCISE **77**

4.5 EXERCISES

CONCEPTS

1. Let's solve the exponential equation $2e^x = 50$.

  (a) First, we isolate e^x to get the equivalent equation _____.

  (b) Next, we take ln of each side to get the equivalent equation

  _____.

  (c) Now we use a calculator to find $x =$ _____.

2. Let's solve the logarithmic equation
  $\log 3 + \log(x - 2) = \log x$.

  (a) First, we combine the logarithms to get the equivalent

  equation _____.

  (b) Next, we write each side in exponential form to get the

  equivalent equation _____.

  (c) Now we find $x =$ _____.

SKILLS

3–28 ■ Find the solution of the exponential equation, rounded to four decimal places.

3. $10^x = 25$

4. $10^{-x} = 4$

5. $e^{-2x} = 7$

6. $e^{3x} = 12$

7. $2^{1-x} = 3$

8. $3^{2x-1} = 5$

9. $3e^x = 10$

10. $2e^{12x} = 17$

11. $e^{1-4x} = 2$

12. $4(1 + 10^{5x}) = 9$

13. $4 + 3^{5x} = 8$

14. $2^{3x} = 34$

15. $8^{0.4x} = 5$

16. $3^{x/14} = 0.1$

17. $5^{-x/100} = 2$

18. $e^{3-5x} = 16$

19. $e^{2x+1} = 200$

20. $\left(\frac{1}{4}\right)^x = 75$

21. $5^x = 4^{x+1}$

22. $10^{1-x} = 6^x$

23. $2^{3x+1} = 3^{x-2}$

24. $7^{x/2} = 5^{1-x}$

25. $\dfrac{50}{1 + e^{-x}} = 4$

26. $\dfrac{10}{1 + e^{-x}} = 2$

27. $100(1.04)^{2t} = 300$

28. $(1.00625)^{12t} = 2$

29–36 ■ Solve the equation.

29. $e^{2x} - 3e^x + 2 = 0$

30. $e^{2x} - e^x - 6 = 0$

31. $e^{4x} + 4e^{2x} - 21 = 0$

32. $e^x - 12e^{-x} - 1 = 0$

33. $x^2 2^x - 2^x = 0$

34. $x^2 10^x - x10^x = 2(10^x)$

35. $4x^3 e^{-3x} - 3x^4 e^{-3x} = 0$

36. $x^2 e^x + xe^x - e^x = 0$

37–54 ■ Solve the logarithmic equation for x.

37. $\ln x = 10$

38. $\ln(2 + x) = 1$

39. $\log x = -2$

40. $\log(x - 4) = 3$

41. $\log(3x + 5) = 2$

42. $\log_3(2 - x) = 3$

43. $4 - \log(3 - x) = 3$

44. $\log_2(x^2 - x - 2) = 2$

45. $\log_2 3 + \log_2 x = \log_2 5 + \log_2(x - 2)$

46. $2 \log x = \log 2 + \log(3x - 4)$

47. $\log x + \log(x - 1) = \log(4x)$

48. $\log_5 x + \log_5(x + 1) = \log_5 20$

49. $\log_5(x + 1) - \log_5(x - 1) = 2$

50. $\log_3(x + 15) - \log_3(x - 1) = 2$

51. $\log_2 x + \log_2(x - 3) = 2$

52. $\log x + \log(x - 3) = 1$

53. $\log_9(x - 5) + \log_9(x + 3) = 1$

54. $\ln(x - 1) + \ln(x + 2) = 1$

55. For what value of x is the following true?
$$\log(x + 3) = \log x + \log 3$$

56. For what value of x is it true that $(\log x)^3 = 3 \log x$?

57. Solve for x: $\quad 2^{2/\log_5 x} = \frac{1}{16}$

58. Solve for x: $\quad \log_2(\log_3 x) = 4$

DRILL QUESTION

If I invest \$2000 at an annual interest rate of 3%, compounded continuously, how long will it take the investment to double?

Answer

$\dfrac{\ln 2}{0.03} \approx 23$ years

59–66 ■ Use a graphing device to find all solutions of the equation, rounded to two decimal places.

59. $\ln x = 3 - x$

60. $\log x = x^2 - 2$

61. $x^3 - x = \log(x + 1)$

62. $x = \ln(4 - x^2)$

63. $e^x = -x$

64. $2^{-x} = x - 1$

65. $4^{-x} = \sqrt{x}$

66. $e^{x^2} - 2 = x^3 - x$

67–70 ■ Solve the inequality.

67. $\log(x - 2) + \log(9 - x) < 1$

68. $3 \le \log_2 x \le 4$

69. $2 < 10^x < 5$

70. $x^2 e^x - 2e^x < 0$

71–74 ■ Find the inverse function of f.

71. $f(x) = 2^{2x}$

72. $f(x) = 3^{x+1}$

73. $f(x) = \log_2(x - 1)$

74. $f(x) = \log 3x$

APPLICATIONS

75. Compound Interest A man invests $5000 in an account that pays 8.5% interest per year, compounded quarterly.
(a) Find the amount after 3 years.
(b) How long will it take for the investment to double?

76. Compound Interest A woman invests $6500 in an account that pays 6% interest per year, compounded continuously.
(a) What is the amount after 2 years?
(b) How long will it take for the amount to be $8000?

77. Compound Interest Find the time required for an investment of $5000 to grow to $8000 at an interest rate of 7.5% per year, compounded quarterly.

78. Compound Interest Nancy wants to invest $4000 in saving certificates that bear an interest rate of 9.75% per year, compounded semiannually. How long a time period should she choose to save an amount of $5000?

79. Doubling an Investment How long will it take for an investment of $1000 to double in value if the interest rate is 8.5% per year, compounded continuously?

80. Interest Rate A sum of $1000 was invested for 4 years, and the interest was compounded semiannually. If this sum amounted to $1435.77 in the given time, what was the interest rate?

81. Radioactive Decay A 15-g sample of radioactive iodine decays in such a way that the mass remaining after t days is given by $m(t) = 15e^{-0.087t}$, where $m(t)$ is measured in grams. After how many days is there only 5 g remaining?

82. Sky Diving The velocity of a sky diver t seconds after jumping is given by $v(t) = 80(1 - e^{-0.2t})$. After how many seconds is the velocity 70 ft/s?

83. Fish Population A small lake is stocked with a certain species of fish. The fish population is modeled by the function

$$P = \frac{10}{1 + 4e^{-0.8t}}$$

where P is the number of fish in thousands and t is measured in years since the lake was stocked.
(a) Find the fish population after 3 years.
(b) After how many years will the fish population reach 5000 fish?

84. Transparency of a Lake Environmental scientists measure the intensity of light at various depths in a lake to find the "transparency" of the water. Certain levels of transparency are required for the biodiversity of the submerged macrophyte population. In a certain lake the intensity of light at depth x is given by

$$I = 10e^{-0.008x}$$

where I is measured in lumens and x in feet.
(a) Find the intensity I at a depth of 30 ft.
(b) At what depth has the light intensity dropped to $I = 5$?

85. Atmospheric Pressure Atmospheric pressure P (in kilopascals, kPa) at altitude h (in kilometers, km) is governed by the formula

$$\ln\left(\frac{P}{P_0}\right) = -\frac{h}{k}$$

where $k = 7$ and $P_0 = 100$ kPa are constants.
(a) Solve the equation for P.
(b) Use part (a) to find the pressure P at an altitude of 4 km.

86. Cooling an Engine Suppose you're driving your car on a cold winter day (20°F outside) and the engine overheats (at about 220°F). When you park, the engine begins to cool down. The temperature T of the engine t minutes after you park satisfies the equation

$$\ln\left(\frac{T - 20}{200}\right) = -0.11t$$

(a) Solve the equation for T.
(b) Use part (a) to find the temperature of the engine after 20 min ($t = 20$).

87. Electric Circuits An electric circuit contains a battery that produces a voltage of 60 volts (V), a resistor with a resistance of 13 ohms (Ω), and an inductor with an inductance of 5 henrys (H), as shown in the figure. Using calculus, it can be shown that the current $I = I(t)$ (in amperes, A) t seconds after the switch is closed is $I = \frac{60}{13}(1 - e^{-13t/5})$.
(a) Use this equation to express the time t as a function of the current I.
(b) After how many seconds is the current 2 A?

88. Learning Curve A *learning curve* is a graph of a function $P(t)$ that measures the performance of someone learning a skill as a function of the training time t. At first, the rate of learning is rapid. Then, as performance increases and approaches a maximal value M, the rate of learning decreases. It has been found that the function

$$P(t) = M - Ce^{-kt}$$

where k and C are positive constants and $C < M$ is a reasonable model for learning.

(a) Express the learning time t as a function of the performance level P.

(b) For a pole-vaulter in training, the learning curve is given by

$$P(t) = 20 - 14e^{-0.024t}$$

where $P(t)$ is the height he is able to pole-vault after t months. After how many months of training is he able to vault 12 ft?

(c) Draw a graph of the learning curve in part (b).

DISCOVERY ▪ DISCUSSION ▪ WRITING

89. Estimating a Solution Without actually solving the equation, find two whole numbers between which the solution of $9^t = 20$ must lie. Do the same for $9^t = 100$. Explain how you reached your conclusions.

90. A Surprising Equation Take logarithms to show that the equation

$$x^{1/\log x} = 5$$

has no solution. For what values of k does the equation

$$x^{1/\log x} = k$$

have a solution? What does this tell us about the graph of the function $f(x) = x^{1/\log x}$? Confirm your answer using a graphing device.

91. Disguised Equations Each of these equations can be transformed into an equation of linear or quadratic type by applying the hint. Solve each equation.

(a) $(x - 1)^{\log(x-1)} = 100(x - 1)$ [Take log of each side.]

(b) $\log_2 x + \log_4 x + \log_8 x = 11$ [Change all logs to base 2.]

(c) $4^x - 2^{x+1} = 3$ [Write as a quadratic in 2^x.]

4.6 MODELING WITH EXPONENTIAL AND LOGARITHMIC FUNCTIONS

Exponential Growth (Doubling Time) ▶ Exponential Growth (Relative Growth Rate) ▶ Radioactive Decay ▶ Newton's Law of Cooling ▶ Logarithmic Scales

Many processes that occur in nature, such as population growth, radioactive decay, heat diffusion, and numerous others, can be modeled by using exponential functions. Logarithmic functions are used in models for the loudness of sounds, the intensity of earthquakes, and many other phenomena. In this section we study exponential and logarithmic models.

▼ Exponential Growth (Doubling Time)

Suppose we start with a single bacterium, which divides every hour. After one hour we have 2 bacteria, after two hours we have 2^2 or 4 bacteria, after three hours we have 2^3 or 8 bacteria, and so on (see Figure 1). We see that we can model the bacteria population after t hours by $f(t) = 2^t$.

FIGURE 1 Bacteria population

| 0 | 1 | 2 | 3 | 4 | 5 | 6 |

SUGGESTED TIME AND EMPHASIS

$\frac{1}{2}$–1 class, recommended material (may be combined with Section 4.5)

TEXT QUESTION

Recall that Newton's Law of Cooling is given by

$$T(t) = T_s + D_0 e^{-kt}$$

Which of the constants in this law correspond to surrounding temperature? Which represents the initial difference between the object and its surroundings? How do you know?

Answer

T_s, D_0. There is a horizontal asymptote at T_s, which would have to correspond to the surrounding temperature, because things cool off to the surrounding temperature. Their initial difference is D_0, because when $t = 0$ we know that $T = T_s + D_0$.

If we start with 10 of these bacteria, then the population is modeled by $f(t) = 10 \cdot 2^t$. A slower-growing strain of bacteria doubles every 3 hours; in this case the population is modeled by $f(t) = 10 \cdot 2^{t/3}$. In general, we have the following.

EXPONENTIAL GROWTH (DOUBLING TIME)

If the initial size of a population is n_0 and the doubling time is a, then the size of the population at time t is

$$n(t) = n_0 2^{t/a}$$

where a and t are measured in the same time units (minutes, hours, days, years, and so on).

EXAMPLE 1 | Bacteria Population

Under ideal conditions a certain bacteria population doubles every three hours. Initially there are 1000 bacteria in a colony.

(a) Find a model for the bacteria population after t hours.

(b) How many bacteria are in the colony after 15 hours?

(c) When will the bacteria count reach 100,000?

SOLUTION

(a) The population at time t is modeled by

$$n(t) = 1000 \cdot 2^{t/3}$$

where t is measured in hours.

(b) After 15 hours the number of bacteria is

$$n(15) = 1000 \cdot 2^{15/3} = 32{,}000$$

(c) We set $n(t) = 100{,}000$ in the model that we found in part (a) and solve the resulting exponential equation for t.

$100{,}000 = 1000 \cdot 2^{t/3}$	$n(t) = 1000 \cdot 2^{t/3}$
$100 = 2^{t/3}$	Divide by 1000
$\log 100 = \log 2^{t/3}$	Take log of each side
$2 = \dfrac{t}{3} \log 2$	Properties of log
$t = \dfrac{6}{\log 2} \approx 19.93$	Solve for t

For guidelines on working with significant figures, see the Appendix, Calculations and Significant Figures.

The bacteria level reaches 100,000 in about 20 hours.

 NOW TRY EXERCISE **1**

EXAMPLE 2 | Rabbit Population

A certain breed of rabbit was introduced onto a small island 8 months ago. The current rabbit population on the island is estimated to be 4100 and doubling every 3 months.

(a) What was the initial size of the rabbit population?

(b) Estimate the population one year after the rabbits were introduced to the island.

(c) Sketch a graph of the rabbit population.

IN-CLASS MATERIALS

Show that the expression $y = e^{kt}$ can be written as $y = a^t$ and vice versa. Continue by demonstrating that e^{kt+c} is equivalent to Ae^{kt} for suitable constants k, c and A.

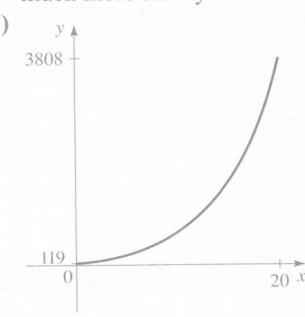

IN-CLASS MATERIALS

One way to measure the growth of the Internet is to measure the number of Internet hosts over time. The following data show the number of Internet hosts over a 20-year period starting in 1981, when BITNET was created. Try to determine along with students whether this is exponential growth. (Note: Do not show the students the third column right away. Let them come up with the idea of finding growth rates between data points.)

Month	Hosts	Growth
Aug 1981	213	—
May 1982	235	1.1404
Aug 1983	562	2.0065
Oct 1984	1,024	1.6701
Oct 1985	1,961	1.9150
Feb 1986	2,308	1.6217
Nov 1986	5,089	2.8782
Dec 1987	28,174	4.8615
Jul 1988	33,000	1.3112
Oct 1988	56,000	8.1509
Jan 1989	80,000	4.1168
Jul 1989	130,000	2.6620
Oct 1989	159,000	2.2231
Oct 1990	313,000	1.9686
Jan 1991	376,000	2.0824
Jul 1991	535,000	2.0364
Oct 1991	617,000	1.7608
Jan 1992	727,000	1.9172
Apr 1992	890,000	2.2511
Jul 1992	992,000	1.5453
Oct 1992	1,136,000	1.7122
Jan 1993	1,313,000	1.7762
Apr 1993	1,486,000	1.6520
Jul 1993	1,776,000	2.0443
Oct 1993	2,056,000	1.7875
Jan 1994	2,217,000	1.3487
Jul 1994	3,212,000	2.1120
Oct 1994	3,864,000	2.0818
Jan 1995	4,852,000	2.4618
Jul 1995	6,642,000	1.8739
Jan 1996	9,472,000	2.0357
Jul 1996	12,881,000	1.8525
Jan 1997	16,146,000	1.5654
Jul 1997	19,540,000	1.4692
Jan 1998	29,670,000	2.2900
Jul 1998	36,739,000	1.5387
Jan 1999	43,230,000	1.3809
Jul 1999	56,218,000	1.6985
Jan 2000	72,398,092	1.6516
Jul 2000	93,047,785	1.6541
Jan 2001	109,574,429	1.3831

SOLUTION

(a) The doubling time is $a = 3$, so the population at time t is

$$n(t) = n_0 2^{t/3} \qquad \text{Model}$$

where n_0 is the initial population. Since the population is 4100 when t is 8 months, we have

$$n(8) = n_0 2^{8/3} \qquad \text{From model}$$

$$4100 = n_0 2^{8/3} \qquad \text{Because } n(8) = 4100$$

$$n_0 = \frac{4100}{2^{8/3}} \qquad \text{Divide by } 2^{8/3} \text{ and switch sides}$$

$$n_0 \approx 645 \qquad \text{Calculate}$$

Thus we estimate that 645 rabbits were introduced onto the island.

(b) From part (a) we know that the initial population is $n_0 = 645$, so we can model the population after t months by

$$n(t) = 645 \cdot 2^{t/3} \qquad \text{Model}$$

After one year $t = 12$, so

$$n(12) = 645 \cdot 2^{12/3} \approx 10,320$$

So after one year there would be about 10,000 rabbits.

(c) We first note that the domain is $t \geq 0$. The graph is shown in Figure 2.

❀. NOW TRY EXERCISE **3**

FIGURE 2 $n(t) = 645 \cdot 2^{t/3}$

For guidelines on working with significant figures, see the Appendix, *Calculations and Significant Figures.*

▼ Exponential Growth (Relative Growth Rate)

We have used an exponential function with base 2 to model population growth (in terms of the doubling time). We could also model the same population with an exponential function with base 3 (in terms of the tripling time). In fact, we can find an exponential model with any base. If we use the base e, we get the following model of a population in terms of the **relative growth rate** r: the rate of population growth expressed as a proportion of the population at any time. For instance, if $r = 0.02$, then at any time t the growth rate is 2% of the population at time t.

EXPONENTIAL GROWTH (RELATIVE GROWTH RATE)

A population that experiences **exponential growth** increases according to the model

$$n(t) = n_0 e^{rt}$$

where
- $n(t)$ = population at time t
- n_0 = initial size of the population
- r = relative rate of growth (expressed as a proportion of the population)
- t = time

Notice that the formula for population growth is the same as that for continuously compounded interest. In fact, the same principle is at work in both cases: The growth of a population (or an investment) per time period is proportional to the size of the population (or

Answer

We can graph the data and get a curve that looks like exponential growth. We can also graph growth rate and see (except for two spikes in the late 1980s) a more or less constant growth rate.

the amount of the investment). A population of 1,000,000 will increase more in one year than a population of 1000; in exactly the same way, an investment of $1,000,000 will increase more in one year than an investment of $1000.

In the following examples we assume that the populations grow exponentially.

EXAMPLE 3 | Predicting the Size of a Population

The initial bacterium count in a culture is 500. A biologist later makes a sample count of bacteria in the culture and finds that the relative rate of growth is 40% per hour.

(a) Find a function that models the number of bacteria after t hours.

(b) What is the estimated count after 10 hours?

(c) When will the bacteria count reach 80,000?

(d) Sketch the graph of the function $n(t)$.

SOLUTION

(a) We use the exponential growth model with $n_0 = 500$ and $r = 0.4$ to get

$$n(t) = 500e^{0.4t}$$

where t is measured in hours.

(b) Using the function in part (a), we find that the bacterium count after 10 hours is

$$n(10) = 500e^{0.4(10)} = 500e^4 \approx 27{,}300$$

(c) We set $n(t) = 80{,}000$ and solve the resulting exponential equation for t:

$$80{,}000 = 500 \cdot e^{0.4t} \qquad n(t) = 500 \cdot e^{0.4t}$$

$$160 = e^{0.4t} \qquad \text{Divide by 500}$$

$$\ln 160 = 0.4t \qquad \text{Take ln of each side}$$

$$t = \frac{\ln 160}{0.4} \approx 12.68 \qquad \text{Solve for } t$$

The bacteria level reaches 80,000 in about 12.7 hours.

(d) The graph is shown in Figure 3.

✎ NOW TRY EXERCISE 5   ■

FIGURE 3

EXAMPLE 4 | Comparing Different Rates of Population Growth

In 2000 the population of the world was 6.1 billion, and the relative rate of growth was 1.4% per year. It is claimed that a rate of 1.0% per year would make a significant difference in the total population in just a few decades. Test this claim by estimating the population of the world in the year 2050 using a relative rate of growth of (a) 1.4% per year and (b) 1.0% per year.

Graph the population functions for the next 100 years for the two relative growth rates in the same viewing rectangle.

SOLUTION

(a) By the exponential growth model we have

$$n(t) = 6.1e^{0.014t}$$

where $n(t)$ is measured in billions and t is measured in years since 2000. Because the year 2050 is 50 years after 2000, we find

$$n(50) = 6.1e^{0.014(50)} = 6.1e^{0.7} \approx 12.3$$

The estimated population in the year 2050 is about 12.3 billion.

The relative growth of world population has been declining over the past few decades—from 2% in 1995 to 1.3% in 2006.

Standing Room Only
The population of the world was about 6.1 billion in 2000 and was increasing at 1.4% per year. Assuming that each person occupies an average of 4 ft² of the surface of the earth, the exponential model for population growth projects that by the year 2801 there will be standing room only! (The total land surface area of the world is about 1.8×10^{15} ft².)

IN-CLASS MATERIALS

In 1985 there were 15,948 diagnosed cases of AIDS in the United States. In 1990 there were 156,024 cases. Scientists said that if no research was done, the disease would grow exponentially. Compute the number of cases this model predicts for the year 2000. The actual number was 774,467. Discuss possible flaws in the model with students, and point out the dangers of extrapolation.

$n(t) = 6.1e^{0.014t}$

$n(t) = 6.1e^{0.01t}$

FIGURE 4

(b) We use the function

$$n(t) = 6.1e^{0.010t}$$

and find

$$n(50) = 6.1e^{0.010(50)} = 6.1e^{0.50} \approx 10.1$$

The estimated population in the year 2050 is about 10.1 billion.

The graphs in Figure 4 show that a small change in the relative rate of growth will, over time, make a large difference in population size.

✎. **NOW TRY EXERCISE 7** ▪

EXAMPLE 5 | Expressing a Model in Terms of e

A culture starts with 10,000 bacteria, and the number doubles every 40 minutes.

(a) Find a function $n(t) = n_0 2^{t/a}$ that models the number of bacteria after t minutes.
(b) Find a function $n(t) = n_0 e^{rt}$ that models the number of bacteria after t minutes.
(c) Sketch a graph of the number of bacteria at time t.

SOLUTION

(a) The initial population is $n_0 = 10,000$. The doubling time is $a = 40$ min $= 2/3$ h. Since $1/a = 3/2 = 1.5$, the model is

$$n(t) = 10,000 \cdot 2^{1.5t}$$

(b) The initial population is $n_0 = 10,000$. We need to find the relative growth rate r. Since there are 20,000 bacteria when $t = 2/3$ h, we have

$$20,000 = 10,000e^{r(2/3)} \qquad n(t) = 10,000e^{rt}$$

$$2 = e^{r(2/3)} \qquad \text{Divide by 10,000}$$

$$\ln 2 = \ln e^{r(2/3)} \qquad \text{Take ln of each side}$$

$$\ln 2 = r(2/3) \qquad \text{Property of ln}$$

$$r = \frac{3 \ln 2}{2} \approx 1.0397 \qquad \text{Solve for } r$$

Now that we know the relative growth rate r, we can find the model:

$$n(t) = 10,000e^{1.0397t}$$

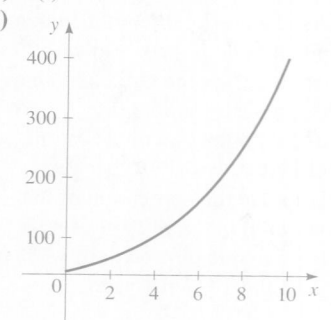

500,000

0   4

FIGURE 5
Graphs of $y = 10,000 \cdot 2^{1.5t}$
and $y = 10,000e^{1.0397t}$

(c) We can graph the model in part (a) or the one in part (b). The graphs are identical. See Figure 5.

✎. **NOW TRY EXERCISE 9** ▪

▼ Radioactive Decay

Radioactive substances decay by spontaneously emitting radiation. The rate of decay is proportional to the mass of the substance. This is analogous to population growth except that the mass *decreases*. Physicists express the rate of decay in terms of **half-life**. For example, the half-life of radium-226 is 1600 years, so a 100-g sample decays to 50 g (or $\frac{1}{2} \times 100$ g) in 1600 years, then to 25 g (or $\frac{1}{2} \times \frac{1}{2} \times 100$ g) in 3200 years, and so on. In

---

ALTERNATE EXAMPLE 5

A certain breed of rabbit is introduced onto a small island. There are 40 rabbits in the initial group and the population doubles every 3 months.

(a) Find a function $n(t) = n_0 2^{t/a}$ that models the number of rabbits after t months.

(b) Find a function $n(t) = n_0 e^{rt}$ that models the number of rabbits after t months.

(c) Sketch a graph of the number of rabbits at time t.

ANSWERS

(a) $n(t) = 40 \cdot 2^{t/3}$

(b) $n(t) = 40 \cdot e^{0.231t}$

(c)

IN-CLASS MATERIALS

Discuss the logistic growth model $P = \dfrac{M}{1 + Ae^{-kt}}$. Have students graph a few of these curves with different values of M and k. This model assumes that an environment has a carrying capacity M. It assumes that when a population is much less than M, a population's growth will look like exponential growth but that when the population approaches M, the population growth gets very slow, asymptotically approaching M. If the population starts out greater than M, then it will decay, exponentially, to M.

The half-lives of **radioactive elements** vary from very long to very short. Here are some examples.

Element	Half-life
Thorium-232	14.5 billion years
Uranium-235	4.5 billion years
Thorium-230	80,000 years
Plutonium-239	24,360 years
Carbon-14	5,730 years
Radium-226	1,600 years
Cesium-137	30 years
Strontium-90	28 years
Polonium-210	140 days
Thorium-234	25 days
Iodine-135	8 days
Radon-222	3.8 days
Lead-211	3.6 minutes
Krypton-91	10 seconds

general, for a radioactive substance with mass m_0 and half-life h, the amount remaining at time t is modeled by

$$m(t) = m_0 2^{-t/h}$$

where h and t are measured in the same time units (minutes, hours, days, years, and so on).

To express this model in the form $m(t) = m_0 e^{rt}$, we need to find the relative decay rate r. Since h is the half-life, we have

$$m(t) = m_0 e^{-rt} \qquad \text{Model}$$

$$\frac{m_0}{2} = m_0 e^{-rh} \qquad \text{h is the half-life}$$

$$\frac{1}{2} = e^{-rh} \qquad \text{Divide by m_0}$$

$$\ln \frac{1}{2} = -rh \qquad \text{Take ln of each side}$$

$$r = \frac{\ln 2}{h} \qquad \text{Solve for r}$$

This last equation allows us to find the rate r from the half-life h.

RADIOACTIVE DECAY MODEL

If m_0 is the initial mass of a radioactive substance with half-life h, then the mass remaining at time t is modeled by the function

$$m(t) = m_0 e^{-rt}$$

where $r = \dfrac{\ln 2}{h}$.

EXAMPLE 6 | Radioactive Decay

Polonium-210 (^{210}Po) has a half-life of 140 days. Suppose a sample of this substance has a mass of 300 mg.

(a) Find a function $m(t) = m_0 2^{-t/h}$ that models the mass remaining after t days.

(b) Find a function $m(t) = m_0 e^{-rt}$ that models the mass remaining after t days.

(c) Find the mass remaining after one year.

(d) How long will it take for the sample to decay to a mass of 200 mg?

(e) Draw a graph of the sample mass as a function of time.

SOLUTION

(a) We have $m_0 = 300$ and $h = 140$, so the amount remaining after t days is

$$m(t) = 300 \cdot 2^{-t/140}$$

(b) We have $m_0 = 300$ and $r = \ln 2/140 \approx -0.00495$, so the amount remaining after t days is

$$m(t) = 300 \cdot e^{-0.00495t}$$

In parts (c) and (d) we can also use the model found in part (a). Check that the result is the same using either model.

(c) We use the function we found in part (a) with $t = 365$ (one year).

$$m(365) = 300e^{-0.00495(365)} \approx 49.256$$

Thus, approximately 49 mg of ^{210}Po remains after one year.

ALTERNATE EXAMPLE 6

Seaborgium has a half-life of 1.94 minutes. A research team successfully synthesizes 1500 atoms of this highly unstable element.

(a) Find a function $m(t) = m_0 2^{-t/k}$ that models the number of atoms remaining after t minutes.

(b) Find a function $m(t) = m_0 e^{-rt}$ that models the number of atoms remaining after t minutes.

(c) Approximate the number of atoms remaining after 5 minutes.

(d) According to your model, how long will it take for there to be only one atom left?

(e) Draw a graph of the number of atoms of seaborgium as a function of time.

ANSWERS

(a) $m(t) = 1500 \cdot 2^{-t/1.94}$

(b) $m(t) = 1500 \cdot e^{-0.357t}$

(c) Approximately 251 atoms

(d) Approximately 20 minutes

(e)

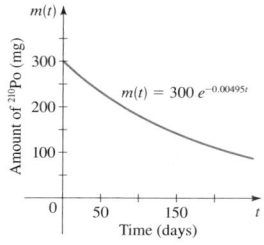
© Joel W. Rogers/CORBIS

Radioactive Waste

Harmful radioactive isotopes are produced whenever a nuclear reaction occurs, whether as the result of an atomic bomb test, a nuclear accident such as the one at Chernobyl in 1986, or the uneventful production of electricity at a nuclear power plant.

One radioactive material that is produced in atomic bombs is the isotope strontium-90 (^{90}Sr), with a half-life of 28 years. This is deposited like calcium in human bone tissue, where it can cause leukemia and other cancers. However, in the decades since atmospheric testing of nuclear weapons was halted, ^{90}Sr levels in the environment have fallen to a level that no longer poses a threat to health.

Nuclear power plants produce radioactive plutonium-239 (^{239}Pu), which has a half-life of 24,360 years. Because of its long half-life, ^{239}Pu could pose a threat to the environment for thousands of years. So great care must be taken to dispose of it properly. The difficulty of ensuring the safety of the disposed radioactive waste is one reason that nuclear power plants remain controversial.

(d) We use the function that we found in part (a) with $m(t) = 200$ and solve the resulting exponential equation for t.

$$300e^{-0.00495t} = 200 \qquad m(t) = m_0 e^{-rt}$$

$$e^{-0.00495t} = \tfrac{2}{3} \qquad \text{Divided by 300}$$

$$\ln e^{-0.00495t} = \ln \tfrac{2}{3} \qquad \text{Take ln of each side}$$

$$-0.00495t = \ln \tfrac{2}{3} \qquad \text{Property of ln}$$

$$t = -\frac{\ln \tfrac{2}{3}}{0.00495} \qquad \text{Solve for } t$$

$$t \approx 81.9 \qquad \text{Calculator}$$

The time required for the sample to decay to 200 mg is about 82 days.

(e) We can graph the model in part (a) or the one in part (b). The graphs are identical. See Figure 6.

FIGURE 6

[Graph: $m(t)$ vs. Time (days); curve labeled $m(t) = 300\,e^{-0.00495t}$; vertical axis "Amount of ^{210}Po (mg)" with marks at 100, 200, 300; horizontal axis marks at 50, 150.]

✎. NOW TRY EXERCISE **17**

▼ Newton's Law of Cooling

Newton's Law of Cooling states that the rate at which an object cools is proportional to the temperature difference between the object and its surroundings, provided that the temperature difference is not too large. By using calculus, the following model can be deduced from this law.

NEWTON'S LAW OF COOLING

If D_0 is the initial temperature difference between an object and its surroundings, and if its surroundings have temperature T_s, then the temperature of the object at time t is modeled by the function

$$T(t) = T_s + D_0 e^{-kt}$$

where k is a positive constant that depends on the type of object.

EXAMPLE 7 | Newton's Law of Cooling

A cup of coffee has a temperature of 200°F and is placed in a room that has a temperature of 70°F. After 10 min the temperature of the coffee is 150°F.

(a) Find a function that models the temperature of the coffee at time t.

(b) Find the temperature of the coffee after 15 min.

ALTERNATE EXAMPLE 7

A cup of coffee has a temperature of 210°F and is placed in a room that has a temperature of 85°F. After 20 minutes the temperature of the coffee is 140°F. Find the temperature of the coffee after 25 minutes.

ANSWER
130°F

(c) When will the coffee have cooled to 100°F?

(d) Illustrate by drawing a graph of the temperature function.

SOLUTION

(a) The temperature of the room is $T_s = 70°F$, and the initial temperature difference is

$$D_0 = 200 - 70 = 130°F$$

So by Newton's Law of Cooling, the temperature after t minutes is modeled by the function

$$T(t) = 70 + 130e^{-kt}$$

We need to find the constant k associated with this cup of coffee. To do this, we use the fact that when $t = 10$, the temperature is $T(10) = 150$. So we have

$$70 + 130e^{-10k} = 150 \qquad \text{$T_s + D_0 e^{-kt} = T(t)$}$$

$$130e^{-10k} = 80 \qquad \text{Subtract 70}$$

$$e^{-10k} = \tfrac{8}{13} \qquad \text{Divide by 130}$$

$$-10k = \ln \tfrac{8}{13} \qquad \text{Take ln of each side}$$

$$k = -\tfrac{1}{10} \ln \tfrac{8}{13} \qquad \text{Solve for k}$$

$$k \approx 0.04855 \qquad \text{Calculator}$$

Substituting this value of k into the expression for $T(t)$, we get

$$T(t) = 70 + 130e^{-0.04855t}$$

(b) We use the function that we found in part (a) with $t = 15$.

$$T(15) = 70 + 130e^{-0.04855(15)} \approx 133°F$$

(c) We use the function that we found in part (a) with $T(t) = 100$ and solve the resulting exponential equation for t.

$$70 + 130e^{-0.04855t} = 100 \qquad \text{$T_s + D_0 e^{-kt} = T(t)$}$$

$$130e^{-0.04855t} = 30 \qquad \text{Subtract 70}$$

$$e^{-0.04855t} = \tfrac{3}{13} \qquad \text{Divide by 130}$$

$$-0.04855t = \ln \tfrac{3}{13} \qquad \text{Take ln of each side}$$

$$t = \frac{\ln \tfrac{3}{13}}{-0.04855} \qquad \text{Solve for t}$$

$$t \approx 30.2 \qquad \text{Calculator}$$

The coffee will have cooled to 100°F after about half an hour.

(d) The graph of the temperature function is sketched in Figure 7. Notice that the line $t = 70$ is a horizontal asymptote. (Why?)

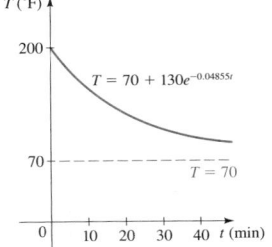

FIGURE 7 Temperature of coffee after t minutes

✎. **NOW TRY EXERCISE 25**   ■

▼ Logarithmic Scales

When a physical quantity varies over a very large range, it is often convenient to take its logarithm in order to have a more manageable set of numbers. We discuss three such situations: the pH scale, which measures acidity; the Richter scale, which measures the intensity of earthquakes; and the decibel scale, which measures the loudness of sounds. Other quantities that are measured on logarithmic scales are light intensity, information capacity, and radiation.

The pH Scale   Chemists measured the acidity of a solution by giving its hydrogen ion concentration until Søren Peter Lauritz Sørensen, in 1909, proposed a more convenient measure. He defined

$$pH = -\log[H^+]$$

where $[H^+]$ is the concentration of hydrogen ions measured in moles per liter (M). He did this to avoid very small numbers and negative exponents. For instance,

$$\text{if} \quad [H^+] = 10^{-4} \text{ M}, \quad \text{then} \quad pH = -\log_{10}(10^{-4}) = -(-4) = 4$$

Solutions with a pH of 7 are defined as *neutral*, those with pH < 7 are *acidic*, and those with pH > 7 are *basic*. Notice that when the pH increases by one unit, $[H^+]$ decreases by a factor of 10.

pH for Some Common Substances	
Substance	**pH**
Milk of magnesia	10.5
Seawater	8.0–8.4
Human blood	7.3–7.5
Crackers	7.0–8.5
Hominy	6.9–7.9
Cow's milk	6.4–6.8
Spinach	5.1–5.7
Tomatoes	4.1–4.4
Oranges	3.0–4.0
Apples	2.9–3.3
Limes	1.3–2.0
Battery acid	1.0

EXAMPLE 8 | pH Scale and Hydrogen Ion Concentration

(a) The hydrogen ion concentration of a sample of human blood was measured to be $[H^+] = 3.16 \times 10^{-8}$ M. Find the pH and classify the blood as acidic or basic.

(b) The most acidic rainfall ever measured occurred in Scotland in 1974; its pH was 2.4. Find the hydrogen ion concentration.

SOLUTION

(a) A calculator gives

$$pH = -\log[H^+] = -\log(3.16 \times 10^{-8}) \approx 7.5$$

Since this is greater than 7, the blood is basic.

(b) To find the hydrogen ion concentration, we need to solve for $[H^+]$ in the logarithmic equation

$$\log[H^+] = -pH$$

So we write it in exponential form.

$$[H^+] = 10^{-pH}$$

In this case pH = 2.4, so

$$[H^+] = 10^{-2.4} \approx 4.0 \times 10^{-3} \text{ M}$$

✎. NOW TRY EXERCISE **29**   ■

The Richter Scale   In 1935 the American geologist Charles Richter (1900–1984) defined the magnitude M of an earthquake to be

$$M = \log \frac{I}{S}$$

where I is the intensity of the earthquake (measured by the amplitude of a seismograph reading taken 100 km from the epicenter of the earthquake) and S is the intensity of a "standard" earthquake (whose amplitude is 1 micron = 10^{-4} cm). The magnitude of a standard earthquake is

$$M = \log \frac{S}{S} = \log 1 = 0$$

Largest Earthquakes		
Location	**Date**	**Magnitude**
Chile	1960	9.5
Alaska	1964	9.2
Sumatra	2004	9.1
Alaska	1957	9.1
Kamchatka	1952	9.0
Chile	2010	8.8
Ecuador	1906	8.8
Alaska	1965	8.7
Sumatra	2005	8.7
Tibet	1950	8.6
Kamchatka	1923	8.5
Indonesia	1938	8.5
Kuril Islands	1963	8.5

ALTERNATE EXAMPLE 8

The hydrogen ion concentration in a sample of human blood was measured to be $[H^+] = 5.41 \times 10^{-8}$ M. Find the pH and classify the blood as acidic or basic.

ANSWER

pH = 7.3, basic

Richter studied many earthquakes that occurred between 1900 and 1950. The largest had magnitude 8.9 on the Richter scale, and the smallest had magnitude 0. This corresponds to a ratio of intensities of 800,000,000, so the Richter scale provides more manageable numbers to work with. For instance, an earthquake of magnitude 6 is ten times stronger than an earthquake of magnitude 5.

EXAMPLE 9 | Magnitude of Earthquakes

The 1906 earthquake in San Francisco had an estimated magnitude of 8.3 on the Richter scale. In the same year a powerful earthquake occurred on the Colombia-Ecuador border that was four times as intense. What was the magnitude of the Colombia-Ecuador earthquake on the Richter scale?

SOLUTION   If I is the intensity of the San Francisco earthquake, then from the definition of magnitude we have

$$M = \log \frac{I}{S} = 8.3$$

The intensity of the Colombia-Ecuador earthquake was $4I$, so its magnitude was

$$M = \log \frac{4I}{S} = \log 4 + \log \frac{I}{S} = \log 4 + 8.3 \approx 8.9$$

✎. NOW TRY EXERCISE **35**   ∎

EXAMPLE 10 | Intensity of Earthquakes

The 1989 Loma Prieta earthquake that shook San Francisco had a magnitude of 7.1 on the Richter scale. How many times more intense was the 1906 earthquake (see Example 9) than the 1989 event?

SOLUTION   If I_1 and I_2 are the intensities of the 1906 and 1989 earthquakes, then we are required to find I_1/I_2. To relate this to the definition of magnitude, we divide the numerator and denominator by S.

$$\log \frac{I_1}{I_2} = \log \frac{I_1/S}{I_2/S} \qquad \text{Divide numerator and denominator by } S$$

$$= \log \frac{I_1}{S} - \log \frac{I_2}{S} \qquad \text{Law 2 of logarithms}$$

$$= 8.3 - 7.1 = 1.2 \qquad \text{Definition of earthquake magnitude}$$

Therefore,

$$\frac{I_1}{I_2} = 10^{\log(I_1/I_2)} = 10^{1.2} \approx 16$$

The 1906 earthquake was about 16 times as intense as the 1989 earthquake.

✎. NOW TRY EXERCISE **37**   ∎

The Decibel Scale   The ear is sensitive to an extremely wide range of sound intensities. We take as a reference intensity $I_0 = 10^{-12}$ W/m² (watts per square meter) at a frequency of 1000 hertz, which measures a sound that is just barely audible (the threshold of hearing). The psychological sensation of loudness varies with the logarithm of the intensity (the Weber-Fechner Law), so the **intensity level** B, measured in decibels (dB), is defined as

$$B = 10 \log \frac{I}{I_0}$$

IN-CLASS MATERIALS

Go over Examples 9 and 10, the Richter scale. Ask students the open-ended question, "How much worse is an earthquake that measures 7 on the Richter scale than an earthquake that measures 6?" and discuss.

ALTERNATE EXAMPLE 9

An earthquake in the United States has an estimated magnitude of 3.7 on the Richter scale. In the same year, an earthquake in Ecuador was four times as intense. What was the magnitude of the Ecuador earthquake on the Richter scale?

ANSWER

4.3

ALTERNATE EXAMPLE 10

A San Francisco earthquake has a magnitude of 7.5 on the Richter scale. Five years before, San Francisco had one with a magnitude of 8.1 on the Richter scale. How many times more intense was the past earthquake than the present one?

ANSWER

4

IN-CLASS MATERIALS

Go over Examples 9 and 10, the Richter scale. Ask students the open-ended question, "How much worse is an earthquake that measures 7 on the Richter scale than an earthquake that measures 6?" and discuss.

The intensity level of the barely audible reference sound is

$$B = 10 \log \frac{I_0}{I_0} = 10 \log 1 = 0 \text{ dB}$$

The **intensity levels of sounds** that we can hear vary from very loud to very soft. Here are some examples of the decibel levels of commonly heard sounds.

Source of sound	B (dB)
Jet takeoff	140
Jackhammer	130
Rock concert	120
Subway	100
Heavy traffic	80
Ordinary traffic	70
Normal conversation	50
Whisper	30
Rustling leaves	10–20
Threshold of hearing	0

ALTERNATE EXAMPLE 11

Find the decibel intensity level of a jet engine during takeoff if the intensity was measured at 10,000 W/m².

ANSWER

160

EXAMPLE 11 | Sound Intensity of a Jet Takeoff

Find the decibel intensity level of a jet engine during takeoff if the intensity was measured at 100 W/m².

SOLUTION From the definition of intensity level we see that

$$B = 10 \log \frac{I}{I_0} = 10 \log \frac{10^2}{10^{-12}} = 10 \log 10^{14} = 140 \text{ dB}$$

Thus, the intensity level is 140 dB.

✎. NOW TRY EXERCISE **41**   ■

The table in the margin lists decibel intensity levels for some common sounds ranging from the threshold of human hearing to the jet takeoff of Example 11. The threshold of pain is about 120 dB.

4.6 EXERCISES

APPLICATIONS

1–16 ■ These exercises use the population growth model.

✎. **1. Bacteria Culture** A certain culture of the bacterium *Streptococcus A* initially has 10 bacteria and is observed to double every 1.5 hours.
  (a) Find an exponential model $n(t) = n_0 2^{t/a}$ for the number of bacteria in the culture after t hours.
  (b) Estimate the number of bacteria after 35 hours.
  (c) When will the bacteria count reach 10,000?

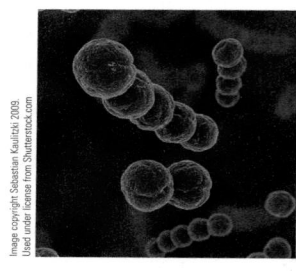

Streptococcus A
(12,000 × magnification)

2. Bacteria Culture A certain culture of the bacterium *Rhodobacter sphaeroides* initially has 25 bacteria and is observed to double every 5 hours.
  (a) Find an exponential model $n(t) = n_0 2^{t/a}$ for the number of bacteria in the culture after t hours.
  (b) Estimate the number of bacteria after 18 hours.

  (c) After how many hours will the bacteria count reach 1 million?

✎. **3. Squirrel Population** A grey squirrel population was introduced in a certain county of Great Britain 30 years ago. Biologists observe that the population doubles every 6 years, and now the population is 100,000.
  (a) What was the initial size of the squirrel population?
  (b) Estimate the squirrel population 10 years from now.
  (c) Sketch a graph of the squirrel population.

4. Bird Population A certain species of bird was introduced in a certain county 25 years ago. Biologists observe that the population doubles every 10 years, and now the population is 13,000.
  (a) What was the initial size of the bird population?
  (b) Estimate the bird population 5 years from now.
  (c) Sketch a graph of the bird population.

✎. **5. Fox Population** The fox population in a certain region has a relative growth rate of 8% per year. It is estimated that the population in 2005 was 18,000.
  (a) Find a function $n(t) = n_0 e^{rt}$ that models the population t years after 2005.
  (b) Use the function from part (a) to estimate the fox population in the year 2013.
  (c) Sketch a graph of the fox population function for the years 2005–2013.

6. Fish Population The population of a certain species of fish has a relative growth rate of 1.2% per year. It is estimated that the population in 2000 was 12 million.
  (a) Find an exponential model $n(t) = n_0 e^{rt}$ for the population t years after 2000.
  (b) Estimate the fish population in the year 2005.
  (c) Sketch a graph of the fish population.

DRILL QUESTIONS

Recall that the pH of a substance is given by $-\log [H^+]$, where H^+ is the concentration of hydrogen ions measured in moles per liter. Also recall that solutions with a pH of 7 are neutral, those with pH > 7 are basic, and those with pH < 7 are acidic.

(a) If a sample were measured to have hydrogen concentration of $[H^+] = 4 \times 10^{-8}$ M, what would the pH be?

(b) What is the hydrogen ion concentration in a neutral substance?

Answers
(a) 7.4
(b) 10^{-7}

7. Population of a Country   The population of a country has a relative growth rate of 3% per year. The government is trying to reduce the growth rate to 2%. The population in 1995 was approximately 110 million. Find the projected population for the year 2020 for the following conditions.

(a) The relative growth rate remains at 3% per year.

(b) The relative growth rate is reduced to 2% per year.

8. Bacteria Culture   It is observed that a certain bacteria culture has a relative growth rate of 12% per hour, but in the presence of an antibiotic the relative growth rate is reduced to 5% per hour. The initial number of bacteria in the culture is 22. Find the projected population after 24 hours for the following conditions.

(a) No antibiotic is present, so the relative growth rate is 12%.

(b) An antibiotic is present in the culture, so the relative growth rate is reduced to 5%.

9. Population of a City   The population of a certain city was 112,000 in 2006, and the observed doubling time for the population is 18 years.

(a) Find an exponential model $n(t) = n_0 2^{t/a}$ for the population t years after 2006.

(b) Find an exponential model $n(t) = n_0 e^{rt}$ for the population t years after 2006.

(c) Sketch a graph of the population at time t.

(d) Estimate when the population will reach 500,000.

10. Bat Population   The bat population in a certain Midwestern county was 350,000 in 2009, and the observed doubling time for the population is 25 years.

(a) Find an exponential model $n(t) = n_0 2^{t/a}$ for the population t years after 2006.

(b) Find an exponential model $n(t) = n_0 e^{rt}$ for the population t years after 2006.

(c) Sketch a graph of the population at time t.

(d) Estimate when the population will reach 2 million.

11. Deer Population   The graph shows the deer population in a Pennsylvania county between 2003 and 2007. Assume that the population grows exponentially.

(a) What was the deer population in 2003?

(b) Find a function that models the deer population t years after 2003.

(c) What is the projected deer population in 2011?

(d) In what year will the deer population reach 100,000?

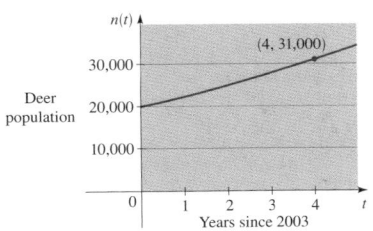

12. Frog Population   Some bullfrogs were introduced into a small pond. The graph shows the bullfrog population for the next few years. Assume that the population grows exponentially.

(a) What was the initial bullfrog population?

(b) Find a function that models the bullfrog population t years since the bullfrogs were put into the pond.

(c) What is the projected bullfrog population after 15 years?

(d) Estimate how long it takes the population to reach 75,000.

13. Bacteria Culture   A culture starts with 8600 bacteria. After one hour the count is 10,000.

(a) Find a function that models the number of bacteria $n(t)$ after t hours.

(b) Find the number of bacteria after 2 hours.

(c) After how many hours will the number of bacteria double?

14. Bacteria Culture   The count in a culture of bacteria was 400 after 2 hours and 25,600 after 6 hours.

(a) What is the relative rate of growth of the bacteria population? Express your answer as a percentage.

(b) What was the initial size of the culture?

(c) Find a function that models the number of bacteria $n(t)$ after t hours.

(d) Find the number of bacteria after 4.5 hours.

(e) When will the number of bacteria be 50,000?

15. Population of California   The population of California was 29.76 million in 1990 and 33.87 million in 2000. Assume that the population grows exponentially.

(a) Find a function that models the population t years after 1990.

(b) Find the time required for the population to double.

(c) Use the function from part (a) to predict the population of California in the year 2010. Look up California's actual population in 2010, and compare.

16. World Population   The population of the world was 5.7 billion in 1995, and the observed relative growth rate was 2% per year.

(a) By what year will the population have doubled?

(b) By what year will the population have tripled?

17–24 ■ These exercises use the radioactive decay model.

17. Radioactive Radium   The half-life of radium-226 is 1600 years. Suppose we have a 22-mg sample.

(a) Find a function $m(t) = m_0 2^{-t/h}$ that models the mass remaining after t years.

(b) Find a function $m(t) = m_0 e^{-rt}$ that models the mass remaining after t years.

(c) How much of the sample will remain after 4000 years?

(d) After how long will only 18 mg of the sample remain?

18. Radioactive Cesium   The half-life of cesium-137 is 30 years. Suppose we have a 10-g sample.

(a) Find a function $m(t) = m_0 2^{-t/h}$ that models the mass remaining after t years.

(b) Find a function $m(t) = m_0 e^{-rt}$ that models the mass remaining after t years.
(c) How much of the sample will remain after 80 years?
(d) After how long will only 2 g of the sample remain?

19. Radioactive Strontium The half-life of strontium-90 is 28 years. How long will it take a 50-mg sample to decay to a mass of 32 mg?

20. Radioactive Radium Radium-221 has a half-life of 30 s. How long will it take for 95% of a sample to decay?

21. Finding Half-life If 250 mg of a radioactive element decays to 200 mg in 48 hours, find the half-life of the element.

22. Radioactive Radon After 3 days a sample of radon-222 has decayed to 58% of its original amount.
(a) What is the half-life of radon-222?
(b) How long will it take the sample to decay to 20% of its original amount?

23. Carbon-14 Dating A wooden artifact from an ancient tomb contains 65% of the carbon-14 that is present in living trees. How long ago was the artifact made? (The half-life of carbon-14 is 5730 years.)

24. Carbon-14 Dating The burial cloth of an Egyptian mummy is estimated to contain 59% of the carbon-14 it contained originally. How long ago was the mummy buried? (The half-life of carbon-14 is 5730 years.)

25–28 ■ These exercises use Newton's Law of Cooling.

25. Cooling Soup A hot bowl of soup is served at a dinner party. It starts to cool according to Newton's Law of Cooling, so its temperature at time t is given by

$$T(t) = 65 + 145e^{-0.05t}$$

where t is measured in minutes and T is measured in °F.
(a) What is the initial temperature of the soup?
(b) What is the temperature after 10 min?
(c) After how long will the temperature be 100°F?

26. Time of Death Newton's Law of Cooling is used in homicide investigations to determine the time of death. The normal body temperature is 98.6°F. Immediately following death, the body begins to cool. It has been determined experimentally that the constant in Newton's Law of Cooling is approximately $k = 0.1947$, assuming that time is measured in hours. Suppose that the temperature of the surroundings is 60°F.
(a) Find a function $T(t)$ that models the temperature t hours after death.
(b) If the temperature of the body is now 72°F, how long ago was the time of death?

27. Cooling Turkey A roasted turkey is taken from an oven when its temperature has reached 185°F and is placed on a table in a room where the temperature is 75°F.

(a) If the temperature of the turkey is 150°F after half an hour, what is its temperature after 45 min?
(b) When will the turkey cool to 100°F?

 28. Boiling Water A kettle full of water is brought to a boil in a room with temperature 20°C. After 15 min the temperature of the water has decreased from 100°C to 75°C. Find the temperature after another 10 min. Illustrate by graphing the temperature function.

29–43 ■ These exercises deal with logarithmic scales.

29. Finding pH The hydrogen ion concentration of a sample of each substance is given. Calculate the pH of the substance.
(a) Lemon juice: $[H^+] = 5.0 \times 10^{-3}$ M
(b) Tomato juice: $[H^+] = 3.2 \times 10^{-4}$ M
(c) Seawater: $[H^+] = 5.0 \times 10^{-9}$ M

30. Finding pH An unknown substance has a hydrogen ion concentration of $[H^+] = 3.1 \times 10^{-8}$ M. Find the pH and classify the substance as acidic or basic.

31. Ion Concentration The pH reading of a sample of each substance is given. Calculate the hydrogen ion concentration of the substance.
(a) Vinegar: pH = 3.0
(b) Milk: pH = 6.5

32. Ion Concentration The pH reading of a glass of liquid is given. Find the hydrogen ion concentration of the liquid.
(a) Beer: pH = 4.6
(b) Water: pH = 7.3

33. Finding pH The hydrogen ion concentrations in cheeses range from 4.0×10^{-7} M to 1.6×10^{-5} M. Find the corresponding range of pH readings.

34. Ion Concentration in Wine The pH readings for wines vary from 2.8 to 3.8. Find the corresponding range of hydrogen ion concentrations.

35. Earthquake Magnitudes If one earthquake is 20 times as intense as another, how much larger is its magnitude on the Richter scale?

36. Earthquake Magnitudes The 1906 earthquake in San Francisco had a magnitude of 8.3 on the Richter scale. At the same time in Japan an earthquake with magnitude 4.9 caused only minor damage. How many times more intense was the San Francisco earthquake than the Japanese earthquake?

37. Earthquake Magnitudes The Alaska earthquake of 1964 had a magnitude of 8.6 on the Richter scale. How many times more intense was this than the 1906 San Francisco earthquake? (See Exercise 36.)

38. Earthquake Magnitudes The Northridge, California, earthquake of 1994 had a magnitude of 6.8 on the Richter scale. A year later, a 7.2-magnitude earthquake struck Kobe, Japan. How many times more intense was the Kobe earthquake than the Northridge earthquake?

39. Earthquake Magnitudes The 1985 Mexico City earthquake had a magnitude of 8.1 on the Richter scale. The 1976 earthquake in Tangshan, China, was 1.26 times as intense. What was the magnitude of the Tangshan earthquake?

40. Subway Noise The intensity of the sound of a subway train was measured at 98 dB. Find the intensity in W/m^2.

41. Traffic Noise The intensity of the sound of traffic at a busy intersection was measured at 2.0×10^{-5} W/m^2. Find the intensity level in decibels.

42. Comparing Decibel Levels The noise from a power mower was measured at 106 dB. The noise level at a rock concert was measured at 120 dB. Find the ratio of the intensity of the rock music to that of the power mower.

43. Inverse Square Law for Sound A law of physics states that the intensity of sound is inversely proportional to the square of the distance d from the source: $I = k/d^2$.
(a) Use this model and the equation

$$B = 10 \log \frac{I}{I_0}$$

(described in this section) to show that the decibel levels B_1 and B_2 at distances d_1 and d_2 from a sound source are related by the equation

$$B_2 = B_1 + 20 \log \frac{d_1}{d_2}$$

(b) The intensity level at a rock concert is 120 dB at a distance 2 m from the speakers. Find the intensity level at a distance of 10 m.

CHAPTER 4 | REVIEW

■ CONCEPT CHECK

1. (a) Write an equation that defines the exponential function with base a.
(b) What is the domain of this function?
(c) What is the range of this function?
(d) Sketch the general shape of the graph of the exponential function for each case.
  (i) $a > 1$ (ii) $0 < a < 1$

2. If x is large, which function grows faster, $y = 2^x$ or $y = x^2$?

3. (a) How is the number e defined?
(b) What is the natural exponential function?

4. (a) How is the logarithmic function $y = \log_a x$ defined?
(b) What is the domain of this function?
(c) What is the range of this function?
(d) Sketch the general shape of the graph of the function $y = \log_a x$ if $a > 1$.
(e) What is the natural logarithm?
(f) What is the common logarithm?

5. State the three Laws of Logarithms.

6. State the Change of Base Formula.

7. (a) How do you solve an exponential equation?
(b) How do you solve a logarithmic equation?

8. Suppose an amount P is invested at an interest rate r and A is the amount after t years.
(a) Write an expression for A if the interest is compounded n times per year.
(b) Write an expression for A if the interest is compounded continuously.

9. The initial size of a population is n_0 and the population grows exponentially.
(a) Write an expression for the population in terms of the doubling time a.
(b) Write an expression for the population in terms of the relative growth rate r.

10. (a) What is the half-life of a radioactive substance?
(b) If a radioactive substance has initial mass m_0 and half-life h, write an expression for the mass $m(t)$ remaining at time t.

11. What does Newton's Law of Cooling say?

12. What do the pH scale, the Richter scale, and the decibel scale have in common? What do they measure?

■ EXERCISES

1–4 ■ Use a calculator to find the indicated values of the exponential function, correct to three decimal places.

1. $f(x) = 5^x$; $f(-1.5), f(\sqrt{2}), f(2.5)$
2. $f(x) = 3 \cdot 2^x$; $f(-2.2), f(\sqrt{7}), f(5.5)$
3. $g(x) = 4 \cdot \left(\frac{2}{3}\right)^{x-2}$; $g(-0.7), g(e), g(\pi)$
4. $g(x) = \frac{7}{4}e^{x+1}$; $g(-2), g(\sqrt{3}), g(3.6)$

5–16 ■ Sketch the graph of the function. State the domain, range, and asymptote.

5. $f(x) = 2^{-x+1}$
6. $f(x) = 3^{x-2}$
7. $g(x) = 3 + 2^x$
8. $g(x) = 5^{-x} - 5$

9. $f(x) = \log_3(x - 1)$ **10.** $g(x) = \log(-x)$

11. $f(x) = 2 - \log_2 x$ **12.** $f(x) = 3 + \log_5(x + 4)$

13. $F(x) = e^x - 1$ **14.** $G(x) = \frac{1}{2}e^{x-1}$

15. $g(x) = 2 \ln x$ **16.** $g(x) = \ln(x^2)$

17–20 ■ Find the domain of the function.

17. $f(x) = 10^{x^2} + \log(1 - 2x)$

18. $g(x) = \log(2 + x - x^2)$

19. $h(x) = \ln(x^2 - 4)$ **20.** $k(x) = \ln|x|$

21–24 ■ Write the equation in exponential form.

21. $\log_2 1024 = 10$ **22.** $\log_6 37 = x$

23. $\log x = y$ **24.** $\ln c = 17$

25–28 ■ Write the equation in logarithmic form.

25. $2^6 = 64$ **26.** $49^{-1/2} = \frac{1}{7}$

27. $10^x = 74$ **28.** $e^k = m$

29–44 ■ Evaluate the expression without using a calculator.

29. $\log_2 128$ **30.** $\log_8 1$

31. $10^{\log 45}$ **32.** $\log 0.000001$

33. $\ln(e^6)$ **34.** $\log_4 8$

35. $\log_3(\frac{1}{27})$ **36.** $2^{\log_2 13}$

37. $\log_5 \sqrt{5}$ **38.** $e^{2\ln 7}$

39. $\log 25 + \log 4$ **40.** $\log_3 \sqrt{243}$

41. $\log_2 16^{23}$ **42.** $\log_5 250 - \log_5 2$

43. $\log_8 6 - \log_8 3 + \log_8 2$ **44.** $\log \log 10^{100}$

45–50 ■ Expand the logarithmic expression.

45. $\log(AB^2C^3)$ **46.** $\log_2(x\sqrt{x^2 + 1})$

47. $\ln\sqrt{\dfrac{x^2 - 1}{x^2 + 1}}$ **48.** $\log\left(\dfrac{4x^3}{y^2(x - 1)^5}\right)$

49. $\log_5\left(\dfrac{x^2(1 - 5x)^{3/2}}{\sqrt{x^3 - x}}\right)$ **50.** $\ln\left(\dfrac{\sqrt[3]{x^4 + 12}}{(x + 16)\sqrt{x - 3}}\right)$

51–56 ■ Combine into a single logarithm.

51. $\log 6 + 4 \log 2$ **52.** $\log x + \log(x^2 y) + 3 \log y$

53. $\frac{3}{2}\log_2(x - y) - 2\log_2(x^2 + y^2)$

54. $\log_5 2 + \log_5(x + 1) - \frac{1}{3}\log_5(3x + 7)$

55. $\log(x - 2) + \log(x + 2) - \frac{1}{2}\log(x^2 + 4)$

56. $\frac{1}{2}[\ln(x - 4) + 5\ln(x^2 + 4x)]$

57–68 ■ Solve the equation. Find the exact solution if possible; otherwise, use a calculator to approximate to two decimals.

57. $3^{2x-7} = 27$ **58.** $5^{4-x} = \frac{1}{125}$

59. $2^{3x-5} = 7$ **60.** $10^{6-3x} = 18$

61. $4^{1-x} = 3^{2x+5}$ **62.** $e^{3x/4} = 10$

63. $x^2 e^{2x} + 2x e^{2x} = 8e^{2x}$ **64.** $3^{2x} - 3^x - 6 = 0$

65. $\log_2(1 - x) = 4$

66. $\log x + \log(x + 1) = \log 12$

67. $\log_8(x + 5) - \log_8(x - 2) = 1$

68. $\ln(2x - 3) + 1 = 0$

69–72 ■ Use a calculator to find the solution of the equation, rounded to six decimal places.

69. $5^{-2x/3} = 0.63$ **70.** $2^{3x-5} = 7$

71. $5^{2x+1} = 3^{4x-1}$ **72.** $e^{-15k} = 10{,}000$

73–76 ■ Draw a graph of the function and use it to determine the asymptotes and the local maximum and minimum values.

73. $y = e^{x/(x+2)}$ **74.** $y = 10^x - 5^x$

75. $y = \log(x^3 - x)$ **76.** $y = 2x^2 - \ln x$

77–78 ■ Find the solutions of the equation, rounded to two decimal places.

77. $3\log x = 6 - 2x$ **78.** $4 - x^2 = e^{-2x}$

79–80 ■ Solve the inequality graphically.

79. $\ln x > x - 2$ **80.** $e^x < 4x^2$

81. Use a graph of $f(x) = e^x - 3e^{-x} - 4x$ to find, approximately, the intervals on which f is increasing and on which f is decreasing.

82. Find an equation of the line shown in the figure.

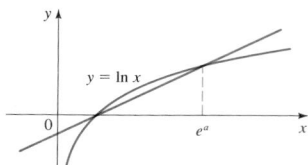

83–86 ■ Use the Change of Base Formula to evaluate the logarithm, rounded to six decimal places.

83. $\log_4 15$ **84.** $\log_7(\frac{3}{4})$

85. $\log_9 0.28$ **86.** $\log_{100} 250$

87. Which is larger, $\log_4 258$ or $\log_5 620$?

88. Find the inverse of the function $f(x) = 2^{3^x}$, and state its domain and range.

89. If \$12,000 is invested at an interest rate of 10% per year, find the amount of the investment at the end of 3 years for each compounding method.
 (a) Semiannually   (b) Monthly
 (c) Daily   (d) Continuously

90. A sum of \$5000 is invested at an interest rate of $8\frac{1}{2}\%$ per year, compounded semiannually.
 (a) Find the amount of the investment after $1\frac{1}{2}$ years.

(b) After what period of time will the investment amount to $7000?

(c) If interest were compounded continously instead of semi-annually, how long would it take for the amount to grow to $7000?

91. A money market account pays 5.2% annual interest, compounded daily. If $100,000 is invested in this account, how long will it take for the account to accumulate $10,000 in interest?

92. A retirement savings plan pays 4.5% interest, compounded continuously. How long will it take for an investment in this plan to double?

93–94 ■ Determine the annual percentage yield (APY) for the given nominal annual interest rate and compounding frequency.

93. 4.25%;   daily   **94.** 3.2%;   monthly

95. The stray-cat population in a small town grows exponentially. In 1999 the town had 30 stray cats, and the relative growth rate was 15% per year.
(a) Find a function that models the stray-cat population $n(t)$ after t years.
(b) Find the projected population after 4 years.
(c) Find the number of years required for the stray-cat population to reach 500.

96. A culture contains 10,000 bacteria initially. After an hour the bacteria count is 25,000.
(a) Find the doubling period.
(b) Find the number of bacteria after 3 hours.

97. Uranium-234 has a half-life of 2.7×10^5 years.
(a) Find the amount remaining from a 10-mg sample after a thousand years.
(b) How long will it take this sample to decompose until its mass is 7 mg?

98. A sample of bismuth-210 decayed to 33% of its original mass after 8 days.
(a) Find the half-life of this element.
(b) Find the mass remaining after 12 days.

99. The half-life of radium-226 is 1590 years.
(a) If a sample has a mass of 150 mg, find a function that models the mass that remains after t years.
(b) Find the mass that will remain after 1000 years.
(c) After how many years will only 50 mg remain?

100. The half-life of palladium-100 is 4 days. After 20 days a sample has been reduced to a mass of 0.375 g.
(a) What was the initial mass of the sample?
(b) Find a function that models the mass remaining after t days.
(c) What is the mass after 3 days?
(d) After how many days will only 0.15 g remain?

101. The graph shows the population of a rare species of bird, where t represents years since 1999 and $n(t)$ is measured in thousands.
(a) Find a function that models the bird population at time t in the form $n(t) = n_0 e^{rt}$.
(b) What is the bird population expected to be in the year 2010?

102. A car engine runs at a temperature of 190°F. When the engine is turned off, it cools according to Newton's Law of Cooling with constant $k = 0.0341$, where the time is measured in minutes. Find the time needed for the engine to cool to 90°F if the surrounding temperature is 60°F.

103. The hydrogen ion concentration of fresh egg whites was measured as

$$[H^+] = 1.3 \times 10^{-8} \, M$$

Find the pH, and classify the substance as acidic or basic.

104. The pH of lime juice is 1.9. Find the hydrogen ion concentration.

105. If one earthquake has magnitude 6.5 on the Richter scale, what is the magnitude of another quake that is 35 times as intense?

106. The drilling of a jackhammer was measured at 132 dB. The sound of whispering was measured at 28 dB. Find the ratio of the intensity of the drilling to that of the whispering.

1. Sketch the graph of each function, and state its domain, range, and asymptote. Show the x- and y-intercepts on the graph.
   (a) $f(x) = 2^{-x} + 4$ (b) $g(x) = \log_3(x + 3)$

2. (a) Write the equation $6^{2x} = 25$ in logarithmic form.
   (b) Write the equation $\ln A = 3$ in exponential form.

3. Find the exact value of each expression.
   (a) $10^{\log 36}$ (b) $\ln e^3$
   (c) $\log_3 \sqrt{27}$ (d) $\log_2 80 - \log_2 10$
   (e) $\log_8 4$ (f) $\log_6 4 + \log_6 9$

4. Use the Laws of Logarithms to expand the expression:
$$\log \sqrt[3]{\frac{x + 2}{x^4(x^2 + 4)}}$$

5. Combine into a single logarithm: $\ln x - 2\ln(x^2 + 1) + \frac{1}{2}\ln(3 - x^4)$

6. Find the solution of the equation, correct to two decimal places.
   (a) $2^{x-1} = 10$ (b) $5\ln(3 - x) = 4$
   (c) $10^{x+3} = 6^{2x}$ (d) $\log_2(x + 2) + \log_2(x - 1) = 2$

7. The initial size of a culture of bacteria is 1000. After one hour the bacteria count is 8000.
   (a) Find a function that models the population after t hours.
   (b) Find the population after 1.5 hours.
   (c) When will the population reach 15,000?
   (d) Sketch the graph of the population function.

8. Suppose that $12,000 is invested in a savings account paying 5.6% interest per year.
   (a) Write the formula for the amount in the account after t years if interest is compounded monthly.
   (b) Find the amount in the account after 3 years if interest is compounded daily.
   (c) How long will it take for the amount in the account to grow to $20,000 if interest is compounded semiannually?

9. The half-life of krypton-91 (^{91}Kr) is 10 seconds. At time $t = 0$ a heavy canister contains 3 g of this radioactive gas.
   (a) Find a function that models the amount $A(t)$ of ^{91}Kr remaining in the canister after t seconds.
   (b) How much ^{91}Kr remains after one minute?
   (c) When will the amount of ^{91}Kr remaining be reduced to 1 μg (1 microgram, or 10^{-6} g)?

10. An earthquake measuring 6.4 on the Richter scale struck Japan in July 2007, causing extensive damage. Earlier that year, a minor earthquake measuring 3.1 on the Richter scale was felt in parts of Pennsylvania. How many times more intense was the Japanese earthquake than the Pennsylvania earthquake?

Fitting Exponential and Power Curves to Data

In a previous *Focus on Modeling* (page 296) we learned that the shape of a scatter plot helps us to choose the type of curve to use in modeling data. The first plot in Figure 1 fairly screams for a line to be fitted through it, and the second one points to a cubic polynomial. For the third plot it is tempting to fit a second-degree polynomial. But what if an exponential curve fits better? How do we decide this? In this section we learn how to fit exponential and power curves to data and how to decide which type of curve fits the data better. We also learn that for scatter plots like those in the last two plots in Figure 1, the data can be modeled by logarithmic or logistic functions.

FIGURE 1

▼ Modeling with Exponential Functions

If a scatter plot shows that the data increase rapidly, we might want to model the data using an *exponential model*, that is, a function of the form

$$f(x) = Ce^{kx}$$

where C and k are constants. In the first example we model world population by an exponential model. Recall from Section 4.6 that population tends to increase exponentially.

TABLE 1
World population

Year (t)	World population (P in millions)
1900	1650
1910	1750
1920	1860
1930	2070
1940	2300
1950	2520
1960	3020
1970	3700
1980	4450
1990	5300
2000	6060

EXAMPLE 1 | An Exponential Model for World Population

Table 1 gives the population of the world in the 20th century.

(a) Draw a scatter plot, and note that a linear model is not appropriate.

(b) Find an exponential function that models population growth.

(c) Draw a graph of the function that you found together with the scatter plot. How well does the model fit the data?

(d) Use the model that you found to predict world population in the year 2020.

SOLUTION

(a) The scatter plot is shown in Figure 2. The plotted points do not appear to lie along a straight line, so a linear model is not appropriate.

FIGURE 2 Scatter plot of world population

357

The population of the world increases exponentially.

(b) Using a graphing calculator and the `ExpReg` command (see Figure 3(a)), we get the exponential model

$$P(t) = (0.0082543) \cdot (1.0137186)^t$$

This is a model of the form $y = Cb^t$. To convert this to the form $y = Ce^{kt}$, we use the properties of exponentials and logarithms as follows:

$$
\begin{aligned}
1.0137186^t &= e^{\ln 1.0137186^t} & A &= e^{\ln A} \\
&= e^{t \ln 1.0137186} & \ln A^B &= B \ln A \\
&= e^{0.013625t} & \ln 1.0137186 &\approx 0.013625
\end{aligned}
$$

Thus, we can write the model as

$$P(t) = 0.0082543e^{0.013625t}$$

(c) From the graph in Figure 3(b) we see that the model appears to fit the data fairly well. The period of relatively slow population growth is explained by the depression of the 1930s and the two world wars.

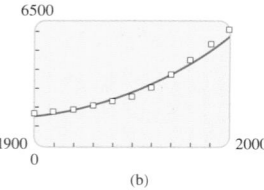

(a)   (b)

FIGURE 3 Exponential model for world population

(d) The model predicts that the world population in 2020 will be

$$P(2020) = 0.0082543e^{(0.013625)(2020)}$$

$$\approx 7,405,400,000$$

▼ Modeling with Power Functions

If the scatter plot of the data we are studying resembles the graph of $y = ax^2$, $y = ax^{1.32}$, or some other power function, then we seek a *power model*, that is, a function of the form

$$f(x) = ax^n$$

where a is a positive constant and n is any real number.

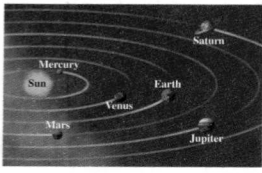

In the next example we seek a power model for some astronomical data. In astronomy, distance in the solar system is often measured in astronomical units. An *astronomical unit* (AU) is the mean distance from the earth to the sun. The *period* of a planet is the time it takes the planet to make a complete revolution around the sun (measured in earth years). In this example we derive the remarkable relationship, first discovered by Johannes Kepler (see page 754), between the mean distance of a planet from the sun and its period.

EXAMPLE 2 | A Power Model for Planetary Periods

Table 2 gives the mean distance d of each planet from the sun in astronomical units and its period T in years.

TABLE 2

Distances and periods of the planets

Planet	d	T
Mercury	0.387	0.241
Venus	0.723	0.615
Earth	1.000	1.000
Mars	1.523	1.881
Jupiter	5.203	11.861
Saturn	9.541	29.457
Uranus	19.190	84.008
Neptune	30.086	164.784
Pluto	39.507	248.350

(a) Sketch a scatter plot. Is a linear model appropriate?

(b) Find a power function that models the data.

(c) Draw a graph of the function you found and the scatter plot on the same graph. How well does the model fit the data?

(d) Use the model that you found to calculate the period of an asteroid whose mean distance from the sun is 5 AU.

SOLUTION

(a) The scatter plot shown in Figure 4 indicates that the plotted points do not lie along a straight line, so a linear model is not appropriate.

FIGURE 4 Scatter plot of planetary data

(b) Using a graphing calculator and the `PwrReg` command (see Figure 5(a)), we get the power model

$$T = 1.000396d^{1.49966}$$

If we round both the coefficient and the exponent to three significant figures, we can write the model as

$$T = d^{1.5}$$

This is the relationship discovered by Kepler (see page 754). Sir Isaac Newton (page 852) later used his Law of Gravity to derive this relationship theoretically, thereby providing strong scientific evidence that the Law of Gravity must be true.

(c) The graph is shown in Figure 5(b). The model appears to fit the data very well.

(a)

(b)

FIGURE 5 Power model for planetary data

(d) In this case $d = 5$ AU, so our model gives

$$T = 1.00039 \cdot 5^{1.49966} \approx 11.22$$

The period of the asteroid is about 11.2 years.

▼ Linearizing Data

We have used the shape of a scatter plot to decide which type of model to use: linear, exponential, or power. This works well if the data points lie on a straight line. But it's difficult to distinguish a scatter plot that is exponential from one that requires a power model. So to help decide which model to use, we can *linearize* the data, that is, apply a function that "straightens" the scatter plot. The inverse of the linearizing function is then an appropriate model. We now describe how to linearize data that can be modeled by exponential or power functions.

▶ **Linearizing exponential data**

If we suspect that the data points (x, y) lie on an exponential curve $y = Ce^{kx}$, then the points

$$(x, \ln y)$$

should lie on a straight line. We can see this from the following calculations:

$$\ln y = \ln Ce^{kx} \qquad \text{Assume that } y = Ce^{kx} \text{ and take ln}$$
$$= \ln e^{kx} + \ln C \qquad \text{Property of ln}$$
$$= kx + \ln C \qquad \text{Property of ln}$$

To see that $\ln y$ is a linear function of x, let $Y = \ln y$ and $A = \ln C$; then

$$Y = kx + A$$

We apply this technique to the world population data (t, P) to obtain the points $(t, \ln P)$ in Table 3. The scatter plot of $(t, \ln P)$ in Figure 6, called a **semi-log plot**, shows that the linearized data lie approximately on a straight line, so an exponential model should be appropriate.

TABLE 3
World population data

t	Population P (in millions)	$\ln P$
1900	1650	21.224
1910	1750	21.283
1920	1860	21.344
1930	2070	21.451
1940	2300	21.556
1950	2520	21.648
1960	3020	21.829
1970	3700	22.032
1980	4450	22.216
1990	5300	22.391
2000	6060	22.525

FIGURE 6 Semi-log plot of data in Table 3

▶ **Linearizing power data**

If we suspect that the data points (x, y) lie on a power curve $y = ax^n$, then the points

$$(\ln x, \ln y)$$

should be on a straight line. We can see this from the following calculations:

$$\ln y = \ln ax^n \qquad \text{Assume that } y = ax^n \text{ and take ln}$$
$$= \ln a + \ln x^n \qquad \text{Property of ln}$$
$$= \ln a + n \ln x \qquad \text{Property of ln}$$

To see that $\ln y$ is a linear function of $\ln x$, let $Y = \ln y$, $X = \ln x$, and $A = \ln a$; then

$$Y = nX + A$$

TABLE 4
Log-log table

$\ln d$	$\ln T$
−0.94933	−1.4230
−0.32435	−0.48613
0	0
0.42068	0.6318
1.6492	2.4733
2.2556	3.3829
2.9544	4.4309
3.4041	5.1046
3.6765	5.5148

We apply this technique to the planetary data (d, T) in Table 2 to obtain the points $(\ln d, \ln T)$ in Table 4. The scatter plot of $(\ln d, \ln T)$ in Figure 7, called a **log-log plot**, shows that the data lie on a straight line, so a power model seems appropriate.

FIGURE 7 Log-log plot of data in Table 4

▼ An Exponential or Power Model?

Suppose that a scatter plot of the data points (x, y) shows a rapid increase. Should we use an exponential function or a power function to model the data? To help us decide, we draw two scatter plots: one for the points $(x, \ln y)$ and the other for the points $(\ln x, \ln y)$. If the first scatter plot appears to lie along a line, then an exponential model is appropriate. If the second plot appears to lie along a line, then a power model is appropriate.

EXAMPLE 3 | An Exponential or Power Model?

Data points (x, y) are shown in Table 5.

(a) Draw a scatter plot of the data.

(b) Draw scatter plots of $(x, \ln y)$ and $(\ln x, \ln y)$.

(c) Is an exponential function or a power function appropriate for modeling this data?

(d) Find an appropriate function to model the data.

SOLUTION

(a) The scatter plot of the data is shown in Figure 8.

TABLE 5

x	y
1	2
2	6
3	14
4	22
5	34
6	46
7	64
8	80
9	102
10	130

FIGURE 8

(b) We use the values from Table 6 to graph the scatter plots in Figures 9 and 10.

TABLE 6

x	ln x	ln y
1	0	0.7
2	0.7	1.8
3	1.1	2.6
4	1.4	3.1
5	1.6	3.5
6	1.8	3.8
7	1.9	4.2
8	2.1	4.4
9	2.2	4.6
10	2.3	4.9

FIGURE 9   Semi-log plot

FIGURE 10   Log-log plot

(c) The scatter plot of $(x, \ln y)$ in Figure 9 does not appear to be linear, so an exponential model is not appropriate. On the other hand, the scatter plot of $(\ln x, \ln y)$ in Figure 10 is very nearly linear, so a power model is appropriate.

(d) Using the `PwrReg` command on a graphing calculator, we find that the power function that best fits the data point is

$$y = 1.85x^{1.82}$$

The graph of this function and the original data points are shown in Figure 11. ■

FIGURE 11

Before graphing calculators and statistical software became common, exponential and power models for data were often constructed by first finding a linear model for the linearized data. Then the model for the actual data was found by taking exponentials. For instance, if we find that $\ln y = A \ln x + B$, then by taking exponentials we get the model $y = e^B \cdot e^{A \ln x}$, or $y = Cx^A$ (where $C = e^B$). Special graphing paper called "log paper" or "log-log paper" was used to facilitate this process.

▼ Modeling with Logistic Functions

A logistic growth model is a function of the form

$$f(t) = \frac{c}{1 + ae^{-bt}}$$

where a, b, and c are positive constants. Logistic functions are used to model populations where the growth is constrained by available resources. (See Exercises 25–28 of Section 4.2.)

EXAMPLE 4 | Stocking a Pond with Catfish

TABLE 7

Week	Catfish
0	1000
15	1500
30	3300
45	4400
60	6100
75	6900
90	7100
105	7800
120	7900

Much of the fish that is sold in supermarkets today is raised on commercial fish farms, not caught in the wild. A pond on one such farm is initially stocked with 1000 catfish, and the fish population is then sampled at 15-week intervals to estimate its size. The population data are given in Table 7.

(a) Find an appropriate model for the data.

(b) Make a scatter plot of the data and graph the model that you found in part (a) on the scatter plot.

(c) How does the model predict that the fish population will change with time?

SOLUTION

(a) Since the catfish population is restricted by its habitat (the pond), a logistic model is appropriate. Using the `Logistic` command on a calculator (see Figure 12(a)), we find the following model for the catfish population $P(t)$:

$$P(t) = \frac{7925}{1 + 7.7e^{-0.052t}}$$

FIGURE 12   (a)   (b) Catfish population $y = P(t)$

(b) The scatter plot and the logistic curve are shown in Figure 12(b).

(c) From the graph of P in Figure 12(b) we see that the catfish population increases rapidly until about $t = 80$ weeks. Then growth slows down, and at about $t = 120$ weeks the population levels off and remains more or less constant at slightly over 7900. ■

The behavior that is exhibited by the catfish population in Example 4 is typical of logistic growth. After a rapid growth phase, the population approaches a constant level called the **carrying capacity** of the environment. This occurs because as $t \to \infty$, we have $e^{-bt} \to 0$ (see Section 4.2), and so

$$P(t) = \frac{c}{1 + ae^{-bt}} \quad \longrightarrow \quad \frac{c}{1 + 0} = c$$

Thus, the carrying capacity is c.

PROBLEMS

1. **U.S. Population**   The U.S. Constitution requires a census every 10 years. The census data for 1790–2000 are given in the table.

   (a) Make a scatter plot of the data.

   (b) Use a calculator to find an exponential model for the data.

   (c) Use your model to predict the population at the 2010 census.

   (d) Use your model to estimate the population in 1965.

   (e) Compare your answers from parts (c) and (d) to the values in the table. Do you think an exponential model is appropriate for these data?

Year	Population (in millions)	Year	Population (in millions)	Year	Population (in millions)
1790	3.9	1870	38.6	1950	151.3
1800	5.3	1880	50.2	1960	179.3
1810	7.2	1890	63.0	1970	203.3
1820	9.6	1900	76.2	1980	226.5
1830	12.9	1910	92.2	1990	248.7
1840	17.1	1920	106.0	2000	281.4
1850	23.2	1930	123.2		
1860	31.4	1940	132.2		

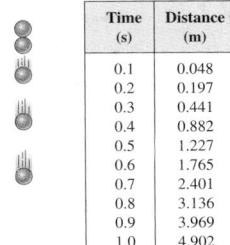

Time (s)	Distance (m)
0.1	0.048
0.2	0.197
0.3	0.441
0.4	0.882
0.5	1.227
0.6	1.765
0.7	2.401
0.8	3.136
0.9	3.969
1.0	4.902

2. **A Falling Ball**   In a physics experiment a lead ball is dropped from a height of 5 m. The students record the distance the ball has fallen every one-tenth of a second. (This can be done by using a camera and a strobe light.)

   (a) Make a scatter plot of the data.

   (b) Use a calculator to find a power model.

   (c) Use your model to predict how far a dropped ball would fall in 3 s.

3. **Health-Care Expenditures**   The U.S. health-care expenditures for 1970–2001 are given in the table below, and a scatter plot of the data is shown in the figure.

   (a) Does the scatter plot shown suggest an exponential model?

   (b) Make a table of the values $(t, \ln E)$ and a scatter plot. Does the scatter plot appear to be linear?

   (c) Find the regression line for the data in part (b).

   (d) Use the results of part (c) to find an exponential model for the growth of health-care expenditures.

   (e) Use your model to predict the total health-care expenditures in 2009.

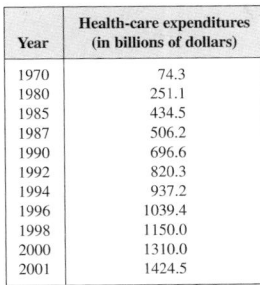

Year	Health-care expenditures (in billions of dollars)
1970	74.3
1980	251.1
1985	434.5
1987	506.2
1990	696.6
1992	820.3
1994	937.2
1996	1039.4
1998	1150.0
2000	1310.0
2001	1424.5

Time (h)	Amount of ^{131}I (g)
0	4.80
8	4.66
16	4.51
24	4.39
32	4.29
40	4.14
48	4.04

Light intensity decreases
exponentially with depth.

4. Half-Life of Radioactive Iodine   A student is trying to determine the half-life of radioactive iodine-131. He measures the amount of iodine-131 in a sample solution every 8 hours. His data are shown in the table in the margin.

(a) Make a scatter plot of the data.

(b) Use a calculator to find an exponential model.

(c) Use your model to find the half-life of iodine-131.

5. The Beer-Lambert Law   As sunlight passes through the waters of lakes and oceans, the light is absorbed, and the deeper it penetrates, the more its intensity diminishes. The light intensity I at depth x is given by the Beer-Lambert Law:

$$I = I_0 e^{-kx}$$

where I_0 is the light intensity at the surface and k is a constant that depends on the murkiness of the water (see page 336). A biologist uses a photometer to investigate light penetration in a northern lake, obtaining the data in the table.

(a) Use a graphing calculator to find an exponential function of the form given by the Beer-Lambert Law to model these data. What is the light intensity I_0 at the surface on this day, and what is the "murkiness" constant k for this lake?   [*Hint:* If your calculator gives you a function of the form $I = ab^x$, convert this to the form you want using the identities $b^x = e^{\ln(b^x)} = e^{x \ln b}$. See Example 1(b).]

(b) Make a scatter plot of the data, and graph the function that you found in part (a) on your scatter plot.

(c) If the light intensity drops below 0.15 lumen (lm), a certain species of algae can't survive because photosynthesis is impossible. Use your model from part (a) to determine the depth below which there is insufficient light to support this algae.

Depth (ft)	Light intensity (lm)	Depth (ft)	Light intensity (lm)
5	13.0	25	1.8
10	7.6	30	1.1
15	4.5	35	0.5
20	2.7	40	0.3

6. Experimenting with "Forgetting" Curves   Every one of us is all too familiar with the phenomenon of forgetting. Facts that we clearly understood at the time we first learned them sometimes fade from our memory by the time the final exam rolls around. Psychologists have proposed several ways to model this process. One such model is Ebbinghaus' Law of Forgetting, described on page 327. Other models use exponential or logarithmic functions. To develop her own model, a psychologist performs an experiment on a group of volunteers by asking them to memorize a list of 100 related words. She then tests how many of these words they can recall after various periods of time. The average results for the group are shown in the table.

(a) Use a graphing calculator to find a *power* function of the form $y = at^b$ that models the average number of words y that the volunteers remember after t hours. Then find an *exponential* function of the form $y = ab^t$ to model the data.

(b) Make a scatter plot of the data, and graph both the functions that you found in part (a) on your scatter plot.

(c) Which of the two functions seems to provide the better model?

Time	Words recalled
15 min	64.3
1 h	45.1
8 h	37.3
1 day	32.8
2 days	26.9
3 days	25.6
5 days	22.9

The number of different bat species
in a cave is related to the size
of the cave by a power function.

7. Modeling the Species-Area Relation   The table gives the areas of several caves in central Mexico and the number of bat species that live in each cave.*

(a) Find a power function that models the data.

(b) Draw a graph of the function you found in part (a) and a scatter plot of the data on the same graph. Does the model fit the data well?

(c) The cave called El Sapo near Puebla, Mexico, has a surface area of $A = 205$ m². Use the model to estimate the number of bat species you would expect to find in that cave.

Cave	Area (m²)	Number of species
La Escondida	18	1
El Escorpion	19	1
El Tigre	58	1
Mision Imposible	60	2
San Martin	128	5
El Arenal	187	4
La Ciudad	344	6
Virgen	511	7

8. Auto Exhaust Emissions   A study by the U.S. Office of Science and Technology in 1972 estimated the cost of reducing automobile emissions by certain percentages. Find an exponential model that captures the "diminishing returns" trend of these data shown in the table below.

Reduction in emissions (%)	Cost per car ($)
50	45
55	55
60	62
65	70
70	80
75	90
80	100
85	200
90	375
95	600

9. Exponential or Power Model?   Data points (x, y) are shown in the table.

(a) Draw a scatter plot of the data.

(b) Draw scatter plots of $(x, \ln y)$ and $(\ln x, \ln y)$.

(c) Which is more appropriate for modeling this data: an exponential function or a power function?

(d) Find an appropriate function to model the data.

x	y
2	0.08
4	0.12
6	0.18
8	0.25
10	0.36
12	0.52
14	0.73
16	1.06

*A. K. Brunet and R. A. Medallin, "The Species-Area Relationship in Bat Assemblages of Tropical Caves." *Journal of Mammalogy, 82*(4):1114–1122, 2001.

x	y
10	29
20	82
30	151
40	235
50	330
60	430
70	546
80	669
90	797

10. Exponential or Power Model?   Data points (x, y) are shown in the table in the margin.

(a) Draw a scatter plot of the data.

(b) Draw scatter plots of $(x, \ln y)$ and $(\ln x, \ln y)$.

(c) Which is more appropriate for modeling this data: an exponential function or a power function?

(d) Find an appropriate function to model the data.

11. Logistic Population Growth   The table and scatter plot give the population of black flies in a closed laboratory container over an 18-day period.

(a) Use the `Logistic` command on your calculator to find a logistic model for these data.

(b) Use the model to estimate the time when there were 400 flies in the container.

Time (days)	Number of flies
0	10
2	25
4	66
6	144
8	262
10	374
12	446
16	492
18	498

12. Logarithmic Models   A **logarithmic model** is a function of the form

$$y = a + b \ln x$$

Many relationships between variables in the real world can be modeled by this type of function. The table and the scatter plot show the coal production (in metric tons) from a small mine in northern British Columbia.

(a) Use the `LnReg` command on your calculator to find a logarithmic model for these production figures.

(b) Use the model to predict coal production from this mine in 2010.

Year	Metric tons of coal
1950	882
1960	889
1970	894
1980	899
1990	905
2000	909

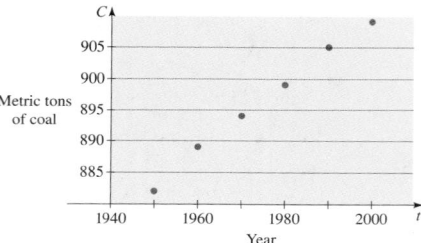

1. Let $f(x) = x^2 - 4x$ and $g(x) = \sqrt{x + 4}$. Find each of the following:

   (a) The domain of f

   (b) The domain of g

   (c) $f(-2), f(0), f(4), g(0), g(8), g(-6)$

   (d) $f(x + 2), g(x + 2), f(2 + h)$

   (e) The average rate of change of g between $x = 5$ and $x = 21$

   (f) $f \circ g, g \circ f, f(g(12)), g(f(12))$

   (g) The inverse of g

2. Let $f(x) = \begin{cases} 4 & \text{if } x \le 2 \\ x - 3 & \text{if } x > 2 \end{cases}$

   (a) Evaluate $f(0), f(1), f(2), f(3)$, and $f(4)$.

   (b) Sketch the graph of f.

3. Let f be the quadratic function $f(x) = -2x^2 + 8x + 5$.

   (a) Express f in standard form.

   (b) Find the maximum or minimum value of f.

   (c) Sketch the graph of f.

   (d) Find the interval on which f is increasing and the interval on which f is decreasing.

   (e) How is the graph of $g(x) = -2x^2 + 8x + 10$ obtained from the graph of f?

   (f) How is the graph of $h(x) = -2(x + 3)^2 + 8(x + 3) + 5$ obtained from the graph of f?

4. Without using a graphing calculator, match each of the following functions to the graphs below. Give reasons for your choices.

   $$f(x) = x^3 - 8x \qquad g(x) = -x^4 + 8x^2 \qquad r(x) = \frac{2x + 3}{x^2 - 9}$$

   $$s(x) = \frac{2x - 3}{x^2 + 9} \qquad h(x) = 2^x - 5 \qquad k(x) = 2^{-x} + 3$$

   A B C D E F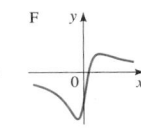

5. Let $P(x) = 2x^3 - 11x^2 + 10x + 8$.

   (a) List all possible rational zeros of P.

   (b) Determine which of the numbers you listed in part (a) actually are zeros of P.

   (c) Factor P completely.

   (d) Sketch a graph of P.

6. Let $Q(x) = x^5 - 3x^4 + 3x^3 + x^2 - 4x + 2$.

   (a) Find all zeros of Q, real and complex, and state their multiplicities.

   (b) Factor Q completely.

   (c) Factor Q into linear and irreducible quadratic factors.

367

7. Let $r(x) = \dfrac{3x^2 + 6x}{x^2 - x - 2}$. Find the x- and y-intercepts and the horizontal and vertical asymptotes. Then sketch the graph of r.

8. Sketch graphs of the following functions on the same coordinate plane.

   (a) $f(x) = 2 - e^x$ **(b)** $g(x) = \ln(x + 1)$

9. **(a)** Find the exact value of $\log_3 16 - 2 \log_3 36$.

   (b) Use the Laws of Logarithms to expand the expression

$$\log\left(\frac{x^5 \sqrt{x - 1}}{2x - 3}\right)$$

10. Solve the equations.

   (a) $\log_2 x + \log_2(x - 2) = 3$

   (b) $2e^{3x} - 11e^{2x} + 10e^x + 8 = 0$ [*Hint:* Compare to the polynomial in Problem 5.]

11. A sum of $25,000 is deposited into an account paying 5.4% interest per year, compounded daily.

   (a) What will the amount in the account be after 3 years?

   (b) When will the account have grown to $35,000?

   (c) How long will it take for the initial deposit to double?

12. After a shipwreck, 120 rats manage to swim from the wreckage to a deserted island. The rat population on the island grows exponentially, and after 15 months there are 280 rats on the island.

   (a) Find a function that models the population t months after the arrival of the rats.

   (b) What will the population be 3 years after the shipwreck?

   (c) When will the population reach 2000?

TRIGONOMETRIC FUNCTIONS: UNIT CIRCLE APPROACH

If you've ever taken a ferris wheel ride, then you know about periodic motion—that is, motion that repeats over and over. Periodic motion is common in nature. Think about the daily rising and setting of the sun (day, night, day, night, . . .), the daily variation in tide levels (high, low, high, low, . . .), or the vibrations of a leaf in the wind (left, right, left, right, . . .). To model such motion, we need a function whose values increase, then decrease, then increase, and so on. To understand how to define such a function, let's look at a person riding on a ferris wheel. The graph shows the height of the person above the center of the wheel at time t. Notice that the graph goes up and down repeatedly.

The trigonometric function *sine* is defined in a similar way, using the unit circle (in place of the ferris wheel). The trigonometric functions can be defined in two different but equivalent ways: as functions of real numbers (Chapter 5) or as functions of angles (Chapter 6). The two approaches are independent of each other, so either Chapter 5 or Chapter 6 may be studied first. We study both approaches because the different approaches are required for different applications.

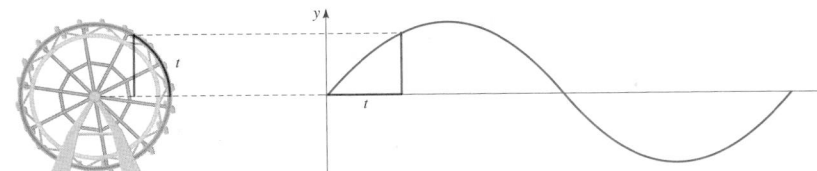

369

SUGGESTED TIME AND EMPHASIS

$\frac{1}{2}$–1 class, essential material

5.1 THE UNIT CIRCLE

| The Unit Circle ▶ Terminal Points on the Unit Curcle ▶ The Reference Number

In this section we explore some properties of the circle of radius 1 centered at the origin. These properties are used in the next section to define the trigonometric functions.

▼ The Unit Circle

The set of points at a distance 1 from the origin is a circle of radius 1 (see Figure 1). In Section 1.8 we learned that the equation of this circle is $x^2 + y^2 = 1$.

FIGURE 1 The unit circle

> **THE UNIT CIRCLE**
>
> The **unit circle** is the circle of radius 1 centered at the origin in the xy-plane. Its equation is
>
> $$x^2 + y^2 = 1$$

EXAMPLE 1 | A Point on the Unit Circle

Show that the point $P\left(\dfrac{\sqrt{3}}{3}, \dfrac{\sqrt{6}}{3}\right)$ is on the unit circle.

SOLUTION We need to show that this point satisfies the equation of the unit circle, that is, $x^2 + y^2 = 1$. Since

$$\left(\frac{\sqrt{3}}{3}\right)^2 + \left(\frac{\sqrt{6}}{3}\right)^2 = \frac{3}{9} + \frac{6}{9} = 1$$

P is on the unit circle.

✎. NOW TRY EXERCISE **3** ∎

ALTERNATE EXAMPLE 1

Is the point $P\left(\dfrac{\sqrt{6}}{6}, \dfrac{\sqrt{7}}{6}\right)$ on the unit circle?

ANSWER
No

EXAMPLE 2 | Locating a Point on the Unit Circle

The point $P(\sqrt{3}/2, y)$ is on the unit circle in Quadrant IV. Find its y-coordinate.

SOLUTION Since the point is on the unit circle, we have

$$\left(\frac{\sqrt{3}}{2}\right)^2 + y^2 = 1$$

$$y^2 = 1 - \frac{3}{4} = \frac{1}{4}$$

$$y = \pm \frac{1}{2}$$

Since the point is in Quadrant IV, its y-coordinate must be negative, so $y = -\frac{1}{2}$.

✎. NOW TRY EXERCISE **9** ∎

ALTERNATE EXAMPLE 2

The point $P(\sqrt{35}/6, y)$ is on the unit circle in Quadrant I. Find its y-coordinate.

ANSWER

$\dfrac{1}{6}$

▼ Terminal Points on the Unit Circle

Suppose t is a real number. Let's mark off a distance t along the unit circle, starting at the point $(1, 0)$ and moving in a counterclockwise direction if t is positive or in a clockwise direction if t is negative (Figure 2). In this way we arrive at a point $P(x, y)$ on the unit cir-

TEXT QUESTION

Is it possible for two different real numbers to have the same reference number?

Answer

Yes

cle. The point $P(x, y)$ obtained in this way is called the **terminal point** determined by the real number t.

 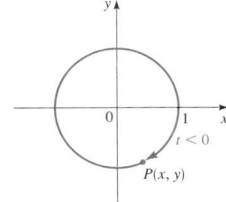

(a) Terminal point $P(x, y)$ determined by $t > 0$

(b) Terminal point $P(x, y)$ determined by $t < 0$

FIGURE 2

The circumference of the unit circle is $C = 2\pi(1) = 2\pi$. So if a point starts at $(1, 0)$ and moves counterclockwise all the way around the unit circle and returns to $(1, 0)$, it travels a distance of 2π. To move halfway around the circle, it travels a distance of $\frac{1}{2}(2\pi) = \pi$. To move a quarter of the distance around the circle, it travels a distance of $\frac{1}{4}(2\pi) = \pi/2$. Where does the point end up when it travels these distances along the circle? From Figure 3 we see, for example, that when it travels a distance of π starting at $(1, 0)$, its terminal point is $(-1, 0)$.

   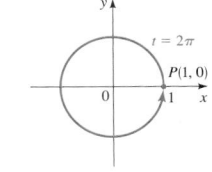

FIGURE 3 Terminal points determined by $t = \frac{\pi}{2}, \pi, \frac{3\pi}{2}$, and 2π

EXAMPLE 3 | Finding Terminal Points

Find the terminal point on the unit circle determined by each real number t.

(a) $t = 3\pi$ **(b)** $t = -\pi$ **(c)** $t = -\dfrac{\pi}{2}$

SOLUTION   From Figure 4 we get the following:

(a) The terminal point determined by 3π is $(-1, 0)$.

(b) The terminal point determined by $-\pi$ is $(-1, 0)$.

(c) The terminal point determined by $-\pi/2$ is $(0, -1)$.

  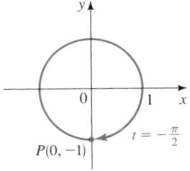

FIGURE 4

Notice that different values of t can determine the same terminal point.

✎. NOW TRY EXERCISE **23**

IN-CLASS MATERIALS

Look at the time, and then ask the class what time it will be 8 hours from now. Then ask about 12 hours from now, 13 hours from now, 25 hours from now, and 50 hours from now. Then ask what time it was 12 hours ago, 11 hours ago, and 13 hours ago. Draw the analogy of the type of arithmetic you are doing when computing future and past times to that of finding reference angles, only instead of freely adding and subtracting 12, we are freely adding and subtracting 2π.

The terminal point $P(x, y)$ determined by $t = \pi/4$ is the same distance from $(1, 0)$ as from $(0, 1)$ along the unit circle (see Figure 5).

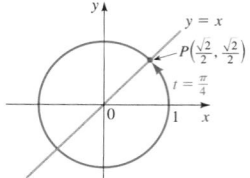

FIGURE 5

Since the unit circle is symmetric with respect to the line $y = x$, it follows that P lies on the line $y = x$. So P is the point of intersection (in the first quadrant) of the circle $x^2 + y^2 = 1$ and the line $y = x$. Substituting x for y in the equation of the circle, we get

$$x^2 + x^2 = 1$$

$$2x^2 = 1 \qquad \text{Combine like terms}$$

$$x^2 = \frac{1}{2} \qquad \text{Divide by 2}$$

$$x = \pm\frac{1}{\sqrt{2}} \qquad \text{Take square roots}$$

Since P is in the first quadrant, $x = 1/\sqrt{2}$ and since $y = x$, we have $y = 1/\sqrt{2}$ also. Thus, the terminal point determined by $\pi/4$ is

$$P\left(\frac{1}{\sqrt{2}}, \frac{1}{\sqrt{2}}\right) = P\left(\frac{\sqrt{2}}{2}, \frac{\sqrt{2}}{2}\right)$$

Similar methods can be used to find the terminal points determined by $t = \pi/6$ and $t = \pi/3$ (see Exercises 57 and 58). Table 1 and Figure 6 give the terminal points for some special values of t.

TABLE 1

t	Terminal point determined by t
0	$(1, 0)$
$\frac{\pi}{6}$	$\left(\frac{\sqrt{3}}{2}, \frac{1}{2}\right)$
$\frac{\pi}{4}$	$\left(\frac{\sqrt{2}}{2}, \frac{\sqrt{2}}{2}\right)$
$\frac{\pi}{3}$	$\left(\frac{1}{2}, \frac{\sqrt{3}}{2}\right)$
$\frac{\pi}{2}$	$(0, 1)$

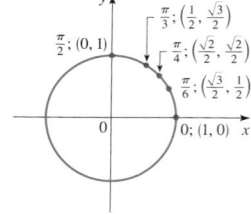

FIGURE 6

EXAMPLE 4 | Finding Terminal Points

Find the terminal point determined by each given real number t.

(a) $t = -\dfrac{\pi}{4}$ (b) $t = \dfrac{3\pi}{4}$ (c) $t = -\dfrac{5\pi}{6}$

IN-CLASS MATERIALS

Point out that finding terminal points is much more difficult than finding reference numbers. If the reference number is not given in Table 1, the students don't have a good method for finding the terminal point. Have them try to estimate a few by measurement. For example, have the students draw a circle with a 1-in. radius, and have them draw arcs of length 2 and 2.5 (by "rolling" the ruler along the circle and measuring the coordinates of the relevant terminal point). $t = 2$ should yield a terminal point at approximately $(-0.4, 0.9)$. $t = 2.5$ should yield a terminal point at approximately $(-0.8, 0.6)$.

SOLUTION

(a) Let P be the terminal point determined by $-\pi/4$, and let Q be the terminal point determined by $\pi/4$. From Figure 7(a) we see that the point P has the same coordinates as Q except for sign. Since P is in quadrant IV, its x-coordinate is positive and its y-coordinate is negative. Thus, the terminal point is $P(\sqrt{2}/2, -\sqrt{2}/2)$.

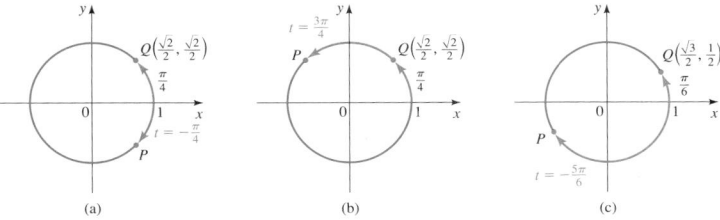

FIGURE 7   (a)   (b)   (c)

(b) Let P be the terminal point determined by $3\pi/4$, and let Q be the terminal point determined by $\pi/4$. From Figure 7(b) we see that the point P has the same coordinates as Q except for sign. Since P is in quadrant II, its x-coordinate is negative and its y-coordinate is positive. Thus, the terminal point is $P(-\sqrt{2}/2, \sqrt{2}/2)$.

(c) Let P be the terminal point determined by $-5\pi/6$, and let Q be the terminal point determined by $\pi/6$. From Figure 7(c) we see that the point P has the same coordinates as Q except for sign. Since P is in quadrant III, its coordinates are both negative. Thus, the terminal point is $P(-\sqrt{3}/2, -\frac{1}{2})$.

✎ NOW TRY EXERCISE **25**   ■

▼ The Reference Number

From Examples 3 and 4 we see that to find a terminal point in any quadrant we need only know the "corresponding" terminal point in the first quadrant. We use the idea of the *reference number* to help us find terminal points.

REFERENCE NUMBER

Let t be a real number. The **reference number** $\bar{t}$ associated with t is the shortest distance along the unit circle between the terminal point determined by t and the x-axis.

Figure 8 shows that to find the reference number $\bar{t}$, it's helpful to know the quadrant in which the terminal point determined by t lies. If the terminal point lies in quadrants I or IV, where x is positive, we find $\bar{t}$ by moving along the circle to the *positive* x-axis. If it lies in quadrants II or III, where x is negative, we find $\bar{t}$ by moving along the circle to the *negative* x-axis.

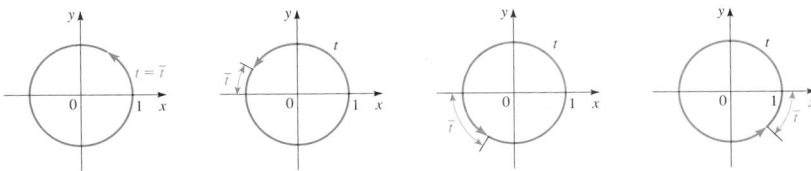

FIGURE 8   The reference number $\bar{t}$ for t

IN-CLASS MATERIALS

The text uses integer multiples of $\dfrac{\pi}{6}$ and $\dfrac{\pi}{4}$ for most of its examples of finding reference numbers. After the students understand these examples, try having them work with different rational multiples of π, such as $-\dfrac{121}{35}\pi$ or $\dfrac{10,001}{5}\pi$. Transition them to numbers whose terminal points lie in quadrants that are easy to figure out, such as $t = 3$, 6, or 1.5. Finally, have them try to find reference numbers of arbitrary real numbers such as 22 and -13.

ALTERNATE EXAMPLE 5

Find the reference number determined by the given real number t:

$t = 5.29$

Please give the answer to two decimal places.

ANSWER

0.99

EXAMPLE 5 | Finding Reference Numbers

Find the reference number for each value of t.

(a) $t = \dfrac{5\pi}{6}$ **(b)** $t = \dfrac{7\pi}{4}$ **(c)** $t = -\dfrac{2\pi}{3}$ **(d)** $t = 5.80$

SOLUTION   From Figure 9 we find the reference numbers as follows:

(a) $\bar{t} = \pi - \dfrac{5\pi}{6} = \dfrac{\pi}{6}$

(b) $\bar{t} = 2\pi - \dfrac{7\pi}{4} = \dfrac{\pi}{4}$

(c) $\bar{t} = \pi - \dfrac{2\pi}{3} = \dfrac{\pi}{3}$

(d) $\bar{t} = 2\pi - 5.80 \approx 0.48$

    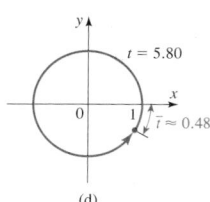

(a)   (b)   (c)   (d)

FIGURE 9

➤ . NOW TRY EXERCISE **35**

USING REFERENCE NUMBERS TO FIND TERMINAL POINTS

To find the terminal point P determined by any value of t, we use the following steps:

1. Find the reference number $\bar{t}$.
2. Find the terminal point $Q(a, b)$ determined by $\bar{t}$.
3. The terminal point determined by t is $P(\pm a, \pm b)$, where the signs are chosen according to the quadrant in which this terminal point lies.

EXAMPLE 6 | Using Reference Numbers to Find Terminal Points

Find the terminal point determined by each given real number t.

(a) $t = \dfrac{5\pi}{6}$ **(b)** $t = \dfrac{7\pi}{4}$ **(c)** $t = -\dfrac{2\pi}{3}$

SOLUTION   The reference numbers associated with these values of t were found in Example 5.

(a) The reference number is $\bar{t} = \pi/6$, which determines the terminal point $\left(\sqrt{3}/2, \tfrac{1}{2}\right)$ from Table 1. Since the terminal point determined by t is in Quadrant II, its x-coordinate is negative and its y-coordinate is positive. Thus, the desired terminal point is

$$\left(-\frac{\sqrt{3}}{2}, \frac{1}{2}\right)$$

EXAMPLE

Some values of t, their reference numbers, and their terminal points:

t	$\bar{t}$	Terminal Point
$-\dfrac{33\pi}{2}$	$\dfrac{\pi}{2}$	$(0, -1)$
$\dfrac{55\pi}{4}$	$\dfrac{\pi}{4}$	$\left(\dfrac{\sqrt{2}}{2}, -\dfrac{\sqrt{2}}{2}\right)$
$\dfrac{48\pi}{6}$	0	$(1, 0)$
$\dfrac{16\pi}{3}$	$\dfrac{\pi}{3}$	$\left(-\dfrac{1}{2}, -\dfrac{\sqrt{3}}{2}\right)$
10	$10 - 3\pi \approx 0.57522204$	$(-0.839, -0.544)$

(b) The reference number is $\bar{t} = \pi/4$, which determines the terminal point $\left(\sqrt{2}/2, \sqrt{2}/2\right)$ from Table 1. Since the terminal point is in Quadrant IV, its x-coordinate is positive and its y-coordinate is negative. Thus, the desired terminal point is

$$\left(\frac{\sqrt{2}}{2}, -\frac{\sqrt{2}}{2}\right)$$

(c) The reference number is $\bar{t} = \pi/3$, which determines the terminal point $\left(\frac{1}{2}, \sqrt{3}/2\right)$ from Table 1. Since the terminal point determined by t is in Quadrant III, its coordinates are both negative. Thus, the desired terminal point is

$$\left(-\frac{1}{2}, -\frac{\sqrt{3}}{2}\right)$$

✎. **NOW TRY EXERCISE 39**   ■

Since the circumference of the unit circle is 2π, the terminal point determined by t is the same as that determined by $t + 2\pi$ or $t - 2\pi$. In general, we can add or subtract 2π any number of times without changing the terminal point determined by t. We use this observation in the next example to find terminal points for large t.

EXAMPLE 7 | Finding the Terminal Point for Large t

Find the terminal point determined by $t = \dfrac{29\pi}{6}$.

SOLUTION   Since

$$t = \frac{29\pi}{6} = 4\pi + \frac{5\pi}{6}$$

we see that the terminal point of t is the same as that of $5\pi/6$ (that is, we subtract 4π). So by Example 6(a) the terminal point is $\left(-\sqrt{3}/2, \frac{1}{2}\right)$. (See Figure 10.)

✎. **NOW TRY EXERCISE 45**   ■

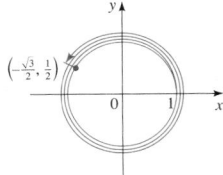

FIGURE 10

5.1 EXERCISES

CONCEPTS

1. (a) The unit circle is the circle centered at _____ with

radius _____.

(b) The equation of the unit circle is _____.

(c) Suppose the point $P(x, y)$ is on the unit circle. Find the missing coordinate:

  (i) $P(1, \blacksquare)$ (ii) $P(\blacksquare, 1)$

  (iii) $P(-1, \blacksquare)$ (iv) $P(\blacksquare, -1)$

2. (a) If we mark off a distance t along the unit circle, starting at $(1, 0)$ and moving in a counterclockwise direction, we

arrive at the _____ point determined by t.

(b) The terminal points determined by $\pi/2, \pi, -\pi/2, 2\pi$

are _____, _____, _____, and _____, respectively.

SKILLS

3–8 ■ Show that the point is on the unit circle.

3. $\left(\dfrac{4}{5}, -\dfrac{3}{5}\right)$ **4.** $\left(-\dfrac{5}{13}, \dfrac{12}{13}\right)$ **5.** $\left(\dfrac{7}{25}, \dfrac{24}{25}\right)$

6. $\left(-\dfrac{5}{7}, -\dfrac{2\sqrt{6}}{7}\right)$ **7.** $\left(-\dfrac{\sqrt{5}}{3}, \dfrac{2}{3}\right)$ **8.** $\left(\dfrac{\sqrt{11}}{6}, \dfrac{5}{6}\right)$

9–14 ■ Find the missing coordinate of P, using the fact that P lies on the unit circle in the given quadrant.

Coordinates	Quadrant
9. $P\left(-\dfrac{3}{5}, \blacksquare\right)$	III
10. $P\left(\blacksquare, -\dfrac{7}{25}\right)$	IV
11. $P\left(\blacksquare, \dfrac{1}{3}\right)$	II

Coordinates	Quadrant
12. $P\left(\frac{2}{3},\ \quad\right)$	I
13. $P\left(\quad,\ -\frac{2}{7}\right)$	IV
14. $P\left(-\frac{2}{3},\ \quad\right)$	II

15–20 ■ The point P is on the unit circle. Find $P(x, y)$ from the given information.

15. The x-coordinate of P is $\frac{4}{5}$, and the y-coordinate is positive.

16. The y-coordinate of P is $-\frac{1}{3}$, and the x-coordinate is positive.

17. The y-coordinate of P is $\frac{2}{3}$, and the x-coordinate is negative.

18. The x-coordinate of P is positive, and the y-coordinate of P is $-\sqrt{5}/5$.

19. The x-coordinate of P is $-\sqrt{2}/3$, and P lies below the x-axis.

20. The x-coordinate of P is $-\frac{2}{5}$, and P lies above the x-axis.

21–22 ■ Find t and the terminal point determined by t for each point in the figure. In Exercise 21, t increases in increments of $\pi/4$; in Exercise 22, t increases in increments of $\pi/6$.

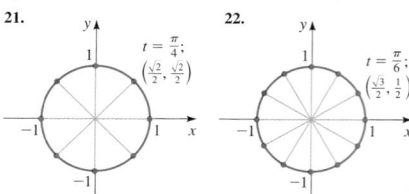

21. $t = \frac{\pi}{4}$; $\left(\frac{\sqrt{2}}{2}, \frac{\sqrt{2}}{2}\right)$

22. $t = \frac{\pi}{6}$; $\left(\frac{\sqrt{3}}{2}, \frac{1}{2}\right)$

23–32 ■ Find the terminal point $P(x, y)$ on the unit circle determined by the given value of t.

23. $t = \frac{\pi}{2}$ **24.** $t = \frac{3\pi}{2}$

25. $t = \frac{5\pi}{6}$ **26.** $t = \frac{7\pi}{6}$

27. $t = -\frac{\pi}{3}$ **28.** $t = \frac{5\pi}{3}$

29. $t = \frac{2\pi}{3}$ **30.** $t = -\frac{\pi}{2}$

31. $t = -\frac{3\pi}{4}$ **32.** $t = \frac{11\pi}{6}$

33. Suppose that the terminal point determined by t is the point $\left(\frac{3}{5}, \frac{4}{5}\right)$ on the unit circle. Find the terminal point determined by each of the following.
  (a) $\pi - t$ (b) $-t$
  (c) $\pi + t$ (d) $2\pi + t$

34. Suppose that the terminal point determined by t is the point $\left(\frac{3}{4}, \sqrt{7}/4\right)$ on the unit circle. Find the terminal point determined by each of the following.
  (a) $-t$ (b) $4\pi + t$
  (c) $\pi - t$ (d) $t - \pi$

35–38 ■ Find the reference number for each value of t.

35. (a) $t = \frac{5\pi}{4}$ (b) $t = \frac{7\pi}{3}$
   (c) $t = -\frac{4\pi}{3}$ (d) $t = \frac{\pi}{6}$

36. (a) $t = \frac{5\pi}{6}$ (b) $t = \frac{7\pi}{6}$
   (c) $t = \frac{11\pi}{3}$ (d) $t = -\frac{7\pi}{4}$

37. (a) $t = \frac{5\pi}{7}$ (b) $t = -\frac{7\pi}{9}$
   (c) $t = -3$ (d) $t = 5$

38. (a) $t = \frac{11\pi}{5}$ (b) $t = -\frac{9\pi}{7}$
   (c) $t = 6$ (d) $t = -7$

39–52 ■ Find (a) the reference number for each value of t and (b) the terminal point determined by t.

39. $t = \frac{2\pi}{3}$ **40.** $t = \frac{4\pi}{3}$

41. $t = \frac{3\pi}{4}$ **42.** $t = \frac{7\pi}{3}$

43. $t = -\frac{2\pi}{3}$ **44.** $t = -\frac{7\pi}{6}$

45. $t = \frac{13\pi}{4}$ **46.** $t = \frac{13\pi}{6}$

47. $t = \frac{7\pi}{6}$ **48.** $t = \frac{17\pi}{4}$

49. $t = -\frac{11\pi}{3}$ **50.** $t = \frac{31\pi}{6}$

51. $t = \frac{16\pi}{3}$ **52.** $t = -\frac{41\pi}{4}$

53–56 ■ Use the figure to find the terminal point determined by the real number t, with coordinates rounded to one decimal place.

53. $t = 1$

54. $t = 2.5$

55. $t = -1.1$

56. $t = 4.2$

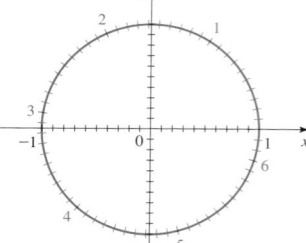

57. Finding the Terminal Point for $\pi/6$ Suppose the terminal point determined by $t = \pi/6$ is $P(x, y)$ and the points Q and R are as shown in the figure. Why are the distances PQ and PR the same? Use this fact, together with the Distance Formula, to show that the coordinates of P satisfy the equation $2y = \sqrt{x^2 + (y - 1)^2}$. Simplify this equation using the fact that $x^2 + y^2 = 1$. Solve the simplified equation to find $P(x, y)$.

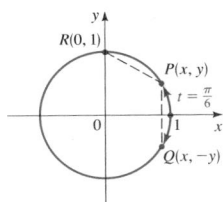

58. Finding the Terminal Point for $\pi/3$ Now that you know the terminal point determined by $t = \pi/6$, use symmetry to find the terminal point determined by $t = \pi/3$ (see the figure). Explain your reasoning.

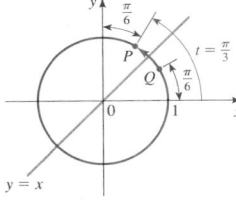

5.2 TRIGONOMETRIC FUNCTIONS OF REAL NUMBERS

The Trigonometric Functions ▶ Values of the Trigonometric Functions ▶ Fundamental Identities

A function is a rule that assigns to each real number another real number. In this section we use properties of the unit circle from the preceding section to define the trigonometric functions.

▼ The Trigonometric Functions

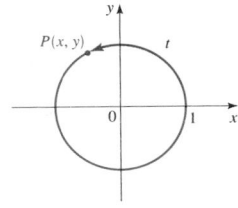

FIGURE 1

Recall that to find the terminal point $P(x, y)$ for a given real number t, we move a distance t along the unit circle, starting at the point $(1, 0)$. We move in a counterclockwise direction if t is positive and in a clockwise direction if t is negative (see Figure 1). We now use the x- and y-coordinates of the point $P(x, y)$ to define several functions. For instance, we define the function called *sine* by assigning to each real number t the y-coordinate of the terminal point $P(x, y)$ determined by t. The functions *cosine*, *tangent*, *cosecant*, *secant*, and *cotangent* are also defined by using the coordinates of $P(x, y)$.

DEFINITION OF THE TRIGONOMETRIC FUNCTIONS

Let t be any real number and let $P(x, y)$ be the terminal point on the unit circle determined by t. We define

$$\sin t = y \qquad\qquad \cos t = x \qquad\qquad \tan t = \frac{y}{x} \quad (x \neq 0)$$

$$\csc t = \frac{1}{y} \quad (y \neq 0) \qquad \sec t = \frac{1}{x} \quad (x \neq 0) \qquad \cot t = \frac{x}{y} \quad (y \neq 0)$$

Because the trigonometric functions can be defined in terms of the unit circle, they are sometimes called the **circular functions**.

SUGGESTED TIME AND EMPHASIS

$\frac{1}{2}$–1 class, essential material

TEXT QUESTION

If $\sin t = \frac{3}{5}$, what is the value of $\csc t$?

Answer

$\dfrac{5}{3}$

ALTERNATE EXAMPLE 1

Find the six trigonometric functions of the given real number $t = \dfrac{\pi}{4}$.

ANSWER

$\dfrac{\sqrt{2}}{2}, \dfrac{\sqrt{2}}{2}, 1, \sqrt{2}, \sqrt{2}, 1$

FIGURE 2

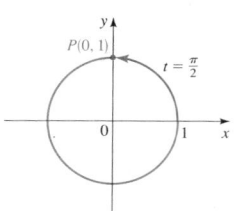

FIGURE 3

EXAMPLE 1 | Evaluating Trigonometric Functions

Find the six trigonometric functions of each given real number t.

(a) $t = \dfrac{\pi}{3}$ **(b)** $t = \dfrac{\pi}{2}$

SOLUTION

(a) From Table 1 on page 372, we see that the terminal point determined by $t = \pi/3$ is $P(\frac{1}{2}, \sqrt{3}/2)$. (See Figure 2.) Since the coordinates are $x = \frac{1}{2}$ and $y = \sqrt{3}/2$, we have

$$\sin\frac{\pi}{3} = \frac{\sqrt{3}}{2} \qquad \cos\frac{\pi}{3} = \frac{1}{2} \qquad \tan\frac{\pi}{3} = \frac{\sqrt{3}/2}{1/2} = \sqrt{3}$$

$$\csc\frac{\pi}{3} = \frac{2\sqrt{3}}{3} \qquad \sec\frac{\pi}{3} = 2 \qquad \cot\frac{\pi}{3} = \frac{1/2}{\sqrt{3}/2} = \frac{\sqrt{3}}{3}$$

(b) The terminal point determined by $\pi/2$ is $P(0, 1)$. (See Figure 3.) So

$$\sin\frac{\pi}{2} = 1 \qquad \cos\frac{\pi}{2} = 0 \qquad \csc\frac{\pi}{2} = \frac{1}{1} = 1 \qquad \cot\frac{\pi}{2} = \frac{0}{1} = 0$$

But $\tan \pi/2$ and $\sec \pi/2$ are undefined because $x = 0$ appears in the denominator in each of their definitions.

✎ NOW TRY EXERCISE **3** ∎

Some special values of the trigonometric functions are listed in Table 1. This table is easily obtained from Table 1 of Section 5.1, together with the definitions of the trigonometric functions.

TABLE 1
Special values of the trigonometric functions

t	$\sin t$	$\cos t$	$\tan t$	$\csc t$	$\sec t$	$\cot t$
0	0	1	0	—	1	—
$\dfrac{\pi}{6}$	$\dfrac{1}{2}$	$\dfrac{\sqrt{3}}{2}$	$\dfrac{\sqrt{3}}{3}$	2	$\dfrac{2\sqrt{3}}{3}$	$\sqrt{3}$
$\dfrac{\pi}{4}$	$\dfrac{\sqrt{2}}{2}$	$\dfrac{\sqrt{2}}{2}$	1	$\sqrt{2}$	$\sqrt{2}$	1
$\dfrac{\pi}{3}$	$\dfrac{\sqrt{3}}{2}$	$\dfrac{1}{2}$	$\sqrt{3}$	$\dfrac{2\sqrt{3}}{3}$	2	$\dfrac{\sqrt{3}}{3}$
$\dfrac{\pi}{2}$	1	0	—	1	—	0

We can easily remember the sines and cosines of the basic angles by writing them in the form $\sqrt{}/2$:

t	$\sin t$	$\cos t$
0	$\sqrt{0}/2$	$\sqrt{4}/2$
$\pi/6$	$\sqrt{1}/2$	$\sqrt{3}/2$
$\pi/4$	$\sqrt{2}/2$	$\sqrt{2}/2$
$\pi/3$	$\sqrt{3}/2$	$\sqrt{1}/2$
$\pi/2$	$\sqrt{4}/2$	$\sqrt{0}/2$

Example 1 shows that some of the trigonometric functions fail to be defined for certain real numbers. So we need to determine their domains. The functions sine and cosine are defined for all values of t. Since the functions cotangent and cosecant have y in the denominator of their definitions, they are not defined whenever the y-coordinate of the terminal point $P(x, y)$ determined by t is 0. This happens when $t = n\pi$ for any integer n, so their domains do not include these points. The functions tangent and secant have x in the denominator in their definitions, so they are not defined whenever $x = 0$. This happens when $t = (\pi/2) + n\pi$ for any integer n.

IN-CLASS MATERIALS

The etymology of the word *sine* is fairly interesting and not that well known. It starts with the Indian word *jya,* meaning "cord of a bowstring." The Arabs translated this word as *jiba.* The written language had no vowels, so it looked like this: jb. In 1145, the Spanish translator Robert of Cheste had to figure out what vowels to put in. Because of the shape of the curve, he thought the word was *jaib,* which meant the opening of a garment that shows a woman's cleavage. So he used the Latin word for the cavity formed by a curve: *sinus.* (This word exists in the English language today—right behind your nose are the sinus cavities.)

Relationship to the Trigonometric Functions of Angles

If you have previously studied trigonometry of right triangles (Chapter 6), you are probably wondering how the sine and cosine of an *angle* relate to those of this section. To see how, let's start with a right triangle, ΔOPQ.

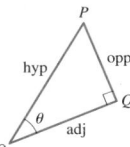

Right triangle OPQ

Place the triangle in the coordinate plane as shown, with angle θ in standard position.

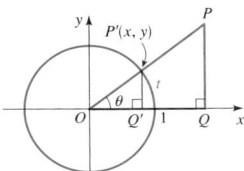

$P'(x, y)$ is the terminal point determined by t.

The point $P'(x, y)$ in the figure is the terminal point determined by the arc t. Note that triangle OPQ is similar to the small triangle $OP'Q'$ whose legs have lengths x and y.

Now, by the definition of the trigonometric functions of the *angle* θ we have

$$\sin \theta = \frac{\text{opp}}{\text{hyp}} = \frac{PQ}{OP} = \frac{P'Q'}{OP'}$$

$$= \frac{y}{1} = y$$

$$\cos \theta = \frac{\text{adj}}{\text{hyp}} = \frac{OQ}{OP} = \frac{OQ'}{OP'}$$

$$= \frac{x}{1} = x$$

By the definition of the trigonometric functions of the *real number t,* we have

$$\sin t = y \qquad \cos t = x$$

Now, if θ is measured in radians, then $\theta = t$ (see the figure). So the trigonometric functions of the angle with radian measure θ are exactly the same as the trigonometric functions defined in terms of the terminal point determined by the real number t.

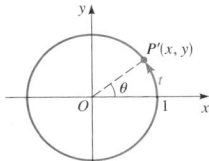

The radian measure of angle θ is t.

Why then study trigonometry in two different ways? Because different applications require that we view the trigonometric functions differently. (Compare Section 5.6 with Sections 6.2, 6.5, and 6.6.)

DOMAINS OF THE TRIGONOMETRIC FUNCTIONS	
Function	**Domain**
sin, cos	All real numbers
tan, sec	All real numbers other than $\dfrac{\pi}{2} + n\pi$ for any integer n
cot, csc	All real numbers other than $n\pi$ for any integer, n

▼ Values of the Trigonometric Functions

The following mnemonic device will help you remember which trigonometric functions are positive in each quadrant: All of them, Sine, Tangent, or Cosine.

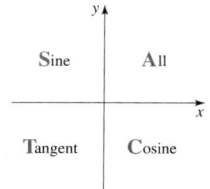

You can remember this as "All Students Take Calculus."

To compute other values of the trigonometric functions, we first determine their signs. The signs of the trigonometric functions depend on the quadrant in which the terminal point of t lies. For example, if the terminal point $P(x, y)$ determined by t lies in Quadrant III, then its coordinates are both negative. So sin t, cos t, csc t, and sec t are all negative, whereas tan t and cot t are positive. You can check the other entries in the following box.

SIGNS OF THE TRIGONOMETRIC FUNCTIONS		
Quadrant	**Positive Functions**	**Negative Functions**
I	all	none
II	sin, csc	cos, sec, tan, cot
III	tan, cot	sin, csc, cos, sec
IV	cos, sec	sin, csc, tan, cot

For example $\cos(2\pi/3) < 0$ because the terminal point of $t = 2\pi/3$ is in Quadrant II, whereas tan $4 > 0$ because the terminal point of $t = 4$ is in Quadrant III.

In Section 5.1 we used the reference number to find the terminal point determined by a real number t. Since the trigonometric functions are defined in terms of the coordinates of terminal points, we can use the reference number to find values of the trigonometric functions. Suppose that $\bar{t}$ is the reference number for t. Then the terminal point of $\bar{t}$ has the same coordinates, except possibly for sign, as the terminal point of t. So the values of the trigonometric functions at t are the same, except possibly for sign, as their values at $\bar{t}$. We illustrate this procedure in the next example.

EXAMPLE 2 | Evaluating Trigonometric Functions

Find each value.

(a) $\cos \dfrac{2\pi}{3}$ **(b)** $\tan\left(-\dfrac{\pi}{3}\right)$ **(c)** $\sin \dfrac{19\pi}{4}$

SOLUTION

(a) The reference number for $2\pi/3$ is $\pi/3$ (see Figure 4(a)). Since the terminal point of $2\pi/3$ is in Quadrant II, $\cos(2\pi/3)$ is negative. Thus,

$$\cos \frac{2\pi}{3} = -\cos \frac{\pi}{3} = -\frac{1}{2}$$

Sign   Reference number   From Table 1

ALTERNATE EXAMPLE 2

(a) Find the value of $\sin \dfrac{2\pi}{3}$.

(b) Find the value of $\tan \left(-\dfrac{4\pi}{3}\right)$.

(c) Find the value of $\cos \dfrac{14\pi}{3}$.

ANSWERS

(a) $\dfrac{\sqrt{3}}{2}$

(b) $-\sqrt{3}$

(c) $-\dfrac{1}{2}$

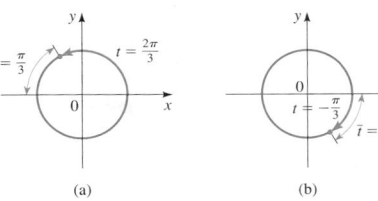

FIGURE 4   (a)   (b)   (c)

(b) The reference number for $-\pi/3$ is $\pi/3$ (see Figure 4(b)). Since the terminal point of $-\pi/3$ is in Quadrant IV, $\tan(-\pi/3)$ is negative. Thus,

$$\tan\left(-\frac{\pi}{3}\right) = -\tan\frac{\pi}{3} = -\sqrt{3}$$

Sign   Reference number   From Table 1

(c) Since $(19\pi/4) - 4\pi = 3\pi/4$, the terminal points determined by $19\pi/4$ and $3\pi/4$ are the same. The reference number for $3\pi/4$ is $\pi/4$ (see Figure 4(c)). Since the terminal point of $3\pi/4$ is in Quadrant II, $\sin(3\pi/4)$ is positive. Thus,

$$\sin\frac{19\pi}{4} = \sin\frac{3\pi}{4} = +\sin\frac{\pi}{4} = \frac{\sqrt{2}}{2}$$

Subtract 4π Sign   Reference number   From Table 1

✎. NOW TRY EXERCISE **7**

So far, we have been able to compute the values of the trigonometric functions only for certain values of t. In fact, we can compute the values of the trigonometric functions whenever t is a multiple of $\pi/6$, $\pi/4$, $\pi/3$, and $\pi/2$. How can we compute the trigonometric functions for other values of t? For example, how can we find $\sin 1.5$? One way is to carefully sketch a diagram and read the value (see Exercises 39–46); however, this method is not very accurate. Fortunately, programmed directly into scientific calculators are mathematical procedures (see the margin note on page 400) that find the values of *sine*, *cosine*, and *tangent* correct to the number of digits in the display. The calculator must be put in *radian mode* to evaluate these functions. To find values of cosecant, secant, and cotangent using a calculator, we need to use the following *reciprocal relations*:

$$\csc t = \frac{1}{\sin t} \qquad \sec t = \frac{1}{\cos t} \qquad \cot t = \frac{1}{\tan t}$$

These identities follow from the definitions of the trigonometric functions. For instance, since $\sin t = y$ and $\csc t = 1/y$, we have $\csc t = 1/y = 1/(\sin t)$. The others follow similarly.

EXAMPLE 3 | Using a Calculator to Evaluate Trigonometric Functions

Making sure our calculator is set to radian mode and rounding the results to six decimal places, we get

(a) $\sin 2.2 \approx 0.808496$ **(b)** $\cos 1.1 \approx 0.453596$

(c) $\cot 28 = \dfrac{1}{\tan 28} \approx -3.553286$ **(d)** $\csc 0.98 = \dfrac{1}{\sin 0.98} \approx 1.204098$

✎. NOW TRY EXERCISES **41** AND **43**

ALTERNATE EXAMPLE 3
Approximate the following with a calculator:
(a) $\sin(0.5236)$
(b) $\cos(3.2)$
(c) $\csc(37)$
(d) $\cot(1.7)$

ANSWERS
(All answers are rounded to five significant figures.)
(a) 0.50000
(b) -0.99829
(c) -1.5539
(d) -0.12993

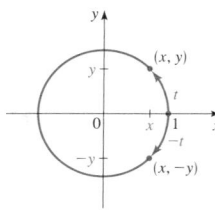

FIGURE 5

Even and odd functions are defined in Section 2.5.

Let's consider the relationship between the trigonometric functions of t and those of $-t$. From Figure 5 we see that

$$\sin(-t) = -y = -\sin t$$

$$\cos(-t) = x = \cos t$$

$$\tan(-t) = \frac{-y}{x} = -\frac{y}{x} = -\tan t$$

These equations show that sine and tangent are odd functions, whereas cosine is an even function. It's easy to see that the reciprocal of an even function is even and the reciprocal of an odd function is odd. This fact, together with the reciprocal relations, completes our knowledge of the even-odd properties for all the trigonometric functions.

EVEN-ODD PROPERTIES

Sine, cosecant, tangent, and cotangent are odd functions; cosine and secant are even functions.

$$\sin(-t) = -\sin t \qquad \cos(-t) = \cos t \qquad \tan(-t) = -\tan t$$

$$\csc(-t) = -\csc t \qquad \sec(-t) = \sec t \qquad \cot(-t) = -\cot t$$

EXAMPLE 4 | Even and Odd Trigonometric Functions

Use the even-odd properties of the trigonometric functions to determine each value.

(a) $\sin\left(-\dfrac{\pi}{6}\right)$ **(b)** $\cos\left(-\dfrac{\pi}{4}\right)$

SOLUTION By the even-odd properties and Table 1 we have

(a) $\sin\left(-\dfrac{\pi}{6}\right) = -\sin\dfrac{\pi}{6} = -\dfrac{1}{2}$ Sine is odd

(b) $\cos\left(-\dfrac{\pi}{4}\right) = \cos\dfrac{\pi}{4} = \dfrac{\sqrt{2}}{2}$ Cosine is even

✎. NOW TRY EXERCISE **13** ∎

▼ **Fundamental Identities**

The trigonometric functions are related to each other through equations called **trigonometric identities**. We give the most important ones in the following box.*

FUNDAMENTAL IDENTITIES

Reciprocal Identities

$$\csc t = \frac{1}{\sin t} \qquad \sec t = \frac{1}{\cos t} \qquad \cot t = \frac{1}{\tan t} \qquad \tan t = \frac{\sin t}{\cos t} \qquad \cot t = \frac{\cos t}{\sin t}$$

Pythagorean Identities

$$\sin^2 t + \cos^2 t = 1 \qquad \tan^2 t + 1 = \sec^2 t \qquad 1 + \cot^2 t = \csc^2 t$$

---

*We follow the usual convention of writing $\sin^2 t$ for $(\sin t)^2$. In general, we write $\sin^n t$ for $(\sin t)^n$ for all integers n except $n = -1$. The exponent $n = -1$ will be assigned another meaning in Section 5.5. Of course, the same convention applies to the other five trigonometric functions.

ALTERNATE EXAMPLE 4

Use the even-odd properties of the trigonometric functions to determine the value of $\cos\left(-\dfrac{\pi}{3}\right)$.

ANSWER

$\dfrac{1}{2}$

EXAMPLE

Use the even-odd properties of the trigonometric functions to determine the value of $\cos\left(-\dfrac{\pi}{3}\right)$.

ANSWER

$\dfrac{1}{2}$

PROOF   The reciprocal identities follow immediately from the definitions on page 377. We now prove the Pythagorean identities. By definition, $\cos t = x$ and $\sin t = y$, where x and y are the coordinates of a point $P(x, y)$ on the unit circle. Since $P(x, y)$ is on the unit circle, we have $x^2 + y^2 = 1$. Thus

$$\sin^2 t + \cos^2 t = 1$$

Dividing both sides by $\cos^2 t$ (provided that $\cos t \neq 0$), we get

$$\frac{\sin^2 t}{\cos^2 t} + \frac{\cos^2 t}{\cos^2 t} = \frac{1}{\cos^2 t}$$

$$\left(\frac{\sin t}{\cos t}\right)^2 + 1 = \left(\frac{1}{\cos t}\right)^2$$

$$\tan^2 t + 1 = \sec^2 t$$

We have used the reciprocal identities $\sin t/\cos t = \tan t$ and $1/\cos t = \sec t$. Similarly, dividing both sides of the first Pythagorean identity by $\sin^2 t$ (provided that $\sin t \neq 0$) gives us $1 + \cot^2 t = \csc^2 t$. ■

As their name indicates, the fundamental identities play a central role in trigonometry because we can use them to relate any trigonometric function to any other. So, if we know the value of any one of the trigonometric functions at t, then we can find the values of all the others at t.

EXAMPLE 5 | **Finding All Trigonometric Functions from the Value of One**

If $\cos t = \frac{3}{5}$ and t is in Quadrant IV, find the values of all the trigonometric functions at t.

SOLUTION   From the Pythagorean identities we have

$$\sin^2 t + \cos^2 t = 1$$

$$\sin^2 t + \left(\tfrac{3}{5}\right)^2 = 1 \qquad \text{Substitute } \cos t = \tfrac{3}{5}$$

$$\sin^2 t = 1 - \tfrac{9}{25} = \tfrac{16}{25} \qquad \text{Solve for } \sin^2 t$$

$$\sin t = \pm\tfrac{4}{5} \qquad \text{Take square roots}$$

Since this point is in Quadrant IV, $\sin t$ is negative, so $\sin t = -\frac{4}{5}$. Now that we know both $\sin t$ and $\cos t$, we can find the values of the other trigonometric functions using the reciprocal identities:

$$\sin t = -\frac{4}{5} \qquad\qquad \cos t = \frac{3}{5} \qquad\qquad \tan t = \frac{\sin t}{\cos t} = \frac{-\frac{4}{5}}{\frac{3}{5}} = -\frac{4}{3}$$

$$\csc t = \frac{1}{\sin t} = -\frac{5}{4} \qquad \sec t = \frac{1}{\cos t} = \frac{5}{3} \qquad \cot t = \frac{1}{\tan t} = -\frac{3}{4}$$

✎. NOW TRY EXERCISE **65**   ■

EXAMPLE 6 | **Writing One Trigonometric Function in Terms of Another**

Write $\tan t$ in terms of $\cos t$, where t is in Quadrant III.

SOLUTION Since $\tan t = \sin t / \cos t$, we need to write $\sin t$ in terms of $\cos t$. By the Pythagorean identities we have

$$\sin^2 t + \cos^2 t = 1$$

$$\sin^2 t = 1 - \cos^2 t \qquad \text{Solve for } \sin^2 t$$

$$\sin t = \pm\sqrt{1 - \cos^2 t} \qquad \text{Take square roots}$$

Since $\sin t$ is negative in Quadrant III, the negative sign applies here. Thus,

$$\tan t = \frac{\sin t}{\cos t} = \frac{-\sqrt{1 - \cos^2 t}}{\cos t}$$

✎ **NOW TRY EXERCISE 55**

EXAMPLES

■ $\sin \dfrac{\pi}{3} = \dfrac{\sqrt{3}}{2}$

■ $\cos \dfrac{7\pi}{6} = -\dfrac{\sqrt{3}}{2}$

■ $\tan \dfrac{11\pi}{4} = -1$

■ $\sec \dfrac{17\pi}{3} = 2$

■ $\csc \dfrac{17\pi}{2} = 1$

■ $\cot \dfrac{121\pi}{6} = \sqrt{3}$

DRILL QUESTION

If $\sin t = \dfrac{3}{5}$ and the terminal point of t is in the second quadrant, what is the value of $\cos t$?

Answer

$-\dfrac{4}{5}$

5.2 EXERCISES

CONCEPTS

1. Let $P(x, y)$ be the terminal point on the unit circle determined by t. Then $\sin t =$ _____, $\cos t =$ _____, and $\tan t =$ _____.

2. If $P(x, y)$ is on the unit circle, then $x^2 + y^2 =$ _____. So for all t we have $\sin^2 t + \cos^2 t =$ _____.

SKILLS

3–4 ■ Find $\sin t$ and $\cos t$ for the values of t whose terminal points are shown on the unit circle in the figure. In Exercise 3, t increases in increments of $\pi/4$; in Exercise 4, t increases in increments of $\pi/6$. (See Exercises 21 and 22 in Section 5.1.)

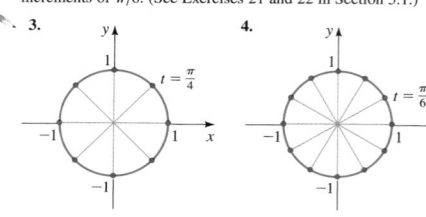

✎ **3.**   **4.**

5–24 ■ Find the exact value of the trigonometric function at the given real number.

5. (a) $\sin \dfrac{2\pi}{3}$ (b) $\cos \dfrac{2\pi}{3}$ (c) $\tan \dfrac{2\pi}{3}$

6. (a) $\sin \dfrac{5\pi}{6}$ (b) $\cos \dfrac{5\pi}{6}$ (c) $\tan \dfrac{5\pi}{6}$

✎ **7.** (a) $\sin \dfrac{7\pi}{6}$ (b) $\sin\left(-\dfrac{\pi}{6}\right)$ (c) $\sin \dfrac{11\pi}{6}$

8. (a) $\cos \dfrac{5\pi}{3}$ (b) $\cos\left(-\dfrac{5\pi}{3}\right)$ (c) $\cos \dfrac{7\pi}{3}$

9. (a) $\cos \dfrac{3\pi}{4}$ (b) $\cos \dfrac{5\pi}{4}$ (c) $\cos \dfrac{7\pi}{4}$

10. (a) $\sin \dfrac{3\pi}{4}$ (b) $\sin \dfrac{5\pi}{4}$ (c) $\sin \dfrac{7\pi}{4}$

11. (a) $\sin \dfrac{7\pi}{3}$ (b) $\csc \dfrac{7\pi}{3}$ (c) $\cot \dfrac{7\pi}{3}$

12. (a) $\cos\left(-\dfrac{\pi}{3}\right)$ (b) $\sec\left(-\dfrac{\pi}{3}\right)$ (c) $\tan\left(-\dfrac{\pi}{3}\right)$

✎ **13.** (a) $\sin\left(-\dfrac{\pi}{2}\right)$ (b) $\cos\left(-\dfrac{\pi}{2}\right)$ (c) $\cot\left(-\dfrac{\pi}{2}\right)$

14. (a) $\sin\left(-\dfrac{3\pi}{2}\right)$ (b) $\cos\left(-\dfrac{3\pi}{2}\right)$ (c) $\cot\left(-\dfrac{3\pi}{2}\right)$

15. (a) $\sec \dfrac{11\pi}{3}$ (b) $\csc \dfrac{11\pi}{3}$ (c) $\sec\left(-\dfrac{\pi}{3}\right)$

16. (a) $\cos \dfrac{7\pi}{6}$ (b) $\sec \dfrac{7\pi}{6}$ (c) $\csc \dfrac{7\pi}{6}$

17. (a) $\tan \dfrac{5\pi}{6}$ (b) $\tan \dfrac{7\pi}{6}$ (c) $\tan \dfrac{11\pi}{6}$

18. (a) $\cot\left(-\dfrac{\pi}{3}\right)$ (b) $\cot \dfrac{2\pi}{3}$ (c) $\cot \dfrac{5\pi}{3}$

19. (a) $\cos\left(-\dfrac{\pi}{4}\right)$ (b) $\csc\left(-\dfrac{\pi}{4}\right)$ (c) $\cot\left(-\dfrac{\pi}{4}\right)$

20. (a) $\sin \dfrac{5\pi}{4}$ (b) $\sec \dfrac{5\pi}{4}$ (c) $\tan \dfrac{5\pi}{4}$

21. (a) $\csc\left(-\dfrac{\pi}{2}\right)$ (b) $\csc \dfrac{\pi}{2}$ (c) $\csc \dfrac{3\pi}{2}$

22. (a) $\sec(-\pi)$ (b) $\sec \pi$ (c) $\sec 4\pi$

23. (a) $\sin 13\pi$ (b) $\cos 14\pi$ (c) $\tan 15\pi$

24. (a) $\sin \dfrac{25\pi}{2}$ (b) $\cos \dfrac{25\pi}{2}$ (c) $\cot \dfrac{25\pi}{2}$

25–28 ■ Find the value of each of the six trigonometric functions (if it is defined) at the given real number t. Use your answers to complete the table.

25. $t = 0$ **26.** $t = \dfrac{\pi}{2}$ **27.** $t = \pi$ **28.** $t = \dfrac{3\pi}{2}$

t	$\sin t$	$\cos t$	$\tan t$	$\csc t$	$\sec t$	$\cot t$
0	0	1		undefined		
$\frac{\pi}{2}$						
π			0			undefined
$\frac{3\pi}{2}$						

29–38 ■ The terminal point $P(x, y)$ determined by a real number t is given. Find $\sin t$, $\cos t$, and $\tan t$.

29. $\left(\dfrac{3}{5}, \dfrac{4}{5}\right)$ **30.** $\left(-\dfrac{3}{5}, \dfrac{4}{5}\right)$

31. $\left(\dfrac{\sqrt{5}}{4}, -\dfrac{\sqrt{11}}{4}\right)$ **32.** $\left(-\dfrac{1}{3}, -\dfrac{2\sqrt{2}}{3}\right)$

33. $\left(-\dfrac{6}{7}, \dfrac{\sqrt{13}}{7}\right)$ **34.** $\left(\dfrac{40}{41}, \dfrac{9}{41}\right)$

35. $\left(-\dfrac{5}{13}, -\dfrac{12}{13}\right)$ **36.** $\left(\dfrac{\sqrt{5}}{5}, \dfrac{2\sqrt{5}}{5}\right)$

37. $\left(-\dfrac{20}{29}, \dfrac{21}{29}\right)$ **38.** $\left(\dfrac{24}{25}, -\dfrac{7}{25}\right)$

39–46 ■ Find an approximate value of the given trigonometric function by using (a) the figure and (b) a calculator. Compare the two values.

39. $\sin 1$

40. $\cos 0.8$

41. $\sin 1.2$

42. $\cos 5$

43. $\tan 0.8$

44. $\tan(-1.3)$

45. $\cos 4.1$

46. $\sin(-5.2)$

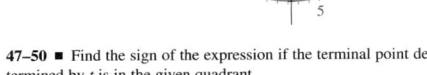

47–50 ■ Find the sign of the expression if the terminal point determined by t is in the given quadrant.

47. $\sin t \cos t$, Quadrant II **48.** $\tan t \sec t$, Quadrant IV

49. $\dfrac{\tan t \sin t}{\cot t}$, Quadrant III **50.** $\cos t \sec t$, any quadrant

51–54 ■ From the information given, find the quadrant in which the terminal point determined by t lies.

51. $\sin t > 0$ and $\cos t < 0$ **52.** $\tan t > 0$ and $\sin t < 0$

53. $\csc t > 0$ and $\sec t < 0$ **54.** $\cos t < 0$ and $\cot t < 0$

55–64 ■ Write the first expression in terms of the second if the terminal point determined by t is in the given quadrant.

55. $\sin t$, $\cos t$; Quadrant II **56.** $\cos t$, $\sin t$; Quadrant IV

57. $\tan t$, $\sin t$; Quadrant IV **58.** $\tan t$, $\cos t$; Quadrant III

59. $\sec t$, $\tan t$; Quadrant II **60.** $\csc t$, $\cot t$; Quadrant III

61. $\tan t$, $\sec t$; Quadrant III **62.** $\sin t$, $\sec t$; Quadrant IV

63. $\tan^2 t$, $\sin t$; any quadrant

64. $\sec^2 t \sin^2 t$, $\cos t$; any quadrant

65–72 ■ Find the values of the trigonometric functions of t from the given information.

65. $\sin t = \frac{3}{5}$, terminal point of t is in Quadrant II

66. $\cos t = -\frac{4}{5}$, terminal point of t is in Quadrant III

67. $\sec t = 3$, terminal point of t is in Quadrant IV

68. $\tan t = \frac{1}{4}$, terminal point of t is in Quadrant III

69. $\tan t = -\frac{3}{4}$, $\cos t > 0$

70. $\sec t = 2$, $\sin t < 0$

71. $\sin t = -\frac{1}{4}$, $\sec t < 0$

72. $\tan t = -4$, $\csc t > 0$

73–80 ■ Determine whether the function is even, odd, or neither.

73. $f(x) = x^2 \sin x$ **74.** $f(x) = x^2 \cos 2x$

75. $f(x) = \sin x \cos x$ **76.** $f(x) = \sin x + \cos x$

77. $f(x) = |x| \cos x$ **78.** $f(x) = x \sin^3 x$

79. $f(x) = x^3 + \cos x$ **80.** $f(x) = \cos(\sin x)$

APPLICATIONS

81. Harmonic Motion   The displacement from equilibrium of an oscillating mass attached to a spring is given by $y(t) = 4 \cos 3\pi t$ where y is measured in inches and t in seconds. Find the displacement at the times indicated in the table.

t	$y(t)$
0	
0.25	
0.50	
0.75	
1.00	
1.25	

82. Circadian Rhythms   Everybody's blood pressure varies over the course of the day. In a certain individual the resting diastolic blood pressure at time t is given by $B(t) = 80 + 7 \sin(\pi t/12)$, where t is measured in hours since midnight and $B(t)$ in mmHg (millimeters of mercury). Find this person's diastolic blood pressure at
(a) 6:00 A.M. (b) 10:30 A.M. (c) Noon (d) 8:00 P.M.

IN-CLASS MATERIALS

Problems such as Exercises 25–28 are crucial when students take calculus. It is vitally important that they go beyond memorizing the answers and truly understand where they come from.

83. Electric Circuit After the switch is closed in the circuit shown, the current t seconds later is $I(t) = 0.8e^{-3t}\sin 10t$. Find the current at the times
(a) $t = 0.1$ s and (b) $t = 0.5$ s.

$$L = 10^3 \text{ h}$$
$$R = 6 \times 10^3 \ \Omega$$
$$C = 9.17 \ \mu\text{f}$$
$$E = 4.8 \times 10^3 \text{ V}$$

84. Bungee Jumping A bungee jumper plummets from a high bridge to the river below and then bounces back over and over again. At time t seconds after her jump, her height H (in meters) above the river is given by $H(t) = 100 + 75e^{-t/20}\cos(\frac{\pi}{4} t)$. Find her height at the times indicated in the table.

t	$H(t)$
0	
1	
2	
4	
6	
8	
12	

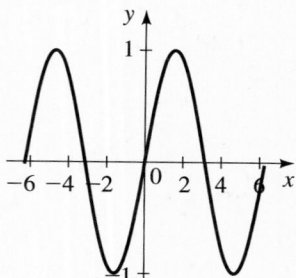

DISCOVERY ▪ DISCUSSION ▪ WRITING

85. Reduction Formulas A *reduction formula* is one that can be used to "reduce" the number of terms in the input for a trigonometric function. Explain how the figure shows that the following reduction formulas are valid:

$$\sin(t + \pi) = -\sin t \qquad \cos(t + \pi) = -\cos t$$
$$\tan(t + \pi) = \tan t$$

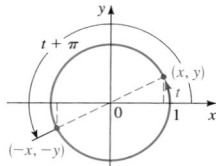

86. More Reduction Formulas By the "Angle-Side-Angle" theorem from elementary geometry, triangles CDO and AOB in the figure are congruent. Explain how this proves that if B has coordinates (x, y), then D has coordinates $(-y, x)$. Then explain how the figure shows that the following reduction formulas are valid:

$$\sin\left(t + \frac{\pi}{2}\right) = \cos t$$
$$\cos\left(t + \frac{\pi}{2}\right) = -\sin t$$
$$\tan\left(t + \frac{\pi}{2}\right) = -\cot t$$

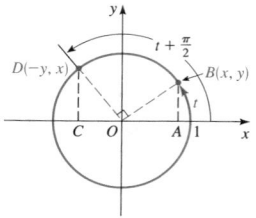

5.3 TRIGONOMETRIC GRAPHS

SUGGESTED TIME AND EMPHASIS

1 class, essential material

> Graphs of Sine and Cosine ▶ Graphs of Transformations of Sine and Cosine ▶ Using Graphing Devices to Graph Trigonometric Functions

The graph of a function gives us a better idea of its behavior. So, in this section we graph the sine and cosine functions and certain transformations of these functions. The other trigonometric functions are graphed in the next section.

▼ Graphs of Sine and Cosine

To help us graph the sine and cosine functions, we first observe that these functions repeat their values in a regular fashion. To see exactly how this happens, recall that the circumference of the unit circle is 2π. It follows that the terminal point $P(x, y)$ determined by the real number t is the same as that determined by $t + 2\pi$. Since the sine and cosine functions are

---

TEXT QUESTION
Sketch $y = \sin x$.

Answer

defined in terms of the coordinates of $P(x, y)$, it follows that their values are unchanged by the addition of any integer multiple of 2π. In other words,

$$\sin(t + 2n\pi) = \sin t \qquad \text{for any integer } n$$

$$\cos(t + 2n\pi) = \cos t \qquad \text{for any integer } n$$

Thus, the sine and cosine functions are *periodic* according to the following definition: A function f is **periodic** if there is a positive number p such that $f(t + p) = f(t)$ for every t. The least such positive number (if it exists) is the **period** of f. If f has period p, then the graph of f on any interval of length p is called **one complete period** of f.

PERIODIC PROPERTIES OF SINE AND COSINE

The functions sine and cosine have period 2π:

$$\sin(t + 2\pi) = \sin t \qquad\qquad \cos(t + 2\pi) = \cos t$$

TABLE 1

t	$\sin t$	$\cos t$
$0 \to \dfrac{\pi}{2}$	$0 \to 1$	$1 \to 0$
$\dfrac{\pi}{2} \to \pi$	$1 \to 0$	$0 \to -1$
$\pi \to \dfrac{3\pi}{2}$	$0 \to -1$	$-1 \to 0$
$\dfrac{3\pi}{2} \to 2\pi$	$-1 \to 0$	$0 \to 1$

So the sine and cosine functions repeat their values in any interval of length 2π. To sketch their graphs, we first graph one period. To sketch the graphs on the interval $0 \le t \le 2\pi$, we could try to make a table of values and use those points to draw the graph. Since no such table can be complete, let's look more closely at the definitions of these functions.

Recall that $\sin t$ is the y-coordinate of the terminal point $P(x, y)$ on the unit circle determined by the real number t. How does the y-coordinate of this point vary as t increases? It's easy to see that the y-coordinate of $P(x, y)$ increases to 1, then decreases to -1 repeatedly as the point $P(x, y)$ travels around the unit circle. (See Figure 1.) In fact, as t increases from 0 to $\pi/2$, $y = \sin t$ increases from 0 to 1. As t increases from $\pi/2$ to π, the value of $y = \sin t$ decreases from 1 to 0. Table 1 shows the variation of the sine and cosine functions for t between 0 and 2π.

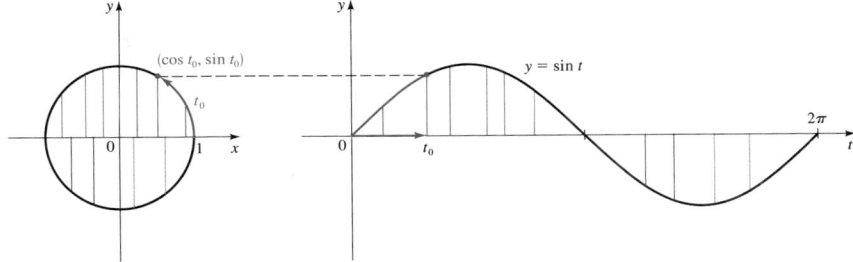

FIGURE 1

To draw the graphs more accurately, we find a few other values of $\sin t$ and $\cos t$ in Table 2. We could find still other values with the aid of a calculator.

TABLE 2

t	0	$\dfrac{\pi}{6}$	$\dfrac{\pi}{3}$	$\dfrac{\pi}{2}$	$\dfrac{2\pi}{3}$	$\dfrac{5\pi}{6}$	π	$\dfrac{7\pi}{6}$	$\dfrac{4\pi}{3}$	$\dfrac{3\pi}{2}$	$\dfrac{5\pi}{3}$	$\dfrac{11\pi}{6}$	2π
$\sin t$	0	$\dfrac{1}{2}$	$\dfrac{\sqrt{3}}{2}$	1	$\dfrac{\sqrt{3}}{2}$	$\dfrac{1}{2}$	0	$-\dfrac{1}{2}$	$-\dfrac{\sqrt{3}}{2}$	-1	$-\dfrac{\sqrt{3}}{2}$	$-\dfrac{1}{2}$	0
$\cos t$	1	$\dfrac{\sqrt{3}}{2}$	$\dfrac{1}{2}$	0	$-\dfrac{1}{2}$	$-\dfrac{\sqrt{3}}{2}$	-1	$-\dfrac{\sqrt{3}}{2}$	$-\dfrac{1}{2}$	0	$\dfrac{1}{2}$	$\dfrac{\sqrt{3}}{2}$	1

IN-CLASS MATERIALS

Ask the class if it is true that the sum of two periodic curves is always periodic. It turns out that although this seems a reasonable proposition, it is actually false. It is a true statement if you add the stipulation that the periods of the two curves are rational multiples of each other.

$\sin 2x + \cos 3x$ is periodic.

$\sin 2x + \cos \pi x$ is not periodic.

Now we use this information to graph the functions $\sin t$ and $\cos t$ for t between 0 and 2π in Figures 2 and 3. These are the graphs of one period. Using the fact that these functions are periodic with period 2π, we get their complete graphs by continuing the same pattern to the left and to the right in every successive interval of length 2π.

The graph of the sine function is symmetric with respect to the origin. This is as expected, since sine is an odd function. Since the cosine function is an even function, its graph is symmetric with respect to the y-axis.

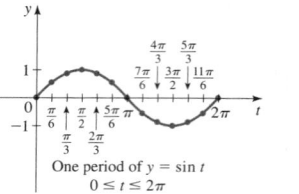

One period of $y = \sin t$
$0 \leq t \leq 2\pi$

FIGURE 2 Graph of $\sin t$

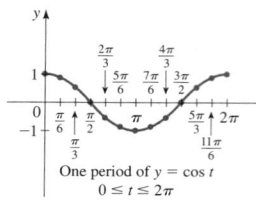

One period of $y = \cos t$
$0 \leq t \leq 2\pi$

FIGURE 3 Graph of $\cos t$

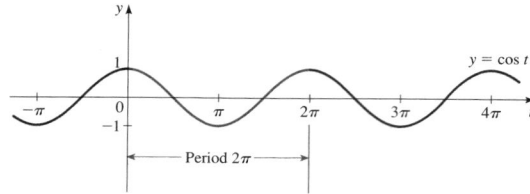

▼ Graphs of Transformations of Sine and Cosine

We now consider graphs of functions that are transformations of the sine and cosine functions. Thus, the graphing techniques of Section 2.5 are very useful here. The graphs we obtain are important for understanding applications to physical situations such as harmonic motion (see Section 5.6), but some of them are beautiful graphs that are interesting in their own right.

It's traditional to use the letter x to denote the variable in the domain of a function. So from here on we use the letter x and write $y = \sin x$, $y = \cos x$, $y = \tan x$, and so on to denote these functions.

EXAMPLE 1 | Cosine Curves

Sketch the graph of each function.

(a) $f(x) = 2 + \cos x$ **(b)** $g(x) = -\cos x$

SOLUTION

(a) The graph of $y = 2 + \cos x$ is the same as the graph of $y = \cos x$, but shifted up 2 units (see Figure 4(a)).

IN-CLASS MATERIALS

Let $f(x) = \sin x + \frac{1}{100} \cos x$. Have students graph this function with their calculators. In the default viewing window, the graph will be indistinguishable from that of $\sin x$. Show that when they zoom in, they can see the "bumps" in the function.

(b) The graph of $y = -\cos x$ in Figure 4(b) is the reflection of the graph of $y = \cos x$ in the x-axis.

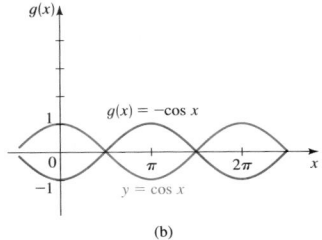

FIGURE 4   (a)   (b)

✎ NOW TRY EXERCISES **3** AND **5**   ■

Let's graph $y = 2 \sin x$. We start with the graph of $y = \sin x$ and multiply the y-coordinate of each point by 2. This has the effect of stretching the graph vertically by a factor of 2. To graph $y = \frac{1}{2} \sin x$, we start with the graph of $y = \sin x$ and multiply the y-coordinate of each point by $\frac{1}{2}$. This has the effect of shrinking the graph vertically by a factor of $\frac{1}{2}$ (see Figure 5).

Vertical stretching and shrinking of graphs is discussed in Section 2.5.

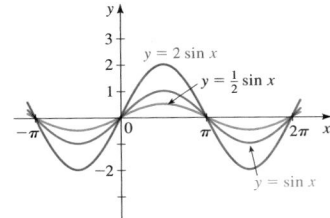

FIGURE 5

In general, for the functions

$$y = a \sin x \qquad \text{and} \qquad y = a \cos x$$

the number $|a|$ is called the **amplitude** and is the largest value these functions attain. Graphs of $y = a \sin x$ for several values of a are shown in Figure 6.

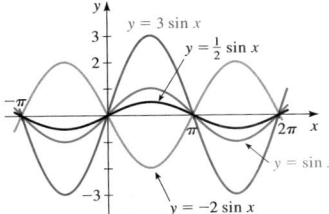

FIGURE 6

IN-CLASS MATERIALS

Have students obtain a table of time of sunrise versus date for your city. Perhaps have each student write down the information for a given month. (Websites such as http://www.usno.navy.mil/USNO/astronomical-applications will do these calculations for you.) Have the students pool and plot the data, and see how the resulting graph resembles a sine or cosine curve.

ALTERNATE EXAMPLE 2

Find the amplitude of $y = \pi \cos x$.

ANSWER

π

EXAMPLE 2 │ Stretching a Cosine Curve

Find the amplitude of $y = -3 \cos x$, and sketch its graph.

SOLUTION The amplitude is $|-3| = 3$, so the largest value the graph attains is 3 and the smallest value is -3. To sketch the graph, we begin with the graph of $y = \cos x$, stretch the graph vertically by a factor of 3, and reflect in the x-axis, arriving at the graph in Figure 7.

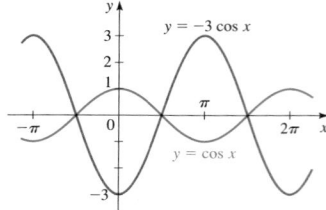

FIGURE 7

🔎. NOW TRY EXERCISE **9**   ■

Since the sine and cosine functions have period 2π, the functions

$$y = a \sin kx \qquad \text{and} \qquad y = a \cos kx \qquad (k > 0)$$

complete one period as kx varies from 0 to 2π, that is, for $0 \le kx \le 2\pi$ or for $0 \le x \le 2\pi/k$. So these functions complete one period as x varies between 0 and $2\pi/k$ and thus have period $2\pi/k$. The graphs of these functions are called **sine curves** and **cosine curves**, respectively. (Collectively, sine and cosine curves are often referred to as **sinusoidal** curves.)

SINE AND COSINE CURVES

The sine and cosine curves

$$y = a \sin kx \qquad \text{and} \qquad y = a \cos kx \qquad (k > 0)$$

have **amplitude** $|a|$ and **period** $2\pi/k$.

An appropriate interval on which to graph one complete period is $[0, 2\pi/k]$.

To see how the value of k affects the graph of $y = \sin kx$, let's graph the sine curve $y = \sin 2x$. Since the period is $2\pi/2 = \pi$, the graph completes one period in the interval $0 \le x \le \pi$ (see Figure 8(a)). For the sine curve $y = \sin \frac{1}{2}x$, the period is $2\pi \div \frac{1}{2} = 4\pi$, so the graph completes one period in the interval $0 \le x \le 4\pi$ (see Figure 8(b)). We see that the effect is to *shrink* the graph horizontally if $k > 1$ or to *stretch* the graph horizontally if $k < 1$.

Horizontal stretching and shrinking of graphs is discussed in Section 2.5.

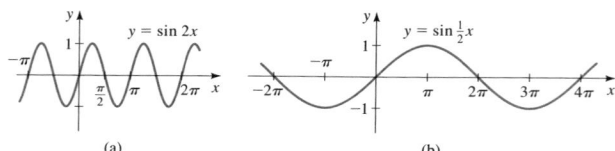

FIGURE 8   (a)   (b)

EXAMPLE

A graph of a transformed sine curve: $y = 3 \sin 2x + 1$ has amplitude 3, period π, and vertical shift 1.

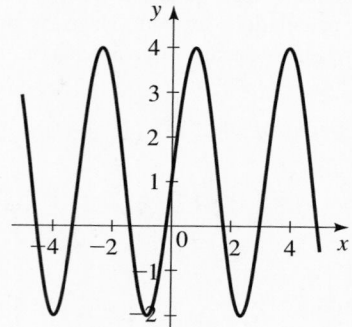

For comparison, in Figure 9 we show the graphs of one period of the sine curve $y = a \sin kx$ for several values of k.

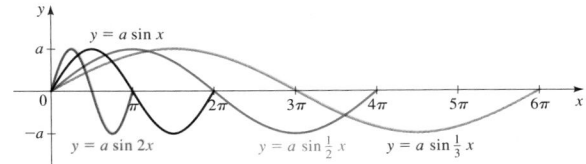

FIGURE 9

EXAMPLE 3 | Amplitude and Period

Find the amplitude and period of each function, and sketch its graph.

(a) $y = 4 \cos 3x$ **(b)** $y = -2 \sin \frac{1}{2}x$

SOLUTION

(a) We get the amplitude and period from the form of the function as follows:

$$\text{amplitude} = |a| = 4$$

$$y = 4 \cos 3x$$

$$\text{period} = \frac{2\pi}{k} = \frac{2\pi}{3}$$

The amplitude is 4 and the period is $2\pi/3$. The graph is shown in Figure 10.

(b) For $y = -2 \sin \frac{1}{2}x$,

$$\text{amplitude} = |a| = |-2| = 2$$

$$\text{period} = \frac{2\pi}{\frac{1}{2}} = 4\pi$$

The graph is shown in Figure 11.

NOW TRY EXERCISES 19 AND 21

FIGURE 10

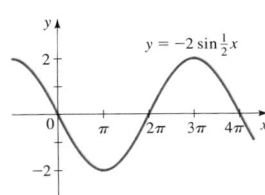

FIGURE 11

The graphs of functions of the form $y = a \sin k(x - b)$ and $y = a \cos k(x - b)$ are simply sine and cosine curves shifted horizontally by an amount $|b|$. They are shifted to the right if $b > 0$ or to the left if $b < 0$. The number b is the *phase shift*. We summarize the properties of these functions in the following box.

SHIFTED SINE AND COSINE CURVES

The sine and cosine curves

$$y = a \sin k(x - b) \qquad \text{and} \qquad y = a \cos k(x - b) \qquad (k > 0)$$

have **amplitude** $|a|$, **period** $2\pi/k$, and **phase shift** b.

An appropriate interval on which to graph one complete period is $[b, b + (2\pi/k)]$.

EXAMPLE

A graph of a transformed cosine curve

$$y = \frac{1}{2} \cos\left[\frac{\pi}{3}(x - 1)\right]$$

has amplitude $\frac{1}{2}$, period 6, and horizontal shift 1.

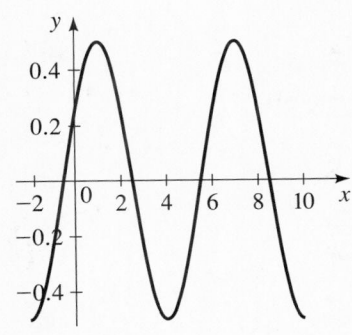

The graphs of $y = \sin\left(x - \frac{\pi}{3}\right)$ and $y = \sin\left(x + \frac{\pi}{6}\right)$ are shown in Figure 12.

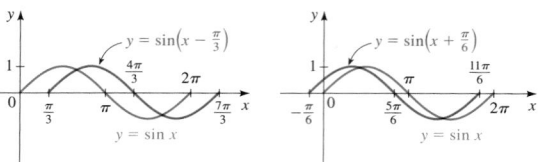

FIGURE 12

EXAMPLE 4 | A Shifted Sine Curve

Find the amplitude, period, and phase shift of $y = 3 \sin 2\left(x - \frac{\pi}{4}\right)$, and graph one complete period.

SOLUTION We get the amplitude, period, and phase shift from the form of the function as follows:

$$\text{amplitude} = |a| = 3 \qquad \text{period} = \frac{2\pi}{k} = \frac{2\pi}{2} = \pi$$

$$y = 3 \sin 2\left(x - \frac{\pi}{4}\right)$$

$$\text{phase shift} = \frac{\pi}{4} \text{ (to the right)}$$

Since the phase shift is $\pi/4$ and the period is π, one complete period occurs on the interval

$$\left[\frac{\pi}{4}, \frac{\pi}{4} + \pi\right] = \left[\frac{\pi}{4}, \frac{5\pi}{4}\right]$$

As an aid in sketching the graph, we divide this interval into four equal parts, then graph a sine curve with amplitude 3 as in Figure 13.

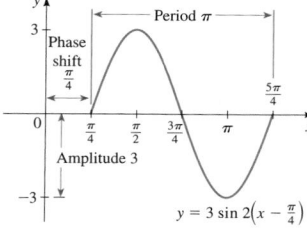

FIGURE 13

NOW TRY EXERCISE 33

EXAMPLE 5 | A Shifted Cosine Curve

Find the amplitude, period, and phase shift of

$$y = \frac{3}{4}\cos\left(2x + \frac{2\pi}{3}\right)$$

and graph one complete period.

Here is another way to find an appropriate interval on which to graph one complete period. Since the period of $y = \sin x$ is 2π, the function $y = 3 \sin 2(x - \frac{\pi}{4})$ will go through one complete period as $2(x - \frac{\pi}{4})$ varies from 0 to 2π.

Start of period: End of period:

$2(x - \frac{\pi}{4}) = 0$ $2(x - \frac{\pi}{4}) = 2\pi$

$x - \frac{\pi}{4} = 0$ $x - \frac{\pi}{4} = \pi$

$x = \frac{\pi}{4}$ $x = \frac{5\pi}{4}$

So we graph one period on the interval $\left[\frac{\pi}{4}, \frac{5\pi}{4}\right]$.

ALTERNATE EXAMPLE 4

(a) Find the amplitude, the period, and the phase shift of $y = -2 \sin 4(x - 1.3)$.
(b) Graph one complete period of $y = -2 \sin 4(x - 1.3)$.

ANSWERS
(a) Amplitude $= 2$, period $= \pi/2$, phase shift $= 1.3$ (to the right)
(b)

SOLUTION   We first write this function in the form $y = a \cos k(x - b)$. To do this, we factor 2 from the expression $2x + \dfrac{2\pi}{3}$ to get

$$y = \frac{3}{4} \cos 2\left[x - \left(-\frac{\pi}{3} \right) \right]$$

Thus we have

$$\text{amplitude} = |a| = \frac{3}{4}$$

$$\text{period} = \frac{2\pi}{k} = \frac{2\pi}{2} = \pi$$

$$\text{phase shift} = b = -\frac{\pi}{3} \qquad \text{Shift } \tfrac{\pi}{3} \text{ to the } \textit{left}$$

We can also find one complete period as follows:

Start of period: End of period:

$2x + \frac{2\pi}{3} = 0$ $2x + \frac{2\pi}{3} = 2\pi$

$2x = -\frac{2\pi}{3}$ $2x = \frac{4\pi}{3}$

$x = -\frac{\pi}{3}$ $x = \frac{2\pi}{3}$

So we graph one period on the interval $\left[-\frac{\pi}{3}, \frac{2\pi}{3} \right]$.

From this information it follows that one period of this cosine curve begins at $-\pi/3$ and ends at $(-\pi/3) + \pi = 2\pi/3$. To sketch the graph over the interval $[-\pi/3, 2\pi/3]$, we divide this interval into four equal parts and graph a cosine curve with amplitude $\frac{3}{4}$ as shown in Figure 14.

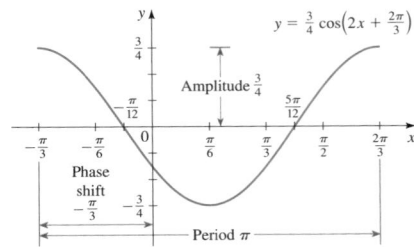

FIGURE 14

NOW TRY EXERCISE **35**

▼ Using Graphing Devices to Graph Trigonometric Functions

See Section 1.9 for guidelines on choosing an appropriate viewing rectangle.

When using a graphing calculator or a computer to graph a function, it is important to choose the viewing rectangle carefully in order to produce a reasonable graph of the function. This is especially true for trigonometric functions; the next example shows that, if care is not taken, it's easy to produce a very misleading graph of a trigonometric function.

EXAMPLE 6 | Choosing the Viewing Rectangle

Graph the function $f(x) = \sin 50x$ in an appropriate viewing rectangle.

The appearance of the graphs in Figure 15 depends on the machine used. The graphs you get with your own graphing device might not look like these figures, but they will also be quite inaccurate.

SOLUTION   Figure 15(a) shows the graph of f produced by a graphing calculator using the viewing rectangle $[-12, 12]$ by $[-1.5, 1.5]$. At first glance the graph appears to be reasonable. But if we change the viewing rectangle to the ones shown in Figure 15, the graphs look very different. Something strange is happening.

   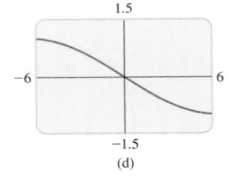

(a)   (b)   (c)   (d)

FIGURE 15   Graphs of $f(x) = \sin 50x$ in different viewing rectangles

---

ALTERNATE EXAMPLE 5
Find the amplitude, period, and phase shift of

$$y = \frac{\sqrt{2}}{2} \cos(3x + 2)$$

and graph one complete period.

ANSWER

Amplitude $= \dfrac{\sqrt{2}}{2}$,

period $= \dfrac{2\pi}{3}$,

phase shift $= 2/3$ to the left

ALTERNATE EXAMPLE 6
Graph the function $f(x) = \cos(x/100)$ in an appropriate viewing rectangle.

ANSWER
Bad viewing window:

Good viewing window:

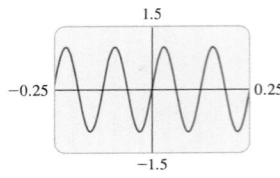

FIGURE 16 $f(x) = \sin 50x$

To explain the big differences in appearance of these graphs and to find an appropriate viewing rectangle, we need to find the period of the function $y = \sin 50x$:

$$\text{period} = \frac{2\pi}{50} = \frac{\pi}{25} \approx 0.126$$

This suggests that we should deal only with small values of x in order to show just a few oscillations of the graph. If we choose the viewing rectangle $[-0.25, 0.25]$ by $[-1.5, 1.5]$, we get the graph shown in Figure 16.

Now we see what went wrong in Figure 15. The oscillations of $y = \sin 50x$ are so rapid that when the calculator plots points and joins them, it misses most of the maximum and minimum points and therefore gives a very misleading impression of the graph.

✎ NOW TRY EXERCISE **51**

The function h in Example 7 is **periodic** with period 2π. In general, functions that are sums of functions from the following list are periodic:

$$1, \cos kx, \cos 2kx, \cos 3kx, \ldots$$

$$\sin kx, \sin 2kx, \sin 3kx, \ldots$$

Although these functions appear to be special, they are actually fundamental to describing all periodic functions that arise in practice. The French mathematician J. B. J. Fourier (see page 501) discovered that nearly every periodic function can be written as a sum (usually an infinite sum) of these functions. This is remarkable because it means that any situation in which periodic variation occurs can be described mathematically using the functions sine and cosine. A modern application of Fourier's discovery is the digital encoding of sound on compact discs.

EXAMPLE 7 | A Sum of Sine and Cosine Curves

Graph $f(x) = 2 \cos x$, $g(x) = \sin 2x$, and $h(x) = 2 \cos x + \sin 2x$ on a common screen to illustrate the method of graphical addition.

SOLUTION Notice that $h = f + g$, so its graph is obtained by adding the corresponding y-coordinates of the graphs of f and g. The graphs of f, g, and h are shown in Figure 17.

FIGURE 17

✎ NOW TRY EXERCISE **59**

EXAMPLE 8 | A Cosine Curve with Variable Amplitude

Graph the functions $y = x^2$, $y = -x^2$, and $y = x^2 \cos 6\pi x$ on a common screen. Comment on and explain the relationship among the graphs.

SOLUTION Figure 18 shows all three graphs in the viewing rectangle $[-1.5, 1.5]$ by $[-2, 2]$. It appears that the graph of $y = x^2 \cos 6\pi x$ lies between the graphs of the functions $y = x^2$ and $y = -x^2$.

To understand this, recall that the values of $\cos 6\pi x$ lie between -1 and 1, that is,

$$-1 \leq \cos 6\pi x \leq 1$$

for all values of x. Multiplying the inequalities by x^2 and noting that $x^2 \geq 0$, we get

$$-x^2 \leq x^2 \cos 6\pi x \leq x^2$$

This explains why the functions $y = x^2$ and $y = -x^2$ form a boundary for the graph of $y = x^2 \cos 6\pi x$. (Note that the graphs touch when $\cos 6\pi x = \pm 1$.)

✎ NOW TRY EXERCISE **63**

Example 8 shows that the function $y = x^2$ controls the amplitude of the graph of $y = x^2 \cos 6\pi x$. In general, if $f(x) = a(x) \sin kx$ or $f(x) = a(x) \cos kx$, the function a determines how the amplitude of f varies, and the graph of f lies between the graphs of $y = -a(x)$ and $y = a(x)$. Here is another example.

ALTERNATE EXAMPLE 7

Graph $f(x) = \sin(x)$, $g(x) = \frac{1}{3}\sin(3x)$, and $h(x) = \sin(x) + \frac{1}{3}\sin(3x)$ on a common screen to illustrate the method of graphical addition.

ANSWER

ALTERNATE EXAMPLE 8

Graph $y = 1.5^x$, $y = -1.5^x$, and $y = 1.5^x \sin(8*x)$ on the same screen and notice the relationship among the graphs.

ANSWER

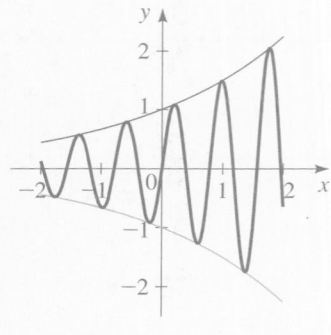

FIGURE 18 $y = x^2 \cos 6\pi x$

EXAMPLE 9 | A Cosine Curve with Variable Amplitude

Graph the function $f(x) = \cos 2\pi x \cos 16\pi x$.

SOLUTION The graph is shown in Figure 19. Although it was drawn by a computer, we could have drawn it by hand, by first sketching the boundary curves $y = \cos 2\pi x$ and $y = -\cos 2\pi x$. The graph of f is a cosine curve that lies between the graphs of these two functions.

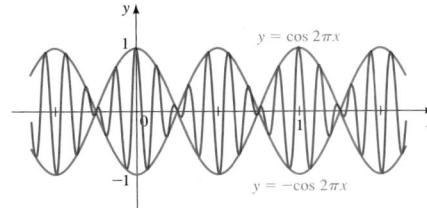

FIGURE 19 $f(x) = \cos 2\pi x \cos 16\pi x$

◥. NOW TRY EXERCISE **65** ■

EXAMPLE 10 | A Sine Curve with Decaying Amplitude

The function $f(x) = \dfrac{\sin x}{x}$ is important in calculus. Graph this function and comment on its behavior when x is close to 0.

SOLUTION The viewing rectangle $[-15, 15]$ by $[-0.5, 1.5]$ shown in Figure 20(a) gives a good global view of the graph of f. The viewing rectangle $[-1, 1]$ by $[-0.5, 1.5]$ in Figure 20(b) focuses on the behavior of f when $x \approx 0$. Notice that although $f(x)$ is not defined when $x = 0$ (in other words, 0 is not in the domain of f), the values of f seem to approach 1 when x gets close to 0. This fact is crucial in calculus.

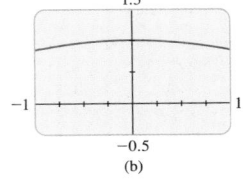

(a)   (b)

FIGURE 20 $f(x) = \dfrac{\sin x}{x}$

◥. NOW TRY EXERCISE **75** ■

The function in Example 10 can be written as

$$f(x) = \frac{1}{x} \sin x$$

and may thus be viewed as a sine function whose amplitude is controlled by the function $a(x) = 1/x$.

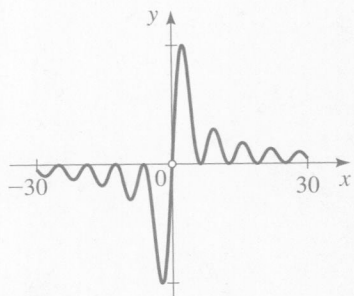

DRILL QUESTION

Sketch $y = 2 \sin \pi x$.

Answer

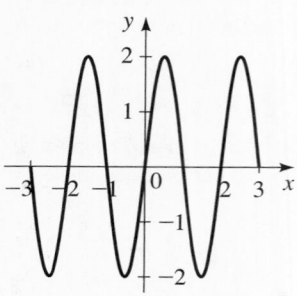

5.3 EXERCISES

CONCEPTS

1. The trigonometric functions $y = \sin x$ and $y = \cos x$ have

amplitude _____ and period _____. Sketch a graph of each function on the interval $[0, 2\pi]$.

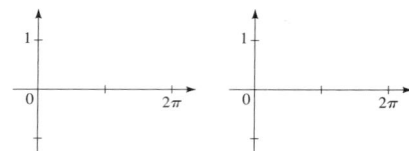

2. The trigonometric function $y = 3 \sin 2x$ has amplitude

_____ and period _____.

SKILLS

3–16 ■ Graph the function.

3. $f(x) = 1 + \cos x$ **4.** $f(x) = 3 + \sin x$

5. $f(x) = -\sin x$ **6.** $f(x) = 2 - \cos x$

7. $f(x) = -2 + \sin x$ **8.** $f(x) = -1 + \cos x$

9. $g(x) = 3 \cos x$ **10.** $g(x) = 2 \sin x$

11. $g(x) = -\frac{1}{2} \sin x$ **12.** $g(x) = -\frac{2}{3} \cos x$

13. $g(x) = 3 + 3 \cos x$ **14.** $g(x) = 4 - 2 \sin x$

15. $h(x) = |\cos x|$ **16.** $h(x) = |\sin x|$

17–28 ■ Find the amplitude and period of the function, and sketch its graph.

17. $y = \cos 2x$ **18.** $y = -\sin 2x$

19. $y = -3 \sin 3x$ **20.** $y = \frac{1}{2} \cos 4x$

21. $y = 10 \sin \frac{1}{2}x$ **22.** $y = 5 \cos \frac{1}{4}x$

23. $y = -\frac{1}{3} \cos \frac{1}{3}x$ **24.** $y = 4 \sin(-2x)$

25. $y = -2 \sin 2\pi x$ **26.** $y = -3 \sin \pi x$

27. $y = 1 + \frac{1}{2} \cos \pi x$ **28.** $y = -2 + \cos 4\pi x$

29–42 ■ Find the amplitude, period, and phase shift of the function, and graph one complete period.

29. $y = \cos\left(x - \frac{\pi}{2}\right)$ **30.** $y = 2 \sin\left(x - \frac{\pi}{3}\right)$

31. $y = -2 \sin\left(x - \frac{\pi}{6}\right)$ **32.** $y = 3 \cos\left(x + \frac{\pi}{4}\right)$

33. $y = -4 \sin 2\left(x + \frac{\pi}{2}\right)$ **34.** $y = \sin \frac{1}{2}\left(x + \frac{\pi}{4}\right)$

35. $y = 5 \cos\left(3x - \frac{\pi}{4}\right)$ **36.** $y = 2 \sin\left(\frac{2}{3}x - \frac{\pi}{6}\right)$

37. $y = \frac{1}{2} - \frac{1}{2} \cos\left(2x - \frac{\pi}{3}\right)$ **38.** $y = 1 + \cos\left(3x + \frac{\pi}{2}\right)$

39. $y = 3 \cos \pi\left(x + \frac{1}{2}\right)$ **40.** $y = 3 + 2 \sin 3(x + 1)$

41. $y = \sin(\pi + 3x)$ **42.** $y = \cos\left(\frac{\pi}{2} - x\right)$

43–50 ■ The graph of one complete period of a sine or cosine curve is given.

(a) Find the amplitude, period, and phase shift.

(b) Write an equation that represents the curve in the form

$$y = a \sin k(x - b) \qquad \text{or} \qquad y = a \cos k(x - b)$$

43.   **44.**

45.   **46.**

47.   **48.**

49.   **50.**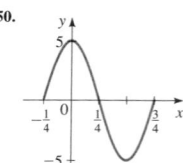

51–58 ■ Determine an appropriate viewing rectangle for each function, and use it to draw the graph.

51. $f(x) = \cos 100x$ **52.** $f(x) = 3 \sin 120x$

53. $f(x) = \sin(x/40)$ **54.** $f(x) = \cos(x/80)$

55. $y = \tan 25x$ **56.** $y = \csc 40x$

57. $y = \sin^2 20x$ **58.** $y = \sqrt{\tan 10\pi x}$

59–60 ■ Graph f, g, and $f + g$ on a common screen to illustrate graphical addition.

 59. $f(x) = x$, $g(x) = \sin x$

60. $f(x) = \sin x$, $g(x) = \sin 2x$

 61–66 ■ Graph the three functions on a common screen. How are the graphs related?

61. $y = x^2$, $y = -x^2$, $y = x^2 \sin x$

62. $y = x$, $y = -x$, $y = x \cos x$

63. $y = \sqrt{x}$, $y = -\sqrt{x}$, $y = \sqrt{x} \sin 5\pi x$

64. $y = \dfrac{1}{1 + x^2}$, $y = -\dfrac{1}{1 + x^2}$, $y = \dfrac{\cos 2\pi x}{1 + x^2}$

65. $y = \cos 3\pi x$, $y = -\cos 3\pi x$, $y = \cos 3\pi x \cos 21\pi x$

66. $y = \sin 2\pi x$, $y = -\sin 2\pi x$, $y = \sin 2\pi x \sin 10\pi x$

 67–70 ■ Find the maximum and minimum values of the function.

67. $y = \sin x + \sin 2x$

68. $y = x - 2 \sin x$, $0 \le x \le 2\pi$

69. $y = 2 \sin x + \sin^2 x$

70. $y = \dfrac{\cos x}{2 + \sin x}$

71–74 ■ Find all solutions of the equation that lie in the interval $[0, \pi]$. State each answer correct to two decimal places.

71. $\cos x = 0.4$

72. $\tan x = 2$

73. $\csc x = 3$

74. $\cos x = x$

75–76 ■ A function f is given.

(a) Is f even, odd, or neither?

(b) Find the x-intercepts of the graph of f.

(c) Graph f in an appropriate viewing rectangle.

(d) Describe the behavior of the function as $x \to \pm\infty$.

(e) Notice that $f(x)$ is not defined when $x = 0$. What happens as x approaches 0?

75. $f(x) = \dfrac{1 - \cos x}{x}$

76. $f(x) = \dfrac{\sin 4x}{2x}$

APPLICATIONS

77. Height of a Wave   As a wave passes by an offshore piling, the height of the water is modeled by the function

$$h(t) = 3 \cos\left(\frac{\pi}{10}t\right)$$

where $h(t)$ is the height in feet above mean sea level at time t seconds.

(a) Find the period of the wave.

(b) Find the wave height, that is, the vertical distance between the trough and the crest of the wave.

78. Sound Vibrations   A tuning fork is struck, producing a pure tone as its tines vibrate. The vibrations are modeled by the function

$$v(t) = 0.7 \sin(880\pi t)$$

where $v(t)$ is the displacement of the tines in millimeters at time t seconds.

(a) Find the period of the vibration.

(b) Find the frequency of the vibration, that is, the number of times the fork vibrates per second.

(c) Graph the function v.

79. Blood Pressure   Each time your heart beats, your blood pressure first increases and then decreases as the heart rests between beats. The maximum and minimum blood pressures are called the *systolic* and *diastolic* pressures, respectively. Your *blood pressure reading* is written as systolic/diastolic. A reading of 120/80 is considered normal.

A certain person's blood pressure is modeled by the function

$$p(t) = 115 + 25 \sin(160\pi t)$$

where $p(t)$ is the pressure in mmHg (millimeters of mercury), at time t measured in minutes.

(a) Find the period of p.

(b) Find the number of heartbeats per minute.

(c) Graph the function p.

(d) Find the blood pressure reading. How does this compare to normal blood pressure?

80. Variable Stars   Variable stars are ones whose brightness varies periodically. One of the most visible is R Leonis; its brightness is modeled by the function

$$b(t) = 7.9 - 2.1 \cos\left(\frac{\pi}{156}t\right)$$

where t is measured in days.

(a) Find the period of R Leonis.

(b) Find the maximum and minimum brightness.

(c) Graph the function b.

DISCOVERY ▪ DISCUSSION ▪ WRITING

81. Compositions Involving Trigonometric Functions
This exercise explores the effect of the inner function g on a composite function $y = f(g(x))$.

(a) Graph the function $y = \sin\sqrt{x}$ using the viewing rectangle $[0, 400]$ by $[-1.5, 1.5]$. In what ways does this graph differ from the graph of the sine function?

(b) Graph the function $y = \sin(x^2)$ using the viewing rectangle $[-5, 5]$ by $[-1.5, 1.5]$. In what ways does this graph differ from the graph of the sine function?

82. Periodic Functions I Recall that a function f is *periodic* if there is a positive number p such that $f(t + p) = f(t)$ for every t, and the least such p (if it exists) is the *period* of f. The graph of a function of period p looks the same on each interval of length p, so we can easily determine the period from the graph. Determine whether the function whose graph is shown is periodic; if it is periodic, find the period.

(a)

(b)

(c)

(d)

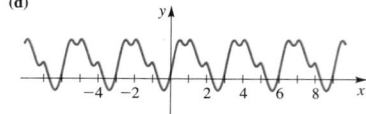

83. Periodic Functions II Use a graphing device to graph the following functions. From the graph, determine whether the function is periodic; if it is periodic, find the period. (See page 156 for the definition of $[\![x]\!]$.)

(a) $y = |\sin x|$

(b) $y = \sin|x|$

(c) $y = 2^{\cos x}$

(d) $y = x - [\![x]\!]$

(e) $y = \cos(\sin x)$

(f) $y = \cos(x^2)$

84. Sinusoidal Curves The graph of $y = \sin x$ is the same as the graph of $y = \cos x$ shifted to the right $\pi/2$ units. So the sine curve $y = \sin x$ is also at the same time a cosine curve: $y = \cos(x - \pi/2)$. In fact, any sine curve is also a cosine curve with a different phase shift, and any cosine curve is also a sine curve. Sine and cosine curves are collectively referred to as *sinusoidal*. For the curve whose graph is shown, find all possible ways of expressing it as a sine curve $y = a \sin(x - b)$ or as a cosine curve $y = a \cos(x - b)$. Explain why you think you have found all possible choices for a and b in each case.

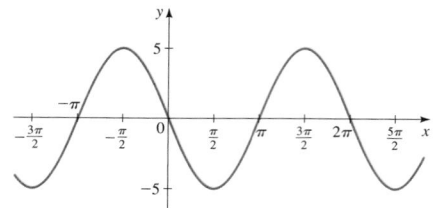

◯ DISCOVERY PROJECT | **Predator/Prey Models**

In this project we explore the use of sine functions in modeling the population of a predator and its prey. You can find the project at the book companion website:
www.stewartmath.com

5.4 MORE TRIGONOMETRIC GRAPHS

Graphs of Tangent, Cotangent, Secant, and Cosecant ▶ Graphs of Transformations of Tangent and Cotangent ▶ Graphs of Transformations of Cosecant and Secant

In this section we graph the tangent, cotangent, secant, and cosecant functions and transformations of these functions.

▼ Graphs of Tangent, Cotangent, Secant, and Cosecant

We begin by stating the periodic properties of these functions. Recall that sine and cosine have period 2π. Since cosecant and secant are the reciprocals of sine and cosine, respectively, they also have period 2π (see Exercise 55). Tangent and cotangent, however, have period π (see Exercise 85 of Section 5.2).

PERIODIC PROPERTIES

The functions tangent and cotangent have period π:

$$\tan(x + \pi) = \tan x \qquad \cot(x + \pi) = \cot x$$

The functions cosecant and secant have period 2π:

$$\csc(x + 2\pi) = \csc x \qquad \sec(x + 2\pi) = \sec x$$

---

x	$\tan x$
0	0
$\pi/6$	0.58
$\pi/4$	1.00
$\pi/3$	1.73
1.4	5.80
1.5	14.10
1.55	48.08
1.57	1,255.77
1.5707	10,381.33

We first sketch the graph of tangent. Since it has period π, we need only sketch the graph on any interval of length π and then repeat the pattern to the left and to the right. We sketch the graph on the interval $(-\pi/2, \pi/2)$. Since $\tan(\pi/2)$ and $\tan(-\pi/2)$ aren't defined, we need to be careful in sketching the graph at points near $\pi/2$ and $-\pi/2$. As x gets near $\pi/2$ through values less than $\pi/2$, the value of $\tan x$ becomes large. To see this, notice that as x gets close to $\pi/2$, $\cos x$ approaches 0 and $\sin x$ approaches 1 and so $\tan x = \sin x/\cos x$ is large. A table of values of $\tan x$ for x close to $\pi/2$ (≈ 1.570796) is shown in the margin.

Thus, by choosing x close enough to $\pi/2$ through values less than $\pi/2$, we can make the value of $\tan x$ larger than any given positive number. We express this by writing

$$\tan x \to \infty \qquad \text{as} \qquad x \to \frac{\pi^-}{2}$$

This is read "tan x approaches infinity as x approaches $\pi/2$ from the left."

In a similar way, by choosing x close to $-\pi/2$ through values greater than $-\pi/2$, we can make tan x smaller than any given negative number. We write this as

$$\tan x \to -\infty \qquad \text{as} \qquad x \to -\frac{\pi^+}{2}$$

Arrow notation is discussed in Section 3.7.

This is read "tan x approaches negative infinity as x approaches $-\pi/2$ from the right."

Thus, the graph of $y = \tan x$ approaches the vertical lines $x = \pi/2$ and $x = -\pi/2$. So these lines are **vertical asymptotes**. With the information we have so far, we sketch the graph of

Asymptotes are discussed in Section 3.7.

SUGGESTED TIME AND EMPHASIS
$\frac{1}{2}$ class, essential material

Text Question
Sketch $y = \tan x$.

Answer

$y = \tan x$ for $-\pi/2 < x < \pi/2$ in Figure 1. The complete graph of tangent (see Figure 5(a) on the next page) is now obtained using the fact that tangent is periodic with period π.

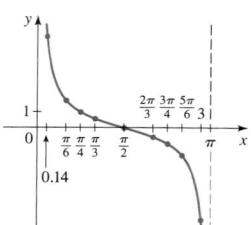

FIGURE 1
One period of $y = \tan x$

FIGURE 2
One period of $y = \cot x$

The function $y = \cot x$ is graphed on the interval $(0, \pi)$ by a similar analysis (see Figure 2). Since $\cot x$ is undefined for $x = n\pi$ with n an integer, its complete graph (in Figure 5(b) on the next page) has vertical asymptotes at these values.

To graph the cosecant and secant functions, we use the reciprocal identities

$$\csc x = \frac{1}{\sin x} \quad \text{and} \quad \sec x = \frac{1}{\cos x}$$

So to graph $y = \csc x$, we take the reciprocals of the y-coordinates of the points of the graph of $y = \sin x$. (See Figure 3.) Similarly, to graph $y = \sec x$, we take the reciprocals of the y-coordinates of the points of the graph of $y = \cos x$. (See Figure 4.)

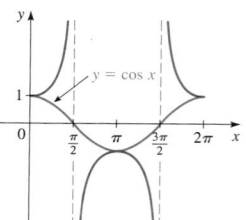

FIGURE 3
One period of $y = \csc x$

FIGURE 4
One period of $y = \sec x$

Let's consider more closely the graph of the function $y = \csc x$ on the interval $0 < x < \pi$. We need to examine the values of the function near 0 and π, since at these values $\sin x = 0$, and $\csc x$ is thus undefined. We see that

$$\csc x \to \infty \qquad \text{as} \qquad x \to 0^+$$
$$\csc x \to \infty \qquad \text{as} \qquad x \to \pi^-$$

Thus, the lines $x = 0$ and $x = \pi$ are vertical asymptotes. In the interval $\pi < x < 2\pi$ the graph is sketched in the same way. The values of $\csc x$ in that interval are the same as those in the interval $0 < x < \pi$ except for sign (see Figure 3). The complete graph in Figure 5(c) is now obtained from the fact that the function cosecant is periodic with period

IN-CLASS MATERIALS

Notice that the functions $\sec x$ and $x^2 + 1$ are very different functions ($\sec x$ has vertical asymptotes, for example, and $x^2 + 1$ does not). When we casually sketch their graphs near $x = 0$, however, the sketches look similar:

$y = \sec x$

$y = x^2 + 1$

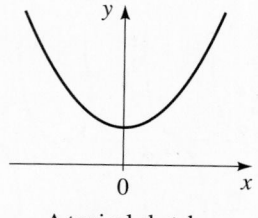

A typical sketch

2π. Note that the graph has vertical asymptotes at the points where $\sin x = 0$, that is, at $x = n\pi$, for n an integer.

(a) $y = \tan x$

(b) $y = \cot x$

(c) $y = \csc x$

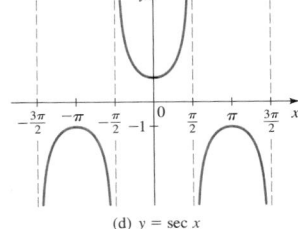

(d) $y = \sec x$

FIGURE 5

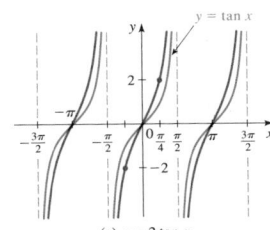

(a) $y = 2 \tan x$

The graph of $y = \sec x$ is sketched in a similar manner. Observe that the domain of $\sec x$ is the set of all real numbers other than $x = (\pi/2) + n\pi$, for n an integer, so the graph has vertical asymptotes at those points. The complete graph is shown in Figure 5(d).

It is apparent that the graphs of $y = \tan x$, $y = \cot x$, and $y = \csc x$ are symmetric about the origin, whereas that of $y = \sec x$ is symmetric about the y-axis. This is because tangent, cotangent, and cosecant are odd functions, whereas secant is an even function.

▼ Graphs of Transformations of Tangent and Cotangent

We now consider graphs of transformations of the tangent and cotangent functions.

EXAMPLE 1 | Graphing Tangent Curves

Graph each function.

(a) $y = 2 \tan x$ (b) $y = -\tan x$

SOLUTION We first graph $y = \tan x$ and then transform it as required.

(a) To graph $y = 2 \tan x$, we multiply the y-coordinate of each point on the graph of $y = \tan x$ by 2. The resulting graph is shown in Figure 6(a).

(b) The graph of $y = -\tan x$ in Figure 6(b) is obtained from that of $y = \tan x$ by reflecting in the x-axis.

✎. NOW TRY EXERCISES **9** AND **11** ■

(b) $y = -\tan x$

FIGURE 6

IN-CLASS MATERIALS

Discuss $\tan x$, x^3, $\sin x$, and $\sinh x$. Notice that, unlike in the previous example (included in the prior In-Class Materials section), these curves don't all look alike at the origin—some are flatter than others.

Since the tangent and cotangent functions have period π, the functions

$$y = a \tan kx \quad \text{and} \quad y = a \cot kx \quad (k > 0)$$

complete one period as kx varies from 0 to π, that is, for $0 \le kx \le \pi$. Solving this inequality, we get $0 \le x \le \pi/k$. So they each have period π/k.

TANGENT AND COTANGENT CURVES

The functions

$$y = a \tan kx \quad \text{and} \quad y = a \cot kx \quad (k > 0)$$

have period π/k.

Thus, one complete period of the graphs of these functions occurs on any interval of length π/k. To sketch a complete period of these graphs, it's convenient to select an interval between vertical asymptotes:

To graph one period of $y = a \tan kx$, an appropriate interval is $\left(-\dfrac{\pi}{2k}, \dfrac{\pi}{2k}\right)$.

To graph one period of $y = a \cot kx$, an appropriate interval is $\left(0, \dfrac{\pi}{k}\right)$.

EXAMPLE 2 | Graphing Tangent Curves

Graph each function.

(a) $y = \tan 2x$ **(b)** $y = \tan 2\left(x - \dfrac{\pi}{4}\right)$

SOLUTION

(a) The period is $\pi/2$ and an appropriate interval is $(-\pi/4, \pi/4)$. The endpoints $x = -\pi/4$ and $x = \pi/4$ are vertical asymptotes. Thus, we graph one complete period of the function on $(-\pi/4, \pi/4)$. The graph has the same shape as that of the tangent function, but is shrunk horizontally by a factor of $\frac{1}{2}$. We then repeat that portion of the graph to the left and to the right. See Figure 7(a).

(b) The graph is the same as that in part (a), but it is shifted to the right $\pi/4$, as shown in Figure 7(b).

 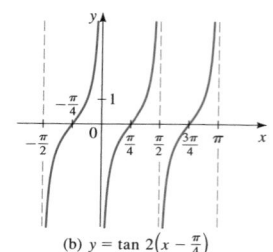

(a) $y = \tan 2x$ (b) $y = \tan 2\left(x - \dfrac{\pi}{4}\right)$

FIGURE 7

Since $y = \tan x$ completes one period between $x = -\frac{\pi}{2}$ and $x = \frac{\pi}{2}$, the function $y = \tan 2(x - \frac{\pi}{4})$ completes one period as $2(x - \frac{\pi}{4})$ varies from $-\frac{\pi}{2}$ to $\frac{\pi}{2}$.

Start of period: End of period:
$$2\left(x - \tfrac{\pi}{4}\right) = -\tfrac{\pi}{2} \qquad 2\left(x - \tfrac{\pi}{4}\right) = \tfrac{\pi}{2}$$
$$x - \tfrac{\pi}{4} = -\tfrac{\pi}{4} \qquad x - \tfrac{\pi}{4} = \tfrac{\pi}{4}$$
$$x = 0 \qquad\qquad x = \tfrac{\pi}{2}$$

So we graph one period on the interval $(0, \frac{\pi}{2})$.

✎. NOW TRY EXERCISES **27** AND **39** ◼

IN-CLASS MATERIALS

Compare the graphs of $\tan x$ and x^3 on the interval $-1 \le x \le 1$. Point out that, although they have some similarities in shape (increasing, concave down followed by concave up), they do look very different. The difference is even more pronounced when we widen the interval to $1.5 \le x \le 1.5$.

EXAMPLE 3 | A Shifted Cotangent Curve

Graph $y = 2 \cot\left(3x - \dfrac{\pi}{2}\right)$.

SOLUTION   We first put this in the form $y = a \cot k(x - b)$ by factoring 3 from the expression $3x - \dfrac{\pi}{2}$:

$$y = 2 \cot\left(3x - \frac{\pi}{2}\right) = 2 \cot 3\left(x - \frac{\pi}{6}\right)$$

Since $y = \cot x$ completes one period between $x = 0$ and $x = \pi$, the function $y = 2 \cot(3x - \frac{\pi}{2})$ completes one period as $3x - \frac{\pi}{2}$ varies from 0 to π.

Start of period: End of period:

$3x - \frac{\pi}{2} = 0$ $3x - \frac{\pi}{2} = \pi$

$3x = \frac{\pi}{2}$ $3x = \frac{3\pi}{2}$

$x = \frac{\pi}{6}$ $x = \frac{\pi}{2}$

So we graph one period on the interval $(\frac{\pi}{6}, \frac{\pi}{2})$.

Thus the graph is the same as that of $y = 2 \cot 3x$ but is shifted to the right $\pi/6$. The period of $y = 2 \cot 3x$ is $\pi/3$, and an appropriate interval is $(0, \pi/3)$. To get the corresponding interval for the desired graph, we shift this interval to the right $\pi/6$. This gives

$$\left(0 + \frac{\pi}{6}, \frac{\pi}{3} + \frac{\pi}{6}\right) = \left(\frac{\pi}{6}, \frac{\pi}{2}\right)$$

Finally, we graph one period in the shape of cotangent on the interval $(\pi/6, \pi/2)$ and repeat that portion of the graph to the left and to the right. (See Figure 8.)

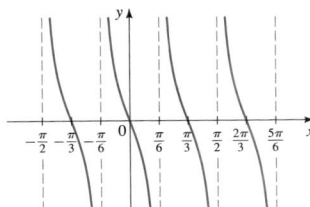

FIGURE 8

$y = 2 \cot\left(3x - \dfrac{\pi}{2}\right)$

✎. NOW TRY EXERCISE **43**   ∎

▼ Graphs of Transformations of Cosecant and Secant

We have already observed that the cosecant and secant functions are the reciprocals of the sine and cosine functions. Thus, the following result is the counterpart of the result for sine and cosine curves in Section 5.3.

COSECANT AND SECANT CURVES

The functions

$$y = a \csc kx \quad \text{and} \quad y = a \sec kx \quad (k > 0)$$

have period $2\pi/k$.

An appropriate interval on which to graph one complete period is $[0, 2\pi/k]$.

EXAMPLE 4 | Graphing Cosecant Curves

Graph each function.

(a) $y = \dfrac{1}{2} \csc 2x$ **(b)** $y = \dfrac{1}{2} \csc\left(2x + \dfrac{\pi}{2}\right)$

IN-CLASS MATERIALS

If we look at the previously mentioned "U-shaped" functions' behavior on a larger interval, their similarity decreases, but some of them would still be hard to tell apart just by looking at the shapes of the curves.

$y = x^2 + 1$

$y = \sec x$

$y = -\cos x + 2$

$y = x^4 + 1$

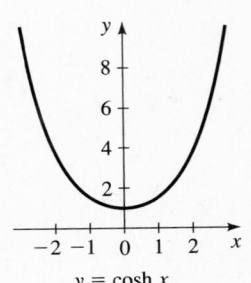

$y = \cosh x$

SOLUTION

(a) The period is $2\pi/2 = \pi$. An appropriate interval is $[0, \pi]$, and the asymptotes occur in this interval whenever $\sin 2x = 0$. So the asymptotes in this interval are $x = 0$, $x = \pi/2$, and $x = \pi$. With this information we sketch on the interval $[0, \pi]$ a graph with the same general shape as that of one period of the cosecant function. The complete graph in Figure 9(a) is obtained by repeating this portion of the graph to the left and to the right.

Since $y = \csc x$ completes one period between $x = 0$ and $x = 2\pi$, the function $y = \frac{1}{2}\csc(2x + \frac{\pi}{2})$ completes one period as $2x + \frac{\pi}{2}$ varies from 0 to 2π.

(b) We first write

$$y = \frac{1}{2}\csc\left(2x + \frac{\pi}{2}\right) = \frac{1}{2}\csc 2\left(x + \frac{\pi}{4}\right)$$

From this we see that the graph is the same as that in part (a) but shifted to the left $\pi/4$. The graph is shown in Figure 9(b).

Start of period: End of period:

$2x + \frac{\pi}{2} = 0$ $2x + \frac{\pi}{2} = 2\pi$

$2x = -\frac{\pi}{2}$ $2x = \frac{3\pi}{2}$

$x = -\frac{\pi}{4}$ $x = \frac{3\pi}{4}$

So we graph one period on the interval $\left(-\frac{\pi}{4}, \frac{3\pi}{4}\right)$.

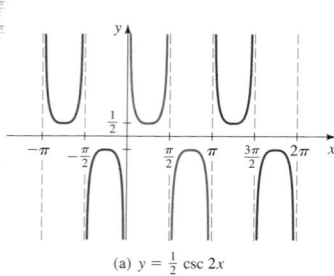

(a) $y = \frac{1}{2}\csc 2x$

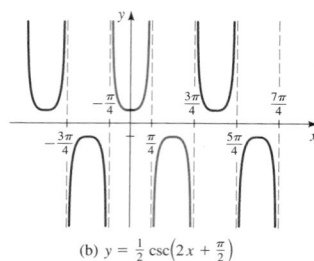

(b) $y = \frac{1}{2}\csc\left(2x + \frac{\pi}{2}\right)$

FIGURE 9

▨. NOW TRY EXERCISES **33** AND **45**

EXAMPLE 5 | Graphing a Secant Curve

Graph $y = 3 \sec \frac{1}{2}x$.

SOLUTION   The period is $2\pi \div \frac{1}{2} = 4\pi$. An appropriate interval is $[0, 4\pi]$, and the asymptotes occur in this interval wherever $\cos \frac{1}{2}x = 0$. Thus, the asymptotes in this interval are $x = \pi$, $x = 3\pi$. With this information we sketch on the interval $[0, 4\pi]$ a graph with the same general shape as that of one period of the secant function. The complete graph in Figure 10 is obtained by repeating this portion of the graph to the left and to the right.

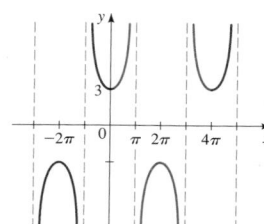

FIGURE 10
$y = 3 \sec \frac{1}{2}x$

▨. NOW TRY EXERCISE **31**

ALTERNATE EXAMPLE 5

Let $f(x) = 2 \sec 4x$. Find the period of f and the equation of its vertical asymptote(s) in the interval $\left[0, \dfrac{\pi}{2}\right]$.

ANSWER

$\dfrac{\pi}{4}, x = \dfrac{\pi}{8}, x = \dfrac{3\pi}{8}$

EXAMPLE

$y = \sec\left[\dfrac{\pi}{3}(x - 1)\right]$ and $y = \csc\left[\dfrac{\pi}{3}(x - 1)\right]$ have period 3 and horizontal shift 1.

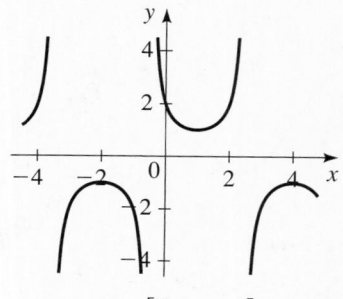

$y = \sec\left[\frac{\pi}{3}(x - 1)\right]$

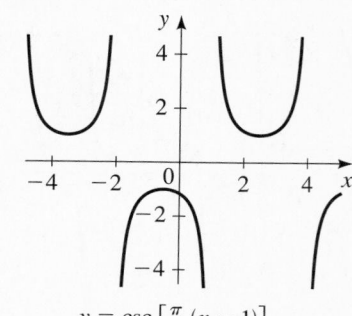

$y = \csc\left[\frac{\pi}{3}(x - 1)\right]$

5.4 EXERCISES

CONCEPTS

1. The trigonometric function $y = \tan x$ has period _____ and asymptotes $x =$ _____. Sketch a graph of this function on the interval $(-\pi/2, \pi/2)$.

2. The trigonometric function $y = \csc x$ has period _____ and asymptotes $x =$ _____. Sketch a graph of this function on the interval $(-\pi, \pi)$.

SKILLS

3–8 ■ Match the trigonometric function with one of the graphs I–VI.

3. $f(x) = \tan\left(x + \dfrac{\pi}{4}\right)$ 4. $f(x) = \sec 2x$

5. $f(x) = \cot 2x$ 6. $f(x) = -\tan x$

7. $f(x) = 2 \sec x$ 8. $f(x) = 1 + \csc x$

I

II

III

IV

V

VI
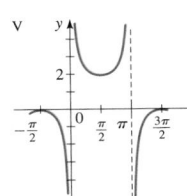

9–54 ■ Find the period and graph the function.

9. $y = 4 \tan x$ 10. $y = -4 \tan x$

11. $y = -\tfrac{1}{2} \tan x$ 12. $y = \tfrac{1}{2} \tan x$

13. $y = -\cot x$ 14. $y = 2 \cot x$

15. $y = 2 \csc x$ 16. $y = \tfrac{1}{2} \csc x$

17. $y = 3 \sec x$ 18. $y = -3 \sec x$

19. $y = \tan\left(x + \dfrac{\pi}{2}\right)$ 20. $y = \tan\left(x - \dfrac{\pi}{4}\right)$

21. $y = \csc\left(x - \dfrac{\pi}{2}\right)$ 22. $y = \sec\left(x + \dfrac{\pi}{4}\right)$

23. $y = \cot\left(x + \dfrac{\pi}{4}\right)$ 24. $y = 2 \csc\left(x - \dfrac{\pi}{3}\right)$

25. $y = \dfrac{1}{2} \sec\left(x - \dfrac{\pi}{6}\right)$ 26. $y = 3 \csc\left(x + \dfrac{\pi}{2}\right)$

27. $y = \tan 4x$ 28. $y = \tan \tfrac{1}{2} x$

29. $y = \tan \dfrac{\pi}{4} x$ 30. $y = \cot \dfrac{\pi}{2} x$

31. $y = \sec 2x$ 32. $y = 5 \csc 3x$

33. $y = \csc 4x$ 34. $y = \csc \tfrac{1}{2} x$

35. $y = 2 \tan 3\pi x$ 36. $y = 2 \tan \dfrac{\pi}{2} x$

37. $y = 5 \csc \dfrac{3\pi}{2} x$ 38. $y = 5 \sec 2\pi x$

39. $y = \tan 2\left(x + \dfrac{\pi}{2}\right)$ 40. $y = \csc 2\left(x + \dfrac{\pi}{2}\right)$

41. $y = \tan 2(x - \pi)$ 42. $y = \sec 2\left(x - \dfrac{\pi}{2}\right)$

43. $y = \cot\left(2x - \dfrac{\pi}{2}\right)$ 44. $y = \tfrac{1}{2} \tan(\pi x - \pi)$

45. $y = 2 \csc\left(\pi x - \dfrac{\pi}{3}\right)$ 46. $y = 2 \sec\left(\dfrac{1}{2} x - \dfrac{\pi}{3}\right)$

47. $y = 5 \sec\left(3x - \dfrac{\pi}{2}\right)$ 48. $y = \tfrac{1}{2} \sec(2\pi x - \pi)$

49. $y = \tan\left(\dfrac{2}{3} x - \dfrac{\pi}{6}\right)$ 50. $y = \tan \dfrac{1}{2}\left(x + \dfrac{\pi}{4}\right)$

51. $y = 3 \sec \pi\left(x + \dfrac{1}{2}\right)$ 52. $y = \sec\left(3x + \dfrac{\pi}{2}\right)$

53. $y = -2 \tan\left(2x - \dfrac{\pi}{3}\right)$ 54. $y = 2 \csc(3x + 3)$

55. (a) Prove that if f is periodic with period p, then $1/f$ is also periodic with period p.
    (b) Prove that cosecant and secant each have period 2π.

56. Prove that if f and g are periodic with period p, then f/g is also periodic, but its period could be smaller than p.

APPLICATIONS

57. **Lighthouse** The beam from a lighthouse completes one rotation every two minutes. At time t, the distance d shown in the figure on the next page is

$$d(t) = 3 \tan \pi t$$

where t is measured in minutes and d in miles.
    (a) Find $d(0.15)$, $d(0.25)$, and $d(0.45)$.

EXAMPLE
Graphs of variants of trigonometric curves:
$y = \tan 2x + 1$ and $y = \cot 2x + 1$
have period $\dfrac{\pi}{2}$ and vertical shift 1.

$y = \tan 2x + 1$

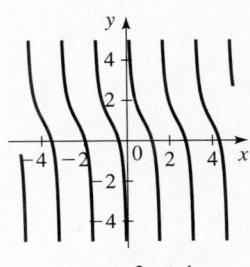

$y = \cot 2x + 1$

DRILL QUESTION
Sketch $y = \tan \pi x$.

Answer

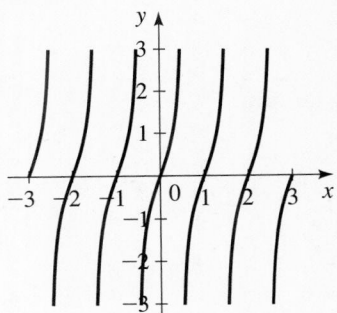

(b) Sketch a graph of the function d for $0 \le t < \frac{1}{2}$.
(c) What happens to the distance d as t approaches $\frac{1}{2}$?

(d) Explain what happens to the shadow as the time approaches 6 P.M. (that is, as $t \to 12^-$).

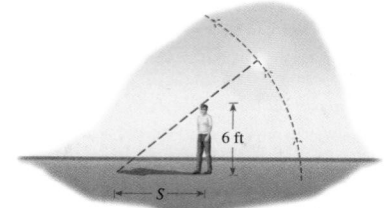

58. Length of a Shadow On a day when the sun passes directly overhead at noon, a six-foot-tall man casts a shadow of length

$$S(t) = 6 \left| \cot \frac{\pi}{12} t \right|$$

where S is measured in feet and t is the number of hours since 6 A.M.

(a) Find the length of the shadow at 8:00 A.M., noon, 2:00 P.M., and 5:45 P.M.
(b) Sketch a graph of the function S for $0 < t < 12$.
(c) From the graph determine the values of t at which the length of the shadow equals the man's height. To what time of day does each of these values correspond?

DISCOVERY ■ DISCUSSION ■ WRITING

59. Reduction Formulas Use the graphs in Figure 5 to explain why the following formulas are true.

$$\tan\left(x - \frac{\pi}{2}\right) = -\cot x$$

$$\sec\left(x - \frac{\pi}{2}\right) = \csc x$$

SUGGESTED TIME AND EMPHASIS

1 class, essential material

5.5 INVERSE TRIGONOMETRIC FUNCTIONS AND THEIR GRAPHS

The Inverse Sine Function ▶ The Inverse Cosine Function ▶ The Inverse Tangent Function ▶ The Inverse Secant, Cosecant, and Cotangent Functions

We study applications of inverse trigonometric functions to triangles in Sections 6.4–6.6.

Recall from Section 2.7 that the inverse of a function f is a function f^{-1} that reverses the rule of f. For a function to have an inverse, it must be one-to-one. Since the trigonometric functions are not one-to-one, they do not have inverses. It is possible, however, to restrict the domains of the trigonometric functions in such a way that the resulting functions are one-to-one.

▼ The Inverse Sine Function

Let's first consider the sine function. There are many ways to restrict the domain of sine so that the new function is one-to-one. A natural way to do this is to restrict the domain to the interval $[-\pi/2, \pi/2]$. The reason for this choice is that sine is one-to-one on this interval and moreover attains each of the values in its range on this interval. From Figure 1 we see that sine is one-to-one on this restricted domain (by the Horizontal Line Test) and so has an inverse.

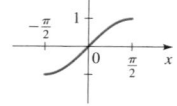

FIGURE 1 Graphs of the sine function and the restricted sine function

$y = \sin x$

$y = \sin x, \ -\frac{\pi}{2} \le x \le \frac{\pi}{2}$

TEXT QUESTION

We can say $\sin^{-1} y = x$ means $y = \sin x$. Given this definition, why does the text need to fuss with domains and ranges?

Answer

For a given y between -1 and 1, there are infinitely many values of x such that $y = \sin x$.

We can now define an inverse sine function on this restricted domain. The graph of $y = \sin^{-1} x$ is shown in Figure 2; it is obtained by reflecting the graph of $y = \sin x$, $-\pi/2 \le x \le \pi/2$, in the line $y = x$.

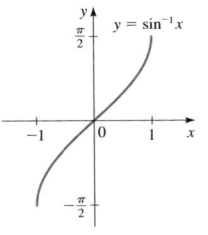

FIGURE 2 Graph of $y = \sin^{-1} x$

DEFINITION OF THE INVERSE SINE FUNCTION

The **inverse sine function** is the function $\sin^{-1}$ with domain $[-1, 1]$ and range $[-\pi/2, \pi/2]$ defined by

$$\sin^{-1} x = y \quad \Leftrightarrow \quad \sin y = x$$

The inverse sine function is also called **arcsine**, denoted by **arcsin**.

Thus, $y = \sin^{-1} x$ *is the number in the interval* $[-\pi/2, \pi/2]$ *whose sine is x.* In other words, $\sin(\sin^{-1} x) = x$. In fact, from the general properties of inverse functions studied in Section 2.7, we have the following **cancellation properties**.

$$\sin(\sin^{-1} x) = x \quad \text{for} \quad -1 \le x \le 1$$
$$\sin^{-1}(\sin x) = x \quad \text{for} \quad -\frac{\pi}{2} \le x \le \frac{\pi}{2}$$

EXAMPLE 1 | Evaluating the Inverse Sine Function

Find each value.

(a) $\sin^{-1} \frac{1}{2}$ **(b)** $\sin^{-1}\left(-\frac{1}{2}\right)$ **(c)** $\sin^{-1} \frac{3}{2}$

SOLUTION

(a) The number in the interval $[-\pi/2, \pi/2]$ whose sine is $\frac{1}{2}$ is $\pi/6$. Thus, $\sin^{-1} \frac{1}{2} = \pi/6$.

(b) The number in the interval $[-\pi/2, \pi/2]$ whose sine is $-\frac{1}{2}$ is $-\pi/6$. Thus, $\sin^{-1}(-\frac{1}{2}) = -\pi/6$.

(c) Since $\frac{3}{2} > 1$, it is not in the domain of $\sin^{-1} x$, so $\sin^{-1} \frac{3}{2}$ is not defined.

✎. NOW TRY EXERCISE **3**

EXAMPLE 2 | Using a Calculator to Evaluate Inverse Sine

Find approximate values for **(a)** $\sin^{-1}(0.82)$ and **(b)** $\sin^{-1} \frac{1}{3}$.

SOLUTION

We use a calculator to approximate these values. Using the $\boxed{\text{SIN}^{-1}}$, or $\boxed{\text{INV}}\boxed{\text{SIN}}$, or $\boxed{\text{ARC}}\boxed{\text{SIN}}$ key(s) on the calculator (with the calculator in radian mode), we get

(a) $\sin^{-1}(0.82) \approx 0.96141$ **(b)** $\sin^{-1} \frac{1}{3} \approx 0.33984$

✎. NOW TRY EXERCISES **11** AND **21**

When evaluating expressions involving $\sin^{-1}$, we need to remember that the range of $\sin^{-1}$ is the interval $[-\pi/2, \pi/2]$.

EXAMPLE 3 | Evaluating Expressions with Inverse Sine

Find each value.

(a) $\sin^{-1}\left(\sin \frac{\pi}{3}\right)$ **(b)** $\sin^{-1}\left(\sin \frac{2\pi}{3}\right)$

ALTERNATE EXAMPLE 1

Find $\sin^{-1} \frac{\sqrt{2}}{2}$, $\sin^{-1}\left(-\frac{\sqrt{2}}{2}\right)$, and $\sin^{-1} \frac{5}{4}$.

ANSWER

$\frac{\pi}{4}, -\frac{\pi}{4}$, undefined

ALTERNATE EXAMPLE 2

Find approximate values for $\sin^{-1} 0.71$ and $\sin^{-1} \frac{6}{7}$. Express your answer in radians and give the answer to five decimal places.

ANSWER

0.7895, 1.0297

ALTERNATE EXAMPLE 3

Compute the following:

(a) $\sin^{-1}\left[\sin\left(\frac{\pi}{6}\right)\right]$

(b) $\sin^{-1}\left[\sin\left(\frac{13\pi}{6}\right)\right]$

ANSWERS

(a) $\frac{\pi}{6}$

(b) $\frac{\pi}{6}$

IN-CLASS MATERIALS

Many students may need a review of notation: $\sin^2 x = (\sin x)^2$, $\sin x^2 = \sin(x^2)$, $(\sin x)^{-1} = \dfrac{1}{\sin x} = \csc x$, $\sin x^{-1} = \sin\left(\dfrac{1}{x}\right)$, but $\sin^{-1} x$ represents the inverse sine of x, the arcsine of x, which is not the same as any of the previous functions.

SOLUTION

(a) Since $\pi/3$ is in the interval $[-\pi/2, \pi/2]$, we can use the above cancellation properties of inverse functions:

$$\sin^{-1}\left(\sin\frac{\pi}{3}\right) = \frac{\pi}{3} \qquad \text{Cancellation property: } -\frac{\pi}{2} \le \frac{\pi}{3} \le \frac{\pi}{2}$$

(b) We first evaluate the expression in the parentheses:

$$\sin^{-1}\left(\sin\frac{2\pi}{3}\right) = \sin^{-1}\left(\frac{\sqrt{3}}{2}\right) \qquad \text{Evaluate}$$

$$= \frac{\pi}{3} \qquad \text{Because } \sin\frac{\pi}{3} = \frac{\sqrt{3}}{2}$$

⊘ Note: $\sin^{-1}(\sin x) = x$ only if $-\frac{\pi}{2} \le x \le \frac{\pi}{2}$.

✎. NOW TRY EXERCISES **31** AND **33**

▼ The Inverse Cosine Function

If the domain of the cosine function is restricted to the interval $[0, \pi]$, the resulting function is one-to-one and so has an inverse. We choose this interval because on it, cosine attains each of its values exactly once (see Figure 3).

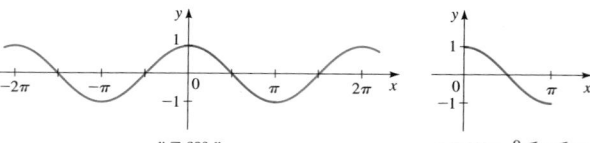

FIGURE 3 Graphs of the cosine function and the restricted cosine function

$y = \cos x$ $y = \cos x, \ 0 \le x \le \pi$

DEFINITION OF THE INVERSE COSINE FUNCTION

The **inverse cosine function** is the function $\cos^{-1}$ with domain $[-1, 1]$ and range $[0, \pi]$ defined by

$$\cos^{-1}x = y \quad \Leftrightarrow \quad \cos y = x$$

The inverse cosine function is also called **arccosine**, denoted by **arccos**.

Thus, $y = \cos^{-1}x$ *is the number in the interval* $[0, \pi]$ *whose cosine is x.* The following **cancellation properties** follow from the inverse function properties.

$$\cos(\cos^{-1}x) = x \quad \text{for} \quad -1 \le x \le 1$$
$$\cos^{-1}(\cos x) = x \quad \text{for} \quad 0 \le x \le \pi$$

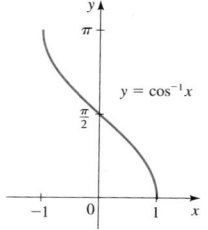

FIGURE 4 Graph of $y = \cos^{-1}x$

The graph of $y = \cos^{-1}x$ is shown in Figure 4; it is obtained by reflecting the graph of $y = \cos x, 0 \le x \le \pi$, in the line $y = x$.

EXAMPLE 4 | Evaluating the Inverse Cosine Function

Find each value.

(a) $\cos^{-1}\frac{\sqrt{3}}{2}$ **(b)** $\cos^{-1}0$ **(c)** $\cos^{-1}\frac{5}{7}$

ALTERNATE EXAMPLE 4

Find $\cos^{-1}\dfrac{\sqrt{2}}{2}$.

ANSWER

$\dfrac{\pi}{4}$

IN-CLASS MATERIALS

It may be helpful to start by reviewing general inverse functions (Section 2.7). If $f(x) = x^3$, what is $f^{-1}(x)$?

Note that $f(2) = 8$ and $f^{-1}(8) = 2$. Now move to $f(x) = \sqrt[5]{3x + 2} \Rightarrow f^{-1}(x) = \dfrac{x^5 - 2}{3}$.

Note that $f(5) \approx 1.762$ and $f^{-1}(1.762) \approx 5$. Now explore $f(x) = x^2$, and point out that even though there is no inverse function, we could make things work out if we were allowed to assume that x was positive. This leads to a natural segue into $f(x) = \sin x$.

SOLUTION

(a) The number in the interval $[0, \pi]$ whose cosine is $\sqrt{3}/2$ is $\pi/6$. Thus, $\cos^{-1}(\sqrt{3}/2) = \pi/6$.

(b) The number in the interval $[0, \pi]$ whose cosine is 0 is $\pi/2$. Thus, $\cos^{-1} 0 = \pi/2$.

(c) Since no rational multiple of π has cosine $\frac{5}{7}$, we use a calculator (in radian mode) to find this value approximately:

$$\cos^{-1}\frac{5}{7} \approx 0.77519$$

✎. **NOW TRY EXERCISES 5 AND 13**   ∎

EXAMPLE 5 | Evaluating Expressions with Inverse Cosine

Find each value.

(a) $\cos^{-1}\left(\cos \dfrac{2\pi}{3} \right)$ (b) $\cos^{-1}\left(\cos \dfrac{5\pi}{3} \right)$

SOLUTION

(a) Since $2\pi/3$ is in the interval $[0, \pi]$ we can use the above cancellation properties:

$$\cos^{-1}\left(\cos \frac{2\pi}{3} \right) = \frac{2\pi}{3} \qquad \text{Cancellation property: } 0 \le \frac{2\pi}{3} \le \pi$$

(b) We first evaluate the expression in the parentheses:

$$\cos^{-1}\left(\cos \frac{5\pi}{3} \right) = \cos^{-1}\left(\tfrac{1}{2}\right) \qquad \text{Evaluate}$$

$$= \frac{\pi}{3} \qquad \text{Because } \cos\frac{\pi}{3} = \frac{1}{2}$$

⊘ Note: $\cos^{-1}(\cos x) = x$ only if $0 \le x \le \pi$.

✎. **NOW TRY EXERCISES 29 AND 35**   ∎

▼ The Inverse Tangent Function

We restrict the domain of the tangent function to the interval $(-\pi/2, \pi/2)$ in order to obtain a one-to-one function.

DEFINITION OF THE INVERSE TANGENT FUNCTION

The **inverse tangent function** is the function $\tan^{-1}$ with domain $\mathbb{R}$ and range $(-\pi/2, \pi/2)$ defined by

$$\tan^{-1} x = y \quad \Leftrightarrow \quad \tan y = x$$

The inverse tangent function is also called **arctangent**, denoted by **arctan**.

Thus, $y = \tan^{-1} x$ *is the number in the interval* $(-\pi/2, \pi/2)$ *whose tangent is x.* The following **cancellation properties** follow from the inverse function properties.

$$\tan(\tan^{-1} x) = x \quad \text{for} \quad x \in \mathbb{R}$$

$$\tan^{-1}(\tan x) = x \quad \text{for} \quad -\frac{\pi}{2} < x < \frac{\pi}{2}$$

ALTERNATE EXAMPLE 5
Compute the following:

(a) $\cos^{-1}\left[\cos\left(\dfrac{5\pi}{6} \right) \right]$

(b) $\cos^{-1}\left[\cos\left(\dfrac{7\pi}{6} \right) \right]$

ANSWERS

(a) $\dfrac{5\pi}{6}$

(b) $\dfrac{5\pi}{6}$

EXAMPLES

- $\sin^{-1}\left(\dfrac{\sqrt{2}}{2} \right) = \dfrac{\pi}{4}$

- $\cos^{-1}\left(-\dfrac{\sqrt{3}}{2} \right) = \dfrac{5\pi}{6}$

- $\tan^{-1} \sqrt{3} = \dfrac{\pi}{3}$

- $\tan^{-1}\left(-\sqrt{3} \right) = -\dfrac{\pi}{3}$

- $\tan\left(\sin^{-1}\dfrac{1}{5} \right) = \dfrac{\sqrt{6}}{12}$

- $\cos\left(\tan^{-1}\dfrac{3}{8} \right) = 8\dfrac{\sqrt{73}}{73}$

- $\sin^{-1}\left(\sin\dfrac{87\pi}{4} \right) = -\dfrac{\pi}{4}$

Figure 5 shows the graph of $y = \tan x$ on the interval $(-\pi/2, \pi/2)$ and the graph of its inverse function, $y = \tan^{-1} x$.

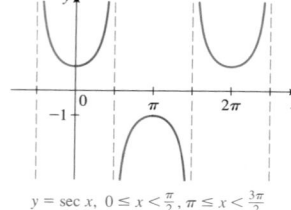

FIGURE 5 Graphs of the restricted tangent function and the inverse tangent function

$y = \tan x, \ -\frac{\pi}{2} < x < \frac{\pi}{2}$

$y = \tan^{-1} x$

See Exercise 44 in Section 6.4 (page 469) for a way of finding the values of these inverse trigonometric functions on a calculator.

EXAMPLE 6 | Evaluating the Inverse Tangent Function

Find each value.

(a) $\tan^{-1} 1$ **(b)** $\tan^{-1} \sqrt{3}$ **(c)** $\tan^{-1}(20)$

SOLUTION

(a) The number in the interval $(-\pi/2, \pi/2)$ with tangent 1 is $\pi/4$. Thus, $\tan^{-1} 1 = \pi/4$.

(b) The number in the interval $(-\pi/2, \pi/2)$ with tangent $\sqrt{3}$ is $\pi/3$. Thus, $\tan^{-1}\sqrt{3} = \pi/3$.

(c) We use a calculator (in radian mode) to find that $\tan^{-1}(20) \approx -1.52084$.

✎ NOW TRY EXERCISES **7** AND **17** ∎

▼ The Inverse Secant, Cosecant, and Cotangent Functions

To define the inverse functions of the secant, cosecant, and cotangent functions, we restrict the domain of each function to a set on which it is one-to-one and on which it attains all its values. Although any interval satisfying these criteria is appropriate, we choose to restrict the domains in a way that simplifies the choice of sign in computations involving inverse trigonometric functions. The choices we make are also appropriate for calculus. This explains the seemingly strange restriction for the domains of the secant and cosecant functions. We end this section by displaying the graphs of the secant, cosecant, and cotangent functions with their restricted domains and the graphs of their inverse functions (Figures 6–8).

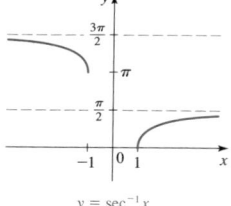

FIGURE 6 The inverse secant function

$y = \sec x, \ 0 \le x < \frac{\pi}{2}, \ \pi \le x < \frac{3\pi}{2}$

$y = \sec^{-1} x$

ALTERNATE EXAMPLE 6

(a) Find $\tan^{-1} 1$, $\tan^{-1} \dfrac{\sqrt{3}}{3}$.

(b) Find the approximate value for $\tan^{-1}(-15)$. Express your answer in radians and give the answer to five decimal places.

ANSWERS

(a) $\dfrac{\pi}{4}, \dfrac{\pi}{6}$

(b) -1.50423

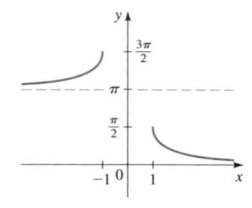

FIGURE 7 The inverse cosecant function

$y = \csc x, \ 0 < x \le \frac{\pi}{2}, \ \pi < x \le \frac{3\pi}{2}$ $y = \csc^{-1} x$

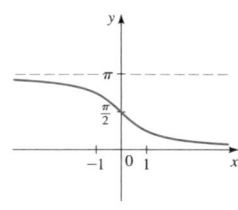

FIGURE 8 The inverse cotangent function

$y = \cot x, \ 0 < x < \pi$ $y = \cot^{-1} x$

5.5 EXERCISES

CONCEPTS

1. (a) To define the inverse sine function, we restrict the domain of sine to the interval _____. On this interval the sine function is one-to-one, and its inverse function $\sin^{-1}$ is defined by $\sin^{-1} x = y \ \Leftrightarrow \ \sin$ ____ = ____. For example, $\sin^{-1} \frac{1}{2} =$ ____ because $\sin$ ____ = ____.

   (b) To define the inverse cosine function we restrict the domain of cosine to the interval _____. On this interval the cosine function is one-to-one and its inverse function $\cos^{-1}$ is defined by $\cos^{-1} x = y \ \Leftrightarrow$ $\cos$ ____ = ____. For example, $\cos^{-1} \frac{1}{2} =$ ____ because $\cos$ ____ = ____.

2. The cancellation property $\sin^{-1}(\sin x) = x$ is valid for x in the interval _____. Which of the following is not true?

   (a) $\sin^{-1}\left(\sin \frac{\pi}{3}\right) = \frac{\pi}{3}$

   (b) $\sin^{-1}\left(\sin \frac{10\pi}{3}\right) = \frac{10\pi}{3}$

SKILLS

3–10 ■ Find the exact value of each expression, if it is defined.

3. (a) $\sin^{-1} 1$ (b) $\sin^{-1} \frac{\sqrt{3}}{2}$ (c) $\sin^{-1} 2$

4. (a) $\sin^{-1}(-1)$ (b) $\sin^{-1} \frac{\sqrt{2}}{2}$ (c) $\sin^{-1}(-2)$

5. (a) $\cos^{-1}(-1)$ (b) $\cos^{-1} \frac{1}{2}$ (c) $\cos^{-1}\left(-\frac{\sqrt{3}}{2}\right)$

6. (a) $\cos^{-1}\left(\frac{\sqrt{2}}{2}\right)$ (b) $\cos^{-1} 1$ (c) $\cos^{-1}\left(-\frac{\sqrt{2}}{2}\right)$

7. (a) $\tan^{-1}(-1)$ (b) $\tan^{-1} \sqrt{3}$ (c) $\tan^{-1} \frac{\sqrt{3}}{3}$

8. (a) $\tan^{-1} 0$ (b) $\tan^{-1}(-\sqrt{3})$ (c) $\tan^{-1}\left(-\frac{\sqrt{3}}{3}\right)$

9. (a) $\cos^{-1}(-\frac{1}{2})$ (b) $\sin^{-1}\left(-\frac{\sqrt{2}}{2}\right)$ (c) $\tan^{-1} 1$

10. (a) $\cos^{-1} 0$ (b) $\sin^{-1} 0$ (c) $\sin^{-1}(-\frac{1}{2})$

11–22 ■ Use a calculator to find an approximate value of each expression correct to five decimal places, if it is defined.

11. $\sin^{-1} \frac{2}{3}$ 12. $\sin^{-1}(-\frac{8}{9})$

13. $\cos^{-1}(-\frac{3}{7})$ 14. $\cos^{-1}(\frac{4}{9})$

15. $\cos^{-1}(-0.92761)$ 16. $\sin^{-1}(0.13844)$

17. $\tan^{-1} 10$ 18. $\tan^{-1}(-26)$

19. $\tan^{-1}(1.23456)$ 20. $\cos^{-1}(1.23456)$

21. $\sin^{-1}(-0.25713)$ 22. $\tan^{-1}(-0.25713)$

DRILL QUESTION

Compute $\sin^{-1}\left(-\frac{1}{2}\right)$ and $\cos^{-1}\left(\frac{\sqrt{3}}{2}\right)$.

Answer

$-\frac{\pi}{6}, \frac{\pi}{6}$

23–44 ■ Find the exact value of the expression, if it is defined.

23. $\sin\left(\sin^{-1}\frac{1}{4}\right)$

24. $\cos\left(\cos^{-1}\frac{2}{3}\right)$

25. $\tan(\tan^{-1} 5)$

26. $\sin(\sin^{-1} 5)$

27. $\sin\left(\sin^{-1}\left(\frac{3}{2}\right)\right)$

28. $\tan\left(\tan^{-1}\left(\frac{3}{2}\right)\right)$

29. $\cos^{-1}\left(\cos\frac{5\pi}{6}\right)$

30. $\tan^{-1}\left(\tan\left(\frac{\pi}{4}\right)\right)$

31. $\sin^{-1}\left(\sin\left(-\frac{\pi}{6}\right)\right)$

32. $\tan^{-1}\left(\tan\left(-\frac{\pi}{4}\right)\right)$

33. $\sin^{-1}\left(\sin\left(\frac{5\pi}{6}\right)\right)$

34. $\cos^{-1}\left(\cos\left(-\frac{\pi}{6}\right)\right)$

35. $\cos^{-1}\left(\cos\left(\frac{17\pi}{6}\right)\right)$

36. $\tan^{-1}\left(\tan\left(\frac{4\pi}{3}\right)\right)$

37. $\tan^{-1}\left(\tan\left(\frac{2\pi}{3}\right)\right)$

38. $\sin^{-1}\left(\sin\left(\frac{11\pi}{4}\right)\right)$

39. $\tan(\sin^{-1}\frac{1}{2})$

40. $\cos(\sin^{-1} 0)$

41. $\cos\left(\sin^{-1}\frac{\sqrt{3}}{2}\right)$

42. $\tan\left(\sin^{-1}\frac{\sqrt{2}}{2}\right)$

43. $\sin(\tan^{-1}(-1))$

44. $\sin(\tan^{-1}(-\sqrt{3}))$

DISCOVERY ■ DISCUSSION ■ WRITING

45. Two Different Compositions Let f and g be the functions

$$f(x) = \sin(\sin^{-1} x)$$

and

$$g(x) = \sin^{-1}(\sin x)$$

By the cancellation properties, $f(x) = x$ and $g(x) = x$ for suitable values of x. But these functions are not the same for all x. Graph both f and g to show how the functions differ. (Think carefully about the domain and range of $\sin^{-1}$).

46–47 ■ **Graphing Inverse Trigonometric Functions**
(a) Graph the function and make a conjecture, and **(b)** prove that your conjecture is true.

46. $y = \sin^{-1} x + \cos^{-1} x$

47. $y = \tan^{-1} x + \tan^{-1}\frac{1}{x}$

SUGGESTED TIME AND EMPHASIS

1 class, optional material

5.6 MODELING HARMONIC MOTION

| Simple Harmonic Motion ▶ Damped Harmonic Motion

Periodic behavior—behavior that repeats over and over again—is common in nature. Perhaps the most familiar example is the daily rising and setting of the sun, which results in the repetitive pattern of day, night, day, night, ... Another example is the daily variation of tide levels at the beach, which results in the repetitive pattern of high tide, low tide, high tide, low tide, ... Certain animal populations increase and decrease in a predictable periodic pattern: A large population exhausts the food supply, which causes the population to dwindle; this in turn results in a more plentiful food supply, which makes it possible for the population to increase; and the pattern then repeats over and over (see the Discovery Project *Predator/Prey Models* referenced on page 398).

Other common examples of periodic behavior involve motion that is caused by vibration or oscillation. A mass suspended from a spring that has been compressed and then allowed to vibrate vertically is a simple example. This "back and forth" motion also occurs in such diverse phenomena as sound waves, light waves, alternating electrical current, and pulsating stars, to name a few. In this section we consider the problem of modeling periodic behavior.

▼ Simple Harmonic Motion

The trigonometric functions are ideally suited for modeling periodic behavior. A glance at the graphs of the sine and cosine functions, for instance, tells us that these functions themselves exhibit periodic behavior. Figure 1 shows the graph of $y = \sin t$. If we think of

TEXT QUESTION

What is the relationship between the period of a harmonic function and its frequency?

Answer

They are reciprocals.

t as time, we see that as time goes on, $y = \sin t$ increases and decreases over and over again. Figure 2 shows that the motion of a vibrating mass on a spring is modeled very accurately by $y = \sin t$.

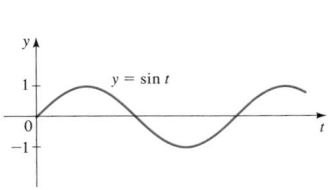

FIGURE 1 $y = \sin t$

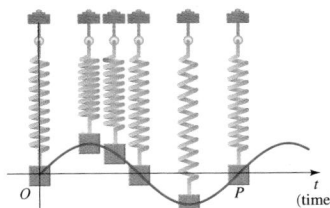

FIGURE 2   Motion of a vibrating spring is modeled by $y = \sin t$.

Notice that the mass returns to its original position over and over again. A **cycle** is one complete vibration of an object, so the mass in Figure 2 completes one cycle of its motion between *O* and *P*. Our observations about how the sine and cosine functions model periodic behavior are summarized in the following box.

The main difference between the two equations describing simple harmonic motion is the starting point. At $t = 0$ we get

$$y = a \sin \omega \cdot 0 = 0$$
$$y = a \cos \omega \cdot 0 = a$$

In the first case the motion "starts" with zero displacement, whereas in the second case the motion "starts" with the displacement at maximum (at the amplitude *a*).

The symbol ω is the lowercase Greek letter "omega," and ν is the letter "nu."

SIMPLE HARMONIC MOTION

If the equation describing the displacement *y* of an object at time *t* is

$$y = a \sin \omega t \qquad \text{or} \qquad y = a \cos \omega t$$

then the object is in **simple harmonic motion**. In this case,

amplitude $= |a|$ Maximum displacement of the object

period $= \dfrac{2\pi}{\omega}$ Time required to complete one cycle

frequency $= \dfrac{\omega}{2\pi}$ Number of cycles per unit of time

---

Notice that the functions

$$y = a \sin 2\pi\nu t \qquad \text{and} \qquad y = a \cos 2\pi\nu t$$

have frequency ν, because $2\pi\nu/(2\pi) = \nu$. Since we can immediately read the frequency from these equations, we often write equations of simple harmonic motion in this form.

EXAMPLE 1 | A Vibrating Spring

Rest position

FIGURE 3

The displacement of a mass suspended by a spring is modeled by the function

$$y = 10 \sin 4\pi t$$

where *y* is measured in inches and *t* in seconds (see Figure 3).

(a) Find the amplitude, period, and frequency of the motion of the mass.

(b) Sketch a graph of the displacement of the mass.

ALTERNATE EXAMPLE 1

The displacement of a mass suspended by a spring is modeled by the function $y = 5 \sin 2\pi t$, where *y* is measured in inches and *t* in seconds. Sketch the graph of the displacement of the mass.

ANSWER

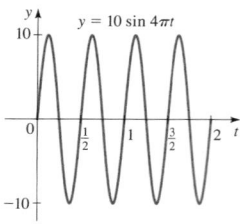

$y = 10 \sin 4\pi t$

FIGURE 4

SOLUTION

(a) From the formulas for amplitude, period, and frequency we get

$$\text{amplitude} = |a| = 10 \text{ in.}$$

$$\text{period} = \frac{2\pi}{\omega} = \frac{2\pi}{4\pi} = \frac{1}{2} \text{ s}$$

$$\text{frequency} = \frac{\omega}{2\pi} = \frac{4\pi}{2\pi} = 2 \text{ cycles per second (Hz)}$$

(b) The graph of the displacement of the mass at time t is shown in Figure 4.

✎ NOW TRY EXERCISE **3**

An important situation in which simple harmonic motion occurs is in the production of sound. Sound is produced by a regular variation in air pressure from the normal pressure. If the pressure varies in simple harmonic motion, then a pure sound is produced. The tone of the sound depends on the frequency, and the loudness depends on the amplitude.

EXAMPLE 2 | Vibrations of a Musical Note

A tuba player plays the note E and sustains the sound for some time. For a pure E the variation in pressure from normal air pressure is given by

$$V(t) = 0.2 \sin 80\pi t$$

where V is measured in pounds per square inch and t is measured in seconds.

(a) Find the amplitude, period, and frequency of V.

(b) Sketch a graph of V.

(c) If the tuba player increases the loudness of the note, how does the equation for V change?

(d) If the player is playing the note incorrectly and it is a little flat, how does the equation for V change?

SOLUTION

(a) From the formulas for amplitude, period, and frequency we get

$$\text{amplitude} = |0.2| = 0.2$$

$$\text{period} = \frac{2\pi}{80\pi} = \frac{1}{40}$$

$$\text{frequency} = \frac{80\pi}{2\pi} = 40$$

(b) The graph of V is shown in Figure 5.

(c) If the player increases the loudness the amplitude increases. So the number 0.2 is replaced by a larger number.

(d) If the note is flat, then the frequency is decreased. Thus, the coefficient of t is less than 80π.

✎ NOW TRY EXERCISE **29**

$y = 0.2 \sin 80\pi t$

FIGURE 5

EXAMPLE 3 | Modeling a Vibrating Spring

A mass is suspended from a spring. The spring is compressed a distance of 4 cm and then released. It is observed that the mass returns to the compressed position after $\frac{1}{3}$ s.

(a) Find a function that models the displacement of the mass.

(b) Sketch the graph of the displacement of the mass.

ALTERNATE EXAMPLE 2

A tuba player plays the note G and sustains the sound for some time. For a pure G, the variation in pressure from normal air pressure is given by $V(t) = 0.2 \sin 49\pi t$, where V is measured in pounds per square inch and t in seconds. Sketch a graph of V.

ANSWER

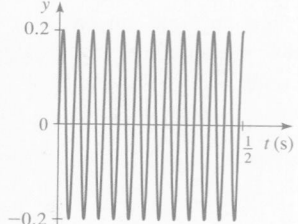

IN-CLASS MATERIALS

Demonstrate simple harmonic motion by bringing a spring (like a Slinky, or another kind of spring, perhaps with a weight attached at the end) and letting it oscillate. Notice how the graph of the height of the end of the spring versus time is a sine (or cosine) curve. Similarly, if you chart the height with respect to time of a point on a spinning disk whose axis is parallel to the floor, you will get a sine or cosine curve.

4 cm

Rest
position

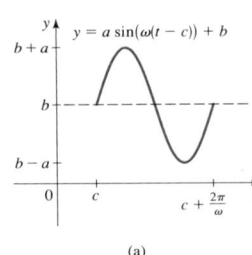

$y = 4 \cos 6\pi t$

FIGURE 6

SOLUTION

(a) The motion of the mass is given by one of the equations for simple harmonic motion. The amplitude of the motion is 4 cm. Since this amplitude is reached at time $t = 0$, an appropriate function that models the displacement is of the form

$$y = a \cos \omega t$$

Since the period is $p = \frac{1}{3}$, we can find ω from the following equation:

$$\text{period} = \frac{2\pi}{\omega}$$

$$\frac{1}{3} = \frac{2\pi}{\omega} \qquad \text{Period} = \tfrac{1}{3}$$

$$\omega = 6\pi \qquad \text{Solve for } \omega$$

So the motion of the mass is modeled by the function

$$y = 4 \cos 6\pi t$$

where y is the displacement from the rest position at time t. Notice that when $t = 0$, the displacement is $y = 4$, as we expect.

(b) The graph of the displacement of the mass at time t is shown in Figure 6.

✎ **NOW TRY EXERCISES 15 AND 35**

In general, the sine or cosine functions representing harmonic motion may be shifted horizontally or vertically. In this case, the equations take the form

$$y = a \sin(\omega(t - c)) + b \qquad \text{or} \qquad y = a \cos(\omega(t - c)) + b$$

The vertical shift b indicates that the variation occurs around an average value b. The horizontal shift c indicates the position of the object at $t = 0$. (See Figure 7.)

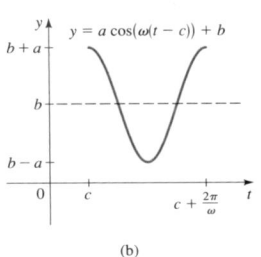

FIGURE 7   (a)   (b)

EXAMPLE 4 | Modeling the Brightness of a Variable Star

A variable star is one whose brightness alternately increases and decreases. For the variable star Delta Cephei, the time between periods of maximum brightness is 5.4 days. The average brightness (or magnitude) of the star is 4.0, and its brightness varies by ± 0.35 magnitude.

(a) Find a function that models the brightness of Delta Cephei as a function of time.

(b) Sketch a graph of the brightness of Delta Cephei as a function of time.

SOLUTION

(a) Let's find a function in the form

$$y = a\cos(\omega(t - c)) + b$$

The amplitude is the maximum variation from average brightness, so the amplitude is $a = 0.35$ magnitude. We are given that the period is 5.4 days, so

$$\omega = \frac{2\pi}{5.4} \approx 1.164$$

Since the brightness varies from an average value of 4.0 magnitudes, the graph is shifted upward by $b = 4.0$. If we take $t = 0$ to be a time when the star is at maximum brightness, there is no horizontal shift, so $c = 0$ (because a cosine curve achieves its maximum at $t = 0$). Thus, the function we want is

$$y = 0.35\cos(1.16t) + 4.0$$

where t is the number of days from a time when the star is at maximum brightness.

(b) The graph is sketched in Figure 8.

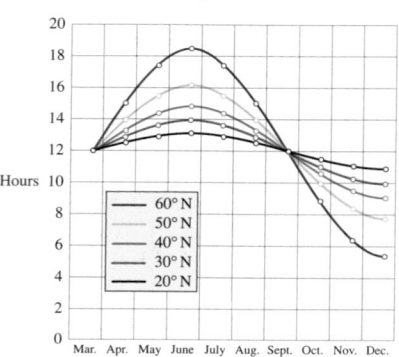

FIGURE 8

🔖 **NOW TRY EXERCISE 39** ∎

The number of hours of daylight varies throughout the course of a year. In the Northern Hemisphere, the longest day is June 21, and the shortest is December 21. The average length of daylight is 12 h, and the variation from this average depends on the latitude. (For example, Fairbanks, Alaska, experiences more than 20 h of daylight on the longest day and less than 4 h on the shortest day!) The graph in Figure 9 shows the number of hours of daylight at different times of the year for various latitudes. It's apparent from the graph that the variation in hours of daylight is simple harmonic.

FIGURE 9 Graph of the length of daylight from March 21 through December 21 at various latitudes

Source: Lucia C. Harrison, *Daylight, Twilight, Darkness and Time*
(New York: Silver, Burdett, 1935), page 40.

EXAMPLE 5 | Modeling the Number of Hours of Daylight

In Philadelphia (40° N latitude) the longest day of the year has 14 h 50 min of daylight, and the shortest day has 9 h 10 min of daylight.

(a) Find a function L that models the length of daylight as a function of t, the number of days from January 1.

(b) An astronomer needs at least 11 hours of darkness for a long exposure astronomical photograph. On what days of the year are such long exposures possible?

IN-CLASS MATERIALS
Musical instruments produce a basic sound, plus a series of overtones. We can think of the basic sound as a sine wave with a (relatively) large amplitude and the overtones as waves whose frequencies are rational multiples of the basic frequency and whose amplitudes are smaller. We add the sine curves together to get a sound wave that looks something like this:

SOLUTION

(a) We need to find a function in the form

$$y = a \sin(\omega(t - c)) + b$$

whose graph is the 40° N latitude curve in Figure 9. From the information given, we see that the amplitude is

$$a = \tfrac{1}{2}\left(14\tfrac{5}{6} - 9\tfrac{1}{6}\right) \approx 2.83 \text{ h}$$

Since there are 365 days in a year, the period is 365, so

$$\omega = \frac{2\pi}{365} \approx 0.0172$$

Since the average length of daylight is 12 h, the graph is shifted upward by 12, so $b = 12$. Since the curve attains the average value (12) on March 21, the 80th day of the year, the curve is shifted 80 units to the right. Thus, $c = 80$. So a function that models the number of hours of daylight is

$$y = 2.83 \sin(0.0172(t - 80)) + 12$$

where t is the number of days from January 1.

15   $t = 101$ $t = 241$

0   365

FIGURE 10

(b) A day has 24 h, so 11 h of night correspond to 13 h of daylight. So we need to solve the inequality $y \leq 13$. To solve this inequality graphically, we graph $y = 2.83 \sin 0.0172(t - 80) + 12$ and $y = 13$ on the same graph. From the graph in Figure 10 we see that there are fewer than 13 h of daylight between day 1 (January 1) and day 101 (April 11) and from day 241 (August 29) to day 365 (December 31).

✎. NOW TRY EXERCISE **41**   ■

Another situation in which simple harmonic motion occurs is in alternating current (AC) generators. Alternating current is produced when an armature rotates about its axis in a magnetic field.

Figure 11 represents a simple version of such a generator. As the wire passes through the magnetic field, a voltage E is generated in the wire. It can be shown that the voltage generated is given by

$$E(t) = E_0 \cos \omega t$$

where E_0 is the maximum voltage produced (which depends on the strength of the magnetic field) and $\omega/(2\pi)$ is the number of revolutions per second of the armature (the frequency).

Magnets

N   S

Wire

FIGURE 11

EXAMPLE 6 | Modeling Alternating Current

Ordinary 110-V household alternating current varies from +155 V to −155 V with a frequency of 60 Hz (cycles per second). Find an equation that describes this variation in voltage.

> Why do we say that household current is 110 V when the maximum voltage produced is 155 V? From the symmetry of the cosine function we see that the average voltage produced is zero. This average value would be the same for all AC generators and so gives no information about the voltage generated. To obtain a more informative measure of voltage, engineers use the **root-mean-square** (rms) method. It can be shown that the rms voltage is $1/\sqrt{2}$ times the maximum voltage. So for household current the rms voltage is
>
> $$155 \times \frac{1}{\sqrt{2}} \approx 110 \text{ V}$$

ALTERNATE EXAMPLE 6

An alternating current varies from +135 V to −135 V with a frequency of 70 Hz (cycles per second). Find an equation that describes this variation in voltage.
(*HINT:* Take $t = 0$ to be a time when the voltage is +135 V.)
The equation is

$E(t) = $ _____.

ANSWER
$E(t) = 135 \cos 140\pi t$

IN-CLASS MATERIALS

An easy way to graph a sine or cosine function given an amplitude and period (no phase shift) is to plot the zeros of one cycle, followed by the maximum and the minimum (between the zeros), and then draw the graph. This method also works with a phase shift, but is not as straightforward.

SOLUTION   The variation in voltage is simple harmonic. Since the frequency is 60 cycles per second, we have

$$\frac{\omega}{2\pi} = 60 \qquad \text{or} \qquad \omega = 120\pi$$

Let's take $t = 0$ to be a time when the voltage is $+155$ V. Then

$$E(t) = a \cos \omega t = 155 \cos 120\pi t$$

✎ NOW TRY EXERCISE **43**   ∎

▼ Damped Harmonic Motion

The spring in Figure 2 on page 413 is assumed to oscillate in a frictionless environment. In this hypothetical case the amplitude of the oscillation will not change. In the presence of friction, however, the motion of the spring eventually "dies down"; that is, the amplitude of the motion decreases with time. Motion of this type is called *damped harmonic motion.*

DAMPED HARMONIC MOTION

If the equation describing the displacement y of an object at time t is

$$y = ke^{-ct} \sin \omega t \qquad \text{or} \qquad y = ke^{-ct} \cos \omega t \qquad (c > 0)$$

then the object is in **damped harmonic motion**. The constant c is the **damping constant**, k is the initial amplitude, and $2\pi/\omega$ is the period.*

Damped harmonic motion is simply harmonic motion for which the amplitude is governed by the function $a(t) = ke^{-ct}$. Figure 12 shows the difference between harmonic motion and damped harmonic motion.

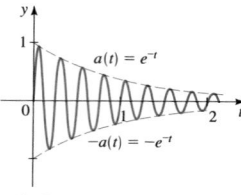

FIGURE 12   (a) Harmonic motion: $y = \sin 8\pi t$ (b) Damped harmonic motion:
                                                                        $y = e^{-t} \sin 8\pi t$

EXAMPLE 7 | Modeling Damped Harmonic Motion

Two mass-spring systems are experiencing damped harmonic motion, both at 0.5 cycles per second and both with an initial maximum displacement of 10 cm. The first has a damping constant of 0.5, and the second has a damping constant of 0.1.

(a) Find functions of the form $g(t) = ke^{-ct} \cos \omega t$ to model the motion in each case.

(b) Graph the two functions you found in part (a). How do they differ?

SOLUTION

Hz is the abbreviation for hertz. One hertz is one cycle per second.

(a) At time $t = 0$ the displacement is 10 cm. Thus, $g(0) = ke^{-c \cdot 0} \cos(\omega \cdot 0) = k$, so $k = 10$. Also, the frequency is $f = 0.5$ Hz, and since $\omega = 2\pi f$ (see page 413), we get $\omega = 2\pi(0.5) = \pi$. Using the given damping constants, we find that the motions of the two springs are given by the functions

$$g_1(t) = 10e^{-0.5t} \cos \pi t \qquad \text{and} \qquad g_2(t) = 10e^{-0.1t} \cos \pi t$$

---

*In the case of damped harmonic motion the term *quasi-period* is often used instead of *period* because the motion is not actually periodic—it diminishes with time. However, we will continue to use the term *period* to avoid confusion.

ALTERNATE EXAMPLE 7

Two mass-spring systems are experiencing damped harmonic motion with an initial maximum displacement of 10 cm. They both have damping constant 0.1. One is oscillating at 0.5 cycles per second, and the other is oscillating at 2 cycles per second.

(a) Find functions of the form $g(t) = ke^{-ct} \cos(\omega t)$ to model the motion in each case.

(b) Graph the two functions you found in part (a) and notice how they differ.

ANSWERS

(a) $g(t) = 10e^{-0.1t} \cos(\pi t)$ and
$g(t) = 10e^{-0.1t} \cos(4\pi t)$

(b)

IN-CLASS MATERIALS

Note that not all periodic functions are trigonometric functions. For example, mark a point on a car tire and plot its distance from the ground versus time as the car moves. The resulting graph is called a *cycloid* and looks like this:

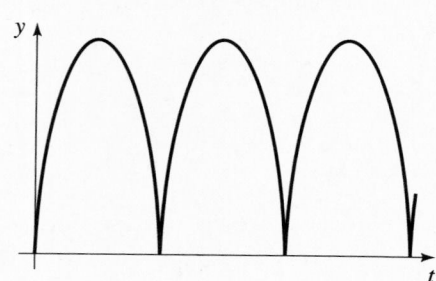

(b) The functions g_1 and g_2 are graphed in Figure 13. From the graphs we see that in the first case (where the damping constant is larger) the motion dies down quickly, whereas in the second case, perceptible motion continues much longer.

 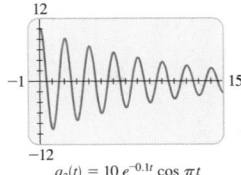

FIGURE 13

$g_1(t) = 10\,e^{-0.5t}\cos \pi t$ $g_2(t) = 10\,e^{-0.1t}\cos \pi t$

✎. NOW TRY EXERCISE **19**

As the preceding example indicates, the larger the damping constant c, the quicker the oscillation dies down. When a guitar string is plucked and then allowed to vibrate freely, a point on that string undergoes damped harmonic motion. We hear the damping of the motion as the sound produced by the vibration of the string fades. How fast the damping of the string occurs (as measured by the size of the constant c) is a property of the size of the string and the material it is made of. Another example of damped harmonic motion is the motion that a shock absorber on a car undergoes when the car hits a bump in the road. In this case the shock absorber is engineered to damp the motion as quickly as possible (large c) and to have the frequency as small as possible (small ω). On the other hand, the sound produced by a tuba player playing a note is undamped as long as the player can maintain the loudness of the note. The electromagnetic waves that produce light move in simple harmonic motion that is not damped.

EXAMPLE 8 | A Vibrating Violin String

The G-string on a violin is pulled a distance of 0.5 cm above its rest position, then released and allowed to vibrate. The damping constant c for this string is determined to be 1.4. Suppose that the note produced is a pure G (frequency = 200 Hz). Find an equation that describes the motion of the point at which the string was plucked.

SOLUTION   Let P be the point at which the string was plucked. We will find a function $f(t)$ that gives the distance at time t of the point P from its original rest position. Since the maximum displacement occurs at $t = 0$, we find an equation in the form

$$y = ke^{-ct}\cos \omega t$$

From this equation we see that $f(0) = k$. But we know that the original displacement of the string is 0.5 cm. Thus, $k = 0.5$. Since the frequency of the vibration is 200, we have $\omega = 2\pi f = 2\pi(200) = 400\pi$. Finally, since we know that the damping constant is 1.4, we get

$$f(t) = 0.5e^{-1.4t}\cos 400\pi t$$

✎. NOW TRY EXERCISE **45**

EXAMPLE 9 | Ripples on a Pond

A stone is dropped in a calm lake, causing waves to form. The up-and-down motion of a point on the surface of the water is modeled by damped harmonic motion. At some time the amplitude of the wave is measured, and 20 s later it is found that the amplitude has dropped to $\frac{1}{10}$ of this value. Find the damping constant c.

EXAMPLE

$$y = 4\sin\left[\pi\left(x - \frac{1}{4}\right)\right]$$

Period = 2, frequency = $\frac{1}{2}$, amplitude = 4

SOLUTION The amplitude is governed by the coefficient ke^{-ct} in the equations for damped harmonic motion. Thus, the amplitude at time t is ke^{-ct}, and 20 s later, it is $ke^{-c(t+20)}$. So, because the later value is $\frac{1}{10}$ the earlier value, we have

$$ke^{-c(t+20)} = \tfrac{1}{10}ke^{-ct}$$

We now solve this equation for c. Canceling k and using the Laws of Exponents, we get

$$e^{-ct} \cdot e^{-20c} = \tfrac{1}{10}e^{-ct}$$

$$e^{-20c} = \tfrac{1}{10} \qquad \text{Cancel } e^{-ct}$$

$$e^{20c} = 10 \qquad \text{Take reciprocals}$$

Taking the natural logarithm of each side gives

$$20c = \ln(10)$$

$$c = \tfrac{1}{20}\ln(10) \approx \tfrac{1}{20}(2.30) \approx 0.12$$

Thus, the damping constant is $c \approx 0.12$.

✎. **NOW TRY EXERCISE 47** ■

5.6 EXERCISES

CONCEPTS

1. For an object in simple harmonic motion with amplitude a and period $2\pi/\omega$, find an equation that models the displacement y at time t if

   (a) $y = 0$ at time $t = 0$: $y =$ _____.

   (b) $y = a$ at time $t = 0$: $y =$ _____.

2. For an object in damped harmonic motion with initial amplitude k, period $2\pi/\omega$, and damping constant c, find an equation that models the displacement y at time t if

   (a) $y = 0$ at time $t = 0$: $y =$ _____.

   (b) $y = a$ at time $t = 0$: $y =$ _____.

SKILLS

3–10 ■ The given function models the displacement of an object moving in simple harmonic motion.
(a) Find the amplitude, period, and frequency of the motion.
(b) Sketch a graph of the displacement of the object over one complete period.

✎. 3. $y = 2\sin 3t$ 4. $y = 3\cos \frac{1}{2}t$

5. $y = -\cos 0.3t$ 6. $y = 2.4\sin 3.6t$

7. $y = -0.25\cos\left(1.5t - \dfrac{\pi}{3}\right)$ 8. $y = -\frac{3}{2}\sin(0.2t + 1.4)$

9. $y = 5\cos(\frac{2}{3}t + \frac{3}{4})$ 10. $y = 1.6\sin(t - 1.8)$

11–14 ■ Find a function that models the simple harmonic motion having the given properties. Assume that the displacement is zero at time $t = 0$.

11. amplitude 10 cm, period 3 s

12. amplitude 24 ft, period 2 min

13. amplitude 6 in., frequency $5/\pi$ Hz

14. amplitude 1.2 m, frequency 0.5 Hz

15–18 ■ Find a function that models the simple harmonic motion having the given properties. Assume that the displacement is at its maximum at time $t = 0$.

✎. 15. amplitude 60 ft, period 0.5 min

16. amplitude 35 cm, period 8 s

17. amplitude 2.4 m, frequency 750 Hz

18. amplitude 6.25 in., frequency 60 Hz

19–26 ■ An initial amplitude k, damping constant c, and frequency f or period p are given. (Recall that frequency and period are related by the equation $f = 1/p$.)
(a) Find a function that models the damped harmonic motion. Use a function of the form $y = ke^{-ct}\cos \omega t$ in Exercises 19–22, and of the form $y = ke^{-ct}\sin \omega t$ in Exercises 23–26.
(b) Graph the function.

✎. 19. $k = 2$, $c = 1.5$, $f = 3$

20. $k = 15$, $c = 0.25$, $f = 0.6$

21. $k = 100$, $c = 0.05$, $p = 4$

22. $k = 0.75$, $c = 3$, $p = 3\pi$

23. $k = 7$, $c = 10$, $p = \pi/6$

24. $k = 1$, $c = 1$, $p = 1$

25. $k = 0.3$, $c = 0.2$, $f = 20$

26. $k = 12$, $c = 0.01$, $f = 8$

APPLICATIONS

27. A Bobbing Cork   A cork floating in a lake is bobbing in simple harmonic motion. Its displacement above the bottom of the lake is modeled by

$$y = 0.2 \cos 20\pi t + 8$$

where y is measured in meters and t is measured in minutes.
(a) Find the frequency of the motion of the cork.
(b) Sketch a graph of y.
(c) Find the maximum displacement of the cork above the lake bottom.

28. FM Radio Signals   The carrier wave for an FM radio signal is modeled by the function

$$y = a \sin(2\pi(9.15 \times 10^7)t)$$

where t is measured in seconds. Find the period and frequency of the carrier wave.

29. Blood Pressure   Each time your heart beats, your blood pressure increases, then decreases as the heart rests between beats. A certain person's blood pressure is modeled by the function

$$p(t) = 115 + 25 \sin(160\pi t)$$

where $p(t)$ is the pressure in mmHg at time t, measured in minutes.
(a) Find the amplitude, period, and frequency of p.
(b) Sketch a graph of p.
(c) If a person is exercising, his or her heart beats faster. How does this affect the period and frequency of p?

30. Predator Population Model   In a predator/prey model the predator population is modeled by the function

$$y = 900 \cos 2t + 8000$$

where t is measured in years.
(a) What is the maximum population?
(b) Find the length of time between successive periods of maximum population.

31. Spring–Mass System   A mass attached to a spring is moving up and down in simple harmonic motion. The graph gives its displacement $d(t)$ from equilibrium at time t. Express the function d in the form $d(t) = a \sin \omega t$.

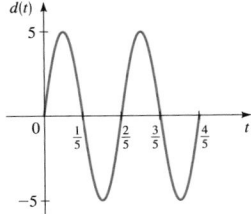

32. Tides   The graph shows the variation of the water level relative to mean sea level in Commencement Bay at Tacoma, Washington, for a particular 24-hour period. Assuming that this varia-

tion is modeled by simple harmonic motion, find an equation of the form $y = a \sin \omega t$ that describes the variation in water level as a function of the number of hours after midnight.

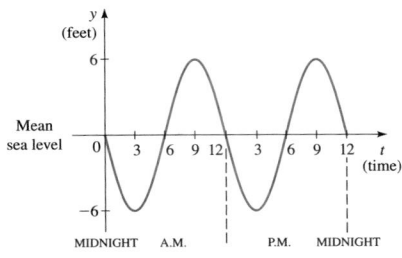

33. Tides   The Bay of Fundy in Nova Scotia has the highest tides in the world. In one 12-hour period the water starts at mean sea level, rises to 21 ft above, drops to 21 ft below, then returns to mean sea level. Assuming that the motion of the tides is simple harmonic, find an equation that describes the height of the tide in the Bay of Fundy above mean sea level. Sketch a graph that shows the level of the tides over a 12-hour period.

34. Spring–Mass System   A mass suspended from a spring is pulled down a distance of 2 ft from its rest position, as shown in the figure. The mass is released at time $t = 0$ and allowed to oscillate. If the mass returns to this position after 1 s, find an equation that describes its motion.

Rest position

2 ft

35. Spring–Mass System   A mass is suspended on a spring. The spring is compressed so that the mass is located 5 cm above its rest position. The mass is released at time $t = 0$ and allowed to oscillate. It is observed that the mass reaches its lowest point $\frac{1}{2}$ s after it is released. Find an equation that describes the motion of the mass.

36. Spring–Mass System   The frequency of oscillation of an object suspended on a spring depends on the stiffness k of the spring (called the *spring constant*) and the mass m of the object. If the spring is compressed a distance a and then allowed to oscillate, its displacement is given by

$$f(t) = a \cos \sqrt{k/m}\, t$$

(a) A 10-g mass is suspended from a spring with stiffness $k = 3$. If the spring is compressed a distance 5 cm and then released, find the equation that describes the oscillation of the spring.
(b) Find a general formula for the frequency (in terms of k and m).

(c) How is the frequency affected if the mass is increased? Is the oscillation faster or slower?

(d) How is the frequency affected if a stiffer spring is used (larger k)? Is the oscillation faster or slower?

37. Ferris Wheel A ferris wheel has a radius of 10 m, and the bottom of the wheel passes 1 m above the ground. If the ferris wheel makes one complete revolution every 20 s, find an equation that gives the height above the ground of a person on the ferris wheel as a function of time.

38. Clock Pendulum The pendulum in a grandfather clock makes one complete swing every 2 s. The maximum angle that the pendulum makes with respect to its rest position is 10°. We know from physical principles that the angle θ between the pendulum and its rest position changes in simple harmonic fashion. Find an equation that describes the size of the angle θ as a function of time. (Take $t = 0$ to be a time when the pendulum is vertical.)

39. Variable Stars The variable star Zeta Gemini has a period of 10 days. The average brightness of the star is 3.8 magnitudes, and the maximum variation from the average is 0.2 magnitude. Assuming that the variation in brightness is simple harmonic, find an equation that gives the brightness of the star as a function of time.

40. Variable Stars Astronomers believe that the radius of a variable star increases and decreases with the brightness of the star. The variable star Delta Cephei (Example 4) has an average radius of 20 million miles and changes by a maximum of 1.5 million miles from this average during a single pulsation. Find an equation that describes the radius of this star as a function of time.

41. Biological Clocks *Circadian rhythms* are biological processes that oscillate with a period of approximately 24 hours. That is, a circadian rhythm is an internal daily biological clock. Blood pressure appears to follow such a rhythm. For a certain individual the average resting blood pressure varies from a maximum of 100 mmHg at 2:00 P.M. to a minimum of 80 mmHg at 2:00 A.M. Find a sine function of the form

$$f(t) = a \sin(\omega(t - c)) + b$$

that models the blood pressure at time t, measured in hours from midnight.

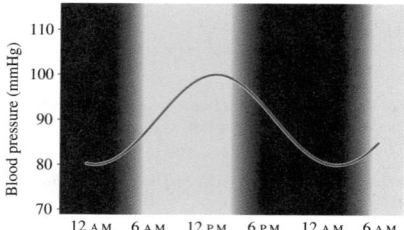

42. Electric Generator The armature in an electric generator is rotating at the rate of 100 revolutions per second (rps). If the maximum voltage produced is 310 V, find an equation that describes this variation in voltage. What is the rms voltage? (See Example 6 and the margin note adjacent to it.)

43. Electric Generator The graph shows an oscilloscope reading of the variation in voltage of an AC current produced by a simple generator.

(a) Find the maximum voltage produced.

(b) Find the frequency (cycles per second) of the generator.

(c) How many revolutions per second does the armature in the generator make?

(d) Find a formula that describes the variation in voltage as a function of time.

44. Doppler Effect When a car with its horn blowing drives by an observer, the pitch of the horn seems higher as it approaches and lower as it recedes (see the figure on the next page). This phenomenon is called the **Doppler effect**. If the sound source is moving at speed v relative to the observer and if the speed of sound is v_0, then the perceived frequency f is related to the actual frequency f_0 as follows:

$$f = f_0\left(\frac{v_0}{v_0 \pm v}\right)$$

We choose the minus sign if the source is moving toward the observer and the plus sign if it is moving away.

Suppose that a car drives at 110 ft/s past a woman standing on the shoulder of a highway, blowing its horn, which has a frequency of 500 Hz. Assume that the speed of sound is 1130 ft/s. (This is the speed in dry air at 70°F.)

(a) What are the frequencies of the sounds that the woman hears as the car approaches her and as it moves away from her?

(b) Let A be the amplitude of the sound. Find functions of the form

$$y = A \sin \omega t$$

that model the perceived sound as the car approaches the woman and as it recedes.

45. Motion of a Building A strong gust of wind strikes a tall building, causing it to sway back and forth in damped harmonic motion. The frequency of the oscillation is 0.5 cycle per second, and the damping constant is $c = 0.9$. Find an equation that describes the motion of the building. (Assume that $k = 1$, and take $t = 0$ to be the instant when the gust of wind strikes the building.)

46. Shock Absorber When a car hits a certain bump on the road, a shock absorber on the car is compressed a distance of 6 in., then released (see the figure). The shock absorber vibrates in damped harmonic motion with a frequency of 2 cycles per second. The damping constant for this particular shock absorber is 2.8.

(a) Find an equation that describes the displacement of the shock absorber from its rest position as a function of time. Take $t = 0$ to be the instant that the shock absorber is released.

(b) How long does it take for the amplitude of the vibration to decrease to 0.5 in?

47. Tuning Fork A tuning fork is struck and oscillates in damped harmonic motion. The amplitude of the motion is measured, and 3 s later it is found that the amplitude has dropped to $\frac{1}{4}$ of this value. Find the damping constant c for this tuning fork.

48. Guitar String A guitar string is pulled at point P a distance of 3 cm above its rest position. It is then released and vibrates in damped harmonic motion with a frequency of 165 cycles per second. After 2 s, it is observed that the amplitude of the vibration at point P is 0.6 cm.

(a) Find the damping constant c.

(b) Find an equation that describes the position of point P above its rest position as a function of time. Take $t = 0$ to be the instant that the string is released.

CHAPTER 5 | REVIEW

■ CONCEPT CHECK

1. (a) What is the unit circle?

(b) Use a diagram to explain what is meant by the terminal point determined by a real number t.

(c) What is the reference number $\bar{t}$ associated with t?

(d) If t is a real number and $P(x, y)$ is the terminal point determined by t, write equations that define $\sin t$, $\cos t$, $\tan t$, $\cot t$, $\sec t$, and $\csc t$.

(e) What are the domains of the six functions that you defined in part (d)?

(f) Which trigonometric functions are positive in Quadrants I, II, III, and IV?

2. (a) What is an even function?

(b) Which trigonometric functions are even?

(c) What is an odd function?

(d) Which trigonometric functions are odd?

3. (a) State the reciprocal identities.

(b) State the Pythagorean identities.

4. (a) What is a periodic function?

(b) What are the periods of the six trigonometric functions?

5. Graph the sine and cosine functions. How is the graph of cosine related to the graph of sine?

6. Write expressions for the amplitude, period, and phase shift of the sine curve $y = a \sin k(x - b)$ and the cosine curve $y = a \cos k(x - b)$.

7. (a) Graph the tangent and cotangent functions.

(b) State the periods of the tangent curve $y = a \tan kx$ and the cotangent curve $y = a \cot kx$.

8. (a) Graph the secant and cosecant functions.

(b) State the periods of the secant curve $y = a \sec kx$ and the cosecant curve $y = a \csc kx$.

9. (a) Define the inverse sine function $\sin^{-1}$. What are its domain and range?

(b) For what values of x is the equation $\sin(\sin^{-1} x) = x$ true?

(c) For what values of x is the equation $\sin^{-1}(\sin x) = x$ true?

10. (a) Define the inverse cosine function $\cos^{-1}$. What are its domain and range?
(b) For what values of x is the equation $\cos(\cos^{-1} x) = x$ true?
(c) For what values of x is the equation $\cos^{-1}(\cos x) = x$ true?

11. (a) Define the inverse tangent function $\tan^{-1}$. What are its domain and range?

(b) For what values of x is the equation $\tan(\tan^{-1} x) = x$ true?
(c) For what values of x is the equation $\tan^{-1}(\tan x) = x$ true?

12. (a) What is simple harmonic motion?
(b) What is damped harmonic motion?
(c) Give three real-life examples of simple harmonic motion and of damped harmonic motion.

■ EXERCISES

1–2 ■ A point $P(x, y)$ is given.
(a) Show that P is on the unit circle.
(b) Suppose that P is the terminal point determined by t. Find $\sin t$, $\cos t$, and $\tan t$.

1. $P\left(-\dfrac{\sqrt{3}}{2}, \dfrac{1}{2}\right)$　　　　**2.** $P\left(\dfrac{3}{5}, -\dfrac{4}{5}\right)$

3–6 ■ A real number t is given.
(a) Find the reference number for t.
(b) Find the terminal point $P(x, y)$ on the unit circle determined by t.
(c) Find the six trigonometric functions of t.

3. $t = \dfrac{2\pi}{3}$　　　　**4.** $t = \dfrac{5\pi}{3}$

5. $t = -\dfrac{11\pi}{4}$　　　　**6.** $t = -\dfrac{7\pi}{6}$

7–16 ■ Find the value of the trigonometric function. If possible, give the exact value; otherwise, use a calculator to find an approximate value correct to five decimal places.

7. (a) $\sin \dfrac{3\pi}{4}$　　　　**(b)** $\cos \dfrac{3\pi}{4}$

8. (a) $\tan \dfrac{\pi}{3}$　　　　**(b)** $\tan\left(-\dfrac{\pi}{3}\right)$

9. (a) $\sin 1.1$　　　　**(b)** $\cos 1.1$

10. (a) $\cos \dfrac{\pi}{5}$　　　　**(b)** $\cos\left(-\dfrac{\pi}{5}\right)$

11. (a) $\cos \dfrac{9\pi}{2}$　　　　**(b)** $\sec \dfrac{9\pi}{2}$

12. (a) $\sin \dfrac{\pi}{7}$　　　　**(b)** $\csc \dfrac{\pi}{7}$

13. (a) $\tan \dfrac{5\pi}{2}$　　　　**(b)** $\cot \dfrac{5\pi}{2}$

14. (a) $\sin 2\pi$　　　　**(b)** $\csc 2\pi$

15. (a) $\tan \dfrac{5\pi}{6}$　　　　**(b)** $\cot \dfrac{5\pi}{6}$

16. (a) $\cos \dfrac{\pi}{3}$　　　　**(b)** $\sin \dfrac{\pi}{6}$

17–20 ■ Use the fundamental identities to write the first expression in terms of the second.

17. $\dfrac{\tan t}{\cos t}$, $\sin t$　　　　**18.** $\tan^2 t \sec t$, $\cos t$

19. $\tan t$, $\sin t$; t in Quadrant IV

20. $\sec t$, $\sin t$; t in Quadrant II

21–24 ■ Find the values of the remaining trigonometric functions at t from the given information.

21. $\sin t = \frac{5}{13}$, $\cos t = -\frac{12}{13}$

22. $\sin t = -\frac{1}{2}$, $\cos t > 0$

23. $\cot t = -\frac{1}{2}$, $\csc t = \sqrt{5}/2$

24. $\cos t = -\frac{3}{5}$, $\tan t < 0$

25. If $\tan t = \frac{1}{4}$ and the terminal point for t is in Quadrant III, find $\sec t + \cot t$.

26. If $\sin t = -\frac{8}{17}$ and the terminal point for t is in Quadrant IV, find $\csc t + \sec t$.

27. If $\cos t = \frac{3}{5}$ and the terminal point for t is in Quadrant I, find $\tan t + \sec t$.

28. If $\sec t = -5$ and the terminal point for t is in Quadrant II, find $\sin^2 t + \cos^2 t$.

29–36 ■ A trigonometric function is given.
(a) Find the amplitude, period, and phase shift of the function.
(b) Sketch the graph.

29. $y = 10 \cos \frac{1}{2} x$　　　　**30.** $y = 4 \sin 2\pi x$

31. $y = -\sin \frac{1}{2} x$　　　　**32.** $y = 2 \sin\left(x - \dfrac{\pi}{4}\right)$

33. $y = 3 \sin(2x - 2)$　　　　**34.** $y = \cos 2\left(x - \dfrac{\pi}{2}\right)$

35. $y = -\cos\left(\dfrac{\pi}{2} x + \dfrac{\pi}{6}\right)$　　　　**36.** $y = 10 \sin\left(2x - \dfrac{\pi}{2}\right)$

37–40 ■ The graph of one period of a function of the form $y = a \sin k(x - b)$ or $y = a \cos k(x - b)$ is shown. Determine the function.

37.

38.

39.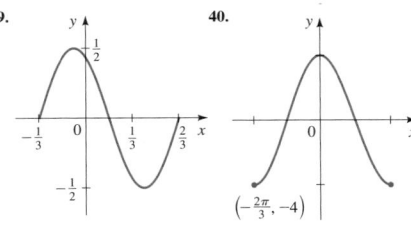

40.

41–48 ■ Find the period, and sketch the graph.

41. $y = 3 \tan x$

42. $y = \tan \pi x$

43. $y = 2 \cot\left(x - \dfrac{\pi}{2}\right)$

44. $y = \sec\left(\dfrac{1}{2}x - \dfrac{\pi}{2}\right)$

45. $y = 4 \csc(2x + \pi)$

46. $y = \tan\left(x + \dfrac{\pi}{6}\right)$

47. $y = \tan\left(\dfrac{1}{2}x - \dfrac{\pi}{8}\right)$

48. $y = -4 \sec 4\pi x$

49–52 ■ Find the exact value of each expression, if it is defined.

49. $\sin^{-1} 1$

50. $\cos^{-1}\left(-\dfrac{1}{2}\right)$

51. $\sin^{-1}\left(\sin \dfrac{13\pi}{6}\right)$

52. $\tan\left(\cos^{-1}\left(\frac{1}{2}\right)\right)$

53–58 ■ A function is given.
(a) Use a graphing device to graph the function.
(b) Determine from the graph whether the function is periodic and, if so, determine the period.
(c) Determine from the graph whether the function is odd, even, or neither.

53. $y = |\cos x|$

54. $y = \sin(\cos x)$

55. $y = \cos(2^{0.1x})$

56. $y = 1 + 2^{\cos x}$

57. $y = |x| \cos 3x$

58. $y = \sqrt{x} \sin 3x \quad (x > 0)$

59–62 ■ Graph the three functions on a common screen. How are the graphs related?

59. $y = x, \quad y = -x, \quad y = x \sin x$

60. $y = 2^{-x}, \quad y = -2^{-x}, \quad y = 2^{-x} \cos 4\pi x$

61. $y = x, \quad y = \sin 4x, \quad y = x + \sin 4x$

62. $y = \sin^2 x, \quad y = \cos^2 x, \quad y = \sin^2 x + \cos^2 x$

63–64 ■ Find the maximum and minimum values of the function.

63. $y = \cos x + \sin 2x$

64. $y = \cos x + \sin^2 x$

65. Find the solutions of $\sin x = 0.3$ in the interval $[0, 2\pi]$.

66. Find the solutions of $\cos 3x = x$ in the interval $[0, \pi]$.

67. Let $f(x) = \dfrac{\sin^2 x}{x}$.
(a) Is the function f even, odd, or neither?
(b) Find the x-intercepts of the graph of f.
(c) Graph f in an appropriate viewing rectangle.
(d) Describe the behavior of the function as x becomes large.
(e) Notice that $f(x)$ is not defined when $x = 0$. What happens as x approaches 0?

68. Let $y_1 = \cos(\sin x)$ and $y_2 = \sin(\cos x)$.
(a) Graph y_1 and y_2 in the same viewing rectangle.
(b) Determine the period of each of these functions from its graph.
(c) Find an inequality between $\sin(\cos x)$ and $\cos(\sin x)$ that is valid for all x.

69. A point P moving in simple harmonic motion completes 8 cycles every second. If the amplitude of the motion is 50 cm, find an equation that describes the motion of P as a function of time. Assume that the point P is at its maximum displacement when $t = 0$.

70. A mass suspended from a spring oscillates in simple harmonic motion at a frequency of 4 cycles per second. The distance from the highest to the lowest point of the oscillation is 100 cm. Find an equation that describes the distance of the mass from its rest position as a function of time. Assume that the mass is at its lowest point when $t = 0$.

71. The graph shows the variation of the water level relative to mean sea level in the Long Beach harbor for a particular 24-hour period. Assuming that this variation is simple harmonic, find an equation of the form $y = a \cos \omega t$ that describes the variation in water level as a function of the number of hours after midnight.

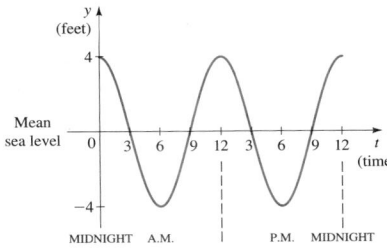

72. The top floor of a building undergoes damped harmonic motion after a sudden brief earthquake. At time $t = 0$ the displacement is at a maximum, 16 cm from the normal position. The damping constant is $c = 0.72$ and the building vibrates at 1.4 cycles per second.
(a) Find a function of the form $y = ke^{-ct} \cos \omega t$ to model the motion.
(b) Graph the function you found in part (a).
(c) What is the displacement at time $t = 10$ s?

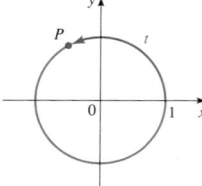

1. The point $P(x, y)$ is on the unit circle in Quadrant IV. If $x = \sqrt{11}/6$, find y.

2. The point P in the figure at the left has y-coordinate $\frac{4}{5}$. Find:
   (a) $\sin t$ (b) $\cos t$
   (c) $\tan t$ (d) $\sec t$

3. Find the exact value.
   (a) $\sin \dfrac{7\pi}{6}$ (b) $\cos \dfrac{13\pi}{4}$
   (c) $\tan\left(-\dfrac{5\pi}{3}\right)$ (d) $\csc \dfrac{3\pi}{2}$

4. Express $\tan t$ in terms of $\sin t$, if the terminal point determined by t is in Quadrant II.

5. If $\cos t = -\frac{8}{17}$ and if the terminal point determined by t is in Quadrant III, find $\tan t \cot t + \csc t$.

6–7 ■ A trigonometric function is given.
   (a) Find the amplitude, period, and phase shift of the function.
   (b) Sketch the graph.

6. $y = -5 \cos 4x$ 7. $y = 2 \sin\left(\dfrac{1}{2}x - \dfrac{\pi}{6}\right)$

8–9 ■ Find the period, and graph the function.

8. $y = -\csc 2x$ 9. $y = \tan\left(2x - \dfrac{\pi}{2}\right)$

10. Find the exact value of each expression, if it is defined.
    (a) $\tan^{-1} 1$ (b) $\cos^{-1}\left(-\dfrac{\sqrt{3}}{2}\right)$
    (c) $\tan^{-1}(\tan 3\pi)$ (d) $\cos(\tan^{-1}(-\sqrt{3}))$

11. The graph shown at left is one period of a function of the form $y = a \sin k(x - b)$. Determine the function.

 12. Let $f(x) = \dfrac{\cos x}{1 + x^2}$.
    (a) Use a graphing device to graph f in an appropriate viewing rectangle.
    (b) Determine from the graph if f is even, odd, or neither.
    (c) Find the minimum and maximum values of f.

13. A mass suspended from a spring oscillates in simple harmonic motion. The mass completes 2 cycles every second, and the distance between the highest point and the lowest point of the oscillation is 10 cm. Find an equation of the form $y = a \sin \omega t$ that gives the distance of the mass from its rest position as a function of time.

14. An object is moving up and down in damped harmonic motion. Its displacement at time $t = 0$ is 16 in; this is its maximum displacement. The damping constant is $c = 0.1$, and the frequency is 12 Hz.
    (a) Find a function that models this motion.
    (b) Graph the function.

Fitting Sinusoidal Curves to Data

In previous *Focus on Modeling* sections, we learned how to fit linear, polynomial, exponential, and power models to data. Figure 1 shows some scatter plots of data. The scatter plots can help guide us in choosing an appropriate model. (Try to determine what type of function would best model the data in each graph.) If the scatter plot indicates simple harmonic motion, then we might try to model the data with a sine or cosine function. The next example illustrates this process.

FIGURE 1

EXAMPLE 1 | Modeling the Height of a Tide

The water depth in a narrow channel varies with the tides. Table 1 shows the water depth over a 12-hour period.

(a) Make a scatter plot of the water depth data.

(b) Find a function that models the water depth with respect to time.

(c) If a boat needs at least 11 ft of water to cross the channel, during which times can it safely do so?

TABLE 1

Time	Depth (ft)
12:00 A.M.	9.8
1:00 A.M.	11.4
2:00 A.M.	11.6
3:00 A.M.	11.2
4:00 A.M.	9.6
5:00 A.M.	8.5
6:00 A.M.	6.5
7:00 A.M.	5.7
8:00 A.M.	5.4
9:00 A.M.	6.0
10:00 A.M.	7.0
11:00 A.M.	8.6
12:00 P.M.	10.0

SOLUTION

(a) A scatter plot of the data is shown in Figure 2.

FIGURE 2

427

FIGURE 3

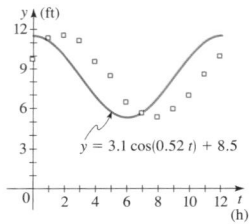

(b) The data appear to lie on a cosine (or sine) curve. But if we graph $y = \cos t$ on the same graph as the scatter plot, the result in Figure 3 is not even close to the data. To fit the data, we need to adjust the vertical shift, amplitude, period, and phase shift of the cosine curve. In other words, we need to find a function of the form

$$y = a\cos(\omega(t - c)) + b$$

We use the following steps, which are illustrated by the graphs in the margin.

▶ **Adjust the Vertical Shift**

The vertical shift b is the average of the maximum and minimum values:

$$b = \text{vertical shift}$$

$$= \frac{1}{2} \cdot (\text{maximum value} + \text{minimum value})$$

$$= \frac{1}{2}(11.6 + 5.4) = 8.5$$

▶ **Adjust the Amplitude**

The amplitude a is half of the difference between the maximum and minimum values:

$$a = \text{amplitude}$$

$$= \frac{1}{2} \cdot (\text{maximum value} - \text{minimum value})$$

$$= \frac{1}{2}(11.6 - 5.4) = 3.1$$

▶ **Adjust the Period**

The time between consecutive maximum and minimum values is half of one period. Thus

$$\frac{2\pi}{\omega} = \text{period}$$

$$= 2 \cdot (\text{time of maximum value} - \text{time of minimum value})$$

$$= 2(8 - 2) = 12$$

Thus, $\omega = 2\pi/12 = 0.52$.

▶ **Adjust the Horizontal Shift**

Since the maximum value of the data occurs at approximately $t = 2.0$, it represents a cosine curve shifted 2 h to the right. So

$$c = \text{phase shift}$$

$$= \text{time of maximum value}$$

$$= 2.0$$

▶ **The Model**

We have shown that a function that models the tides over the given time period is given by

$$y = 3.1\cos(0.52(t - 2.0)) + 8.5$$

A graph of the function and the scatter plot are shown in Figure 4. It appears that the model we found is a good approximation to the data.

(c) We need to solve the inequality $y \geq 11$. We solve this inequality graphically by graphing $y = 3.1 \cos 0.52(t - 2.0) + 8.5$ and $y = 11$ on the same graph. From the graph in Figure 5 we see the water depth is higher than 11 ft between $t \approx 0.8$ and $t \approx 3.2$. This corresponds to the times 12:48 A.M. to 3:12 A.M.

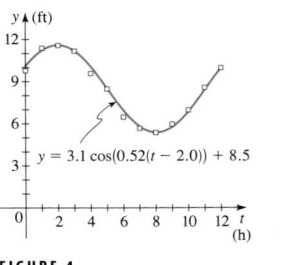

FIGURE 4

FIGURE 5

In Example 1 we used the scatter plot to guide us in finding a cosine curve that gives an approximate model of the data. Some graphing calculators are capable of finding a sine or cosine curve that best fits a given set of data points. The method these calculators use is similar to the method of finding a line of best fit, as explained on page 131.

For the TI-83 and TI-86 the command SinReg (for sine regression) finds the sine curve that best fits the given data.

EXAMPLE 2 │ Fitting a Sine Curve to Data

(a) Use a graphing device to find the sine curve that best fits the depth of water data in Table 1 on page 427.

(b) Compare your result to the model found in Example 1.

SOLUTION

(a) Using the data in Table 1 and the SinReg command on the TI-83 calculator, we get a function of the form

$$y = a \sin(bt + c) + d$$

where

$$a = 3.1 \qquad b = 0.53$$
$$c = 0.55 \qquad d = 8.42$$

So the sine function that best fits the data is

$$y = 3.1 \sin(0.53t + 0.55) + 8.42$$

```
SinReg
y=a*sin(bx+c)+d
a=3.097877596
b=.5268322697
c=.5493035195
d=8.424021899
```

Output of the SinReg function on the TI-83.

(b) To compare this with the function in Example 1, we change the sine function to a cosine function by using the reduction formula $\sin u = \cos(u - \pi/2)$.

$$y = 3.1 \sin(0.53t + 0.55) + 8.42$$

$$= 3.1 \cos\left(0.53t + 0.55 - \frac{\pi}{2}\right) + 8.42 \qquad \text{Reduction formula}$$

$$= 3.1 \cos(0.53t - 1.02) + 8.42$$

$$= 3.1 \cos(0.53(t - 1.92)) + 8.42 \qquad \text{Factor 0.53}$$

Comparing this with the function we obtained in Example 1, we see that there are small differences in the coefficients. In Figure 6 we graph a scatter plot of the data together with the sine function of best fit.

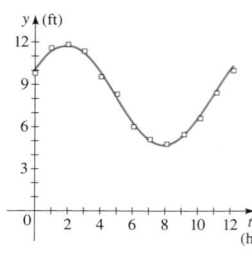

FIGURE 6

In Example 1 we estimated the values of the amplitude, period, and shifts from the data. In Example 2 the calculator computed the sine curve that best fits the data (that is, the curve that deviates least from the data as explained on page 131). The different ways of obtaining the model account for the differences in the functions.

PROBLEMS

1–4 ■ Modeling Periodic Data   A set of data is given.

(a) Make a scatter plot of the data.

(b) Find a cosine function of the form $y = a\cos(\omega(t - c)) + b$ that models the data, as in Example 1.

(c) Graph the function you found in part (b) together with the scatter plot. How well does the curve fit the data?

(d) Use a graphing calculator to find the sine function that best fits the data, as in Example 2.

(e) Compare the functions you found in parts (b) and (d). [Use the reduction formula $\sin u = \cos(u - \pi/2)$.]

1.

t	y
0	2.1
2	1.1
4	−0.8
6	−2.1
8	−1.3
10	0.6
12	1.9
14	1.5

2.

t	y
0	190
25	175
50	155
75	125
100	110
125	95
150	105
175	120
200	140
225	165
250	185
275	200
300	195
325	185
350	165

3.

t	y
0.1	21.1
0.2	23.6
0.3	24.5
0.4	21.7
0.5	17.5
0.6	12.0
0.7	5.6
0.8	2.2
0.9	1.0
1.0	3.5
1.1	7.6
1.2	13.2
1.3	18.4
1.4	23.0
1.5	25.1

4.

t	y
0.0	0.56
0.5	0.45
1.0	0.29
1.5	0.13
2.0	0.05
2.5	−0.10
3.0	0.02
3.5	0.12
4.0	0.26
4.5	0.43
5.0	0.54
5.5	0.63
6.0	0.59

5. **Annual Temperature Change**   The table gives the average monthly temperature in Montgomery County, Maryland.

   (a) Make a scatter plot of the data.

   (b) Find a cosine curve that models the data (as in Example 1).

   (c) Graph the function you found in part (b) together with the scatter plot.

   (d) Use a graphing calculator to find the sine curve that best fits the data (as in Example 2).

Month	Average temperature (°F)	Month	Average temperature (°F)
January	40.0	July	85.8
February	43.1	August	83.9
March	54.6	September	76.9
April	64.2	October	66.8
May	73.8	November	55.5
June	81.8	December	44.5

6. **Circadian Rhythms**   Circadian rhythm (from the Latin *circa*—about, and *diem*—day) is the daily biological pattern by which body temperature, blood pressure, and other physiological variables change. The data in the table below show typical changes in human body temperature over a 24-hour period ($t = 0$ corresponds to midnight).

   (a) Make a scatter plot of the data.

   (b) Find a cosine curve that models the data (as in Example 1).

   (c) Graph the function you found in part (b) together with the scatter plot.

   (d) Use a graphing calculator to find the sine curve that best fits the data (as in Example 2).

Time	Body temperature (°C)	Time	Body temperature (°C)
0	36.8	14	37.3
2	36.7	16	37.4
4	36.6	18	37.3
6	36.7	20	37.2
8	36.8	22	37.0
10	37.0	24	36.8
12	37.2		

Year	Owl population
0	50
1	62
2	73
3	80
4	71
5	60
6	51
7	43
8	29
9	20
10	28
11	41
12	49

7. **Predator Population**   When two species interact in a predator/prey relationship, the populations of both species tend to vary in a sinusoidal fashion. (See the Discovery Project *Predator/Prey Models* referenced on page 398). In a certain midwestern county, the main food source for barn owls consists of field mice and other small mammals. The table gives the population of barn owls in this county every July 1 over a 12-year period.

   (a) Make a scatter plot of the data.

   (b) Find a sine curve that models the data (as in Example 1).

   (c) Graph the function you found in part (b) together with the scatter plot.

   (d) Use a graphing calculator to find the sine curve that best fits the data (as in Example 2). Compare to your answer from part (b).

8. Salmon Survival   For reasons not yet fully understood, the number of fingerling salmon that survive the trip from their riverbed spawning grounds to the open ocean varies approximately sinusoidally from year to year. The table shows the number of salmon that hatch in a certain British Columbia creek and then make their way to the Strait of Georgia. The data is given in thousands of fingerlings, over a period of 16 years.

(a) Make a scatter plot of the data.

(b) Find a sine curve that models the data (as in Example 1).

(c) Graph the function you found in part (b) together with the scatter plot.

(d) Use a graphing calculator to find the sine curve that best fits the data (as in Example 2). Compare to your answer from part (b).

Year	Salmon (× 1000)	Year	Salmon (× 1000)
1985	43	1993	56
1986	36	1994	63
1987	27	1995	57
1988	23	1996	50
1989	26	1997	44
1990	33	1998	38
1991	43	1999	30
1992	50	2000	22

9. Sunspot Activity   Sunspots are relatively "cool" regions on the sun that appear as dark spots when observed through special solar filters. The number of sunspots varies in an 11-year cycle. The table gives the average daily sunspot count for the years 1975–2004.

(a) Make a scatter plot of the data.

(b) Find a cosine curve that models the data (as in Example 1).

(c) Graph the function you found in part (b) together with the scatter plot.

(d) Use a graphing calculator to find the sine curve that best fits the data (as in Example 2). Compare to your answer in part (b).

Solar & Heliospheric Observatory/Photo Researchers

Year	Sunspots	Year	Sunspots
1975	16	1990	143
1976	13	1991	146
1977	28	1992	94
1978	93	1993	55
1979	155	1994	30
1980	155	1995	18
1981	140	1996	9
1982	116	1997	21
1983	67	1998	64
1984	46	1999	93
1985	18	2000	119
1986	13	2001	111
1987	29	2002	104
1988	100	2003	64
1989	158	2004	40

CHAPTER

TRIGONOMETRIC FUNCTIONS: RIGHT TRIANGLE APPROACH

Suppose we want to find the distance from the earth to the sun. Using a tape measure is obviously impractical, so we need something other than simple measurements to tackle this problem. Angles are easier to measure than distances. For example, we can find the angle formed by the sun, earth, and moon by simply pointing to the sun with one arm and to the moon with the other and estimating the angle between them. The key idea is to find relationships between angles and distances. So if we had a way of determining distances from angles, we would be able to find the distance to the sun without having to go there. The trigonometric functions provide us with just the tools we need.

If θ is an angle in a right triangle, then the trigonometric ratio $\sin \theta$ is defined as the length of the side opposite θ divided by the length of the hypotenuse. This ratio is the same in *any* similar right triangle, including the huge triangle formed by the sun, earth, and moon! (See Section 6.2, Exercise 61.)

The trigonometric functions can be defined in two different but equivalent ways: as functions of real numbers (Chapter 5) or as functions of angles (Chapter 6). The two approaches are independent of each other, so either Chapter 5 or Chapter 6 may be studied first. We study both approaches because the different approaches are required for different applications.

433

6.1 ANGLE MEASURE

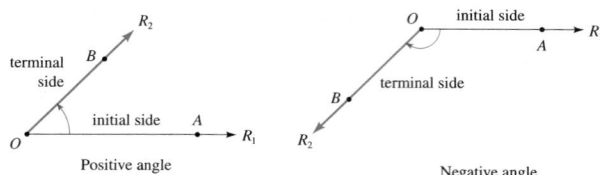

Angle Measure ▶ Angles in Standard Position ▶ Length of a Circular Arc ▶ Area of a Circular Sector ▶ Circular Motion

An **angle** AOB consists of two rays R_1 and R_2 with a common vertex O (see Figure 1). We often interpret an angle as a rotation of the ray R_1 onto R_2. In this case, R_1 is called the **initial side**, and R_2 is called the **terminal side** of the angle. If the rotation is counterclockwise, the angle is considered **positive**, and if the rotation is clockwise, the angle is considered **negative**.

![Positive angle and Negative angle diagrams]

FIGURE 1

▼ Angle Measure

The **measure** of an angle is the amount of rotation about the vertex required to move R_1 onto R_2. Intuitively, this is how much the angle "opens." One unit of measurement for angles is the **degree**. An angle of measure 1 degree is formed by rotating the initial side $\frac{1}{360}$ of a complete revolution. In calculus and other branches of mathematics, a more natural method of measuring angles is used—*radian measure*. The amount an angle opens is measured along the arc of a circle of radius 1 with its center at the vertex of the angle.

Radian measure of θ

FIGURE 2

DEFINITION OF RADIAN MEASURE

If a circle of radius 1 is drawn with the vertex of an angle at its center, then the measure of this angle in **radians** (abbreviated **rad**) is the length of the arc that subtends the angle (see Figure 2).

The circumference of the circle of radius 1 is 2π and so a complete revolution has measure 2π rad, a straight angle has measure π rad, and a right angle has measure $\pi/2$ rad. An angle that is subtended by an arc of length 2 along the unit circle has radian measure 2 (see Figure 3).

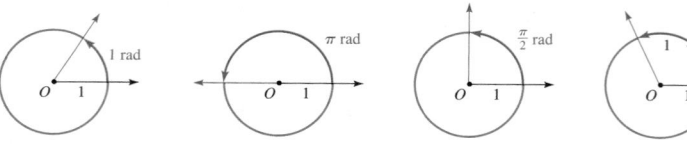

FIGURE 3 Radian measure

Since a complete revolution measured in degrees is 360° and measured in radians is 2π rad, we get the following simple relationship between these two methods of angle measurement.

TEXT QUESTIONS

(a) Which two of the following angles (given in radian measure) are coterminal?

$$0, \frac{\pi}{2}, \pi, \frac{3\pi}{2}, 2\pi$$

(b) Which two of the following angles are coterminal?
45°, −45°, 180°, −180°, 0°

Answers

(a) 0 and 2π

(b) 180° and −180°

RELATIONSHIP BETWEEN DEGREES AND RADIANS

$$180° = \pi \text{ rad} \qquad 1 \text{ rad} = \left(\frac{180}{\pi}\right)° \qquad 1° = \frac{\pi}{180}\text{ rad}$$

1. To convert degrees to radians, multiply by $\frac{\pi}{180}$.

2. To convert radians to degrees, multiply by $\frac{180}{\pi}$.

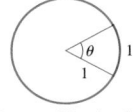

Measure of $\theta = 1$ rad
Measure of $\theta \approx 57.296°$

FIGURE 4

To get some idea of the size of a radian, notice that

$$1 \text{ rad} \approx 57.296° \qquad \text{and} \qquad 1° \approx 0.01745 \text{ rad}$$

An angle θ of measure 1 rad is shown in Figure 4.

EXAMPLE 1 | Converting Between Radians and Degrees

(a) Express 60° in radians. **(b)** Express $\frac{\pi}{6}$ rad in degrees.

SOLUTION The relationship between degrees and radians gives

(a) $60° = 60\left(\frac{\pi}{180}\right)\text{ rad} = \frac{\pi}{3}\text{ rad}$ **(b)** $\frac{\pi}{6}\text{ rad} = \left(\frac{\pi}{6}\right)\left(\frac{180}{\pi}\right) = 30°$

✎ NOW TRY EXERCISES **3** AND **15**

A note on terminology: We often use a phrase such as "a 30° angle" to mean *an angle whose measure is* 30°. Also, for an angle θ, we write $\theta = 30°$ or $\theta = \pi/6$ to mean *the measure of* θ *is* 30° *or* $\pi/6$ *rad*. When no unit is given, the angle is assumed to be measured in radians.

▼ **Angles in Standard Position**

An angle is in **standard position** if it is drawn in the *xy*-plane with its vertex at the origin and its initial side on the positive *x*-axis. Figure 5 gives examples of angles in standard position.

   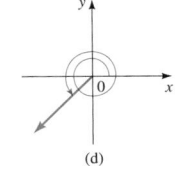

(a) (b) (c) (d)

FIGURE 5 Angles in standard position

Two angles in standard position are **coterminal** if their sides coincide. In Figure 5 the angles in (a) and (c) are coterminal.

EXAMPLE 2 | Coterminal Angles

(a) Find angles that are coterminal with the angle $\theta = 30°$ in standard position.

(b) Find angles that are coterminal with the angle $\theta = \frac{\pi}{3}$ in standard position.

ALTERNATE EXAMPLE 1
(a) Express 20° in radians.
(b) Express $\frac{\pi}{9}$ rad in degrees.

ANSWERS
(a) $\frac{\pi}{9}$
(b) 20°

EXAMPLE
Find an angle between 0 and 2π that is coterminal with 100.

ANSWER
$100 - 30\pi \approx 5.7522$

ALTERNATE EXAMPLE 2
(a) Find angles that are coterminal with the angle $\theta = 62°$ in standard position.
(b) Find angles that are coterminal with the angle $\theta = \frac{5\pi}{6}$ in standard position.

ANSWERS
(a) We add any positive or negative multiple of 360° to 62°. Answers include 422° and −298°.
(b) We add any positive or negative multiple of 2π to $\frac{5\pi}{6}$. Answers include $\frac{17\pi}{6}$ and $-\frac{7\pi}{6}$.

IN-CLASS MATERIALS
Make an analogy between angle measurement and clock measurement. In 48 hours 15 minutes, how far will the minute hand have moved? One answer is that it will go around the clock face $48\frac{1}{4}$ times. Another answer is that it moved one quarter of the way around the clock face, relative to where it started.

EXAMPLE
Find an angle between 0° and 360°
that is coterminal with −3624°.

ANSWER
336°

EXAMPLE
Find an angle between 0 and 2π
that is coterminal with $\dfrac{88\pi}{3}$.

ANSWER
$\dfrac{4\pi}{3}$

ALTERNATE EXAMPLE 3
Find an angle with measure
between 0° and 360° that is
coterminal with the angle of
measure 1635° in standard
position.

ANSWER
195°

SOLUTION

(a) To find positive angles that are coterminal with θ, we add any multiple of 360°. Thus

$$30° + 360° = 390° \quad \text{and} \quad 30° + 720° = 750°$$

are coterminal with $\theta = 30°$. To find negative angles that are coterminal with θ, we subtract any multiple of 360°. Thus

$$30° - 360° = -330° \quad \text{and} \quad 30° - 720° = -690°$$

are coterminal with θ. (See Figure 6.)

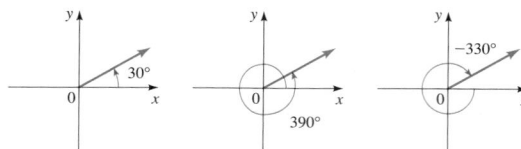

FIGURE 6

(b) To find positive angles that are coterminal with θ, we add any multiple of 2π. Thus

$$\frac{\pi}{3} + 2\pi = \frac{7\pi}{3} \quad \text{and} \quad \frac{\pi}{3} + 4\pi = \frac{13\pi}{3}$$

are coterminal with $\theta = \pi/3$. To find negative angles that are coterminal with θ, we subtract any multiple of 2π. Thus

$$\frac{\pi}{3} - 2\pi = -\frac{5\pi}{3} \quad \text{and} \quad \frac{\pi}{3} - 4\pi = -\frac{11\pi}{3}$$

are coterminal with θ. (See Figure 7.)

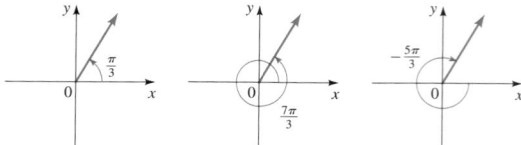

FIGURE 7

✎ NOW TRY EXERCISES **27** AND **29**

EXAMPLE 3 | Coterminal Angles

Find an angle with measure between 0° and 360° that is coterminal with the angle of measure 1290° in standard position.

SOLUTION We can subtract 360° as many times as we wish from 1290°, and the resulting angle will be coterminal with 1290°. Thus, 1290° − 360° = 930° is coterminal with 1290°, and so is the angle 1290° − 2(360)° = 570°.
To find the angle we want between 0° and 360°, we subtract 360° from 1290° as many times as necessary. An efficient way to do this is to determine how many times 360° goes into 1290°, that is, divide 1290 by 360, and the remainder will be the angle we are look-

IN-CLASS MATERIALS
Students often get the false impression that angles with integer measure are always in degrees and that angles with measures that are rational multiples of π are in radians. Ask students to sketch a 1° angle and then a 1 radian angle. Similarly, ask students to sketch angles with measures $\dfrac{\pi}{2}$ radians and $\dfrac{\pi}{2}$ degrees.

ing for. We see that 360 goes into 1290 three times with a remainder of 210. Thus, 210° is the desired angle (see Figure 8).

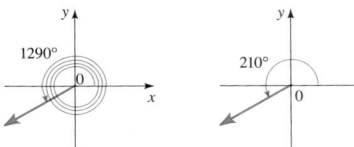

FIGURE 8

✎. NOW TRY EXERCISE **39**   ∎

▼ Length of a Circular Arc

An angle whose radian measure is θ is subtended by an arc that is the fraction $\theta/(2\pi)$ of the circumference of a circle. Thus, in a circle of radius r, the length s of an arc that subtends the angle θ (see Figure 9) is

FIGURE 9 $s = \theta r$

$$s = \frac{\theta}{2\pi} \times \text{circumference of circle}$$

$$= \frac{\theta}{2\pi}(2\pi r) = \theta r$$

LENGTH OF A CIRCULAR ARC

In a circle of radius r, the length s of an arc that subtends a central angle of θ radians is

$$s = r\theta$$

Solving for θ, we get the important formula

$$\theta = \frac{s}{r}$$

This formula allows us to define radian measure using a circle of any radius r: The radian measure of an angle θ is s/r, where s is the length of the circular arc that subtends θ in a circle of radius r (see Figure 10).

 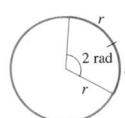

FIGURE 10   The radian measure of θ is the number of "radiuses" that can fit in the arc that subtends θ; hence the term *radian*.

EXAMPLE 4 | Arc Length and Angle Measure

(a) Find the length of an arc of a circle with radius 10 m that subtends a central angle of 30°.

(b) A central angle θ in a circle of radius 4 m is subtended by an arc of length 6 m. Find the measure of θ in radians.

SOLUTION

(a) From Example 1(b) we see that $30° = \pi/6$ rad. So the length of the arc is

$$s = r\theta = (10)\frac{\pi}{6} = \frac{5\pi}{3}\text{ m}$$

(b) By the formula $\theta = s/r$, we have

$$\theta = \frac{s}{r} = \frac{6}{4} = \frac{3}{2}\text{ rad}$$

✎ **NOW TRY EXERCISES 55 AND 57** ∎

⊘ The formula $s = r\theta$ is true only when θ is measured in radians.

▼ Area of a Circular Sector

The area of a circle of radius r is $A = \pi r^2$. A sector of this circle with central angle θ has an area that is the fraction $\theta/(2\pi)$ of the area of the entire circle (see Figure 11). So the area of this sector is

$$A = \frac{\theta}{2\pi} \times \text{area of circle}$$

$$= \frac{\theta}{2\pi}(\pi r^2) = \frac{1}{2}r^2\theta$$

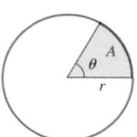

FIGURE 11
$A = \frac{1}{2}r^2\theta$

AREA OF A CIRCULAR SECTOR

In a circle of radius r, the area A of a sector with a central angle of θ radians is

$$A = \frac{1}{2}r^2\theta$$

EXAMPLE 5 | Area of a Sector

Find the area of a sector of a circle with central angle 60° if the radius of the circle is 3 m.

SOLUTION To use the formula for the area of a circular sector, we must find the central angle of the sector in radians: $60° = 60(\pi/180)$ rad $= \pi/3$ rad. Thus, the area of the sector is

$$A = \frac{1}{2}r^2\theta = \frac{1}{2}(3)^2\left(\frac{\pi}{3}\right) = \frac{3\pi}{2}\text{ m}^2$$

⊘ The formula $A = \frac{1}{2}r^2\theta$ is true only when θ is measured in radians.

✎ **NOW TRY EXERCISE 61** ∎

▼ Circular Motion

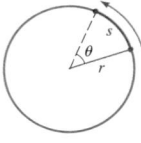

FIGURE 12

Suppose a point moves along a circle as shown in Figure 12. There are two ways to describe the motion of the point: linear speed and angular speed. **Linear speed** is the rate at which the distance traveled is changing, so linear speed is the distance traveled divided by the time elapsed. **Angular speed** is the rate at which the central angle θ is changing, so angular speed is the number of radians this angle changes divided by the time elapsed.

IN-CLASS MATERIALS

One can demonstrate the relationship between linear and angular speed this way: The teacher sits in a rotating office chair and spins at a rate of, say, 2π radians per 5 seconds. Now have one student stand close to the professor, and one stand farther away; have them both try to run in circles at that rate. Note that the one farther away has to travel much faster, demonstrating that if the angular speed is held constant and r is increased, then v is increased as well.

LINEAR SPEED AND ANGULAR SPEED

Suppose a point moves along a circle of radius r and the ray from the center of the circle to the point traverses θ radians in time t. Let $s = r\theta$ be the distance the point travels in time t. Then the speed of the object is given by

The symbol ω is the Greek letter "omega."

$$\text{Angular speed} \qquad \omega = \frac{\theta}{t}$$

$$\text{Linear speed} \qquad v = \frac{s}{t}$$

EXAMPLE 6 | Finding Linear and Angular Speed

A boy rotates a stone in a 3-ft-long sling at the rate of 15 revolutions every 10 seconds. Find the angular and linear velocities of the stone.

SOLUTION   In 10 s, the angle θ changes by $15 \cdot 2\pi = 30\pi$ radians. So the *angular speed* of the stone is

$$\omega = \frac{\theta}{t} = \frac{30\pi \text{ rad}}{10 \text{ s}} = 3\pi \text{ rad/s}$$

The distance traveled by the stone in 10 s is $s = 15 \cdot 2\pi r = 15 \cdot 2\pi \cdot 3 = 90\pi$ ft. So the *linear speed* of the stone is

$$v = \frac{s}{t} = \frac{90\pi \text{ ft}}{10 \text{ s}} = 9\pi \text{ ft/s}$$

✎ NOW TRY EXERCISE **79** ∎

Notice that angular speed does *not* depend on the radius of the circle, but only on the angle θ. However, if we know the angular speed ω and the radius r, we can find linear speed as follows: $v = s/t = r\theta/t = r(\theta/t) = r\omega$.

RELATIONSHIP BETWEEN LINEAR AND ANGULAR SPEED

If a point moves along a circle of radius r with angular speed ω, then its linear speed v is given by

$$v = r\omega$$

EXAMPLE 7 | Finding Linear Speed from Angular Speed

A woman is riding a bicycle whose wheels are 26 inches in diameter. If the wheels rotate at 125 revolutions per minute (rpm), find the speed at which she is traveling, in mi/h.

SOLUTION   The angular speed of the wheels is $2\pi \cdot 125 = 250\pi$ rad/min. Since the wheels have radius 13 in. (half the diameter), the linear speed is

$$v = r\omega = 13 \cdot 250\pi \approx 10{,}210.2 \text{ in./min}$$

Since there are 12 inches per foot, 5280 feet per mile, and 60 minutes per hour, her speed in miles per hour is

$$\frac{10{,}210.2 \text{ in./min} \times 60 \text{ min/h}}{12 \text{ in./ft} \times 5280 \text{ ft/mi}} = \frac{612{,}612 \text{ in./h}}{63{,}360 \text{ in./mi}}$$

$$\approx 9.7 \text{ mi/h}$$

✎ NOW TRY EXERCISE **81** ∎

ALTERNATE EXAMPLE 6

A disk with a 12-in. diameter spins at the rate of 45 revolutions per minute. Find the angular and linear velocities of a point at the edge of the disk in radians per second and inches per second, respectively.

ANSWER

Angular speed $= \dfrac{3}{2}\pi$ rad/s

Linear speed $= 18\pi$ in/s

ALTERNATE EXAMPLE 7

A woman is riding a bicycle whose wheels are 30 inches in diameter. If the wheels rotate at 150 revolutions per minute, find the speed at which she is traveling in mi/h.

ANSWER

13.4 mi/h

IN-CLASS MATERIALS

If the students have taken some physics, present them with this paradox: We know that Einstein said that the speed of an object cannot exceed 186,000 miles per second, regardless of reference frame. Let the reference frame be a basketball. Have them calculate how fast the sun is moving if the basketball is spinning on a finger, relative to the frame of reference of the basketball. Then have them calculate how fast the stars are moving. These numbers will be faster than the speed of light! This "paradox" is actually a misunderstanding of relativity. The rules about the speed of light being a maximum, and most of relativity in general, apply to what is called an "inertial" reference frame—one where objects in motion remain in motion and objects at rest remain at rest. The reference frames of a spinning basketball or an accelerating train are not inertial reference frames.

DRILL QUESTION

Find an angle with measure (in radians) between $-\dfrac{\pi}{2}$ and $\dfrac{\pi}{2}$ that is coterminal with the angle of measure $\dfrac{11\pi}{3}$ in standard position.

Answer

$-\dfrac{\pi}{3}$ rad

6.1 EXERCISES

CONCEPTS

1. (a) The radian measure of an angle θ is the length of the _____ that subtends the angle in a circle of radius _____.

   (b) To convert degrees to radians, we multiply by _____.

   (c) To convert radians to degrees, we multiply by _____.

2. A central angle θ is drawn in a circle of radius r.

   (a) The length of the arc subtended by θ is $s =$ _____.

   (b) The area of the sector with central angle θ is $A =$ _____.

SKILLS

3–14 ■ Find the radian measure of the angle with the given degree measure.

3. $72°$
4. $54°$
5. $-45°$
6. $-60°$
7. $-75°$
8. $-300°$
9. $1080°$
10. $3960°$
11. $96°$
12. $15°$
13. $7.5°$
14. $202.5°$

15–26 ■ Find the degree measure of the angle with the given radian measure.

15. $\dfrac{7\pi}{6}$
16. $\dfrac{11\pi}{3}$
17. $-\dfrac{5\pi}{4}$
18. $-\dfrac{3\pi}{2}$
19. 3
20. -2
21. -1.2
22. 3.4
23. $\dfrac{\pi}{10}$
24. $\dfrac{5\pi}{18}$
25. $-\dfrac{2\pi}{15}$
26. $-\dfrac{13\pi}{12}$

27–32 ■ The measure of an angle in standard position is given. Find two positive angles and two negative angles that are coterminal with the given angle.

27. $50°$
28. $135°$
29. $\dfrac{3\pi}{4}$
30. $\dfrac{11\pi}{6}$
31. $-\dfrac{\pi}{4}$
32. $-45°$

33–38 ■ The measures of two angles in standard position are given. Determine whether the angles are coterminal.

33. $70°$, $430°$
34. $-30°$, $330°$
35. $\dfrac{5\pi}{6}$, $\dfrac{17\pi}{6}$
36. $\dfrac{32\pi}{3}$, $\dfrac{11\pi}{3}$
37. $155°$, $875°$
38. $50°$, $340°$

39–44 ■ Find an angle between $0°$ and $360°$ that is coterminal with the given angle.

39. $733°$
40. $361°$
41. $1110°$
42. $-100°$
43. $-800°$
44. $1270°$

45–50 ■ Find an angle between 0 and 2π that is coterminal with the given angle.

45. $\dfrac{17\pi}{6}$
46. $-\dfrac{7\pi}{3}$
47. 87π
48. 10
49. $\dfrac{17\pi}{4}$
50. $\dfrac{51\pi}{2}$

51. Find the length of the arc s in the figure.

52. Find the angle θ in the figure.

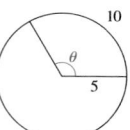

53. Find the radius r of the circle in the figure.

54. Find the length of an arc that subtends a central angle of $45°$ in a circle of radius 10 m.

55. Find the length of an arc that subtends a central angle of 2 rad in a circle of radius 2 mi.

56. A central angle θ in a circle of radius 5 m is subtended by an arc of length 6 m. Find the measure of θ in degrees and in radians.

57. An arc of length 100 m subtends a central angle θ in a circle of radius 50 m. Find the measure of θ in degrees and in radians.

58. A circular arc of length 3 ft subtends a central angle of $25°$. Find the radius of the circle.

59. Find the radius of the circle if an arc of length 6 m on the circle subtends a central angle of $\pi/6$ rad.

60. Find the radius of the circle if an arc of length 4 ft on the circle subtends a central angle of $135°$.

61. Find the area of the sector shown in each figure.

(a)

(b)

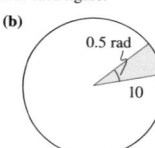

EXAMPLE

We can approximate the shape of the earth by a sphere of radius 3960 miles. If we wanted to walk far enough to traverse exactly one degree in latitude, how far a trip would we have to take?

ANSWER

$3960 \cdot 1 \cdot \dfrac{\pi}{180} \approx 69$ mi

62. Find the radius of each circle if the area of the sector is 12.

(a) **(b)**

  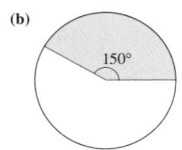

63. Find the area of a sector with central angle 1 rad in a circle of radius 10 m.

64. A sector of a circle has a central angle of 60°. Find the area of the sector if the radius of the circle is 3 mi.

65. The area of a sector of a circle with a central angle of 2 rad is 16 m². Find the radius of the circle.

66. A sector of a circle of radius 24 mi has an area of 288 mi². Find the central angle of the sector.

67. The area of a circle is 72 cm². Find the area of a sector of this circle that subtends a central angle of $\pi/6$ rad.

68. Three circles with radii 1, 2, and 3 ft are externally tangent to one another, as shown in the figure. Find the area of the sector of the circle of radius 1 that is cut off by the line segments joining the center of that circle to the centers of the other two circles.

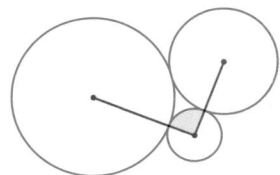

APPLICATIONS

69. Travel Distance A car's wheels are 28 in. in diameter. How far (in miles) will the car travel if its wheels revolve 10,000 times without slipping?

70. Wheel Revolutions How many revolutions will a car wheel of diameter 30 in. make as the car travels a distance of one mile?

71. Latitudes Pittsburgh, Pennsylvania, and Miami, Florida, lie approximately on the same meridian. Pittsburgh has a latitude of 40.5° N, and Miami has a latitude of 25.5° N. Find the distance between these two cities. (The radius of the earth is 3960 mi.)

72. Latitudes Memphis, Tennessee, and New Orleans, Louisiana, lie approximately on the same meridian. Memphis has a latitude of 35° N, and New Orleans has a latitude of 30° N. Find the distance between these two cities. (The radius of the earth is 3960 mi.)

73. Orbit of the Earth Find the distance that the earth travels in one day in its path around the sun. Assume that a year has 365 days and that the path of the earth around the sun is a circle of radius 93 million miles. [The path of the earth around the sun is actually an *ellipse* with the sun at one focus (see Section 10.2). This ellipse, however, has very small eccentricity, so it is nearly circular.]

74. Circumference of the Earth The Greek mathematician Eratosthenes (ca. 276–195 B.C.) measured the circumference of the earth from the following observations. He noticed that on a certain day the sun shone directly down a deep well in Syene (modern Aswan). At the same time in Alexandria, 500 miles north (on the same meridian), the rays of the sun shone at an angle of 7.2° to the zenith. Use this information and the figure to find the radius and circumference of the earth.

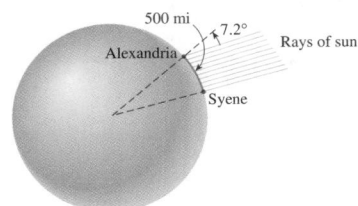

75. Nautical Miles Find the distance along an arc on the surface of the earth that subtends a central angle of 1 minute (1 minute = $\frac{1}{60}$ degree). This distance is called a *nautical mile*. (The radius of the earth is 3960 mi.)

76. Irrigation An irrigation system uses a straight sprinkler pipe 300 ft long that pivots around a central point as shown. Due to an obstacle the pipe is allowed to pivot through 280° only. Find the area irrigated by this system.

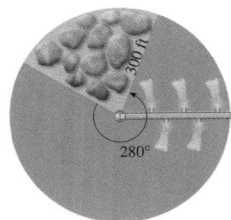

77. Windshield Wipers The top and bottom ends of a wind-shield wiper blade are 34 in. and 14 in., respectively, from the pivot point. While in operation, the wiper sweeps through 135°. Find the area swept by the blade.

78. The Tethered Cow A cow is tethered by a 100-ft rope to the inside corner of an L-shaped building, as shown in the figure. Find the area that the cow can graze.

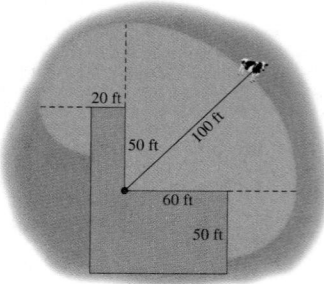

79. Fan A ceiling fan with 16-in. blades rotates at 45 rpm.
(a) Find the angular speed of the fan in rad/min.
(b) Find the linear speed of the tips of the blades in in./min.

80. Radial Saw A radial saw has a blade with a 6-in. radius. Suppose that the blade spins at 1000 rpm.
(a) Find the angular speed of the blade in rad/min.
(b) Find the linear speed of the sawteeth in ft/s.

81. Winch A winch of radius 2 ft is used to lift heavy loads. If the winch makes 8 revolutions every 15 s, find the speed at which the load is rising.

82. Speed of a Car The wheels of a car have radius 11 in. and are rotating at 600 rpm. Find the speed of the car in mi/h.

83. Speed at the Equator The earth rotates about its axis once every 23 h 56 min 4 s, and the radius of the earth is 3960 mi. Find the linear speed of a point on the equator in mi/h.

84. Truck Wheels A truck with 48-in.-diameter wheels is traveling at 50 mi/h.
(a) Find the angular speed of the wheels in rad/min.
(b) How many revolutions per minute do the wheels make?

85. Speed of a Current To measure the speed of a current, scientists place a paddle wheel in the stream and observe the rate at which it rotates. If the paddle wheel has radius 0.20 m and rotates at 100 rpm, find the speed of the current in m/s.

86. Bicycle Wheel The sprockets and chain of a bicycle are shown in the figure. The pedal sprocket has a radius of 4 in., the wheel sprocket a radius of 2 in., and the wheel a radius of 13 in. The cyclist pedals at 40 rpm.
(a) Find the angular speed of the wheel sprocket.
(b) Find the speed of the bicycle. (Assume that the wheel turns at the same rate as the wheel sprocket.)

87. Conical Cup A conical cup is made from a circular piece of paper with radius 6 cm by cutting out a sector and joining the edges as shown on the next page. Suppose $\theta = 5\pi/3$.
(a) Find the circumference C of the opening of the cup.
(b) Find the radius r of the opening of the cup. [*Hint:* Use $C = 2\pi r$.]
(c) Find the height h of the cup. [*Hint:* Use the Pythagorean Theorem.]

(d) Find the volume of the cup.

 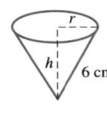

88. Conical Cup In this exercise we find the volume of the conical cup in Exercise 87 for any angle θ.

(a) Follow the steps in Exercise 87 to show that the volume of the cup as a function of θ is

$$V(\theta) = \frac{9}{\pi^2} \theta^2 \sqrt{4\pi^2 - \theta^2}, \qquad 0 < \theta < 2\pi$$

(b) Graph the function V.

(c) For what angle θ is the volume of the cup a maximum?

DISCOVERY ▪ DISCUSSION ▪ WRITING

89. Different Ways of Measuring Angles The custom of measuring angles using degrees, with 360° in a circle, dates back to the ancient Babylonians, who used a number system based on groups of 60. Another system of measuring angles divides the circle into 400 units, called *grads*. In this system a right angle is 100 grad, so this fits in with our base 10 number system.

Write a short essay comparing the advantages and disadvantages of these two systems and the radian system of measuring angles. Which system do you prefer? Why?

90. Clocks and Angles In one hour, the minute hand on a clock moves through a complete circle, and the hour hand moves through $\frac{1}{12}$ of a circle. Through how many radians do the minute and the hour hand move between 1:00 P.M. and 6:45 P.M. (on the same day)?

6.2 TRIGONOMETRY OF RIGHT TRIANGLES

Trigonometric Ratios ▶ Special Triangles ▶ Applications of Trigonometry of Right Triangles

In this section we study certain ratios of the sides of right triangles, called trigonometric ratios, and give several applications.

▼ Trigonometric Ratios

Consider a right triangle with θ as one of its acute angles. The trigonometric ratios are defined as follows (see Figure 1).

FIGURE 1

THE TRIGONOMETRIC RATIOS

$$\sin \theta = \frac{\text{opposite}}{\text{hypotenuse}} \qquad \cos \theta = \frac{\text{adjacent}}{\text{hypotenuse}} \qquad \tan \theta = \frac{\text{opposite}}{\text{adjacent}}$$

$$\csc \theta = \frac{\text{hypotenuse}}{\text{opposite}} \qquad \sec \theta = \frac{\text{hypotenuse}}{\text{adjacent}} \qquad \cot \theta = \frac{\text{adjacent}}{\text{opposite}}$$

The symbols we use for these ratios are abbreviations for their full names: **sine, cosine, tangent, cosecant, secant, cotangent.** Since any two right triangles with angle θ are

SUGGESTED TIME AND EMPHASIS

1 class, essential material

TEXT QUESTION
Define *angle of elevation*.

Answer
Answers will vary.

similar, these ratios are the same, regardless of the size of the triangle; the trigonometric ratios depend only on the angle θ (see Figure 2).

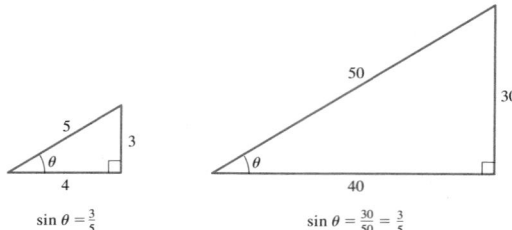

FIGURE 2

$\sin \theta = \frac{3}{5}$ $\sin \theta = \frac{30}{50} = \frac{3}{5}$

ALTERNATE EXAMPLE 1

Find the six trigonometric ratios of the angle θ in this figure.

ANSWER

$\sin(\theta) = \dfrac{2}{3}$, $\cos(\theta) = \dfrac{\sqrt{5}}{3}$,

$\tan(\theta) = \dfrac{2}{\sqrt{5}}$, $\cot(\theta) = \dfrac{\sqrt{5}}{2}$,

$\sec(\theta) = \dfrac{3}{\sqrt{5}}$, $\csc(\theta) = \dfrac{3}{2}$

ALTERNATE EXAMPLE 2

Consider a right triangle with α as one of its acute angles. If $\cos \alpha = \frac{7}{8}$, find the other five trigonometric ratios of α.

ANSWER

$\sin(\alpha) = \dfrac{\sqrt{15}}{8}$, $\tan(\alpha) = \dfrac{\sqrt{15}}{7}$,

$\csc(\alpha) = \dfrac{8}{\sqrt{15}}$, $\sec(\alpha) = \dfrac{8}{7}$,

$\cot(\alpha) = \dfrac{7}{\sqrt{15}}$

FIGURE 3

EXAMPLE 1 | Finding Trigonometric Ratios

Find the six trigonometric ratios of the angle θ in Figure 3.

SOLUTION

$$\sin \theta = \frac{2}{3} \qquad \cos \theta = \frac{\sqrt{5}}{3} \qquad \tan \theta = \frac{2}{\sqrt{5}}$$

$$\csc \theta = \frac{3}{2} \qquad \sec \theta = \frac{3}{\sqrt{5}} \qquad \cot \theta = \frac{\sqrt{5}}{2}$$

✏ NOW TRY EXERCISE **3**   ■

EXAMPLE 2 | Finding Trigonometric Ratios

If $\cos \alpha = \frac{3}{4}$, sketch a right triangle with acute angle α, and find the other five trigonometric ratios of α.

SOLUTION Since $\cos \alpha$ is defined as the ratio of the adjacent side to the hypotenuse, we sketch a triangle with hypotenuse of length 4 and a side of length 3 adjacent to α. If the opposite side is x, then by the Pythagorean Theorem, $3^2 + x^2 = 4^2$ or $x^2 = 7$, so $x = \sqrt{7}$. We then use the triangle in Figure 4 to find the ratios.

$$\sin \alpha = \frac{\sqrt{7}}{4} \qquad \cos \alpha = \frac{3}{4} \qquad \tan \alpha = \frac{\sqrt{7}}{3}$$

$$\csc \alpha = \frac{4}{\sqrt{7}} \qquad \sec \alpha = \frac{4}{3} \qquad \cot \alpha = \frac{3}{\sqrt{7}}$$

✏ NOW TRY EXERCISE **19**   ■

FIGURE 4

▼ Special Triangles

Certain right triangles have ratios that can be calculated easily from the Pythagorean Theorem. Since they are used frequently, we mention them here.

The first triangle is obtained by drawing a diagonal in a square of side 1 (see Figure 5). By the Pythagorean Theorem this diagonal has length $\sqrt{2}$. The resulting triangle has angles 45°, 45°, and 90° (or $\pi/4$, $\pi/4$, and $\pi/2$). To get the second triangle, we start with an equilateral triangle ABC of side 2 and draw the perpendicular bisector DB of the base, as in Figure 6. By the Pythagorean Theorem the length of DB is $\sqrt{3}$. Since DB bisects angle ABC, we obtain a triangle with angles 30°, 60°, and 90° (or $\pi/6$, $\pi/3$, and $\pi/2$).

IN-CLASS MATERIALS

Note: If Chapter 5 was covered, this point may already have been discussed.

The etymology of the word *sine* is fairly interesting and not that well known. It starts with the Indian word *jya,* meaning "cord of a bowstring." The Arabs translated this word as *jiba.* The written language had no vowels, so it looked like this: jb. In 1145, the Spanish translator Robert of Cheste had to figure out what vowels to put in. Because of the shape of the curve, he thought the word was *jaib,* which meant the opening of a garment that shows a woman's cleavage. So he used the Latin word for the cavity formed by a curve: *sinus.* (This word exists in the English language today—right behind your nose are the sinus cavities.)

FIGURE 5

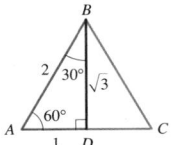

FIGURE 6

For an explanation of numerical methods, see the margin note on page 400.

We can now use the special triangles in Figures 5 and 6 to calculate the trigonometric ratios for angles with measures 30°, 45°, and 60° (or $\pi/6$, $\pi/4$, and $\pi/3$). These are listed in Table 1.

TABLE 1
Values of the trigonometric ratios for special angles

θ in degrees	θ in radians	$\sin \theta$	$\cos \theta$	$\tan \theta$	$\csc \theta$	$\sec \theta$	$\cot \theta$
30°	$\dfrac{\pi}{6}$	$\dfrac{1}{2}$	$\dfrac{\sqrt{3}}{2}$	$\dfrac{\sqrt{3}}{3}$	2	$\dfrac{2\sqrt{3}}{3}$	$\sqrt{3}$
45°	$\dfrac{\pi}{4}$	$\dfrac{\sqrt{2}}{2}$	$\dfrac{\sqrt{2}}{2}$	1	$\sqrt{2}$	$\sqrt{2}$	1
60°	$\dfrac{\pi}{3}$	$\dfrac{\sqrt{3}}{2}$	$\dfrac{1}{2}$	$\sqrt{3}$	$\dfrac{2\sqrt{3}}{3}$	2	$\dfrac{\sqrt{3}}{3}$

It's useful to remember these special trigonometric ratios because they occur often. Of course, they can be recalled easily if we remember the triangles from which they are obtained.

To find the values of the trigonometric ratios for other angles, we use a calculator. Mathematical methods (called *numerical methods*) used in finding the trigonometric ratios are programmed directly into scientific calculators. For instance, when the $\boxed{\text{SIN}}$ key is pressed, the calculator computes an approximation to the value of the sine of the given angle. Calculators give the values of sine, cosine, and tangent; the other ratios can be easily calculated from these by using the following *reciprocal relations*:

$$\csc t = \frac{1}{\sin t} \qquad \sec t = \frac{1}{\cos t} \qquad \cot t = \frac{1}{\tan t}$$

You should check that these relations follow immediately from the definitions of the trigonometric ratios.

We follow the convention that when we write $\sin t$, *we mean the sine of the angle whose radian measure is t.* For instance, $\sin 1$ means the sine of the angle whose radian measure is 1. When using a calculator to find an approximate value for this number, set your calculator to radian mode; you will find that

$$\sin 1 \approx 0.841471$$

If you want to find the sine of the angle whose measure is 1°, set your calculator to degree mode; you will find that

$$\sin 1° \approx 0.0174524$$

▼ Applications of Trigonometry of Right Triangles

A triangle has six parts: three angles and three sides. To **solve a triangle** means to determine all of its parts from the information known about the triangle, that is, to determine the lengths of the three sides and the measures of the three angles.

EXAMPLE 3 | Solving a Right Triangle

Solve triangle ABC, shown in Figure 7 on the next page.

IN-CLASS MATERIALS

Note: If Chapter 5 was covered, this point may already have been discussed.

There is an inconsistency in mathematical notation that can be made explicit at this time. We say that $\dfrac{1}{3} = 3^{-1}$. Similarly, we say that $\dfrac{1}{\pi} = \pi^{-1}$. But $\dfrac{1}{\sin x}$ is written as $\csc x$. Unfortunately, there is a symbol, $\sin^{-1} x$, that means something entirely different—the arcsine of x. Even worse, as noted in the section, $\sin^2 x = (\sin x)^2$ and $\sin^3 x = (\sin x)^3$. The exponent -1 is a notational anomaly.

ALTERNATE EXAMPLE 3

Solve triangle *ABC*, shown in this figure (find the sides *a* and *b*, and the third unknown angle).

ANSWER

$7, 7\sqrt{3}, 60$

ALTERNATE EXAMPLE 4

A giant redwood tree casts a shadow 452 ft long. Find the height of the tree if the angle of elevation of the sun is 12.3°.

ANSWER

176 ft

FIGURE 7

FIGURE 8
$a = r \sin \theta$
$b = r \cos \theta$

> **ARISTARCHUS OF SAMOS** (310–230 B.C.) was a famous Greek scientist, musician, astronomer, and geometer. In his book *On the Sizes and Distances of the Sun and the Moon,* he estimated the distance to the sun by observing that when the moon is exactly half full, the triangle formed by the sun, moon, and the earth has a right angle at the moon. His method was similar to the one described in Exercise 61 in this section. Aristarchus was the first to advance the theory that the earth and planets move around the sun, an idea that did not gain full acceptance until after the time of Copernicus, 1800 years later. For this reason Aristarchus is often called "the Copernicus of antiquity."

SOLUTION   It's clear that $\angle B = 60°$. To find *a*, we look for an equation that relates *a* to the lengths and angles we already know. In this case, we have $\sin 30° = a/12$, so

$$a = 12 \sin 30° = 12\left(\tfrac{1}{2}\right) = 6$$

Similarly, $\cos 30° = b/12$, so

$$b = 12 \cos 30° = 12\left(\frac{\sqrt{3}}{2}\right) = 6\sqrt{3}$$

NOW TRY EXERCISE 31

Figure 8 shows that if we know the hypotenuse *r* and an acute angle θ in a right triangle, then the legs *a* and *b* are given by

$$a = r \sin \theta \qquad \text{and} \qquad b = r \cos \theta$$

The ability to solve right triangles by using the trigonometric ratios is fundamental to many problems in navigation, surveying, astronomy, and the measurement of distances. The applications we consider in this section always involve right triangles, but as we will see in the next three sections, trigonometry is also useful in solving triangles that are not right triangles.

To discuss the next examples, we need some terminology. If an observer is looking at an object, then the line from the eye of the observer to the object is called the **line of sight** (Figure 9). If the object being observed is above the horizontal, then the angle between the line of sight and the horizontal is called the **angle of elevation**. If the object is below the horizontal, then the angle between the line of sight and the horizontal is called the **angle of depression**. In many of the examples and exercises in this chapter, angles of elevation and depression will be given for a hypothetical observer at ground level. If the line of sight follows a physical object, such as an inclined plane or a hillside, we use the term **angle of inclination**.

FIGURE 9

The next example gives an important application of trigonometry to the problem of measurement: We measure the height of a tall tree without having to climb it! Although the example is simple, the result is fundamental to understanding how the trigonometric ratios are applied to such problems.

EXAMPLE 4 | Finding the Height of a Tree

A giant redwood tree casts a shadow 532 ft long. Find the height of the tree if the angle of elevation of the sun is 25.7°.

IN-CLASS MATERIALS

It is relatively easy to make a device to measure angle of elevation. Tape a soda straw to the bottom of a protractor, and tie a string with a weight to the center. When you sight an object through the straw, you can figure out the angle by noticing where the string falls. The name of such a device is a *clinometer.* These days, it is possible to get a clinometer application for a smartphone!

SOLUTION Let the height of the tree be h. From Figure 10 we see that

$$\frac{h}{532} = \tan 25.7° \qquad \text{Definition of tangent}$$

$$h = 532 \tan 25.7° \qquad \text{Multiply by 532}$$

$$\approx 532(0.48127) \approx 256 \qquad \text{Use a calculator}$$

Therefore, the height of the tree is about 256 ft.

FIGURE 10

✎. NOW TRY EXERCISE **47**

EXAMPLE 5 | A Problem Involving Right Triangles

From a point on the ground 500 ft from the base of a building, an observer finds that the angle of elevation to the top of the building is 24° and that the angle of elevation to the top of a flagpole atop the building is 27°. Find the height of the building and the length of the flagpole.

SOLUTION Figure 11 illustrates the situation. The height of the building is found in the same way that we found the height of the tree in Example 4.

$$\frac{h}{500} = \tan 24° \qquad \text{Definition of tangent}$$

$$h = 500 \tan 24° \qquad \text{Multiply by 500}$$

$$\approx 500(0.4452) \approx 223 \qquad \text{Use a calculator}$$

The height of the building is approximately 223 ft.

To find the length of the flagpole, let's first find the height from the ground to the top of the pole:

$$\frac{k}{500} = \tan 27°$$

$$k = 500 \tan 27°$$

$$\approx 500(0.5095)$$

$$\approx 255$$

To find the length of the flagpole, we subtract h from k. So the length of the pole is approximately $255 - 223 = 32$ ft.

✎. NOW TRY EXERCISE **55**

FIGURE 11

6.2 EXERCISES

CONCEPTS

1. A right triangle with an angle θ is shown in the figure.

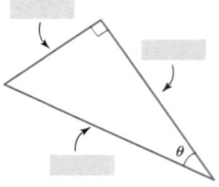

(a) Label the "opposite" and "adjacent" sides of θ and the hypotenuse of the triangle.

(b) The trigonometric functions of the angle θ are defined as follows:

$\sin\theta =$ _____ $\cos\theta =$ _____ $\tan\theta =$ _____

(c) The trigonometric ratios do not depend on the size of the triangle. This is because all right triangles with an acute angle θ are _____.

2. The reciprocal identities state that

$$\csc\theta = \frac{1}{} \qquad \sec\theta = \frac{1}{} \qquad \cot\theta = \frac{1}{}$$

SKILLS

3–8 ■ Find the exact values of the six trigonometric ratios of the angle θ in the triangle.

3.

4.

5.

6.

7.

8.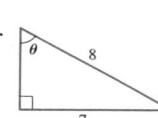

9–10 ■ Find (a) $\sin\alpha$ and $\cos\beta$, (b) $\tan\alpha$ and $\cot\beta$, and (c) $\sec\alpha$ and $\csc\beta$.

9.

10.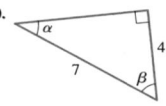

11–16 ■ Find the side labeled x. In Exercises 13 and 14 state your answer rounded to five decimal places.

11.

12.

13.

14.

15.

16.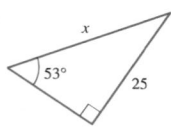

17–18 ■ Express x and y in terms of trigonometric ratios of θ.

17.

18.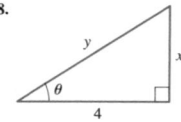

19–24 ■ Sketch a triangle that has acute angle θ, and find the other five trigonometric ratios of θ.

19. $\sin\theta = \frac{3}{5}$ **20.** $\cos\theta = \frac{9}{40}$

21. $\cot\theta = 1$ **22.** $\tan\theta = \sqrt{3}$

23. $\sec\theta = \frac{7}{2}$ **24.** $\csc\theta = \frac{13}{12}$

25–30 ■ Evaluate the expression without using a calculator.

25. $\sin\dfrac{\pi}{6} + \cos\dfrac{\pi}{6}$

26. $\sin 30° \csc 30°$

27. $\sin 30° \cos 60° + \sin 60° \cos 30°$

28. $(\sin 60°)^2 + (\cos 60°)^2$

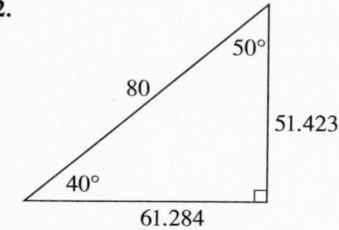

29. $(\cos 30°)^2 - (\sin 30°)^2$

30. $\left(\sin \dfrac{\pi}{3} \cos \dfrac{\pi}{4} - \sin \dfrac{\pi}{4} \cos \dfrac{\pi}{3}\right)^2$

31–38 ■ Solve the right triangle.

31.

32.

33.

34.

35.

36.

37.

38.

39. Use a ruler to carefully measure the sides of the triangle, and then use your measurements to estimate the six trigonometric ratios of θ.

40. Using a protractor, sketch a right triangle that has the acute angle 40°. Measure the sides carefully, and use your results to estimate the six trigonometric ratios of 40°.

41–44 ■ Find x rounded to one decimal place.

41.

42.

43.

44.

45. Express the length x in terms of the trigonometric ratios of θ.

46. Express the length a, b, c, and d in the figure in terms of the trigonometric ratios of θ.

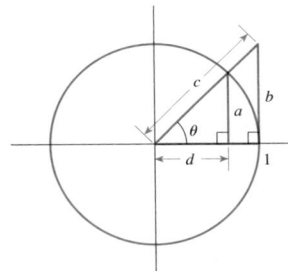

APPLICATIONS

47. Height of a Building   The angle of elevation to the top of the Empire State Building in New York is found to be 11° from the ground at a distance of 1 mi from the base of the building. Using this information, find the height of the Empire State Building.

48. Gateway Arch A plane is flying within sight of the Gateway Arch in St. Louis, Missouri, at an elevation of 35,000 ft. The pilot would like to estimate her distance from the Gateway Arch. She finds that the angle of depression to a point on the ground below the arch is 22°.
  (a) What is the distance between the plane and the arch?
  (b) What is the distance between a point on the ground directly below the plane and the arch?

49. Deviation of a Laser Beam A laser beam is to be directed toward the center of the moon, but the beam strays 0.5° from its intended path.
  (a) How far has the beam diverged from its assigned target when it reaches the moon? (The distance from the earth to the moon is 240,000 mi.)
  (b) The radius of the moon is about 1000 mi. Will the beam strike the moon?

50. Distance at Sea From the top of a 200-ft lighthouse, the angle of depression to a ship in the ocean is 23°. How far is the ship from the base of the lighthouse?

51. Leaning Ladder A 20-ft ladder leans against a building so that the angle between the ground and the ladder is 72°. How high does the ladder reach on the building?

52. Height of a Tower A 600-ft guy wire is attached to the top of a communications tower. If the wire makes an angle of 65° with the ground, how tall is the communications tower?

53. Elevation of a Kite A man is lying on the beach, flying a kite. He holds the end of the kite string at ground level, and estimates the angle of elevation of the kite to be 50°. If the string is 450 ft long, how high is the kite above the ground?

54. Determining a Distance A woman standing on a hill sees a flagpole that she knows is 60 ft tall. The angle of depression to the bottom of the pole is 14°, and the angle of elevation to the top of the pole is 18°. Find her distance x from the pole.

55. Height of a Tower A water tower is located 325 ft from a building (see the figure). From a window in the building, an observer notes that the angle of elevation to the top of the tower is 39° and that the angle of depression to the bottom of the tower is 25°. How tall is the tower? How high is the window?

56. Determining a Distance An airplane is flying at an elevation of 5150 ft, directly above a straight highway. Two motorists are driving cars on the highway on opposite sides of the plane, and the angle of depression to one car is 35° and to the other is 52°. How far apart are the cars?

57. Determining a Distance If both cars in Exercise 56 are on one side of the plane and if the angle of depression to one car is 38° and to the other car is 52°, how far apart are the cars?

58. Height of a Balloon A hot-air balloon is floating above a straight road. To estimate their height above the ground, the balloonists simultaneously measure the angle of depression to two consecutive mileposts on the road on the same side of the balloon. The angles of depression are found to be 20° and 22°. How high is the balloon?

59. Height of a Mountain To estimate the height of a mountain above a level plain, the angle of elevation to the top of the mountain is measured to be 32°. One thousand feet closer to the mountain along the plain, it is found that the angle of elevation is 35°. Estimate the height of the mountain.

60. Height of Cloud Cover To measure the height of the cloud cover at an airport, a worker shines a spotlight upward at an angle 75° from the horizontal. An observer 600 m away measures the angle of elevation to the spot of light to be 45°. Find the height h of the cloud cover.

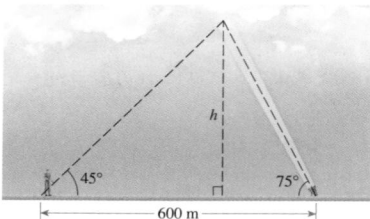

61. Distance to the Sun When the moon is exactly half full, the earth, moon, and sun form a right angle (see the figure). At that time the angle formed by the sun, earth, and moon is measured to be 89.85°. If the distance from the earth to the moon is 240,000 mi, estimate the distance from the earth to the sun.

62. Distance to the Moon To find the distance to the sun as in Exercise 61, we needed to know the distance to the moon. Here is a way to estimate that distance: When the moon is seen at its zenith at a point A on the earth, it is observed to be at the horizon from point B (see the following figure). Points *A* and *B* are 6155 mi apart, and the radius of the earth is 3960 mi.

(a) Find the angle θ in degrees.

(b) Estimate the distance from point *A* to the moon.

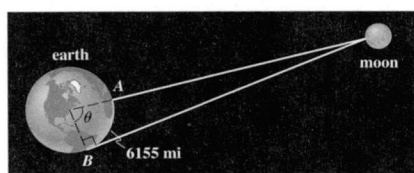

63. Radius of the Earth In Exercise 74 of Section 6.1 a method was given for finding the radius of the earth. Here is a more modern method: From a satellite 600 mi above the earth, it is observed that the angle formed by the vertical and the line of sight to the horizon is 60.276°. Use this information to find the radius of the earth.

64. Parallax To find the distance to nearby stars, the method of parallax is used. The idea is to find a triangle with the star at one vertex and with a base as large as possible. To do this, the star is observed at two different times exactly 6 months apart, and its apparent change in position is recorded. From these two observations, $\angle E_1 S E_2$ can be calculated. (The times are chosen so that $\angle E_1 S E_2$ is as large as possible, which guarantees that $\angle E_1 O S$ is 90°.) The angle $E_1 S O$ is called the *parallax* of the star. Alpha Centauri, the star nearest the earth, has a

parallax of 0.000211°. Estimate the distance to this star. (Take the distance from the earth to the sun to be 9.3×10^7 mi.)

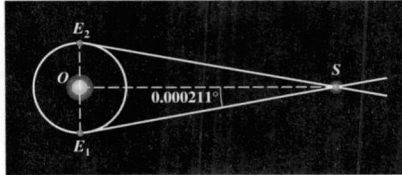

65. Distance from Venus to the Sun The **elongation** α of a planet is the angle formed by the planet, earth, and sun (see the figure). When Venus achieves its maximum elongation of 46.3°, the earth, Venus, and the sun form a triangle with a right angle at Venus. Find the distance between Venus and the sun in astronomical units (AU). (By definition the distance between the earth and the sun is 1 AU.)

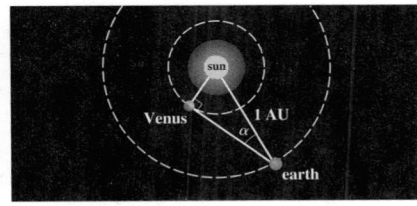

DISCOVERY ▪ DISCUSSION ▪ WRITING

66. Similar Triangles If two triangles are similar, what properties do they share? Explain how these properties make it possible to define the trigonometric ratios without regard to the size of the triangle.

6.3 TRIGONOMETRIC FUNCTIONS OF ANGLES

| Trigonometric Functions of Angles ▶ Evaluating Trigonometric Functions at Any Angle ▶ Trigonometric Identities ▶ Areas of Triangles

In the preceding section we defined the trigonometric ratios for acute angles. Here we extend the trigonometric ratios to all angles by defining the trigonometric functions of angles. With these functions we can solve practical problems that involve angles that are not necessarily acute.

SUGGESTED TIME AND EMPHASIS

1 class, essential material

TEXT QUESTION

Is it possible for two different angles to have the same reference angle?

Answer

Yes

▼ Trigonometric Functions of Angles

Let POQ be a right triangle with acute angle θ as shown in Figure 1(a). Place θ in standard position as shown in Figure 1(b).

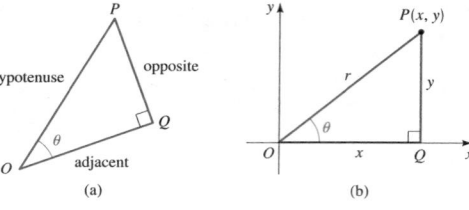

FIGURE 1

Then $P = P(x, y)$ is a point on the terminal side of θ. In triangle POQ, the opposite side has length y and the adjacent side has length x. Using the Pythagorean Theorem, we see that the hypotenuse has length $r = \sqrt{x^2 + y^2}$. So

$$\sin \theta = \frac{y}{r} \qquad \cos \theta = \frac{x}{r} \qquad \tan \theta = \frac{y}{x}$$

The other trigonometric ratios can be found in the same way.

These observations allow us to extend the trigonometric ratios to any angle. We define the trigonometric functions of angles as follows (see Figure 2).

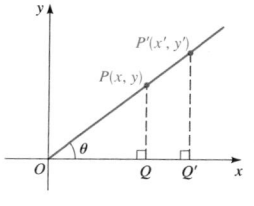

FIGURE 2

DEFINITION OF THE TRIGONOMETRIC FUNCTIONS

Let θ be an angle in standard position and let $P(x, y)$ be a point on the terminal side. If $r = \sqrt{x^2 + y^2}$ is the distance from the origin to the point $P(x, y)$, then

$$\sin \theta = \frac{y}{r} \qquad\qquad \cos \theta = \frac{x}{r} \qquad\qquad \tan \theta = \frac{y}{x} \ \ (x \neq 0)$$

$$\csc \theta = \frac{r}{y} \ \ (y \neq 0) \qquad \sec \theta = \frac{r}{x} \ \ (x \neq 0) \qquad \cot \theta = \frac{x}{y} \ \ (y \neq 0)$$

Since division by 0 is an undefined operation, certain trigonometric functions are not defined for certain angles. For example, $\tan 90° = y/x$ is undefined because $x = 0$. The angles for which the trigonometric functions may be undefined are the angles for which either the x- or y-coordinate of a point on the terminal side of the angle is 0. These are **quadrantal angles**—angles that are coterminal with the coordinate axes.

It is a crucial fact that the values of the trigonometric functions do *not* depend on the choice of the point $P(x, y)$. This is because if $P'(x', y')$ is any other point on the terminal side, as in Figure 3, then triangles POQ and $P'OQ'$ are similar.

FIGURE 3

▼ Evaluating Trigonometric Functions at Any Angle

From the definition we see that the values of the trigonometric functions are all positive if the angle θ has its terminal side in Quadrant I. This is because x and y are positive in this quadrant. [Of course, r is always positive, since it is simply the distance from the origin to the point $P(x, y)$.] If the terminal side of θ is in Quadrant II, however, then x is

---

IN-CLASS MATERIALS

Students often make the mistake of assuming that the trig functions are linear functions. Since the class will probably involve computing a few trig functions, one can kill two birds with one stone by computing $\sin\left(\dfrac{\pi}{2} + \dfrac{\pi}{3}\right)$, $\sin\dfrac{\pi}{2}$, and $\sin\dfrac{\pi}{3}$ to demonstrate that, for example, $\sin\left(\dfrac{\pi}{2} + \dfrac{\pi}{3}\right) \neq \sin\dfrac{\pi}{2} + \sin\dfrac{\pi}{3}$. Return to this point several times; they will be grateful when they avoid that mistake in later courses.

Relationship to the Trigonometric Functions of Real Numbers

You may have already studied the trigonometric functions defined using the unit circle (Chapter 5). To see how they relate to the trigonometric functions of an *angle*, let's start with the unit circle in the coordinate plane.

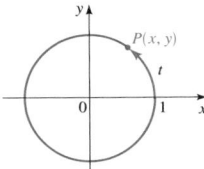

$P(x, y)$ is the terminal point determined by t.

Let $P(x, y)$ be the terminal point determined by an arc of length t on the unit circle. Then t subtends an angle θ at the center of the circle. If we drop a perpendicular from P onto the point Q on the x-axis, then triangle ΔOPQ is a right triangle with legs of length x and y, as shown in the figure.

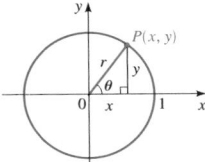

Triangle OPQ is a right triangle.

Now, by the definition of the trigonometric functions of the *real number* t we have

$$\sin t = y$$
$$\cos t = x$$

By the definition of the trigonometric functions of the *angle* θ we have

$$\sin \theta = \frac{\text{opp}}{\text{hyp}} = \frac{y}{1} = y$$

$$\cos \theta = \frac{\text{adj}}{\text{hyp}} = \frac{x}{1} = x$$

If θ is measured in radians, then $\theta = t$. (See the figure below.) Comparing the two ways of defining the trigonometric functions, we see that they are identical. In other words, as functions, they assign identical values to a given real number. (The real number is the radian measure of θ in one case or the length t of an arc in the other.)

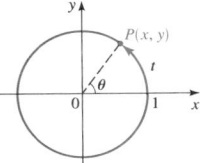

The radian measure of angle θ is t.

Why then do we study trigonometry in two different ways? Because different applications require that we view the trigonometric functions differently. (See *Focus on Modeling*, pages 427, 489, and 533, and Sections 6.2, 6.5, and 6.6.)

The following mnemonic device can be used to remember which trigonometric functions are positive in each quadrant: All of them, Sine, Tangent, or Cosine.

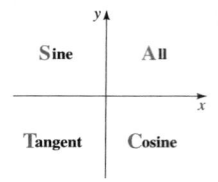

You can remember this as "All Students Take Calculus."

negative and y is positive. Thus, in Quadrant II the functions $\sin\theta$ and $\csc\theta$ are positive, and all the other trigonometric functions have negative values. You can check the other entries in the following table.

SIGNS OF THE TRIGONOMETRIC FUNCTIONS

Quadrant	Positive Functions	Negative Functions
I	all	none
II	sin, csc	cos, sec, tan, cot
III	tan, cot	sin, csc, cos, sec
IV	cos, sec	sin, csc, tan, cot

We now turn our attention to finding the values of the trigonometric functions for angles that are not acute.

EXAMPLE 1 | Finding Trigonometric Functions of Angles

Find **(a)** cos 135° and **(b)** tan 390°.

SOLUTION

(a) From Figure 4 we see that $\cos 135° = -x/r$. But $\cos 45° = x/r$, and since $\cos 45° = \sqrt{2}/2$, we have

$$\cos 135° = -\frac{\sqrt{2}}{2}$$

(b) The angles 390° and 30° are coterminal. From Figure 5 it's clear that $\tan 390° = \tan 30°$ and, since $\tan 30° = \sqrt{3}/3$, we have

$$\tan 390° = \frac{\sqrt{3}}{3}$$

FIGURE 4

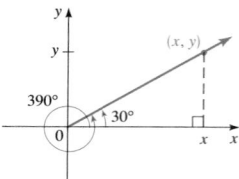

FIGURE 5

✎. NOW TRY EXERCISES **11** AND **13**

From Example 1 we see that the trigonometric functions for angles that aren't acute have the same value, except possibly for sign, as the corresponding trigonometric functions of an acute angle. That acute angle will be called the *reference angle*.

REFERENCE ANGLE

Let θ be an angle in standard position. The **reference angle** $\bar{\theta}$ associated with θ is the acute angle formed by the terminal side of θ and the x-axis.

ALTERNATE EXAMPLE 1

(a) Find cos 60°.

(b) Find tan 240°.

ANSWERS

(a) $\dfrac{1}{2}$

(b) $\sqrt{3}$

IN-CLASS MATERIALS

Don't allow the students to use the mnemonic given in the text (All Students Take Calculus) as a way to avoid all understanding of the sign of the various trigonometric functions in different quadrants. Make sure they are able to articulate why, for example, the cosine function is positive in Quadrants I and IV and negative in Quadrants II and III.

Figure 6 shows that to find a reference angle $\bar{\theta}$, it's useful to know the quadrant in which the terminal side of the angle θ lies.

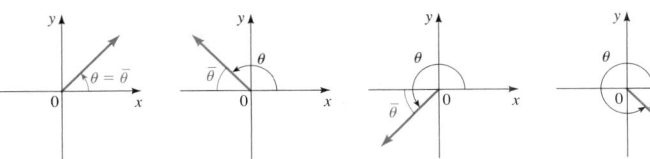

FIGURE 6 The reference angle $\bar{\theta}$ for an angle θ

FIGURE 7

FIGURE 8

EXAMPLE 2 | Finding Reference Angles

Find the reference angle for **(a)** $\theta = \dfrac{5\pi}{3}$ and **(b)** $\theta = 870°$.

SOLUTION

(a) The reference angle is the acute angle formed by the terminal side of the angle $5\pi/3$ and the x-axis (see Figure 7). Since the terminal side of this angle is in Quadrant IV, the reference angle is

$$\bar{\theta} = 2\pi - \frac{5\pi}{3} = \frac{\pi}{3}$$

(b) The angles 870° and 150° are coterminal [because $870 - 2(360) = 150$]. Thus, the terminal side of this angle is in Quadrant II (see Figure 8). So the reference angle is

$$\bar{\theta} = 180° - 150° = 30°$$

✎ NOW TRY EXERCISES **3** AND **7** ■

EVALUATING TRIGONOMETRIC FUNCTIONS FOR ANY ANGLE

To find the values of the trigonometric functions for any angle θ, we carry out the following steps.

1. Find the reference angle $\bar{\theta}$ associated with the angle θ.

2. Determine the sign of the trigonometric function of θ by noting the quadrant in which θ lies.

3. The value of the trigonometric function of θ is the same, except possibly for sign, as the value of the trigonometric function of $\bar{\theta}$.

EXAMPLE 3 | Using the Reference Angle to Evaluate Trigonometric Functions

Find **(a)** sin 240° and **(b)** cot 495°.

SOLUTION

(a) This angle has its terminal side in Quadrant III, as shown in Figure 9. The reference angle is therefore $240° - 180° = 60°$, and the value of sin 240° is negative. Thus

$$\sin 240° = -\sin 60° = -\frac{\sqrt{3}}{2}$$

Sign   Reference angle

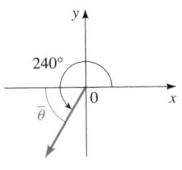

FIGURE 9

$\dfrac{S \mid A}{T \mid C}$ sin 240° is *negative*.

ALTERNATE EXAMPLE 2

(a) Find the reference angle for $\theta = \dfrac{13\pi}{7}$.

(b) $\theta = 600°$

ANSWERS

(a) $\dfrac{\pi}{7}$

(b) $60°$

ALTERNATE EXAMPLE 3

Find sin 120°.

ANSWER

$-\dfrac{1}{2}$

FIGURE 10

$\begin{array}{c|c} S & A \\ \hline T & C \end{array}$ *tan* 495° *is negative,*
so cot 495° *is negative.*

(b) The angle 495° is coterminal with the angle 135°, and the terminal side of this angle is in Quadrant II, as shown in Figure 10. So the reference angle is $180° - 135° = 45°$, and the value of cot 495° is negative. We have

$$\cot 495° = \cot 135° = -\cot 45° = -1$$

Coterminal angles   Sign   Reference angle

⟋ **NOW TRY EXERCISES 17 AND 19** ◼

EXAMPLE 4 | Using the Reference Angle to Evaluate Trigonometric Functions

Find **(a)** $\sin\dfrac{16\pi}{3}$ and **(b)** $\sec\left(-\dfrac{\pi}{4}\right)$.

SOLUTION

(a) The angle $16\pi/3$ is coterminal with $4\pi/3$, and these angles are in Quadrant III (see Figure 11). Thus, the reference angle is $(4\pi/3) - \pi = \pi/3$. Since the value of sine is negative in Quadrant III, we have

$$\sin\frac{16\pi}{3} = \sin\frac{4\pi}{3} = -\sin\frac{\pi}{3} = -\frac{\sqrt{3}}{2}$$

Coterminal angles   Sign   Reference angle

(b) The angle $-\pi/4$ is in Quadrant IV, and its reference angle is $\pi/4$ (see Figure 12). Since secant is positive in this quadrant, we get

$$\sec\left(-\frac{\pi}{4}\right) = +\sec\frac{\pi}{4} = \sqrt{2}$$

Sign   Reference angle

FIGURE 11

$\begin{array}{c|c} S & A \\ \hline T & C \end{array}$ $\sin\frac{16\pi}{3}$ *is negative.*

FIGURE 12

$\begin{array}{c|c} S & A \\ \hline T & C \end{array}$ $\cos(-\frac{\pi}{4})$ *is positive,*
so $\sec(-\frac{\pi}{4})$ *is positive.*

⟋ **NOW TRY EXERCISES 23 AND 25** ◼

▼ Trigonometric Identities

The trigonometric functions of angles are related to each other through several important equations called **trigonometric identities**. We've already encountered the reciprocal identities. These identities continue to hold for any angle θ, provided that both sides of the equation are defined. The Pythagorean identities are a consequence of the Pythagorean Theorem.*

FUNDAMENTAL IDENTITIES

Reciprocal Identities

$$\csc \theta = \frac{1}{\sin \theta} \qquad \sec \theta = \frac{1}{\cos \theta} \qquad \cot \theta = \frac{1}{\tan \theta}$$

$$\tan \theta = \frac{\sin \theta}{\cos \theta} \qquad \cot \theta = \frac{\cos \theta}{\sin \theta}$$

Pythagorean Identities

$$\sin^2\theta + \cos^2\theta = 1 \qquad \tan^2\theta + 1 = \sec^2\theta \qquad 1 + \cot^2\theta = \csc^2\theta$$

FIGURE 13

PROOF Let's prove the first Pythagorean identity. Using $x^2 + y^2 = r^2$ (the Pythagorean Theorem) in Figure 13, we have

$$\sin^2\theta + \cos^2\theta = \left(\frac{y}{r}\right)^2 + \left(\frac{x}{r}\right)^2 = \frac{x^2 + y^2}{r^2} = \frac{r^2}{r^2} = 1$$

Thus, $\sin^2\theta + \cos^2\theta = 1$. (Although the figure indicates an acute angle, you should check that the proof holds for all angles θ.) ■

See Exercises 61 and 62 for the proofs of the other two Pythagorean identities.

EXAMPLE 5 | **Expressing One Trigonometric Function in Terms of Another**

(a) Express $\sin \theta$ in terms of $\cos \theta$.

(b) Express $\tan \theta$ in terms of $\sin \theta$, where θ is in Quadrant II.

SOLUTION

(a) From the first Pythagorean identity we get

$$\sin \theta = \pm\sqrt{1 - \cos^2\theta}$$

where the sign depends on the quadrant. If θ is in Quadrant I or II, then $\sin \theta$ is positive, and so

$$\sin \theta = \sqrt{1 - \cos^2\theta}$$

whereas if θ is in Quadrant III or IV, $\sin \theta$ is negative, and so

$$\sin \theta = -\sqrt{1 - \cos^2\theta}$$

(b) Since $\tan \theta = \sin \theta/\cos \theta$, we need to write $\cos \theta$ in terms of $\sin \theta$. By part (a)

$$\cos \theta = \pm\sqrt{1 - \sin^2\theta}$$

and since $\cos \theta$ is negative in Quadrant II, the negative sign applies here. Thus

$$\tan \theta = \frac{\sin \theta}{\cos \theta} = \frac{\sin \theta}{-\sqrt{1 - \sin^2\theta}}$$

✎. NOW TRY EXERCISE **39** ■

---

* We follow the usual convention of writing $\sin^2\theta$ for $(\sin \theta)^2$. In general, we write $\sin^n\theta$ for $(\sin \theta)^n$ for all integers n except $n = -1$. The exponent $n = -1$ will be assigned another meaning in Section 6.4. Of course, the same convention applies to the other five trigonometric functions.

ALTERNATE EXAMPLE 5

Express $\tan \theta$ in terms of $\sin \theta$, where θ is in Quadrant III.

ANSWER

$$-\frac{\sin(\theta)}{\sqrt{1 - \sin^2(\theta)}}$$

ALTERNATE EXAMPLE 6

If $\tan \theta = \frac{1}{2}$ and θ is in Quadrant IV, find $\cos \theta$.

ANSWER

$$\frac{2}{\sqrt{5}}$$

ALTERNATE EXAMPLE 7

If $\sec \theta = 6$ and θ is in Quadrant IV, find the other five trigonometric functions of θ.

ANSWER

$\sin (\theta) = -\dfrac{\sqrt{35}}{6}$

$\cos (\theta) = \dfrac{1}{6}$

$\tan (\theta) = -\sqrt{35}$

$\cot (\theta) = -\dfrac{1}{\sqrt{35}}$

$\csc (\theta) = -\dfrac{6}{\sqrt{35}}$

EXAMPLE 6 | Evaluating a Trigonometric Function

If $\tan \theta = \frac{2}{3}$ and θ is in Quadrant III, find $\cos \theta$.

SOLUTION 1 We need to write $\cos \theta$ in terms of $\tan \theta$. From the identity $\tan^2\theta + 1 = \sec^2\theta$ we get $\sec \theta = \pm\sqrt{\tan^2\theta + 1}$. In Quadrant III, $\sec \theta$ is negative, so

$$\sec \theta = -\sqrt{\tan^2\theta + 1}$$

If you wish to rationalize the denominator, you can express $\cos \theta$ as

$$-\frac{3}{\sqrt{13}} \cdot \frac{\sqrt{13}}{\sqrt{13}} = -\frac{3\sqrt{13}}{13}$$

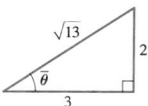

FIGURE 14

Thus,

$$\cos \theta = \frac{1}{\sec \theta} = \frac{1}{-\sqrt{\tan^2\theta + 1}}$$

$$= \frac{1}{-\sqrt{\left(\frac{2}{3}\right)^2 + 1}} = \frac{1}{-\sqrt{\frac{13}{9}}} = -\frac{3}{\sqrt{13}}$$

SOLUTION 2 This problem can be solved more easily by using the method of Example 2 of Section 6.2. Recall that, except for sign, the values of the trigonometric functions of any angle are the same as those of an acute angle (the reference angle). So, ignoring the sign for the moment, let's sketch a right triangle with an acute angle $\bar{\theta}$ satisfying $\tan \bar{\theta} = \frac{2}{3}$ (see Figure 14). By the Pythagorean Theorem the hypotenuse of this triangle has length $\sqrt{13}$. From the triangle in Figure 14 we immediately see that $\cos \bar{\theta} = 3/\sqrt{13}$. Since θ is in Quadrant III, $\cos \theta$ is negative, so

$$\cos \theta = -\frac{3}{\sqrt{13}}$$

🔊 NOW TRY EXERCISE **45** ∎

EXAMPLE 7 | Evaluating Trigonometric Functions

If $\sec \theta = 2$ and θ is in Quadrant IV, find the other five trigonometric functions of θ.

SOLUTION We sketch a triangle as in Figure 15 so that $\sec \bar{\theta} = 2$. Taking into account the fact that θ is in Quadrant IV, we get

$$\sin \theta = -\frac{\sqrt{3}}{2} \qquad \cos \theta = \frac{1}{2} \qquad \tan \theta = -\sqrt{3}$$

$$\csc \theta = -\frac{2}{\sqrt{3}} \qquad \sec \theta = 2 \qquad \cot \theta = -\frac{1}{\sqrt{3}}$$

FIGURE 15

🔊 NOW TRY EXERCISE **47** ∎

▼ Areas of Triangles

We conclude this section with an application of the trigonometric functions that involves angles that are not necessarily acute. More extensive applications appear in the next two sections.

The area of a triangle is $\mathcal{A} = \frac{1}{2} \times$ base $\times$ height. If we know two sides and the included angle of a triangle, then we can find the height using the trigonometric functions, and from this we can find the area.

If θ is an acute angle, then the height of the triangle in Figure 16(a) is given by $h = b \sin \theta$. Thus the area is

$$\mathcal{A} = \tfrac{1}{2} \times \text{base} \times \text{height} = \tfrac{1}{2}ab \sin \theta$$

If the angle θ is not acute, then from Figure 16(b) we see that the height of the triangle is

$$h = b \sin(180° - \theta) = b \sin \theta$$

(a)

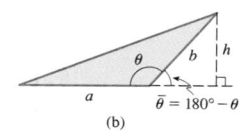

(b)

FIGURE 16

This is so because the reference angle of θ is the angle $180° - \theta$. Thus, in this case also, the area of the triangle is

$$\mathcal{A} = \tfrac{1}{2} \times \text{base} \times \text{height} = \tfrac{1}{2}ab \sin \theta$$

AREA OF A TRIANGLE

The area $\mathcal{A}$ of a triangle with sides of lengths a and b and with included angle θ is

$$\mathcal{A} = \tfrac{1}{2}ab \sin \theta$$

EXAMPLE 8 | Finding the Area of a Triangle

Find the area of triangle ABC shown in Figure 17.

SOLUTION   The triangle has sides of length 10 cm and 3 cm, with included angle 120°. Therefore

$$\mathcal{A} = \tfrac{1}{2}ab \sin \theta$$
$$= \tfrac{1}{2}(10)(3) \sin 120°$$
$$= 15 \sin 60° \qquad \text{Reference angle}$$
$$= 15\frac{\sqrt{3}}{2} \approx 13 \text{ cm}^2$$

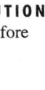

FIGURE 17

NOW TRY EXERCISE 55 ∎

ALTERNATE EXAMPLE 8
Find the area of triangle ABC shown in the figure.

ANSWER
$27 \cdot \dfrac{\sqrt{3}}{2}$

6.3 EXERCISES

CONCEPTS

1. If the angle θ is in standard position and $P(x, y)$ is a point on the terminal side of θ, and r is the distance from the origin to P, then

$\sin \theta = $ ____ $\cos \theta = $ ____ $\tan \theta = $ ____

2. The sign of a trigonometric function of θ depends on the

_____ in which the terminal side of the angle θ lies.

In Quadrant II, $\sin \theta$ is _____ (positive / negative).

In Quadrant III, $\cos \theta$ is _____ (positive / negative).

In Quadrant IV, $\sin \theta$ is _____ (positive / negative).

SKILLS

3–10 ■ Find the reference angle for the given angle.

3. (a) 150°   **(b)** 330°   **(c)** −30°

4. (a) 120°   **(b)** −210°   **(c)** 780°

5. (a) 225°   **(b)** 810°   **(c)** −105°

6. (a) 99°   **(b)** −199°   **(c)** 359°

7. (a) $\dfrac{11\pi}{4}$ **(b)** $-\dfrac{11\pi}{6}$ **(c)** $\dfrac{11\pi}{3}$

8. (a) $\dfrac{4\pi}{3}$ **(b)** $\dfrac{33\pi}{4}$ **(c)** $-\dfrac{23\pi}{6}$

9. (a) $\dfrac{5\pi}{7}$ **(b)** -1.4π **(c)** 1.4

10. (a) 2.3π **(b)** 2.3   **(c)** -10π

11–34 ■ Find the exact value of the trigonometric function.

11. $\sin 150°$ **12.** $\sin 225°$ **13.** $\cos 210°$

14. $\cos(-60°)$ **15.** $\tan(-60°)$ **16.** $\sec 300°$

17. $\csc(-630°)$ **18.** $\cot 210°$ **19.** $\cos 570°$

20. $\sec 120°$ **21.** $\tan 750°$ **22.** $\cos 660°$

23. $\sin \dfrac{2\pi}{3}$ **24.** $\sin \dfrac{5\pi}{3}$ **25.** $\sin \dfrac{3\pi}{2}$

26. $\cos \dfrac{7\pi}{3}$ **27.** $\cos\left(-\dfrac{7\pi}{3}\right)$ **28.** $\tan \dfrac{5\pi}{6}$

29. $\sec \dfrac{17\pi}{3}$ **30.** $\csc \dfrac{5\pi}{4}$ **31.** $\cot\left(-\dfrac{\pi}{4}\right)$

32. $\cos \dfrac{7\pi}{4}$ **33.** $\tan \dfrac{5\pi}{2}$ **34.** $\sin \dfrac{11\pi}{6}$

DRILL QUESTION
If $\theta = \dfrac{17\pi}{6}$, find its reference angle $\bar{\theta}$. In what quadrant is θ?

Answer
$\bar{\theta} = \dfrac{\pi}{6}$. θ is in the second quadrant.

35–38 ■ Find the quadrant in which θ lies from the information given.

35. $\sin \theta < 0$ and $\cos \theta < 0$

36. $\tan \theta < 0$ and $\sin \theta < 0$

37. $\sec \theta > 0$ and $\tan \theta < 0$

38. $\csc \theta > 0$ and $\cos \theta < 0$

39–44 ■ Write the first trigonometric function in terms of the second for θ in the given quadrant.

39. $\tan \theta$, $\cos \theta$; θ in Quadrant III

40. $\cot \theta$, $\sin \theta$; θ in Quadrant II

41. $\cos \theta$, $\sin \theta$; θ in Quadrant IV

42. $\sec \theta$, $\sin \theta$; θ in Quadrant I

43. $\sec \theta$, $\tan \theta$; θ in Quadrant II

44. $\csc \theta$, $\cot \theta$; θ in Quadrant III

45–52 ■ Find the values of the trigonometric functions of θ from the information given.

45. $\sin \theta = \frac{3}{5}$, θ in Quadrant II

46. $\cos \theta = -\frac{7}{12}$, θ in Quadrant III

47. $\tan \theta = -\frac{3}{4}$, $\cos \theta > 0$

48. $\sec \theta = 5$, $\sin \theta < 0$

49. $\csc \theta = 2$, θ in Quadrant I

50. $\cot \theta = \frac{1}{4}$, $\sin \theta < 0$

51. $\cos \theta = -\frac{2}{7}$, $\tan \theta < 0$

52. $\tan \theta = -4$, $\sin \theta > 0$

53. If $\theta = \pi/3$, find the value of each expression.
   (a) $\sin 2\theta$, $2 \sin \theta$ **(b)** $\sin \frac{1}{2}\theta$, $\frac{1}{2} \sin \theta$
   (c) $\sin^2\theta$, $\sin(\theta^2)$

54. Find the area of a triangle with sides of length 7 and 9 and included angle 72°.

55. Find the area of a triangle with sides of length 10 and 22 and included angle 10°.

56. Find the area of an equilateral triangle with side of length 10.

57. A triangle has an area of 16 in², and two of the sides of the triangle have lengths 5 in. and 7 in. Find the angle included by these two sides.

58. An isosceles triangle has an area of 24 cm², and the angle between the two equal sides is $5\pi/6$. What is the length of the two equal sides?

59–60 ■ Find the area of the shaded region in the figure.

59.

60.

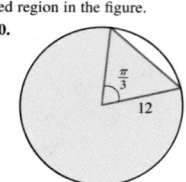

61. Use the first Pythagorean identity to prove the second. [*Hint:* Divide by $\cos^2\theta$.]

62. Use the first Pythagorean identity to prove the third.

APPLICATIONS

63. Height of a Rocket   A rocket fired straight up is tracked by an observer on the ground a mile away.
   (a) Show that when the angle of elevation is θ, the height of the rocket in feet is $h = 5280 \tan \theta$.
   (b) Complete the table to find the height of the rocket at the given angles of elevation.

θ	20°	60°	80°	85°
h				

64. Rain Gutter   A rain gutter is to be constructed from a metal sheet of width 30 cm by bending up one-third of the sheet on each side through an angle θ.
   (a) Show that the cross-sectional area of the gutter is modeled by the function
   $$A(\theta) = 100 \sin \theta + 100 \sin \theta \cos \theta$$
   (b) Graph the function A for $0 \le \theta \le \pi/2$.
   (c) For what angle θ is the largest cross-sectional area achieved?

65. Wooden Beam   A rectangular beam is to be cut from a cylindrical log of diameter 20 cm. The figures show different ways this can be done.
   (a) Express the cross-sectional area of the beam as a function of the angle θ in the figures.
   (b) Graph the function you found in part (a).
   (c) Find the dimensions of the beam with largest cross-sectional area.

66. Strength of a Beam The strength of a beam is proportional to the width and the square of the depth. A beam is cut from a log as in Exercise 65. Express the strength of the beam as a function of the angle θ in the figures.

67. Throwing a Shot Put The range R and height H of a shot put thrown with an initial velocity of v_0 ft/s at an angle θ are given by

$$R = \frac{v_0^2 \sin(2\theta)}{g}$$

$$H = \frac{v_0^2 \sin^2\theta}{2g}$$

On the earth $g = 32$ ft/s^2 and on the moon $g = 5.2$ ft/s^2. Find the range and height of a shot put thrown under the given conditions.
(a) On the earth with $v_0 = 12$ ft/s and $\theta = \pi/6$
(b) On the moon with $v_0 = 12$ ft/s and $\theta = \pi/6$

68. Sledding The time in seconds that it takes for a sled to slide down a hillside inclined at an angle θ is

$$t = \sqrt{\frac{d}{16 \sin \theta}}$$

where d is the length of the slope in feet. Find the time it takes to slide down a 2000-ft slope inclined at 30°.

69. Beehives In a beehive each cell is a regular hexagonal prism, as shown in the figure. The amount of wax W in the cell depends on the apex angle θ and is given by

$$W = 3.02 - 0.38 \cot \theta + 0.65 \csc \theta$$

Bees instinctively choose θ so as to use the least amount of wax possible.
(a) Use a graphing device to graph W as a function of θ for $0 < \theta < \pi$.

(b) For what value of θ does W have its minimum value? [*Note:* Biologists have discovered that bees rarely deviate from this value by more than a degree or two.]

70. Turning a Corner A steel pipe is being carried down a hallway that is 9 ft wide. At the end of the hall there is a right-angled turn into a narrower hallway 6 ft wide.
(a) Show that the length of the pipe in the figure is modeled by the function

$$L(\theta) = 9 \csc \theta + 6 \sec \theta$$

(b) Graph the function L for $0 < \theta < \pi/2$.
(c) Find the minimum value of the function L.
(d) Explain why the value of L you found in part (c) is the length of the longest pipe that can be carried around the corner.

71. Rainbows Rainbows are created when sunlight of different wavelengths (colors) is refracted and reflected in raindrops. The angle of elevation θ of a rainbow is always the same. It can be shown that $\theta = 4\beta - 2\alpha$, where

$$\sin \alpha = k \sin \beta$$

and $\alpha = 59.4°$ and $k = 1.33$ is the index of refraction of water. Use the given information to find the angle of elevation θ of a rainbow. (For a mathematical explanation of rainbows see *Calculus Early Transcendentals,* 7th Edition, by James Stewart, page 282.)

DISCOVERY ■ DISCUSSION ■ WRITING

72. Using a Calculator To solve a certain problem, you need to find the sine of 4 rad. Your study partner uses his calculator and tells you that

$$\sin 4 = 0.0697564737$$

On your calculator you get

$$\sin 4 = -0.7568024953$$

What is wrong? What mistake did your partner make?

73. Viète's Trigonometric Diagram In the 16th century the French mathematician François Viète (see page 49) published the following remarkable diagram. Each of the six trigonometric functions of θ is equal to the length of a line segment in the figure. For instance, $\sin \theta = |PR|$, since from $\triangle OPR$ we see that

$$\sin \theta = \frac{\text{opp}}{\text{hyp}} = \frac{|PR|}{|OR|}$$

$$= \frac{|PR|}{1} = |PR|$$

For each of the five other trigonometric functions, find a line segment in the figure whose length equals the value of the function at θ. (*Note:* The radius of the circle is 1, the center is O, segment QS is tangent to the circle at R, and $\angle SOQ$ is a right angle.)

DISCOVERY PROJECT | **Similarity**

In this project we explore the idea of similarity and some of its consequences for any type of figure. You can find the project at the book companion website: **www.stewartmath.com**

SUGGESTED TIME AND EMPHASIS

1 class, essential material

6.4 INVERSE TRIGONOMETRIC FUNCTIONS AND RIGHT TRIANGLES

The Inverse Sine, Inverse Cosine, and Inverse Tangent Functions ▶ Solving for Angles in Right Triangles ▶ Evaluating Expressions Involving Inverse Trigonometric Functions

The graphs of the inverse trigonometric functions are studied in Section 5.5.

Recall that for a function to have an inverse, it must be one-to-one. Since the trigonometric functions are not one-to-one, they do not have inverses. So we restrict the domain of each of the trigonometric functions to intervals on which they attain all their values and on which they are one-to-one. The resulting functions have the same range as the original functions but are one-to-one.

▼ The Inverse Sine, Inverse Cosine, and Inverse Tangent Functions

Let's first consider the sine function. We restrict the domain of the sine function to angles θ with $-\pi/2 \le \theta \le \pi/2$. From Figure 1 we see that on this domain the sine function attains each of the values in the interval $[-1, 1]$ exactly once and so is one-to-one. Similarly, we restrict the domains of cosine and tangent as shown in Figure 1.

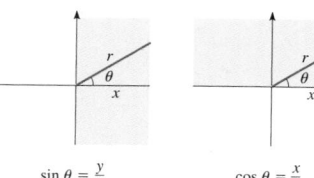

FIGURE 1 Restricted domains of the sine, cosine, and tangent functions

$$\sin \theta = \frac{y}{r}$$
$$-\frac{\pi}{2} \le \theta \le \frac{\pi}{2}$$

$$\cos \theta = \frac{x}{r}$$
$$0 \le \theta \le \pi$$

$$\tan \theta = \frac{x}{y}$$
$$-\frac{\pi}{2} < \theta < \frac{\pi}{2}$$

Text Question

We can say $\sin^{-1} y = x$ means $y = \sin x$. Given this definition, why does the text need to fuss with domains and ranges?

Answer

For a given y between -1 and 1, there are infinitely many values of x such that $y = \sin x$.

On these restricted domains we can define an inverse for each of these functions. By the definition of inverse function we have

$$\sin^{-1} x = y \iff \sin y = x$$
$$\cos^{-1} x = y \iff \cos y = x$$
$$\tan^{-1} x = y \iff \tan y = x$$

We summarize the domains and ranges of the inverse trigonometric functions in the following box.

THE INVERSE SINE, INVERSE COSINE, AND INVERSE TANGENT FUNCTIONS

The sine, cosine, and tangent functions on the restricted domains $[-\pi/2, \pi/2]$, $[0, \pi]$, and $(-\pi/2, \pi/2)$, respectively, are one-to one and so have inverses. The inverse functions have domain and range as follows.

Function	Domain	Range
$\sin^{-1}$	$[-1, 1]$	$[-\pi/2, \pi/2]$
$\cos^{-1}$	$[-1, 1]$	$[0, \pi]$
$\tan^{-1}$	$\mathbb{R}$	$(-\pi/2, \pi/2)$

The functions $\sin^{-1}$, $\cos^{-1}$, and $\tan^{-1}$ are sometimes called **arcsine, arccosine**, and **arctangent**, respectively.

Since these are inverse functions, they reverse the rule of the original function. For example, since $\sin \pi/6 = \frac{1}{2}$, it follows that $\sin^{-1} \frac{1}{2} = \pi/6$. The following example gives further illustrations.

EXAMPLE 1 | Evaluating Inverse Trigonometric Functions

Find the exact value.

(a) $\sin^{-1} \dfrac{\sqrt{3}}{2}$ **(b)** $\cos^{-1}\left(-\frac{1}{2}\right)$ **(c)** $\tan^{-1} 1$

SOLUTION

(a) The angle in the interval $[-\pi/2, \pi/2]$ whose sine is $\sqrt{3}/2$ is $\pi/3$. Thus $\sin^{-1}(\sqrt{3}/2) = \pi/3$.

(b) The angle in the interval $[0, \pi]$ whose cosine is $-\frac{1}{2}$ is $2\pi/3$. Thus $\cos^{-1}(-\frac{1}{2}) = 2\pi/3$.

(c) The angle in the interval $[-\pi/2, \pi/2]$ whose tangent is 1 is $\pi/4$. Thus $\tan^{-1} 1 = \pi/4$.

✎ NOW TRY EXERCISE **3** ∎

EXAMPLE 2 | Evaluating Inverse Trigonometric Functions

Find approximate values for the given expression.

(a) $\sin^{-1}(0.71)$ **(b)** $\tan^{-1}(2)$ **(c)** $\cos^{-1} 2$

SOLUTION We use a calculator to approximate these values.

(a) Using the INV SIN, or SIN⁻¹, or ARC SIN key(s) on the calculator (with the calculator in radian mode), we get

$$\sin^{-1}(0.71) \approx 0.78950$$

EXAMPLES

- $\sin^{-1}\left(\dfrac{\sqrt{2}}{2}\right) = \dfrac{\pi}{4}$

- $\cos^{-1}\left(-\dfrac{\sqrt{3}}{2}\right) = \dfrac{5\pi}{6}$

- $\tan^{-1} \sqrt{3} = \dfrac{\pi}{3}$

- $\tan^{-1}\left(-\sqrt{3}\right) = -\dfrac{\pi}{3}$

- $\tan\left(\sin^{-1} \dfrac{1}{5}\right) = \dfrac{\sqrt{6}}{12}$

- $\cos\left(\tan^{-1} \dfrac{3}{8}\right) = 8 \dfrac{\sqrt{73}}{73}$

- $\sin^{-1}\left(\sin \dfrac{87\pi}{4}\right) = -\dfrac{\pi}{4}$

ALTERNATE EXAMPLE 1

Find $\sin^{-1} \dfrac{\sqrt{2}}{2}$, $\sin^{-1}\left(-\dfrac{\sqrt{2}}{2}\right)$, and $\sin^{-1} \dfrac{5}{4}$.

ANSWER

$\dfrac{\pi}{4}$, $-\dfrac{\pi}{4}$, undefined

ALTERNATE EXAMPLE 2

Find approximate values for $\sin^{-1} 1$, $\cos^{-1} 1$, and $\tan^{-1} 1$.

ANSWER

$\dfrac{\pi}{2}$, 0, and $\dfrac{\pi}{4}$

IN-CLASS MATERIALS

Many students may need a review of notation: $\sin^2 x = (\sin x)^2$, $\sin x^2 = \sin(x^2)$, $(\sin x)^{-1} = \dfrac{1}{\sin x} = \csc x$, $\sin x^{-1} = \sin\left(\dfrac{1}{x}\right)$, but $\sin^{-1} x$ represents the inverse sine of x, the arcsine of x, which is not the same as any of the previous functions.

(b) Using the [INV][TAN], or [TAN⁻¹], or [ARC][TAN] key(s) on the calculator (with the calculator in radian mode), we get

$$\tan^{-1} 2 \approx 1.10715$$

(c) Since $2 > 1$, it is not in the domain of $\cos^{-1}$, so $\cos^{-1} 2$ is not defined.

✎. NOW TRY EXERCISES **7**, **11**, AND **13** ∎

▼ Solving for Angles in Right Triangles

In Section 6.2 we solved triangles by using the trigonometric functions to find the unknown sides. We now use the inverse trigonometric functions to solve for *angles* in a right triangle.

EXAMPLE 3 | Finding an Angle in a Right Triangle

Find the angle θ in the triangle shown in Figure 2.

SOLUTION Since θ is the angle opposite the side of length 10 and the hypotenuse has length 50, we have

$$\sin \theta = \frac{10}{50} = \frac{1}{5} \qquad \sin \theta = \frac{\text{opp}}{\text{hyp}}$$

Now we can use $\sin^{-1}$ to find θ:

$$\theta = \sin^{-1} \tfrac{1}{5} \qquad \text{Definition of } \sin^{-1}$$

$$\theta \approx 11.5° \qquad \text{Calculator (in degree mode)}$$

✎. NOW TRY EXERCISE **15** ∎

EXAMPLE 4 | Solving for an Angle in a Right Triangle

A 40-ft ladder leans against a building. If the base of the ladder is 6 ft from the base of the building, what is the angle formed by the ladder and the building?

SOLUTION First we sketch a diagram as in Figure 3. If θ is the angle between the ladder and the building, then

$$\sin \theta = \frac{6}{40} = 0.15 \qquad \sin \theta = \frac{\text{opp}}{\text{hyp}}$$

Now we use $\sin^{-1}$ to find θ:

$$\theta = \sin^{-1}(0.15) \qquad \text{Definition of } \sin^{-1}$$

$$\theta \approx 8.6° \qquad \text{Calculator (in degree mode)}$$

FIGURE 3

✎. NOW TRY EXERCISE **37** ∎

FIGURE 2

IN-CLASS MATERIALS

It may be helpful to start by reviewing general inverse functions (Section 2.7). If $f(x) = x^3$, what is $f^{-1}(x)$?

Note that $f(2) = 8$ and $f^{-1}(8) = 2$. Now move to $f(x) = \sqrt[5]{3x + 2} \Rightarrow f^{-1}(x) = \frac{x^5 - 2}{3}$.

Note that $f(5) \approx 1.762$ and $f^{-1}(1.762) \approx 5$. Now explore $f(x) = x^2$, and point out that even though there is no inverse function, we could make things work out if we were allowed to assume that x was positive. This leads to a natural segue into $f(x) = \sin x$.

EXAMPLE 5 | The Angle of a Beam of Light

A lighthouse is located on an island that is 2 mi off a straight shoreline (see Figure 4). Express the angle formed by the beam of light and the shoreline in terms of the distance d in the figure.

SOLUTION From the figure we see that

$$\tan \theta = \frac{2}{d} \qquad\qquad \tan \theta = \frac{\text{opp}}{\text{adj}}$$

Taking the inverse tangent of both sides, we get

$$\tan^{-1}(\tan \theta) = \tan^{-1}\left(\frac{2}{d}\right) \qquad \text{Take } \tan^{-1} \text{ of both sides}$$

$$\theta = \tan^{-1}\left(\frac{2}{d}\right) \qquad \text{Property of inverse functions: } \tan^{-1}(\tan \theta) = \theta$$

shoreline

lighthouse

2 mi

FIGURE 4

◥. NOW TRY EXERCISE **39** ■

In Section 6.5 we learn how to solve any triangle (not necessarily a right triangle). The angles in a triangle are always in the interval $[0, \pi]$ (or between 0° and 180°). We'll see that to solve such triangles we need to find all angles in the interval $[0, \pi]$ that have a specified sine or cosine. We do this in the next example.

EXAMPLE 6 | Solving a Basic Trigonometric Equation on an Interval

Find all angles θ between 0° and 180° satisfying the given equation.

(a) $\sin \theta = 0.4$ **(b)** $\cos \theta = 0.4$

SOLUTION

(a) We use $\sin^{-1}$ to find one solution in the interval $[-\pi/2, \pi/2]$.

$$\sin \theta = 0.4 \qquad \text{Equation}$$

$$\theta = \sin^{-1}(0.4) \qquad \text{Take } \sin^{-1} \text{ of each side}$$

$$\theta \approx 23.6° \qquad \text{Calculator (in degree mode)}$$

Another solution with θ between 0° and 180° is obtained by taking the supplement of the angle: $180° - 23.6° = 156.4°$ (see Figure 5). So the solutions of the equation with θ between 0° and 180° are

$$\theta \approx 23.6° \qquad \text{and} \qquad \theta \approx 156.4°$$

(b) The cosine function is one-to-one on the interval $[0, \pi]$, so there is only one solution of the equation with θ between 0° and 180°. We find that solution by taking $\cos^{-1}$ of each side.

$$\cos \theta = 0.4$$

$$\theta = \cos^{-1}(0.4) \qquad \text{Take } \cos^{-1} \text{ of each side}$$

$$\theta \approx 66.4° \qquad \text{Calculator (in degree mode)}$$

The solution is $\theta \approx 66.4°$

156.4°

23.6°

FIGURE 5

◥. NOW TRY EXERCISES **23** AND **25** ■

▼ Evaluating Expressions Involving Inverse Trigonometric Functions

Expressions like $\cos(\sin^{-1} x)$ arise in calculus. We find exact values of such expressions using trigonometric identities or right triangles.

IN-CLASS MATERIALS

In calculus, when integrating certain functions (such as those containing terms of the form $a^2 \pm x^2$), we often obtain unwieldy answers like $\sin(\tan^{-1} x)$. The technique presented in Example 7 and Example 8 (Solution 1) is very useful in that situation.

ALTERNATE EXAMPLE 7

Find the exact value of

$$\cos\left(\sin^{-1}\frac{5}{13}\right).$$

ANSWER

$$\frac{12}{13}$$

EXAMPLE 7 | Composing Trigonometric Functions and Their Inverses

Find $\cos(\sin^{-1}\frac{3}{5})$.

SOLUTION 1

Let $\theta = \sin^{-1}\frac{3}{5}$. Then θ is the number in the interval $[-\pi/2, \pi/2]$ whose sine is $\frac{3}{5}$. Let's interpret θ as an angle and draw a right triangle with θ as one of its acute angles, with opposite side 3 and hypotenuse 5 (see Figure 6). The remaining leg of the triangle is found by the Pythagorean Theorem to be 4. From the figure we get

$$\cos(\sin^{-1}\tfrac{3}{5}) = \cos\theta \qquad \theta = \sin^{-1}\tfrac{3}{5}$$
$$= \frac{4}{5} \qquad \cos\theta = \frac{\text{adj}}{\text{hyp}}$$

So $\cos(\sin^{-1}\frac{3}{5}) = \frac{4}{5}$.

FIGURE 6 $\cos\theta = \frac{4}{5}$

SOLUTION 2

It's easy to find $\sin(\sin^{-1}\frac{3}{5})$. In fact, by the cancellation properties of inverse functions, this value is exactly $\frac{3}{5}$. To find $\cos(\sin^{-1}\frac{3}{5})$, we first write the cosine function in terms of the sine function. Let $u = \sin^{-1}\frac{3}{5}$. Since $-\pi/2 \le u \le \pi/2$, $\cos u$ is positive, and we can write the following:

$$\cos u = +\sqrt{1 - \sin^2 u} \qquad \cos^2 u + \sin^2 u = 1$$
$$= \sqrt{1 - \sin^2(\sin^{-1}\tfrac{3}{5})} \qquad u = \sin^{-1}\tfrac{3}{5}$$
$$= \sqrt{1 - (\tfrac{3}{5})^2} \qquad \text{Property of inverse functions: } \sin(\sin^{-1}\tfrac{3}{5}) = \tfrac{3}{5}$$
$$= \sqrt{1 - \tfrac{9}{25}} = \sqrt{\tfrac{16}{25}} = \tfrac{4}{5} \qquad \text{Calculate}$$

So $\cos(\sin^{-1}\frac{3}{5}) = \frac{4}{5}$.

✎. NOW TRY EXERCISE **27**

ALTERNATE EXAMPLE 8

Write $\cos(\sin^{-1} x)$ as an algebraic expression in x, for $-1 < x < 1$.

ANSWER

$$\sqrt{1 - x^2}$$

EXAMPLE 8 | Composing Trigonometric Functions and Their Inverses

Write $\sin(\cos^{-1} x)$ and $\tan(\cos^{-1} x)$ as algebraic expressions in x for $-1 \le x \le 1$.

SOLUTION 1

Let $\theta = \cos^{-1} x$; then $\cos\theta = x$. In Figure 7 we sketch a right triangle with an acute angle θ, adjacent side x, and hypotenuse 1. By the Pythagorean Theorem the remaining leg is $\sqrt{1 - x^2}$. From the figure we have

$$\sin(\cos^{-1} x) = \sin\theta = \sqrt{1 - x^2} \quad \text{and} \quad \tan(\cos^{-1} x) = \tan\theta = \frac{\sqrt{1 - x^2}}{x}$$

FIGURE 7 $\cos\theta = \frac{x}{1} = x$

SOLUTION 2

Let $u = \cos^{-1} x$. We need to find $\sin u$ and $\tan u$ in terms of x. As in Example 5 the idea here is to write sine and tangent in terms of cosine. Note that $0 \le u \le \pi$ because $u = \cos^{-1} x$. We have

$$\sin u = \pm\sqrt{1 - \cos^2 u} \quad \text{and} \quad \tan u = \frac{\sin u}{\cos u} = \frac{\pm\sqrt{1 - \cos^2 u}}{\cos u}$$

IN-CLASS MATERIALS

Present students with this problem: An airplane is flying at 3000 ft and is approaching a photographer. The photographer wants to take a picture of the plane when it is 4000 ft away from her. At what angle should she set the camera so that the plane will be in the shot at the right time?

The answer is $\sin^{-1}\dfrac{3}{4} \approx 0.848$ radians or $48.59°$.

To choose the proper signs, note that u lies in the interval $[0, \pi]$ because $u = \cos^{-1} x$. Since $\sin u$ is positive on this interval, the $+$ sign is the correct choice. Substituting $u = \cos^{-1} x$ in the displayed equations and using the cancellation property $\cos(\cos^{-1} x) = x$, we get

$$\sin(\cos^{-1} x) = \sqrt{1 - x^2} \qquad \text{and} \qquad \tan(\cos^{-1} x) = \frac{\sqrt{1 - x^2}}{x}$$

✎ NOW TRY EXERCISES **33** AND **35**   ■

Note: In Solution 1 of Example 8 it might seem that because we are sketching a triangle, the angle $\theta = \cos^{-1} x$ must be acute. But it turns out that the triangle method works for any x. The domains and ranges of all six inverse trigonometric functions have been chosen in such a way that we can always use a triangle to find $S(T^{-1}(x))$, where S and T are any trigonometric functions.

6.4 EXERCISES

CONCEPTS

1. The inverse sine, inverse cosine, and inverse tangent functions have the followings domains and ranges.

   (a) The function $\sin^{-1}$ has domain _____ and range _____.

   (b) The function $\cos^{-1}$ has domain _____ and range _____.

   (c) The function $\tan^{-1}$ has domain _____ and range _____.

2. In the triangle shown, we can find the angle θ as follows:

   (a) $\theta = \sin^{-1} \dfrac{\;\;}{\;\;}$

   (b) $\theta = \cos^{-1} \dfrac{\;\;}{\;\;}$

   (c) $\theta = \tan^{-1} \dfrac{\;\;}{\;\;}$

SKILLS

3–6 ■ Find the exact value of each expression, if it is defined.

3. (a) $\sin^{-1} \dfrac{1}{2}$ (b) $\cos^{-1}\left(-\dfrac{\sqrt{3}}{2}\right)$ (c) $\tan^{-1}(-1)$

4. (a) $\sin^{-1}\left(-\dfrac{\sqrt{3}}{2}\right)$ (b) $\cos^{-1}\left(-\dfrac{\sqrt{2}}{2}\right)$ (c) $\tan^{-1}(-\sqrt{3})$

5. (a) $\sin^{-1}\left(-\dfrac{1}{2}\right)$ (b) $\cos^{-1}\dfrac{1}{2}$ (c) $\tan^{-1}\left(\dfrac{\sqrt{3}}{3}\right)$

6. (a) $\sin^{-1}(-1)$ (b) $\cos^{-1} 1$ (c) $\tan^{-1} 0$

7–14 ■ Use a calculator to find an approximate value of each expression rounded to five decimal places, if it is defined.

7. $\sin^{-1}(0.45)$ 8. $\cos^{-1}(-0.75)$

9. $\cos^{-1}\left(-\dfrac{1}{4}\right)$ 10. $\sin^{-1}\dfrac{1}{3}$

11. $\tan^{-1} 3$ 12. $\tan^{-1}(-4)$

13. $\cos^{-1} 3$ 14. $\sin^{-1}(-2)$

15–20 ■ Find the angle θ in degrees, rounded to one decimal.

15.   16.

17.   18.

19.   20.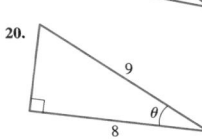

21–26 ■ Find all angles θ between $0°$ and $180°$ satisfying the given equation.

21. $\sin \theta = \dfrac{1}{2}$ 22. $\sin \theta = \dfrac{\sqrt{3}}{2}$

---

23. $\sin\theta = 0.7$

24. $\sin\theta = \dfrac{1}{4}$

25. $\cos\theta = 0.7$

26. $\cos\theta = \dfrac{1}{9}$

27–32 ■ Find the exact value of the expression.

27. $\sin(\cos^{-1}\frac{3}{5})$

28. $\tan(\sin^{-1}\frac{4}{5})$

29. $\sec(\sin^{-1}\frac{12}{13})$

30. $\csc(\cos^{-1}\frac{7}{25})$

31. $\tan(\sin^{-1}\frac{12}{13})$

32. $\cot(\sin^{-1}\frac{2}{3})$

33–36 ■ Rewrite the expression as an algebraic expression in x.

33. $\cos(\sin^{-1}x)$

34. $\sin(\tan^{-1}x)$

35. $\tan(\sin^{-1}x)$

36. $\cos(\tan^{-1}x)$

APPLICATIONS

37. Leaning Ladder A 20-ft ladder is leaning against a building. If the base of the ladder is 6 ft from the base of the building, what is the angle of elevation of the ladder? How high does the ladder reach on the building?

38. Angle of the Sun A 96-ft tree casts a shadow that is 120 ft long. What is the angle of elevation of the sun?

39. Height of the Space Shuttle An observer views the space shuttle from a distance of 2 mi from the launch pad.
   (a) Express the height of the space shuttle as a function of the angle of elevation θ.
   (b) Express the angle of elevation θ as a function of the height h of the space shuttle.

40. Height of a Pole A 50-ft pole casts a shadow as shown in the figure.
   (a) Express the angle of elevation θ of the sun as a function of the length s of the shadow.
   (b) Find the angle θ of elevation of the sun when the shadow is 20 ft long.

41. Height of a Balloon A 680-ft rope anchors a hot-air balloon as shown in the figure.
   (a) Express the angle θ as a function of the height h of the balloon.

   (b) Find the angle θ if the balloon is 500 ft high.

42. View from a Satellite The figures indicate that the higher the orbit of a satellite, the more of the earth the satellite can "see." Let θ, s, and h be as in the figure, and assume the earth is a sphere of radius 3960 mi.
   (a) Express the angle θ as a function of h.
   (b) Express the distance s as a function of θ.
   (c) Express the distance s as a function of h. [*Hint:* Find the composition of the functions in parts (a) and (b).]
   (d) If the satellite is 100 mi above the earth, what is the distance s that it can see?
   (e) How high does the satellite have to be to see both Los Angeles and New York, 2450 mi apart?

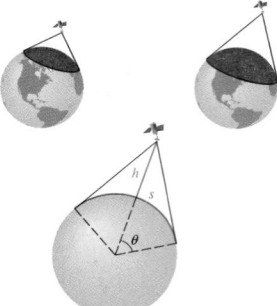

43. Surfing the Perfect Wave For a wave to be surfable, it can't break all at once. Robert Guza and Tony Bowen have shown that a wave has a surfable shoulder if it hits the shoreline at an angle θ given by

$$\theta = \sin^{-1}\left(\frac{1}{(2n+1)\tan\beta}\right)$$

where β is the angle at which the beach slopes down and where $n = 0, 1, 2, \ldots.$
   (a) For $\beta = 10°$, find θ when $n = 3$.
   (b) For $\beta = 15°$, find θ when $n = 2, 3,$ and 4. Explain why the formula does not give a value for θ when $n = 0$ or 1.

44. Inverse Trigonometric Functions on a Calculator
Most calculators do not have keys for $\sec^{-1}$, $\csc^{-1}$, or $\cot^{-1}$. Prove the following identities, and then use these identities and a calculator to find $\sec^{-1} 2$, $\csc^{-1} 3$, and $\cot^{-1} 4$.

$$\sec^{-1} x = \cos^{-1}\left(\frac{1}{x}\right), \qquad x \geq 1$$

$$\csc^{-1} x = \sin^{-1}\left(\frac{1}{x}\right), \qquad x \geq 1$$

$$\cot^{-1} x = \tan^{-1}\left(\frac{1}{x}\right), \qquad x > 0$$

6.5 THE LAW OF SINES

> **SUGGESTED TIME AND EMPHASIS**
> $\frac{1}{2}$–1 class, essential material

| The Law of Sines ▶ The Ambiguous Case

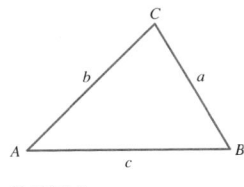

FIGURE 1

In Section 6.2 we used the trigonometric ratios to solve right triangles. The trigonometric functions can also be used to solve *oblique triangles*, that is, triangles with no right angles. To do this, we first study the Law of Sines here and then the Law of Cosines in the next section. To state these laws (or formulas) more easily, we follow the convention of labeling the angles of a triangle as A, B, C and the lengths of the corresponding opposite sides as a, b, c, as in Figure 1.

To solve a triangle, we need to know certain information about its sides and angles. To decide whether we have enough information, it's often helpful to make a sketch. For instance, if we are given two angles and the included side, then it's clear that one and only one triangle can be formed (see Figure 2(a)). Similarly, if two sides and the included angle are known, then a unique triangle is determined (Figure 2(c)). But if we know all three angles and no sides, we cannot uniquely determine the triangle because many triangles can have the same three angles. (All these triangles would be similar, of course.) So we won't consider this last case.

(a) ASA or SAA

(b) SSA

(c) SAS

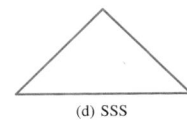
(d) SSS

FIGURE 2

In general, a triangle is determined by three of its six parts (angles and sides) as long as at least one of these three parts is a side. So the possibilities, illustrated in Figure 2, are as follows.

Case 1   One side and two angles (ASA or SAA)

Case 2   Two sides and the angle opposite one of those sides (SSA)

Case 3   Two sides and the included angle (SAS)

Case 4   Three sides (SSS)

Cases 1 and 2 are solved by using the Law of Sines; Cases 3 and 4 require the Law of Cosines.

▼ The Law of Sines

The **Law of Sines** says that in any triangle the lengths of the sides are proportional to the sines of the corresponding opposite angles.

THE LAW OF SINES

In triangle ABC we have

$$\frac{\sin A}{a} = \frac{\sin B}{b} = \frac{\sin C}{c}$$

TEXT QUESTION
Why does the book say that SSA is the ambiguous case?

Answer
It is possible to form two different triangles given two sides and an opposite angle.

FIGURE 3

PROOF   To see why the Law of Sines is true, refer to Figure 3. By the formula in Section 6.3 the area of triangle ABC is $\frac{1}{2}ab \sin C$. By the same formula the area of this triangle is also $\frac{1}{2}ac \sin B$ and $\frac{1}{2}bc \sin A$. Thus,

$$\tfrac{1}{2}bc \sin A = \tfrac{1}{2}ac \sin B = \tfrac{1}{2}ab \sin C$$

Multiplying by $2/(abc)$ gives the Law of Sines.   ∎

ALTERNATE EXAMPLE 1

Two people who live 20 mi apart look at an overhead airplane simultaneously. The angle of elevation relative to the first person is 80°, and the angle of elevation relative to the second person is 15°. What is the distance between the first person and the airplane?

ANSWER
5.2 mi

EXAMPLE 1 | Tracking a Satellite (ASA)

A satellite orbiting the earth passes directly overhead at observation stations in Phoenix and Los Angeles, 340 mi apart. At an instant when the satellite is between these two stations, its angle of elevation is simultaneously observed to be 60° at Phoenix and 75° at Los Angeles. How far is the satellite from Los Angeles?

SOLUTION   We need to find the distance b in Figure 4. Since the sum of the angles in any triangle is 180°, we see that $\angle C = 180° - (75° + 60°) = 45°$ (see Figure 4), so we have

$$\frac{\sin B}{b} = \frac{\sin C}{c} \qquad \text{Law of Sines}$$

$$\frac{\sin 60°}{b} = \frac{\sin 45°}{340} \qquad \text{Substitute}$$

$$b = \frac{340 \sin 60°}{\sin 45°} \approx 416 \qquad \text{Solve for } b$$

The distance of the satellite from Los Angeles is approximately 416 mi.

✎. NOW TRY EXERCISES **5** AND **33**   ∎

Los Angeles $c = 340$ mi   Phoenix

FIGURE 4

EXAMPLE 2 | Solving a Triangle (SAA)

Solve the triangle in Figure 5.

SOLUTION   First, $\angle B = 180° - (20° + 25°) = 135°$. Since side c is known, to find side a we use the relation

$$\frac{\sin A}{a} = \frac{\sin C}{c} \qquad \text{Law of Sines}$$

$$a = \frac{c \sin A}{\sin C} = \frac{80.4 \sin 20°}{\sin 25°} \approx 65.1 \qquad \text{Solve for } a$$

Similarly, to find b, we use

$$\frac{\sin B}{b} = \frac{\sin C}{c} \qquad \text{Law of Sines}$$

$$b = \frac{c \sin B}{\sin C} = \frac{80.4 \sin 135°}{\sin 25°} \approx 134.5 \qquad \text{Solve for } b$$

✎. NOW TRY EXERCISE **13**   ∎

ALTERNATE EXAMPLE 2

Solve the triangle. Find the solution for the value of $\angle B$ and the solutions for the values of the sides a and b.

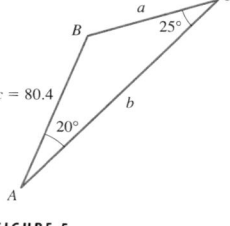

ANSWER
125°, 32.3, 62.6

FIGURE 5

▼ The Ambiguous Case

In Examples 1 and 2 a unique triangle was determined by the information given. This is always true of Case 1 (ASA or SAA). But in Case 2 (SSA) there may be two triangles, one triangle, or no triangle with the given properties. For this reason, Case 2 is sometimes

---

IN-CLASS MATERIALS

One can demonstrate the ambiguous case physically, using two rulers taped together to make a fixed angle, and a piece of string. See Figure 6 in the text.

called the **ambiguous case**. To see why this is so, we show in Figure 6 the possibilities when angle A and sides a and b are given. In part (a) no solution is possible, since side a is too short to complete the triangle. In part (b) the solution is a right triangle. In part (c) two solutions are possible, and in part (d) there is a unique triangle with the given properties. We illustrate the possibilities of Case 2 in the following examples.

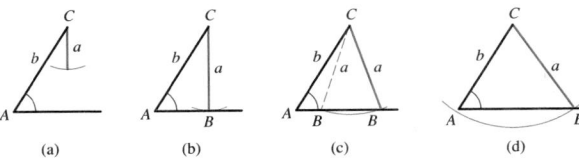

FIGURE 6 The ambiguous case

(a)   (b)   (c)   (d)

EXAMPLE 3 | SSA, the One-Solution Case

Solve triangle ABC, where $\angle A = 45°$, $a = 7\sqrt{2}$, and $b = 7$.

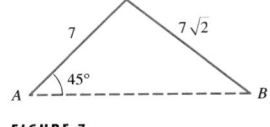

FIGURE 7

We consider only angles smaller than 180°, since no triangle can contain an angle of 180° or larger.

SOLUTION We first sketch the triangle with the information we have (see Figure 7). Our sketch is necessarily tentative, since we don't yet know the other angles. Nevertheless, we can now see the possibilities.

We first find $\angle B$.

$$\frac{\sin A}{a} = \frac{\sin B}{b} \qquad \text{Law of Sines}$$

$$\sin B = \frac{b \sin A}{a} = \frac{7}{7\sqrt{2}} \sin 45° = \left(\frac{1}{\sqrt{2}}\right)\left(\frac{\sqrt{2}}{2}\right) = \frac{1}{2} \qquad \text{Solve for } \sin B$$

Which angles B have $\sin B = \frac{1}{2}$? From the preceding section we know that there are two such angles smaller than 180° (they are 30° and 150°). Which of these angles is compatible with what we know about triangle ABC? Since $\angle A = 45°$, we cannot have $\angle B = 150°$, because $45° + 150° > 180°$. So $\angle B = 30°$, and the remaining angle is $\angle C = 180° - (30° + 45°) = 105°$.

Now we can find side c.

$$\frac{\sin B}{b} = \frac{\sin C}{c} \qquad \text{Law of Sines}$$

$$c = \frac{b \sin C}{\sin B} = \frac{7 \sin 105°}{\sin 30°} = \frac{7 \sin 105°}{\frac{1}{2}} \approx 13.5 \qquad \text{Solve for } c$$

 . NOW TRY EXERCISE **19**

In Example 3 there were two possibilities for angle B, and one of these was not compatible with the rest of the information. In general, if $\sin A < 1$, we must check the angle and its supplement as possibilities, because any angle smaller than 180° can be in the triangle. To decide whether either possibility works, we check to see whether the resulting sum of the angles exceeds 180°. It can happen, as in Figure 6(c), that both possibilities are compatible with the given information. In that case, two different triangles are solutions to the problem.

The *supplement* of an angle θ (where $0 \le \theta \le 180°$) is the angle $180° - \theta$.

EXAMPLE 4 | SSA, the Two-Solution Case

Solve triangle ABC if $\angle A = 43.1°$, $a = 186.2$, and $b = 248.6$.

ALTERNATE EXAMPLE 3
Solve triangle ABC, where $\angle A = 45°$, $a = 9\sqrt{2}$, and $b = 9.0$. Find the length of the side c and the values of angles B and C.

ANSWER
$B = 30°$, $C = 105$, $c = 17.39$

ALTERNATE EXAMPLE 4
Solve triangle ABC if $\angle A = 45.3°$, $a = 167.1$, and $b = 185.2$.

ANSWERS
(52, 82.7, 233.2), (128, 6.7, 27.4)

IN-CLASS MATERIALS

Make sure that students express some answers in degrees and some in radians so that they become comfortable with both.

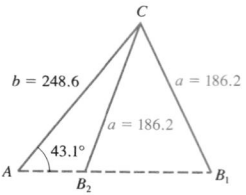

Surveying is a method of land measurement used for mapmaking. Surveyors use a process called *triangulation* in which a network of thousands of interlocking triangles is created on the area to be mapped. The process is started by measuring the length of a *baseline* between two surveying stations. Then, with the use of an instrument called a *theodolite*, the angles between these two stations and a third station are measured. The Law of Sines is then used to calculate the two other sides of the triangle formed by the three stations. The calculated sides are used as baselines, and the process is repeated over and over to create a network of triangles. In this method the only distance measured is the initial baseline; all other distances are calculated from the Law of Sines. This method is practical because it is much easier to measure angles than distances.

One of the most ambitious mapmaking efforts of all time was the Great Trigonometric Survey of India (see Problem 8, page 492) which required several expeditions and took over a century to complete. The famous expedition of 1823, led by **Sir George Everest**, lasted 20 years. Ranging over treacherous terrain and encountering the dreaded malaria-carrying mosquitoes, this expedition reached the foothills of the Himalayas. A later expedition, using triangulation, calculated the height of the highest peak of the Himalayas to be 29,002 ft. The peak was named in honor of Sir George Everest.

Today, with the use of satellites, the height of Mt. Everest is estimated to be 29,028 ft. The very close agreement of these two estimates shows the great accuracy of the trigonometric method.

SOLUTION   From the given information we sketch the triangle shown in Figure 8. Note that side a may be drawn in two possible positions to complete the triangle. From the Law of Sines

$$\sin B = \frac{b \sin A}{a} = \frac{248.6 \sin 43.1^\circ}{186.2} \approx 0.91225$$

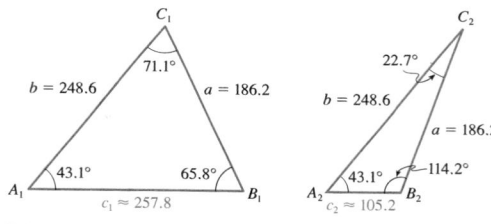

FIGURE 8

There are two possible angles B between 0° and 180° such that $\sin B = 0.91225$. Using a calculator, we find that one of the angles is $\sin^{-1}(0.91225) \approx 65.8^\circ$. The other angle is approximately $180^\circ - 65.8^\circ = 114.2^\circ$. We denote these two angles by B_1 and B_2 so that

$$\angle B_1 \approx 65.8^\circ \qquad \text{and} \qquad \angle B_2 \approx 114.2^\circ$$

Thus two triangles satisfy the given conditions: triangle $A_1B_1C_1$ and triangle $A_2B_2C_2$.

Solve triangle $A_1B_1C_1$:

$$\angle C_1 \approx 180^\circ - (43.1^\circ + 65.8^\circ) = 71.1^\circ \qquad \text{Find } \angle C_1$$

Thus $c_1 = \dfrac{a_1 \sin C_1}{\sin A_1} \approx \dfrac{186.2 \sin 71.1^\circ}{\sin 43.1^\circ} \approx 257.8 \qquad$ Law of Sines

Solve triangle $A_2B_2C_2$:

$$\angle C_2 \approx 180^\circ - (43.1^\circ + 114.2^\circ) = 22.7^\circ \qquad \text{Find } \angle C_2$$

Thus $c_2 = \dfrac{a_2 \sin C_2}{\sin A_2} \approx \dfrac{186.2 \sin 22.7^\circ}{\sin 43.1^\circ} \approx 105.2 \qquad$ Law of Sines

Triangles $A_1B_1C_1$ and $A_2B_2C_2$ are shown in Figure 9.

FIGURE 9

✎. NOW TRY EXERCISE **23**

EXAMPLES

▪ **ASA**

1. $A = 30^\circ$, $B = 40^\circ$, $c = 100$
2. $A = 0.75$ rad, $B = 0.8$ rad, $c = 100$

ANSWERS

1. $A = 30^\circ$, $B = 40^\circ$, $C = 110^\circ$, $a \approx 53.2$, $b \approx 68.4$, $c = 100$
2. $A = 0.75$ rad, $B = 0.8$ rad, $C \approx \pi - 1.55 \approx 1.59$ rad, $a \approx 68.18$, $b \approx 71.75$, $c = 100$

The next example presents a situation for which no triangle is compatible with the given data.

EXAMPLE 5 | SSA, the No-Solution Case

Solve triangle ABC, where $\angle A = 42°$, $a = 70$, and $b = 122$.

SOLUTION To organize the given information, we sketch the diagram in Figure 10. Let's try to find $\angle B$. We have

$$\frac{\sin A}{a} = \frac{\sin B}{b} \qquad \text{Law of Sines}$$

$$\sin B = \frac{b \sin A}{a} = \frac{122 \sin 42°}{70} \approx 1.17 \qquad \text{Solve for } \sin B$$

Since the sine of an angle is never greater than 1, we conclude that no triangle satisfies the conditions given in this problem.

FIGURE 10

✎ NOW TRY EXERCISE **21**

6.5 EXERCISES

CONCEPTS

1. In triangle ABC with sides a, b, and c the Law of Sines states that

$$\frac{\square}{\square} = \frac{\square}{\square} = \frac{\square}{\square}$$

2. In which of the following cases can we use the Law of Sines to solve a triangle?

ASA   SSS   SAS   SSA

SKILLS

3–8 ■ Use the Law of Sines to find the indicated side x or angle θ.

3.

4.

5.

6.

7.

8.

9–12 ■ Solve the triangle using the Law of Sines.

9. **10.**

11. **12.**

13–18 ■ Sketch each triangle, and then solve the triangle using the Law of Sines.

13. $\angle A = 50°$, $\angle B = 68°$, $c = 230$
14. $\angle A = 23°$, $\angle B = 110°$, $c = 50$
15. $\angle A = 30°$, $\angle C = 65°$, $b = 10$
16. $\angle A = 22°$, $\angle B = 95°$, $a = 420$
17. $\angle B = 29°$, $\angle C = 51°$, $b = 44$
18. $\angle B = 10°$, $\angle C = 100°$, $c = 115$

19–28 ■ Use the Law of Sines to solve for all possible triangles that satisfy the given conditions.

19. $a = 28$, $b = 15$, $\angle A = 110°$
20. $a = 30$, $c = 40$, $\angle A = 37°$
21. $a = 20$, $c = 45$, $\angle A = 125°$
22. $b = 45$, $c = 42$, $\angle C = 38°$

ALTERNATE EXAMPLE 5
Solve triangle ABC, where $\angle A = 41°$, $a = 40$, and $b = 89$. Find the length of the side c and the values of angles B and C.

ANSWER
No solution

DRILL QUESTION
Find x in the following diagram:

Answer
$x \approx 14.119$

EXAMPLES

■ **SSA:** For each of the following, have students draw triangles to try to guess how many solutions there are.
1. $A = 80°$, $b = 100$, $a = 10$
2. $A = 80°$, $b = 10$, $a = 100$
3. $A = 80°$, $b = 121$, $a = 120$
4. $A = 0.2$ rad, $b = 50$, $a = 40$

ANSWERS
1. No solution
2. One solution:
$A = 80°, B \approx 5.65°, C \approx 94.35°, a = 100, b = 10, c \approx 101.25$
3. Two solutions:
$A = 80°, B \approx 83.2°, C \approx 16.8°, a = 120, b = 121, c \approx 35.2$;
$A = 80°, B \approx 96.8°, C \approx 3.2°, a = 120, b = 121, c \approx 6.9$
4. Two solutions:
$A = 0.2$ rad, $B \approx 0.25$ rad, $C \approx 2.69$ rad, $a = 40, b = 50, c \approx 87.8$;
$A = 0.2$ rad, $B \approx 2.89$ rad, $C \approx 0.05$ rad, $a = 40, b = 50, c \approx 10.3$

23. $b = 25$, $c = 30$, $\angle B = 25°$

24. $a = 75$, $b = 100$, $\angle A = 30°$

25. $a = 50$, $b = 100$, $\angle A = 50°$

26. $a = 100$, $b = 80$, $\angle A = 135°$

27. $a = 26$, $c = 15$, $\angle C = 29°$

28. $b = 73$, $c = 82$, $\angle B = 58°$

29. For the triangle shown, find
    (a) $\angle BCD$ and
    (b) $\angle DCA$.

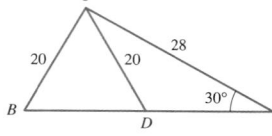

30. For the triangle shown, find the length AD.

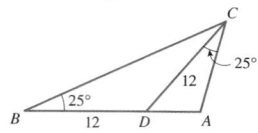

31. In triangle ABC, $\angle A = 40°$, $a = 15$, and $b = 20$.
    (a) Show that there are two triangles, ABC and $A'B'C'$, that satisfy these conditions.
    (b) Show that the areas of the triangles in part (a) are proportional to the sines of the angles C and C', that is,

$$\frac{\text{area of } \triangle ABC}{\text{area of } \triangle A'B'C'} = \frac{\sin C}{\sin C'}$$

32. Show that, given the three angles A, B, C of a triangle and one side, say a, the area of the triangle is

$$\text{area} = \frac{a^2 \sin B \sin C}{2 \sin A}$$

APPLICATIONS

33. Tracking a Satellite   The path of a satellite orbiting the earth causes it to pass directly over two tracking stations A and B, which are 50 mi apart. When the satellite is on one side of the two stations, the angles of elevation at A and B are measured to be 87.0° and 84.2°, respectively.
    (a) How far is the satellite from station A?
    (b) How high is the satellite above the ground?

34. Flight of a Plane   A pilot is flying over a straight highway. He determines the angles of depression to two mileposts, 5 mi apart, to be 32° and 48°, as shown in the figure.
    (a) Find the distance of the plane from point A.
    (b) Find the elevation of the plane.

35. Distance Across a River   To find the distance across a river, a surveyor chooses points A and B, which are 200 ft apart on one side of the river (see the figure). She then chooses a reference point C on the opposite side of the river and finds that $\angle BAC \approx 82°$ and $\angle ABC \approx 52°$. Approximate the distance from A to C.

36. Distance Across a Lake   Points A and B are separated by a lake. To find the distance between them, a surveyor locates a point C on land such that $\angle CAB = 48.6°$. He also measures CA as 312 ft and CB as 527 ft. Find the distance between A and B.

37. The Leaning Tower of Pisa   The bell tower of the cathedral in Pisa, Italy, leans 5.6° from the vertical. A tourist stands 105 m from its base, with the tower leaning directly toward her. She measures the angle of elevation to the top of the tower to be 29.2°. Find the length of the tower to the nearest meter.

38. Radio Antenna   A short-wave radio antenna is supported by two guy wires, 165 ft and 180 ft long. Each wire is attached to the top of the antenna and anchored to the ground, at two anchor points on opposite sides of the antenna. The shorter wire makes an angle of 67° with the ground. How far apart are the anchor points?

39. Height of a Tree   A tree on a hillside casts a shadow 215 ft down the hill. If the angle of inclination of the hillside is 22° to the horizontal and the angle of elevation of the sun is 52°, find the height of the tree.

40. Length of a Guy Wire A communications tower is located at the top of a steep hill, as shown. The angle of inclination of the hill is 58°. A guy wire is to be attached to the top of the tower and to the ground, 100 m downhill from the base of the tower. The angle α in the figure is determined to be 12°. Find the length of cable required for the guy wire.

41. Calculating a Distance Observers at P and Q are located on the side of a hill that is inclined 32° to the horizontal, as shown. The observer at P determines the angle of elevation to a hot-air balloon to be 62°. At the same instant the observer at Q measures the angle of elevation to the balloon to be 71°. If P is 60 m down the hill from Q, find the distance from Q to the balloon.

42. Calculating an Angle A water tower 30 m tall is located at the top of a hill. From a distance of 120 m down the hill, it is observed that the angle formed between the top and base of the tower is 8°. Find the angle of inclination of the hill.

43. Distances to Venus The *elongation* α of a planet is the angle formed by the planet, earth, and sun (see the figure). It is known that the distance from the sun to Venus is 0.723 AU (see Exercise 65 in Section 6.2). At a certain time the elongation of

Venus is found to be 39.4°. Find the possible distances from the earth to Venus at that time in astronomical units (AU).

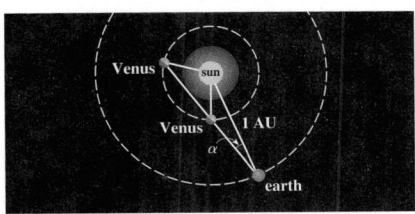

44. Soap Bubbles When two bubbles cling together in midair, their common surface is part of a sphere whose center D lies on the line passing throught the centers of the bubbles (see the figure). Also, angles ACB and ACD each have measure 60°.

(a) Show that the radius r of the common face is given by

$$r = \frac{ab}{a - b}$$

[*Hint:* Use the Law of Sines together with the fact that an angle θ and its supplement $180° - \theta$ have the same sine.]

(b) Find the radius of the common face if the radii of the bubbles are 4 cm and 3 cm.

(c) What shape does the common face take if the two bubbles have equal radii?

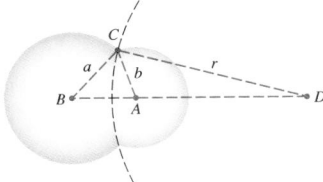

DISCOVERY ▪ DISCUSSION ▪ WRITING

45. Number of Solutions in the Ambiguous Case We have seen that when the Law of Sines is used to solve a triangle in the SSA case, there may be two, one, or no solution(s). Sketch triangles like those in Figure 6 to verify the criteria in the table for the number of solutions if you are given $\angle A$ and sides a and b.

Criterion	Number of solutions
$a \geq b$	1
$b > a > b \sin A$	2
$a = b \sin A$	1
$a < b \sin A$	0

If $\angle A = 30°$ and $b = 100$, use these criteria to find the range of values of a for which the triangle ABC has two solutions, one solution, or no solution.

SUGGESTED TIME
AND EMPHASIS

1 class, essential material

6.6 THE LAW OF COSINES

| The Law of Cosines ▶ Navigation: Heading and Bearing ▶ The Area of a Triangle

▼ The Law of Cosines

The Law of Sines cannot be used directly to solve triangles if we know two sides and the angle between them or if we know all three sides (these are Cases 3 and 4 of the preceding section). In these two cases the **Law of Cosines** applies.

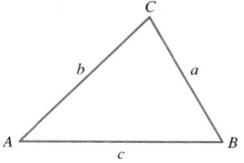

FIGURE 1

THE LAW OF COSINES

In any triangle ABC (see Figure 1), we have

$$a^2 = b^2 + c^2 - 2bc \cos A$$

$$b^2 = a^2 + c^2 - 2ac \cos B$$

$$c^2 = a^2 + b^2 - 2ab \cos C$$

PROOF To prove the Law of Cosines, place triangle ABC so that $\angle A$ is at the origin, as shown in Figure 2. The coordinates of vertices B and C are $(c, 0)$ and $(b \cos A, b \sin A)$, respectively. (You should check that the coordinates of these points will be the same if we draw angle A as an acute angle.) Using the Distance Formula, we get

$$a^2 = (b \cos A - c)^2 + (b \sin A - 0)^2$$

$$= b^2 \cos^2 A - 2bc \cos A + c^2 + b^2 \sin^2 A$$

$$= b^2(\cos^2 A + \sin^2 A) - 2bc \cos A + c^2$$

$$= b^2 + c^2 - 2bc \cos A \qquad \text{Because } \sin^2 A + \cos^2 A = 1$$

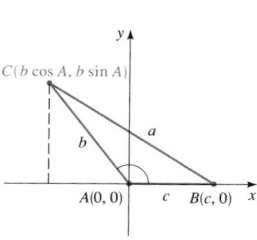

FIGURE 2

This proves the first formula. The other two formulas are obtained in the same way by placing each of the other vertices of the triangle at the origin and repeating the preceding argument. ∎

In words, the Law of Cosines says that the square of any side of a triangle is equal to the sum of the squares of the other two sides, minus twice the product of those two sides times the cosine of the included angle.

If one of the angles of a triangle, say $\angle C$, is a right angle, then $\cos C = 0$, and the Law of Cosines reduces to the Pythagorean Theorem, $c^2 = a^2 + b^2$. Thus the Pythagorean Theorem is a special case of the Law of Cosines.

EXAMPLE 1 | Length of a Tunnel

A tunnel is to be built through a mountain. To estimate the length of the tunnel, a surveyor makes the measurements shown in Figure 3. Use the surveyor's data to approximate the length of the tunnel.

SOLUTION To approximate the length c of the tunnel, we use the Law of Cosines:

$$c^2 = a^2 + b^2 - 2ab \cos C \qquad \text{Law of Cosines}$$

$$= 388^2 + 212^2 - 2(388)(212) \cos 82.4° \qquad \text{Substitute}$$

$$\approx 173730.2367 \qquad \text{Use a calculator}$$

$$c \approx \sqrt{173730.2367} \approx 416.8 \qquad \text{Take square roots}$$

Thus the tunnel will be approximately 417 ft long.

FIGURE 3

✎ NOW TRY EXERCISES **3** AND **39** ∎

ALTERNATE EXAMPLE 1

A tunnel is to be built through a mountain. To estimate the length of the tunnel, a surveyor makes the measurements shown in this figure. Use the surveyor's data to approximate the length of the tunnel.

ANSWER
388.8 ft

TEXT QUESTION

Is it possible to find the area of a triangle if the side lengths are known, but the angles are not?

Answer

Yes

EXAMPLE 2 | SSS, the Law of Cosines

The sides of a triangle are $a = 5$, $b = 8$, and $c = 12$ (see Figure 4). Find the angles of the triangle.

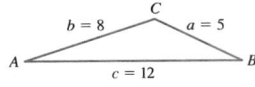

FIGURE 4

SOLUTION We first find $\angle A$. From the Law of Cosines, $a^2 = b^2 + c^2 - 2bc \cos A$. Solving for $\cos A$, we get

$$\cos A = \frac{b^2 + c^2 - a^2}{2bc} = \frac{8^2 + 12^2 - 5^2}{2(8)(12)} = \frac{183}{192} = 0.953125$$

Using a calculator, we find that $\angle A = \cos^{-1}(0.953125) \approx 18°$. In the same way we get

$$\cos B = \frac{a^2 + c^2 - b^2}{2ac} = \frac{5^2 + 12^2 - 8^2}{2(5)(12)} = 0.875$$

$$\cos C = \frac{a^2 + b^2 - c^2}{2ab} = \frac{5^2 + 8^2 - 12^2}{2(5)(8)} = -0.6875$$

Using a calculator, we find that

$$\angle B = \cos^{-1}(0.875) \approx 29° \quad \text{and} \quad \angle C = \cos^{-1}(-0.6875) \approx 133°$$

Of course, once two angles have been calculated, the third can more easily be found from the fact that the sum of the angles of a triangle is 180°. However, it's a good idea to calculate all three angles using the Law of Cosines and add the three angles as a check on your computations.

✎ NOW TRY EXERCISE **7**

EXAMPLE 3 | SAS, the Law of Cosines

Solve triangle ABC, where $\angle A = 46.5°$, $b = 10.5$, and $c = 18.0$.

SOLUTION We can find a using the Law of Cosines.

$$a^2 = b^2 + c^2 - 2bc \cos A$$
$$= (10.5)^2 + (18.0)^2 - 2(10.5)(18.0)(\cos 46.5°) \approx 174.05$$

Thus, $a \approx \sqrt{174.05} \approx 13.2$. We also use the Law of Cosines to find $\angle B$ and $\angle C$, as in Example 2.

$$\cos B = \frac{a^2 + c^2 - b^2}{2ac} = \frac{13.2^2 + 18.0^2 - 10.5^2}{2(13.2)(18.0)} \approx 0.816477$$

$$\cos C = \frac{a^2 + b^2 - c^2}{2ab} = \frac{13.2^2 + 10.5^2 - 18.0^2}{2(13.2)(10.5)} \approx -0.142532$$

Using a calculator, we find that

$$\angle B = \cos^{-1}(0.816477) \approx 35.3° \quad \text{and} \quad \angle C = \cos^{-1}(-0.142532) \approx 98.2°$$

To summarize: $\angle B \approx 35.3°$, $\angle C \approx 98.2°$, and $a \approx 13.2$. (See Figure 5.)

✎ NOW TRY EXERCISE **13**

FIGURE 5

We could have used the Law of Sines to find $\angle B$ and $\angle C$ in Example 3, since we knew all three sides and an angle in the triangle. But knowing the sine of an angle does not uniquely specify the angle, since an angle θ and its supplement $180° - \theta$ both have the

IN-CLASS MATERIALS
Have the class apply the Law of Cosines to the special case where C is a right angle. Note that the Law of Cosines is actually a generalization of the Pythagorean Theorem.

same sine. Thus, we would need to decide which of the two angles is the correct choice. This ambiguity does not arise when we use the Law of Cosines, because every angle between 0° and 180° has a unique cosine. So using only the Law of Cosines is preferable in problems like Example 3.

▼ Navigation: Heading and Bearing

In navigation a direction is often given as a **bearing**, that is, as an acute angle measured from due north or due south. The bearing N 30° E, for example, indicates a direction that points 30° to the east of due north (see Figure 6).

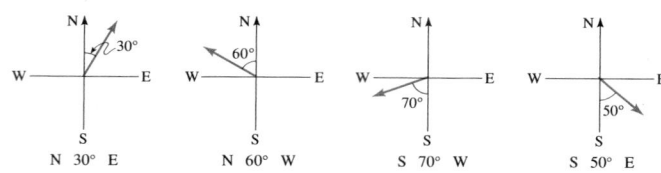

FIGURE 6

EXAMPLE 4 | Navigation

A pilot sets out from an airport and heads in the direction N 20° E, flying at 200 mi/h. After one hour, he makes a course correction and heads in the direction N 40° E. Half an hour after that, engine trouble forces him to make an emergency landing.

(a) Find the distance between the airport and his final landing point.

(b) Find the bearing from the airport to his final landing point.

SOLUTION

(a) In one hour the plane travels 200 mi, and in half an hour it travels 100 mi, so we can plot the pilot's course as in Figure 7. When he makes his course correction, he turns 20° to the right, so the angle between the two legs of his trip is 180° − 20° = 160°. So by the Law of Cosines we have

$$b^2 = 200^2 + 100^2 - 2 \cdot 200 \cdot 100 \cos 160°$$

$$\approx 87{,}587.70$$

Thus, $b \approx 295.95$. The pilot lands about 296 mi from his starting point.

(b) We first use the Law of Sines to find $\angle A$.

$$\frac{\sin A}{100} = \frac{\sin 160°}{295.95}$$

$$\sin A = 100 \cdot \frac{\sin 160°}{295.95}$$

$$\approx 0.11557$$

Another angle with sine 0.11557 is 180° − 6.636° = 173.364°. But this is clearly too large to be $\angle A$ in $\angle ABC$.

Using the SIN⁻¹ key on a calculator, we find that $\angle A \approx 6.636°$. From Figure 7 we see that the line from the airport to the final landing site points in the direction 20° + 6.636° = 26.636° east of due north. Thus, the bearing is about N 26.6° E.

✎. NOW TRY EXERCISE **45** ∎

FIGURE 7

ALTERNATE EXAMPLE 4

To find the distance across a small lake, a surveyor has taken the measurements shown in this figure. Find the distance across the lake (in miles) using this information.

ANSWER
2.44 mi

IN-CLASS MATERIALS

Notice that the ability to easily find areas of triangles can be used to help find areas of polygons, because they can be decomposed into triangles.

▼ The Area of a Triangle

An interesting application of the Law of Cosines involves a formula for finding the area of a triangle from the lengths of its three sides (see Figure 8).

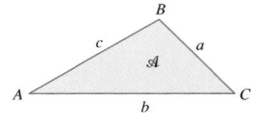

FIGURE 8

HERON'S FORMULA

The area $\mathcal{A}$ of triangle ABC is given by

$$\mathcal{A} = \sqrt{s(s-a)(s-b)(s-c)}$$

where $s = \frac{1}{2}(a + b + c)$ is the **semiperimeter** of the triangle; that is, s is half the perimeter.

PROOF   We start with the formula $\mathcal{A} = \frac{1}{2}ab \sin C$ from Section 6.3. Thus

$$\mathcal{A}^2 = \tfrac{1}{4}a^2b^2 \sin^2 C$$

$$= \tfrac{1}{4}a^2b^2(1 - \cos^2 C) \qquad \text{Pythagorean identity}$$

$$= \tfrac{1}{4}a^2b^2(1 - \cos C)(1 + \cos C) \qquad \text{Factor}$$

Next, we write the expressions $1 - \cos C$ and $1 + \cos C$ in terms of a, b, and c. By the Law of Cosines we have

$$\cos C = \frac{a^2 + b^2 - c^2}{2ab} \qquad \text{Law of Cosines}$$

$$1 + \cos C = 1 + \frac{a^2 + b^2 - c^2}{2ab} \qquad \text{Add 1}$$

$$= \frac{2ab + a^2 + b^2 - c^2}{2ab} \qquad \text{Common denominator}$$

$$= \frac{(a + b)^2 - c^2}{2ab} \qquad \text{Factor}$$

$$= \frac{(a + b + c)(a + b - c)}{2ab} \qquad \text{Difference of squares}$$

Similarly

$$1 - \cos C = \frac{(c + a - b)(c - a + b)}{2ab}$$

Substituting these expressions in the formula we obtained for $\mathcal{A}^2$ gives

To see that the factors in the last two products are equal, note for example that

$$\frac{a + b - c}{2} = \frac{a + b + c}{2} - c$$

$$= s - c$$

$$\mathcal{A}^2 = \tfrac{1}{4}a^2b^2 \frac{(a + b + c)(a + b - c)}{2ab} \frac{(c + a - b)(c - a + b)}{2ab}$$

$$= \frac{(a + b + c)}{2} \frac{(a + b - c)}{2} \frac{(c + a - b)}{2} \frac{(c - a + b)}{2}$$

$$= s(s - c)(s - b)(s - a)$$

Heron's Formula now follows by taking the square root of each side.   ■

EXAMPLE
SAS: $A = 25°$, $b = 10$, $c = 20$

ANSWER
$a \approx 11.725$, $B \approx 21.1°$, $C \approx 133.9°$

EXAMPLE
SSS: $a = 4$, $b = 8$, $c = 11$

ANSWER
$A \approx 16.2°$, $B \approx 33.9°$, $C \approx 129.8°$

FIGURE 9

EXAMPLE 5 | Area of a Lot

A businessman wishes to buy a triangular lot in a busy downtown location (see Figure 9). The lot frontages on the three adjacent streets are 125, 280, and 315 ft. Find the area of the lot.

SOLUTION The semiperimeter of the lot is

$$s = \frac{125 + 280 + 315}{2} = 360$$

By Heron's Formula the area is

$$\mathcal{A} = \sqrt{360(360 - 125)(360 - 280)(360 - 315)} \approx 17{,}451.6$$

Thus, the area is approximately 17,452 ft^2.

✎ NOW TRY EXERCISES **29** AND **53** ■

6.6 EXERCISES

CONCEPTS

1. For triangle ABC with sides a, b, and c the Law of Cosines states

$c^2 = $ _____

2. In which of the following cases must the Law of Cosines be used to solve a triangle?

ASA   SSS   SAS   SSA

SKILLS

3–10 ■ Use the Law of Cosines to determine the indicated side x or angle θ.

3.

4.

5.

6.

7.

8.

9.

10.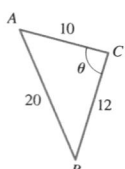

11–20 ■ Solve triangle ABC.

11.

12.

13. $a = 3.0$, $b = 4.0$, $\angle C = 53°$

14. $b = 60$, $c = 30$, $\angle A = 70°$

15. $a = 20$, $b = 25$, $c = 22$

16. $a = 10$, $b = 12$, $c = 16$

17. $b = 125$, $c = 162$, $\angle B = 40°$

18. $a = 65$, $c = 50$, $\angle C = 52°$

19. $a = 50$, $b = 65$, $\angle A = 55°$

20. $a = 73.5$, $\angle B = 61°$, $\angle C = 83°$

21–28 ■ Find the indicated side x or angle θ. (Use either the Law of Sines or the Law of Cosines, as appropriate.)

21.

22.

23.

24.

25.

26.

27.

28.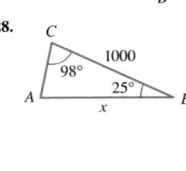

29–32 ■ Find the area of the triangle whose sides have the given lengths.

29. $a = 9$, $b = 12$, $c = 15$ **30.** $a = 1$, $b = 2$, $c = 2$

31. $a = 7$, $b = 8$, $c = 9$

32. $a = 11$, $b = 100$, $c = 101$

33–36 ■ Find the area of the shaded figure, rounded to two decimals.

33.

34.

35.

36.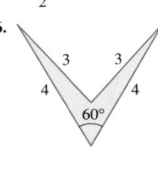

37. Three circles of radii 4, 5, and 6 cm are mutually tangent. Find the shaded area enclosed between the circles.

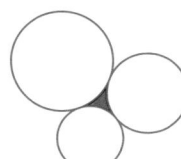

38. Prove that in triangle ABC

$$a = b \cos C + c \cos B$$
$$b = c \cos A + a \cos C$$
$$c = a \cos B + b \cos A$$

These are called the *Projection Laws.*   [*Hint:* To get the first equation, add the second and third equations in the Law of Cosines and solve for a.]

APPLICATIONS

39. Surveying   To find the distance across a small lake, a surveyor has taken the measurements shown. Find the distance across the lake using this information.

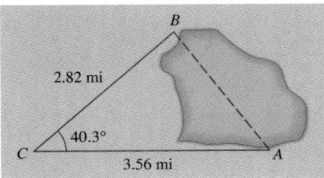

40. Geometry   A parallelogram has sides of lengths 3 and 5, and one angle is 50°. Find the lengths of the diagonals.

41. Calculating Distance   Two straight roads diverge at an angle of 65°. Two cars leave the intersection at 2:00 P.M., one traveling at 50 mi/h and the other at 30 mi/h. How far apart are the cars at 2:30 P.M.?

42. Calculating Distance   A car travels along a straight road, heading east for 1 h, then traveling for 30 min on another road that leads northeast. If the car has maintained a constant speed of 40 mi/h, how far is it from its starting position?

43. Dead Reckoning   A pilot flies in a straight path for 1 h 30 min. She then makes a course correction, heading 10° to the right of her original course, and flies 2 h in the new direction. If she maintains a constant speed of 625 mi/h, how far is she from her starting position?

44. Navigation   Two boats leave the same port at the same time. One travels at a speed of 30 mi/h in the direction N 50° E and the other travels at a speed of 26 mi/h in a direction S 70° E (see the figure). How far apart are the two boats after one hour?

45. Navigation A fisherman leaves his home port and heads in the direction N 70° W. He travels 30 mi and reaches Egg Island. The next day he sails N 10° E for 50 mi, reaching Forrest Island.

(a) Find the distance between the fisherman's home port and Forrest Island.

(b) Find the bearing from Forrest Island back to his home port.

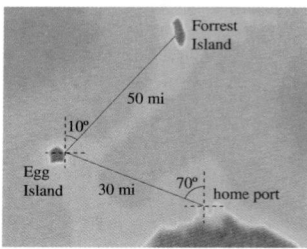

46. Navigation Airport B is 300 mi from airport A at a bearing N 50° E (see the figure). A pilot wishing to fly from A to B mistakenly flies due east at 200 mi/h for 30 minutes, when he notices his error.

(a) How far is the pilot from his destination at the time he notices the error?

(b) What bearing should he head his plane in order to arrive at airport B?

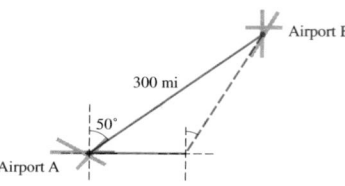

47. Triangular Field A triangular field has sides of lengths 22, 36, and 44 yd. Find the largest angle.

48. Towing a Barge Two tugboats that are 120 ft apart pull a barge, as shown. If the length of one cable is 212 ft and the length of the other is 230 ft, find the angle formed by the two cables.

49. Flying Kites A boy is flying two kites at the same time. He has 380 ft of line out to one kite and 420 ft to the other. He estimates the angle between the two lines to be 30°. Approximate the distance between the kites.

50. Securing a Tower A 125-ft tower is located on the side of a mountain that is inclined 32° to the horizontal. A guy wire is to be attached to the top of the tower and anchored at a point 55 ft downhill from the base of the tower. Find the shortest length of wire needed.

51. Cable Car A steep mountain is inclined 74° to the horizontal and rises 3400 ft above the surrounding plain. A cable car is to be installed from a point 800 ft from the base to the top of the mountain, as shown. Find the shortest length of cable needed.

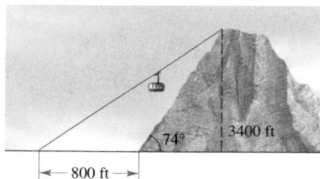

52. CN Tower The CN Tower in Toronto, Canada, is the tallest free-standing structure in North America. A woman on the observation deck, 1150 ft above the ground, wants to determine the distance between two landmarks on the ground below. She observes that the angle formed by the lines of sight to these two landmarks is 43°. She also observes that the angle between the vertical and the line of sight to one of the landmarks is 62° and to the other landmark is 54°. Find the distance between the two landmarks.

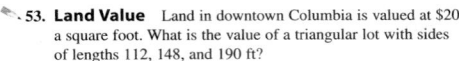

53. Land Value Land in downtown Columbia is valued at $20 a square foot. What is the value of a triangular lot with sides of lengths 112, 148, and 190 ft?

DISCOVERY ▪ DISCUSSION ▪ WRITING

54. Solving for the Angles in a Triangle The paragraph that follows the solution of Example 3 on page 477 explains an alternative method for finding $\angle B$ and $\angle C$, using the Law of Sines. Use this method to solve the triangle in the example, finding $\angle B$ first and then $\angle C$. Explain how you chose the appropriate value for the measure of $\angle B$. Which method do you prefer for solving an SAS triangle problem, the one explained in Example 3 or the one you used in this exercise?

CHAPTER 6 | REVIEW

■ CONCEPT CHECK

1. (a) Explain the difference between a positive angle and a negative angle.
   (b) How is an angle of measure 1 degree formed?
   (c) How is an angle of measure 1 radian formed?
   (d) How is the radian measure of an angle θ defined?
   (e) How do you convert from degrees to radians?
   (f) How do you convert from radians to degrees?

2. (a) When is an angle in standard position?
   (b) When are two angles coterminal?

3. (a) What is the length s of an arc of a circle with radius r that subtends a central angle of θ radians?
   (b) What is the area A of a sector of a circle with radius r and central angle θ radians?

4. If θ is an acute angle in a right triangle, define the six trigonometric ratios in terms of the adjacent and opposite sides and the hypotenuse.

5. What does it mean to solve a triangle?

6. If θ is an angle in standard position, $P(x, y)$ is a point on the terminal side, and r is the distance from the origin to P, write expressions for the six trigonometric functions of θ.

7. Which trigonometric functions are positive in Quadrants I, II, III, and IV?

8. If θ is an angle in standard position, what is its reference angle $\bar{\theta}$?

9. (a) State the reciprocal identities.
   (b) State the Pythagorean identities.

10. (a) What is the area of a triangle with sides of length a and b and with included angle θ?
   (b) What is the area of a triangle with sides of length a, b, and c?

11. Define the inverse sine function $\sin^{-1}$. What are its domain and range?

12. Define the inverse cosine function $\cos^{-1}$. What are its domain and range?

13. Define the inverse tangent function $\tan^{-1}$. What are its domain and range?

14. (a) State the Law of Sines.
   (b) State the Law of Cosines.

15. Explain the ambiguous case in the Law of Sines.

■ EXERCISES

1–2 ■ Find the radian measure that corresponds to the given degree measure.

1. (a) 60°   **(b)** 330°   **(c)** −135°   **(d)** −90°

2. (a) 24°   **(b)** −330°   **(c)** 750°   **(d)** 5°

3–4 ■ Find the degree measure that corresponds to the given radian measure.

3. (a) $\dfrac{5\pi}{2}$ **(b)** $-\dfrac{\pi}{6}$ **(c)** $\dfrac{9\pi}{4}$ **(d)** 3.1

4. (a) 8   **(b)** $-\dfrac{5}{2}$ **(c)** $\dfrac{11\pi}{6}$ **(d)** $\dfrac{3\pi}{5}$

5. Find the length of an arc of a circle of radius 8 m if the arc subtends a central angle of 1 rad.

6. Find the measure of a central angle θ in a circle of radius 5 ft if the angle is subtended by an arc of length 7 ft.

7. A circular arc of length 100 ft subtends a central angle of 70°. Find the radius of the circle.

8. How many revolutions will a car wheel of diameter 28 in. make over a period of half an hour if the car is traveling at 60 mi/h?

9. New York and Los Angeles are 2450 mi apart. Find the angle that the arc between these two cities subtends at the center of the earth. (The radius of the earth is 3960 mi.)

10. Find the area of a sector with central angle 2 rad in a circle of radius 5 m.

11. Find the area of a sector with central angle 52° in a circle of radius 200 ft.

12. A sector in a circle of radius 25 ft has an area of 125 ft². Find the central angle of the sector.

13. A potter's wheel with radius 8 in. spins at 150 rpm. Find the angular and linear speeds of a point on the rim of the wheel.

14. In an automobile transmission a *gear ratio* g is the ratio

$$g = \frac{\text{angular speed of engine}}{\text{angular speed of wheels}}$$

The angular speed of the engine is shown on the tachometer (in rpm).

A certain sports car has wheels with radius 11 in. Its gear ratios are shown in the following table. Suppose the car is in fourth gear and the tachometer reads 3500 rpm.
   (a) Find the angular speed of the engine.
   (b) Find the angular speed of the wheels.
   (c) How fast (in mi/h) is the car traveling?

Gear	Ratio
1st	4.1
2nd	3.0
3rd	1.6
4th	0.9
5th	0.7

15–16 ■ Find the values of the six trigonometric ratios of θ.

15.

16.

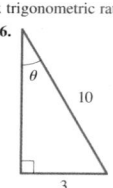

17–20 ■ Find the sides labeled x and y, rounded to two decimal places.

17.

18.

19.

20.

21–24 ■ Solve the triangle.

21.

22.

23.

24.

25. Express the lengths a and b in the figure in terms of the trigonometric ratios of θ.

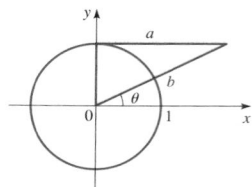

26. The highest free-standing tower in North America is the CN Tower in Toronto, Canada. From a distance of 1 km from its base, the angle of elevation to the top of the tower is 28.81°. Find the height of the tower.

27. Find the perimeter of a regular hexagon that is inscribed in a circle of radius 8 m.

28. The pistons in a car engine move up and down repeatedly to turn the crankshaft, as shown. Find the height of the point P above the center O of the crankshaft in terms of the angle θ.

29. As viewed from the earth, the angle subtended by the full moon is $0.518°$. Use this information and the fact that the distance AB from the earth to the moon is $236{,}900$ mi to find the radius of the moon.

30. A pilot measures the angles of depression to two ships to be $40°$ and $52°$ (see the figure). If the pilot is flying at an elevation of $35{,}000$ ft, find the distance between the two ships.

31–42 ■ Find the exact value.

31. $\sin 315°$

32. $\csc \dfrac{9\pi}{4}$

33. $\tan(-135°)$

34. $\cos \dfrac{5\pi}{6}$

35. $\cot\left(-\dfrac{22\pi}{3}\right)$

36. $\sin 405°$

37. $\cos 585°$

38. $\sec \dfrac{22\pi}{3}$

39. $\csc \dfrac{8\pi}{3}$

40. $\sec \dfrac{13\pi}{6}$

41. $\cot(-390°)$

42. $\tan \dfrac{23\pi}{4}$

43. Find the values of the six trigonometric ratios of the angle θ in standard position if the point $(-5, 12)$ is on the terminal side of θ.

44. Find $\sin \theta$ if θ is in standard position and its terminal side intersects the circle of radius 1 centered at the origin at the point $(-\sqrt{3}/2, \tfrac{1}{2})$.

45. Find the acute angle that is formed by the line $y - \sqrt{3}x + 1 = 0$ and the x-axis.

46. Find the six trigonometric ratios of the angle θ in standard position if its terminal side is in Quadrant III and is parallel to the line $4y - 2x - 1 = 0$.

47–50 ■ Write the first expression in terms of the second, for θ in the given quadrant.

47. $\tan \theta$, $\cos \theta$; θ in Quadrant II

48. $\sec \theta$, $\sin \theta$; θ in Quadrant III

49. $\tan^2\theta$, $\sin \theta$; θ in any quadrant

50. $\csc^2\theta\,\cos^2\theta$, $\sin \theta$; θ in any quadrant

51–54 ■ Find the values of the six trigonometric functions of θ from the information given.

51. $\tan \theta = \sqrt{7}/3$, $\sec \theta = \tfrac{4}{3}$

52. $\sec \theta = \tfrac{41}{40}$, $\csc \theta = -\tfrac{41}{9}$

53. $\sin \theta = \tfrac{3}{5}$, $\cos \theta < 0$

54. $\sec \theta = -\tfrac{13}{5}$, $\tan \theta > 0$

55. If $\tan \theta = -\tfrac{1}{2}$ for θ in Quadrant II, find $\sin \theta + \cos \theta$.

56. If $\sin \theta = \tfrac{1}{2}$ for θ in Quadrant I, find $\tan \theta + \sec \theta$.

57. If $\tan \theta = -1$, find $\sin^2\theta + \cos^2\theta$.

58. If $\cos \theta = -\sqrt{3}/2$ and $\pi/2 < \theta < \pi$, find $\sin 2\theta$.

59–62 ■ Find the exact value of the expression.

59. $\sin^{-1}(\sqrt{3}/2)$

60. $\tan^{-1}(\sqrt{3}/3)$

61. $\tan(\sin^{-1}\tfrac{2}{5})$

62. $\sin(\cos^{-1}\tfrac{3}{8})$

63–64 ■ Rewrite the expression as an algebraic expression in x.

63. $\sin(\tan^{-1}x)$

64. $\sec(\sin^{-1}x)$

65–66 ■ Express θ in terms of x.

65.

66.

67–76 ■ Find the side labeled x or the angle labeled θ.

67.

68.

69.

70.

71.

72.

73.

74.

75.
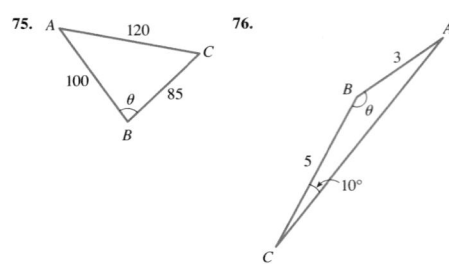

76.

77. Two ships leave a port at the same time. One travels at 20 mi/h in a direction N 32° E, and the other travels at 28 mi/h in a direction S 42° E (see the figure). How far apart are the two ships after 2 h?

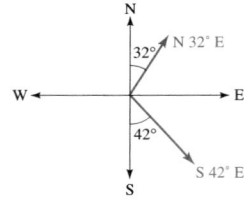

78. From a point A on the ground, the angle of elevation to the top of a tall building is 24.1°. From a point B, which is 600 ft closer to the building, the angle of elevation is measured to be 30.2°. Find the height of the building.

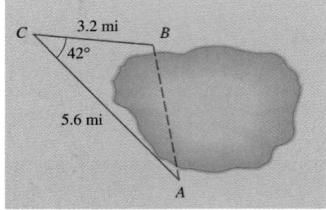

79. Find the distance between points A and B on opposite sides of a lake from the information shown.

80. A boat is cruising the ocean off a straight shoreline. Points A and B are 120 mi apart on the shore, as shown. It is found that $\angle A = 42.3°$ and $\angle B = 68.9°$. Find the shortest distance from the boat to the shore.

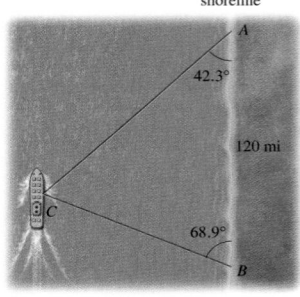

shoreline

81. Find the area of a triangle with sides of length 8 and 14 and included angle 35°.

82. Find the area of a triangle with sides of length 5, 6, and 8.

1. Find the radian measures that correspond to the degree measures $330°$ and $-135°$.

2. Find the degree measures that correspond to the radian measures $\dfrac{4\pi}{3}$ and -1.3.

3. The rotor blades of a helicopter are 16 ft long and are rotating at 120 rpm.
   (a) Find the angular speed of the rotor.
   (b) Find the linear speed of a point on the tip of a blade.

4. Find the exact value of each of the following.
   (a) $\sin 405°$ (b) $\tan(-150°)$ (c) $\sec \dfrac{5\pi}{3}$ (d) $\csc \dfrac{5\pi}{2}$

5. Find $\tan \theta + \sin \theta$ for the angle θ shown.

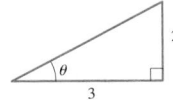

6. Express the lengths a and b shown in the figure in terms of θ.

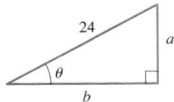

7. If $\cos \theta = -\frac{1}{3}$ and θ is in Quadrant III, find $\tan \theta \cot \theta + \csc \theta$.

8. If $\sin \theta = \frac{5}{13}$ and $\tan \theta = -\frac{5}{12}$, find $\sec \theta$.

9. Express $\tan \theta$ in terms of $\sec \theta$ for θ in Quadrant II.

10. The base of the ladder in the figure is 6 ft from the building, and the angle formed by the ladder and the ground is $73°$. How high up the building does the ladder touch?

11. Express θ in each figure in terms of x.
    (a)

    (b)

12. Find the exact value of $\cos\left(\tan^{-1} \frac{9}{40}\right)$.

487

13–18 ■ Find the side labeled x or the angle labeled θ.

13.

14.

15.

16.

17.

18.

19. Refer to the figure below.

    (a) Find the area of the shaded region.

    (b) Find the perimeter of the shaded region.

20. Refer to the figure below.

    (a) Find the angle opposite the longest side.

    (b) Find the area of the triangle.

21. Two wires tether a balloon to the ground, as shown. How high is the balloon above the ground?

How can we measure the height of a mountain or the distance across a lake? Obviously, it may be difficult, inconvenient, or impossible to measure these distances directly (that is, by using a tape measure or a yardstick). On the other hand, it is easy to measure *angles* involving distant objects. That's where trigonometry comes in: the trigonometric ratios relate angles to distances, so they can be used to *calculate* distances from the *measured* angles. In this *Focus* we examine how trigonometry is used to map a town. Modern mapmaking methods use satellites and the Global Positioning System, but mathematics remains at the core of the process.

▼ Mapping a Town

A student wants to draw a map of his hometown. To construct an accurate map (or scale model), he needs to find distances between various landmarks in the town. The student makes the measurements shown in Figure 1. Note that only one distance is measured, between City Hall and the first bridge. All other measurements are angles.

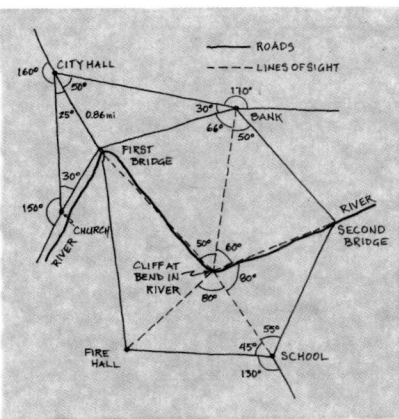

FIGURE 1

The distances between other landmarks can now be found by using the Law of Sines. For example, the distance x from the bank to the first bridge is calculated by applying the Law of Sines to the triangle with vertices at City Hall, the bank, and the first bridge:

$$\frac{x}{\sin 50°} = \frac{0.86}{\sin 30°} \qquad \text{Law of Sines}$$

$$x = \frac{0.86 \sin 50°}{\sin 30°} \qquad \text{Solve for } x$$

$$\approx 1.32 \text{ mi} \qquad \text{Calculator}$$

So the distance between the bank and the first bridge is 1.32 mi.

The distance we just found can now be used to find other distances. For instance, we find the distance y between the bank and the cliff as follows:

$$\frac{y}{\sin 64°} = \frac{1.32}{\sin 50°} \qquad \text{Law of Sines}$$

$$y = \frac{1.32 \sin 64°}{\sin 50°} \qquad \text{Solve for } y$$

$$\approx 1.55 \text{ mi} \qquad \text{Calculator}$$

Continuing in this fashion, we can calculate all the distances between the landmarks shown in the rough sketch in Figure 1. We can use this information to draw the map shown in Figure 2.

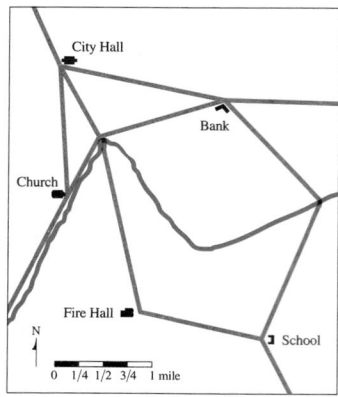

FIGURE 2

To make a topographic map, we need to measure elevation. This concept is explored in Problems 4–6.

PROBLEMS

1. **Completing the Map**   Find the distance between the church and City Hall.

2. **Completing the Map**   Find the distance between the fire hall and the school. (You will need to find other distances first.)

3. **Determining a Distance**   A surveyor on one side of a river wishes to find the distance between points A and B on the opposite side of the river. On her side, she chooses points C and D, which are 20 m apart, and measures the angles shown in the figure below. Find the distance between A and B.

4. **Height of a Cliff**   To measure the height of an inaccessible cliff on the opposite side of a river, a surveyor makes the measurements shown in the figure at the left. Find the height of the cliff.

5. **Height of a Mountain**   To calculate the height h of a mountain, angle α, β, and distance d are measured, as shown in the figure below.

   (a) Show that

   $$h = \frac{d}{\cot \alpha - \cot \beta}$$

   (b) Show that

   $$h = d \frac{\sin \alpha \sin \beta}{\sin(\beta - \alpha)}$$

   (c) Use the formulas from parts (a) and (b) to find the height of a mountain if $\alpha = 25°$, $\beta = 29°$, and $d = 800$ ft. Do you get the same answer from each formula?

6. **Determining a Distance**   A surveyor has determined that a mountain is 2430 ft high. From the top of the mountain he measures the angles of depression to two landmarks at the base of the mountain and finds them to be 42° and 39°. (Observe that these are the same as the angles of elevation from the landmarks as shown in the figure at the left.) The angle between the lines of sight to the landmarks is 68°. Calculate the distance between the two landmarks.

7. **Surveying Building Lots**   A surveyor surveys two adjacent lots and makes the following rough sketch showing his measurements. Calculate all the distances shown in the figure, and use your result to draw an accurate map of the two lots.

8. **Great Survey of India**   The Great Trigonometric Survey of India was one of the most massive mapping projects ever undertaken (see the margin note on page 472). Do some research at your library or on the Internet to learn more about the Survey, and write a report on your findings.

© Sony Pictures Classics/Courtesy of Everett Collection

CHAPTER | 7

ANALYTIC TRIGONOMETRY

In Chapters 5 and 6 we studied graphical and geometric properties of the trigonometric functions. In this chapter we study algebraic properties of these functions, that is, simplifying and factoring expressions and solving equations that involve trigonometric functions.

We have used the trigonometric functions to model different real-world phenomena, including periodic motion (such as the motion of an ocean wave). To obtain information from a model, we often need to solve equations. If the model involves trigonometric functions, we need to solve trigonometric equations. Solving trigonometric equations often involves using trigonometric identities. We've already encountered some basic trigonometric identities in the preceding chapters. We begin this chapter by finding many new identities.

493

SUGGESTED TIME AND EMPHASIS

$\frac{1}{2}$–1 class, essential material

7.1 TRIGONOMETRIC IDENTITIES

| Simplifying Trigonometric Expressions ▶ Proving Trigonometric Identities

We begin by listing some of the basic trigonometric identities. We studied most of these in Chapters 5 and 6; you are asked to prove the cofunction identities in Exercise 102.

FUNDAMENTAL TRIGONOMETRIC IDENTITIES

Reciprocal Identities

$$\csc x = \frac{1}{\sin x} \qquad \sec x = \frac{1}{\cos x} \qquad \cot x = \frac{1}{\tan x}$$

$$\tan x = \frac{\sin x}{\cos x} \qquad \cot x = \frac{\cos x}{\sin x}$$

Pythagorean Identities

$$\sin^2 x + \cos^2 x = 1 \qquad \tan^2 x + 1 = \sec^2 x \qquad 1 + \cot^2 x = \csc^2 x$$

Even-Odd Identities

$$\sin(-x) = -\sin x \qquad \cos(-x) = \cos x \qquad \tan(-x) = -\tan x$$

Cofunction Identities

$$\sin\left(\frac{\pi}{2} - u\right) = \cos u \qquad \tan\left(\frac{\pi}{2} - u\right) = \cot u \qquad \sec\left(\frac{\pi}{2} - u\right) = \csc u$$

$$\cos\left(\frac{\pi}{2} - u\right) = \sin u \qquad \cot\left(\frac{\pi}{2} - u\right) = \tan u \qquad \csc\left(\frac{\pi}{2} - u\right) = \sec u$$

▼ Simplifying Trigonometric Expressions

Identities enable us to write the same expression in different ways. It is often possible to rewrite a complicated-looking expression as a much simpler one. To simplify algebraic expressions, we used factoring, common denominators, and the Special Product Formulas. To simplify trigonometric expressions, we use these same techniques together with the fundamental trigonometric identities.

EXAMPLE 1 | Simplifying a Trigonometric Expression

Simplify the expression $\cos t + \tan t \sin t$.

SOLUTION   We start by rewriting the expression in terms of sine and cosine:

$$\cos t + \tan t \sin t = \cos t + \left(\frac{\sin t}{\cos t}\right)\sin t \qquad \text{Reciprocal identity}$$

$$= \frac{\cos^2 t + \sin^2 t}{\cos t} \qquad \text{Common denominator}$$

$$= \frac{1}{\cos t} \qquad \text{Pythagorean identity}$$

$$= \sec t \qquad \text{Reciprocal identity}$$

✎. NOW TRY EXERCISE **3**   ∎

ALTERNATE EXAMPLE 1
Simplify the expression
$(1 + \sin y)(\sec y - \tan y)$.

ANSWER
$\cos y$

TEXT QUESTION
Given that $\sin^2 x + \cos^2 x = 1$, find an identity for $\tan^2 x + 1$ and show that it is valid.

Answer

$$\frac{\sin^2 x}{\cos^2 x} + \frac{\cos^2 x}{\cos^2 x} = \frac{1}{\cos^2 x}$$
$$\Rightarrow \tan^2 x + 1$$
$$= \sec^2 x$$

EXAMPLE 2 | Simplifying by Combining Fractions

Simplify the expression $\dfrac{\sin\theta}{\cos\theta} + \dfrac{\cos\theta}{1+\sin\theta}$.

SOLUTION We combine the fractions by using a common denominator:

$$\frac{\sin\theta}{\cos\theta} + \frac{\cos\theta}{1+\sin\theta} = \frac{\sin\theta\,(1+\sin\theta)+\cos^2\theta}{\cos\theta\,(1+\sin\theta)} \qquad \text{Common denominator}$$

$$= \frac{\sin\theta + \sin^2\theta + \cos^2\theta}{\cos\theta\,(1+\sin\theta)} \qquad \text{Distribute } \sin\theta$$

$$= \frac{\sin\theta + 1}{\cos\theta\,(1+\sin\theta)} \qquad \text{Pythagorean identity}$$

$$= \frac{1}{\cos\theta} = \sec\theta \qquad \text{Cancel and use reciprocal identity}$$

 NOW TRY EXERCISE **21**

▼ Proving Trigonometric Identities

Many identities follow from the fundamental identities. In the examples that follow, we learn how to prove that a given trigonometric equation is an identity, and in the process we will see how to discover new identities.

First, it's easy to decide when a given equation is *not* an identity. All we need to do is show that the equation does not hold for some value of the variable (or variables). Thus the equation

$$\sin x + \cos x = 1$$

is not an identity, because when $x = \pi/4$, we have

$$\sin\frac{\pi}{4} + \cos\frac{\pi}{4} = \frac{\sqrt{2}}{2} + \frac{\sqrt{2}}{2} = \sqrt{2} \neq 1$$

To verify that a trigonometric equation is an identity, we transform one side of the equation into the other side by a series of steps, each of which is itself an identity.

GUIDELINES FOR PROVING TRIGONOMETRIC IDENTITIES

1. **Start with one side.** Pick one side of the equation and write it down. Your goal is to transform it into the other side. It's usually easier to start with the more complicated side.

2. **Use known identities.** Use algebra and the identities you know to change the side you started with. Bring fractional expressions to a common denominator, factor, and use the fundamental identities to simplify expressions.

3. **Convert to sines and cosines.** If you are stuck, you may find it helpful to rewrite all functions in terms of sines and cosines.

⊘ Warning: To prove an identity, we do *not* just perform the same operations on both sides of the equation. For example, if we start with an equation that is not an identity, such as

(1) $$\sin x = -\sin x$$

and square both sides, we get the equation

(2) $$\sin^2 x = \sin^2 x$$

which is clearly an identity. Does this mean that the original equation is an identity? Of course not. The problem here is that the operation of squaring is not **reversible** in the sense

---

ALTERNATE EXAMPLE 2
Simplify the expression
$$\frac{\sin\theta + \cot\theta\cos\theta}{\cot\theta}.$$

ANSWER
$\sec\theta$

IN-CLASS MATERIALS
Students often do not grasp the difference between an equation and an identity. Have students classify the following:

$$2x + x = 2x + 2 \qquad \text{(equation)}$$
$$2x + x = 3x \qquad \text{(identity)}$$
$$x + 1 = 2x + 2 \qquad \text{(equation)}$$
$$2(x + 1) = 2x + 2 \qquad \text{(identity)}$$
$$\sin 2x = 2\sin x\cos x \qquad \text{(identity)}$$
$$2\sin^2 2x + 2\cos^2 2x = 2 \qquad \text{(identity)}$$
$$2\sin^2 2x = 1 \qquad \text{(equation)}$$

ALTERNATE EXAMPLE 3

Consider the equation
$$\frac{1}{\cos\theta\,\tan\theta} = \csc\theta.$$

(a) Verify algebraically that the equation is an identity.
(b) Confirm graphically that the equation is an identity.

ANSWERS

(a) $\dfrac{1}{\cos\theta\,\tan\theta} =$

$\dfrac{1}{\cos\theta\,\dfrac{\sin\theta}{\cos\theta}} =$

$\dfrac{1}{\sin\theta} =$

$\csc\theta$

(b)

ALTERNATE EXAMPLE 4

Verify the identity
$$\frac{1-\cos\theta}{\sin\theta} - \frac{\sin\theta}{1+\cos\theta} = 0.$$

ANSWER

Steps:

$\dfrac{1-\cos\theta}{\sin\theta} - \dfrac{\sin\theta}{1+\cos\theta}$

$= \dfrac{(1+\cos\theta)(1-\cos\theta)}{\sin\theta\,(1+\cos\theta)}$

$- \dfrac{\sin^2\theta}{\sin\theta\,(1+\cos\theta)}$

$= \dfrac{(1+\cos\theta)(1-\cos\theta) - \sin^2\theta}{\sin\theta(1+\cos\theta)}$

$= \dfrac{\sin^2\theta - \sin^2\theta}{\sin\theta\,(1+\cos\theta)} = 0$

---

that we cannot arrive back at (1) from (2) by taking square roots (reversing the procedure). Only operations that are reversible will necessarily transform an identity into an identity.

EXAMPLE 3 | Proving an Identity by Rewriting in Terms of Sine and Cosine

Consider the equation $\cos\theta\,(\sec\theta - \cos\theta) = \sin^2\theta$.

(a) Verify algebraically that the equation is an identity.
(b) Confirm graphically that the equation is an identity.

SOLUTION

(a) The left-hand side looks more complicated, so we start with it and try to transform it into the right-hand side:

$\text{LHS} = \cos\theta\,(\sec\theta - \cos\theta)$

$= \cos\theta\left(\dfrac{1}{\cos\theta} - \cos\theta\right)$ Reciprocal identity

$= 1 - \cos^2\theta$ Expand

$= \sin^2\theta = \text{RHS}$ Pythagorean identity

(b) We graph each side of the equation to see whether the graphs coincide. From Figure 1 we see that the graphs of $y = \cos\theta\,(\sec\theta - \cos\theta)$ and $y = \sin^2\theta$ are identical. This confirms that the equation is an identity.

FIGURE 1

✎ NOW TRY EXERCISE **27**   ∎

In Example 3 it isn't easy to see how to change the right-hand side into the left-hand side, but it's definitely possible. Simply notice that each step is reversible. In other words, if we start with the last expression in the proof and work backward through the steps, the right-hand side is transformed into the left-hand side. You will probably agree, however, that it's more difficult to prove the identity this way. That's why it's often better to change the more complicated side of the identity into the simpler side.

EXAMPLE 4 | Proving an Identity by Combining Fractions

Verify the identity

$$2\tan x\,\sec x = \frac{1}{1-\sin x} - \frac{1}{1+\sin x}$$

SOLUTION   Finding a common denominator and combining the fractions on the right-hand side of this equation, we get

$\text{RHS} = \dfrac{1}{1-\sin x} - \dfrac{1}{1+\sin x}$

$= \dfrac{(1+\sin x) - (1-\sin x)}{(1-\sin x)(1+\sin x)}$ Common denominator

$= \dfrac{2\sin x}{1-\sin^2 x}$ Simplify

$= \dfrac{2\sin x}{\cos^2 x}$ Pythagorean identity

$= 2\,\dfrac{\sin x}{\cos x}\left(\dfrac{1}{\cos x}\right)$ Factor

$= 2\tan x\,\sec x = \text{LHS}$ Reciprocal identities

✎ NOW TRY EXERCISE **79**   ∎

IN-CLASS MATERIALS

Point out the difference between a reversible operation and an irreversible one. Note the importance—reversible operations can be used to prove identities. Have students classify the following:

x^2 (irreversible)
x^3 (reversible)
$\sqrt[3]{x}$ (reversible)
$x + c$ (reversible)
cx (reversible if $c \neq 0$)

See the Prologue: *Principles of Problem Solving,* pages P1–P4.

In Example 5 we introduce "something extra" to the problem by multiplying the numerator and the denominator by a trigonometric expression, chosen so that we can simplify the result.

EXAMPLE 5 | Proving an Identity by Introducing Something Extra

Verify the identity $\dfrac{\cos u}{1 - \sin u} = \sec u + \tan u$.

SOLUTION We start with the left-hand side and multiply the numerator and denominator by $1 + \sin u$:

We multiply by $1 + \sin u$ because we know by the difference of squares formula that $(1 - \sin u)(1 + \sin u) = 1 - \sin^2 u$, and this is just $\cos^2 u$, a simpler expression.

$$
\begin{aligned}
\text{LHS} &= \frac{\cos u}{1 - \sin u} \\
&= \frac{\cos u}{1 - \sin u} \cdot \frac{1 + \sin u}{1 + \sin u} && \text{Multiply numerator and denominator by } 1 + \sin u \\
&= \frac{\cos u (1 + \sin u)}{1 - \sin^2 u} && \text{Expand denominator} \\
&= \frac{\cos u (1 + \sin u)}{\cos^2 u} && \text{Pythagorean identity} \\
&= \frac{1 + \sin u}{\cos u} && \text{Cancel common factor} \\
&= \frac{1}{\cos u} + \frac{\sin u}{\cos u} && \text{Separate into two fractions} \\
&= \sec u + \tan u && \text{Reciprocal identities}
\end{aligned}
$$

NOW TRY EXERCISE 53

Here is another method for proving that an equation is an identity. If we can transform each side of the equation *separately*, by way of identities, to arrive at the same result, then the equation is an identity. Example 6 illustrates this procedure.

EXAMPLE 6 | Proving an Identity by Working with Both Sides Separately

Verify the identity $\dfrac{1 + \cos \theta}{\cos \theta} = \dfrac{\tan^2 \theta}{\sec \theta - 1}$.

SOLUTION We prove the identity by changing each side separately into the same expression. Supply the reasons for each step:

$$
\text{LHS} = \frac{1 + \cos \theta}{\cos \theta} = \frac{1}{\cos \theta} + \frac{\cos \theta}{\cos \theta} = \sec \theta + 1
$$

$$
\text{RHS} = \frac{\tan^2 \theta}{\sec \theta - 1} = \frac{\sec^2 \theta - 1}{\sec \theta - 1} = \frac{(\sec \theta - 1)(\sec \theta + 1)}{\sec \theta - 1} = \sec \theta + 1
$$

It follows that LHS = RHS, so the equation is an identity.

NOW TRY EXERCISE 81

We conclude this section by describing the technique of *trigonometric substitution,* which we use to convert algebraic expressions to trigonometric ones. This is often useful in calculus, for instance, in finding the area of a circle or an ellipse.

EUCLID (circa 300 B.C.) taught in Alexandria. His *Elements* is the most widely influential scientific book in history. For 2000 years it was the standard introduction to geometry in the schools, and for many generations it was considered the best way to develop logical reasoning. Abraham Lincoln, for instance, studied the *Elements* as a way to sharpen his mind. The story is told that King Ptolemy once asked Euclid if there was a faster way to learn geometry than through the *Elements.* Euclid replied that there is "no royal road to geometry"—meaning by this that mathematics does not respect wealth or social status. Euclid was revered in his own time and was referred to by the title "The Geometer" or "The Writer of the *Elements.*" The greatness of the *Elements* stems from its precise, logical, and systematic treatment of geometry. For dealing with equality, Euclid lists the following rules, which he calls "common notions."

1. Things that are equal to the same thing are equal to each other.
2. If equals are added to equals, the sums are equal.
3. If equals are subtracted from equals, the remainders are equal.
4. Things that coincide with one another are equal.
5. The whole is greater than the part.

ALTERNATE EXAMPLE 5
Verify the identity
$$\frac{\sin^3 u}{1 + \cos u} = \sin u (1 - \cos u).$$

ANSWER
$$
\begin{aligned}
\frac{\sin^3 u}{1 + \cos u} &= \\
&= \frac{\sin^3 u (1 - \cos u)}{(1 + \cos u)(1 - \cos u)} \\
&= \frac{\sin^3 u (1 - \cos u)}{1 - \cos^2 u} \\
&= \sin u (1 - \cos u)
\end{aligned}
$$

ALTERNATE EXAMPLE 6
Verify the identity
$$\sin \theta[\sin \theta + \cos \theta(1 + \cot \theta)] = \cos \theta(\sin \theta + \cos \theta + \sin \theta \tan \theta).$$

ANSWER
LHS:
$$
\begin{aligned}
&\sin \theta[\sin \theta + \cos \theta(1 + \cot \theta)] = \\
&\sin \theta(\sin \theta + \cos \theta + \cos \theta \tan \theta) = \\
&\quad \sin \theta \cos \theta + \sin^2 \theta + \cos^2 \theta = \\
&\qquad\qquad\qquad\qquad \sin \theta \cos \theta + 1
\end{aligned}
$$

RHS:
$$
\begin{aligned}
&\cos \theta(\sin \theta + \cos \theta + \sin \theta \tan \theta) = \\
&\quad \cos \theta \sin \theta + \cos^2 \theta + \sin^2 \theta = \\
&\qquad\qquad\qquad\qquad \sin \theta \cos \theta + 1
\end{aligned}
$$

EXAMPLE
Verify the identity
$$\frac{\cos(2\theta) - \cos(4\theta)}{\sin(2\theta) + \sin(4\theta)} = \tan(\theta).$$

Steps:
$$
\begin{aligned}
\cos(2\theta) &= \cos^2(\theta) - \sin^2(\theta) \\
&= 1 - 2\sin^2(\theta) \\
\sin(2\theta) &= 2\sin(\theta)\cos(\theta) \\
\cos(4\theta) &= \cos^2(2\theta) - \sin^2(2\theta) \\
&= 1 - 2\sin^2(2\theta) \\
\sin(4\theta) &= 2\sin(2\theta)\cos(2\theta)
\end{aligned}
$$

EXAMPLE
Proving an identity by introducing something extra:
$$\frac{\csc \theta}{\tan \theta + \cot \theta} = \cos \theta$$

PROOF
$$
\frac{\csc \theta}{\tan \theta + \cot \theta} = \frac{\csc \theta}{\tan \theta + \cot \theta} \cdot \frac{\tan \theta}{\tan \theta} = \frac{\sec \theta}{\tan^2 \theta + 1} = \frac{\sec \theta}{\sec^2 \theta} = \cos \theta
$$

ALTERNATE EXAMPLE 7

Verify the identity

$\sqrt{1 + x^2}, x = \tan \theta.$

ANSWER

$x = \tan \theta;$

then $\sqrt{1 + x^2} = \sqrt{1 + \tan^2 \theta}$

$\qquad = \sqrt{\sec^2 \theta}$

$\qquad = \sec \theta$

EXAMPLE 7 | Trigonometric Substitution

Substitute $\sin \theta$ for x in the expression $\sqrt{1 - x^2}$ and simplify. Assume that $0 \le \theta \le \pi/2$.

SOLUTION   Setting $x = \sin \theta$, we have

$$\sqrt{1 - x^2} = \sqrt{1 - \sin^2\theta} \qquad \text{Substitute } x = \sin \theta$$
$$= \sqrt{\cos^2\theta} \qquad \text{Pythagorean identity}$$
$$= \cos \theta \qquad \text{Take square root}$$

The last equality is true because $\cos \theta \ge 0$ for the values of θ in question.

✎ NOW TRY EXERCISE **91**   ∎

7.1 EXERCISES

CONCEPTS

1. An equation is called an identity if it is valid for _____ values of the variable. The equation $2x = x + x$ is an algebraic identity, and the equation $\sin^2 x + \cos^2 x =$ _____ is a trigonometric identity.

2. For any x it is true that $\cos(-x)$ has the same value as $\cos x$.

We express this fact as the identity _____.

SKILLS

3–12 ■ Write the trigonometric expression in terms of sine and cosine, and then simplify.

3. $\cos t \tan t$

4. $\cos t \csc t$

5. $\sin \theta \sec \theta$

6. $\tan \theta \csc \theta$

7. $\tan^2 x - \sec^2 x$

8. $\dfrac{\sec x}{\csc x}$

9. $\sin u + \cot u \cos u$

10. $\cos^2\theta \, (1 + \tan^2\theta)$

11. $\dfrac{\sec \theta - \cos \theta}{\sin \theta}$

12. $\dfrac{\cot \theta}{\csc \theta - \sin \theta}$

13–26 ■ Simplify the trigonometric expression.

13. $\dfrac{\sin x \sec x}{\tan x}$

14. $\cos^3 x + \sin^2 x \cos x$

15. $\dfrac{1 + \cos y}{1 + \sec y}$

16. $\dfrac{\tan x}{\sec(-x)}$

17. $\dfrac{\sec^2 x - 1}{\sec^2 x}$

18. $\dfrac{\sec x - \cos x}{\tan x}$

19. $\dfrac{1 + \csc x}{\cos x + \cot x}$

20. $\dfrac{\sin x}{\csc x} + \dfrac{\cos x}{\sec x}$

21. $\dfrac{1 + \sin u}{\cos u} + \dfrac{\cos u}{1 + \sin u}$

22. $\tan x \cos x \csc x$

23. $\dfrac{2 + \tan^2 x}{\sec^2 x} - 1$

24. $\dfrac{1 + \cot A}{\csc A}$

25. $\tan \theta + \cos(-\theta) + \tan(-\theta)$

26. $\dfrac{\cos x}{\sec x + \tan x}$

27–28 ■ Consider the given equation. **(a)** Verify algebraically that the equation is an identity. **(b)** Confirm graphically that the equation is an identity.

✎ **27.** $\dfrac{\cos x}{\sec x \sin x} = \csc x - \sin x$ **28.** $\dfrac{\tan y}{\csc y} = \sec y - \cos y$

29–90 ■ Verify the identity.

29. $\dfrac{\sin \theta}{\tan \theta} = \cos \theta$

30. $\dfrac{\tan x}{\sec x} = \sin x$

31. $\dfrac{\cos u \sec u}{\tan u} = \cot u$

32. $\dfrac{\cot x \sec x}{\csc x} = 1$

33. $\sin B + \cos B \cot B = \csc B$

34. $\cos(-x) - \sin(-x) = \cos x + \sin x$

35. $\cot(-\alpha) \cos(-\alpha) + \sin(-\alpha) = -\csc \alpha$

36. $\csc x \, [\csc x + \sin(-x)] = \cot^2 x$

37. $\tan \theta + \cot \theta = \sec \theta \csc \theta$

38. $(\sin x + \cos x)^2 = 1 + 2 \sin x \cos x$

39. $(1 - \cos \beta)(1 + \cos \beta) = \dfrac{1}{\csc^2 \beta}$

40. $\dfrac{\cos x}{\sec x} + \dfrac{\sin x}{\csc x} = 1$

41. $\dfrac{(\sin x + \cos x)^2}{\sin^2 x - \cos^2 x} = \dfrac{\sin^2 x - \cos^2 x}{(\sin x - \cos x)^2}$

42. $(\sin x + \cos x)^4 = (1 + 2 \sin x \cos x)^2$

43. $\dfrac{\sec t - \cos t}{\sec t} = \sin^2 t$

44. $\dfrac{1 - \sin x}{1 + \sin x} = (\sec x - \tan x)^2$

45. $\dfrac{1}{1 - \sin^2 y} = 1 + \tan^2 y$ **46.** $\csc x - \sin x = \cos x \cot x$

47. $(\cot x - \csc x)(\cos x + 1) = -\sin x$

48. $\sin^4 \theta - \cos^4 \theta = \sin^2 \theta - \cos^2 \theta$

49. $(1 - \cos^2 x)(1 + \cot^2 x) = 1$

DRILL QUESTION

Prove that $\sin^3 x + \sin x \cos^2 x = \sin x$ is an identity.

Answer

$\sin^3 x + \sin x \cos^2 x = \sin x \, (\sin^2 x + \cos^2 x) = \sin x$

50. $\cos^2 x - \sin^2 x = 2\cos^2 x - 1$

51. $2\cos^2 x - 1 = 1 - 2\sin^2 x$

52. $(\tan y + \cot y)\sin y \cos y = 1$

53. $\dfrac{1 - \cos\alpha}{\sin\alpha} = \dfrac{\sin\alpha}{1 + \cos\alpha}$

54. $\sin^2\alpha + \cos^2\alpha + \tan^2\alpha = \sec^2\alpha$

55. $\tan^2\theta - \sin^2\theta = \tan^2\theta\,\sin^2\theta$

56. $\cot^2\theta\,\cos^2\theta = \cot^2\theta - \cos^2\theta$

57. $\dfrac{\sin x - 1}{\sin x + 1} = \dfrac{-\cos^2 x}{(\sin x + 1)^2}$

58. $\dfrac{\sin w}{\sin w + \cos w} = \dfrac{\tan w}{1 + \tan w}$

59. $\dfrac{(\sin t + \cos t)^2}{\sin t \cos t} = 2 + \sec t \csc t$

60. $\sec t \csc t\,(\tan t + \cot t) = \sec^2 t + \csc^2 t$

61. $\dfrac{1 + \tan^2 u}{1 - \tan^2 u} = \dfrac{1}{\cos^2 u - \sin^2 u}$

62. $\dfrac{1 + \sec^2 x}{1 + \tan^2 x} = 1 + \cos^2 x$

63. $\dfrac{\sec x}{\sec x - \tan x} = \sec x\,(\sec x + \tan x)$

64. $\dfrac{\sec x + \csc x}{\tan x + \cot x} = \sin x + \cos x$

65. $\sec v - \tan v = \dfrac{1}{\sec v + \tan v}$

66. $\dfrac{\sin A}{1 - \cos A} - \cot A = \csc A$

67. $\dfrac{\sin x + \cos x}{\sec x + \csc x} = \sin x \cos x$

68. $\dfrac{1 - \cos x}{\sin x} + \dfrac{\sin x}{1 - \cos x} = 2\csc x$

69. $\dfrac{\csc x - \cot x}{\sec x - 1} = \cot x$ **70.** $\dfrac{\csc^2 x - \cot^2 x}{\sec^2 x} = \cos^2 x$

71. $\tan^2 u - \sin^2 u = \tan^2 u\,\sin^2 u$

72. $\dfrac{\tan v \sin v}{\tan v + \sin v} = \dfrac{\tan v - \sin v}{\tan v \sin v}$

73. $\sec^4 x - \tan^4 x = \sec^2 x + \tan^2 x$

74. $\dfrac{\cos\theta}{1 - \sin\theta} = \sec\theta + \tan\theta$

75. $\dfrac{\cos\theta}{1 - \sin\theta} = \dfrac{\sin\theta - \csc\theta}{\cos\theta - \cot\theta}$

76. $\dfrac{1 + \tan x}{1 - \tan x} = \dfrac{\cos x + \sin x}{\cos x - \sin x}$

77. $\dfrac{\cos^2 t + \tan^2 t - 1}{\sin^2 t} = \tan^2 t$

78. $\dfrac{1}{1 - \sin x} - \dfrac{1}{1 + \sin x} = 2\sec x \tan x$

79. $\dfrac{1}{\sec x + \tan x} + \dfrac{1}{\sec x - \tan x} = 2\sec x$

80. $\dfrac{1 + \sin x}{1 - \sin x} - \dfrac{1 - \sin x}{1 + \sin x} = 4\tan x \sec x$

81. $(\tan x + \cot x)^2 = \sec^2 x + \csc^2 x$

82. $\tan^2 x - \cot^2 x = \sec^2 x - \csc^2 x$

83. $\dfrac{\sec u - 1}{\sec u + 1} = \dfrac{1 - \cos u}{1 + \cos u}$ **84.** $\dfrac{\cot x + 1}{\cot x - 1} = \dfrac{1 + \tan x}{1 - \tan x}$

85. $\dfrac{\sin^3 x + \cos^3 x}{\sin x + \cos x} = 1 - \sin x \cos x$

86. $\dfrac{\tan v - \cot v}{\tan^2 v - \cot^2 v} = \sin v \cos v$

87. $\dfrac{1 + \sin x}{1 - \sin x} = (\tan x + \sec x)^2$

88. $\dfrac{\tan x + \tan y}{\cot x + \cot y} = \tan x \tan y$

89. $(\tan x + \cot x)^4 = \csc^4 x \sec^4 x$

90. $(\sin\alpha - \tan\alpha)(\cos\alpha - \cot\alpha) = (\cos\alpha - 1)(\sin\alpha - 1)$

91–96 ■ Make the indicated trigonometric substitution in the given algebraic expression and simplify (see Example 7). Assume that $0 \le \theta < \pi/2$.

91. $\dfrac{x}{\sqrt{1 - x^2}},\quad x = \sin\theta$ **92.** $\sqrt{1 + x^2},\quad x = \tan\theta$

93. $\sqrt{x^2 - 1},\quad x = \sec\theta$ **94.** $\dfrac{1}{x^2\sqrt{4 + x^2}},\quad x = 2\tan\theta$

95. $\sqrt{9 - x^2},\quad x = 3\sin\theta$ **96.** $\dfrac{\sqrt{x^2 - 25}}{x},\quad x = 5\sec\theta$

97–100 ■ Graph f and g in the same viewing rectangle. Do the graphs suggest that the equation $f(x) = g(x)$ is an identity? Prove your answer.

97. $f(x) = \cos^2 x - \sin^2 x,\quad g(x) = 1 - 2\sin^2 x$

98. $f(x) = \tan x\,(1 + \sin x),\quad g(x) = \dfrac{\sin x \cos x}{1 + \sin x}$

99. $f(x) = (\sin x + \cos x)^2,\quad g(x) = 1$

100. $f(x) = \cos^4 x - \sin^4 x,\quad g(x) = 2\cos^2 x - 1$

101. Show that the equation is not an identity.

  (a) $\sin 2x = 2\sin x$ (b) $\sin(x + y) = \sin x + \sin y$

  (c) $\sec^2 x + \csc^2 x = 1$

  (d) $\dfrac{1}{\sin x + \cos x} = \csc x + \sec x$

DISCOVERY ■ DISCUSSION ■ WRITING

102. Cofunction Identities   In the right triangle shown, explain why $v = (\pi/2) - u$. Explain how you can obtain all six cofunction identities from this triangle for $0 < u < \pi/2$.

103. Graphs and Identities   Suppose you graph two functions, f and g, on a graphing device and their graphs appear identical in the viewing rectangle. Does this prove that the equation $f(x) = g(x)$ is an identity? Explain.

104. Making Up Your Own Identity   If you start with a trigonometric expression and rewrite it or simplify it,

then setting the original expression equal to the rewritten expression yields a trigonometric identity. For instance, from Example 1 we get the identity

$$\cos t + \tan t \sin t = \sec t$$

Use this technique to make up your own identity, then give it to a classmate to verify.

SUGGESTED TIME AND EMPHASIS

$\frac{1}{2}$–1 class, recommended material

7.2   ADDITION AND SUBTRACTION FORMULAS

Addition and Subtraction Formulas ▶ Evaluating Expressions Involving Inverse Trigonometric Functions ▶ Expressions of the form $A \sin x + B \cos x$

▼ Addition and Subtraction Formulas

We now derive identities for trigonometric functions of sums and differences.

ADDITION AND SUBTRACTION FORMULAS

Formulas for sine:
$$\sin(s + t) = \sin s \cos t + \cos s \sin t$$
$$\sin(s - t) = \sin s \cos t - \cos s \sin t$$

Formulas for cosine:
$$\cos(s + t) = \cos s \cos t - \sin s \sin t$$
$$\cos(s - t) = \cos s \cos t + \sin s \sin t$$

Formulas for tangent:
$$\tan(s + t) = \frac{\tan s + \tan t}{1 - \tan s \tan t}$$
$$\tan(s - t) = \frac{\tan s - \tan t}{1 + \tan s \tan t}$$

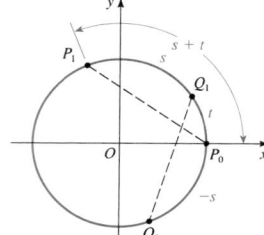

FIGURE 1

PROOF OF ADDITION FORMULA FOR COSINE   To prove the formula $\cos(s + t) = \cos s \cos t - \sin s \sin t$, we use Figure 1. In the figure, the distances t, $s + t$, and $-s$ have been marked on the unit circle, starting at $P_0(1, 0)$ and terminating at Q_1, P_1, and Q_0, respectively. The coordinates of these points are

$$P_0(1, 0) \qquad\qquad Q_0(\cos(-s), \sin(-s))$$
$$P_1(\cos(s + t), \sin(s + t)) \qquad Q_1(\cos t, \sin t)$$

Since $\cos(-s) = \cos s$ and $\sin(-s) = -\sin s$, it follows that the point Q_0 has the coordinates $Q_0(\cos s, -\sin s)$. Notice that the distances between P_0 and P_1 and between Q_0 and Q_1 measured along the arc of the circle are equal. Since equal arcs are subtended by equal chords, it follows that $d(P_0, P_1) = d(Q_0, Q_1)$. Using the Distance Formula, we get

$$\sqrt{[\cos(s + t) - 1]^2 + [\sin(s + t) - 0]^2} = \sqrt{(\cos t - \cos s)^2 + (\sin t + \sin s)^2}$$

Squaring both sides and expanding, we have

$$\overbrace{\cos^2(s + t) - 2 \cos(s + t) + 1 + \sin^2(s + t)}^{\text{These add to 1}}$$
$$= \underbrace{\cos^2 t - 2 \cos s \cos t + \cos^2 s + \sin^2 t + 2 \sin s \sin t + \sin^2 s}_{}$$

with the notes "These add to 1" marked under the expanded terms.

TEXT QUESTION

The text has an example in which $\cos 75°$ is calculated. How is this done?

Answer

Write $\cos 75° = \cos(30° + 45°)$ and use an addition formula.

JEAN BAPTISTE JOSEPH FOURIER
(1768–1830) is responsible for the most
powerful application of the trigonometric functions (see the margin note
on page 394). He used sums of these
functions to describe such physical
phenomena as the transmission of
sound and the flow of heat.
Orphaned as a young boy, Fourier
was educated in a military school,
where he became a mathematics
teacher at the age of 20. He was later
appointed professor at the École Polytechnique but resigned this position to
accompany Napoleon on his expedition to Egypt, where Fourier served as
governor. After returning to France he
began conducting experiments on
heat. The French Academy refused to
publish his early papers on this subject
because of his lack of rigor. Fourier
eventually became Secretary of the
Academy and in this capacity had his
papers published in their original form.
Probably because of his study of heat
and his years in the deserts of Egypt,
Fourier became obsessed with keeping
himself warm—he wore several layers
of clothes, even in the summer, and
kept his rooms at unbearably high
temperatures. Evidently, these habits
overburdened his heart and contributed to his death at the age of 62.

Using the Pythagorean identity $\sin^2\theta + \cos^2\theta = 1$ three times gives

$$2 - 2\cos(s + t) = 2 - 2\cos s \cos t + 2 \sin s \sin t$$

Finally, subtracting 2 from each side and dividing both sides by -2, we get

$$\cos(s + t) = \cos s \cos t - \sin s \sin t$$

which proves the Addition Formula for Cosine. ■

PROOF OF SUBTRACTION FORMULA FOR COSINE Replacing t with $-t$ in the Addition Formula for Cosine, we get

$$\cos(s - t) = \cos(s + (-t))$$
$$= \cos s \cos(-t) - \sin s \sin(-t) \qquad \text{Addition Formula for Cosine}$$
$$= \cos s \cos t + \sin s \sin t \qquad \text{Even-odd identities}$$

This proves the Subtraction Formula for Cosine. ■

See Exercises 70 and 71 for proofs of the other Addition Formulas.

EXAMPLE 1 | Using the Addition and Subtraction Formulas

Find the exact value of each expression.

(a) $\cos 75°$ (b) $\cos \dfrac{\pi}{12}$

SOLUTION

(a) Notice that $75° = 45° + 30°$. Since we know the exact values of sine and cosine at 45° and 30°, we use the Addition Formula for Cosine to get

$$\cos 75° = \cos(45° + 30°)$$
$$= \cos 45° \cos 30° - \sin 45° \sin 30°$$
$$= \frac{\sqrt{2}}{2}\frac{\sqrt{3}}{2} - \frac{\sqrt{2}}{2}\frac{1}{2} = \frac{\sqrt{2}\sqrt{3} - \sqrt{2}}{4} = \frac{\sqrt{6} - \sqrt{2}}{4}$$

(b) Since $\dfrac{\pi}{12} = \dfrac{\pi}{4} - \dfrac{\pi}{6}$, the Subtraction Formula for Cosine gives

$$\cos \frac{\pi}{12} = \cos\left(\frac{\pi}{4} - \frac{\pi}{6}\right)$$
$$= \cos \frac{\pi}{4} \cos \frac{\pi}{6} + \sin \frac{\pi}{4} \sin \frac{\pi}{6}$$
$$= \frac{\sqrt{2}}{2}\frac{\sqrt{3}}{2} + \frac{\sqrt{2}}{2}\frac{1}{2} = \frac{\sqrt{6} + \sqrt{2}}{4}$$

✎ NOW TRY EXERCISES **3** AND **9** ■

EXAMPLE 2 | Using the Addition Formula for Sine

Find the exact value of the expression $\sin 20° \cos 40° + \cos 20° \sin 40°$.

SOLUTION We recognize the expression as the right-hand side of the Addition Formula for Sine with $s = 20°$ and $t = 40°$. So we have

$$\sin 20° \cos 40° + \cos 20° \sin 40° = \sin(20° + 40°) = \sin 60° = \frac{\sqrt{3}}{2}$$

✎ NOW TRY EXERCISE **15** ■

ALTERNATE EXAMPLE 1
Find the exact value of the expression $\cos 15°$.

ANSWER
$$\frac{\sqrt{6} + \sqrt{2}}{4}$$

ALTERNATE EXAMPLE 2
Find the exact value of the expression $\sin 10° \cos 50° + \cos 10° \sin 50°$.

ANSWER
$$\frac{\sqrt{3}}{2}$$

IN-CLASS MATERIALS

It might be a good idea for the class to work together to come up with some mnemonics to help them remember the addition formulas. The very act of trying to invent such a mnemonic forces students to look at the formulas carefully and think about them, which is a memory aid in itself. Students might come up with such things as "the sign of the sine doesn't change," or "the cosine keeps like functions together, while the sine switches them."

ALTERNATE EXAMPLE 3

Prove the cofunction identity

$$\cos\left(\frac{3\pi}{2} - t\right) = -\sin(t).$$

ANSWER

$$\cos\left(\frac{3\pi}{2} - t\right) =$$

$$\cos\left(\frac{3\pi}{2}\right)\cos(t) + \sin\left(\frac{3\pi}{2}\right)\sin(t) =$$

$$0 - \sin(t) =$$

$$-\sin(t)$$

ALTERNATE EXAMPLE 4

Verify the identity

$$\tan\left(\frac{\pi}{4} - x\right) = \frac{1 - \tan(x)}{1 + \tan(x)}.$$

ANSWER

$$\tan\left(\frac{\pi}{4} - x\right) =$$

$$\frac{\tan\left(\frac{\pi}{4}\right) - \tan(x)}{1 + \tan\left(\frac{\pi}{4}\right)\tan(x)} = \frac{1 - \tan(x)}{1 + \tan(x)}$$

EXAMPLE 3 | Proving a Cofunction Identity

Prove the cofunction identity $\cos\left(\frac{\pi}{2} - u\right) = \sin u$.

SOLUTION   By the Subtraction Formula for Cosine, we have

$$\cos\left(\frac{\pi}{2} - u\right) = \cos\frac{\pi}{2}\cos u + \sin\frac{\pi}{2}\sin u$$

$$= 0 \cdot \cos u + 1 \cdot \sin u = \sin u$$

✎. NOW TRY EXERCISE **21**   ■

The cofunction identity in Example 3, as well as the other cofunction identities, can also be derived from the figure in the margin.

$$\cos\left(\frac{\pi}{2} - u\right) = \frac{b}{r} = \sin u$$

EXAMPLE 4 | Proving an Identity

Verify the identity $\frac{1 + \tan x}{1 - \tan x} = \tan\left(\frac{\pi}{4} + x\right)$.

SOLUTION   Starting with the right-hand side and using the Addition Formula for Tangent, we get

$$\text{RHS} = \tan\left(\frac{\pi}{4} + x\right) = \frac{\tan\frac{\pi}{4} + \tan x}{1 - \tan\frac{\pi}{4}\tan x}$$

$$= \frac{1 + \tan x}{1 - \tan x} = \text{LHS}$$

✎. NOW TRY EXERCISE **25**   ■

The next example is a typical use of the Addition and Subtraction Formulas in calculus.

EXAMPLE 5 | An Identity from Calculus

If $f(x) = \sin x$, show that

$$\frac{f(x + h) - f(x)}{h} = \sin x \left(\frac{\cos h - 1}{h}\right) + \cos x \left(\frac{\sin h}{h}\right)$$

SOLUTION

$$\frac{f(x + h) - f(x)}{h} = \frac{\sin(x + h) - \sin x}{h}$$ Definition of f

$$= \frac{\sin x \cos h + \cos x \sin h - \sin x}{h}$$ Addition Formula for Sine

$$= \frac{\sin x\,(\cos h - 1) + \cos x \sin h}{h}$$ Factor

$$= \sin x \left(\frac{\cos h - 1}{h}\right) + \cos x \left(\frac{\sin h}{h}\right)$$ Separate the fraction

✎. NOW TRY EXERCISE **61**   ■

▼ Evaluating Expressions Involving Inverse Trigonometric Functions

Expressions involving trigonometric functions and their inverses arise in calculus. In the next examples we illustrate how to evaluate such expressions.

IN-CLASS MATERIALS

Students can test the formulas by seeing if they work for values of sine and cosine that they know. For example, they can look at $\sin(2 - 2)$ and $\cos(\beta - \beta)$ to make sure they get 0 and 1, respectively. They can look at $\sin(60° + 30°)$ and $\cos\left(\frac{\pi}{4} + \frac{\pi}{2}\right)$ to make sure things work out as they should.

$$\cos \theta = x$$

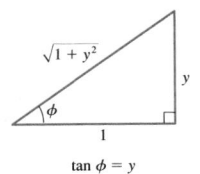

$$\tan \phi = y$$

FIGURE 2

EXAMPLE 6 | Simplifying an Expression Involving Inverse Trigonometric Functions

Write $\sin(\cos^{-1}x + \tan^{-1}y)$ as an algebraic expression in x and y, where $-1 \le x \le 1$ and y is any real number.

SOLUTION Let $\theta = \cos^{-1}x$ and $\phi = \tan^{-1}y$. Using the methods of Section 6.4, we sketch triangles with angles θ and ϕ such that $\cos \theta = x$ and $\tan \phi = y$ (see Figure 2). From the triangles we have

$$\sin \theta = \sqrt{1 - x^2} \qquad \cos \phi = \frac{1}{\sqrt{1 + y^2}} \qquad \sin \phi = \frac{y}{\sqrt{1 + y^2}}$$

From the Addition Formula for Sine we have

$$\sin(\cos^{-1}x + \tan^{-1}y) = \sin(\theta + \phi)$$

$$= \sin \theta \cos \phi + \cos \theta \sin \phi \qquad \text{Addition Formula for Sine}$$

$$= \sqrt{1 - x^2}\,\frac{1}{\sqrt{1 + y^2}} + x\,\frac{y}{\sqrt{1 + y^2}} \qquad \text{From triangles}$$

$$= \frac{1}{\sqrt{1 + y^2}}(\sqrt{1 - x^2} + xy) \qquad \text{Factor } \frac{1}{\sqrt{1 + y^2}}$$

✎ NOW TRY EXERCISES **43** AND **47** ∎

EXAMPLE 7 | Evaluating an Expression Involving Trigonometric Functions

Evaluate $\sin(\theta + \phi)$, where $\sin \theta = \frac{12}{13}$ with θ in Quadrant II and $\tan \phi = \frac{3}{4}$ with ϕ in Quadrant III.

SOLUTION We first sketch the angles θ and ϕ in standard position with terminal sides in the appropriate quadrants as in Figure 3. Since $\sin \theta = y/r = \frac{12}{13}$ we can label a side and the hypotenuse in the triangle in Figure 3(a). To find the remaining side, we use the Pythagorean Theorem:

$$x^2 + y^2 = r^2 \qquad \text{Pythagorean Theorem}$$

$$x^2 + 12^2 = 13^2 \qquad y = 12, \quad r = 13$$

$$x^2 = 25 \qquad \text{Solve for } x^2$$

$$x = -5 \qquad \text{Because } x < 0$$

Similarly, since $\tan \phi = y/x = \frac{3}{4}$, we can label two sides of the triangle in Figure 3(b) and then use the Pythagorean Theorem to find the hypotenuse.

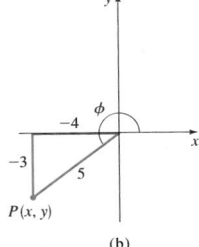

FIGURE 3   (a)   (b)

IN-CLASS MATERIALS
Have students predict which will be bigger, the sum of the first two graphs or the sum of the second two. Note that the sum of the amplitudes of each pair of graphs is 5. Then use the formula from the section to show the first sum has an amplitude of $\sqrt{17}$ and the second has an amplitude of $\sqrt{12.5}$. Finally, show them the graphs of the sums.

$\sin x + 4 \cos x$

$2.5 \sin x + 2.5 \cos x$

EXAMPLE

Given that $\sin\dfrac{\pi}{5} \approx 0.58779$, find $\cos\dfrac{11}{30}\pi$.

ANSWER

We verify that $\dfrac{\pi}{5} + \dfrac{\pi}{6} = \dfrac{11}{30}\pi$

and calculate $\cos\dfrac{11}{30}\pi = \cos\dfrac{\pi}{5} \times$

$\cos\dfrac{\pi}{6} - \sin\dfrac{\pi}{5}\sin\dfrac{\pi}{6}$. Since $\dfrac{\pi}{5}$ is

in the first quadrant, we have

$\cos\dfrac{\pi}{5} \approx 0.80902$. Therefore,

$\cos\dfrac{11}{30}\pi \approx 0.40674$.

Now, to find $\sin(\theta + \phi)$, we use the Addition Formula for Sine and the triangles in Figure 3:

$$\sin(\theta + \phi) = \sin\theta\cos\phi + \cos\theta\sin\phi \qquad \text{Addition Formula}$$

$$= \left(\tfrac{12}{13}\right)\left(-\tfrac{4}{5}\right) + \left(-\tfrac{5}{13}\right)\left(-\tfrac{3}{5}\right) \qquad \text{From triangles}$$

$$= -\tfrac{33}{65} \qquad \text{Calculate}$$

◣ NOW TRY EXERCISE **51**

▼ Expressions of the Form $A\sin x + B\cos x$

We can write expressions of the form $A\sin x + B\cos x$ in terms of a single trigonometric function using the Addition Formula for Sine. For example, consider the expression

$$\frac{1}{2}\sin x + \frac{\sqrt{3}}{2}\cos x$$

If we set $\phi = \pi/3$, then $\cos\phi = \tfrac{1}{2}$ and $\sin\phi = \sqrt{3}/2$, and we can write

$$\frac{1}{2}\sin x + \frac{\sqrt{3}}{2}\cos x = \cos\phi\sin x + \sin\phi\cos x$$

$$= \sin(x + \phi) = \sin\left(x + \frac{\pi}{3}\right)$$

We are able to do this because the coefficients $\tfrac{1}{2}$ and $\sqrt{3}/2$ are precisely the cosine and sine of a particular number, in this case, $\pi/3$. We can use this same idea in general to write $A\sin x + B\cos x$ in the form $k\sin(x + \phi)$. We start by multiplying the numerator and denominator by $\sqrt{A^2 + B^2}$ to get

$$A\sin x + B\cos x = \sqrt{A^2 + B^2}\left(\frac{A}{\sqrt{A^2 + B^2}}\sin x + \frac{B}{\sqrt{A^2 + B^2}}\cos x\right)$$

We need a number ϕ with the property that

$$\cos\phi = \frac{A}{\sqrt{A^2 + B^2}} \qquad \text{and} \qquad \sin\phi = \frac{B}{\sqrt{A^2 + B^2}}$$

FIGURE 4

Figure 4 shows that the point (A, B) in the plane determines a number ϕ with precisely this property. With this ϕ we have

$$A\sin x + B\cos x = \sqrt{A^2 + B^2}(\cos\phi\sin x + \sin\phi\cos x)$$

$$= \sqrt{A^2 + B^2}\sin(x + \phi)$$

We have proved the following theorem.

SUMS OF SINES AND COSINES

If A and B are real numbers, then

$$A\sin x + B\cos x = k\sin(x + \phi)$$

where $k = \sqrt{A^2 + B^2}$ and ϕ satisfies

$$\cos\phi = \frac{A}{\sqrt{A^2 + B^2}} \qquad \text{and} \qquad \sin\phi = \frac{B}{\sqrt{A^2 + B^2}}$$

EXAMPLE 8 | A Sum of Sine and Cosine Terms

Express $3 \sin x + 4 \cos x$ in the form $k \sin(x + \phi)$.

SOLUTION By the preceding theorem, $k = \sqrt{A^2 + B^2} = \sqrt{3^2 + 4^2} = 5$. The angle ϕ has the property that $\sin \phi = \frac{4}{5}$ and $\cos \phi = \frac{3}{5}$. Using a calculator, we find $\phi \approx 53.1°$. Thus

$$3 \sin x + 4 \cos x \approx 5 \sin(x + 53.1°)$$

✎. NOW TRY EXERCISE **55** ▪

EXAMPLE 9 | Graphing a Trigonometric Function

Write the function $f(x) = -\sin 2x + \sqrt{3} \cos 2x$ in the form $k \sin(2x + \phi)$, and use the new form to graph the function.

SOLUTION Since $A = -1$ and $B = \sqrt{3}$, we have $k = \sqrt{A^2 + B^2} = \sqrt{1 + 3} = 2$. The angle ϕ satisfies $\cos \phi = -\frac{1}{2}$ and $\sin \phi = \sqrt{3}/2$. From the signs of these quantities we conclude that ϕ is in Quadrant II. Thus $\phi = 2\pi/3$. By the preceding theorem we can write

$$f(x) = -\sin 2x + \sqrt{3} \cos 2x = 2 \sin\left(2x + \frac{2\pi}{3}\right)$$

Using the form

$$f(x) = 2 \sin 2\left(x + \frac{\pi}{3}\right)$$

we see that the graph is a sine curve with amplitude 2, period $2\pi/2 = \pi$, and phase shift $-\pi/3$. The graph is shown in Figure 5.

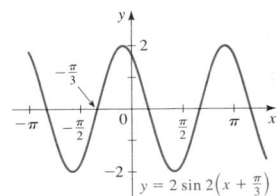

$$y = 2 \sin 2\left(x + \frac{\pi}{3}\right)$$

FIGURE 5

✎. NOW TRY EXERCISE **59** ▪

7.2 EXERCISES

CONCEPTS

1. If we know the values of the sine and cosine of x and y, we can

find the value of $\sin(x + y)$ by using the _____ Formula for

Sine. State the formula: $\sin(x + y) =$ _____.

2. If we know the values of the sine and cosine of x and y, we can

find the value of $\cos(x - y)$ by using the _____ Formula for

Cosine. State the formula: $\cos(x - y) =$ _____.

SKILLS

3–14 ■ Use an Addition or Subtraction Formula to find the exact value of the expression, as demonstrated in Example 1.

✎. **3.** $\sin 75°$ **4.** $\sin 15°$

5. $\cos 105°$ **6.** $\cos 195°$

7. $\tan 15°$ **8.** $\tan 165°$

✎. **9.** $\sin \dfrac{19\pi}{12}$ **10.** $\cos \dfrac{17\pi}{12}$

11. $\tan\left(-\dfrac{\pi}{12}\right)$ **12.** $\sin\left(-\dfrac{5\pi}{12}\right)$

13. $\cos \dfrac{11\pi}{12}$ **14.** $\tan \dfrac{7\pi}{12}$

15–20 ■ Use an Addition or Subtraction Formula to write the expression as a trigonometric function of one number, and then find its exact value.

✎. **15.** $\sin 18° \cos 27° + \cos 18° \sin 27°$

16. $\cos 10° \cos 80° - \sin 10° \sin 80°$

17. $\cos \dfrac{3\pi}{7} \cos \dfrac{2\pi}{21} + \sin \dfrac{3\pi}{7} \sin \dfrac{2\pi}{21}$

18. $\dfrac{\tan \dfrac{\pi}{18} + \tan \dfrac{\pi}{9}}{1 - \tan \dfrac{\pi}{18} \tan \dfrac{\pi}{9}}$

DRILL QUESTION

Find $\sin\left(\dfrac{\pi}{3} + x\right)$ if $\sin x \approx 0.42264$ and $\cos x \approx -0.75984$.

Answer

$$\sin\left(\dfrac{\pi}{3} + x\right) = \sin \dfrac{\pi}{3} \cos x + \cos \dfrac{\pi}{3} \sin x \approx \dfrac{\sqrt{3}}{2}(-0.75984) + \dfrac{1}{2}(0.42264) \approx -0.44672$$

19. $\dfrac{\tan 73° - \tan 13°}{1 + \tan 73° \tan 13°}$

20. $\cos \dfrac{13\pi}{15} \cos\left(-\dfrac{\pi}{5}\right) - \sin \dfrac{13\pi}{15} \sin\left(-\dfrac{\pi}{5}\right)$

21–24 ■ Prove the cofunction identity using the Addition and Subtraction Formulas.

21. $\tan\left(\dfrac{\pi}{2} - u\right) = \cot u$ **22.** $\cot\left(\dfrac{\pi}{2} - u\right) = \tan u$

23. $\sec\left(\dfrac{\pi}{2} - u\right) = \csc u$ **24.** $\csc\left(\dfrac{\pi}{2} - u\right) = \sec u$

25–42 ■ Prove the identity.

25. $\sin\left(x - \dfrac{\pi}{2}\right) = -\cos x$

26. $\cos\left(x - \dfrac{\pi}{2}\right) = \sin x$

27. $\sin(x - \pi) = -\sin x$ **28.** $\cos(x - \pi) = -\cos x$

29. $\tan(x - \pi) = \tan x$

30. $\sin\left(\dfrac{\pi}{2} - x\right) = \sin\left(\dfrac{\pi}{2} + x\right)$

31. $\cos\left(x + \dfrac{\pi}{6}\right) + \sin\left(x - \dfrac{\pi}{3}\right) = 0$

32. $\tan\left(x - \dfrac{\pi}{4}\right) = \dfrac{\tan x - 1}{\tan x + 1}$

33. $\sin(x + y) - \sin(x - y) = 2 \cos x \sin y$

34. $\cos(x + y) + \cos(x - y) = 2 \cos x \cos y$

35. $\cot(x - y) = \dfrac{\cot x \cot y + 1}{\cot y - \cot x}$

36. $\cot(x + y) = \dfrac{\cot x \cot y - 1}{\cot x + \cot y}$

37. $\tan x - \tan y = \dfrac{\sin(x - y)}{\cos x \cos y}$

38. $1 - \tan x \tan y = \dfrac{\cos(x + y)}{\cos x \cos y}$

39. $\dfrac{\sin(x + y) - \sin(x - y)}{\cos(x + y) + \cos(x - y)} = \tan y$

40. $\cos(x + y) \cos(x - y) = \cos^2 x - \sin^2 y$

41. $\sin(x + y + z) = \sin x \cos y \cos z + \cos x \sin y \cos z$
$+ \cos x \cos y \sin z - \sin x \sin y \sin z$

42. $\tan(x - y) + \tan(y - z) + \tan(z - x)$
$= \tan(x - y) \tan(y - z) \tan(z - x)$

43–46 ■ Write the given expression in terms of x and y only.

43. $\cos(\sin^{-1} x - \tan^{-1} y)$ **44.** $\tan(\sin^{-1} x + \cos^{-1} y)$

45. $\sin(\tan^{-1} x - \tan^{-1} y)$ **46.** $\sin(\sin^{-1} x + \cos^{-1} y)$

47–50 ■ Find the exact value of the expression.

47. $\sin\left(\cos^{-1} \frac{1}{2} + \tan^{-1} 1\right)$ **48.** $\cos\left(\sin^{-1} \frac{\sqrt{3}}{2} + \cot^{-1} \sqrt{3}\right)$

49. $\tan\left(\sin^{-1} \frac{3}{4} - \cos^{-1} \frac{1}{3}\right)$ **50.** $\sin\left(\cos^{-1} \frac{2}{3} - \tan^{-1} \frac{1}{2}\right)$

51–54 ■ Evaluate each expression under the given conditions.

51. $\cos(\theta - \phi)$; $\cos \theta = \frac{3}{5}$, θ in Quadrant IV, $\tan \phi = -\sqrt{3}$, ϕ in Quadrant II.

52. $\sin(\theta - \phi)$; $\tan \theta = \frac{4}{3}$, θ in Quadrant III, $\sin \phi = -\sqrt{10}/10$, ϕ in Quadrant IV

53. $\sin(\theta + \phi)$; $\sin \theta = \frac{5}{13}$, θ in Quadrant I, $\cos \phi = -2\sqrt{5}/5$, ϕ in Quadrant II

54. $\tan(\theta + \phi)$; $\cos \theta = -\frac{1}{3}$, θ in Quadrant III, $\sin \phi = \frac{1}{4}$, ϕ in Quadrant II

55–58 ■ Write the expression in terms of sine only.

55. $-\sqrt{3} \sin x + \cos x$ **56.** $\sin x + \cos x$

57. $5(\sin 2x - \cos 2x)$ **58.** $3 \sin \pi x + 3\sqrt{3} \cos \pi x$

59–60 ■ (a) Express the function in terms of sine only. (b) Graph the function.

59. $g(x) = \cos 2x + \sqrt{3} \sin 2x$ **60.** $f(x) = \sin x + \cos x$

61. Let $g(x) = \cos x$. Show that

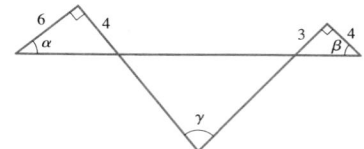

$$\frac{g(x + h) - g(x)}{h} = -\cos x\left(\frac{1 - \cos h}{h}\right) - \sin x\left(\frac{\sin h}{h}\right)$$

62. Show that if $\beta - \alpha = \pi/2$, then

$$\sin(x + \alpha) + \cos(x + \beta) = 0$$

63. Refer to the figure. Show that $\alpha + \beta = \gamma$, and find $\tan \gamma$.

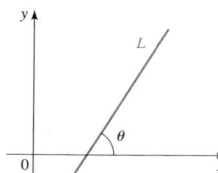

64. (a) If L is a line in the plane and θ is the angle formed by the line and the x-axis as shown in the figure, show that the slope m of the line is given by

$$m = \tan \theta$$

(b) Let L_1 and L_2 be two nonparallel lines in the plane with slopes m_1 and m_2, respectively. Let ψ be the acute angle formed by the two lines (see the following figure). Show that

$$\tan \psi = \frac{m_2 - m_1}{1 + m_1 m_2}$$

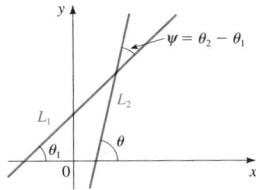

(c) Find the acute angle formed by the two lines

$$y = \tfrac{1}{3}x + 1 \qquad \text{and} \qquad y = -\tfrac{1}{2}x - 3$$

(d) Show that if two lines are perpendicular, then the slope of one is the negative reciprocal of the slope of the other. [*Hint:* First find an expression for cot ψ.]

 65–66 ■ (a) Graph the function and make a conjecture, then (b) prove that your conjecture is true.

65. $y = \sin^2\left(x + \dfrac{\pi}{4}\right) + \sin^2\left(x - \dfrac{\pi}{4}\right)$

66. $y = -\tfrac{1}{2}[\cos(x + \pi) + \cos(x - \pi)]$

67. Find $\angle A + \angle B + \angle C$ in the figure. [*Hint:* First use an addition formula to find $\tan(A + B)$.]

APPLICATIONS

 68. Adding an Echo A digital delay device echoes an input signal by repeating it a fixed length of time after it is received. If such a device receives the pure note $f_1(t) = 5 \sin t$ and echoes the pure note $f_2(t) = 5 \cos t$, then the combined sound is $f(t) = f_1(t) + f_2(t)$.
(a) Graph $y = f(t)$ and observe that the graph has the form of a sine curve $y = k \sin(t + \phi)$.
(b) Find k and ϕ.

69. Interference Two identical tuning forks are struck, one a fraction of a second after the other. The sounds produced are modeled by $f_1(t) = C \sin \omega t$ and $f_2(t) = C \sin(\omega t + \alpha)$. The two sound waves interfere to produce a single sound modeled by the sum of these functions

$$f(t) = C \sin \omega t + C \sin(\omega t + \alpha)$$

(a) Use the Addition Formula for Sine to show that f can be written in the form $f(t) = A \sin \omega t + B \cos \omega t$, where A and B are constants that depend on α.
(b) Suppose that $C = 10$ and $\alpha = \pi/3$. Find constants k and ϕ so that $f(t) = k \sin(\omega t + \phi)$.

DISCOVERY ■ DISCUSSION ■ WRITING

70. Addition Formula for Sine In the text we proved only the Addition and Subtraction Formulas for Cosine. Use these formulas and the cofunction identities

$$\sin x = \cos\left(\dfrac{\pi}{2} - x\right)$$

$$\cos x = \sin\left(\dfrac{\pi}{2} - x\right)$$

to prove the Addition Formula for Sine. [*Hint:* To get started, use the first cofunction identity to write

$$\sin(s + t) = \cos\left(\dfrac{\pi}{2} - (s + t)\right)$$

$$= \cos\left(\left(\dfrac{\pi}{2} - s\right) - t\right)$$

and use the Subtraction Formula for Cosine.]

71. Addition Formula for Tangent Use the Addition Formulas for Cosine and Sine to prove the Addition Formula for Tangent. [*Hint:* Use

$$\tan(s + t) = \dfrac{\sin(s + t)}{\cos(s + t)}$$

and divide the numerator and denominator by $\cos s \cos t$.]

7.3 DOUBLE-ANGLE, HALF-ANGLE, AND PRODUCT-SUM FORMULAS

| Double-Angle Formulas ▶ Half-Angle Formulas ▶ Simplifying Expressions Involving Inverse Trigonometric Functions ▶ Product-Sum Formulas

The identities we consider in this section are consequences of the addition formulas. The **Double-Angle Formulas** allow us to find the values of the trigonometric functions at $2x$ from their values at x. The **Half-Angle Formulas** relate the values of the trigonometric functions at $\tfrac{1}{2}x$ to their values at x. The **Product-Sum Formulas** relate products of sines and cosines to sums of sines and cosines.

TEXT QUESTION
How did we obtain the formula $\sin 2x = 2 \sin x \cos x$?

Answer
We wrote $\sin 2x = \sin(x + x)$ and used an Addition Formula.

▼ Double-Angle Formulas

The formulas in the following box are immediate consequences of the addition formulas, which we proved in the preceding section.

DOUBLE-ANGLE FORMULAS

Formula for sine:	$\sin 2x = 2 \sin x \cos x$
Formulas for cosine:	$\cos 2x = \cos^2 x - \sin^2 x$
	$= 1 - 2 \sin^2 x$
	$= 2 \cos^2 x - 1$
Formula for tangent:	$\tan 2x = \dfrac{2 \tan x}{1 - \tan^2 x}$

The proofs for the formulas for cosine are given here. You are asked to prove the remaining formulas in Exercises 35 and 36.

PROOF OF DOUBLE-ANGLE FORMULAS FOR COSINE

$$\cos 2x = \cos(x + x)$$
$$= \cos x \cos x - \sin x \sin x$$
$$= \cos^2 x - \sin^2 x$$

The second and third formulas for $\cos 2x$ are obtained from the formula we just proved and the Pythagorean identity. Substituting $\cos^2 x = 1 - \sin^2 x$ gives

$$\cos 2x = \cos^2 x - \sin^2 x$$
$$= (1 - \sin^2 x) - \sin^2 x$$
$$= 1 - 2 \sin^2 x$$

The third formula is obtained in the same way, by substituting $\sin^2 x = 1 - \cos^2 x$. ■

EXAMPLE 1 | Using the Double-Angle Formulas

If $\cos x = -\frac{2}{3}$ and x is in Quadrant II, find $\cos 2x$ and $\sin 2x$.

SOLUTION Using one of the Double-Angle Formulas for Cosine, we get

$$\cos 2x = 2 \cos^2 x - 1$$
$$= 2\left(-\frac{2}{3}\right)^2 - 1 = \frac{8}{9} - 1 = -\frac{1}{9}$$

To use the formula $\sin 2x = 2 \sin x \cos x$, we need to find $\sin x$ first. We have

$$\sin x = \sqrt{1 - \cos^2 x} = \sqrt{1 - \left(-\frac{2}{3}\right)^2} = \frac{\sqrt{5}}{3}$$

where we have used the positive square root because $\sin x$ is positive in Quadrant II. Thus

$$\sin 2x = 2 \sin x \cos x$$
$$= 2\left(\frac{\sqrt{5}}{3}\right)\left(-\frac{2}{3}\right) = -\frac{4\sqrt{5}}{9}$$

✎ NOW TRY EXERCISE **3** ■

ALTERNATE EXAMPLE 1

If $\cos x = -\frac{6}{11}$ and x is in Quadrant II, find $\sin 2x$ and $\cos 2x$.

ANSWER

$$\sin(2x) = -\frac{12\sqrt{85}}{121},$$
$$\cos(2x) = -\frac{49}{121}$$

IN-CLASS MATERIALS

One can illustrate many of the formulas in this section graphically. For example, this is how you can illustrate $\sin 2x = \dfrac{1 - \cos 2x}{2}$:

$\sin 2x$

$\cos 2x$

$-\cos 2x$

$1 - \cos 2x$

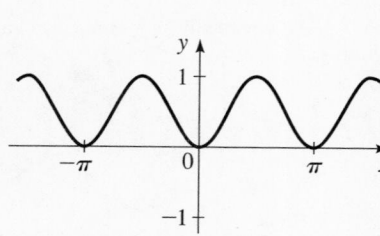

$\dfrac{1 - \cos 2x}{2}$

EXAMPLE 2 | A Triple-Angle Formula

Write $\cos 3x$ in terms of $\cos x$.

SOLUTION

$$
\begin{aligned}
\cos 3x &= \cos(2x + x) \\
&= \cos 2x \cos x - \sin 2x \sin x &&\text{Addition formula} \\
&= (2\cos^2 x - 1)\cos x - (2\sin x \cos x)\sin x &&\text{Double-Angle Formulas} \\
&= 2\cos^3 x - \cos x - 2\sin^2 x \cos x &&\text{Expand} \\
&= 2\cos^3 x - \cos x - 2\cos x(1 - \cos^2 x) &&\text{Pythagorean identity} \\
&= 2\cos^3 x - \cos x - 2\cos x + 2\cos^3 x &&\text{Expand} \\
&= 4\cos^3 x - 3\cos x &&\text{Simplify}
\end{aligned}
$$

NOW TRY EXERCISE 101

Example 2 shows that $\cos 3x$ can be written as a polynomial of degree 3 in $\cos x$. The identity $\cos 2x = 2\cos^2 x - 1$ shows that $\cos 2x$ is a polynomial of degree 2 in $\cos x$. In fact, for any natural number n, we can write $\cos nx$ as a polynomial in $\cos x$ of degree n (see the note following Exercise 101). The analogous result for $\sin nx$ is not true in general.

EXAMPLE 3 | Proving an Identity

Prove the identity $\dfrac{\sin 3x}{\sin x \cos x} = 4\cos x - \sec x$.

SOLUTION We start with the left-hand side:

$$
\begin{aligned}
\frac{\sin 3x}{\sin x \cos x} &= \frac{\sin(x + 2x)}{\sin x \cos x} \\
&= \frac{\sin x \cos 2x + \cos x \sin 2x}{\sin x \cos x} &&\text{Addition Formula} \\
&= \frac{\sin x(2\cos^2 x - 1) + \cos x(2\sin x \cos x)}{\sin x \cos x} &&\text{Double-Angle Formulas} \\
&= \frac{\sin x(2\cos^2 x - 1)}{\sin x \cos x} + \frac{\cos x(2\sin x \cos x)}{\sin x \cos x} &&\text{Separate fraction} \\
&= \frac{2\cos^2 x - 1}{\cos x} + 2\cos x &&\text{Cancel} \\
&= 2\cos x - \frac{1}{\cos x} + 2\cos x &&\text{Separate fraction} \\
&= 4\cos x - \sec x &&\text{Reciprocal identity}
\end{aligned}
$$

NOW TRY EXERCISE 81

▼ Half-Angle Formulas

The following formulas allow us to write any trigonometric expression involving even powers of sine and cosine in terms of the first power of cosine only. This technique is important in calculus. The Half-Angle Formulas are immediate consequences of these formulas.

ALTERNATE EXAMPLE 2
Write $\cos 3\theta$ in terms of $\cos\theta$.

ANSWER
$\cos 3\theta = 4\cos^3\theta - 3\cos\theta$

ALTERNATE EXAMPLE 3
Prove the identity
$\dfrac{\cos 2x + 1}{2\cos^4 x} = 1 + \tan^2 x.$

ANSWER
$$
\begin{aligned}
\frac{\cos 2x + 1}{2\cos^4 x} &= \frac{2\cos^2 x - 1 + 1}{2\cos^4 x} \\
&= \frac{1}{\cos^2 x} = \sec^2 x \\
&= 1 + \tan^2 x
\end{aligned}
$$

IN-CLASS MATERIALS
Note that we can derive the formula for $\tan\dfrac{u}{2}$ by dividing the formula for $\sin\dfrac{u}{2}$ by the formula for $\cos\dfrac{u}{2}$.

FORMULAS FOR LOWERING POWERS

$$\sin^2 x = \frac{1 - \cos 2x}{2} \qquad \cos^2 x = \frac{1 + \cos 2x}{2}$$

$$\tan^2 x = \frac{1 - \cos 2x}{1 + \cos 2x}$$

PROOF   The first formula is obtained by solving for $\sin^2 x$ in the double-angle formula $\cos 2x = 1 - 2\sin^2 x$. Similarly, the second formula is obtained by solving for $\cos^2 x$ in the Double-Angle Formula $\cos 2x = 2\cos^2 x - 1$.

The last formula follows from the first two and the reciprocal identities:

$$\tan^2 x = \frac{\sin^2 x}{\cos^2 x} = \frac{\dfrac{1 - \cos 2x}{2}}{\dfrac{1 + \cos 2x}{2}} = \frac{1 - \cos 2x}{1 + \cos 2x} \qquad \blacksquare$$

EXAMPLE 4 | Lowering Powers in a Trigonometric Expression

Express $\sin^2 x \cos^2 x$ in terms of the first power of cosine.

SOLUTION   We use the formulas for lowering powers repeatedly:

$$\sin^2 x \cos^2 x = \left(\frac{1 - \cos 2x}{2}\right)\left(\frac{1 + \cos 2x}{2}\right)$$

$$= \frac{1 - \cos^2 2x}{4} = \frac{1}{4} - \frac{1}{4}\cos^2 2x$$

$$= \frac{1}{4} - \frac{1}{4}\left(\frac{1 + \cos 4x}{2}\right) = \frac{1}{4} - \frac{1}{8} - \frac{\cos 4x}{8}$$

$$= \frac{1}{8} - \frac{1}{8}\cos 4x = \frac{1}{8}(1 - \cos 4x)$$

Another way to obtain this identity is to use the Double-Angle Formula for Sine in the form $\sin x \cos x = \frac{1}{2}\sin 2x$. Thus

$$\sin^2 x \cos^2 x = \frac{1}{4}\sin^2 2x = \frac{1}{4}\left(\frac{1 - \cos 4x}{2}\right)$$

$$= \frac{1}{8}(1 - \cos 4x)$$

✎ NOW TRY EXERCISE **11**   ■

HALF-ANGLE FORMULAS

$$\sin\frac{u}{2} = \pm\sqrt{\frac{1 - \cos u}{2}} \qquad \cos\frac{u}{2} = \pm\sqrt{\frac{1 + \cos u}{2}}$$

$$\tan\frac{u}{2} = \frac{1 - \cos u}{\sin u} = \frac{\sin u}{1 + \cos u}$$

The choice of the + or − sign depends on the quadrant in which $u/2$ lies.

IN-CLASS MATERIALS

One fun way to verify the formulas in this section is to compute $\sin x = \sin\left(2 \cdot \frac{1}{2}x\right)$ "the long way." (An even more fun method is to have your students do it.)

PROOF   We substitute $x = u/2$ in the formulas for lowering powers and take the square root of each side. This gives the first two Half-Angle Formulas. In the case of the Half-Angle Formula for Tangent we get

$$\tan\frac{u}{2} = \pm\sqrt{\frac{1 - \cos u}{1 + \cos u}}$$

$$= \pm\sqrt{\left(\frac{1 - \cos u}{1 + \cos u}\right)\left(\frac{1 - \cos u}{1 - \cos u}\right)} \qquad \text{Multiply numerator and} \\ \text{denominator by } 1 - \cos u$$

$$= \pm\sqrt{\frac{(1 - \cos u)^2}{1 - \cos^2 u}} \qquad \text{Simplify}$$

$$= \pm\frac{|1 - \cos u|}{|\sin u|} \qquad \sqrt{A^2} = |A| \\ \text{and} \quad 1 - \cos^2 u = \sin^2 u$$

Now, $1 - \cos u$ is nonnegative for all values of u. It is also true that $\sin u$ and $\tan(u/2)$ always have the same sign. (Verify this.) It follows that

$$\tan\frac{u}{2} = \frac{1 - \cos u}{\sin u}$$

The other Half-Angle Formula for Tangent is derived from this by multiplying the numerator and denominator by $1 + \cos u$.   ■

EXAMPLE 5 | Using a Half-Angle Formula

Find the exact value of $\sin 22.5°$.

SOLUTION   Since $22.5°$ is half of $45°$, we use the Half-Angle Formula for Sine with $u = 45°$. We choose the $+$ sign because $22.5°$ is in the first quadrant:

$$\sin\frac{45°}{2} = \sqrt{\frac{1 - \cos 45°}{2}} \qquad \text{Half-Angle Formula}$$

$$= \sqrt{\frac{1 - \sqrt{2}/2}{2}} \qquad \cos 45° = \sqrt{2}/2$$

$$= \sqrt{\frac{2 - \sqrt{2}}{4}} \qquad \text{Common denominator}$$

$$= \tfrac{1}{2}\sqrt{2 - \sqrt{2}} \qquad \text{Simplify}$$

✎ NOW TRY EXERCISE **17**   ■

EXAMPLE 6 | Using a Half-Angle Formula

Find $\tan(u/2)$ if $\sin u = \frac{2}{5}$ and u is in Quadrant II.

SOLUTION   To use the Half-Angle Formula for Tangent, we first need to find $\cos u$. Since cosine is negative in Quadrant II, we have

$$\cos u = -\sqrt{1 - \sin^2 u}$$

$$= -\sqrt{1 - \left(\tfrac{2}{5}\right)^2} = -\frac{\sqrt{21}}{5}$$

Thus

$$\tan\frac{u}{2} = \frac{1 - \cos u}{\sin u}$$

$$= \frac{1 + \sqrt{21}/5}{\tfrac{2}{5}} = \frac{5 + \sqrt{21}}{2}$$

✎ NOW TRY EXERCISE **37**   ■

ALTERNATE EXAMPLE 5
Find the exact value of $\cos 22.5°$.

ANSWER
$\dfrac{1}{2}\sqrt{2 + \sqrt{2}}$

ALTERNATE EXAMPLE 6
Find $\sin\left(\dfrac{u}{2}\right)$ if $\tan u = \dfrac{12}{35}$ and u is in Quadrant III.

ANSWER
$-\dfrac{6\sqrt{37}}{37}$

EXAMPLE

$$\sin 15° \cos 45° = \frac{1}{2}[\sin 60° + \sin(-30°)] = \frac{\sqrt{3} - 1}{4}$$

EXAMPLE

$$\tan^2 22.5° = \frac{1 - \cos 45°}{1 + \cos 45°}$$

$$= \frac{2 - \sqrt{2}}{2 + \sqrt{2}}$$

ALTERNATE EXAMPLE 7

Write $\sin\left(\dfrac{\tan^{-1}x}{2}\right)$ as an

algebraic expression in x only.

ANSWER

$$\pm\sqrt{\dfrac{1 - \dfrac{1}{\sqrt{1 + x^2}}}{2}} =$$

$$\pm\frac{1}{2}\sqrt{2 - \frac{2}{\sqrt{1 + x^2}}}$$

ALTERNATE EXAMPLE 8

Evaluate $\cos\left(\dfrac{\theta}{2}\right)$, where

$\tan \theta = -3/4$ with θ in

Quadrant IV.

ANSWER

$$\frac{3\sqrt{10}}{10}$$

▼ Evaluating Expressions Involving Inverse Trigonometric Functions

Expressions involving trigonometric functions and their inverses arise in calculus. In the next examples we illustrate how to evaluate such expressions.

EXAMPLE 7 | Simplifying an Expression Involving an Inverse Trigonometric Function

Write $\sin(2 \cos^{-1}x)$ as an algebraic expression in x only, where $-1 \le x \le 1$.

SOLUTION Let $\theta = \cos^{-1}x$, and sketch a triangle as in Figure 1. We need to find $\sin 2\theta$, but from the triangle we can find trigonometric functions of θ only, not 2θ. So we use the Double-Angle Formula for Sine.

$$\sin(2 \cos^{-1}x) = \sin 2\theta \qquad \cos^{-1}x = \theta$$

$$= 2 \sin \theta \cos \theta \qquad \text{Double-Angle Formula}$$

$$= 2x\sqrt{1 - x^2} \qquad \text{From the triangle}$$

✎ NOW TRY EXERCISES **43** AND **47** ∎

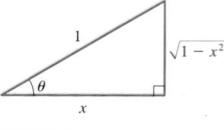

FIGURE 1

EXAMPLE 8 | Evaluating an Expression Involving Inverse Trigonometric Functions

Evaluate $\sin 2\theta$, where $\cos \theta = -\frac{2}{5}$ with θ in Quadrant II.

SOLUTION We first sketch the angle θ in standard position with terminal side in Quadrant II as in Figure 2. Since $\cos \theta = x/r = -\frac{2}{5}$, we can label a side and the hypotenuse of the triangle in Figure 2. To find the remaining side, we use the Pythagorean Theorem:

$$x^2 + y^2 = r^2 \qquad \text{Pythagorean Theorem}$$

$$(-2)^2 + y^2 = 5^2 \qquad x = -2, \quad r = 5$$

$$y = \pm\sqrt{21} \qquad \text{Solve for } y^2$$

$$y = +\sqrt{21} \qquad \text{Because } y > 0$$

We can now use the Double-Angle Formula for Sine:

$$\sin 2\theta = 2 \sin \theta \cos \theta \qquad \text{Double-Angle Formula}$$

$$= 2\left(\frac{\sqrt{21}}{5}\right)\left(-\frac{2}{5}\right) \qquad \text{From the triangle}$$

$$= -\frac{4\sqrt{21}}{25} \qquad \text{Simplify}$$

✎ NOW TRY EXERCISE **51** ∎

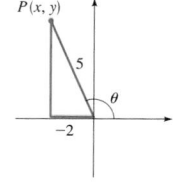

$P(x, y)$

FIGURE 2

▼ Product-Sum Formulas

It is possible to write the product $\sin u \cos v$ as a sum of trigonometric functions. To see this, consider the addition and subtraction formulas for the sine function:

$$\sin(u + v) = \sin u \cos v + \cos u \sin v$$

$$\sin(u - v) = \sin u \cos v - \cos u \sin v$$

Adding the left- and right-hand sides of these formulas gives

$$\sin(u + v) + \sin(u - v) = 2 \sin u \cos v$$

Dividing by 2 gives the formula

$$\sin u \cos v = \tfrac{1}{2}[\sin(u + v) + \sin(u - v)]$$

The other three **Product-to-Sum Formulas** follow from the addition formulas in a similar way.

PRODUCT-TO-SUM FORMULAS

$$\sin u \cos v = \tfrac{1}{2}[\sin(u + v) + \sin(u - v)]$$

$$\cos u \sin v = \tfrac{1}{2}[\sin(u + v) - \sin(u - v)]$$

$$\cos u \cos v = \tfrac{1}{2}[\cos(u + v) + \cos(u - v)]$$

$$\sin u \sin v = \tfrac{1}{2}[\cos(u - v) - \cos(u + v)]$$

EXAMPLE 9 | Expressing a Trigonometric Product as a Sum

Express $\sin 3x \sin 5x$ as a sum of trigonometric functions.

SOLUTION   Using the fourth Product-to-Sum Formula with $u = 3x$ and $v = 5x$ and the fact that cosine is an even function, we get

$$\sin 3x \sin 5x = \tfrac{1}{2}[\cos(3x - 5x) - \cos(3x + 5x)]$$

$$= \tfrac{1}{2}\cos(-2x) - \tfrac{1}{2}\cos 8x$$

$$= \tfrac{1}{2}\cos 2x - \tfrac{1}{2}\cos 8x$$

✎. NOW TRY EXERCISE **55**   ◼

The Product-to-Sum Formulas can also be used as Sum-to-Product Formulas. This is possible because the right-hand side of each Product-to-Sum Formula is a sum and the left side is a product. For example, if we let

$$u = \frac{x + y}{2} \quad \text{and} \quad v = \frac{x - y}{2}$$

in the first Product-to-Sum Formula, we get

$$\sin \frac{x + y}{2} \cos \frac{x - y}{2} = \tfrac{1}{2}(\sin x + \sin y)$$

so

$$\sin x + \sin y = 2 \sin \frac{x + y}{2} \cos \frac{x - y}{2}$$

The remaining three of the following **Sum-to-Product Formulas** are obtained in a similar manner.

SUM-TO-PRODUCT FORMULAS

$$\sin x + \sin y = 2 \sin \frac{x + y}{2} \cos \frac{x - y}{2}$$

$$\sin x - \sin y = 2 \cos \frac{x + y}{2} \sin \frac{x - y}{2}$$

$$\cos x + \cos y = 2 \cos \frac{x + y}{2} \cos \frac{x - y}{2}$$

$$\cos x - \cos y = -2 \sin \frac{x + y}{2} \sin \frac{x - y}{2}$$

ALTERNATE EXAMPLE 9

Express $\sin 2x \sin 4x$ as a sum of trigonometric functions.

ANSWER

$$\frac{1}{2}\cos(2x) - \frac{1}{2}\cos(6x)$$

ALTERNATE EXAMPLE 10
Write $\sin 11x + \sin 5x$ as a product.

ANSWER
$\sin(11x) + \sin(5x)$
$= 2\sin(8x)\cos(3x)$

ALTERNATE EXAMPLE 11
Verify the identity
$\dfrac{\sin(4x) + \sin(2x)}{\sin(2x)} = \dfrac{\sin(3x)}{\sin(x)}.$

ANSWER
$\dfrac{\sin(4x) + \sin(2x)}{\sin(2x)}$

$= \dfrac{2\sin(3x)\cos(x)}{2\sin(x)\cos(x)}$

$= \dfrac{\sin(3x)}{\sin(x)}$

EXAMPLE 10 | Expressing a Trigonometric Sum as a Product

Write $\sin 7x + \sin 3x$ as a product.

SOLUTION   The first Sum-to-Product Formula gives

$$\sin 7x + \sin 3x = 2\sin\frac{7x + 3x}{2}\cos\frac{7x - 3x}{2}$$

$$= 2\sin 5x \cos 2x$$

✎ NOW TRY EXERCISE **61**   ∎

EXAMPLE 11 | Proving an Identity

Verify the identity $\dfrac{\sin 3x - \sin x}{\cos 3x + \cos x} = \tan x.$

SOLUTION   We apply the second Sum-to-Product Formula to the numerator and the third formula to the denominator:

$$\text{LHS} = \frac{\sin 3x - \sin x}{\cos 3x + \cos x} = \frac{2\cos\dfrac{3x + x}{2}\sin\dfrac{3x - x}{2}}{2\cos\dfrac{3x + x}{2}\cos\dfrac{3x - x}{2}} \qquad \text{Sum-to-Product Formulas}$$

$$= \frac{2\cos 2x \sin x}{2\cos 2x \cos x} \qquad \text{Simplify}$$

$$= \frac{\sin x}{\cos x} = \tan x = \text{RHS} \qquad \text{Cancel}$$

✎ NOW TRY EXERCISE **89**   ∎

7.3 EXERCISES

CONCEPTS

1. If we know the values of $\sin x$ and $\cos x$, we can find the value of $\sin 2x$ by using the _____ Formula for Sine. State the formula: $\sin 2x = $ _____.

2. If we know the value of $\cos x$ and the quadrant in which $x/2$ lies, we can find the value of $\sin(x/2)$ by using the _____ Formula for Sine. State the formula:

$\sin(x/2) = $ _____.

SKILLS

3–10 ■ Find $\sin 2x$, $\cos 2x$, and $\tan 2x$ from the given information.

✎ **3.** $\sin x = \frac{5}{13}$, x in Quadrant I

4. $\tan x = -\frac{4}{3}$, x in Quadrant II

5. $\cos x = \frac{4}{5}$, $\csc x < 0$ **6.** $\csc x = 4$, $\tan x < 0$

7. $\sin x = -\frac{3}{5}$, x in Quadrant III

8. $\sec x = 2$, x in Quadrant IV

9. $\tan x = -\frac{1}{3}$, $\cos x > 0$

10. $\cot x = \frac{2}{3}$, $\sin x > 0$

11–16 ■ Use the formulas for lowering powers to rewrite the expression in terms of the first power of cosine, as in Example 4.

✎ **11.** $\sin^4 x$ **12.** $\cos^4 x$

13. $\cos^2 x \sin^4 x$ **14.** $\cos^4 x \sin^2 x$

15. $\cos^4 x \sin^4 x$ **16.** $\cos^6 x$

17–28 ■ Use an appropriate Half-Angle Formula to find the exact value of the expression.

✎ **17.** $\sin 15°$ **18.** $\tan 15°$

19. $\tan 22.5°$ **20.** $\sin 75°$

21. $\cos 165°$ **22.** $\cos 112.5°$

DRILL QUESTION
Use Product-to-Sum Formulas to compute $\sin 15° \cos 15°$.

Answer
$\sin 15° \cos 15°$
$= \dfrac{1}{2}(\sin 30° + \sin 0°) = \dfrac{1}{4}$

23. $\tan \dfrac{\pi}{8}$ **24.** $\cos \dfrac{3\pi}{8}$

25. $\cos \dfrac{\pi}{12}$ **26.** $\tan \dfrac{5\pi}{12}$

27. $\sin \dfrac{9\pi}{8}$ **28.** $\sin \dfrac{11\pi}{12}$

29–34 ■ Simplify the expression by using a Double-Angle Formula or a Half-Angle Formula.

29. (a) $2 \sin 18° \cos 18°$ **(b)** $2 \sin 3\theta \cos 3\theta$

30. (a) $\dfrac{2 \tan 7°}{1 - \tan^2 7°}$ **(b)** $\dfrac{2 \tan 7\theta}{1 - \tan^2 7\theta}$

31. (a) $\cos^2 34° - \sin^2 34°$ **(b)** $\cos^2 5\theta - \sin^2 5\theta$

32. (a) $\cos^2 \dfrac{\theta}{2} - \sin^2 \dfrac{\theta}{2}$ **(b)** $2 \sin \dfrac{\theta}{2} \cos \dfrac{\theta}{2}$

33. (a) $\dfrac{\sin 8°}{1 + \cos 8°}$ **(b)** $\dfrac{1 - \cos 4\theta}{\sin 4\theta}$

34. (a) $\sqrt{\dfrac{1 - \cos 30°}{2}}$ **(b)** $\sqrt{\dfrac{1 - \cos 8\theta}{2}}$

35. Use the Addition Formula for Sine to prove the Double-Angle Formula for Sine.

36. Use the Addition Formula for Tangent to prove the Double-Angle Formula for Tangent.

37–42 ■ Find $\sin \dfrac{x}{2}$, $\cos \dfrac{x}{2}$, and $\tan \dfrac{x}{2}$ from the given information.

37. $\sin x = \tfrac{3}{5}, \quad 0° < x < 90°$

38. $\cos x = -\tfrac{4}{5}, \quad 180° < x < 270°$

39. $\csc x = 3, \quad 90° < x < 180°$

40. $\tan x = 1, \quad 0° < x < 90°$

41. $\sec x = \tfrac{3}{2}, \quad 270° < x < 360°$

42. $\cot x = 5, \quad 180° < x < 270°$

43–46 ■ Write the given expression as an algebraic expression in x.

43. $\sin(2 \tan^{-1} x)$ **44.** $\tan(2 \cos^{-1} x)$

45. $\sin(\tfrac{1}{2} \cos^{-1} x)$ **46.** $\cos(2 \sin^{-1} x)$

47–50 ■ Find the exact value of the given expression.

47. $\sin(2 \cos^{-1} \tfrac{7}{25})$ **48.** $\cos(2 \tan^{-1} \tfrac{12}{5})$

49. $\sec(2 \sin^{-1} \tfrac{1}{4})$ **50.** $\tan(\tfrac{1}{2} \cos^{-1} \tfrac{2}{3})$

51–54 ■ Evaluate each expression under the given conditions.

51. $\cos 2\theta$; $\sin \theta = -\tfrac{3}{5}$, θ in Quadrant III

52. $\sin(\theta/2)$; $\tan \theta = -\tfrac{5}{12}$, θ in Quadrant IV

53. $\sin 2\theta$; $\sin \theta = \tfrac{1}{7}$, θ in Quadrant II

54. $\tan 2\theta$; $\cos \theta = \tfrac{3}{5}$, θ in Quadrant I

55–60 ■ Write the product as a sum.

55. $\sin 2x \cos 3x$ **56.** $\sin x \sin 5x$

57. $\cos x \sin 4x$ **58.** $\cos 5x \cos 3x$

59. $3 \cos 4x \cos 7x$ **60.** $11 \sin \dfrac{x}{2} \cos \dfrac{x}{4}$

61–66 ■ Write the sum as a product.

61. $\sin 5x + \sin 3x$ **62.** $\sin x - \sin 4x$

63. $\cos 4x - \cos 6x$ **64.** $\cos 9x + \cos 2x$

65. $\sin 2x - \sin 7x$ **66.** $\sin 3x + \sin 4x$

67–72 ■ Find the value of the product or sum.

67. $2 \sin 52.5° \sin 97.5°$ **68.** $3 \cos 37.5° \cos 7.5°$

69. $\cos 37.5° \sin 7.5°$ **70.** $\sin 75° + \sin 15°$

71. $\cos 255° - \cos 195°$

72. $\cos \dfrac{\pi}{12} + \cos \dfrac{5\pi}{12}$

73–90 ■ Prove the identity.

73. $\cos^2 5x - \sin^2 5x = \cos 10x$

74. $\sin 8x = 2 \sin 4x \cos 4x$

75. $(\sin x + \cos x)^2 = 1 + \sin 2x$

76. $\dfrac{2 \tan x}{1 + \tan^2 x} = \sin 2x$

77. $\dfrac{\sin 4x}{\sin x} = 4 \cos x \cos 2x$

78. $\dfrac{1 + \sin 2x}{\sin 2x} = 1 + \tfrac{1}{2} \sec x \csc x$

79. $\dfrac{2(\tan x - \cot x)}{\tan^2 x - \cot^2 x} = \sin 2x$

80. $\cot 2x = \dfrac{1 - \tan^2 x}{2 \tan x}$

81. $\tan 3x = \dfrac{3 \tan x - \tan^3 x}{1 - 3 \tan^2 x}$

82. $4(\sin^6 x + \cos^6 x) = 4 - 3 \sin^2 2x$

83. $\cos^4 x - \sin^4 x = \cos 2x$

84. $\tan^2 \left(\dfrac{x}{2} + \dfrac{\pi}{4} \right) = \dfrac{1 + \sin x}{1 - \sin x}$

85. $\dfrac{\sin x + \sin 5x}{\cos x + \cos 5x} = \tan 3x$

86. $\dfrac{\sin 3x + \sin 7x}{\cos 3x - \cos 7x} = \cot 2x$

87. $\dfrac{\sin 10x}{\sin 9x + \sin x} = \dfrac{\cos 5x}{\cos 4x}$

88. $\dfrac{\sin x + \sin 3x + \sin 5x}{\cos x + \cos 3x + \cos 5x} = \tan 3x$

89. $\dfrac{\sin x + \sin y}{\cos x + \cos y} = \tan \left(\dfrac{x + y}{2} \right)$

90. $\tan y = \dfrac{\sin(x + y) - \sin(x - y)}{\cos(x + y) + \cos(x - y)}$

91. Show that $\sin 130° - \sin 110° = -\sin 10°$.

92. Show that $\cos 100° - \cos 200° = \sin 50°$.

93. Show that $\sin 45° + \sin 15° = \sin 75°$.

94. Show that $\cos 87° + \cos 33° = \sin 63°$.

95. Prove the identity

$$\frac{\sin x + \sin 2x + \sin 3x + \sin 4x + \sin 5x}{\cos x + \cos 2x + \cos 3x + \cos 4x + \cos 5x} = \tan 3x$$

96. Use the identity

$$\sin 2x = 2 \sin x \cos x$$

n times to show that

$$\sin(2^n x) = 2^n \sin x \cos x \cos 2x \cos 4x \cdots \cos 2^{n-1} x$$

97. (a) Graph $f(x) = \dfrac{\sin 3x}{\sin x} - \dfrac{\cos 3x}{\cos x}$ and make a conjecture.

   (b) Prove the conjecture you made in part (a).

98. (a) Graph $f(x) = \cos 2x + 2 \sin^2 x$ and make a conjecture.

   (b) Prove the conjecture you made in part (a).

99. Let $f(x) = \sin 6x + \sin 7x$.

   (a) Graph $y = f(x)$.

   (b) Verify that $f(x) = 2 \cos \frac{1}{2}x \sin \frac{13}{2}x$.

   (c) Graph $y = 2 \cos \frac{1}{2}x$ and $y = -2 \cos \frac{1}{2}x$, together with the graph in part (a), in the same viewing rectangle. How are these graphs related to the graph of f?

100. Let $3x = \pi/3$ and let $y = \cos x$. Use the result of Example 2 to show that y satisfies the equation

$$8y^3 - 6y - 1 = 0$$

NOTE This equation has roots of a certain kind that are used to show that the angle $\pi/3$ cannot be trisected by using a ruler and compass only.

101. (a) Show that there is a polynomial $P(t)$ of degree 4 such that $\cos 4x = P(\cos x)$ (see Example 2).

   (b) Show that there is a polynomial $Q(t)$ of degree 5 such that $\cos 5x = Q(\cos x)$.

NOTE In general, there is a polynomial $P_n(t)$ of degree n such that $\cos nx = P_n(\cos x)$. These polynomials are called *Tchebycheff polynomials*, after the Russian mathematician P. L. Tchebycheff (1821–1894).

102. In triangle ABC (see the figure) the line segment s bisects angle C. Show that the length of s is given by

$$s = \frac{2ab \cos x}{a + b}$$

[*Hint:* Use the Law of Sines.]

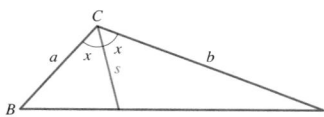

103. If A, B, and C are the angles in a triangle, show that

$$\sin 2A + \sin 2B + \sin 2C = 4 \sin A \sin B \sin C$$

104. A rectangle is to be inscribed in a semicircle of radius 5 cm as shown in the following figure.

   (a) Show that the area of the rectangle is modeled by the function

$$A(\theta) = 25 \sin 2\theta$$

   (b) Find the largest possible area for such an inscribed rectangle.

   (c) Find the dimensions of the inscribed rectangle with the largest possible area.

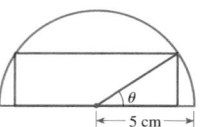

APPLICATIONS

105. Sawing a Wooden Beam A rectangular beam is to be cut from a cylindrical log of diameter 20 in.

   (a) Show that the cross-sectional area of the beam is modeled by the function

$$A(\theta) = 200 \sin 2\theta$$

   where θ is as shown in the figure.

   (b) Show that the maximum cross-sectional area of such a beam is 200 in². [*Hint:* Use the fact that $\sin u$ achieves its maximum value at $u = \pi/2$.]

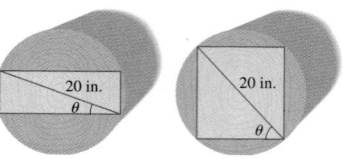

106. Length of a Fold The lower right-hand corner of a long piece of paper 6 in. wide is folded over to the left-hand edge as shown. The length L of the fold depends on the angle θ. Show that

$$L = \frac{3}{\sin \theta \cos^2 \theta}$$

107. Sound Beats When two pure notes that are close in frequency are played together, their sounds interfere to produce *beats*; that is, the loudness (or amplitude) of the sound alternately increases and decreases. If the two notes are given by

$$f_1(t) = \cos 11t \quad \text{and} \quad f_2(t) = \cos 13t$$

the resulting sound is $f(t) = f_1(t) + f_2(t)$.

   (a) Graph the function $y = f(t)$.

   (b) Verify that $f(t) = 2 \cos t \cos 12t$.

(c) Graph $y = 2 \cos t$ and $y = -2 \cos t$, together with the graph in part (a), in the same viewing rectangle. How do these graphs describe the variation in the loudness of the sound?

108. Touch-Tone Telephones When a key is pressed on a touch-tone telephone, the keypad generates two pure tones, which combine to produce a sound that uniquely identifies the key. The figure shows the low frequency f_1 and the high frequency f_2 associated with each key. Pressing a key produces the sound wave $y = \sin(2\pi f_1 t) + \sin(2\pi f_2 t)$.

(a) Find the function that models the sound produced when the 4 key is pressed.
(b) Use a Sum-to-Product Formula to express the sound generated by the 4 key as a product of a sine and a cosine function.
(c) Graph the sound wave generated by the 4 key, from $t = 0$ to $t = 0.006$ s.

High frequency f_2

1209 1336 1477 Hz

	1209	1336	1477
697 Hz	1	2	3
770 Hz	4	5	6
852 Hz	7	8	9
941 Hz	*	0	#

Low frequency f_1

DISCOVERY ▪ DISCUSSION ▪ WRITING

109. Geometric Proof of a Double-Angle Formula Use the figure to prove that $\sin 2\theta = 2 \sin \theta \cos \theta$.

[*Hint:* Find the area of triangle ABC in two different ways. You will need the following facts from geometry:

An angle inscribed in a semicircle is a right angle, so $\angle ACB$ is a right angle.

The central angle subtended by the chord of a circle is twice the angle subtended by the chord on the circle, so $\angle BOC$ is 2θ.]

7.4 BASIC TRIGONOMETRIC EQUATIONS

Basic Trigonometric Equations ▶ Solving Trigonometric Equations by Factoring

An equation that contains trigonometric functions is called a **trigonometric equation**. For example, the following are trigonometric equations:

$$\sin^2\theta + \cos^2\theta = 1 \qquad 2\sin\theta - 1 = 0 \qquad \tan 2\theta - 1 = 0$$

The first equation is an *identity*—that is, it is true for every value of the variable θ. The other two equations are true only for certain values of θ. To solve a trigonometric equation, we find all the values of the variable that make the equation true.

▼ Basic Trigonometric Equations

Solving any trigonometric equation always reduces to solving a **basic trigonometric equation**—an equation of the form $T(\theta) = c$, where T is a trigonometric function and c is a constant. In the next three examples we solve such basic equations.

EXAMPLE 1 | Solving a Basic Trigonometric Equation

Solve the equation $\sin \theta = \dfrac{1}{2}$.

SUGGESTED TIME AND EMPHASIS

1 class, essential material

ALTERNATE EXAMPLE 1

Solve the equation $\cos \theta = -\dfrac{\sqrt{2}}{2}$.

ANSWER

$\dfrac{3\pi}{4} + 2k\pi, \dfrac{5\pi}{4} + 2k\pi$

TEXT QUESTION
In the text, the equation $2\cos^2 x - 7\cos x + 3 = 0$ is solved. The authors wrote it this way: $(2\cos x - 1)(\cos x - 3) = 0$. They then dealt with the first of the two terms but ignored the second. Why?

Answer
There is no x such that $\cos x = 3$.

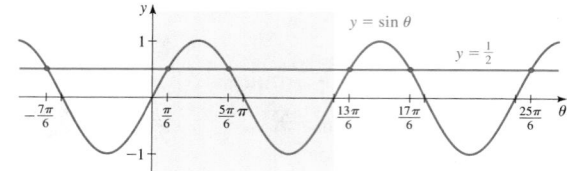

FIGURE 1

SOLUTION

Find the solutions in one period. Because sine has period 2π, we first find the solutions in any interval of length 2π. To find these solutions, we look at the unit circle in Figure 1. We see that $\sin\theta = \frac{1}{2}$ in Quadrants I and II, so the solutions in the interval $[0, 2\pi)$ are

$$\theta = \frac{\pi}{6} \qquad \theta = \frac{5\pi}{6}$$

Find all solutions. Because the sine function repeats its values every 2π units, we get all solutions of the equation by adding integer multiples of 2π to these solutions:

$$\theta = \frac{\pi}{6} + 2k\pi \qquad \theta = \frac{5\pi}{6} + 2k\pi$$

where k is any integer. Figure 2 gives a graphical representation of the solutions.

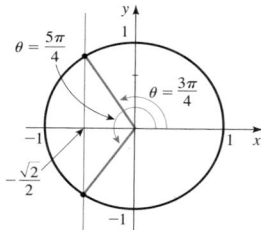

FIGURE 2

✎ NOW TRY EXERCISE **5**

ALTERNATE EXAMPLE 2

Solve the equation $\sin\theta = \dfrac{1}{2}$ and list eight specific solutions.

ANSWER

$$-\frac{11\pi}{6}, -\frac{7\pi}{6}, \frac{\pi}{6}, \frac{5\pi}{6}, \frac{13\pi}{6}, \frac{17\pi}{6},$$
$$\frac{25\pi}{6}, \frac{29\pi}{6}$$

EXAMPLE 2 | Solving a Basic Trigonometric Equation

Solve the equation $\cos\theta = -\dfrac{\sqrt{2}}{2}$, and list eight specific solutions.

SOLUTION

Find the solutions in one period. Because cosine has period 2π, we first find the solutions in any interval of length 2π. From the unit circle in Figure 3 we see that $\cos\theta = -\sqrt{2}/2$ in Quadrants II and III, so the solutions in the interval $[0, 2\pi)$ are

$$\theta = \frac{3\pi}{4} \qquad \theta = \frac{5\pi}{4}$$

FIGURE 3

Find all solutions. Because the cosine function repeats its values every 2π units, we get all solutions of the equation by adding integer multiples of 2π to these solutions:

$$\theta = \frac{3\pi}{4} + 2k\pi \qquad \theta = \frac{5\pi}{4} + 2k\pi$$

IN-CLASS MATERIALS

Assume we want to solve $\sin x = \frac{1}{3}$. We want our students to enter $\sin^{-1}\frac{1}{3}$ into a calculator, obtaining 0.33983691. Then we want them to write down one answer $(0.33983691 + 2\pi k)$ and figure out another $(2.8017557 + 2\pi k)$. This process requires a very different use of technology than the kind to which the students are accustomed. Most of their mathematical experiences with technology involve a problem that ends when the "=" key is pressed, save for (perhaps) checking their answer or interpreting the result. This time, the "=" key signals only the beginning of their thinking, which causes many of them difficulty.

where k is any integer. You can check that for $k = -1, 0, 1, 2$ we get the following specific solutions:

$$\theta = -\underbrace{\frac{5\pi}{4}, -\frac{3\pi}{4}}_{k=-1}, \underbrace{\frac{3\pi}{4}, \frac{5\pi}{4}}_{k=0}, \underbrace{\frac{11\pi}{4}, \frac{13\pi}{4}}_{k=1}, \underbrace{\frac{19\pi}{4}, \frac{21\pi}{4}}_{k=2}$$

Figure 4 gives a graphical representation of the solutions.

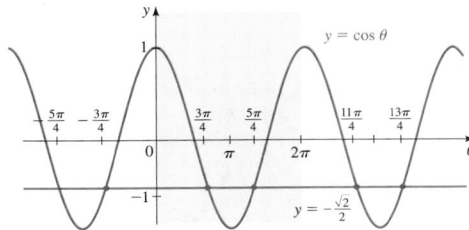

FIGURE 4

✎. NOW TRY EXERCISE **17**

EXAMPLE 3 | Solving a Basic Trigonometric Equation

Solve the equation $\cos \theta = 0.65$.

SOLUTION

Find the solutions in one period.   We first find one solution by taking $\cos^{-1}$ of each side of the equation.

$$\cos \theta = 0.65 \qquad \text{Given equation}$$
$$\theta = \cos^{-1}(0.65) \qquad \text{Take } \cos^{-1} \text{ of each side}$$
$$\theta \approx 0.86 \qquad \text{Calculator (in radian mode)}$$

Because cosine has period 2π, we next find the solutions in any interval of length 2π. To find these solutions, we look at the unit circle in Figure 5. We see that $\cos \theta = 0.85$ in Quadrants I and IV, so the solutions are

$$\theta \approx 0.86 \qquad \theta \approx 2\pi - 0.86 \approx 5.42$$

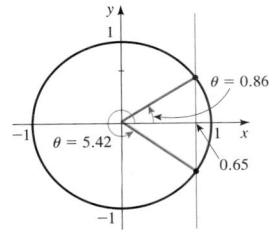

FIGURE 5

Find all solutions.   To get all solutions of the equation, we add integer multiples of 2π to these solutions:

$$\theta \approx 0.86 + 2k\pi \qquad \theta \approx 5.42 + 2k\pi$$

where k is any integer.

✎. NOW TRY EXERCISE **21**

ALTERNATE EXAMPLE 3
Solve the equation $\sin \theta = 0.28$.

ANSWER
$0.284 + 2k\pi, 2.858 + 2k\pi$

EXAMPLE
An equation in quadratic form: $25 \cos^2 \theta - 5 \cos \theta - 2$. This equation factors into
$\cos \theta = -\frac{2}{5}, \cos \theta = \frac{1}{5}$.

ANSWER
$x \approx \pm 1.9823132 + 2\pi k$ or $\pm 1.3694384 + 2\pi k$

ALTERNATE EXAMPLE 4

Solve the equation $\tan \theta = 10$.

ANSWER

$1.471 + k\pi$

EXAMPLE

Solve $\cos x \tan x + \dfrac{1}{2} \tan x = 0$.

ANSWER

$x = \pi k$ or $\pm \dfrac{2\pi}{3} + 2\pi k$

ALTERNATE EXAMPLE 5

(a) Solve the equation
$2 \cos b - 1 = 0$.

(b) Solve the equation
$\tan^3 x = \dfrac{1}{3\sqrt{3}}$.

ANSWERS

(a) $\dfrac{\pi}{3} + 2k\pi, \dfrac{5\pi}{3} + 2k\pi$

(b) $\dfrac{\pi}{6} + k\pi$

EXAMPLE 4 | Solving a Basic Trigonometric Equation

Solve the equation $\tan \theta = 2$.

SOLUTION

Find the solutions in one period. We first find one solution by taking $\tan^{-1}$ of each side of the equation:

$$\tan \theta = 2 \qquad \text{Given equation}$$
$$\theta = \tan^{-1}(2) \qquad \text{Take } \tan^{-1} \text{ of each side}$$
$$\theta \approx 1.12 \qquad \text{Calculator (in radian mode)}$$

By the definition of $\tan^{-1}$, the solution that we obtained is the only solution in the interval $(-\pi/2, \pi/2)$ (which is an interval of length π).

Find all solutions. Since tangent has period π, we get all solutions of the equation by adding integer multiples of π:

$$\theta \approx 1.12 + k\pi$$

where k is any integer. A graphical representation of the solutions is shown in Figure 6. You can check that the solutions shown in the graph correspond to $k = -1, 0, 1, 2, 3$.

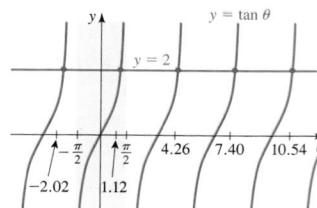

FIGURE 6

✎. NOW TRY EXERCISE **23**

In the next example we solve trigonometric equations that are algebraically equivalent to basic trigonometric equations.

EXAMPLE 5 | Solving Trigonometric Equations

Find all solutions of the equation.
(a) $2 \sin \theta - 1 = 0$ (b) $\tan^2 \theta - 3 = 0$

SOLUTION

(a) We start by isolating $\sin \theta$:

$$2 \sin \theta - 1 = 0 \qquad \text{Given equation}$$
$$2 \sin \theta = 1 \qquad \text{Add 1}$$
$$\sin \theta = \dfrac{1}{2} \qquad \text{Divide by 2}$$

This last equation is the same as that in Example 1. The solutions are

$$\theta = \dfrac{\pi}{6} + 2k\pi \qquad \theta = \dfrac{5\pi}{6} + 2k\pi$$

where k is any integer.

(b) We start by isolating $\tan\theta$:

$$\tan^2\theta - 3 = 0 \qquad \text{Given equation}$$

$$\tan^2\theta = 3 \qquad \text{Add 3}$$

$$\tan\theta = \pm\sqrt{3} \qquad \text{Take the square root}$$

Because tangent has period π, we first find the solutions in any interval of length π. In the interval $(-\pi/2, \pi/2)$ the solutions are $\theta = \pi/3$ and $\theta = -\pi/3$. To get all solutions, we add integer multiples of π to these solutions:

$$\theta = \frac{\pi}{3} + k\pi \qquad \theta = -\frac{\pi}{3} + k\pi$$

where k is any integer.

✎ NOW TRY EXERCISES **27** AND **33**   ∎

▼ Solving Trigonometric Equations by Factoring

Factoring is one of the most useful techniques for solving equations, including trigonometric equations. The idea is to move all terms to one side of the equation, factor, and then use the Zero-Product Property (see Section 1.5).

Zero-Product Property
If $AB = 0$, then $A = 0$ or $B = 0$.

EXAMPLE 6 | A Trigonometric Equation of Quadratic Type

Solve the equation $2\cos^2\theta - 7\cos\theta + 3 = 0$.

SOLUTION   We factor the left-hand side of the equation.

Equation of Quadratic Type
$$2C^2 - 7C + 3 = 0$$
$$(2C - 1)(C - 3) = 0$$

$$2\cos^2\theta - 7\cos\theta + 3 = 0 \qquad \text{Given equation}$$

$$(2\cos\theta - 1)(\cos\theta - 3) = 0 \qquad \text{Factor}$$

$$2\cos\theta - 1 = 0 \quad \text{or} \quad \cos\theta - 3 = 0 \qquad \text{Set each factor equal to 0}$$

$$\cos\theta = \frac{1}{2} \quad \text{or} \quad \cos\theta = 3 \qquad \text{Solve for } \cos\theta$$

Because cosine has period 2π, we first find the solutions in the interval $[0, 2\pi)$. For the first equation the solutions are $\theta = \pi/3$ and $\theta = 5\pi/3$ (see Figure 7). The second equation has no solution because $\cos\theta$ is never greater than 1. Thus the solutions are

$$\theta = \frac{\pi}{3} + 2k\pi \qquad \theta = \frac{5\pi}{3} + 2k\pi$$

where k is any integer.

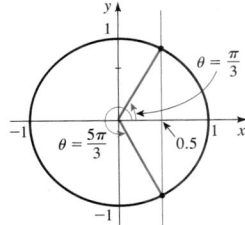

FIGURE 7

✎ NOW TRY EXERCISE **41**   ∎

ALTERNATE EXAMPLE 6
Solve the equation
$$2\sin^2 x - 13\sin x + 6 = 0.$$

ANSWER
$$\frac{\pi}{6} + 2k\pi, \ \frac{5\pi}{6} + 2k\pi$$

ALTERNATE EXAMPLE 7

Solve the equation

$$\sin^3 x \tan x + \frac{1}{8} \tan x = 0.$$

ANSWER

$$\frac{\pi}{6} + 2k\pi, \frac{5\pi}{6} + 2k\pi, k\pi$$

DRILL QUESTION

Find all solutions to $\tan x = -1$.

ANSWER

$$x = \frac{3\pi}{4} + k\pi$$

EXAMPLE 7 | Solving a Trigonometric Equation by Factoring

Solve the equation $5 \sin \theta \cos \theta + 4 \cos \theta = 0$.

SOLUTION We factor the left-hand side of the equation:

$$5 \sin \theta \cos \theta + 2 \cos \theta = 0 \qquad \text{Given equation}$$
$$\cos \theta (5 \sin \theta + 2) = 0 \qquad \text{Factor}$$
$$\cos \theta = 0 \quad \text{or} \quad 5 \sin \theta + 4 = 0 \qquad \text{Set each factor equal to 0}$$
$$\sin \theta = -0.8 \qquad \text{Solve for } \sin \theta$$

Because sine and cosine have period 2π, we first find the solutions of these equations in an interval of length 2π. For the first equation the solutions in the interval $[0, 2\pi)$ are $\theta = \pi/2$ and $\theta = 3\pi/2$. To solve the second equation, we take $\sin^{-1}$ of each side:

$$\sin \theta = -0.80 \qquad \text{Second equation}$$
$$\theta = \sin^{-1}(-0.80) \qquad \text{Take } \sin^{-1} \text{ of each side}$$
$$\theta \approx -0.93 \qquad \text{Calculator (in radian mode)}$$

So the solutions in an interval of length 2π are $\theta = -0.93$ and $\theta = \pi + 0.93 \approx 4.07$ (see Figure 8). We get all the solutions of the equation by adding integer multiples of 2π to these solutions.

$$\theta = \frac{\pi}{2} + 2k\pi, \qquad \theta = \frac{3\pi}{2} + 2k\pi, \qquad \theta \approx -0.93 + 2k\pi, \qquad \theta \approx 4.07 + 2k\pi$$

where k is any integer.

✎ NOW TRY EXERCISE **53** ∎

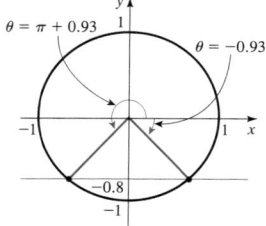

$\theta = \pi + 0.93$

$\theta = -0.93$

FIGURE 8

7.4 EXERCISES

CONCEPTS

1. Because the trigonometric functions are periodic, if a basic trigonometric equation has one solution, it has _____ (several/infinitely many) solutions.

2. The basic equation $\sin x = 2$ has _____ (no/one/infinitely many) solutions, whereas the basic equation $\sin x = 0.3$ has _____ (no/one/infinitely many) solutions.

3. We can find some of the solutions of $\sin x = 0.3$ graphically by graphing $y = \sin x$ and $y =$ _____. Use the graph below to estimate some of the solutions.

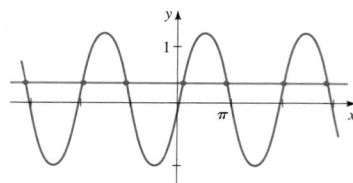

4. We can find the solutions of $\sin x = 0.3$ algebraically.
(a) First we find the solutions in the interval $[-\pi, \pi]$. We get one such solution by taking $\sin^{-1}$ to get $x =$ _____. The other solution in this interval is $x =$ _____.

(b) We find all solutions by adding multiples of _____ to the solutions in $[-\pi, \pi]$. The solutions are

$$x = \underline{\quad\quad} \text{ and } x = \underline{\quad\quad}.$$

SKILLS

5–16 ■ Solve the given equation.

✎ **5.** $\sin \theta = \dfrac{\sqrt{3}}{2}$

6. $\sin \theta = -\dfrac{\sqrt{2}}{2}$

7. $\cos \theta = -1$

8. $\cos \theta = \dfrac{\sqrt{3}}{2}$

9. $\cos \theta = \frac{1}{4}$

10. $\sin \theta = -0.3$

11. $\sin \theta = -0.45$

12. $\cos \theta = 0.32$

13. $\tan \theta = -\sqrt{3}$

14. $\tan \theta = 1$

15. $\tan \theta = 5$

16. $\tan \theta = -\frac{1}{3}$

17–24 ■ Solve the given equation, and list six specific solutions.

17. $\cos \theta = -\dfrac{\sqrt{3}}{2}$

18. $\cos \theta = \dfrac{1}{2}$

19. $\sin \theta = \dfrac{\sqrt{2}}{2}$

20. $\sin \theta = -\dfrac{\sqrt{3}}{2}$

21. $\cos \theta = 0.28$

22. $\tan \theta = 2.5$

23. $\tan \theta = -10$

24. $\sin \theta = -0.9$

25–38 ■ Find all solutions of the given equation.

25. $\cos \theta + 1 = 0$

26. $\sin \theta + 1 = 0$

27. $\sqrt{2} \sin \theta + 1 = 0$

28. $\sqrt{2} \cos \theta - 1 = 0$

29. $5 \sin \theta - 1 = 0$

30. $4 \cos \theta + 1 = 0$

31. $3 \tan^2 \theta - 1 = 0$

32. $\cot \theta + 1 = 0$

33. $2 \cos^2 \theta - 1 = 0$

34. $4 \sin^2 \theta - 3 = 0$

35. $\tan^2 \theta - 4 = 0$

36. $9 \sin^2 \theta - 1 = 0$

37. $\sec^2 \theta - 2 = 0$

38. $\csc^2 \theta - 4 = 0$

39–56 ■ Solve the given equation.

39. $(\tan^2 \theta - 4)(2 \cos \theta + 1) = 0$

40. $(\tan \theta - 2)(16 \sin^2 \theta - 1) = 0$

41. $4 \cos^2 \theta - 4 \cos \theta + 1 = 0$

42. $2 \sin^2 \theta - \sin \theta - 1 = 0$

43. $3 \sin^2 \theta - 7 \sin \theta + 2 = 0$

44. $\tan^4 \theta - 13 \tan^2 \theta + 36 = 0$

45. $2 \cos^2 \theta - 7 \cos \theta + 3 = 0$

46. $\sin^2 \theta - \sin \theta - 2 = 0$

47. $\cos^2 \theta - \cos \theta - 6 = 0$ **48.** $2 \sin^2 \theta + 5 \sin \theta - 12 = 0$

49. $\sin^2 \theta = 2 \sin \theta + 3$ **50.** $3 \tan^3 \theta = \tan \theta$

51. $\cos \theta (2 \sin \theta + 1) = 0$ **52.** $\sec \theta (2 \cos \theta - \sqrt{2}) = 0$

53. $\cos \theta \sin \theta - 2 \cos \theta = 0$ **54.** $\tan \theta \sin \theta + \sin \theta = 0$

55. $3 \tan \theta \sin \theta - 2 \tan \theta = 0$ **56.** $4 \cos \theta \sin \theta + 3 \cos \theta = 0$

APPLICATIONS

57. Refraction of Light   It has been observed since ancient times that light refracts or "bends" as it travels from one medium to another (from air to water, for example). If v_1 is the speed of light in one medium and v_2 its speed in another medium, then according to **Snell's Law,**

$$\frac{\sin \theta_1}{\sin \theta_2} = \frac{v_1}{v_2}$$

where θ_1 is the *angle of incidence* and θ_2 is the *angle of refraction* (see the figure). The number v_1/v_2 is called the *index of refraction*. The index of refraction for several substances is given in the table.

If a ray of light passes through the surface of a lake at an angle of incidence of 70°, what is the angle of refraction?

Substance	Refraction from air to substance
Water	1.33
Alcohol	1.36
Glass	1.52
Diamond	2.41

58. Total Internal Reflection   When light passes from a more-dense to a less-dense medium—from glass to air, for example—the angle of refraction predicted by Snell's Law (see Exercise 57) can be 90° or larger. In this case the light beam is actually reflected back into the denser medium. This phenomenon, called *total internal reflection*, is the principle behind fiber optics. Set $\theta_2 = 90°$ in Snell's Law, and solve for θ_1 to determine the critical angle of incidence at which total internal reflection begins to occur when light passes from glass to air. (Note that the index of refraction from glass to air is the reciprocal of the index from air to glass.)

59. Phases of the Moon   As the moon revolves around the earth, the side that faces the earth is usually just partially illuminated by the sun. The phases of the moon describe how much of the surface appears to be in sunlight. An astronomical measure of phase is given by the fraction F of the lunar disc that is lit. When the angle between the sun, earth, and moon is θ ($0 \le \theta \le 360°$), then

$$F = \frac{1}{2}(1 - \cos \theta)$$

Determine the angles θ that correspond to the following phases:
(a) $F = 0$ (new moon)
(b) $F = 0.25$ (a crescent moon)
(c) $F = 0.5$ (first or last quarter)
(d) $F = 1$ (full moon)

DISCOVERY ▪ DISCUSSION ▪ WRITING

60. Equations and Identities   Which of the following statements is true?
   A. Every identity is an equation.
   B. Every equation is an identity.

Give examples to illustrate your answer. Write a short paragraph to explain the difference between an equation and an identity.

**SUGGESTED TIME
AND EMPHASIS**

1 class, essential material

7.5 MORE TRIGONOMETRIC EQUATIONS

| Solving Trigonometric Equations by Using Identities ▶ Equations
with Trigonometric Functions of Multiples of Angles

In this section we solve trigonometric equations by first using identities to simplify the equation. We also solve trigonometric equations in which the terms contain multiples of angles.

▼ Solving Trigonometric Equations by Using Identities

In the next two examples we use trigonometric identities to express a trigonometric equation in a form in which it can be factored.

EXAMPLE 1 | Using a Trigonometric Identity

Solve the equation $1 + \sin\theta = 2\cos^2\theta$.

SOLUTION We first need to rewrite this equation so that it contains only one trigonometric function. To do this, we use a trigonometric identity:

$$
\begin{aligned}
1 + \sin\theta &= 2\cos^2\theta && \text{Given equation} \\
1 + \sin\theta &= 2(1 - \sin^2\theta) && \text{Pythagorean identity} \\
2\sin^2\theta + \sin\theta - 1 &= 0 && \text{Put all terms on one side} \\
(2\sin\theta - 1)(\sin\theta + 1) &= 0 && \text{Factor}
\end{aligned}
$$

$$
2\sin\theta - 1 = 0 \quad \text{or} \quad \sin\theta + 1 = 0 \qquad \text{Set each factor equal to 0}
$$

$$
\sin\theta = \frac{1}{2} \quad \text{or} \quad \sin\theta = -1 \qquad \text{Solve for } \sin\theta
$$

$$
\theta = \frac{\pi}{6}, \frac{5\pi}{6} \quad \text{or} \quad \theta = \frac{3\pi}{2} \qquad \begin{array}{l}\text{Solve for } \theta \text{ in the}\\ \text{interval } [0, 2\pi)\end{array}
$$

Because sine has period 2π, we get all the solutions of the equation by adding integer multiples of 2π to these solutions. Thus the solutions are

$$
\theta = \frac{\pi}{6} + 2k\pi \qquad \theta = \frac{5\pi}{6} + 2k\pi \qquad \theta = \frac{3\pi}{2} + 2k\pi
$$

where k is any integer.

✎. NOW TRY EXERCISE **3** ■

EXAMPLE 2 | Using a Trigonometric Identity

Solve the equation $\sin 2\theta - \cos\theta = 0$.

SOLUTION The first term is a function of 2θ, and the second is a function of θ, so we begin by using a trigonometric identity to rewrite the first term as a function of θ only:

$$
\begin{aligned}
\sin 2\theta - \cos\theta &= 0 && \text{Given equation} \\
2\sin\theta\cos\theta - \cos\theta &= 0 && \text{Double-Angle Formula} \\
\cos\theta\,(2\sin\theta - 1) &= 0 && \text{Factor}
\end{aligned}
$$

ALTERNATE EXAMPLE 1

Solve the equation
$-7 + \cos x = 4\sin^2 x$.

ANSWER

$\cos(x) = -1$ or $\cos(x) = \frac{3}{4}$

$\begin{aligned} x &= \pi + 2\pi k \\ &= -\pi + 2\pi k \end{aligned}$

Thus,

$\begin{aligned} &= 0.7227 + 2\pi k \\ &= -0.7227 + 2\pi k \end{aligned}$

ALTERNATE EXAMPLE 2

Solve the equation

$\tan\left(\dfrac{x}{2}\right) = 1 - \cos x$.

ANSWER

$\tan\left(\dfrac{x}{2}\right) = 1 - \cos x$

$\dfrac{\sin x}{1 + \cos x} = 1 - \cos x$

$\sin x = (1 - \cos x)(1 + \cos x)$

$\sin x = 1 - \cos^2 x$

$0 = \sin^2 x - \sin x$

$ = \sin x(\sin x - 1)$

$k\pi, \dfrac{\pi}{2} + 2k\pi$

TEXT QUESTION

True or false? One set of solutions to $\left(\sin x - \dfrac{1}{2}\right)\left(\cos x + \dfrac{\sqrt{3}}{2}\right) = 1$ will be the solutions to the simpler equation $\left(\sin x - \dfrac{1}{2}\right) = 1$.

Answer

False

$$\cos \theta = 0 \quad \text{or} \quad 2 \sin \theta - 1 = 0 \qquad \text{Set each factor equal to 0}$$

$$\sin \theta = \frac{1}{2} \qquad \text{Solve for } \sin \theta$$

$$\theta = \frac{\pi}{2}, \frac{3\pi}{2} \quad \text{or} \quad \theta = \frac{\pi}{6}, \frac{5\pi}{6} \qquad \text{Solve for } \theta \text{ in } [0, 2\pi)$$

Both sine and cosine have period 2π, so we get all the solutions of the equation by adding integer multiples of 2π to these solutions. Thus the solutions are

$$\theta = \frac{\pi}{2} + 2k\pi \qquad \theta = \frac{3\pi}{2} + 2k\pi \qquad \theta = \frac{\pi}{6} + 2k\pi \qquad \theta = \frac{5\pi}{6} + 2k\pi$$

where k is any integer.

✎. NOW TRY EXERCISES **7** AND **11**   ■

EXAMPLE 3 | Squaring and Using an Identity

Solve the equation $\cos \theta + 1 = \sin \theta$ in the interval $[0, 2\pi)$.

SOLUTION   To get an equation that involves either sine only or cosine only, we square both sides and use a Pythagorean identity:

$$\cos \theta + 1 = \sin \theta \qquad \text{Given equation}$$

$$\cos^2\theta + 2 \cos \theta + 1 = \sin^2\theta \qquad \text{Square both sides}$$

$$\cos^2\theta + 2 \cos \theta + 1 = 1 - \cos^2\theta \qquad \text{Pythagorean identity}$$

$$2 \cos^2\theta + 2 \cos \theta = 0 \qquad \text{Simplify}$$

$$2 \cos \theta(\cos \theta + 1) = 0 \qquad \text{Factor}$$

$$2 \cos \theta = 0 \quad \text{or} \quad \cos \theta + 1 = 0 \qquad \text{Set each factor equal to 0}$$

$$\cos \theta = 0 \quad \text{or} \quad \cos \theta = -1 \qquad \text{Solve for } \cos \theta$$

$$\theta = \frac{\pi}{2}, \frac{3\pi}{2} \quad \text{or} \quad \theta = \pi \qquad \text{Solve for } \theta \text{ in } [0, 2\pi)$$

Because we squared both sides, we need to check for extraneous solutions. From *Check Your Answers* we see that the solutions of the given equation are $\pi/2$ and π.

CHECK YOUR ANSWER

$$\theta = \frac{\pi}{2} \qquad\qquad \theta = \frac{3\pi}{2} \qquad\qquad \theta = \pi$$

$$\cos \frac{\pi}{2} + 1 = \sin \frac{\pi}{2} \qquad \cos \frac{3\pi}{2} + 1 = \sin \frac{3\pi}{2} \qquad \cos \pi + 1 = \sin \pi$$

$$0 + 1 = 1 \quad ✔ \qquad 0 + 1 \overset{?}{=} -1 \quad ✗ \qquad -1 + 1 = 0 \quad ✔$$

✎. NOW TRY EXERCISE **13**   ■

EXAMPLE 4 | Finding Intersection Points

Find the values of x for which the graphs of $f(x) = \sin x$ and $g(x) = \cos x$ intersect.

ALTERNATE EXAMPLE 3
Solve $\sin \theta + 3 = 3 \cos \theta$.

ANSWER

$$\sin \theta + 3 = 3 \cos \theta$$
$$\sin^2 \theta + 6 \sin \theta + 9 = 9 \cos^2 \theta$$
$$\sin^2 \theta + 6 \sin \theta + 9 = 9 - 9 \sin^2 \theta$$
$$10 \sin^2 \theta + 6 \sin \theta = 0$$
$$2 \sin \theta(5 \sin \theta + 3) = 0$$
$$\theta = k\pi, -0.644 + 2k\pi, 3.785 + 2k\pi$$

Checking for and eliminating extraneous solutions yields
$$\theta = 2k\pi, -0.644 + 2k\pi.$$

ALTERNATE EXAMPLE 4
Find the values of x for which the graphs of $f(x) = \sin x$ and $g(x) = \cot x$ intersect.

ANSWER
This can be solved graphically or algebraically as in the text. The algebraic solution requires a calculator approximation at the end.
$$0.905 + 2k\pi, -0.905 + 2k\pi$$

IN-CLASS MATERIALS

When we solve trigonometric equations, we often have to deal with restricted domains. Solve $\sin 3x = 0.15$ with the condition that $5\pi \leq x \leq 7\pi$.

Answer
$x \approx 16.80535, 18.8997, 20.9941$

SOLUTION 1: Graphical

The graphs intersect where $f(x) = g(x)$. In Figure 1 we graph $y_1 = \sin x$ and $y_2 = \cos x$ on the same screen, for x between 0 and 2π. Using TRACE or the intersect command on the graphing calculator, we see that the two points of intersection in this interval occur where $x \approx 0.785$ and $x \approx 3.927$. Since sine and cosine are periodic with period 2π, the intersection points occur where

$$x \approx 0.785 + 2k\pi \qquad \text{and} \qquad x \approx 3.927 + 2k\pi$$

where k is any integer.

FIGURE 1   (a)   (b)

SOLUTION 2: Algebraic

To find the exact solution, we set $f(x) = g(x)$ and solve the resulting equation algebraically:

$$\sin x = \cos x \qquad \text{Equate functions}$$

Since the numbers x for which $\cos x = 0$ are not solutions of the equation, we can divide both sides by $\cos x$:

$$\frac{\sin x}{\cos x} = 1 \qquad \text{Divide by } \cos x$$

$$\tan x = 1 \qquad \text{Reciprocal identity}$$

The only solution of this equation in the interval $(-\pi/2, \pi/2)$ is $x = \pi/4$. Since tangent has period π, we get all solutions of the equation by adding integer multiples of π:

$$x = \frac{\pi}{4} + k\pi$$

where k is any integer. The graphs intersect for these values of x. You should use your calculator to check that, rounded to three decimals, these are the same values that we obtained in Solution 1.

✎. NOW TRY EXERCISE **35**   ■

▼ Equations with Trigonometric Functions of Multiples of Angles

When solving trigonometric equations that involve functions of multiples of angles, we first solve for the multiple of the angle, then divide to solve for the angle.

EXAMPLE 5 | A Trigonometric Equation Involving a Multiple of an Angle

Consider the equation $2 \sin 3\theta - 1 = 0$.

(a) Find all solutions of the equation.

(b) Find the solutions in the interval $[0, 2\pi)$.

EXAMPLE

Solve $\dfrac{\sec 5x}{2} = \cos 5x$.

ANSWER

$x = \pm\dfrac{\pi}{20} + 2\pi k$

SOLUTION

(a) We first isolate $\sin 3\theta$ and then solve for the angle 3θ.

$$2 \sin 3\theta - 1 = 0 \qquad \text{Given equation}$$

$$2 \sin 3\theta = 1 \qquad \text{Add 1}$$

$$\sin 3\theta = \frac{1}{2} \qquad \text{Divide by 2}$$

$$3\theta = \frac{\pi}{6}, \frac{5\pi}{6} \qquad \text{Solve for } 3\theta \text{ in the interval } [0, 2\pi) \text{ (see Figure 2)}$$

To get all solutions, we add integer multiples of 2π to these solutions. So the solutions are of the form

$$3\theta = \frac{\pi}{6} + 2k\pi \qquad 3\theta = \frac{5\pi}{6} + 2k\pi$$

To solve for θ, we divide by 3 to get the solutions

$$\theta = \frac{\pi}{18} + \frac{2k\pi}{3} \qquad \theta = \frac{5\pi}{18} + \frac{2k\pi}{3}$$

where k is any integer.

(b) The solutions from part (a) that are in the interval $[0, 2\pi)$ correspond to $k = 0, 1$, and 2. For all other values of k the corresponding values of θ lie outside this interval. So the solutions in the interval $[0, 2\pi)$ are

$$\theta = \underbrace{\frac{\pi}{18}, \frac{5\pi}{18}}_{k=0}, \underbrace{\frac{13\pi}{18}, \frac{17\pi}{18}}_{k=1}, \underbrace{\frac{25\pi}{18}, \frac{29\pi}{18}}_{k=2}$$

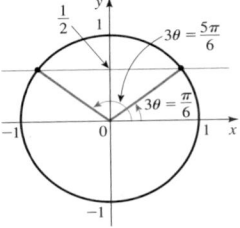

FIGURE 2

NOW TRY EXERCISE **17**

EXAMPLE 6 | A Trigonometric Equation Involving a Half Angle

Consider the equation $\sqrt{3} \tan \dfrac{\theta}{2} - 1 = 0$.

(a) Find all solutions of the equation.

(b) Find the solutions in the interval $[0, 4\pi)$.

ALTERNATE EXAMPLE 6

Find all solutions of the equation $\sin\left(\dfrac{\theta}{2}\right) = -\dfrac{1}{2}$ in the interval $[0, 7\pi)$.

ANSWER

$\dfrac{7\pi}{3}, \dfrac{19\pi}{3}, \dfrac{11\pi}{3}$

IN-CLASS MATERIALS

If your students are having difficulty visualizing or understanding solving trigonometric equations over a given interval, solve Example 6 with them, and then draw the graphs of $y = \sqrt{3} \tan \dfrac{\theta}{2}$ and $y = 1$ on the same axis, over the interval $[0, 4\pi)$.

SOLUTION

(a) We start by isolating $\tan\dfrac{\theta}{2}$:

$$\sqrt{3}\tan\frac{\theta}{2} - 1 = 0 \qquad \text{Given equation}$$

$$\sqrt{3}\tan\frac{\theta}{2} = 1 \qquad \text{Add 1}$$

$$\tan\frac{\theta}{2} = \frac{1}{\sqrt{3}} \qquad \text{Divide by } \sqrt{3}$$

$$\frac{\theta}{2} = \frac{\pi}{6} \qquad \text{Solve for } \frac{\theta}{2} \text{ in the interval } \left(-\frac{\pi}{2}, \frac{\pi}{2}\right)$$

Since tangent has period π, to get all solutions we add integer multiples of π to this solution. So the solutions are of the form

$$\frac{\theta}{2} = \frac{\pi}{6} + k\pi$$

Multiplying by 2, we get the solutions

$$\theta = \frac{\pi}{3} + 2k\pi$$

where k is any integer.

(b) The solutions from part (a) that are in the interval $[0, 4\pi)$ correspond to $k = 0$ and $k = 1$. For all other values of k the corresponding values of x lie outside this interval. Thus the solutions in the interval $[0, 4\pi)$ are

$$x = \frac{\pi}{3}, \frac{7\pi}{3}$$

◥ NOW TRY EXERCISE **23**

7.5 EXERCISES

CONCEPTS

1–2 ■ We can use identities to help us solve trigonometric equations.

1. Using a Pythagorean identity we see that the equation $\sin x + \sin^2 x + \cos^2 x = 1$ is equivalent to the basic equation
_____ whose solutions are $x =$ _____.

2. Using a Double-Angle Formula we see that the equation $\sin x + \sin 2x = 0$ is equivalent to the equation _____. Factoring we see that solving this equation is equivalent to solving the two basic equations _____ and _____.

SKILLS

3–16 ■ Solve the given equation.

3. $2\cos^2\theta + \sin\theta = 1$
4. $\sin^2\theta = 4 - 2\cos^2\theta$
5. $\tan^2\theta - 2\sec\theta = 2$
6. $\csc^2\theta = \cot\theta + 3$

7. $2\sin 2\theta - 3\sin\theta = 0$
8. $3\sin 2\theta - 2\sin\theta = 0$
9. $\cos 2\theta = 3\sin\theta - 1$
10. $\cos 2\theta = \cos^2\theta - \frac{1}{2}$
11. $2\sin^2\theta - \cos\theta = 1$
12. $\tan\theta - 3\cot\theta = 0$
13. $\sin\theta - 1 = \cos\theta$
14. $\cos\theta - \sin\theta = 1$
15. $\tan\theta + 1 = \sec\theta$
16. $2\tan\theta + \sec^2\theta = 4$

17–34 ■ An equation is given. (a) Find all solutions of the equation. (b) Find the solutions in the interval $[0, 2\pi)$.

17. $2\cos 3\theta = 1$
18. $3\csc^2\theta = 4$
19. $2\cos 2\theta + 1 = 0$
20. $2\sin 3\theta + 1 = 0$
21. $\sqrt{3}\tan 3\theta + 1 = 0$
22. $\sec 4\theta - 2 = 0$
23. $\cos\dfrac{\theta}{2} - 1 = 0$
24. $\tan\dfrac{\theta}{4} + \sqrt{3} = 0$
25. $2\sin\dfrac{\theta}{3} + \sqrt{3} = 0$
26. $\sec\dfrac{\theta}{2} = \cos\dfrac{\theta}{2}$

DRILL QUESTION

Solve $x\sin 3x + \dfrac{1}{2}x = 0$.

Answer

$x = 0$, $x = \dfrac{7\pi}{18} + \dfrac{2}{3}\pi k$, or $x = \dfrac{35\pi}{18} + \dfrac{2}{3}\pi k$

27. $\sin 2\theta = 3 \cos 2\theta$ **28.** $\csc 3\theta = 5 \sin 3\theta$

29. $\sec \theta - \tan \theta = \cos \theta$ **30.** $\tan 3\theta + 1 = \sec 3\theta$

31. $3 \tan^3 \theta - 3 \tan^2 \theta - \tan \theta + 1 = 0$

32. $4 \sin \theta \cos \theta + 2 \sin \theta - 2 \cos \theta - 1 = 0$

33. $2 \sin \theta \tan \theta - \tan \theta = 1 - 2 \sin \theta$

34. $\sec \theta \tan \theta - \cos \theta \cot \theta = \sin \theta$

35–38 ■ (a) Graph f and g in the given viewing rectangle and find the intersection points graphically, rounded to two decimal places. (b) Find the intersection points of f and g algebraically. Give exact answers.

35. $f(x) = 3 \cos x + 1, g(x) = \cos x - 1$; $[-2\pi, 2\pi]$ by $[-2.5, 4.5]$

36. $f(x) = \sin 2x + 1, g(x) = 2 \sin 2x + 1$; $[-2\pi, 2\pi]$ by $[-1.5, 3.5]$

37. $f(x) = \tan x, g(x) = \sqrt{3}$; $\left[-\frac{\pi}{2}, \frac{\pi}{2}\right]$ by $[-10, 10]$

38. $f(x) = \sin x - 1, g(x) = \cos x$; $[-2\pi, 2\pi]$ by $[-2.5, 1.5]$

39–42 ■ Use an Addition or Subtraction Formula to simplify the equation. Then find all solutions in the interval $[0, 2\pi)$.

39. $\cos \theta \cos 3\theta - \sin \theta \sin 3\theta = 0$

40. $\cos \theta \cos 2\theta + \sin \theta \sin 2\theta = \frac{1}{2}$

41. $\sin 2\theta \cos \theta - \cos 2\theta \sin \theta = \sqrt{3}/2$

42. $\sin 3\theta \cos \theta - \cos 3\theta \sin \theta = 0$

43–52 ■ Use a Double- or Half-Angle Formula to solve the equation in the interval $[0, 2\pi)$.

43. $\sin 2\theta + \cos \theta = 0$ **44.** $\tan \frac{\theta}{2} - \sin \theta = 0$

45. $\cos 2\theta + \cos \theta = 2$ **46.** $\tan \theta + \cot \theta = 4 \sin 2\theta$

47. $\cos 2\theta - \cos^2 \theta = 0$ **48.** $2 \sin^2 \theta = 2 + \cos 2\theta$

49. $\cos 2\theta - \cos 4\theta = 0$ **50.** $\sin 3\theta - \sin 6\theta = 0$

51. $\cos \theta - \sin \theta = \sqrt{2} \sin \frac{\theta}{2}$ **52.** $\sin \theta - \cos \theta = \frac{1}{2}$

53–56 ■ Solve the equation by first using a Sum-to-Product Formula.

53. $\sin \theta + \sin 3\theta = 0$ **54.** $\cos 5\theta - \cos 7\theta = 0$

55. $\cos 4\theta + \cos 2\theta = \cos \theta$ **56.** $\sin 5\theta - \sin 3\theta = \cos 4\theta$

57–62 ■ Use a graphing device to find the solutions of the equation, correct to two decimal places.

57. $\sin 2x = x$ **58.** $\cos x = \frac{x}{3}$

59. $2^{\sin x} = x$ **60.** $\sin x = x^3$

61. $\frac{\cos x}{1 + x^2} = x^2$ **62.** $\cos x = \frac{1}{2}(e^x + e^{-x})$

APPLICATIONS

63. Range of a Projectile If a projectile is fired with velocity v_0 at an angle θ, then its *range*, the horizontal distance it travels (in feet), is modeled by the function

$$R(\theta) = \frac{v_0^2 \sin 2\theta}{32}$$

(See page 576.) If $v_0 = 2200$ ft/s, what angle (in degrees) should be chosen for the projectile to hit a target on the ground 5000 ft away?

64. Damped Vibrations The displacement of a spring vibrating in damped harmonic motion is given by

$$y = 4e^{-3t} \sin 2\pi t$$

Find the times when the spring is at its equilibrium position ($y = 0$).

65. Hours of Daylight In Philadelphia the number of hours of daylight on day t (where t is the number of days after January 1) is modeled by the function

$$L(t) = 12 + 2.83 \sin\left(\frac{2\pi}{365}(t - 80)\right)$$

(a) Which days of the year have about 10 hours of daylight?
(b) How many days of the year have more than 10 hours of daylight?

66. Belts and Pulleys A thin belt of length L surrounds two pulleys of radii R and r, as shown in the figure.
(a) Show that the angle θ (in radians) where the belt crosses itself satisfies the equation

$$\theta + 2 \cot \frac{\theta}{2} = \frac{L}{R + r} - \pi$$

[*Hint:* Express L in terms of R, r, and θ by adding up the lengths of the curved and straight parts of the belt.]
(b) Suppose that $R = 2.42$ ft, $r = 1.21$ ft, and $L = 27.78$ ft. Find θ by solving the equation in part (a) graphically. Express your answer both in radians and in degrees.

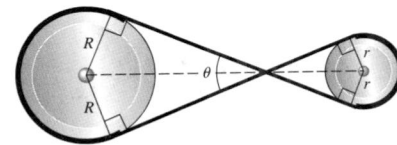

DISCOVERY ■ DISCUSSION ■ WRITING

67. A Special Trigonometric Equation What makes the equation $\sin(\cos x) = 0$ different from all the other equations we've looked at in this section? Find all solutions of this equation.

CHAPTER 7 | REVIEW

■ CONCEPT CHECK

1. **(a)** State the reciprocal identities.
   (b) State the Pythagorean identities.
   (c) State the even-odd identities.
   (d) State the cofunction identities.

2. Explain the difference between an equation and an identity.

3. How do you prove a trigonometric identity?

4. **(a)** State the Addition Formulas for Sine, Cosine, and Tangent.
   (b) State the Subtraction Formulas for Sine, Cosine, and Tangent.

5. **(a)** State the Double-Angle Formulas for Sine, Cosine, and Tangent.
   (b) State the formulas for lowering powers.
   (c) State the Half-Angle Formulas.

6. **(a)** State the Product-to-Sum Formulas.
   (b) State the Sum-to-Product Formulas.

7. Explain how you solve a trigonometric equation by factoring.

8. What identity would you use to solve the equation $\cos x - \sin 2x = 0$?

■ EXERCISES

1–24 ■ Verify the identity.

1. $\sin \theta \, (\cot \theta + \tan \theta) = \sec \theta$

2. $(\sec \theta - 1)(\sec \theta + 1) = \tan^2 \theta$

3. $\cos^2 x \csc x - \csc x = -\sin x$

4. $\dfrac{1}{1 - \sin^2 x} = 1 + \tan^2 x$

5. $\dfrac{\cos^2 x - \tan^2 x}{\sin^2 x} = \cot^2 x - \sec^2 x$

6. $\dfrac{1 + \sec x}{\sec x} = \dfrac{\sin^2 x}{1 - \cos x}$

7. $\dfrac{\cos^2 x}{1 - \sin x} = \dfrac{\cos x}{\sec x - \tan x}$

8. $(1 - \tan x)(1 - \cot x) = 2 - \sec x \csc x$

9. $\sin^2 x \cot^2 x + \cos^2 x \tan^2 x = 1$

10. $(\tan x + \cot x)^2 = \csc^2 x \sec^2 x$

11. $\dfrac{\sin 2x}{1 + \cos 2x} = \tan x$

12. $\dfrac{\cos(x + y)}{\cos x \sin y} = \cot y - \tan x$

13. $\tan \dfrac{x}{2} = \csc x - \cot x$

14. $\dfrac{\sin(x + y) + \sin(x - y)}{\cos(x + y) + \cos(x - y)} = \tan x$

15. $\sin(x + y) \sin(x - y) = \sin^2 x - \sin^2 y$

16. $\csc x - \tan \dfrac{x}{2} = \cot x$

17. $1 + \tan x \tan \dfrac{x}{2} = \sec x$

18. $\dfrac{\sin 3x + \cos 3x}{\cos x - \sin x} = 1 + 2 \sin 2x$

19. $\left(\cos \dfrac{x}{2} - \sin \dfrac{x}{2} \right)^2 = 1 - \sin x$

20. $\dfrac{\cos 3x - \cos 7x}{\sin 3x + \sin 7x} = \tan 2x$

21. $\dfrac{\sin 2x}{\sin x} - \dfrac{\cos 2x}{\cos x} = \sec x$

22. $(\cos x + \cos y)^2 + (\sin x - \sin y)^2 = 2 + 2 \cos(x + y)$

23. $\tan \left(x + \dfrac{\pi}{4} \right) = \dfrac{1 + \tan x}{1 - \tan x}$

24. $\dfrac{\sec x - 1}{\sin x \sec x} = \tan \dfrac{x}{2}$

25–28 ■ **(a)** Graph f and g. **(b)** Do the graphs suggest that the equation $f(x) = g(x)$ is an identity? Prove your answer.

25. $f(x) = 1 - \left(\cos \dfrac{x}{2} - \sin \dfrac{x}{2} \right)^2, \quad g(x) = \sin x$

26. $f(x) = \sin x + \cos x, \quad g(x) = \sqrt{\sin^2 x + \cos^2 x}$

27. $f(x) = \tan x \tan \dfrac{x}{2}, \quad g(x) = \dfrac{1}{\cos x}$

28. $f(x) = 1 - 8 \sin^2 x + 8 \sin^4 x, \quad g(x) = \cos 4x$

29–30 ■ **(a)** Graph the function(s) and make a conjecture, and **(b)** prove your conjecture.

29. $f(x) = 2 \sin^2 3x + \cos 6x$

30. $f(x) = \sin x \cot \dfrac{x}{2}, \quad g(x) = \cos x$

31–48 ■ Solve the equation in the interval $[0, 2\pi)$.

31. $4 \sin \theta - 3 = 0$

32. $5 \cos \theta + 3 = 0$

33. $\cos x \sin x - \sin x = 0$

34. $\sin x - 2 \sin^2 x = 0$

35. $2 \sin^2 x - 5 \sin x + 2 = 0$

36. $\sin x - \cos x - \tan x = -1$

37. $2 \cos^2 x - 7 \cos x + 3 = 0$

38. $4 \sin^2 x + 2 \cos^2 x = 3$

39. $\dfrac{1 - \cos x}{1 + \cos x} = 3$

40. $\sin x = \cos 2x$

41. $\tan^3 x + \tan^2 x - 3 \tan x - 3 = 0$

42. $\cos 2x \csc^2 x = 2 \cos 2x$

43. $\tan \frac{1}{2}x + 2 \sin 2x = \csc x$

44. $\cos 3x + \cos 2x + \cos x = 0$

45. $\tan x + \sec x = \sqrt{3}$

46. $2 \cos x - 3 \tan x = 0$

 47. $\cos x = x^2 - 1$

 48. $e^{\sin x} = x$

49. If a projectile is fired with velocity v_0 at an angle θ, then the maximum height it reaches (in feet) is modeled by the function

$$M(\theta) = \frac{v_0^2 \sin^2 \theta}{64}$$

Suppose $v_0 = 400$ ft/s.
(a) At what angle θ should the projectile be fired so that the maximum height it reaches is 2000 ft?
(b) Is it possible for the projectile to reach a height of 3000 ft?
(c) Find the angle θ for which the projectile will travel highest.

50. The displacement of an automobile shock absorber is modeled by the function

$$f(t) = 2^{-0.2t} \sin 4\pi t$$

Find the times when the shock absorber is at its equilibrium position (that is, when $f(t) = 0$). [*Hint:* $2^x > 0$ for all real x.]

51–60 ■ Find the exact value of the expression.

51. $\cos 15°$

52. $\sin \dfrac{5\pi}{12}$

53. $\tan \dfrac{\pi}{8}$

54. $2 \sin \dfrac{\pi}{12} \cos \dfrac{\pi}{12}$

55. $\sin 5° \cos 40° + \cos 5° \sin 40°$

56. $\dfrac{\tan 66° - \tan 6°}{1 + \tan 66° \tan 6°}$

57. $\cos^2 \dfrac{\pi}{8} - \sin^2 \dfrac{\pi}{8}$

58. $\dfrac{1}{2} \cos \dfrac{\pi}{12} + \dfrac{\sqrt{3}}{2} \sin \dfrac{\pi}{12}$

59. $\cos 37.5° \cos 7.5°$

60. $\cos 67.5° + \cos 22.5°$

61–66 ■ Find the exact value of the expression given that $\sec x = \frac{3}{2}$, $\csc y = 3$, and x and y are in Quadrant I.

61. $\sin(x + y)$

62. $\cos(x - y)$

63. $\tan(x + y)$

64. $\sin 2x$

65. $\cos \dfrac{y}{2}$

66. $\tan \dfrac{y}{2}$

67–68 ■ Find the exact value of the expression.

67. $\tan\left(2 \cos^{-1} \frac{3}{7}\right)$

68. $\sin\left(\tan^{-1} \frac{3}{4} + \cos^{-1} \frac{5}{13}\right)$

69–70 ■ Write the expression as an algebraic expression in the variable(s).

69. $\tan(2 \tan^{-1} x)$

70. $\cos(\sin^{-1} x + \cos^{-1} y)$

71. A 10-ft-wide highway sign is adjacent to a roadway, as shown in the figure. As a driver approaches the sign, the viewing angle θ changes.
(a) Express viewing angle θ as a function of the distance x between the driver and the sign.
(b) The sign is legible when the viewing angle is $2°$ or greater. At what distance x does the sign first become legible?

72. A 380-ft-tall building supports a 40-ft communications tower (see the figure). As a driver approaches the building, the viewing angle θ of the tower changes.
(a) Express the viewing angle θ as a function of the distance x between the driver and the building.
(b) At what distance from the building is the viewing angle θ as large as possible?

1. Verify each identity.

   (a) $\tan\theta\sin\theta + \cos\theta = \sec\theta$

   (b) $\dfrac{\tan x}{1 - \cos x} = \csc x\,(1 + \sec x)$

   (c) $\dfrac{2\tan x}{1 + \tan^2 x} = \sin 2x$

2. Let $x = 2\sin\theta,\ -\pi/2 < \theta < \pi/2$. Simplify the expression

$$\frac{x}{\sqrt{4 - x^2}}$$

3. Find the exact value of each expression.

   (a) $\sin 8°\cos 22° + \cos 8°\sin 22°$
   (b) $\sin 75°$
   (c) $\sin\dfrac{\pi}{12}$

4. For the angles α and β in the figures, find $\cos(\alpha + \beta)$.

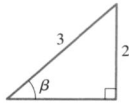

5. (a) Write $\sin 3x\cos 5x$ as a sum of trigonometric functions.

   (b) Write $\sin 2x - \sin 5x$ as a product of trigonometric functions.

6. If $\sin\theta = -\frac{4}{5}$ and θ is in Quadrant III, find $\tan(\theta/2)$.

7. Solve each trigonometric equation in the interval $[0, 2\pi)$, rounded to two decimal places.

   (a) $3\sin\theta - 1 = 0$

   (b) $(2\cos\theta - 1)(\sin\theta - 1) = 0$

   (c) $2\cos^2\theta + 5\cos\theta + 2 = 0$

   (d) $\sin 2\theta - \cos\theta = 0$

8. Find all solutions in the interval $[0, 2\pi)$, rounded to five decimal places:

$$5\cos 2\theta = 2$$

9. Find the exact value of $\cos\!\left(2\tan^{-1}\frac{9}{40}\right)$.

10. Rewrite the expression as an algebraic function of x and y:

$$\sin(\cos^{-1}x - \tan^{-1}y)$$

We've learned that the position of a particle in simple harmonic motion is described by a function of the form $y = A \sin \omega t$ (see Section 5.6). For example, if a string is moved up and down as in Figure 1, then the red dot on the string moves up and down in simple harmonic motion. Of course, the same holds true for each point on the string.

FIGURE 1

What function describes the shape of the whole string? If we fix an instant in time ($t = 0$) and snap a photograph of the string, we get the shape in Figure 2, which is modeled by

$$y = A \sin kx$$

where y is the height of the string above the x-axis at the point x.

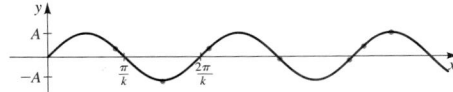

FIGURE 2 $y = A \sin kx$

▼ Traveling Waves

If we snap photographs of the string at other instants, as in Figure 3, it appears that the waves in the string "travel" or shift to the right.

FIGURE 3

The **velocity** of the wave is the rate at which it moves to the right. If the wave has velocity v, then it moves to the right a distance vt in time t. So the graph of the shifted wave at time t is

$$y(x, t) = A \sin k(x - vt)$$

This function models the position of any point x on the string at any time t. We use the notation $y(x, t)$ to indicate that the function depends on the *two* variables x and t. Here is how this function models the motion of the string.

- **If we fix x**, then $y(x, t)$ is a function of t only, which gives the position of the fixed point x at time t.
- **If we fix t**, then $y(x, t)$ is a function of x only, whose graph is the shape of the string at the fixed time t.

533

EXAMPLE 1 | A Traveling Wave

A traveling wave is described by the function

$$y(x, t) = 3 \sin\left(2x - \frac{\pi}{2}t\right), \qquad x \geq 0$$

(a) Find the function that models the position of the point $x = \pi/6$ at any time t. Observe that the point moves in simple harmonic motion.

(b) Sketch the shape of the wave when $t = 0, 0.5, 1.0, 1.5,$ and 2.0. Does the wave appear to be traveling to the right?

(c) Find the velocity of the wave.

SOLUTION

(a) Substituting $x = \pi/6$ we get

$$y\left(\frac{\pi}{6}, t\right) = 3 \sin\left(2 \cdot \frac{\pi}{6} - \frac{\pi}{2}t\right) = 3 \sin\left(\frac{\pi}{3} - \frac{\pi}{2}t\right)$$

The function $y = 3 \sin\left(\frac{\pi}{3} - \frac{\pi}{2}t\right)$ describes simple harmonic motion with amplitude 3 and period $2\pi/(\pi/2) = 4$.

(b) The graphs are shown in Figure 4. As t increases, the wave moves to the right.

(c) We express the given function in the standard form $y(x, t) = A \sin k(x - vt)$:

$$y(x, t) = 3 \sin\left(2x - \frac{\pi}{2}t\right) \qquad \text{Given}$$

$$= 3 \sin 2\left(x - \frac{\pi}{4}t\right) \qquad \text{Factor 2}$$

Comparing this to the standard form, we see that the wave is moving with velocity $v = \pi/4$. ∎

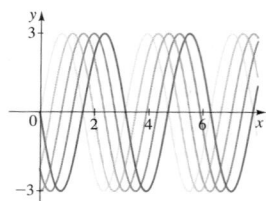

FIGURE 4 Traveling wave

▼ Standing Waves

If two waves are traveling along the same string, then the movement of the string is determined by the sum of the two waves. For example, if the string is attached to a wall, then the waves bounce back with the same amplitude and speed but in the opposite direction. In this case, one wave is described by $y = A \sin k(x - vt)$ and the reflected wave by $y = A \sin k(x + vt)$. The resulting wave is

$$y(x, t) = A \sin k(x - vt) + A \sin k(x + vt) \qquad \text{Add the two waves}$$

$$= 2A \sin kx \cos kvt \qquad \text{Sum-to-Product Formula}$$

The points where kx is a multiple of 2π are special, because at these points $y = 0$ for any time t. In other words, these points never move. Such points are called **nodes**. Figure 5 shows the graph of the wave for several values of t. We see that the wave does not travel, but simply vibrates up and down. Such a wave is called a **standing wave**.

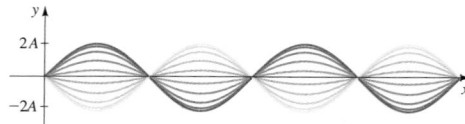

FIGURE 5 A standing wave

EXAMPLE 2 | A Standing Wave

Traveling waves are generated at each end of a wave tank 30 ft long, with equations

$$y = 1.5 \sin\left(\frac{\pi}{5}x - 3t\right)$$

and

$$y = 1.5 \sin\left(\frac{\pi}{5}x + 3t\right)$$

(a) Find the equation of the combined wave, and find the nodes.

(b) Sketch the graph for $t = 0, 0.17, 0.34, 0.51, 0.68, 0.85,$ and 1.02. Is this a standing wave?

SOLUTION

(a) The combined wave is obtained by adding the two equations:

$$y = 1.5 \sin\left(\frac{\pi}{5}x - 3t\right) + 1.5 \sin\left(\frac{\pi}{5}x + 3t\right) \qquad \text{Add the two waves}$$

$$= 3 \sin\frac{\pi}{5}x \cos 3t \qquad\qquad\qquad \text{Sum-to-Product Formula}$$

The nodes occur at the values of x for which $\sin\frac{\pi}{5}x = 0$, that is, where $\frac{\pi}{5}x = k\pi$ (k an integer). Solving for x, we get $x = 5k$. So the nodes occur at

$$x = 0, 5, 10, 15, 20, 25, 30$$

(b) The graphs are shown in Figure 6. From the graphs we see that this is a standing wave.

| $t = 0$ | $t = 0.17$ | $t = 0.34$ | $t = 0.51$ | $t = 0.68$ | $t = 0.85$ | $t = 1.02$ |

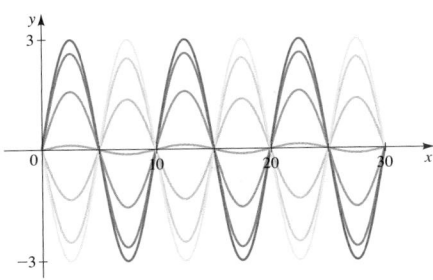

FIGURE 6 $y(x, t) = 3 \sin\dfrac{\pi}{5}x \cos 3t$

PROBLEMS

1. **Wave on a Canal**   A wave on the surface of a long canal is described by the function

$$y(x, t) = 5 \sin\left(2x - \frac{\pi}{2}t\right), \quad x \geq 0$$

   (a) Find the function that models the position of the point $x = 0$ at any time t.
   (b) Sketch the shape of the wave when $t = 0, 0.4, 0.8, 1.2,$ and 1.6. Is this a traveling wave?
   (c) Find the velocity of the wave.

2. **Wave in a Rope**   Traveling waves are generated at each end of a tightly stretched rope 24 ft long, with equations

$$y = 0.2 \sin(1.047x - 0.524t) \quad \text{and} \quad y = 0.2 \sin(1.047x + 0.524t)$$

   (a) Find the equation of the combined wave, and find the nodes.
   (b) Sketch the graph for $t = 0, 1, 2, 3, 4, 5,$ and 6. Is this a standing wave?

3. **Traveling Wave**   A traveling wave is graphed at the instant $t = 0$. If it is moving to the right with velocity 6, find an equation of the form $y(x, t) = A \sin(kx - kvt)$ for this wave.

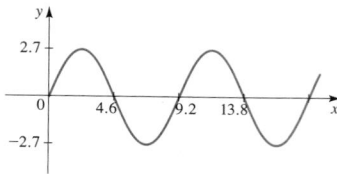

4. **Traveling Wave**   A traveling wave has period $2\pi/3$, amplitude 5, and velocity 0.5.
   (a) Find the equation of the wave.
   (b) Sketch the graph for $t = 0, 0.5, 1, 1.5,$ and 2.

5. **Standing Wave**   A standing wave with amplitude 0.6 is graphed at several times t as shown in the figure. If the vibration has a frequency of 20 Hz, find an equation of the form $y(x, t) = A \sin \alpha x \cos \beta t$ that models this wave.

$t = 0$ s

$t = 0.010$ s

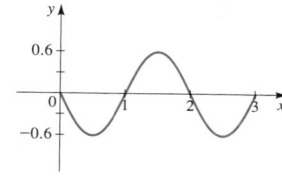

$t = 0.025$ s

6. **Standing Wave**   A standing wave has maximum amplitude 7 and nodes at 0, $\pi/2$, π, $3\pi/2$, 2π, as shown in the figure. Each point that is not a node moves up and down with period 4π. Find a function of the form $y(x, t) = A \sin \alpha x \cos \beta t$ that models this wave.

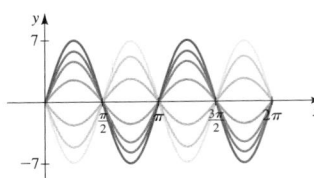

7. **Vibrating String**   When a violin string vibrates, the sound produced results from a combination of standing waves that have evenly placed nodes. The figure illustrates some of the possible standing waves. Let's assume that the string has length π.

   (a) For fixed t, the string has the shape of a sine curve $y = A \sin \alpha x$. Find the appropriate value of α for each of the illustrated standing waves.

   (b) Do you notice a pattern in the values of α that you found in part (a)? What would the next two values of α be? Sketch rough graphs of the standing waves associated with these new values of α.

   (c) Suppose that for fixed t, each point on the string that is not a node vibrates with frequency 440 Hz. Find the value of β for which an equation of the form $y = A \cos \beta t$ would model this motion.

   (d) Combine your answers for parts (a) and (c) to find functions of the form $y(x, t) = A \sin \alpha x \cos \beta t$ that model each of the standing waves in the figure. (Assume that $A = 1$.)

8. **Waves in a Tube**   Standing waves in a violin string must have nodes at the ends of the string because the string is fixed at its endpoints. But this need not be the case with sound waves in a tube (such as a flute or an organ pipe). The figure shows some possible standing waves in a tube.

   Suppose that a standing wave in a tube 37.7 ft long is modeled by the function

   $$y(x, t) = 0.3 \cos \tfrac{1}{2}x \cos 50\pi t$$

   Here $y(x, t)$ represents the variation from normal air pressure at the point x feet from the end of the tube, at time t seconds.

   (a) At what points x are the nodes located? Are the endpoints of the tube nodes?

   (b) At what frequency does the air vibrate at points that are not nodes?

1. The point $P(x, y)$ shown in the figure has y-coordinate $\sqrt{5}/3$. Find:
   (a) $\sin t$ (b) $\cos t$ (c) $\tan t$ (d) $\csc t$

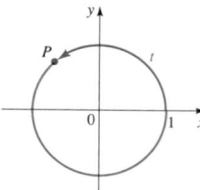

2. For the angle θ shown in the figure, find:
   (a) $\sin \theta$ (b) $\sec \theta$ (c) $\cot \theta$

3. Find the exact value:

   (a) $\cos \dfrac{7\pi}{6}$ (b) $\tan 135°$ (c) $\csc 240°$ (d) $\sin\left(-\dfrac{9\pi}{2}\right)$

4. Suppose that $\cos t = \dfrac{7}{25}$ and $\tan t < 0$. Find the values of $\sin t$, $\tan t$, $\cot t$, $\sec t$, and $\csc t$.

5. Let $f(x) = -2 \sin\left(2x - \dfrac{\pi}{2}\right)$.

   (a) Find the amplitude, period, and phase shift of f.
   (b) Sketch the graph of one complete period of f.

6. One period of a function of the form $y = a \cos k(x - b)$ is shown in the figure. Determine the function.

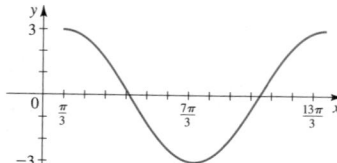

7. The figure below shows a model ferris wheel that a child has constructed using a toy building kit. The wheel has a radius of 40 cm, and the center of the wheel is 45 cm above the floor. An electric motor turns the wheel at 4 rotations per minute.

   (a) Let $h(t)$ be the vertical distance between the point P and the floor at the time t. Express the function h in the form $h(t) = a + b \cos kt$. (Assume that at $t = 0$ the point P is at the lowest point of its travel.)

   (b) The support struts AB and AC are each 50 cm long. Find the distance between B and C.

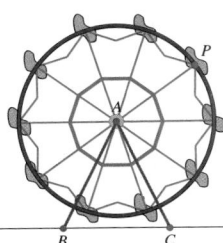

8. Find the side or angle labeled x:

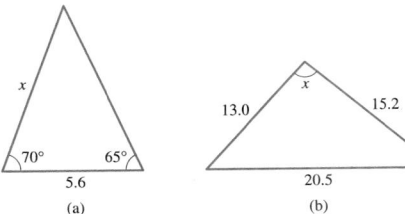

   (a)   (b)

9. Verify each identity:

   (a) $\dfrac{\sec \theta - 1}{\tan \theta} = \dfrac{\tan \theta}{\sec \theta + 1}$ (b) $8 \sin^2\theta \cos^2\theta = 1 - \cos 4\theta$

10. Write $\cos 3x + \cos 4x$ as a product of trigonometric functions.

11. (a) What are the domain and range of the function $f(x) = \cos^{-1} x$? Sketch a graph of this function.

    (b) Find the exact value of $\cos^{-1}(\cos(7\pi/6))$.

    (c) Express $\tan(\cos^{-1} x)$ as an algebraic function of x.

12. Find all solutions of the equation $\cos 2x - \sin x = 0$ in the interval $[0, 2\pi)$.

POLAR COORDINATES AND PARAMETRIC EQUATIONS

In Section 1.8 we learned how to graph points in rectangular coordinates. In this chapter we study a different way of locating points in the plane, called *polar coordinates*. Using rectangular coordinates is like describing a location in a city by saying that it's at the corner of 2nd Street and 4th Avenue; these directions would help a taxi driver find the location. But we may also describe this same location "as the crow flies"; we can say that it's 1.5 miles northeast of City Hall. So instead of specifying the location with respect to a grid of streets and avenues, we specify it by giving its distance and direction from a fixed reference point. That's what we do in the polar coordinate system. In polar coordinates the location of a point is given by an ordered pair of numbers: the distance of the point from the origin (or pole) and the angle from the positive x-axis.

Why do we study different coordinate systems? It's because certain curves are more naturally described in one coordinate system rather than another. For example, in rectangular coordinates lines and parabolas have simple equations, but equations of circles are rather complicated. We'll see that in polar coordinates circles have very simple equations.

541

8.1 POLAR COORDINATES

| Definition of Polar Coordinates ▶ Relationship Between Polar
| and Rectangular Coordinates ▶ Polar Equations

In this section we define polar coordinates, and we learn how polar coordinates are related to rectangular coordinates.

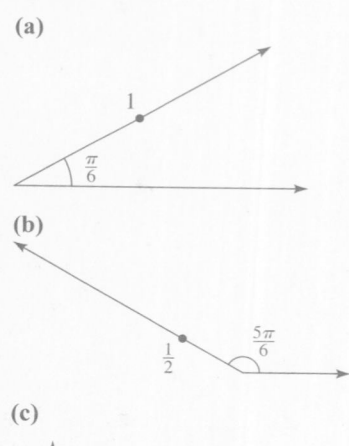

FIGURE 1

FIGURE 2

▼ Definition of Polar Coordinates

The **polar coordinate system** uses distances and directions to specify the location of a point in the plane. To set up this system, we choose a fixed point O in the plane called the **pole** (or **origin**) and draw from O a ray (half-line) called the **polar axis** as in Figure 1. Then each point P can be assigned polar coordinates $P(r, \theta)$ where

r is the *distance* from O to P

θ is the *angle* between the polar axis and the segment $\overline{OP}$

We use the convention that θ is positive if measured in a counterclockwise direction from the polar axis or negative if measured in a clockwise direction. If r is negative, then $P(r, \theta)$ is defined to be the point that lies $|r|$ units from the pole in the direction opposite to that given by θ (see Figure 2).

EXAMPLE 1 | Plotting Points in Polar Coordinates

Plot the points whose polar coordinates are given.

(a) $(1, 3\pi/4)$ **(b)** $(3, -\pi/6)$ **(c)** $(3, 3\pi)$ **(d)** $(-4, \pi/4)$

SOLUTION The points are plotted in Figure 3. Note that the point in part (d) lies 4 units from the origin along the angle $5\pi/4$, because the given value of r is negative.

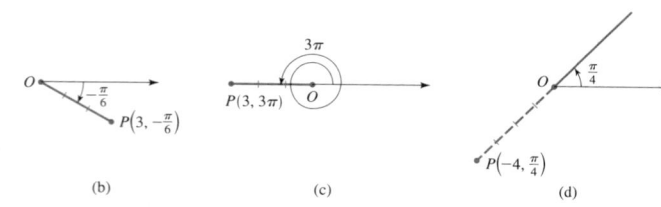

FIGURE 3

☜. NOW TRY EXERCISES **3** AND **5**

Note that the coordinates (r, θ) and $(-r, \theta + \pi)$ represent the same point, as shown in Figure 4. Moreover, because the angles $\theta + 2n\pi$ (where n is any integer) all have the same terminal side as the angle θ, each point in the plane has infinitely many representations in polar coordinates. In fact, any point $P(r, \theta)$ can also be represented by

$$P(r, \theta + 2n\pi) \quad \text{and} \quad P(-r, \theta + (2n + 1)\pi)$$

for any integer n.

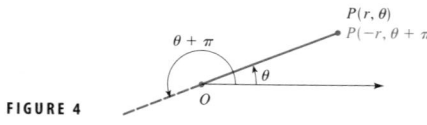

FIGURE 4

TEXT QUESTION

Where do the conversion equations $x = r \cos\theta$, $y = r \sin\theta$ come from?

Answer

Several correct answers are possible. Anything addressing the definitions of sine and cosine, for example, should be given credit.

EXAMPLE 2 | Different Polar Coordinates for the Same Point

(a) Graph the point with polar coordinates $P(2, \pi/3)$.

(b) Find two other polar coordinate representations of P with $r > 0$ and two with $r < 0$.

SOLUTION

(a) The graph is shown in Figure 5(a).

(b) Other representations with $r > 0$ are

$$\left(2, \frac{\pi}{3} + 2\pi\right) = \left(2, \frac{7\pi}{3}\right) \qquad \text{Add } 2\pi \text{ to } \theta$$

$$\left(2, \frac{\pi}{3} - 2\pi\right) = \left(2, -\frac{5\pi}{3}\right) \qquad \text{Add } -2\pi \text{ to } \theta$$

Other representations with $r < 0$ are

$$\left(-2, \frac{\pi}{3} + \pi\right) = \left(-2, \frac{4\pi}{3}\right) \qquad \text{Replace } r \text{ by } -r \text{ and add } \pi \text{ to } \theta$$

$$\left(-2, \frac{\pi}{3} - \pi\right) = \left(-2, -\frac{2\pi}{3}\right) \qquad \text{Replace } r \text{ by } -r \text{ and add } -\pi \text{ to } \theta$$

The graphs in Figure 5 explain why these coordinates represent the same point.

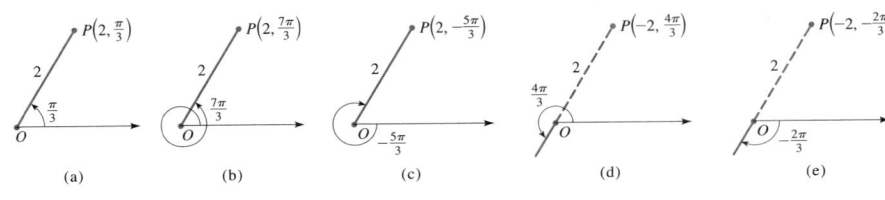

    (a)   (b)   (c)   (d)   (e)

FIGURE 5

✎ NOW TRY EXERCISE **9**

▼ Relationship Between Polar and Rectangular Coordinates

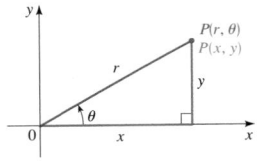

FIGURE 6

Situations often arise in which we need to consider polar and rectangular coordinates simultaneously. The connection between the two systems is illustrated in Figure 6, where the polar axis coincides with the positive x-axis. The formulas in the following box are obtained from the figure using the definitions of the trigonometric functions and the Pythagorean Theorem. (Although we have pictured the case where $r > 0$ and θ is acute, the formulas hold for any angle θ and for any value of r.)

RELATIONSHIP BETWEEN POLAR AND RECTANGULAR COORDINATES

1. To change from polar to rectangular coordinates, use the formulas

$$x = r \cos \theta \qquad \text{and} \qquad y = r \sin \theta$$

2. To change from rectangular to polar coordinates, use the formulas

$$r^2 = x^2 + y^2 \qquad \text{and} \qquad \tan \theta = \frac{y}{x} \quad (x \neq 0)$$

IN-CLASS MATERIALS

Begin with an intuitive definition of polar coordinates and then derive the algebraic formulas, noting that the graph of a polar function need not pass the Vertical Line Test.

ALTERNATE EXAMPLE 3

Find the rectangular coordinates for the point whose polar coordinates are $\left(-4, \dfrac{5\pi}{2}\right)$.

ANSWER

The rectangular coordinates for the given point are $(0, -4)$.

ALTERNATE EXAMPLE 4

Find two polar coordinates for the point that has rectangular coordinates $(-7, -7)$.

ANSWER

$\left(7\sqrt{2}, -\dfrac{3\pi}{4}\right), \left(-7\sqrt{2}, -\dfrac{\pi}{4}\right)$

ALTERNATE EXAMPLE 5

Convert the equation $x = 1$ to polar form.

ANSWER

$r = \sec(\theta)$

EXAMPLE 3 | Converting Polar Coordinates to Rectangular Coordinates

Find rectangular coordinates for the point that has polar coordinates $(4, 2\pi/3)$.

SOLUTION Since $r = 4$ and $\theta = 2\pi/3$, we have

$$x = r \cos \theta = 4 \cos \frac{2\pi}{3} = 4 \cdot \left(-\frac{1}{2}\right) = -2$$

$$y = r \sin \theta = 4 \sin \frac{2\pi}{3} = 4 \cdot \frac{\sqrt{3}}{2} = 2\sqrt{3}$$

Thus the point has rectangular coordinates $(-2, 2\sqrt{3})$.

■. NOW TRY EXERCISE **27**

EXAMPLE 4 | Converting Rectangular Coordinates to Polar Coordinates

Find polar coordinates for the point that has rectangular coordinates $(2, -2)$.

SOLUTION Using $x = 2$, $y = -2$, we get

$$r^2 = x^2 + y^2 = 2^2 + (-2)^2 = 8$$

so $r = 2\sqrt{2}$ or $-2\sqrt{2}$. Also

$$\tan \theta = \frac{y}{x} = \frac{-2}{2} = -1$$

so $\theta = 3\pi/4$ or $-\pi/4$. Since the point $(2, -2)$ lies in Quadrant IV (see Figure 7), we can represent it in polar coordinates as $(2\sqrt{2}, -\pi/4)$ or $(-2\sqrt{2}, 3\pi/4)$.

■. NOW TRY EXERCISE **35**

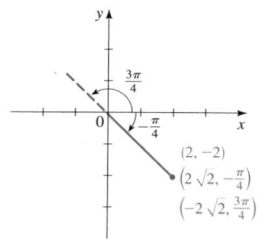

FIGURE 7

⊘ Note that the equations relating polar and rectangular coordinates do not uniquely determine r or θ. When we use these equations to find the polar coordinates of a point, we must be careful that the values we choose for r and θ give us a point in the correct quadrant, as we did in Example 4.

▼ Polar Equations

In Examples 3 and 4 we converted points from one coordinate system to the other. Now we consider the same problem for equations.

EXAMPLE 5 | Converting an Equation from Rectangular to Polar Coordinates

Express the equation $x^2 = 4y$ in polar coordinates.

SOLUTION We use the formulas $x = r \cos \theta$ and $y = r \sin \theta$:

$x^2 = 4y$	Rectangular equation
$(r \cos \theta)^2 = 4(r \sin \theta)$	Substitute $x = r \cos \theta$, $y = r \sin \theta$
$r^2 \cos^2\theta = 4r \sin \theta$	Expand
$r = 4 \dfrac{\sin \theta}{\cos^2\theta}$	Divide by $r \cos^2\theta$
$r = 4 \sec \theta \tan \theta$	Simplify

■. NOW TRY EXERCISE **45**

IN-CLASS MATERIALS

Point out how some equations are simpler to consider in rectangular coordinates ($y = \ln x$ is easier than $r \sin \theta = \ln r + \ln \cos \theta$) but some equations are simpler in polar coordinates [$r = \theta$, the simple spiral, is much easier than $\pm\sqrt{x^2 + y^2} = \tan^{-1}(y/x)$]. You can foreshadow Chapter 11 at this point, pointing out that there are curves called rotated ellipses, hyperbolas, and parabolas, that turn out to be very nice when considered as polar equations.

As Example 5 shows, converting from rectangular to polar coordinates is straightforward: Just replace x by $r \cos \theta$ and y by $r \sin \theta$, and then simplify. But converting polar equations to rectangular form often requires more thought.

EXAMPLE 6 | Converting Equations from Polar to Rectangular Coordinates

Express the polar equation in rectangular coordinates. If possible, determine the graph of the equation from its rectangular form.

(a) $r = 5 \sec \theta$ **(b)** $r = 2 \sin \theta$ **(c)** $r = 2 + 2 \cos \theta$

SOLUTION

(a) Since $\sec \theta = 1/\cos \theta$, we multiply both sides by $\cos \theta$:

$$r = 5 \sec \theta \qquad \text{Polar equation}$$
$$r \cos \theta = 5 \qquad \text{Multiply by } \cos \theta$$
$$x = 5 \qquad \text{Substitute } x = r \cos \theta$$

The graph of $x = 5$ is the vertical line in Figure 8.

(b) We multiply both sides of the equation by r, because then we can use the formulas $r^2 = x^2 + y^2$ and $r \sin \theta = y$:

$$r = 2 \sin \theta \qquad \text{Polar equation}$$
$$r^2 = 2r \sin \theta \qquad \text{Multiply by } r$$
$$x^2 + y^2 = 2y \qquad r^2 = x^2 + y^2 \text{ and } r \sin \theta = y$$
$$x^2 + y^2 - 2y = 0 \qquad \text{Subtract } 2y$$
$$x^2 + (y - 1)^2 = 1 \qquad \text{Complete the square in } y$$

This is the equation of a circle of radius 1 centered at the point $(0, 1)$. It is graphed in Figure 9.

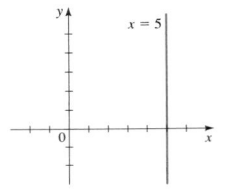

FIGURE 8   **FIGURE 9**

(c) We first multiply both sides of the equation by r:

$$r^2 = 2r + 2r \cos \theta$$

Using $r^2 = x^2 + y^2$ and $x = r \cos \theta$, we can convert two terms in the equation into rectangular coordinates, but eliminating the remaining r requires more work:

$$x^2 + y^2 = 2r + 2x \qquad r^2 = x^2 + y^2 \text{ and } r \cos \theta = x$$
$$x^2 + y^2 - 2x = 2r \qquad \text{Subtract } 2x$$
$$(x^2 + y^2 - 2x)^2 = 4r^2 \qquad \text{Square both sides}$$
$$(x^2 + y^2 - 2x)^2 = 4(x^2 + y^2) \qquad r^2 = x^2 + y^2$$

In this case the rectangular equation looks more complicated than the polar equation. Although we cannot easily determine the graph of the equation from its rectangular form, we will see in the next section how to graph it using the polar equation.

NOW TRY EXERCISES **53, 55,** AND **57** ∎

ALTERNATE EXAMPLE 6
(a) Express the polar equation $r = 4 \sin \theta$ in rectangular coordinates.
(b) Convert the equation $r = 5 + 4 \cos \theta$ to rectangular coordinates.

ANSWERS
(a) $x^2 + (y - 2)^2 = 4$
(b) $(x^2 + y^2 - 4x)^2 = 25(x^2 + y^2)$

EXAMPLE
Equation conversion:
Rectangular $x^2 + y^2 = 9$ is the same as polar $r = 9$.
Polar $\tan \theta = 1$ is the same as rectangular $y = x$.

IN-CLASS MATERIALS
Do several examples of converting Cartesian equations into polar equations, such as $y^2 = 4x$ to $r = 4 \csc \theta \cot \theta$, and of converting polar equations into Cartesian equations (the results of which are sometimes implicit equations), such as $r = 2 \sec \theta$ to $x = 2$ and $r = 2(1 + \cos \theta)$ to $(x^2 + y^2 - 2x)^2 = 4(x^2 + y^2)$.

Convert the equation
$r \sin \theta = 3r \cos \theta + 2$ to polar form.

Answer

$y = 3x + 2$

8.1 EXERCISES

CONCEPTS

1. We can describe the location of a point in the plane using different _____ systems. The point P shown in the figure has rectangular coordinates (⬚ , ⬚) and polar coordinates (⬚ , ⬚).

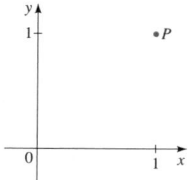

2. Let P be a point in the plane.

(a) If P has polar coordinates (r, θ) then it has rectangular coordinates (x, y) where $x =$ _____ and $y =$ _____.

(b) If P has rectangular coordinates (x, y) then it has polar coordinates (r, θ) where $r^2 =$ _____ and $\tan \theta =$ _____.

SKILLS

3–8 ■ Plot the point that has the given polar coordinates.

3. $(4, \pi/4)$ **4.** $(1, 0)$ **5.** $(6, -7\pi/6)$

6. $(3, -2\pi/3)$ **7.** $(-2, 4\pi/3)$ **8.** $(-5, -17\pi/6)$

9–14 ■ Plot the point that has the given polar coordinates. Then give two other polar coordinate representations of the point, one with $r < 0$ and the other with $r > 0$.

9. $(3, \pi/2)$ **10.** $(2, 3\pi/4)$ **11.** $(-1, 7\pi/6)$

12. $(-2, -\pi/3)$ **13.** $(-5, 0)$ **14.** $(3, 1)$

15–22 ■ Determine which point in the figure, P, Q, R, or S, has the given polar coordinates.

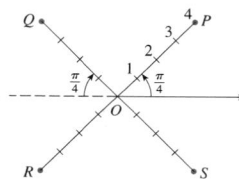

15. $(4, 3\pi/4)$ **16.** $(4, -3\pi/4)$

17. $(-4, -\pi/4)$ **18.** $(-4, 13\pi/4)$

19. $(4, -23\pi/4)$ **20.** $(-4, 23\pi/4)$

21. $(-4, 101\pi/4)$ **22.** $(4, 103\pi/4)$

23–24 ■ A point is graphed in rectangular form. Find polar coordinates for the point, with $r > 0$ and $0 < \theta < 2\pi$.

23.   **24.**

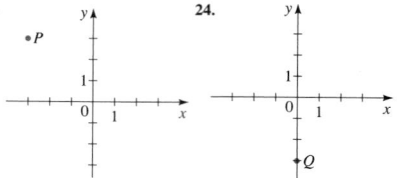

25–26 ■ A point is graphed in polar form. Find its rectangular coordinates.

25.   **26.**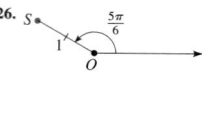

27–34 ■ Find the rectangular coordinates for the point whose polar coordinates are given.

27. $(4, \pi/6)$ **28.** $(6, 2\pi/3)$

29. $(\sqrt{2}, -\pi/4)$ **30.** $(-1, 5\pi/2)$

31. $(5, 5\pi)$ **32.** $(0, 13\pi)$

33. $(6\sqrt{2}, 11\pi/6)$ **34.** $(\sqrt{3}, -5\pi/3)$

35–42 ■ Convert the rectangular coordinates to polar coordinates with $r > 0$ and $0 \leq \theta < 2\pi$.

35. $(-1, 1)$ **36.** $(3\sqrt{3}, -3)$

37. $(\sqrt{8}, \sqrt{8})$ **38.** $(-\sqrt{6}, -\sqrt{2})$

39. $(3, 4)$ **40.** $(1, -2)$

41. $(-6, 0)$ **42.** $(0, -\sqrt{3})$

43–48 ■ Convert the equation to polar form.

43. $x = y$ **44.** $x^2 + y^2 = 9$

45. $y = x^2$ **46.** $y = 5$

47. $x = 4$ **48.** $x^2 - y^2 = 1$

49–68 ■ Convert the polar equation to rectangular coordinates.

49. $r = 7$ **50.** $r = -3$

51. $\theta = -\dfrac{\pi}{2}$ **52.** $\theta = \pi$

53. $r \cos \theta = 6$ **54.** $r = 2 \csc \theta$

55. $r = 4 \sin \theta$

56. $r = 6 \cos \theta$

57. $r = 1 + \cos \theta$

58. $r = 3(1 - \sin \theta)$

59. $r = 1 + 2 \sin \theta$

60. $r = 2 - \cos \theta$

61. $r = \dfrac{1}{\sin \theta - \cos \theta}$

62. $r = \dfrac{1}{1 + \sin \theta}$

63. $r = \dfrac{4}{1 + 2 \sin \theta}$

64. $r = \dfrac{2}{1 - \cos \theta}$

65. $r^2 = \tan \theta$

66. $r^2 = \sin 2\theta$

67. $\sec \theta = 2$

68. $\cos 2\theta = 1$

DISCOVERY ▪ DISCUSSION ▪ WRITING

69. The Distance Formula in Polar Coordinates

(a) Use the Law of Cosines to prove that the distance between the polar points (r_1, θ_1) and (r_2, θ_2) is

$$d = \sqrt{r_1^2 + r_2^2 - 2r_1 r_2 \cos(\theta_2 - \theta_1)}$$

(b) Find the distance between the points whose polar coordinates are $(3, 3\pi/4)$ and $(1, 7\pi/6)$, using the formula from part (a).

(c) Now convert the points in part (b) to rectangular coordinates. Find the distance between them using the usual Distance Formula. Do you get the same answer?

8.2 GRAPHS OF POLAR EQUATIONS

| Graphing Polar Equations ▶ Symmetry ▶ Graphing Polar Equations with Graphing Devices

The **graph of a polar equation** $r = f(\theta)$ consists of all points P that have at least one polar representation (r, θ) whose coordinates satisfy the equation. Many curves that arise in mathematics and its applications are more easily and naturally represented by polar equations than by rectangular equations.

▼ Graphing Polar Equations

A rectangular grid is helpful for plotting points in rectangular coordinates (see Figure 1(a)). To plot points in polar coordinates, it is convenient to use a grid consisting of circles centered at the pole and rays emanating from the pole, as in Figure 1(b). We will use such grids to help us sketch polar graphs.

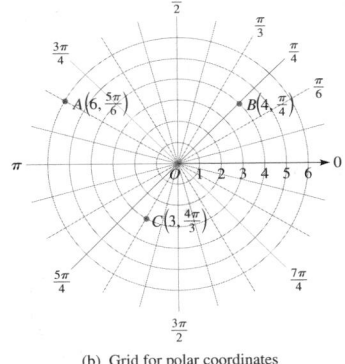

FIGURE 1   (a) Grid for rectangular coordinates   (b) Grid for polar coordinates

SUGGESTED TIME AND EMPHASIS

1 class, recommended material

TEXT QUESTION

Sketch the graph of $r = \cos \theta$.

Answer

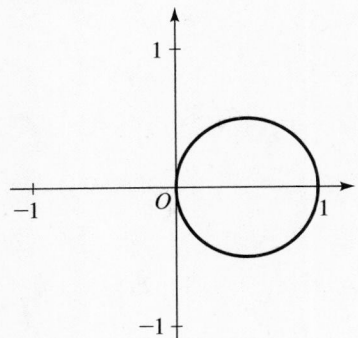

ALTERNATE EXAMPLE 1

Sketch the graph of the equation

$$r = \frac{1}{\sqrt{\theta}}.$$

ANSWER

ALTERNATE EXAMPLE 2

Express the equation $\theta = 2$ in rectangular coordinates and sketch its graph.

ANSWER

$y = -2.185x$

In Examples 1 and 2 we see that circles centered at the origin and lines that pass through the origin have particularly simple equations in polar coordinates.

EXAMPLE 1 | Sketching the Graph of a Polar Equation

Sketch a graph of the equation $r = 3$, and express the equation in rectangular coordinates.

SOLUTION The graph consists of all points whose r-coordinate is 3, that is, all points that are 3 units away from the origin. So the graph is a circle of radius 3 centered at the origin, as shown in Figure 2.

Squaring both sides of the equation, we get

$$r^2 = 3^2 \qquad \text{Square both sides}$$
$$x^2 + y^2 = 9 \qquad \text{Substitute } r^2 = x^2 + y^2$$

So the equivalent equation in rectangular coordinates is $x^2 + y^2 = 9$.

✎ **NOW TRY EXERCISE 17** ∎

FIGURE 2

In general, the graph of the equation $r = a$ is a circle of radius $|a|$ centered at the origin. Squaring both sides of this equation, we see that the equivalent equation in rectangular coordinates is $x^2 + y^2 = a^2$.

EXAMPLE 2 | Sketching the Graph of a Polar Equation

Sketch a graph of the equation $\theta = \pi/3$, and express the equation in rectangular coordinates.

SOLUTION The graph consists of all points whose θ-coordinate is $\pi/3$. This is the straight line that passes through the origin and makes an angle of $\pi/3$ with the polar axis (see Figure 3). Note that the points $(r, \pi/3)$ on the line with $r > 0$ lie in Quadrant I, whereas those with $r < 0$ lie in Quadrant III. If the point (x, y) lies on this line, then

$$\frac{y}{x} = \tan \theta = \tan \frac{\pi}{3} = \sqrt{3}$$

Thus, the rectangular equation of this line is $y = \sqrt{3}x$.

✎ **NOW TRY EXERCISE 19** ∎

FIGURE 3

To sketch a polar curve whose graph isn't as obvious as the ones in the preceding examples, we plot points calculated for sufficiently many values of θ and then join them in a continuous curve. (This is what we did when we first learned to graph functions in rectangular coordinates.)

EXAMPLE 3 | Sketching the Graph of a Polar Equation

Sketch a graph of the polar equation $r = 2 \sin \theta$.

SOLUTION We first use the equation to determine the polar coordinates of several points on the curve. The results are shown in the following table.

θ	0	$\pi/6$	$\pi/4$	$\pi/3$	$\pi/2$	$2\pi/3$	$3\pi/4$	$5\pi/6$	π
$r = 2 \sin \theta$	0	1	$\sqrt{2}$	$\sqrt{3}$	2	$\sqrt{3}$	$\sqrt{2}$	1	0

We plot these points in Figure 4 and then join them to sketch the curve. The graph appears to be a circle. We have used values of θ only between 0 and π, since the same points (this time expressed with negative r-coordinates) would be obtained if we allowed θ to range from π to 2π.

IN-CLASS MATERIALS

After showing students how to graph polar functions on a calculator, give them a chance to experiment and try to come up with interesting-looking polar graphs. Make sure they know that if their graphs appear to have a lot of cusps, it could be that their Δt is set too large.

The polar equation $r = 2 \sin \theta$ in rectangular coordinates is
$$x^2 + (y - 1)^2 = 1$$
(see Section 8.1, Example 6(b)). From the rectangular form of the equation we see that the graph is a circle of radius 1 centered at $(0, 1)$.

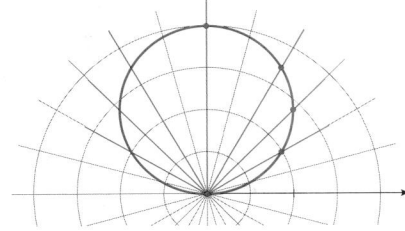

FIGURE 4 $r = 2 \sin \theta$

▲ NOW TRY EXERCISE **21**

In general, the graphs of equations of the form
$$r = 2a \sin \theta \qquad \text{and} \qquad r = 2a \cos \theta$$
are **circles** with radius $|a|$ centered at the points with polar coordinates $(a, \pi/2)$ and $(a, 0)$, respectively.

EXAMPLE 4 | Sketching the Graph of a Cardioid

Sketch a graph of $r = 2 + 2 \cos \theta$.

SOLUTION Instead of plotting points as in Example 3, we first sketch the graph of $r = 2 + 2 \cos \theta$ in *rectangular* coordinates in Figure 5. We can think of this graph as a table of values that enables us to read at a glance the values of r that correspond to increasing values of θ. For instance, we see that as θ increases from 0 to $\pi/2$, r (the distance from O) decreases from 4 to 2, so we sketch the corresponding part of the polar graph in Figure 6(a). As θ increases from $\pi/2$ to π, Figure 5 shows that r decreases from 2 to 0, so we sketch the next part of the graph as in Figure 6(b). As θ increases from π to $3\pi/2$, r increases from 0 to 2, as shown in part (c). Finally, as θ increases from $3\pi/2$ to 2π, r increases from 2 to 4, as shown in part (d). If we let θ increase beyond 2π or decrease beyond 0, we would simply retrace our path. Combining the portions of the graph from parts (a) through (d) of Figure 6, we sketch the complete graph in part (e).

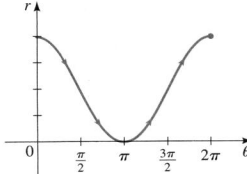

FIGURE 5 $r = 2 + 2 \cos \theta$

    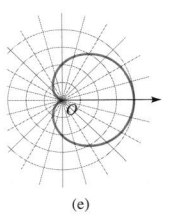

(a) (b) (c) (d) (e)

FIGURE 6 Steps in sketching $r = 2 + 2 \cos \theta$

The polar equation $r = 2 + 2 \cos \theta$ in rectangular coordinates is
$$(x^2 + y^2 - 2x)^2 = 4(x^2 + y^2)$$
(see Section 8.1, Example 6(c)). The simpler form of the polar equation shows that it is more natural to describe cardioids using polar coordinates.

▲ NOW TRY EXERCISE **25**

The curve in Figure 6 is called a **cardioid** because it is heart-shaped. In general, the graph of any equation of the form
$$r = a(1 \pm \cos \theta) \qquad \text{or} \qquad r = a(1 \pm \sin \theta)$$
is a cardioid.

ALTERNATE EXAMPLE 3
Sketch the graph of the polar equation $r = -\cos \theta$ by plotting points as done in the text.

ANSWER

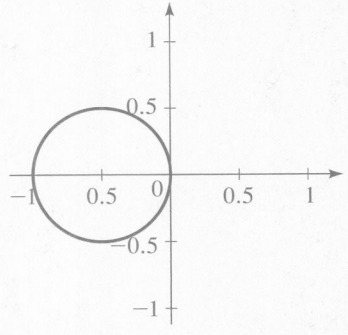

ALTERNATE EXAMPLE 4
Sketch the graph of $r = \dfrac{\cos 3\theta}{2}$.

ANSWER

IN-CLASS MATERIALS
Do a problem where $r = f(\theta)$ is graphed both as a function in rectangular coordinates and as a polar function. For example, if $r = (1.5)^\theta$, we get the two graphs shown here.

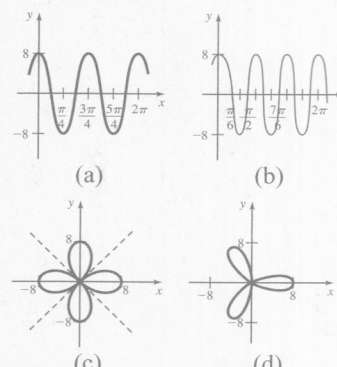
EXAMPLE 5 | Sketching the Graph of a Four-Leaved Rose

Sketch the curve $r = \cos 2\theta$.

SOLUTION   As in Example 4, we first sketch the graph of $r = \cos 2\theta$ in *rectangular* coordinates, as shown in Figure 7. As θ increases from 0 to $\pi/4$, Figure 7 shows that r decreases from 1 to 0, so we draw the corresponding portion of the polar curve in Figure 8 (indicated by ①). As θ increases from $\pi/4$ to $\pi/2$, the value of r goes from 0 to -1. This means that the distance from the origin increases from 0 to 1, but instead of being in Quadrant I, this portion of the polar curve (indicated by ②) lies on the opposite side of the origin in Quadrant III. The remainder of the curve is drawn in a similar fashion, with the arrows and numbers indicating the order in which the portions are traced out. The resulting curve has four petals and is called a **four-leaved rose**.

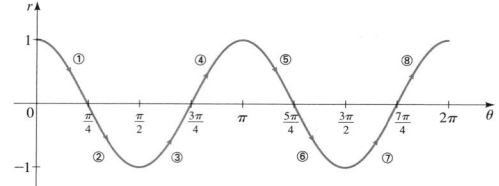

FIGURE 7   Graph of $r = \cos 2\theta$ sketched in rectangular coordinates

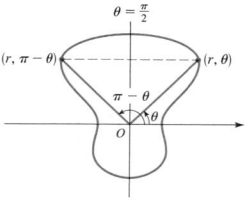

FIGURE 8   Four-leaved rose $r = \cos 2\theta$ sketched in polar coordinates

✎ NOW TRY EXERCISE **29**

In general, the graph of an equation of the form

$$r = a \cos n\theta \qquad \text{or} \qquad r = a \sin n\theta$$

is an ***n*-leaved rose** if n is odd or a $2n$-leaved rose if n is even (as in Example 5).

▼ Symmetry

In graphing a polar equation, it's often helpful to take advantage of symmetry. We list three tests for symmetry; Figure 9 shows why these tests work.

TESTS FOR SYMMETRY

1. If a polar equation is unchanged when we replace θ by $-\theta$, then the graph is symmetric about the polar axis (Figure 9(a)).

2. If the equation is unchanged when we replace r by $-r$, then the graph is symmetric about the pole (Figure 9(b)).

3. If the equation is unchanged when we replace θ by $\pi - \theta$, the graph is symmetric about the vertical line $\theta = \pi/2$ (the y-axis) (Figure 9(c)).

   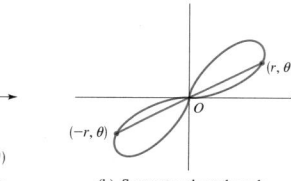

FIGURE 9   (a) Symmetry about the polar axis   (b) Symmetry about the pole   (c) Symmetry about the line $\theta = \frac{\pi}{2}$

IN-CLASS MATERIALS

An interesting graph to look at is $r = 1 - \dfrac{1}{\theta}, r \geq 1$.

Have the class try to figure out if, as $\theta \to \infty$, the curve will get arbitrarily close to the curve $r = 1$. Have them discuss whether it will ever intersect that curve. If this curve is combined with the circle $r = 1$, the resulting set of points is what topologists call "connected, but not path-connected." The set of points is not path-connected because there is no path from the origin that touches the outer circle. It is called "connected" because (to simplify things somewhat) there is no curve that separates the two components without touching either.

The graphs in Figures 2, 6(e), and 8 are symmetric about the polar axis. The graph in Figure 8 is also symmetric about the pole. Figures 4 and 8 show graphs that are symmetric about $\theta = \pi/2$. Note that the four-leaved rose in Figure 8 meets all three tests for symmetry.

In rectangular coordinates, the zeros of the function $y = f(x)$ correspond to the x-intercepts of the graph. In polar coordinates, the zeros of the function $r = f(\theta)$ are the angles θ at which the curve crosses the pole. The zeros help us sketch the graph, as is illustrated in the next example.

EXAMPLE 6 | Using Symmetry to Sketch a Limaçon

Sketch a graph of the equation $r = 1 + 2 \cos \theta$.

SOLUTION   We use the following as aids in sketching the graph:

Symmetry: Since the equation is unchanged when θ is replaced by $-\theta$, the graph is symmetric about the polar axis.

Zeros: To find the zeros, we solve

$$0 = 1 + 2 \cos \theta$$
$$\cos \theta = -\frac{1}{2}$$
$$\theta = \frac{2\pi}{3}, \frac{4\pi}{3}$$

Table of values: As in Example 4, we sketch the graph of $r = 1 + 2 \cos \theta$ in *rectangular* coordinates to serve as a table of values (Figure 10).

Now we sketch the polar graph of $r = 1 + 2 \cos \theta$ from $\theta = 0$ to $\theta = \pi$, and then use symmetry to complete the graph in Figure 11.

✎ **NOW TRY EXERCISE 35** ∎

The curve in Figure 11 is called a **limaçon**, after the Middle French word for snail. In general, the graph of an equation of the form

$$r = a \pm b \cos \theta \qquad \text{or} \qquad r = a \pm b \sin \theta$$

is a limaçon. The shape of the limaçon depends on the relative size of a and b (see the table on the next page).

▼ Graphing Polar Equations with Graphing Devices

Although it's useful to be able to sketch simple polar graphs by hand, we need a graphing calculator or computer when the graph is as complicated as the one in Figure 12. Fortunately, most graphing calculators are capable of graphing polar equations directly.

EXAMPLE 7 | Drawing the Graph of a Polar Equation

Graph the equation $r = \cos(2\theta/3)$.

SOLUTION   We need to determine the domain for θ. So we ask ourselves: How many times must θ go through a complete rotation (2π radians) before the graph starts to repeat itself? The graph repeats itself when the same value of r is obtained at θ and $\theta + 2n\pi$. Thus we need to find an integer n, so that

$$\cos \frac{2(\theta + 2n\pi)}{3} = \cos \frac{2\theta}{3}$$

For this equality to hold, $4n\pi/3$ must be a multiple of 2π, and this first happens when $n = 3$. Therefore, we obtain the entire graph if we choose values of θ between $\theta = 0$ and $\theta = 0 + 2(3)\pi = 6\pi$. The graph is shown in Figure 13.

✎ **NOW TRY EXERCISE 43** ∎

FIGURE 10

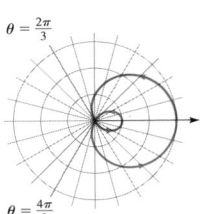

FIGURE 11 $r = 1 + 2 \cos \theta$

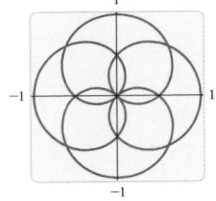

FIGURE 12 $r = \sin \theta + \sin^3(5\theta/2)$

FIGURE 13 $r = \cos(2\theta/3)$

ALTERNATE EXAMPLE 6
Sketch the graph of the equation
$r = 1 - 2 \cos \theta$,

ANSWER

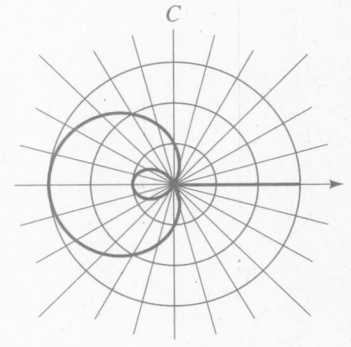

ALTERNATE EXAMPLE 7
For the graph of the equation
$r = \cos \dfrac{\theta}{2}$, determine the number of complete rotations required before the graph starts to repeat itself.

ANSWER
2

EXAMPLE
Sketch a graph of the polar curve $r = f(\theta)$ where $f(\theta)$ is the function whose representation in rectangular coordinates is given here.

ANSWER

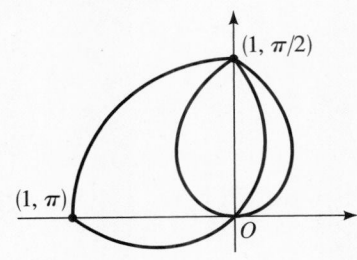

EXAMPLE 8 | A Family of Polar Equations

Graph the family of polar equations $r = 1 + c \sin \theta$ for $c = 3, 2.5, 2, 1.5, 1$. How does the shape of the graph change as c changes?

SOLUTION   Figure 14 shows computer-drawn graphs for the given values of c. When $c > 1$, the graph has an inner loop; the loop decreases in size as c decreases. When $c = 1$, the loop disappears, and the graph becomes a cardioid (see Example 4).

| $c = 3.0$ | $c = 2.5$ | $c = 2.0$ | $c = 1.5$ | $c = 1.0$ |

FIGURE 14   A family of limaçons $r = 1 + c \sin \theta$ in the viewing rectangle $[-2.5, 2.5]$ by $[-0.5, 4.5]$

NOW TRY EXERCISE 47

The box below gives a summary of some of the basic polar graphs used in calculus.

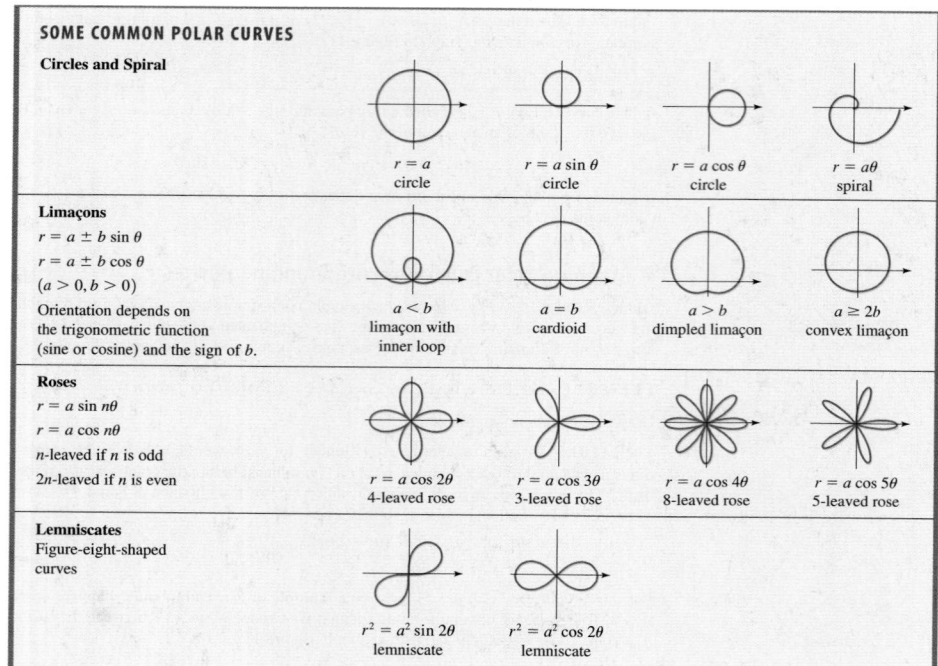

SOME COMMON POLAR CURVES

Circles and Spiral

$r = a$ $r = a \sin \theta$ $r = a \cos \theta$ $r = a\theta$
circle   circle   circle   spiral

Limaçons
$r = a \pm b \sin \theta$
$r = a \pm b \cos \theta$
$(a > 0, b > 0)$
Orientation depends on the trigonometric function (sine or cosine) and the sign of b.

$a < b$ $a = b$ $a > b$ $a \geq 2b$
limaçon with inner loop   cardioid   dimpled limaçon   convex limaçon

Roses
$r = a \sin n\theta$
$r = a \cos n\theta$
n-leaved if n is odd
$2n$-leaved if n is even

$r = a \cos 2\theta$ $r = a \cos 3\theta$ $r = a \cos 4\theta$ $r = a \cos 5\theta$
4-leaved rose   3-leaved rose   8-leaved rose   5-leaved rose

Lemniscates
Figure-eight-shaped curves

$r^2 = a^2 \sin 2\theta$ $r^2 = a^2 \cos 2\theta$
lemniscate   lemniscate

8.2 EXERCISES

CONCEPTS

1. To plot points in polar coordinates, we use a grid consisting of

   _____ centered at the pole and _____ emanating from the pole.

2. **(a)** To graph a polar equation $r = f(\theta)$, we plot all the points

   (r, θ) that _____ the equation.

   (b) The simplest polar equations are obtained by setting r or θ equal to a constant. The graph of the polar equation

   $r = 3$ is a _____ with radius _____ centered at

   the _____. The graph of the polar equation $\theta = \pi/4$

   is a _____ passing through the _____ with slope

   _____. Graph these polar equations below.

 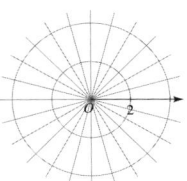

SKILLS

3–8 ■ Match the polar equation with the graphs labeled I–VI. Use the table on page 552 to help you.

3. $r = 3 \cos \theta$

4. $r = 3$

5. $r = 2 + 2 \sin \theta$

6. $r = 1 + 2 \cos \theta$

7. $r = \sin 3\theta$

8. $r = \sin 4\theta$

I

II

III

IV

V

VI

9–16 ■ Test the polar equation for symmetry with respect to the polar axis, the pole, and the line $\theta = \pi/2$.

9. $r = 2 - \sin \theta$

10. $r = 4 + 8 \cos \theta$

11. $r = 3 \sec \theta$

12. $r = 5 \cos \theta \, \csc \theta$

13. $r = \dfrac{4}{3 - 2 \sin \theta}$

14. $r = \dfrac{5}{1 + 3 \cos \theta}$

15. $r^2 = 4 \cos 2\theta$

16. $r^2 = 9 \sin \theta$

17–22 ■ Sketch a graph of the polar equation, and express the equation in rectangular coordinates.

17. $r = 2$

18. $r = -1$

19. $\theta = -\pi/2$

20. $\theta = 5\pi/6$

21. $r = 6 \sin \theta$

22. $r = \cos \theta$

23–42 ■ Sketch a graph of the polar equation.

23. $r = -2 \cos \theta$

24. $r = 2 \sin \theta + 2 \cos \theta$

25. $r = 2 - 2 \cos \theta$

26. $r = 1 + \sin \theta$

27. $r = -3(1 + \sin \theta)$

28. $r = \cos \theta - 1$

29. $r = \sin 2\theta$

30. $r = 2 \cos 3\theta$

31. $r = -\cos 5\theta$

32. $r = \sin 4\theta$

33. $r = \sqrt{3} - 2 \sin \theta$

34. $r = 2 + \sin \theta$

35. $r = \sqrt{3} + \cos \theta$

36. $r = 1 - 2 \cos \theta$

37. $r^2 = \cos 2\theta$

38. $r^2 = 4 \sin 2\theta$

39. $r = \theta, \quad \theta \geq 0$ (spiral)

40. $r\theta = 1, \quad \theta > 0$ (reciprocal spiral)

41. $r = 2 + \sec \theta$ (conchoid)

42. $r = \sin \theta \tan \theta$ (cissoid)

43–46 ■ Use a graphing device to graph the polar equation. Choose the domain of θ to make sure you produce the entire graph.

43. $r = \cos(\theta/2)$

44. $r = \sin(8\theta/5)$

45. $r = 1 + 2 \sin(\theta/2)$ (nephroid)

46. $r = \sqrt{1 - 0.8 \sin^2\theta}$ (hippopede)

47. Graph the family of polar equations $r = 1 + \sin n\theta$ for $n = 1, 2, 3, 4$, and 5. How is the number of loops related to n?

48. Graph the family of polar equations $r = 1 + c \sin 2\theta$ for $c = 0.3, 0.6, 1, 1.5$, and 2. How does the graph change as c increases?

49–52 ■ Match the polar equation with the graphs labeled I–IV. Give reasons for your answers.

49. $r = \sin(\theta/2)$ **50.** $r = 1/\sqrt{\theta}$

51. $r = \theta \sin \theta$ **52.** $r = 1 + 3 \cos(3\theta)$

I   II

III   IV

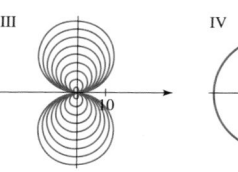

53–56 ■ Sketch a graph of the rectangular equation. [*Hint:* First convert the equation to polar coordinates.]

53. $(x^2 + y^2)^3 = 4x^2y^2$

54. $(x^2 + y^2)^3 = (x^2 - y^2)^2$

55. $(x^2 + y^2)^2 = x^2 - y^2$

56. $x^2 + y^2 = (x^2 + y^2 - x)^2$

57. Show that the graph of $r = a \cos \theta + b \sin \theta$ is a circle, and find its center and radius.

58. (a) Graph the polar equation $r = \tan \theta \sec \theta$ in the viewing rectangle $[-3, 3]$ by $[-1, 9]$.
    (b) Note that your graph in part (a) looks like a parabola (see Section 2.5). Confirm this by converting the equation to rectangular coordinates.

APPLICATIONS

59. Orbit of a Satellite   Scientists and engineers often use polar equations to model the motion of satellites in earth orbit. Let's consider a satellite whose orbit is modeled by the equation $r = 22500/(4 - \cos \theta)$, where r is the distance in miles between the satellite and the center of the earth and θ is the angle shown in the following figure.
    (a) On the same viewing screen, graph the circle $r = 3960$ (to represent the earth, which we will assume to be a sphere of radius 3960 mi) and the polar equation of the satellite's orbit. Describe the motion of the satellite as θ increases from 0 to 2π.

(b) For what angle θ is the satellite closest to the earth? Find the height of the satellite above the earth's surface for this value of θ.

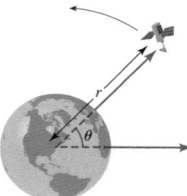

60. An Unstable Orbit   The orbit described in Exercise 59 is stable because the satellite traverses the same path over and over as θ increases. Suppose that a meteor strikes the satellite and changes its orbit to

$$r = \frac{22500\left(1 - \dfrac{\theta}{40}\right)}{4 - \cos \theta}$$

(a) On the same viewing screen, graph the circle $r = 3960$ and the new orbit equation, with θ increasing from 0 to 3π. Describe the new motion of the satellite.

(b) Use the [TRACE] feature on your graphing calculator to find the value of θ at the moment the satellite crashes into the earth.

DISCOVERY ■ DISCUSSION ■ WRITING

61. A Transformation of Polar Graphs   How are the graphs of

$$r = 1 + \sin\left(\theta - \frac{\pi}{6}\right)$$

and $$r = 1 + \sin\left(\theta - \frac{\pi}{3}\right)$$

related to the graph of $r = 1 + \sin \theta$? In general, how is the graph of $r = f(\theta - \alpha)$ related to the graph of $r = f(\theta)$?

62. Choosing a Convenient Coordinate System   Compare the polar equation of the circle $r = 2$ with its equation in rectangular coordinates. In which coordinate system is the equation simpler? Do the same for the equation of the four-leaved rose $r = \sin 2\theta$. Which coordinate system would you choose to study these curves?

63. Choosing a Convenient Coordinate System   Compare the rectangular equation of the line $y = 2$ with its polar equation. In which coordinate system is the equation simpler? Which coordinate system would you choose to study lines?

8.3 POLAR FORM OF COMPLEX NUMBERS; DE MOIVRE'S THEOREM

Graphing Complex Numbers ▶ Polar Form of Complex Numbers ▶
De Moivre's Theorem ▶ nth Roots of Complex Numbers

In this section we represent complex numbers in polar (or trigonometric) form. This enables us to find the nth roots of complex numbers. To describe the polar form of complex numbers, we must first learn to work with complex numbers graphically.

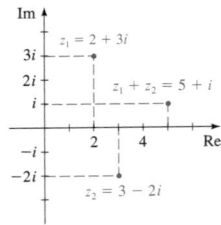

FIGURE 1

▼ Graphing Complex Numbers

To graph real numbers or sets of real numbers, we have been using the number line, which has just one dimension. Complex numbers, however, have two components: a real part and an imaginary part. This suggests that we need two axes to graph complex numbers: one for the real part and one for the imaginary part. We call these the **real axis** and the **imaginary axis**, respectively. The plane determined by these two axes is called the **complex plane**. To graph the complex number $a + bi$, we plot the ordered pair of numbers (a, b) in this plane, as indicated in Figure 1.

FIGURE 2

EXAMPLE 1 | Graphing Complex Numbers

Graph the complex numbers $z_1 = 2 + 3i$, $z_2 = 3 - 2i$, and $z_1 + z_2$.

SOLUTION We have $z_1 + z_2 = (2 + 3i) + (3 - 2i) = 5 + i$. The graph is shown in Figure 2.

✎. NOW TRY EXERCISE **19** ■

EXAMPLE 2 | Graphing Sets of Complex Numbers

Graph each set of complex numbers.
(a) $S = \{a + bi \mid a \geq 0\}$
(b) $T = \{a + bi \mid a < 1, b \geq 0\}$

SOLUTION

(a) S is the set of complex numbers whose real part is nonnegative. The graph is shown in Figure 3(a).

(b) T is the set of complex numbers for which the real part is less than 1 and the imaginary part is nonnegative. The graph is shown in Figure 3(b).

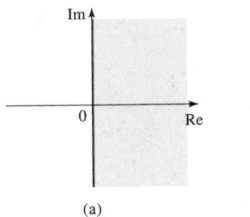

FIGURE 3   (a)   (b)

✎. NOW TRY EXERCISE **21** ■

ALTERNATE EXAMPLE 1
Graph the complex numbers
$z_1 = 3 - 4i$, $z_2 = -2i + 1$,
$z_1 + z_2$.

ANSWER

ALTERNATE EXAMPLE 2
Graph the set of complex numbers
$S = \{a + bi \mid 2 \leq a \leq 3\}$.

ANSWER

Text Question
Graph the following set of complex numbers: $\{z \mid |z| = 1\}$

Answer

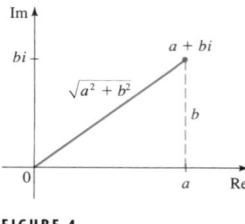

FIGURE 4

Recall that the absolute value of a real number can be thought of as its distance from the origin on the real number line (see Section 1.1). We define absolute value for complex numbers in a similar fashion. Using the Pythagorean Theorem, we can see from Figure 4 that the distance between $a + bi$ and the origin in the complex plane is $\sqrt{a^2 + b^2}$. This leads to the following definition.

MODULUS OF A COMPLEX NUMBER

The **modulus** (or **absolute value**) of the complex number $z = a + bi$ is

$$|z| = \sqrt{a^2 + b^2}$$

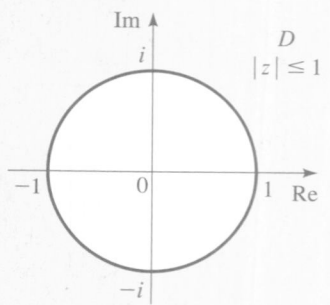
The plural of modulus is moduli.

EXAMPLE 3 | Calculating the Modulus

Find the moduli of the complex numbers $3 + 4i$ and $8 - 5i$.

SOLUTION

$$|3 + 4i| = \sqrt{3^2 + 4^2} = \sqrt{25} = 5$$
$$|8 - 5i| = \sqrt{8^2 + (-5)^2} = \sqrt{89}$$

✎. **NOW TRY EXERCISE 9**

EXAMPLE 4 | Absolute Value of Complex Numbers

Graph each set of complex numbers.
(a) $C = \{z|\, |z| = 1\}$ (b) $D = \{z|\, |z| \leq 1\}$

SOLUTION

(a) C is the set of complex numbers whose distance from the origin is 1. Thus, C is a circle of radius 1 with center at the origin, as shown in Figure 5.

(b) D is the set of complex numbers whose distance from the origin is less than or equal to 1. Thus, D is the disk that consists of all complex numbers on and inside the circle C of part (a), as shown in Figure 6.

FIGURE 5

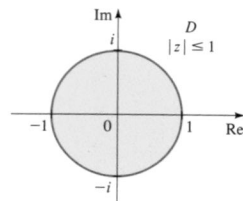

FIGURE 6

✎. **NOW TRY EXERCISES 23 AND 25**

▼ Polar Form of Complex Numbers

Let $z = a + bi$ be a complex number, and in the complex plane let's draw the line segment joining the origin to the point $a + bi$ (see Figure 7). The length of this line segment is $r = |z| = \sqrt{a^2 + b^2}$. If θ is an angle in standard position whose terminal side

FIGURE 7

IN-CLASS MATERIALS

Verify, using the multiplication of complex numbers in polar form, that $i^2 = -1$. This leads to another way to view complex numbers, one that is more intuitively justifiable for some than allowing negative square roots. We define a "complex number" as a point in the plane where we want to define addition in a certain way (which will parallel vector addition defined in the next section) and multiplication of quantities of the same magnitude to correspond to a rotation. The idea that the point $(0, 1)$ times itself is $(-1, 0)$ is then a logical consequence of this definition of multiplication. Then, if we define the point $(1, 0)$ to be "1" and the point $(0, 1)$ to be "i," we obtain $i^2 = -1$. This is not violating the laws of conventional mathematics; it is just a result of our definitions of operations on these point quantities. In the real world, it turns out there are quantities (such as waveforms, impedance of an AC circuit, etc.) that are most usefully represented in this way.

coincides with this line segment, then by the definitions of sine and cosine (see Section 6.2)

$$a = r \cos \theta \qquad \text{and} \qquad b = r \sin \theta$$

so $z = r \cos \theta + ir \sin \theta = r(\cos \theta + i \sin \theta)$. We have shown the following.

POLAR FORM OF COMPLEX NUMBERS

A complex number $z = a + bi$ has the **polar form** (or **trigonometric form**)

$$z = r(\cos \theta + i \sin \theta)$$

where $r = |z| = \sqrt{a^2 + b^2}$ and $\tan \theta = b/a$. The number r is the **modulus** of z, and θ is an **argument** of z.

The argument of z is not unique, but any two arguments of z differ by a multiple of 2π. When determining the argument, we must consider the quadrant in which z lies, as we see in the next example.

EXAMPLE 5 | Writing Complex Numbers in Polar Form

Write each complex number in polar form.

(a) $1 + i$ (b) $-1 + \sqrt{3}i$ (c) $-4\sqrt{3} - 4i$ (d) $3 + 4i$

SOLUTION These complex numbers are graphed in Figure 8, which helps us find their arguments.

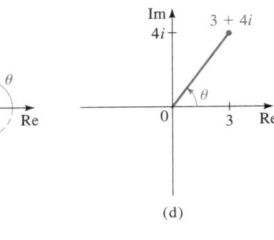

(a)   (b)   (c)   (d)

FIGURE 8

$\tan \theta = \frac{1}{1} = 1$

$\theta = \frac{\pi}{4}$

(a) An argument is $\theta = \pi/4$ and $r = \sqrt{1 + 1} = \sqrt{2}$. Thus

$$1 + i = \sqrt{2}\left(\cos \frac{\pi}{4} + i \sin \frac{\pi}{4}\right)$$

$\tan \theta = \frac{\sqrt{3}}{-1} = -\sqrt{3}$

$\theta = \frac{2\pi}{3}$

(b) An argument is $\theta = 2\pi/3$ and $r = \sqrt{1 + 3} = 2$. Thus

$$-1 + \sqrt{3}i = 2\left(\cos \frac{2\pi}{3} + i \sin \frac{2\pi}{3}\right)$$

$\tan \theta = \frac{-4}{-4\sqrt{3}} = \frac{1}{\sqrt{3}}$

$\theta = \frac{7\pi}{6}$

(c) An argument is $\theta = 7\pi/6$ (or we could use $\theta = -5\pi/6$), and $r = \sqrt{48 + 16} = 8$. Thus

$$-4\sqrt{3} - 4i = 8\left(\cos \frac{7\pi}{6} + i \sin \frac{7\pi}{6}\right)$$

$\tan \theta = \frac{4}{3}$

$\theta = \tan^{-1} \frac{4}{3}$

(d) An argument is $\theta = \tan^{-1} \frac{4}{3}$ and $r = \sqrt{3^2 + 4^2} = 5$. So

$$3 + 4i = 5[\cos(\tan^{-1} \tfrac{4}{3}) + i \sin(\tan^{-1} \tfrac{4}{3})]$$

✎ NOW TRY EXERCISES **29, 31, AND 33** ∎

ALTERNATE EXAMPLE 5

Write the complex number $-1 - i$ in trigonometric form.

ANSWER

$$\sqrt{2}\left[\cos\left(\frac{5\pi}{4}\right) + i \sin\left(\frac{5\pi}{4}\right)\right]$$

IN-CLASS MATERIALS

Notice that we now have three distinct ways of representing the same quantity. Each has advantages and disadvantages. For example, it is cumbersome to compute

$$3\left(\cos \frac{\pi}{2} + i \sin \frac{\pi}{2}\right) + 2\left(\cos \frac{\pi}{6} + i \sin \frac{\pi}{6}\right) = \sqrt{19}\,(\cos 1.162 + i \sin 1.162),$$

but not too hard to compute

$$3i + (\sqrt{3} + i) = \sqrt{3} + 4i.$$

Similarly, it is annoying to divide

$$\frac{3 - 6i}{4 + 2i} = \frac{3}{2}i,$$

but it is not hard to divide

$$\frac{8(\cos 4 + i \sin 4)}{4[\cos(-1) + i \sin(-1)]} = 2(\cos 5 + i \sin 5).$$

The Addition Formulas for Sine and Cosine that we discussed in Section 7.2 greatly simplify the multiplication and division of complex numbers in polar form. The following theorem shows how.

MULTIPLICATION AND DIVISION OF COMPLEX NUMBERS

If the two complex numbers z_1 and z_2 have the polar forms

$$z_1 = r_1(\cos\theta_1 + i\sin\theta_1) \quad \text{and} \quad z_2 = r_2(\cos\theta_2 + i\sin\theta_2)$$

then

$$z_1 z_2 = r_1 r_2 [\cos(\theta_1 + \theta_2) + i\sin(\theta_1 + \theta_2)] \qquad \text{Multiplication}$$

$$\frac{z_1}{z_2} = \frac{r_1}{r_2}[\cos(\theta_1 - \theta_2) + i\sin(\theta_1 - \theta_2)] \quad (z_2 \neq 0) \qquad \text{Division}$$

This theorem says:

> To multiply two complex numbers, multiply the moduli and add the arguments.
> To divide two complex numbers, divide the moduli and subtract the arguments.

PROOF To prove the Multiplication Formula, we simply multiply the two complex numbers:

$$z_1 z_2 = r_1 r_2 (\cos\theta_1 + i\sin\theta_1)(\cos\theta_2 + i\sin\theta_2)$$

$$= r_1 r_2 [\cos\theta_1 \cos\theta_2 - \sin\theta_1 \sin\theta_2 + i(\sin\theta_1 \cos\theta_2 + \cos\theta_1 \sin\theta_2)]$$

$$= r_1 r_2 [\cos(\theta_1 + \theta_2) + i\sin(\theta_1 + \theta_2)]$$

In the last step we used the Addition Formulas for Sine and Cosine.
The proof of the Division Formula is left as an exercise. ∎

EXAMPLE 6 | Multiplying and Dividing Complex Numbers

Let

$$z_1 = 2\left(\cos\frac{\pi}{4} + i\sin\frac{\pi}{4}\right) \quad \text{and} \quad z_2 = 5\left(\cos\frac{\pi}{3} + i\sin\frac{\pi}{3}\right)$$

Find **(a)** $z_1 z_2$ and **(b)** z_1/z_2.

SOLUTION

(a) By the Multiplication Formula

$$z_1 z_2 = (2)(5)\left[\cos\left(\frac{\pi}{4} + \frac{\pi}{3}\right) + i\sin\left(\frac{\pi}{4} + \frac{\pi}{3}\right)\right]$$

$$= 10\left(\cos\frac{7\pi}{12} + i\sin\frac{7\pi}{12}\right)$$

To approximate the answer, we use a calculator in radian mode and get

$$z_1 z_2 \approx 10(-0.2588 + 0.9659i)$$

$$= -2.588 + 9.659i$$

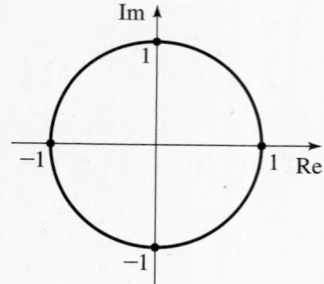
Now ask about the third roots of 1 and fifth roots of 1. You will probably have to do these as an example on the board. Draw them, and point out that the nth roots of one are always equally spaced around the unit circle.

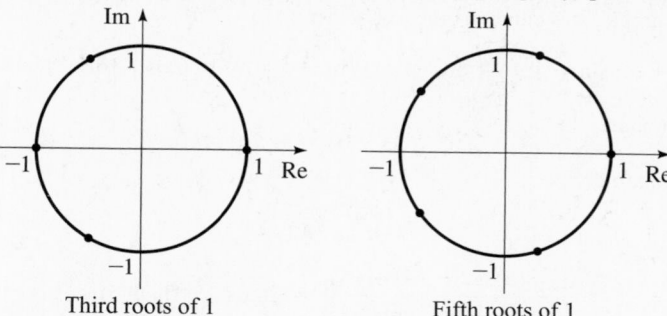

Third roots of 1   Fifth roots of 1

(b) By the Division Formula

$$\frac{z_1}{z_2} = \frac{2}{5}\left[\cos\left(\frac{\pi}{4} - \frac{\pi}{3}\right) + i\sin\left(\frac{\pi}{4} - \frac{\pi}{3}\right)\right]$$

$$= \frac{2}{5}\left[\cos\left(-\frac{\pi}{12}\right) + i\sin\left(-\frac{\pi}{12}\right)\right]$$

$$= \frac{2}{5}\left(\cos\frac{\pi}{12} - i\sin\frac{\pi}{12}\right)$$

Using a calculator in radian mode, we get the approximate answer:

$$\frac{z_1}{z_2} \approx \frac{2}{5}(0.9659 - 0.2588i) = 0.3864 - 0.1035i$$

✎ NOW TRY EXERCISE **55**   ∎

▼ De Moivre's Theorem

Repeated use of the Multiplication Formula gives the following useful formula for raising a complex number to a power n for any positive integer n.

DE MOIVRE'S THEOREM

If $z = r(\cos\theta + i\sin\theta)$, then for any integer n

$$z^n = r^n(\cos n\theta + i\sin n\theta)$$

This theorem says: *To take the nth power of a complex number, we take the nth power of the modulus and multiply the argument by n.*

PROOF   By the Multiplication Formula

$$z^2 = zz = r^2[\cos(\theta + \theta) + i\sin(\theta + \theta)]$$

$$= r^2(\cos 2\theta + i\sin 2\theta)$$

Now we multiply z^2 by z to get

$$z^3 = z^2 z = r^3[\cos(2\theta + \theta) + i\sin(2\theta + \theta)]$$

$$= r^3(\cos 3\theta + i\sin 3\theta)$$

Repeating this argument, we see that for any positive integer n

$$z^n = r^n(\cos n\theta + i\sin n\theta)$$

A similar argument using the Division Formula shows that this also holds for negative integers.   ∎

EXAMPLE 7 | Finding a Power Using De Moivre's Theorem

Find $\left(\frac{1}{2} + \frac{1}{2}i\right)^{10}$.

SOLUTION   Since $\frac{1}{2} + \frac{1}{2}i = \frac{1}{2}(1 + i)$, it follows from Example 5(a) that

$$\frac{1}{2} + \frac{1}{2}i = \frac{\sqrt{2}}{2}\left(\cos\frac{\pi}{4} + i\sin\frac{\pi}{4}\right)$$

EXAMPLES

Switching between forms:

- $4\left(\cos\dfrac{5\pi}{4} + i\sin\dfrac{5\pi}{4}\right) = -2\sqrt{2} - 2\sqrt{2}i$

- $4(\cos 1 + i\sin 1) \approx 2.161 + 3.366i$

- $3(\cos 20° + i\sin 20°) \approx 2.81907786 + 1.02606043i$

- $(4 - 3i)^5 = -3116 + 237i$

So by De Moivre's Theorem

$$\left(\frac{1}{2}+\frac{1}{2}i\right)^{10}=\left(\frac{\sqrt{2}}{2}\right)^{10}\left(\cos\frac{10\pi}{4}+i\sin\frac{10\pi}{4}\right)$$

$$=\frac{2^5}{2^{10}}\left(\cos\frac{5\pi}{2}+i\sin\frac{5\pi}{2}\right)=\frac{1}{32}i$$

✎. NOW TRY EXERCISE **69**   ■

▼ *n*th Roots of Complex Numbers

An ***n*th root** of a complex number z is any complex number w such that $w^n = z$. De Moivre's Theorem gives us a method for calculating the nth roots of any complex number.

---

*n*th ROOTS OF COMPLEX NUMBERS

If $z = r(\cos\theta + i\sin\theta)$ and n is a positive integer, then z has the n distinct nth roots

$$w_k = r^{1/n}\left[\cos\left(\frac{\theta+2k\pi}{n}\right)+i\sin\left(\frac{\theta+2k\pi}{n}\right)\right]$$

for $k = 0, 1, 2, \ldots, n-1$.

PROOF   To find the nth roots of z, we need to find a complex number w such that

$$w^n = z$$

Let's write z in polar form:

$$z = r(\cos\theta + i\sin\theta)$$

One nth root of z is

$$w = r^{1/n}\left(\cos\frac{\theta}{n}+i\sin\frac{\theta}{n}\right)$$

since by De Moivre's Theorem, $w^n = z$. But the argument θ of z can be replaced by $\theta + 2k\pi$ for any integer k. Since this expression gives a different value of w for $k = 0, 1, 2, \ldots, n-1$, we have proved the formula in the theorem.   ■

The following observations help us use the preceding formula.

FINDING THE *n*th ROOTS OF $z = r(\cos\theta + i\sin\theta)$

1. The modulus of each nth root is $r^{1/n}$.
2. The argument of the first root is θ/n.
3. We repeatedly add $2\pi/n$ to get the argument of each successive root.

These observations show that, when graphed, the nth roots of z are spaced equally on the circle of radius $r^{1/n}$.

EXAMPLE 8 | Finding Roots of a Complex Number

Find the six sixth roots of $z = -64$, and graph these roots in the complex plane.

ALTERNATE EXAMPLE 8
Find the six sixth roots of $z = -729$.

ANSWER
$\frac{3\sqrt{3}}{2}+\frac{3}{2}i, 3i, -\frac{3\sqrt{3}}{2}+\frac{3}{2}i,$

$-\frac{3\sqrt{3}}{2}-\frac{3}{2}i, -3i, \frac{3\sqrt{3}}{2}-\frac{3}{2}i$

SOLUTION In polar form, $z = 64(\cos \pi + i \sin \pi)$. Applying the formula for nth roots with $n = 6$, we get

$$w_k = 64^{1/6}\left[\cos\left(\frac{\pi + 2k\pi}{6}\right) + i\sin\left(\frac{\pi + 2k\pi}{6}\right)\right]$$

for $k = 0, 1, 2, 3, 4, 5$. Using $64^{1/6} = 2$, we find that the six sixth roots of -64 are

We add $2\pi/6 = \pi/3$ to each argument to get the argument of the next root.

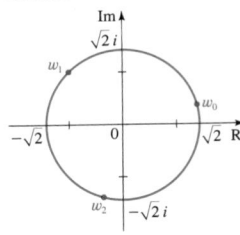

$$w_0 = 2\left(\cos\frac{\pi}{6} + i\sin\frac{\pi}{6}\right) = \sqrt{3} + i$$

$$w_1 = 2\left(\cos\frac{\pi}{2} + i\sin\frac{\pi}{2}\right) = 2i$$

$$w_2 = 2\left(\cos\frac{5\pi}{6} + i\sin\frac{5\pi}{6}\right) = -\sqrt{3} + i$$

$$w_3 = 2\left(\cos\frac{7\pi}{6} + i\sin\frac{7\pi}{6}\right) = -\sqrt{3} - i$$

$$w_4 = 2\left(\cos\frac{3\pi}{2} + i\sin\frac{3\pi}{2}\right) = -2i$$

$$w_5 = 2\left(\cos\frac{11\pi}{6} + i\sin\frac{11\pi}{6}\right) = \sqrt{3} - i$$

FIGURE 9 The six sixth roots of $z = -64$

All these points lie on a circle of radius 2, as shown in Figure 9.

✎ **NOW TRY EXERCISE 85** ∎

When finding roots of complex numbers, we sometimes write the argument θ of the complex number in degrees. In this case the nth roots are obtained from the formula

$$w_k = r^{1/n}\left[\cos\left(\frac{\theta + 360°k}{n}\right) + i\sin\left(\frac{\theta + 360°k}{n}\right)\right]$$

for $k = 0, 1, 2, \ldots, n - 1$.

EXAMPLE 9 | Finding Cube Roots of a Complex Number

Find the three cube roots of $z = 2 + 2i$, and graph these roots in the complex plane.

SOLUTION First we write z in polar form using degrees. We have $r = \sqrt{2^2 + 2^2} = 2\sqrt{2}$ and $\theta = 45°$. Thus

$$z = 2\sqrt{2}(\cos 45° + i\sin 45°)$$

We add $360°/3 = 120°$ to each argument to get the argument of the next root.

Applying the formula for nth roots (in degrees) with $n = 3$, we find that the cube roots of z are of the form

$$w_k = (2\sqrt{2})^{1/3}\left[\cos\left(\frac{45° + 360°k}{3}\right) + i\sin\left(\frac{45° + 360°k}{3}\right)\right]$$

where $k = 0, 1, 2$. Thus the three cube roots are

$$w_0 = \sqrt{2}(\cos 15° + i\sin 15°) \approx 1.366 + 0.366i \qquad (2\sqrt{2})^{1/3} = (2^{3/2})^{1/3} = 2^{1/2} = \sqrt{2}$$

$$w_1 = \sqrt{2}(\cos 135° + i\sin 135°) = -1 + i$$

$$w_2 = \sqrt{2}(\cos 255° + i\sin 255°) \approx -0.366 - 1.366i$$

The three cube roots of z are graphed in Figure 10. These roots are spaced equally on a circle of radius $\sqrt{2}$.

FIGURE 10 The three cube roots of $z = 2 + 2i$

✎ **NOW TRY EXERCISE 81** ∎

ALTERNATE EXAMPLE 9
Find the three cube roots of $8i$.

ANSWER
$-2i, -\sqrt{3} + i, \sqrt{3} + i$

ALTERNATE EXAMPLE 10

Solve the equation $z^6 + 729 = 0$.

ANSWER

$$\frac{3\sqrt{3}}{2} + \frac{3}{2}i,\ 3i,\ -\frac{3\sqrt{3}}{2} + \frac{3}{2}i,$$

$$-\frac{3\sqrt{3}}{2} - \frac{3}{2}i,\ -3i,\ \frac{3\sqrt{3}}{2} - \frac{3}{2}i$$

DRILL QUESTION

Compute $(\sqrt{3} - i)^{10}$.

Answer

$512 + 512\sqrt{3}i$

EXAMPLE 10 | Solving an Equation Using the *n*th Roots Formula

Solve the equation $z^6 + 64 = 0$.

SOLUTION This equation can be written as $z^6 = -64$. Thus the solutions are the sixth roots of -64, which we found in Example 8.

✎. **NOW TRY EXERCISE 91** ∎

8.3 EXERCISES

CONCEPTS

1. A complex number $z = a + bi$ has two parts: a is the
_____ part, and b is the _____ part. To graph $a + bi$, we graph the ordered pair (☐ , ☐) in the complex plane.

2. Let $z = a + bi$.
   (a) The modulus of z is $r =$ _____, and an argument of z is an angle θ satisfying $\tan \theta =$ _____.
   (b) We can express z in polar form as $z =$ _____, where r is the modulus of z and θ is the argument of z.

3. (a) The complex number $z = -1 + i$ in polar form is
   $z =$ _____. The complex number
   $z = 2\left(\cos \dfrac{\pi}{6} + i \sin \dfrac{\pi}{6}\right)$ in rectangular form is
   $z =$ _____.
   (b) The complex number graphed below can be expressed in rectangular form as _____ or in polar form as _____.

4. How many different *n*th roots does a nonzero complex number have? _____. The number 16 has _____ fourth roots. These roots are _____, _____, _____, and _____. In the complex plane these roots all lie on a circle of radius _____. Graph the roots on the following graph.

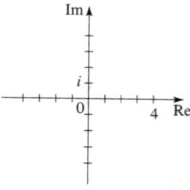

SKILLS

5–14 ■ Graph the complex number and find its modulus.

5. $4i$ **6.** $-3i$

7. -2 **8.** 6

9. $5 + 2i$ **10.** $7 - 3i$

11. $\sqrt{3} + i$ **12.** $-1 - \dfrac{\sqrt{3}}{3}i$

13. $\dfrac{3 + 4i}{5}$ **14.** $\dfrac{-\sqrt{2} + i\sqrt{2}}{2}$

15–16 ■ Sketch the complex number z, and also sketch $2z$, $-z$, and $\frac{1}{2}z$ on the same complex plane.

15. $z = 1 + i$ **16.** $z = -1 + i\sqrt{3}$

17–18 ■ Sketch the complex number z and its complex conjugate $\bar{z}$ on the same complex plane.

17. $z = 8 + 2i$ **18.** $z = -5 + 6i$

19–20 ■ Sketch z_1, z_2, $z_1 + z_2$, and $z_1 z_2$ on the same complex plane.

19. $z_1 = 2 - i$, $z_2 = 2 + i$

20. $z_1 = -1 + i$, $z_2 = 2 - 3i$

21–28 ■ Sketch the set in the complex plane.

21. $\{z = a + bi \mid a \leq 0, b \geq 0\}$

22. $\{z = a + bi \mid a > 1, b > 1\}$

23. $\{z \mid |z| = 3\}$ **24.** $\{z \mid |z| \geq 1\}$

25. $\{z \mid |z| < 2\}$ **26.** $\{z \mid 2 \leq |z| \leq 5\}$

27. $\{z = a + bi \mid a + b < 2\}$

28. $\{z = a + bi \mid a \geq b\}$

29–52 ■ Write the complex number in polar form with argument θ between 0 and 2π.

29. $1 + i$ **30.** $1 + \sqrt{3}i$ **31.** $\sqrt{2} - \sqrt{2}i$

32. $1 - i$ **33.** $2\sqrt{3} - 2i$ **34.** $-1 + i$

35. $-3i$ **36.** $-3 - 3\sqrt{3}i$ **37.** $5 + 5i$

38. 4 **39.** $4\sqrt{3} - 4i$ **40.** $8i$

41. -20 **42.** $\sqrt{3} + i$ **43.** $3 + 4i$

44. $i(2 - 2i)$ **45.** $3i(1 + i)$ **46.** $2(1 - i)$

47. $4(\sqrt{3} + i)$ **48.** $-3 - 3i$ **49.** $2 + i$

50. $3 + \sqrt{3}\,i$ **51.** $\sqrt{2} + \sqrt{2}\,i$ **52.** $-\pi i$

53–60 ■ Find the product $z_1 z_2$ and the quotient z_1/z_2. Express your answer in polar form.

53. $z_1 = \cos \pi + i \sin \pi, \quad z_2 = \cos \dfrac{\pi}{3} + i \sin \dfrac{\pi}{3}$

54. $z_1 = \cos \dfrac{\pi}{4} + i \sin \dfrac{\pi}{4}, \quad z_2 = \cos \dfrac{3\pi}{4} + i \sin \dfrac{3\pi}{4}$

55. $z_1 = 3\left(\cos \dfrac{\pi}{6} + i \sin \dfrac{\pi}{6}\right), \quad z_2 = 5\left(\cos \dfrac{4\pi}{3} + i \sin \dfrac{4\pi}{3}\right)$

56. $z_1 = 7\left(\cos \dfrac{9\pi}{8} + i \sin \dfrac{9\pi}{8}\right), \quad z_2 = 2\left(\cos \dfrac{\pi}{8} + i \sin \dfrac{\pi}{8}\right)$

57. $z_1 = 4(\cos 120° + i \sin 120°),$
    $z_2 = 2(\cos 30° + i \sin 30°)$

58. $z_1 = \sqrt{2}(\cos 75° + i \sin 75°),$
    $z_2 = 3\sqrt{2}(\cos 60° + i \sin 60°)$

59. $z_1 = 4(\cos 200° + i \sin 200°),$
    $z_2 = 25(\cos 150° + i \sin 150°)$

60. $z_1 = \frac{4}{5}(\cos 25° + i \sin 25°),$
    $z_2 = \frac{1}{5}(\cos 155° + i \sin 155°)$

61–68 ■ Write z_1 and z_2 in polar form, and then find the product $z_1 z_2$ and the quotients z_1/z_2 and $1/z_1$.

61. $z_1 = \sqrt{3} + i, \quad z_2 = 1 + \sqrt{3}\,i$

62. $z_1 = \sqrt{2} - \sqrt{2}\,i, \quad z_2 = 1 - i$

63. $z_1 = 2\sqrt{3} - 2i, \quad z_2 = -1 + i$

64. $z_1 = -\sqrt{2}\,i, \quad z_2 = -3 - 3\sqrt{3}\,i$

65. $z_1 = 5 + 5i, \quad z_2 = 4$ **66.** $z_1 = 4\sqrt{3} - 4i, \quad z_2 = 8i$

67. $z_1 = -20, \quad z_2 = \sqrt{3} + i$ **68.** $z_1 = 3 + 4i, \quad z_2 = 2 - 2i$

69–80 ■ Find the indicated power using De Moivre's Theorem.

69. $(1 + i)^{20}$ **70.** $(1 - \sqrt{3}\,i)^5$

71. $(2\sqrt{3} + 2i)^5$ **72.** $(1 - i)^8$

73. $\left(\dfrac{\sqrt{2}}{2} + \dfrac{\sqrt{2}}{2}i\right)^{12}$ **74.** $(\sqrt{3} - i)^{-10}$

75. $(2 - 2i)^8$ **76.** $\left(-\dfrac{1}{2} - \dfrac{\sqrt{3}}{2}i\right)^{15}$

77. $(-1 - i)^7$ **78.** $(3 + \sqrt{3}\,i)^4$

79. $(2\sqrt{3} + 2i)^{-5}$ **80.** $(1 - i)^{-8}$

81–90 ■ Find the indicated roots, and graph the roots in the complex plane.

81. The square roots of $4\sqrt{3} + 4i$

82. The cube roots of $4\sqrt{3} + 4i$

83. The fourth roots of $-81i$

84. The fifth roots of 32

85. The eighth roots of 1

86. The cube roots of $1 + i$

87. The cube roots of i

88. The fifth roots of i

89. The fourth roots of -1

90. The fifth roots of $-16 - 16\sqrt{3}i$

91–96 ■ Solve the equation.

91. $z^4 + 1 = 0$ **92.** $z^8 - i = 0$

93. $z^3 - 4\sqrt{3} - 4i = 0$ **94.** $z^6 - 1 = 0$

95. $z^3 + 1 = -i$ **96.** $z^3 - 1 = 0$

97. (a) Let $w = \cos \dfrac{2\pi}{n} + i \sin \dfrac{2\pi}{n}$ where n is a positive integer. Show that $1, w, w^2, w^3, \ldots, w^{n-1}$ are the n distinct nth roots of 1.

   (b) If $z \neq 0$ is any complex number and $s^n = z$, show that the n distinct nth roots of z are

$$s, sw, sw^2, sw^3, \ldots, sw^{n-1}$$

DISCOVERY ■ DISCUSSION ■ WRITING

98. Sums of Roots of Unity Find the exact values of all three cube roots of 1 (see Exercise 97) and then add them. Do the same for the fourth, fifth, sixth, and eighth roots of 1. What do you think is the sum of the nth roots of 1 for any n?

99. Products of Roots of Unity Find the product of the three cube roots of 1 (see Exercise 97). Do the same for the fourth, fifth, sixth, and eighth roots of 1. What do you think is the product of the nth roots of 1 for any n?

100. Complex Coefficients and the Quadratic Formula The quadratic formula works whether the coefficients of the equation are real or complex. Solve these equations using the quadratic formula and, if necessary, De Moivre's Theorem.

   (a) $z^2 + (1 + i)z + i = 0$

   (b) $z^2 - iz + 1 = 0$

   (c) $z^2 - (2 - i)z - \frac{1}{4}i = 0$

⬤ **DISCOVERY PROJECT** **Fractals**

In this project we use graphs of complex numbers to create fractal images. You can find the project at the book companion website: **www.stewartmath.com**

8.4 PLANE CURVES AND PARAMETRIC EQUATIONS

| Plane Curves and Parametric Equations ▶ Eliminating the Parameter ▶ Finding Parametric Equations for a Curve ▶ Using Graphing Devices to Graph Parametric Curves

So far, we have described a curve by giving an equation (in rectangular or polar coordinates) that the coordinates of all the points on the curve must satisfy. But not all curves in the plane can be described in this way. In this section we study parametric equations, which are a general method for describing any curve.

▼ Plane Curves and Parametric Equations

We can think of a curve as the path of a point moving in the plane; the x- and y-coordinates of the point are then functions of time. This idea leads to the following definition.

PLANE CURVES AND PARAMETRIC EQUATIONS

If f and g are functions defined on an interval I, then the set of points $(f(t), g(t))$ is a **plane curve**. The equations

$$x = f(t) \qquad y = g(t)$$

where $t \in I$, are **parametric equations** for the curve, with **parameter** t.

EXAMPLE 1 | Sketching a Plane Curve

Sketch the curve defined by the parametric equations

$$x = t^2 - 3t \qquad y = t - 1$$

SOLUTION   For every value of t, we get a point on the curve. For example, if $t = 0$, then $x = 0$ and $y = -1$, so the corresponding point is $(0, -1)$. In Figure 1 we plot the points (x, y) determined by the values of t shown in the following table.

t	x	y
-2	10	-3
-1	4	-2
0	0	-1
1	-2	0
2	-2	1
3	0	2
4	4	3
5	10	4

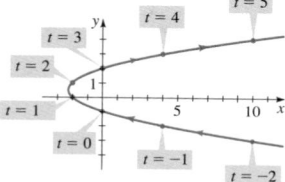

FIGURE 1

As t increases, a particle whose position is given by the parametric equations moves along the curve in the direction of the arrows.

✎. NOW TRY EXERCISE **3**   ■

TEXT QUESTION
What is the difference between a function and a parametric curve?

Answer
Many answers are possible. The graph of a function can be made into a parametric curve, but not necessarily the other way around. A function has to pass the Vertical Line Test and a parametric curve does not.

If we replace t by $-t$ in Example 1, we obtain the parametric equations

$$x = t^2 + 3t \qquad y = -t - 1$$

The graph of these parametric equations (see Figure 2) is the same as the curve in Figure 1, but traced out in the opposite direction. On the other hand, if we replace t by $2t$ in Example 1, we obtain the parametric equations

$$x = 4t^2 - 6t \qquad y = 2t - 1$$

The graph of these parametric equations (see Figure 3) is again the same, but is traced out "twice as fast." *Thus, a parametrization contains more information than just the shape of the curve; it also indicates how the curve is being traced out.*

MARIA GAETANA AGNESI (1718–1799) is famous for having written *Instituzioni Analitiche*, one of the first calculus textbooks.

Maria was born into a wealthy family in Milan, Italy, the oldest of 21 children. She was a child prodigy, mastering many languages at an early age, including Latin, Greek, and Hebrew. At the age of 20 she published a series of essays on philosophy and natural science. After Maria's mother died, she took on the task of educating her brothers. In 1748 Agnesi published her famous textbook, which she originally wrote as a text for tutoring her brothers. The book compiled and explained the mathematical knowledge of the day. It contains many carefully chosen examples, one of which is the curve now known as the "witch of Agnesi" (see Exercise 64, page 571). One review calls her book an "exposition by examples rather than by theory." The book gained Agnesi immediate recognition. Pope Benedict XIV appointed her to a position at the University of Bologna, writing, "we have had the idea that you should be awarded the well-known chair of mathematics, by which it comes of itself that you should not thank us but we you." This appointment was an extremely high honor for a woman, since very few women then were even allowed to attend university. Just two years later, Agnesi's father died, and she left mathematics completely. She became a nun and devoted the rest of her life and her wealth to caring for sick and dying women, herself dying in poverty at a poorhouse of which she had once been director.

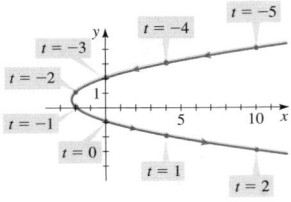

FIGURE 2 $x = t^2 + 3t,\ y = -t - 1$

FIGURE 3 $x = 4t^2 - 6t,\ y = 2t - 1$

▼ Eliminating the Parameter

Often a curve given by parametric equations can also be represented by a single rectangular equation in x and y. The process of finding this equation is called *eliminating the parameter*. One way to do this is to solve for t in one equation, then substitute into the other.

EXAMPLE 2 | Eliminating the Parameter

Eliminate the parameter in the parametric equations of Example 1.

SOLUTION   First we solve for t in the simpler equation, then we substitute into the other equation. From the equation $y = t - 1$, we get $t = y + 1$. Substituting into the equation for x, we get

$$x = t^2 - 3t = (y + 1)^2 - 3(y + 1) = y^2 - y - 2$$

Thus the curve in Example 1 has the rectangular equation $x = y^2 - y - 2$, so it is a parabola.

✎. **NOW TRY EXERCISE 5**   ◾

Eliminating the parameter often helps us identify the shape of a curve, as we see in the next two examples.

EXAMPLE 3 | Modeling Circular Motion

The following parametric equations model the position of a moving object at time t (in seconds):

$$x = \cos t \qquad y = \sin t \qquad t \geq 0$$

Describe and graph the path of the object.

ALTERNATE EXAMPLE 2
For the curve defined by the parametric equations $x = t^2 - 7t$ and $y = t - 3$, eliminate the parameter t and obtain a single equation for the curve in variables x and y.

ANSWER
$x = y^2 - y - 12t$

ALTERNATE EXAMPLE 3
Eliminate the parameter t to obtain a single equation for the curve $x = 5 \cos t$, $y = 5 \sin t$ in the variables x and y.

ANSWER
$x^2 + y^2 = 25$

IN-CLASS MATERIALS

Give an example of a curve such as $x(t) = \cos(et)$, $y(t) = \sin(\sqrt{3}t)$. This curve essentially fills the square $-1 \leq x \leq 1$, $-1 \leq y \leq 1$ in that the curve gets arbitrarily close to any point in the square. (It is not what mathematicians call a "space-filling curve" because it does not actually hit every point in the square.) It can be simulated using a graphing calculator with the approximations $e \approx 2.7183$ and $\sqrt{3} \approx 1.7321$. The range $0 \leq t \leq 200$ should be sufficient to convey this property to the students. Next, describe the family of functions $x(t) = a \cos(et)$, $y(t) = b \sin(\sqrt{3}t)$. If the students are following well, perhaps consider the family $x(t) = \cos(at)$, $y(t) = \sin(\sqrt{3}t)$. The students might be tempted to conclude that all these curves behave the same way, but they do not for some values of a, such as $a = 2\sqrt{3}$.

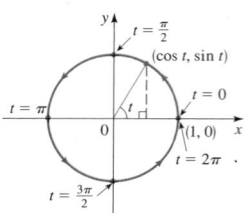

FIGURE 4

SOLUTION To identify the curve, we eliminate the parameter. Since $\cos^2 t + \sin^2 t = 1$ and since $x = \cos t$ and $y = \sin t$ for every point (x, y) on the curve, we have

$$x^2 + y^2 = (\cos t)^2 + (\sin t)^2 = 1$$

This means that all points on the curve satisfy the equation $x^2 + y^2 = 1$, so the graph is a circle of radius 1 centered at the origin. As t increases from 0 to 2π, the point given by the parametric equations starts at $(1, 0)$ and moves counterclockwise once around the circle, as shown in Figure 4. So the object completes one revolution around the circle in 2π seconds. Notice that the parameter t can be interpreted as the angle shown in the figure.

✎. **NOW TRY EXERCISE 25**   ■

ALTERNATE EXAMPLE 4

For the graph of a curve defined by the parametric equations $x = \sin t$ and $y = 7 - \cos 2t$, find a single equation and its domain.

ANSWER

$y = 6 + x^2, x \in [-1, 1]$

EXAMPLE 4 | Sketching a Parametric Curve

Eliminate the parameter, and sketch the graph of the parametric equations

$$x = \sin t \qquad y = 2 - \cos^2 t$$

SOLUTION To eliminate the parameter, we first use the trigonometric identity $\cos^2 t = 1 - \sin^2 t$ to change the second equation:

$$y = 2 - \cos^2 t = 2 - (1 - \sin^2 t) = 1 + \sin^2 t$$

Now we can substitute $\sin t = x$ from the first equation to get

$$y = 1 + x^2$$

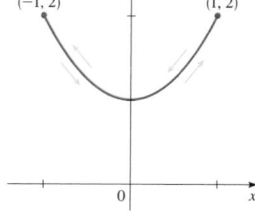

FIGURE 5

so the point (x, y) moves along the parabola $y = 1 + x^2$. However, since $-1 \le \sin t \le 1$, we have $-1 \le x \le 1$, so the parametric equations represent only the part of the parabola between $x = -1$ and $x = 1$. Since $\sin t$ is periodic, the point $(x, y) = (\sin t, 2 - \cos^2 t)$ moves back and forth infinitely often along the parabola between the points $(-1, 2)$ and $(1, 2)$, as shown in Figure 5.

✎. **NOW TRY EXERCISE 17**   ■

▼ Finding Parametric Equations for a Curve

It is often possible to find parametric equations for a curve by using some geometric properties that define the curve, as in the next two examples.

ALTERNATE EXAMPLE 5

Find a single equation for the curve in the variables x and y for the line of slope 9 that passes through the point (4, 36).

ANSWER

$y = 9x$

EXAMPLE 5 | Finding Parametric Equations for a Graph

Find parametric equations for the line of slope 3 that passes through the point $(2, 6)$.

SOLUTION Let's start at the point $(2, 6)$ and move up and to the right along this line. Because the line has slope 3, for every 1 unit we move to the right, we must move up 3 units. In other words, if we increase the x-coordinate by t units, we must correspondingly increase the y-coordinate by $3t$ units. This leads to the parametric equations

$$x = 2 + t \qquad y = 6 + 3t$$

To confirm that these equations give the desired line, we eliminate the parameter. We solve for t in the first equation and substitute into the second to get

$$y = 6 + 3(x - 2) = 3x$$

FIGURE 6

Thus the slope-intercept form of the equation of this line is $y = 3x$, which is a line of slope 3 that does pass through $(2, 6)$ as required. The graph is shown in Figure 6.

✎. **NOW TRY EXERCISE 29**   ■

IN-CLASS MATERIALS

Discuss the process of going from a parametric curve to a relation between x and y. The figure at right is meant to help students see how parametrized curves are sketched out over time. First sketch $(x(t), y(t))$, starting at the initial point (the origin) and moving up and to the right. (Try to keep your speed constant.) Stop when the cycle is about to repeat. Then, to the right of the figure, graph the motion in the y-direction only. Then, below the figure, graph the motion in the x-direction. That graph is sideways because the x-axis is horizontal.

EXAMPLE 6 | Parametric Equations for the Cycloid

As a circle rolls along a straight line, the curve traced out by a fixed point P on the circumference of the circle is called a **cycloid** (see Figure 7). If the circle has radius a and rolls along the x-axis, with one position of the point P being at the origin, find parametric equations for the cycloid.

FIGURE 7

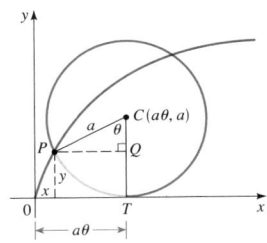

FIGURE 8

SOLUTION Figure 8 shows the circle and the point P after the circle has rolled through an angle θ (in radians). The distance $d(O, T)$ that the circle has rolled must be the same as the length of the arc PT, which, by the arc length formula, is $a\theta$ (see Section 6.1). This means that the center of the circle is $C(a\theta, a)$.

Let the coordinates of P be (x, y). Then from Figure 8 (which illustrates the case $0 < \theta < \pi/2$), we see that

$$x = d(O, T) - d(P, Q) = a\theta - a \sin \theta = a(\theta - \sin \theta)$$

$$y = d(T, C) - d(Q, C) = a - a \cos \theta = a(1 - \cos \theta)$$

so parametric equations for the cycloid are

$$x = a(\theta - \sin \theta) \qquad y = a(1 - \cos \theta)$$

✎ NOW TRY EXERCISE **57** ∎

The cycloid has a number of interesting physical properties. It is the "curve of quickest descent" in the following sense. Let's choose two points P and Q that are not directly above each other, and join them with a wire. Suppose we allow a bead to slide down the wire under the influence of gravity (ignoring friction). Of all possible shapes into which the wire can be bent, the bead will slide from P to Q the fastest when the shape is half of an arch of an inverted cycloid (see Figure 9). The cycloid is also the "curve of equal descent" in the sense that no matter where we place a bead B on a cycloid-shaped wire, it takes the same time to slide to the bottom (see Figure 10). These rather surprising properties of the cycloid were proved (using calculus) in the 17th century by several mathematicians and physicists, including Johann Bernoulli, Blaise Pascal, and Christiaan Huygens.

Cycloid

FIGURE 9

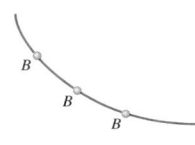

FIGURE 10

▼ Using Graphing Devices to Graph Parametric Curves

Most graphing calculators and computer graphing programs can be used to graph parametric equations. Such devices are particularly useful in sketching complicated curves like the one shown in Figure 11.

EXAMPLE 7 | Graphing Parametric Curves

Use a graphing device to draw the following parametric curves. Discuss their similarities and differences.

(a) $x = \sin 2t$
$y = 2 \cos t$

(b) $x = \sin 3t$
$y = 2 \cos t$

FIGURE 11 $x = t + 2 \sin 2t$,
$y = t + 2 \cos 5t$

IN-CLASS MATERIALS

Show how reversing the functions $x(t)$ and $y(t)$ yields the inverse of a given relation. For example,

$\begin{cases} x(t) = t \\ y(t) = \sin t \end{cases}$ is the sine function, so $\begin{cases} x(t) = \sin t \\ y(t) = t \end{cases}$ is the general arcsine function. Display an inverse

for $f(x) = x^3 + x + 2$ graphically using parametric equations. Explain the difficulties with the algebraic approach.

ALTERNATE EXAMPLE 7
Use a graphing device to draw the following parametric curves. Compare the two curves.

(a) $x = \cos t$
$y = \sin t$

(b) $x = 2 \cos t$
$y = 4 \sin t$

ANSWERS
(a)

(b)

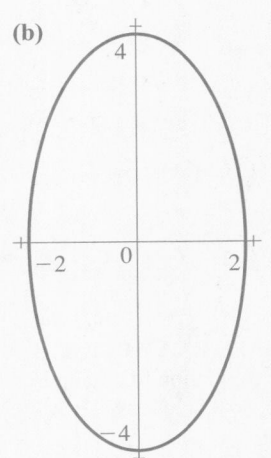

The first curve is a circle. The second one stretches the x- and y-coordinates by different factors, resulting in an ellipse.

EXAMPLE
Construction of an ellipse with center $(-1, -2)$ and axis lengths 2 and 3: We start with the circle $x = \cos \theta, y = \sin \theta$. We stretch it into shape: $x = 2 \cos \theta, y = 3 \sin \theta$. Then we move it into position: $x = 2\cos \theta - 1, y = 3 \sin \theta - 2$.

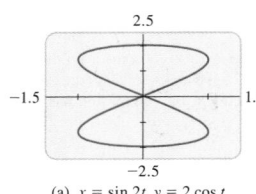

(a) $x = \sin 2t, y = 2 \cos t$

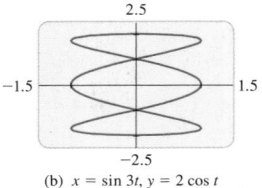

(b) $x = \sin 3t, y = 2 \cos t$

FIGURE 12

SOLUTION In both parts (a) and (b) the graph will lie inside the rectangle given by $-1 \le x \le 1$, $-2 \le y \le 2$, since both the sine and the cosine of any number will be between -1 and 1. Thus, we may use the viewing rectangle $[-1.5, 1.5]$ by $[-2.5, 2.5]$.

(a) Since $2 \cos t$ is periodic with period 2π (see Section 5.3) and since $\sin 2t$ has period π, letting t vary over the interval $0 \le t \le 2\pi$ gives us the complete graph, which is shown in Figure 12(a).

(b) Again, letting t take on values between 0 and 2π gives the complete graph shown in Figure 12(b).

Both graphs are *closed curves*, which means they form loops with the same starting and ending point; also, both graphs cross over themselves. However, the graph in Figure 12(a) has two loops, like a figure eight, whereas the graph in Figure 12(b) has three loops.

✎. NOW TRY EXERCISE **43** ■

The curves graphed in Example 7 are called Lissajous figures. A **Lissajous figure** is the graph of a pair of parametric equations of the form

$$x = A \sin \omega_1 t \qquad y = B \cos \omega_2 t$$

where A, B, ω_1, and ω_2 are real constants. Since $\sin \omega_1 t$ and $\cos \omega_2 t$ are both between -1 and 1, a Lissajous figure will lie inside the rectangle determined by $-A \le x \le A$, $-B \le y \le B$. This fact can be used to choose a viewing rectangle when graphing a Lissajous figure, as in Example 7.

Recall from Section 8.1 that rectangular coordinates (x, y) and polar coordinates (r, θ) are related by the equations $x = r \cos \theta$, $y = r \sin \theta$. Thus we can graph the polar equation $r = f(\theta)$ by changing it to parametric form as follows:

$$x = r \cos \theta = f(\theta) \cos \theta \qquad \text{Since } r = f(\theta)$$

$$y = r \sin \theta = f(\theta) \sin \theta$$

Replacing θ by the standard parametric variable t, we have the following result.

POLAR EQUATIONS IN PARAMETRIC FORM

The graph of the polar equation $r = f(\theta)$ is the same as the graph of the parametric equations

$$x = f(t) \cos t \qquad y = f(t) \sin t$$

ALTERNATE EXAMPLE 8
Express the equation in parametric form:
$r = 3 \ln \theta$

ANSWER
$x = 3 \ln (t) \cdot \cos (t)$,
$y = 3 \ln (t) \cdot \sin (t)$

EXAMPLE 8 | Parametric Form of a Polar Equation

Consider the polar equation $r = \theta$, $1 \le \theta \le 10\pi$.

(a) Express the equation in parametric form.

(b) Draw a graph of the parametric equations from part (a).

SOLUTION

(a) The given polar equation is equivalent to the parametric equations

$$x = t \cos t \qquad y = t \sin t$$

(b) Since $10\pi \approx 31.42$, we use the viewing rectangle $[-32, 32]$ by $[-32, 32]$, and we let t vary from 1 to 10π. The resulting graph shown in Figure 13 is a *spiral*.

✎. NOW TRY EXERCISE **51** ■

FIGURE 13 $x = t \cos t, y = t \sin t$

IN-CLASS MATERIALS

Have the students get into groups, and have each group try to come up with the most interesting-looking parametric curve. After displaying their best ones, perhaps show them the following examples:

8.4 EXERCISES

CONCEPTS

1. (a) The parametric equations $x = f(t)$ and $y = g(t)$ give the coordinates of a point $(x, y) = (f(t), g(t))$ for appropriate values of t. The variable t is called a _____.

   (b) Suppose that the parametric equations $x = t$, $y = t^2$, $t \geq 0$, model the position of a moving object at time t. When $t = 0$, the object is at (□, □), and when $t = 1$, the object is at (□, □).

   (c) If we eliminate the parameter in part (b), we get the equation $y =$ _____. We see from this equation that the path of the moving object is a _____.

2. (a) *True or false?* The same curve can be described by parametric equations in many different ways.

   (b) The parametric equations $x = 2t$, $y = (2t)^2$ model the position of a moving object at time t. When $t = 0$, the object is at (□, □), and when $t = 1$, the object is at (□, □).

   (c) If we eliminate the parameter, we get the equation $y =$ _____, which is the same equation as in Exercise 1(b). So the objects in Exercises 1(b) and 2(b) move along the same _____ but traverse the path differently. Indicate the position of each object when $t = 0$ and when $t = 1$ on the following graph.

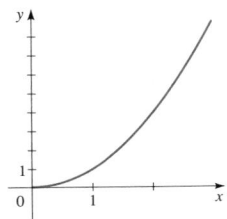

SKILLS

3–24 ■ A pair of parametric equations is given. **(a)** Sketch the curve represented by the parametric equations. **(b)** Find a rectangular-coordinate equation for the curve by eliminating the parameter.

3. $x = 2t$, $y = t + 6$

4. $x = 6t - 4$, $y = 3t$, $t \geq 0$

5. $x = t^2$, $y = t - 2$, $2 \leq t \leq 4$

6. $x = 2t + 1$, $y = \left(t + \frac{1}{2}\right)^2$

7. $x = \sqrt{t}$, $y = 1 - t$

8. $x = t^2$, $y = t^4 + 1$

9. $x = \dfrac{1}{t}$, $y = t + 1$ 10. $x = t + 1$, $y = \dfrac{t}{t + 1}$

11. $x = 4t^2$, $y = 8t^3$ 12. $x = |t|$, $y = |1 - |t||$

13. $x = 2 \sin t$, $y = 2 \cos t$, $0 \leq t \leq \pi$

14. $x = 2 \cos t$, $y = 3 \sin t$, $0 \leq t \leq 2\pi$

15. $x = \sin^2 t$, $y = \sin^4 t$ 16. $x = \sin^2 t$, $y = \cos t$

17. $x = \cos t$, $y = \cos 2t$ 18. $x = \cos 2t$, $y = \sin 2t$

19. $x = \sec t$, $y = \tan t$, $0 \leq t < \pi/2$

20. $x = \cot t$, $y = \csc t$, $0 < t < \pi$

21. $x = \tan t$, $y = \cot t$, $0 < t < \pi/2$

22. $x = \sec t$, $y = \tan^2 t$, $0 \leq t < \pi/2$

23. $x = \cos^2 t$, $y = \sin^2 t$

24. $x = \cos^3 t$, $y = \sin^3 t$, $0 \leq t \leq 2\pi$

25–28 ■ The position of an object in circular motion is modeled by the given parametric equations. Describe the path of the object by stating the radius of the circle, the position at time $t = 0$, the orientation of the motion (clockwise or counterclockwise), and the time t that it takes to complete one revolution around the circle.

25. $x = 3 \cos t$, $y = 3 \sin t$ 26. $x = 2 \sin t$, $y = 2 \cos t$

27. $x = \sin 2t$, $y = \cos 2t$ 28. $x = 4 \cos 3t$, $y = 4 \sin 3t$

29–34 ■ Find parametric equations for the line with the given properties.

29. Slope $\frac{1}{2}$, passing through $(4, -1)$

30. Slope -2, passing through $(-10, -20)$

31. Passing through $(6, 7)$ and $(7, 8)$

32. Passing through $(12, 7)$ and the origin

33. Find parametric equations for the circle $x^2 + y^2 = a^2$.

34. Find parametric equations for the ellipse
$$\frac{x^2}{a^2} + \frac{y^2}{b^2} = 1$$

35. Show by eliminating the parameter θ that the following parametric equations represent a hyperbola:
$$x = a \tan \theta \qquad y = b \sec \theta$$

36. Show that the following parametric equations represent a part of the hyperbola of Exercise 35:
$$x = a\sqrt{t} \qquad y = b\sqrt{t + 1}$$

37–40 ■ Sketch the curve given by the parametric equations.

37. $x = t \cos t$, $y = t \sin t$, $t \geq 0$

38. $x = \sin t$, $y = \sin 2t$

39. $x = \dfrac{3t}{1 + t^3}$, $y = \dfrac{3t^2}{1 + t^3}$

40. $x = \cot t$, $y = 2 \sin^2 t$, $0 < t < \pi$

41. If a projectile is fired with an initial speed of v_0 ft/s at an angle α above the horizontal, then its position after t seconds is given by the parametric equations
$$x = (v_0 \cos \alpha)t \qquad y = (v_0 \sin \alpha)t - 16t^2$$
(where x and y are measured in feet). Show that the path of the projectile is a parabola by eliminating the parameter t.

42. Referring to Exercise 41, suppose a gun fires a bullet into the air with an initial speed of 2048 ft/s at an angle of 30° to the horizontal.

    (a) After how many seconds will the bullet hit the ground?

    (b) How far from the gun will the bullet hit the ground?

    (c) What is the maximum height attained by the bullet?

43–48 ■ Use a graphing device to draw the curve represented by the parametric equations.

43. $x = \sin t$, $y = 2 \cos 3t$

44. $x = 2 \sin t$, $y = \cos 4t$

45. $x = 3 \sin 5t$, $y = 5 \cos 3t$

46. $x = \sin 4t$, $y = \cos 3t$

47. $x = \sin(\cos t)$, $y = \cos(t^{3/2})$, $0 \le t \le 2\pi$

48. $x = 2 \cos t + \cos 2t$, $y = 2 \sin t - \sin 2t$

49–52 ■ A polar equation is given. **(a)** Express the polar equation in parametric form. **(b)** Use a graphing device to graph the parametric equations you found in part (a).

49. $r = 2^{\theta/12}$, $0 \le \theta \le 4\pi$ **50.** $r = \sin\theta + 2\cos\theta$

51. $r = \dfrac{4}{2 - \cos\theta}$ **52.** $r = 2^{\sin\theta}$

53–56 ■ Match the parametric equations with the graphs labeled I–IV. Give reasons for your answers.

53. $x = t^3 - 2t$, $y = t^2 - t$

54. $x = \sin 3t$, $y = \sin 4t$

55. $x = t + \sin 2t$, $y = t + \sin 3t$

56. $x = \sin(t + \sin t)$, $y = \cos(t + \cos t)$

I

II

III

IV
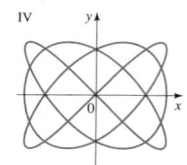

57. (a) In Example 6 suppose the point P that traces out the curve lies not on the edge of the circle, but rather at a fixed point inside the rim, at a distance b from the center (with $b < a$). The curve traced out by P is called a **curtate cycloid** (or **trochoid**). Show that parametric equations for the curtate cycloid are

$$x = a\theta - b\sin\theta \qquad y = a - b\cos\theta$$

 (b) Sketch the graph using $a = 3$ and $b = 2$.

58. (a) In Exercise 57 if the point P lies *outside* the circle at a distance b from the center (with $b > a$), then the curve traced out by P is called a **prolate cycloid**. Show that parametric equations for the prolate cycloid are the same as the equations for the curtate cycloid.

    (b) Sketch the graph for the case in which $a = 1$ and $b = 2$.

59. A circle C of radius b rolls on the inside of a larger circle of radius a centered at the origin. Let P be a fixed point on the smaller circle, with initial position at the point $(a, 0)$ as shown in the figure. The curve traced out by P is called a **hypocycloid**.

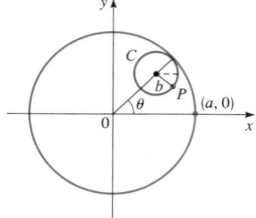

    (a) Show that parametric equations for the hypocycloid are

$$x = (a - b)\cos\theta + b\cos\left(\frac{a - b}{b}\theta\right)$$

$$y = (a - b)\sin\theta - b\sin\left(\frac{a - b}{b}\theta\right)$$

    (b) If $a = 4b$, the hypocycloid is called an **astroid**. Show that in this case the parametric equations can be reduced to

$$x = a\cos^3\theta \qquad y = a\sin^3\theta$$

    Sketch the curve. Eliminate the parameter to obtain an equation for the astroid in rectangular coordinates.

60. If the circle C of Exercise 59 rolls on the *outside* of the larger circle, the curve traced out by P is called an **epicycloid**. Find parametric equations for the epicycloid.

61. In the figure, the circle of radius a is stationary, and for every θ, the point P is the midpoint of the segment QR. The curve traced out by P for $0 < \theta < \pi$ is called the **longbow curve**. Find parametric equations for this curve.

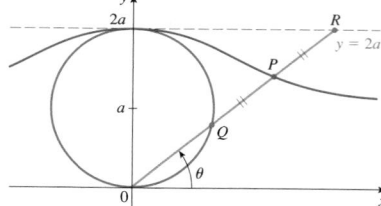

62. Two circles of radius a and b are centered at the origin, as shown in the figure. As the angle θ increases, the point P traces out a curve that lies between the circles.

(a) Find parametric equations for the curve, using θ as the parameter.

(b) Graph the curve using a graphing device, with $a = 3$ and $b = 2$.

(c) Eliminate the parameter, and identify the curve.

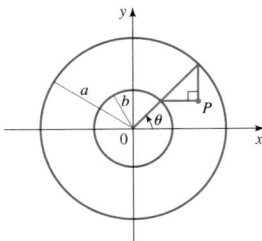

63. Two circles of radius a and b are centered at the origin, as shown in the figure.

(a) Find parametric equations for the curve traced out by the point P, using the angle θ as the parameter. (Note that the line segment AB is always tangent to the larger circle.)

(b) Graph the curve using a graphing device, with $a = 3$ and $b = 2$.

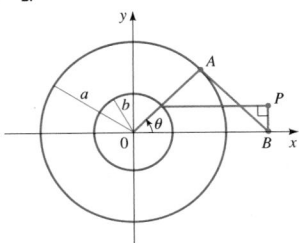

64. A curve, called a **witch of Agnesi**, consists of all points P determined as shown in the figure.

(a) Show that parametric equations for this curve can be written as

$$x = 2a \cot \theta \qquad y = 2a \sin^2 \theta$$

(b) Graph the curve using a graphing device, with $a = 3$.

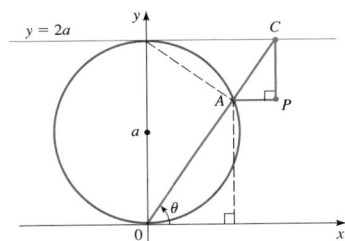

65. Eliminate the parameter θ in the parametric equations for the cycloid (Example 6) to obtain a rectangular coordinate equation for the section of the curve given by $0 \le \theta \le \pi$.

APPLICATIONS

66. The Rotary Engine   The Mazda RX-8 uses an unconventional engine (invented by Felix Wankel in 1954) in which the pistons are replaced by a triangular rotor that turns in a special housing as shown in the figure. The vertices of the rotor maintain contact with the housing at all times, while the center of the triangle traces out a circle of radius r, turning the drive shaft. The shape of the housing is given by the parametric equations below (where R is the distance between the vertices and center of the rotor):

$$x = r \cos 3\theta + R \cos \theta \qquad y = r \sin 3\theta + R \sin \theta$$

(a) Suppose that the drive shaft has radius $r = 1$. Graph the curve given by the parametric equations for the following values of R: 0.5, 1, 3, 5.

(b) Which of the four values of R given in part (a) seems to best model the engine housing illustrated in the figure?

67. Spiral Path of a Dog   A dog is tied to a circular tree trunk of radius 1 ft by a long leash. He has managed to wrap the entire leash around the tree while playing in the yard, and he finds himself at the point $(1, 0)$ in the figure. Seeing a squirrel, he runs around the tree counterclockwise, keeping the leash taut while chasing the intruder.

(a) Show that parametric equations for the dog's path (called an **involute of a circle**) are

$$x = \cos \theta + \theta \sin \theta \qquad y = \sin \theta - \theta \cos \theta$$

[*Hint:* Note that the leash is always tangent to the tree, so OT is perpendicular to TD.]

(b) Graph the path of the dog for $0 \le \theta \le 4\pi$.

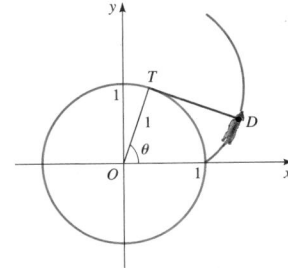

DISCOVERY ■ DISCUSSION ■ WRITING

68. More Information in Parametric Equations In this section we stated that parametric equations contain more information than just the shape of a curve. Write a short paragraph explaining this statement. Use the following example and your answers to parts (a) and (b) below in your explanation.

The position of a particle is given by the parametric equations

$$x = \sin t \qquad y = \cos t$$

where t represents time. We know that the shape of the path of the particle is a circle.

(a) How long does it take the particle to go once around the circle? Find parametric equations if the particle moves twice as fast around the circle.

(b) Does the particle travel clockwise or counterclockwise around the circle? Find parametric equations if the particle moves in the opposite direction around the circle.

69. Different Ways of Tracing Out a Curve The curves C, D, E, and F are defined parametrically as follows, where the parameter t takes on all real values unless otherwise stated:

$$C: \quad x = t, \quad y = t^2$$
$$D: \quad x = \sqrt{t}, \quad y = t, \quad t \geq 0$$
$$E: \quad x = \sin t, \quad y = \sin^2 t$$
$$F: \quad x = 3^t, \quad y = 3^{2t}$$

(a) Show that the points on all four of these curves satisfy the same rectangular coordinate equation.

(b) Draw the graph of each curve and explain how the curves differ from one another.

CHAPTER 8 | REVIEW

■ CONCEPT CHECK

1. Describe how polar coordinates represent the position of a point in the plane.

2. (a) What equations do you use to change from polar to rectangular coordinates?
   (b) What equations do you use to change from rectangular to polar coordinates?

3. How do you sketch the graph of a polar equation $r = f(\theta)$?

4. What type of curve has a polar equation of the given form?
   (a) $r = a \cos \theta$ or $r = a \sin \theta$
   (b) $r = a(1 \pm \cos \theta)$ or $r = a(1 \pm \sin \theta)$
   (c) $r = a \pm b \cos \theta$ or $r = a \pm b \sin \theta$
   (d) $r = a \cos n\theta$ or $r = a \sin n\theta$

5. How do you graph a complex number z? What is the polar form of a complex number z? What is the modulus of z? What is the argument of z?

6. (a) How do you multiply two complex numbers if they are given in polar form?
   (b) How do you divide two such numbers?

7. (a) State De Moivre's Theorem.
   (b) How do you find the nth roots of a complex number?

8. A curve is given by the parametric equations $x = f(t), y = g(t)$.
   (a) How do you sketch the curve?
   (b) How do you eliminate the parameter?

■ EXERCISES

1–6 ■ A point $P(r, \theta)$ is given in polar coordinates.
(a) Plot the point P. (b) Find rectangular coordinates for P.

1. $\left(12, \frac{\pi}{6}\right)$
2. $\left(8, -\frac{3\pi}{4}\right)$
3. $\left(-3, \frac{7\pi}{4}\right)$
4. $\left(-\sqrt{3}, \frac{2\pi}{3}\right)$
5. $\left(4\sqrt{3}, -\frac{5\pi}{3}\right)$
6. $\left(-6\sqrt{2}, -\frac{\pi}{4}\right)$

7–12 ■ A point $P(x, y)$ is given in rectangular coordinates.
(a) Plot the point P. (b) Find polar coordinates for P with $r \geq 0$.
(c) Find polar coordinates for P with $r \leq 0$.

7. $(8, 8)$
8. $(-\sqrt{2}, \sqrt{6})$
9. $(-6\sqrt{2}, -6\sqrt{2})$
10. $(3\sqrt{3}, 3)$
11. $(-3, \sqrt{3})$
12. $(4, -4)$

13–16 ■ (a) Convert the equation to polar coordinates and simplify. (b) Graph the equation. [*Hint:* Use the form of the equation that you find easier to graph.]

13. $x + y = 4$
14. $xy = 1$
15. $x^2 + y^2 = 4x + 4y$
16. $(x^2 + y^2)^2 = 2xy$

17–24 ■ (a) Sketch the graph of the polar equation.
(b) Express the equation in rectangular coordinates.

17. $r = 3 + 3 \cos \theta$
18. $r = 3 \sin \theta$
19. $r = 2 \sin 2\theta$
20. $r = 4 \cos 3\theta$
21. $r^2 = \sec 2\theta$
22. $r^2 = 4 \sin 2\theta$
23. $r = \sin \theta + \cos \theta$
24. $r = \dfrac{4}{2 + \cos \theta}$

25–28 ■ Use a graphing device to graph the polar equation. Choose the domain of θ to make sure you produce the entire graph.

25. $r = \cos(\theta/3)$

26. $r = \sin(9\theta/4)$

27. $r = 1 + 4\cos(\theta/3)$

28. $r = \theta \sin \theta, \quad -6\pi \le \theta \le 6\pi$

29–34 ■ A complex number is given. **(a)** Graph the complex number in the complex plane. **(b)** Find the modulus and argument. **(c)** Write the number in polar form.

29. $4 + 4i$ **30.** $-10i$

31. $5 + 3i$ **32.** $1 + \sqrt{3}\,i$

33. $-1 + i$ **34.** -20

35–38 ■ Use De Moivre's Theorem to find the indicated power.

35. $(1 - \sqrt{3}\,i)^4$ **36.** $(1 + i)^8$

37. $(\sqrt{3} + i)^{-4}$ **38.** $\left(\dfrac{1}{2} + \dfrac{\sqrt{3}}{2}i\right)^{20}$

39–42 ■ Find the indicated roots.

39. The square roots of $-16i$

40. The cube roots of $4 + 4\sqrt{3}\,i$

41. The sixth roots of 1

42. The eighth roots of i

43–46 ■ A pair of parametric equations is given. **(a)** Sketch the curve represented by the parametric equations. **(b)** Find a rectangular-coordinate equation for the curve by eliminating the parameter.

43. $x = 1 - t^2, \quad y = 1 + t$

44. $x = t^2 - 1, \quad y = t^2 + 1$

45. $x = 1 + \cos t, \quad y = 1 - \sin t, \quad 0 \le t \le \pi/2$

46. $x = \dfrac{1}{t} + 2, \quad y = \dfrac{2}{t^2}, \quad 0 < t \le 2$

47–48 ■ Use a graphing device to draw the parametric curve.

47. $x = \cos 2t, \quad y = \sin 3t$

48. $x = \sin(t + \cos 2t), \quad y = \cos(t + \sin 3t)$

49. In the figure, the point P is the midpoint of the segment QR and $0 \le \theta < \pi/2$. Using θ as the parameter, find a parametric representation for the curve traced out by P.

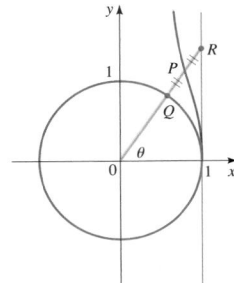

1. (a) Convert the point whose polar coordinates are $(8, 5\pi/4)$ to rectangular coordinates.
   (b) Find two polar coordinate representations for the rectangular coordinate point $(-6, 2\sqrt{3})$, one with $r > 0$ and one with $r < 0$ and both with $0 \leq \theta < 2\pi$.

2. (a) Graph the polar equation $r = 8 \cos \theta$. What type of curve is this?
   (b) Convert the equation to rectangular coordinates.

3. Graph the polar equation $r = 3 + 6 \sin \theta$. What type of curve is this?

4. Let $z = 1 + \sqrt{3}i$.
   (a) Graph z in the complex plane.
   (b) Write z in polar form.
   (c) Find the complex number z^9.

5. Let $z_1 = 4\left(\cos \dfrac{7\pi}{12} + i \sin \dfrac{7\pi}{12}\right)$ and $z_2 = 2\left(\cos \dfrac{5\pi}{12} + i \sin \dfrac{5\pi}{12}\right)$.
   Find $z_1 z_2$ and $\dfrac{z_1}{z_2}$.

6. Find the cube roots of $27i$, and sketch these roots in the complex plane.

7. (a) Sketch the graph of the parametric curve
$$x = 3 \sin t + 3 \qquad y = 2 \cos t \qquad (0 \leq t \leq \pi)$$
   (b) Eliminate the parameter t in part (a) to obtain an equation for this curve in rectangular coordinates.

8. Find parametric equations for the line of slope 2 that passes through the point $(3, 5)$.

574

The Path of a Projectile

Modeling motion is one of the most important ideas in both classical and modern physics. Much of Isaac Newton's work dealt with creating a mathematical model for how objects move and interact—this was the main reason for his invention of calculus. Albert Einstein developed his Special Theory of Relativity in the early 1900s to refine Newton's laws of motion.

In this section we use coordinate geometry to model the motion of a projectile, such as a ball thrown upward into the air, a bullet fired from a gun, or any other sort of missile. A similar model was created by Galileo, but we have the advantage of using our modern mathematical notation to make describing the model much easier than it was for Galileo!

▼ Parametric Equations for the Path of a Projectile

Suppose that we fire a projectile into the air from ground level, with an initial speed v_0 and at an angle θ upward from the ground. If there were no gravity (and no air resistance), the projectile would just keep moving indefinitely at the same speed and in the same direction. Since distance = speed × time, the projectile would travel a distance v_0t, so its position at time t would therefore be given by the following parametric equations (assuming that the origin of our coordinate system is placed at the initial location of the projectile; see Figure 1):

$$x = (v_0 \cos \theta)t \qquad y = (v_0 \sin \theta)t \qquad \text{No gravity}$$

But, of course, we know that gravity will pull the projectile back to ground level. By using calculus, it can be shown that the effect of gravity can be accounted for by subtracting $\frac{1}{2}gt^2$ from the vertical position of the projectile. In this expression, g is the gravitational acceleration: $g \approx 32 \text{ ft/s}^2 \approx 9.8 \text{ m/s}^2$. Thus we have the following parametric equations for the path of the projectile:

$$x = (v_0 \cos \theta)t \qquad y = (v_0 \sin \theta)t - \frac{1}{2}gt^2 \qquad \text{With gravity}$$

EXAMPLE | The Path of a Cannonball

Find parametric equations that model the path of a cannonball fired into the air with an initial speed of 150.0 m/s at a 30° angle of elevation. Sketch the path of the cannonball.

SOLUTION Substituting the given initial speed and angle into the general parametric equations of the path of a projectile, we get

$$x = (150.0 \cos 30°)t \qquad y = (150.0 \sin 30°)t - \frac{1}{2}(9.8)t^2 \qquad \begin{array}{l}\text{Substitute}\\ v_0 = 150.0, \theta = 30°\end{array}$$

$$x = 129.9t \qquad\qquad y = 75.0t - 4.9t^2 \qquad \text{Simplify}$$

This path is graphed in Figure 2.

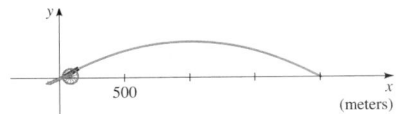

FIGURE 2 Path of a cannonball

FIGURE 1

▼ Range of a Projectile

How can we tell where and when the cannonball of the above example hits the ground? Since ground level corresponds to $y = 0$, we substitute this value for y and solve for t:

$$0 = 75.0t - 4.9t^2 \qquad \text{Set } y = 0$$

$$0 = t(75.0 - 4.9t) \qquad \text{Factor}$$

$$t = 0 \quad \text{or} \quad t = \frac{75.0}{4.9} \approx 15.3 \qquad \text{Solve for } t$$

The first solution, $t = 0$, is the time when the cannon was fired; the second solution means that the cannonball hits the ground after 15.3 s of flight. To see *where* this happens, we substitute this value into the equation for x, the horizontal location of the cannonball.

$$x = 129.9(15.3) \approx 1987.5 \text{ m}$$

The cannonball travels almost 2 km before hitting the ground.

Figure 3 shows the paths of several projectiles, all fired with the same initial speed but at different angles. From the graphs we see that if the firing angle is too high or too low, the projectile doesn't travel very far.

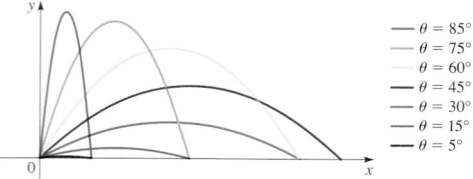

FIGURE 3 Paths of projectiles

Let's try to find the optimal firing angle—the angle that shoots the projectile as far as possible. We'll go through the same steps as we did in the preceding example, but we'll use the general parametric equations instead. First, we solve for the time when the projectile hits the ground by substituting $y = 0$:

$$0 = (v_0 \sin \theta)t - \tfrac{1}{2}gt^2 \qquad \text{Substitute } y = 0$$

$$0 = t(v_0 \sin \theta - \tfrac{1}{2}gt) \qquad \text{Factor}$$

$$0 = v_0 \sin \theta - \tfrac{1}{2}gt \qquad \text{Set second factor equal to 0}$$

$$t = \frac{2v_0 \sin \theta}{g} \qquad \text{Solve for } t$$

GALILEO GALILEI (1564–1642) was born in Pisa, Italy. He studied medicine but later abandoned this in favor of science and mathematics. At the age of 25, by dropping cannonballs of various sizes from the Leaning Tower of Pisa, he demonstrated that light objects fall at the same rate as heavier ones. This contradicted the then-accepted view of Aristotle that heavier objects fall more quickly. He also showed that the distance an object falls is proportional to the square of the time it has been falling, and from this he was able to prove that the path of a projectile is a parabola.

Galileo constructed the first telescope and, using it, discovered the moons of Jupiter. His advocacy of the Copernican view that the earth revolves around the sun (rather than being stationary) led to his being called before the Inquisition. By then an old man, he was forced to recant his views, but he is said to have muttered under his breath, "Nevertheless, it does move." Galileo revolutionized science by expressing scientific principles in the language of mathematics. He said, "The great book of nature is written in mathematical symbols."

Now we substitute this into the equation for x to see how far the projectile has traveled horizontally when it hits the ground:

$$x = (v_0 \cos \theta)t \qquad \text{Parametric equation for } x$$

$$= (v_0 \cos \theta)\left(\frac{2v_0 \sin \theta}{g}\right) \qquad \text{Substitute } t = (2v_0 \sin \theta)/g$$

$$= \frac{2v_0^2 \sin \theta \cos \theta}{g} \qquad \text{Simplify}$$

$$= \frac{v_0^2 \sin 2\theta}{g} \qquad \text{Use identity } \sin 2\theta = 2 \sin \theta \cos \theta$$

We want to choose θ so that x is as large as possible. The largest value that the sine of any angle can have is 1, the sine of 90°. Thus we want $2\theta = 90°$, or $\theta = 45°$. So to send the projectile as far as possible, it should be shot up at an angle of 45°. From the last equation in the preceding display, we can see that it will then travel a distance $x = v_0^2/g$.

PROBLEMS

1. **Trajectories Are Parabolas** From the graphs in Figure 3 the paths of projectiles appear to be parabolas that open downward. Eliminate the parameter t from the general parametric equations to verify that these are indeed parabolas.

2. **Path of a Baseball** Suppose a baseball is thrown at 30 ft/s at a 60° angle to the horizontal from a height of 4 ft above the ground.

    (a) Find parametric equations for the path of the baseball, and sketch its graph.

    (b) How far does the baseball travel, and when does it hit the ground?

3. **Path of a Rocket** Suppose that a rocket is fired at an angle of 5° from the vertical with an initial speed of 1000 ft/s.

    (a) Find the length of time the rocket is in the air.

    (b) Find the greatest height it reaches.

    (c) Find the horizontal distance it has traveled when it hits the ground.

    (d) Graph the rocket's path.

4. **Firing a Missile** The initial speed of a missile is 330 m/s.

    (a) At what angle should the missile be fired so that it hits a target 10 km away? (You should find that there are two possible angles.) Graph the missile paths for both angles.

    (b) For which angle is the target hit sooner?

5. **Maximum Height** Show that the maximum height reached by a projectile as a function of its initial speed v_0 and its firing angle θ is

$$y = \frac{v_0^2 \sin^2\theta}{2g}$$

6. **Shooting Into the Wind** Suppose that a projectile is fired into a headwind that pushes it back so as to reduce its horizontal speed by a constant amount w. Find parametric equations for the path of the projectile.

7. **Shooting Into the Wind** Using the parametric equations you derived in Problem 6, draw graphs of the path of a projectile with initial speed $v_0 = 32$ ft/s, fired into a headwind of $w = 24$ ft/s, for the angles $\theta = 5°, 15°, 30°, 40°, 45°, 55°, 60°$, and 75°. Is it still true that the greatest range is attained when firing at 45°? Draw some more graphs for different angles, and use these graphs to estimate the optimal firing angle.

8. Simulating the Path of a Projectile The path of a projectile can be simulated on a graphing calculator. On the TI-83, use the "Path" graph style to graph the general parametric equations for the path of a projectile, and watch as the circular cursor moves, simulating the motion of the projectile. Selecting the size of the $\mathtt{Tstep}$ determines the speed of the "projectile."

(a) Simulate the path of a projectile. Experiment with various values of θ. Use $v_0 = 10$ ft/s and $\mathtt{Tstep} = 0.02$. Part (a) of the figure below shows one such path.

(b) Simulate the path of two projectiles, fired simultaneously, one at $\theta = 30°$ and the other at $\theta = 60°$. This can be done on the TI-83 using $\mathtt{Simul}$ mode ("simultaneous" mode). Use $v_0 = 10$ ft/s and $\mathtt{Tstep} = 0.02$. See part (b) of the figure. Where do the projectiles land? Which lands first?

(c) Simulate the path of a ball thrown straight up ($\theta = 90°$). Experiment with values of v_0 between 5 and 20 ft/s. Use the "Animate" graph style and $\mathtt{Tstep} = 0.02$. Simulate the path of two balls thrown simultaneously at different speeds. To better distinguish the two balls, place them at different x-coordinates (for example, $x = 1$ and $x = 2$). See part (c) of the figure. How does doubling v_0 change the maximum height the ball reaches?

(a)

(b)

(c)

© James L. Amos/SuperStock

VECTORS IN TWO AND THREE DIMENSIONS

9.1 Vectors in Two Dimensions

9.2 The Dot Product

9.3 Three-Dimensional Coordinate Geometry

9.4 Vectors in Three Dimensions

9.5 The Cross Product

9.6 Equations of Lines and Planes

FOCUS ON MODELING
  Vector Fields

Many real-world quantities are described mathematically by just one number: their "size" or magnitude. For example, quantities such as mass, volume, distance, and temperature are described by their magnitude. But many other real-world quantities involve both magnitude *and* direction. Such quantities are described mathematically by vectors. For example, if you push a car with a certain force, the direction in which you push on the car is important; you get different results if you push the car forward, backward, or perhaps sideways. So force is a vector. The result of several forces acting on an object can be evaluated by using vectors. For example, we'll see how we can combine the vector forces of wind and water on the sails and hull of a sailboat to find the direction in which the boat will sail. Analyzing these vector forces helps sailors to sail against the wind by tacking. (See the Discovery Project *Sailing Against the Wind* referenced on page 597.)

Vector forces

Tacking against the wind

579

CHAPTER 9   Vectors in Two and Three Dimensions   579

**SUGGESTED TIME
AND EMPHASIS**

1 class, essential material

9.1 VECTORS IN TWO DIMENSIONS

| Geometric Description of Vectors ▶ Vectors in the Coordinate Plane
| ▶ Using Vectors to Model Velocity and Force

In applications of mathematics, certain quantities are determined completely by their magnitude—for example, length, mass, area, temperature, and energy. We speak of a length of 5 m or a mass of 3 kg; only one number is needed to describe each of these quantities. Such a quantity is called a **scalar**.

On the other hand, to describe the displacement of an object, two numbers are required: the *magnitude* and the *direction* of the displacement. To describe the velocity of a moving object, we must specify both the *speed* and the *direction* of travel. Quantities such as displacement, velocity, acceleration, and force that involve magnitude as well as direction are called *directed quantities*. One way to represent such quantities mathematically is through the use of *vectors*.

▼ Geometric Description of Vectors

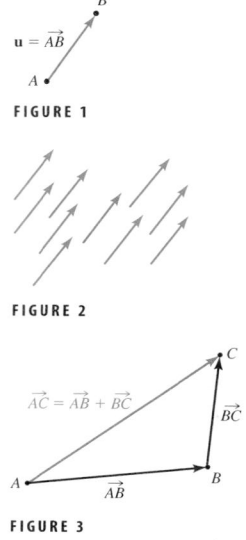

FIGURE 1

FIGURE 2

A **vector** in the plane is a line segment with an assigned direction. We sketch a vector as shown in Figure 1 with an arrow to specify the direction. We denote this vector by $\vec{AB}$. Point A is the **initial point**, and B is the **terminal point** of the vector $\vec{AB}$. The length of the line segment AB is called the **magnitude** or **length** of the vector and is denoted by $|\vec{AB}|$. We use boldface letters to denote vectors. Thus we write $\mathbf{u} = \vec{AB}$.

Two vectors are considered **equal** if they have equal magnitude and the same direction. Thus all the vectors in Figure 2 are equal. This definition of equality makes sense if we think of a vector as representing a displacement. Two such displacements are the same if they have equal magnitudes and the same direction. So the vectors in Figure 2 can be thought of as the *same* displacement applied to objects in different locations in the plane.

If the displacement $\mathbf{u} = \vec{AB}$ is followed by the displacement $\mathbf{v} = \vec{BC}$, then the resulting displacement is $\vec{AC}$ as shown in Figure 3. In other words, the single displacement represented by the vector $\vec{AC}$ has the same effect as the other two displacements together. We call the vector $\vec{AC}$ the **sum** of the vectors $\vec{AB}$ and $\vec{BC}$, and we write $\vec{AC} = \vec{AB} + \vec{BC}$. (The **zero vector**, denoted by $\mathbf{0}$, represents no displacement.) Thus to find the sum of any two vectors $\mathbf{u}$ and $\mathbf{v}$, we sketch vectors equal to $\mathbf{u}$ and $\mathbf{v}$ with the initial point of one at the terminal point of the other (see Figure 4(a)). If we draw $\mathbf{u}$ and $\mathbf{v}$ starting at the same point, then $\mathbf{u} + \mathbf{v}$ is the vector that is the diagonal of the parallelogram formed by $\mathbf{u}$ and $\mathbf{v}$ shown in Figure 4(b).

FIGURE 3

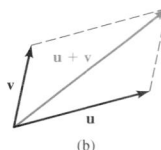

FIGURE 4   Addition of vectors

(a)   (b)

If a is a real number and $\mathbf{v}$ is a vector, we define a new vector $a\mathbf{v}$ as follows: The vector $a\mathbf{v}$ has magnitude $|a|\,|\mathbf{v}|$ and has the same direction as $\mathbf{v}$ if $a > 0$ and the opposite direction if $a < 0$. If $a = 0$, then $a\mathbf{v} = \mathbf{0}$, the zero vector. This process is called **multiplication of a vector by a scalar**. Multiplying a vector by a scalar has the effect of stretching or shrinking the vector. Figure 5 shows graphs of the vector $a\mathbf{v}$ for different values of a. We write the vector $(-1)\mathbf{v}$ as $-\mathbf{v}$. Thus $-\mathbf{v}$ is the vector with the same length as $\mathbf{v}$ but with the opposite direction.

TEXT QUESTION

What are the components of the vector from (3, 3) to (4, 4)?

Answer

$\langle 1, 1 \rangle$

The **difference** of two vectors **u** and **v** is defined by $\mathbf{u} - \mathbf{v} = \mathbf{u} + (-\mathbf{v})$. Figure 6 shows that the vector $\mathbf{u} - \mathbf{v}$ is the other diagonal of the parallelogram formed by **u** and **v**.

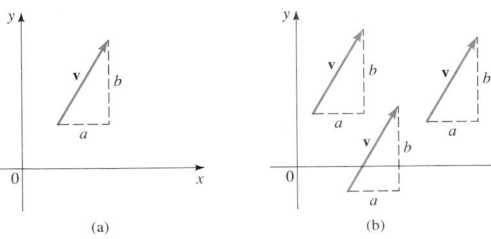

FIGURE 5 Multiplication of a vector by a scalar

FIGURE 6 Subtraction of vectors

▼ Vectors in the Coordinate Plane

So far, we've discussed vectors geometrically. By placing a vector in a coordinate plane, we can describe it analytically (that is, by using components). In Figure 7(a), to go from the initial point of the vector **v** to the terminal point, we move a units to the right and b units upward. We represent **v** as an ordered pair of real numbers.

Note the distinction between the *vector* $\langle a, b \rangle$ and the *point* (a, b).

$$\mathbf{v} = \langle a, b \rangle$$

where a is the **horizontal component** of **v** and b is the **vertical component** of **v**. Remember that a vector represents a magnitude and a direction, not a particular arrow in the plane. Thus the vector $\langle a, b \rangle$ has many different representations, depending on its initial point (see Figure 7(b)).

(a)

(b)

FIGURE 7

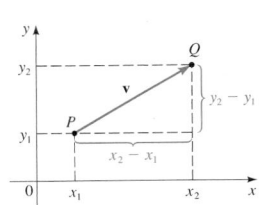

FIGURE 8

Using Figure 8, we can state the relationship between a geometric representation of a vector and the analytic one as follows.

COMPONENT FORM OF A VECTOR

If a vector **v** is represented in the plane with initial point $P(x_1, y_1)$ and terminal point $Q(x_2, y_2)$, then

$$\mathbf{v} = \langle x_2 - x_1, y_2 - y_1 \rangle$$

EXAMPLE 1 | Describing Vectors in Component Form

(a) Find the component form of the vector **u** with initial point $(-2, 5)$ and terminal point $(3, 7)$.

(b) If the vector $\mathbf{v} = \langle 3, 7 \rangle$ is sketched with initial point $(2, 4)$, what is its terminal point?

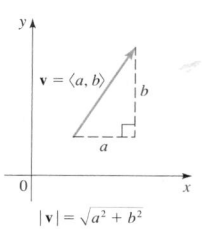

FIGURE 9

FIGURE 10

$$|\mathbf{v}| = \sqrt{a^2 + b^2}$$

FIGURE 11

(c) Sketch representations of the vector $\mathbf{w} = \langle 2, 3 \rangle$ with initial points at $(0, 0)$, $(2, 2)$, $(-2, -1)$, and $(1, 4)$.

SOLUTION

(a) The desired vector is

$$\mathbf{u} = \langle 3 - (-2), 7 - 5 \rangle = \langle 5, 2 \rangle$$

(b) Let the terminal point of $\mathbf{v}$ be (x, y). Then

$$\langle x - 2, y - 4 \rangle = \langle 3, 7 \rangle$$

So $x - 2 = 3$ and $y - 4 = 7$, or $x = 5$ and $y = 11$. The terminal point is $(5, 11)$.

(c) Representations of the vector $\mathbf{w}$ are sketched in Figure 9.

✎. NOW TRY EXERCISES **11, 19,** AND **23**

We now give analytic definitions of the various operations on vectors that we have described geometrically. Let's start with equality of vectors. We've said that two vectors are equal if they have equal magnitude and the same direction. For the vectors $\mathbf{u} = \langle a_1, b_1 \rangle$ and $\mathbf{v} = \langle a_2, b_2 \rangle$, this means that $a_1 = a_2$ and $b_1 = b_2$. In other words, two vectors are **equal** if and only if their corresponding components are equal. Thus all the arrows in Figure 7(b) represent the same vector, as do all the arrows in Figure 9.

Applying the Pythagorean Theorem to the triangle in Figure 10, we obtain the following formula for the magnitude of a vector.

MAGNITUDE OF A VECTOR

The **magnitude** or **length** of a vector $\mathbf{v} = \langle a, b \rangle$ is

$$|\mathbf{v}| = \sqrt{a^2 + b^2}$$

EXAMPLE 2 | Magnitudes of Vectors

Find the magnitude of each vector.
(a) $\mathbf{u} = \langle 2, -3 \rangle$ **(b)** $\mathbf{v} = \langle 5, 0 \rangle$ **(c)** $\mathbf{w} = \langle \frac{3}{5}, \frac{4}{5} \rangle$

SOLUTION

(a) $|\mathbf{u}| = \sqrt{2^2 + (-3)^2} = \sqrt{13}$

(b) $|\mathbf{v}| = \sqrt{5^2 + 0^2} = \sqrt{25} = 5$

(c) $|\mathbf{w}| = \sqrt{\left(\frac{3}{5}\right)^2 + \left(\frac{4}{5}\right)^2} = \sqrt{\frac{9}{25} + \frac{16}{25}} = 1$

✎. NOW TRY EXERCISE **37**

The following definitions of addition, subtraction, and scalar multiplication of vectors correspond to the geometric descriptions given earlier. Figure 11 shows how the analytic definition of addition corresponds to the geometric one.

ALGEBRAIC OPERATIONS ON VECTORS

If $\mathbf{u} = \langle a_1, b_1 \rangle$ and $\mathbf{v} = \langle a_2, b_2 \rangle$, then

$$\mathbf{u} + \mathbf{v} = \langle a_1 + a_2, b_1 + b_2 \rangle$$
$$\mathbf{u} - \mathbf{v} = \langle a_1 - a_2, b_1 - b_2 \rangle$$
$$c\mathbf{u} = \langle ca_1, cb_1 \rangle, \qquad c \in \mathbb{R}$$

IN-CLASS MATERIALS

Ask students to find r and s such that $\langle 3, 2 \rangle = r\langle 1, 1 \rangle + s\langle 0, 4 \rangle$. Repeat for $\langle 3, 2 \rangle = r\langle 1, 1 \rangle - s\langle 0, 4 \rangle$. Ask students if there is a vector $\langle x, y \rangle$ such that we cannot find r and s with $\langle x, y \rangle = r\langle 1, 1 \rangle + s\langle 0, 4 \rangle$. Note that this kind of question becomes very important in linear algebra.

EXAMPLE 3 | Operations with Vectors

If $\mathbf{u} = \langle 2, -3 \rangle$ and $\mathbf{v} = \langle -1, 2 \rangle$, find $\mathbf{u} + \mathbf{v}, \mathbf{u} - \mathbf{v}, 2\mathbf{u}, -3\mathbf{v}$, and $2\mathbf{u} + 3\mathbf{v}$.

SOLUTION By the definitions of the vector operations we have

$$\mathbf{u} + \mathbf{v} = \langle 2, -3 \rangle - \langle -1, 2 \rangle = \langle 1, -1 \rangle$$

$$\mathbf{u} - \mathbf{v} = \langle 2, -3 \rangle - \langle -1, 2 \rangle = \langle 3, -5 \rangle$$

$$2\mathbf{u} = 2\langle 2, -3 \rangle = \langle 4, -6 \rangle$$

$$-3\mathbf{v} = -3\langle -1, 2 \rangle = \langle 3, -6 \rangle$$

$$2\mathbf{u} + 3\mathbf{v} = 2\langle 2, -3 \rangle + 3\langle -1, 2 \rangle = \langle 4, -6 \rangle + \langle -3, 6 \rangle = \langle 1, 0 \rangle$$

✎. NOW TRY EXERCISE **31** ∎

The following properties for vector operations can be easily proved from the definitions. The **zero vector** is the vector $\mathbf{0} = \langle 0, 0 \rangle$. It plays the same role for addition of vectors as the number 0 does for addition of real numbers.

PROPERTIES OF VECTORS

Vector addition	Multiplication by a scalar
$\mathbf{u} + \mathbf{v} = \mathbf{v} + \mathbf{u}$	$c(\mathbf{u} + \mathbf{v}) = c\mathbf{u} + c\mathbf{v}$
$\mathbf{u} + (\mathbf{v} + \mathbf{w}) = (\mathbf{u} + \mathbf{v}) + \mathbf{w}$	$(c + d)\mathbf{u} = c\mathbf{u} + d\mathbf{u}$
$\mathbf{u} + \mathbf{0} = \mathbf{u}$	$(cd)\mathbf{u} = c(d\mathbf{u}) = d(c\mathbf{u})$
$\mathbf{u} + (-\mathbf{u}) = \mathbf{0}$	$1\mathbf{u} = \mathbf{u}$
Length of a vector	$0\mathbf{u} = \mathbf{0}$
$|c\mathbf{u}| = |c||\mathbf{u}|$	$c\mathbf{0} = \mathbf{0}$

A vector of length 1 is called a **unit vector**. For instance, in Example 2(c) the vector $\mathbf{w} = \langle \frac{3}{5}, \frac{4}{5} \rangle$ is a unit vector. Two useful unit vectors are $\mathbf{i}$ and $\mathbf{j}$, defined by

$$\mathbf{i} = \langle 1, 0 \rangle \qquad \mathbf{j} = \langle 0, 1 \rangle$$

(See Figure 12.) These vectors are special because any vector can be expressed in terms of them. (See Figure 13.)

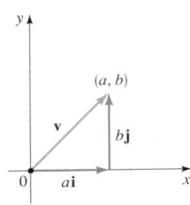

FIGURE 12

VECTORS IN TERMS OF $\mathbf{i}$ AND $\mathbf{j}$

The vector $\mathbf{v} = \langle a, b \rangle$ can be expressed in terms of $\mathbf{i}$ and $\mathbf{j}$ by

$$\mathbf{v} = \langle a, b \rangle = a\mathbf{i} + b\mathbf{j}$$

FIGURE 13

EXAMPLE 4 | Vectors in Terms of $\mathbf{i}$ and $\mathbf{j}$

(a) Write the vector $\mathbf{u} = \langle 5, -8 \rangle$ in terms of $\mathbf{i}$ and $\mathbf{j}$.

(b) If $\mathbf{u} = 3\mathbf{i} + 2\mathbf{j}$ and $\mathbf{v} = -\mathbf{i} + 6\mathbf{j}$, write $2\mathbf{u} + 5\mathbf{v}$ in terms of $\mathbf{i}$ and $\mathbf{j}$.

SOLUTION

(a) $\mathbf{u} = 5\mathbf{i} + (-8)\mathbf{j} = 5\mathbf{i} - 8\mathbf{j}$

IN-CLASS MATERIALS

Go over the properties of vectors from both algebraic and geometric perspectives.

(b) The properties of addition and scalar multiplication of vectors show that we can manipulate vectors in the same way as algebraic expressions. Thus

$$2\mathbf{u} + 5\mathbf{v} = 2(3\mathbf{i} + 2\mathbf{j}) + 5(-\mathbf{i} + 6\mathbf{j})$$
$$= (6\mathbf{i} + 4\mathbf{j}) + (-5\mathbf{i} + 30\mathbf{j})$$
$$= \mathbf{i} + 34\mathbf{j}$$

✎. NOW TRY EXERCISES **27** AND **35** ◼

FIGURE 14

Let $\mathbf{v}$ be a vector in the plane with its initial point at the origin. The **direction** of $\mathbf{v}$ is θ, the smallest positive angle in standard position formed by the positive x-axis and $\mathbf{v}$ (see Figure 14). If we know the magnitude and direction of a vector, then Figure 14 shows that we can find the horizontal and vertical components of the vector.

HORIZONTAL AND VERTICAL COMPONENTS OF A VECTOR

Let $\mathbf{v}$ be a vector with magnitude $|\mathbf{v}|$ and direction θ.
Then $\mathbf{v} = \langle a, b \rangle = a\mathbf{i} + b\mathbf{j}$, where

$$a = |\mathbf{v}| \cos \theta \qquad \text{and} \qquad b = |\mathbf{v}| \sin \theta$$

Thus we can express $\mathbf{v}$ as

$$\mathbf{v} = |\mathbf{v}| \cos \theta \, \mathbf{i} + |\mathbf{v}| \sin \theta \, \mathbf{j}$$

ALTERNATE EXAMPLE 5

(a) A vector $\mathbf{v}$ has length 4 and direction $\frac{\pi}{6}$. Write $\mathbf{v}$ in terms of $\mathbf{i}$ and $\mathbf{j}$ by finding its horizontal and vertical components.

(b) Find the direction of the vector $\mathbf{u} = 100\mathbf{i} + 301\mathbf{j}$.

ANSWERS

(a) $2\sqrt{3}\,\mathbf{i} + 2\mathbf{j}$

(b) Approximately 1.25 radians

EXAMPLE 5 | Components and Direction of a Vector

(a) A vector $\mathbf{v}$ has length 8 and direction $\pi/3$. Find the horizontal and vertical components, and write $\mathbf{v}$ in terms of $\mathbf{i}$ and $\mathbf{j}$.

(b) Find the direction of the vector $\mathbf{u} = -\sqrt{3}\mathbf{i} + \mathbf{j}$.

SOLUTION

(a) We have $\mathbf{v} = \langle a, b \rangle$, where the components are given by

$$a = 8 \cos \frac{\pi}{3} = 4 \qquad \text{and} \qquad b = 8 \sin \frac{\pi}{3} = 4\sqrt{3}$$

Thus $\mathbf{v} = \langle 4, 4\sqrt{3} \rangle = 4\mathbf{i} + 4\sqrt{3}\mathbf{j}$.

(b) From Figure 15 we see that the direction θ has the property that

$$\tan \theta = \frac{1}{-\sqrt{3}} = -\frac{\sqrt{3}}{3}$$

Thus the reference angle for θ is $\pi/6$. Since the terminal point of the vector $\mathbf{u}$ is in Quadrant II, it follows that $\theta = 5\pi/6$.

✎. NOW TRY EXERCISES **41** AND **51** ◼

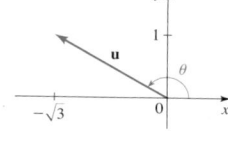

FIGURE 15

The use of bearings (such as N 30° E) to describe directions is explained on page 478 in Section 6.6.

▼ Using Vectors to Model Velocity and Force

The **velocity** of a moving object is modeled by a vector whose direction is the direction of motion and whose magnitude is the speed. Figure 16 on the next page shows some vectors $\mathbf{u}$, representing the velocity of wind flowing in the direction N 30° E, and a vector $\mathbf{v}$, representing the velocity of an airplane flying through this wind at the point P. It's obvious from our experience that wind affects both the speed and the direction of an airplane.

Figure 17 indicates that the true velocity of the plane (relative to the ground) is given by the vector $\mathbf{w} = \mathbf{u} + \mathbf{v}$.

FIGURE 16   **FIGURE 17**

EXAMPLE 6 | The True Speed and Direction of an Airplane

An airplane heads due north at 300 mi/h. It experiences a 40 mi/h crosswind flowing in the direction N 30° E, as shown in Figure 16.

(a) Express the velocity $\mathbf{v}$ of the airplane relative to the air, and the velocity $\mathbf{u}$ of the wind, in component form.

(b) Find the true velocity of the airplane as a vector.

(c) Find the true speed and direction of the airplane.

SOLUTION

(a) The velocity of the airplane relative to the air is $\mathbf{v} = 0\mathbf{i} + 300\mathbf{j} = 300\mathbf{j}$. By the formulas for the components of a vector, we find that the velocity of the wind is

$$\mathbf{u} = (40 \cos 60°)\mathbf{i} + (40 \sin 60°)\mathbf{j}$$
$$= 20\mathbf{i} + 20\sqrt{3}\mathbf{j}$$
$$\approx 20\mathbf{i} + 34.64\mathbf{j}$$

(b) The true velocity of the airplane is given by the vector $\mathbf{w} = \mathbf{u} + \mathbf{v}$:

$$\mathbf{w} = \mathbf{u} + \mathbf{v} = (20\mathbf{i} + 20\sqrt{3}\mathbf{j}) + (300\mathbf{j})$$
$$= 20\mathbf{i} + (20\sqrt{3} + 300)\mathbf{j}$$
$$\approx 20\mathbf{i} + 334.64\mathbf{j}$$

(c) The true speed of the airplane is given by the magnitude of $\mathbf{w}$:

$$|\mathbf{w}| \approx \sqrt{(20)^2 + (334.64)^2} \approx 335.2 \text{ mi/h}$$

The direction of the airplane is the direction θ of the vector $\mathbf{w}$. The angle θ has the property that $\tan \theta \approx 334.64/20 = 16.732$, so $\theta \approx 86.6°$. Thus the airplane is heading in the direction N 3.4° E.

. NOW TRY EXERCISE **59**   ■

EXAMPLE 7 | Calculating a Heading

A woman launches a boat from one shore of a straight river and wants to land at the point directly on the opposite shore. If the speed of the boat (relative to the water) is 10 mi/h and the river is flowing east at the rate of 5 mi/h, in what direction should she head the boat in order to arrive at the desired landing point?

ALTERNATE EXAMPLE 6

An airplane heads due north at 280 mi/h. It experiences a 38 mi/h crosswind flowing in the direction N 60° E. Find the true velocity of the airplane as a vector expressed in terms of $\mathbf{i}$ and $\mathbf{j}$. Find the true speed of the airplane.

ANSWER

$19\sqrt{3}\,\mathbf{i} + 299\,\mathbf{j}$, 300.81 mi/h

ALTERNATE EXAMPLE 7

A woman launches a boat from one shore of a straight river and wants to land at the point directly opposite on the other shore. If the speed of the boat (in still water) is 16 mi/h and the river is flowing east at the rate of 8 mi/h, in what direction (you should find the angle θ) should she head the boat in order to arrive at the desired landing point?

ANSWER
120°

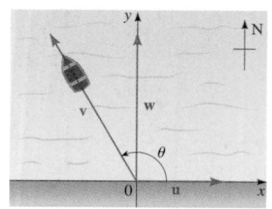

FIGURE 18

SOLUTION We choose a coordinate system with the origin at the initial position of the boat as shown in Figure 18. Let **u** and **v** represent the velocities of the river and the boat, respectively. Clearly, **u** = 5**i**, and since the speed of the boat is 10 mi/h, we have $|\mathbf{v}| = 10$, so

$$\mathbf{v} = (10 \cos \theta)\mathbf{i} + (10 \sin \theta)\mathbf{j}$$

where the angle θ is as shown in Figure 16. The true course of the boat is given by the vector $\mathbf{w} = \mathbf{u} + \mathbf{v}$. We have

$$\mathbf{w} = \mathbf{u} + \mathbf{v} = 5\mathbf{i} + (10 \cos \theta)\mathbf{i} + (10 \sin \theta)\mathbf{j}$$
$$= (5 + 10 \cos \theta)\mathbf{i} + (10 \sin \theta)\mathbf{j}$$

Since the woman wants to land at a point directly across the river, her direction should have horizontal component 0. In other words, she should choose θ in such a way that

$$5 + 10 \cos \theta = 0$$
$$\cos \theta = -\tfrac{1}{2}$$
$$\theta = 120°$$

Thus she should head the boat in the direction $\theta = 120°$ (or N 30° W).

✎. NOW TRY EXERCISE **57**

Force is also represented by a vector. Intuitively, we can think of force as describing a push or a pull on an object, for example, a horizontal push of a book across a table or the downward pull of the earth's gravity on a ball. Force is measured in pounds (or in newtons, in the metric system). For instance, a man weighing 200 lb exerts a force of 200 lb downward on the ground. If several forces are acting on an object, the **resultant force** experienced by the object is the vector sum of these forces.

EXAMPLE 8 | Resultant Force

Two forces $\mathbf{F}_1$ and $\mathbf{F}_2$ with magnitudes 10 and 20 lb, respectively, act on an object at a point P as shown in Figure 19. Find the resultant force acting at P.

SOLUTION We write $\mathbf{F}_1$ and $\mathbf{F}_2$ in component form:

$$\mathbf{F}_1 = (10 \cos 45°)\mathbf{i} + (10 \sin 45°)\mathbf{j} = 10 \frac{\sqrt{2}}{2}\mathbf{i} + 10 \frac{\sqrt{2}}{2}\mathbf{j}$$
$$= 5\sqrt{2}\,\mathbf{i} + 5\sqrt{2}\,\mathbf{j}$$
$$\mathbf{F}_2 = (20 \cos 150°)\mathbf{i} + (20 \sin 150°)\mathbf{j} = -20 \frac{\sqrt{3}}{2}\mathbf{i} + 20\left(\frac{1}{2}\right)\mathbf{j}$$
$$= -10\sqrt{3}\,\mathbf{i} + 10\mathbf{j}$$

So the resultant force $\mathbf{F}$ is

$$\mathbf{F} = \mathbf{F}_1 + \mathbf{F}_2$$
$$= (5\sqrt{2}\,\mathbf{i} + 5\sqrt{2}\,\mathbf{j}) + (-10\sqrt{3}\,\mathbf{i} + 10\mathbf{j})$$
$$= (5\sqrt{2} - 10\sqrt{3})\mathbf{i} + (5\sqrt{2} + 10)\mathbf{j}$$
$$\approx -10\mathbf{i} + 17\mathbf{j}$$

The resultant force $\mathbf{F}$ is shown in Figure 20.

✎. NOW TRY EXERCISE **67**

FIGURE 19

FIGURE 20

ALTERNATE EXAMPLE 8

Two forces $\mathbf{F}_1$ and $\mathbf{F}_2$ with magnitudes 6 and 24 lb, respectively, act on an object at a point P, as shown in the following figure. Find the resultant force acting at P as a vector expressed in terms of **i** and **j**. Round the horizontal and vertical components of the vector to the nearest integer.

ANSWER
$-8\mathbf{i} + 25\mathbf{j}$

9.1 EXERCISES

CONCEPTS

1. (a) A vector in the plane is a line segment with an assigned direction. In Figure I below, the vector **u** has initial point _____ and terminal point _____. Sketch the vectors 2**u** and **u** + **v**.

   (b) A vector in a coordinate plane is expressed by using components. In Figure II below, the vector **u** has initial point ([ ] , [ ]) and terminal point ([ ] , [ ]). In component form we write **u** = ⟨ [ ] , [ ] ⟩, and **v** = ⟨ [ ] , [ ] ⟩. Then 2**u** = ⟨ [ ] , [ ] ⟩ and **u** + **v** = ⟨ [ ] , [ ] ⟩.

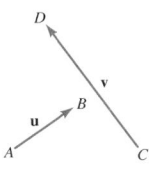

I   II

2. (a) The length of a vector **w** = ⟨a, b⟩ is |**w**| = _____, so the length of the vector **u** in Figure II is

   |**u**| = _____.

   (b) If we know the length |**w**| and direction θ of a vector **w**, then we can express the vector in component form as

   w = ⟨ _____ , _____ ⟩.

SKILLS

3–8 ■ Sketch the vector indicated. (The vectors **u** and **v** are shown in the figure.)

3. 2**u**

4. −**v**

5. **u** + **v**

6. **u** − **v**

7. **v** − 2**u**

8. 2**u** + **v**

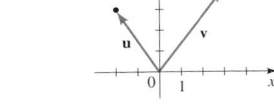

9–18 ■ Express the vector with initial point P and terminal point Q in component form.

9.

10.

11.

12.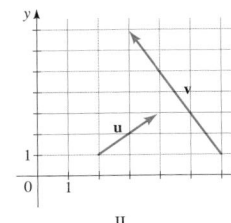

13. $P(3, 2)$, $Q(8, 9)$

14. $P(1, 1)$, $Q(9, 9)$

15. $P(5, 3)$, $Q(1, 0)$

16. $P(-1, 3)$, $Q(-6, -1)$

17. $P(-1, -1)$, $Q(-1, 1)$

18. $P(-8, -6)$, $Q(-1, -1)$

19–22 ■ Sketch the given vector with initial point (4, 3), and find the terminal point.

19. **u** = ⟨2, 4⟩

20. **u** = ⟨−1, 2⟩

21. **u** = ⟨4, −3⟩

22. **u** = ⟨−8, −1⟩

23–26 ■ Sketch representations of the given vector with initial points at (0, 0), (2, 3), and (−3, 5).

23. **u** = ⟨3, 5⟩

24. **u** = ⟨4, −6⟩

25. **u** = ⟨−7, 2⟩

26. **u** = ⟨0, −9⟩

27–30 ■ Write the given vector in terms of **i** and **j**.

27. **u** = ⟨1, 4⟩

28. **u** = ⟨−2, 10⟩

29. **u** = ⟨3, 0⟩

30. **u** = ⟨0, −5⟩

31–36 ■ Find 2**u**, −3**v**, **u** + **v**, and 3**u** − 4**v** for the given vectors **u** and **v**.

31. **u** = ⟨2, 7⟩, **v** = ⟨3, 1⟩

32. **u** = ⟨−2, 5⟩, **v** = ⟨2, −8⟩

33. **u** = ⟨0, −1⟩, **v** = ⟨−2, 0⟩

34. **u** = **i**, **v** = −2**j**

35. **u** = 2**i**, **v** = 3**i** − 2**j**   36. **u** = **i** + **j**, **v** = **i** − **j**

37–40 ■ Find |**u**|, |**v**|, |2**u**|, |$\frac{1}{2}$**v**|, |**u** + **v**|, |**u** − **v**|, and |**u**| − |**v**|.

37. **u** = 2**i** + **j**, **v** = 3**i** − 2**j**

38. **u** = −2**i** + 3**j**, **v** = **i** − 2**j**

39. **u** = ⟨10, −1⟩, **v** = ⟨−2, −2⟩

40. **u** = ⟨−6, 6⟩, **v** = ⟨−2, −1⟩

41–46 ■ Find the horizontal and vertical components of the vector with given length and direction, and write the vector in terms of the vectors **i** and **j**.

41. |**v**| = 40, θ = 30°

42. |**v**| = 50, θ = 120°

43. |**v**| = 1, θ = 225°

44. |**v**| = 800, θ = 125°

45. |**v**| = 4, θ = 10°

46. |**v**| = √3, θ = 300°

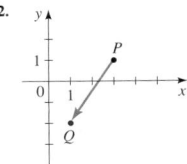

47–52 ■ Find the magnitude and direction (in degrees) of the vector.

47. $\mathbf{v} = \langle 3, 4 \rangle$

48. $\mathbf{v} = \left\langle -\dfrac{\sqrt{2}}{2}, -\dfrac{\sqrt{2}}{2} \right\rangle$

49. $\mathbf{v} = \langle -12, 5 \rangle$

50. $\mathbf{v} = \langle 40, 9 \rangle$

51. $\mathbf{v} = \mathbf{i} + \sqrt{3}\,\mathbf{j}$

52. $\mathbf{v} = \mathbf{i} + \mathbf{j}$

APPLICATIONS

53. Components of a Force A man pushes a lawn mower with a force of 30 lb exerted at an angle of 30° to the ground. Find the horizontal and vertical components of the force.

54. Components of a Velocity A jet is flying in a direction N 20° E with a speed of 500 mi/h. Find the north and east components of the velocity.

55. Velocity A river flows due south at 3 mi/h. A swimmer attempting to cross the river heads due east swimming at 2 mi/h relative to the water. Find the true velocity of the swimmer as a vector.

56. Velocity Suppose that in Exercise 55 the current is flowing at 1.2 mi/h due south. In what direction should the swimmer head in order to arrive at a landing point due east of his starting point?

57. Velocity The speed of an airplane is 300 mi/h relative to the air. The wind is blowing due north with a speed of 30 mi/h. In what direction should the airplane head in order to arrive at a point due west of its location?

58. Velocity A migrating salmon heads in the direction N 45° E, swimming at 5 mi/h relative to the water. The prevailing ocean currents flow due east at 3 mi/h. Find the true velocity of the fish as a vector.

59. True Velocity of a Jet A pilot heads his jet due east. The jet has a speed of 425 mi/h relative to the air. The wind is blowing due north with a speed of 40 mi/h.
(a) Express the velocity of the wind as a vector in component form.
(b) Express the velocity of the jet relative to the air as a vector in component form.
(c) Find the true velocity of the jet as a vector.
(d) Find the true speed and direction of the jet.

60. True Velocity of a Jet A jet is flying through a wind that is blowing with a speed of 55 mi/h in the direction N 30° E (see the figure). The jet has a speed of 765 mi/h relative to the air, and the pilot heads the jet in the direction N 45° E.
(a) Express the velocity of the wind as a vector in component form.
(b) Express the velocity of the jet relative to the air as a vector in component form.
(c) Find the true velocity of the jet as a vector.
(d) Find the true speed and direction of the jet.

61. True Velocity of a Jet Find the true speed and direction of the jet in Exercise 60 if the pilot heads the plane in the direction N 30° W.

62. True Velocity of a Jet In what direction should the pilot in Exercise 60 head the plane for the true course to be due north?

63. Velocity of a Boat A straight river flows east at a speed of 10 mi/h. A boater starts at the south shore of the river and heads in a direction 60° from the shore (see the figure). The motorboat has a speed of 20 mi/h relative to the water.
(a) Express the velocity of the river as a vector in component form.
(b) Express the velocity of the motorboat relative to the water as a vector in component form.
(c) Find the true velocity of the motorboat.
(d) Find the true speed and direction of the motorboat.

64. Velocity of a Boat The boater in Exercise 63 wants to arrive at a point on the north shore of the river directly opposite the starting point. In what direction should the boat be headed?

65. Velocity of a Boat A boat heads in the direction N 72° E. The speed of the boat relative to the water is 24 mi/h. The water is flowing directly south. It is observed that the true direction of the boat is directly east.

(a) Express the velocity of the boat relative to the water as a vector in component form.

(b) Find the speed of the water and the true speed of the boat.

66. Velocity A woman walks due west on the deck of an ocean liner at 2 mi/h. The ocean liner is moving due north at a speed of 25 mi/h. Find the speed and direction of the woman relative to the surface of the water.

67–72 ■ Equilibrium of Forces The forces $\mathbf{F}_1, \mathbf{F}_2, \ldots, \mathbf{F}_n$ acting at the same point P are said to be in equilibrium if the resultant force is zero, that is, if $\mathbf{F}_1 + \mathbf{F}_2 + \cdots + \mathbf{F}_n = 0$. Find (a) the resultant forces acting at P, and (b) the additional force required (if any) for the forces to be in equilibrium.

 67. $\mathbf{F}_1 = \langle 2, 5 \rangle, \quad \mathbf{F}_2 = \langle 3, -8 \rangle$

68. $\mathbf{F}_1 = \langle 3, -7 \rangle, \quad \mathbf{F}_2 = \langle 4, -2 \rangle, \quad \mathbf{F}_3 = \langle -7, 9 \rangle$

69. $\mathbf{F}_1 = 4\mathbf{i} - \mathbf{j}, \quad \mathbf{F}_2 = 3\mathbf{i} - 7\mathbf{j}, \quad \mathbf{F}_3 = -8\mathbf{i} + 3\mathbf{j},$
$\mathbf{F}_4 = \mathbf{i} + \mathbf{j}$

70. $\mathbf{F}_1 = \mathbf{i} - \mathbf{j}, \quad \mathbf{F}_2 = \mathbf{i} + \mathbf{j}, \quad \mathbf{F}_3 = -2\mathbf{i} + \mathbf{j}$

71.

72.

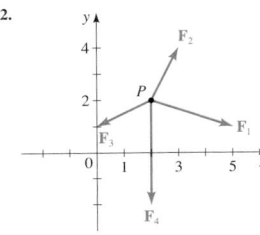

73. Equilibrium of Tensions A 100-lb weight hangs from a string as shown in the figure. Find the tensions $\mathbf{T}_1$ and $\mathbf{T}_2$ in the string.

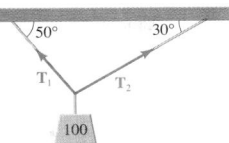

74. Equilibrium of Tensions The cranes in the figure are lifting an object that weighs 18,278 lb. Find the tensions $\mathbf{T}_1$ and $\mathbf{T}_2$.

DISCOVERY ■ DISCUSSION ■ WRITING

75. Vectors That Form a Polygon Suppose that n vectors can be placed head to tail in the plane so that they form a polygon. (The figure shows the case of a hexagon.) Explain why the sum of these vectors is **0**.

9.2 THE DOT PRODUCT

> The Dot Product of Vectors ▶ The Component of **u** Along **v** ▶ The Projection of **u** Onto **v** ▶ Work

In this section we define an operation on vectors called the dot product. This concept is especially useful in calculus and in applications of vectors to physics and engineering.

▼ The Dot Product of Vectors

We begin by defining the dot product of two vectors.

DEFINITION OF THE DOT PRODUCT

If $\mathbf{u} = \langle a_1, b_1 \rangle$ and $\mathbf{v} = \langle a_2, b_2 \rangle$ are vectors, then their **dot product**, denoted by $\mathbf{u} \cdot \mathbf{v}$, is defined by

$$\mathbf{u} \cdot \mathbf{v} = a_1 a_2 + b_1 b_2$$

Thus to find the dot product of **u** and **v**, we multiply corresponding components and add. The dot product is *not* a vector; it is a real number, or scalar.

EXAMPLE 1 | Calculating Dot Products

(a) If $\mathbf{u} = \langle 3, -2 \rangle$ and $\mathbf{v} = \langle 4, 5 \rangle$ then

$$\mathbf{u} \cdot \mathbf{v} = (3)(4) + (-2)(5) = 2$$

(b) If $\mathbf{u} = 2\mathbf{i} + \mathbf{j}$ and $\mathbf{v} = 5\mathbf{i} - 6\mathbf{j}$, then

$$\mathbf{u} \cdot \mathbf{v} = (2)(5) + (1)(-6) = 4$$

✎. NOW TRY EXERCISES **5(a)** AND **11(a)** ∎

The proofs of the following properties of the dot product follow easily from the definition.

PROPERTIES OF THE DOT PRODUCT

1. $\mathbf{u} \cdot \mathbf{v} = \mathbf{v} \cdot \mathbf{u}$

2. $(a\mathbf{u}) \cdot \mathbf{v} = a(\mathbf{u} \cdot \mathbf{v}) = \mathbf{u} \cdot (a\mathbf{v})$

3. $(\mathbf{u} + \mathbf{v}) \cdot \mathbf{w} = \mathbf{u} \cdot \mathbf{w} + \mathbf{v} \cdot \mathbf{w}$

4. $|\mathbf{u}|^2 = \mathbf{u} \cdot \mathbf{u}$

PROOF We prove only the last property. The proofs of the others are left as exercises. Let $\mathbf{u} = \langle a, b \rangle$. Then

$$\mathbf{u} \cdot \mathbf{u} = \langle a, b \rangle \cdot \langle a, b \rangle = a^2 + b^2 = |\mathbf{u}|^2 \qquad \blacksquare$$

Let **u** and **v** be vectors, and sketch them with initial points at the origin. We define the **angle θ between u and v** to be the smaller of the angles formed by these representations of **u** and **v** (see Figure 1). Thus $0 \le \theta \le \pi$. The next theorem relates the angle between two vectors to their dot product.

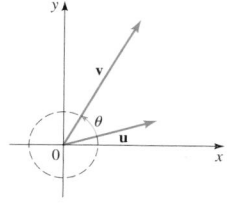

FIGURE 1

THE DOT PRODUCT THEOREM

If θ is the angle between two nonzero vectors **u** and **v**, then

$$\mathbf{u} \cdot \mathbf{v} = |\mathbf{u}||\mathbf{v}|\cos\theta$$

PROOF Applying the Law of Cosines to triangle AOB in Figure 2 gives

$$|\mathbf{u} - \mathbf{v}|^2 = |\mathbf{u}|^2 + |\mathbf{v}|^2 - 2|\mathbf{u}||\mathbf{v}|\cos\theta$$

IN-CLASS MATERIALS

Demonstrate the proper formation of statements involving dot products. For example, the statement $c(\mathbf{a} \cdot \mathbf{b})$ makes sense, while the statements $\mathbf{d} \cdot (\mathbf{a} \cdot \mathbf{b})$ and $c \cdot \mathbf{a}$ do not.

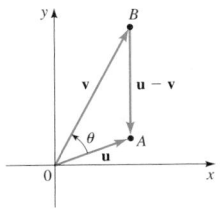

FIGURE 2

Using the properties of the dot product, we write the left-hand side as follows:

$$|\mathbf{u} - \mathbf{v}|^2 = (\mathbf{u} - \mathbf{v}) \cdot (\mathbf{u} - \mathbf{v})$$
$$= \mathbf{u} \cdot \mathbf{u} - \mathbf{u} \cdot \mathbf{v} - \mathbf{v} \cdot \mathbf{u} + \mathbf{v} \cdot \mathbf{v}$$
$$= |\mathbf{u}|^2 - 2(\mathbf{u} \cdot \mathbf{v}) + |\mathbf{v}|^2$$

Equating the right-hand sides of the displayed equations, we get

$$|\mathbf{u}|^2 - 2(\mathbf{u} \cdot \mathbf{v}) + |\mathbf{v}|^2 = |\mathbf{u}|^2 + |\mathbf{v}|^2 - 2|\mathbf{u}||\mathbf{v}|\cos\theta$$
$$-2(\mathbf{u} \cdot \mathbf{v}) = -2|\mathbf{u}||\mathbf{v}|\cos\theta$$
$$\mathbf{u} \cdot \mathbf{v} = |\mathbf{u}||\mathbf{v}|\cos\theta$$

This proves the theorem. ∎

The Dot Product Theorem is useful because it allows us to find the angle between two vectors if we know the components of the vectors. The angle is obtained simply by solving the equation in the Dot Product Theorem for $\cos\theta$. We state this important result explicitly.

> **ANGLE BETWEEN TWO VECTORS**
>
> If θ is the angle between two nonzero vectors $\mathbf{u}$ and $\mathbf{v}$, then
>
> $$\cos\theta = \frac{\mathbf{u} \cdot \mathbf{v}}{|\mathbf{u}||\mathbf{v}|}$$

EXAMPLE 2 | Finding the Angle Between Two Vectors

Find the angle between the vectors $\mathbf{u} = \langle 2, 5 \rangle$ and $\mathbf{v} = \langle 4, -3 \rangle$.

SOLUTION By the formula for the angle between two vectors we have

$$\cos\theta = \frac{\mathbf{u} \cdot \mathbf{v}}{|\mathbf{u}||\mathbf{v}|} = \frac{(2)(4) + (5)(-3)}{\sqrt{4 + 25}\sqrt{16 + 9}} = \frac{-7}{5\sqrt{29}}$$

Thus the angle between $\mathbf{u}$ and $\mathbf{v}$ is

$$\theta = \cos^{-1}\left(\frac{-7}{5\sqrt{29}}\right) \approx 105.1°$$

✎ NOW TRY EXERCISES **5(b)** AND **11(b)** ∎

Two nonzero vectors $\mathbf{u}$ and $\mathbf{v}$ are called **perpendicular**, or **orthogonal**, if the angle between them is $\pi/2$. The following theorem shows that we can determine whether two vectors are perpendicular by finding their dot product.

> **ORTHOGONAL VECTORS**
>
> Two nonzero vectors $\mathbf{u}$ and $\mathbf{v}$ are perpendicular if and only if $\mathbf{u} \cdot \mathbf{v} = 0$.

PROOF If $\mathbf{u}$ and $\mathbf{v}$ are perpendicular, then the angle between them is $\pi/2$, so

$$\mathbf{u} \cdot \mathbf{v} = |\mathbf{u}||\mathbf{v}|\cos\frac{\pi}{2} = 0$$

Conversely, if $\mathbf{u} \cdot \mathbf{v} = 0$, then

$$|\mathbf{u}||\mathbf{v}|\cos\theta = 0$$

Since $\mathbf{u}$ and $\mathbf{v}$ are nonzero vectors, we conclude that $\cos\theta = 0$, so $\theta = \pi/2$. Thus $\mathbf{u}$ and $\mathbf{v}$ are orthogonal. ∎

ALTERNATE EXAMPLE 2
Find the angle between the vectors $\mathbf{u} = 4\mathbf{i} + \mathbf{j}$ and $\mathbf{v} = 6\mathbf{i} - 5\mathbf{j}$.

ANSWER
53.84°

IN-CLASS MATERIALS

Demonstrate the Distributive Property in general. Note that while the dot product is commutative and distributive, the Associative Property makes no sense, as it is not possible to take the dot product of three vectors.

ALTERNATE EXAMPLE 3

Determine whether the vectors in each pair are perpendicular.

(a) **a** = $\langle 1, 6 \rangle$ **b** = $\langle 12, -2 \rangle$

(b) **a** = $\langle 3, 4 \rangle$ **b** = $\langle -3, 4 \rangle$

ANSWERS

(a) **a** · **b** = 0, so they are perpendicular.

(b) **a** · **b** = 7 ≠ 0, so they are not perpendicular.

IN-CLASS MATERIALS

This is a nice, direct application of vector projections. It is clear that a weight will slide more quickly down ramp 2 than down ramp 1:

Ramp 1

Ramp 2

EXAMPLE 3 | Checking Vectors for Perpendicularity

Determine whether the vectors in each pair are perpendicular.

(a) **u** = $\langle 3, 5 \rangle$ and **v** = $\langle 2, -8 \rangle$ (b) **u** = $\langle 2, 1 \rangle$ and **v** = $\langle -1, 2 \rangle$

SOLUTION

(a) **u** · **v** = $(3)(2) + (5)(-8) = -34 \neq 0$, so **u** and **v** are not perpendicular.

(b) **u** · **v** = $(2)(-1) + (1)(2) = 0$, so **u** and **v** are perpendicular.

✎ . NOW TRY EXERCISES **15** AND **17**   ■

▼ The Component of u Along v

The **component of u along v** (or the **component of u in the direction of v**) is defined to be

$$|\mathbf{u}| \cos \theta$$

where θ is the angle between **u** and **v**. Figure 3 gives a geometric interpretation of this concept. Intuitively, the component of **u** along **v** is the magnitude of the portion of **u** that points in the direction of **v**. Notice that the component of **u** along **v** is negative if $\pi/2 < \theta \le \pi$.

Note that the component of **u** along **v** is a scalar, not a vector.

FIGURE 3

In analyzing forces in physics and engineering, it's often helpful to express a vector as a sum of two vectors lying in perpendicular directions. For example, suppose a car is parked on an inclined driveway as in Figure 4. The weight of the car is a vector **w** that points directly downward. We can write

$$\mathbf{w} = \mathbf{u} + \mathbf{v}$$

where **u** is parallel to the driveway and **v** is perpendicular to the driveway. The vector **u** is the force that tends to roll the car down the driveway, and **v** is the force experienced by the surface of the driveway. The magnitudes of these forces are the components of **w** along **u** and **v**, respectively.

FIGURE 4

EXAMPLE 4 | Resolving a Force into Components

A car weighing 3000 lb is parked on a driveway that is inclined 15° to the horizontal, as shown in Figure 5.

(a) Find the magnitude of the force required to prevent the car from rolling down the driveway.

Gravity is the same in both cases, yet there is a definite difference in speed. The reason behind this is interesting. Gravity is doing two things at once: It is letting the weight slide down, and it is also preventing the weight from floating off the ramp and flying into outer space. We can draw a "free body diagram" that shows how the gravity available to let the weight slide down is affected by the angle of the ramp.

A block slides faster on a steeper slope because the projection of the gravitational force in the direction of the slope is larger. There is more force pushing the block down the slope and less of a force holding it to the surface of the slope.

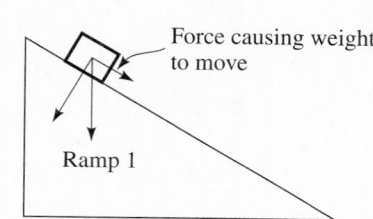

Force causing weight to move

Ramp 1

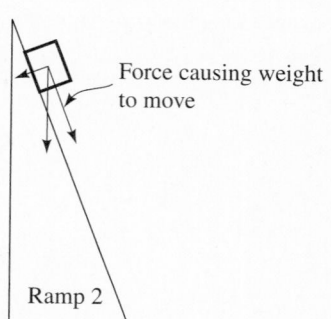

Force causing weight to move

Ramp 2

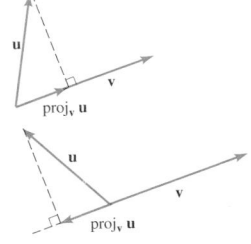

FIGURE 5

(b) Find the magnitude of the force experienced by the driveway due to the weight of the car.

SOLUTION   The car exerts a force **w** of 3000 lb directly downward. We resolve **w** into the sum of two vectors **u** and **v**, one parallel to the surface of the driveway and the other perpendicular to it, as shown in Figure 5.

(a) The magnitude of the part of the force **w** that causes the car to roll down the driveway is

$$|\mathbf{u}| = \text{component of } \mathbf{w} \text{ along } \mathbf{u} = 3000 \cos 75° \approx 776$$

Thus the force needed to prevent the car from rolling down the driveway is about 776 lb.

(b) The magnitude of the force exerted by the car on the driveway is

$$|\mathbf{v}| = \text{component of } \mathbf{w} \text{ along } \mathbf{v} = 3000 \cos 15° \approx 2898$$

The force experienced by the driveway is about 2898 lb.

✎. NOW TRY EXERCISE **49**　　　　　　　　　　　　　　■

The component of **u** along **v** can be computed by using dot products:

$$|\mathbf{u}| \cos \theta = \frac{|\mathbf{v}||\mathbf{u}| \cos \theta}{|\mathbf{v}|} = \frac{\mathbf{u} \cdot \mathbf{v}}{|\mathbf{v}|}$$

We have shown the following.

CALCULATING COMPONENTS

The component of **u** along **v** is $\dfrac{\mathbf{u} \cdot \mathbf{v}}{|\mathbf{v}|}$.

EXAMPLE 5 | Finding Components

Let $\mathbf{u} = \langle 1, 4 \rangle$ and $\mathbf{v} = \langle -2, 1 \rangle$. Find the component of **u** along **v**.

SOLUTION   We have

$$\text{component of } \mathbf{u} \text{ along } \mathbf{v} = \frac{\mathbf{u} \cdot \mathbf{v}}{|\mathbf{v}|} = \frac{(1)(-2) + (4)(1)}{\sqrt{4 + 1}} = \frac{2}{\sqrt{5}}$$

✎. NOW TRY EXERCISE **25**　　　　　　　　　　　　　　■

▼ The Projection of u Onto v

Figure 6 shows representations of the vectors **u** and **v**. The projection of **u** onto **v**, denoted by proj$_\mathbf{v}$ **u**, is the vector *parallel* to **v** and whose *length* is the component of **u** along **v** as shown in Figure 6. To find an expression for proj$_\mathbf{v}$ **u**, we first find a unit vector in the direction of **v** and then multiply it by the component of **u** along **v**:

$$\text{proj}_\mathbf{v}\, \mathbf{u} = (\text{component of } \mathbf{u} \text{ along } \mathbf{v})(\text{unit vector in direction of } \mathbf{v})$$

$$= \left(\frac{\mathbf{u} \cdot \mathbf{v}}{|\mathbf{v}|}\right) \frac{\mathbf{v}}{|\mathbf{v}|} = \left(\frac{\mathbf{u} \cdot \mathbf{v}}{|\mathbf{v}|^2}\right) \mathbf{v}$$

We often need to **resolve** a vector **u** into the sum of two vectors, one parallel to **v** and one orthogonal to **v**. That is, we want to write $\mathbf{u} = \mathbf{u}_1 + \mathbf{u}_2$, where $\mathbf{u}_1$ is parallel to **v** and $\mathbf{u}_2$ is orthogonal to **v**. In this case, $\mathbf{u}_1 = \text{proj}_\mathbf{v}\, \mathbf{u}$ and $\mathbf{u}_2 = \mathbf{u} - \text{proj}_\mathbf{v}\, \mathbf{u}$ (see Exercise 43).

FIGURE 6

IN-CLASS MATERIALS

Assume that $\mathbf{a} \cdot \mathbf{b} = \mathbf{a} \cdot \mathbf{c}$ and $\mathbf{a} \neq 0$. Pose the question, "Is it necessarily true that $\mathbf{b} = \mathbf{c}$?" When you've convinced the students (perhaps by example) that the answer is "no," the next logical question to ask is, "What *can* we say about **b** and **c**?" It can be shown that **b** and **c** have the same projection onto **a**, since $\mathbf{a} \perp (\mathbf{b} - \mathbf{c})$.

CALCULATING PROJECTIONS

The **projection of u onto v** is the vector proj$_v$ **u** given by

$$\text{proj}_v\, \mathbf{u} = \left(\frac{\mathbf{u}\cdot\mathbf{v}}{|\mathbf{v}|^2}\right)\mathbf{v}$$

If the vector **u** is **resolved** into $\mathbf{u}_1$ and $\mathbf{u}_2$, where $\mathbf{u}_1$ is parallel to **v** and $\mathbf{u}_2$ is orthogonal to **v**, then

$$\mathbf{u}_1 = \text{proj}_v\, \mathbf{u} \qquad \text{and} \qquad \mathbf{u}_2 = \mathbf{u} - \text{proj}_v\, \mathbf{u}$$

EXAMPLE 6 | Resolving a Vector into Orthogonal Vectors

Let $\mathbf{u} = \langle -2, 9\rangle$ and $\mathbf{v} = \langle -1, 2\rangle$.

(a) Find proj$_v$ **u**.

(b) Resolve **u** into $\mathbf{u}_1$ and $\mathbf{u}_2$, where $\mathbf{u}_1$ is parallel to **v** and $\mathbf{u}_2$ is orthogonal to **v**.

SOLUTION

(a) By the formula for the projection of one vector onto another we have

$$\text{proj}_v\, \mathbf{u} = \left(\frac{\mathbf{u}\cdot\mathbf{v}}{|\mathbf{v}|^2}\right)\mathbf{v} \qquad \text{Formula for projection}$$

$$= \left(\frac{\langle -2,9\rangle\cdot\langle -1,2\rangle}{(-1)^2+2^2}\right)\langle -1,2\rangle \qquad \text{Definition of } \mathbf{u} \text{ and } \mathbf{v}$$

$$= 4\langle -1,2\rangle = \langle -4,8\rangle$$

(b) By the formula in the preceding box we have $\mathbf{u} = \mathbf{u}_1 + \mathbf{u}_2$, where

$$\mathbf{u}_1 = \text{proj}_v\, \mathbf{u} = \langle -4,8\rangle \qquad \text{From part (a)}$$

$$\mathbf{u}_2 = \mathbf{u} - \text{proj}_v\, \mathbf{u} = \langle -2,9\rangle - \langle -4,8\rangle = \langle 2,1\rangle$$

✎. NOW TRY EXERCISE **29**

▼ Work

One use of the dot product occurs in calculating work. In everyday use, the term *work* means the total amount of effort required to perform a task. In physics, *work* has a technical meaning that conforms to this intuitive meaning. If a constant force of magnitude F moves an object through a distance d along a straight line, then the **work** done is

$$W = Fd \qquad \text{or} \qquad \text{work} = \text{force} \times \text{distance}$$

If F is measured in pounds and d in feet, then the unit of work is a foot-pound (ft-lb). For example, how much work is done in lifting a 20-lb weight 6 ft off the ground? Since a force of 20 lb is required to lift this weight and since the weight moves through a distance of 6 ft, the amount of work done is

$$W = Fd = (20)(6) = 120 \text{ ft-lb}$$

This formula applies only when the force is directed along the direction of motion. In the general case, if the force **F** moves an object from P to Q, as in Figure 7, then only the component of the force in the direction of $\mathbf{D} = \overrightarrow{PQ}$ affects the object. Thus the effective magnitude of the force on the object is

$$\text{component of } \mathbf{F} \text{ along } \mathbf{D} = |\mathbf{F}|\cos\theta$$

So the work done is

$$W = \text{force}\times\text{distance} = (|\mathbf{F}|\cos\theta)|\mathbf{D}| = |\mathbf{F}||\mathbf{D}|\cos\theta = \mathbf{F}\cdot\mathbf{D}$$

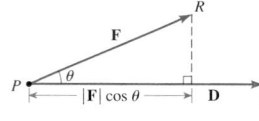

FIGURE 7

ALTERNATE EXAMPLE 6
Let $u = \langle 3, 8\rangle$ and $v = \langle -1, 1\rangle$.
(a) Find proj$_v$ **u**.
(b) Resolve **u** into $\mathbf{u}_1$ and $\mathbf{u}_2$, where $\mathbf{u}_1$ is parallel to **v** and $\mathbf{u}_2$ is orthogonal to **v**.

ANSWER

(a) $\left\langle -\dfrac{5}{2}, \dfrac{5}{2}\right\rangle$

(b) $\mathbf{u}_1 = \left\langle -\dfrac{5}{2}, \dfrac{5}{2}\right\rangle$

$\mathbf{u}_2 = \left\langle \dfrac{11}{2}, \dfrac{11}{2}\right\rangle$

EXAMPLES

- $\langle 5,6,2\rangle\cdot\langle -3,1,0\rangle = -9$
- Two vectors that are orthogonal:
  $\mathbf{a} = \langle 5,6,2\rangle$,
  $\mathbf{b} = \left\langle 1,-1,\dfrac{1}{2}\right\rangle$
- Projections: If $\mathbf{a} = \langle 2,1,-1\rangle$ and $\mathbf{b} = \langle 3,2,7\rangle$, then
  $\text{proj}_a\, \mathbf{b} = \left\langle \dfrac{1}{3}, \dfrac{1}{6}, \dfrac{1}{6}\right\rangle$,
  $\text{proj}_b\, \mathbf{a} = \left\langle \dfrac{3}{62}, \dfrac{1}{31}, -\dfrac{7}{62}\right\rangle$,
  and $|\mathbf{a}| = \sqrt{6}$.

We have derived the following simple formula for calculating work.

WORK

The **work** W done by a force $\mathbf{F}$ in moving along a vector $\mathbf{D}$ is

$$W = \mathbf{F} \cdot \mathbf{D}$$

EXAMPLE 7 | Calculating Work

A force is given by the vector $\mathbf{F} = \langle 2, 3 \rangle$ and moves an object from the point $(1, 3)$ to the point $(5, 9)$. Find the work done.

SOLUTION   The displacement vector is

$$\mathbf{D} = \langle 5 - 1, 9 - 3 \rangle = \langle 4, 6 \rangle$$

So the work done is

$$W = \mathbf{F} \cdot \mathbf{D} = \langle 2, 3 \rangle \cdot \langle 4, 6 \rangle = 26$$

If the unit of force is pounds and the distance is measured in feet, then the work done is 26 ft-lb.

✎. NOW TRY EXERCISE **35**   ■

EXAMPLE 8 | Calculating Work

A man pulls a wagon horizontally by exerting a force of 20 lb on the handle. If the handle makes an angle of 60° with the horizontal, find the work done in moving the wagon 100 ft.

SOLUTION   We choose a coordinate system with the origin at the initial position of the wagon (see Figure 8). That is, the wagon moves from the point $P(0, 0)$ to the point $Q(100, 0)$. The vector that represents this displacement is

$$\mathbf{D} = 100\,\mathbf{i}$$

The force on the handle can be written in terms of components (see Section 9.1) as

$$\mathbf{F} = (20 \cos 60°)\mathbf{i} + (20 \sin 60°)\mathbf{j} = 10\,\mathbf{i} + 10\sqrt{3}\,\mathbf{j}$$

Thus the work done is

$$W = \mathbf{F} \cdot \mathbf{D} = (10\,\mathbf{i} + 10\sqrt{3}\,\mathbf{j}) \cdot (100\,\mathbf{i}) = 1000 \text{ ft-lb}$$

✎. NOW TRY EXERCISE **47**   ■

FIGURE 8

9.2 EXERCISES

CONCEPTS

1–2 ■ Let $\mathbf{a} = \langle a_1, a_2 \rangle$ and $\mathbf{b} = \langle b_1, b_2 \rangle$ be nonzero vectors in the plane, and let θ be the angle between them.

1. The dot product of $\mathbf{a}$ and $\mathbf{b}$ is defined by

$$\mathbf{a} \cdot \mathbf{b} = \underline{\hspace{3cm}}$$

The dot product of two vectors is a _____, not a vector.

2. The angle θ satisfies

$$\cos \theta = \frac{}{}$$

So if $\mathbf{a} \cdot \mathbf{b} = 0$, the vectors are _____.

DRILL QUESTION

Consider the following pairs of vectors, all of which have length l:

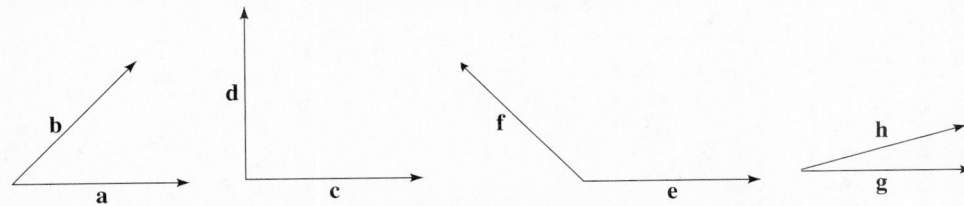

Put the following quantities in order, from smallest to largest: $\mathbf{a} \cdot \mathbf{b}, \mathbf{c} \cdot \mathbf{d}, \mathbf{e} \cdot \mathbf{f}, \mathbf{g} \cdot \mathbf{h}$

Answer

$\mathbf{e} \cdot \mathbf{f}, \mathbf{c} \cdot \mathbf{d}, \mathbf{a} \cdot \mathbf{b}, \mathbf{g} \cdot \mathbf{h}$

3. (a) The component of **a** along **b** is the scalar $|a| \cos \theta$ and can be expressed in terms of the dot product as

_____. Sketch this component in the figure below.

(b) The projection of **a** onto **b** is the vector

$\text{proj}_b \, \mathbf{a} =$ _____. Sketch this projection in the figure below.

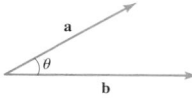

4. The work done by a force **F** in moving an object along a vector **D** is $W =$ _____.

SKILLS

5–14 ■ Find **(a)** $\mathbf{u} \cdot \mathbf{v}$ and **(b)** the angle between **u** and **v** to the nearest degree.

5. $\mathbf{u} = \langle 2, 0 \rangle$, $\quad \mathbf{v} = \langle 1, 1 \rangle$

6. $\mathbf{u} = \mathbf{i} + \sqrt{3}\mathbf{j}$, $\quad \mathbf{v} = -\sqrt{3}\mathbf{i} + \mathbf{j}$

7. $\mathbf{u} = \langle 2, 7 \rangle$, $\quad \mathbf{v} = \langle 3, 1 \rangle$

8. $\mathbf{u} = \langle -6, 6 \rangle$, $\quad \mathbf{v} = \langle 1, -1 \rangle$

9. $\mathbf{u} = \langle 3, -2 \rangle$, $\quad \mathbf{v} = \langle 1, 2 \rangle$

10. $\mathbf{u} = 2\mathbf{i} + \mathbf{j}$, $\quad \mathbf{v} = 3\mathbf{i} - 2\mathbf{j}$

11. $\mathbf{u} = -5\mathbf{j}$, $\quad \mathbf{v} = -\mathbf{i} - \sqrt{3}\mathbf{j}$

12. $\mathbf{u} = \mathbf{i} + \mathbf{j}$, $\quad \mathbf{v} = \mathbf{i} - \mathbf{j}$

13. $\mathbf{u} = \mathbf{i} + 3\mathbf{j}$, $\quad \mathbf{v} = 4\mathbf{i} - \mathbf{j}$

14. $\mathbf{u} = 3\mathbf{i} + 4\mathbf{j}$, $\quad \mathbf{v} = -2\mathbf{i} - \mathbf{j}$

15–20 ■ Determine whether the given vectors are perpendicular.

15. $\mathbf{u} = \langle 6, 4 \rangle$, $\quad \mathbf{v} = \langle -2, 3 \rangle$ **16.** $\mathbf{u} = \langle 0, -5 \rangle$, $\quad \mathbf{v} = \langle 4, 0 \rangle$

17. $\mathbf{u} = \langle -2, 6 \rangle$, $\quad \mathbf{v} = \langle 4, 2 \rangle$ **18.** $\mathbf{u} = 2\mathbf{i}$, $\quad \mathbf{v} = -7\mathbf{j}$

19. $\mathbf{u} = 2\mathbf{i} - 8\mathbf{j}$, $\quad \mathbf{v} = -12\mathbf{i} - 3\mathbf{j}$

20. $\mathbf{u} = 4\mathbf{i}$, $\quad \mathbf{v} = -\mathbf{i} + 3\mathbf{j}$

21–24 ■ Find the indicated quantity, assuming $\mathbf{u} = 2\mathbf{i} + \mathbf{j}$, $\mathbf{v} = \mathbf{i} - 3\mathbf{j}$, and $\mathbf{w} = 3\mathbf{i} + 4\mathbf{j}$.

21. $\mathbf{u} \cdot \mathbf{v} + \mathbf{u} \cdot \mathbf{w}$ **22.** $\mathbf{u} \cdot (\mathbf{v} + \mathbf{w})$

23. $(\mathbf{u} + \mathbf{v}) \cdot (\mathbf{u} - \mathbf{v})$ **24.** $(\mathbf{u} \cdot \mathbf{v})(\mathbf{u} \cdot \mathbf{w})$

25–28 ■ Find the component of **u** along **v**.

25. $\mathbf{u} = \langle 4, 6 \rangle$, $\quad \mathbf{v} = \langle 3, -4 \rangle$

26. $\mathbf{u} = \langle -3, 5 \rangle$, $\quad \mathbf{v} = \langle 1/\sqrt{2}, 1/\sqrt{2} \rangle$

27. $\mathbf{u} = 7\mathbf{i} - 24\mathbf{j}$, $\quad \mathbf{v} = \mathbf{j}$

28. $\mathbf{u} = 7\mathbf{i}$, $\quad \mathbf{v} = 8\mathbf{i} + 6\mathbf{j}$

29–34 ■ **(a)** Calculate $\text{proj}_v \, \mathbf{u}$. **(b)** Resolve **u** into $\mathbf{u}_1$ and $\mathbf{u}_2$, where $\mathbf{u}_1$ is parallel to **v** and $\mathbf{u}_2$ is orthogonal to **v**.

29. $\mathbf{u} = \langle -2, 4 \rangle$, $\quad \mathbf{v} = \langle 1, 1 \rangle$

30. $\mathbf{u} = \langle 7, -4 \rangle$, $\quad \mathbf{v} = \langle 2, 1 \rangle$

31. $\mathbf{u} = \langle 1, 2 \rangle$, $\quad \mathbf{v} = \langle 1, -3 \rangle$

32. $\mathbf{u} = \langle 11, 3 \rangle$, $\quad \mathbf{v} = \langle -3, -2 \rangle$

33. $\mathbf{u} = \langle 2, 9 \rangle$, $\quad \mathbf{v} = \langle -3, 4 \rangle$

34. $\mathbf{u} = \langle 1, 1 \rangle$, $\quad \mathbf{v} = \langle 2, -1 \rangle$

35–38 ■ Find the work done by the force **F** in moving an object from P to Q.

35. $\mathbf{F} = 4\mathbf{i} - 5\mathbf{j}$; $\quad P(0, 0)$, $Q(3, 8)$

36. $\mathbf{F} = 400\mathbf{i} + 50\mathbf{j}$; $\quad P(-1, 1)$, $Q(200, 1)$

37. $\mathbf{F} = 10\mathbf{i} + 3\mathbf{j}$; $\quad P(2, 3)$, $Q(6, -2)$

38. $\mathbf{F} = -4\mathbf{i} + 20\mathbf{j}$; $\quad P(0, 10)$, $Q(5, 25)$

39–42 ■ Let **u**, **v**, and **w** be vectors, and let a be a scalar. Prove the given property.

39. $\mathbf{u} \cdot \mathbf{v} = \mathbf{v} \cdot \mathbf{u}$

40. $(a\mathbf{u}) \cdot \mathbf{v} = a(\mathbf{u} \cdot \mathbf{v}) = \mathbf{u} \cdot (a\mathbf{v})$

41. $(\mathbf{u} + \mathbf{v}) \cdot \mathbf{w} = \mathbf{u} \cdot \mathbf{w} + \mathbf{v} \cdot \mathbf{w}$

42. $(\mathbf{u} - \mathbf{v}) \cdot (\mathbf{u} + \mathbf{v}) = |\mathbf{u}|^2 - |\mathbf{v}|^2$

43. Show that the vectors $\text{proj}_v \, \mathbf{u}$ and $\mathbf{u} - \text{proj}_v \, \mathbf{u}$ are orthogonal.

44. Evaluate $\mathbf{v} \cdot \text{proj}_v \, \mathbf{u}$.

APPLICATIONS

45. Work The force $\mathbf{F} = 4\mathbf{i} - 7\mathbf{j}$ moves an object 4 ft along the x-axis in the positive direction. Find the work done if the unit of force is the pound.

46. Work A constant force $\mathbf{F} = \langle 2, 8 \rangle$ moves an object along a straight line from the point $(2, 5)$ to the point $(11, 13)$. Find the work done if the distance is measured in feet and the force is measured in pounds.

47. Work A lawn mower is pushed a distance of 200 ft along a horizontal path by a constant force of 50 lb. The handle of the lawn mower is held at an angle of 30° from the horizontal (see the figure). Find the work done.

48. Work A car drives 500 ft on a road that is inclined 12° to the horizontal, as shown in the following figure. The car weighs 2500 lb. Thus gravity acts straight down on the car with a constant force $\mathbf{F} = -2500\mathbf{j}$. Find the work done by the car in overcoming gravity.

$-2500\mathbf{j}$

49. Force A car is on a driveway that is inclined 25° to the horizontal. If the car weighs 2755 lb, find the force required to keep it from rolling down the driveway.

50. Force A car is on a driveway that is inclined 10° to the horizontal. A force of 490 lb is required to keep the car from rolling down the driveway.
(a) Find the weight of the car.
(b) Find the force the car exerts against the driveway.

51. Force A package that weighs 200 lb is placed on an inclined plane. If a force of 80 lb is just sufficient to keep the package from sliding, find the angle of inclination of the plane. (Ignore the effects of friction.)

52. Force A cart weighing 40 lb is placed on a ramp inclined at 15° to the horizontal. The cart is held in place by a rope inclined at 60° to the horizontal, as shown in the figure. Find the force that the rope must exert on the cart to keep it from rolling down the ramp.

DISCOVERY ▪ DISCUSSION ▪ WRITING

53. Distance from a Point to a Line Let L be the line $2x + 4y = 8$ and let P be the point $(3, 4)$.
(a) Show that the points $Q(0, 2)$ and $R(2, 1)$ lie on L.
(b) Let $\mathbf{u} = \overrightarrow{QP}$ and $\mathbf{v} = \overrightarrow{QR}$, as shown in the figure. Find $\mathbf{w} = \text{proj}_{\mathbf{v}}\, \mathbf{u}$.
(c) Sketch a graph that explains why $|\mathbf{u} - \mathbf{w}|$ is the distance from P to L. Find this distance.
(d) Write a short paragraph describing the steps you would take to find the distance from a given point to a given line.

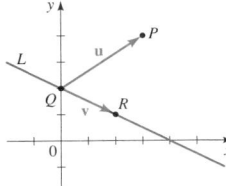

DISCOVERY PROJECT   **Sailing Against the Wind**

In this project we study how sailors use the method of taking a zigzag path, or *tacking*, to sail against the wind. You can find the project at the book companion website:
www.stewartmath.com

9.3 THREE-DIMENSIONAL COORDINATE GEOMETRY

The Three-Dimensional Rectangular Coordinate System ▶ Distance Formula in Three Dimensions ▶ The Equation of a Sphere

To locate a point in a plane, two numbers are necessary. We know that any point in the Cartesian plane can be represented as an ordered pair (a, b) of real numbers, where a is the x-coordinate and b is the y-coordinate. In three-dimensional space, a third dimension is added, so any point in space is represented by an ordered triple (a, b, c) of real numbers.

SUGGESTED TIME AND EMPHASIS

$\frac{1}{2}$–1 class, essential material

TEXT QUESTION

Explain why the equation $x = 3$ is the equation of a plane, not a line, in three-dimensional space.

Answer

Since the coordinates y and z are not specified, they can take on any value, extending the line $x = 3$ into a three-dimensional plane.

▼ The Three-Dimensional Rectangular Coordinate System

To represent points in space, we first choose a fixed point O (the origin) and three directed lines through O that are perpendicular to each other, called the **coordinate axes** and labeled the x-axis, y-axis, and z-axis. Usually we think of the x- and y-axes as being horizontal and the z-axis as being vertical, and we draw the orientation of the axes as in Figure 1.

The three coordinate axes determine the three **coordinate planes** illustrated in Figure 2(a). The xy-plane is the plane that contains the x- and y-axes; the yz-plane is the plane that contains the y- and z-axes; the xz-plane is the plane that contains the x- and z-axes. These three coordinate planes divide space into eight parts, called **octants**.

FIGURE 1 Coordinate axes

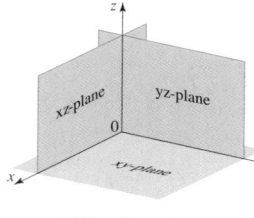

FIGURE 2   (a) Coordinate planes   (b) Coordinate "walls"

Because people often have difficulty visualizing diagrams of three-dimensional figures, you may find it helpful to do the following (see Figure 2(b)). Look at any bottom corner of a room and call the corner the origin. The wall on your left is in the xz-plane, the wall on your right is in the yz-plane, and the floor is in the xy-plane. The x-axis runs along the intersection of the floor and the left wall; the y-axis runs along the intersection of the floor and the right wall. The z-axis runs up from the floor toward the ceiling along the intersection of the two walls.

Now any point P in space can be located by a unique **ordered triple** of real numbers (a, b, c), as shown in Figure 3. The first number a is the x-coordinate of P, the second number b is the y-coordinate of P, and the third number c is the z-coordinate of P. The set of all ordered triples $\{(x, y, z) \mid x, y, z \in \mathbb{R}\}$ forms the **three-dimensional rectangular coordinate system**.

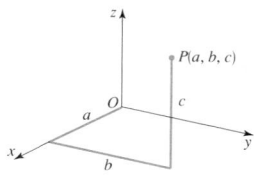

FIGURE 3 Point $P(a, b, c)$

EXAMPLE 1 | Plotting Points in Three Dimensions

Plot the points $(2, 4, 7)$ and $(-4, 3, -5)$.

SOLUTION The points are plotted in Figure 4.

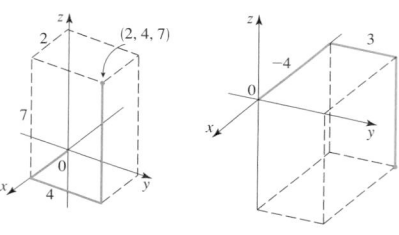

FIGURE 4

✏. NOW TRY EXERCISE **3(a)** ∎

In two-dimensional geometry the graph of an equation involving x and y is a *curve* in the plane. In three-dimensional geometry an equation in x, y, and z represents a *surface* in space.

ALTERNATE EXAMPLE 1

Plot the point $(3, 1, 4)$.

ANSWER

IN CLASS MATERIALS

- If possible, mark off one corner of the lecture room with electrical tape. Determine the coordinates of various objects in the room and/or find the equation of the plane of the chalkboard.

- Explain why the equation $z = \sqrt{R^2 - (x^2 + y^2)}$ represents the hemisphere $z \geq 0$, whereas the equation $x^2 + y^2 + z^2 = R^2$ represents a full sphere, perhaps making a two-dimensional analogy.

- Introduce the equation of a circular cylinder as an extension to $\mathbb{R}^3$ of the equation of the circle $x^2 + y^2 = r^2$.

EXAMPLE 2 | Surfaces in Three-Dimensional Space

Describe and sketch the surfaces represented by the following equations:

(a) $z = 3$ **(b)** $y = 5$

SOLUTION

(a) The surface consists of the points $P(x, y, z)$ where the z-coordinate is 3. This is the horizontal plane that is parallel to the xy-plane and three units above it, as in Figure 5.

(b) The surface consists of the points $P(x, y, z)$ where the y-coordinate is 5. This is the vertical plane that is parallel to the xz-plane and five units to the right of it, as in Figure 6.

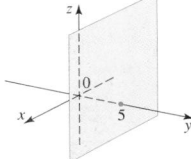

FIGURE 5   The plane $z = 3$ **FIGURE 6**   The plane $y = 5$

✎. NOW TRY EXERCISE **7**

▼ Distance Formula in Three Dimensions

The familiar formula for the distance between two points in a plane is easily extended to the following three-dimensional formula.

DISTANCE FORMULA IN THREE DIMENSIONS

The distance between the points $P(x_1, y_1, z_1)$ and $Q(x_2, y_2, z_2)$ is

$$d(P, Q) = \sqrt{(x_2 - x_1)^2 + (y_2 - y_1)^2 + (z_2 - z_1)^2}$$

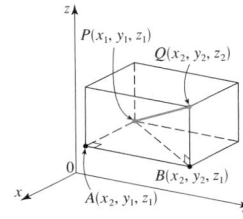

FIGURE 7

PROOF   To prove this formula, we construct a rectangular box as in Figure 7, where $P(x_1, y_1, z_1)$ and $Q(x_2, y_2, z_2)$ are diagonally opposite vertices and the faces of the box are parallel to the coordinate planes. If A and B are the vertices of the box that are indicated in the figure, then

$$d(P, A) = |x_2 - x_1| \qquad d(A, B) = |y_2 - y_1| \qquad d(Q, B) = |z_2 - z_1|$$

Triangles PAB and PBQ are right triangles, so by the Pythagorean Theorem we have

$$(d(P, Q))^2 = (d(P, B))^2 + (d(Q, B))^2$$
$$(d(P, B))^2 = (d(P, A))^2 + (d(A, B))^2$$

Combining these equations, we get

$$(d(P, Q))^2 = (d(P, A))^2 + (d(A, B))^2 + (d(Q, B))^2$$
$$= |x_2 - x_1|^2 + |y_2 - y_1|^2 + |z_2 - z_1|^2$$

Therefore

$$d(P, Q) = \sqrt{(x_2 - x_1)^2 + (y_2 - y_1)^2 + (z_2 - z_1)^2}$$

ALTERNATE EXAMPLE 2

Describe the surface represented by the equation $x = 2$.

ANSWER

It is a plane, parallel to the yz-plane (perpendicular to the x-axis), going through the point $(2, 0, 0)$.

EXAMPLES

One sphere in three forms:

(a) Description: sphere with center $(1, 2, 3)$ and radius 4

(b) $(x - 1)^2 + (y - 2)^2 + (z - 3)^2 = 16$

(c) $x^2 - 2x + y^2 - 4y + z^2 - 6z - 2 = 0$

ALTERNATE EXAMPLE 3
Find the distance between the points $P(2, 9, 6)$ and $Q(4, -1, -5)$.

ANSWER

15

ALTERNATE EXAMPLE 4
Find an equation of a sphere with radius 3 and center $C(6, -1, 2)$.

ANSWER
$(x - 6)^2 + (y + 1)^2 + (z - 2)^2 = 9$

ALTERNATE EXAMPLE 5
Show that $x^2 + y^2 + z^2 - 18x + 16y + 6z + 6 + 54 = 0$ is the equation of a sphere, and find its center and radius.

ANSWER
Center: $(9, -8, -3)$, radius: 10

EXAMPLE 3 | Using the Distance Formula

Find the distance between the points $P(2, -1, 7)$ and $Q(1, -3, 5)$.

SOLUTION   We use the Distance Formula:

$$d(P, Q) = \sqrt{(1 - 2)^2 + (-3 - (-1))^2 + (5 - 7)^2} = \sqrt{1 + 4 + 4} = 3$$

✎. NOW TRY EXERCISE **3(b)**   ∎

▼ The Equation of a Sphere

We can use the Distance Formula to find an equation for a sphere in a three-dimensional coordinate space.

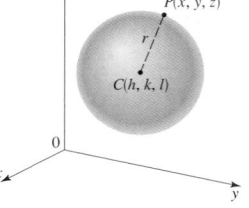

FIGURE 8 Sphere with radius r and center $C(h, k, l)$

EQUATION OF A SPHERE

An equation of a sphere with center $C(h, k, l)$ and radius r is

$$(x - h)^2 + (y - k)^2 + (z - l)^2 = r^2$$

PROOF   A sphere with radius r is the set of all points $P(x, y, z)$ whose distance from the center C is the constant r (see Figure 8). By the Distance Formula we have

$$[d(P, C)]^2 = (x - h)^2 + (y - k)^2 + (z - l)^2$$

Since the distance $d(P, C)$ is equal to r, we get the desired formula.   ∎

EXAMPLE 4 | Finding the Equation of a Sphere

Find an equation of a sphere with radius 5 and center $C(-2, 1, 3)$.

SOLUTION   We use the general equation of a sphere, with $r = 5$, $h = -2$, $k = 1$, and $l = 3$:

$$(x + 2)^2 + (y - 1)^2 + (z - 3)^2 = 25$$

✎. NOW TRY EXERCISE **11**   ∎

EXAMPLE 5 | Finding the Center and Radius of a Sphere

Show that $x^2 + y^2 + z^2 + 4x - 6y + 2z + 6 = 0$ is the equation of a sphere, and find its center and radius.

SOLUTION   We complete the squares in the x-, y-, and z-terms to rewrite the given equation in the form of an equation of a sphere:

$$x^2 + y^2 + z^2 + 4x - 6y + 2z + 6 = 0 \qquad \text{Given equation}$$
$$(x^2 + 4x + 4) + (y^2 - 6y + 9) + (z^2 + 2z + 1) = -6 + 4 + 9 + 1 \qquad \text{Complete squares}$$
$$(x + 2)^2 + (y - 3)^2 + (z + 1)^2 = 8 \qquad \text{Factor into squares}$$

Comparing this with the standard equation of a sphere, we can see that the center is $(-2, 3, -1)$ and the radius is $\sqrt{8} = 2\sqrt{2}$.

✎. NOW TRY EXERCISE **15**   ∎

The intersection of a sphere with a plane is called the **trace** of the sphere in a plane.

EXAMPLE 6 | Finding the Trace of a Sphere

Describe the trace of the sphere $(x - 2)^2 + (y - 4)^2 + (z - 5)^2 = 36$ in
(a) the xy-plane and **(b)** the plane $z = 9$.

SOLUTION

(a) In the xy-plane the z-coordinate is 0. So the trace of the sphere in the xy-plane consists of all the points on the sphere whose z-coordinate is 0. We replace z by 0 in
the equation of the sphere and get

$$(x - 2)^2 + (y - 4)^2 + (0 - 5)^2 = 36 \qquad \text{Replace } z \text{ by } 0$$
$$(x - 2)^2 + (y - 4)^2 + 25 = 36 \qquad \text{Calculate}$$
$$(x - 2)^2 + (y - 4)^2 = 11 \qquad \text{Subtract } 25$$

Thus the trace of the sphere is the circle

$$(x - 2)^2 + (y - 4)^2 = 11, \qquad z = 0$$

which is a circle of radius $\sqrt{11}$ that is in the xy-plane, centered at $(2, 4, 0)$ (see
Figure 9(a)).

(b) The trace of the sphere in the plane $z = 9$ consists of all the points on the sphere
whose z-coordinate is 9. So we replace z by 9 in the equation of the sphere and get

$$(x - 2)^2 + (y - 4)^2 + (9 - 5)^2 = 36 \qquad \text{Replace } z \text{ by } 0$$
$$(x - 2)^2 + (y - 4)^2 + 16 = 36 \qquad \text{Calculate}$$
$$(x - 2)^2 + (y - 4)^2 = 20 \qquad \text{Subtract } 16$$

Thus the trace of the sphere is the circle

$$(x - 2)^2 + (y - 4)^2 = 20, \qquad z = 9$$

which is a circle of radius $\sqrt{20}$ that is 9 units above the xy-plane, centered at
$(2, 4, 9)$ (see Figure 9(b)).

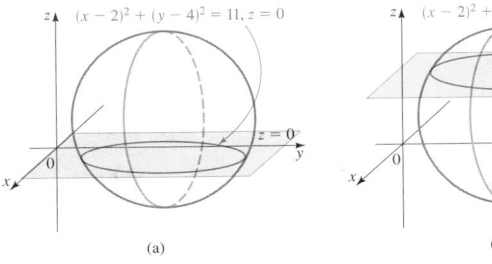

(a)   (b)

FIGURE 9 The trace of a sphere in the planes $z = 0$ and $z = 9$

NOW TRY EXERCISE **19**

DRILL QUESTION

What is the distance between the points $(-1, -1, -1)$ and $(-4, -1, 3)$?

Answer

5

9.3 EXERCISES

CONCEPTS

1–2 ■ Refer to the figure.

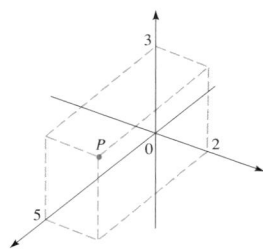

1. In a three-dimensional coordinate system the three mutually perpendicular axes are called the ___-axis, the ___-axis, and the ___-axis. Label the axes in the figure. The point P in the figure has coordinates (▢ , ▢ , ▢). The equation of the plane passing through P and parallel to the xz-plane is

_____.

2. The distance between the point $P(x_1, y_1, z_1)$ and $Q(x_2, y_2, z_2)$ is given by the formula $d(P, Q) = $ _____.
The distance between the point P in the figure and the origin is _____. The equation of the sphere centered at P with radius 3 is _____.

SKILLS

3–6 ■ Two points P and Q are given. **(a)** Plot P and Q. **(b)** Find the distance between P and Q.

3. $P(3, 1, 0)$, $Q(-1, 2, -5)$

4. $P(5, 0, 10)$, $Q(3, -6, 7)$

5. $P(-2, -1, 0)$, $Q(-12, 3, 0)$

6. $P(5, -4, -6)$, $Q(8, -7, 4)$

7–10 ■ Describe and sketch the surface represented by the given equation.

7. $x = 4$　　　　　　　**8.** $y = -2$

9. $z = 8$　　　　　　　**10.** $y = -1$

11–14 ■ Find an equation of a sphere with the given radius r and center C.

11. $r = 5$;　$C(2, -5, 3)$

12. $r = 3$;　$C(-1, 4, -7)$

13. $r = \sqrt{6}$;　$C(3, -1, 0)$

14. $r = \sqrt{11}$;　$C(-10, 0, 1)$

15–18 ■ Show that the equation represents a sphere, and find its center and radius.

15. $x^2 + y^2 + z^2 - 10x + 2y + 8z = 9$

16. $x^2 + y^2 + z^2 + 4x - 6y + 2z = 10$

17. $x^2 + y^2 + z^2 = 12x + 2y$

18. $x^2 + y^2 + z^2 = 14y - 6z$

19. Describe the trace of the sphere

$$(x + 1)^2 + (y - 2)^2 + (z + 10)^2 = 100$$

in **(a)** the yz-plane and **(b)** the plane $x = 4$.

20. Describe the trace of the sphere

$$x^2 + (y - 4)^2 + (z - 3)^2 = 144$$

in **(a)** the xz-plane and in **(b)** the plane $z = -2$.

APPLICATIONS

21. Spherical Water Tank　A water tank is in the shape of a sphere of radius 5 feet. The tank is supported on a metal circle 4 feet below the center of the sphere, as shown in the figure. Find the radius of the metal circle.

22. A Spherical Buoy　A spherical buoy of radius 2 feet floats in a calm lake. Six inches of the buoy are submerged. Place a coordinate system with the origin at the center of the sphere.
(a) Find an equation of the sphere.
(b) Find an equation of the circle formed at the waterline of the buoy.

DISCOVERY ▪ DISCUSSION ▪ WRITING

23. Visualizing a Set in Space Try to visualize the set of all points (x, y, z) in a coordinate space that are equidistant from the points $P(0, 0, 0)$ and $Q(0, 3, 0)$. Use the Distance Formula to find an equation for this surface, and observe that it is a plane.

24. Visualizing a Set in Space Try to visualize the set of all points (x, y, z) in a coordinate space that are twice as far from the points $Q(0, 3, 0)$ as from the point $P(0, 0, 0)$. Use the Distance Formula to show that the set is a sphere, and find its center and radius.

9.4 VECTORS IN THREE DIMENSIONS

Vectors in Space ▶ Combining Vectors in Space ▶ The Dot Product for Vectors in Space

Recall that vectors are used to indicate a quantity that has both magnitude and direction. In Section 9.1 we studied vectors in the coordinate plane, where the direction is restricted to two dimensions. Vectors in space have a direction that is in three-dimensional space. The properties that hold for vectors in the plane hold for vectors in space as well.

▼ Vectors in Space

Recall from Section 9.1 that a vector can be described geometrically by its initial point and terminal point. When we place a vector **a** in space with its initial point at the origin, we can describe it algebraically as an ordered triple:

$$\mathbf{a} = \langle a_1, a_2, a_3 \rangle$$

where a_1, a_2, and a_3 are the **components** of **a** (see Figure 1). Recall also that a vector has many different representations, depending on its initial point. The following definition gives the relationship between the algebraic and geometric representations of a vector.

FIGURE 1 $\mathbf{a} = \langle a_1, a_2, a_3 \rangle$

COMPONENT FORM OF A VECTOR IN SPACE

If a vector **a** is represented in space with initial point $P(x_1, y_1, z_1)$ and terminal point $Q(x_2, y_2, z_2)$, then

$$\mathbf{a} = \langle x_2 - x_1, y_2 - y_1, z_2 - z_1 \rangle$$

EXAMPLE 1 | Describing Vectors in Component Form

(a) Find the components of the vector **a** with initial point $P(1, -4, 5)$ and terminal point $Q(3, 1, -1)$.

(b) If the vector $\mathbf{b} = \langle -2, 1, 3 \rangle$ has initial point $(2, 1, -1)$, what is its terminal point?

SOLUTION

(a) The desired vector is

$$\mathbf{a} = \langle 3 - 1, 1 - (-4), -1 - 5 \rangle = \langle 2, 5, -6 \rangle$$

See Figure 2.

(b) Let the terminal point of **b** be (x, y, z). Then

$$\mathbf{b} = \langle x - 2, y - 1, z - (-1) \rangle$$

Since $\mathbf{b} = \langle -2, 1, 3 \rangle$ we have $x - 2 = -2$, $y - 1 = 1$, and $z + 1 = 3$. So $x = 0$, $y = 2$, and $z = 2$, and the terminal point is $(0, 2, 2)$.

FIGURE 2 $\mathbf{a} = \langle 2, 5, -6 \rangle$

◥ NOW TRY EXERCISES **3** AND **7**   ■

SUGGESTED TIME AND EMPHASIS

$\frac{1}{2}$ class, essential material

ALTERNATE EXAMPLE 1

(a) Find the components of the vector **a** with initial point $P(8, 6, 7)$ and terminal point $Q(5, 3, 0)$.

(b) If the vector $\mathbf{b} = \langle 3, 0, -4 \rangle$ has initial point $(-3, -4, 8)$, what is its terminal point?

ANSWERS

(a) $\langle -3, -3, -7 \rangle$

(b) $(0, -4, 4)$

TEXT QUESTION

If $\mathbf{a} = \langle a_1, a_2, a_3 \rangle$ has $a_2 > 0$ and $a_3 < 0$, then is the z-component of $-3\mathbf{a}$ positive or negative?

Answer

Positive

ALTERNATE EXAMPLE 2

Find the magnitude of the vector $\langle 3, -4, 12 \rangle$.

ANSWER

13

ALTERNATE EXAMPLE 3

If $\mathbf{u} = \langle -3, 0, 2 \rangle$ and $\mathbf{v} = \langle 4, 1, -2 \rangle$, find $\mathbf{u} + \mathbf{v}$, $\mathbf{u} - \mathbf{v}$, and $2\mathbf{u} - 4\mathbf{v}$.

ANSWER

$\langle 1, 1, 0 \rangle$, $\langle -7, -1, 4 \rangle$, $\langle -22, -4, 12 \rangle$

IN-CLASS MATERIALS

- Picture two students standing on opposite sides of a giant cube, 8 ft on a side, pushing toward the center. Have the students describe in what direction the cube will probably move (toward one of the two students or not at all if the students have the same strength). Now have them picture the students standing on adjacent sides, "kitty-corner." Now have them describe the resultant motion, and try to get them to justify their answers. Lead into how vectors give us a very natural way of describing the situation and predicting the outcome.

The following formula is a consequence of the Distance Formula, since the vector $\mathbf{a} = \langle a_1, a_2, a_3 \rangle$ in standard position has initial point $(0, 0, 0)$ and terminal point (a_1, a_2, a_3).

MAGNITUDE OF A VECTOR IN THREE DIMENSIONS

The magnitude of the vector $\mathbf{a} = \langle a_1, a_2, a_3 \rangle$ is

$$|\mathbf{a}| = \sqrt{a_1^2 + a_2^2 + a_3^2}$$

EXAMPLE 2 | Magnitude of Vectors in Three Dimensions

Find the magnitude of the given vector.

(a) $\mathbf{u} = \langle 3, 2, 5 \rangle$ (b) $\mathbf{v} = \langle 0, 3, -1 \rangle$ (c) $\mathbf{w} = \langle 0, 0, -1 \rangle$

SOLUTION

(a) $|\mathbf{u}| = \sqrt{3^2 + 2^2 + 5^2} = \sqrt{38}$

(b) $|\mathbf{v}| = \sqrt{0^2 + 3^2 + (-1)^2} = \sqrt{10}$

(c) $|\mathbf{w}| = \sqrt{0^2 + 0^2 + (-1)^2} = 1$

✎. NOW TRY EXERCISE **11** ∎

▼ Combining Vectors in Space

We now give definitions of the algebraic operations involving vectors in three dimensions.

ALGEBRAIC OPERATIONS ON VECTORS IN THREE DIMENSIONS

If $\mathbf{a} = \langle a_1, a_2, a_3 \rangle$, $\mathbf{b} = \langle b_1, b_2, b_3 \rangle$, and c is a scalar, then

$$\mathbf{a} + \mathbf{b} = \langle a_1 + b_1, a_2 + b_2, a_3 + b_3 \rangle$$
$$\mathbf{a} - \mathbf{b} = \langle a_1 - b_1, a_2 - b_2, a_3 - b_3 \rangle$$
$$c\mathbf{a} = \langle ca_1, ca_2, ca_3 \rangle$$

EXAMPLE 3 | Operations with Three-Dimensional Vectors

If $\mathbf{u} = \langle 1, -2, 4 \rangle$ and $\mathbf{v} = \langle 6, -1, 1 \rangle$ find $\mathbf{u} + \mathbf{v}$, $\mathbf{u} - \mathbf{v}$, and $5\mathbf{u} - 3\mathbf{v}$.

SOLUTION Using the definitions of algebraic operations we have

$$\mathbf{u} + \mathbf{v} = \langle 1 + 6, -2 - 1, 4 + 1 \rangle = \langle 7, -3, 5 \rangle$$
$$\mathbf{u} - \mathbf{v} = \langle 1 - 6, -2 - (-1), 4 - 1 \rangle = \langle -5, -1, 3 \rangle$$
$$5\mathbf{u} - 3\mathbf{v} = 5\langle 1, -2, 4 \rangle - 3\langle 6, -1, 1 \rangle = \langle 5, -10, 20 \rangle - \langle 18, -3, 3 \rangle = \langle -13, -7, 17 \rangle$$

✎. NOW TRY EXERCISE **15** ∎

Recall that a unit vector is a vector of length 1. The vector $\mathbf{w}$ in Example 2(c) is an example of a unit vector. Some other unit vectors in three dimensions are

$$\mathbf{i} = \langle 1, 0, 0 \rangle \qquad \mathbf{j} = \langle 0, 1, 0 \rangle \qquad \mathbf{k} = \langle 0, 0, 1 \rangle$$

as shown in Figure 3. Any vector in three dimensions can be written in terms of these three vectors (see Figure 4).

FIGURE 3

FIGURE 4

- Show how it is tough, by inspection, to determine whether a three-dimensional triangle is a right triangle, but three-dimensional vectors make it simple. For example, consider the triangle with vertices $(2, 1, 2)$, $(3, 3, 1)$, $(2, 2, 4)$. We create vectors between the vertices and find that the dot product of two of these vectors is zero.

- Point out that even though it isn't easy to picture four-dimensional space, it is simple to generalize all our three-dimensional formulas and results. You can put these four vectors on the board $\mathbf{u} = \langle 1, 2, -2, 6 \rangle$, $\mathbf{v} = \langle 2, 1, 3, 0 \rangle$ and the students can figure out that the dot product "should be" -2 without ever formally defining a four-dimensional dot product. Similarly, we can determine the magnitudes of four-dimensional vectors, their sums, differences, and scalar multiples.

EXPRESSING VECTORS IN TERMS OF i, j, AND k

The vector $\mathbf{a} = \langle a_1, a_2, a_3 \rangle$ can be expressed in terms of $\mathbf{i}$, $\mathbf{j}$, and $\mathbf{k}$ by

$$\mathbf{a} = \langle a_1, a_2, a_3 \rangle = a_1\mathbf{i} + a_2\mathbf{j} + a_3\mathbf{k}$$

All the properties of vectors on page 583 in Section 9.1 hold for vectors in three dimensions as well. We use these properties in the next example.

EXAMPLE 4 | Vectors in Terms of **i, j,** and **k**

(a) Write the vector $\mathbf{u} = \langle 5, -3, 6 \rangle$ in terms of **i, j,** and **k**.

(b) If $\mathbf{u} = \mathbf{i} + 2\mathbf{j} - 3\mathbf{k}$ and $\mathbf{v} = 4\mathbf{i} + 7\mathbf{k}$, express the vector $2\mathbf{u} + 3\mathbf{v}$ in terms of **i, j,** and **k**.

SOLUTION

(a) $\mathbf{u} = 5\mathbf{i} + (-3)\mathbf{j} + 6\mathbf{k} = 5\mathbf{i} - 3\mathbf{j} + 6\mathbf{k}$

(b) We use the properties of vectors to get the following:

$$2\mathbf{u} + 3\mathbf{v} = 2(2\mathbf{i} + 2\mathbf{j} - 3\mathbf{k}) + 3(4\mathbf{i} + 7\mathbf{k})$$
$$= 4\mathbf{i} + 4\mathbf{j} - 6\mathbf{k} + 12\mathbf{i} + 21\mathbf{k}$$
$$= 16\mathbf{i} + 4\mathbf{j} + 15\mathbf{k}$$

✎. NOW TRY EXERCISE **19**

▼ **The Dot Product for Vectors in Space**

We define the dot product for vectors in three dimensions. All the properties of the dot product, including the Dot Product Theorem (page 590), hold for vectors in three dimensions.

DEFINITION OF THE DOT PRODUCT FOR VECTORS IN THREE DIMENSIONS

If $\mathbf{a} = \langle a_1, a_2, a_3 \rangle$ and $\mathbf{b} = \langle b_1, b_2, b_3 \rangle$ are vectors in three dimensions, then their **dot product** is defined by

$$\mathbf{a} \cdot \mathbf{b} = a_1b_1 + a_2b_2 + a_3b_3$$

EXAMPLE 5 | Calculating Dot Products for Vectors in Three Dimensions

Find the given dot product.

(a) $\langle -1, 2, 3 \rangle \cdot \langle 6, 5, -1 \rangle$

(b) $(2\mathbf{i} - 3\mathbf{j} - \mathbf{k}) \cdot (-\mathbf{i} + 2\mathbf{j} + 8\mathbf{k})$

SOLUTION

(a) $\langle -1, 2, 3 \rangle \cdot \langle 6, 5, -1 \rangle = (-1)(6) + (2)(5) + (3)(-1) = 1$

(b) $(2\mathbf{i} - 3\mathbf{j} - \mathbf{k}) \cdot (-\mathbf{i} + 2\mathbf{j} + 8\mathbf{k}) = \langle 2, -3, -1 \rangle \cdot \langle -1, 2, 8 \rangle$
$$= (2)(-1) + (-3)(2) + (-1)(8) = -16$$

✎. NOW TRY EXERCISES **25** AND **27**

ALTERNATE EXAMPLE 4
If $\mathbf{u} = \langle 4, 2, 8 \rangle$ and $\mathbf{v} = \langle 1, 5, 1 \rangle$, express the vector $2\mathbf{u} - \mathbf{v}$ in terms of **i, j,** and **k**.

ANSWER
$7\mathbf{i} - \mathbf{j} + 15\mathbf{k}$

ALTERNATE EXAMPLE 5
Find the given dot product.
(a) $\langle -2, -3, 7 \rangle \cdot \langle -4, -4, 4 \rangle$
(b) $(2\mathbf{j} + 7\mathbf{k}) \cdot (-\mathbf{i} + 2\mathbf{j} + 3\mathbf{k})$

ANSWERS
(a) 48
(b) 25

EXAMPLE
Two perpendicular three-dimensional vectors: $\langle -2, 5, 1 \rangle$, $\langle 5, 4, -10 \rangle$

Recall that the cosine of the angle between two vectors can be calculated using the dot product (page 591). The same property holds for vectors in three dimensions. We restate this property here for emphasis.

ANGLE BETWEEN TWO VECTORS

Let **u** and **v** be vectors in space and θ be the angle between them. Then

$$\cos \theta = \frac{\mathbf{u} \cdot \mathbf{v}}{|\mathbf{u}|\,|\mathbf{v}|}$$

In particular, **u** and **v** are **perpendicular** (or **orthogonal**) if and only if $\mathbf{u} \cdot \mathbf{v} = 0$.

ALTERNATE EXAMPLE 6
Show that the vector
$\mathbf{u} = 3\,\mathbf{i} - \mathbf{j} + 2\,\mathbf{k}$ is not
perpendicular to
$\mathbf{v} = 3\,\mathbf{i} + 6\,\mathbf{j} - 3\,\mathbf{k}$.

ANSWER

$\mathbf{u} \cdot \mathbf{v} = -3 \neq 0$. Since the dot product is not zero, the vectors are not perpendicular.

EXAMPLE 6 | Checking Vectors for Perpendicularity

Show that the vector $\mathbf{u} = 2\,\mathbf{i} + 2\,\mathbf{j} - \mathbf{k}$ is perpendicular to $5\,\mathbf{i} - 4\,\mathbf{j} + 2\,\mathbf{k}$.

SOLUTION   We find the dot product.

$$(2\,\mathbf{i} + 2\,\mathbf{j} - \mathbf{k}) \cdot (5\,\mathbf{i} - 4\,\mathbf{j} + 2\,\mathbf{k}) = (2)(5) + (2)(-4) + (-1)(2) = 0$$

Since the dot product is 0, the vectors are perpendicular. See Figure 5.

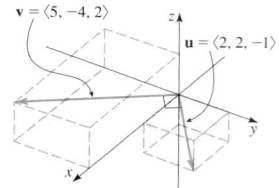

FIGURE 5   The vectors **u** and **v** are perpendicular.

▲. NOW TRY EXERCISE **29**

▼ Direction Angles of a Vector

The **direction angles** of a nonzero vector $\mathbf{a} = a_1\,\mathbf{i} + a_2\,\mathbf{j} + a_3\,\mathbf{k}$ are the angles α, β, and γ in the interval $[0, \pi]$ that the vector **a** makes with the positive x-, y-, and z-axes (see Figure 6). The cosines of these angles, $\cos \alpha$, $\cos \beta$, and $\cos \gamma$, are called the **direction cosines** of the vector **a**. By using the formula for the angle between two vectors, we can find the direction cosines of **a**:

$$\cos \alpha = \frac{\mathbf{a} \cdot \mathbf{i}}{|\mathbf{a}|\,|\mathbf{i}|} = \frac{a_1}{|\mathbf{a}|} \qquad \cos \beta = \frac{\mathbf{a} \cdot \mathbf{j}}{|\mathbf{a}|\,|\mathbf{j}|} = \frac{a_2}{|\mathbf{a}|} \qquad \cos \gamma = \frac{\mathbf{a} \cdot \mathbf{k}}{|\mathbf{a}|\,|\mathbf{k}|} = \frac{a_3}{|\mathbf{a}|}$$

FIGURE 6   Direction angles of the vector **a**

DIRECTION ANGLES OF A VECTOR

If $\mathbf{a} = a_1\mathbf{i} + a_2\mathbf{j} + a_3\mathbf{k}$ is a nonzero vector in space, the direction angles α, β, and γ satisfy

$$\cos \alpha = \frac{a_1}{|\mathbf{a}|} \qquad \cos \beta = \frac{a_2}{|\mathbf{a}|} \qquad \cos \gamma = \frac{a_3}{|\mathbf{a}|}$$

In particular, if $|\mathbf{a}| = 1$ then the direction cosines of $\mathbf{a}$ are simply the components of $\mathbf{a}$.

EXAMPLE 7 | Finding the Direction Angles of a Vector

Find the direction angles of the vector $\mathbf{a} = \mathbf{i} + 2\mathbf{j} + 3\mathbf{k}$.

SOLUTION The length of the vector $\mathbf{a}$ is $|\mathbf{a}| = \sqrt{1^2 + 2^2 + 3^2} = \sqrt{14}$. From the above box we get

$$\cos \alpha = \frac{1}{\sqrt{14}} \qquad \cos \beta = \frac{2}{\sqrt{14}} \qquad \cos \gamma = \frac{3}{\sqrt{14}}$$

Since the direction angles are in the interval $[0, \pi]$ and since $\cos^{-1}$ gives angles in that same interval, we get α, β, and γ by simply taking $\cos^{-1}$ of the above equations.

$$\alpha = \cos^{-1}\frac{1}{\sqrt{14}} \approx 74° \qquad \beta = \cos^{-1}\frac{2}{\sqrt{14}} \approx 58° \qquad \gamma = \cos^{-1}\frac{3}{\sqrt{14}} \approx 37°$$

NOW TRY EXERCISE **37**

The direction angles of a vector uniquely determine its direction, but not its length. If we also know the length of the vector $\mathbf{a}$, the expressions for the direction cosines of $\mathbf{a}$ allow us to express the vector as

$$\mathbf{a} = \langle\, |\mathbf{a}|\cos \alpha, |\mathbf{a}|\cos \beta, |\mathbf{a}|\cos \gamma \,\rangle$$

From this we get

$$\mathbf{a} = |\mathbf{a}|\langle \cos \alpha, \cos \beta, \cos \gamma \rangle$$

$$\frac{\mathbf{a}}{|\mathbf{a}|} = \langle \cos \alpha, \cos \beta, \cos \gamma \rangle$$

Since $\mathbf{a}/|\mathbf{a}|$ is a unit vector we get the following.

PROPERTY OF DIRECTION COSINES

The direction angles α, β, and γ of a nonzero vector $\mathbf{a}$ in space satisfy the following equation:

$$\cos^2\alpha + \cos^2\beta + \cos^2\gamma = 1$$

This property indicates that if we know two of the direction cosines of a vector, we can find the third up to its sign.

ALTERNATE EXAMPLE 7

Find the direction angles of the vector $a = 4\mathbf{i} + 2\mathbf{j} + 2\mathbf{k}$.

ANSWER

$\alpha \approx 35.36°$
$\beta \approx 65.91°$
$\gamma \approx 65.91°$

ALTERNATE EXAMPLE 8

A vector makes an angle $\alpha = \pi/3$ with the positive x-axis and an angle $\beta = \pi/3$ with the positive y-axis. Find all possible values of the angle γ that the vector makes with the positive z-axis.

ANSWER

$\gamma = \pi/4$ or $\gamma = 7\pi/4$

An angle θ is **acute** if $0 \le \theta < \pi/2$ and is **obtuse** if $\pi/2 < \theta \le \pi$.

EXAMPLE 8 | Finding the Direction Angles of a Vector

A vector makes an angle $\alpha = \pi/3$ with the positive x-axis and an angle $\beta = 3\pi/4$ with the positive y-axis. Find the angle γ that the vector makes with the positive z-axis, given that γ is an obtuse angle.

SOLUTION   By the property of the direction angles we have

$$\cos^2 \alpha + \cos^2 \beta + \cos^2 \gamma = 1$$

$$\cos^2 \frac{\pi}{3} + \cos^2 \frac{3\pi}{4} + \cos^2 \gamma = 1$$

$$\left(\frac{1}{2}\right)^2 + \left(-\frac{1}{\sqrt{2}}\right)^2 + \cos^2 \gamma = 1$$

$$\cos^2 \gamma = \frac{1}{4}$$

$$\cos \gamma = \frac{1}{2} \qquad \text{or} \qquad \cos \gamma = -\frac{1}{2}$$

$$\gamma = \frac{\pi}{3} \qquad \text{or} \qquad \gamma = \frac{2\pi}{3}$$

Since we require γ to be an obtuse angle, we conclude that $\gamma = 2\pi/3$.

✎. NOW TRY EXERCISE **41**

9.4 EXERCISES

CONCEPTS

1. A vector in three dimensions can be written in either of two forms: in coordinate form as $\mathbf{a} = \langle a_1, a_2, a_3 \rangle$ and in terms of

the _____ vectors $\mathbf{i}$, $\mathbf{j}$, and $\mathbf{k}$ as $\mathbf{a} =$ _____.

The magnitude of the vector $\mathbf{a}$ is $|\mathbf{a}| =$ _____.

So $\langle 4, -2, 4 \rangle = \square\,\mathbf{i} + \square\,\mathbf{j} + \square\,\mathbf{k}$ and

$7\mathbf{j} - 24\mathbf{k} = \langle \square, \square, \square \rangle$.

2. The angle θ between the vectors $\mathbf{u}$ and $\mathbf{v}$ satisfies

$\cos \theta =$ _____. So if $\mathbf{u}$ and $\mathbf{v}$ are perpendicular, then

$\mathbf{u} \cdot \mathbf{v} =$ _____. If $\mathbf{u} = \langle 4, 5, 6 \rangle$ and $\mathbf{v} = \langle 3, 0, -2 \rangle$ then

$\mathbf{u} \cdot \mathbf{v} =$ _____, so $\mathbf{u}$ and $\mathbf{v}$ are _____.

SKILLS

3–6 ■ Find the vector $\mathbf{v}$ with initial point P and terminal point Q.

3. $P(1, -1, 0)$, $Q(0, -2, 5)$ **4.** $P(1, 2, -1)$, $Q(3, -1, 2)$

5. $P(6, -1, 0)$, $Q(0, -3, 0)$ **6.** $P(1, -1, -1)$, $Q(0, 0, -1)$

7–10 ■ If the vector $\mathbf{v}$ has initial point P, what is its terminal point?

7. $\mathbf{v} = \langle 3, 4, -2 \rangle$, $P(2, 0, 1)$

8. $\mathbf{v} = \langle 0, 0, 1 \rangle$, $P(0, 1, -1)$

9. $\mathbf{v} = \langle -2, 0, 2 \rangle$, $P(3, 0, -3)$

10. $\mathbf{v} = \langle 23, -5, 12 \rangle$, $P(-6, 4, 2)$

11–14 ■ Find the magnitude of the given vector.

11. $\langle -2, 1, 2 \rangle$

12. $\langle 5, 0, -12 \rangle$

13. $\langle 3, 5, -4 \rangle$

14. $\langle 1, -6, 2\sqrt{2} \rangle$

15–18 ■ Find the vectors $\mathbf{u} + \mathbf{v}$, $\mathbf{u} - \mathbf{v}$, and $3\mathbf{u} - \frac{1}{2}\mathbf{v}$.

15. $\mathbf{u} = \langle 2, -7, 3 \rangle$, $\mathbf{v} = \langle 0, 4, -1 \rangle$

16. $\mathbf{u} = \langle 0, 1, -3 \rangle$, $\mathbf{v} = \langle 4, 2, 0 \rangle$

17. $\mathbf{u} = \mathbf{i} + \mathbf{j}$, $\mathbf{v} = -\mathbf{j} - 2\mathbf{k}$

18. $\mathbf{u} = \langle a, 2b, 3c \rangle$, $\mathbf{v} = \langle -4a, b, -2c \rangle$

DRILL QUESTION

Compute the magnitude of $\langle 4, 13, 16 \rangle$.

Answer

21

19–22 ■ Express the given vector in terms of the unit vectors **i**, **j**, and **k**.

19. $\langle 12, 0, 2 \rangle$ **20.** $\langle 0, -3, 5 \rangle$

21. $\langle 3, -3, 0 \rangle$ **22.** $\langle -a, \frac{1}{3}a, 4 \rangle$

23–24 ■ Two vectors **u** and **v** are given. Express the vector $-2\mathbf{u} + 3\mathbf{v}$ **(a)** in component form $\langle a_1, a_2, a_3 \rangle$ and **(b)** in terms of the unit vectors **i**, **j**, and **k**.

23. $\mathbf{u} = \langle 0, -2, 1 \rangle$, $\mathbf{v} = \langle 1, -1, 0 \rangle$

24. $\mathbf{u} = \langle 3, 1, 0 \rangle$, $\mathbf{v} = \langle 3, 0, -5 \rangle$

25–28 ■ Two vectors **u** and **v** are given. Find their dot product $\mathbf{u} \cdot \mathbf{v}$.

25. $\mathbf{u} = \langle 2, 5, 0 \rangle$, $\mathbf{v} = \langle \frac{1}{2}, -1, 10 \rangle$

26. $\mathbf{u} = \langle -3, 0, 4 \rangle$, $\mathbf{v} = \langle 2, 4, \frac{1}{2} \rangle$

27. $\mathbf{u} = 6\mathbf{i} - 4\mathbf{j} - 2\mathbf{k}$, $\mathbf{v} = \frac{5}{6}\mathbf{i} + \frac{3}{2}\mathbf{j} - \mathbf{k}$

28. $\mathbf{u} = 3\mathbf{j} - 2\mathbf{k}$, $\mathbf{v} = \frac{5}{6}\mathbf{i} - \frac{5}{3}\mathbf{j}$

29–32 ■ Determine whether or not the given vectors are perpendicular.

29. $\langle 4, -2, -4 \rangle$, $\langle 1, -2, 2 \rangle$ **30.** $4\mathbf{j} - \mathbf{k}$, $\mathbf{i} + 2\mathbf{j} + 9\mathbf{k}$

31. $\langle 0.3, 1.2, -0.9 \rangle$, $\langle 10, -5, 10 \rangle$

32. $\langle x, -2x, 3x \rangle$, $\langle 5, 7, 3 \rangle$

33–36 ■ Two vectors **u** and **v** are given. Find the angle (expressed in degrees) between **u** and **v**.

33. $\mathbf{u} = \langle 2, -2, -1 \rangle$, $\mathbf{v} = \langle 1, 2, 2 \rangle$

34. $\mathbf{u} = \langle 4, 0, 2 \rangle$, $\mathbf{v} = \langle 2, -1, 0 \rangle$

35. $\mathbf{u} = \mathbf{j} + \mathbf{k}$, $\mathbf{v} = \mathbf{i} + 2\mathbf{j} - 3\mathbf{k}$

36. $\mathbf{u} = \mathbf{i} + 2\mathbf{j} - 2\mathbf{k}$, $\mathbf{v} = 4\mathbf{i} - 3\mathbf{k}$

37–40 ■ Find the direction angles of the given vector, rounded to the nearest degree.

37. $3\mathbf{i} + 4\mathbf{j} + 5\mathbf{k}$ **38.** $\mathbf{i} - 2\mathbf{j} - \mathbf{k}$

39. $\langle 2, 3, -6 \rangle$ **40.** $\langle 2, -1, 2 \rangle$

41–44 ■ Two direction angles of a vector are given. Find the third direction angle, given that it is either obtuse or acute as indicated. (In Exercises 43 and 44, round your answers to the nearest degree.)

41. $\alpha = \frac{\pi}{3}$, $\gamma = \frac{2\pi}{3}$; β is acute

42. $\beta = \frac{2\pi}{3}$, $\gamma = \frac{\pi}{4}$; α is acute

43. $\alpha = 60°$, $\beta = 50°$; γ is obtuse

44. $\alpha = 75°$, $\gamma = 15°$

45–46 ■ Explain why it is impossible for a vector to have the given direction angles.

45. $\alpha = 20°$, $\beta = 45°$ **46.** $\alpha = 150°$, $\gamma = 25°$

APPLICATIONS

47. Resultant of Four Forces   An object located at the origin in a three-dimensional coordinate system is held in equilibrium by four forces. One has magnitude 7 lb and points in the direction of the positive x-axis, so it is represented by the vector $7\mathbf{i}$. The second has magnitude 24 lb and points in the direction of the positive y-axis. The third has magnitude 25 lb and points in the direction of the *negative z*-axis.
  (a) Use the fact that the four forces are in equilibrium (that is, their sum is **0**) to find the fourth force. Express it in terms of the unit vectors **i**, **j**, and **k**.
  (b) What is the magnitude of the fourth force?

48. Central Angle of a Tetrahedron   A *tetrahedron* is a solid with four triangular faces, four vertices, and six edges, as shown in the figure. In a *regular* tetrahedron, the edges are all of the same length. Consider the tetrahedron with vertices $A(1, 0, 0)$, $B(0, 1, 0)$, $C(0, 0, 1)$, and $D(1, 1, 1)$.
  (a) Show that the tetrahedron is regular.
  (b) The center of the tetrahedron is the point $E(\frac{1}{2}, \frac{1}{2}, \frac{1}{2})$ (the "average" of the vertices). Find the angle between the vectors that join the center to any two of the vertices (for instance, $\angle AEB$). This angle is called the *central angle* of the tetrahedron.

NOTE: In a molecule of methane (CH_4) the four hydrogen atoms form the vertices of a regular tetrahedron with the carbon atom at the center. In this case chemists refer to the central angle as the *bond angle*. In the figure, the tetrahedron in the exercise is shown, with the vertices labeled H for hydrogen, and the center labeled C for carbon.

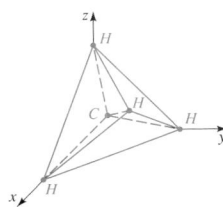

DISCOVERY ■ DISCUSSION ■ WRITING

49. Parallel Vectors   Two nonzero vectors are *parallel* if they point in the same direction or in opposite directions. This means that if two vectors are parallel, one must be a scalar multiple of the other. Determine whether the given vectors **u** and **v** are parallel. If they are, express **v** as a scalar multiple of **u**.
  (a) $\mathbf{u} = \langle 3, -2, 4 \rangle$, $\mathbf{v} = \langle -6, 4, -8 \rangle$
  (b) $\mathbf{u} = \langle -9, -6, 12 \rangle$, $\mathbf{v} = \langle 12, 8, -16 \rangle$
  (c) $\mathbf{u} = \mathbf{i} + \mathbf{j} + \mathbf{k}$, $\mathbf{v} = 2\mathbf{i} + 2\mathbf{j} - 2\mathbf{k}$

50. Unit Vectors   A *unit vector* is a vector of magnitude 1. Multiplying a vector by a scalar changes its magnitude but not its direction.
  (a) If a vector **v** has magnitude m, what scalar multiple of **v** has magnitude 1 (i.e., is a unit vector)?

(b) Multiply each of the following vectors by an appropriate scalar to change them into unit vectors:

$$\langle 1, -2, 2 \rangle \quad \langle -6, 8, -10 \rangle \quad \langle 6, 5, 9 \rangle$$

51. Vector Equation of a Sphere Let $\mathbf{a} = \langle 2, 2, 2 \rangle$, $\mathbf{b} = \langle -2, -2, 0 \rangle$, and $\mathbf{r} = \langle x, y, z \rangle$.
   (a) Show that the vector equation $(\mathbf{r} - \mathbf{a}) \cdot (\mathbf{r} - \mathbf{b}) = 0$ represents a sphere, by expanding the dot product and simplifying the resulting algebraic equation.
   (b) Find the center and radius of the sphere.

(c) Interpret the result of part (a) geometrically, using the fact that the dot product of two vectors is 0 only if the vectors are perpendicular. [*Hint:* Draw a diagram showing the endpoints of the vectors $\mathbf{a}$, $\mathbf{b}$, and $\mathbf{r}$, noting that the endpoints of $\mathbf{a}$ and $\mathbf{b}$ are the endpoints of a diameter and the endpoint of $\mathbf{r}$ is an arbitrary point on the sphere.]

(d) Using your observations from part (a), find a vector equation for the sphere in which the points $(0, 1, 3)$ and $(2, -1, 4)$ form the endpoints of a diameter. Simplify the vector equation to obtain an algebraic equation for the sphere. What are its center and radius?

9.5 THE CROSS PRODUCT

> The Cross Product ▶ Properties of the Cross Product ▶ Area of a Parallelogram ▶ Volume of a Parallelepiped

In this section we define an operation on vectors that allows us to find a vector which is perpendicular to two given vectors.

▼ The Cross Product

Given two vectors $\mathbf{a} = \langle a_1, a_2, a_3 \rangle$ and $\mathbf{b} = \langle b_1, b_2, b_3 \rangle$ we often need to find a vector $\mathbf{c}$ perpendicular to both $\mathbf{a}$ and $\mathbf{b}$. If we write $\mathbf{c} = \langle c_1, c_2, c_3 \rangle$ then $\mathbf{a} \cdot \mathbf{c} = 0$ and $\mathbf{b} \cdot \mathbf{c} = 0$, so

$$a_1 c_1 + a_2 c_2 + a_3 c_3 = 0$$
$$b_1 c_1 + b_2 c_2 + b_3 c_3 = 0$$

You can check that one of the solutions of this system of equations is the vector $\mathbf{c} = \langle a_2 b_3 - a_3 b_2, a_3 b_1 - a_1 b_3, a_1 b_2 - a_2 b_1 \rangle$. This vector is called the *cross product* of $\mathbf{a}$ and $\mathbf{b}$ and is denoted by $\mathbf{a} \times \mathbf{b}$.

THE CROSS PRODUCT

If $\mathbf{a} = \langle a_1, a_2, a_3 \rangle$ and $\mathbf{b} = \langle b_1, b_2, b_3 \rangle$ are three-dimensional vectors, then the **cross product** of $\mathbf{a}$ and $\mathbf{b}$ is the vector

$$\mathbf{a} \times \mathbf{b} = \langle a_2 b_3 - a_3 b_2, \; a_3 b_1 - a_1 b_3, \; a_1 b_2 - a_2 b_1 \rangle$$

The *cross product* $\mathbf{a} \times \mathbf{b}$ of two vectors $\mathbf{a}$ and $\mathbf{b}$, unlike the dot product, is a vector (not a scalar). For this reason it is also called the *vector product*. Note that $\mathbf{a} \times \mathbf{b}$ is defined only when $\mathbf{a}$ and $\mathbf{b}$ are vectors in *three dimensions*.

Determinants and their properties are studied in Section 10.7.

To help us remember the definition of the cross product, we use the notation of determinants. A **determinant of order two** is defined by

$$\begin{vmatrix} a & b \\ c & d \end{vmatrix} = ad - bc$$

For example,

$$\begin{vmatrix} 2 & 1 \\ -6 & 4 \end{vmatrix} = 2(4) - 1(-6) = 14$$

TEXT QUESTION
Why is it that if $\mathbf{a} \cdot (\mathbf{b} \times \mathbf{c}) = 0$, then $\mathbf{a}$, $\mathbf{b}$, and $\mathbf{c}$ are coplanar?

Answer
$\mathbf{b} \times \mathbf{c}$ must be perpendicular to $\mathbf{a}$, and since $\mathbf{b} \times \mathbf{c}$ is also perpendicular to $\mathbf{b}$ and $\mathbf{c}$, we see that $\mathbf{a}$, $\mathbf{b}$, and $\mathbf{c}$ are coplanar.

A **determinant of order three** is defined in terms of second-order determinants as

$$\begin{vmatrix} a_1 & a_2 & a_3 \\ b_1 & b_2 & b_3 \\ c_1 & c_2 & c_3 \end{vmatrix} = a_1 \begin{vmatrix} b_2 & b_3 \\ c_2 & c_3 \end{vmatrix} - a_2 \begin{vmatrix} b_1 & b_3 \\ c_1 & c_3 \end{vmatrix} + a_3 \begin{vmatrix} b_1 & b_2 \\ c_1 & c_2 \end{vmatrix}$$

Observe that each term on the right side of the above equation involves a number a_i in the first row of the determinant, and a_i is multiplied by the second-order determinant obtained from the left side by deleting the row and column in which a_i appears. Notice also the minus sign in the second term. For example,

$$\begin{vmatrix} 1 & 2 & -1 \\ 3 & 0 & 1 \\ -5 & 4 & 2 \end{vmatrix} = 1 \begin{vmatrix} 0 & 1 \\ 4 & 2 \end{vmatrix} - 2 \begin{vmatrix} 3 & 1 \\ -5 & 2 \end{vmatrix} + (-1) \begin{vmatrix} 3 & 0 \\ -5 & 4 \end{vmatrix}$$

$$= 1(0 - 4) - 2(6 - (-5)) + (-1)(12 - 0) = -38$$

We can write the definition of the cross product using determinants as

$$\begin{vmatrix} \mathbf{i} & \mathbf{j} & \mathbf{k} \\ a_1 & a_2 & a_3 \\ b_1 & b_2 & b_3 \end{vmatrix} = \begin{vmatrix} a_2 & a_3 \\ b_2 & b_3 \end{vmatrix} \mathbf{i} - \begin{vmatrix} a_1 & a_3 \\ b_1 & b_3 \end{vmatrix} \mathbf{j} + \begin{vmatrix} a_1 & a_2 \\ b_1 & b_2 \end{vmatrix} \mathbf{k}$$

$$= (a_2 b_3 - a_3 b_2)\mathbf{i} + (a_3 b_1 - a_1 b_3)\mathbf{j} + (a_1 b_2 - a_2 b_1)\mathbf{k}$$

Although the first row of the above determinant consists of vectors, we expand it as if it were an ordinary determinant of order 3. The symbolic formula given by the above determinant is probably the easiest way to remember and compute cross products.

EXAMPLE 1 | Finding a Cross Product

If $\mathbf{a} = \langle 0, -1, 3 \rangle$ and $\mathbf{b} = \langle 2, 0, -1 \rangle$, find $\mathbf{a} \times \mathbf{b}$.

SOLUTION We use the formula above to find the cross product of $\mathbf{a}$ and $\mathbf{b}$:

$$\mathbf{a} \times \mathbf{b} = \begin{vmatrix} \mathbf{i} & \mathbf{j} & \mathbf{k} \\ 0 & -1 & 3 \\ 2 & 0 & -1 \end{vmatrix}$$

$$= \begin{vmatrix} -1 & 3 \\ 0 & -1 \end{vmatrix} \mathbf{i} - \begin{vmatrix} 0 & 3 \\ 2 & -1 \end{vmatrix} \mathbf{j} + \begin{vmatrix} 0 & -1 \\ 2 & 0 \end{vmatrix} \mathbf{k}$$

$$= (1 - 0)\mathbf{i} - (0 - 6)\mathbf{j} + (0 - (-2))\mathbf{k}$$

$$= \mathbf{i} + 6\mathbf{j} + 2\mathbf{k}$$

So the desired vector is $\mathbf{i} + 6\mathbf{j} + 2\mathbf{k}$.

✎ . NOW TRY EXERCISE **3**

▼ Properties of the Cross Product

One of the most important properties of the cross product is the following theorem.

> **CROSS PRODUCT THEOREM**
>
> The vector $\mathbf{a} \times \mathbf{b}$ is orthogonal (perpendicular) to both $\mathbf{a}$ and $\mathbf{b}$.

WILLIAM ROWAN HAMILTON
(1805–1865) was an Irish mathematician and physicist. He was raised by his uncle (a linguist) who noticed that Hamilton had a remarkable ability to learn languages. When he was five years old, he could read Latin, Greek, and Hebrew. At age eight he added French and Italian, and by age ten he had mastered Arabic and Sanskrit.

Hamilton was also a calculating prodigy and competed in contests of mental arithmetic. He entered Trinity College in Dublin, Ireland, where he studied science; he was appointed Professor of Astronomy there while still an undergraduate.

Hamilton made many contributions to mathematics and physics, but he is best known for his invention of quaternions. Hamilton knew that we can multiply vectors in the plane by considering them as complex numbers. He was looking for a similar multiplication for points in space. After thinking about this problem for over 20 years he discovered the solution in a flash of insight while walking near Brougham Bridge in Dublin: He realized that a fourth dimension is needed to make the multiplication work. He carved the formula for his quaternions into the bridge, where it still stands. Later, the American mathematician Josiah Willard Gibbs extracted the dot product and cross product of vectors from the properties of quaternion multiplication. Quaternions are used today in computer graphics because of their ability to easily describe special rotations.

ALTERNATE EXAMPLE 1
If $\mathbf{a} = \langle 1, -5, 4 \rangle$ and $\mathbf{b} = \langle 4, 0, -3 \rangle$, find $\mathbf{a} \times \mathbf{b}$.

ANSWER
$15\,\mathbf{i} + 19\,\mathbf{j} + 20\,\mathbf{k}$

IN-CLASS MATERIALS
Note that the correct pronunciation of the solid discussed is parallelepiped, a shortening of the original parallelepipedon, from the Greek words *para* (beside), *allele* (other), *epi* (upon), and *pedon* (ground). This reflects the fact that the solid always has a face parallel to the one on the ground.

PROOF   To show that $\mathbf{a} \times \mathbf{b}$ is orthogonal to $\mathbf{a}$, we compute their dot product and show that it is 0:

$$(\mathbf{a} \times \mathbf{b}) \cdot \mathbf{a} = \begin{vmatrix} a_2 & a_3 \\ b_2 & b_3 \end{vmatrix} a_1 - \begin{vmatrix} a_1 & a_3 \\ b_1 & b_3 \end{vmatrix} a_2 + \begin{vmatrix} a_1 & a_2 \\ b_1 & b_2 \end{vmatrix} a_3$$

$$= a_1(a_2 b_3 - a_3 b_2) - a_2(a_1 b_3 - a_3 b_1) + a_3(a_1 b_2 - a_2 b_1)$$

$$= a_1 a_2 b_3 - a_1 a_3 b_2 - a_1 a_2 b_3 + a_2 a_3 b_1 + a_1 a_3 b_2 - a_2 a_3 b_1$$

$$= 0$$

A similar computation shows that $(\mathbf{a} \times \mathbf{b}) \cdot \mathbf{b} = 0$. Therefore, $\mathbf{a} \times \mathbf{b}$ is orthogonal to $\mathbf{a}$ and to $\mathbf{b}$. ∎

ALTERNATE EXAMPLE 2

If $\mathbf{a} = -\mathbf{i} - 2\mathbf{j}$ and $\mathbf{b} = -\mathbf{i} + \mathbf{j} - 3\mathbf{k}$, find a unit vector that is orthogonal to the plane containing the vectors $\mathbf{a}$ and $\mathbf{b}$.

ANSWER

$$\frac{\sqrt{6}}{3}\mathbf{i} - \frac{\sqrt{6}}{6}\mathbf{j} - \frac{\sqrt{6}}{6}\mathbf{k}$$

ALTERNATE EXAMPLE 3

Find a vector perpendicular to the plane that passes through the points $P(5, -2, 7)$, $Q(-4, 1, 7)$, and $R(3, -2, -3)$.

ANSWER

$\overrightarrow{PQ} = \langle 9, -3, 0 \rangle$

$\overrightarrow{PR} = \langle 2, 0, 10 \rangle$

$\overrightarrow{PQ} \times \overrightarrow{PR} = \langle -30, -90, 6 \rangle$

Final answer: any nonzero scalar multiple of $\langle 5, 15, -1 \rangle$

FIGURE 1 The vector $\mathbf{a} \times \mathbf{b}$ is perpendicular to $\mathbf{a}$ and $\mathbf{b}$.

EXAMPLE 2 | Finding an Orthogonal Vector

If $\mathbf{a} = -\mathbf{j} + 3\mathbf{k}$ and $\mathbf{b} = 2\mathbf{i} - \mathbf{k}$, find a unit vector that is orthogonal to the plane containing the vectors $\mathbf{a}$ and $\mathbf{b}$.

SOLUTION   By the Cross Product Theorem the vector $\mathbf{a} \times \mathbf{b}$ is orthogonal to the plane containing the vectors $\mathbf{a}$ and $\mathbf{b}$. (See Figure 1.) In Example 1 we found $\mathbf{a} \times \mathbf{b} = \mathbf{i} + 6\mathbf{j} + 2\mathbf{k}$. To obtain an orthogonal unit vector, we multiply $\mathbf{a} \times \mathbf{b}$ by the scalar $1/|\mathbf{a} \times \mathbf{b}|$:

$$\frac{\mathbf{a} \times \mathbf{b}}{|\mathbf{a} \times \mathbf{b}|} = \frac{\mathbf{i} + 6\mathbf{j} + 2\mathbf{k}}{\sqrt{1^2 + 6^2 + 2^2}} = \frac{\mathbf{i} + 6\mathbf{j} + 2\mathbf{k}}{\sqrt{41}}$$

So the desired vector is $\dfrac{1}{\sqrt{41}}(\mathbf{i} + 6\mathbf{j} + 2\mathbf{k})$.

✎. NOW TRY EXERCISE **9** ∎

EXAMPLE 3 | Finding a Vector Perpendicular to a Plane

Find a vector perpendicular to the plane that passes through the points $P(1, 4, 6)$, $Q(-2, 5, -1)$, and $R(1, -1, 1)$.

SOLUTION   By the Cross Product Theorem, the vector $\overrightarrow{PQ} \times \overrightarrow{PR}$ is perpendicular to both $\overrightarrow{PQ}$ and $\overrightarrow{PR}$, and is therefore perpendicular to the plane through P, Q, and R. We know that

$$\overrightarrow{PQ} = (-2 - 1)\mathbf{i} + (5 - 4)\mathbf{j} + (-1 - 6)\mathbf{k} = -3\mathbf{i} + \mathbf{j} - 7\mathbf{k}$$

$$\overrightarrow{PR} = (1 - 1)\mathbf{i} + ((-1) - 4)\mathbf{j} + (1 - 6)\mathbf{k} = -5\mathbf{j} - 5\mathbf{k}$$

We compute the cross product of these vectors:

$$\overrightarrow{PQ} \times \overrightarrow{PR} = \begin{vmatrix} \mathbf{i} & \mathbf{j} & \mathbf{k} \\ -3 & 1 & -7 \\ 0 & -5 & -5 \end{vmatrix}$$

$$= (-5 - 35)\mathbf{i} - (15 - 0)\mathbf{j} + (15 - 0)\mathbf{k} = -40\mathbf{i} - 15\mathbf{j} + 15\mathbf{k}$$

So the vector $\langle -40, -15, 15 \rangle$ is perpendicular to the given plane. Notice that any nonzero scalar multiple of this vector, such as $\langle -8, -3, 3 \rangle$, is also perpendicular to the plane.

✎. NOW TRY EXERCISE **17** ∎

If $\mathbf{a}$ and $\mathbf{b}$ are represented by directed line segments with the same initial point (as in Figure 2), then the Cross Product Theorem says that the cross product $\mathbf{a} \times \mathbf{b}$ points in a

---

IN-CLASS MATERIALS

Pose the problem of finding a vector perpendicular to two given vectors (without considering the length of the resultant vector). Show that there is an obvious solution for $\langle 1, 0, 0 \rangle$ and $\langle 0, 1, 0 \rangle$. Then look at the two vectors $\langle 1, 0, 1 \rangle$ and $\langle 0, 1, 1 \rangle$. Repeat for $\langle -3, 1, -7 \rangle$ and $\langle 0, -5, -5 \rangle$. Point out that in this case an alternate algebraic solution using dot products gives $-3x + y - 7z = -5y - 5z$, $y = -z$, $x = -\frac{8}{3}z$, so $\mathbf{c} = \langle -\frac{8}{3}, -1, 1 \rangle$ works. Note that $\mathbf{c}$ is a scalar multiple of $\mathbf{a} \times \mathbf{b} = \langle -40, -15, -15 \rangle$. This suggests the general idea behind the cross product.

EXAMPLES

A nonzero cross product: $\langle 4, 5, 2 \rangle \times \langle 1, 3, 6 \rangle = \langle 24, -22, 7 \rangle$

A zero cross product: $\langle 1, -2, 5 \rangle \times \langle -3, 6, -15 \rangle = \langle 0, 0, 0 \rangle$

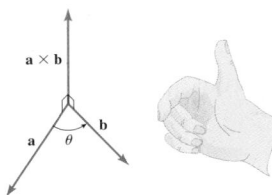

FIGURE 2 Right-hand rule

direction perpendicular to the plane through **a** and **b**. It turns out that the direction of **a** × **b** is given by the *right-hand rule:* If the fingers of your right hand curl in the direction of a rotation (through an angle less than 180°) from **a** to **b**, then your thumb points in the direction of **a** × **b** (as in Figure 2). You can check that the vector **a** × **b** in Figure 1 satisfies the right-hand rule.

Now that we know the direction of the vector **a** × **b**, the remaining thing we need is the length $|\mathbf{a} \times \mathbf{b}|$.

LENGTH OF THE CROSS PRODUCT

If θ is the angle between **a** and **b** (so $0 \le \theta \le \pi$), then

$$|\mathbf{a} \times \mathbf{b}| = |\mathbf{a}|\,|\mathbf{b}|\sin\theta$$

In particular, two nonzero vectors **a** and **b** are parallel if and only if

$$\mathbf{a} \times \mathbf{b} = \mathbf{0}$$

PROOF   We apply the definitions of the cross product and length of a vector. You can verify the algebra in the first step by expanding the right-hand sides of the first and second lines, and then comparing the results.

$$
\begin{aligned}
|\mathbf{a} \times \mathbf{b}|^2 &= (a_2b_3 - a_3b_2)^2 + (a_3b_1 - a_1b_3)^2 + (a_1b_2 - a_2b_1)^2 && \text{Definitions} \\
&= (a_1^2 + a_2^2 + a_3^2)(b_1^2 + b_2^2 + b_3^2) - (a_1b_1 + a_2b_2 + a_3b_3)^2 && \text{Verify algebra} \\
&= |\mathbf{a}|^2|\mathbf{b}|^2 - (\mathbf{a}\cdot\mathbf{b})^2 && \text{Definitions} \\
&= |\mathbf{a}|^2|\mathbf{b}|^2 - |\mathbf{a}|^2|\mathbf{b}|^2\cos^2\theta && \text{Property of Dot Product} \\
&= |\mathbf{a}|^2|\mathbf{b}|^2(1 - \cos^2\theta) && \text{Factor} \\
&= |\mathbf{a}|^2|\mathbf{b}|^2\sin^2\theta && \text{Pythagorean Identity}
\end{aligned}
$$

The result follows by taking square roots and observing that $\sqrt{\sin^2\theta} = \sin\theta$ because $\sin\theta \ge 0$ when $0 \le \theta \le \pi$. ∎

We have now completely determined the vector **a** × **b** geometrically. The vector **a** × **b** is perpendicular to both **a** and **b**, and its orientation is determined by the right-hand rule. The length of **a** × **b** is $|\mathbf{a}|\,|\mathbf{b}|\sin\theta$.

▼ Area of a Parallelogram

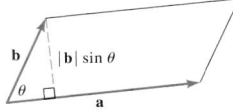

FIGURE 3 Parallelogram determined by **a** and **b**

We can use the cross product to find the area of a parallelogram. If **a** and **b** are represented by directed line segments with the same initial point, then they determine a parallelogram with base $|\mathbf{a}|$, altitude $|\mathbf{b}|\sin\theta$, and area

$$A = |\mathbf{a}|(|\mathbf{b}|\sin\theta) = |\mathbf{a} \times \mathbf{b}|$$

(See Figure 3.) Thus we have the following way of interpreting the magnitude of a cross product.

AREA OF A PARALLELOGRAM

The length of the cross product **a** × **b** is the area of the parallelogram determined by **a** and **b**.

IN-CLASS MATERIALS

A common mistake made by right-handed students can be avoided if they are reminded to *put down their pencils* before using the right-hand rule!

ALTERNATE EXAMPLE 4

Find the area of the triangle with vertices $P(5, -2, 7)$, $Q(-4, 1, 7)$, and $R(3, -2, -3)$.

ANSWER

$3\sqrt{251}$

EXAMPLE 4 | Finding the Area of a Triangle

Find the area of the triangle with vertices $P(1, 4, 6)$, $Q(-2, 5, -1)$, and $R(1, -1, 1)$.

SOLUTION   In Example 3 we computed that $\overrightarrow{PQ} \times \overrightarrow{PR} = \langle -40, -15, 15 \rangle$. The area of the parallelogram with adjacent sides PQ and PR is the length of this cross product:

$$| \overrightarrow{PQ} \times \overrightarrow{PR} | = \sqrt{(-40)^2 + (-15)^2 + 15^2} = 5\sqrt{82}$$

The area A of the triangle PQR is half the area of this parallelogram, that is, $\frac{5}{2}\sqrt{82}$.

✎ NOW TRY EXERCISES **21** AND **25** ∎

▼ Volume of a Parallelepiped

The product $\mathbf{a} \cdot (\mathbf{b} \times \mathbf{c})$ is called the **scalar triple product** of the vectors $\mathbf{a}$, $\mathbf{b}$, and $\mathbf{c}$. You can check that the scalar triple product can be written as the following determinant:

$$\mathbf{a} \cdot (\mathbf{b} \times \mathbf{c}) = \begin{vmatrix} a_1 & a_2 & a_3 \\ b_1 & b_2 & b_3 \\ c_1 & c_2 & c_3 \end{vmatrix}$$

The geometric significance of the scalar triple product can be seen by considering the parallelepiped* determined by the vectors $\mathbf{a}$, $\mathbf{b}$, and $\mathbf{c}$ (see Figure 4). The area of the base parallelogram is $A = |\mathbf{b} \times \mathbf{c}|$. If θ is the angle between $\mathbf{a}$ and $\mathbf{b} \times \mathbf{c}$, then the height h of the parallelepiped is $h = |\mathbf{a}||\cos \theta|$. (We must use $|\cos \theta|$ instead of $\cos \theta$ in case $\theta > \pi/2$.) Therefore, the volume of the parallelepiped is

$$V = Ah = |\mathbf{b} \times \mathbf{c}||\mathbf{a}||\cos \theta| = |\mathbf{a} \cdot (\mathbf{b} \times \mathbf{c})|$$

The last equality follows from the Dot Product Theorem on page 590.

FIGURE 4   Parallelepiped determined by $\mathbf{a}$, $\mathbf{b}$, and $\mathbf{c}$

We have proved the following formula.

VOLUME OF A PARALLELEPIPED

The volume of the parallelepiped determined by the vectors $\mathbf{a}$, $\mathbf{b}$, and $\mathbf{c}$ is the magnitude of their scalar triple product:

$$V = |\mathbf{a} \cdot (\mathbf{b} \times \mathbf{c})|$$

In particular, if the volume of the parallelepiped is 0, then the vectors $\mathbf{a}$, $\mathbf{b}$, and $\mathbf{c}$ are coplanar.

EXAMPLE 5 | Coplanar Vectors

Use the scalar triple product to show that the vectors $\mathbf{a} = \langle 1, 4, -7 \rangle$, $\mathbf{b} = \langle 2, -1, 4 \rangle$, and $\mathbf{c} = \langle 0, -9, 18 \rangle$ are coplanar, that is, lie in the same plane.

_____

*The word *parallelepiped* is derived from Greek roots which together mean, roughly, "parallel faces." While the word is often pronounced "par-al-lel-uh-PIE-ped," the more etymologically correct pronunciation is "par-al-lel-EP-uh-ped."

ALTERNATE EXAMPLE 5

Use the scalar triple product to show that the vectors $\mathbf{a} = \langle 6, -5, 6 \rangle$, $\mathbf{b} = \langle 0, 0, -7 \rangle$, and $\mathbf{c} = \langle 2, 1, 4 \rangle$ are not coplanar.

ANSWER

$\mathbf{a} \cdot (\mathbf{b} \times \mathbf{c}) = 112$, which is not zero; therefore, the vectors are not coplanar.

IN-CLASS MATERIALS

Point out that while $\mathbf{a} \times \mathbf{b}$ and $\mathbf{b} \times \mathbf{a}$ have the same length, $\mathbf{b} \times \mathbf{a}$ points in the opposite direction to that of $\mathbf{a} \times \mathbf{b}$, by the right-hand rule. Thus, $\mathbf{b} \times \mathbf{a} = -(\mathbf{a} \times \mathbf{b})$.

SOLUTION   We compute the scalar triple product:

$$\mathbf{a} \cdot (\mathbf{b} \times \mathbf{c}) = \begin{vmatrix} 1 & 4 & -7 \\ 2 & -1 & 4 \\ 0 & -9 & 18 \end{vmatrix}$$

$$= 1 \begin{vmatrix} -1 & 4 \\ -9 & 18 \end{vmatrix} - 4 \begin{vmatrix} 2 & 4 \\ 0 & 18 \end{vmatrix} + (-7) \begin{vmatrix} 2 & -1 \\ 0 & -9 \end{vmatrix}$$

$$= 1(18) - 4(36) - 7(-18) = 0$$

So the volume of the parallelepiped is 0, and hence the vectors **a**, **b**, and **c** are coplanar.

▸. NOW TRY EXERCISE **29**   ■

9.5 EXERCISES

CONCEPTS

1. The cross product of the vectors $\mathbf{a} = \langle a_1, a_2, a_3 \rangle$ and $\mathbf{b} = \langle b_1, b_2, b_3 \rangle$ is the vector

$$\mathbf{a} \times \mathbf{b} = \begin{vmatrix} \mathbf{i} & \mathbf{j} & \mathbf{k} \\ & & \\ & & \end{vmatrix}$$

$$= \underline{\hspace{1cm}} \mathbf{i} + \underline{\hspace{1cm}} \mathbf{j} + \underline{\hspace{1cm}} \mathbf{k}$$

So the cross product of $\mathbf{a} = \langle 1, 0, 1 \rangle$ and $\mathbf{b} = \langle 2, 3, 0 \rangle$

is $\mathbf{a} \times \mathbf{b} = \underline{\hspace{2cm}}$.

2. The cross product of two vectors **a** and **b** is _____ to **a** and to **b**. Thus if both vectors **a** and **b** lie in a plane, the vector $\mathbf{a} \times \mathbf{b}$ is _____ to the plane.

SKILLS

3–8 ■ For the given vectors **a** and **b**, find the cross product $\mathbf{a} \times \mathbf{b}$.

▸. **3.** $\mathbf{a} = \langle 1, 0, -3 \rangle$, $\mathbf{b} = \langle 2, 3, 0 \rangle$

4. $\mathbf{a} = \langle 0, -4, 1 \rangle$, $\mathbf{b} = \langle 1, 1, -2 \rangle$

5. $\mathbf{a} = \langle 6, -2, 8 \rangle$, $\mathbf{b} = \langle -9, 3, -12 \rangle$

6. $\mathbf{a} = \langle -2, 3, 4 \rangle$, $\mathbf{b} = \langle \frac{1}{6}, -\frac{1}{4}, -\frac{1}{3} \rangle$

7. $\mathbf{a} = \mathbf{i} + \mathbf{j} + \mathbf{k}$, $\mathbf{b} = 3\mathbf{i} - 4\mathbf{k}$

8. $\mathbf{a} = 3\mathbf{i} - \mathbf{j}$, $\mathbf{b} = -3\mathbf{j} + \mathbf{k}$

9–12 ■ Two vectors **a** and **b** are given. **(a)** Find a vector perpendicular to both **a** and **b**. **(b)** Find a unit vector perpendicular to both **a** and **b**.

▸. **9.** $\mathbf{a} = \langle 1, 1, -1 \rangle$, $\mathbf{b} = \langle -1, 1, -1 \rangle$

10. $\mathbf{a} = \langle 2, 5, 3 \rangle$, $\mathbf{b} = \langle 3, -2, -1 \rangle$

11. $\mathbf{a} = \frac{1}{2}\mathbf{i} - \mathbf{j} + \frac{2}{3}\mathbf{k}$, $\mathbf{b} = 6\mathbf{i} - 12\mathbf{j} - 6\mathbf{k}$

12. $\mathbf{a} = 3\mathbf{j} + 5\mathbf{k}$, $\mathbf{b} = -\mathbf{i} + 2\mathbf{k}$

13–16 ■ The lengths of two vectors **a** and **b** and the angle θ between them are given. Find the length of their cross product, $|\mathbf{a} \times \mathbf{b}|$.

13. $|\mathbf{a}| = 6$, $|\mathbf{b}| = \frac{1}{2}$, $\theta = 60°$

14. $|\mathbf{a}| = 4$, $|\mathbf{b}| = 5$, $\theta = 30°$

15. $|\mathbf{a}| = 10$, $|\mathbf{b}| = 10$, $\theta = 90°$

16. $|\mathbf{a}| = 0.12$, $|\mathbf{b}| = 1.25$, $\theta = 75°$

17–20 ■ Find a vector that is perpendicular to the plane passing through the three given points.

▸. **17.** $P(0, 1, 0)$, $Q(1, 2, -1)$, $R(-2, 1, 0)$

18. $P(3, 4, 5)$, $Q(1, 2, 3)$, $R(4, 7, 6)$

19. $P(1, 1, -5)$, $Q(2, 2, 0)$, $R(0, 0, 0)$

20. $P(3, 0, 0)$, $Q(0, 2, -5)$, $R(-2, 0, 6)$

21–24 ■ Find the area of the parallelogram determined by the given vectors.

▸. **21.** $\mathbf{u} = \langle 3, 2, 1 \rangle$, $\mathbf{v} = \langle 1, 2, 3 \rangle$

22. $\mathbf{u} = \langle 0, -3, 2 \rangle$, $\mathbf{v} = \langle 5, -6, 0 \rangle$

23. $\mathbf{u} = 2\mathbf{i} - \mathbf{j} + 4\mathbf{k}$, $\mathbf{v} = \frac{1}{2}\mathbf{i} + 2\mathbf{j} - \frac{3}{2}\mathbf{k}$

24. $\mathbf{u} = \mathbf{i} - \mathbf{j} + \mathbf{k}$, $\mathbf{v} = \mathbf{i} + \mathbf{j} - \mathbf{k}$

25–28 ■ Find the area of $\triangle PQR$.

▸. **25.** $P(1, 0, 1)$, $Q(0, 1, 0)$, $R(2, 3, 4)$

26. $P(2, 1, 0)$, $Q(0, 0, -1)$, $R(-4, 2, 0)$

27. $P(6, 0, 0)$, $Q(0, -6, 0)$, $R(0, 0, -6)$

28. $P(3, -2, 6)$, $Q(-1, -4, -6)$, $R(3, 4, 6)$

IN-CLASS MATERIALS

If $\mathbf{a} = \alpha \mathbf{b} + \beta \mathbf{c}$, with α and β constant, show that $\mathbf{a} \cdot (\mathbf{b} \times \mathbf{c}) = 0$.

29–34 ■ Three vectors **a**, **b**, and **c** are given. **(a)** Find their scalar triple product $\mathbf{a} \cdot (\mathbf{b} \times \mathbf{c})$. **(b)** Are the vectors coplanar? If not, find the volume of the parallelepiped that they determine.

29. $\mathbf{a} = \langle 1, 2, 3 \rangle$, $\quad \mathbf{b} = \langle -3, 2, 1 \rangle$, $\quad \mathbf{c} = \langle 0, 8, 10 \rangle$

30. $\mathbf{a} = \langle 3, 0, -4 \rangle$, $\quad \mathbf{b} = \langle 1, 1, 1 \rangle$, $\quad \mathbf{c} = \langle 7, 4, 0 \rangle$

31. $\mathbf{a} = \langle 2, 3, -2 \rangle$, $\quad \mathbf{b} = \langle -1, 4, 0 \rangle$, $\quad \mathbf{c} = \langle 3, -1, 3 \rangle$

32. $\mathbf{a} = \langle 1, -1, 0 \rangle$, $\quad \mathbf{b} = \langle -1, 0, 1 \rangle$, $\quad \mathbf{c} = \langle 0, -1, 1 \rangle$

33. $\mathbf{a} = \mathbf{i} - \mathbf{j} + \mathbf{k}$, $\quad \mathbf{b} = -\mathbf{j} + \mathbf{k}$, $\quad \mathbf{c} = \mathbf{i} + \mathbf{j} + \mathbf{k}$

34. $\mathbf{a} = 2\mathbf{i} - 2\mathbf{j} - 3\mathbf{k}$, $\quad \mathbf{b} = 3\mathbf{i} - \mathbf{j} - \mathbf{k}$, $\quad \mathbf{c} = 6\mathbf{i}$

APPLICATIONS

35. Volume of a Fish Tank A fish tank in an avant-garde restaurant is in the shape of a parallelepiped with a rectangular base that is 300 cm long and 120 cm wide. The front and back faces are vertical, but the left and right faces are slanted at 30° from the vertical and measure 120 cm by 150 cm. (See the figure.)

(a) Let **a**, **b**, and **c** be the three vectors shown in the figure. Find $\mathbf{a} \cdot (\mathbf{b} \times \mathbf{c})$. [*Hint:* Recall that $\mathbf{u} \cdot \mathbf{v} = |\mathbf{u}| |\mathbf{v}| \cos \theta$ and $|\mathbf{u} \times \mathbf{v}| = |\mathbf{u}| |\mathbf{v}| \sin \theta$.]

(b) What is the capacity of the tank in liters? [*Note:* 1 L = 1000 cm³.]

36. Rubik's Tetrahedron Rubik's Cube, a puzzle craze of the 1980s that remains popular to this day, inspired many similar puzzles. The one illustrated in the figure is called Rubik's Tetrahedron; it is in the shape of a regular tetrahedron, with each edge $\sqrt{2}$ inches long. The volume of a regular tetrahedron is one-sixth the volume of the parallelepiped determined by any three edges that meet at a corner.

(a) Use the triple product to find the volume of Rubik's Tetrahedron. [*Hint:* See Exercise 48 in Section 9.4, which gives the corners of a tetrahedron that has the same shape and size as Rubik's Tetrahedron.]

(b) Construct six identical regular tetrahedra using modeling clay. Experiment to see how they can be put together to create a parallelepiped that is determined by three edges of one of the tetrahedra (thus confirming the above statement about the volume of a regular tetrahedron).

DISCOVERY ■ DISCUSSION ■ WRITING

37. Order of Operations in the Triple Product Given three vectors **u**, **v**, and **w**, their scalar triple product can be performed in six different orders:

$$\mathbf{u} \cdot (\mathbf{v} \times \mathbf{w}), \quad \mathbf{u} \cdot (\mathbf{w} \times \mathbf{v}), \quad \mathbf{v} \cdot (\mathbf{u} \times \mathbf{w}),$$
$$\mathbf{v} \cdot (\mathbf{w} \times \mathbf{u}), \quad \mathbf{w} \cdot (\mathbf{u} \times \mathbf{v}), \quad \mathbf{w} \cdot (\mathbf{v} \times \mathbf{u})$$

(a) Calculate each of these six triple products for the vectors:

$$\mathbf{u} = \langle 0, 1, 1 \rangle, \quad \mathbf{v} = \langle 1, 0, 1 \rangle, \quad \mathbf{w} = \langle 1, 1, 0 \rangle$$

(b) On the basis of your observations in part (a), make a conjecture about the relationships between these six triple products.

(c) Prove the conjecture you made in part (b).

SUGGESTED TIME AND EMPHASIS

1 class, essential material

9.6 EQUATIONS OF LINES AND PLANES

| Equations of Lines ▶ Equations of Planes

In this section we find equations for lines and planes in a three-dimensional coordinate space. We use vectors to help us find such equations.

▼ Equations of Lines

The **position vector** of a point (a_1, a_2, a_3) is the vector $\langle a_1, a_2, a_3 \rangle$; that is, it is the vector from the origin to the point.

A line L in three-dimensional space is determined when we know a point $P_0(x_0, y_0, z_0)$ on L and the direction of L. In three dimensions the direction of a line is described by a vector **v** parallel to L. If we let $\mathbf{r}_0$ be the position vector of P_0 (that is, the vector $\overrightarrow{OP_0}$), then for all real numbers t, the terminal points P of the position vectors $\mathbf{r}_0 + t\mathbf{v}$ trace out a line

---

TEXT QUESTION

When specifying the equation of a line in space, the text says you need a point on the line and a vector parallel to the line. Why can't you determine a line in space simply by using one vector?

Answer

One vector would give the direction of the line, but it could be placed anywhere in space. It would be analogous to trying to specify a line in $\mathbb{R}^2$ using only a slope.

FIGURE 1

parallel to $\mathbf{v}$ and passing through P_0 (see Figure 1). Each value of the parameter t gives a point P on L. So the line L is given by the position vector $\mathbf{r}$, where

$$\mathbf{r} = \mathbf{r}_0 + t\mathbf{v}$$

for $t \in \mathbb{R}$. This is the **vector equation of a line**.

Let's write the vector $\mathbf{v}$ in component form $\mathbf{v} = \langle a, b, c \rangle$ and let $\mathbf{r}_0 = \langle x_0, y_0, z_0 \rangle$ and $\mathbf{r} = \langle x, y, z \rangle$. Then the vector equation of the line becomes

$$\langle x, y, z \rangle = \langle x_0, y_0, z_0 \rangle + t\langle a, b, c \rangle$$
$$= \langle x_0 + ta, y_0 + tb, z_0 + tc \rangle$$

Since two vectors are equal if and only if their corresponding components are equal, we have the following result.

PARAMETRIC EQUATIONS FOR A LINE

A line passing through the point $P(x_0, y_0, z_0)$ and parallel to the vector $\mathbf{v} = \langle a, b, c \rangle$ is described by the parametric equations

$$x = x_0 + at$$
$$y = y_0 + bt$$
$$z = z_0 + ct$$

where t is any real number.

EXAMPLE 1 | Equations of a Line

Find parametric equations for the line that passes through the point $(5, -2, 3)$ and is parallel to the vector $\mathbf{v} = \langle 3, -4, 2 \rangle$.

SOLUTION We use the above formula to find the parametric equations:

$$x = 5 + 3t$$
$$y = -2 - 4t$$
$$z = 3 + 2t$$

where t is any real number. (See Figure 2.)

NOW TRY EXERCISE **3**

FIGURE 2 Line through $(5, -2, 3)$ with direction $\mathbf{v} = \langle 3, -4, 2 \rangle$

EXAMPLE 2 | Equations of a Line

Find parametric equations for the line that passes through the points $(-1, 2, 6)$ and $(2, -3, -7)$.

SOLUTION We first find a vector determined by the two points:

$$\mathbf{v} = \langle 2 - (-1), -3 - 2, -7 - 6 \rangle = \langle 3, -5, -13 \rangle$$

Now we use $\mathbf{v}$ and the point $(-1, 2, 6)$ to find the parametric equations:

$$x = -1 + 3t$$
$$y = 2 - 5t$$
$$z = 6 - 13t$$

where t is any real number. A graph of the line is shown in Figure 3.

NOW TRY EXERCISE **9**

FIGURE 3 Line through $(-1, 2, 6)$ and $(2, -3, -7)$

IN-CLASS MATERIALS

- An overall theme for this section could be that a "line" is determined by a point and a direction and a "plane" is determined by a point and a normal vector, or a point and two directions.
- Review parametric representation of lines in $\mathbb{R}^2$ and then generalize to $\mathbb{R}^3$. Recall that in two dimensions, a line can be determined by a point and a slope. Ask for the slope of the line between the points $(0, 0)$ and $(1, 2)$. Start with the line $y = mx + b$ and write it parametrically as $x = t, y = mt + b$. Then write the vector equation with $\mathbf{r}_0 = \langle 0, b \rangle$ and $\mathbf{d} = \langle 1, m \rangle$, a vector whose direction has slope m. Next ask for the slope of the line between $(0, 0, 0)$ and $(1, 2, 3)$. Note that there is no answer—we lose the idea of "slope" when going from two to three dimensions. So a vector is our only way of specifying direction in three dimensions.

In Example 2 we used the point $(-1, 2, 6)$ to get the parametric equations of the line. We could instead use the point $(2, -3, -7)$. The resulting parametric equations would look different but would still describe the same line (see Exercise 37).

▼ Equations of Planes

Although a line in space is determined by a point and a direction, the "direction" of a plane cannot be described by a vector in the plane. In fact, different vectors in a plane can have different directions. But a vector perpendicular to a plane *does* completely specify the direction of the plane. Thus a plane in space is determined by a point $P_0(x_0, y_0, z_0)$ in the plane and a vector $\mathbf{n}$ that is orthogonal to the plane. This orthogonal vector $\mathbf{n}$ is called a **normal vector**. To determine whether a point $P(x, y, z)$ is in the plane, we check whether the vector $\overrightarrow{P_0P}$ with initial point P_0 and terminal point P is orthogonal to the normal vector. Let $\mathbf{r}_0$ and $\mathbf{r}$ be the position vectors of P_0 and P, respectively. Then the vector $\overrightarrow{P_0P}$ is represented by $\mathbf{r} - \mathbf{r}_0$ (see Figure 4). So the plane is described by the tips of the vectors $\mathbf{r}$ satisfying

$$\mathbf{n} \cdot (\mathbf{r} - \mathbf{r}_0) = 0$$

This is the **vector equation of the plane**.

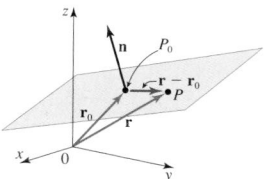

FIGURE 4

Let's write the normal vector $\mathbf{n}$ in component form $\mathbf{n} = \langle a, b, c \rangle$ and let $\mathbf{r}_0 = \langle x_0, y_0, z_0 \rangle$ and $\mathbf{r} = \langle x, y, z \rangle$. Then the vector equation of the plane becomes

$$\langle a, b, c \rangle \cdot \langle x - x_0, y - y_0, z - z_0 \rangle = 0$$

Performing the dot product, we arrive at the following equation of the plane in the variables x, y, and z.

EQUATION OF A PLANE

The plane containing the point $P(x_0, y_0, z_0)$ and having the normal vector $\mathbf{n} = \langle a, b, c \rangle$ is described by the equation

$$a(x - x_0) + b(y - y_0) + c(z - z_0) = 0$$

EXAMPLE 3 | Finding an Equation for a Plane

A plane has normal vector $\mathbf{n} = \langle 4, -6, 3 \rangle$ and passes through the point $P(3, -1, -2)$.

(a) Find an equation of the plane.

(b) Find the intercepts, and sketch a graph of the plane.

SOLUTION

(a) By the above formula for the equation of a plane we have

$$4(x - 3) - 6(y - (-1)) + 3(z - (-2)) = 0 \qquad \text{Formula}$$
$$4x - 12 - 6y - 6 + 3z + 6 = 0 \qquad \text{Expand}$$
$$4x - 6y + 3z = 12 \qquad \text{Simplify}$$

Thus an equation of the plane is $4x - 6y + 3z = 32$.

ALTERNATE EXAMPLE 3

A plane has normal vector $\mathbf{n} = \langle 5, -7, -4 \rangle$ and passes through the point $P(4, 5, -4)$.

(a) Find an equation of the plane.

(b) Find the intercepts.

ANSWERS

(a) $5(x - 4) - 7(y - 5) - 4(z + 4) = 0$
$$5x - 7y - 4z = 1$$

(b) $\left(\dfrac{1}{5}, 0, 0\right)$

$\left(0, -\dfrac{1}{7}, 0\right)$

$\left(0, 0, -\dfrac{1}{4}\right)$

EXAMPLE

A plane that is relatively easy to sketch: $10x + 5y + 5z = 10$ (The intercepts are $x = 1$, $y = 2$, and $z = 2$.)

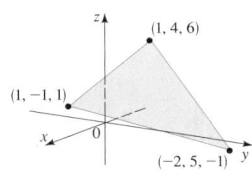

FIGURE 5 The plane
$4x - 6y + 3z = 32$

Notice that in Figure 5 the axes have been rotated so that we get a better view.

FIGURE 6 A plane through three points

(b) To find the *x*-intercept, we set $y = 0$ and $z = 0$ in the equation of the plane and solve for *x*. Similarly, we find the *y*- and *z*- intercepts.

x-intercept: Setting $y = 0$, $z = 0$, we get $x = 3$.

y-intercept: Setting $x = 0$, $z = 0$, we get $y = -2$.

z-intercept: Setting $x = 0$, $y = 0$, we get $z = 4$.

So the graph of the plane intersects the coordinate axes at the points $(3, 0, 0)$, $(0, -2, 0)$, and $(0, 0, 4)$. This enables us to sketch the portion of the plane shown in Figure 5.

NOW TRY EXERCISE 15

EXAMPLE 4 | Finding an Equation for a Plane

Find an equation of the plane that passes through the points $P(1, 4, 6)$, $Q(-2, 5, -1)$, and $R(1, -1, 1)$.

SOLUTION   The vector $\mathbf{n} = \overrightarrow{PQ} \times \overrightarrow{PR}$ is perpendicular to both $\overrightarrow{PQ}$ and $\overrightarrow{PR}$ and is therefore perpendicular to the plane through P, Q, and R. In Example 3 of Section 9.5 we found $\overrightarrow{PQ} \times \overrightarrow{PR} = \langle -40, -15, 15 \rangle$. Using the formula for an equation of a plane, we have

$$-40(x - 1) - 15(y - 4) + 15(z - 6) = 0 \qquad \text{Formula}$$
$$-40x + 40 - 15y + 60 + 15z - 90 = 0 \qquad \text{Expand}$$
$$-40x - 15y + 15z = -10 \qquad \text{Simplify}$$
$$-8x - 3y + 3z = -2 \qquad \text{Divide by 5}$$

So an equation of the plane is $-8x - 3y + 3z = -2$. A graph of this plane is shown in Figure 6.

NOW TRY EXERCISE 21

In Example 4 we used the point P to obtain the equation of the plane. You can check that using Q or R gives the same equation.

9.6 EXERCISES

CONCEPTS

1. A line in space is described algebraically by using

_____ equations. The line that passes through the point $P(x_0, y_0, z_0)$ and is parallel to the vector $\mathbf{v} = \langle a, b, c \rangle$ is described by the equations $x = $ _____,

$y = $ _____, $z = $ _____.

2. The plane containing the point $P(x_0, y_0, z_0)$ and having the normal vector $\mathbf{n} = \langle a, b, c \rangle$ is described algebraically by the

equation _____.

SKILLS

3–8 ■ Find parametric equations for the line that passes through the point P and is parallel to the vector $\mathbf{v}$.

3. $P(1, 0, -2)$, $\mathbf{v} = \langle 3, 2, -3 \rangle$

4. $P(0, -5, 3)$, $\mathbf{v} = \langle 2, 0, -4 \rangle$

5. $P(3, 2, 1)$, $\mathbf{v} = \langle 0, -4, 2 \rangle$

6. $P(0, 0, 0)$, $\mathbf{v} = \langle -4, 3, 5 \rangle$

7. $P(1, 0, -2)$, $\mathbf{v} = 2\mathbf{i} - 5\mathbf{k}$

8. $P(1, 1, 1)$, $\mathbf{v} = \mathbf{i} - \mathbf{j} + \mathbf{k}$

9–14 ■ Find parametric equations for the line that passes through the points P and Q.

9. $P(1, -3, 2)$, $Q(2, 1, -1)$ **10.** $P(2, -1, -2)$, $Q(0, 1, -3)$

11. $P(1, 1, 0)$, $Q(0, 2, 2)$ **12.** $P(3, 3, 3)$, $Q(7, 0, 0)$

13. $P(3, 7, -5)$, $Q(7, 3, -5)$

14. $P(12, 16, 18)$, $Q(12, -6, 0)$

15–20 ■ A plane has normal vector $\mathbf{n}$ and passes through the point P. **(a)** Find an equation for the plane. **(b)** Find the intercepts and sketch a graph of the plane.

15. $\mathbf{n} = \langle 1, 1, -1 \rangle$, $P(0, 2, -3)$

16. $\mathbf{n} = \langle 3, 2, 0 \rangle$, $P(1, 2, 7)$

17. $\mathbf{n} = \langle 3, 0, -\frac{1}{2} \rangle$, $P(2, 4, 8)$

18. $\mathbf{n} = \langle -\frac{2}{3}, -\frac{1}{3}, 1 \rangle$, $P(-6, 0, -3)$

19. $\mathbf{n} = 3\mathbf{i} - \mathbf{j} + 2\mathbf{k}$, $P(0, 2, -3)$

20. $\mathbf{n} = \mathbf{i} + 4\mathbf{j}$, $P(1, 0, -9)$

21–26 ■ Find an equation of the plane that passes through the points P, Q, and R.

21. $P(6, -2, 1)$, $Q(5, -3, -1)$, $R(7, 0, 0)$

22. $P(3, 4, 5)$, $Q(1, 2, 3)$, $R(4, 7, 6)$

23. $P(3, \frac{1}{3}, -5)$, $Q(4, \frac{2}{3}, -3)$, $R(2, 0, 1)$

24. $P(\frac{3}{2}, 4, -2)$, $Q(-\frac{1}{2}, 2, 0)$, $R(-\frac{1}{2}, 0, 2)$

25. $P(6, 1, 1)$, $Q(3, 2, 0)$, $R(0, 0, 0)$

26. $P(2, 0, 0)$, $Q(0, 2, -2)$, $R(0, 0, 4)$

27–30 ■ A description of a line is given. Find parametric equations for the line.

27. The line crosses the z-axis where $z = 4$ and crosses the xy-plane where $x = 2$ and $y = 5$.

28. The line crosses the x-axis where $x = -2$ and crosses the z-axis where $z = 10$.

29. The line perpendicular to the xz-plane that contains the point $(2, -1, 5)$.

30. The line parallel to the y-axis that crosses the xz-plane where $x = -3$ and $z = 2$.

31–34 ■ A description of a plane is given. Find an equation for the plane.

31. The plane that crosses the x-axis where $x = 1$, the y-axis where $y = 3$, and the z-axis where $z = 4$.

32. The plane that crosses the x-axis where $x = -2$, the y-axis where $y = -1$, and the z-axis where $z = 3$.

33. The plane that is parallel to the plane $x - 2y + 4z = 6$ and contains the origin.

34. The plane that contains the line $x = 1 - t$, $y = 2 + t$, $z = -3t$ and the point $P(2, 0, -6)$. [*Hint:* A vector from any point on the line to P will lie in the plane.]

DISCOVERY ■ DISCUSSION ■ WRITING

35. Intersection of a Line and a Plane A line has parametric equations

$$x = 2 + t, \qquad y = 3t, \qquad z = 5 - t$$

and a plane has equation $5x - 2y - 2z = 1$.
  (a) For what value of t does the corresponding point on the line intersect the plane?
  (b) At what point do the line and the plane intersect?

36. Lines and Planes A line is parallel to the vector $\mathbf{v}$, and a plane has normal vector $\mathbf{n}$.
  (a) If the line is perpendicular to the plane, what is the relationship between $\mathbf{v}$ and $\mathbf{n}$ (parallel or perpendicular)?
  (b) If the line is parallel to the plane (that is, the line and the plane do not intersect), what is the relationship between $\mathbf{v}$ and $\mathbf{n}$ (parallel or perpendicular)?
  (c) Parametric equations for two lines are given. Which line is parallel to the plane $x - y + 4z = 6$? Which line is perpendicular to this plane?

  Line 1: $x = 2t$, $\quad y = 3 - 2t$, $\quad z = 4 + 8t$

  Line 2: $x = -2t$, $\quad y = 5 + 2t$, $\quad z = 3 + t$

37. Same Line: Different Parametric Equations Every line can be described by infinitely many different sets of parametric equations, since *any* point on the line and *any* vector parallel to the line can be used to construct the equations. But how can we tell whether two sets of parametric equations represent the same line? Consider the following two sets of parametric equations:

  Line 1: $x = 1 - t$, $\quad y = 3t$, $\quad z = -6 + 5t$

  Line 2: $x = -1 + 2t$, $\quad y = 6 - 6t$, $\quad z = 4 - 10t$

  (a) Find two points that lie on Line 1 by setting $t = 0$ and $t = 1$ in its parametric equations. Then show that these points also lie on Line 2 by finding two values of the parameter that give these points when substituted into the parametric equations for Line 2.
  (b) Show that the following two lines are not the same by finding a point on Line 3 and then showing that it does not lie on Line 4.

  Line 3: $x = 4t$, $\quad y = 3 - 6t$, $\quad z = -5 + 2t$

  Line 4: $x = 8 - 2t$, $\quad y = -9 + 3t$, $\quad z = 6 - t$

CHAPTER 9 | REVIEW

■ CONCEPT CHECK

1. (a) What is the difference between a scalar and a vector?
  (b) Draw a diagram to show how to add two vectors.
  (c) Draw a diagram to show how to subtract two vectors.
  (d) Draw a diagram to show how to multiply a vector by the scalars $2, \frac{1}{2}, -2,$ and $-\frac{1}{2}$.

2. If $\mathbf{u} = \langle u_1, u_2 \rangle$ and $\mathbf{v} = \langle v_1, v_2 \rangle$ are vectors in two dimensions and c is a scalar, write expressions for $\mathbf{u} + \mathbf{v}$, $\mathbf{u} - \mathbf{v}$, and $c\mathbf{u}$.

3. If $\mathbf{u} = \langle u_1, u_2 \rangle$ and $\mathbf{v} = \langle v_1, v_2, v_3 \rangle$ are vectors in two and three dimensions, respectively, write expressions for their magnitudes $|\mathbf{u}|$ and $|\mathbf{v}|$.

4. (a) If $\mathbf{u} = \langle u_1, u_2 \rangle$, write $\mathbf{u}$ in terms of $\mathbf{i}$ and $\mathbf{j}$.
  (b) If $\mathbf{v} = \langle v_1, v_2, v_3 \rangle$, write $\mathbf{v}$ in terms of $\mathbf{i}$, $\mathbf{j}$, and $\mathbf{k}$.

5. Write the components of the vector $\mathbf{u} = \langle u_1, u_2 \rangle$ in terms of its magnitude $|\mathbf{u}|$ and direction θ.

6. Express the dot product $\mathbf{u} \cdot \mathbf{v}$ in terms of the components of the vectors.
   (a) $\mathbf{u} = \langle u_1, u_2 \rangle$, $\quad \mathbf{v} = \langle v_1, v_2 \rangle$
   (b) $\mathbf{u} = \langle u_1, u_2, u_3 \rangle$, $\quad \mathbf{v} = \langle v_1, v_2, v_3 \rangle$

7. (a) How do you use the dot product to find the angle between two vectors?
   (b) How do you use the dot product to determine whether two vectors are perpendicular?

8. What is the component of $\mathbf{u}$ along $\mathbf{v}$, and how do you calculate it?

9. What is the projection of $\mathbf{u}$ onto $\mathbf{v}$, and how do you calculate it?

10. How much work is done by the force $\mathbf{F}$ in moving an object along a displacement $\mathbf{D}$?

11. How do you find the distance between two points $P(x_1, y_1, z_1)$ and $Q(x_2, y_2, z_2)$ in three-dimensional space?

12. What is the equation of the sphere with center $C(a, b, c)$ and radius r?

13. (a) How do you calculate the cross product $\mathbf{a} \times \mathbf{b}$ if you know the components of $\mathbf{a}$ and $\mathbf{b}$?
    (b) How do you calculate $\mathbf{a} \times \mathbf{b}$ if you know the lengths of $\mathbf{a}$ and $\mathbf{b}$ and the angle between them?
    (c) What is the angle between $\mathbf{a} \times \mathbf{b}$ and each of $\mathbf{a}$ and $\mathbf{b}$?

14. (a) How do you find the area of the parallelogram determined by $\mathbf{a}$ and $\mathbf{b}$?
    (b) How do you find the volume of the parallelepiped determined by $\mathbf{a}$, $\mathbf{b}$, and $\mathbf{c}$?

15. Write parametric equations for the line that contains the point $P(x_0, y_0, z_0)$ and that is parallel to the vector $\mathbf{v} = \langle a, b, c \rangle$.

16. Write an equation for the plane that contains the point $P(x_0, y_0, z_0)$ and has normal vector $\mathbf{n} = \langle a, b, c \rangle$.

17. How do you find parametric equations for the line that contains the points $P(x_1, y_1, z_1)$ and $Q(x_2, y_2, z_2)$?

18. How do you find an equation for the plane that contains the points $P(x_1, y_1, z_1)$, $Q(x_2, y_2, z_2)$, and $R(x_3, y_3, z_3)$?

■ EXERCISES

Exercises 1–24 deal with vectors in two dimensions.

1–4 ■ Find $|\mathbf{u}|$, $\mathbf{u} + \mathbf{v}$, $\mathbf{u} - \mathbf{v}$, $2\mathbf{u}$, and $3\mathbf{u} - 2\mathbf{v}$.

1. $\mathbf{u} = \langle -2, 3 \rangle$, $\quad \mathbf{v} = \langle 8, 1 \rangle$

2. $\mathbf{u} = \langle 5, -2 \rangle$, $\quad \mathbf{v} = \langle -3, 0 \rangle$

3. $\mathbf{u} = 2\mathbf{i} + \mathbf{j}$, $\quad \mathbf{v} = \mathbf{i} - 2\mathbf{j}$

4. $\mathbf{u} = 3\mathbf{j}$, $\quad \mathbf{v} = -\mathbf{i} + 2\mathbf{j}$

5. Find the vector with initial point $P(0, 3)$ and terminal point $Q(3, -1)$.

6. If the vector $5\mathbf{i} - 8\mathbf{j}$ is placed in the plane with its initial point at $P(5, 6)$, find its terminal point.

7–8 ■ Find the length and direction of the given vector.

7. $\mathbf{u} = \langle -2, 2\sqrt{3} \rangle$ $\qquad$ 8. $\mathbf{v} = 2\mathbf{i} - 5\mathbf{j}$

9–10 ■ The length $|\mathbf{u}|$ and direction θ of a vector $\mathbf{u}$ are given. Express $\mathbf{u}$ in component form.

9. $|\mathbf{u}| = 20$, $\quad \theta = 60°$ $\qquad$ 10. $|\mathbf{u}| = 13.5$, $\quad \theta = 125°$

11. Two tugboats are pulling a barge as shown in the figure. One pulls with a force of 2.0×10^4 lb in the direction N 50° E, and the other pulls with a force of 3.4×10^4 lb in the direction S 75° E.
    (a) Find the resultant force on the barge as a vector.
    (b) Find the magnitude and direction of the resultant force.

12. An airplane heads N 60° E at a speed of 600 mi/h relative to the air. A wind begins to blow in the direction N 30° W at 50 mi/h. (See the figure.)
    (a) Find the velocity of the airplane as a vector.
    (b) Find the true speed and direction of the airplane.

13–16 ■ Find the vectors $|\mathbf{u}|$, $\mathbf{u} \cdot \mathbf{u}$, and $\mathbf{u} \cdot \mathbf{v}$.

13. $\mathbf{u} = \langle 4, -3 \rangle$, $\quad \mathbf{v} = \langle 9, -8 \rangle$

14. $\mathbf{u} = \langle 5, 12 \rangle$, $\quad \mathbf{v} = \langle 10, -4 \rangle$

15. $\mathbf{u} = -2\mathbf{i} + 2\mathbf{j}$, $\quad \mathbf{v} = \mathbf{i} + \mathbf{j}$

16. $\mathbf{u} = 10\mathbf{j}$, $\quad \mathbf{v} = 5\mathbf{i} - 3\mathbf{j}$

17–20 ■ Are $\mathbf{u}$ and $\mathbf{v}$ orthogonal? If not, find the angle between them.

17. $\mathbf{u} = \langle -4, 2 \rangle$, $\quad \mathbf{v} = \langle 3, 6 \rangle$

18. $\mathbf{u} = \langle 5, 3 \rangle$, $\quad \mathbf{v} = \langle -2, 6 \rangle$

19. $\mathbf{u} = 2\mathbf{i} + \mathbf{j}$, $\quad \mathbf{v} = \mathbf{i} + 3\mathbf{j}$

20. $\mathbf{u} = \mathbf{i} - \mathbf{j}$, $\quad \mathbf{v} = \mathbf{i} + \mathbf{j}$

21–24 ■ Two vectors **u** and **v** are given.
  (a) Find the component of **u** along **v**.
  (b) Find $\text{proj}_v\,\mathbf{u}$.
  (c) Resolve **u** into the vectors $\mathbf{u}_1$ and $\mathbf{u}_2$, where $\mathbf{u}_1$ is parallel to **v** and $\mathbf{u}_2$ is perpendicular to **v**.

21. $\mathbf{u} = \langle 3, 1 \rangle, \quad \mathbf{v} = \langle 6, -1 \rangle$

22. $\mathbf{u} = \langle -8, 6 \rangle, \quad \mathbf{v} = \langle 20, 20 \rangle$

23. $\mathbf{u} = \mathbf{i} + 2\mathbf{j}, \quad \mathbf{v} = 4\mathbf{i} - 9\mathbf{j}$

24. $\mathbf{u} = 2\mathbf{i} + 4\mathbf{j}, \quad \mathbf{v} = 10\mathbf{j}$

Exercises 25–54 deal with three-dimensional coordinate geometry.

25–26 ■ Plot the given points, and find the distance between them.

25. $P(1, 0, 2), \quad Q(3, -2, 3)$ **26.** $P(0, 2, 4), \quad Q(1, 3, 0)$

27–28 ■ Find an equation of the sphere with the given radius r and center C.

27. $r = 6, \quad C(0, 0, 0)$ **28.** $r = 2, \quad C(1, -2, 4)$

29–30 ■ Show that the equation represents a sphere, and find its center and radius.

29. $x^2 + y^2 + z^2 - 2x - 6y + 4z = 2$

30. $x^2 + y^2 + z^2 = 4y + 4z$

31–32 ■ Find $|\mathbf{u}|$, $\mathbf{u} + \mathbf{v}$, $\mathbf{u} - \mathbf{v}$, and $\frac{3}{4}\mathbf{u} - 2\mathbf{v}$.

31. $\mathbf{u} = \langle 4, -2, 4 \rangle, \quad \mathbf{v} = \langle 2, 3, -1 \rangle$

32. $\mathbf{u} = 6\mathbf{i} - 8\mathbf{k}, \quad \mathbf{v} = \mathbf{i} - \mathbf{j} + \mathbf{k}$

33–36 ■ Two vectors **u** and **v** are given.
  (a) Find their dot product $\mathbf{u} \cdot \mathbf{v}$.
  (b) Are **u** and **v** perpendicular? If not, find the angle between them.

33. $\mathbf{u} = \langle 3, -2, 4 \rangle, \quad \mathbf{v} = \langle 3, 1, -2 \rangle$

34. $\mathbf{u} = \langle 2, -6, 5 \rangle, \quad \mathbf{v} = \langle 1, -\frac{1}{2}, -1 \rangle$

35. $\mathbf{u} = 2\mathbf{i} - \mathbf{j} + 4\mathbf{k}, \quad \mathbf{v} = 3\mathbf{i} + 2\mathbf{j} - \mathbf{k}$

36. $\mathbf{u} = \mathbf{j} - \mathbf{k}, \quad \mathbf{v} = \mathbf{i} + \mathbf{j}$

37–40 ■ Two vectors **a** and **b** are given.
  (a) Find their cross product $\mathbf{a} \times \mathbf{b}$.
  (b) Find a unit vector **u** that is perpendicular to both **a** and **b**.

37. $\mathbf{a} = \langle 1, 1, 3 \rangle, \quad \mathbf{b} = \langle 5, 0, -2 \rangle$

38. $\mathbf{a} = \langle 2, 3, 0 \rangle, \quad \mathbf{b} = \langle 0, 4, -1 \rangle$

39. $\mathbf{a} = \mathbf{i} - \mathbf{j}, \quad \mathbf{b} = 2\mathbf{j} - \mathbf{k}$

40. $\mathbf{a} = \mathbf{i} + \mathbf{j} - \mathbf{k}, \quad \mathbf{b} = \mathbf{i} - \mathbf{j} + \mathbf{k}$

41. Find the area of the triangle with vertices $P(2, 1, 1)$, $Q(0, 0, 3)$, and $R(-2, 4, 0)$.

42. Find the area of the parallelogram determined by the vectors $\mathbf{a} = \langle 4, 1, 1 \rangle$ and $\mathbf{b} = \langle -1, 2, 2 \rangle$.

43. Find the volume of the parallelepiped determined by the vectors $\mathbf{a} = 2\mathbf{i} - \mathbf{j}$, $\mathbf{b} = 2\mathbf{j} + \mathbf{k}$, and $\mathbf{c} = 3\mathbf{i} + \mathbf{j} - \mathbf{k}$.

44. A parallelepiped has one vertex at the origin; the three edges that have the origin as one endpoint extend to the points $P(0, 2, 2)$, $Q(3, 1, -1)$, and $R(1, 4, 1)$. Find the volume of the parallelepiped.

45–46 ■ Find parametric equations for the line that passes through P and is parallel to **v**.

45. $P(2, 0, -6), \quad \mathbf{v} = \langle 3, 1, 0 \rangle$

46. $P(5, 2, 8), \quad \mathbf{v} = 2\mathbf{i} - \mathbf{j} + 5\mathbf{k}$

47–48 ■ Find parametric equations for the line that passes through the points P and Q.

47. $P(6, -2, -3), \quad Q(4, 1, -2)$

48. $P(1, 0, 0), \quad Q(3, -4, 2)$

49–50 ■ Find an equation for the plane with normal vector **n** and passing through the point P.

49. $\mathbf{n} = \langle 2, 3, -5 \rangle, \quad P(2, 1, 1)$

50. $\mathbf{n} = -\mathbf{i} - 2\mathbf{j} + 7\mathbf{k}, \quad P(-2, 5, 2)$

51–52 ■ Find an equation of the plane that passes through the points P, Q, and R.

51. $P(1, 1, 1), \quad Q(3, -4, 2), \quad R(6, -1, 0)$

52. $P(4, 0, 0), \quad Q(0, -3, 0), \quad R(0, 0, -5)$

53. Find parametric equations for the line that crosses the x-axis where $x = 2$ and the z-axis where $z = -4$.

54. Find an equation of the plane that contains the line $x = 2 + 2t, y = 4t, z = -6$ and the point $P(5, 3, 0)$.

1. Let **u** be the vector with initial point $P(3, -1)$ and terminal point $Q(-3, 9)$.
   (a) Graph **u** in the coordinate plane.
   (b) Express **u** in terms of **i** and **j**.
   (c) Find the length of **u**.

2. Let $\mathbf{u} = \langle 1, 3 \rangle$ and $\mathbf{v} = \langle -6, 2 \rangle$.
   (a) Find $\mathbf{u} - 3\mathbf{v}$.
   (b) Find $|\mathbf{u} + \mathbf{v}|$.
   (c) Find $\mathbf{u} \cdot \mathbf{v}$.
   (d) Are **u** and **v** perpendicular?

3. Let $\mathbf{u} = \langle -4\sqrt{3}, 4 \rangle$.
   (a) Graph **u** in the coordinate plane, with initial point $(0, 0)$.
   (b) Find the length and direction of **u**.

4. A river is flowing due east at 8 mi/h. A man heads his motorboat in the direction N 30° E in the river. The speed of the motorboat relative to the water is 12 mi/h.
   (a) Express the true velocity of the motorboat as a vector.
   (b) Find the true speed and direction of the motorboat.

5. Let $\mathbf{u} = 3\mathbf{i} + 2\mathbf{j}$ and $\mathbf{v} = 5\mathbf{i} - \mathbf{j}$.
   (a) Find the angle between **u** and **v**.
   (b) Find the component of **u** along **v**.
   (c) Find $\text{proj}_\mathbf{v}\, \mathbf{u}$.

6. Find the work done by the force $\mathbf{F} = 3\mathbf{i} - 5\mathbf{j}$ in moving an object from the point $(2, 2)$ to the point $(7, -13)$.

7. Let $P(4, 3, -1)$ and $Q(6, -1, 3)$ be two points in three-dimensional space.
   (a) Find the distance between P and Q.
   (b) Find an equation for the sphere whose center is P and for which the segment $\overrightarrow{PQ}$ is a radius of the sphere.
   (c) The vector **u** has initial point P and terminal point Q. Express **u** both in component form and using the vectors **i**, **j**, and **k**.

8. Calculate the given quantity if
   $$\mathbf{a} = \mathbf{i} + \mathbf{j} - 2\mathbf{k} \qquad \mathbf{b} = 3\mathbf{i} - 2\mathbf{j} + \mathbf{k} \qquad \mathbf{c} = \mathbf{j} - 5\mathbf{k}$$

   (a) $2\mathbf{a} + 3\mathbf{b}$ (b) $|\mathbf{a}|$
   (c) $\mathbf{a} \cdot \mathbf{b}$ (d) $\mathbf{a} \times \mathbf{b}$
   (e) $|\mathbf{b} \times \mathbf{c}|$ (f) $\mathbf{a} \cdot (\mathbf{b} \times \mathbf{c})$
   (g) The angle between **a** and **b** (rounded to the nearest degree)

9. Find two unit vectors that are perpendicular to both $\mathbf{j} + 2\mathbf{k}$ and $\mathbf{i} - 2\mathbf{j} + 3\mathbf{k}$.

10. (a) Find a vector perpendicular to the plane that contains the points $P(1, 0, 0)$, $Q(2, 0, -1)$, and $R(1, 4, 3)$.
    (b) Find an equation for the plane that contains P, Q, and R.
    (c) Find the area of triangle PQR.

11. Find parametric equations for the line that contains the points $P(2, -4, 7)$ and $Q(0, -3, 5)$.

623

Vector Fields

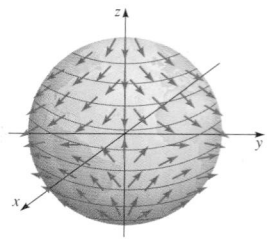

FIGURE 1 Wind represented by a vector field

To model the gravitational force near the earth or the flow of wind on a surface of the earth, we use vectors. For example, at each point on the surface of the earth air flows with a certain speed and direction. We represent the air currents by vectors. If we graph many of these vectors we get a "picture" or a graph of the flow of the air. (See Figure 1.)

▼ Vector Fields in the Plane

A **vector field** in the coordinate plane is a function that assigns a vector to each point in the plane (or to each point in some subset of the plane). For example,

$$\mathbf{F}(x, y) = x\mathbf{i} + y\mathbf{j}$$

is a vector field that assigns the vector $x\mathbf{i} + y\mathbf{j}$ to the point (x, y). We graph this vector field in the next example.

EXAMPLE 1 | Graphing a Vector Field in the Plane

Graph the vector field $\mathbf{F}(x, y) = x\mathbf{i} + y\mathbf{j}$. What does the graph indicate?

SOLUTION The table gives the vector field at several points. In Figure 2 we sketch the vectors in the table together with several other vectors in the vector field.

(x, y)	$\mathbf{F} = x\mathbf{i} + y\mathbf{j}$
$(1, 3)$	$\mathbf{i} + 3\mathbf{j}$
$(3, 3)$	$3\mathbf{i} + 3\mathbf{j}$
$(-4, 6)$	$-4\mathbf{i} + 6\mathbf{j}$
$(-6, -1)$	$-6\mathbf{i} - \mathbf{j}$
$(6, -6)$	$6\mathbf{i} - 6\mathbf{j}$

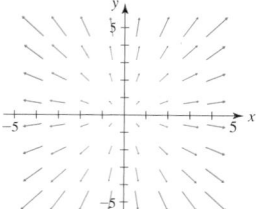

FIGURE 2

We see from the graph that the vectors in the field point away from the origin, and the farther from the origin, the greater the magnitude of the vector. ■

EXAMPLE 2 | Graphing a Vector Field in the Plane

A potter's wheel has a radius of 5 inches. The velocity of each point on the wheel is given by the vector field $\mathbf{F}(x, y) = -y\mathbf{i} + x\mathbf{j}$. What does the graph indicate?

SOLUTION The table gives the vector field at several points. In Figure 3 we sketch the vectors in the table.

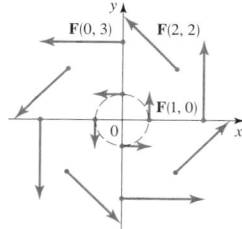

FIGURE 3

(x, y)	$\mathbf{F}(x, y)$	(x, y)	$\mathbf{F}(x, y)$
$(1, 0)$	$\langle 0, 1 \rangle$	$(-1, 0)$	$\langle 0, -1 \rangle$
$(2, 2)$	$\langle -2, 2 \rangle$	$(-2, -2)$	$\langle 2, -2 \rangle$
$(3, 0)$	$\langle 0, 3 \rangle$	$(-3, 0)$	$\langle 0, -3 \rangle$
$(0, 1)$	$\langle -1, 0 \rangle$	$(0, -1)$	$\langle 1, 0 \rangle$
$(-2, 2)$	$\langle -2, -2 \rangle$	$(2, -2)$	$\langle 2, 2 \rangle$
$(0, 3)$	$\langle -3, 0 \rangle$	$(0, -3)$	$\langle 3, 0 \rangle$

We see from the graph that the wheel is rotating counterclockwise and that the points at the edge of the wheel have a higher velocity than do the points near the center of the wheel. ■

624

Graphing vector fields requires graphing a lot of vectors. Some graphing calculators and computer programs are capable of graphing vector fields. You can also find many Internet sites that have applets for graphing vector fields. The vector field in Example 2 is graphed with a computer program in Figure 4. Notice how the computer scales the lengths of the vectors so that they are not too long yet are proportional to their true lengths.

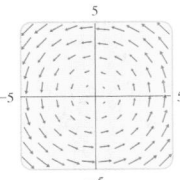

FIGURE 4

▼ Vector Fields in Space

A **vector field** in three-dimensional space is a function that assigns a vector to each point in space (or to each point in some subset of space). For example,

$$\mathbf{F}(x, y, z) = 2x\,\mathbf{i} - y\,\mathbf{j} + z^2\,\mathbf{k}$$

is a vector field that assigns the vector $2x\,\mathbf{i} - y\,\mathbf{j} + z^3\,\mathbf{k}$ to the point (x, y, z). In general, it is difficult to draw a vector field in space by hand, since we must draw many vectors with the proper perspective. The vector field in the next example is particularly simple, so we'll sketch it by hand.

EXAMPLE 3 │ Graphing a Vector Field in Space

Graph the vector field $\mathbf{F}(x, y, z) = z\,\mathbf{k}$. What does the graph indicate?

SOLUTION   A graph is shown in Figure 5. Notice that all vectors are vertical and point upward above the xy-plane and downward below it. The magnitude of each vector increases with the distance from the xy-plane.

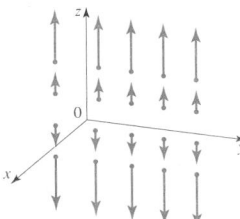

FIGURE 5

The gravitational pull of the earth in the space surrounding it is mathematically modeled by a vector field. According to Newton's Law of Gravitation, the gravitational force **F** is directed toward the center of the earth and is inversely proportional to the distance from the center of the earth. The magnitude of the force is

$$F = G\frac{Mm}{r^2}$$

where M is the mass of the earth, m is mass of an object in proximity to the earth, r is the distance from the object to the center of the earth, and G is the universal gravitational constant.

To model the gravitational force, let's place a three-dimensional coordinate system with the origin at the center of the earth. The gravitational force at the point (x, y, z) is directed toward the origin. A unit vector pointing toward the origin is

$$\mathbf{u} = -\frac{x\mathbf{i} + y\mathbf{j} + z\mathbf{k}}{\sqrt{x^2 + y^2 + z^2}}$$

To obtain the gravitational vector field, we multiply this unit vector by the appropriate magnitude, namely, GMm/r^2. Since the distance r from the point (x, y, z) to the origin is $r = \sqrt{x^2 + y^2 + z^2}$, it follows that $r^2 = x^2 + y^2 + z^2$. So we can express the gravitational vector field as

$$\mathbf{F}(x, y, z) = -GMm\frac{x\mathbf{i} + y\mathbf{j} + z\mathbf{k}}{(x^2 + y^2 + z^2)^{3/2}}$$

Some of the vectors in the gravitational field **F** are pictured in Figure 6.

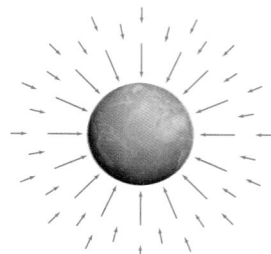

FIGURE 6   The gravitational field

PROBLEMS

1–6 ■ Sketch the vector field **F** by drawing a diagram as in Figure 3.

1. $\mathbf{F}(x, y) = \frac{1}{2}\mathbf{i} + \frac{1}{2}\mathbf{j}$

2. $\mathbf{F}(x, y) = \mathbf{i} + x\mathbf{j}$

3. $\mathbf{F}(x, y) = y\mathbf{i} + \frac{1}{2}\mathbf{j}$

4. $\mathbf{F}(x, y) = (x - y)\mathbf{i} + x\mathbf{j}$

5. $\mathbf{F}(x, y) = \dfrac{y\mathbf{i} + x\mathbf{j}}{\sqrt{x^2 + y^2}}$

6. $\mathbf{F}(x, y) = \dfrac{y\mathbf{i} - x\mathbf{j}}{\sqrt{x^2 + y^2}}$

7–10 ■ Sketch the vector field **F** by drawing a diagram as in Figure 5.

7. $\mathbf{F}(x, y, z) = \mathbf{j}$

8. $\mathbf{F}(x, y, z) = \mathbf{j} - \mathbf{k}$

9. $\mathbf{F}(x, y, z) = z\mathbf{j}$

10. $\mathbf{F}(x, y, z) = y\mathbf{k}$

11–14 ■ Match the vector field **F** with the graphs labeled I–IV.

11. $\mathbf{F}(x, y) = \langle y, x \rangle$

12. $\mathbf{F}(x, y) = \langle 1, \sin y \rangle$

13. $\mathbf{F}(x, y) = \langle x - 2, y + 1 \rangle$

14. $\mathbf{F}(x, y) = \langle y, 1/x \rangle$

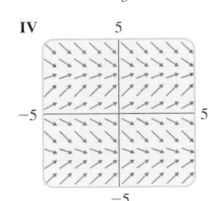

15–18 ■ Match the vector field **F** with the graphs labeled I–IV.

15. $\mathbf{F}(x, y, z) = \mathbf{i} + 2\mathbf{j} + 3\mathbf{k}$

16. $\mathbf{F}(x, y, z) = \mathbf{i} + 2\mathbf{j} + z\mathbf{k}$

17. $\mathbf{F}(x, y, z) = x\mathbf{i} + y\mathbf{j} + 3\mathbf{k}$

18. $\mathbf{F}(x, y, z) = x\mathbf{i} + y\mathbf{j} + z\mathbf{k}$

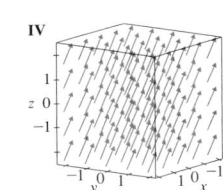

19. Flow Lines in a Current   The current in a turbulent bay is described by the velocity vector field

$$\mathbf{F}(x, y) = (x + y)\mathbf{i} + (x - y)\mathbf{j}$$

A graph of the vector field **F** is shown. If a small toy boat is put in this bay, we can tell from the graph of the vector field what path the boat would follow. Such paths are called **flow lines** (or **streamlines**) of the vector field. A streamline starting at $(1, -3)$ is shown in blue in the figure. Sketch streamlines starting at the given point.

(a) $(1, 4)$ **(b)** $(-2, 1)$ **(c)** $(-1, -2)$

1. Find two polar coordinate representations of the point $(8, -8)$, one with $r > 0$ and one with $r < 0$, and both with $0 \leq \theta < 2\pi$.

2. The graph of the equation $r = 2 \sin 2\theta$ is called a *four-leafed rose*.
   (a) Sketch a graph of this equation.
   (b) Convert the equation to rectangular coordinates.

3. Let $z = \sqrt{3} - i$ and let $w = 6\left(\cos \dfrac{5\pi}{12} + i \sin \dfrac{5\pi}{12}\right)$.
   (a) Write z in polar form.
   (b) Find zw and z/w.
   (c) Find z^{10}.
   (d) Find the three cube roots of z.

4. (a) Sketch a graph of the parametric equations
$$x = 2 - \sin^2 t \qquad y = \cos t$$
   (b) Eliminate the parameter to obtain an equation for this curve in rectangular coordinates. What type of curve is this?

5. Let $\mathbf{u} = \langle 8, 6 \rangle$ and $\mathbf{v} = 5\mathbf{i} - 10\mathbf{j}$.
   (a) Graph $\mathbf{u}$ and $\mathbf{v}$ in the coordinate plane, with initial point $(0, 0)$.
   (b) Find $\mathbf{u} + \mathbf{v}$, $2\mathbf{u} - \mathbf{v}$, the angle between $\mathbf{u}$ and $\mathbf{v}$, and $\text{proj}_{\mathbf{v}}\, \mathbf{u}$.
   (c) Assuming $\mathbf{u}$ is a force vector, calculate the work done by $\mathbf{u}$ when a particle moves under its influence from $(2, 0)$ to $(10, 3)$.

6. Let $P(1, -1, 3)$ and $Q(3, -2, 1)$ be two points in three-dimensional space.
   (a) Find the distance between P and Q.
   (b) Find an equation for the sphere that has center P and for which Q is a point on its surface.
   (c) Find parametric equations for the line that contains P and Q.

7. Let $\mathbf{a} = \langle 2, 1, -3 \rangle$ and $\mathbf{b} = 3\mathbf{i} + 2\mathbf{k}$ be two vectors in three-dimensional space.
   (a) Find $\mathbf{a} \cdot \mathbf{b}$ and $\mathbf{a} \times \mathbf{b}$. Are $\mathbf{a}$ and $\mathbf{b}$ perpendicular, parallel, or neither?
   (b) Find an equation for the plane that is parallel to both $\mathbf{a}$ and $\mathbf{b}$, and that contains the point $(3, 0, -5)$.

SYSTEMS OF EQUATIONS AND INEQUALITIES

Throughout the preceding chapters we modeled real-world situations by equations. But many real-world situations involve too many variables to be modeled by a single equation. For example, weather depends on the relationship among many variables, including temperature, wind speed, air pressure, and humidity. So to model (and forecast) the weather, scientists use many equations, each having many variables. Such collections of equations, called systems of equations, *work together* to describe the weather. Systems of equations with hundreds of variables are used by airlines to establish consistent flight schedules and by telecommunications companies to find efficient routings for telephone calls. In this chapter we learn how to solve systems of equations that consist of several equations in several variables.

AP Photo/Mark Duncan, File

629

SUGGESTED TIME AND EMPHASIS

$1\frac{1}{2}$–2 classes, essential material

10.1 SYSTEMS OF LINEAR EQUATIONS IN TWO VARIABLES

Systems of Linear Equations and Their Solutions ▶ Substitution Method ▶ Elimination Method ▶ Graphical Method ▶ The Number of Solutions of a Linear System in Two Variables ▶ Modeling with Linear Systems

▼ Systems of Linear Equations and Their Solutions

A linear equation in two variables is an equation of the form

$$ax + by = c$$

The graph of a linear equation is a line (see Section 1.10).

A **system of equations** is a set of equations that involve the same variables. A **system of linear equations** is a system of equations in which each equation is linear. A **solution** of a system is an assignment of values for the variables that makes *each* equation in the system true. To **solve** a system means to find all solutions of the system.

Here is an example of a system of linear equations in two variables:

$$\begin{cases} 2x - y = 5 & \text{Equation 1} \\ x + 4y = 7 & \text{Equation 2} \end{cases}$$

We can check that $x = 3$ and $y = 1$ is a solution of this system.

Equation 1	**Equation 2**
$2x - y = 5$	$x + 4y = 7$
$2(3) - 1 = 5$ ✔	$3 + 4(1) = 7$ ✔

The solution can also be written as the ordered pair $(3, 1)$.

Note that the graphs of Equations 1 and 2 are lines (see Figure 1). Since the solution $(3, 1)$ satisfies each equation, the point $(3, 1)$ lies on each line. So it is the point of intersection of the two lines.

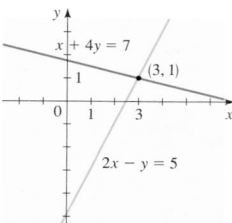

FIGURE 1

▼ Substitution Method

In the **substitution method** we start with one equation in the system and solve for one variable in terms of the other variable. The following box describes the procedure.

SUBSTITUTION METHOD

1. **Solve for One Variable.**   Choose one equation, and solve for one variable in terms of the other variable.
2. **Substitute.**   Substitute the expression you found in Step 1 into the other equation to get an equation in one variable, then solve for that variable.
3. **Back-Substitute.**   Substitute the value you found in Step 2 back into the expression found in Step 1 to solve for the remaining variable.

TEXT QUESTION

Why does the dependent system $x + y = 2$, $2x + 2y = 4$ have infinitely many solutions?

Answer

For any given x, there is a y that satisfies both equations.

TEXT QUESTION

The textbook says that given the system

$$\begin{cases} 3x + 2y = 14 \\ x - 2y = 2 \end{cases}$$

we can add the equations to eliminate y, obtaining $4x = 16$ and thus determining $x = 4$ and $y = 1$. Could this system be solved using the substitution method? If not, why not? If so, would the answers be the same?

Answer

It could, and the answers would be the same.

EXAMPLE 1 | Substitution Method

Find all solutions of the system.

$$\begin{cases} 2x + y = 1 & \text{Equation 1} \\ 3x + 4y = 14 & \text{Equation 2} \end{cases}$$

SOLUTION **Solve for one variable.** We solve for y in the first equation.

$$y = 1 - 2x \qquad \text{Solve for } y \text{ in Equation 1}$$

Substitute. Now we substitute for y in the second equation and solve for x.

$$3x + 4(1 - 2x) = 14 \qquad \text{Substitute } y = 1 - 2x \text{ into Equation 2}$$
$$3x + 4 - 8x = 14 \qquad \text{Expand}$$
$$-5x + 4 = 14 \qquad \text{Simplify}$$
$$-5x = 10 \qquad \text{Subtract 4}$$
$$x = -2 \qquad \text{Solve for } x$$

Back-substitute. Next we back-substitute $x = -2$ into the equation $y = 1 - 2x$.

$$y = 1 - 2(-2) = 5 \qquad \text{Back-substitute}$$

Thus $x = -2$ and $y = 5$, so the solution is the ordered pair $(-2, 5)$. Figure 2 shows that the graphs of the two equations intersect at the point $(-2, 5)$.

CHECK YOUR ANSWER

$x = -2, y = 5$:

$$\begin{cases} 2(-2) + 5 = 1 \\ 3(-2) + 4(5) = 14 \end{cases} \checkmark$$

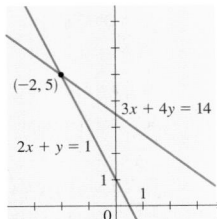

FIGURE 2

✎ NOW TRY EXERCISE **5**

▼ Elimination Method

To solve a system using the **elimination method**, we try to combine the equations using sums or differences so as to eliminate one of the variables.

ELIMINATION METHOD

1. **Adjust the Coefficients.** Multiply one or more of the equations by appropriate numbers so that the coefficient of one variable in one equation is the negative of its coefficient in the other equation.

2. **Add the Equations.** Add the two equations to eliminate one variable, then solve for the remaining variable.

3. **Back-Substitute.** Substitute the value that you found in Step 2 back into one of the original equations, and solve for the remaining variable.

IN-CLASS MATERIALS

This may be a good time to point out that a system of equations can have zero, one, more than one, or infinitely many solutions. The students will be able to solve systems that have one or more than one solution:

$$\begin{cases} 2x + y = 3 \\ -2x + 3y = 3 \end{cases} \qquad \begin{cases} x^2 = y \\ -x^2 + 8 = y \end{cases} \qquad \begin{cases} y = x^3 - x^2 - 4x \\ y = 4 \end{cases}$$

When demonstrating these systems, it is important to show the graphical solution as well as an analytic solution. Then have the students graphically show a system of equations with no solutions and then one with infinitely many solutions.

ALTERNATE EXAMPLE 2

Find all solutions of the system.

$$\begin{cases} 5x + 4y = 54 \\ x - 4y = -18 \end{cases}$$

ANSWER

$(6, 6)$

EXAMPLE 2 | Elimination Method

Find all solutions of the system.

$$\begin{cases} 3x + 2y = 14 & \text{Equation 1} \\ x - 2y = 2 & \text{Equation 2} \end{cases}$$

SOLUTION Since the coefficients of the y-terms are negatives of each other, we can add the equations to eliminate y.

$$\begin{cases} 3x + 2y = 14 \\ x - 2y = 2 \end{cases} \quad \text{System}$$

$$\begin{aligned} 4x &= 16 && \text{Add} \\ x &= 4 && \text{Solve for } x \end{aligned}$$

Now we back-substitute $x = 4$ into one of the original equations and solve for y. Let's choose the second equation because it looks simpler.

$$\begin{aligned} x - 2y &= 2 && \text{Equation 2} \\ 4 - 2y &= 2 && \text{Back-substitute } x = 4 \text{ into Equation 2} \\ -2y &= -2 && \text{Subtract 4} \\ y &= 1 && \text{Solve for } y \end{aligned}$$

The solution is $(4, 1)$. Figure 3 shows that the graphs of the equations in the system intersect at the point $(4, 1)$.

↰ NOW TRY EXERCISE **9** ■

FIGURE 3

Graph showing lines $3x + 2y = 14$ and $x - 2y = 2$ intersecting at $(4, 1)$.

▼ Graphical Method

In the **graphical method** we use a graphing device to solve the system of equations.

> **GRAPHICAL METHOD**
>
> 1. **Graph Each Equation.** Express each equation in a form suitable for the graphing calculator by solving for y as a function of x. Graph the equations on the same screen.
> 2. **Find the Intersection Points.** The solutions are the x- and y-coordinates of the points of intersection.

MATHEMATICS IN THE MODERN WORLD

Weather Prediction

Modern meteorologists do much more than predict tomorrow's weather. They research long-term weather patterns, depletion of the ozone layer, global warming, and other effects of human activity on the weather. But daily weather prediction is still a major part of meteorology; its value is measured by the innumerable human lives that are saved each year through accurate prediction of hurricanes, blizzards, and other catastrophic weather phenomena. Early in the 20th century mathematicians proposed to model weather with equations that used the current values of hundreds of atmospheric variables. Although this model worked in principle, it was impossible to predict future weather patterns with it because of the difficulty of measuring all the variables accurately and solving all the equations. Today, new mathematical models combined with high-speed computer simulations and better data have vastly improved weather prediction. As a result, many human as well as economic disasters have been averted. Mathematicians at the National Oceanographic and Atmospheric Administration (NOAA) are continually researching better methods of weather prediction.

© Rachel Epstein/Photo Edit

IN-CLASS MATERIALS

Many students will want to learn just one method of solving systems of equations and stick with it. It is important that they be familiar with all three. One reason is that some systems are easier to solve with one method than with another. Another reason is that if they take mathematics classes in the future, their teachers will use their own favorite methods in class.

Either have the students try to come up with three sample systems, each lending itself to a different method, or use these:

$$\begin{aligned} y &= 3x + 2 \\ \sqrt{y^2 - 8x^2 - 12x - 4} &= 4 \end{aligned} \qquad \text{Substitution easiest}$$

$$\begin{aligned} 3x + \frac{5}{11}y &= 2 \\ -3x + \frac{6}{11}y &= 3 \end{aligned} \qquad \text{Elimination easiest}$$

$$\begin{aligned} y &= x^3 - x \\ y &= e^x \end{aligned} \qquad \begin{array}{l} \text{Exact solution impossible—a} \\ \text{graph can give an approximation} \end{array}$$

EXAMPLE 3 | Graphical Method

Find all solutions of the system

$$\begin{cases} 1.35x - 2.13y = -2.36 \\ 2.16x + 0.32y = 1.06 \end{cases}$$

SOLUTION   Solving for y in terms of x, we get the equivalent system

$$\begin{cases} y = 0.63x + 1.11 \\ y = -6.75x + 3.31 \end{cases}$$

where we have rounded the coefficients to two decimals. Figure 4 shows that the two lines intersect. Zooming in, we see that the solution is approximately $(0.30, 1.3)$.

✎. NOW TRY EXERCISES **13** AND **49**

FIGURE 4

▼ The Number of Solutions of a Linear System in Two Variables

The graph of a linear system in two variables is a pair of lines, so to solve the system graphically, we must find the intersection point(s) of the lines. Two lines may intersect in a single point, they may be parallel, or they may coincide, as shown in Figure 5. So there are three possible outcomes in solving such a system.

NUMBER OF SOLUTIONS OF A LINEAR SYSTEM IN TWO VARIABLES

For a system of linear equations in two variables, exactly one of the following is true. (See Figure 5.)

1. The system has exactly one solution.

2. The system has no solution.

3. The system has infinitely many solutions.

A system that has no solution is said to be **inconsistent**. A system with infinitely many solutions is called **dependent**.

  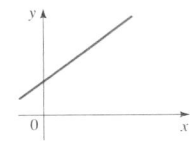

FIGURE 5

(a) Lines intersect at a single point. The system has one solution.

(b) Lines are parallel and do not intersect. The system has no solution.

(c) Lines coincide—equations are for the same line. The system has infinitely many solutions.

EXAMPLE 4 | A Linear System with One Solution

Solve the system and graph the lines.

$$\begin{cases} 3x - y = 0 & \text{Equation 1} \\ 5x + 2y = 22 & \text{Equation 2} \end{cases}$$

IN-CLASS MATERIALS

The text has shown examples of systems of linear equations with zero, one, and infinitely many solutions. Ask the students to try to come up with an example of a system with a different outcome or to explain why it is not possible. Discussing graphical solutions to these systems will not only make the answer apparent, it will also reinforce the nomenclature *linear equation*.

ALTERNATE EXAMPLE 3

Find all solutions of the system.

$$\begin{cases} 0.32x - y = -1.42 \\ 0.41x + 1.8y = 2.31 \end{cases}$$

ANSWER

From the graph, we estimate the solution to be roughly $x = 0.25$, $y = 1.35$. A closer approximation, achieved through algebraic methods, is $x = -0.24949$, $y = 1.34016$.

IN-CLASS MATERIALS

Note that some systems that are not technically linear can be solved by similar means. For example, given

$$\begin{cases} \sqrt{x} + 2^y = 10 \\ 5\sqrt{x} - 3(2^y) = -14 \end{cases}$$

one can use elimination to obtain $\sqrt{x} = 2$, $2^y = 8 \Rightarrow x = 4$, $y = 3$.

ALTERNATE EXAMPLE 4

Solve the system.

$$\begin{cases} 4x - y = 0 \\ 5x + 2y = 52 \end{cases}$$

If the system is inconsistent, indicate this.

ANSWER

$(4, 16)$

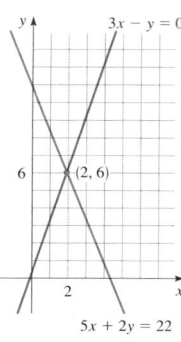

FIGURE 6

CHECK YOUR ANSWER

$x = 2, \quad y = 6$:

$$\begin{cases} 3(2) - (6) = 0 \\ 5(2) + 2(6) = 22 \end{cases} ✔$$

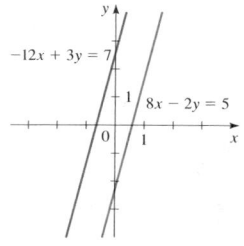

FIGURE 7

ALTERNATE EXAMPLE 5
Solve the system.
$$\begin{cases} 12x - 3y = 7 \\ -20x + 5y = 4 \end{cases}$$
If the system is inconsistent, indicate this.

ANSWER
Inconsistent

ALTERNATE EXAMPLE 6
Solve the system.
$$\begin{cases} 2x - 6y = 24 \\ 3x - 9y = 36 \end{cases}$$
If the system is inconsistent, indicate this.

ANSWER
$\left(x, \dfrac{1}{3}x - 4 \right)$

SOLUTION We eliminate y from the equations and solve for x.

$$\begin{cases} 6x - 2y = 0 & \quad 2 \times \text{Equation 1} \\ 5x + 2y = 22 \\ \hline 11x \quad\;\; = 22 & \quad \text{Add} \\ x = 2 & \quad \text{Solve for } x \end{cases}$$

Now we back-substitute into the first equation and solve for y:

$$6(2) - 2y = 0 \qquad \text{Back-substitute } x = 2$$
$$-2y = -12 \qquad \text{Subtract } 6 \times 2 = 12$$
$$y = 6 \qquad \text{Solve for } y$$

The solution of the system is the ordered pair $(2, 6)$, that is,

$$x = 2, \qquad y = 6$$

The graph in Figure 6 shows that the lines in the system intersect at the point $(2, 6)$.

✎ **NOW TRY EXERCISE 23** ▪

EXAMPLE 5 | A Linear System with No Solution

Solve the system.

$$\begin{cases} 8x - 2y = 5 & \quad \text{Equation 1} \\ -12x + 3y = 7 & \quad \text{Equation 2} \end{cases}$$

SOLUTION This time we try to find a suitable combination of the two equations to eliminate the variable y. Multiplying the first equation by 3 and the second equation by 2 gives

$$\begin{cases} 24x - 6y = 15 & \quad 3 \times \text{Equation 1} \\ -24x + 6y = 14 & \quad 2 \times \text{Equation 2} \\ \hline 0 = 29 & \quad \text{Add} \end{cases}$$

Adding the two equations eliminates *both x and y* in this case, and we end up with $0 = 29$, which is obviously false. No matter what values we assign to x and y, we cannot make this statement true, so the system has *no solution*. Figure 7 shows that the lines in the system are parallel and do not intersect. The system is inconsistent.

✎ **NOW TRY EXERCISE 35** ▪

EXAMPLE 6 | A Linear System with Infinitely Many Solutions

Solve the system.

$$\begin{cases} 3x - 6y = 12 & \quad \text{Equation 1} \\ 4x - 8y = 16 & \quad \text{Equation 2} \end{cases}$$

SOLUTION We multiply the first equation by 4 and the second by 3 to prepare for subtracting the equations to eliminate x. The new equations are

$$\begin{cases} 12x - 24y = 48 & \quad 4 \times \text{Equation 1} \\ 12x - 24y = 48 & \quad 3 \times \text{Equation 2} \end{cases}$$

We see that the two equations in the original system are simply different ways of expressing the equation of one single line. The coordinates of any point on this line give a

---

IN-CLASS MATERIALS

Complex arithmetic can be reviewed at this time. Ask the students if this is a system of linear equations in two variables and (if so) to solve it:

$$(2 - i)x + 4y = 5$$
$$(4 - 3i)x - 2y = 3 + i$$

solution of the system. Writing the equation in slope-intercept form, we have $y = \frac{1}{2}x - 2$. So if we let t represent any real number, we can write the solution as

$$x = t$$

$$y = \frac{1}{2}t - 2$$

We can also write the solution in ordered-pair form as

$$\left(t, \frac{1}{2}t - 2\right)$$

where t is any real number. The system has infinitely many solutions (see Figure 8).

⟡ NOW TRY EXERCISE **37**   ◼

In Example 3, to get specific solutions we have to assign values to t. For instance, if $t = 1$, we get the solution $\left(1, -\frac{3}{2}\right)$. If $t = 4$, we get the solution $(4, 0)$. For every value of t we get a different solution. (See Figure 8.)

▼ Modeling with Linear Systems

Frequently, when we use equations to solve problems in the sciences or in other areas, we obtain systems like the ones we've been considering. When modeling with systems of equations, we use the following guidelines, which are similar to those in Section 1.6.

GUIDELINES FOR MODELING WITH SYSTEMS OF EQUATIONS

1. **Identify the Variables.**   Identify the quantities that the problem asks you to find. These are usually determined by a careful reading of the question posed at the end of the problem. Introduce notation for the variables (call them x and y or some other letters).

2. **Express All Unknown Quantities in Terms of the Variables.**   Read the problem again, and express all the quantities mentioned in the problem in terms of the variables you defined in Step 1.

3. **Set Up a System of Equations.**   Find the crucial facts in the problem that give the relationships between the expressions you found in Step 2. Set up a system of equations (or a model) that expresses these relationships.

4. **Solve the System and Interpret the Results.**   Solve the system you found in Step 3, check your solutions, and state your final answer as a sentence that answers the question posed in the problem.

The next two examples illustrate how to model with systems of equations.

EXAMPLE 7 | A Distance-Speed-Time Problem

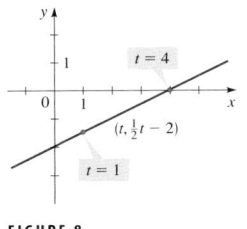

current

4 mi

A woman rows a boat upstream from one point on a river to another point 4 mi away in $1\frac{1}{2}$ hours. The return trip, traveling with the current, takes only 45 min. How fast does she row relative to the water, and at what speed is the current flowing?

SOLUTION   Identify the variables.   We are asked to find the rowing speed and the speed of the current, so we let

$$x = \text{rowing speed (mi/h)}$$

$$y = \text{current speed (mi/h)}$$

FIGURE 8

ALTERNATE EXAMPLE 7

A woman rows a boat upstream from one point on a river to another point 7 mi away in $1\frac{1}{4}$ hours. The return trip, traveling with the current, takes only 50 min. How fast does she row relative to the water (in mi/h), and at what speed is the current flowing (in mi/h)?

ANSWER

7 mi/h, $\dfrac{7}{5}$ mi/h

EXAMPLE

A straightforward word problem:

Retaining bricks for gardens are usually either 6 in. or 12 in. long. A 6-in. brick costs \$0.80, and a 12-in. brick costs \$1.20. Assume we have a garden with an 8-ft perimeter and we spend \$10.80. How many bricks of each type did we buy?

ANSWER

6 small bricks and 5 large ones

Express unknown quantites in terms of the variable. The woman's speed when she rows upstream is her rowing speed minus the speed of the current; her speed downstream is her rowing speed plus the speed of the current. Now we translate this information into the language of algebra.

In Words	In Algebra
Rowing speed	x
Current speed	y
Speed upstream	$x - y$
Speed downstream	$x + y$

Set up a system of equations. The distance upstream and downstream is 4 mi, so using the fact that speed × time = distance for both legs of the trip, we get

$$\boxed{\text{speed upstream}} \times \boxed{\text{time upstream}} = \boxed{\text{distance traveled}}$$

$$\boxed{\text{speed downstream}} \times \boxed{\text{time downstream}} = \boxed{\text{distance traveled}}$$

In algebraic notation this translates into the following equations.

$$(x - y)\tfrac{3}{2} = 4 \qquad \text{Equation 1}$$
$$(x + y)\tfrac{3}{4} = 4 \qquad \text{Equation 2}$$

(The times have been converted to hours, since we are expressing the speeds in miles per *hour*.)

Solve the system. We multiply the equations by 2 and 4, respectively, to clear the denominators.

$$\begin{cases} 3x - 3y = 8 & \quad 2 \times \text{Equation 1} \\ 3x + 3y = 16 & \quad 4 \times \text{Equation 2} \end{cases}$$

$$\begin{aligned} 6x &= 24 & \text{Add} \\ x &= 4 & \text{Solve for } x \end{aligned}$$

Back-substituting this value of x into the first equation (the second works just as well) and solving for y gives

$$\begin{aligned} 3(4) - 3y &= 8 & \text{Back-substitute } x = 4 \\ -3y &= 8 - 12 & \text{Subtract 12} \\ y &= \tfrac{4}{3} & \text{Solve for } y \end{aligned}$$

The woman rows at 4 mi/h, and the current flows at $1\tfrac{1}{3}$ mi/h.

CHECK YOUR ANSWER

Speed upstream is

$$\frac{\text{distance}}{\text{time}} = \frac{4 \text{ mi}}{1\frac{1}{2}\text{ h}} = 2\tfrac{2}{3}\text{ mi/h}$$

and this should equal

rowing speed − current flow

$$= 4 \text{ mi/h} - \tfrac{4}{3}\text{ mi/h} = 2\tfrac{2}{3}\text{ mi/h}$$

Speed downstream is

$$\frac{\text{distance}}{\text{time}} = \frac{4 \text{ mi}}{\frac{3}{4}\text{ h}} = 5\tfrac{1}{3}\text{ mi/h}$$

and this should equal

rowing speed + current flow

$$= 4 \text{ mi/h} + \tfrac{4}{3}\text{ mi/h} = 5\tfrac{1}{3}\text{ mi/h} \quad ✔$$

↖. NOW TRY EXERCISE **63**

EXAMPLE

A "mixture problem": Peanuts cost $4.00 per pound, and cashews cost $7.50 per pound. If I buy a 5-lb bag consisting of peanuts and cashews and I pay $23.50 for the bag, how many pounds of cashews are in it?

ANSWER

1 lb cashews, 4 lb peanuts

EXAMPLE 8 | A Mixture Problem

A vintner fortifies wine that contains 10% alcohol by adding a 70% alcohol solution to it. The resulting mixture has an alcoholic strength of 16% and fills 1000 one-liter bottles. How many liters (L) of the wine and of the alcohol solution does the vintner use?

SOLUTION   **Identify the variables.**   Since we are asked for the amounts of wine and alcohol, we let

$$x = \text{amount of wine used (L)}$$

$$y = \text{amount of alcohol solution used (L)}$$

Express all unknown quantities in terms of the variable.   From the fact that the wine contains 10% alcohol and the solution contains 70% alcohol, we get the following.

In Words	In Algebra
Amount of wine used (L)	x
Amount of alcohol solution used (L)	y
Amount of alcohol in wine (L)	$0.10x$
Amount of alcohol in solution (L)	$0.70y$

Set up a system of equations.   The volume of the mixture must be the total of the two volumes the vintner is adding together, so

$$x + y = 1000$$

Also, the amount of alcohol in the mixture must be the total of the alcohol contributed by the wine and by the alcohol solution, that is,

$0.10x + 0.70y = (0.16)1000$	
$0.10x + 0.70y = 160$	Simplify
$x + 7y = 1600$	Multiply by 10 to clear decimals

Thus we get the system

$$\begin{cases} x + y = 1000 & \text{Equation 1} \\ x + 7y = 1600 & \text{Equation 2} \end{cases}$$

Solve the system.   Subtracting the first equation from the second eliminates the variable x, and we get

$6y = 600$	Subtract Equation 1 from Equation 2
$y = 100$	Solve for y

We now back-substitute $y = 100$ into the first equation and solve for x.

$x + 100 = 1000$	Back-substitute $y = 100$
$x = 900$	Solve for x

The vintner uses 900 L of wine and 100 L of the alcohol solution.

✎. NOW TRY EXERCISE **65**

ALTERNATE EXAMPLE 8
A vintner fortifies wine that contains 10% alcohol by adding a 60% alcohol solution to it. The resulting mixture has an alcoholic strength of 12% and fills 1100 one-liter bottles. How many liters (L) of the wine and of the alcohol solution does he use?

ANSWER
1056 L, 44 L

DRILL QUESTION

Solve this system of equations.

$$\begin{cases} x + y = 2 \\ 4x - 2y = -1 \end{cases}$$

Answer

$$x = \frac{1}{2}, y = \frac{3}{2}$$

10.1 EXERCISES

CONCEPTS

1. The system of equations

$$\begin{cases} 2x + 3y = 7 \\ 5x - y = 9 \end{cases}$$

is a system of two equations in the two variables _____

and _____. To determine whether $(5, -1)$ is a solution of this system, we check whether $x = 5$ and $y = -1$ satisfy each

_____ in the system. Which of the following are solutions of this system?

$$(5, -1), \quad (-1, 3), \quad (2, 1)$$

2. A system of equations in two variables can be solved by the

_____ method, the _____ method, or the _____ method.

3. A system of two linear equations in two variables can have one

solution, _____ solution, or _____ _____ solutions.

4. The following is a system of two linear equations in two variables.

$$\begin{cases} x + y = 1 \\ 2x + 2y = 2 \end{cases}$$

The graph of the first equation is the same as the graph of the

second equation, so the system has _____ _____ solutions. We express these solutions by writing

$$x = t$$
$$y = \underline{\quad}$$

where t is any real number. Some of the solutions of this

system are $(1, \underline{\quad})$, $(-3, \underline{\quad})$, and $(5, \underline{\quad})$.

SKILLS

5–8 ■ Use the substitution method to find all solutions of the system of equations.

5. $\begin{cases} x - y = 1 \\ 4x + 3y = 18 \end{cases}$

6. $\begin{cases} 3x + y = 1 \\ 5x + 2y = 1 \end{cases}$

7. $\begin{cases} x - y = 2 \\ 2x + 3y = 9 \end{cases}$

8. $\begin{cases} 2x + y = 7 \\ x + 2y = 2 \end{cases}$

9–12 ■ Use the elimination method to find all solutions of the system of equations.

9. $\begin{cases} 3x + 4y = 10 \\ x - 4y = -2 \end{cases}$

10. $\begin{cases} 2x + 5y = 15 \\ 4x + y = 21 \end{cases}$

11. $\begin{cases} x + 2y = 5 \\ 2x + 3y = 8 \end{cases}$

12. $\begin{cases} 4x - 3y = 11 \\ 8x + 4y = 12 \end{cases}$

13–14 ■ Two equations and their graphs are given. Find the intersection point(s) of the graphs by solving the system.

13. $\begin{cases} 2x + y = -1 \\ x - 2y = -8 \end{cases}$

14. $\begin{cases} x + y = 2 \\ 2x + y = 5 \end{cases}$

15–20 ■ Graph each linear system, either by hand or using a graphing device. Use the graph to determine whether the system has one solution, no solution, or infinitely many solutions. If there is exactly one solution, use the graph to find it.

15. $\begin{cases} x - y = 4 \\ 2x + y = 2 \end{cases}$

16. $\begin{cases} 2x - y = 4 \\ 3x + y = 6 \end{cases}$

17. $\begin{cases} 2x - 3y = 12 \\ -x + \frac{3}{2}y = 4 \end{cases}$

18. $\begin{cases} 2x + 6y = 0 \\ -3x - 9y = 18 \end{cases}$

19. $\begin{cases} -x + \frac{1}{2}y = -5 \\ 2x - y = 10 \end{cases}$

20. $\begin{cases} 12x + 15y = -18 \\ 2x + \frac{5}{2}y = -3 \end{cases}$

21–48 ■ Solve the system, or show that it has no solution. If the system has infinitely many solutions, express them in the ordered-pair form given in Example 6.

21. $\begin{cases} x + y = 4 \\ -x + y = 0 \end{cases}$

22. $\begin{cases} x - y = 3 \\ x + 3y = 7 \end{cases}$

23. $\begin{cases} 2x - 3y = 9 \\ 4x + 3y = 9 \end{cases}$

24. $\begin{cases} 3x + 2y = 0 \\ -x - 2y = 8 \end{cases}$

25. $\begin{cases} x + 3y = 5 \\ 2x - y = 3 \end{cases}$

26. $\begin{cases} x + y = 7 \\ 2x - 3y = -1 \end{cases}$

27. $\begin{cases} -x + y = 2 \\ 4x - 3y = -3 \end{cases}$

28. $\begin{cases} 4x - 3y = 28 \\ 9x - y = -6 \end{cases}$

29. $\begin{cases} x + 2y = 7 \\ 5x - y = 2 \end{cases}$

30. $\begin{cases} -4x + 12y = 0 \\ 12x + 4y = 160 \end{cases}$

31. $\begin{cases} \frac{1}{2}x + \frac{1}{3}y = 2 \\ \frac{1}{5}x - \frac{2}{3}y = 8 \end{cases}$

32. $\begin{cases} 0.2x - 0.2y = -1.8 \\ -0.3x + 0.5y = 3.3 \end{cases}$

33. $\begin{cases} 3x + 2y = 8 \\ x - 2y = 0 \end{cases}$

34. $\begin{cases} 4x + 2y = 16 \\ x - 5y = 70 \end{cases}$

35. $\begin{cases} x + 4y = 8 \\ 3x + 12y = 2 \end{cases}$

36. $\begin{cases} -3x + 5y = 2 \\ 9x - 15y = 6 \end{cases}$

37. $\begin{cases} 2x - 6y = 10 \\ -3x + 9y = -15 \end{cases}$

38. $\begin{cases} 2x - 3y = -8 \\ 14x - 21y = 3 \end{cases}$

DRILL QUESTION

A woman rows a boat upstream from one point on a river to another point 4 mi away in 3 hours. The return trip, traveling with the current, takes 2 hours. How fast does she row relative to the water, and at what speed is the current flowing?

Answer

She rows at $\frac{5}{3}$ mi/h and the current flows at $\frac{1}{3}$ mi/h.

39. $\begin{cases} 6x + 4y = 12 \\ 9x + 6y = 18 \end{cases}$

40. $\begin{cases} 25x - 75y = 100 \\ -10x + 30y = -40 \end{cases}$

41. $\begin{cases} 8s - 3t = -3 \\ 5s - 2t = -1 \end{cases}$

42. $\begin{cases} u - 30v = -5 \\ -3u + 80v = 5 \end{cases}$

43. $\begin{cases} \frac{1}{2}x + \frac{3}{5}y = 3 \\ \frac{5}{3}x + 2y = 10 \end{cases}$

44. $\begin{cases} \frac{3}{2}x - \frac{1}{3}y = \frac{1}{2} \\ 2x - \frac{1}{2}y = -\frac{1}{2} \end{cases}$

45. $\begin{cases} 0.4x + 1.2y = 14 \\ 12x - 5y = 10 \end{cases}$

46. $\begin{cases} 26x - 10y = -4 \\ -0.6x + 1.2y = 3 \end{cases}$

47. $\begin{cases} \frac{1}{3}x - \frac{1}{4}y = 2 \\ -8x + 6y = 10 \end{cases}$

48. $\begin{cases} -\frac{1}{10}x + \frac{1}{2}y = 4 \\ 2x - 10y = -80 \end{cases}$

49–52 ■ Use a graphing device to graph both lines in the same viewing rectangle. (Note that you must solve for y in terms of x before graphing if you are using a graphing calculator.) Solve the system rounded to two decimal places, either by zooming in and using TRACE or by using Intersect.

49. $\begin{cases} 0.21x + 3.17y = 9.51 \\ 2.35x - 1.17y = 5.89 \end{cases}$

50. $\begin{cases} 18.72x - 14.91y = 12.33 \\ 6.21x - 12.92y = 17.82 \end{cases}$

51. $\begin{cases} 2371x - 6552y = 13,591 \\ 9815x + 992y = 618,555 \end{cases}$

52. $\begin{cases} -435x + 912y = 0 \\ 132x + 455y = 994 \end{cases}$

53–56 ■ Find x and y in terms of a and b.

53. $\begin{cases} x + y = 0 \\ x + ay = 1 \end{cases}$ $(a \neq 1)$

54. $\begin{cases} ax + by = 0 \\ x + y = 1 \end{cases}$ $(a \neq b)$

55. $\begin{cases} ax + by = 1 \\ bx + ay = 1 \end{cases}$ $(a^2 - b^2 \neq 0)$

56. $\begin{cases} ax + by = 0 \\ a^2x + b^2y = 1 \end{cases}$ $(a \neq 0, b \neq 0, a \neq b)$

APPLICATIONS

57. Number Problem   Find two numbers whose sum is 34 and whose difference is 10.

58. Number Problem   The sum of two numbers is twice their difference. The larger number is 6 more than twice the smaller. Find the numbers.

59. Value of Coins   A man has 14 coins in his pocket, all of which are dimes and quarters. If the total value of his change is $2.75, how many dimes and how many quarters does he have?

60. Admission Fees   The admission fee at an amusement park is $1.50 for children and $4.00 for adults. On a certain day,

2200 people entered the park, and the admission fees that were collected totaled $5050. How many children and how many adults were admitted?

61. Gas Station   A gas station sells regular gas for $2.20 per gallon and premium gas for $3.00 a gallon. At the end of a business day 280 gallons of gas were sold, and receipts totaled $680. How many gallons of each type of gas were sold?

62. Fruit Stand   A fruit stand sells two varieties of strawberries: standard and deluxe. A box of standard strawberries sells for $7, and a box of deluxe strawberries sells for $10. In one day the stand sells 135 boxes of strawberries for a total of $1110. How many boxes of each type were sold?

63. Airplane Speed   A man flies a small airplane from Fargo to Bismarck, North Dakota—a distance of 180 mi. Because he is flying into a head wind, the trip takes him 2 hours. On the way back, the wind is still blowing at the same speed, so the return trip takes only 1 h 12 min. What is his speed in still air, and how fast is the wind blowing?

64. Boat Speed   A boat on a river travels downstream between two points, 20 mi apart, in one hour. The return trip against the current takes $2\frac{1}{2}$ hours. What is the boat's speed, and how fast does the current in the river flow?

65. Nutrition   A researcher performs an experiment to test a hypothesis that involves the nutrients niacin and retinol. She feeds one group of laboratory rats a daily diet of precisely 32 units of niacin and 22,000 units of retinol. She uses two types of commercial pellet foods. Food A contains 0.12 unit of niacin and 100 units of retinol per gram. Food B contains 0.20 unit of niacin and 50 units of retinol per gram. How many grams of each food does she feed this group of rats each day?

66. Coffee Blends A customer in a coffee shop purchases a blend of two coffees: Kenyan, costing $3.50 a pound, and Sri Lankan, costing $5.60 a pound. He buys 3 lb of the blend, which costs him $11.55. How many pounds of each kind went into the mixture?

67. Mixture Problem A chemist has two large containers of sulfuric acid solution, with different concentrations of acid in each container. Blending 300 mL of the first solution and 600 mL of the second gives a mixture that is 15% acid, whereas blending 100 mL of the first with 500 mL of the second gives a $12\frac{1}{2}\%$ acid mixture. What are the concentrations of sulfuric acid in the original containers?

68. Mixture Problem A biologist has two brine solutions, one containing 5% salt and another containing 20% salt. How many milliliters of each solution should she mix to obtain 1 L of a solution that contains 14% salt?

69. Investments A woman invests a total of $20,000 in two accounts, one paying 5% and the other paying 8% simple interest per year. Her annual interest is $1180. How much did she invest at each rate?

70. Investments A man invests his savings in two accounts, one paying 6% and the other paying 10% simple interest per year. He puts twice as much in the lower-yielding account because it is less risky. His annual interest is $3520. How much did he invest at each rate?

71. Distance, Speed, and Time John and Mary leave their house at the same time and drive in opposite directions. John drives at 60 mi/h and travels 35 mi farther than Mary, who drives at 40 mi/h. Mary's trip takes 15 min longer than John's. For what length of time does each of them drive?

72. Aerobic Exercise A woman keeps fit by bicycling and running every day. On Monday she spends $\frac{1}{2}$ hour at each activity, covering a total of $12\frac{1}{2}$ mi. On Tuesday she runs for 12 min and cycles for 45 min, covering a total of 16 mi. Assuming that her running and cycling speeds don't change from day to day, find these speeds.

73. Number Problem The sum of the digits of a two-digit number is 7. When the digits are reversed, the number is increased by 27. Find the number.

74. Area of a Triangle Find the area of the triangle that lies in the first quadrant (with its base on the x-axis) and that is bounded by the lines $y = 2x - 4$ and $y = -4x + 20$.

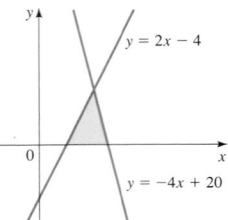

DISCOVERY ■ DISCUSSION ■ WRITING

75. The Least Squares Line The *least squares* line or *regression* line is the line that best fits a set of points in the plane. We studied this line in the *Focus on Modeling* that follows Chapter 1 (see page 130). By using calculus, it can be shown that the line that best fits the n data points $(x_1, y_1), (x_2, y_2), \ldots, (x_n, y_n)$ is the line $y = ax + b$, where the coefficients a and b satisfy the following pair of linear equations. (The notation $\sum_{k=1}^{n} x_k$ stands for the sum of all the x's. See Section 12.1 for a complete description of sigma (Σ) notation.)

$$\left(\sum_{k=1}^{n} x_k\right)a + nb = \sum_{k=1}^{n} y_k$$

$$\left(\sum_{k=1}^{n} x_k^2\right)a + \left(\sum_{k=1}^{n} x_k\right)b = \sum_{k=1}^{n} x_k y_k$$

Use these equations to find the least squares line for the following data points.

$$(1, 3), \quad (2, 5), \quad (3, 6), \quad (5, 6), \quad (7, 9)$$

Sketch the points and your line to confirm that the line fits these points well. If your calculator computes regression lines, see whether it gives you the same line as the formulas.

10.2 SYSTEMS OF LINEAR EQUATIONS IN SEVERAL VARIABLES

| Solving a Linear System ▶ The Number of Solutions of a Linear System ▶ Modeling Using Linear Systems

A **linear equation in n variables** is an equation that can be put in the form

$$a_1x_1 + a_2x_2 + \cdots + a_nx_n = c$$

where $a_1, a_2, \ldots, a_n$ and c are real numbers, and $x_1, x_2, \ldots, x_n$ are the variables. If we have only three or four variables, we generally use x, y, z, and w instead of x_1, x_2, x_3, and x_4. Such equations are called *linear* because if we have just two variables, the equation is $a_1x + a_2y = c$, which is the equation of a line. Here are some examples of equations in three variables that illustrate the difference between linear and nonlinear equations.

TEXT QUESTION

Consider this system of three equations:

$$\begin{cases} x - 2y + 3z = 1 \\ x + 2y - z = 13 \\ 3x + 2y - 5z = 3 \end{cases}$$

Is the following system equivalent to the first one? Why or why not?

$$\begin{cases} x - 2y + 3z = 1 \\ 100x + 200y - 100z = 1300 \\ 3x + 2y - 5z = 3 \end{cases}$$

Answer

It is. The second equation was simply multiplied by a nonzero constant.

Linear equations	Nonlinear equations	
$6x_1 - 3x_2 + \sqrt{5}x_3 = 10$	$x^2 + 3y - \sqrt{z} = 5$	Not linear because it contains the square and the square root of a variable
$x + y + z = 2w - \frac{1}{2}$	$x_1x_2 + 6x_3 = -6$	Not linear because it contains a product of variables

In this section we study systems of linear equations in three or more variables.

▼ Solving a Linear System

The following are two examples of systems of linear equations in three variables. The second system is in **triangular form**; that is, the variable x doesn't appear in the second equation, and the variables x and y do not appear in the third equation.

A system of linear equations

$$\begin{cases} x - 2y - z = 1 \\ -x + 3y + 3z = 4 \\ 2x - 3y + z = 10 \end{cases}$$

A system in triangular form

$$\begin{cases} x - 2y - z = 1 \\ y + 2z = 5 \\ z = 3 \end{cases}$$

It's easy to solve a system that is in triangular form by using back-substitution. So our goal in this section is to start with a system of linear equations and change it to a system in triangular form that has the same solutions as the original system. We begin by showing how to use back-substitution to solve a system that is already in triangular form.

EXAMPLE 1 | Solving a Triangular System Using Back-Substitution

Solve the system using back-substitution:

$$\begin{cases} x - 2y - z = 1 & \text{Equation 1} \\ y + 2z = 5 & \text{Equation 2} \\ z = 3 & \text{Equation 3} \end{cases}$$

SOLUTION From the last equation we know that $z = 3$. We back-substitute this into the second equation and solve for y.

$$y + 2(3) = 5 \quad \text{Back-substitute } z = 3 \text{ into Equation 2}$$
$$y = -1 \quad \text{Solve for } y$$

Then we back-substitute $y = -1$ and $z = 3$ into the first equation and solve for x.

$$x - 2(-1) - (3) = 1 \quad \text{Back-substitute } y = -1 \text{ and } z = 3 \text{ into Equation 1}$$
$$x = 2 \quad \text{Solve for } x$$

The solution of the system is $x = 2$, $y = -1$, $z = 3$. We can also write the solution as the ordered triple $(2, -1, 3)$.

✎ NOW TRY EXERCISE **7**

To change a system of linear equations to an **equivalent system** (that is, a system with the same solutions as the original system), we use the elimination method. This means that we can use the following operations.

ALTERNATE EXAMPLE 1
Solve the system using back-substitution.

$$\begin{cases} x - 5y - z = 22 \\ y + 4z = 8 \\ z = 3 \end{cases}$$

If the system is dependent or inconsistent, indicate this.

ANSWER
$(5, -4, 3)$

IN-CLASS MATERIALS

Have the students go over the applied problems from their homework for the previous section. Ask them to try to come up with similar problems involving three or four variables. For example, Exercise 72 in Section 10.1 can be expanded this way:

A woman keeps fit by bicycling, running, and swimming every day. On Monday she spends $\frac{1}{2}$ hour at each activity, covering a total of 14.25 mi. On Tuesday she runs for 12 min, cycles for 45 min, and swims for 30 min, covering a total of 15.45 mi. On Wednesday she runs for 30 min, cycles for 10 min, and swims for 30 min, covering a total of 9.25 mi. Assuming her running and cycling speeds don't change from day to day, find these speeds.

Make sure to point out that, for the problem to be solvable, the students now need three pieces of information instead of two (that is, if there is a Monday and a Tuesday in the problem, we now need a Wednesday). Also, they need to make sure that their problem has a solution. In two dimensions, it is very easy to get a consistent system, using random numbers. In three dimensions, it is a bit tougher.

> **OPERATIONS THAT YIELD AN EQUIVALENT SYSTEM**
> **1.** Add a nonzero multiple of one equation to another.
> **2.** Multiply an equation by a nonzero constant.
> **3.** Interchange the positions of two equations.

To solve a linear system, we use these operations to change the system to an equivalent triangular system. Then we use back-substitution as in Example 1. This process is called **Gaussian elimination**.

EXAMPLE 2 | Solving a System of Three Equations in Three Variables

Solve the system using Gaussian elimination.

$$\begin{cases} x - 2y + 3z = 1 & \text{Equation 1} \\ x + 2y - z = 13 & \text{Equation 2} \\ 3x + 2y - 5z = 3 & \text{Equation 3} \end{cases}$$

SOLUTION We need to change this to a triangular system, so we begin by eliminating the x-term from the second equation.

$$\begin{array}{l} x + 2y - z = 13 \qquad \text{Equation 2} \\ \underline{x - 2y + 3z = 1} \qquad \text{Equation 1} \\ \quad 4y - 4z = 12 \qquad \text{Equation 2} + (-1) \times \text{Equation 1} = \text{new Equation 2} \end{array}$$

This gives us a new, equivalent system that is one step closer to triangular form.

$$\begin{cases} x - 2y + 3z = 1 & \text{Equation 1} \\ 4y - 4z = 12 & \text{Equation 2} \\ 3x + 2y - 5z = 3 & \text{Equation 3} \end{cases}$$

Now we eliminate the x-term from the third equation.

$$\begin{cases} x - 2y + 3z = 1 \\ 4y - 4z = 12 \\ 8y - 14z = 0 \quad \text{Equation 3} + (-3) \times \text{Equation 1} = \text{new Equation 3} \end{cases}$$

Then we eliminate the y-term from the third equation.

$$\begin{cases} x - 2y + 3z = 1 \\ 4y - 4z = 12 \\ -6z = -24 \quad \text{Equation 3} + (-2) \times \text{Equation 2} = \text{new Equation 3} \end{cases}$$

The system is now in triangular form, but it will be easier to work with if we divide the second and third equations by the common factors of each term.

$$\begin{cases} x - 2y + 3z = 1 \\ y - z = 3 \quad \frac{1}{4} \times \text{Equation 2} = \text{new Equation 2} \\ z = 4 \quad -\frac{1}{6} \times \text{Equation 3} = \text{new Equation 3} \end{cases}$$

Now we use back-substitution to solve the system. From the third equation we get $z = 4$. We back-substitute this into the second equation and solve for y.

$$y - (4) = 3 \qquad \text{Back-substitute } z = 4 \text{ into Equation 2}$$
$$y = 7 \qquad \text{Solve for } y$$

$$\begin{array}{l} 3x + 2y - 5z = 3 \\ \underline{-3x + 6y - 9z = -3} \\ 8y - 14z = 0 \end{array}$$

$$\begin{array}{l} 8y - 14z = 0 \\ \underline{-8y + 8z = -24} \\ -6z = -24 \end{array}$$

IN-CLASS MATERIALS

If students have learned to use their calculators to solve linear systems, they may not realize the calculator's limitations. Have them attempt to solve a 5 × 5 system using their calculators, and record the length of time it takes. Then have them attempt a 10 × 10 system. It turns out that the length of time required to solve an arbitrary linear system grows very quickly with the number of variables involved. When doing a system by hand, it is possible to take advantage of properties of the particular system in question. For example, show them this system:

$$\begin{cases} -v & - 2y + z = 1 \\ v + & 2y = 3 \\ v + w - x + 2y = 2 \\ -v & + x - 2y = 7 \\ v + w + x + y + z = 26 \end{cases}$$

One can go through the traditional algorithm (or have a calculator do it), and it will take some time. (The time it takes to enter it into a calculator counts!) But, by looking at the individual equations, one can get w, x, and z instantly (add equations 1 and 2, 2 and 4, and 3 and 4) and then v and y come easily as well.

$x = 3, y = 7, z = 4$:

$$(3) - 2(7) + 3(4) = 1$$
$$(3) + 2(7) - (4) = 13$$
$$3(3) + 2(7) - 5(4) = 3 \checkmark$$

Now we back-substitute $y = 7$ and $z = 4$ into the first equation and solve for x.

$$x - 2(7) + 3(4) = 1 \qquad \text{Back-substitute } y = 7 \text{ and } z = 4 \text{ into Equation 1}$$
$$x = 3 \qquad \text{Solve for } x$$

The solution of the system is $x = 3, y = 7, z = 4$, which we can write as the ordered triple $(3, 7, 4)$.

✎. **NOW TRY EXERCISE 17** ■

▼ The Number of Solutions of a Linear System

The graph of a linear equation in three variables is a plane in three dimensional space (see Section 9.6). A system of three equations in three variables represents three planes in space. The solutions of the system are the points where all three planes intersect. Three planes may intersect in a point, a line, not at all, or all three planes may coincide. Figure 1 illustrates some of these possibilities. Checking these possibilities we see that there are three possible outcomes when solving such a system.

NUMBER OF SOLUTIONS OF A LINEAR SYSTEM

For a system of linear equations, exactly one of the following is true.

1. The system has exactly one solution.

2. The system has no solution.

3. The system has infinitely many solutions.

A system with no solutions is said to be **inconsistent**, and a system with infinitely many solutions is said to be **dependent**. As we see in the next example, a linear system has no solution if we end up with a *false equation* after applying Gaussian elimination to the system.

(a) The three planes intersect at a single point. **The system has one solution.**

(b) The three planes intersect at more than one point. **The system has infinitely many solutions.**

(c) The three planes have no point in common. **The system has no solution.**

FIGURE 1

EXAMPLE 3 | A System with No Solution

Solve the following system.

$$\begin{cases} x + 2y - 2z = 1 & \text{Equation 1} \\ 2x + 2y - z = 6 & \text{Equation 2} \\ 3x + 4y - 3z = 5 & \text{Equation 3} \end{cases}$$

ALTERNATE EXAMPLE 3

Solve the following system.

$$\begin{cases} x + 7y - 7z = 3 \\ 3x + 14y - 16z = 17 \\ 2x + 7y - 9z = 10 \end{cases}$$

If the system is dependent or inconsistent, indicate this.

ANSWER

Inconsistent

IN-CLASS MATERIALS

One can discuss the geometry of systems of three variables as an extension of the geometry of two variables, replacing lines with planes. Ask the class how they could think of a four-variable system. This is not a trivial question. We are looking at the intersection of three hyperplanes in four-dimensional space. Even though you may not get a satisfactory answer (but then again, you may), there is value in trying to come up with visual interpretations for complex, abstract mathematical concepts.

SOLUTION To put this in triangular form, we begin by eliminating the x-terms from the second equation and the third equation.

$$\begin{cases} x + 2y - 2z = 1 \\ \quad\;\; -2y + 3z = 4 \\ 3x + 4y + 3z = 5 \end{cases} \quad \text{Equation 2} + (-2) \times \text{Equation 1} = \text{new Equation 2}$$

$$\begin{cases} x + 2y - 2z = 1 \\ \quad\;\; -2y + 3z = 4 \\ \quad\;\; -2y + 3z = 2 \end{cases} \quad \text{Equation 3} + (-3) \times \text{Equation 1} = \text{new Equation 3}$$

Now we eliminate the y-term from the third equation.

$$\begin{cases} x + 2y - 2z = 1 \\ \quad\;\; -2y + 3z = 4 \\ \qquad\qquad 0 = 2 \end{cases} \quad \text{Equation 3} + (-1) \times \text{Equation 2} = \text{new Equation 3}$$

The system is now in triangular form, but the third equation says $0 = 2$, which is false. No matter what values we assign to x, y, and z, the third equation will never be true. This means that the system has *no solution*.

✎. NOW TRY EXERCISE **27** ∎

ALTERNATE EXAMPLE 4

Solve the following system.

$$\begin{cases} x - \;\;\; y + \;\; 5z = -2 \\ 3x + \;\;\; y + \;\; 3z = \;\;\; 2 \\ 3x + 9y - 21z = \;\; 18 \end{cases}$$

If the system is dependent or inconsistent, indicate this.

ANSWER

$(-2t, 3t + 2, t)$

EXAMPLE 4 | A System with Infinitely Many Solutions

Solve the following system.

$$\begin{cases} x - \;\; y + 5z = -2 & \text{Equation 1} \\ 2x + \;\; y + 4z = \;\;\; 2 & \text{Equation 2} \\ 2x + 4y - 2z = \;\;\; 8 & \text{Equation 3} \end{cases}$$

SOLUTION To put this in triangular form, we begin by eliminating the x-terms from the second equation and the third equation.

$$\begin{cases} x - \;\; y + 5z = -2 \\ \quad\;\;\; 3y - 6z = \;\;\; 6 \\ 2x + 4y - 2z = \;\;\; 8 \end{cases} \quad \text{Equation 2} + (-2) \times \text{Equation 1} = \text{new Equation 2}$$

$$\begin{cases} x - y + \;\; 5z = -2 \\ \quad\; 3y - \;\; 6z = \;\;\; 6 \\ \quad\; 6y - 12z = \;\; 12 \end{cases} \quad \text{Equation 3} + (-2) \times \text{Equation 1} = \text{new Equation 3}$$

Now we eliminate the y-term from the third equation.

$$\begin{cases} x - y + 5z = -2 \\ \quad\; 3y - 6z = \;\;\; 6 \\ \qquad\qquad 0 = \;\;\; 0 \end{cases} \quad \text{Equation 3} + (-2) \times \text{Equation 2} = \text{new Equation 3}$$

The new third equation is true, but it gives us no new information, so we can drop it from the system. Only two equations are left. We can use them to solve for x and y in terms of z, but z can take on any value, so there are infinitely many solutions.

To find the complete solution of the system, we begin by solving for y in terms of z, using the new second equation.

$$\begin{aligned} 3y - 6z &= 6 & \text{Equation 2} \\ y - 2z &= 2 & \text{Multiply by } \tfrac{1}{3} \\ y &= 2z + 2 & \text{Solve for } y \end{aligned}$$

SECTION 10.2 | Systems of Linear Equations in Several Variables **645**

Then we solve for x in terms of z, using the first equation.

$$x - (2z + 2) + 5z = -2 \qquad \text{Substitute } y = 2z + 2 \text{ into Equation 1}$$
$$x + 3z - 2 = -2 \qquad \text{Simplify}$$
$$x = -3z \qquad \text{Solve for } x$$

To describe the complete solution, we let t represent any real number. The solution is

$$x = -3t$$
$$y = 2t + 2$$
$$z = t$$

We can also write this as the ordered triple $(-3t, 2t + 2, t)$.

✎. NOW TRY EXERCISE **25**

In the solution of Example 4 the variable t is called a **parameter**. To get a specific solution, we give a specific value to the parameter t. For instance, if we set $t = 2$, we get

$$x = -3(2) = -6$$
$$y = 2(2) + 2 = 6$$
$$z = 2$$

Thus $(-6, 6, 2)$ is a solution of the system. Here are some other solutions of the system obtained by substituting other values for the parameter t.

Parameter t	Solution $(-3t, 2t + 2, t)$
-1	$(3, 0, -1)$
0	$(0, 2, 0)$
3	$(-9, 8, 3)$
10	$(-30, 22, 10)$

You should check that these points satisfy the original equations. There are infinitely many choices for the parameter t, so the system has infinitely many solutions.

▼ Modeling Using Linear Systems

Linear systems are used to model situations that involve several varying quantities. In the next example we consider an application of linear systems to finance.

EXAMPLE 5 | Modeling a Financial Problem
Using a Linear System

Jason receives an inheritance of $50,000. His financial advisor suggests that he invest this in three mutual funds: a money-market fund, a blue-chip stock fund, and a high-tech stock fund. The advisor estimates that the money-market fund will return 5% over the next year, the blue-chip fund 9%, and the high-tech fund 16%. Jason wants a total first-year return of $4000. To avoid excessive risk, he decides to invest three times as much in the money-market fund as in the high-tech stock fund. How much should he invest in each fund?

EXAMPLE
A consistent 3×3 system:
$$\begin{cases} 3x + 2y + z = 4 \\ x - y - z = 1 \\ 2x - 4y - z = -1 \end{cases}$$

ANSWER
$x = 1, y = 1, z = -1$

EXAMPLE
An inconsistent 3×3 system:
$$\begin{cases} x - y + z = 3 \\ 2x - y + 2z = 4 \\ 3x - 2y + 3z = 8 \end{cases}$$

EXAMPLE
A dependent 3×3 system:
$$\begin{cases} x + 5y - z = 4 \\ 2x + 3y + 4z = 0 \\ 3x + 8y + 3z = 4 \end{cases}$$

ALTERNATE EXAMPLE 5
John receives an inheritance of $50,000. He invests in three mutual funds: a money-market fund, a blue-chip stock fund, and a high-risk entrepreneurial fund. If past trends hold true, the money-market fund will return 2% over the next year; the blue-chip fund, 8%; and the entrepreneurial fund, 12%. John wants a total first-year return of $5000. He is going to invest twice as much in the entrepreneurial fund as in the other two funds combined. How much should he invest in each fund?

ANSWER
$$x + y + z = 50{,}000$$
$$0.02x + 0.08y + 0.12z = 5000 \rightarrow$$
$$x = 5555.56, y = 11{,}111.11,$$
$$z = 33{,}333.33$$
$$2x + 2y - z = 0$$

CHAPTER 10 Systems of Equations and Inequalities **645**

DRILL QUESTION

Solve this system using Gaussian elimination.

$$\begin{cases} x - 2y + z = 1 \\ -x + y - z = 4 \\ -x + 2y - 4z = 8 \end{cases}$$

Answer

$x = -6,\ y = -5,\ z = -3$

SOLUTION

Let x = amount invested in the money-market fund

y = amount invested in the blue-chip stock fund

z = amount invested in the high-tech stock fund

We convert each fact given in the problem into an equation.

$$x + y + z = 50{,}000 \qquad \text{Total amount invested is \$50,000}$$

$$0.05x + 0.09y + 0.16z = 4000 \qquad \text{Total investment return is \$4000}$$

$$x = 3z \qquad \text{Money-market amount is } 3 \times \text{high-tech amount}$$

Multiplying the second equation by 100 and rewriting the third gives the following system, which we solve using Gaussian elimination.

$$\begin{cases} x + y + z = 50{,}000 \\ 5x + 9y + 16z = 400{,}000 & 100 \times \text{Equation 2} \\ x \qquad - 3z = 0 & \text{Subtract } 3z \end{cases}$$

$$\begin{cases} x + y + z = 50{,}000 \\ 4y + 11z = 150{,}000 & \text{Equation 2} + (-5) \times \text{Equation 1} = \text{new Equation 2} \\ -y - 4z = -50{,}000 & \text{Equation 3} + (-1) \times \text{Equation 1} = \text{new Equation 3} \end{cases}$$

$$\begin{cases} x + y + z = 50{,}000 \\ -5z = -50{,}000 & \text{Equation 2} + 4 \times \text{Equation 3} = \text{new Equation 3} \\ -y - 4z = -50{,}000 \end{cases}$$

$$\begin{cases} x + y + z = 50{,}000 \\ z = 10{,}000 & \left(-\frac{1}{5}\right) \times \text{Equation 2} \\ y + 4z = 50{,}000 & (-1) \times \text{Equation 3} \end{cases}$$

$$\begin{cases} x + y + z = 50{,}000 \\ y + 4z = 50{,}000 & \text{Interchange Equations 2 and 3} \\ z = 10{,}000 \end{cases}$$

Now that the system is in triangular form, we use back-substitution to find that $x = 30{,}000$, $y = 10{,}000$, and $z = 10{,}000$. This means that Jason should invest

$30,000 in the money-market fund

$10,000 in the blue-chip stock fund

$10,000 in the high-tech stock fund

✏ NOW TRY EXERCISE **37** ∎

10.2 EXERCISES

CONCEPTS

1–2 ■ These exercises refer to the following system.

$$\begin{cases} x - y + z = 2 \\ -x + 2y + z = -3 \\ 3x + y - 2z = 2 \end{cases}$$

1. If we add 2 times the first equation to the second equation, the second equation becomes _____ = ____ .

2. To eliminate x from the third equation, we add _____ times the first equation to the third equation. The third equation becomes _____ = ____ .

SKILLS

3–6 ■ State whether the equation or system of equations is linear.

3. $6x - \sqrt{3}y + \frac{1}{2}z = 0$ **4.** $x^2 + y^2 + z^2 = 4$

5. $\begin{cases} xy - 3y + z = 5 \\ x - y^2 + 5z = 0 \\ 2x + yz = 3 \end{cases}$ **6.** $\begin{cases} x - 2y + 3z = 10 \\ 2x + 5y = 2 \\ y + 2z = 4 \end{cases}$

7–12 ■ Use back-substitution to solve the triangular system.

7. $\begin{cases} x - 2y + 4z = 3 \\ y + 2z = 7 \\ z = 2 \end{cases}$ **8.** $\begin{cases} x + y - 3z = 8 \\ y - 3z = 5 \\ z = -1 \end{cases}$

9. $\begin{cases} x + 2y + z = 7 \\ -y + 3z = 9 \\ 2z = 6 \end{cases}$ **10.** $\begin{cases} x - 2y + 3z = 10 \\ 2y - z = 2 \\ 3z = 12 \end{cases}$

11. $\begin{cases} 2x - y + 6z = 5 \\ y + 4z = 0 \\ -2z = 1 \end{cases}$ **12.** $\begin{cases} 4x + 3z = 10 \\ 2y - z = -6 \\ \frac{1}{2}z = 4 \end{cases}$

13–16 ■ Perform an operation on the given system that eliminates the indicated variable. Write the new equivalent system.

13. $\begin{cases} x - 2y - z = 4 \\ x - y + 3z = 0 \\ 2x + y + z = 0 \end{cases}$ **14.** $\begin{cases} x + y - 3z = 3 \\ -2x + 3y + z = 2 \\ x - y + 2z = 0 \end{cases}$

Eliminate the x-term from the second equation.   Eliminate the x-term from the second equation.

15. $\begin{cases} 2x - y + 3z = 2 \\ x + 2y - z = 4 \\ -4x + 5y + z = 10 \end{cases}$ **16.** $\begin{cases} x - 4y + z = 3 \\ y - 3z = 10 \\ 3y - 8z = 24 \end{cases}$

Eliminate the x-term from the third equation.   Eliminate the y-term from the third equation.

17–36 ■ Find the complete solution of the linear system, or show that it is inconsistent.

17. $\begin{cases} x - y - z = 4 \\ 2y + z = -1 \\ -x + y - 2z = 5 \end{cases}$ **18.** $\begin{cases} x - y + z = 0 \\ y + 2z = -2 \\ x + y - z = 2 \end{cases}$

19. $\begin{cases} x + y + z = 4 \\ x + 3y + 3z = 10 \\ 2x + y - z = 3 \end{cases}$ **20.** $\begin{cases} x + y + z = 0 \\ -x + 2y + 5z = 3 \\ 3x - y = 6 \end{cases}$

21. $\begin{cases} x - 4z = 1 \\ 2x - y - 6z = 4 \\ 2x + 3y - 2z = 8 \end{cases}$ **22.** $\begin{cases} x - y + 2z = 2 \\ 3x + y + 5z = 8 \\ 2x - y - 2z = -7 \end{cases}$

23. $\begin{cases} 2x + 4y - z = 2 \\ x + 2y - 3z = -4 \\ 3x - y + z = 1 \end{cases}$ **24.** $\begin{cases} 2x + y - z = -8 \\ -x + y + z = 3 \\ -2x + 4z = 18 \end{cases}$

25. $\begin{cases} y - 2z = 0 \\ 2x + 3y = 2 \\ -x - 2y + z = -1 \end{cases}$ **26.** $\begin{cases} 2y + z = 3 \\ 5x + 4y + 3z = -1 \\ x - 3y = -2 \end{cases}$

27. $\begin{cases} x + 2y - z = 1 \\ 2x + 3y - 4z = -3 \\ 3x + 6y - 3z = 4 \end{cases}$ **28.** $\begin{cases} -x + 2y + 5z = 4 \\ x - 2z = 0 \\ 4x - 2y - 11z = 2 \end{cases}$

29. $\begin{cases} 2x + 3y - z = 1 \\ x + 2y = 3 \\ x + 3y + z = 4 \end{cases}$ **30.** $\begin{cases} x - 2y - 3z = 5 \\ 2x + y - z = 5 \\ 4x - 3y - 7z = 5 \end{cases}$

31. $\begin{cases} x + y - z = 0 \\ x + 2y - 3z = -3 \\ 2x + 3y - 4z = -3 \end{cases}$ **32.** $\begin{cases} x - 2y + z = 3 \\ 2x - 5y + 6z = 7 \\ 2x - 3y - 2z = 5 \end{cases}$

33. $\begin{cases} x + 3y - 2z = 0 \\ 2x + 4z = 4 \\ 4x + 6y = 4 \end{cases}$ **34.** $\begin{cases} 2x + 4y - z = 3 \\ x + 2y + 4z = 6 \\ x + 2y - 2z = 0 \end{cases}$

35. $\begin{cases} x + z + 2w = 6 \\ y - 2z = -3 \\ x + 2y - z = -2 \\ 2x + y + 3z - 2w = 0 \end{cases}$

36. $\begin{cases} x + y + z + w = 0 \\ x + y + 2z + 2w = 0 \\ 2x + 2y + 3z + 4w = 1 \\ 2x + 3y + 4z + 5w = 2 \end{cases}$

APPLICATIONS

37–38 ■ **Finance** An investor has $100,000 to invest in three types of bonds: short-term, intermediate-term, and long-term. How much should she invest in each type to satisfy the given conditions?

37. Short-term bonds pay 4% annually, intermediate-term bonds pay 5%, and long-term bonds pay 6%. The investor wishes to realize a total annual income of 5.1%, with equal amounts invested in short- and intermediate-term bonds.

38. Short-term bonds pay 4% annually, intermediate-term bonds pay 6%, and long-term bonds pay 8%. The investor wishes to have a total annual return of $6700 on her investment, with equal amounts invested in intermediate- and long-term bonds.

39. Agriculture A farmer has 1200 acres of land on which he grows corn, wheat, and soybeans. It costs $45 per acre to grow corn, $60 to grow wheat, and $50 to grow soybeans. Because of market demand, the farmer will grow twice as many acres of wheat as of corn. He has allocated $63,750 for the cost of growing his crops. How many acres of each crop should he plant?

40. Gas Station A gas station sells three types of gas: Regular for $3.00 a gallon, Performance Plus for $3.20 a gallon, and Premium for $3.30 a gallon. On a particular day 6500 gallons of gas were sold for a total of $20,050. Three times as many gallons of Regular as Premium gas were sold. How many gallons of each type of gas were sold that day?

41. Nutrition A biologist is performing an experiment on the effects of various combinations of vitamins. She wishes to feed each of her laboratory rabbits a diet that contains exactly 9 mg of niacin, 14 mg of thiamin, and 32 mg of riboflavin. She has available three different types of commercial rabbit pellets; their vitamin content (per ounce) is given in the table. How many ounces of each type of food should each rabbit be given daily to satisfy the experiment requirements?

	Type A	Type B	Type C
Niacin (mg)	2	3	1
Thiamin (mg)	3	1	3
Riboflavin (mg)	8	5	7

42. Diet Program Nicole started a new diet that requires each meal to have 460 calories, 6 grams of fiber, and 11 grams of fat. The table shows the fiber, fat, and calorie content of one serving of each of three breakfast foods. How many servings of each food should Nicole eat to follow her diet?

Food	Fiber	Fat	Calories
Toast	2	1	100
Cottage cheese	0	5	120
Fruit	2	0	60

43. Juice Blends The Juice Company offers three kinds of smoothies: Midnight Mango, Tropical Torrent, and Pineapple Power. Each smoothie contains the amounts of juices shown in the table.

Smoothie	Mango juice (oz)	Pineapple juice (oz)	Orange juice (oz)
Midnight Mango	8	3	3
Tropical Torrent	6	5	3
Pineapple Power	2	8	4

On a particular day the Juice Company used 820 oz of mango juice, 690 oz of pineapple juice, and 450 oz of orange juice. How many smoothies of each kind were sold that day?

44. Appliance Manufacturing Kitchen Korner produces refrigerators, dishwashers, and stoves at three different factories. The table gives the number of each product produced at each factory per day. Kitchen Korner receives an order for 110 refrigerators, 150 dishwashers, and 114 ovens. How many days should each plant be scheduled to fill this order?

Appliance	Factory A	Factory B	Factory C
Refrigerators	8	10	14
Dishwashers	16	12	10
Stoves	10	18	6

45. Stock Portfolio An investor owns three stocks: A, B, and C. The closing prices of the stocks on three successive trading days are given in the table.

	Stock A	Stock B	Stock C
Monday	$10	$25	$29
Tuesday	$12	$20	$32
Wednesday	$16	$15	$32

Despite the volatility in the stock prices, the total value of the investor's stocks remained unchanged at $74,000 at the end of each of these three days. How many shares of each stock does the investor own?

46. Electricity By using Kirchhoff's Laws, it can be shown that the currents I_1, I_2, and I_3 that pass through the three branches of the circuit in the figure satisfy the given linear system. Solve the system to find I_1, I_2, and I_3.

$$\begin{cases} I_1 + I_2 - I_3 = 0 \\ 16I_1 - 8I_2 \quad\quad = 4 \\ \quad\quad 8I_2 + 4I_3 = 5 \end{cases}$$

DISCOVERY ▪ DISCUSSION ▪ WRITING

47. Can a Linear System Have Exactly Two Solutions?
(a) Suppose that (x_0, y_0, z_0) and (x_1, y_1, z_1) are solutions of the system

$$\begin{cases} a_1x + b_1y + c_1z = d_1 \\ a_2x + b_2y + c_2z = d_2 \\ a_3x + b_3y + c_3z = d_3 \end{cases}$$

Show that $\left(\dfrac{x_0 + x_1}{2}, \dfrac{y_0 + y_1}{2}, \dfrac{z_0 + z_1}{2}\right)$ is also a solution.

(b) Use the result of part (a) to prove that if the system has two different solutions, then it has infinitely many solutions.

⬤ **DISCOVERY PROJECT**   **Best Fit Versus Exact Fit**

In this project we use linear systems to find quadratic functions whose graphs pass through a set of given points. You can find the project at the book companion website: **www.stewartmath.com**

10.3 MATRICES AND SYSTEMS OF LINEAR EQUATIONS

Matrices ▶ The Augmented Matrix of a Linear System ▶ Elementary Row
Operations ▶ Gaussian Elimination ▶ Gauss-Jordan Elimination ▶
Inconsistent and Dependent Systems ▶ Modeling with Linear Systems

A *matrix* is simply a rectangular array of numbers. Matrices* are used to organize information into categories that correspond to the rows and columns of the matrix. For example, a scientist might organize information on a population of endangered whales as follows:

$$\begin{array}{c} \\ \text{Male} \\ \text{Female} \end{array} \begin{array}{ccc} \text{Immature} & \text{Juvenile} & \text{Adult} \\ \begin{bmatrix} 12 & 52 & 18 \\ 15 & 42 & 11 \end{bmatrix} \end{array}$$

This is a compact way of saying that there are 12 immature males, 15 immature females, 18 adult males, and so on.

In this section we represent a linear system by a matrix, called the *augmented matrix* of the system:

Linear system   **Augmented matrix**

$$\begin{cases} 2x - y = 5 & \text{Equation 1} \\ x + 4y = 7 & \text{Equation 2} \end{cases} \qquad \begin{bmatrix} 2 & -1 & 5 \\ 1 & 4 & 7 \end{bmatrix}$$

$$ x \quad y$$

The augmented matrix contains the same information as the system, but in a simpler form. The operations we learned for solving systems of equations can now be performed on the augmented matrix.

▼ Matrices

We begin by defining the various elements that make up a matrix.

DEFINITION OF MATRIX

An $m \times n$ **matrix** is a rectangular array of numbers with m **rows** and n **columns**.

$$\begin{bmatrix} a_{11} & a_{12} & a_{13} & \cdots & a_{1n} \\ a_{21} & a_{22} & a_{23} & \cdots & a_{2n} \\ a_{31} & a_{32} & a_{33} & \cdots & a_{3n} \\ \vdots & \vdots & \vdots & \ddots & \vdots \\ a_{m1} & a_{m2} & a_{m3} & \cdots & a_{mn} \end{bmatrix} \begin{array}{l} \leftarrow \\ \leftarrow \\ \leftarrow \\ \\ \leftarrow \end{array} \right\} m \text{ rows}$$

$$\underbrace{\phantom{a_{11} \quad a_{12} \quad a_{13} \quad \cdots \quad a_{1n}}}_{n \text{ columns}}$$

We say that the matrix has **dimension** $m \times n$. The numbers a_{ij} are the **entries** of the matrix. The subscript on the entry a_{ij} indicates that it is in the ith row and the jth column.

---

*The plural of *matrix* is *matrices*.

TEXT QUESTIONS

Which of the following matrices are in row-echelon form? Which are in reduced row-echelon form?

$$\text{(a)} \begin{bmatrix} 1 & 4 & 0 & 0 & 0 \\ 0 & 0 & 1 & 0 & -5 \\ 0 & 0 & 0 & 1 & \pi \\ 0 & 0 & 0 & 0 & 0 \end{bmatrix} \quad \text{(b)} \begin{bmatrix} 1 & 0 & 0 & 0 & 0 \\ 0 & 0 & 1 & 0 & 0 \\ 0 & 1 & 0 & 1 & 0 \\ 0 & 1 & 0 & 0 & 1 \end{bmatrix} \quad \text{(c)} \begin{bmatrix} 1 & 4 & 3 & 0 & 5 \\ 0 & 0 & 1 & 2 & -5 \\ 0 & 0 & 0 & 1 & \pi \\ 0 & 0 & 0 & 0 & 0 \end{bmatrix}$$

Answers

(a) and (c) are in row-echelon form; (a) is in reduced row-echelon form.

Here are some examples of matrices.

Matrix	Dimension	
$\begin{bmatrix} 1 & 3 & 0 \\ 2 & 4 & -1 \end{bmatrix}$	2×3	2 rows by 3 columns
$\begin{bmatrix} 6 & -5 & 0 & 1 \end{bmatrix}$	1×4	1 row by 4 columns

▼ The Augmented Matrix of a Linear System

We can write a system of linear equations as a matrix, called the **augmented matrix** of the system, by writing only the coefficients and constants that appear in the equations. Here is an example.

Linear system	Augmented matrix
$\begin{cases} 3x - 2y + z = 5 \\ x + 3y - z = 0 \\ -x + 4z = 11 \end{cases}$	$\begin{bmatrix} 3 & -2 & 1 & 5 \\ 1 & 3 & -1 & 0 \\ -1 & 0 & 4 & 11 \end{bmatrix}$

Notice that a missing variable in an equation corresponds to a 0 entry in the augmented matrix.

EXAMPLE 1 | Finding the Augmented Matrix of a Linear System

Write the augmented matrix of the system of equations.

$$\begin{cases} 6x - 2y - z = 4 \\ x + 3z = 1 \\ 7y + z = 5 \end{cases}$$

SOLUTION First we write the linear system with the variables lined up in columns.

$$\begin{cases} 6x - 2y - z = 4 \\ x + 3z = 1 \\ 7y + z = 5 \end{cases}$$

The augmented matrix is the matrix whose entries are the coefficients and the constants in this system.

$$\begin{bmatrix} 6 & -2 & -1 & 4 \\ 1 & 0 & 3 & 1 \\ 0 & 7 & 1 & 5 \end{bmatrix}$$

✎ NOW TRY EXERCISE **2**

▼ Elementary Row Operations

The operations that we used in Section 10.2 to solve linear systems correspond to operations on the rows of the augmented matrix of the system. For example, adding a multiple of one equation to another corresponds to adding a multiple of one row to another.

ELEMENTARY ROW OPERATIONS

1. Add a multiple of one row to another.

2. Multiply a row by a nonzero constant.

3. Interchange two rows.

ALTERNATE EXAMPLE 1

Write the augmented matrix of the system of equations.

$$\begin{cases} 7x - 2y - z = 4 \\ x + 3z = 6 \\ 4y + z = 7 \end{cases}$$

ANSWER

$$\begin{bmatrix} 7 & -2 & -1 & 4 \\ 1 & 0 & 3 & 6 \\ 0 & 4 & 1 & 7 \end{bmatrix}$$

IN-CLASS MATERIALS

Point out that, as noted in the text, the row-echelon form of a given matrix is not unique, but the reduced row-echelon form is unique. In fact, it can be shown that if two matrices have the same reduced row-echelon form, you can transform one into the other via elementary row operations.

Note that performing any of these operations on the augmented matrix of a system does not change its solution. We use the following notation to describe the elementary row operations:

Symbol	Description
$R_i + kR_j \rightarrow R_i$	Change the ith row by adding k times row j to it, and then put the result back in row i.
kR_i	Multiply the ith row by k.
$R_i \leftrightarrow R_j$	Interchange the ith and jth rows.

In the next example we compare the two ways of writing systems of linear equations.

EXAMPLE 2 | Using Elementary Row Operations to Solve a Linear System

Solve the system of linear equations.

$$\begin{cases} x - y + 3z = 4 \\ x + 2y - 2z = 10 \\ 3x - y + 5z = 14 \end{cases}$$

SOLUTION   Our goal is to eliminate the x-term from the second equation and the x- and y-terms from the third equation. For comparison, we write both the system of equations and its augmented matrix.

System

$$\begin{cases} x - y + 3z = 4 \\ x + 2y - 2z = 10 \\ 3x - y + 5z = 14 \end{cases}$$

Add $(-1) \times$ Equation 1 to Equation 2.
Add $(-3) \times$ Equation 1 to Equation 3.

$$\begin{cases} x - y + 3z = 4 \\ 3y - 5z = 6 \\ 2y - 4z = 2 \end{cases}$$

Multiply Equation 3 by $\frac{1}{2}$.

$$\begin{cases} x - y + 3z = 4 \\ 3y - 5z = 6 \\ y - 2z = 1 \end{cases}$$

Add $(-3) \times$ Equation 3 to Equation 2 (to eliminate y from Equation 2).

$$\begin{cases} x - y + 3z = 4 \\ z = 3 \\ y - 2z = 1 \end{cases}$$

Interchange Equations 2 and 3.

$$\begin{cases} x - y + 3z = 4 \\ y - 2z = 1 \\ z = 3 \end{cases}$$

Augmented matrix

$$\begin{bmatrix} 1 & -1 & 3 & 4 \\ 1 & 2 & -2 & 10 \\ 3 & -1 & 5 & 14 \end{bmatrix}$$

$\xrightarrow{\substack{R_2 - R_1 \rightarrow R_2 \\ R_3 - 3R_1 \rightarrow R_3}}$
$$\begin{bmatrix} 1 & -1 & 3 & 4 \\ 0 & 3 & -5 & 6 \\ 0 & 2 & -4 & 2 \end{bmatrix}$$

$\xrightarrow{\frac{1}{2}R_3}$
$$\begin{bmatrix} 1 & -1 & 3 & 4 \\ 0 & 3 & -5 & 6 \\ 0 & 1 & -2 & 1 \end{bmatrix}$$

$\xrightarrow{R_2 - 3R_3 \rightarrow R_2}$
$$\begin{bmatrix} 1 & -1 & 3 & 4 \\ 0 & 0 & 1 & 3 \\ 0 & 1 & -2 & 1 \end{bmatrix}$$

$\xrightarrow{R_2 \leftrightarrow R_3}$
$$\begin{bmatrix} 1 & -1 & 3 & 4 \\ 0 & 1 & -2 & 1 \\ 0 & 0 & 1 & 3 \end{bmatrix}$$

Now we use back-substitution to find that $x = 2$, $y = 7$, and $z = 3$. The solution is $(2, 7, 3)$.

◥ **NOW TRY EXERCISE 19**   ■

▼ Gaussian Elimination

In general, to solve a system of linear equations using its augmented matrix, we use elementary row operations to arrive at a matrix in a certain form. This form is described in the following box.

EXAMPLE
A system with infinitely many solutions:

$$\begin{cases} x + 2y - 3z = 12 \\ -2x + y + 4z = 2 \\ x + 7y - 5z = 38 \end{cases}$$

ANSWER
$x = \dfrac{11}{5}t + \dfrac{8}{5}, \; y = \dfrac{2}{5}t + \dfrac{26}{5},$

$z = t$

Note: The representation of this set of solutions is not unique.

ROW-ECHELON FORM AND REDUCED ROW-ECHELON FORM OF A MATRIX

A matrix is in **row-echelon form** if it satisfies the following conditions.

1. The first nonzero number in each row (reading from left to right) is 1. This is called the **leading entry**.

2. The leading entry in each row is to the right of the leading entry in the row immediately above it.

3. All rows consisting entirely of zeros are at the bottom of the matrix.

A matrix is in **reduced row-echelon** form if it is in row-echelon form and also satisfies the following condition.

4. Every number above and below each leading entry is a 0.

In the following matrices, the first one is not in row-echelon form. The second one *is* in row-echelon form, and the third one is in reduced row-echelon form. The entries in red are the leading entries.

Not in row-echelon form	Row-echelon form	Reduced row-echelon form
$\begin{bmatrix} 0 & 1 & -\frac{1}{2} & 0 & 6 \\ 1 & 0 & 3 & 4 & -5 \\ 0 & 0 & 0 & 1 & 0.4 \\ 0 & 1 & 1 & 0 & 0 \end{bmatrix}$	$\begin{bmatrix} 1 & 3 & -6 & 10 & 0 \\ 0 & 0 & 1 & 4 & -3 \\ 0 & 0 & 0 & 1 & \frac{1}{2} \\ 0 & 0 & 0 & 0 & 0 \end{bmatrix}$	$\begin{bmatrix} 1 & 3 & 0 & 0 & 0 \\ 0 & 0 & 1 & 0 & -3 \\ 0 & 0 & 0 & 1 & \frac{1}{2} \\ 0 & 0 & 0 & 0 & 0 \end{bmatrix}$
Leading 1's do *not* shift to the right in successive rows	Leading 1's shift to the right in successive rows	Leading 1's have 0's above and below them

Here is a systematic way to put a matrix in row-echelon form using elementary row operations:

- Start by obtaining 1 in the top left corner. Then obtain zeros below that 1 by adding appropriate multiples of the first row to the rows below it.

- Next, obtain a leading 1 in the next row, and then obtain zeros below that 1.

- At each stage make sure that every leading entry is to the right of the leading entry in the row above it—rearrange the rows if necessary.

- Continue this process until you arrive at a matrix in row-echelon form.

This is how the process might work for a 3×4 matrix:

$$\begin{bmatrix} 1 & \blacksquare & \blacksquare & \blacksquare \\ 0 & \blacksquare & \blacksquare & \blacksquare \\ 0 & \blacksquare & \blacksquare & \blacksquare \end{bmatrix} \quad \begin{bmatrix} 1 & \blacksquare & \blacksquare & \blacksquare \\ 0 & 1 & \blacksquare & \blacksquare \\ 0 & 0 & \blacksquare & \blacksquare \end{bmatrix} \quad \begin{bmatrix} 1 & \blacksquare & \blacksquare & \blacksquare \\ 0 & 1 & \blacksquare & \blacksquare \\ 0 & 0 & 1 & \blacksquare \end{bmatrix}$$

Once an augmented matrix is in row-echelon form, we can solve the corresponding linear system using back-substitution. This technique is called **Gaussian elimination**, in honor of its inventor, the German mathematician C. F. Gauss (see page 272).

SOLVING A SYSTEM USING GAUSSIAN ELIMINATION

1. **Augmented Matrix.** Write the augmented matrix of the system.

2. **Row-Echelon Form.** Use elementary row operations to change the augmented matrix to row-echelon form.

3. **Back-Substitution.** Write the new system of equations that corresponds to the row-echelon form of the augmented matrix and solve by back-substitution.

IN-CLASS MATERIALS

Point out that the techniques in this section are extendable in a way that some ad hoc techniques are not. One can solve an 8×8 or even a 100×100 system (in theory) using this method. If you want to pursue this line further, it is interesting to estimate the complexity of using this technique. Have the students solve a 2×2 system, keeping track of every multiplication they do, and every addition, then have them do the same for a 3×3. They can then do the same for a 4×4—not necessarily bothering to actually do all the additions and multiplications, just doing the count. Notice that the increase in complexity grows faster than a linear function.

EXAMPLE 3 | Solving a System Using Row-Echelon Form

Solve the system of linear equations using Gaussian elimination.

$$\begin{cases} 4x + 8y - 4z = 4 \\ 3x + 8y + 5z = -11 \\ -2x + y + 12z = -17 \end{cases}$$

SOLUTION   We first write the augmented matrix of the system, and then we use elementary row operations to put it in row-echelon form.

Augmented matrix:
$$\begin{bmatrix} 4 & 8 & -4 & 4 \\ 3 & 8 & 5 & -11 \\ -2 & 1 & 12 & -17 \end{bmatrix}$$ Need a 1 here

$\frac{1}{4}R_1$
$$\begin{bmatrix} 1 & 2 & -1 & 1 \\ 3 & 8 & 5 & -11 \\ -2 & 1 & 12 & -17 \end{bmatrix}$$ Need 0's here

$\begin{matrix} R_2 - 3R_1 \rightarrow R_2 \\ R_3 + 2R_1 \rightarrow R_3 \end{matrix}$
$$\begin{bmatrix} 1 & 2 & -1 & 1 \\ 0 & 2 & 8 & -14 \\ 0 & 5 & 10 & -15 \end{bmatrix}$$ Need a 1 here

$\frac{1}{2}R_2$
$$\begin{bmatrix} 1 & 2 & -1 & 1 \\ 0 & 1 & 4 & -7 \\ 0 & 5 & 10 & -15 \end{bmatrix}$$ Need a 0 here

$R_3 - 5R_2 \rightarrow R_3$
$$\begin{bmatrix} 1 & 2 & -1 & 1 \\ 0 & 1 & 4 & -7 \\ 0 & 0 & -10 & 20 \end{bmatrix}$$ Need a 1 here

Row-echelon form:
$-\frac{1}{10}R_3$
$$\begin{bmatrix} 1 & 2 & -1 & 1 \\ 0 & 1 & 4 & -7 \\ 0 & 0 & 1 & -2 \end{bmatrix}$$

We now have an equivalent matrix in row-echelon form, and the corresponding system of equations is

$$\begin{cases} x + 2y - z = 1 \\ y + 4z = -7 \\ z = -2 \end{cases}$$

Back-substitute: We use back-substitution to solve the system.

$y + 2(-2) = -3$ Back-substitute $z = -2$ into Equation 2

$y = 1$ Solve for y

$x + 2(1) - (-2) = 1$ Back-substitute $y = 1$ and $z = -2$ into Equation 1

$x = -3$ Solve for x

So the solution of the system is $(-3, 1, -2)$.

✎ **NOW TRY EXERCISE 21**

Graphing calculators have a "row-echelon form" command that puts a matrix in row-echelon form. (On the TI-83 this command is `ref`.) For the augmented matrix in Example 3 the `ref` command gives the output shown in Figure 1. Notice that the

```
ref([A])
  [[1 2 -1 1 ]
   [0 1 2 -3]
   [0 0 1 -2]]
```

FIGURE 1

ALTERNATE EXAMPLE 3
Solve the system of linear equations using Gaussian elimination.

$$\begin{cases} 11x + 22y - 11z = 22 \\ 7x + 14y + 5z = -10 \\ -6x + y + 58z = -51 \end{cases}$$

If the system is dependent or inconsistent, indicate this.

ANSWER
$(-10, 5, -2)$

EXAMPLE

A pet shop has 100 puppies, kittens, and turtles. A puppy costs $30, a kitten costs $20, and a turtle costs $5. If there are twice as many kittens as puppies, and if the stock is worth $1050, how many of each type of animal is there?

ANSWER

$$\begin{aligned} p + k + t &= 100 \\ 30p + 20k + 5t &= 1050 \\ 2p - k + 0t &= 0 \end{aligned}$$

10 puppies, 20 kittens, 70 turtles

row-echelon form that is obtained by the calculator differs from the one we got in Example 3. This is because the calculator used different row operations than we did. You should check that your calculator's row-echelon form leads to the same solution as ours.

▼ Gauss-Jordan Elimination

If we put the augmented matrix of a linear system in *reduced* row-echelon form, then we don't need to back-substitute to solve the system. To put a matrix in reduced row-echelon form, we use the following steps.

- Use the elementary row operations to put the matrix in row-echelon form.
- Obtain zeros above each leading entry by adding multiples of the row containing that entry to the rows above it. Begin with the last leading entry and work up.

Here is how the process works for a 3×4 matrix:

$$\begin{bmatrix} 1 & \blacksquare & \blacksquare & \blacksquare \\ 0 & 1 & \blacksquare & \blacksquare \\ 0 & 0 & 1 & \blacksquare \end{bmatrix} \rightarrow \begin{bmatrix} 1 & \blacksquare & 0 & \blacksquare \\ 0 & 1 & 0 & \blacksquare \\ 0 & 0 & 1 & \blacksquare \end{bmatrix} \rightarrow \begin{bmatrix} 1 & 0 & 0 & \blacksquare \\ 0 & 1 & 0 & \blacksquare \\ 0 & 0 & 1 & \blacksquare \end{bmatrix}$$

Using the reduced row-echelon form to solve a system is called **Gauss-Jordan elimination**. The process is illustrated in the next example.

EXAMPLE 4 | Solving a System Using Reduced Row-Echelon Form

Solve the system of linear equations, using Gauss-Jordan elimination.

$$\begin{cases} 4x + 8y - 4z = 4 \\ 3x + 8y + 5z = -11 \\ -2x + y + 12z = -17 \end{cases}$$

SOLUTION   In Example 3 we used Gaussian elimination on the augmented matrix of this system to arrive at an equivalent matrix in row-echelon form. We continue using elementary row operations on the last matrix in Example 3 to arrive at an equivalent matrix in reduced row-echelon form.

Need 0's here

$$\begin{bmatrix} 1 & 2 & \boxed{-1} & 1 \\ 0 & 1 & \boxed{4} & -7 \\ 0 & 0 & 1 & -2 \end{bmatrix}$$

Need a 0 here

$$\xrightarrow[\substack{R_2 - 4R_3 \rightarrow R_2 \\ R_1 + R_3 \rightarrow R_1}]{} \begin{bmatrix} 1 & \boxed{2} & 0 & -1 \\ 0 & 1 & 0 & 1 \\ 0 & 0 & 1 & -2 \end{bmatrix}$$

$$\xrightarrow[R_1 - 2R_2 \rightarrow R_1]{} \begin{bmatrix} 1 & 0 & 0 & -3 \\ 0 & 1 & 0 & 1 \\ 0 & 0 & 1 & -2 \end{bmatrix}$$

We now have an equivalent matrix in reduced row-echelon form, and the corresponding system of equations is

Since the system is in reduced row-echelon form, back-subsitution is not required to get the solution.

$$\begin{cases} x = -3 \\ y = 1 \\ z = -2 \end{cases}$$

Hence we immediately arrive at the solution $(-3, 1, -2)$.

✎. NOW TRY EXERCISE **23**   ∎

ALTERNATE EXAMPLE 4

Solve the system of linear equations, using Gauss-Jordan elimination.

$$\begin{cases} 6x + 18y - 6z = 24 \\ 5x + 15y + 3z = -20 \\ -3x + y + 33z = -42 \end{cases}$$

If the system is dependent or inconsistent, indicate this.

ANSWER

$(-37, 12, -5)$

EXAMPLE

I have $6.50 in nickels, dimes, and quarters. I have twice as many nickels as dimes. That's a lot of nickels. In fact, if you add the number of dimes I have to twice the number of quarters I have, you get the number of nickels I have. How many nickels do I have?

ANSWER

$$\begin{aligned} 5n + 10d + 25q &= 650 \\ n - 2d + 0q &= 0 \\ -n + d + 2q &= 0 \end{aligned}$$

40 nickels, 20 dimes, 10 quarters

```
rref([A])
    [[1 0 0 -3]
     [0 1 0 1 ]
     [0 0 1 -2]]
```

FIGURE 2

Graphing calculators also have a command that puts a matrix in reduced row-echelon form. (On the TI-83 this command is `rref`.) For the augmented matrix in Example 4, the `rref` command gives the output shown in Figure 2. The calculator gives the same reduced row-echelon form as the one we got in Example 4. This is because every matrix has a *unique* reduced row-echelon form.

▼ Inconsistent and Dependent Systems

The systems of linear equations that we considered in Examples 1–4 had exactly one solution. But as we know from Section 10.2, a linear system may have one solution, no solution, or infinitely many solutions. Fortunately, the row-echelon form of a system allows us to determine which of these cases applies, as described in the following box.

First we need some terminology. A **leading variable** in a linear system is one that corresponds to a leading entry in the row-echelon form of the augmented matrix of the system.

THE SOLUTIONS OF A LINEAR SYSTEM IN ROW-ECHELON FORM

Suppose the augmented matrix of a system of linear equations has been transformed by Gaussian elimination into row-echelon form. Then exactly one of the following is true.

1. **No solution.** If the row-echelon form contains a row that represents the equation $0 = c$, where c is not zero, then the system has no solution. A system with no solution is called **inconsistent**.

2. **One solution.** If each variable in the row-echelon form is a leading variable, then the system has exactly one solution, which we find using back-substitution or Gauss-Jordan elimination.

3. **Infinitely many solutions.** If the variables in the row-echelon form are not all leading variables and if the system is not inconsistent, then it has infinitely many solutions. In this case the system is called **dependent**. We solve the system by putting the matrix in reduced row-echelon form and then expressing the leading variables in terms of the nonleading variables. The nonleading variables may take on any real numbers as their values.

The matrices below, all in row-echelon form, illustrate the three cases described above.

No solution

$$\begin{bmatrix} 1 & 2 & 5 & 7 \\ 0 & 1 & 3 & 4 \\ 0 & 0 & 0 & 1 \end{bmatrix}$$

Last equation says $0 = 1$

One solution

$$\begin{bmatrix} 1 & 6 & -1 & 3 \\ 0 & 1 & 2 & -2 \\ 0 & 0 & 1 & 8 \end{bmatrix}$$

Each variable is a leading variable

Infinitely many solutions

$$\begin{bmatrix} 1 & 2 & -3 & 1 \\ 0 & 1 & 5 & -2 \\ 0 & 0 & 0 & 0 \end{bmatrix}$$

z is not a leading variable

EXAMPLE 5 | A System with No Solution

Solve the system.

$$\begin{cases} x - 3y + 2z = 12 \\ 2x - 5y + 5z = 14 \\ x - 2y + 3z = 20 \end{cases}$$

ALTERNATE EXAMPLE 5

Solve the system.

$$\begin{cases} x - 8y + 4z = 11 \\ 2x - 12y + 12z = 17 \\ x - 4y + 8z = 22 \end{cases}$$

If the system is dependent or inconsistent, indicate this.

ANSWER

Inconsistent

SOLUTION   We transform the system into row-echelon form.

$$\begin{bmatrix} 1 & -3 & 2 & 12 \\ 2 & -5 & 5 & 14 \\ 1 & -2 & 3 & 20 \end{bmatrix} \xrightarrow[\substack{R_2 - 2R_1 \to R_2 \\ R_3 - R_1 \to R_3}]{} \begin{bmatrix} 1 & -3 & 2 & 12 \\ 0 & 1 & 1 & -10 \\ 0 & 1 & 1 & 8 \end{bmatrix}$$

$$\xrightarrow{R_3 - R_2 \to R_3} \begin{bmatrix} 1 & -3 & 2 & 12 \\ 0 & 1 & 1 & -10 \\ 0 & 0 & 0 & 18 \end{bmatrix} \xrightarrow{\frac{1}{18}R_3} \begin{bmatrix} 1 & -3 & 2 & 12 \\ 0 & 1 & 1 & -10 \\ 0 & 0 & 0 & 1 \end{bmatrix}$$

This last matrix is in row-echelon form, so we can stop the Gaussian elimination process. Now if we translate the last row back into equation form, we get $0x + 0y + 0z = 1$, or $0 = 1$, which is false. No matter what values we pick for x, y, and z, the last equation will never be a true statement. This means that the system *has no solution*.

✎. NOW TRY EXERCISE **29**   ■

Figure 3 shows the row-echelon form produced by a TI-83 calculator for the augmented matrix in Example 5. You should check that this gives the same solution.

```
ref([A])
[[1 -2.5 2.5 7   ]
 [0  1    1   -10]
 [0  0    0    1  ]]
```

FIGURE 3

EXAMPLE 6 | A System with Infinitely Many Solutions

Find the complete solution of the system.

$$\begin{cases} -3x - 5y + 36z = 10 \\ -x \qquad + 7z = 5 \\ x + y - 10z = -4 \end{cases}$$

SOLUTION   We transform the system into reduced row-echelon form.

$$\begin{bmatrix} -3 & -5 & 36 & 10 \\ -1 & 0 & 7 & 5 \\ 1 & 1 & -10 & -4 \end{bmatrix} \xrightarrow{R_1 \leftrightarrow R_3} \begin{bmatrix} 1 & 1 & -10 & -4 \\ -1 & 0 & 7 & 5 \\ -3 & -5 & 36 & 10 \end{bmatrix}$$

$$\xrightarrow[\substack{R_2 + R_1 \to R_2 \\ R_3 + 3R_1 \to R_3}]{} \begin{bmatrix} 1 & 1 & -10 & -4 \\ 0 & 1 & -3 & 1 \\ 0 & -2 & 6 & -2 \end{bmatrix} \xrightarrow{R_3 + 2R_2 \to R_3} \begin{bmatrix} 1 & 1 & -10 & -4 \\ 0 & 1 & -3 & 1 \\ 0 & 0 & 0 & 0 \end{bmatrix}$$

$$\xrightarrow{R_1 - R_2 \to R_1} \begin{bmatrix} 1 & 0 & -7 & -5 \\ 0 & 1 & -3 & 1 \\ 0 & 0 & 0 & 0 \end{bmatrix}$$

Reduced row-echelon form on the TI-83 calculator:

```
rref([A])
[[1 0 -7 -5]
 [0 1 -3  1 ]
 [0 0  0  0 ]]
```

The third row corresponds to the equation $0 = 0$. This equation is always true, no matter what values are used for x, y, and z. Since the equation adds no new information about the variables, we can drop it from the system. So the last matrix corresponds to the system

$$\begin{cases} x \qquad - 7z = -5 & \text{Equation 1} \\ \quad y - 3z = 1 & \text{Equation 2} \end{cases}$$

Leading variables

Now we solve for the leading variables x and y in terms of the nonleading variable z:

$$x = 7z - 5 \qquad \text{Solve for } x \text{ in Equation 1}$$

$$y = 3z + 1 \qquad \text{Solve for } y \text{ in Equation 2}$$

ALTERNATE EXAMPLE 6

Find the complete solution of the system.

$$\begin{cases} -5x - 10y + 75z = 10 \\ -x \qquad + 7z = 4 \\ x + y - 11z = -3 \end{cases}$$

ANSWER

$(7k - 4, 4k + 1, k)$

To obtain the complete solution, we let t represent any real number, and we express x, y, and z in terms of t:

$$x = 7t - 5$$
$$y = 3t + 1$$
$$z = t$$

We can also write the solution as the ordered triple $(7t - 5, 3t + 1, t)$, where t is any real number.

✎. NOW TRY EXERCISE **31** ■

In Example 6, to get specific solutions, we give a specific value to t. For example, if $t = 1$, then

$$x = 7(1) - 5 = 2$$
$$y = 3(1) + 1 = 4$$
$$z = 1$$

Here are some other solutions of the system obtained by substituting other values for the parameter t.

Parameter t	Solution $(7t - 5, 3t + 1, t)$
-1	$(-12, -2, -1)$
0	$(-5, 1, 0)$
2	$(9, 7, 2)$
5	$(30, 16, 5)$

EXAMPLE 7 | A System with Infinitely Many Solutions

Find the complete solution of the system.

$$\begin{cases} x + 2y - 3z - 4w = 10 \\ x + 3y - 3z - 4w = 15 \\ 2x + 2y - 6z - 8w = 10 \end{cases}$$

SOLUTION We transform the system into reduced row-echelon form.

$$\begin{bmatrix} 1 & 2 & -3 & -4 & 10 \\ 1 & 3 & -3 & -4 & 15 \\ 2 & 2 & -6 & -8 & 10 \end{bmatrix} \xrightarrow[R_3 - 2R_1 \to R_3]{R_2 - R_1 \to R_2} \begin{bmatrix} 1 & 2 & -3 & -4 & 10 \\ 0 & 1 & 0 & 0 & 5 \\ 0 & -2 & 0 & 0 & -10 \end{bmatrix}$$

$$\xrightarrow{R_1 + 2R_2 \to R_3} \begin{bmatrix} 1 & 2 & -3 & -4 & 10 \\ 0 & 1 & 0 & 0 & 5 \\ 0 & 0 & 0 & 0 & 0 \end{bmatrix} \xrightarrow{R_1 - 2R_2 \to R_1} \begin{bmatrix} 1 & 0 & -3 & -4 & 0 \\ 0 & 1 & 0 & 0 & 5 \\ 0 & 0 & 0 & 0 & 0 \end{bmatrix}$$

This is in reduced row-echelon form. Since the last row represents the equation $0 = 0$, we may discard it. So the last matrix corresponds to the system

$$\begin{cases} x & -3z - 4w = 0 \\ y & = 5 \end{cases}$$

Leading variables

ALTERNATE EXAMPLE 7
Find the complete solution of the system.

$$\begin{cases} x + 2y - 4z - 5w = 14 \\ x + 3y - 4z - 5w = 21 \\ 2x + 2y - 8z - 10w = 14 \end{cases}$$

ANSWER
$(4m + 5n, 7, m, n)$

To obtain the complete solution, we solve for the leading variables x and y in terms of the nonleading variables z and w, and we let z and w be any real numbers. Thus the complete solution is

$$x = 3s + 4t$$
$$y = 5$$
$$z = s$$
$$w = t$$

where s and t are any real numbers.

✎. NOW TRY EXERCISE **51**   ■

 Note that s and t do *not* have to be the *same* real number in the solution for Example 7. We can choose arbitrary values for each if we wish to construct a specific solution to the system. For example, if we let $s = 1$ and $t = 2$, then we get the solution $(11, 5, 1, 2)$. You should check that this does indeed satisfy all three of the original equations in Example 7.

Examples 6 and 7 illustrate this general fact: If a system in row-echelon form has n nonzero equations in m variables $(m > n)$, then the complete solution will have $m - n$ nonleading variables. For instance, in Example 6 we arrived at *two* nonzero equations in the *three* variables x, y, and z, which gave us $3 - 2 = 1$ nonleading variable.

▼ Modeling with Linear Systems

Linear equations, often containing hundreds or even thousands of variables, occur frequently in the applications of algebra to the sciences and to other fields. For now, let's consider an example that involves only three variables.

EXAMPLE 8 | Nutritional Analysis Using a System of Linear Equations

A nutritionist is performing an experiment on student volunteers. He wishes to feed one of his subjects a daily diet that consists of a combination of three commercial diet foods: MiniCal, LiquiFast, and SlimQuick. For the experiment it is important that the subject consume exactly 500 mg of potassium, 75 g of protein, and 1150 units of vitamin D every day. The amounts of these nutrients in one ounce of each food are given in the table. How many ounces of each food should the subject eat every day to satisfy the nutrient requirements exactly?

	MiniCal	LiquiFast	SlimQuick
Potassium (mg)	50	75	10
Protein (g)	5	10	3
Vitamin D (units)	90	100	50

SOLUTION Let x, y, and z represent the number of ounces of MiniCal, LiquiFast, and SlimQuick, respectively, that the subject should eat every day. This means that he will get $50x$ mg of potassium from MiniCal, $75y$ mg from LiquiFast, and $10z$ mg from SlimQuick, for a total of $50x + 75y + 10z$ mg potassium in all. Since the potassium requirement is 500 mg, we get the first equation below. Similar reasoning for the protein and vitamin D requirements leads to the system

$$\begin{cases} 50x + 75y + 10z = 500 & \text{Potassium} \\ 5x + 10y + 3z = 75 & \text{Protein} \\ 90x + 100y + 50z = 1150 & \text{Vitamin D} \end{cases}$$

```
rref([A])
    [[1 0 0 5 ]
     [0 1 0 2 ]
     [0 0 1 10]]
```

FIGURE 4

CHECK YOUR ANSWER

$x = 5, y = 2, z = 10$:

$$\begin{cases} 10(5) + 15(2) + 2(10) = 100 \\ 5(5) + 10(2) + 3(10) = 75 \\ 9(5) + 10(2) + 5(10) = 115 \end{cases} \checkmark$$

Dividing the first equation by 5 and the third one by 10 gives the system

$$\begin{cases} 10x + 15y + 2z = 100 \\ 5x + 10y + 3z = 75 \\ 9x + 10y + 5z = 115 \end{cases}$$

We can solve this system using Gaussian elimination, or we can use a graphing calculator to find the reduced row-echelon form of the augmented matrix of the system. Using the rref command on the TI-83, we get the output in Figure 4. From the reduced row-echelon form we see that $x = 5$, $y = 2$, $z = 10$. The subject should be fed 5 oz of Mini-Cal, 2 oz of LiquiFast, and 10 oz of SlimQuick every day.

✎ **NOW TRY EXERCISE 55** ■

A more practical application might involve dozens of foods and nutrients rather than just three. Such problems lead to systems with large numbers of variables and equations. Computers or graphing calculators are essential for solving such large systems.

10.3 EXERCISES

CONCEPTS

1. If a system of linear equations has infinitely many solutions, then the system is called _____. If a system of linear equations has no solution, then the system is called _____.

2. Write the augmented matrix of the following system of equations.

System	Augmented matrix
$\begin{cases} x + y - z = 1 \\ x + 2z = -3 \\ 2y - z = 3 \end{cases}$	$\begin{bmatrix} \blacksquare & \blacksquare & \blacksquare & \blacksquare \\ \blacksquare & \blacksquare & \blacksquare & \blacksquare \\ \blacksquare & \blacksquare & \blacksquare & \blacksquare \end{bmatrix}$

3. The following matrix is the augmented matrix of a system of linear equations in the variables x, y, and z. (It is given in reduced row-echelon form.)

$$\begin{bmatrix} 1 & 0 & -1 & 3 \\ 0 & 1 & 2 & 5 \\ 0 & 0 & 0 & 0 \end{bmatrix}$$

(a) The leading variables are _____.

(b) Is the system inconsistent or dependent?_____

(c) The solution of the system is:

$x = $ _____, $y = $ _____, $z = $ _____

4. The augmented matrix of a system of linear equations is given in reduced row-echelon form. Find the solution of the system.

(a) $\begin{bmatrix} 1 & 0 & 0 & 2 \\ 0 & 1 & 0 & 1 \\ 0 & 0 & 1 & 3 \end{bmatrix}$ (b) $\begin{bmatrix} 1 & 0 & 1 & 2 \\ 0 & 1 & 1 & 1 \\ 0 & 0 & 0 & 0 \end{bmatrix}$ (c) $\begin{bmatrix} 1 & 0 & 0 & 2 \\ 0 & 1 & 0 & 1 \\ 0 & 0 & 0 & 3 \end{bmatrix}$

$x = $ _____ $x = $ _____ $x = $ _____
$y = $ _____ $y = $ _____ $y = $ _____
$z = $ _____ $z = $ _____ $z = $ _____

SKILLS

5–10 ■ State the dimension of the matrix.

5. $\begin{bmatrix} 2 & 7 \\ 0 & -1 \\ 5 & -3 \end{bmatrix}$ **6.** $\begin{bmatrix} -1 & 5 & 4 & 0 \\ 0 & 2 & 11 & 3 \end{bmatrix}$ **7.** $\begin{bmatrix} 12 \\ 35 \end{bmatrix}$

8. $\begin{bmatrix} -3 \\ 0 \\ 1 \end{bmatrix}$ **9.** $\begin{bmatrix} 1 & 4 & 7 \end{bmatrix}$ **10.** $\begin{bmatrix} 1 & 0 \\ 0 & 1 \end{bmatrix}$

11–18 ■ A matrix is given. (a) Determine whether the matrix is in row-echelon form. (b) Determine whether the matrix is in reduced row-echelon form. (c) Write the system of equations for which the given matrix is the augmented matrix.

11. $\begin{bmatrix} 1 & 0 & -3 \\ 0 & 1 & 5 \end{bmatrix}$ **12.** $\begin{bmatrix} 1 & 3 & -3 \\ 0 & 1 & 5 \end{bmatrix}$

13. $\begin{bmatrix} 1 & 2 & 8 & 0 \\ 0 & 1 & 3 & 2 \\ 0 & 0 & 0 & 0 \end{bmatrix}$ **14.** $\begin{bmatrix} 1 & 0 & -7 & 0 \\ 0 & 1 & 3 & 0 \\ 0 & 0 & 0 & 1 \end{bmatrix}$

15. $\begin{bmatrix} 1 & 0 & 0 & 0 \\ 0 & 0 & 0 & 0 \\ 0 & 1 & 5 & 1 \end{bmatrix}$ **16.** $\begin{bmatrix} 1 & 0 & 0 & 1 \\ 0 & 1 & 0 & 2 \\ 0 & 0 & 1 & 3 \end{bmatrix}$

17. $\begin{bmatrix} 1 & 3 & 0 & -1 & 0 \\ 0 & 0 & 1 & 2 & 0 \\ 0 & 0 & 0 & 0 & 1 \\ 0 & 0 & 0 & 0 & 0 \end{bmatrix}$ **18.** $\begin{bmatrix} 1 & 3 & 0 & 1 & 0 & 0 \\ 0 & 1 & 0 & 4 & 0 & 0 \\ 0 & 0 & 0 & 1 & 1 & 2 \\ 0 & 0 & 0 & 1 & 0 & 0 \end{bmatrix}$

19–28 ■ The system of linear equations has a unique solution. Find the solution using Gaussian elimination or Gauss-Jordan elimination.

19. $\begin{cases} x - 2y + z = 1 \\ y + 2z = 5 \\ x + y + 3z = 8 \end{cases}$ **20.** $\begin{cases} x + y + 6z = 3 \\ x + y + 3z = 3 \\ x + 2y + 4z = 7 \end{cases}$

DRILL QUESTION

Consider this system of equations:

$$\begin{cases} x + y = -1 \\ 2x - 3y = 8 \end{cases}$$

(a) Find the augmented matrix of this system.

(b) Put the matrix in reduced row-echelon form.

Answers

(a) $\begin{bmatrix} 1 & 1 & -1 \\ 2 & -3 & 8 \end{bmatrix}$

(b) $\begin{bmatrix} 1 & 0 & 1 \\ 0 & 1 & -2 \end{bmatrix}$

21. $\begin{cases} x + y + z = 2 \\ 2x - 3y + 2z = 4 \\ 4x + y - 3z = 1 \end{cases}$

22. $\begin{cases} x + y + z = 4 \\ -x + 2y + 3z = 17 \\ 2x - y = -7 \end{cases}$

23. $\begin{cases} x + 2y - z = -2 \\ x + z = 0 \\ 2x - y - z = -3 \end{cases}$

24. $\begin{cases} 2y + z = 4 \\ x + y = 4 \\ 3x + 3y - z = 10 \end{cases}$

25. $\begin{cases} x_1 + 2x_2 - x_3 = 9 \\ 2x_1 - x_3 = -2 \\ 3x_1 + 5x_2 + 2x_3 = 22 \end{cases}$

26. $\begin{cases} 2x_1 + x_2 = 7 \\ 2x_1 - x_2 + x_3 = 6 \\ 3x_1 - 2x_2 + 4x_3 = 11 \end{cases}$

27. $\begin{cases} 2x - 3y - z = 13 \\ -x + 2y - 5z = 6 \\ 5x - y - z = 49 \end{cases}$

28. $\begin{cases} 10x + 10y - 20z = 60 \\ 15x + 20y + 30z = -25 \\ -5x + 30y - 10z = 45 \end{cases}$

29–38 ■ Determine whether the system of linear equations is inconsistent or dependent. If it is dependent, find the complete solution.

29. $\begin{cases} x + y + z = 2 \\ y - 3z = 1 \\ 2x + y + 5z = 0 \end{cases}$

30. $\begin{cases} x + 3z = 3 \\ 2x + y - 2z = 5 \\ -y + 8z = 8 \end{cases}$

31. $\begin{cases} 2x - 3y - 9z = -5 \\ x + 3z = 2 \\ -3x + y - 4z = -3 \end{cases}$

32. $\begin{cases} x - 2y + 5z = 3 \\ -2x + 6y - 11z = 1 \\ 3x - 16y - 20z = -26 \end{cases}$

33. $\begin{cases} x - y + 3z = 3 \\ 4x - 8y + 32z = 24 \\ 2x - 3y + 11z = 4 \end{cases}$

34. $\begin{cases} -2x + 6y - 2z = -12 \\ x - 3y + 2z = 10 \\ -x + 3y + 2z = 6 \end{cases}$

35. $\begin{cases} x + 4y - 2z = -3 \\ 2x - y + 5z = 12 \\ 8x + 5y + 11z = 30 \end{cases}$

36. $\begin{cases} 3r + 2s - 3t = 10 \\ r - s - t = -5 \\ r + 4s - t = 20 \end{cases}$

37. $\begin{cases} 2x + y - 2z = 12 \\ -x - \frac{1}{2}y + z = -6 \\ 3x + \frac{3}{2}y - 3z = 18 \end{cases}$

38. $\begin{cases} y - 5z = 7 \\ 3x + 2y = 12 \\ 3x + 10z = 80 \end{cases}$

39–54 ■ Solve the system of linear equations.

39. $\begin{cases} 4x - 3y + z = -8 \\ -2x + y - 3z = -4 \\ x - y + 2z = 3 \end{cases}$

40. $\begin{cases} 2x - 3y + 5z = 14 \\ 4x - y - 2z = -17 \\ -x - y + z = 3 \end{cases}$

41. $\begin{cases} 2x + y + 3z = 9 \\ -x - 7z = 10 \\ 3x + 2y - z = 4 \end{cases}$

42. $\begin{cases} -4x - y + 36z = 24 \\ x - 2y + 9z = 3 \\ -2x + y + 6z = 6 \end{cases}$

43. $\begin{cases} x + 2y - 3z = -5 \\ -2x - 4y - 6z = 10 \\ 3x + 7y - 2z = -13 \end{cases}$

44. $\begin{cases} 3x + y = 2 \\ -4x + 3y + z = 4 \\ 2x + 5y + z = 0 \end{cases}$

45. $\begin{cases} x - y + 6z = 8 \\ x + z = 5 \\ x + 3y - 14z = -4 \end{cases}$

46. $\begin{cases} 3x - y + 2z = -1 \\ 4x - 2y + z = -7 \\ -x + 3y - 2z = -1 \end{cases}$

47. $\begin{cases} -x + 2y + z - 3w = 3 \\ 3x - 4y + z + w = 9 \\ -x - y + z + w = 0 \\ 2x + y + 4z - 2w = 3 \end{cases}$

48. $\begin{cases} x + y - z - w = 6 \\ 2x + z - 3w = 8 \\ x - y + 4w = -10 \\ 3x + 5y - z - w = 20 \end{cases}$

49. $\begin{cases} x + y + 2z - w = -2 \\ 3y + z + 2w = 2 \\ x + y + 3w = 2 \\ -3x + z + 2w = 5 \end{cases}$

50. $\begin{cases} x - 3y + 2z + w = -2 \\ x - 2y - 2w = -10 \\ z + 5w = 15 \\ 3x + 2z + w = -3 \end{cases}$

51. $\begin{cases} x - y + w = 0 \\ 3x - z + 2w = 0 \\ x - 4y + z + 2w = 0 \end{cases}$

52. $\begin{cases} 2x - y + 2z + w = 5 \\ -x + y + 4z - w = 3 \\ 3x - 2y - z = 0 \end{cases}$

53. $\begin{cases} x + z + w = 4 \\ y - z = -4 \\ x - 2y + 3z + w = 12 \\ 2x - 2z + 5w = -1 \end{cases}$

54. $\begin{cases} y - z + 2w = 0 \\ 3x + 2y + w = 0 \\ 2x + 4w = 12 \\ -2x - 2z + 5w = 6 \end{cases}$

APPLICATIONS

55. Nutrition A doctor recommends that a patient take 50 mg each of niacin, riboflavin, and thiamin daily to alleviate a vitamin deficiency. In his medicine chest at home the patient finds three brands of vitamin pills. The amounts of the relevant vitamins per pill are given in the table. How many pills of each type should he take every day to get 50 mg of each vitamin?

	VitaMax	Vitron	VitaPlus
Niacin (mg)	5	10	15
Riboflavin (mg)	15	20	0
Thiamin (mg)	10	10	10

56. Mixtures A chemist has three acid solutions at various concentrations. The first is 10% acid, the second is 20%, and the third is 40%. How many milliliters of each should she use to make 100 mL of 18% solution, if she has to use four times as much of the 10% solution as the 40% solution?

57. Distance, Speed, and Time Amanda, Bryce, and Corey enter a race in which they have to run, swim, and cycle over a marked course. Their average speeds are given in the table. Corey finishes first with a total time of 1 h 45 min. Amanda comes in second with a time of 2 h 30 min. Bryce finishes last with a time of 3 h. Find the distance (in miles) for each part of the race.

	Average speed (mi/h)		
	Running	Swimming	Cycling
Amanda	10	4	20
Bryce	$7\frac{1}{2}$	6	15
Corey	15	3	40

58. Classroom Use A small school has 100 students who occupy three classrooms: A, B, and C. After the first period of the school day, half the students in room A move to room B, one-fifth of the students in room B move to room C, and one-third of the students in room C move to room A. Nevertheless, the total number of students in each room is the same for both periods. How many students occupy each room?

59. Manufacturing Furniture A furniture factory makes wooden tables, chairs, and armoires. Each piece of furniture requires three operations: cutting the wood, assembling, and finishing. Each operation requires the number of hours (h) given in the table. The workers in the factory can provide 300 hours of cutting, 400 hours of assembling, and 590 hours of finishing each work week. How many tables, chairs, and armoires should be produced so that all available labor-hours are used? Or is this impossible?

	Table	Chair	Armoire
Cutting (h)	$\frac{1}{2}$	1	1
Assembling (h)	$\frac{1}{2}$	$1\frac{1}{2}$	1
Finishing (h)	1	$1\frac{1}{2}$	2

60. Traffic Flow A section of a city's street network is shown in the figure. The arrows indicate one-way streets, and the numbers show how many cars enter or leave this section of the city via the indicated street in a certain one-hour period. The variables x, y, z, and w represent the number of cars that travel along the portions of First, Second, Avocado, and Birch Streets during this period. Find x, y, z, and w, assuming that none of the cars stop or park on any of the streets shown.

DISCOVERY ▪ DISCUSSION ▪ WRITING

61. Polynomials Determined by a Set of Points We all know that two points uniquely determine a line $y = ax + b$ in the coordinate plane. Similarly, three points uniquely determine a quadratic (second-degree) polynomial

$$y = ax^2 + bx + c$$

four points uniquely determine a cubic (third-degree) polynomial

$$y = ax^3 + bx^2 + cx + d$$

and so on. (Some exceptions to this rule are if the three points actually lie on a line, or the four points lie on a quadratic or line, and so on.) For the following set of five points, find the line that contains the first two points, the quadratic that contains the first three points, the cubic that contains the first four points, and the fourth-degree polynomial that contains all five points.

$$(0, 0), \quad (1, 12), \quad (2, 40), \quad (3, 6), \quad (-1, -14)$$

Graph the points and functions in the same viewing rectangle using a graphing device.

10.4 THE ALGEBRA OF MATRICES

Equality of Matrices ▶ Addition, Subtraction, and Scalar Multiplication of Matrices ▶ Multiplication of Matrices ▶ Properties of Matrix Multiplication ▶ Applications of Matrix Multiplication ▶ Computer Graphics

Thus far, we have used matrices simply for notational convenience when solving linear systems. Matrices have many other uses in mathematics and the sciences, and for most of these applications a knowledge of matrix algebra is essential. Like numbers, matrices can be added, subtracted, multiplied, and divided. In this section we learn how to perform these algebraic operations on matrices.

▼ Equality of Matrices

Two matrices are equal if they have the same entries in the same positions.

SUGGESTED TIME AND EMPHASIS

1 class, recommended material

TEXT QUESTIONS

True or false?

(a) $\begin{bmatrix} 3 & 4 \\ 1 & 2 \end{bmatrix} \begin{bmatrix} -1 & 5 \\ 1 & 0 \end{bmatrix} = \begin{bmatrix} -3 & 20 \\ 1 & 0 \end{bmatrix}$

(b) $\begin{bmatrix} 3 & 4 \\ 1 & 2 \end{bmatrix} + \begin{bmatrix} -1 & 5 \\ 1 & 0 \end{bmatrix} = \begin{bmatrix} 2 & 9 \\ 2 & 2 \end{bmatrix}$

Answers
(a) False
(b) True

Equal matrices

$$\begin{bmatrix} \sqrt{4} & 2^2 & e^0 \\ 0.5 & 1 & 1-1 \end{bmatrix} = \begin{bmatrix} 2 & 4 & 1 \\ \frac{1}{2} & \frac{2}{2} & 0 \end{bmatrix}$$

Unequal matrices

$$\begin{bmatrix} 1 & 2 \\ 3 & 4 \\ 5 & 6 \end{bmatrix} \neq \begin{bmatrix} 1 & 3 & 5 \\ 2 & 4 & 6 \end{bmatrix}$$

EQUALITY OF MATRICES

The matrices $A = [a_{ij}]$ and $B = [b_{ij}]$ are **equal** if and only if they have the same dimension $m \times n$, and corresponding entries are equal, that is,

$$a_{ij} = b_{ij}$$

for $i = 1, 2, \ldots, m$ and $j = 1, 2, \ldots, n$.

ALTERNATE EXAMPLE 1

Find a, b, c, and d if

$$\begin{bmatrix} a & 2 \\ 3 & b \end{bmatrix} = \begin{bmatrix} 4 & c \\ d & 2 \end{bmatrix}$$

ANSWER

$a = 4, b = 2, c = 2, d = 3$

EXAMPLE 1 | Equal Matrices

Find a, b, c, and d, if

$$\begin{bmatrix} a & b \\ c & d \end{bmatrix} = \begin{bmatrix} 1 & 3 \\ 5 & 2 \end{bmatrix}$$

SOLUTION Since the two matrices are equal, corresponding entries must be the same. So we must have $a = 1$, $b = 3$, $c = 5$, and $d = 2$.

NOW TRY EXERCISE **5** ∎

▼ Addition, Subtraction, and Scalar Multiplication of Matrices

Two matrices can be added or subtracted if they have the same dimension. (Otherwise, their sum or difference is undefined.) We add or subtract the matrices by adding or subtracting corresponding entries. To multiply a matrix by a number, we multiply every element of the matrix by that number. This is called the *scalar product*.

SUM, DIFFERENCE, AND SCALAR PRODUCT OF MATRICES

Let $A = [a_{ij}]$ and $B = [b_{ij}]$ be matrices of the same dimension $m \times n$, and let c be any real number.

1. The **sum** $A + B$ is the $m \times n$ matrix obtained by adding corresponding entries of A and B.

$$A + B = [a_{ij} + b_{ij}]$$

2. The **difference** $A - B$ is the $m \times n$ matrix obtained by subtracting corresponding entries of A and B.

$$A - B = [a_{ij} - b_{ij}]$$

3. The **scalar product** cA is the $m \times n$ matrix obtained by multiplying each entry of A by c.

$$cA = [ca_{ij}]$$

EXAMPLE 2 | Performing Algebraic Operations on Matrices

Let

$$A = \begin{bmatrix} 2 & -3 \\ 0 & 5 \\ 7 & -\frac{1}{2} \end{bmatrix} \quad B = \begin{bmatrix} 1 & 0 \\ -3 & 1 \\ 2 & 2 \end{bmatrix}$$

$$C = \begin{bmatrix} 7 & -3 & 0 \\ 0 & 1 & 5 \end{bmatrix} \quad D = \begin{bmatrix} 6 & 0 & -6 \\ 8 & 1 & 9 \end{bmatrix}$$

IN-CLASS MATERIALS

The text describes which properties of real number addition and multiplication carry over to matrix addition, matrix multiplication, and scalar multiplication. Discuss how some of their consequences carry over as well. Ask the students if they believe that $(A + B)(A + B) = AA + 2AB + BB$. Let them discuss and argue. It turns out that this is false, because of commutativity. It is true that $(A + B)(A + B) = AA + AB + BA + BB$. Have the class look at $(A + B)(A - B)$ next.

Carry out each indicated operation, or explain why it cannot be performed.

(a) $A + B$ (b) $C - D$ (c) $C + A$ (d) $5A$

SOLUTION

(a) $A + B = \begin{bmatrix} 2 & -3 \\ 0 & 5 \\ 7 & -\frac{1}{2} \end{bmatrix} + \begin{bmatrix} 1 & 0 \\ -3 & 1 \\ 2 & 2 \end{bmatrix} = \begin{bmatrix} 3 & -3 \\ -3 & 6 \\ 9 & \frac{3}{2} \end{bmatrix}$

(b) $C - D = \begin{bmatrix} 7 & -3 & 0 \\ 0 & 1 & 5 \end{bmatrix} - \begin{bmatrix} 6 & 0 & -6 \\ 8 & 1 & 9 \end{bmatrix}$

$= \begin{bmatrix} 1 & -3 & 6 \\ -8 & 0 & -4 \end{bmatrix}$

(c) $C + A$ is undefined because we can't add matrices of different dimensions.

(d) $5A = 5 \begin{bmatrix} 2 & -3 \\ 0 & 5 \\ 7 & -\frac{1}{2} \end{bmatrix} = \begin{bmatrix} 10 & -15 \\ 0 & 25 \\ 35 & -\frac{5}{2} \end{bmatrix}$

✎ **NOW TRY EXERCISES 21 AND 23** ∎

The properties in the box follow from the definitions of matrix addition and scalar multiplication and the corresponding properties of real numbers.

PROPERTIES OF ADDITION AND SCALAR MULTIPLICATION OF MATRICES

Let A, B, and C be $m \times n$ matrices and let c and d be scalars.

$A + B = B + A$	Commutative Property of Matrix Addition
$(A + B) + C = A + (B + C)$	Associative Property of Matrix Addition
$c(dA) = cdA$	Associative Property of Scalar Multiplication
$(c + d)A = cA + dA$	Distributive Properties of Scalar Multiplication
$c(A + B) = cA + cB$	

EXAMPLE 3 | Solving a Matrix Equation

Solve the matrix equation

$$2X - A = B$$

for the unknown matrix X, where

$$A = \begin{bmatrix} 2 & 3 \\ -5 & 1 \end{bmatrix} \qquad B = \begin{bmatrix} 4 & -1 \\ 1 & 3 \end{bmatrix}$$

SOLUTION   We use the properties of matrices to solve for X.

$2X - A = B$	Given equation
$2X = B + A$	Add the matrix A to each side
$X = \frac{1}{2}(B + A)$	Multiply each side by the scalar $\frac{1}{2}$

ALTERNATE EXAMPLE 2

Let $A = \begin{bmatrix} 6 & 0 \\ -2 & 4 \\ 1 & 2 \end{bmatrix}$

$B = \begin{bmatrix} 4 & 2 \\ 0 & 0 \\ 12 & -2 \end{bmatrix}$

$C = \begin{bmatrix} 3 & 2 & 5 \\ 1 & 2 & 9 \end{bmatrix}$

$D = \begin{bmatrix} -5 & 4 & 1 \\ 1 & -6 & 2 \end{bmatrix}$

Carry out each indicated operation or explain why it can't be performed.

(a) $C + D$
(b) $B - C$
(c) $A + 2B$
(d) $3B$

ANSWERS

(a) $C + D = \begin{bmatrix} -2 & 6 & 6 \\ 2 & -4 & 11 \end{bmatrix}$

(b) Not possible; the dimensions are not the same.

(c) $A + 2B = \begin{bmatrix} 14 & 4 \\ -2 & 4 \\ 25 & -2 \end{bmatrix}$

(d) $3B = \begin{bmatrix} 12 & 6 \\ 0 & 0 \\ 36 & -6 \end{bmatrix}$

ALTERNATE EXAMPLE 3

Solve the matrix equation
$$3X - 4A = B$$
for the unknown matrix X where

$A = \begin{bmatrix} 4 & -1 \\ 3 & 2 \end{bmatrix}$ and

$B = \begin{bmatrix} -13 & 1 \\ -3 & -2 \end{bmatrix}$.

ANSWER

$X = \begin{bmatrix} 1 & -1 \\ 3 & 2 \end{bmatrix}$

IN-CLASS MATERIALS

Let A and B be 2×2 matrices. Although AB may not be equal to BA, there are special matrices for which $AB = BA$. One necessary (but not sufficient) condition for this to happen is that $a_{12}b_{21} = a_{21}b_{12}$. It is relatively simple to show this condition by explicitly multiplying out AB and BA. After demonstrating this condition, challenge the students to find a pair of distinct matrices, without zero elements, such that $AB = BA$. The process of searching for them will give students good practice multiplying matrices. One example that works is

$$A = \begin{bmatrix} 1 & 2 \\ 3 & 4 \end{bmatrix}, B = \begin{bmatrix} -1 & 2 \\ 3 & 2 \end{bmatrix}$$

So $\qquad X = \dfrac{1}{2}\left(\begin{bmatrix} 4 & -1 \\ 1 & 3 \end{bmatrix} + \begin{bmatrix} 2 & 3 \\ -5 & 1 \end{bmatrix}\right)$ Substitute the matrices A and B

$\qquad\qquad = \dfrac{1}{2}\begin{bmatrix} 6 & 2 \\ -4 & 4 \end{bmatrix}$ Add matrices

$\qquad\qquad = \begin{bmatrix} 3 & 1 \\ -2 & 2 \end{bmatrix}$ Multiply by the scalar $\frac{1}{2}$

✎ **NOW TRY EXERCISE 15**   ■

▼ Multiplication of Matrices

Multiplying two matrices is more difficult to describe than other matrix operations. In later examples we will see why multiplying matrices involves a rather complex procedure, which we now describe.

First, the product AB (or $A \cdot B$) of two matrices A and B is defined only when the number of columns in A is equal to the number of rows in B. This means that if we write their dimensions side by side, the two inner numbers must match:

Matrices	A	B
Dimensions	$m \times n$	$n \times k$

	Columns in A	Rows in B

If we think of the row of A and the column of B as vectors, then their inner product is the same as their dot product (see Sections 9.2 and 9.4).

If the dimensions of A and B match in this fashion, then the product AB is a matrix of dimension $m \times k$. Before describing the procedure for obtaining the elements of AB, we define the *inner product* of a row of A and a column of B.

If $[a_1 \quad a_2 \quad \cdots \quad a_n]$ is a row of A, and if $\begin{bmatrix} b_1 \\ b_2 \\ \vdots \\ b_n \end{bmatrix}$ is a column of B, then their **inner product**

is the number $a_1b_1 + a_2b_2 + \cdots + a_nb_n$. For example, taking the inner product of

$[2 \quad -1 \quad 0 \quad 4]$ and $\begin{bmatrix} 5 \\ 4 \\ -3 \\ \frac{1}{2} \end{bmatrix}$ gives

$$2 \cdot 5 + (-1) \cdot 4 + 0 \cdot (-3) + 4 \cdot \tfrac{1}{2} = 8$$

We now define the **product** AB of two matrices.

MATRIX MULTIPLICATION

If $A = [a_{ij}]$ is an $m \times n$ matrix and $B = [b_{ij}]$ an $n \times k$ matrix, then their product is the $m \times k$ matrix

$$C = [c_{ij}]$$

where c_{ij} is the inner product of the ith row of A and the jth column of B. We write the product as

$$C = AB$$

IN-CLASS MATERIALS

Foreshadow the next section by having students compute

$$\begin{bmatrix} 2 & 5 & 1 \\ 4 & 2 & 1 \\ 5 & 3 & 1 \end{bmatrix}\begin{bmatrix} x \\ y \\ z \end{bmatrix}.$$

This definition of matrix product says that each entry in the matrix AB is obtained from a *row* of A and a *column* of B as follows: The entry c_{ij} in the ith row and jth column of the matrix AB is obtained by multiplying the entries in the ith row of A with the corresponding entries in the jth column of B and adding the results.

$$
\underset{i\text{th row of } A}{} \begin{bmatrix} \blacksquare & \blacksquare & \blacksquare \end{bmatrix} \quad \overset{j\text{th column of } B}{\begin{bmatrix} \blacksquare \\ \blacksquare \\ \blacksquare \end{bmatrix}} \quad \overset{\text{Entry in } i\text{th row and } j\text{th column of } AB}{\begin{bmatrix} c_{ij} \end{bmatrix}}
$$

EXAMPLE 4 | Multiplying Matrices

Let

$$
A = \begin{bmatrix} 1 & 3 \\ -1 & 0 \end{bmatrix} \quad \text{and} \quad B = \begin{bmatrix} -1 & 5 & 2 \\ 0 & 4 & 7 \end{bmatrix}
$$

Calculate, if possible, the products AB and BA.

SOLUTION   Since A has dimension 2×2 and B has dimension 2×3, the product AB is defined and has dimension 2×3. We can therefore write

> Inner numbers match, so product is defined
>
> 2×2 2×3
>
> Outer numbers give dimension of product: 2×3

$$
AB = \begin{bmatrix} 1 & 3 \\ -1 & 0 \end{bmatrix} \begin{bmatrix} -1 & 5 & 2 \\ 0 & 4 & 7 \end{bmatrix} = \begin{bmatrix} ? & ? & ? \\ ? & ? & ? \end{bmatrix}
$$

where the question marks must be filled in using the rule defining the product of two matrices. If we define $C = AB = [c_{ij}]$, then the entry c_{11} is the inner product of the first row of A and the first column of B:

$$
\begin{bmatrix} 1 & 3 \\ -1 & 0 \end{bmatrix} \begin{bmatrix} -1 & 5 & 2 \\ 0 & 4 & 7 \end{bmatrix} \qquad 1 \cdot (-1) + 3 \cdot 0 = -1
$$

Similarly, we calculate the remaining entries of the product as follows.

Entry	Inner product of:	Value	Product matrix
c_{12}	$\begin{bmatrix} 1 & 3 \\ -1 & 0 \end{bmatrix} \begin{bmatrix} -1 & 5 & 2 \\ 0 & 4 & 7 \end{bmatrix}$	$1 \cdot 5 + 3 \cdot 4 = 17$	$\begin{bmatrix} -1 & 17 & \\ & & \end{bmatrix}$
c_{13}	$\begin{bmatrix} 1 & 3 \\ -1 & 0 \end{bmatrix} \begin{bmatrix} -1 & 5 & 2 \\ 0 & 4 & 7 \end{bmatrix}$	$1 \cdot 2 + 3 \cdot 7 = 23$	$\begin{bmatrix} -1 & 17 & 23 \\ & & \end{bmatrix}$
c_{21}	$\begin{bmatrix} 1 & 3 \\ -1 & 0 \end{bmatrix} \begin{bmatrix} -1 & 5 & 2 \\ 0 & 4 & 7 \end{bmatrix}$	$(-1) \cdot (-1) + 0 \cdot 0 = 1$	$\begin{bmatrix} -1 & 17 & 23 \\ 1 & & \end{bmatrix}$
c_{22}	$\begin{bmatrix} 1 & 3 \\ -1 & 0 \end{bmatrix} \begin{bmatrix} -1 & 5 & 2 \\ 0 & 4 & 7 \end{bmatrix}$	$(-1) \cdot 5 + 0 \cdot 4 = -5$	$\begin{bmatrix} -1 & 17 & 23 \\ 1 & -5 & \end{bmatrix}$
c_{23}	$\begin{bmatrix} 1 & 3 \\ -1 & 0 \end{bmatrix} \begin{bmatrix} -1 & 5 & 2 \\ 0 & 4 & 7 \end{bmatrix}$	$(-1) \cdot 2 + 0 \cdot 7 = -2$	$\begin{bmatrix} -1 & 17 & 23 \\ 1 & -5 & -2 \end{bmatrix}$

Thus, we have

$$
AB = \begin{bmatrix} -1 & 17 & 23 \\ 1 & -5 & -2 \end{bmatrix}
$$

> Not equal, so product not defined
>
> 2×3 2×2

The product BA is not defined, however, because the dimensions of B and A are

$$
2 \times 3 \quad \text{and} \quad 2 \times 2
$$

The inner two numbers are not the same, so the rows and columns won't match up when we try to calculate the product.

✎ NOW TRY EXERCISE 25   ■

IN-CLASS MATERIALS

This is a good time to discuss permutation matrices. A permutation matrix is a matrix that is all zeros except for a single 1 in each row and each column.

$$
\begin{bmatrix}
0 & 0 & 1 & 0 & 0 \\
1 & 0 & 0 & 0 & 0 \\
0 & 0 & 0 & 1 & 0 \\
0 & 1 & 0 & 0 & 0 \\
0 & 0 & 0 & 0 & 1
\end{bmatrix}
$$

Have the class figure out if the sum of two permutation matrices must always be a permutation matrix (no) and if the product of two permutation matrices must always be a permutation matrix (yes). Finally, have the students multiply arbitrary matrices by permutation matrices to see what happens to them (the rows or columns get rearranged, depending on whether the permutation matrix was multiplied on the left or on the right).

```
[A]*[B]
   [[-1  17  23]
    [1   -5  -2]]
```

FIGURE 1

Graphing calculators and computers are capable of performing matrix algebra. For instance, if we enter the matrices in Example 4 into the matrix variables `[A]` and `[B]` on a TI-83 calculator, then the calculator finds their product as shown in Figure 1.

▼ Properties of Matrix Multiplication

Although matrix multiplication is not commutative, it does obey the Associative and Distributive Properties.

PROPERTIES OF MATRIX MULTIPLICATION

Let A, B, and C be matrices for which the following products are defined. Then

$$A(BC) = (AB)C \qquad \text{Associative Property}$$

$$A(B + C) = AB + AC$$
$$(B + C)A = BA + CA \qquad \text{Distributive Property}$$

⊘ The next example shows that even when both AB and BA are defined, they aren't necessarily equal. This result proves that matrix multiplication is *not* commutative.

EXAMPLE 5 | Matrix Multiplication Is Not Commutative

Let

$$A = \begin{bmatrix} 5 & 7 \\ -3 & 0 \end{bmatrix} \quad \text{and} \quad B = \begin{bmatrix} 1 & 2 \\ 9 & -1 \end{bmatrix}$$

Calculate the products AB and BA.

SOLUTION Since both matrices A and B have dimension 2×2, both products AB and BA are defined, and each product is also a 2×2 matrix.

$$AB = \begin{bmatrix} 5 & 7 \\ -3 & 0 \end{bmatrix}\begin{bmatrix} 1 & 2 \\ 9 & -1 \end{bmatrix} = \begin{bmatrix} 5 \cdot 1 + 7 \cdot 9 & 5 \cdot 2 + 7 \cdot (-1) \\ (-3) \cdot 1 + 0 \cdot 9 & (-3) \cdot 2 + 0 \cdot (-1) \end{bmatrix}$$

$$= \begin{bmatrix} 68 & 3 \\ -3 & -6 \end{bmatrix}$$

$$BA = \begin{bmatrix} 1 & 2 \\ 9 & -1 \end{bmatrix}\begin{bmatrix} 5 & 7 \\ -3 & 0 \end{bmatrix} = \begin{bmatrix} 1 \cdot 5 + 2 \cdot (-3) & 1 \cdot 7 + 2 \cdot 0 \\ 9 \cdot 5 + (-1) \cdot (-3) & 9 \cdot 7 + (-1) \cdot 0 \end{bmatrix}$$

$$= \begin{bmatrix} -1 & 7 \\ 48 & 63 \end{bmatrix}$$

This shows that, in general, $AB \neq BA$. In fact, in this example AB and BA don't even have an entry in common.

✎. NOW TRY EXERCISE **27** ■

▼ Applications of Matrix Multiplication

We now consider some applied examples that give some indication of why mathematicians chose to define the matrix product in such an apparently bizarre fashion. Example 6 shows how our definition of matrix product allows us to express a system of linear equations as a single matrix equation.

ALTERNATE EXAMPLE 5

Let $A = \begin{bmatrix} 1 & 2 \\ -1 & 4 \end{bmatrix}$ and

$B = \begin{bmatrix} 6 & 0 \\ 2 & 3 \end{bmatrix}$. Calculate the products AB and BA. Does $AB = BA$?

ANSWER

$AB = \begin{bmatrix} 10 & 6 \\ 2 & 12 \end{bmatrix}$

$BA = \begin{bmatrix} 6 & 12 \\ -1 & 16 \end{bmatrix}$

They are not equal.

EXAMPLES

Let $A = \begin{bmatrix} 3 & 1 \\ -1 & 0 \\ 3 & 2 \end{bmatrix}$, $B = \begin{bmatrix} 5 & 1 \\ 1 & 2 \\ -6 & -1 \end{bmatrix}$, and $C = \begin{bmatrix} 3 & 1 \\ 2 & 5 \end{bmatrix}$.

$A + B = \begin{bmatrix} 8 & 2 \\ 0 & 2 \\ -3 & 1 \end{bmatrix}$ $\quad B - A = \begin{bmatrix} 2 & 0 \\ 2 & 2 \\ -9 & -3 \end{bmatrix}$ $\quad AC = \begin{bmatrix} 11 & 8 \\ -3 & -1 \\ 13 & 13 \end{bmatrix}$ $\quad BC = \begin{bmatrix} 17 & 10 \\ 7 & 11 \\ -20 & -11 \end{bmatrix}$ $\quad (A + B)C = \begin{bmatrix} 28 & 18 \\ 4 & 10 \\ -7 & 2 \end{bmatrix}$

If using these examples, occasionally throw in an undefined operation such as $A + C$ or AB.

EXAMPLE 6 | Writing a Linear System as a Matrix Equation

Show that the following matrix equation is equivalent to the system of equations in Example 2 of Section 10.3.

$$\begin{bmatrix} 1 & -1 & 3 \\ 1 & 2 & -2 \\ 3 & -1 & 5 \end{bmatrix} \begin{bmatrix} x \\ y \\ z \end{bmatrix} = \begin{bmatrix} 4 \\ 10 \\ 14 \end{bmatrix}$$

> Matrix equations like this one are described in more detail on page 677.

SOLUTION   If we perform matrix multiplication on the left side of the equation, we get

$$\begin{bmatrix} x - y + 3z \\ x + 2y - 2z \\ 3x - y + 5z \end{bmatrix} = \begin{bmatrix} 4 \\ 10 \\ 14 \end{bmatrix}$$

Because two matrices are equal only if their corresponding entries are equal, we equate entries to get

$$\begin{cases} x - y + 3z = 4 \\ x + 2y - 2z = 10 \\ 3x - y + 5z = 14 \end{cases}$$

This is exactly the system of equations in Example 2 of Section 10.3.

✎ NOW TRY EXERCISE **39** ∎

EXAMPLE 7 | Representing Demographic Data by Matrices

In a certain city the proportions of voters in each age group who are registered as Democrats, Republicans, or Independents are given by the following matrix.

Age

	18–30	31–50	Over 50
Democrat	0.30	0.60	0.50
Republican	0.50	0.35	0.25
Independent	0.20	0.05	0.25

$= A$

The next matrix gives the distribution, by age and sex, of the voting population of this city.

Age

		Male	Female
	18–30	5,000	6,000
	31–50	10,000	12,000
	Over 50	12,000	15,000

$= B$

For this problem, let's make the (highly unrealistic) assumption that within each age group, political preference is not related to gender. That is, the percentage of Democrat males in the 18–30 group, for example, is the same as the percentage of Democrat females in this group.

(a) Calculate the product AB.

(b) How many males are registered as Democrats in this city?

(c) How many females are registered as Republicans?

ALTERNATE EXAMPLE 6

Find a system of equations that is equivalent to the following matrix equation:

$$\begin{bmatrix} 1 & 1 & 1 \\ 2 & -3 & 0 \\ 2 & 6 & 2 \end{bmatrix} \begin{bmatrix} x \\ y \\ z \end{bmatrix} = \begin{bmatrix} 1 \\ 2 \\ 5 \end{bmatrix}$$

ANSWER

$x + y + z = 1$
$2x - 3y = 2$
$2x + 6y + 2z = 5$

ALTERNATE EXAMPLE 7

In a certain city the proportion of voters in each age group who are registered as Democrats, Republicans, or Independents is given by the following matrix.

Age

	18–30	31–50	Over 50
Democrat	0.35	0.55	0.50
Republican	0.50	0.20	0.25
Independent	0.15	0.25	0.25

$= A$

The next matrix gives the distribution, by age and sex, of the voting population of this city.

		Male	Female
	18–30	7,000	8,000
Age	31–50	15,000	18,000
	Over 50	18,000	19,000

$= B$

For this problem, let's make the assumption that within each age group, political preference is not related to gender. That is, the percentage of Democratic males in the 18–30 group, for example, is the same as the percentage of Democratic females in this group. Find how many females are registered as Independents in this city.

ANSWER

10,450

OLGA TAUSSKY-TODD (1906–1995) was instrumental in developing applications of matrix theory. Described as "in love with anything matrices can do," she successfully applied matrices to aerodynamics, a field used in the design of airplanes and rockets. Taussky-Todd was also famous for her work in number theory, which deals with prime numbers and divisibility. Although number theory has often been called the least applicable branch of mathematics, it is now used in significant ways throughout the computer industry.

Taussky-Todd studied mathematics at a time when young women rarely aspired to be mathematicians. She said, "When I entered university I had no idea what it meant to study mathematics." One of the most respected mathematicians of her day, she was for many years a professor of mathematics at Caltech in Pasadena.

SOLUTION

(a) $AB = \begin{bmatrix} 0.30 & 0.60 & 0.50 \\ 0.50 & 0.35 & 0.25 \\ 0.20 & 0.05 & 0.25 \end{bmatrix} \begin{bmatrix} 5{,}000 & 6{,}000 \\ 10{,}000 & 12{,}000 \\ 12{,}000 & 15{,}000 \end{bmatrix} = \begin{bmatrix} 13{,}500 & 16{,}500 \\ 9{,}000 & 10{,}950 \\ 4{,}500 & 5{,}550 \end{bmatrix}$

(b) When we take the inner product of a row in A with a column in B, we are adding the number of people in each age group who belong to the category in question. For example, the entry c_{21} of AB (the 9000) is obtained by taking the inner product of the Republican row in A with the Male column in B. This number is therefore the total number of male Republicans in this city. We can label the rows and columns of AB as follows.

	Male	Female
Democrat	13,500	16,500
Republican	9,000	10,950
Independent	4,500	5,550

$= AB$

Thus 13,500 males are registered as Democrats in this city.

(c) There are 10,950 females registered as Republicans.

✎ **NOW TRY EXERCISE 45** ■

In Example 7 the entries in each column of A add up to 1. (Can you see why this has to be true, given what the matrix describes?) A matrix with this property is called **stochastic**. Stochastic matrices are used extensively in statistics, where they arise frequently in situations like the one described here.

▼ Computer Graphics

One important use of matrices is in the digital representation of images. A digital camera or a scanner converts an image into a matrix by dividing the image into a rectangular array of elements called pixels. Each pixel is assigned a value that represents the color, brightness, or some other feature of that location. For example, in a 256-level gray-scale image each pixel is assigned a value between 0 and 255, where 0 represents white, 255 represents black, and the numbers in between represent increasing gradations of gray. The gradations of a much simpler 8-level gray scale are shown in Figure 2. We use this eight-level gray scale to illustrate the process.

To digitize the black and white image in Figure 3(a), we place a grid over the picture as shown in Figure 3(b). Each cell in the grid is compared to the gray scale and then assigned a value between 0 and 7 depending on which gray square in the scale most closely matches

0 1 2 3 4 5 6 7

FIGURE 2

(a) Original image

(b) 10 × 10 grid

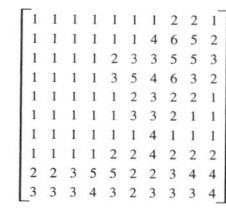

$\begin{bmatrix} 1 & 1 & 1 & 1 & 1 & 1 & 1 & 2 & 2 & 1 \\ 1 & 1 & 1 & 1 & 1 & 1 & 4 & 6 & 5 & 2 \\ 1 & 1 & 1 & 1 & 2 & 3 & 3 & 5 & 5 & 3 \\ 1 & 1 & 1 & 1 & 3 & 5 & 4 & 6 & 3 & 2 \\ 1 & 1 & 1 & 1 & 1 & 2 & 3 & 2 & 2 & 1 \\ 1 & 1 & 1 & 1 & 1 & 3 & 3 & 2 & 1 & 1 \\ 1 & 1 & 1 & 1 & 1 & 1 & 4 & 1 & 1 & 1 \\ 1 & 1 & 1 & 2 & 2 & 4 & 2 & 2 & 2 \\ 2 & 2 & 3 & 5 & 5 & 2 & 2 & 3 & 4 & 4 \\ 3 & 3 & 3 & 4 & 3 & 2 & 3 & 3 & 3 & 4 \end{bmatrix}$

(c) Matrix representation

(d) Digital image

FIGURE 3

the "darkness" of the cell. (If the cell is not uniformly gray, an average value is assigned.) The values are stored in the matrix shown in Figure 3(c). The digital image corresponding to this matrix is shown in Figure 3(d). Obviously, the grid that we have used is far too coarse to provide good image resolution. In practice, currently available high-resolution digital cameras use matrices with dimension as large as 2048 × 2048.

Once the image is stored as a matrix, it can be manipulated by using matrix operations. For example, to darken the image, we add a constant to each entry in the matrix; to lighten the image, we subtract a constant. To increase the contrast, we darken the darker areas and lighten the lighter areas, so we could add 1 to each entry that is 4, 5, or 6 and subtract 1 from each entry that is 1, 2, or 3. (Note that we cannot darken an entry of 7 or lighten a 0.) Applying this process to the matrix in Figure 3(c) produces the new matrix in Figure 4(a). This generates the high-contrast image shown in Figure 4(b).

$$\begin{bmatrix} 0 & 0 & 0 & 0 & 0 & 0 & 0 & 1 & 1 & 0 \\ 0 & 0 & 0 & 0 & 0 & 0 & 5 & 7 & 6 & 1 \\ 0 & 0 & 0 & 0 & 1 & 2 & 2 & 6 & 6 & 2 \\ 0 & 0 & 0 & 0 & 2 & 6 & 5 & 7 & 2 & 1 \\ 0 & 0 & 0 & 0 & 0 & 1 & 2 & 1 & 1 & 0 \\ 0 & 0 & 0 & 0 & 0 & 2 & 2 & 1 & 0 & 0 \\ 0 & 0 & 0 & 0 & 0 & 0 & 5 & 0 & 0 & 0 \\ 0 & 0 & 0 & 0 & 1 & 1 & 5 & 1 & 1 & 1 \\ 1 & 1 & 2 & 6 & 6 & 1 & 1 & 2 & 5 & 5 \\ 2 & 2 & 2 & 5 & 2 & 1 & 2 & 2 & 2 & 5 \end{bmatrix}$$

(a) Matrix modified to increase contrast

(b) High contrast image

FIGURE 4

Other ways of representing and manipulating images using matrices are discussed in the Discovery Projects *Computer Graphics I* and *II* at the book companion website: **www.stewartmath.com.**

10.4 EXERCISES

CONCEPTS

1. We can add (or subtract) two matrices only if they have the same _____.

2. (a) We can multiply two matrices only if the number of _____ in the first matrix is the same as the number of _____ in the second matrix.

(b) If A is a 3×3 matrix and B is a 4×3 matrix, which of the following matrix multiplications are possible?

(i) AB (ii) BA (iii) AA (iv) BB

3. Which of the following operations can we perform for a matrix A of any dimension?

(i) $A + A$ (ii) $2A$ (iii) $A \cdot A$

4. Fill in the missing entries in the product matrix.

$$\begin{bmatrix} 3 & 1 & 2 \\ -1 & 2 & 0 \\ 1 & 3 & -2 \end{bmatrix} \begin{bmatrix} -1 & 3 & -2 \\ 3 & -2 & -1 \\ 2 & 1 & 0 \end{bmatrix} = \begin{bmatrix} 4 & \blacksquare & -7 \\ 7 & -7 & \blacksquare \\ \blacksquare & -5 & -5 \end{bmatrix}$$

SKILLS

5–6 ■ Determine whether the matrices A and B are equal.

5. $A = \begin{bmatrix} 1 & -2 & 0 \\ \frac{1}{2} & 6 & 0 \end{bmatrix}$ $B = \begin{bmatrix} 1 & -2 \\ \frac{1}{2} & 6 \end{bmatrix}$

6. $A = \begin{bmatrix} \frac{1}{4} & \ln 1 \\ 2 & 3 \end{bmatrix}$ $B = \begin{bmatrix} 0.25 & 0 \\ \sqrt{4} & \frac{6}{2} \end{bmatrix}$

7–14 ■ Perform the matrix operation, or if it is impossible, explain why.

7. $\begin{bmatrix} 2 & 6 \\ -5 & 3 \end{bmatrix} + \begin{bmatrix} -1 & -3 \\ 6 & 2 \end{bmatrix}$ **8.** $\begin{bmatrix} 0 & 1 & 1 \\ 1 & 1 & 0 \end{bmatrix} - \begin{bmatrix} 2 & 1 & -1 \\ 1 & 3 & -2 \end{bmatrix}$

9. $3\begin{bmatrix} 1 & 2 \\ 4 & -1 \\ 1 & 0 \end{bmatrix}$ **10.** $2\begin{bmatrix} 1 & 1 & 0 \\ 1 & 0 & 1 \\ 0 & 1 & 1 \end{bmatrix} + \begin{bmatrix} 1 & 1 \\ 2 & 1 \\ 3 & 1 \end{bmatrix}$

11. $\begin{bmatrix} 2 & 6 \\ 1 & 3 \\ 2 & 4 \end{bmatrix} \begin{bmatrix} 1 & -2 \\ 3 & 6 \\ -2 & 0 \end{bmatrix}$ **12.** $\begin{bmatrix} 2 & 1 & 2 \\ 6 & 3 & 4 \end{bmatrix} \begin{bmatrix} 1 & -2 \\ 3 & 6 \\ -2 & 0 \end{bmatrix}$

13. $\begin{bmatrix} 1 & 2 \\ -1 & 4 \end{bmatrix}\begin{bmatrix} 1 & -2 & 3 \\ 2 & 2 & -1 \end{bmatrix}$ **14.** $\begin{bmatrix} 2 & -3 \\ 0 & 1 \\ 1 & 2 \end{bmatrix}\begin{bmatrix} 5 \\ 1 \end{bmatrix}$

15–20 ■ Solve the matrix equation for the unknown matrix X, or explain why no solution exists.

$$A = \begin{bmatrix} 4 & 6 \\ 1 & 3 \end{bmatrix} \qquad B = \begin{bmatrix} 2 & 5 \\ 3 & 7 \end{bmatrix}$$

$$C = \begin{bmatrix} 2 & 3 \\ 1 & 0 \\ 0 & 2 \end{bmatrix} \qquad D = \begin{bmatrix} 10 & 20 \\ 30 & 20 \\ 10 & 0 \end{bmatrix}$$

15. $2X + A = B$ **16.** $3X - B = C$

17. $2(B - X) = D$ **18.** $5(X - C) = D$

19. $\frac{1}{5}(X + D) = C$ **20.** $2A = B - 3X$

21–34 ■ The matrices A, B, C, D, E, F, G and H are defined as follows.

$$A = \begin{bmatrix} 2 & -5 \\ 0 & 7 \end{bmatrix} \qquad B = \begin{bmatrix} 3 & \frac{1}{2} & 5 \\ 1 & -1 & 3 \end{bmatrix} \qquad C = \begin{bmatrix} 2 & -\frac{5}{2} & 0 \\ 0 & 2 & -3 \end{bmatrix}$$

$$D = \begin{bmatrix} 7 & 3 \end{bmatrix} \qquad E = \begin{bmatrix} 1 \\ 2 \\ 0 \end{bmatrix} \qquad F = \begin{bmatrix} 1 & 0 & 0 \\ 0 & 1 & 0 \\ 0 & 0 & 1 \end{bmatrix}$$

$$G = \begin{bmatrix} 5 & -3 & 10 \\ 6 & 1 & 0 \\ -5 & 2 & 2 \end{bmatrix} \qquad H = \begin{bmatrix} 3 & 1 \\ 2 & -1 \end{bmatrix}$$

Carry out the indicated algebraic operation, or explain why it cannot be performed.

21. (a) $B + C$ (b) $B + F$

22. (a) $C - B$ (b) $2C - 6B$

23. (a) $5A$ (b) $C - 5A$

24. (a) $3B + 2C$ (b) $2H + D$

25. (a) AD (b) DA

26. (a) DH (b) HD

27. (a) AH (b) HA

28. (a) BC (b) BF

29. (a) GF (b) GE

30. (a) B^2 (b) F^2

31. (a) A^2 (b) A^3

32. (a) $(DA)B$ (b) $D(AB)$

33. (a) ABE (b) AHE

34. (a) $DB + DC$ (b) $BF + FE$

35–38 ■ Solve for x and y.

35. $\begin{bmatrix} x & 2y \\ 4 & 6 \end{bmatrix} = \begin{bmatrix} 2 & -2 \\ 2x & -6y \end{bmatrix}$ **36.** $3\begin{bmatrix} x & y \\ y & x \end{bmatrix} = \begin{bmatrix} 6 & -9 \\ -9 & 6 \end{bmatrix}$

37. $2\begin{bmatrix} x & y \\ x+y & x-y \end{bmatrix} = \begin{bmatrix} 2 & -4 \\ -2 & 6 \end{bmatrix}$

38. $\begin{bmatrix} x & y \\ -y & x \end{bmatrix} - \begin{bmatrix} y & x \\ x & -y \end{bmatrix} = \begin{bmatrix} 4 & -4 \\ -6 & 6 \end{bmatrix}$

39–42 ■ Write the system of equations as a matrix equation (see Example 6).

39. $\begin{cases} 2x - 5y = 7 \\ 3x + 2y = 4 \end{cases}$ **40.** $\begin{cases} 6x - y + z = 12 \\ 2x + z = 7 \\ y - 2z = 4 \end{cases}$

41. $\begin{cases} 3x_1 + 2x_2 - x_3 + x_4 = 0 \\ x_1 - x_3 = 5 \\ 3x_2 + x_3 - x_4 = 4 \end{cases}$

42. $\begin{cases} x - y + z = 2 \\ 4x - 2y - z = 2 \\ x + y + 5z = 2 \\ -x - y - z = 2 \end{cases}$

43. Let

$$A = \begin{bmatrix} 1 & 0 & 6 & -1 \\ 2 & \frac{1}{2} & 4 & 0 \end{bmatrix} \qquad C = \begin{bmatrix} 1 \\ 0 \\ -1 \\ -2 \end{bmatrix}$$

$$B = \begin{bmatrix} 1 & 7 & -9 & 2 \end{bmatrix}$$

Determine which of the following products are defined, and calculate the ones that are.

ABC	ACB	BAC
BCA	CAB	CBA

44. (a) Prove that if A and B are 2×2 matrices, then

$$(A + B)^2 = A^2 + AB + BA + B^2$$

(b) If A and B are 2×2 matrices, is it necessarily true that

$$(A + B)^2 \stackrel{?}{=} A^2 + 2AB + B^2$$

APPLICATIONS

45. Fast-Food Sales A small fast-food chain with restaurants in Santa Monica, Long Beach, and Anaheim sells only hamburgers, hot dogs, and milk shakes. On a certain day, sales were distributed according to the following matrix.

	Number of items sold		
	Santa Monica	Long Beach	Anaheim
Hamburgers	4000	1000	3500
Hot dogs	400	300	200
Milk shakes	700	500	9000

$= A$

The price of each item is given by the following matrix.

Hamburger	Hot dog	Milk shake
[$0.90	$0.80	$1.10] $= B$

(a) Calculate the product BA.

(b) Interpret the entries in the product matrix BA.

46. Car-Manufacturing Profits A specialty-car manufacturer has plants in Auburn, Biloxi, and Chattanooga. Three models are produced, with daily production given in the following matrix.

Cars produced each day

	Model K	Model R	Model W
Auburn	12	10	0
Biloxi	4	4	20
Chattanooga	8	9	12

$= A$

Because of a wage increase, February profits are lower than January profits. The profit per car is tabulated by model in the following matrix.

	January	February
Model K	$1000	$500
Model R	$2000	$1200
Model W	$1500	$1000

$= B$

(a) Calculate AB.

(b) Assuming that all cars produced were sold, what was the daily profit in January from the Biloxi plant?

(c) What was the total daily profit (from all three plants) in February?

47. Canning Tomato Products Jaeger Foods produces tomato sauce and tomato paste, canned in small, medium, large, and giant sized cans. The matrix A gives the size (in ounces) of each container.

	Small	Medium	Large	Giant
Ounces	6	10	14	28

$= A$

The matrix B tabulates one day's production of tomato sauce and tomato paste.

	Cans of sauce	Cans of paste
Small	2000	2500
Medium	3000	1500
Large	2500	1000
Giant	1000	500

$= B$

(a) Calculate the product of AB.

(b) Interpret the entries in the product matrix AB.

48. Produce Sales A farmer's three children, Amy, Beth, and Chad, run three roadside produce stands during the summer months. One weekend they all sell watermelons, yellow squash, and tomatoes. The matrices A and B tabulate the number of pounds of each product sold by each sibling on Saturday and Sunday.

Saturday

	Melons	Squash	Tomatoes
Amy	120	50	60
Beth	40	25	30
Chad	60	30	20

$= A$

Sunday

	Melons	Squash	Tomatoes
Amy	100	60	30
Beth	35	20	20
Chad	60	25	30

$= B$

The matrix C gives the price per pound (in dollars) for each type of produce that they sell.

Price per pound

Melons	0.10
Squash	0.50
Tomatoes	1.00

$= C$

Perform each of the following matrix operations, and interpret the entries in each result.

(a) AC **(b)** BC **(c)** $A + B$ **(d)** $(A + B)C$

49. Digital Images A four-level gray scale is shown below.

(a) Use the gray scale to find a 6×6 matrix that digitally represents the image in the figure.

(b) Find a matrix that represents a darker version of the image in the figure.

(c) The **negative** of an image is obtained by reversing light and dark, as in the negative of a photograph. Find the matrix that represents the negative of the image in the figure. How do you change the elements of the matrix to create the negative?

(d) Increase the contrast of the image by changing each 1 to a 0 and each 2 to a 3 in the matrix you found in part (b). Draw the image represented by the resulting matrix. Does this clarify the image?

(e) Draw the image represented by the matrix I. Can you recognize what this is? If you don't, try increasing the contrast.

$$I = \begin{bmatrix} 1 & 2 & 3 & 3 & 2 & 0 \\ 0 & 3 & 0 & 1 & 0 & 1 \\ 1 & 3 & 2 & 3 & 0 & 0 \\ 0 & 3 & 0 & 1 & 0 & 1 \\ 1 & 3 & 3 & 2 & 3 & 0 \\ 0 & 1 & 0 & 1 & 0 & 1 \end{bmatrix}$$

DISCOVERY ▪ DISCUSSION ▪ WRITING

50. When Are Both Products Defined? What must be true about the dimensions of the matrices A and B if both products AB and BA are defined?

51. Powers of a Matrix Let

$$A = \begin{bmatrix} 1 & 1 \\ 0 & 1 \end{bmatrix}$$

Calculate $A^2, A^3, A^4, \ldots$ until you detect a pattern. Write a general formula for A^n.

52. Powers of a Matrix Let $A = \begin{bmatrix} 1 & 1 \\ 1 & 1 \end{bmatrix}$. Calculate A^2, $A^3, A^4, \ldots$ until you detect a pattern. Write a general formula for A^n.

53. Square Roots of Matrices A **square root** of a matrix B is a matrix A with the property that $A^2 = B$. (This is the same definition as for a square root of a number.) Find as many square roots as you can of each matrix:

$$\begin{bmatrix} 4 & 0 \\ 0 & 9 \end{bmatrix} \qquad \begin{bmatrix} 1 & 5 \\ 0 & 9 \end{bmatrix}$$

[*Hint:* If $A = \begin{bmatrix} a & b \\ c & d \end{bmatrix}$, write the equations that a, b, c, and d would have to satisfy if A is the square root of the given matrix.]

⊙ DISCOVERY PROJECT **Will the Species Survive?**

In this project we investigate matrix models for species populations and how multiplication by a transition matrix can predict future population trends. You can find the project at the book companion website: **www.stewartmath.com**

10.5 INVERSES OF MATRICES AND MATRIX EQUATIONS

The Inverse of a Matrix ▶ Finding the Inverse of a 2 × 2 Matrix ▶ Finding the Inverse of an $n \times n$ Matrix ▶ Matrix Equations ▶ Modeling with Matrix Equations

In the preceding section we saw that when the dimensions are appropriate, matrices can be added, subtracted, and multiplied. In this section we investigate division of matrices. With this operation we can solve equations that involve matrices.

▼ The Inverse of a Matrix

First, we define *identity matrices*, which play the same role for matrix multiplication as the number 1 does for ordinary multiplication of numbers; that is, $1 \cdot a = a \cdot 1 = a$ for all numbers a. A **square matrix** is one that has the same number of rows as columns. The **main diagonal** of a square matrix consists of the entries whose row and column numbers are the same. These entries stretch diagonally down the matrix, from top left to bottom right.

IDENTITY MATRIX

The **identity matrix** I_n is the $n \times n$ matrix for which each main diagonal entry is a 1 and for which all other entries are 0.

Thus the 2 × 2, 3 × 3, and 4 × 4 identity matrices are

$$I_2 = \begin{bmatrix} 1 & 0 \\ 0 & 1 \end{bmatrix} \qquad I_3 = \begin{bmatrix} 1 & 0 & 0 \\ 0 & 1 & 0 \\ 0 & 0 & 1 \end{bmatrix} \qquad I_4 = \begin{bmatrix} 1 & 0 & 0 & 0 \\ 0 & 1 & 0 & 0 \\ 0 & 0 & 1 & 0 \\ 0 & 0 & 0 & 1 \end{bmatrix}$$

TEXT QUESTION

If $AB = I$, where I is the identity matrix, is it necessarily true that $BA = I$?

Answer

Yes

Identity matrices behave like the number 1 in the sense that

$$A \cdot I_n = A \qquad \text{and} \qquad I_n \cdot B = B$$

whenever these products are defined.

EXAMPLE 1 | Identity Matrices

The following matrix products show how multiplying a matrix by an identity matrix of the appropriate dimension leaves the matrix unchanged.

$$\begin{bmatrix} 1 & 0 \\ 0 & 1 \end{bmatrix} \begin{bmatrix} 3 & 5 & 6 \\ -1 & 2 & 7 \end{bmatrix} = \begin{bmatrix} 3 & 5 & 6 \\ -1 & 2 & 7 \end{bmatrix}$$

$$\begin{bmatrix} -1 & 7 & \frac{1}{2} \\ 12 & 1 & 3 \\ -2 & 0 & 7 \end{bmatrix} \begin{bmatrix} 1 & 0 & 0 \\ 0 & 1 & 0 \\ 0 & 0 & 1 \end{bmatrix} = \begin{bmatrix} -1 & 7 & \frac{1}{2} \\ 12 & 1 & 3 \\ -2 & 0 & 7 \end{bmatrix}$$

✎. NOW TRY EXERCISE **1(a), (b)** ∎

If A and B are $n \times n$ matrices, and if $AB = BA = I_n$, then we say that B is the *inverse* of A, and we write $B = A^{-1}$. The concept of the inverse of a matrix is analogous to that of the reciprocal of a real number.

> **INVERSE OF A MATRIX**
>
> Let A be a square $n \times n$ matrix. If there exists an $n \times n$ matrix A^{-1} with the property that
>
> $$AA^{-1} = A^{-1}A = I_n$$
>
> then we say that A^{-1} is the **inverse** of A.

EXAMPLE 2 | Verifying That a Matrix Is an Inverse

Verify that B is the inverse of A, where

$$A = \begin{bmatrix} 2 & 1 \\ 5 & 3 \end{bmatrix} \qquad \text{and} \qquad B = \begin{bmatrix} 3 & -1 \\ -5 & 2 \end{bmatrix}$$

SOLUTION We perform the matrix multiplications to show that $AB = I$ and $BA = I$.

$$\begin{bmatrix} 2 & 1 \\ 5 & 3 \end{bmatrix} \begin{bmatrix} 3 & -1 \\ -5 & 2 \end{bmatrix} = \begin{bmatrix} 2 \cdot 3 + 1(-5) & 2(-1) + 1 \cdot 2 \\ 5 \cdot 3 + 3(-5) & 5(-1) + 3 \cdot 2 \end{bmatrix} = \begin{bmatrix} 1 & 0 \\ 0 & 1 \end{bmatrix}$$

$$\begin{bmatrix} 3 & -1 \\ -5 & 2 \end{bmatrix} \begin{bmatrix} 2 & 1 \\ 5 & 3 \end{bmatrix} = \begin{bmatrix} 3 \cdot 2 + (-1)5 & 3 \cdot 1 + (-1)3 \\ (-5)2 + 2 \cdot 5 & (-5)1 + 2 \cdot 3 \end{bmatrix} = \begin{bmatrix} 1 & 0 \\ 0 & 1 \end{bmatrix}$$

✎. NOW TRY EXERCISE **3** ∎

▼ Finding the Inverse of a 2 × 2 Matrix

The following rule provides a simple way for finding the inverse of a 2×2 matrix, when it exists. For larger matrices there is a more general procedure for finding inverses, which we consider later in this section.

ALTERNATE EXAMPLE 1

$$\begin{bmatrix} 1 & 2 \\ 3 & -1 \\ 5 & 8 \end{bmatrix} \begin{bmatrix} 1 & 0 \\ 0 & 1 \end{bmatrix}$$

$$= \begin{bmatrix} 1 & 2 \\ 3 & -1 \\ 5 & 8 \end{bmatrix}$$

ALTERNATE EXAMPLE 2

Verify that B is the inverse of A.

$$A = \begin{bmatrix} 3 & 2 \\ 4 & 3 \end{bmatrix} \text{ and}$$

$$B = \begin{bmatrix} 3 & -2 \\ -4 & 3 \end{bmatrix}$$

ANSWER

$$AB = BA = \begin{bmatrix} 1 & 0 \\ 0 & 1 \end{bmatrix}$$

IN-CLASS MATERIALS

Perhaps take this opportunity to talk about the inverse of a complex number: How do we find $\dfrac{1}{3 + 4i}$?

The technique, multiplying by $\dfrac{3 - 4i}{3 - 4i}$, is not as important as the concept that given a real, complex, or matrix quantity it is often possible to find an inverse that will reduce it to unity. One can also add "inverse functions" to this discussion—in this case $f(x) = x$ is the identity function, referred to as such because it leaves inputs unchanged (analogous to multiplying by 1). Try to get the students to see the conceptual similarities in solving the three following equations:

$$3x = 2$$
$$(3 + i)x = 2 - 4i$$
$$\begin{bmatrix} 2 & 1 \\ 3 & -4 \end{bmatrix} \begin{bmatrix} x \\ y \end{bmatrix} = \begin{bmatrix} 3 \\ 1 \end{bmatrix}$$

ARTHUR CAYLEY (1821–1895) was an English mathematician who was instrumental in developing the theory of matrices. He was the first to use a single symbol such as A to represent a matrix, thereby introducing the idea that a matrix is a single entity rather than just a collection of numbers. Cayley practiced law until the age of 42, but his primary interest from adolescence was mathematics, and he published almost 200 articles on the subject in his spare time. In 1863 he accepted a professorship in mathematics at Cambridge, where he taught until his death. Cayley's work on matrices was of purely theoretical interest in his day, but in the 20th century many of his results found application in physics, the social sciences, business, and other fields. One of the most common uses of matrices today is in computers, where matrices are employed for data storage, error correction, image manipulation, and many other purposes. These applications have made matrix algebra more useful than ever.

ALTERNATE EXAMPLE 3

Find the inverse of $\begin{bmatrix} 6 & 4 \\ 4 & 3 \end{bmatrix}$.

ANSWER

$$\frac{1}{2}\begin{bmatrix} 3 & -4 \\ -4 & 6 \end{bmatrix} = \begin{bmatrix} \frac{3}{2} & -2 \\ -2 & 3 \end{bmatrix}$$

INVERSE OF A 2 × 2 MATRIX

If $A = \begin{bmatrix} a & b \\ c & d \end{bmatrix}$, then

$$A^{-1} = \frac{1}{ad - bc}\begin{bmatrix} d & -b \\ -c & a \end{bmatrix}$$

If $ad - bc = 0$, then A has no inverse.

EXAMPLE 3 | Finding the Inverse of a 2 × 2 Matrix

Let

$$A = \begin{bmatrix} 4 & 5 \\ 2 & 3 \end{bmatrix}$$

Find A^{-1}, and verify that $AA^{-1} = A^{-1}A = I_2$.

SOLUTION Using the rule for the inverse of a 2 × 2 matrix, we get

$$A^{-1} = \frac{1}{4 \cdot 3 - 5 \cdot 2}\begin{bmatrix} 3 & -5 \\ -2 & 4 \end{bmatrix} = \frac{1}{2}\begin{bmatrix} 3 & -5 \\ -2 & 4 \end{bmatrix} = \begin{bmatrix} \frac{3}{2} & -\frac{5}{2} \\ -1 & 2 \end{bmatrix}$$

To verify that this is indeed the inverse of A, we calculate AA^{-1} and $A^{-1}A$:

$$AA^{-1} = \begin{bmatrix} 4 & 5 \\ 2 & 3 \end{bmatrix}\begin{bmatrix} \frac{3}{2} & -\frac{5}{2} \\ -1 & 2 \end{bmatrix} = \begin{bmatrix} 4 \cdot \frac{3}{2} + 5(-1) & 4(-\frac{5}{2}) + 5 \cdot 2 \\ 2 \cdot \frac{3}{2} + 3(-1) & 2(-\frac{5}{2}) + 3 \cdot 2 \end{bmatrix} = \begin{bmatrix} 1 & 0 \\ 0 & 1 \end{bmatrix}$$

$$A^{-1}A = \begin{bmatrix} \frac{3}{2} & -\frac{5}{2} \\ -1 & 2 \end{bmatrix}\begin{bmatrix} 4 & 5 \\ 2 & 3 \end{bmatrix} = \begin{bmatrix} \frac{3}{2} \cdot 4 + (-\frac{5}{2})2 & \frac{3}{2} \cdot 5 + (-\frac{5}{2})3 \\ (-1)4 + 2 \cdot 2 & (-1)5 + 2 \cdot 3 \end{bmatrix} = \begin{bmatrix} 1 & 0 \\ 0 & 1 \end{bmatrix}$$

✎. NOW TRY EXERCISE **9** ∎

The quantity $ad - bc$ that appears in the rule for calculating the inverse of a 2 × 2 matrix is called the **determinant** of the matrix. If the determinant is 0, then the matrix does not have an inverse (since we cannot divide by 0).

▼ Finding the Inverse of an $n \times n$ Matrix

For 3 × 3 and larger square matrices the following technique provides the most efficient way to calculate their inverses. If A is an $n \times n$ matrix, we first construct the $n \times 2n$ matrix that has the entries of A on the left and of the identity matrix I_n on the right:

$$\begin{bmatrix} a_{11} & a_{12} & \cdots & a_{1n} & 1 & 0 & \cdots & 0 \\ a_{21} & a_{22} & \cdots & a_{2n} & 0 & 1 & \cdots & 0 \\ \vdots & \vdots & \ddots & \vdots & \vdots & \vdots & \ddots & \vdots \\ a_{n1} & a_{n2} & \cdots & a_{nn} & 0 & 0 & \cdots & 1 \end{bmatrix}$$

We then use the elementary row operations on this new large matrix to change the left side into the identity matrix. (This means that we are changing the large matrix to reduced row-echelon form.) The right side is transformed automatically into A^{-1}. (We omit the proof of this fact.)

IN-CLASS MATERIALS

It is straightforward to demonstrate that $(A - 1)^{-1} = A$ for specific 2 × 2 or 3 × 3 matrices. Students can pick up why it should be true, given the definition of inverse. A general algebraic proof is a little messy:

$$(A^{-1})^{-1} = \begin{bmatrix} \dfrac{d}{ad - bc} & -\dfrac{b}{ad - bc} \\ -\dfrac{c}{ad - bc} & \dfrac{a}{ad - bc} \end{bmatrix}^{-1}$$

$$= \frac{1}{\left(\dfrac{a}{ad - bc}\right)\left(\dfrac{d}{ad - bc}\right) - \left(\dfrac{b}{ad - bc}\right)\left(\dfrac{c}{ad - bc}\right)}\begin{bmatrix} \dfrac{a}{ad - bc} & -\dfrac{b}{ad - bc} \\ -\dfrac{c}{ad - bc} & \dfrac{d}{ad - bc} \end{bmatrix} = \frac{1}{1/(ad - bc)} \cdot \frac{1}{ad - bc} \cdot \begin{bmatrix} a & b \\ c & d \end{bmatrix} = \begin{bmatrix} a & b \\ c & d \end{bmatrix} = A$$

Note that there is a formula for 3 × 3 inverses, just as there is a formula for 2 × 2 inverses. Unfortunately, it is so complicated that it is easier to do 3 × 3 inverses manually than to use a formula.

$$\begin{bmatrix} a & b & c \\ d & e & f \\ g & h & i \end{bmatrix}^{-1} = \frac{1}{afh - aei + bdi - bfg + ceg - cdh}\begin{bmatrix} fh - ei & bi - ch & ce - bf \\ di - fg & cg - ai & af - cd \\ eg - dh & ah - bg & bd - ae \end{bmatrix}$$

EXAMPLE 4 | Finding the Inverse of a 3 × 3 Matrix

Let A be the matrix

$$A = \begin{bmatrix} 1 & -2 & -4 \\ 2 & -3 & -6 \\ -3 & 6 & 15 \end{bmatrix}$$

(a) Find A^{-1}.

(b) Verify that $AA^{-1} = A^{-1}A = I_3$.

SOLUTION

(a) We begin with the 3 × 6 matrix whose left half is A and whose right half is the identity matrix.

$$\begin{bmatrix} 1 & -2 & -4 & | & 1 & 0 & 0 \\ 2 & -3 & -6 & | & 0 & 1 & 0 \\ -3 & 6 & 15 & | & 0 & 0 & 1 \end{bmatrix}$$

We then transform the left half of this new matrix into the identity matrix by performing the following sequence of elementary row operations on the *entire* new matrix.

$$\xrightarrow[R_3 + 3R_1 \rightarrow R_3]{R_2 - 2R_1 \rightarrow R_2} \begin{bmatrix} 1 & -2 & -4 & | & 1 & 0 & 0 \\ 0 & 1 & 2 & | & -2 & 1 & 0 \\ 0 & 0 & 3 & | & 3 & 0 & 1 \end{bmatrix}$$

$$\xrightarrow{\frac{1}{3}R_3} \begin{bmatrix} 1 & -2 & -4 & | & 1 & 0 & 0 \\ 0 & 1 & 2 & | & -2 & 1 & 0 \\ 0 & 0 & 1 & | & 1 & 0 & \frac{1}{3} \end{bmatrix}$$

$$\xrightarrow{R_1 + 2R_2 \rightarrow R_1} \begin{bmatrix} 1 & 0 & 0 & | & -3 & 2 & 0 \\ 0 & 1 & 2 & | & -2 & 1 & 0 \\ 0 & 0 & 1 & | & 1 & 0 & \frac{1}{3} \end{bmatrix}$$

$$\xrightarrow{R_2 - 2R_3 \rightarrow R_2} \begin{bmatrix} 1 & 0 & 0 & | & -3 & 2 & 0 \\ 0 & 1 & 0 & | & -4 & 1 & -\frac{2}{3} \\ 0 & 0 & 1 & | & 1 & 0 & \frac{1}{3} \end{bmatrix}$$

We have now transformed the left half of this matrix into an identity matrix. (This means that we have put the entire matrix in reduced row-echelon form.) Note that to do this in as systematic a fashion as possible, we first changed the elements below the main diagonal to zeros, just as we would if we were using Gaussian elimination. We then changed each main diagonal element to a 1 by multiplying by the appropriate constant(s). Finally, we completed the process by changing the remaining entries on the left side to zeros.

The right half is now A^{-1}.

$$A^{-1} = \begin{bmatrix} -3 & 2 & 0 \\ -4 & 1 & -\frac{2}{3} \\ 1 & 0 & \frac{1}{3} \end{bmatrix}$$

ALTERNATE EXAMPLE 4

Find the inverse of the following matrix:

$$\begin{bmatrix} 3 & -8 & 1 \\ 1 & -1 & 0 \\ 2 & 1 & 1 \end{bmatrix}$$

ANSWER

$$\begin{bmatrix} -\frac{1}{8} & \frac{9}{8} & \frac{1}{8} \\ -\frac{1}{8} & \frac{1}{8} & \frac{1}{8} \\ \frac{3}{8} & -\frac{19}{8} & \frac{5}{8} \end{bmatrix}$$

IN-CLASS MATERIALS

Example 7 is particularly important, because Section 10.3 presented a straightforward method of solving an $n \times n$ system. The advantage of finding the inverse matrix really kicks in when solving a series of systems with the same coefficient matrix.

(b) We calculate AA^{-1} and $A^{-1}A$ and verify that both products give the identity matrix I_3.

$$AA^{-1} = \begin{bmatrix} 1 & -2 & -4 \\ 2 & -3 & -6 \\ -3 & 6 & 15 \end{bmatrix} \begin{bmatrix} -3 & 2 & 0 \\ -4 & 1 & -\frac{2}{3} \\ 1 & 0 & \frac{1}{3} \end{bmatrix} = \begin{bmatrix} 1 & 0 & 0 \\ 0 & 1 & 0 \\ 0 & 0 & 1 \end{bmatrix}$$

$$A^{-1}A = \begin{bmatrix} -3 & 2 & 0 \\ -4 & 1 & -\frac{2}{3} \\ 1 & 0 & \frac{1}{3} \end{bmatrix} \begin{bmatrix} 1 & -2 & -4 \\ 2 & -3 & -6 \\ -3 & 6 & 15 \end{bmatrix} = \begin{bmatrix} 1 & 0 & 0 \\ 0 & 1 & 0 \\ 0 & 0 & 1 \end{bmatrix}$$

✎. **NOW TRY EXERCISE 17** ▪

```
[A]⁻¹▶Frac
    [[-3 2  0   ]
     [-4 1 -2/3]
     [1  0 1/3 ]]
```

FIGURE 1

Graphing calculators are also able to calculate matrix inverses. On the TI-83 and TI-84 calculators, matrices are stored in memory using names such as [A], [B], [C], ... To find the inverse of [A], we key in

[A] $\boxed{x^{-1}}$ $\boxed{\text{ENTER}}$

For the matrix of Example 4 this results in the output shown in Figure 1 (where we have also used the ▶Frac command to display the output in fraction form rather than in decimal form).

The next example shows that not every square matrix has an inverse.

EXAMPLE 5 | A Matrix That Does Not Have an Inverse

Find the inverse of the matrix.

$$\begin{bmatrix} 2 & -3 & -7 \\ 1 & 2 & 7 \\ 1 & 1 & 4 \end{bmatrix}$$

SOLUTION   We proceed as follows.

$$\begin{bmatrix} 2 & -3 & -7 & | & 1 & 0 & 0 \\ 1 & 2 & 7 & | & 0 & 1 & 0 \\ 1 & 1 & 4 & | & 0 & 0 & 1 \end{bmatrix} \xrightarrow{R_1 \leftrightarrow R_2} \begin{bmatrix} 1 & 2 & 7 & | & 0 & 1 & 0 \\ 2 & -3 & -7 & | & 1 & 0 & 0 \\ 1 & 1 & 4 & | & 0 & 0 & 1 \end{bmatrix}$$

$$\xrightarrow[R_3 - R_1 \to R_3]{R_2 - 2R_1 \to R_2} \begin{bmatrix} 1 & 2 & 7 & | & 0 & 1 & 0 \\ 0 & -7 & -21 & | & 1 & -2 & 0 \\ 0 & -1 & -3 & | & 0 & -1 & 1 \end{bmatrix}$$

$$\xrightarrow{-\frac{1}{7}R_2} \begin{bmatrix} 1 & 2 & 7 & | & 0 & 1 & 0 \\ 0 & 1 & 3 & | & -\frac{1}{7} & \frac{2}{7} & 0 \\ 0 & -1 & -3 & | & 0 & -1 & 1 \end{bmatrix}$$

$$\xrightarrow[R_1 - 2R_2 \to R_1]{R_3 + R_2 \to R_3} \begin{bmatrix} 1 & 0 & 1 & | & \frac{2}{7} & \frac{3}{7} & 0 \\ 0 & 1 & 3 & | & -\frac{1}{7} & \frac{2}{7} & 0 \\ 0 & 0 & 0 & | & -\frac{1}{7} & -\frac{5}{7} & 1 \end{bmatrix}$$

At this point we would like to change the 0 in the $(3, 3)$ position of this matrix to a 1 without changing the zeros in the $(3, 1)$ and $(3, 2)$ positions. But there is no way to accomplish this, because no matter what multiple of rows 1 and/or 2 we add to row 3, we can't change the third zero in row 3 without changing the first or second zero as well. Thus we cannot change the left half to the identity matrix, so the original matrix doesn't have an inverse.

✎. **NOW TRY EXERCISE 19** ▪

ALTERNATE EXAMPLE 5

Show that the following matrix does not have an inverse.

$$\begin{bmatrix} 3 & -8 & 1 \\ 1 & -1 & 0 \\ 5 & -15 & 2 \end{bmatrix}$$

ANSWER

When we try to find the inverse, we wind up with a row of zeros.

IN-CLASS MATERIALS

After doing a standard example or two, throw a singular matrix on the board before defining singularity. "Unexpectedly" run into trouble and thus discover, with your class, that not every matrix has an inverse.

```
ERR:SINGULAR MAT
1▪Quit
2:Goto
```

FIGURE 2

If we encounter a row of zeros on the left when trying to find an inverse, as in Example 5, then the original matrix does not have an inverse. If we try to calculate the inverse of the matrix from Example 5 on a TI-83 calculator, we get the error message shown in Figure 2. (A matrix that has no inverse is called *singular*.)

▼ Matrix Equations

We saw in Example 6 in Section 10.4 that a system of linear equations can be written as a single matrix equation. For example, the system

$$\begin{cases} x - 2y - 4z = 7 \\ 2x - 3y - 6z = 5 \\ -3x + 6y + 15z = 0 \end{cases}$$

is equivalent to the matrix equation

$$\underbrace{\begin{bmatrix} 1 & -2 & -4 \\ 2 & -3 & -6 \\ -3 & 6 & 15 \end{bmatrix}}_{A} \underbrace{\begin{bmatrix} x \\ y \\ z \end{bmatrix}}_{X} = \underbrace{\begin{bmatrix} 7 \\ 5 \\ 0 \end{bmatrix}}_{B}$$

If we let

$$A = \begin{bmatrix} 1 & -2 & -4 \\ 2 & -3 & -6 \\ -3 & 6 & 15 \end{bmatrix} \qquad X = \begin{bmatrix} x \\ y \\ z \end{bmatrix} \qquad B = \begin{bmatrix} 7 \\ 5 \\ 0 \end{bmatrix}$$

then this matrix equation can be written as

$$AX = B$$

The matrix A is called the **coefficient matrix**.

We solve this matrix equation by multiplying each side by the inverse of A (provided that this inverse exists):

Solving the matrix equation $AX = B$ is very similar to solving the simple real-number equation

$$3x = 12$$

which we do by multiplying each side by the reciprocal (or inverse) of 3.

$$\tfrac{1}{3}(3x) = \tfrac{1}{3}(12)$$

$$x = 4$$

$$AX = B$$
$$A^{-1}(AX) = A^{-1}B \qquad \text{Multiply on left by } A^{-1}$$
$$(A^{-1}A)X = A^{-1}B \qquad \text{Associative Property}$$
$$I_3 X = A^{-1}B \qquad \text{Property of inverses}$$
$$X = A^{-1}B \qquad \text{Property of identity matrix}$$

In Example 4 we showed that

$$A^{-1} = \begin{bmatrix} -3 & 2 & 0 \\ -4 & 1 & -\tfrac{2}{3} \\ 1 & 0 & \tfrac{1}{3} \end{bmatrix}$$

So from $X = A^{-1}B$ we have

$$\underbrace{\begin{bmatrix} x \\ y \\ z \end{bmatrix}}_{X} = \underbrace{\begin{bmatrix} -3 & 2 & 0 \\ -4 & 1 & -\tfrac{2}{3} \\ 1 & 0 & \tfrac{1}{3} \end{bmatrix}}_{A^{-1}} \underbrace{\begin{bmatrix} 7 \\ 5 \\ 0 \end{bmatrix}}_{B} = \begin{bmatrix} -11 \\ -23 \\ 7 \end{bmatrix}$$

Thus $x = -11$, $y = -23$, $z = 7$ is the solution of the original system.

EXAMPLES
- **Nonsingular real matrices**

$$\begin{bmatrix} -2 & 1 \\ 3 & 3 \end{bmatrix}^{-1} = \begin{bmatrix} -\tfrac{1}{3} & \tfrac{1}{9} \\ \tfrac{1}{3} & \tfrac{2}{9} \end{bmatrix}$$

$$\begin{bmatrix} -1 & 1 & 1 \\ 4 & -1 & 1 \\ 4 & 2 & 1 \end{bmatrix}^{-1}$$
$$= \begin{bmatrix} -\tfrac{1}{5} & \tfrac{1}{15} & \tfrac{2}{15} \\ 0 & -\tfrac{1}{3} & \tfrac{1}{3} \\ \tfrac{4}{5} & \tfrac{2}{5} & -\tfrac{1}{5} \end{bmatrix}$$

$$\begin{bmatrix} 0 & 2 & 0 & 0 \\ 2 & 0 & 0 & 0 \\ 0 & 0 & 5 & 0 \\ 0 & 1 & 0 & 6 \end{bmatrix}^{-1}$$
$$= \begin{bmatrix} 0 & \tfrac{1}{2} & 0 & 0 \\ \tfrac{1}{2} & 0 & 0 & 0 \\ 0 & 0 & \tfrac{1}{5} & 0 \\ -\tfrac{1}{12} & 0 & 0 & \tfrac{1}{6} \end{bmatrix}$$

- **Singular real matrices**

$$\begin{bmatrix} 5 & 4 \\ 15 & 24 \end{bmatrix}$$

$$\begin{bmatrix} 1 & 2 & 3 \\ -1 & 3 & -2 \\ -1 & 8 & -1 \end{bmatrix}$$

$$\begin{bmatrix} 8 & 3 & 5 & -8 \\ -7 & 6 & 0 & -6 \\ -5 & -3 & 7 & 9 \\ -4 & 6 & 12 & -5 \end{bmatrix}$$

- A complex matrix and its inverse

$$\begin{bmatrix} 1 & 2i \\ 1-i & 1 \end{bmatrix}^{-1} = \frac{1}{-1-2i}\begin{bmatrix} 1 & -2i \\ -1+i & 1 \end{bmatrix} = \begin{bmatrix} -\tfrac{1}{5}+\tfrac{2}{5}i & \tfrac{4}{5}+\tfrac{2}{5}i \\ -\tfrac{1}{5}-\tfrac{3}{5}i & -\tfrac{1}{5}+\tfrac{2}{5}i \end{bmatrix}$$

We have proved that the matrix equation $AX = B$ can be solved by the following method.

SOLVING A MATRIX EQUATION

If A is a square $n \times n$ matrix that has an inverse A^{-1} and if X is a variable matrix and B a known matrix, both with n rows, then the solution of the matrix equation

$$AX = B$$

is given by

$$X = A^{-1}B$$

EXAMPLE 6 | Solving a System Using a Matrix Inverse

A system of equations is given.

(a) Write the system of equations as a matrix equation.

(b) Solve the system by solving the matrix equation.

$$\begin{cases} 2x - 5y = 15 \\ 3x - 6y = 36 \end{cases}$$

SOLUTION

(a) We write the system as a matrix equation of the form $AX = B$.

$$\underbrace{\begin{bmatrix} 2 & -5 \\ 3 & -6 \end{bmatrix}}_{A} \underbrace{\begin{bmatrix} x \\ y \end{bmatrix}}_{X} = \underbrace{\begin{bmatrix} 15 \\ 36 \end{bmatrix}}_{B}$$

(b) Using the rule for finding the inverse of a 2×2 matrix, we get

$$A^{-1} = \begin{bmatrix} 2 & -5 \\ 3 & -6 \end{bmatrix}^{-1} = \frac{1}{2(-6) - (-5)3} \begin{bmatrix} -6 & -(-5) \\ -3 & 2 \end{bmatrix} = \frac{1}{3}\begin{bmatrix} -6 & 5 \\ -3 & 2 \end{bmatrix}$$

Multiplying each side of the matrix equation by this inverse matrix, we get

$$\underbrace{\begin{bmatrix} x \\ y \end{bmatrix}}_{X} = \underbrace{\frac{1}{3}\begin{bmatrix} -6 & 5 \\ -3 & 2 \end{bmatrix}}_{A^{-1}} \underbrace{\begin{bmatrix} 15 \\ 36 \end{bmatrix}}_{B} = \begin{bmatrix} 30 \\ 9 \end{bmatrix}$$

So $x = 30$ and $y = 9$.

✎ NOW TRY EXERCISE **25** ■

▼ Modeling with Matrix Equations

Suppose we need to solve several systems of equations with the same coefficient matrix. Then converting the systems to matrix equations provides an efficient way to obtain the solutions, because we need to find the inverse of the coefficient matrix only once. This

---

ALTERNATE EXAMPLE 6

Consider the following system of equations:

$$\begin{cases} 4x + y = 14 \\ 12x - y = 2 \end{cases}$$

(a) Write the system as a matrix equation.

(b) Solve the system by solving the matrix equation.

ANSWERS

(a) $\begin{bmatrix} 4 & 1 \\ 12 & -1 \end{bmatrix}\begin{bmatrix} x \\ y \end{bmatrix} = \begin{bmatrix} 14 \\ 2 \end{bmatrix}$

(b) $x = 1, y = 10$

$\left(\text{Alternatively, } \begin{bmatrix} x \\ y \end{bmatrix} = \begin{bmatrix} 1 \\ 10 \end{bmatrix} \right)$

procedure is particularly convenient if we use a graphing calculator to perform the matrix
operations, as in the next example.

EXAMPLE 7 | Modeling Nutritional Requirements
Using Matrix Equations

A pet-store owner feeds his hamsters and gerbils different mixtures of three types
of rodent food: KayDee Food, Pet Pellets, and Rodent Chow. He wishes to feed his
animals the correct amount of each brand to satisfy their daily requirements for protein, fat, and carbohydrates exactly. Suppose that hamsters require 340 mg of protein,
280 mg of fat, and 440 mg of carbohydrates, and gerbils need 480 mg of protein,
360 mg of fat, and 680 mg of carbohydrates each day. The amount of each nutrient
(in mg) in one gram of each brand is given in the following table. How many grams
of each food should the storekeeper feed his hamsters and gerbils daily to satisfy their
nutrient requirements?

	KayDee Food	Pet Pellets	Rodent Chow
Protein (mg)	10	0	20
Fat (mg)	10	20	10
Carbohydrates (mg)	5	10	30

SOLUTION We let $x_1, x_2,$ and x_3 be the respective amounts (in grams) of KayDee Food,
Pet Pellets, and Rodent Chow that the hamsters should eat and $y_1, y_2,$ and y_3 be the corresponding amounts for the gerbils. Then we want to solve the matrix equations

$$\begin{bmatrix} 10 & 0 & 20 \\ 10 & 20 & 10 \\ 5 & 10 & 30 \end{bmatrix} \begin{bmatrix} x_1 \\ x_2 \\ x_3 \end{bmatrix} = \begin{bmatrix} 340 \\ 280 \\ 440 \end{bmatrix} \quad \text{Hamster equation}$$

$$\begin{bmatrix} 10 & 0 & 20 \\ 10 & 20 & 10 \\ 5 & 10 & 30 \end{bmatrix} \begin{bmatrix} y_1 \\ y_2 \\ y_3 \end{bmatrix} = \begin{bmatrix} 480 \\ 360 \\ 680 \end{bmatrix} \quad \text{Gerbil equation}$$

Let

$$A = \begin{bmatrix} 10 & 0 & 20 \\ 10 & 20 & 10 \\ 5 & 10 & 30 \end{bmatrix} \quad B = \begin{bmatrix} 340 \\ 280 \\ 440 \end{bmatrix} \quad C = \begin{bmatrix} 480 \\ 360 \\ 680 \end{bmatrix} \quad X = \begin{bmatrix} x_1 \\ x_2 \\ x_3 \end{bmatrix} \quad Y = \begin{bmatrix} y_1 \\ y_2 \\ y_3 \end{bmatrix}$$

Then we can write these matrix equations as

$$AX = B \quad \text{Hamster equation}$$

$$AY = C \quad \text{Gerbil equation}$$

We want to solve for X and Y, so we multiply both sides of each equation by A^{-1}, the inverse of the coefficient matrix. We could find A^{-1} by hand, but it is more convenient to
use a graphing calculator as shown in Figure 3.

```
[A]⁻¹*[B]
          [[10]
           [3 ]
           [12]]
```

```
[A]⁻¹*[C]
          [[8 ]
           [4 ]
           [20]]
```

FIGURE 3   (a)   (b)

So

$$X = A^{-1}B = \begin{bmatrix} 10 \\ 3 \\ 12 \end{bmatrix} \qquad Y = A^{-1}C = \begin{bmatrix} 8 \\ 4 \\ 20 \end{bmatrix}$$

Thus each hamster should be fed 10 g of KayDee Food, 3 g of Pet Pellets, and 12 g of Rodent Chow; and each gerbil should be fed 8 g of KayDee Food, 4 g of Pet Pellets, and 20 g of Rodent Chow daily.

✎. **NOW TRY EXERCISE 47**   ■

10.5 EXERCISES

CONCEPTS

✎. **1. (a)** The matrix $I = \begin{bmatrix} 1 & 0 \\ 0 & 1 \end{bmatrix}$ is called an _____ matrix.

(b) If A is a 2×2 matrix, then $A \times I =$ _____ and $I \times A =$ _____.

(c) If A and B are 2×2 matrices with $AB = I$, then B is the _____ of A.

2. (a) Write the following system as a matrix equation $AX = B$.

System	Matrix equation
	$A \quad \cdot \quad X \ = \ B$
$5x + 3y = 4$	$\begin{bmatrix} \blacksquare & \blacksquare \\ \blacksquare & \blacksquare \end{bmatrix} \begin{bmatrix} \blacksquare \\ \blacksquare \end{bmatrix} = \begin{bmatrix} \blacksquare \\ \blacksquare \end{bmatrix}$
$3x + 2y = 3$	

(b) The inverse of A is $A^{-1} = \begin{bmatrix} \blacksquare & \blacksquare \\ \blacksquare & \blacksquare \end{bmatrix}$.

(c) The solution of the matrix equation is $X = A^{-1}B$.

$$X \ = \ A^{-1} \quad B$$
$$\begin{bmatrix} x \\ y \end{bmatrix} = \begin{bmatrix} \blacksquare & \blacksquare \\ \blacksquare & \blacksquare \end{bmatrix} \begin{bmatrix} \blacksquare \\ \blacksquare \end{bmatrix} = \begin{bmatrix} \blacksquare \\ \blacksquare \end{bmatrix}$$

(d) The solution of the system is $x =$ _____, $y =$ _____.

SKILLS

3–6 ■ Calculate the products AB and BA to verify that B is the inverse of A.

✎. **3.** $A = \begin{bmatrix} 4 & 1 \\ 7 & 2 \end{bmatrix}$ $\quad B = \begin{bmatrix} 2 & -1 \\ -7 & 4 \end{bmatrix}$

4. $A = \begin{bmatrix} 2 & -3 \\ 4 & -7 \end{bmatrix}$ $\quad B = \begin{bmatrix} \frac{7}{2} & -\frac{3}{2} \\ 2 & -1 \end{bmatrix}$

5. $A = \begin{bmatrix} 1 & 3 & -1 \\ 1 & 4 & 0 \\ -1 & -3 & 2 \end{bmatrix}$ $B = \begin{bmatrix} 8 & -3 & 4 \\ -2 & 1 & -1 \\ 1 & 0 & 1 \end{bmatrix}$

6. $A = \begin{bmatrix} 3 & 2 & 4 \\ 1 & 1 & -6 \\ 2 & 1 & 12 \end{bmatrix}$ $B = \begin{bmatrix} 9 & -10 & -8 \\ -12 & 14 & 11 \\ -\frac{1}{2} & \frac{1}{2} & \frac{1}{2} \end{bmatrix}$

7–8 ■ Find the inverse of the matrix and verify that $A^{-1}A = AA^{-1} = I_2$ and $B^{-1}B = BB^{-1} = I_3$.

7. $A = \begin{bmatrix} 7 & 4 \\ 3 & 2 \end{bmatrix}$ **8.** $B = \begin{bmatrix} 1 & 3 & 2 \\ 0 & 2 & 2 \\ -2 & -1 & 0 \end{bmatrix}$

9–24 ■ Find the inverse of the matrix if it exists.

✎. **9.** $\begin{bmatrix} -3 & -5 \\ 2 & 3 \end{bmatrix}$ **10.** $\begin{bmatrix} 3 & 4 \\ 7 & 9 \end{bmatrix}$

11. $\begin{bmatrix} 2 & 5 \\ -5 & -13 \end{bmatrix}$ **12.** $\begin{bmatrix} -7 & 4 \\ 8 & -5 \end{bmatrix}$

13. $\begin{bmatrix} 6 & -3 \\ -8 & 4 \end{bmatrix}$ **14.** $\begin{bmatrix} \frac{1}{2} & \frac{1}{3} \\ 5 & 4 \end{bmatrix}$

15. $\begin{bmatrix} 0.4 & -1.2 \\ 0.3 & 0.6 \end{bmatrix}$ **16.** $\begin{bmatrix} 4 & 2 & 3 \\ 3 & 3 & 2 \\ 1 & 0 & 1 \end{bmatrix}$

✎. **17.** $\begin{bmatrix} 2 & 4 & 1 \\ -1 & 1 & -1 \\ 1 & 4 & 0 \end{bmatrix}$ **18.** $\begin{bmatrix} 5 & 7 & 4 \\ 3 & -1 & 3 \\ 6 & 7 & 5 \end{bmatrix}$

✎. **19.** $\begin{bmatrix} 1 & 2 & 3 \\ 4 & 5 & -1 \\ 1 & -1 & -10 \end{bmatrix}$ **20.** $\begin{bmatrix} 2 & 1 & 0 \\ 1 & 1 & 4 \\ 2 & 1 & 2 \end{bmatrix}$

21. $\begin{bmatrix} 0 & -2 & 2 \\ 3 & 1 & 3 \\ 1 & -2 & 3 \end{bmatrix}$ **22.** $\begin{bmatrix} 3 & -2 & 0 \\ 5 & 1 & 1 \\ 2 & -2 & 0 \end{bmatrix}$

23. $\begin{bmatrix} 1 & 2 & 0 & 3 \\ 0 & 1 & 1 & 1 \\ 0 & 1 & 0 & 1 \\ 1 & 2 & 0 & 2 \end{bmatrix}$ **24.** $\begin{bmatrix} 1 & 0 & 1 & 0 \\ 0 & 1 & 0 & 1 \\ 1 & 1 & 1 & 0 \\ 1 & 1 & 1 & 1 \end{bmatrix}$

25–32 ■ Solve the system of equations by converting to a matrix equation and using the inverse of the coefficient matrix, as in Example 6. Use the inverses from Exercises 9–12, 17, 18, 21, and 23.

✎. **25.** $\begin{cases} -3x - 5y = 4 \\ 2x + 3y = 0 \end{cases}$ **26.** $\begin{cases} 3x + 4y = 10 \\ 7x + 9y = 20 \end{cases}$

27. $\begin{cases} 2x + 5y = 2 \\ -5x - 13y = 20 \end{cases}$ **28.** $\begin{cases} -7x + 4y = 0 \\ 8x - 5y = 100 \end{cases}$

29. $\begin{cases} 2x + 4y + z = 7 \\ -x + y - z = 0 \\ x + 4y = -2 \end{cases}$ 30. $\begin{cases} 5x + 7y + 4z = 1 \\ 3x - y + 3z = 1 \\ 6x + 7y + 5z = 1 \end{cases}$

31. $\begin{cases} -2y + 2z = 12 \\ 3x + y + 3z = -2 \\ x - 2y + 3z = 8 \end{cases}$ 32. $\begin{cases} x + 2y + 3w = 0 \\ y + z + w = 1 \\ y + w = 2 \\ x + 2y + 2w = 3 \end{cases}$

33–38 ■ Use a calculator that can perform matrix operations to solve the system, as in Example 7.

33. $\begin{cases} x + y - 2z = 3 \\ 2x + 5z = 11 \\ 2x + 3y = 12 \end{cases}$ 34. $\begin{cases} 3x + 4y - z = 2 \\ 2x - 3y + z = -5 \\ 5x - 2y + 2z = -3 \end{cases}$

35. $\begin{cases} 12x + \frac{1}{2}y - 7z = 21 \\ 11x - 2y + 3z = 43 \\ 13x + y - 4z = 29 \end{cases}$ 36. $\begin{cases} x + \frac{1}{2}y - \frac{1}{3}z = 4 \\ x - \frac{1}{4}y + \frac{1}{6}z = 7 \\ x + y - z = -6 \end{cases}$

37. $\begin{cases} x + y - 3w = 0 \\ x - 2z = 8 \\ 2y - z + w = 5 \\ 2x + 3y - 2w = 13 \end{cases}$

38. $\begin{cases} x + y + z + w = 15 \\ x - y + z - w = 5 \\ x + 2y + 3z + 4w = 26 \\ x - 2y + 3z - 4w = 2 \end{cases}$

39–40 ■ Solve the matrix equation by multiplying each side by the appropriate inverse matrix.

39. $\begin{bmatrix} 3 & -2 \\ -4 & 3 \end{bmatrix} \begin{bmatrix} x & y & z \\ u & v & w \end{bmatrix} = \begin{bmatrix} 1 & 0 & -1 \\ 2 & 1 & 3 \end{bmatrix}$

40. $\begin{bmatrix} 0 & -2 & 2 \\ 3 & 1 & 3 \\ 1 & -2 & 3 \end{bmatrix} \begin{bmatrix} x & u \\ y & v \\ z & w \end{bmatrix} = \begin{bmatrix} 3 & 6 \\ 6 & 12 \\ 0 & 0 \end{bmatrix}$

41–42 ■ Find the inverse of the matrix.

41. $\begin{bmatrix} a & -a \\ a & a \end{bmatrix}$
$(a \neq 0)$

42. $\begin{bmatrix} a & 0 & 0 & 0 \\ 0 & b & 0 & 0 \\ 0 & 0 & c & 0 \\ 0 & 0 & 0 & d \end{bmatrix}$
$(abcd \neq 0)$

43–46 ■ Find the inverse of the matrix. For what value(s) of x, if any, does the matrix have no inverse?

43. $\begin{bmatrix} 2 & x \\ x & x^2 \end{bmatrix}$ 44. $\begin{bmatrix} e^x & -e^{2x} \\ e^{2x} & e^{3x} \end{bmatrix}$

45. $\begin{bmatrix} 1 & e^x & 0 \\ e^x & -e^{2x} & 0 \\ 0 & 0 & 2 \end{bmatrix}$ 46. $\begin{bmatrix} x & 1 \\ -x & \dfrac{1}{x-1} \end{bmatrix}$

APPLICATIONS

47. Nutrition A nutritionist is studying the effects of the nutrients folic acid, choline, and inositol. He has three types

of food available, and each type contains the following amounts of these nutrients per ounce.

	Type A	Type B	Type C
Folic acid (mg)	3	1	3
Choline (mg)	4	2	4
Inositol (mg)	3	2	4

(a) Find the inverse of the matrix
$$\begin{bmatrix} 3 & 1 & 3 \\ 4 & 2 & 4 \\ 3 & 2 & 4 \end{bmatrix}$$
and use it to solve the remaining parts of this problem.

(b) How many ounces of each food should the nutritionist feed his laboratory rats if he wants their daily diet to contain 10 mg of folic acid, 14 mg of choline, and 13 mg of inositol?

(c) How much of each food is needed to supply 9 mg of folic acid, 12 mg of choline, and 10 mg of inositol?

(d) Will any combination of these foods supply 2 mg of folic acid, 4 mg of choline, and 11 mg of inositol?

48. Nutrition Refer to Exercise 47. Suppose food type C has been improperly labeled, and it actually contains 4 mg of folic acid, 6 mg of choline, and 5 mg of inositol per ounce. Would it still be possible to use matrix inversion to solve parts (b), (c), and (d) of Exercise 47? Why or why not?

49. Sales Commissions An encyclopedia saleswoman works for a company that offers three different grades of bindings for its encyclopedias: standard, deluxe, and leather. For each set that she sells, she earns a commission based on the set's binding grade. One week she sells one standard, one deluxe, and two leather sets and makes $675 in commission. The next week she sells two standard, one deluxe, and one leather set for a $600 commission. The third week she sells one standard, two deluxe, and one leather set, earning $625 in commission.

(a) Let x, y, and z represent the commission she earns on standard, deluxe, and leather sets, respectively. Translate the given information into a system of equations in x, y, and z.

(b) Express the system of equations you found in part (a) as a matrix equation of the form $AX = B$.

(c) Find the inverse of the coefficient matrix A and use it to solve the matrix equation in part (b). How much commission does the saleswoman earn on a set of encyclopedias in each grade of binding?

DISCOVERY ■ DISCUSSION ■ WRITING

50. No Zero-Product Property for Matrices We have used the Zero-Product Property to solve algebraic equations. Matrices do *not* have this property. Let O represent the **2 × 2 zero matrix**
$$O = \begin{bmatrix} 0 & 0 \\ 0 & 0 \end{bmatrix}$$

Find 2 × 2 matrices $A \neq O$ and $B \neq O$ such that $AB = O$. Can you find a matrix $A \neq O$ such that $A^2 = O$?

SUGGESTED TIME AND EMPHASIS

1 class, recommended material: determinants; optional material: Cramer's Rule

10.6 DETERMINANTS AND CRAMER'S RULE

Determinant of a 2 × 2 Matrix ▶ Determinant of an $n \times n$ Matrix ▶ Row and Column Transformations ▶ Cramer's Rule ▶ Areas of Triangles Using Determinants

If a matrix is **square** (that is, if it has the same number of rows as columns), then we can assign to it a number called its *determinant*. Determinants can be used to solve systems of linear equations, as we will see later in this section. They are also useful in determining whether a matrix has an inverse.

▼ Determinant of a 2 × 2 Matrix

We denote the determinant of a square matrix A by the symbol $\det(A)$ or $|A|$. We first define $\det(A)$ for the simplest cases. If $A = [a]$ is a 1×1 matrix, then $\det(A) = a$. The following box gives the definition of a 2 × 2 determinant.

We will use both notations, $\det(A)$ and $|A|$, for the determinant of A. Although the symbol $|A|$ looks like the absolute value symbol, it will be clear from the context which meaning is intended.

DETERMINANT OF A 2 × 2 MATRIX

The **determinant** of the 2 × 2 matrix $A = \begin{bmatrix} a & b \\ c & d \end{bmatrix}$ is

$$\det(A) = |A| = \begin{vmatrix} a & b \\ c & d \end{vmatrix} = ad - bc$$

ALTERNATE EXAMPLE 1

Evaluate $|A|$.

$A = \begin{bmatrix} 5 & -9 \\ 1 & 2 \end{bmatrix}$

ANSWER

19

EXAMPLE 1 | Determinant of a 2 × 2 Matrix

Evaluate $|A|$ for $A = \begin{bmatrix} 6 & -3 \\ 2 & 3 \end{bmatrix}$.

SOLUTION

To evaluate a 2 × 2 determinant, we take the product of the diagonal from top left to bottom right and subtract the product from top right to bottom left, as indicated by the arrows.

$$\begin{vmatrix} 6 & -3 \\ 2 & 3 \end{vmatrix} = 6 \cdot 3 - (-3)2 = 18 - (-6) = 24$$

✎ NOW TRY EXERCISE **5**   ∎

▼ Determinant of an $n \times n$ Matrix

To define the concept of determinant for an arbitrary $n \times n$ matrix, we need the following terminology.

MINORS AND COFACTORS

Let A be an $n \times n$ matrix.

1. The **minor** M_{ij} of the element a_{ij} is the determinant of the matrix obtained by deleting the ith row and jth column of A.

2. The **cofactor** A_{ij} of the element a_{ij} is

$$A_{ij} = (-1)^{i+j} M_{ij}$$

TEXT QUESTION

Name one application of determinants.

Answer

Any of the following: determining the singularity of a matrix, solving systems with Cramer's Rule, finding the area of a triangle.

For example, if A is the matrix

$$\begin{bmatrix} 2 & 3 & -1 \\ 0 & 2 & 4 \\ -2 & 5 & 6 \end{bmatrix}$$

then the minor M_{12} is the determinant of the matrix obtained by deleting the first row and second column from A. Thus

$$M_{12} = \begin{vmatrix} 2 & 3 & -1 \\ 0 & 2 & 4 \\ -2 & 5 & 6 \end{vmatrix} = \begin{vmatrix} 0 & 4 \\ -2 & 6 \end{vmatrix} = 0(6) - 4(-2) = 8$$

So the cofactor $A_{12} = (-1)^{1+2}M_{12} = -8$. Similarly,

$$M_{33} = \begin{vmatrix} 2 & 3 & -1 \\ 0 & 2 & 4 \\ -2 & 5 & 6 \end{vmatrix} = \begin{vmatrix} 2 & 3 \\ 0 & 2 \end{vmatrix} = 2 \cdot 2 - 3 \cdot 0 = 4$$

So $A_{33} = (-1)^{3+3}M_{33} = 4$.

Note that the cofactor of a_{ij} is simply the minor of a_{ij} multiplied by either 1 or -1, depending on whether $i + j$ is even or odd. Thus in a 3×3 matrix we obtain the cofactor of any element by prefixing its minor with the sign obtained from the following checkerboard pattern.

$$\begin{bmatrix} + & - & + \\ - & + & - \\ + & - & + \end{bmatrix}$$

We are now ready to define the determinant of any square matrix.

THE DETERMINANT OF A SQUARE MATRIX

If A is an $n \times n$ matrix, then the **determinant** of A is obtained by multiplying each element of the first row by its cofactor and then adding the results. In symbols,

$$\det(A) = |A| = \begin{vmatrix} a_{11} & a_{12} & \cdots & a_{1n} \\ a_{21} & a_{22} & \cdots & a_{2n} \\ \vdots & \vdots & \ddots & \vdots \\ a_{n1} & a_{n2} & \cdots & a_{nn} \end{vmatrix} = a_{11}A_{11} + a_{12}A_{12} + \cdots + a_{1n}A_{1n}$$

EXAMPLE 2 | Determinant of a 3×3 Matrix

Evaluate the determinant of the matrix.

$$A = \begin{bmatrix} 2 & 3 & -1 \\ 0 & 2 & 4 \\ -2 & 5 & 6 \end{bmatrix}$$

DAVID HILBERT (1862–1943) was born in Königsberg, Germany, and became a professor at Göttingen University. He is considered by many to be the greatest mathematician of the 20th century. At the International Congress of Mathematicians held in Paris in 1900, Hilbert set the direction of mathematics for the about-to-dawn 20th century by posing 23 problems that he believed to be of crucial importance. He said that "these are problems whose solutions we expect from the future." Most of Hilbert's problems have now been solved (see Julia Robinson, page 663, and Alan Turing, page 100), and their solutions have led to important new areas of mathematical research. Yet as we proceed into the new millennium, some of his problems remain unsolved. In his work, Hilbert emphasized structure, logic, and the foundations of mathematics. Part of his genius lay in his ability to see the most general possible statement of a problem. For instance, Euler proved that every whole number is the sum of four squares; Hilbert proved a similar statement for all powers of positive integers.

EXAMPLE
A 4×4 determinant:

$$\begin{bmatrix} 1 & 1 & 1 & 1 \\ 2 & -1 & 0 & 5 \\ 0 & 8 & 1 & 2 \\ 0 & 2 & 1 & 3 \end{bmatrix}$$

Expand by row 3:

$$D = -8 \begin{bmatrix} 1 & 1 & 1 \\ 2 & 0 & 5 \\ 0 & 1 & 3 \end{bmatrix} +$$

$$\begin{bmatrix} 1 & 1 & 1 \\ 2 & -1 & 5 \\ 0 & 2 & 3 \end{bmatrix} - 2 \begin{bmatrix} 1 & 1 & 1 \\ 2 & -1 & 0 \\ 0 & 2 & 1 \end{bmatrix}$$

$$= -8(-9) + (-15) - 2(1) = 55$$

ALTERNATE EXAMPLE 2
Evaluate the determinant of the matrix.

$$A = \begin{bmatrix} 9 & 3 & -1 \\ 0 & 3 & 2 \\ -4 & 2 & 4 \end{bmatrix}$$

ANSWER
36

IN-CLASS MATERIALS
Discuss computational complexity. If a 2×2 determinant requires 3 arithmetical operations (2 multiplications and a subtraction), then a 3×3 determinant requires 12 and a 4×4 requires 52. If we let $f(n)$ be the number of arithmetical operations for an $n \times n$ matrix, we get the formula $f(n) = nf(n-1) + n$: there are n determinants of

---

$(n-1) \times (n-1)$ matrices and n extra multiplications (when expanding by a row). So we can generate the following table:

n	Number of Operations	n	Number of Operations
2	3	9	804,969
3	12	10	8,049,700
4	52	11	88,546,711
5	265	.	.
6	1,596	.	.
7	11,179	.	.
8	89,440	20	5,396,862,315,159,760,000

Students can observe this rapid growth on their calculators; it will take the calculator 10 times as long to do a 10×10 determinant as it takes to do a 9×9. In fact, $f(n)$ grows a little more rapidly than $n!$

SOLUTION

$$\det(A) = \begin{vmatrix} 2 & 3 & -1 \\ 0 & 2 & 4 \\ -2 & 5 & 6 \end{vmatrix} = 2 \begin{vmatrix} 2 & 4 \\ 5 & 6 \end{vmatrix} - 3 \begin{vmatrix} 0 & 4 \\ -2 & 6 \end{vmatrix} + (-1) \begin{vmatrix} 0 & 2 \\ -2 & 5 \end{vmatrix}$$

$$= 2(2 \cdot 6 - 4 \cdot 5) - 3[0 \cdot 6 - 4(-2)] - [0 \cdot 5 - 2(-2)]$$

$$= -16 - 24 - 4$$

$$= -44$$

✎. **NOW TRY EXERCISE 19**   ■

In our definition of the determinant we used the cofactors of elements in the first row only. This is called **expanding the determinant by the first row**. In fact, *we can expand the determinant by any row or column in the same way and obtain the same result in each case* (although we won't prove this). The next example illustrates this principle.

EXAMPLE 3 │ **Expanding a Determinant About a Row and a Column**

Let A be the matrix of Example 2. Evaluate the determinant of A by expanding

(a) by the second row

(b) by the third column

Verify that each expansion gives the same value.

SOLUTION

(a) Expanding by the second row, we get

$$\det(A) = \begin{vmatrix} 2 & 3 & -1 \\ 0 & 2 & 4 \\ -2 & 5 & 6 \end{vmatrix} = -0 \begin{vmatrix} 3 & -1 \\ 5 & 6 \end{vmatrix} + 2 \begin{vmatrix} 2 & -1 \\ -2 & 6 \end{vmatrix} - 4 \begin{vmatrix} 2 & 3 \\ -2 & 5 \end{vmatrix}$$

$$= 0 + 2[2 \cdot 6 - (-1)(-2)] - 4[2 \cdot 5 - 3(-2)]$$

$$= 0 + 20 - 64 = -44$$

(b) Expanding by the third column gives

$$\det(A) = \begin{vmatrix} 2 & 3 & -1 \\ 0 & 2 & 4 \\ -2 & 5 & 6 \end{vmatrix}$$

$$= -1 \begin{vmatrix} 0 & 2 \\ -2 & 5 \end{vmatrix} - 4 \begin{vmatrix} 2 & 3 \\ -2 & 5 \end{vmatrix} + 6 \begin{vmatrix} 2 & 3 \\ 0 & 2 \end{vmatrix}$$

$$= -[0 \cdot 5 - 2(-2)] - 4[2 \cdot 5 - 3(-2)] + 6(2 \cdot 2 - 3 \cdot 0)$$

$$= -4 - 64 + 24 = -44$$

In both cases we obtain the same value for the determinant as when we expanded by the first row in Example 2.

✎. **NOW TRY EXERCISE 31**   ■

Graphing calculators are capable of computing determinants. Here is the output when the TI-83 is used to calculate the determinant in Example 3:

```
[A]
        [[2  3  -1]
         [0  2   4 ]
         [-2 5   6 ]]
det([A])
                  -44
```

684   CHAPTER 10 Systems of Equations and Inequalities

ALTERNATE EXAMPLE 3

Evaluate the determinant of the matrix by expanding by the second row and by expanding by the third column.

$$A = \begin{bmatrix} 6 & 6 & -1 \\ 0 & 9 & 8 \\ -2 & 2 & 9 \end{bmatrix}$$

ANSWER

276, 276

IN-CLASS MATERIALS

Show the students the "basket" method of computing a 3×3 determinant. Stress that this method does not generalize to higher dimensions. One rewrites the first two columns of the matrix and then multiplies along the diagonals, adding the top-to-bottom diagonals and subtracting the bottom-to-top ones. In the example

shown here, we calculate the determinant of $\begin{bmatrix} 1 & 4 & 7 \\ 2 & 5 & 8 \\ 3 & 6 & 9 \end{bmatrix}$ to be $105 + 48 + 72 - (45 + 96 + 84) = 0$.

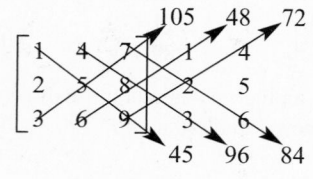

The following criterion allows us to determine whether a square matrix has an inverse without actually calculating the inverse. This is one of the most important uses of the determinant in matrix algebra, and it is the reason for the name *determinant*.

INVERTIBILITY CRITERION

If A is a square matrix, then A has an inverse if and only if $\det(A) \neq 0$.

We will not prove this fact, but from the formula for the inverse of a 2×2 matrix (page 674) you can see why it is true in the 2×2 case.

EXAMPLE 4 | Using the Determinant to Show That a Matrix Is Not Invertible

Show that the matrix A has no inverse.

$$A = \begin{bmatrix} 1 & 2 & 0 & 4 \\ 0 & 0 & 0 & 3 \\ 5 & 6 & 2 & 6 \\ 2 & 4 & 0 & 9 \end{bmatrix}$$

SOLUTION We begin by calculating the determinant of A. Since all but one of the elements of the second row is zero, we expand the determinant by the second row. If we do this, we see from the following equation that only the cofactor A_{24} will have to be calculated.

$$\det(A) = \begin{vmatrix} 1 & 2 & 0 & 4 \\ 0 & 0 & 0 & 3 \\ 5 & 6 & 2 & 6 \\ 2 & 4 & 0 & 9 \end{vmatrix}$$

$$= -0 \cdot A_{21} + 0 \cdot A_{22} - 0 \cdot A_{23} + 3 \cdot A_{24} = 3A_{24}$$

$$= 3 \begin{vmatrix} 1 & 2 & 0 \\ 5 & 6 & 2 \\ 2 & 4 & 0 \end{vmatrix} \qquad \text{Expand this by column 3}$$

$$= 3(-2) \begin{vmatrix} 1 & 2 \\ 2 & 4 \end{vmatrix}$$

$$= 3(-2)(1 \cdot 4 - 2 \cdot 2) = 0$$

Since the determinant of A is zero, A cannot have an inverse, by the Invertibility Criterion.

🖱 NOW TRY EXERCISE **23** ∎

▼ Row and Column Transformations

The preceding example shows that if we expand a determinant about a row or column that contains many zeros, our work is reduced considerably because we don't have to evaluate the cofactors of the elements that are zero. The following principle often simplifies the process of finding a determinant by introducing zeros into the matrix without changing the value of the determinant.

ALTERNATE EXAMPLE 4

Does the matrix A have an inverse?

$$A = \begin{bmatrix} 1 & 2 & 0 & 1 \\ 0 & 0 & 0 & 1 \\ 8 & 2 & 1 & 5 \\ 4 & 8 & 0 & 9 \end{bmatrix}$$

ANSWER

No

IN-CLASS MATERIALS

Make sure the students see the fundamentally recursive nature of determinants. Draw a 6×6 matrix on the board and expand by a row, showing how you would then have to compute six 5×5 determinants, which would require the computation of thirty 4×4 determinants, and so forth.

ALTERNATE EXAMPLE 5

Evaluate the determinant of the matrix.

$$A = \begin{bmatrix} 6 & 2 & 1 & -3 \\ 1 & 2 & 6 & 9 \\ 18 & 6 & 7 & -9 \\ 18 & 8 & 3 & -9 \end{bmatrix}$$

Does the matrix A have an inverse?

ANSWER

−456, yes

The Granger Collection, New York

EMMY NOETHER (1882–1935) was one of the foremost mathematicians of the early 20th century. Her ground-breaking work in abstract algebra pro-vided much of the foundation for this field, and her work in invariant theory was essential in the development of Einstein's theory of general relativity. Although women weren't allowed to study at German universities at that time, she audited courses unofficially and went on to receive a doctorate at Erlangen *summa cum laude*, despite the opposition of the academic senate, which declared that women students would "overthrow all academic order." She subsequently taught mathematics at Göttingen, Moscow, and Frankfurt. In 1933 she left Germany to escape Nazi persecution, accepting a position at Bryn Mawr College in suburban Philadelphia. She lectured there and at the Institute for Advanced Study in Princeton, New Jersey, until her un-timely death in 1935.

ROW AND COLUMN TRANSFORMATIONS OF A DETERMINANT

If A is a square matrix and if the matrix B is obtained from A by adding a multiple of one row to another or a multiple of one column to another, then $\det(A) = \det(B)$.

EXAMPLE 5 | Using Row and Column Transformations to Calculate a Determinant

Find the determinant of the matrix A. Does it have an inverse?

$$A = \begin{bmatrix} 8 & 2 & -1 & -4 \\ 3 & 5 & -3 & 11 \\ 24 & 6 & 1 & -12 \\ 2 & 2 & 7 & -1 \end{bmatrix}$$

SOLUTION If we add −3 times row 1 to row 3, we change all but one element of row 3 to zeros:

$$\begin{bmatrix} 8 & 2 & -1 & -4 \\ 3 & 5 & -3 & 11 \\ 0 & 0 & 4 & 0 \\ 2 & 2 & 7 & -1 \end{bmatrix}$$

This new matrix has the same determinant as A, and if we expand its determinant by the third row, we get

$$\det(A) = 4 \begin{vmatrix} 8 & 2 & -4 \\ 3 & 5 & 11 \\ 2 & 2 & -1 \end{vmatrix}$$

Now, adding 2 times column 3 to column 1 in this determinant gives us

$$\det(A) = 4 \begin{vmatrix} 0 & 2 & -4 \\ 25 & 5 & 11 \\ 0 & 2 & -1 \end{vmatrix} \quad \text{Expand this by column 1}$$

$$= 4(-25) \begin{vmatrix} 2 & -4 \\ 2 & -1 \end{vmatrix}$$

$$= 4(-25)[2(-1) - (-4)2] = -600$$

Since the determinant of A is not zero, A does have an inverse.

✎ NOW TRY EXERCISE **27** ∎

▼ Cramer's Rule

The solutions of linear equations can sometimes be expressed by using determinants. To il-lustrate, let's solve the following pair of linear equations for the variable x.

$$\begin{cases} ax + by = r \\ cx + dy = s \end{cases}$$

IN-CLASS MATERIALS

Determinants have many nice properties. For example, if a row or column consists of all zeros, it is trivial to prove that the determinant is zero. The row/column transformation rule given in the text then lets us conclude that if two rows of a matrix are identical, the determinant is zero. Also, the determinant of a product is the product of the determinants.

To eliminate the variable y, we multiply the first equation by d and the second by b and subtract.

$$\begin{aligned} adx + bdy &= rd \\ bcx + bdy &= bs \\ \hline adx - bcx &= rd - bs \end{aligned}$$

Factoring the left-hand side, we get $(ad - bc)x = rd - bs$. Assuming that $ad - bc \neq 0$, we can now solve this equation for x:

$$x = \frac{rd - bs}{ad - bc}$$

Similarly, we find

$$y = \frac{as - cr}{ad - bc}$$

The numerator and denominator of the fractions for x and y are determinants of 2×2 matrices. So we can express the solution of the system using determinants as follows.

CRAMER'S RULE FOR SYSTEMS IN TWO VARIABLES

The linear system

$$\begin{cases} ax + by = r \\ cx + dy = s \end{cases}$$

has the solution

$$x = \frac{\begin{vmatrix} r & b \\ s & d \end{vmatrix}}{\begin{vmatrix} a & b \\ c & d \end{vmatrix}} \qquad y = \frac{\begin{vmatrix} a & r \\ c & s \end{vmatrix}}{\begin{vmatrix} a & b \\ c & d \end{vmatrix}}$$

provided that $\begin{vmatrix} a & b \\ c & d \end{vmatrix} \neq 0$.

Using the notation

$$D = \begin{bmatrix} a & b \\ c & d \end{bmatrix} \qquad D_x = \begin{bmatrix} r & b \\ s & d \end{bmatrix} \qquad D_y = \begin{bmatrix} a & r \\ c & s \end{bmatrix}$$

Coefficient matrix | Replace first column of D by r and s | Replace second column of D by r and s

we can write the solution of the system as

$$x = \frac{|D_x|}{|D|} \qquad \text{and} \qquad y = \frac{|D_y|}{|D|}$$

EXAMPLE
Cramer's Rule:

$$\begin{aligned} x - y + z &= 8 \\ -x - y - z &= -9 \\ x - 2y - 4z &= 5 \end{aligned}$$

$$D = \begin{bmatrix} 1 & -1 & 1 \\ -1 & -1 & -1 \\ 1 & -2 & -4 \end{bmatrix} = 10,$$

$$D_x = \begin{bmatrix} 8 & -1 & 1 \\ -9 & -1 & -1 \\ 5 & -2 & -4 \end{bmatrix} = 80,$$

$$D_y = \begin{bmatrix} 1 & 8 & 1 \\ -1 & -9 & -1 \\ 1 & 5 & -4 \end{bmatrix} = 5,$$

and

$$D_z = \begin{bmatrix} 1 & -1 & 8 \\ -1 & -1 & -9 \\ 1 & -2 & 5 \end{bmatrix} = 5,$$

so we have $x = 8$, $y = \frac{1}{2}$, and $z = \frac{1}{2}$.

IN-CLASS MATERIALS

When solving a single $n \times n$ system, Cramer's Rule doesn't have much of an advantage over Gaussian elimination. There are, however, some circumstances in which Cramer's Rule is vastly superior. One such situation is when there is a large system (say, 100 equations with 100 unknowns) and we are interested in only one variable. Gaussian elimination requires us to do the work to solve the complete system. Finding the inverse of the matrix also requires us to do all the work necessary to find all the variables. Cramer's Rule, however, allows us to find two (admittedly large) determinants to get our answer.

Another situation is when the coefficient matrix is sparse—a large percentage of the entries are zero. It is usually very quick to find determinants of sparse matrices, and in that case Cramer's Rule can be very quick.

ALTERNATE EXAMPLE 6

Use Cramer's Rule to solve the system.

$$\begin{cases} 3x + 10y = -4 \\ x + 4y = -1 \end{cases}$$

If the equations of the system are dependent, or if a system is inconsistent, so indicate.

ANSWER

$$\left(-3, \frac{1}{2}\right)$$

EXAMPLE 6 │ Using Cramer's Rule to Solve a System with Two Variables

Use Cramer's Rule to solve the system.

$$\begin{cases} 2x + 6y = -1 \\ x + 8y = 2 \end{cases}$$

SOLUTION For this system we have

$$|D| = \begin{vmatrix} 2 & 6 \\ 1 & 8 \end{vmatrix} = 2 \cdot 8 - 6 \cdot 1 = 10$$

$$|D_x| = \begin{vmatrix} -1 & 6 \\ 2 & 8 \end{vmatrix} = (-1)8 - 6 \cdot 2 = -20$$

$$|D_y| = \begin{vmatrix} 2 & -1 \\ 1 & 2 \end{vmatrix} = 2 \cdot 2 - (-1)1 = 5$$

The solution is

$$x = \frac{|D_x|}{|D|} = \frac{-20}{10} = -2$$

$$y = \frac{|D_y|}{|D|} = \frac{5}{10} = \frac{1}{2}$$

✎. NOW TRY EXERCISE **33**   ■

Cramer's Rule can be extended to apply to any system of n linear equations in n variables in which the determinant of the coefficient matrix is not zero. As we saw in the preceding section, any such system can be written in matrix form as

$$\begin{bmatrix} a_{11} & a_{12} & \cdots & a_{1n} \\ a_{21} & a_{22} & \cdots & a_{2n} \\ \vdots & \vdots & \ddots & \vdots \\ a_{n1} & a_{n2} & \cdots & a_{nn} \end{bmatrix} \begin{bmatrix} x_1 \\ x_2 \\ \vdots \\ x_n \end{bmatrix} = \begin{bmatrix} b_1 \\ b_2 \\ \vdots \\ b_n \end{bmatrix}$$

By analogy with our derivation of Cramer's Rule in the case of two equations in two unknowns, we let D be the coefficient matrix in this system, and D_{x_i} be the matrix obtained by replacing the ith column of D by the numbers $b_1, b_2, \ldots, b_n$ that appear to the right of the equal sign. The solution of the system is then given by the following rule.

CRAMER'S RULE

If a system of n linear equations in the n variables $x_1, x_2, \ldots, x_n$ is equivalent to the matrix equation $DX = B$, and if $|D| \neq 0$, then its solutions are

$$x_1 = \frac{|D_{x_1}|}{|D|} \qquad x_2 = \frac{|D_{x_2}|}{|D|} \qquad \cdots \qquad x_n = \frac{|D_{x_n}|}{|D|}$$

where D_{x_i} is the matrix obtained by replacing the ith column of D by the $n \times 1$ matrix B.

EXAMPLE 7 | Using Cramer's Rule to Solve a System with Three Variables

Use Cramer's Rule to solve the system.

$$\begin{cases} 2x - 3y + 4z = 1 \\ x \qquad + 6z = 0 \\ 3x - 2y \qquad = 5 \end{cases}$$

SOLUTION First, we evaluate the determinants that appear in Cramer's Rule. Note that D is the coefficient matrix and that D_x, D_y, and D_z are obtained by replacing the first, second, and third columns of D by the constant terms.

$$|D| = \begin{vmatrix} 2 & -3 & 4 \\ 1 & 0 & 6 \\ 3 & -2 & 0 \end{vmatrix} = -38 \qquad |D_x| = \begin{vmatrix} 1 & -3 & 4 \\ 0 & 0 & 6 \\ 5 & -2 & 0 \end{vmatrix} = -78$$

$$|D_y| = \begin{vmatrix} 2 & 1 & 4 \\ 1 & 0 & 6 \\ 3 & 5 & 0 \end{vmatrix} = -22 \qquad |D_z| = \begin{vmatrix} 2 & -3 & 1 \\ 1 & 0 & 0 \\ 3 & -2 & 5 \end{vmatrix} = 13$$

Now we use Cramer's Rule to get the solution:

$$x = \frac{|D_x|}{|D|} = \frac{-78}{-38} = \frac{39}{19} \qquad\qquad y = \frac{|D_y|}{|D|} = \frac{-22}{-38} = \frac{11}{19}$$

$$z = \frac{|D_z|}{|D|} = \frac{13}{-38} = -\frac{13}{38}$$

✎. NOW TRY EXERCISE **39** ■

Solving the system in Example 7 using Gaussian elimination would involve matrices whose elements are fractions with fairly large denominators. Thus in cases like Examples 6 and 7, Cramer's Rule gives us an efficient way to solve systems of linear equations. But in systems with more than three equations, evaluating the various determinants that are involved is usually a long and tedious task (unless you are using a graphing calculator). Moreover, the rule doesn't apply if $|D| = 0$ or if D is not a square matrix. So Cramer's Rule is a useful alternative to Gaussian elimination, but only in some situations.

▼ Areas of Triangles Using Determinants

Determinants provide a simple way to calculate the area of a triangle in the coordinate plane.

AREA OF A TRIANGLE

If a triangle in the coordinate plane has vertices (a_1, b_1), (a_2, b_2), and (a_3, b_3), then its area is

$$\mathcal{A} = \pm\tfrac{1}{2}\begin{vmatrix} a_1 & b_1 & 1 \\ a_2 & b_2 & 1 \\ a_3 & b_3 & 1 \end{vmatrix}$$

where the sign is chosen to make the area positive.

You are asked to prove this formula in Exercise 63.

ALTERNATE EXAMPLE 8

Find the area of a triangle with vertices $(0, 2)$, $(3, 5)$, and $(-4, 0)$.

ANSWER

$$\pm \frac{1}{2} \begin{vmatrix} 0 & 2 & 1 \\ 3 & 5 & 1 \\ -4 & 0 & 1 \end{vmatrix} = \pm 3,$$

so the area is 3 square units.

DRILL QUESTION

Find $\begin{bmatrix} 2 & 1 & 3 \\ 1 & 0 & 0 \\ 0 & 2 & -1 \end{bmatrix}$.

Answer

7

EXAMPLE 8 | Area of a Triangle

Find the area of the triangle shown in Figure 1.

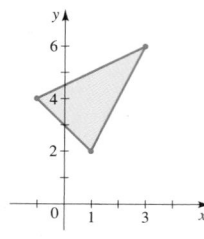

FIGURE 1

We can calculate the determinant by hand or by using a graphing calculator.

```
[A]
        [[-1 4 1]
         [3  6 1]
         [1  2 1]]
det([A])
               -12
```

SOLUTION   The vertices are $(1, 2)$, $(3, 6)$, and $(-1, 4)$. Using the formula in the preceding box, we get

$$\mathcal{A} = \pm \frac{1}{2} \begin{vmatrix} -1 & 4 & 1 \\ 3 & 6 & 1 \\ 1 & 2 & 1 \end{vmatrix} = \pm \frac{1}{2}(-12)$$

To make the area positive, we choose the negative sign in the formula. Thus, the area of the triangle is

$$\mathcal{A} = -\tfrac{1}{2}(-12) = 6$$

✎ NOW TRY EXERCISE 55 ■

10.6 EXERCISES

CONCEPTS

1. *True or false?* det(A) is defined only for a square matrix A.

2. *True or false?* det(A) is a number, not a matrix.

3. *True or false?* If det(A) = 0, then A is not invertible.

4. Fill in the blanks with appropriate numbers to calculate the determinant. Where there is "$\pm$", choose the appropriate sign (+ or −).

(a) $\begin{vmatrix} 2 & 1 \\ -3 & 4 \end{vmatrix} = \blacksquare\blacksquare - \blacksquare\blacksquare = $ _____

(b) $\begin{vmatrix} 1 & 0 & 2 \\ 3 & 2 & 1 \\ 0 & -3 & 4 \end{vmatrix} = \pm\blacksquare(\blacksquare\blacksquare - \blacksquare\blacksquare) \pm \blacksquare(\blacksquare\blacksquare - \blacksquare\blacksquare)$

$\pm \blacksquare(\blacksquare\blacksquare - \blacksquare\blacksquare) = $ _____

SKILLS

5–12 ■ Find the determinant of the matrix, if it exists.

5. $\begin{bmatrix} 2 & 0 \\ 0 & 3 \end{bmatrix}$

6. $\begin{bmatrix} 0 & -1 \\ 2 & 0 \end{bmatrix}$

7. $\begin{bmatrix} 4 & 5 \\ 0 & -1 \end{bmatrix}$

8. $\begin{bmatrix} -2 & 1 \\ 3 & -2 \end{bmatrix}$

9. $\begin{bmatrix} 2 & 5 \end{bmatrix}$

10. $\begin{bmatrix} 3 \\ 0 \end{bmatrix}$

11. $\begin{bmatrix} \frac{1}{2} & \frac{1}{8} \\ 1 & \frac{1}{2} \end{bmatrix}$

12. $\begin{bmatrix} 2.2 & -1.4 \\ 0.5 & 1.0 \end{bmatrix}$

13–18 ■ Evaluate the minor and cofactor using the matrix A.

$$A = \begin{bmatrix} 1 & 0 & \frac{1}{2} \\ -3 & 5 & 2 \\ 0 & 0 & 4 \end{bmatrix}$$

13. M_{11}, A_{11}

14. M_{33}, A_{33}

15. M_{12}, A_{12}

16. M_{13}, A_{13}

17. M_{23}, A_{23}

18. M_{32}, A_{32}

19–26 ■ Find the determinant of the matrix. Determine whether the matrix has an inverse, but don't calculate the inverse.

19. $\begin{bmatrix} 2 & 1 & 0 \\ 0 & -2 & 4 \\ 0 & 1 & -3 \end{bmatrix}$ **20.** $\begin{bmatrix} 1 & 2 & 5 \\ -2 & -3 & 2 \\ 3 & 5 & 3 \end{bmatrix}$

21. $\begin{bmatrix} 30 & 0 & 20 \\ 0 & -10 & -20 \\ 40 & 0 & 10 \end{bmatrix}$ **22.** $\begin{bmatrix} -2 & -\frac{3}{2} & \frac{1}{2} \\ 2 & 4 & 0 \\ \frac{1}{2} & 2 & 1 \end{bmatrix}$

23. $\begin{bmatrix} 1 & 3 & 7 \\ 2 & 0 & 8 \\ 0 & 2 & 2 \end{bmatrix}$ **24.** $\begin{bmatrix} 0 & -1 & 0 \\ 2 & 6 & 4 \\ 1 & 0 & 3 \end{bmatrix}$

25. $\begin{bmatrix} 1 & 3 & 3 & 0 \\ 0 & 2 & 0 & 1 \\ -1 & 0 & 0 & 2 \\ 1 & 6 & 4 & 1 \end{bmatrix}$ **26.** $\begin{bmatrix} 1 & 2 & 0 & 2 \\ 3 & -4 & 0 & 4 \\ 0 & 1 & 6 & 0 \\ 1 & 0 & 2 & 0 \end{bmatrix}$

27–30 ■ Evaluate the determinant, using row or column operations whenever possible to simplify your work.

27. $\begin{vmatrix} 0 & 0 & 4 & 6 \\ 2 & 1 & 1 & 3 \\ 2 & 1 & 2 & 3 \\ 3 & 0 & 1 & 7 \end{vmatrix}$ **28.** $\begin{vmatrix} -2 & 3 & -1 & 7 \\ 4 & 6 & -2 & 3 \\ 7 & 7 & 0 & 5 \\ 3 & -12 & 4 & 0 \end{vmatrix}$

29. $\begin{vmatrix} 1 & 2 & 3 & 4 & 5 \\ 0 & 2 & 4 & 6 & 8 \\ 0 & 0 & 3 & 6 & 9 \\ 0 & 0 & 0 & 4 & 8 \\ 0 & 0 & 0 & 0 & 5 \end{vmatrix}$ **30.** $\begin{vmatrix} 2 & -1 & 6 & 4 \\ 7 & 2 & -2 & 5 \\ 4 & -2 & 10 & 8 \\ 6 & 1 & 1 & 4 \end{vmatrix}$

31. Let

$$B = \begin{bmatrix} 4 & 1 & 0 \\ -2 & -1 & 1 \\ 4 & 0 & 3 \end{bmatrix}$$

(a) Evaluate det(B) by expanding by the second row.
(b) Evaluate det(B) by expanding by the third column.
(c) Do your results in parts (a) and (b) agree?

32. Consider the system

$$\begin{cases} x + 2y + 6z = 5 \\ -3x - 6y + 5z = 8 \\ 2x + 6y + 9z = 7 \end{cases}$$

(a) Verify that $x = -1, y = 0, z = 1$ is a solution of the system.
(b) Find the determinant of the coefficient matrix.
(c) Without solving the system, determine whether there are any other solutions.
(d) Can Cramer's Rule be used to solve this system? Why or why not?

33–48 ■ Use Cramer's Rule to solve the system.

33. $\begin{cases} 2x - y = -9 \\ x + 2y = 8 \end{cases}$ **34.** $\begin{cases} 6x + 12y = 33 \\ 4x + 7y = 20 \end{cases}$

35. $\begin{cases} x - 6y = 3 \\ 3x + 2y = 1 \end{cases}$ **36.** $\begin{cases} \frac{1}{2}x + \frac{1}{3}y = 1 \\ \frac{1}{4}x - \frac{1}{6}y = -\frac{3}{2} \end{cases}$

37. $\begin{cases} 0.4x + 1.2y = 0.4 \\ 1.2x + 1.6y = 3.2 \end{cases}$ **38.** $\begin{cases} 10x - 17y = 21 \\ 20x - 31y = 39 \end{cases}$

39. $\begin{cases} x - y + 2z = 0 \\ 3x + z = 11 \\ -x + 2y = 0 \end{cases}$ **40.** $\begin{cases} 5x - 3y + z = 6 \\ 4y - 6z = 22 \\ 7x + 10y = -13 \end{cases}$

41. $\begin{cases} 2x_1 + 3x_2 - 5x_3 = 1 \\ x_1 + x_2 - x_3 = 2 \\ 2x_2 + x_3 = 8 \end{cases}$ **42.** $\begin{cases} -2a + c = 2 \\ a + 2b - c = 9 \\ 3a + 5b + 2c = 22 \end{cases}$

43. $\begin{cases} \frac{1}{3}x - \frac{1}{5}y + \frac{1}{2}z = \frac{7}{10} \\ -\frac{2}{3}x + \frac{2}{5}y + \frac{3}{2}z = \frac{11}{10} \\ x - \frac{4}{5}y + z = \frac{9}{5} \end{cases}$ **44.** $\begin{cases} 2x - y = 5 \\ 5x + 3z = 19 \\ 4y + 7z = 17 \end{cases}$

45. $\begin{cases} 3y + 5z = 4 \\ 2x - z = 10 \\ 4x + 7y = 0 \end{cases}$ **46.** $\begin{cases} 2x - 5y = 4 \\ x + y - z = 8 \\ 3x + 5z = 0 \end{cases}$

47. $\begin{cases} x + y + z + w = 0 \\ 2x + w = 0 \\ y - z = 0 \\ x + 2z = 1 \end{cases}$ **48.** $\begin{cases} x + y = 1 \\ y + z = 2 \\ z + w = 3 \\ w - x = 4 \end{cases}$

49–50 ■ Evaluate the determinants.

49. $\begin{vmatrix} a & 0 & 0 & 0 & 0 \\ 0 & b & 0 & 0 & 0 \\ 0 & 0 & c & 0 & 0 \\ 0 & 0 & 0 & d & 0 \\ 0 & 0 & 0 & 0 & e \end{vmatrix}$ **50.** $\begin{vmatrix} a & a & a & a & a \\ 0 & a & a & a & a \\ 0 & 0 & a & a & a \\ 0 & 0 & 0 & a & a \\ 0 & 0 & 0 & 0 & a \end{vmatrix}$

51–54 ■ Solve for x.

51. $\begin{vmatrix} x & 12 & 13 \\ 0 & x - 1 & 23 \\ 0 & 0 & x - 2 \end{vmatrix} = 0$ **52.** $\begin{vmatrix} x & 1 & 1 \\ 1 & 1 & x \\ x & 1 & x \end{vmatrix} = 0$

53. $\begin{vmatrix} 1 & 0 & x \\ x^2 & 1 & 0 \\ x & 0 & 1 \end{vmatrix} = 0$ **54.** $\begin{vmatrix} a & b & x - a \\ x & x + b & x \\ 0 & 1 & 1 \end{vmatrix} = 0$

55–58 ■ Sketch the triangle with the given vertices, and use a determinant to find its area.

55. $(0, 0), (6, 2), (3, 8)$ **56.** $(1, 0), (3, 5), (-2, 2)$

57. $(-1, 3), (2, 9), (5, -6)$ **58.** $(-2, 5), (7, 2), (3, -4)$

59. Show that $\begin{vmatrix} 1 & x & x^2 \\ 1 & y & y^2 \\ 1 & z & z^2 \end{vmatrix} = (x - y)(y - z)(z - x)$

APPLICATIONS

60. Buying Fruit A roadside fruit stand sells apples at 75¢ a pound, peaches at 90¢ a pound, and pears at 60¢ a pound. Muriel buys 18 pounds of fruit at a total cost of $13.80. Her peaches and pears together cost $1.80 more than her apples.
   (a) Set up a linear system for the number of pounds of apples, peaches, and pears that she bought.
   (b) Solve the system using Cramer's Rule.

61. The Arch of a Bridge The opening of a railway bridge over a roadway is in the shape of a parabola. A surveyor measures the heights of three points on the bridge, as shown in the figure. He wishes to find an equation of the form

$$y = ax^2 + bx + c$$

to model the shape of the arch.
   (a) Use the surveyed points to set up a system of linear equations for the unknown coefficients a, b, and c.
   (b) Solve the system using Cramer's Rule.

62. A Triangular Plot of Land An outdoors club is purchasing land to set up a conservation area. The last remaining piece they need to buy is the triangular plot shown in the figure. Use the determinant formula for the area of a triangle to find the area of the plot.

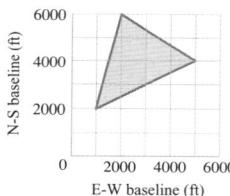

DISCOVERY ▪ DISCUSSION ▪ WRITING

63. Determinant Formula for the Area of a Triangle
The figure shows a triangle in the plane with vertices (a_1, b_1), (a_2, b_2), and (a_3, b_3).

(a) Find the coordinates of the vertices of the surrounding rectangle, and find its area.
(b) Find the area of the red triangle by subtracting the areas of the three blue triangles from the area of the rectangle.
(c) Use your answer to part (b) to show that the area of the red triangle is given by

$$\text{area} = \pm\frac{1}{2} \begin{vmatrix} a_1 & b_1 & 1 \\ a_2 & b_2 & 1 \\ a_3 & b_3 & 1 \end{vmatrix}$$

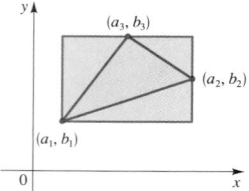

64. Collinear Points and Determinants
   (a) If three points lie on a line, what is the area of the "triangle" that they determine? Use the answer to this question, together with the determinant formula for the area of a triangle, to explain why the points (a_1, b_1), (a_2, b_2), and (a_3, b_3) are collinear if and only if

$$\begin{vmatrix} a_1 & b_1 & 1 \\ a_2 & b_2 & 1 \\ a_3 & b_3 & 1 \end{vmatrix} = 0$$

   (b) Use a determinant to check whether each set of points is collinear. Graph them to verify your answer.
   (i) $(-6, 4)$, $(2, 10)$, $(6, 13)$
   (ii) $(-5, 10)$, $(2, 6)$, $(15, -2)$

65. Determinant Form for the Equation of a Line
   (a) Use the result of Exercise 64(a) to show that the equation of the line containing the points (x_1, y_1) and (x_2, y_2) is

$$\begin{vmatrix} x & y & 1 \\ x_1 & y_1 & 1 \\ x_2 & y_2 & 1 \end{vmatrix} = 0$$

   (b) Use the result of part (a) to find an equation for the line containing the points $(20, 50)$ and $(-10, 25)$.

66. Matrices with Determinant Zero Use the definition of determinant and the elementary row and column operations to explain why matrices of the following types have determinant 0.
   (a) A matrix with a row or column consisting entirely of zeros
   (b) A matrix with two rows the same or two columns the same
   (c) A matrix in which one row is a multiple of another row, or one column is a multiple of another column

67. Solving Linear Systems Suppose you have to solve a linear system with five equations and five variables without the assistance of a calculator or computer. Which method would you prefer: Cramer's Rule or Gaussian elimination? Write a short paragraph explaining the reasons for your answer.

⬤ **DISCOVERY PROJECT**   **Computer Graphics I**

In this project we investigate how matrices are used to manipulate images on a computer screen by compressing, stretching, reflecting, and shearing. You can find the project at the book companion website: **www.stewartmath.com**

10.7 PARTIAL FRACTIONS

> Distinct Linear Factors ▶ Repeated Linear Factors ▶ Irreducible Quadratic
> Factors ▶ Repeated Irreducible Quadratic Factors

Common denominator
$$\frac{1}{x-1}+\frac{1}{2x+1}=\frac{3x}{2x^2-x-1}$$
Partial fractions

To write a sum or difference of fractional expressions as a single fraction, we bring them to a common denominator. For example,

$$\frac{1}{x-1}+\frac{1}{2x+1}=\frac{(2x+1)+(x-1)}{(x-1)(2x+1)}=\frac{3x}{2x^2-x-1}$$

But for some applications of algebra to calculus we must reverse this process—that is, we must express a fraction such as $3x/(2x^2-x-1)$ as the sum of the simpler fractions $1/(x-1)$ and $1/(2x+1)$. These simpler fractions are called *partial fractions*; we learn how to find them in this section.

Let r be the rational function

$$r(x)=\frac{P(x)}{Q(x)}$$

where the degree of P is less than the degree of Q. By the Linear and Quadratic Factors Theorem in Section 3.6, every polynomial with real coefficients can be factored completely into linear and irreducible quadratic factors, that is, factors of the form $ax+b$ and ax^2+bx+c, where a, b, and c are real numbers. For instance,

$$x^4-1=(x^2-1)(x^2+1)=(x-1)(x+1)(x^2+1)$$

After we have completely factored the denominator Q of r, we can express $r(x)$ as a sum of **partial fractions** of the form

$$\frac{A}{(ax+b)^i}\qquad\text{and}\qquad\frac{Ax+B}{(ax^2+bx+c)^j}$$

This sum is called the **partial fraction decomposition** of r. Let's examine the details of the four possible cases.

▼ Distinct Linear Factors

We first consider the case in which the denominator factors into distinct linear factors.

CASE 1: THE DENOMINATOR IS A PRODUCT OF DISTINCT LINEAR FACTORS

Suppose that we can factor $Q(x)$ as

$$Q(x)=(a_1x+b_1)(a_2x+b_2)\cdots(a_nx+b_n)$$

with no factor repeated. In this case the partial fraction decomposition of $P(x)/Q(x)$ takes the form

$$\frac{P(x)}{Q(x)}=\frac{A}{a_1x+b_1}+\frac{A_2}{a_2x+b_2}+\cdots+\frac{A_n}{a_nx+b_n}$$

SUGGESTED TIME AND EMPHASIS

$\frac{1}{2}$–1 class, optional material

EXAMPLE
Case 1:
$$\frac{x-7}{(x-2)(x+3)}=\frac{-1}{x-2}+\frac{2}{x+3}$$

TEXT QUESTION
What does it mean to express a rational expression as partial fractions?

Answer
It means to write the expression as a sum of fractions with simpler denominators.

ALTERNATE EXAMPLE 1

Find the partial fraction decomposition of

$$\frac{13x + 17}{x^3 \cdot + 2x^2 - x - 2}$$

ANSWER

$$\frac{5}{x - 1} - \frac{2}{x + 1} - \frac{3}{x + 2}$$

The Rhind Papyrus is the oldest known mathematical document. It is an Egyptian scroll written in 1650 B.C. by the scribe Ahmes, who explains that it is an exact copy of a scroll written 200 years earlier. Ahmes claims that his papyrus contains "a thorough study of all things, insight into all that exists, knowledge of all obscure secrets." Actually, the document contains rules for doing arithmetic, including multiplication and division of fractions and several exercises with solutions. The exercise shown below reads: "A heap and its seventh make nineteen; how large is the heap?" In solving problems of this sort, the Egyptians used partial fractions because their number system required all fractions to be written as sums of reciprocals of whole numbers. For example, $\frac{7}{12}$ would be written as $\frac{1}{3} + \frac{1}{4}$.

The papyrus gives a correct formula for the volume of a truncated pyramid, which the ancient Egyptians used when building the pyramids at Giza. It also gives the formula $A = \left(\frac{8}{9}d\right)^2$ for the area of a circle with diameter d. How close is this to the actual area?

The constants $A_1, A_2, \ldots , A_n$ are determined as in the following example.

EXAMPLE 1 | Distinct Linear Factors

Find the partial fraction decomposition of $\dfrac{5x + 7}{x^3 + 2x^2 - x - 2}$.

SOLUTION   The denominator factors as follows.

$$x^3 + 2x^2 - x - 2 = x^2(x + 2) - (x + 2) = (x^2 - 1)(x + 2)$$
$$= (x - 1)(x + 1)(x + 2)$$

This gives us the partial fraction decomposition

$$\frac{5x + 7}{x^3 + 2x^2 - x - 2} = \frac{A}{x - 1} + \frac{B}{x + 1} + \frac{C}{x + 2}$$

Multiplying each side by the common denominator, $(x - 1)(x + 1)(x + 2)$, we get

$$5x + 7 = A(x + 1)(x + 2) + B(x - 1)(x + 2) + C(x - 1)(x + 1)$$
$$= A(x^2 + 3x + 2) + B(x^2 + x - 2) + C(x^2 - 1) \qquad \text{Expand}$$
$$= (A + B + C)x^2 + (3A + B)x + (2A - 2B - C) \qquad \text{Combine like terms}$$

If two polynomials are equal, then their coefficients are equal. Thus since $5x + 7$ has no x^2-term, we have $A + B + C = 0$. Similarly, by comparing the coefficients of x, we see that $3A + B = 5$, and by comparing constant terms, we get $2A - 2B - C = 7$. This leads to the following system of linear equations for A, B, and C.

$$\begin{cases} A + B + C = 0 & \text{Equation 1: Coefficients of } x^2 \\ 3A + B = 5 & \text{Equation 2: Coefficients of } x \\ 2A - 2B - C = 7 & \text{Equation 3: Constant coefficients} \end{cases}$$

We use Gaussian elimination to solve this system.

$$\begin{cases} A + B + C = 0 & \\ -2B - 3C = 5 & \text{Equation 2 + (-3) × Equation 1} \\ -4B - 3C = 7 & \text{Equation 3 + (-2) × Equation 1} \end{cases}$$

$$\begin{cases} A + B + C = 0 & \\ -2B - 3C = 5 & \\ 3C = -3 & \text{Equation 3 + (-2) × Equation 2} \end{cases}$$

From the third equation we get $C = -1$. Back-substituting, we find that $B = -1$ and $A = 2$. So the partial fraction decomposition is

$$\frac{5x + 7}{x^3 + 2x^2 - x - 2} = \frac{2}{x - 1} + \frac{-1}{x + 1} + \frac{-1}{x + 2}$$

✎ **NOW TRY EXERCISES 3 AND 13**

The same approach works in the remaining cases. We set up the partial fraction decomposition with the unknown constants A, B, C, ... Then we multiply each side of the resulting equation by the common denominator, simplify the right-hand side of the equation, and equate coefficients. This gives a set of linear equations that will always have a unique solution (provided that the partial fraction decomposition has been set up correctly).

▼ Repeated Linear Factors

We now consider the case in which the denominator factors into linear factors, some of which are repeated.

IN-CLASS MATERIALS

Remind students of the process of polynomial division, perhaps by rewriting $\dfrac{2x^3 + 3x^2 + 7x + 4}{2x + 1}$ as $x^2 + x + 3 + \dfrac{1}{2x + 1}$. Be sure to indicate that, in order to use partial fractions, the degree of the numerator has to be less than the degree of the denominator.

CASE 2: THE DENOMINATOR IS A PRODUCT OF LINEAR FACTORS, SOME OF WHICH ARE REPEATED

Suppose the complete factorization of $Q(x)$ contains the linear factor $ax + b$ repeated k times; that is, $(ax + b)^k$ is a factor of $Q(x)$. Then, corresponding to each such factor, the partial fraction decomposition for $P(x)/Q(x)$ contains

$$\frac{A_1}{ax + b} + \frac{A_2}{(ax + b)^2} + \cdots + \frac{A_k}{(ax + b)^k}$$

EXAMPLE 2 | Repeated Linear Factors

Find the partial fraction decomposition of $\dfrac{x^2 + 1}{x(x - 1)^3}$.

SOLUTION Because the factor $x - 1$ is repeated three times in the denominator, the partial fraction decomposition has the form

$$\frac{x^2 + 1}{x(x - 1)^3} = \frac{A}{x} + \frac{B}{x - 1} + \frac{C}{(x - 1)^2} + \frac{D}{(x - 1)^3}$$

Multiplying each side by the common denominator, $x(x - 1)^3$, gives

$$x^2 + 1 = A(x - 1)^3 + Bx(x - 1)^2 + Cx(x - 1) + Dx$$
$$= A(x^3 - 3x^2 + 3x - 1) + B(x^3 - 2x^2 + x) + C(x^2 - x) + Dx \quad \text{Expand}$$
$$= (A + B)x^3 + (-3A - 2B + C)x^2 + (3A + B - C + D)x - A \quad \text{Combine like terms}$$

Equating coefficients, we get the following equations.

$$\begin{cases} A + B & = 0 & \text{Coefficients of } x^3 \\ -3A - 2B + C & = 1 & \text{Coefficients of } x^2 \\ 3A + B - C + D & = 0 & \text{Coefficients of } x \\ -A & = 1 & \text{Constant coefficients} \end{cases}$$

If we rearrange these equations by putting the last one in the first position, we can easily see (using substitution) that the solution to the system is $A = -1, B = 1, C = 0, D = 2$, so the partial fraction decomposition is

$$\frac{x^2 + 1}{x(x - 1)^3} = \frac{-1}{x} + \frac{1}{x - 1} + \frac{2}{(x - 1)^3}$$

NOW TRY EXERCISES 5 AND 29

▼ Irreducible Quadratic Factors

We now consider the case in which the denominator has distinct irreducible quadratic factors.

CASE 3: THE DENOMINATOR HAS IRREDUCIBLE QUADRATIC FACTORS, NONE OF WHICH IS REPEATED

Suppose the complete factorization of $Q(x)$ contains the quadratic factor $ax^2 + bx + c$ (which can't be factored further). Then, corresponding to this, the partial fraction decomposition of $P(x)/Q(x)$ will have a term of the form

$$\frac{Ax + B}{ax^2 + bx + c}$$

EXAMPLE
Case 2:
$$\frac{3x^2 - x - 3}{x^2(x + 1)} = \frac{1}{x + 1} + \frac{2}{x} - \frac{3}{x^2}$$

ALTERNATE EXAMPLE 2
Find the partial fraction decomposition of $\dfrac{6x^2 + 6}{x(x - 1)^3}$.

ANSWER
$$\frac{6}{x} + \frac{6}{x - 1} + \frac{12}{(x - 1)^3}$$

EXAMPLE
Case 3:
$$\frac{3}{(x - 1)(x^2 + 2)} = \frac{1}{x - 1} - \frac{x + 1}{x^2 + 2}$$

IN-CLASS MATERIALS
Find the coefficients for the partial fraction decomposition for $\dfrac{x + 3}{(x - 2)(x - 1)}$ in two different ways: first using two linear equations and then using the method of creating zeros [setting $x = 1$ and then $x = -2$ in $x + 3 = A(x + 2) + B(x - 1)$].

ALTERNATE EXAMPLE 3

Find the partial fraction decomposition of

$$\frac{11x^2 - 2x + 24}{x^3 + 4x}.$$

ANSWER

$$\frac{6}{x} + \frac{5x - 2}{x^2 + 4}$$

EXAMPLE 3 | Distinct Quadratic Factors

Find the partial fraction decomposition of $\dfrac{2x^2 - x + 4}{x^3 + 4x}$.

SOLUTION Since $x^3 + 4x = x(x^2 + 4)$, which can't be factored further, we write

$$\frac{2x^2 - x + 4}{x^3 + 4x} = \frac{A}{x} + \frac{Bx + C}{x^2 + 4}$$

Multiplying by $x(x^2 + 4)$, we get

$$2x^2 - x + 4 = A(x^2 + 4) + (Bx + C)x$$
$$= (A + B)x^2 + Cx + 4A$$

Equating coefficients gives us the equations

$$\begin{cases} A + B = & 2 & \text{Coefficients of } x^2 \\ C = & -1 & \text{Coefficients of } x \\ 4A = & 4 & \text{Constant coefficients} \end{cases}$$

so $A = 1$, $B = 1$, and $C = -1$. The required partial fraction decomposition is

$$\frac{2x^2 - x + 4}{x^3 + 4x} = \frac{1}{x} + \frac{x - 1}{x^2 + 4}$$

✎. NOW TRY EXERCISES **7** AND **37** ∎

▼ **Repeated Irreducible Quadratic Factors**

We now consider the case in which the denominator has irreducible quadratic factors, some of which are repeated.

CASE 4: THE DENOMINATOR HAS A REPEATED IRREDUCIBLE QUADRATIC FACTOR

Suppose the complete factorization of $Q(x)$ contains the factor $(ax^2 + bx + c)^k$, where $ax^2 + bx + c$ can't be factored further. Then the partial fraction decomposition of $P(x)/Q(x)$ will have the terms

$$\frac{A_1x + B_1}{ax^2 + bx + c} + \frac{A_2x + B_2}{(ax^2 + bx + c)^2} + \cdots + \frac{A_kx + B_k}{(ax^2 + bx + c)^k}$$

EXAMPLE
Case 4:

$$\frac{1}{(x^2 + 1)^2 x} = \frac{1}{x} - \frac{x}{x^2 + 1}$$
$$- \frac{x}{(x^2 + 1)^2}$$

EXAMPLE 4 | Repeated Quadratic Factors

Write the form of the partial fraction decomposition of

$$\frac{x^5 - 3x^2 + 12x - 1}{x^3(x^2 + x + 1)(x^2 + 2)^3}$$

SOLUTION

$$\frac{x^5 - 3x^2 + 12x - 1}{x^3(x^2 + x + 1)(x^2 + 2)^3}$$

$$= \frac{A}{x} + \frac{B}{x^2} + \frac{C}{x^3} + \frac{Dx + E}{x^2 + x + 1} + \frac{Fx + G}{x^2 + 2} + \frac{Hx + I}{(x^2 + 2)^2} + \frac{Jx + K}{(x^2 + 2)^3}$$

✎. NOW TRY EXERCISES **11** AND **41** ∎

ALTERNATE EXAMPLE 4
Write the form of the partial fraction decomposition of the following:

$$\frac{x^2 + 12}{(x + 1)^2 (x^2 + 2x + 30)^3 (x - 2)}$$

ANSWER

$$\frac{A}{x - 2} + \frac{B}{(x + 1)} + \frac{C}{(x + 1)^2}$$
$$+ \frac{Dx + E}{(x^2 + 2x + 30)}$$
$$+ \frac{Fx + G}{(x^2 + 2x + 30)^2}$$
$$+ \frac{Hx + I}{(x^2 + 2x + 30)^3}$$

IN-CLASS MATERIALS

Point out that the quadratic in the denominator of $f(x) = \dfrac{1}{x^2 + x - 6}$ is not irreducible. It can be factored into the two linear terms $x - 2$ and $x + 3$, so the partial fraction decomposition is found by writing $\dfrac{1}{x^2 + x - 6} = \dfrac{A}{x + 2} + \dfrac{B}{x - 3}$ and solving for A and B. Therefore it is important, when factoring the denominator, to make sure all quadratics are irreducible.

To find the values of A, B, C, D, E, F, G, H, I, J, and K in Example 4, we would have to solve a system of 11 linear equations. Although possible, this would certainly involve a great deal of work!

The techniques that we have described in this section apply only to rational functions $P(x)/Q(x)$ in which the degree of P is less than the degree of Q. If this isn't the case, we must first use long division to divide Q into P.

EXAMPLE 5 | Using Long Division to Prepare for Partial Fractions

Find the partial fraction decomposition of

$$\frac{2x^4 + 4x^3 - 2x^2 + x + 7}{x^3 + 2x^2 - x - 2}$$

SOLUTION   Since the degree of the numerator is larger than the degree of the denominator, we use long division to obtain

$$
\begin{array}{r}
2x \\
x^3 + 2x^2 - x - 2\overline{\smash{)}2x^4 + 4x^3 - 2x^2 + x + 7} \\
\underline{2x^4 + 4x^3 - 2x^2 - 4x} \\
5x + 7
\end{array}
$$

$$\frac{2x^4 + 4x^3 - 2x^2 + x + 7}{x^3 + 2x^2 - x - 2} = 2x + \frac{5x + 7}{x^3 + 2x^2 - x - 2}$$

The remainder term now satisfies the requirement that the degree of the numerator is less than the degree of the denominator. At this point we proceed as in Example 1 to obtain the decomposition

$$\frac{2x^4 + 4x^3 - 2x^2 + x + 7}{x^3 + 2x^2 - x - 2} = 2x + \frac{2}{x - 1} + \frac{-1}{x + 1} + \frac{-1}{x + 2}$$

✎. NOW TRY EXERCISE **43**   ■

10.7 EXERCISES

CONCEPTS

1–2 ■ For each rational function r, choose from (i)–(iv) the appropriate form for its partial fraction decomposition.

1. $r(x) = \dfrac{4}{x(x - 2)^2}$

(i) $\dfrac{A}{x} + \dfrac{B}{x - 2}$ (ii) $\dfrac{A}{x} + \dfrac{B}{(x - 2)^2}$

(iii) $\dfrac{A}{x} + \dfrac{B}{x - 2} + \dfrac{C}{(x - 2)^2}$ (iv) $\dfrac{A}{x} + \dfrac{B}{x - 2} + \dfrac{Cx + D}{(x - 2)^2}$

2. $r(x) = \dfrac{2x + 8}{(x - 1)(x^2 + 4)}$

(i) $\dfrac{A}{x - 1} + \dfrac{B}{x^2 + 4}$

(ii) $\dfrac{A}{x - 1} + \dfrac{Bx + C}{x^2 + 4}$

(iii) $\dfrac{A}{x - 1} + \dfrac{B}{x + 2} + \dfrac{C}{x^2 + 4}$

(iv) $\dfrac{Ax + B}{x - 1} + \dfrac{Cx + D}{x^2 + 4}$

SKILLS

3–12 ■ Write the form of the partial fraction decomposition of the function (as in Example 4). Do not determine the numerical values of the coefficients.

✎. **3.** $\dfrac{1}{(x - 1)(x + 2)}$ **4.** $\dfrac{x}{x^2 + 3x - 4}$

✎. **5.** $\dfrac{x^2 - 3x + 5}{(x - 2)^2(x + 4)}$ **5.** $\dfrac{1}{x^4 - x^3}$

✎. **7.** $\dfrac{x^2}{(x - 3)(x^2 + 4)}$ **8.** $\dfrac{1}{x^4 - 1}$

9. $\dfrac{x^3 - 4x^2 + 2}{(x^2 + 1)(x^2 + 2)}$ **10.** $\dfrac{x^4 + x^2 + 1}{x^2(x^2 + 4)^2}$

✎. **11.** $\dfrac{x^3 + x + 1}{x(2x - 5)^3(x^2 + 2x + 5)^2}$ **12.** $\dfrac{1}{(x^3 - 1)(x^2 - 1)}$

13–44 ■ Find the partial fraction decomposition of the rational function.

✎. **13.** $\dfrac{2}{(x - 1)(x + 1)}$ **14.** $\dfrac{2x}{(x - 1)(x + 1)}$

IN-CLASS MATERIALS

It is possible to cover this section without covering every single case. For example, one might just cover the idea of linear factors (Cases 1 and 2) and mention that it is also possible to work with irreducible quadratic factors. Notice that just because every rational expression can be decomposed in theory doesn't mean it is always possible in practice, because there is no closed-form formula for factoring a polynomial of degree 5 or higher.

IN-CLASS MATERIALS

Show the class how a complicated partial fractions problem would be set up, without trying to solve it.

15. $\dfrac{5}{(x-1)(x+4)}$

16. $\dfrac{x+6}{x(x+3)}$

17. $\dfrac{12}{x^2-9}$

18. $\dfrac{x-12}{x^2-4x}$

19. $\dfrac{4}{x^2-4}$

20. $\dfrac{2x+1}{x^2+x-2}$

21. $\dfrac{x+14}{x^2-2x-8}$

22. $\dfrac{8x-3}{2x^2-x}$

23. $\dfrac{x}{8x^2-10x+3}$

24. $\dfrac{7x-3}{x^3+2x^2-3x}$

25. $\dfrac{9x^2-9x+6}{2x^3-x^2-8x+4}$

26. $\dfrac{-3x^2-3x+27}{(x+2)(2x^2+3x-9)}$

27. $\dfrac{x^2+1}{x^3+x^2}$

28. $\dfrac{3x^2+5x-13}{(3x+2)(x^2-4x+4)}$

29. $\dfrac{2x}{4x^2+12x+9}$

30. $\dfrac{x-4}{(2x-5)^2}$

31. $\dfrac{4x^2-x-2}{x^4+2x^3}$

32. $\dfrac{x^3-2x^2-4x+3}{x^4}$

33. $\dfrac{-10x^2+27x-14}{(x-1)^3(x+2)}$

34. $\dfrac{-2x^2+5x-1}{x^4-2x^3+2x-1}$

35. $\dfrac{3x^3+22x^2+53x+41}{(x+2)^2(x+3)^2}$

36. $\dfrac{3x^2+12x-20}{x^4-8x^2+16}$

37. $\dfrac{x-3}{x^3+3x}$

38. $\dfrac{3x^2-2x+8}{x^3-x^2+2x-2}$

39. $\dfrac{2x^3+7x+5}{(x^2+x+2)(x^2+1)}$

40. $\dfrac{x^2+x+1}{2x^4+3x^2+1}$

41. $\dfrac{x^4+x^3+x^2-x+1}{x(x^2+1)^2}$

42. $\dfrac{2x^2-x+8}{(x^2+4)^2}$

43. $\dfrac{x^5-2x^4+x^3+x+5}{x^3-2x^2+x-2}$

44. $\dfrac{x^5-3x^4+3x^3-4x^2+4x+12}{(x-2)^2(x^2+2)}$

45. Determine A and B in terms of a and b.

$$\frac{ax+b}{x^2-1}=\frac{A}{x-1}+\frac{B}{x+1}$$

46. Determine A, B, C, and D in terms of a and b.

$$\frac{ax^3+bx^2}{(x^2+1)^2}=\frac{Ax+B}{x^2+1}+\frac{Cx+D}{(x^2+1)^2}$$

DISCOVERY ■ DISCUSSION ■ WRITING

47. **Recognizing Partial Fraction Decompositions** For each expression, determine whether it is already a partial fraction decomposition or whether it can be decomposed further.

(a) $\dfrac{x}{x^2+1}+\dfrac{1}{x+1}$

(b) $\dfrac{x}{(x+1)^2}$

(c) $\dfrac{1}{x+1}+\dfrac{2}{(x+1)^2}$

(d) $\dfrac{x+2}{(x^2+1)^2}$

48. **Assembling and Disassembling Partial Fractions** The following expression is a partial fraction decomposition.

$$\frac{2}{x-1}+\frac{1}{(x-1)^2}+\frac{1}{x+1}$$

Use a common denominator to combine the terms into one fraction. Then use the techniques of this section to find its partial fraction decomposition. Did you get back the original expression?

10.8 SYSTEMS OF NONLINEAR EQUATIONS

| Substitution and Elimination Methods ▶ Graphical Method

In this section we solve systems of equations in which the equations are not all linear. The methods we learned in Section 10.1 can also be used to solve nonlinear systems.

▼ Substitution and Elimination Methods

To solve a system of nonlinear equations, we can use the substitution or elimination method, as illustrated in the next examples.

EXAMPLE 1 | Substitution Method

Find all solutions of the system.

$$\begin{cases} x^2 + y^2 = 100 & \text{Equation 1} \\ 3x - y = 10 & \text{Equation 2} \end{cases}$$

SUGGESTED TIME AND EMPHASIS

$\frac{1}{2}$–1 class, essential material

ALTERNATE EXAMPLE 1
Find all solutions of the system.
$$\begin{cases} x^2 + y^2 = 625 \\ 3x - y = -25 \end{cases}$$

ANSWER
$(0, 25)$, $(-15, -20)$

TEXT QUESTIONS

Give an example of a linear system of two equations and a nonlinear system of two equations.

Answer

Answers will vary.

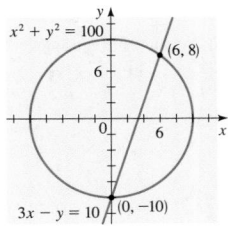

$x^2 + y^2 = 100$

(6, 8)

$3x - y = 10$ (0, −10)

FIGURE 1

CHECK YOUR ANSWERS

$x = 0, y = -10$:

$$\begin{cases} (0)^2 + (-10)^2 = 100 \\ 3(0) - (-10) = 10 \end{cases} ✔$$

$x = 6, y = 8$:

$$\begin{cases} (6)^2 + (8)^2 = 36 + 64 = 100 \\ 3(6) - (8) = 18 - 8 = 10 \end{cases} ✔$$

SOLUTION   **Solve for one variable.**   We start by solving for y in the second equation:

$$y = 3x - 10 \qquad \text{Solve for } y \text{ in Equation 2}$$

Substitute.   Next we substitute for y in the first equation and solve for x:

$$x^2 + (3x - 10)^2 = 100 \qquad \text{Substitute } y = 3x - 10 \text{ into Equation 1}$$

$$x^2 + (9x^2 - 60x + 100) = 100 \qquad \text{Expand}$$

$$10x^2 - 60x = 0 \qquad \text{Simplify}$$

$$10x(x - 6) = 0 \qquad \text{Factor}$$

$$x = 0 \quad \text{or} \quad x = 6 \qquad \text{Solve for } x$$

Back-subsitute.   Now we back-substitute these values of x into the equation $y = 3x - 10$:

$$\text{For} \quad x = 0: \qquad y = 3(0) - 10 = -10 \qquad \text{Back-substitute}$$

$$\text{For} \quad x = 6: \qquad y = 3(6) - 10 = \quad 8 \qquad \text{Back-substitute}$$

So we have two solutions: $(0, -10)$ and $(6, 8)$.

The graph of the first equation is a circle, and the graph of the second equation is a line; Figure 1 shows that the graphs intersect at the two points $(0, -10)$ and $(6, 8)$.

✎ NOW TRY EXERCISE **5**   ■

EXAMPLE 2 | Elimination Method

Find all solutions of the system.

$$\begin{cases} 3x^2 + 2y = 26 & \text{Equation 1} \\ 5x^2 + 7y = 3 & \text{Equation 2} \end{cases}$$

SOLUTION   We choose to eliminate the x-term, so we multiply the first equation by 5 and the second equation by -3. Then we add the two equations and solve for y.

$$\begin{cases} 15x^2 + 10y = \quad 130 & \quad 5 \times \text{Equation 1} \\ -15x^2 - 21y = \quad -9 & \quad (-3) \times \text{Equation 2} \end{cases}$$

$$-11y = 121 \qquad \text{Add}$$

$$y = -11 \qquad \text{Solve for } y$$

Now we back-substitute $y = -11$ into one of the original equations, say $3x^2 + 2y = 26$, and solve for x.

$$3x^2 + 2(-11) = 26 \qquad \text{Back-substitute } y = -11 \text{ into Equation 1}$$

$$3x^2 = 48 \qquad \text{Add 22}$$

$$x^2 = 16 \qquad \text{Divide by 3}$$

$$x = -4 \quad \text{or} \quad x = 4 \qquad \text{Solve for } x$$

So we have two solutions: $(-4, -11)$ and $(4, -11)$.

The graphs of both equations are parabolas (see Section 3.1). Figure 2 shows that the graphs intersect at the two points $(-4, -11)$ and $(4, -11)$.

✎ NOW TRY EXERCISE **11**   ■

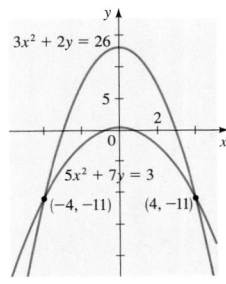

$3x^2 + 2y = 26$

$5x^2 + 7y = 3$

$(-4, -11)$ $(4, -11)$

FIGURE 2

CHECK YOUR ANSWERS

$x = -4, y = -11$:

$$\begin{cases} 3(-4)^2 + 2(-11) = 26 \\ 5(-4)^2 + 7(-11) = 3 \end{cases} ✔$$

$x = 4, y = -11$:

$$\begin{cases} 3(4)^2 + 2(-11) = 26 \\ 5(4)^2 + 7(-11) = 3 \end{cases} ✔$$

IN-CLASS MATERIALS

- Point out that, as opposed to systems of linear equations, a system of nonlinear equations can have any number of solutions. Sketch the system $y = x, y = x^3$ to show a very simple system that has exactly three solutions.
- Have the students discuss the maximum number of solutions of a system consisting of a linear equation and a polynomial equation of degree d.

ALTERNATE EXAMPLE 3

Find all solutions of the system, correct to one decimal place.

$$\begin{cases} y = x^3 - x \\ x^2 + y^2 = 2 \end{cases}$$

ANSWER

$x \approx 1.2, y \approx 0.7$, and $x \approx -1.2$, $y \approx -0.7$

EXAMPLE

A nonlinear system with an integer solution:

$$\begin{cases} x^3 - y^2 = 23 \\ 2x - 3y = 0 \end{cases}$$

ANSWER

$x = 3, y = 2$

EXAMPLE

A nonlinear system with a transcendental solution:

$$\begin{cases} e^x + 2y = 5 \\ -e^x + 5y = 2 \end{cases}$$

ANSWER

$x = \ln 3, y = 1$

▼ Graphical Method

The graphical method is particularly useful in solving systems of nonlinear equations.

EXAMPLE 3 | Graphical Method

Find all solutions of the system

$$\begin{cases} x^2 - y = 2 \\ 2x - y = -1 \end{cases}$$

SOLUTION **Graph each equation.** Solving for y in terms of x, we get the equivalent system

$$\begin{cases} y = x^2 - 2 \\ y = 2x + 1 \end{cases}$$

Find intersection points. Figure 3 shows that the graphs of these equations intersect at two points. Zooming in, we see that the solutions are

$$(-1, -1) \quad \text{and} \quad (3, 7)$$

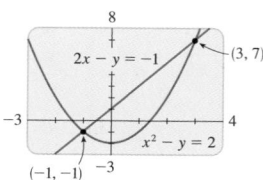

FIGURE 3

╔══════════════════════════╗
║ CHECK YOUR ANSWERS ║
╚══════════════════════════╝

$x = -1, y = -1$: $\qquad\qquad$ $x = 3, y = 7$:

$$\begin{cases} (-1)^2 - (-1) = 2 \\ 2(-1) - (-1) = -1 \end{cases} ✔ \qquad \begin{cases} 3^2 - 7 = 2 \\ 2(3) - 7 = -1 \end{cases} ✔$$

✎ NOW TRY EXERCISE **33** ■

MATHEMATICS IN THE MODERN WORLD

Global Positioning System (GPS)

Courtesy of NASA

On a cold, foggy day in 1707 a British naval fleet was sailing home at a fast clip. The fleet's navigators didn't know it, but the fleet was only a few yards from the rocky shores of England. In the ensuing disaster the fleet was totally destroyed. This tragedy could have been avoided had the navigators known their positions. In those days latitude was determined by the position of the North Star (and this could only be done at night in good weather), and longitude by the position of the sun relative to where it would be in England *at that same time.* So navigation required an accurate method of telling time on ships. (The invention of the spring-loaded clock brought about the eventual solution.)

Since then, several different methods have been developed to determine position, and all rely heavily on mathematics (see LORAN, page 747). The latest method, called the Global Positioning System (GPS), uses triangulation. In this system, 24 satellites are strategically located above the surface of the earth. A handheld GPS device measures distance from a satellite, using the travel time of radio signals emitted from the satellite. Knowing the distances to three different satellites tells us that we are at the point of intersection of three different spheres. This uniquely determines our position (see Exercise 47, page 703).

EXAMPLE 4 | Solving a System of Equations Graphically

Find all solutions of the system, correct to one decimal place.

$$\begin{cases} x^2 + y^2 = 12 & \text{Equation 1} \\ y = 2x^2 - 5x & \text{Equation 2} \end{cases}$$

SOLUTION   The graph of the first equation is a circle, and the graph of the second is a parabola. To graph the circle on a graphing calculator, we must first solve for y in terms of x (see Section 1.9).

$$x^2 + y^2 = 12$$

$$y^2 = 12 - x^2 \qquad \text{Isolate } y^2 \text{ on LHS}$$

$$y = \pm\sqrt{12 - x^2} \qquad \text{Take square roots}$$

To graph the circle, we must graph both functions.

$$y = \sqrt{12 - x^2} \qquad \text{and} \qquad y = -\sqrt{12 - x^2}$$

In Figure 4 the graph of the circle is shown in red, and the parabola is shown in blue. The graphs intersect in Quadrants I and II. Zooming in, or using the `Intersect` command, we see that the intersection points are $(-0.559, 3.419)$ and $(2.847, 1.974)$. There also appears to be an intersection point in Quadrant IV. However, when we zoom in, we see that the curves come close to each other but don't intersect (see Figure 5). Thus the system has two solutions; rounded to the nearest tenth, they are

$$(-0.6, 3.4) \quad \text{and} \quad (2.8, 2.0)$$

(a)

(b)

FIGURE 4 $x^2 + y^2 = 12$, $y = 2x^2 - 5x$

FIGURE 5   Zooming in

✎. NOW TRY EXERCISE **37**

10.8 EXERCISES

CONCEPTS

1–2 ■ The system of equations

$$\begin{cases} 2y - x^2 = 0 \\ y - x = 4 \end{cases}$$

is graphed to the right.

1. Use the graph to find the solution(s) of the system.

2. Check that the solutions you found in Exercise 1 satisfy the system.

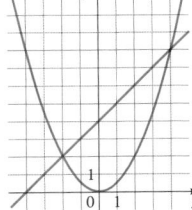

Find all solutions of the system.
$$\begin{cases} x^2 - y = 1 \\ 3x - y = -3 \end{cases}$$

ANSWER
$(4, 15), (-1, 0)$

DRILL QUESTIONS
Solve the following system:
$$\begin{cases} x^2 + 2y = 6 \\ 3x^2 - 4y = 8 \end{cases}$$

Answer
$x = 2, y = 1$ and $x = -2, y = 1$

SKILLS

3–8 ■ Use the substitution method to find all solutions of the system of equations.

3. $\begin{cases} y = x^2 \\ y = x + 12 \end{cases}$

4. $\begin{cases} x^2 + y^2 = 25 \\ y = 2x \end{cases}$

5. $\begin{cases} x^2 + y^2 = 8 \\ x + y = 0 \end{cases}$

6. $\begin{cases} x^2 + y = 9 \\ x - y + 3 = 0 \end{cases}$

7. $\begin{cases} x + y^2 = 0 \\ 2x + 5y^2 = 75 \end{cases}$

8. $\begin{cases} x^2 - y = 1 \\ 2x^2 + 3y = 17 \end{cases}$

9–14 ■ Use the elimination method to find all solutions of the system of equations.

9. $\begin{cases} x^2 - 2y = 1 \\ x^2 + 5y = 29 \end{cases}$

10. $\begin{cases} 3x^2 + 4y = 17 \\ 2x^2 + 5y = 2 \end{cases}$

11. $\begin{cases} 3x^2 - y^2 = 11 \\ x^2 + 4y^2 = 8 \end{cases}$

12. $\begin{cases} 2x^2 + 4y = 13 \\ x^2 - y^2 = \frac{7}{2} \end{cases}$

13. $\begin{cases} x - y^2 + 3 = 0 \\ 2x^2 + y^2 - 4 = 0 \end{cases}$

14. $\begin{cases} x^2 - y^2 = 1 \\ 2x^2 - y^2 = x + 3 \end{cases}$

15–18 ■ Two equations and their graphs are given. Find the intersection point(s) of the graphs by solving the system.

15. $\begin{cases} x^2 + y = 8 \\ x - 2y = -6 \end{cases}$

16. $\begin{cases} x - y^2 = -4 \\ x - y = 2 \end{cases}$

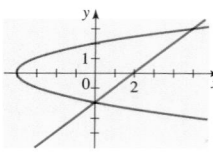

17. $\begin{cases} x^2 + y = 0 \\ x^3 - 2x - y = 0 \end{cases}$

18. $\begin{cases} x^2 + y^2 = 4x \\ x = y^2 \end{cases}$

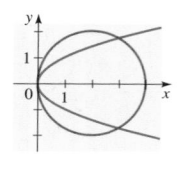

19–32 ■ Find all solutions of the system of equations.

19. $\begin{cases} y + x^2 = 4x \\ y + 4x = 16 \end{cases}$

20. $\begin{cases} x - y^2 = 0 \\ y - x^2 = 0 \end{cases}$

21. $\begin{cases} x - 2y = 2 \\ y^2 - x^2 = 2x + 4 \end{cases}$

22. $\begin{cases} y = 4 - x^2 \\ y = x^2 - 4 \end{cases}$

23. $\begin{cases} x - y = 4 \\ xy = 12 \end{cases}$

24. $\begin{cases} xy = 24 \\ 2x^2 - y^2 + 4 = 0 \end{cases}$

25. $\begin{cases} x^2y = 16 \\ x^2 + 4y + 16 = 0 \end{cases}$

26. $\begin{cases} x + \sqrt{y} = 0 \\ y^2 - 4x^2 = 12 \end{cases}$

27. $\begin{cases} x^2 + y^2 = 9 \\ x^2 - y^2 = 1 \end{cases}$

28. $\begin{cases} x^2 + 2y^2 = 2 \\ 2x^2 - 3y = 15 \end{cases}$

29. $\begin{cases} 2x^2 - 8y^3 = 19 \\ 4x^2 + 16y^3 = 34 \end{cases}$

30. $\begin{cases} x^4 + y^3 = 17 \\ 3x^4 + 5y^3 = 53 \end{cases}$

31. $\begin{cases} \dfrac{2}{x} - \dfrac{3}{y} = 1 \\ -\dfrac{4}{x} + \dfrac{7}{y} = 1 \end{cases}$

32. $\begin{cases} \dfrac{4}{x^2} + \dfrac{6}{y^4} = \dfrac{7}{2} \\ \dfrac{1}{x^2} - \dfrac{2}{y^4} = 0 \end{cases}$

33–40 ■ Use the graphical method to find all solutions of the system of equations, rounded to two decimal places.

33. $\begin{cases} y = x^2 + 8x \\ y = 2x + 16 \end{cases}$

34. $\begin{cases} y = x^2 - 4x \\ 2x - y = 2 \end{cases}$

35. $\begin{cases} x^2 + y^2 = 25 \\ x + 3y = 2 \end{cases}$

36. $\begin{cases} x^2 + y^2 = 17 \\ x^2 - 2x + y^2 = 13 \end{cases}$

37. $\begin{cases} \dfrac{x^2}{9} + \dfrac{y^2}{18} = 1 \\ y = -x^2 + 6x - 2 \end{cases}$

38. $\begin{cases} x^2 - y^2 = 3 \\ y = x^2 - 2x - 8 \end{cases}$

39. $\begin{cases} x^4 + 16y^4 = 32 \\ x^2 + 2x + y = 0 \end{cases}$

40. $\begin{cases} y = e^x + e^{-x} \\ y = 5 - x^2 \end{cases}$

APPLICATIONS

41. Dimensions of a Rectangle A rectangle has an area of 180 cm^2 and a perimeter of 54 cm. What are its dimensions?

42. Legs of a Right Triangle A right triangle has an area of 84 ft^2 and a hypotenuse 25 ft long. What are the lengths of its other two sides?

43. Dimensions of a Rectangle The perimeter of a rectangle is 70, and its diagonal is 25. Find its length and width.

44. Dimensions of a Rectangle A circular piece of sheet metal has a diameter of 20 in. The edges are to be cut off to form a rectangle of area 160 in^2 (see the figure). What are the dimensions of the rectangle?

45. Flight of a Rocket A hill is inclined so that its "slope" is $\frac{1}{2}$, as shown in the figure. We introduce a coordinate system with the origin at the base of the hill and with the scales on the axes measured in meters. A rocket is fired from the base of the hill in such a way that its trajectory is the parabola $y = -x^2 + 401x$. At what point does the rocket strike the hillside? How far is this point from the base of the hill (to the nearest centimeter)?

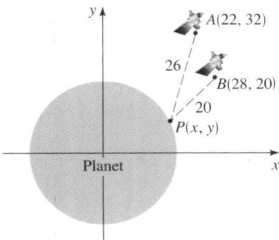

46. Making a Stovepipe A rectangular piece of sheet metal with an area of 1200 in^2 is to be bent into a cylindrical length of stovepipe having a volume of 600 in^3. What are the dimensions of the sheet metal?

47. Global Positioning System (GPS) The Global Positioning System determines the location of an object from its distances to satellites in orbit around the earth. In the simplified, two-dimensional situation shown in the following figure, determine the coordinates of P from the fact that P is 26 units from satellite A and 20 units from satellite B.

DISCOVERY ■ DISCUSSION ■ WRITING

48. Intersection of a Parabola and a Line On a sheet of graph paper or using a graphing calculator, draw the parabola $y = x^2$. Then draw the graphs of the linear equation $y = x + k$ on the same coordinate plane for various values of k. Try to choose values of k so that the line and the parabola intersect at two points for some of your k's and not for others. For what value of k is there exactly one intersection point? Use the results of your experiment to make a conjecture about the values of k for which the following system has two solutions, one solution, and no solution. Prove your conjecture.

$$\begin{cases} y = x^2 \\ y = x + k \end{cases}$$

49. Some Trickier Systems Follow the hints and solve the systems.

(a) $\begin{cases} \log x + \log y = \frac{3}{2} \\ 2\log x - \log y = 0 \end{cases}$ [*Hint:* Add the equations.]

(b) $\begin{cases} 2^x + 2^y = 10 \\ 4^x + 4^y = 68 \end{cases}$ [*Hint:* Note that $4^x = 2^{2x} = (2^x)^2$.]

(c) $\begin{cases} x - y = 3 \\ x^3 - y^3 = 387 \end{cases}$ [*Hint:* Factor the left-hand side of the second equation.]

(d) $\begin{cases} x^2 + xy = 1 \\ xy + y^2 = 3 \end{cases}$ [*Hint:* Add the equations, and factor the result.]

10.9 SYSTEMS OF INEQUALITIES

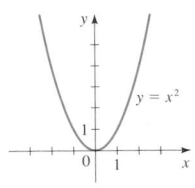

FIGURE 1

| Graphing an Inequality ▶ Systems of Inequalities ▶ Systems of Linear Inequalities ▶ Application: Feasible Regions

In this section we study systems of inequalities in two variables from a graphical point of view.

▼ Graphing an Inequality

We begin by considering the graph of a single inequality. We already know that the graph of $y = x^2$, for example, is the *parabola* in Figure 1. If we replace the equal sign by the symbol $\geq$, we obtain the *inequality*

$$y \geq x^2$$

SUGGESTED TIME AND EMPHASIS

1 class, recommended material

TEXT QUESTION

Consider the system of inequalities.

$$\begin{cases} x^2 + y^2 < 25 \\ x + 2y \geq 5 \end{cases}$$

Which one of the following sentences is true?

1. The solution set of this system is all the points that satisfy at least one of these inequalities.
2. The solution set of this system is all the points that satisfy exactly one of these inequalities.
3. The solution set of this system is all the points that satisfy both of these inequalities.

Answer

Only 3 is true.

EXAMPLES

- $\{5x - 3y < 3, x - 2y > 4,$
  $x + y \leq 1\}$

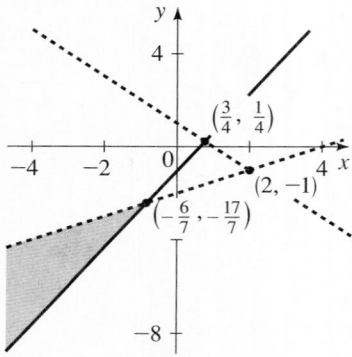

- $\{y > x^2 - 4, y \leq 4 - x^2\}$

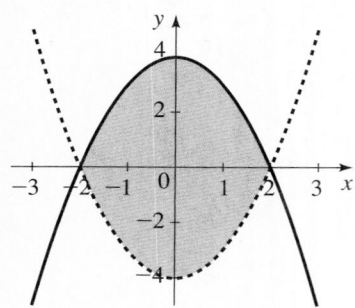

ALTERNATE EXAMPLE 1

(a) For the graph of the inequality $x^2 + y^2 < 81$, determine whether the inside or the outside of the circle satisfies the inequality.

(b) For the graph of the inequality $x + 4y \geq 9$, determine whether the points above or below the boundary line satisfy the inequality.

ANSWERS

(a) Inside

(b) Above

Its graph consists of not just the parabola in Figure 1, but also every point whose y-coordinate is *larger* than x^2. We indicate the solution in Figure 2(a) by shading the points *above* the parabola.

Similarly, the graph of $y \leq x^2$ in Figure 2(b) consists of all points on and *below* the parabola. However, the graphs of $y > x^2$ and $y < x^2$ do not include the points on the parabola itself, as indicated by the dashed curves in Figures 2(c) and 2(d).

(a) $y \geq x^2$

(b) $y \leq x^2$

(c) $y > x^2$

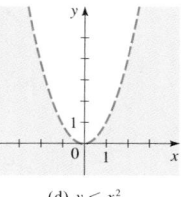

(d) $y < x^2$

FIGURE 2

The graph of an inequality, in general, consists of a region in the plane whose boundary is the graph of the equation obtained by replacing the inequality sign ($\geq$, $\leq$, $>$, or $<$) with an equal sign. To determine which side of the graph gives the solution set of the inequality, we need only check **test points**.

GRAPHING INEQUALITIES

To graph an inequality, we carry out the following steps.

1. **Graph Equation.** Graph the equation corresponding to the inequality. Use a dashed curve for $>$ or $<$ and a solid curve for $\leq$ or $\geq$.

2. **Test Points.** Test one point in each region formed by the graph in Step 1. If the point satisfies the inequality, then all the points in that region satisfy the inequality. (In that case, shade the region to indicate that it is part of the graph.) If the test point does not satisfy the inequality, then the region isn't part of the graph.

EXAMPLE 1 | Graphs of Inequalities

Graph each inequality.

(a) $x^2 + y^2 < 25$ (b) $x + 2y \geq 5$

SOLUTION

(a) The graph of $x^2 + y^2 = 25$ is a circle of radius 5 centered at the origin. The points on the circle itself do not satisfy the inequality because it is of the form $<$, so we graph the circle with a dashed curve, as shown in Figure 3.

To determine whether the inside or the outside of the circle satisfies the inequality, we use the test points $(0, 0)$ on the inside and $(6, 0)$ on the outside. To do this, we substitute the coordinates of each point into the inequality and check whether the result satisfies the inequality. (Note that *any* point inside or outside the circle can serve as a test point. We have chosen these points for simplicity.)

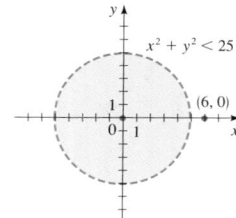

Test point	$x^2 + y^2 < 25$	Conclusion
$(0, 0)$	$0^2 + 0^2 = 0 < 25$	Part of graph
$(6, 0)$	$6^2 + 0^2 = 36 \not< 25$	Not part of graph

FIGURE 3

Thus the graph of $x^2 + y^2 < 25$ is the set of all points *inside* the circle (see Figure 3).

IN-CLASS MATERIALS

Surprisingly, many students are not able to answer this question correctly: "True or false? If $a < b$ then $a \leq b$." Perhaps take a minute or two to remind the students of the basics of inequalities. From straightforward statements involving inequalities, make the transition to some very simple regions such as $x > 2$, $y \leq 3$, etc. The idea is to make sure that the students are crystal-clear on the objects they are working with before working with them.

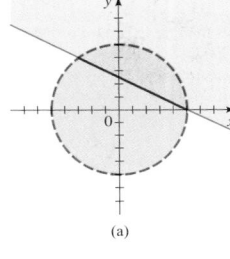

FIGURE 4

(b) The graph of $x + 2y = 5$ is the line shown in Figure 4. We use the test points $(0, 0)$ and $(5, 5)$ on opposite sides of the line.

Test point	$x + 2y \geq 5$	Conclusion
$(0, 0)$	$0 + 2(0) = 0 \not\geq 5$	Not part of graph
$(5, 5)$	$5 + 2(5) = 15 \geq 5$	Part of graph

Our check shows that the points *above* the line satisfy the inequality.

Alternatively, we could put the inequality into slope-intercept form and graph it directly:

$$x + 2y \geq 5$$
$$2y \geq -x + 5$$
$$y \geq -\tfrac{1}{2}x + \tfrac{5}{2}$$

From this form we see that the graph includes all points whose y-coordinates are *greater* than those on the line $y = -\tfrac{1}{2}x + \tfrac{5}{2}$; that is, the graph consists of the points *on or above* this line, as shown in Figure 4.

✎ **NOW TRY EXERCISES 7 AND 15** ◼

▼ Systems of Inequalities

We now consider *systems* of inequalities. The solution of such a system is the set of all points in the coordinate plane that satisfy every inequality in the system.

EXAMPLE 2 | A System of Two Inequalities

Graph the solution of the system of inequalities, and label its vertices.

$$\begin{cases} x^2 + y^2 < 25 \\ x + 2y \geq 5 \end{cases}$$

SOLUTION These are the two inequalities of Example 1. In this example we wish to graph only those points that simultaneously satisfy both inequalities. The solution consists of the intersection of the graphs in Example 1. In Figure 5(a) we show the two regions on the same coordinate plane (in different colors), and in Figure 5(b) we show their intersection.

Vertices The points $(-3, 4)$ and $(5, 0)$ in Figure 5(b) are the **vertices** of the solution set. They are obtained by solving the system of *equations*

$$\begin{cases} x^2 + y^2 = 25 \\ x + 2y = 5 \end{cases}$$

We solve this system of equations by substitution. Solving for x in the second equation gives $x = 5 - 2y$, and substituting this into the first equation gives

$$(5 - 2y)^2 + y^2 = 25 \qquad \text{Substitute } x = 5 - 2y$$
$$(25 - 20y + 4y^2) + y^2 = 25 \qquad \text{Expand}$$
$$-20y + 5y^2 = 0 \qquad \text{Simplify}$$
$$-5y(4 - y) = 0 \qquad \text{Factor}$$

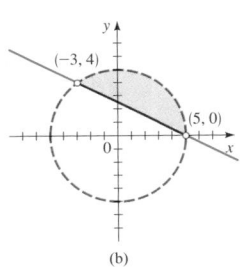

FIGURE 5 $\begin{cases} x^2 + y^2 < 25 \\ x + 2y \geq 5 \end{cases}$

Thus $y = 0$ or $y = 4$. When $y = 0$, we have $x = 5 - 2(0) = 5$, and when $y = 4$, we have $x = 5 - 2(4) = -3$. So the points of intersection of these curves are $(5, 0)$ and $(-3, 4)$.

ALTERNATE EXAMPLE 2
Find the vertices of the graph of the solution set of the system.

$$\begin{cases} x^2 + y^2 < 25 \\ x + 3y \geq 5 \end{cases}$$

ANSWER
$(-4, 3), (5, 0)$

IN-CLASS MATERIALS
Have the students come up with examples of systems of two cubic inequalities with varying numbers of separate solution spaces.

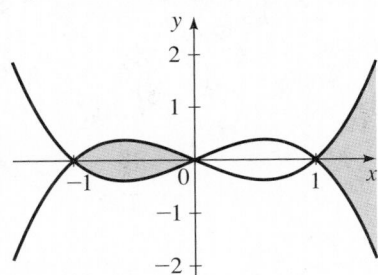

$\{y \leq x^3 - x, y \geq -x^3 + x\}$, two solution spaces

$\{y \leq x^3, y \geq x^3 - 5\}$, one solution space

Note that in this case the vertices are not part of the solution set, since they don't satisfy the inequality $x^2 + y^2 < 25$ (so they are graphed as open circles in the figure). They simply show where the "corners" of the solution set lie.

✎. NOW TRY EXERCISE **33**

▼ Systems of Linear Inequalities

An inequality is **linear** if it can be put into one of the following forms:

$$ax + by \geq c \qquad ax + by \leq c \qquad ax + by > c \qquad ax + by < c$$

In the next example we graph the solution set of a system of linear inequalities.

EXAMPLE 3 | A System of Four Linear Inequalities

Graph the solution set of the system, and label its vertices.

$$\begin{cases} x + 3y \leq 12 \\ x + \ y \leq 8 \\ \quad x \geq 0 \\ \quad y \geq 0 \end{cases}$$

SOLUTION   In Figure 6 we first graph the lines given by the equations that correspond to each inequality. To determine the graphs of the linear inequalities, we need to check only one test point. For simplicity let's use the point $(0, 0)$.

Inequality	Test point $(0, 0)$	Conclusion
$x + 3y \leq 12$	$0 + 3(0) = 0 \leq 12$	Satisfies inequality
$x + y \leq 8$	$0 + 0 = 0 \leq 8$	Satisfies inequality

Since $(0, 0)$ is below the line $x + 3y = 12$, our check shows that the region on or below the line must satisfy the inequality. Likewise, since $(0, 0)$ is below the line $x + y = 8$, our check shows that the region on or below this line must satisfy the inequality. The inequalities $x \geq 0$ and $y \geq 0$ say that x and y are nonnegative. These regions are sketched in Figure 6(a), and the intersection—the solution set—is sketched in Figure 6(b).

Vertices   The coordinates of each vertex are obtained by simultaneously solving the equations of the lines that intersect at that vertex. From the system

$$\begin{cases} x + 3y = 12 \\ x + \ y = \ 8 \end{cases}$$

we get the vertex $(6, 2)$. The origin $(0, 0)$ is also clearly a vertex. The other two vertices are at the x- and y-intercepts of the corresponding lines: $(8, 0)$ and $(0, 4)$. In this case all the vertices *are* part of the solution set.

✎. NOW TRY EXERCISE **39**

EXAMPLE 4 | A System of Linear Inequalities

Graph the solution set of the system.

$$\begin{cases} x + 2y \geq 8 \\ -x + 2y \leq 4 \\ 3x - 2y \leq 8 \end{cases}$$

FIGURE 6

ALTERNATE EXAMPLE 3

Sketch the solution set of the following system, and specify its vertices.

$$\begin{cases} x + 5y \leq 15 \\ x + \ y \leq 11 \\ \quad x \geq 0 \\ \quad y \geq 0 \end{cases}$$

ANSWER

$(10, 1)$, $(0, 3)$, $(11, 0)$

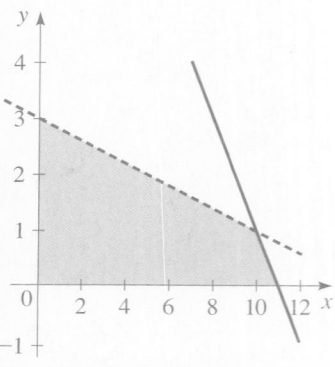

ALTERNATE EXAMPLE 4

Graph the solution set of the system.

$$\begin{cases} x + \ y \geq 3 \\ -2x + \ y \leq 5 \\ \quad x - 2y \leq 12 \end{cases}$$

ANSWER

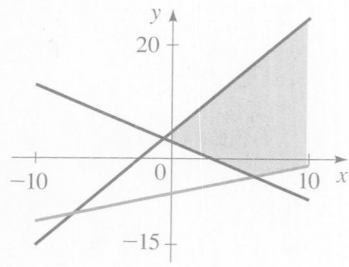

IN-CLASS MATERIALS

If areas are discussed, then the idea of infinite regions with finite areas can be discussed. It is interesting that these regions have finite area:
$$\{x \geq 1, 0 \leq y \leq e^{-x}\}$$
$$\left\{x \geq 1, 0 \leq y \leq \frac{1}{x^2}\right\}$$
$$\left\{x \geq 1, 0 \leq y \leq \frac{1}{x^{1.01}}\right\}$$

Whereas these regions do not:
$$\left\{x \geq 1, 0 \leq y \leq \frac{1}{x}\right\}$$
$$\left\{x \geq 1, 0 \leq y \leq \frac{1}{x\ln(x + 1)}\right\}$$
$$\left\{x \geq 1, 0 \leq y \leq \frac{x}{100(x^2 + x + 1)}\right\}$$

FIGURE 7

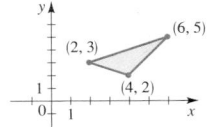

FIGURE 8

SOLUTION We must graph the lines that correspond to these inequalities and then shade the appropriate regions, as in Example 3. We will use a graphing calculator, so we must first isolate y on the left-hand side of each inequality.

$$\begin{cases} y \geq -\frac{1}{2}x + 4 \\ y \leq \frac{1}{2}x + 2 \\ y \geq \frac{3}{2}x - 4 \end{cases}$$

Using the shading feature of the calculator, we obtain the graph in Figure 7. The solution set is the triangular region that is shaded in all three patterns. We then use $\boxed{\text{TRACE}}$ or the $\texttt{Intersect}$ command to find the vertices of the region. The solution set is graphed in Figure 8.

✎. NOW TRY EXERCISE **47**   ■

When a region in the plane can be covered by a (sufficiently large) circle, it is said to be **bounded**. A region that is not bounded is called **unbounded**. For example, the regions graphed in Figures 3, 5(b), 6(b), and 8 are bounded, whereas those in Figures 2 and 4 are unbounded. An unbounded region cannot be "fenced in"—it extends infinitely far in at least one direction.

▼ Application: Feasible Regions

Many applied problems involve *constraints* on the variables. For instance, a factory manager has only a certain number of workers who can be assigned to perform jobs on the factory floor. A farmer deciding what crops to cultivate has only a certain amount of land that can be seeded. Such constraints or limitations can usually be expressed as systems of inequalities. When dealing with applied inequalities, we usually refer to the solution set of a system as a *feasible region*, because the points in the solution set represent feasible (or possible) values for the quantities being studied.

EXAMPLE 5 | Restricting Pollutant Outputs

A factory produces two agricultural pesticides, A and B. For every barrel of A, the factory emits 0.25 kg of carbon monoxide (CO) and 0.60 kg of sulfur dioxide (SO_2); and for every barrel of B, it emits 0.50 kg of CO and 0.20 kg of SO_2. Pollution laws restrict the factory's output of CO to a maximum of 75 kg and SO_2 to a maximum of 90 kg per day.

(a) Find a system of inequalities that describes the number of barrels of each pesticide the factory can produce and still satisfy the pollution laws. Graph the feasible region.

(b) Would it be legal for the factory to produce 100 barrels of A and 80 barrels of B per day?

(c) Would it be legal for the factory to produce 60 barrels of A and 160 barrels of B per day?

SOLUTION

(a) To set up the required inequalities, it is helpful to organize the given information into a table.

	A	B	Maximum
CO (kg)	0.25	0.50	75
SO₂ (kg)	0.60	0.20	90

We let

$$x = \text{number of barrels of A produced per day}$$

$$y = \text{number of barrels of B produced per day}$$

IN-CLASS MATERIALS

This section allows one to foreshadow the concept of area. For example, students should be able to compute the area of the regions defined by the following systems:

$$\{x \geq 1, x \leq 3, y \leq 2, y \geq 0\}$$
$$\{y \geq 2, x \geq 1, y + 2x \geq 0\}$$
$$\{y \geq 2x, (x - 3)^2 + (y - 6)^2 \leq 4\}$$

DRILL QUESTION

Graph the solution set of the system of inequalities.

$$\begin{cases} -\dfrac{1}{2}x^2 + y \geq -2 \\ x - y < 0 \end{cases}$$

Answer

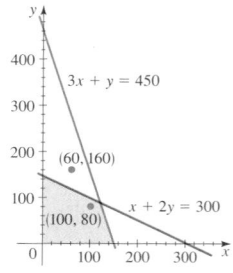

FIGURE 9

From the data in the table and the fact that x and y can't be negative, we obtain the following inequalities.

$$\begin{cases} 0.25x + 0.50y \leq 75 & \text{CO inequality} \\ 0.60x + 0.20y \leq 90 & \text{SO}_2 \text{ inequality} \\ x \geq 0, \quad y \geq 0 \end{cases}$$

Multiplying the first inequality by 4 and the second by 5 simplifies this to

$$\begin{cases} x + 2y \leq 300 \\ 3x + y \leq 450 \\ x \geq 0, \quad y \geq 0 \end{cases}$$

The feasible region is the solution of this system of inequalities, shown in Figure 9.

(b) Since the point $(100, 80)$ lies inside the feasible region, this production plan is legal (see Figure 9).

(c) Since the point $(60, 160)$ lies outside the feasible region, this production plan is not legal. It violates the CO restriction, although it does not violate the SO$_2$ restriction (see Figure 9).

✎. NOW TRY EXERCISE **51**

10.9 EXERCISES

CONCEPTS

1. To graph an inequality, we first graph the corresponding _____. So to graph $y \leq x + 1$, we first graph the equation _____. To decide which side of the graph of the equation is the graph of the inequality, we use _____ points. Using $(0, 0)$ as such a point, graph the inequality by shading the appropriate region.

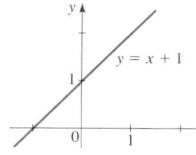

2. Shade the solution of each system of inequalities on the given graph.

(a) $\begin{cases} x - y \geq 0 \\ x + y \geq 2 \end{cases}$ **(b)** $\begin{cases} x - y \leq 0 \\ x + y \leq 2 \end{cases}$

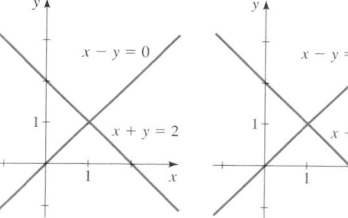

(c) $\begin{cases} x - y \geq 0 \\ x + y \leq 2 \end{cases}$ **(d)** $\begin{cases} x - y \leq 0 \\ x + y \geq 2 \end{cases}$

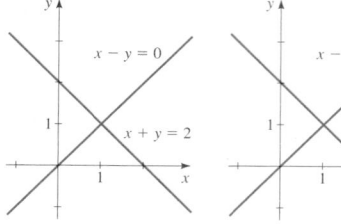

SKILLS

3–16 ■ Graph the inequality.

3. $x < 3$

4. $y \geq -2$

5. $y > x$

6. $y < x + 2$

✎. **7.** $y \leq 2x + 2$

8. $y < -x + 5$

9. $2x - y \leq 8$

10. $3x + 4y + 12 > 0$

11. $4x + 5y < 20$

12. $-x^2 + y \geq 10$

13. $y > x^2 + 1$

14. $x^2 + y^2 \geq 9$

✎. **15.** $x^2 + y^2 \leq 25$

16. $x^2 + (y - 1)^2 \leq 1$

17–20 ■ An equation and its graph are given. Find an inequality whose solution is the shaded region.

17. $y = \frac{1}{2}x - 1$ **18.** $y = x^2 + 2$

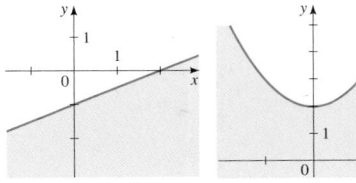

19. $x^2 + y^2 = 4$ **20.** $y = x^3 - 4x$

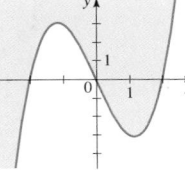

37. $\begin{cases} x + 2y \le 14 \\ 3x - y \ge 0 \\ x - y \ge 2 \end{cases}$ **38.** $\begin{cases} y < x + 6 \\ 3x + 2y \ge 12 \\ x - 2y \le 2 \end{cases}$

39. $\begin{cases} x \ge 0 \\ y \ge 0 \\ x \le 5 \\ x + y \le 7 \end{cases}$ **40.** $\begin{cases} x \ge 0 \\ y \ge 0 \\ y \le 4 \\ 2x + y \le 8 \end{cases}$

41. $\begin{cases} y > x + 1 \\ x + 2y \le 12 \\ x + 1 > 0 \end{cases}$ **42.** $\begin{cases} x + y > 12 \\ y < \frac{1}{2}x - 6 \\ 3x + y < 6 \end{cases}$

43. $\begin{cases} x^2 + y^2 \le 8 \\ x \ge 2 \\ y \ge 0 \end{cases}$

44. $\begin{cases} x^2 - y \ge 0 \\ x + y < 6 \\ x - y < 6 \end{cases}$

45. $\begin{cases} x^2 + y^2 < 9 \\ x + y > 0 \\ x \le 0 \end{cases}$

46. $\begin{cases} y \ge x^3 \\ y \le 2x + 4 \\ x + y \ge 0 \end{cases}$

21–46 ■ Graph the solution of the system of inequalities. Find the coordinates of all vertices, and determine whether the solution set is bounded.

21. $\begin{cases} x + y \le 4 \\ y \ge x \end{cases}$ **22.** $\begin{cases} 2x + 3y > 12 \\ 3x - y < 21 \end{cases}$

23. $\begin{cases} y < \frac{1}{4}x + 2 \\ y \ge 2x - 5 \end{cases}$ **24.** $\begin{cases} x - y > 0 \\ 4 + y \le 2x \end{cases}$

25. $\begin{cases} y \le -2x + 8 \\ y \le -\frac{1}{2}x + 5 \\ x \ge 0, \quad y \ge 0 \end{cases}$ **26.** $\begin{cases} 4x + 3y \le 18 \\ 2x + y \le 8 \\ x \ge 0, \quad y \ge 0 \end{cases}$

27. $\begin{cases} x \ge 0 \\ y \ge 0 \\ 3x + 5y \le 15 \\ 3x + 2y \le 9 \end{cases}$ **28.** $\begin{cases} x > 2 \\ y < 12 \\ 2x - 4y > 8 \end{cases}$

29. $\begin{cases} y \le 9 - x^2 \\ x \ge 0, \quad y \ge 0 \end{cases}$ **30.** $\begin{cases} y \ge x^2 \\ y \le 4 \\ x \ge 0 \end{cases}$

31. $\begin{cases} y < 9 - x^2 \\ y \ge x + 3 \end{cases}$ **32.** $\begin{cases} y \ge x^2 \\ x + y \ge 6 \end{cases}$

33. $\begin{cases} x^2 + y^2 \le 4 \\ x - y > 0 \end{cases}$ **34.** $\begin{cases} x > 0 \\ y > 0 \\ x + y < 10 \\ x^2 + y^2 > 9 \end{cases}$

35. $\begin{cases} x^2 - y \le 0 \\ 2x^2 + y \le 12 \end{cases}$ **36.** $\begin{cases} x^2 + y^2 < 9 \\ 2x + y^2 \ge 1 \end{cases}$

47–50 ■ Use a graphing calculator to graph the solution of the system of inequalities. Find the coordinates of all vertices, rounded to one decimal place.

47. $\begin{cases} y \ge x - 3 \\ y \ge -2x + 6 \\ y \le 8 \end{cases}$ **48.** $\begin{cases} x + y \ge 12 \\ 2x + y \le 24 \\ x - y \ge -6 \end{cases}$

49. $\begin{cases} y \le 6x - x^2 \\ x + y \ge 4 \end{cases}$ **50.** $\begin{cases} y \ge x^3 \\ 2x + y \ge 0 \\ y \le 2x + 6 \end{cases}$

APPLICATIONS

51. Publishing Books A publishing company publishes a total of no more than 100 books every year. At least 20 of these are nonfiction, but the company always publishes at least as much fiction as nonfiction. Find a system of inequalities that describes the possible numbers of fiction and nonfiction books that the company can produce each year consistent with these policies. Graph the solution set.

52. Furniture Manufacturing A man and his daughter manufacture unfinished tables and chairs. Each table requires 3 hours of sawing and 1 hour of assembly. Each chair requires 2 hours of sawing and 2 hours of assembly. Between the two of them, they can put in up to 12 hours of sawing and 8 hours of assembly work each day. Find a system of inequalities that describes all possible combinations of tables and chairs that they can make daily. Graph the solution set.

53. Coffee Blends A coffee merchant sells two different coffee blends. The Standard blend uses 4 oz of arabica and 12 oz of robusta beans per package; the Deluxe blend uses 10 oz of arabica and 6 oz of robusta beans per package. The merchant has 80 lb of arabica and 90 lb of robusta beans available. Find a system of inequalities that describes the possible number of Standard and Deluxe packages the merchant can make. Graph the solution set.

54. Nutrition A cat food manufacturer uses fish and beef byproducts. The fish contains 12 g of protein and 3 g of fat per ounce. The beef contains 6 g of protein and 9 g of fat per ounce. Each can of cat food must contain at least 60 g of protein and 45 g of fat. Find a system of inequalities that describes the possible number of ounces of fish and beef that can be used in each can to satisfy these minimum requirements. Graph the solution set.

DISCOVERY ▪ DISCUSSION ▪ WRITING

55. Shading Unwanted Regions To graph the solution of a system of inequalities, we have shaded the solution of each inequality in a different color; the solution of the system is the region where all the shaded parts overlap. Here is a different method: For each inequality, shade the region that does *not* satisfy the inequality. Explain why the part of the plane that is left unshaded is the solution of the system. Solve the following system by both methods. Which do you prefer? Why?

$$\begin{cases} x + 2y > 4 \\ -x + y < 1 \\ x + 3y < 9 \\ x < 3 \end{cases}$$

CHAPTER 10 | REVIEW

■ CONCEPT CHECK

1. Suppose you are asked to solve a system of two equations in two variables. Explain how you would solve the system
   (a) by the substitution method
   (b) by the elimination method
   (c) graphically

2. Suppose you are asked to solve a system of two *linear* equations in two variables.
   (a) Would you prefer to use the substitution method or the elimination method?
   (b) How many solutions are possible? Draw diagrams to illustrate the possibilities.

3. What operations can be performed on a linear system that result in an equivalent system?

4. Explain how Gaussian elimination works. Your explanation should include a discussion of the steps used to obtain a system in triangular form, and back-substitution.

5. What does it mean to say that A is a matrix with dimension $m \times n$?

6. What is the augmented matrix of a system? Describe the role of elementary row operations, row-echelon form, back-substitution, and leading variables when solving a system in matrix form.

7. (a) What is meant by an inconsistent system?
   (b) What is meant by a dependent system?

8. Suppose you have used Gaussian elimination to transform the augmented matrix of a linear system into row-echelon form. How can you tell whether the system has
   (a) exactly one solution?
   (b) no solution?
   (c) infinitely many solutions?

9. How can you tell whether a matrix is in reduced row-echelon form?

10. How do Gaussian elimination and Gauss-Jordan elimination differ? What advantage does Gauss-Jordan elimination have?

11. If A and B are matrices with the same dimension and k is a real number, how do you find $A + B$, $A - B$, and kA?

12. (a) What must be true of the dimensions of A and B for the product AB to be defined?
   (b) If the product AB is defined, how do you calculate it?

13. (a) What is the identity matrix I_n?
   (b) If A is a square $n \times n$ matrix, what is its inverse matrix?
   (c) Write a formula for the inverse of a 2×2 matrix.
   (d) Explain how you would find the inverse of a 3×3 matrix.

14. (a) Explain how to express a linear system as a matrix equation of the form $AX = B$.
   (b) If A has an inverse, how would you solve the matrix equation $AX = B$?

15. Suppose A is an $n \times n$ matrix.
   (a) What is the minor M_{ij} of the element a_{ij}?
   (b) What is the cofactor A_{ij}?
   (c) How do you find the determinant of A?
   (d) How can you tell if A has an inverse?

16. State Cramer's Rule for solving a system of linear equations in terms of determinants. Do you prefer to use Cramer's Rule or Gaussian elimination? Explain.

17. Explain how to find the partial fraction decomposition of a rational expression. Include in your explanation a discussion of each of the four cases that arise.

18. How do you graph an inequality in two variables?

19. How do you graph the solution set of a system of inequalities?

■ EXERCISES

1–6 ■ Solve the system of equations, and graph the lines.

1. $\begin{cases} 3x - y = 5 \\ 2x + y = 5 \end{cases}$ **2.** $\begin{cases} y = 2x + 6 \\ y = -x + 3 \end{cases}$

3. $\begin{cases} 2x - 7y = 28 \\ y = \frac{2}{7}x - 4 \end{cases}$ **4.** $\begin{cases} 6x - 8y = 15 \\ -\frac{3}{2}x + 2y = -4 \end{cases}$

5. $\begin{cases} 2x - y = 1 \\ x + 3y = 10 \\ 3x + 4y = 15 \end{cases}$ **6.** $\begin{cases} 2x + 5y = 9 \\ -x + 3y = 1 \\ 7x - 2y = 14 \end{cases}$

7–10 ■ Solve the system of equations.

7. $\begin{cases} y = x^2 + 2x \\ y = 6 + x \end{cases}$ **8.** $\begin{cases} x^2 + y^2 = 8 \\ y = x + 2 \end{cases}$

9. $\begin{cases} 3x + \dfrac{4}{y} = 6 \\ x - \dfrac{8}{y} = 4 \end{cases}$ **10.** $\begin{cases} x^2 + y^2 = 10 \\ x^2 + 2y^2 - 7y = 0 \end{cases}$

11–14 ■ Use a graphing device to solve the system, rounded to the nearest hundredth.

11. $\begin{cases} 0.32x + 0.43y = 0 \\ 7x - 12y = 341 \end{cases}$ **12.** $\begin{cases} \sqrt{12}x - 3\sqrt{2}y = 660 \\ 7137x + 3931y = 20{,}000 \end{cases}$

13. $\begin{cases} x - y^2 = 10 \\ x = \frac{1}{22}y + 12 \end{cases}$ **14.** $\begin{cases} y = 5^x + x \\ y = x^5 + 5 \end{cases}$

15–20 ■ A matrix is given.
  (a) State the dimension of the matrix.
  (b) Is the matrix in row-echelon form?
  (c) Is the matrix in reduced row-echelon form?
  (d) Write the system of equations for which the given matrix is the augmented matrix.

15. $\begin{bmatrix} 1 & 2 & -5 \\ 0 & 1 & 3 \end{bmatrix}$ **16.** $\begin{bmatrix} 1 & 0 & 6 \\ 0 & 1 & 0 \end{bmatrix}$

17. $\begin{bmatrix} 1 & 0 & 8 & 0 \\ 0 & 1 & 5 & -1 \\ 0 & 0 & 0 & 0 \end{bmatrix}$ **18.** $\begin{bmatrix} 1 & 3 & 6 & 2 \\ 2 & 1 & 0 & 5 \\ 0 & 0 & 1 & 0 \end{bmatrix}$

19. $\begin{bmatrix} 0 & 1 & -3 & 4 \\ 1 & 1 & 0 & 7 \\ 1 & 2 & 1 & 2 \end{bmatrix}$ **20.** $\begin{bmatrix} 1 & 8 & 6 & -4 \\ 0 & 1 & -3 & 5 \\ 0 & 0 & 2 & -7 \\ 1 & 1 & 1 & 0 \end{bmatrix}$

21–42 ■ Find the complete solution of the system, or show that the system has no solution.

21. $\begin{cases} x + y + 2z = 6 \\ 2x + 5z = 12 \\ x + 2y + 3z = 9 \end{cases}$ **22.** $\begin{cases} x - 2y + 3z = 1 \\ x - 3y - z = 0 \\ 2x - 6z = 6 \end{cases}$

23. $\begin{cases} x - 2y + 3z = 1 \\ 2x - y + z = 3 \\ 2x - 7y + 11z = 2 \end{cases}$ **24.** $\begin{cases} x + y + z + w = 2 \\ 2x - 3z = 5 \\ x - 2y + 4w = 9 \\ x + y + 2z + 3w = 5 \end{cases}$

25. $\begin{cases} x + 2y + 2z = 6 \\ x - y = -1 \\ 2x + y + 3z = 7 \end{cases}$ **26.** $\begin{cases} x - y + z = 2 \\ x + y + 3z = 6 \\ 2y + 3z = 5 \end{cases}$

27. $\begin{cases} x - 2y + 3z = -2 \\ 2x - y + z = 2 \\ 2x - 7y + 11z = -9 \end{cases}$ **28.** $\begin{cases} x - y + z = 2 \\ x + y + 3z = 6 \\ 3x - y + 5z = 10 \end{cases}$

29. $\begin{cases} x + y + z + w = 0 \\ x - y - 4z - w = -1 \\ x - 2y + 4w = -7 \\ 2x + 2y + 3z + 4w = -3 \end{cases}$

30. $\begin{cases} x + 3z = -1 \\ y - 4w = 5 \\ 2y + z + w = 0 \\ 2x + y + 5z - 4w = 4 \end{cases}$

31. $\begin{cases} x - 3y + z = 4 \\ 4x - y + 15z = 5 \end{cases}$ **32.** $\begin{cases} 2x - 3y + 4z = 3 \\ 4x - 5y + 9z = 13 \\ 2x + 7z = 0 \end{cases}$

33. $\begin{cases} -x + 4y + z = 8 \\ 2x - 6y + z = -9 \\ x - 6y - 4z = -15 \end{cases}$ **34.** $\begin{cases} x - z + w = 2 \\ 2x + y - 2w = 12 \\ 3y + z + w = 4 \\ x + y - z = 10 \end{cases}$

35. $\begin{cases} x - y + 3z = 2 \\ 2x + y + z = 2 \\ 3x + 4z = 4 \end{cases}$ **36.** $\begin{cases} x - y = 1 \\ x + y + 2z = 3 \\ x - 3y - 2z = -1 \end{cases}$

37. $\begin{cases} x - y + z - w = 0 \\ 3x - y - z - w = 2 \end{cases}$ **38.** $\begin{cases} x - y = 3 \\ 2x + y = 6 \\ x - 2y = 9 \end{cases}$

39. $\begin{cases} x - y + z = 0 \\ 3x + 2y - z = 6 \\ x + 4y - 3z = 3 \end{cases}$ **40.** $\begin{cases} x + 2y + 3z = 2 \\ 2x - y - 5z = 1 \\ 4x + 3y + z = 6 \end{cases}$

41. $\begin{cases} x + y - z - w = 2 \\ x - y + z - w = 0 \\ 2x + 2w = 2 \\ 2x + 4y - 4z - 2w = 6 \end{cases}$

42. $\begin{cases} x - y - 2z + 3w = 0 \\ y - z + w = 1 \\ 3x - 2y - 7z + 10w = 2 \end{cases}$

43. A man invests his savings in two accounts, one paying 6% interest per year and the other paying 7%. He has twice as much invested in the 7% account as in the 6% account, and his annual interest income is $600. How much is invested in each account?

44. A piggy bank contains 50 coins, all of them nickels, dimes, or quarters. The total value of the coins is $5.60, and the value of the dimes is five times the value of the nickels. How many coins of each type are there?

45. Clarisse invests $60,000 in money-market accounts at three different banks. Bank A pays 2% interest per year, bank B pays 2.5%, and bank C pays 3%. She decides to invest twice as much in bank B as in the other two banks. After one year, Clarisse has earned $1575 in interest. How much did she invest in each bank?

46. A commercial fisherman fishes for haddock, sea bass, and red snapper. He is paid $1.25 a pound for haddock, $0.75 a pound for sea bass, and $2.00 a pound for red snapper. Yesterday he caught 560 lb of fish worth $575. The haddock and red snapper together are worth $320. How many pounds of each fish did he catch?

47–58 ■ Let

$$A = [2 \quad 0 \quad -1] \qquad B = \begin{bmatrix} 1 & 2 & 4 \\ -2 & 1 & 0 \end{bmatrix}$$

$$C = \begin{bmatrix} \frac{1}{2} & 3 \\ 2 & \frac{3}{2} \\ -2 & 1 \end{bmatrix} \qquad D = \begin{bmatrix} 1 & 4 \\ 0 & -1 \\ 2 & 0 \end{bmatrix}$$

$$E = \begin{bmatrix} 2 & -1 \\ -\frac{1}{2} & 1 \end{bmatrix} \qquad F = \begin{bmatrix} 4 & 0 & 2 \\ -1 & 1 & 0 \\ 7 & 5 & 0 \end{bmatrix}$$

$$G = [5]$$

Carry out the indicated operation, or explain why it cannot be performed.

47. $A + B$ **48.** $C - D$ **49.** $2C + 3D$

50. $5B - 2C$ **51.** GA **52.** AG

53. BC **54.** CB **55.** BF

56. FC **57.** $(C + D)E$ **58.** $F(2C - D)$

59–60 ■ Verify that the matrices A and B are inverses of each other by calculating the products AB and BA.

59. $A = \begin{bmatrix} 2 & -5 \\ -2 & 6 \end{bmatrix}$, $B = \begin{bmatrix} 3 & \frac{5}{2} \\ 1 & 1 \end{bmatrix}$

60. $A = \begin{bmatrix} 2 & -1 & 3 \\ 2 & -2 & 1 \\ 0 & 1 & 1 \end{bmatrix}$, $B = \begin{bmatrix} -\frac{3}{2} & 2 & \frac{5}{2} \\ -1 & 1 & 2 \\ 1 & -1 & -1 \end{bmatrix}$

61–66 ■ Solve the matrix equation for the unknown matrix, X, or show that no solution exists, where

$$A = \begin{bmatrix} 2 & 1 \\ 3 & 2 \end{bmatrix}, \quad B = \begin{bmatrix} 1 & -2 \\ -2 & 4 \end{bmatrix}, \quad C = \begin{bmatrix} 0 & 1 & 3 \\ -2 & 4 & 0 \end{bmatrix}$$

61. $A + 3X = B$ **62.** $\frac{1}{2}(X - 2B) = A$

63. $2(X - A) = 3B$ **64.** $2X + C = 5A$

65. $AX = C$ **66.** $AX = B$

67–74 ■ Find the determinant and, if possible, the inverse of the matrix.

67. $\begin{bmatrix} 1 & 4 \\ 2 & 9 \end{bmatrix}$ **68.** $\begin{bmatrix} 2 & 2 \\ 1 & -3 \end{bmatrix}$

69. $\begin{bmatrix} 4 & -12 \\ -2 & 6 \end{bmatrix}$ **70.** $\begin{bmatrix} 2 & 4 & 0 \\ -1 & 1 & 2 \\ 0 & 3 & 2 \end{bmatrix}$

71. $\begin{bmatrix} 3 & 0 & 1 \\ 2 & -3 & 0 \\ 4 & -2 & 1 \end{bmatrix}$ **72.** $\begin{bmatrix} 1 & 2 & 3 \\ 2 & 4 & 5 \\ 2 & 5 & 6 \end{bmatrix}$

73. $\begin{bmatrix} 1 & 0 & 0 & 1 \\ 0 & 2 & 0 & 2 \\ 0 & 0 & 3 & 3 \\ 0 & 0 & 0 & 4 \end{bmatrix}$ **74.** $\begin{bmatrix} 1 & 0 & 1 & 0 \\ 0 & 1 & 0 & 1 \\ 1 & 1 & 1 & 2 \\ 1 & 2 & 1 & 2 \end{bmatrix}$

75–78 ■ Express the system of linear equations as a matrix equation. Then solve the matrix equation by multiplying each side by the inverse of the coefficient matrix.

75. $\begin{cases} 12x - 5y = 10 \\ 5x - 2y = 17 \end{cases}$ **76.** $\begin{cases} 6x - 5y = 1 \\ 8x - 7y = -1 \end{cases}$

77. $\begin{cases} 2x + y + 5z = \frac{1}{3} \\ x + 2y + 2z = \frac{1}{4} \\ x + 3z = \frac{1}{6} \end{cases}$ **78.** $\begin{cases} 2x + 3z = 5 \\ x + y + 6z = 0 \\ 3x - y + z = 5 \end{cases}$

79–82 ■ Solve the system using Cramer's Rule.

79. $\begin{cases} 2x + 7y = 13 \\ 6x + 16y = 30 \end{cases}$

80. $\begin{cases} 12x - 11y = 140 \\ 7x + 9y = 20 \end{cases}$

81. $\begin{cases} 2x - y + 5z = 0 \\ -x + 7y = 9 \\ 5x + 4y + 3z = -9 \end{cases}$

82. $\begin{cases} 3x + 4y - z = 10 \\ x - 4z = 20 \\ 2x + y + 5z = 30 \end{cases}$

83–84 ■ Use the determinant formula for the area of a triangle to find the area of the triangle in the figure.

83. **84.**

 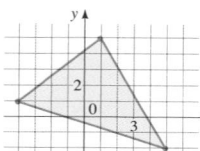

85–90 ■ Find the partial fraction decomposition of the rational function.

85. $\dfrac{3x + 1}{x^2 - 2x - 15}$ **86.** $\dfrac{8}{x^3 - 4x}$

87. $\dfrac{2x - 4}{x(x - 1)^2}$ **88.** $\dfrac{x + 6}{x^3 - 2x^2 + 4x - 8}$

89. $\dfrac{2x - 1}{x^3 + x}$ **90.** $\dfrac{5x^2 - 3x + 10}{x^4 + x^2 - 2}$

91–94 ■ Two equations and their graphs are given. Find the intersection point(s) of the graphs by solving the system.

91. $\begin{cases} 2x + 3y = 7 \\ x - 2y = 0 \end{cases}$ **92.** $\begin{cases} 3x + y = 8 \\ y = x^2 - 5x \end{cases}$

93. $\begin{cases} x^2 + y = 2 \\ x^2 - 3x - y = 0 \end{cases}$ **94.** $\begin{cases} x - y = -2 \\ x^2 + y^2 - 4y = 4 \end{cases}$

   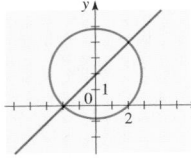

95–96 ■ An equation and its graph are given. Find an inequality whose solution is the shaded region.

95. $x + y^2 = 4$ **96.** $x^2 + y^2 = 8$

   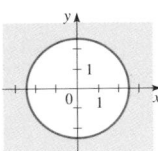

97–100 ■ Graph the inequality.

97. $3x + y \leq 6$ **98.** $y \geq x^2 - 3$

99. $x^2 + y^2 > 9$ **100.** $x - y^2 < 4$

101–104 ■ The figure shows the graphs of the equations corresponding to the given inequalities. Shade the solution set of the system of inequalities.

101. $\begin{cases} y \geq x^2 - 3x \\ y \leq \frac{1}{3}x - 1 \end{cases}$ **102.** $\begin{cases} y \geq x - 1 \\ x^2 + y^2 \leq 1 \end{cases}$

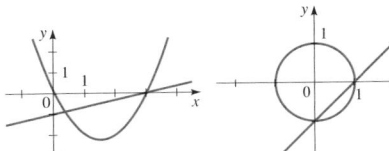

103. $\begin{cases} x + y \geq 2 \\ y - x \leq 2 \\ x \leq 3 \end{cases}$ **104.** $\begin{cases} y \geq -2x \\ y \leq 2x \\ y \leq -\frac{1}{2}x + 2 \end{cases}$

   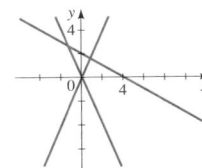

105–108 ■ Graph the solution set of the system of inequalities. Find the coordinates of all vertices, and determine whether the solution set is bounded or unbounded.

105. $\begin{cases} x^2 + y^2 < 9 \\ x + y < 0 \end{cases}$

106. $\begin{cases} y - x^2 \geq 4 \\ y < 20 \end{cases}$

107. $\begin{cases} x \geq 0, \quad y \geq 0 \\ x + 2y \leq 12 \\ y \leq x + 4 \end{cases}$

108. $\begin{cases} x \geq 4 \\ x + y \geq 24 \\ x \leq 2y + 12 \end{cases}$

109–110 ■ Solve for x, y, and z in terms of a, b, and c.

109. $\begin{cases} -x + y + z = a \\ x - y + z = b \\ x + y - z = c \end{cases}$

110. $\begin{cases} ax + by + cz = a - b + c \\ bx + by + cz = c \\ cx + cy + cz = c \end{cases}$ $(a \neq b, b \neq c, c \neq 0)$

111. For what values of k do the following three lines have a common point of intersection?

$$x + y = 12$$
$$kx - y = 0$$
$$y - x = 2k$$

112. For what value of k does the following system have infinitely many solutions?

$$\begin{cases} kx + y + z = 0 \\ x + 2y + kz = 0 \\ -x \quad\quad + 3z = 0 \end{cases}$$

1–2 ■ A system of equations is given. **(a)** Determine whether the system is linear or nonlinear. **(b)** Find all solutions of the system.

1. $\begin{cases} x + 3y = 7 \\ 5x + 2y = -4 \end{cases}$

2. $\begin{cases} 6x + y^2 = 10 \\ 3x - y = 5 \end{cases}$

3. Use a graphing device to find all solutions of the system rounded to two decimal places.

$$\begin{cases} x - 2y = 1 \\ y = x^3 - 2x^2 \end{cases}$$

4. In $2\frac{1}{2}$ h an airplane travels 600 km against the wind. It takes 50 min to travel 300 km with the wind. Find the speed of the wind and the speed of the airplane in still air.

5. Determine whether each matrix is in reduced row-echelon form, row-echelon form, or neither.

(a) $\begin{bmatrix} 1 & 2 & 4 & -6 \\ 0 & 1 & -3 & 0 \end{bmatrix}$

(b) $\begin{bmatrix} 1 & 0 & -1 & 0 & 0 \\ 0 & 1 & 3 & 0 & 0 \\ 0 & 0 & 0 & 1 & 0 \\ 0 & 0 & 0 & 0 & 1 \end{bmatrix}$

(c) $\begin{bmatrix} 1 & 1 & 0 \\ 0 & 0 & 1 \\ 0 & 1 & 3 \end{bmatrix}$

6. Use Gaussian elimination to find the complete solution of the system, or show that no solution exists.

(a) $\begin{cases} x - y + 2z = 0 \\ 2x - 4y + 5z = -5 \\ 2y - 3z = 5 \end{cases}$

(b) $\begin{cases} 2x - 3y + z = 3 \\ x + 2y + 2z = -1 \\ 4x + y + 5z = 4 \end{cases}$

7. Use Gauss-Jordan elimination to find the complete solution of the system.

$$\begin{cases} x + 3y - z = 0 \\ 3x + 4y - 2z = -1 \\ -x + 2y = 1 \end{cases}$$

8. Anne, Barry, and Cathy enter a coffee shop. Anne orders two coffees, one juice, and two doughnuts and pays $6.25. Barry orders one coffee and three doughnuts and pays $3.75. Cathy orders three coffees, one juice, and four doughnuts and pays $9.25. Find the price of coffee, juice, and doughnuts at this coffee shop.

9. Let

$$A = \begin{bmatrix} 2 & 3 \\ 2 & 4 \end{bmatrix} \qquad B = \begin{bmatrix} 2 & 4 \\ -1 & 1 \\ 3 & 0 \end{bmatrix} \qquad C = \begin{bmatrix} 1 & 0 & 4 \\ -1 & 1 & 2 \\ 0 & 1 & 3 \end{bmatrix}$$

Carry out the indicated operation, or explain why it cannot be performed.

(a) $A + B$ (b) AB (c) $BA - 3B$ (d) CBA
(e) A^{-1} (f) B^{-1} (g) $\det(B)$ (h) $\det(C)$

10. (a) Write a matrix equation equivalent to the following system.

$$\begin{cases} 4x - 3y = 10 \\ 3x - 2y = 30 \end{cases}$$

(b) Find the inverse of the coefficient matrix, and use it to solve the system.

11. Only one of the following matrices has an inverse. Find the determinant of each matrix, and use the determinants to identify the one that has an inverse. Then find the inverse.

$$A = \begin{bmatrix} 1 & 4 & 1 \\ 0 & 2 & 0 \\ 1 & 0 & 1 \end{bmatrix} \qquad B = \begin{bmatrix} 1 & 4 & 0 \\ 0 & 2 & 0 \\ -3 & 0 & 1 \end{bmatrix}$$

714

12. Solve using Cramer's Rule:

$$\begin{cases} 2x \quad\ \ - \ z = 14 \\ 3x - \ y + 5z = \ \ 0 \\ 4x + 2y + 3z = -2 \end{cases}$$

13. Find the partial fraction decomposition of the rational function.

(a) $\dfrac{4x - 1}{(x - 1)^2(x + 2)}$

(b) $\dfrac{2x - 3}{x^3 + 3x}$

14. Graph the solution set of the system of inequalities. Label the vertices with their coordinates.

(a) $\begin{cases} 2x + \ y \le \ \ 8 \\ x - \ y \ge -2 \\ x + 2y \ge \ \ 4 \end{cases}$

(b) $\begin{cases} x^2 + y \le 5 \\ y \le 2x + 5 \end{cases}$

Linear programming is a modeling technique that is used to determine the optimal allocation of resources in business, the military, and other areas of human endeavor. For example, a manufacturer who makes several different products from the same raw materials can use linear programming to determine how much of each product should be produced to maximize the profit. This modeling technique is probably the most important practical application of systems of linear inequalities. In 1975 Leonid Kantorovich and T. C. Koopmans won the Nobel Prize in economics for their work in the development of this technique.

Although linear programming can be applied to very complex problems with hundreds or even thousands of variables, we consider only a few simple examples to which the graphical methods of Section 10.9 can be applied. (For large numbers of variables a linear programming method based on matrices is used.) Let's examine a typical problem.

EXAMPLE 1 | Manufacturing for Maximum Profit

A small shoe manufacturer makes two styles of shoes: oxfords and loafers. Two machines are used in the process: a cutting machine and a sewing machine. Each type of shoe requires 15 min per pair on the cutting machine. Oxfords require 10 min of sewing per pair, and loafers require 20 min of sewing per pair. Because the manufacturer can hire only one operator for each machine, each process is available for just 8 hours per day. If the profit is $15 on each pair of oxfords and $20 on each pair of loafers, how many pairs of each type should be produced per day for maximum profit?

Because loafers produce more profit, it would seem best to manufacture only loafers. Surprisingly, this does not turn out to be the most profitable solution.

SOLUTION   First we organize the given information into a table. To be consistent, let's convert all times to hours.

	Oxfords	Loafers	Time available
Time on cutting machine (h)	$\frac{1}{4}$	$\frac{1}{4}$	8
Time on sewing machine (h)	$\frac{1}{6}$	$\frac{1}{3}$	8
Profit	$15	$20	

We describe the model and solve the problem in four steps.

▶ **Choose the Variables.**   To make a mathematical model, we first give names to the variable quantities. For this problem we let

$$x = \text{number of pairs of oxfords made daily}$$

$$y = \text{number of pairs of loafers made daily}$$

▶ **Find the Objective Function.**   Our goal is to determine which values for x and y give maximum profit. Since each pair of oxfords provides $15 profit and each pair of loafers $20, the total profit is given by

$$P = 15x + 20y$$

This function is called the *objective function*.

▶ **Graph the Feasible Region.**   The larger x and y are, the greater is the profit. But we cannot choose arbitrarily large values for these variables because of the restrictions, or *constraints*, in the problem. Each restriction is an inequality in the variables.

716

In this problem the total number of cutting hours needed is $\frac{1}{4}x + \frac{1}{4}y$. Since only 8 hours are available on the cutting machine, we have

$$\tfrac{1}{4}x + \tfrac{1}{4}y \le 8$$

Similarly, by considering the amount of time needed and available on the sewing machine, we get

$$\tfrac{1}{6}x + \tfrac{1}{3}y \le 8$$

We cannot produce a negative number of shoes, so we also have

$$x \ge 0 \qquad \text{and} \qquad y \ge 0$$

Thus, x and y must satisfy the constraints

$$\begin{cases} \tfrac{1}{4}x + \tfrac{1}{4}y \le 8 \\ \tfrac{1}{6}x + \tfrac{1}{3}y \le 8 \\ \qquad\quad x \ge 0 \\ \qquad\quad y \ge 0 \end{cases}$$

If we multiply the first inequality by 4 and the second by 6, we obtain the simplified system

$$\begin{cases} x + \;\; y \le 32 \\ x + 2y \le 48 \\ \qquad x \le 0 \\ \qquad y \le 0 \end{cases}$$

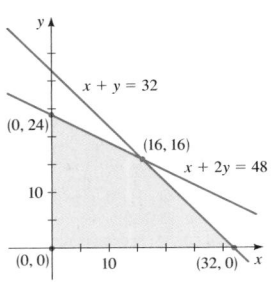

FIGURE 1

The solution of this system (with vertices labeled) is sketched in Figure 1. The only values that satisfy the restrictions of the problem are the ones that correspond to points of the shaded region in Figure 1. This is called the *feasible region* for the problem.

▶ **Find the Maximum Profit.** As x or y increases, profit increases as well. Thus it seems reasonable that the maximum profit will occur at a point on one of the outside edges of the feasible region, where it is impossible to increase x or y without going outside the region. In fact, it can be shown that the maximum value occurs at a vertex. This means that we need to check the profit only at the vertices. The largest value of P occurs at the point $(16, 16)$, where $P = \$560$. Thus the manufacturer should make 16 pairs of oxfords and 16 pairs of loafers, for a maximum daily profit of $\$560$.

Vertex	$P = 15x + 20y$
$(0, 0)$	0
$(0, 24)$	$15(0) \; + 20(24) = \$480$
$(16, 16)$	$15(16) + 20(16) = \$560$ — Maximum profit
$(32, 0)$	$15(32) + 20(0) \; = \$480$

The linear programming problems that we consider all follow the pattern of Example 1. Each problem involves two variables. The problem describes restrictions, called **constraints**, that lead to a system of linear inequalities whose solution is called the **feasible region**. The function that we wish to maximize or minimize is called the **objective function**. This function always attains its largest and smallest values at the **vertices** of the feasible region. This modeling technique involves four steps, summarized in the following box.

Linear Programming helps the telephone industry to determine the most efficient way to route telephone calls. The computerized routing decisions must be made very rapidly so that callers are not kept waiting for connections. Since the database of customers and routes is huge, an extremely fast method for solving linear programming problems is essential. In 1984 the 28-year-old mathematician **Narendra Karmarkar**, working at Bell Labs in Murray Hill, New Jersey, discovered just such a method. His idea is so ingenious and his method so fast that the discovery caused a sensation in the mathematical world. Although mathematical discoveries rarely make the news, this one was reported in *Time*, on December 3, 1984. Today airlines routinely use Karmarkar's technique to minimize costs in scheduling passengers, flight personnel, fuel, baggage, and maintenance workers.

GUIDELINES FOR LINEAR PROGRAMMING

1. **Choose the Variables.**   Decide what variable quantities in the problem should be named x and y.

2. **Find the Objective Function.**   Write an expression for the function we want to maximize or minimize.

3. **Graph the Feasible Region.**   Express the constraints as a system of inequalities, and graph the solution of this system (the feasible region).

4. **Find the Maximum or Minimum.**   Evaluate the objective function at the vertices of the feasible region to determine its maximum or minimum value.

EXAMPLE 2 | A Shipping Problem

A car dealer has warehouses in Millville and Trenton and dealerships in Camden and Atlantic City. Every car that is sold at the dealerships must be delivered from one of the warehouses. On a certain day the Camden dealers sell 10 cars, and the Atlantic City dealers sell 12. The Millville warehouse has 15 cars available, and the Trenton warehouse has 10. The cost of shipping one car is $50 from Millville to Camden, $40 from Millville to Atlantic City, $60 from Trenton to Camden, and $55 from Trenton to Atlantic City. How many cars should be moved from each warehouse to each dealership to fill the orders at minimum cost?

SOLUTION   Our first step is to organize the given information. Rather than construct a table, we draw a diagram to show the flow of cars from the warehouses to the dealerships (see Figure 2 below). The diagram shows the number of cars available at each warehouse or required at each dealership and the cost of shipping between these locations.

▶ **Choose the Variables.**   The arrows in Figure 2 indicate four possible routes, so the problem seems to involve four variables. But we let

$$x = \text{number of cars to be shipped from Millville to Camden}$$

$$y = \text{number of cars to be shipped from Millville to Atlantic City}$$

To fill the orders, we must have

$$10 - x = \text{number of cars shipped from Trenton to Camden}$$

$$12 - y = \text{number of cars shipped from Trenton to Atlantic City}$$

So the only variables in the problem are x and y.

FIGURE 2

► **Find the Objective Function.**   The objective of this problem is to minimize cost. From Figure 2 we see that the total cost C of shipping the cars is

$$C = 50x + 40y + 60(10 - x) + 55(12 - y)$$
$$= 50x + 40y + 600 - 60x + 660 - 55y$$
$$= 1260 - 10x - 15y$$

This is the objective function.

► **Graph the Feasible Region.**   Now we derive the constraint inequalities that define the feasible region. First, the number of cars shipped on each route can't be negative, so we have

$$x \geq 0 \qquad\qquad y \geq 0$$
$$10 - x \geq 0 \qquad 12 - y \geq 0$$

Second, the total number of cars shipped from each warehouse can't exceed the number of cars available there, so

$$x + y \leq 15$$
$$(10 - x) + (12 - y) \leq 10$$

Simplifying the latter inequality, we get

$$22 - x - y \leq 10$$
$$-x - y \leq -12$$
$$x + y \geq 12$$

The inequalities $10 - x \geq 0$ and $12 - y \geq 0$ can be rewritten as $x \leq 10$ and $y \leq 12$. Thus the feasible region is described by the constraints

$$\begin{cases} x + y \leq 15 \\ x + y \geq 12 \\ 0 \leq x \leq 10 \\ 0 \leq y \leq 12 \end{cases}$$

The feasible region is graphed in Figure 3.

FIGURE 3

► **Find the Minimum Cost.**   We check the value of the objective function at each vertex of the feasible region.

Vertex	$C = 1260 - 10x - 15y$	
(0, 12)	$1260 - 10(0)\ \ - 15(12) = \$1080$	
(3, 12)	$1260 - 10(3)\ \ - 15(12) = \$1050$	Minimum cost
(10, 5)	$1260 - 10(10) - 15(5)\ \ = \$1085$	
(10, 2)	$1260 - 10(10) - 15(2)\ \ = \$1130$	

The lowest cost is incurred at the point (3, 12). Thus, the dealer should ship

3 cars from Millville to Camden
12 cars from Millville to Atlantic City
7 cars from Trenton to Camden
0 cars from Trenton to Atlantic City   ■

In the 1940s mathematicians developed matrix methods for solving linear programming problems that involve more than two variables. These methods were first used by the Allies in World War II to solve supply problems similar to (but, of course, much more complicated than) Example 2. Improving such matrix methods is an active and exciting area of current mathematical research.

PROBLEMS

1–4 ■ Find the maximum and minimum values of the given objective function on the indicated feasible region.

1. $M = 200 - x - y$

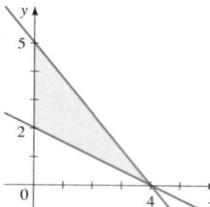

2. $N = \frac{1}{2}x + \frac{1}{4}y + 40$

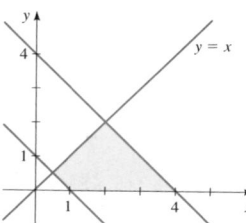

3. $P = 140 - x + 3y$

$$\begin{cases} x \geq 0, y \geq 0 \\ 2x + y \leq 10 \\ 2x + 4y \leq 28 \end{cases}$$

4. $Q = 70x + 82y$

$$\begin{cases} x \geq 0, y \geq 0 \\ x \leq 10, y \leq 20 \\ x + y \geq 5 \\ x + 2y \leq 18 \end{cases}$$

5. Making Furniture A furniture manufacturer makes wooden tables and chairs. The production process involves two basic types of labor: carpentry and finishing. A table requires 2 hours of carpentry and 1 hour of finishing, and a chair requires 3 hours of carpentry and $\frac{1}{2}$ hour of finishing. The profit is $35 per table and $20 per chair. The manufacturer's employees can supply a maximum of 108 hours of carpentry work and 20 hours of finishing work per day. How many tables and chairs should be made each day to maximize profit?

6. A Housing Development A housing contractor has subdivided a farm into 100 building lots. She has designed two types of homes for these lots: colonial and ranch style. A colonial requires $30,000 of capital and produces a profit of $4000 when sold. A ranch-style house requires $40,000 of capital and provides an $8000 profit. If the contractor has $3.6 million of capital on hand, how many houses of each type should she build for maximum profit? Will any of the lots be left vacant?

7. Hauling Fruit A trucker hauls citrus fruit from Florida to Montreal. Each crate of oranges is 4 ft³ in volume and weighs 80 lb. Each crate of grapefruit has a volume of 6 ft³ and weighs 100 lb. His truck has a maximum capacity of 300 ft³ and can carry no more than 5600 lb. Moreover, he is not permitted to carry more crates of grapefruit than crates of oranges. If his profit is $2.50 on each crate of oranges and $4 on each crate of grapefruit, how many crates of each fruit should he carry for maximum profit?

8. **Manufacturing Calculators**   A manufacturer of calculators produces two models: standard and scientific. Long-term demand for the two models mandates that the company manufacture at least 100 standard and 80 scientific calculators each day. However, because of limitations on production capacity, no more than 200 standard and 170 scientific calculators can be made daily. To satisfy a shipping contract, a total of at least 200 calculators must be shipped every day.

   (a) If the production cost is \$5 for a standard calculator and \$7 for a scientific one, how many of each model should be produced daily to minimize this cost?

   (b) If each standard calculator results in a \$2 loss but each scientific one produces a \$5 profit, how many of each model should be made daily to maximize profit?

9. **Shipping Stereos**   An electronics discount chain has a sale on a certain brand of stereo. The chain has stores in Santa Monica and El Toro and warehouses in Long Beach and Pasadena. To satisfy rush orders, 15 sets must be shipped from the warehouses to the Santa Monica store, and 19 must be shipped to the El Toro store. The cost of shipping a set is \$5 from Long Beach to Santa Monica, \$6 from Long Beach to El Toro, \$4 from Pasadena to Santa Monica, and \$5.50 from Pasadena to El Toro. If the Long Beach warehouse has 24 sets and the Pasadena warehouse has 18 sets in stock, how many sets should be shipped from each warehouse to each store to fill the orders at a minimum shipping cost?

10. **Delivering Plywood**   A man owns two building supply stores, one on the east side and one on the west side of a city. Two customers order some $\frac{1}{2}$-inch plywood. Customer A needs 50 sheets, and customer B needs 70 sheets. The east-side store has 80 sheets, and the west-side store has 45 sheets of this plywood in stock. The east-side store's delivery costs per sheet are \$0.50 to customer A and \$0.60 to customer B. The west-side store's delivery costs per sheet are \$0.40 to customer A and \$0.55 to customer B. How many sheets should be shipped from each store to each customer to minimize delivery costs?

11. **Packaging Nuts**   A confectioner sells two types of nut mixtures. The standard-mixture package contains 100 g of cashews and 200 g of peanuts and sells for \$1.95. The deluxe-mixture package contains 150 g of cashews and 50 g of peanuts and sells for \$2.25. The confectioner has 15 kg of cashews and 20 kg of peanuts available. On the basis of past sales, the confectioner needs to have at least as many standard as deluxe packages available. How many bags of each mixture should he package to maximize his revenue?

12. **Feeding Lab Rabbits**   A biologist wishes to feed laboratory rabbits a mixture of two types of foods. Type I contains 8 g of fat, 12 g of carbohydrate, and 2 g of protein per ounce. Type II contains 12 g of fat, 12 g of carbohydrate, and 1 g of protein per ounce. Type I costs \$0.20 per ounce and type II costs \$0.30 per ounce. The rabbits each receive a daily minimum of 24 g of fat, 36 g of carbohydrate, and 4 g of protein, but get no more than 5 oz of food per day. How many ounces of each food type should be fed to each rabbit daily to satisfy the dietary requirements at minimum cost?

13. **Investing in Bonds**   A woman wishes to invest \$12,000 in three types of bonds: municipal bonds paying 7% interest per year, bank investment certificates paying 8%, and high-risk bonds paying 12%. For tax reasons she wants the amount invested in municipal bonds to be at least three times the amount invested in bank certificates. To keep her level of risk manageable, she will invest no more than \$2000 in high-risk bonds. How much should she invest in each type of bond to maximize her annual interest yield?   [*Hint:* Let x = amount in municipal bonds and y = amount in bank certificates. Then the amount in high-risk bonds will be $12,000 - x - y$.]

14. **Annual Interest Yield**   Refer to Problem 13. Suppose the investor decides to increase the maximum invested in high-risk bonds to \$3000 but leaves the other conditions unchanged. By how much will her maximum possible interest yield increase?

15. **Business Strategy**   A small software company publishes computer games and educational and utility software. Their business strategy is to market a total of 36 new programs each year, at least four of these being games. The number of utility programs published is never more than twice the number of educational programs. On average, the company makes an annual profit of \$5000 on each computer game, \$8000 on each educational program, and \$6000 on each utility program. How many of each type of software should the company publish annually for maximum profit?

16. Feasible Region   All parts of this problem refer to the following feasible region and objective function.

$$\begin{cases} x \geq 0 \\ x \geq y \\ x + 2y \leq 12 \\ x + y \leq 10 \end{cases}$$

$$P = x + 4y$$

(a) Graph the feasible region.

(b) On your graph from part (a), sketch the graphs of the linear equations obtained by setting P equal to 40, 36, 32, and 28.

(c) If you continue to decrease the value of P, at which vertex of the feasible region will these lines first touch the feasible region?

(d) Verify that the maximum value of P on the feasible region occurs at the vertex you chose in part (c).

CONIC SECTIONS

Conic sections are the curves we get when we make a straight cut in a cone, as shown in the figure. For example, if a cone is cut horizontally, the cross section is a circle. So a circle is a conic section. Other ways of cutting a cone produce parabolas, ellipses, and hyperbolas.

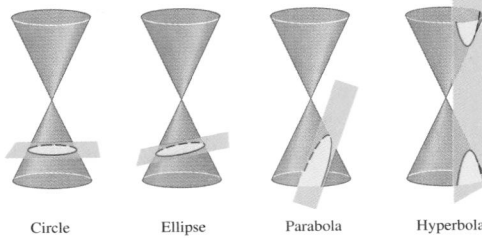

| Circle | Ellipse | Parabola | Hyperbola |

Our goal in this chapter is to find equations whose graphs are the conic sections. We already know from Section 1.8 that the graph of the equation $x^2 + y^2 = r^2$ is a circle. We will find equations for each of the other conic sections by analyzing their *geometric* properties.

The conic sections have interesting properties that make them useful for many real-world applications. For instance, a reflecting surface with parabolic cross-sections concentrates light at a single point. This property of a parabola is used in the construction of solar power plants, like the one in California pictured above.

723

SUGGESTED TIME AND EMPHASIS

$\frac{1}{2}$ class, essential material

11.1 PARABOLAS

Geometric Definition of a Parabola ▶ Equations and Graphs of Parabolas ▶ Applications

▼ Geometric Definition of a Parabola

We saw in Section 3.1 that the graph of the equation

$$y = ax^2 + bx + c$$

is a U-shaped curve called a *parabola* that opens either upward or downward, depending on whether the sign of a is positive or negative.

In this section we study parabolas from a geometric rather than an algebraic point of view. We begin with the geometric definition of a parabola and show how this leads to the algebraic formula that we are already familiar with.

GEOMETRIC DEFINITION OF A PARABOLA

A **parabola** is the set of points in the plane that are equidistant from a fixed point F (called the **focus**) and a fixed line l (called the **directrix**).

This definition is illustrated in Figure 1. The **vertex** V of the parabola lies halfway between the focus and the directrix, and the **axis of symmetry** is the line that runs through the focus perpendicular to the directrix.

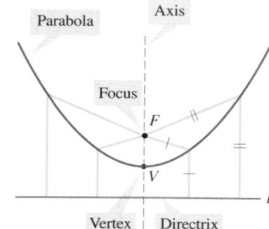

FIGURE 1

In this section we restrict our attention to parabolas that are situated with the vertex at the origin and that have a vertical or horizontal axis of symmetry. (Parabolas in more general positions will be considered in Sections 11.4 and 11.5.) If the focus of such a parabola is the point $F(0, p)$, then the axis of symmetry must be vertical, and the directrix has the equation $y = -p$. Figure 2 illustrates the case $p > 0$.

If $P(x, y)$ is any point on the parabola, then the distance from P to the focus F (using the Distance Formula) is

$$\sqrt{x^2 + (y - p)^2}$$

The distance from P to the directrix is

$$|y - (-p)| = |y + p|$$

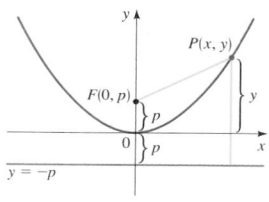

FIGURE 2

TEXT QUESTION
How can you tell if the axis of a parabola is vertical or horizontal?

Answer
If there is a y^2 term, it is horizontal; if there is an x^2 term, it is vertical.

By the definition of a parabola these two distances must be equal:

$$\sqrt{x^2 + (y - p)^2} = |y + p|$$

$$x^2 + (y - p)^2 = |y + p|^2 = (y + p)^2 \qquad \text{Square both sides}$$

$$x^2 + y^2 - 2py + p^2 = y^2 + 2py + p^2 \qquad \text{Expand}$$

$$x^2 - 2py = 2py \qquad \text{Simplify}$$

$$x^2 = 4py$$

If $p > 0$, then the parabola opens upward; but if $p < 0$, it opens downward. When x is replaced by $-x$, the equation remains unchanged, so the graph is symmetric about the y-axis.

▼ Equations and Graphs of Parabolas

The following box summarizes what we have just proved about the equation and features of a parabola with a vertical axis.

PARABOLA WITH VERTICAL AXIS

The graph of the equation

$$x^2 = 4py$$

is a parabola with the following properties.

VERTEX	$V(0, 0)$
FOCUS	$F(0, p)$
DIRECTRIX	$y = -p$

The parabola opens upward if $p > 0$ or downward if $p < 0$.

$x^2 = 4py$ with $p > 0$ $x^2 = 4py$ with $p < 0$

EXAMPLE 1 | Finding the Equation of a Parabola

Find an equation for the parabola with vertex $V(0, 0)$ and focus $F(0, 2)$, and sketch its graph.

SOLUTION   Since the focus is $F(0, 2)$, we conclude that $p = 2$ (so the directrix is $y = -2$). Thus the equation of the parabola is

$$x^2 = 4(2)y \qquad x^2 = 4py \text{ with } p = 2$$

$$x^2 = 8y$$

Since $p = 2 > 0$, the parabola opens upward. See Figure 3.

✎. NOW TRY EXERCISES **29** AND **41**   ∎

FIGURE 3

ALTERNATE EXAMPLE 1

Find the equation of the parabola with vertex $V(0, 0)$ and focus $F(0, -8)$.

ANSWER

$x^2 = -32y$

IN-CLASS MATERIALS

Have students sketch a parabola "from scratch." Hand out a sheet of paper with focus and directrix, and hand out rulers. Get the students to plot points where the distance from the point to the directrix is equal to the distance from the point to the focus. Have them keep plotting points until a parabolic shape emerges.

ALTERNATE EXAMPLE 2

Find the focus and directrix of the parabola $y = -5x^2$.

ANSWER

$$\left(0, \frac{1}{20}\right), y = \frac{1}{20}$$

EXAMPLE 2 | Finding the Focus and Directrix of a Parabola from Its Equation

Find the focus and directrix of the parabola $y = -x^2$, and sketch the graph.

SOLUTION   To find the focus and directrix, we put the given equation in the standard form $x^2 = -y$. Comparing this to the general equation $x^2 = 4py$, we see that $4p = -1$, so $p = -\frac{1}{4}$. Thus the focus is $F\left(0, -\frac{1}{4}\right)$, and the directrix is $y = \frac{1}{4}$. The graph of the parabola, together with the focus and the directrix, is shown in Figure 4(a). We can also draw the graph using a graphing calculator as shown in Figure 4(b).

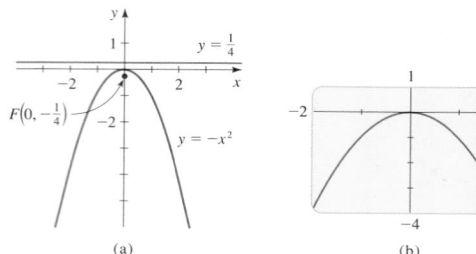

FIGURE 4

(a)   (b)

✎ . NOW TRY EXERCISE **11**

Reflecting the graph in Figure 2 about the diagonal line $y = x$ has the effect of interchanging the roles of x and y. This results in a parabola with horizontal axis. By the same method as before, we can prove the following properties.

PARABOLA WITH HORIZONTAL AXIS

The graph of the equation

$$y^2 = 4px$$

is a parabola with the following properties.

> **VERTEX** $V(0, 0)$
>
> **FOCUS** $F(p, 0)$
>
> **DIRECTRIX** $x = -p$

The parabola opens to the right if $p > 0$ or to the left if $p < 0$.

$y^2 = 4px$ with $p > 0$ $y^2 = 4px$ with $p < 0$

IN-CLASS MATERIALS

As of this writing, it is possible to purchase a parabolic listening device for about $40 on eBay, or about $60 new. If this is feasible, many experiments and demonstrations can be done. For example, students can whisper from a long distance away and be heard using the device.

EXAMPLE 3 | A Parabola with Horizontal Axis

A parabola has the equation $6x + y^2 = 0$.

(a) Find the focus and directrix of the parabola, and sketch the graph.

(b) Use a graphing calculator to draw the graph.

SOLUTION

(a) To find the focus and directrix, we put the given equation in the standard form $y^2 = -6x$. Comparing this to the general equation $y^2 = 4px$, we see that $4p = -6$, so $p = -\frac{3}{2}$. Thus the focus is $F\left(-\frac{3}{2}, 0\right)$ and the directrix is $x = \frac{3}{2}$. Since $p < 0$, the parabola opens to the left. The graph of the parabola, together with the focus and the directrix, is shown in Figure 5(a) below.

(b) To draw the graph using a graphing calculator, we need to solve for y.

$$6x + y^2 = 0$$

$$y^2 = -6x \qquad \text{Subtract } 6x$$

$$y = \pm\sqrt{-6x} \qquad \text{Take square roots}$$

To obtain the graph of the parabola, we graph both functions

$$y = \sqrt{-6x} \qquad \text{and} \qquad y = -\sqrt{-6x}$$

as shown in Figure 5(b).

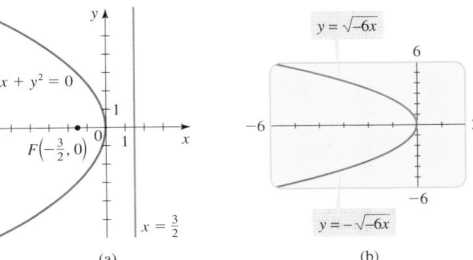

FIGURE 5   (a)   (b)

✎. NOW TRY EXERCISE **13**

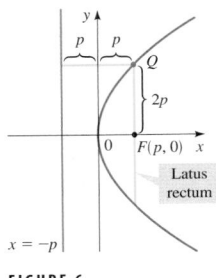

FIGURE 6

The equation $y^2 = 4px$, does not define y as a function of x (see page 158). So to use a graphing calculator to graph a parabola with a horizontal axis, we must first solve for y. This leads to two functions: $y = \sqrt{4px}$ and $y = -\sqrt{4px}$. We need to graph both functions to get the complete graph of the parabola. For example, in Figure 5(b) we had to graph both $y = \sqrt{-6x}$ and $y = -\sqrt{-6x}$ to graph the parabola $y^2 = -6x$.

We can use the coordinates of the focus to estimate the "width" of a parabola when sketching its graph. The line segment that runs through the focus perpendicular to the axis, with endpoints on the parabola, is called the **latus rectum**, and its length is the **focal diameter** of the parabola. From Figure 6 we can see that the distance from an endpoint Q of the latus rectum to the directrix is $|2p|$. Thus the distance from Q to the focus must be $|2p|$ as well (by the definition of a parabola), so the focal diameter is $|4p|$. In the next example we use the focal diameter to determine the "width" of a parabola when graphing it.

IN-CLASS MATERIALS

Make the connection between quadratic functions and parabolas explicit. Point out that any equation of the form $y = ax^2 + bx + c$ can be written as $y = n(x - h)^2 + k$ by completing the square, yielding a (possibly shifted) parabola. The constant n, of course, can be written as $4p$. Note that if $a = 0$, we have a line. So we can call a line a degenerate parabola.

ALTERNATE EXAMPLE 4

Find the focus, directrix, and focal diameter of the parabola.

$$y = \frac{4}{9}x^2$$

ANSWER

$$\left(0, \frac{9}{16}\right), y = -\frac{9}{16}, \frac{9}{4}$$

ALTERNATE EXAMPLE 5

Find equations for the parabolas with vertex at the origin and foci:

$$F_1\left(0, \frac{1}{8}\right), F_2\left(0, \frac{1}{4}\right), F_3(0, 1),$$

$$F_4(0, 4)$$

ANSWER

$$y = 2x^2, y = x^2, y = 0.25x^2,$$

$$y = 0.0625x^2$$

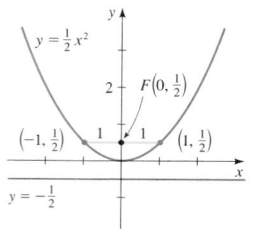

FIGURE 7

EXAMPLE 4 │ The Focal Diameter of a Parabola

Find the focus, directrix, and focal diameter of the parabola $y = \frac{1}{2}x^2$, and sketch its graph.

SOLUTION We first put the equation in the form $x^2 = 4py$.

$$y = \frac{1}{2}x^2$$

$$x^2 = 2y \qquad \text{Multiply by 2, switch sides}$$

From this equation we see that $4p = 2$, so the focal diameter is 2. Solving for p gives $p = \frac{1}{2}$, so the focus is $\left(0, \frac{1}{2}\right)$ and the directrix is $y = -\frac{1}{2}$. Since the focal diameter is 2, the latus rectum extends 1 unit to the left and 1 unit to the right of the focus. The graph is sketched in Figure 7.

✎. NOW TRY EXERCISE **15**   ∎

In the next example we graph a family of parabolas, to show how changing the distance between the focus and the vertex affects the "width" of a parabola.

EXAMPLE 5 │ A Family of Parabolas

(a) Find equations for the parabolas with vertex at the origin and foci $F_1\left(0, \frac{1}{8}\right), F_2\left(0, \frac{1}{2}\right), F_3(0, 1),$ and $F_4(0, 4)$.

(b) Draw the graphs of the parabolas in part (a). What do you conclude?

SOLUTION

(a) Since the foci are on the positive y-axis, the parabolas open upward and have equations of the form $x^2 = 4py$. This leads to the following equations.

Focus	p	Equation $x^2 = 4py$	Form of the equation for graphing calculator
$F_1(0, \frac{1}{8})$	$p = \frac{1}{8}$	$x^2 = \frac{1}{2}y$	$y = 2x^2$
$F_2(0, \frac{1}{2})$	$p = \frac{1}{2}$	$x^2 = 2y$	$y = 0.5x^2$
$F_3(0, 1)$	$p = 1$	$x^2 = 4y$	$y = 0.25x^2$
$F_4(0, 4)$	$p = 4$	$x^2 = 16y$	$y = 0.0625x^2$

(b) The graphs are drawn in Figure 8. We see that the closer the focus is to the vertex, the narrower the parabola.

$y = 2x^2$

$y = 0.5x^2$

$y = 0.25x^2$

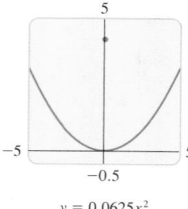
$y = 0.0625x^2$

FIGURE 8 A family of parabolas

✎. NOW TRY EXERCISE **51**   ∎

IN-CLASS MATERIALS

Using dental floss and modeling compound (such as clay or Play-Doh), it is easy for the students to make half a cone and slice it. Have the class attempt to do so to get a parabola. Most of them will wind up creating half of a hyperbola. Refer these students to the chapter overview. Make sure they note that a parabola is not as easy to create in this way as a hyperbola or an ellipse. If the cut is made at the wrong angle, even slightly, one of these two shapes will be formed instead of a parabola.

▼ Applications

Parabolas have an important property that makes them useful as reflectors for lamps and telescopes. Light from a source placed at the focus of a surface with parabolic cross section will be reflected in such a way that it travels parallel to the axis of the parabola (see Figure 9). Thus, a parabolic mirror reflects the light into a beam of parallel rays. Conversely, light approaching the reflector in rays parallel to its axis of symmetry is concentrated to the focus. This *reflection property*, which can be proved by using calculus, is used in the construction of reflecting telescopes.

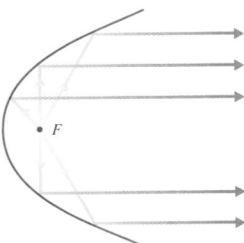

FIGURE 9 Parabolic reflector

EXAMPLE 6 | Finding the Focal Point of a Searchlight Reflector

A searchlight has a parabolic reflector that forms a "bowl," which is 12 in. wide from rim to rim and 8 in. deep, as shown in Figure 10. If the filament of the light bulb is located at the focus, how far from the vertex of the reflector is it?

FIGURE 10 A parabolic reflector

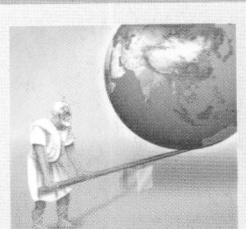

ARCHIMEDES (287–212 B.C.) was the greatest mathematician of the ancient world. He was born in Syracuse, a Greek colony on Sicily, a generation after Euclid (see page 497). One of his many discoveries is the Law of the Lever (see page 71). He famously said, "Give me a place to stand and a fulcrum for my lever, and I can lift the earth." Renowned as a mechanical genius for his many engineering inventions, he designed pulleys for lifting heavy ships and the spiral screw for transporting water to higher levels. He is said to have used parabolic mirrors to concentrate the rays of the sun to set fire to Roman ships attacking Syracuse.

King Hieron II of Syracuse once suspected a goldsmith of keeping part of the gold intended for the king's crown and replacing it with an equal amount of silver. The king asked Archimedes for advice. While in deep thought at a public bath, Archimedes discovered the solution to the king's problem when he noticed that his body's volume was the same as the volume of water it displaced from the tub. Using this insight he was able to measure the volume of each crown, and so determine which was the denser, all-gold crown. As the story is told, he ran home naked, shouting "Eureka, eureka!" ("I have found it, I have found it!") This incident attests to his enormous powers of concentration.

In spite of his engineering prowess, Archimedes was most proud of his mathematical discoveries. These include the formulas for the volume of a sphere, $(V = \frac{4}{3}\pi r^3)$ and the surface area of a sphere $(S = 4\pi r^2)$ and a careful analysis of the properties of parabolas and other conics.

EXAMPLE
A shifted parabola:
$$y = 2x^2 - 8x + 2$$
$$= 2(x^2 - 4x) + 2$$
$$= 2(x^2 - 4x + 4) - 6$$
$$= 2(x - 2)^2 - 6$$

$p = \frac{1}{2}$, focus $\left(0 + 2, \frac{1}{2} - 6\right)$
$= \left(2, -\frac{11}{2}\right)$, directrix $y =$
$-\frac{1}{2} - 6 = -\frac{13}{2}$

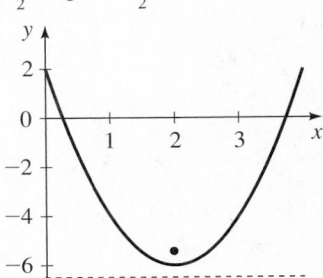

ALTERNATE EXAMPLE 6
A searchlight has a parabolic reflector that forms a "bowl," which is 18 in. wide from rim to rim and 10 in. deep, as shown in the figure. If the filament of the lightbulb is located at the focus, how far from the vertex of the reflector is it?

ANSWER
$\dfrac{81}{40}$

IN-CLASS MATERIALS

Discuss the reflection properties of parabolas: A beam of light originating at the origin will emerge parallel to the parabola's axis of symmetry, and a beam of light that is parallel to the parabola's axis of symmetry will reflect off the parabola in a direction that goes through its focus. One nice project is to construct a parabolic pool table or miniature golf hole. The students accurately graph a parabola and glue erasers or wood along its border, placing the "hole" at the focus. A golf ball or pool ball that is rolled in a direction parallel to the axis will always bounce into the hole.

DRILL QUESTION

Find the focus and directrix of $y = \dfrac{1}{16}x^2$ and sketch its graph.

Answer

Focus $(0, 4)$, directrix $y = -4$

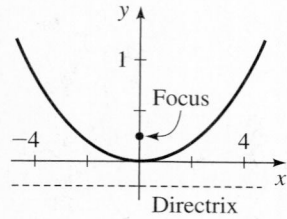

SOLUTION We introduce a coordinate system and place a parabolic cross section of the reflector so that its vertex is at the origin and its axis is vertical (see Figure 11). Then the equation of this parabola has the form $x^2 = 4py$. From Figure 11 we see that the point $(6, 8)$ lies on the parabola. We use this to find p.

$$6^2 = 4p(8) \qquad \text{The point } (6, 8) \text{ satisfies the equation } x^2 = 4py$$

$$36 = 32p$$

$$p = \tfrac{9}{8}$$

The focus is $F\left(0, \tfrac{9}{8}\right)$, so the distance between the vertex and the focus is $\tfrac{9}{8} = 1\tfrac{1}{8}$ in. Because the filament is positioned at the focus, it is located $1\tfrac{1}{8}$ in. from the vertex of the reflector.

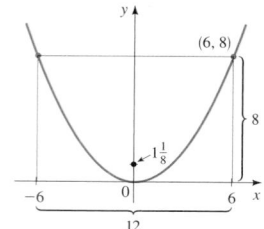

FIGURE 11

✎. **NOW TRY EXERCISE 53**

11.1 EXERCISES

CONCEPTS

1. A parabola is the set of all points in the plane that are equidistant from a fixed point called the _____ and a fixed line called the _____ of the parabola.

2. The graph of the equation $x^2 = 4py$ is a parabola with focus $F(\_\_, \_\_)$ and directrix $y = \_\_\_\_$. So the graph of $x^2 = 12y$ is a parabola with focus $F(\_\_, \_\_)$ and directrix $y = \_\_\_\_$.

3. The graph of the equation $y^2 = 4px$ is a parabola with focus $F(\_\_, \_\_)$ and directrix $x = \_\_\_\_$. So the graph of $y^2 = 12x$ is a parabola with focus $F(\_\_, \_\_)$ and directrix $x = \_\_\_\_$.

4. Label the focus, directrix, and vertex on the graphs given for the parabolas in Exercises 2 and 3.
   (a) $x^2 = 12y$ (b) $y^2 = 12x$

 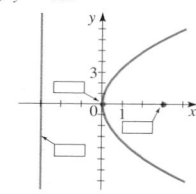

SKILLS

5–10 ■ Match the equation with the graphs labeled I–VI. Give reasons for your answers.

5. $y^2 = 2x$
6. $y^2 = -\tfrac{1}{4}x$
7. $x^2 = -6y$
8. $2x^2 = y$

9. $y^2 - 8x = 0$ 10. $12y + x^2 = 0$

I   II

III   IV

V   VI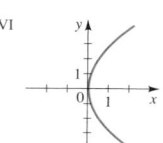

11–22 ■ Find the focus, directrix, and focal diameter of the parabola, and sketch its graph.

✎. 11. $x^2 = 9y$ 12. $x^2 = y$
✎. 13. $y^2 = 4x$ 14. $y^2 = 3x$
✎. 15. $y = 5x^2$ 16. $y = -2x^2$
    17. $x = -8y^2$ 18. $x = \tfrac{1}{2}y^2$
    19. $x^2 + 6y = 0$ 20. $x - 7y^2 = 0$
    21. $5x + 3y^2 = 0$ 22. $8x^2 + 12y = 0$

23–28 ■ Use a graphing device to graph the parabola.

23. $x^2 = 16y$ **24.** $x^2 = -8y$

25. $y^2 = -\frac{1}{3}x$ **26.** $8y^2 = x$

27. $4x + y^2 = 0$ **28.** $x - 2y^2 = 0$

29–40 ■ Find an equation for the parabola that has its vertex at the origin and satisfies the given condition(s).

29. Focus: $F(0, 2)$ **30.** Focus: $F\left(0, -\frac{1}{2}\right)$

31. Focus: $F(-8, 0)$ **32.** Focus: $F(5, 0)$

33. Directrix: $x = 2$ **34.** Directrix: $y = 6$

35. Directrix: $y = -10$ **36.** Directrix: $x = -\frac{1}{8}$

37. Focus on the positive x-axis, 2 units away from the directrix

38. Directrix has y-intercept 6

39. Opens upward with focus 5 units from the vertex

40. Focal diameter 8 and focus on the negative y-axis

41–50 ■ Find an equation of the parabola whose graph is shown.

41.

42.

43.

44.

45.

46.

47.

48.

49.

50.
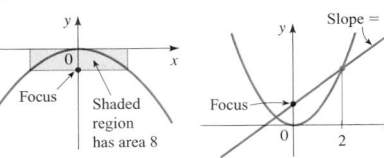

51. (a) Find equations for the family of parabolas with vertex at the origin and with directrixes $y = \frac{1}{2}$, $y = 1$, $y = 4$, and $y = 8$.
  (b) Draw the graphs. What do you conclude?

52. (a) Find equations for the family of parabolas with vertex at the origin, focus on the positive y-axis, and with focal diameters 1, 2, 4, and 8.
  (b) Draw the graphs. What do you conclude?

APPLICATIONS

53. Parabolic Reflector A lamp with a parabolic reflector is shown in the figure. The bulb is placed at the focus, and the focal diameter is 12 cm.
  (a) Find an equation of the parabola.
  (b) Find the diameter $d(C, D)$ of the opening, 20 cm from the vertex.

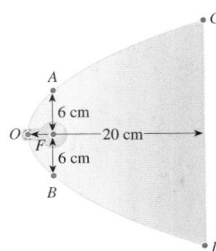

54. Satellite Dish A reflector for a satellite dish is parabolic in cross section, with the receiver at the focus F. The reflector is 1 ft deep and 20 ft wide from rim to rim (see the figure). How far is the receiver from the vertex of the parabolic reflector?

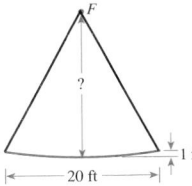

55. Suspension Bridge In a suspension bridge the shape of
the suspension cables is parabolic. The bridge shown in the
figure has towers that are 600 m apart, and the lowest point of
the suspension cables is 150 m below the top of the towers.
Find the equation of the parabolic part of the cables, placing
the origin of the coordinate system at the vertex. [*Note*: This
equation is used to find the length of cable needed in the construction of the bridge.]

56. Reflecting Telescope The Hale telescope at the Mount
Palomar Observatory has a 200-in. mirror, as shown in the figure. The mirror is constructed in a parabolic shape that collects
light from the stars and focuses it at the **prime focus**, that is,
the focus of the parabola. The mirror is 3.79 in. deep at its
center. Find the **focal length** of this parabolic mirror, that is,
the distance from the vertex to the focus.

57. Parabolas in the Real World Several examples of the
uses of parabolas are given in the text. Find other situations in
real life in which parabolas occur. Consult a scientific encyclopedia in the reference section of your library, or search the
Internet.

58. Light Cone from a Flashlight A flashlight is held to
form a lighted area on the ground, as shown in the figure. Is it
possible to angle the flashlight in such a way that the boundary of the lighted area is a parabola? Explain your answer.

> **⊙ DISCOVERY PROJECT** **Rolling Down a Ramp**
>
> In this project we investigate the process of modeling the
> motion of falling objects using a calculator-based motion
> detector. You can find the project at the book companion
> website: **www.stewartmath.com**

11.2 ELLIPSES

| Geometric Definition of an Ellipse ▶ Equations and Graphs of Ellipses
▶ Eccentricity of an Ellipse

▼ Geometric Definition of an Ellipse

An ellipse is an oval curve that looks like an elongated circle. More precisely, we have the
following definition.

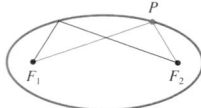

FIGURE 1

> **GEOMETRIC DEFINITION OF AN ELLIPSE**
>
> An **ellipse** is the set of all points in the plane the sum of whose distances from
> two fixed points F_1 and F_2 is a constant. (See Figure 1.) These two fixed points
> are the **foci** (plural of **focus**) of the ellipse.

TEXT QUESTION

Does $\dfrac{x^2}{5^2} + \dfrac{y^2}{6^2} = 1$ describe a horizontal or a vertical ellipse? How do you know?

Answer

It is vertical because the denominator of the y^2 term is larger than that of the x^2 term.

The geometric definition suggests a simple method for drawing an ellipse. Place a sheet of paper on a drawing board, and insert thumbtacks at the two points that are to be the foci of the ellipse. Attach the ends of a string to the tacks, as shown in Figure 2(a). With the point of a pencil, hold the string taut. Then carefully move the pencil around the foci, keeping the string taut at all times. The pencil will trace out an ellipse, because the sum of the distances from the point of the pencil to the foci will always equal the length of the string, which is constant.

If the string is only slightly longer than the distance between the foci, then the ellipse that is traced out will be elongated in shape, as in Figure 2(a), but if the foci are close together relative to the length of the string, the ellipse will be almost circular, as shown in Figure 2(b).

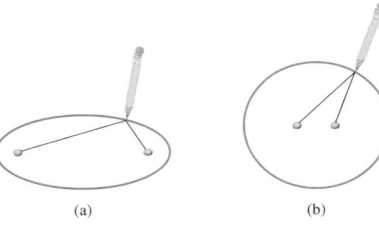

(a)   (b)

FIGURE 2

To obtain the simplest equation for an ellipse, we place the foci on the x-axis at $F_1(-c, 0)$ and $F_2(c, 0)$ so that the origin is halfway between them (see Figure 3).

For later convenience we let the sum of the distances from a point on the ellipse to the foci be $2a$. Then if $P(x, y)$ is any point on the ellipse, we have

$$d(P, F_1) + d(P, F_2) = 2a$$

So from the Distance Formula we have

$$\sqrt{(x + c)^2 + y^2} + \sqrt{(x - c)^2 + y^2} = 2a$$

or

$$\sqrt{(x - c)^2 + y^2} = 2a - \sqrt{(x + c)^2 + y^2}$$

Squaring each side and expanding, we get

$$x^2 - 2cx + c^2 + y^2 = 4a^2 - 4a\sqrt{(x + c)^2 + y^2} + (x^2 + 2cx + c^2 + y^2)$$

which simplifies to

$$4a\sqrt{(x + c)^2 + y^2} = 4a^2 + 4cx$$

Dividing each side by 4 and squaring again, we get

$$a^2[(x + c)^2 + y^2] = (a^2 + cx)^2$$

$$a^2x^2 + 2a^2cx + a^2c^2 + a^2y^2 = a^4 + 2a^2cx + c^2x^2$$

$$(a^2 - c^2)x^2 + a^2y^2 = a^2(a^2 - c^2)$$

Since the sum of the distances from P to the foci must be larger than the distance between the foci, we have that $2a > 2c$, or $a > c$. Thus $a^2 - c^2 > 0$, and we can divide each side of the preceding equation by $a^2(a^2 - c^2)$ to get

$$\frac{x^2}{a^2} + \frac{y^2}{a^2 - c^2} = 1$$

For convenience let $b^2 = a^2 - c^2$ (with $b > 0$). Since $b^2 < a^2$, it follows that $b < a$. The preceding equation then becomes

$$\frac{x^2}{a^2} + \frac{y^2}{b^2} = 1 \qquad \text{with } a > b$$

FIGURE 3

$F_1(-c, 0)$ 0 $F_2(c, 0)$ $P(x, y)$

IN-CLASS MATERIALS

Many representational artists never draw circles, noting that it is rare in nature to see a circle, since we are usually looking at an angle, thus seeing an ellipse. Perhaps have the students bring in photographs of manhole covers and other "circular" objects, noting that if the camera angle is not straight on, the resultant image is elliptical. (Because of the optical illusion of perspective, it makes things easier to draw the outline of the "circle" with a marker to see that it is an ellipse.)

Doug Shaw

EXAMPLE

A vertical ellipse: $\dfrac{x^2}{16} + \dfrac{y^2}{25} = 1$

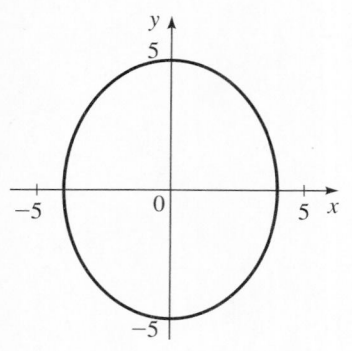

EXAMPLE

A horizontal ellipse:

$$\frac{x^2}{9} + 4y^2 = 1$$

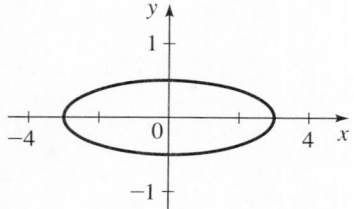

In the standard equation for an ellipse, a^2 is the *larger* denominator and b^2 is the *smaller*. To find c^2, we subtract: larger denominator minus smaller denominator.

This is the equation of the ellipse. To graph it, we need to know the x- and y-intercepts. Setting $y = 0$, we get

$$\frac{x^2}{a^2} = 1$$

so $x^2 = a^2$, or $x = \pm a$. Thus, the ellipse crosses the x-axis at $(a, 0)$ and $(-a, 0)$, as in Figure 4. These points are called the **vertices** of the ellipse, and the segment that joins them is called the **major axis**. Its length is $2a$.

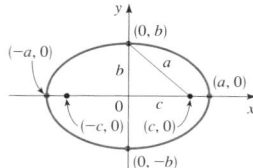

FIGURE 4
$\dfrac{x^2}{a^2} + \dfrac{y^2}{b^2} = 1$ with $a > b$

Similarly, if we set $x = 0$, we get $y = \pm b$, so the ellipse crosses the y-axis at $(0, b)$ and $(0, -b)$. The segment that joins these points is called the **minor axis**, and it has length $2b$. Note that $2a > 2b$, so the major axis is longer than the minor axis. The origin is the **center** of the ellipse.

If the foci of the ellipse are placed on the y-axis at $(0, \pm c)$ rather than on the x-axis, then the roles of x and y are reversed in the preceding discussion, and we get a vertical ellipse.

▼ Equations and Graphs of Ellipses

The following box summarizes what we have just proved about the equation and features of an ellipse centered at the origin.

ELLIPSE WITH CENTER AT THE ORIGIN

The graph of each of the following equations is an ellipse with center at the origin and having the given properties.

EQUATION	$\dfrac{x^2}{a^2} + \dfrac{y^2}{b^2} = 1$	$\dfrac{x^2}{b^2} + \dfrac{y^2}{a^2} = 1$
	$a > b > 0$	$a > b > 0$
VERTICES	$(\pm a, 0)$	$(0, \pm a)$
MAJOR AXIS	Horizontal, length $2a$	Vertical, length $2a$
MINOR AXIS	Vertical, length $2b$	Horizontal, length $2b$
FOCI	$(\pm c, 0)$, $c^2 = a^2 - b^2$	$(0, \pm c)$, $c^2 = a^2 - b^2$
GRAPH		

IN-CLASS MATERIALS

Note that if $a = b$ then we have only one focus, at $(0, 0)$. In this case, the geometric definition breaks down, but it is clear from the equation that we have a circle. This is why a circle can be thought of as a degenerate ellipse.

EXAMPLE 1 | Sketching an Ellipse

An ellipse has the equation

$$\frac{x^2}{9} + \frac{y^2}{4} = 1$$

(a) Find the foci, the vertices, and the lengths of the major and minor axes, and sketch the graph.

 (b) Draw the graph using a graphing calculator.

SOLUTION

(a) Since the denominator of x^2 is larger, the ellipse has a horizontal major axis. This gives $a^2 = 9$ and $b^2 = 4$, so $c^2 = a^2 - b^2 = 9 - 4 = 5$. Thus $a = 3$, $b = 2$, and $c = \sqrt{5}$.

FOCI	$(\pm\sqrt{5}, 0)$
VERTICES	$(\pm 3, 0)$
LENGTH OF MAJOR AXIS	6
LENGTH OF MINOR AXIS	4

The graph is shown in Figure 5(a).

(b) To draw the graph using a graphing calculator, we need to solve for y.

$$\frac{x^2}{9} + \frac{y^2}{4} = 1$$

$$\frac{y^2}{4} = 1 - \frac{x^2}{9} \qquad \text{Subtract } \frac{x^2}{9}$$

$$y^2 = 4\left(1 - \frac{x^2}{9}\right) \qquad \text{Multiply by 4}$$

$$y = \pm 2\sqrt{1 - \frac{x^2}{9}} \qquad \text{Take square roots}$$

To obtain the graph of the ellipse, we graph both functions

$$y = 2\sqrt{1 - x^2/9} \qquad \text{and} \qquad y = -2\sqrt{1 - x^2/9}$$

as shown in Figure 5(b).

Note that the equation of an ellipse does not define y as a function of x (see page 158). That's why we need to graph two functions to graph an ellipse.

The orbits of the planets are ellipses, with the sun at one focus.

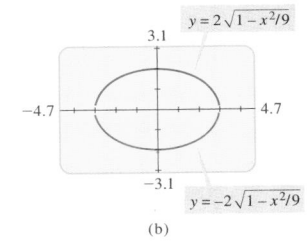

FIGURE 5
$$\frac{x^2}{9} + \frac{y^2}{4} = 1$$

(a)   (b)

✎. NOW TRY EXERCISE **9**

IN-CLASS MATERIALS

Have students sketch an ellipse with thumbtacks and string, as suggested in the text. Have some use foci that are close together and some that are farther apart. Make sure they see the connection between this activity and the idea that the summed distance from the foci is a constant.

ALTERNATE EXAMPLE 2

Find the foci of the ellipse $9x^2 + 4y^2 = 36$.

ANSWER

$(0, \sqrt{5}), (0, -\sqrt{5})$

EXAMPLE 2 | Finding the Foci of an Ellipse

Find the foci of the ellipse $16x^2 + 9y^2 = 144$, and sketch its graph.

SOLUTION First we put the equation in standard form. Dividing by 144, we get

$$\frac{x^2}{9} + \frac{y^2}{16} = 1$$

Since $16 > 9$, this is an ellipse with its foci on the y-axis and with $a = 4$ and $b = 3$. We have

$$c^2 = a^2 - b^2 = 16 - 9 = 7$$
$$c = \sqrt{7}$$

Thus the foci are $(0, \pm\sqrt{7})$. The graph is shown in Figure 6(a).

We can also draw the graph using a graphing calculator as shown in Figure 6(b).

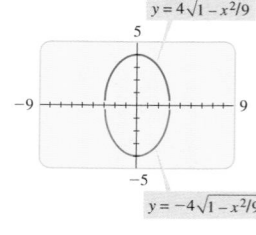

FIGURE 6
$16x^2 + 9y^2 = 144$

(a)

(b)

✎. NOW TRY EXERCISE **11** ∎

EXAMPLE 3 | Finding the Equation of an Ellipse

The vertices of an ellipse are $(\pm 4, 0)$, and the foci are $(\pm 2, 0)$. Find its equation, and sketch the graph.

SOLUTION Since the vertices are $(\pm 4, 0)$, we have $a = 4$ and the major axis is horizontal. The foci are $(\pm 2, 0)$, so $c = 2$. To write the equation, we need to find b. Since $c^2 = a^2 - b^2$, we have

$$2^2 = 4^2 - b^2$$
$$b^2 = 16 - 4 = 12$$

Thus the equation of the ellipse is

$$\frac{x^2}{16} + \frac{y^2}{12} = 1$$

The graph is shown in Figure 7.

✎. NOW TRY EXERCISES **25** AND **33** ∎

ALTERNATE EXAMPLE 3

The vertices of an ellipse are $(\pm 6, 0)$ and the foci are $(\pm 4, 0)$. Find its equation.

ANSWER

$$\frac{x^2}{36} + \frac{y^2}{20} = 1$$

FIGURE 7
$\frac{x^2}{16} + \frac{y^2}{12} = 1$

▼ Eccentricity of an Ellipse

We saw earlier in this section (Figure 2) that if $2a$ is only slightly greater than $2c$, the ellipse is long and thin, whereas if $2a$ is much greater than $2c$, the ellipse is almost circular. We measure the deviation of an ellipse from being circular by the ratio of a and c.

IN-CLASS MATERIALS

As noted in Section 11.1, one can use dental floss and a modeling compound (such as clay or Play-Doh) to make half a cone and slice it. Have the class attempt to do so to get a circle. Note that if their angle is slightly off, they will get an ellipse. Make the analogy that just as a square is a particular kind of rectangle, a circle is a particular kind of ellipse.

> **DEFINITION OF ECCENTRICITY**
>
> For the ellipse $\dfrac{x^2}{a^2} + \dfrac{y^2}{b^2} = 1$ or $\dfrac{x^2}{b^2} + \dfrac{y^2}{a^2} = 1$ (with $a > b > 0$), the **eccentricity e** is the number
>
> $$e = \frac{c}{a}$$
>
> where $c = \sqrt{a^2 - b^2}$. The eccentricity of every ellipse satisfies $0 < e < 1$.

Thus if e is close to 1, then c is almost equal to a, and the ellipse is elongated in shape, but if e is close to 0, then the ellipse is close to a circle in shape. The eccentricity is a measure of how "stretched" the ellipse is.

In Figure 8 we show a number of ellipses to demonstrate the effect of varying the eccentricity e.

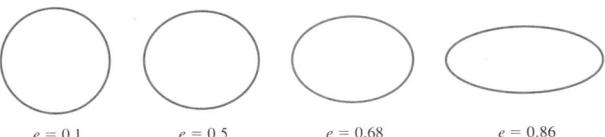

$e = 0.1$ $\qquad$ $e = 0.5$ $\qquad$ $e = 0.68$ $\qquad$ $e = 0.86$

FIGURE 8 Ellipses with various eccentricities

EXAMPLE 4 | Finding the Equation of an Ellipse from Its Eccentricity and Foci

Find the equation of the ellipse with foci $(0, \pm 8)$ and eccentricity $e = \frac{4}{5}$, and sketch its graph.

SOLUTION We are given $e = \frac{4}{5}$ and $c = 8$. Thus

$$\frac{4}{5} = \frac{8}{a} \qquad \text{Eccentricity } e = \frac{c}{a}$$

$$4a = 40 \qquad \text{Cross-multiply}$$

$$a = 10$$

To find b, we use the fact that $c^2 = a^2 - b^2$.

$$8^2 = 10^2 - b^2$$

$$b^2 = 10^2 - 8^2 = 36$$

$$b = 6$$

Thus the equation of the ellipse is

$$\frac{x^2}{36} + \frac{y^2}{100} = 1$$

Because the foci are on the y-axis, the ellipse is oriented vertically. To sketch the ellipse, we find the intercepts: The x-intercepts are ± 6, and the y-intercepts are ± 10. The graph is sketched in Figure 9.

✎. NOW TRY EXERCISE **43**

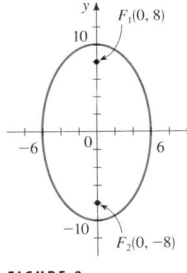

FIGURE 9
$\dfrac{x^2}{36} + \dfrac{y^2}{100} = 1$

IN-CLASS MATERIALS

Discuss the reflection property of an ellipse: A beam of light originating at one focus will reflect off the ellipse and pass through the other focus. One nice project is to construct an elliptical pool table. The students accurately graph an ellipse and glue erasers or wood along its border, placing the "hole" at one focus and marking the second. A golf ball or pool ball that is placed on the mark and struck in any direction will ricochet into the hole.

DRILL QUESTION

Find the vertices and foci of the ellipse $4x^2 + y^2 = 1$ and sketch its graph.

Answer

Vertices: $(0, 1)$, $(0, -1)$, $\left(\dfrac{1}{2}, 0\right)$, $\left(-\dfrac{1}{2}, 0\right)$

Foci: $\left(0, \dfrac{\sqrt{3}}{2}\right)\left(0, -\dfrac{\sqrt{3}}{2}\right)$

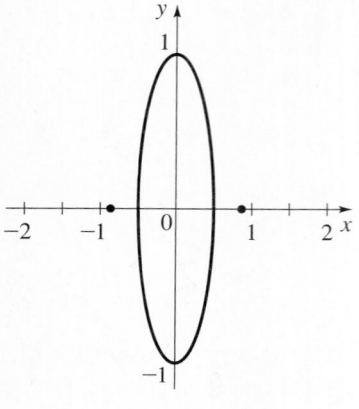

Eccentricities of the Orbits of the Planets

The orbits of the planets are ellipses with the sun at one focus. For most planets these ellipses have very small eccentricity, so they are nearly circular. However, Mercury and Pluto, the innermost and outermost known planets, have visibly elliptical orbits.

Planet	Eccentricity
Mercury	0.206
Venus	0.007
Earth	0.017
Mars	0.093
Jupiter	0.048
Saturn	0.056
Uranus	0.046
Neptune	0.010
Pluto	0.248

Gravitational attraction causes the planets to move in elliptical orbits around the sun with the sun at one focus. This remarkable property was first observed by Johannes Kepler and was later deduced by Isaac Newton from his inverse square Law of Gravity, using calculus. The orbits of the planets have different eccentricities, but most are nearly circular (see the margin).

Ellipses, like parabolas, have an interesting *reflection property* that leads to a number of practical applications. If a light source is placed at one focus of a reflecting surface with elliptical cross sections, then all the light will be reflected off the surface to the other focus, as shown in Figure 10. This principle, which works for sound waves as well as for light, is used in *lithotripsy*, a treatment for kidney stones. The patient is placed in a tub of water with elliptical cross sections in such a way that the kidney stone is accurately located at one focus. High-intensity sound waves generated at the other focus are reflected to the stone and destroy it with minimal damage to surrounding tissue. The patient is spared the trauma of surgery and recovers within days instead of weeks.

The reflection property of ellipses is also used in the construction of *whispering galleries*. Sound coming from one focus bounces off the walls and ceiling of an elliptical room and passes through the other focus. In these rooms even quiet whispers spoken at one focus can be heard clearly at the other. Famous whispering galleries include the National Statuary Hall of the U.S. Capitol in Washington, D.C. (see page 776), and the Mormon Tabernacle in Salt Lake City, Utah.

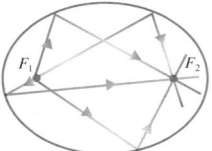

FIGURE 10

11.2 EXERCISES

CONCEPTS

1. An ellipse is the set of all points in the plane for which the _____ of the distances from two fixed points F_1 and F_2 is constant. The points F_1 and F_2 are called the _____ of the ellipse.

2. The graph of the equation $\dfrac{x^2}{a^2} + \dfrac{y^2}{b^2} = 1$ with $a > b > 0$ is an ellipse with vertices (___, ___) and (___, ___) and foci $(\pm c, 0)$, where $c = $ _____. So the graph of $\dfrac{x^2}{5^2} + \dfrac{y^2}{4^2} = 1$ is an ellipse with vertices (___, ___) and (___, ___) and foci (___, ___) and (___, ___).

3. The graph of the equation $\dfrac{x^2}{b^2} + \dfrac{y^2}{a^2} = 1$ with $a > b > 0$ is an ellipse with vertices (___, ___) and (___, ___) and foci $(0, \pm c)$, where $c = $ _____. So the graph of $\dfrac{x^2}{4^2} + \dfrac{y^2}{5^2} = 1$

is an ellipse with vertices (___, ___) and (___, ___) and foci (___, ___) and (___, ___).

4. Label the vertices and foci on the graphs given for the ellipses in Exercises 2 and 3.

(a) $\dfrac{x^2}{5^2} + \dfrac{y^2}{4^2} = 1$ **(b)** $\dfrac{x^2}{4^2} + \dfrac{y^2}{5^2} = 1$

SKILLS

5–8 ■ Match the equation with the graphs labeled I–IV. Give reasons for your answers.

5. $\dfrac{x^2}{16} + \dfrac{y^2}{4} = 1$

6. $x^2 + \dfrac{y^2}{9} = 1$

7. $4x^2 + y^2 = 4$

8. $16x^2 + 25y^2 = 400$

I

II

III

IV

9–22 ■ Find the vertices, foci, and eccentricity of the ellipse. Determine the lengths of the major and minor axes, and sketch the graph.

9. $\dfrac{x^2}{25} + \dfrac{y^2}{9} = 1$

10. $\dfrac{x^2}{16} + \dfrac{y^2}{25} = 1$

11. $9x^2 + 4y^2 = 36$

12. $4x^2 + 25y^2 = 100$

13. $x^2 + 4y^2 = 16$

14. $4x^2 + y^2 = 16$

15. $2x^2 + y^2 = 3$

16. $5x^2 + 6y^2 = 30$

17. $x^2 + 4y^2 = 1$

18. $9x^2 + 4y^2 = 1$

19. $\frac{1}{2}x^2 + \frac{1}{8}y^2 = \frac{1}{4}$

20. $x^2 = 4 - 2y^2$

21. $y^2 = 1 - 2x^2$

22. $20x^2 + 4y^2 = 5$

23–28 ■ Find an equation for the ellipse whose graph is shown.

23.

24.

25.

26.

27.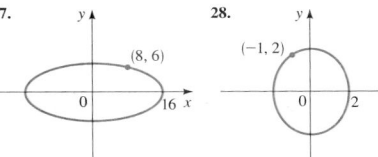

28.

29–32 ■ Use a graphing device to graph the ellipse.

29. $\dfrac{x^2}{25} + \dfrac{y^2}{20} = 1$

30. $x^2 + \dfrac{y^2}{12} = 1$

31. $6x^2 + y^2 = 36$

32. $x^2 + 2y^2 = 8$

33–44 ■ Find an equation for the ellipse that satisfies the given conditions.

33. Foci: $(\pm 4, 0)$, vertices: $(\pm 5, 0)$

34. Foci: $(0, \pm 3)$, vertices: $(0, \pm 5)$

35. Length of major axis: 4, length of minor axis: 2, foci on y-axis

36. Length of major axis: 6, length of minor axis: 4, foci on x-axis

37. Foci: $(0, \pm 2)$, length of minor axis: 6

38. Foci: $(\pm 5, 0)$, length of major axis: 12

39. Endpoints of major axis: $(\pm 10, 0)$, distance between foci: 6

40. Endpoints of minor axis: $(0, \pm 3)$, distance between foci: 8

41. Length of major axis: 10, foci on x-axis, ellipse passes through the point $(\sqrt{5}, 2)$

42. Eccentricity: $\frac{1}{9}$, foci: $(0, \pm 2)$

43. Eccentricity: 0.8, foci: $(\pm 1.5, 0)$

44. Eccentricity: $\sqrt{3}/2$, foci on y-axis, length of major axis: 4

45–47 ■ Find the intersection points of the pair of ellipses. Sketch the graphs of each pair of equations on the same coordinate axes, and label the points of intersection.

45. $\begin{cases} 4x^2 + y^2 = 4 \\ 4x^2 + 9y^2 = 36 \end{cases}$

46. $\begin{cases} \dfrac{x^2}{16} + \dfrac{y^2}{9} = 1 \\ \dfrac{x^2}{9} + \dfrac{y^2}{16} = 1 \end{cases}$

47. $\begin{cases} 100x^2 + 25y^2 = 100 \\ x^2 + \dfrac{y^2}{9} = 1 \end{cases}$

48. The **ancillary circle** of an ellipse is the circle with radius equal to half the length of the minor axis and center the same as the ellipse (see the figure). The ancillary circle is thus the largest circle that can fit within an ellipse.

(a) Find an equation for the ancillary circle of the ellipse $x^2 + 4y^2 = 16$.

(b) For the ellipse and ancillary circle of part (a), show that if (s, t) is a point on the ancillary circle, then $(2s, t)$ is a point on the ellipse.

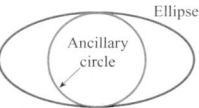

49. (a) Use a graphing device to sketch the top half (the portion in the first and second quadrants) of the family of ellipses $x^2 + ky^2 = 100$ for $k = 4, 10, 25,$ and 50.

(b) What do the members of this family of ellipses have in common? How do they differ?

50. If $k > 0$, the following equation represents an ellipse:

$$\frac{x^2}{k} + \frac{y^2}{4+k} = 1$$

Show that all the ellipses represented by this equation have the same foci, no matter what the value of k.

APPLICATIONS

51. Perihelion and Aphelion The planets move around the sun in elliptical orbits with the sun at one focus. The point in the orbit at which the planet is closest to the sun is called **perihelion**, and the point at which it is farthest is called **aphelion**. These points are the vertices of the orbit. The earth's distance from the sun is 147,000,000 km at perihelion and 153,000,000 km at aphelion. Find an equation for the earth's orbit. (Place the origin at the center of the orbit with the sun on the x-axis.)

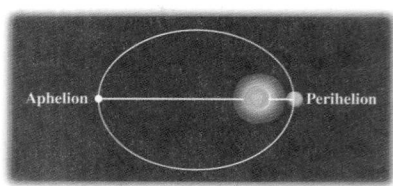

52. The Orbit of Pluto With an eccentricity of 0.25, Pluto's orbit is the most eccentric in the solar system. The length of the minor axis of its orbit is approximately 10,000,000,000 km. Find the distance between Pluto and the sun at perihelion and at aphelion. (See Exercise 51.)

53. Lunar Orbit For an object in an elliptical orbit around the moon, the points in the orbit that are closest to and farthest from the center of the moon are called **perilune** and **apolune**, respectively. These are the vertices of the orbit. The center of the moon is at one focus of the orbit. The *Apollo 11* spacecraft was placed in a lunar orbit with perilune at 68 mi and apolune at 195 mi above the surface of the moon. Assuming that the moon is a sphere of radius 1075 mi, find an equation for the orbit of *Apollo 11*. (Place the coordinate axes so that the origin is at the center of the orbit and the foci are located on the x-axis.)

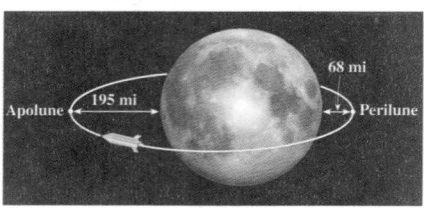

54. Plywood Ellipse A carpenter wishes to construct an elliptical table top from a sheet of plywood, 4 ft by 8 ft. He will trace out the ellipse using the "thumbtack and string" method illustrated in Figures 2 and 3. What length of string should he use, and how far apart should the tacks be located, if the ellipse is to be the largest possible that can be cut out of the plywood sheet?

55. Sunburst Window A "sunburst" window above a doorway is constructed in the shape of the top half of an ellipse, as shown in the figure. The window is 20 in. tall at its highest point and 80 in. wide at the bottom. Find the height of the window 25 in. from the center of the base.

DISCOVERY ▪ DISCUSSION ▪ WRITING

56. Drawing an Ellipse on a Blackboard Try drawing an ellipse as accurately as possible on a blackboard. How would a piece of string and two friends help this process?

57. Light Cone from a Flashlight A flashlight shines on a wall, as shown in the figure. What is the shape of the boundary of the lighted area? Explain your answer.

58. How Wide Is an Ellipse at Its Foci? A *latus rectum* for an ellipse is a line segment perpendicular to the major axis at a focus, with endpoints on the ellipse, as shown in the figure at the top of the next column. Show that the length of a latus rectum is $2b^2/a$ for the ellipse

$$\frac{x^2}{a^2} + \frac{y^2}{b^2} = 1 \qquad \text{with } a > b$$

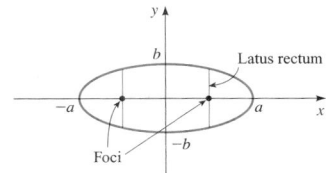

59. Is It an Ellipse? A piece of paper is wrapped around a cylindrical bottle, and then a compass is used to draw a circle on the paper, as shown in the figure. When the paper is laid flat, is the shape drawn on the paper an ellipse? (You don't need to prove your answer, but you might want to do the experiment and see what you get.)

11.3 HYPERBOLAS

| Geometric Definition of a Hyperbola ▶ Equations and Graphs of Hyperbolas

▼ Geometric Definition of a Hyperbola

Although ellipses and hyperbolas have completely different shapes, their definitions and equations are similar. Instead of using the *sum* of distances from two fixed foci, as in the case of an ellipse, we use the *difference* to define a hyperbola.

> **GEOMETRIC DEFINITION OF A HYPERBOLA**
>
> A **hyperbola** is the set of all points in the plane, the difference of whose distances from two fixed points F_1 and F_2 is a constant. (See Figure 1.) These two fixed points are the **foci** of the hyperbola.

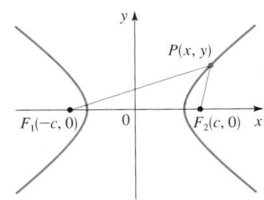

FIGURE 1 P is on the hyperbola if $|d(P, F_1) - d(P, F_2)| = 2a$.

As in the case of the ellipse, we get the simplest equation for the hyperbola by placing the foci on the x-axis at $(\pm c, 0)$, as shown in Figure 1. By definition, if $P(x, y)$ lies on the hyperbola, then either $d(P, F_1) - d(P, F_2)$ or $d(P, F_2) - d(P, F_1)$ must equal some positive constant, which we call $2a$. Thus we have

$$d(P, F_1) - d(P, F_2) = \pm 2a$$

or

$$\sqrt{(x + c)^2 + y^2} - \sqrt{(x - c)^2 + y^2} = \pm 2a$$

SUGGESTED TIME AND EMPHASIS

$\frac{1}{2}$ class, optional material

TEXT QUESTION

Is $\dfrac{x^2}{5^2} - \dfrac{y^2}{6^2} = 1$ the equation of a horizontal or a vertical hyperbola? How do you know?

Answer

It is horizontal because the x^2 term is positive.

Proceeding as we did in the case of the ellipse (Section 11.2), we simplify this to

$$(c^2 - a^2)x^2 - a^2y^2 = a^2(c^2 - a^2)$$

From triangle PF_1F_2 in Figure 1 we see that $| d(P, F_1) - d(P, F_2) | < 2c$. It follows that $2a < 2c$, or $a < c$. Thus $c^2 - a^2 > 0$, so we can set $b^2 = c^2 - a^2$. We then simplify the last displayed equation to get

$$\frac{x^2}{a^2} - \frac{y^2}{b^2} = 1$$

This is the *equation of the hyperbola.* If we replace x by $-x$ or y by $-y$ in this equation, it remains unchanged, so the hyperbola is symmetric about both the x- and y-axes and about the origin. The x-intercepts are $\pm a$, and the points $(a, 0)$ and $(-a, 0)$ are the **vertices** of the hyperbola. There is no y-intercept, because setting $x = 0$ in the equation of the hyperbola leads to $-y^2 = b^2$, which has no real solution. Furthermore, the equation of the hyperbola implies that

$$\frac{x^2}{a^2} = \frac{y^2}{b^2} + 1 \geq 1$$

so $x^2/a^2 \geq 1$; thus $x^2 \geq a^2$, and hence $x \geq a$ or $x \leq -a$. This means that the hyperbola consists of two parts, called its **branches**. The segment joining the two vertices on the separate branches is the **transverse axis** of the hyperbola, and the origin is called its **center**.

If we place the foci of the hyperbola on the y-axis rather than on the x-axis, this has the effect of reversing the roles of x and y in the derivation of the equation of the hyperbola. This leads to a hyperbola with a vertical transverse axis.

▼ Equations and Graphs of Hyperbolas

The main properties of hyperbolas are listed in the following box.

HYPERBOLA WITH CENTER AT THE ORIGIN

The graph of each of the following equations is a hyperbola with center at the origin and having the given properties.

EQUATION	$\dfrac{x^2}{a^2} - \dfrac{y^2}{b^2} = 1 \quad (a > 0, b > 0)$	$\dfrac{y^2}{a^2} - \dfrac{x^2}{b^2} = 1 \quad (a > 0, b > 0)$
VERTICES	$(\pm a, 0)$	$(0, \pm a)$
TRANSVERSE AXIS	Horizontal, length $2a$	Vertical, length $2a$
ASYMPTOTES	$y = \pm \dfrac{b}{a} x$	$y = \pm \dfrac{a}{b} x$
FOCI	$(\pm c, 0), \quad c^2 = a^2 + b^2$	$(0, \pm c), \quad c^2 = a^2 + b^2$
GRAPH		

IN-CLASS MATERIALS

Have students sketch a hyperbola "from scratch." Hand out a sheet of paper with two foci, and hand out rulers. Get the students to plot points where the difference of the distances between the points and the foci is 1 in. Have them keep plotting points until a hyperbolic shape emerges.

Asymptotes of rational functions are discussed in Section 3.7.

The *asymptotes* mentioned in this box are lines that the hyperbola approaches for large values of x and y. To find the asymptotes in the first case in the box, we solve the equation for y to get

$$y = \pm \frac{b}{a} \sqrt{x^2 - a^2}$$

$$= \pm \frac{b}{a} x \sqrt{1 - \frac{a^2}{x^2}}$$

As x gets large, a^2/x^2 gets closer to zero. In other words, as $x \to \infty$, we have $a^2/x^2 \to 0$. So for large x the value of y can be approximated as $y = \pm(b/a)x$. This shows that these lines are asymptotes of the hyperbola.

Asymptotes are an essential aid for graphing a hyperbola; they help us to determine its shape. A convenient way to find the asymptotes, for a hyperbola with horizontal transverse axis, is to first plot the points $(a, 0)$, $(-a, 0)$, $(0, b)$, and $(0, -b)$. Then sketch horizontal and vertical segments through these points to construct a rectangle, as shown in Figure 2(a). We call this rectangle the **central box** of the hyperbola. The slopes of the diagonals of the central box are $\pm b/a$, so by extending them, we obtain the asymptotes $y = \pm(b/a)x$, as sketched in Figure 2(b). Finally, we plot the vertices and use the asymptotes as a guide in sketching the hyperbola shown in Figure 2(c). (A similar procedure applies to graphing a hyperbola that has a vertical transverse axis.)

(a) Central box

(b) Asymptotes

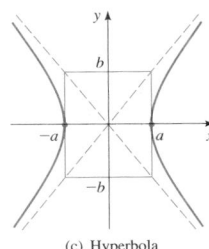

(c) Hyperbola

FIGURE 2 Steps in graphing the hyperbola $\dfrac{x^2}{a^2} - \dfrac{y^2}{b^2} = 1$

HOW TO SKETCH A HYPERBOLA

1. **Sketch the Central Box.** This is the rectangle centered at the origin, with sides parallel to the axes, that crosses one axis at $\pm a$, the other at $\pm b$.

2. **Sketch the Asymptotes.** These are the lines obtained by extending the diagonals of the central box.

3. **Plot the Vertices.** These are the two x-intercepts or the two y-intercepts.

4. **Sketch the Hyperbola.** Start at a vertex, and sketch a branch of the hyperbola, approaching the asymptotes. Sketch the other branch in the same way.

EXAMPLE 1 | A Hyperbola with Horizontal Transverse Axis

A hyperbola has the equation

$$9x^2 - 16y^2 = 144$$

(a) Find the vertices, foci, and asymptotes, and sketch the graph.

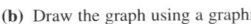 (b) Draw the graph using a graphing calculator.

ALTERNATE EXAMPLE 1
Find the vertices, foci, and asymptotes of the hyperbola $25x^2 - 144y^2 = 3600$.

ANSWER
$(\pm 12, 0)$, $(\pm 13, 0)$,
$y = \pm \dfrac{5}{12} x$

IN-CLASS MATERIALS

As noted in Section 11.1, one can use dental floss and a modeling compound (such as clay or Play-Doh) to make a half-cone and slice it. Have the students attempt to do so to get a hyperbola. Notice that the slice does not have to be straight up and down, as shown in the prologue to the chapter. As long as the slice would cut the other half of the cone, the resultant curve is a hyperbola.

SOLUTION

(a) First we divide both sides of the equation by 144 to put it into standard form:

$$\frac{x^2}{16} - \frac{y^2}{9} = 1$$

Because the x^2-term is positive, the hyperbola has a horizontal transverse axis; its vertices and foci are on the x-axis. Since $a^2 = 16$ and $b^2 = 9$, we get $a = 4$, $b = 3$, and $c = \sqrt{16 + 9} = 5$. Thus we have

VERTICES	$(\pm 4, 0)$
FOCI	$(\pm 5, 0)$
ASYMPTOTES	$y = \pm\frac{3}{4}x$

After sketching the central box and asymptotes, we complete the sketch of the hyperbola as in Figure 3(a).

Note that the equation of a hyperbola does not define y as a function of x (see page 158). That's why we need to graph two functions to graph a hyperbola.

(b) To draw the graph using a graphing calculator, we need to solve for y.

$$9x^2 - 16y^2 = 144$$

$$-16y^2 = -9x^2 + 144 \qquad \text{Subtract } 9x^2$$

$$y^2 = 9\left(\frac{x^2}{16} - 1\right) \qquad \text{Divide by } -16 \text{ and factor } 9$$

$$y = \pm 3\sqrt{\frac{x^2}{16} - 1} \qquad \text{Take square roots}$$

To obtain the graph of the hyperbola, we graph the functions

$$y = 3\sqrt{(x^2/16) - 1} \qquad \text{and} \qquad y = -3\sqrt{(x^2/16) - 1}$$

as shown in Figure 3(b).

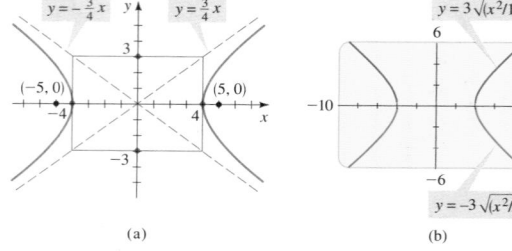

FIGURE 3
$9x^2 - 16y^2 = 144$

(a)

(b)

✎. NOW TRY EXERCISE **9**

EXAMPLE 2 | A Hyperbola with Vertical Transverse Axis

Find the vertices, foci, and asymptotes of the hyperbola, and sketch its graph.

$$x^2 - 9y^2 + 9 = 0$$

ALTERNATE EXAMPLE 2

Find the vertices, foci, and asymptotes of the hyperbola $25x^2 - 144y^2 + 3600 = 0$.

ANSWER

We can write $144y^2 - 25x^2 = 3600$.

Vertices $(0, \pm 5)$, foci $(0, \pm 13)$, asymptotes $y = \pm\frac{5}{12}x$

IN-CLASS MATERIALS

Discuss the reflection property of hyperbolas: Take a point between the branches, and aim a beam of light at one of the foci. It will reflect off the hyperbola and go in a path aimed directly at the other focus. This reflection property is harder to model physically than those of the ellipse and the parabola.

Paths of Comets
The path of a comet is an ellipse, a parabola, or a hyperbola with the sun at a focus. This fact can be proved by using calculus and Newton's laws of motion.* If the path is a parabola or a hyperbola, the comet will never return. If the path is an ellipse, it can be determined precisely when and where the comet can be seen again. Halley's comet has an elliptical path and returns every 75 years; it was last seen in 1987. The brightest comet of the 20th century was comet Hale-Bopp, seen in 1997. Its orbit is a very eccentric ellipse; it is expected to return to the inner solar system around the year 4377.

---

*James Stewart, *Calculus*, 7th ed. (Belmont, CA: Brooks/Cole, 2012), pages 868 and 872.

FIGURE 4
$x^2 - 9y^2 + 9 = 0$

SOLUTION We begin by writing the equation in the standard form for a hyperbola.

$$x^2 - 9y^2 = -9$$

$$y^2 - \frac{x^2}{9} = 1 \qquad \text{Divide by } -9$$

Because the y^2-term is positive, the hyperbola has a vertical transverse axis; its foci and vertices are on the y-axis. Since $a^2 = 1$ and $b^2 = 9$, we get $a = 1$, $b = 3$, and $c = \sqrt{1 + 9} = \sqrt{10}$. Thus we have

VERTICES	$(0, \pm 1)$
FOCI	$(0, \pm\sqrt{10})$
ASYMPTOTES	$y = \pm\frac{1}{3}x$

We sketch the central box and asymptotes, then complete the graph, as shown in Figure 4(a). We can also draw the graph using a graphing calculator, as shown in Figure 4(b).

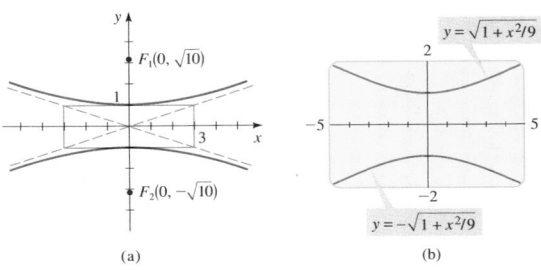

(a) (b)

✎ **NOW TRY EXERCISE 17**

EXAMPLE 3 | Finding the Equation of a Hyperbola from Its Vertices and Foci

Find the equation of the hyperbola with vertices $(\pm 3, 0)$ and foci $(\pm 4, 0)$. Sketch the graph.

SOLUTION Since the vertices are on the x-axis, the hyperbola has a horizontal transverse axis. Its equation is of the form

$$\frac{x^2}{3^2} - \frac{y^2}{b^2} = 1$$

We have $a = 3$ and $c = 4$. To find b, we use the relation $a^2 + b^2 = c^2$:

$$3^2 + b^2 = 4^2$$

$$b^2 = 4^2 - 3^2 = 7$$

$$b = \sqrt{7}$$

Thus the equation of the hyperbola is

$$\frac{x^2}{9} - \frac{y^2}{7} = 1$$

EXAMPLE
A horizontal hyperbola:
$$\frac{x^2}{9} - 2y^2 = 1$$
Vertices $(\pm 3, 0)$, asymptotes
$$y = \pm\frac{1}{3\sqrt{2}}x,$$
foci $\left(\pm\sqrt{\frac{37}{2}}, 0\right)$

ALTERNATE EXAMPLE 3
Find the equation of the hyperbola in standard form with vertices $(\pm 2, 0)$ and foci $(\pm 3, 0)$.

ANSWER
$$\frac{x^2}{4} - \frac{y^2}{5} = 1$$

The graph is shown in Figure 5.

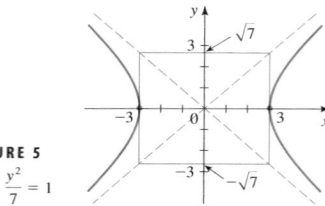

FIGURE 5
$$\frac{x^2}{9} - \frac{y^2}{7} = 1$$

✎. NOW TRY EXERCISES **21** AND **31**

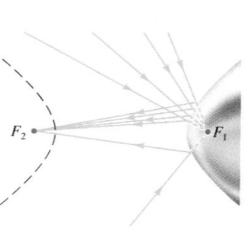

FIGURE 6
$$\frac{y^2}{4} - x^2 = 1$$

EXAMPLE 4 | Finding the Equation of a Hyperbola from Its Vertices and Asymptotes

Find the equation and the foci of the hyperbola with vertices $(0, \pm2)$ and asymptotes $y = \pm2x$. Sketch the graph.

SOLUTION Since the vertices are on the y-axis, the hyperbola has a vertical transverse axis with $a = 2$. From the asymptote equation we see that $a/b = 2$. Since $a = 2$, we get $2/b = 2$, so $b = 1$. Thus the equation of the hyperbola is

$$\frac{y^2}{4} - x^2 = 1$$

To find the foci, we calculate $c^2 = a^2 + b^2 = 2^2 + 1^2 = 5$, so $c = \sqrt{5}$. Thus the foci are $(0, \pm\sqrt{5})$. The graph is shown in Figure 6.

✎. NOW TRY EXERCISES **25** AND **35**

Like parabolas and ellipses, hyperbolas have an interesting *reflection property*. Light aimed at one focus of a hyperbolic mirror is reflected toward the other focus, as shown in Figure 7. This property is used in the construction of Cassegrain-type telescopes. A hyperbolic mirror is placed in the telescope tube so that light reflected from the primary parabolic reflector is aimed at one focus of the hyperbolic mirror. The light is then refocused at a more accessible point below the primary reflector (Figure 8).

FIGURE 7 Reflection property of hyperbolas

FIGURE 8 Cassegrain-type telescope

The LORAN (LOng RAnge Navigation) system was used until the early 1990s; it has now been superseded by the GPS system (see page 700). In the LORAN system, hyperbolas are used onboard a ship to determine its location. In Figure 9, radio stations at A and B transmit signals simultaneously for reception by the ship at P. The onboard computer converts the time difference in reception of these signals into a distance difference $d(P, A) - d(P, B)$. From the definition of a hyperbola this locates the ship on one branch of a hyperbola with foci at A and B (sketched in black in the figure). The same procedure is carried out with two other radio stations at C and D, and this locates the ship on a second hyperbola (shown in red in the figure). (In practice, only three stations are needed because one station can be used as a focus for both hyperbolas.) The coordinates of the intersection point of these two hyperbolas, which can be calculated precisely by the computer, give the location of P.

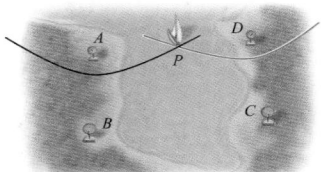

FIGURE 9 LORAN system for finding the location of a ship

11.3 EXERCISES

CONCEPTS

1. A hyperbola is the set of all points in the plane for which the _____ of the distances from two fixed points F_1 and F_2 is constant. The points F_1 and F_2 are called the _____ of the hyperbola.

2. The graph of the equation $\dfrac{x^2}{a^2} - \dfrac{y^2}{b^2} = 1$ with $a > 0, b > 0$

   is a hyperbola with vertices (___, ___) and (___, ___) and

   foci $(\pm c, 0)$, where $c = $ _____. So the graph of

   $\dfrac{x^2}{4^2} - \dfrac{y^2}{3^2} = 1$ is a hyperbola with vertices (___, ___) and

   (___, ___) and foci (___, ___) and (___, ___).

3. The graph of the equation $\dfrac{y^2}{a^2} - \dfrac{x^2}{b^2} = 1$ with $a > 0, b > 0$

   is a hyperbola with vertices (___, ___) and (___, ___) and

   foci $(0, \pm c)$, where $c = $ _____. So the graph of

   $\dfrac{y^2}{4^2} - \dfrac{x^2}{3^2} = 1$ is a hyperbola with vertices (___, ___) and

   (___, ___) and foci (___, ___) and (___, ___).

4. Label the vertices, foci, and asymptotes on the graphs given for the hyperbolas in Exercises 2 and 3.

   (a) $\dfrac{x^2}{4^2} - \dfrac{y^2}{3^2} = 1$

   (b) $\dfrac{y^2}{4^2} - \dfrac{x^2}{3^2} = 1$

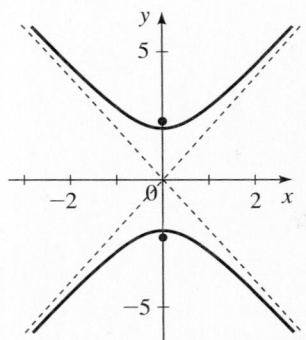

SKILLS

5–8 ■ Match the equation with the graphs labeled I–IV. Give reasons for your answers.

5. $\dfrac{x^2}{4} - y^2 = 1$ **6.** $y^2 - \dfrac{x^2}{9} = 1$

7. $16y^2 - x^2 = 144$ **8.** $9x^2 - 25y^2 = 225$

I

II

III

IV

9–20 ■ Find the vertices, foci, and asymptotes of the hyperbola, and sketch its graph.

9. $\dfrac{x^2}{4} - \dfrac{y^2}{16} = 1$ **10.** $\dfrac{y^2}{9} - \dfrac{x^2}{16} = 1$

11. $y^2 - \dfrac{x^2}{25} = 1$ **12.** $\dfrac{x^2}{2} - y^2 = 1$

13. $x^2 - y^2 = 1$ **14.** $9x^2 - 4y^2 = 36$

15. $25y^2 - 9x^2 = 225$ **16.** $x^2 - y^2 + 4 = 0$

17. $x^2 - 4y^2 - 8 = 0$ **18.** $x^2 - 2y^2 = 3$

19. $4y^2 - x^2 = 1$ **20.** $9x^2 - 16y^2 = 1$

21–26 ■ Find the equation for the hyperbola whose graph is shown.

21.

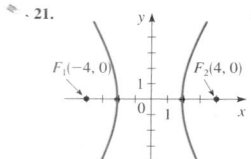

$F_1(-4, 0)$ $F_2(4, 0)$

22.

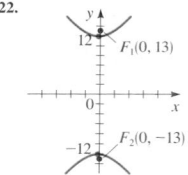

$F_1(0, 13)$

$F_2(0, -13)$

23.

$(3, -5)$

24.

$(4, 4)$

$2\sqrt{3}$

25.

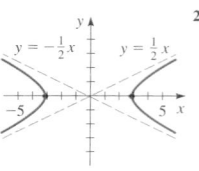

$y = -\tfrac{1}{2}x$ $y = \tfrac{1}{2}x$

26.

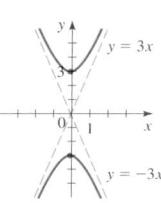

$y = 3x$

$y = -3x$

27–30 ■ Use a graphing device to graph the hyperbola.

27. $x^2 - 2y^2 = 8$ **28.** $3y^2 - 4x^2 = 24$

29. $\dfrac{y^2}{2} - \dfrac{x^2}{6} = 1$ **30.** $\dfrac{x^2}{100} - \dfrac{y^2}{64} = 1$

31–42 ■ Find an equation for the hyperbola that satisfies the given conditions.

31. Foci: $(\pm 5, 0)$, vertices: $(\pm 3, 0)$

32. Foci: $(0, \pm 10)$, vertices: $(0, \pm 8)$

33. Foci: $(0, \pm 2)$, vertices: $(0, \pm 1)$

34. Foci: $(\pm 6, 0)$, vertices: $(\pm 2, 0)$

35. Vertices: $(\pm 1, 0)$, asymptotes: $y = \pm 5x$

36. Vertices: $(0, \pm 6)$, asymptotes: $y = \pm \tfrac{1}{3}x$

37. Foci: $(0, \pm 8)$, asymptotes: $y = \pm \tfrac{1}{2}x$

38. Vertices: $(0, \pm 6)$, hyperbola passes through $(-5, 9)$

39. Asymptotes: $y = \pm x$, hyperbola passes through $(5, 3)$

40. Foci: $(\pm 3, 0)$, hyperbola passes through $(4, 1)$

41. Foci: $(\pm 5, 0)$, length of transverse axis: 6

42. Foci: $(0, \pm 1)$, length of transverse axis: 1

43. (a) Show that the asymptotes of the hyperbola $x^2 - y^2 = 5$ are perpendicular to each other.
(b) Find an equation for the hyperbola with foci $(\pm c, 0)$ and with asymptotes perpendicular to each other.

44. The hyperbolas

$$\frac{x^2}{a^2} - \frac{y^2}{b^2} = 1 \quad \text{and} \quad \frac{x^2}{a^2} - \frac{y^2}{b^2} = -1$$

are said to be **conjugate** to each other.
(a) Show that the hyperbolas

$$x^2 - 4y^2 + 16 = 0 \quad \text{and} \quad 4y^2 - x^2 + 16 = 0$$

are conjugate to each other, and sketch their graphs on the same coordinate axes.
(b) What do the hyperbolas of part (a) have in common?
(c) Show that any pair of conjugate hyperbolas have the relationship you discovered in part (b).

45. In the derivation of the equation of the hyperbola at the beginning of this section, we said that the equation

$$\sqrt{(x + c)^2 + y^2} - \sqrt{(x - c)^2 + y^2} = \pm 2a$$

simplifies to

$$(c^2 - a^2)x^2 - a^2y^2 = a^2(c^2 - a^2)$$

Supply the steps needed to show this.

46. (a) For the hyperbola

$$\frac{x^2}{9} - \frac{y^2}{16} = 1$$

determine the values of a, b, and c, and find the coordinates of the foci F_1 and F_2.
   (b) Show that the point $P(5, \frac{16}{3})$ lies on this hyperbola.
   (c) Find $d(P, F_1)$ and $d(P, F_2)$.
   (d) Verify that the difference between $d(P, F_1)$ and $d(P, F_2)$ is $2a$.

47. Hyperbolas are called **confocal** if they have the same foci.
   (a) Show that the hyperbolas

$$\frac{y^2}{k} - \frac{x^2}{16 - k} = 1 \quad \text{with } 0 < k < 16$$

are confocal.
   (b) Use a graphing device to draw the top branches of the family of hyperbolas in part (a) for $k = 1$, 4, 8, and 12. How does the shape of the graph change as k increases?

APPLICATIONS

48. Navigation In the figure, the LORAN stations at A and B are 500 mi apart, and the ship at P receives station A's signal 2640 microseconds (μs) before it receives the signal from station B.
   (a) Assuming that radio signals travel at 980 ft/μs, find $d(P, A) - d(P, B)$.
   (b) Find an equation for the branch of the hyperbola indicated in red in the figure. (Use miles as the unit of distance.)
   (c) If A is due north of B and if P is due east of A, how far is P from A?

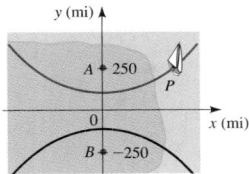

49. Comet Trajectories Some comets, such as Halley's comet, are a permanent part of the solar system, traveling in elliptical orbits around the sun. Other comets pass through the solar system only once, following a hyperbolic path with the sun at a focus. The figure at the top of the next column shows the path of such a comet. Find an equation for the path, assuming that the closest the comet comes to the sun is 2×10^9 mi and that the path the comet was taking before it neared the solar system is at a right angle to the path it continues on after leaving the solar system.

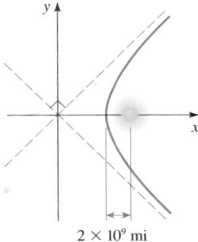

2×10^9 mi

50. Ripples in Pool Two stones are dropped simultaneously into a calm pool of water. The crests of the resulting waves form equally spaced concentric circles, as shown in the figures. The waves interact with each other to create certain interference patterns.
   (a) Explain why the red dots lie on an ellipse.
   (b) Explain why the blue dots lie on a hyperbola.

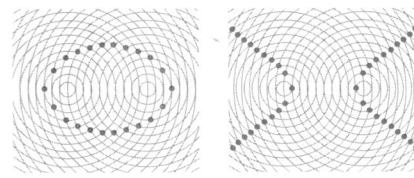

DISCOVERY ▪ DISCUSSION ▸ WRITING

51. Hyperbolas in the Real World Several examples of the uses of hyperbolas are given in the text. Find other situations in real life in which hyperbolas occur. Consult a scientific encyclopedia in the reference section of your library, or search the Internet.

52. Light from a Lamp The light from a lamp forms a lighted area on a wall, as shown in the figure. Why is the boundary of this lighted area a hyperbola? How can one hold a flashlight so that its beam forms a hyperbola on the ground?

SUGGESTED TIME AND EMPHASIS

$\frac{1}{2}$–1 class, optional material (may be combined with Sections 11.1–11.3).

11.4 SHIFTED CONICS

| Shifting Graphs of Equations ▶ Shifted Ellipses ▶ Shifted Parabolas ▶
| Shifted Hyperbolas ▶ The General Equation of a Shifted Conic

In the preceding sections we studied parabolas with vertices at the origin and ellipses and hyperbolas with centers at the origin. We restricted ourselves to these cases because these equations have the simplest form. In this section we consider conics whose vertices and centers are not necessarily at the origin, and we determine how this affects their equations.

▼ Shifting Graphs of Equations

In Section 2.5 we studied transformations of functions that have the effect of shifting their graphs. In general, for any equation in x and y, if we replace x by $x - h$ or by $x + h$, the graph of the new equation is simply the old graph shifted horizontally; if y is replaced by $y - k$ or by $y + k$, the graph is shifted vertically. The following box gives the details.

SHIFTING GRAPHS OF EQUATIONS

If h and k are positive real numbers, then replacing x by $x - h$ or by $x + h$ and replacing y by $y - k$ or by $y + k$ has the following effect(s) on the graph of any equation in x and y.

Replacement	How the graph is shifted
1. x replaced by $x - h$	Right h units
2. x replaced by $x + h$	Left h units
3. y replaced by $y - k$	Upward k units
4. y replaced by $y + k$	Downward k units

EXAMPLE

A nondegenerate ellipse:

$25x^2 + 4y^2 - 150x + 40y$

$+ 324 = 0 \Longleftrightarrow$

$$\frac{(x - 3)^2}{4} + \frac{(y + 5)^2}{25} = 1$$

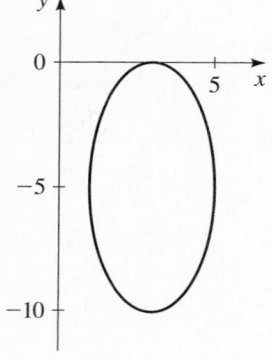

▼ Shifted Ellipses

Let's apply horizontal and vertical shifting to the ellipse with equation

$$\frac{x^2}{a^2} + \frac{y^2}{b^2} = 1$$

whose graph is shown in Figure 1. If we shift it so that its center is at the point (h, k) instead of at the origin, then its equation becomes

$$\frac{(x - h)^2}{a^2} + \frac{(y - k)^2}{b^2} = 1$$

FIGURE 1   Shifted ellipse

TEXT QUESTION

Identify the conic section with equation $9x^2 - 36x + 4y^2 = 0$.

Answer

Ellipse

EXAMPLE 1 | Sketching the Graph of a Shifted Ellipse

Sketch a graph of the ellipse

$$\frac{(x + 1)^2}{4} + \frac{(y - 2)^2}{9} = 1$$

and determine the coordinates of the foci.

SOLUTION The ellipse

$$\frac{(x + 1)^2}{4} + \frac{(y - 2)^2}{9} = 1 \qquad \text{Shifted ellipse}$$

is shifted so that its center is at $(-1, 2)$. It is obtained from the ellipse

$$\frac{x^2}{4} + \frac{y^2}{9} = 1 \qquad \text{Ellipse with center at origin}$$

by shifting it left 1 unit and upward 2 units. The endpoints of the minor and major axes of the ellipse with center at the origin are $(2, 0)$, $(-2, 0)$, $(0, 3)$, $(0, -3)$. We apply the required shifts to these points to obtain the corresponding points on the shifted ellipse:

$$(2, 0) \ \rightarrow \ (2 - 1, 0 + 2) = (1, 2)$$
$$(-2, 0) \ \rightarrow \ (-2 - 1, 0 + 2) = (-3, 2)$$
$$(0, 3) \ \rightarrow \ (0 - 1, 3 + 2) = (-1, 5)$$
$$(0, -3) \ \rightarrow \ (0 - 1, -3 + 2) = (-1, -1)$$

This helps us sketch the graph in Figure 2.

To find the foci of the shifted ellipse, we first find the foci of the ellipse with center at the origin. Since $a^2 = 9$ and $b^2 = 4$, we have $c^2 = 9 - 4 = 5$, so $c = \sqrt{5}$. So the foci are $(0, \pm\sqrt{5})$. Shifting left 1 unit and upward 2 units, we get

$$\left(0, \sqrt{5}\right) \ \rightarrow \ \left(0 - 1, \sqrt{5} + 2\right) = \left(-1, 2 + \sqrt{5}\right)$$
$$\left(0, -\sqrt{5}\right) \ \rightarrow \ \left(0 - 1, -\sqrt{5} + 2\right) = \left(-1, 2 - \sqrt{5}\right)$$

Thus the foci of the shifted ellipse are

$$\left(-1, 2 + \sqrt{5}\right) \qquad \text{and} \qquad \left(-1, 2 - \sqrt{5}\right)$$

✎ NOW TRY EXERCISE **7** ∎

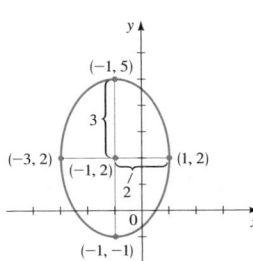

FIGURE 2
$$\frac{(x + 1)^2}{4} + \frac{(y - 2)^2}{9} = 1$$

▼ Shifted Parabolas

Applying shifts to parabolas leads to the equations and graphs shown in Figure 3.

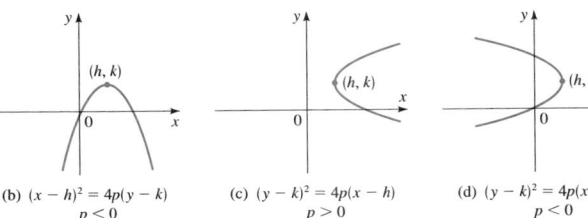

(a) $(x - h)^2 = 4p(y - k)$
$p > 0$

(b) $(x - h)^2 = 4p(y - k)$
$p < 0$

(c) $(y - k)^2 = 4p(x - h)$
$p > 0$

(d) $(y - k)^2 = 4p(x - h)$
$p < 0$

FIGURE 3 Shifted parabolas

IN-CLASS MATERIALS

Class time can be saved if this section is covered along with Sections 11.1–11.3. For example, after discussing parabolas, immediately do an example of a shifted parabola. Teach ellipses and hyperbolas similarly.

EXAMPLE 2 | Graphing a Shifted Parabola

Determine the vertex, focus, and directrix, and sketch a graph of the parabola.

$$x^2 - 4x = 8y - 28$$

SOLUTION We complete the square in x to put this equation into one of the forms in Figure 3.

$$x^2 - 4x + 4 = 8y - 28 + 4 \qquad \text{Add 4 to complete the square}$$

$$(x - 2)^2 = 8y - 24$$

$$(x - 2)^2 = 8(y - 3) \qquad \text{Shifted parabola}$$

This parabola opens upward with vertex at $(2, 3)$. It is obtained from the parabola

$$x^2 = 8y \qquad \text{Parabola with vertex at origin}$$

by shifting right 2 units and upward 3 units. Since $4p = 8$, we have $p = 2$, so the focus is 2 units above the vertex and the directrix is 2 units below the vertex. Thus the focus is $(2, 5)$, and the directrix is $y = 1$. The graph is shown in Figure 4.

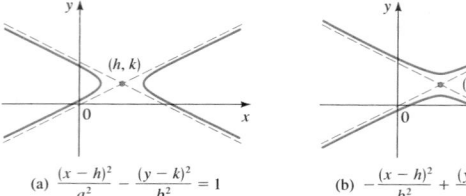

FIGURE 4
$x^2 - 4x = 8y - 28$

✎. NOW TRY EXERCISES **9** AND **23**

▼ Shifted Hyperbolas

Applying shifts to hyperbolas leads to the equations and graphs shown in Figure 5.

FIGURE 5 Shifted hyperbolas

(a) $\dfrac{(x - h)^2}{a^2} - \dfrac{(y - k)^2}{b^2} = 1$

(b) $-\dfrac{(x - h)^2}{b^2} + \dfrac{(y - k)^2}{a^2} = 1$

EXAMPLE 3 | Graphing a Shifted Hyperbola

A shifted conic has the equation

$$9x^2 - 72x - 16y^2 - 32y = 16$$

(a) Complete the square in x and y to show that the equation represents a hyperbola.

(b) Find the center, vertices, foci, and asymptotes of the hyperbola, and sketch its graph.

(c) Draw the graph using a graphing calculator.

SOLUTION

(a) We complete the squares in both x and y:

$$9(x^2 - 8x \qquad) - 16(y^2 + 2y \qquad) = 16 \qquad \text{Group terms and factor}$$

$$9(x^2 - 8x + 16) - 16(y^2 + 2y + 1) = 16 + 9 \cdot 16 - 16 \cdot 1 \qquad \text{Complete the squares}$$

$$9(x - 4)^2 - 16(y + 1)^2 = 144 \qquad \text{Divide this by 144}$$

$$\frac{(x - 4)^2}{16} - \frac{(y + 1)^2}{9} = 1 \qquad \text{Shifted hyperbola}$$

Comparing this to Figure 5(a), we see that this is the equation of a shifted hyperbola.

IN-CLASS MATERIALS

Help the class recognize the difference between the formulas of conic sections by pointing out that the equation of a parabola has degree 2 in only one variable (which variable it is determines which type of parabola it is). Equations of ellipses and hyperbolas have degree 2 in both variables; for ellipses the second-degree terms have the same sign, and for hyperbolas they have opposite signs.

(b) The shifted hyperbola has center $(4, -1)$ and a horizontal transverse axis.

$$\text{CENTER} \quad (4, -1)$$

Its graph will have the same shape as the unshifted hyperbola

$$\frac{x^2}{16} - \frac{y^2}{9} = 1 \qquad \text{Hyperbola with center at origin}$$

Since $a^2 = 16$ and $b^2 = 9$, we have $a = 4$, $b = 3$, and $c = \sqrt{a^2 + b^2} = \sqrt{16 + 9} = 5$. Thus the foci lie 5 units to the left and to the right of the center, and the vertices lie 4 units to either side of the center.

$$\text{FOCI} \qquad (-1, -1) \quad \text{and} \quad (9, -1)$$

$$\text{VERTICES} \quad (0, -1) \quad \text{and} \quad (8, -1)$$

The asymptotes of the unshifted hyperbola are $y = \pm\frac{3}{4}x$, so the asymptotes of the shifted hyperbola are found as follows.

$$\text{ASYMPTOTES} \quad y + 1 = \pm\tfrac{3}{4}(x - 4)$$
$$y + 1 = \pm\tfrac{3}{4}x \mp 3$$
$$y = \tfrac{3}{4}x - 4 \quad \text{and} \quad y = -\tfrac{3}{4}x + 2$$

To help us sketch the hyperbola, we draw the central box; it extends 4 units left and right from the center and 3 units upward and downward from the center. We then draw the asymptotes and complete the graph of the shifted hyperbola as shown in Figure 6(a).

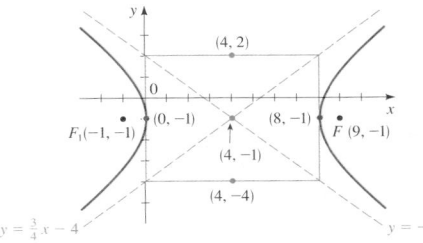

(a)

(b)

FIGURE 6 $\quad 9x^2 - 72x - 16y^2 - 32y = 16$

(c) To draw the graph using a graphing calculator, we need to solve for y. The given equation is a quadratic equation in y, so we use the Quadratic Formula to solve for y. Writing the equation in the form

$$16y^2 + 32y - 9x^2 + 72x + 16 = 0$$

Note that the equation of a hyperbola does not define y as a function of x (see page 158). That's why we need to graph two functions to graph a hyperbola.

we get

$$y = \frac{-32 \pm \sqrt{32^2 - 4(16)(-9x^2 + 72x + 16)}}{2(16)} \qquad \text{Quadratic Formula}$$

$$= \frac{-32 \pm \sqrt{576x^2 - 4608x}}{32} \qquad \text{Expand}$$

$$= \frac{-32 \pm 24\sqrt{x^2 - 8x}}{32} \qquad \text{Factor 576 from under the radical}$$

$$= -1 \pm \tfrac{3}{4}\sqrt{x^2 - 8x} \qquad \text{Simplify}$$

EXAMPLE

A degenerate hyperbola:

$$x^2 - y^2 - 4x - 2y + 3 = 0$$
$$\Leftrightarrow (x - 2)^2 - (y + 1)^2 = 0$$

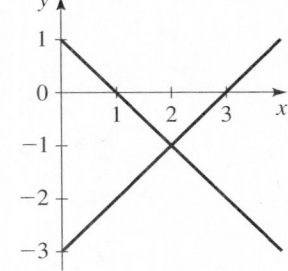

IN-CLASS MATERIALS

The text's guide to the general equation of a shifted conic is important, but students should not memorize it blindly. Point out that if they've learned the previous section, these rules of thumb should make perfect sense. Have them look at the three general formulas they have learned, generalizing them to allow for a shift:

$$y = 4p\,(x - h)^2$$
$$\frac{(x - h)^2}{a^2} + \frac{(y - k)^2}{b^2} = 1$$
$$\frac{(x - h)^2}{a^2} - \frac{(y - k)^2}{b^2} = 1$$

To obtain the graph of the hyperbola, we graph the functions

$$y = -1 + 0.75\sqrt{x^2 - 8x}$$

and

$$y = -1 - 0.75\sqrt{x^2 - 8x}$$

as shown in Figure 6(b).

▼ NOW TRY EXERCISES **13** AND **25**

JOHANNES KEPLER (1571–1630) was the first to give a correct description of the motion of the planets. The cosmology of his time postulated complicated systems of circles moving on circles to describe these motions. Kepler sought a simpler and more harmonious description. As the official astronomer at the imperial court in Prague, he studied the astronomical observations of the Danish astronomer Tycho Brahe, whose data were the most accurate available at the time. After numerous attempts to find a theory, Kepler made the momentous discovery that the orbits of the planets are elliptical. His three great laws of planetary motion are

1. The orbit of each planet is an ellipse with the sun at one focus.

2. The line segment that joins the sun to a planet sweeps out equal areas in equal time (see the figure).

3. The square of the period of revolution of a planet is proportional to the cube of the length of the major axis of its orbit.

His formulation of these laws is perhaps the most impressive deduction from empirical data in the history of science.

▼ The General Equation of a Shifted Conic

If we expand and simplify the equations of any of the shifted conics illustrated in Figures 1, 3, and 5, then we will always obtain an equation of the form

$$Ax^2 + Cy^2 + Dx + Ey + F = 0$$

where A and C are not both 0. Conversely, if we begin with an equation of this form, then we can complete the square in x and y to see which type of conic section the equation represents. In some cases the graph of the equation turns out to be just a pair of lines or a single point, or there might be no graph at all. These cases are called **degenerate conics**. If the equation is not degenerate, then we can tell whether it represents a parabola, an ellipse, or a hyperbola simply by examining the signs of A and C, as described in the box below.

GENERAL EQUATION OF A SHIFTED CONIC

The graph of the equation

$$Ax^2 + Cy^2 + Dx + Ey + F = 0$$

where A and C are not both 0, is a conic or a degenerate conic. In the nondegenerate cases the graph is

1. a parabola if A or C is 0,

2. an ellipse if A and C have the same sign (or a circle if $A = C$),

3. a hyperbola if A and C have opposite signs.

EXAMPLE 4 | An Equation That Leads to a Degenerate Conic

Sketch the graph of the equation

$$9x^2 - y^2 + 18x + 6y = 0$$

SOLUTION   Because the coefficients of x^2 and y^2 are of opposite sign, this equation looks as if it should represent a hyperbola (like the equation of Example 3). To see whether this is in fact the case, we complete the squares:

$$9(x^2 + 2x \quad) - (y^2 - 6y \quad) = 0 \qquad \text{Group terms and factor 9}$$

$$9(x^2 + 2x + 1) - (y^2 - 6y + 9) = 0 + 9 \cdot 1 - 9 \qquad \text{Complete the squares}$$

$$9(x + 1)^2 - (y - 3)^2 = 0 \qquad \text{Factor}$$

$$(x + 1)^2 - \frac{(y - 3)^2}{9} = 0 \qquad \text{Divide by 9}$$

ALTERNATE EXAMPLE 4

The graph of the equation $49x^2 - y^2 + 196x + 28y = 0$ is equivalent to a pair of intersecting lines. Find the equations of these lines.

ANSWER

$y = 7x + 28, y = -7x$

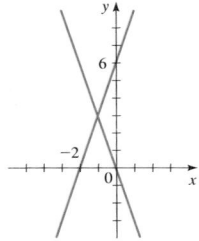

FIGURE 7
$9x^2 - y^2 + 18x + 6y = 0$

For this to fit the form of the equation of a hyperbola, we would need a nonzero constant to the right of the equal sign. In fact, further analysis shows that this is the equation of a pair of intersecting lines:

$$(y - 3)^2 = 9(x + 1)^2$$

$$y - 3 = \pm 3(x + 1) \qquad \text{Take square roots}$$

$$y = 3(x + 1) + 3 \qquad \text{or} \qquad y = -3(x + 1) + 3$$

$$y = 3x + 6 \qquad\qquad\qquad y = -3x$$

These lines are graphed in Figure 7.

✎. NOW TRY EXERCISE **31**

Because the equation in Example 4 looked at first glance like the equation of a hyperbola but, in fact, turned out to represent simply a pair of lines, we refer to its graph as a **degenerate hyperbola**. Degenerate ellipses and parabolas can also arise when we complete the square(s) in an equation that seems to represent a conic. For example, the equation

$$4x^2 + y^2 - 8x + 2y + 6 = 0$$

looks as if it should represent an ellipse, because the coefficients of x^2 and y^2 have the same sign. But completing the squares leads to

$$(x - 1)^2 + \frac{(y + 1)^2}{4} = -\frac{1}{4}$$

which has no solution at all (since the sum of two squares cannot be negative). This equation is therefore degenerate.

11.4 EXERCISES

CONCEPTS

1. Suppose we want to graph an equation in x and y.

   (a) If we replace x by $x - 3$, the graph of the equation is shifted to the _____ by 3 units. If we replace x by $x + 3$, the graph of the equation is shifted to the _____ by 3 units.

   (b) If we replace y by $y - 1$, the graph of the equation is shifted _____ by 1 unit. If we replace y by $y + 1$, the graph of the equation is shifted _____ by 1 unit.

2. The graphs of $x^2 = 12y$ and $(x - 3)^2 = 12(y - 1)$ are given. Label the focus, directrix, and vertex on each parabola.

    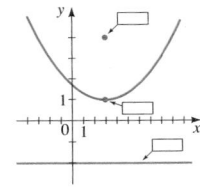

3. The graphs of $\dfrac{x^2}{5^2} + \dfrac{y^2}{4^2} = 1$ and $\dfrac{(x - 3)^2}{5^2} + \dfrac{(y - 1)^2}{4^2} = 1$

   are given. Label the vertices and foci on each ellipse.

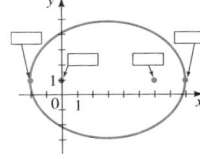

DRILL QUESTION

Graph the conic section with equation

$$4x^2 - 16x + 9y^2 - 20 = 0.$$

Answer

$$4x^2 - 16x + 9y^2 - 20 = 0$$

$$\Leftrightarrow 4(x - 2)^2 + 9y^2 = 36$$

$$\Leftrightarrow \frac{(x - 2)^2}{9} + \frac{y^2}{4} = 1$$

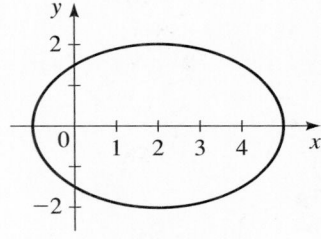

4. The graphs of $\dfrac{x^2}{4^2} - \dfrac{y^2}{3^2} = 1$ and $\dfrac{(x-3)^2}{4^2} - \dfrac{(y-1)^2}{3^2} = 1$

are given. Label the vertices, foci, and asymptotes on each hyperbola.

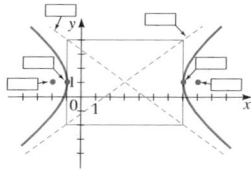

SKILLS

5–8 ■ Find the center, foci, and vertices of the ellipse, and determine the lengths of the major and minor axes. Then sketch the graph.

5. $\dfrac{(x-2)^2}{9} + \dfrac{(y-1)^2}{4} = 1$ **6.** $\dfrac{(x-3)^2}{16} + (y+3)^2 = 1$

7. $\dfrac{x^2}{9} + \dfrac{(y+5)^2}{25} = 1$ **8.** $\dfrac{(x+2)^2}{4} + y^2 = 1$

9–12 ■ Find the vertex, focus, and directrix of the parabola. Then sketch the graph.

9. $(x-3)^2 = 8(y+1)$ **10.** $(y+5)^2 = -6x + 12$

11. $-4\left(x + \tfrac{1}{2}\right)^2 = y$ **12.** $y^2 = 16x - 8$

13–16 ■ Find the center, foci, vertices, and asymptotes of the hyperbola. Then sketch the graph.

13. $\dfrac{(x+1)^2}{9} - \dfrac{(y-3)^2}{16} = 1$ **14.** $(x-8)^2 - (y+6)^2 = 1$

15. $y^2 - \dfrac{(x+1)^2}{4} = 1$ **16.** $\dfrac{(y-1)^2}{25} - (x+3)^2 = 1$

17–22 ■ Find an equation for the conic whose graph is shown.

17.

18.

19.

20.

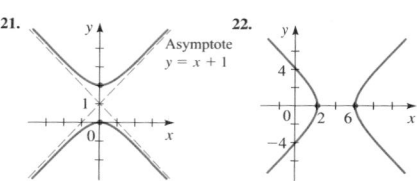

21.

22.

23–34 ■ Complete the square to determine whether the equation represents an ellipse, a parabola, a hyperbola, or a degenerate conic. If the graph is an ellipse, find the center, foci, vertices, and lengths of the major and minor axes. If it is a parabola, find the vertex, focus, and directrix. If it is a hyperbola, find the center, foci, vertices, and asymptotes. Then sketch the graph of the equation. If the equation has no graph, explain why.

23. $y^2 = 4(x + 2y)$

24. $9x^2 - 36x + 4y^2 = 0$

25. $x^2 - 4y^2 - 2x + 16y = 20$

26. $x^2 + 6x + 12y + 9 = 0$

27. $4x^2 + 25y^2 - 24x + 250y + 561 = 0$

28. $2x^2 + y^2 = 2y + 1$

29. $16x^2 - 9y^2 - 96x + 288 = 0$

30. $4x^2 - 4x - 8y + 9 = 0$

31. $x^2 + 16 = 4(y^2 + 2x)$

32. $x^2 - y^2 = 10(x - y) + 1$

33. $3x^2 + 4y^2 - 6x - 24y + 39 = 0$

34. $x^2 + 4y^2 + 20x - 40y + 300 = 0$

35–38 ■ Use a graphing device to graph the conic.

35. $2x^2 - 4x + y + 5 = 0$

36. $4x^2 + 9y^2 - 36y = 0$

37. $9x^2 + 36 = y^2 + 36x + 6y$

38. $x^2 - 4y^2 + 4x + 8y = 0$

39. Determine what the value of F must be if the graph of the equation

$$4x^2 + y^2 + 4(x - 2y) + F = 0$$

is **(a)** an ellipse, **(b)** a single point, or **(c)** the empty set.

40. Find an equation for the ellipse that shares a vertex and a focus with the parabola $x^2 + y = 100$ and has its other focus at the origin.

41. This exercise deals with **confocal parabolas**, that is, families of parabolas that have the same focus.
   (a) Draw graphs of the family of parabolas

$$x^2 = 4p(y + p)$$

   for $p = -2, -\frac{3}{2}, -1, -\frac{1}{2}, \frac{1}{2}, 1, \frac{3}{2}, 2$.

   (b) Show that each parabola in this family has its focus at the origin.
   (c) Describe the effect on the graph of moving the vertex closer to the origin.

APPLICATIONS

42. Path of a Cannonball A cannon fires a cannonball as shown in the figure. The path of the cannonball is a parabola with vertex at the highest point of the path. If the cannonball lands 1600 ft from the cannon and the highest point it reaches is 3200 ft above the ground, find an equation for the path of the cannonball. Place the origin at the location of the cannon.

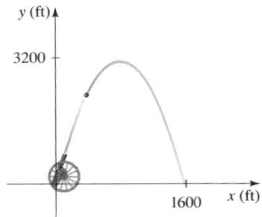

43. Orbit of a Satellite A satellite is in an elliptical orbit around the earth with the center of the earth at one focus, as shown in the figure at the top of the right-hand column. The height of the satellite above the earth varies between 140 mi and 440 mi. Assume that the earth is a sphere with radius 3960 mi. Find an equation for the path of the satellite with the origin at the center of the earth.

DISCOVERY ▪ DISCUSSION ▪ WRITING

44. A Family of Confocal Conics Conics that share a focus are called **confocal**. Consider the family of conics that have a focus at $(0, 1)$ and a vertex at the origin, as shown in the figure.
   (a) Find equations of two different ellipses that have these properties.
   (b) Find equations of two different hyperbolas that have these properties.
   (c) Explain why only one parabola satisfies these properties. Find its equation.
   (d) Sketch the conics you found in parts (a), (b), and (c) on the same coordinate axes (for the hyperbolas, sketch the top branches only).
   (e) How are the ellipses and hyperbolas related to the parabola?

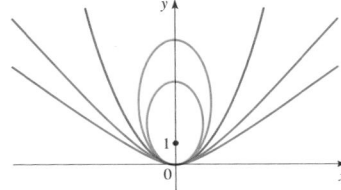

11.5 ROTATION OF AXES

▎Rotation of Axes ▶ General Equation of a Conic ▶ The Discriminant

In Section 11.4 we studied conics with equations of the form

$$Ax^2 + Cy^2 + Dx + Ey + F = 0$$

We saw that the graph is always an ellipse, parabola, or hyperbola with horizontal or vertical axes (except in the degenerate cases). In this section we study the most general second-degree equation

$$Ax^2 + Bxy + Cy^2 + Dx + Ey + F = 0$$

SUGGESTED TIME AND EMPHASIS

1 class, optional material

TEXT QUESTION

If you are presented with the equation of a conic such as $3x^2 + 5xy - 2y^2 + x - y + 4 = 0$, how would you go about finding whether it is an ellipse, parabola, or hyperbola?

Answer

Evaluate the discriminant.

FIGURE 1

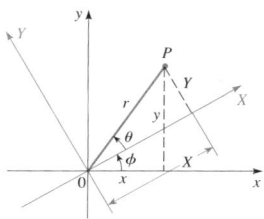

FIGURE 2

We will see that the graph of an equation of this form is also a conic. In fact, by rotating the coordinate axes through an appropriate angle, we can eliminate the term Bxy and then use our knowledge of conic sections to analyze the graph.

▼ Rotation of Axes

In Figure 1 the x- and y-axes have been rotated through an acute angle ϕ about the origin to produce a new pair of axes, which we call the X- and Y-axes. A point P that has coordinates (x, y) in the old system has coordinates (X, Y) in the new system. If we let r denote the distance of P from the origin and let θ be the angle that the segment OP makes with the new X-axis, then we can see from Figure 2 (by considering the two right triangles in the figure) that

$$X = r \cos \theta \qquad\qquad Y = r \sin \theta$$
$$x = r \cos(\theta + \phi) \qquad y = r \sin(\theta + \phi)$$

Using the Addition Formula for Cosine, we see that

$$
\begin{aligned}
x &= r \cos(\theta + \phi) \\
&= r(\cos \theta \cos \phi - \sin \theta \sin \phi) \\
&= (r \cos \theta) \cos \phi - (r \sin \theta) \sin \phi \\
&= X \cos \phi - Y \sin \phi
\end{aligned}
$$

Similarly, we can apply the Addition Formula for Sine to the expression for y to obtain $y = X \sin \phi + Y \cos \phi$. By treating these equations for x and y as a system of linear equations in the variables X and Y (see Exercise 35), we obtain expressions for X and Y in terms of x and y, as detailed in the following box.

ROTATION OF AXES FORMULAS

Suppose the x- and y-axes in a coordinate plane are rotated through the acute angle ϕ to produce the X- and Y-axes, as shown in Figure 1. Then the coordinates (x, y) and (X, Y) of a point in the xy- and the XY-planes are related as follows:

$$x = X \cos \phi - Y \sin \phi \qquad\qquad X = x \cos \phi + y \sin \phi$$
$$y = X \sin \phi + Y \cos \phi \qquad\qquad Y = -x \sin \phi + y \cos \phi$$

EXAMPLE 1 | Rotation of Axes

If the coordinate axes are rotated through 30°, find the XY-coordinates of the point with xy-coordinates $(2, -4)$.

SOLUTION   Using the Rotation of Axes Formulas with $x = 2$, $y = -4$, and $\phi = 30°$, we get

$$X = 2 \cos 30° + (-4) \sin 30° = 2\left(\frac{\sqrt{3}}{2}\right) - 4\left(\frac{1}{2}\right) = \sqrt{3} - 2$$

$$Y = -2 \sin 30° + (-4) \cos 30° = -2\left(\frac{1}{2}\right) - 4\left(\frac{\sqrt{3}}{2}\right) = -1 - 2\sqrt{3}$$

The XY-coordinates are $(-2 + \sqrt{3}, -1 - 2\sqrt{3})$.

✎. NOW TRY EXERCISE **3**   ■

ALTERNATE EXAMPLE 1

If the coordinate axes are rotated through an angle of $\frac{\pi}{3}$, find the XY coordinates of the point with xy coordinates $(1, 4)$.

ANSWER

$$\left(\frac{1 + 4\sqrt{3}}{2}, \frac{4 - \sqrt{3}}{2}\right)$$

IN-CLASS MATERIALS

Point out the progression of the past few sections. Write out $Ax^2 + Bxy + Cy^2 + Dx + Ey + F = 0$. When the course started, we studied lines, which was just the case where $A = B = C = 0$. When we discussed circles, that was the case where $A = C$, $B = D = E = 0$. Shifting the center of a circle allowed D and E to take on nonzero values. Our study of conic sections removed the restriction that $A = C$, so this section really is the last step in a logical progression.

EXAMPLE 2 | Rotating a Hyperbola

Rotate the coordinate axes through 45° to show that the graph of the equation $xy = 2$ is a hyperbola.

SOLUTION   We use the Rotation of Axes Formulas with $\phi = 45°$ to obtain

$$x = X \cos 45° - Y \sin 45° = \frac{X}{\sqrt{2}} - \frac{Y}{\sqrt{2}}$$

$$y = X \sin 45° + Y \cos 45° = \frac{X}{\sqrt{2}} + \frac{Y}{\sqrt{2}}$$

Substituting these expressions into the original equation gives

$$\left(\frac{X}{\sqrt{2}} - \frac{Y}{\sqrt{2}} \right) \left(\frac{X}{\sqrt{2}} + \frac{Y}{\sqrt{2}} \right) = 2$$

$$\frac{X^2}{2} - \frac{Y^2}{2} = 2$$

$$\frac{X^2}{4} - \frac{Y^2}{4} = 1$$

We recognize this as a hyperbola with vertices $(\pm 2, 0)$ in the XY-coordinate system. Its asymptotes are $Y = \pm X$, which correspond to the coordinate axes in the xy-system (see Figure 3).

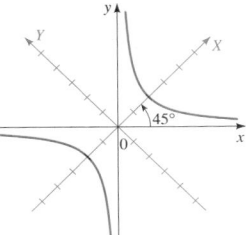

FIGURE 3
$xy = 2$

↖. NOW TRY EXERCISE **11**

▼ General Equation of a Conic

The method of Example 2 can be used to transform any equation of the form

$$Ax^2 + Bxy + Cy^2 + Dx + Ey + F = 0$$

into an equation in X and Y that doesn't contain an XY-term by choosing an appropriate angle of rotation. To find the angle that works, we rotate the axes through an angle ϕ and substitute for x and y using the Rotation of Axes Formulas:

$$A(X \cos \phi - Y \sin \phi)^2 + B(X \cos \phi - Y \sin \phi)(X \sin \phi + Y \cos \phi)$$
$$+ C(X \sin \phi + Y \cos \phi)^2 + D(X \cos \phi - Y \sin \phi)$$
$$+ E(X \sin \phi + Y \cos \phi) + F = 0$$

IN-CLASS MATERIALS
This is a very good section to teach with the aid of a CAS, or even a good place to introduce such a device. A great deal of the work in graphing an arbitrary conic section is multiplying out long algebraic expressions, which a CAS can do easily.

If we expand this and collect like terms, we obtain an equation of the form

$$A'X^2 + B'XY + C'Y^2 + D'X + E'Y + F' = 0$$

where

$$A' = A\cos^2\phi + B\sin\phi\cos\phi + C\sin^2\phi$$

$$B' = 2(C - A)\sin\phi\cos\phi + B(\cos^2\phi - \sin^2\phi)$$

$$C' = A\sin^2\phi - B\sin\phi\cos\phi + C\cos^2\phi$$

$$D' = D\cos\phi + E\sin\phi$$

$$E' = -D\sin\phi + E\cos\phi$$

$$F' = F$$

Double-Angle Formulas

$\sin 2\phi = 2\sin\phi\cos\phi$

$\cos 2\phi = \cos^2\phi - \sin^2\phi$

To eliminate the XY-term, we would like to choose ϕ so that $B' = 0$, that is,

$$2(C - A)\sin\phi\cos\phi + B(\cos^2\phi - \sin^2\phi) = 0$$

Double-Angle Formulas for Sine and Cosine

$$(C - A)\sin 2\phi + B\cos 2\phi = 0$$

$$B\cos 2\phi = (A - C)\sin 2\phi$$

$$\cot 2\phi = \frac{A - C}{B} \qquad \text{Divide by } B\sin 2\phi$$

The preceding calculation proves the following theorem.

SIMPLIFYING THE GENERAL CONIC EQUATION

To eliminate the xy-term in the general conic equation

$$Ax^2 + Bxy + Cy^2 + Dx + Ey + F = 0$$

rotate the axes through the acute angle ϕ that satisfies

$$\cot 2\phi = \frac{A - C}{B}$$

EXAMPLE 3 | Eliminating the xy-Term

Use a rotation of axes to eliminate the xy-term in the equation

$$6\sqrt{3}x^2 + 6xy + 4\sqrt{3}y^2 = 21\sqrt{3}$$

Identify and sketch the curve.

SOLUTION To eliminate the xy-term, we rotate the axes through an angle ϕ that satisfies

$$\cot 2\phi = \frac{A - C}{B} = \frac{6\sqrt{3} - 4\sqrt{3}}{6} = \frac{\sqrt{3}}{3}$$

Thus $2\phi = 60°$ and hence $\phi = 30°$. With this value of ϕ, we get

$$x = X\left(\frac{\sqrt{3}}{2}\right) - Y\left(\frac{1}{2}\right) \qquad \text{Rotation of Axes Formulas}$$

$$y = X\left(\frac{1}{2}\right) + Y\left(\frac{\sqrt{3}}{2}\right) \qquad \cos\phi = \frac{\sqrt{3}}{2}, \sin\phi = \frac{1}{2}$$

ALTERNATE EXAMPLE 3

Use rotation of axes to eliminate the xy-term in the equation $7x^2 - 6\sqrt{3}xy + 13y^2 = 16$.

ANSWER

Rotation angle:

$$\cot 2\phi = \frac{1}{\sqrt{3}}$$

$$\phi = \frac{\pi}{6}$$

Transformation equations:

$$x = \frac{\sqrt{3}}{2}X - \frac{1}{2}Y$$

$$y = \frac{1}{2}X + \frac{\sqrt{3}}{2}Y$$

New equation:

$$4X^2 + 16Y^2 = 16$$

IN-CLASS MATERIALS

If the students are going to be moving on to linear algebra in the future, Exercise 37 is an excellent one to go over in class. It addresses the idea of linear transformations, which will be a major topic in that course.

Substituting these values for x and y into the given equation leads to

$$6\sqrt{3}\left(\frac{X\sqrt{3}}{2} - \frac{Y}{2}\right)^2 + 6\left(\frac{X\sqrt{3}}{2} - \frac{Y}{2}\right)\left(\frac{X}{2} + \frac{Y\sqrt{3}}{2}\right) + 4\sqrt{3}\left(\frac{X}{2} + \frac{Y\sqrt{3}}{2}\right)^2 = 21\sqrt{3}$$

Expanding and collecting like terms, we get

$$7\sqrt{3}X^2 + 3\sqrt{3}Y^2 = 21\sqrt{3}$$

$$\frac{X^2}{3} + \frac{Y^2}{7} = 1 \qquad \text{Divide by } 21\sqrt{3}$$

This is the equation of an ellipse in the XY-coordinate system. The foci lie on the Y-axis. Because $a^2 = 7$ and $b^2 = 3$, the length of the major axis is $2\sqrt{7}$, and the length of the minor axis is $2\sqrt{3}$. The ellipse is sketched in Figure 4.

✎. **NOW TRY EXERCISE 17** ◼

FIGURE 4
$6\sqrt{3}x^2 + 6xy + 4\sqrt{3}y^2 = 21\sqrt{3}$

In the preceding example we were able to determine ϕ without difficulty, since we remembered that $\cot 60° = \sqrt{3}/3$. In general, finding ϕ is not quite so easy. The next example illustrates how the following Half-Angle Formulas, which are valid for $0 < \phi < \pi/2$, are useful in determining ϕ (see Section 7.3).

$$\cos\phi = \sqrt{\frac{1 + \cos 2\phi}{2}} \qquad \sin\phi = \sqrt{\frac{1 - \cos 2\phi}{2}}$$

EXAMPLE 4 | Graphing a Rotated Conic

A conic has the equation

$$64x^2 + 96xy + 36y^2 - 15x + 20y - 25 = 0$$

(a) Use a rotation of axes to eliminate the xy-term.
(b) Identify and sketch the graph.
(c) Draw the graph using a graphing calculator.

SOLUTION

(a) To eliminate the xy-term, we rotate the axes through an angle ϕ that satisfies

$$\cot 2\phi = \frac{A - C}{B} = \frac{64 - 36}{96} = \frac{7}{24}$$

In Figure 5 we sketch a triangle with $\cot 2\phi = \frac{7}{24}$. We see that

$$\cos 2\phi = \frac{7}{25}$$

so, using the Half-Angle Formulas, we get

$$\cos\phi = \sqrt{\frac{1 + \frac{7}{25}}{2}} = \sqrt{\frac{16}{25}} = \frac{4}{5}$$

$$\sin\phi = \sqrt{\frac{1 - \frac{7}{25}}{2}} = \sqrt{\frac{9}{25}} = \frac{3}{5}$$

The Rotation of Axes Formulas then give

$$x = \tfrac{4}{5}X - \tfrac{3}{5}Y \qquad \text{and} \qquad y = \tfrac{3}{5}X + \tfrac{4}{5}Y$$

Substituting into the given equation, we have

$$64(\tfrac{4}{5}X - \tfrac{3}{5}Y)^2 + 96(\tfrac{4}{5}X - \tfrac{3}{5}Y)(\tfrac{3}{5}X + \tfrac{4}{5}Y)$$
$$+ 36(\tfrac{3}{5}X + \tfrac{4}{5}Y)^2 - 15(\tfrac{4}{5}X - \tfrac{3}{5}Y) + 20(\tfrac{3}{5}X + \tfrac{4}{5}Y) - 25 = 0$$

FIGURE 5

ALTERNATE EXAMPLE 4
A conic has the equation
$$7x^2 - 6\sqrt{3}xy + 13y^2 = 16.$$

(a) Identify and sketch the graph.
(b) Draw the graph using a graphing device.

ANSWERS

(a) As shown in Alternate Example 3, this is a conic rotated by 30° with equation $4X^2 + 16Y^2 = 16$. The sketch will be the ellipse

$$\frac{x^2}{4} + y^2 = 1 \text{ with axes rotated by } 30°.$$

(b)

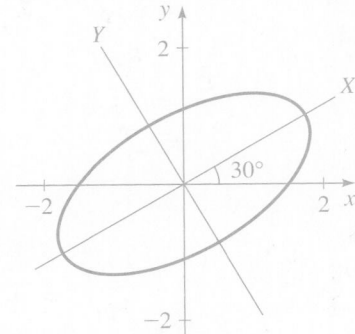

EXAMPLE
The rotated parabola $x^2 + 2xy + y^2 + 2x - 4y = 0$: $\cot(2\phi) = 0 \Rightarrow 2\phi = \dfrac{\pi}{2} \Rightarrow \phi = \pi$. Now we have $x = \sqrt{2}X - \sqrt{2}Y, y = \sqrt{2}X + \sqrt{2}Y$.

After substituting and a lot of algebra, we get $8x^2 - 2\sqrt{2}x - 6\sqrt{2}y = 0$. Completing the square,

$$y = \frac{2\sqrt{2}}{3}\left(x - \frac{\sqrt{2}}{8}\right)^2 - \frac{\sqrt{2}}{48} \approx 0.9(x - 0.2)^2 \text{ (for sketching purposes).}$$

Expanding and collecting like terms, we get

$$100X^2 + 25Y - 25 = 0$$

$$-4X^2 = Y - 1 \qquad \text{Simplify}$$

$$X^2 = -\tfrac{1}{4}(Y - 1) \qquad \text{Divide by 4}$$

(b) We recognize this as the equation of a parabola that opens along the negative Y-axis and has vertex $(0, 1)$ in XY-coordinates. Since $4p = -\tfrac{1}{4}$, we have $p = -\tfrac{1}{16}$, so the focus is $\left(0, \tfrac{15}{16}\right)$ and the directrix is $Y = \tfrac{17}{16}$. Using

$$\phi = \cos^{-1} \tfrac{4}{5} \approx 37°$$

we sketch the graph in Figure 6(a).

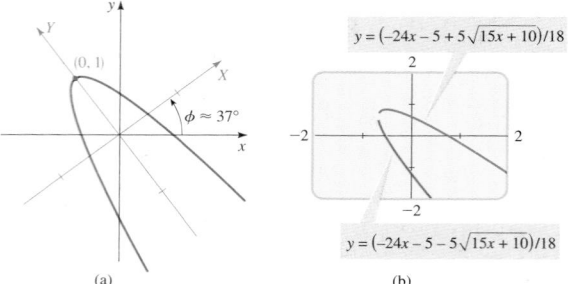

FIGURE 6

$64x^2 + 96xy + 36y^2 - 15x + 20y - 25 = 0$

(a)

(b)

(c) To draw the graph using a graphing calculator, we need to solve for y. The given equation is a quadratic equation in y, so we can use the Quadratic Formula to solve for y. Writing the equation in the form

$$36y^2 + (96x + 20)y + (64x^2 - 15x - 25) = 0$$

we get

$$y = \frac{-(96x + 20) \pm \sqrt{(96x + 20)^2 - 4(36)(64x^2 - 15x - 25)}}{2(36)} \qquad \text{Quadratic Formula}$$

$$= \frac{-(96x + 20) \pm \sqrt{6000x + 4000}}{72} \qquad \text{Expand}$$

$$= \frac{-96x - 20 \pm 20\sqrt{15x + 10}}{72} \qquad \text{Simplify}$$

$$= \frac{-24x - 5 \pm 5\sqrt{15x + 10}}{18} \qquad \text{Simplify}$$

To obtain the graph of the parabola, we graph the functions

$$y = \left(-24x - 5 + 5\sqrt{15x + 10}\right)/18 \qquad \text{and} \qquad y = \left(-24x - 5 - 5\sqrt{15x + 10}\right)/18$$

as shown in Figure 6(b).

. NOW TRY EXERCISE 23

▼ The Discriminant

In Examples 3 and 4 we were able to identify the type of conic by rotating the axes. The next theorem gives rules for identifying the type of conic directly from the equation, without rotating axes.

IDENTIFYING CONICS BY THE DISCRIMINANT

The graph of the equation

$$Ax^2 + Bxy + Cy^2 + Dx + Ey + F = 0$$

is either a conic or a degenerate conic. In the nondegenerate cases, the graph is

1. a parabola if $B^2 - 4AC = 0$

2. an ellipse if $B^2 - 4AC < 0$

3. a hyperbola if $B^2 - 4AC > 0$

The quantity $B^2 - 4AC$ is called the **discriminant** of the equation.

PROOF   If we rotate the axes through an angle ϕ, we get an equation of the form

$$A'X^2 + B'XY + C'Y^2 + D'X + E'Y + F' = 0$$

where A', B', C', . . . are given by the formulas on page 760. A straightforward calculation shows that

$$(B')^2 - 4A'C' = B^2 - 4AC$$

Thus the expression $B^2 - 4AC$ remains unchanged for any rotation. In particular, if we choose a rotation that eliminates the xy-term ($B' = 0$), we get

$$A'X^2 + C'Y^2 + D'X + E'Y + F' = 0$$

In this case, $B^2 - 4AC = -4A'C'$. So $B^2 - 4AC = 0$ if either A' or C' is zero; $B^2 - 4AC < 0$ if A' and C' have the same sign; and $B^2 - 4AC > 0$ if A' and C' have opposite signs. According to the box on page 754, these cases correspond to the graph of the last displayed equation being a parabola, an ellipse, or a hyperbola, respectively. ■

In the proof we indicated that the discriminant is unchanged by any rotation; for this reason, the discriminant is said to be **invariant** under rotation.

EXAMPLE 5 | Identifying a Conic by the Discriminant

A conic has the equation

$$3x^2 + 5xy - 2y^2 + x - y + 4 = 0$$

(a) Use the discriminant to identify the conic.

(b) Confirm your answer to part (a) by graphing the conic with a graphing calculator.

SOLUTION

(a) Since $A = 3$, $B = 5$, and $C = -2$, the discriminant is

$$B^2 - 4AC = 5^2 - 4(3)(-2) = 49 > 0$$

So the conic is a hyperbola.

DRILL QUESTION

Consider the equation
$3x^2 + 5xy - 2y^2 + x - y + 4 = 0$.
What shape is its graph?

Answer

It is a hyperbola.

(b) Using the Quadratic Formula, we solve for y to get

$$y = \frac{5x - 1 \pm \sqrt{49x^2 - 2x + 33}}{4}$$

We graph these functions in Figure 7. The graph confirms that this is a hyperbola.

$y = (5x - 1 + \sqrt{49x^2 - 2x + 33})/4$

FIGURE 7 $y = (5x - 1 - \sqrt{49x^2 - 2x + 33})/4$

NOW TRY EXERCISE 29

11.5 EXERCISES

CONCEPTS

1. Suppose the x- and y-axes are rotated through an acute angle ϕ to produce the new X- and Y-axes. A point P in the plane can be described by its xy-coordinates (x, y) or its XY-coordinates (X, Y). These coordinates are related by the following formulas.

$x = $ _____ $X = $ _____

$y = $ _____ $Y = $ _____

2. Consider the equation

$$Ax^2 + Bxy + Cy^2 + Dx + Ey + F = 0$$

(a) In general, the graph of this equation is a _____.

(b) To eliminate the xy-term from this equation, we rotate the axes through an angle ϕ that satisfies

$\cot 2\phi = $ _____.

(c) The discriminant of this equation is _____.

If the discriminant is 0, the graph is a _____;

if it is negative, the graph is _____; and

if it is positive, the graph is _____.

SKILLS

3–8 ■ Determine the XY-coordinates of the given point if the co-ordinate axes are rotated through the indicated angle.

3. $(1, 1)$, $\phi = 45°$ **4.** $(-2, 1)$, $\phi = 30°$

5. $(3, -\sqrt{3})$, $\phi = 60°$ **6.** $(2, 0)$, $\phi = 15°$

7. $(0, 2)$, $\phi = 55°$ **8.** $(\sqrt{2}, 4\sqrt{2})$, $\phi = 45°$

9–14 ■ Determine the equation of the given conic in XY-coordinates when the coordinate axes are rotated through the indicated angle.

9. $x^2 - 3y^2 = 4$, $\phi = 60°$

10. $y = (x - 1)^2$, $\phi = 45°$

11. $x^2 - y^2 = 2y$, $\phi = \cos^{-1}\frac{3}{5}$

12. $x^2 + 2y^2 = 16$, $\phi = \sin^{-1}\frac{3}{5}$

13. $x^2 + 2\sqrt{3}xy - y^2 = 4$, $\phi = 30°$

14. $xy = x + y$, $\phi = \pi/4$

15–28 ■ **(a)** Use the discriminant to determine whether the graph of the equation is a parabola, an ellipse, or a hyperbola. **(b)** Use a rotation of axes to eliminate the xy-term. **(c)** Sketch the graph.

15. $xy = 8$

16. $xy + 4 = 0$

17. $x^2 + 2\sqrt{3}xy - y^2 + 2 = 0$

18. $13x^2 + 6\sqrt{3}xy + 7y^2 = 16$

19. $11x^2 - 24xy + 4y^2 + 20 = 0$

20. $21x^2 + 10\sqrt{3}xy + 31y^2 = 144$

21. $\sqrt{3}x^2 + 3xy = 3$

22. $153x^2 + 192xy + 97y^2 = 225$

23. $x^2 + 2xy + y^2 + x - y = 0$

24. $25x^2 - 120xy + 144y^2 - 156x - 65y = 0$

25. $2\sqrt{3}x^2 - 6xy + \sqrt{3}x + 3y = 0$

26. $9x^2 - 24xy + 16y^2 = 100(x - y - 1)$

27. $52x^2 + 72xy + 73y^2 = 40x - 30y + 75$

28. $(7x + 24y)^2 = 600x - 175y + 25$

 29–32 ■ **(a)** Use the discriminant to identify the conic.
(b) Confirm your answer by graphing the conic using a graphing device.

29. $2x^2 - 4xy + 2y^2 - 5x - 5 = 0$

30. $x^2 - 2xy + 3y^2 = 8$

31. $6x^2 + 10xy + 3y^2 - 6y = 36$

32. $9x^2 - 6xy + y^2 + 6x - 2y = 0$

33. (a) Use rotation of axes to show that the following equation represents a hyperbola.

$$7x^2 + 48xy - 7y^2 - 200x - 150y + 600 = 0$$

   (b) Find the XY- and xy-coordinates of the center, vertices, and foci.
   (c) Find the equations of the asymptotes in XY- and xy-coordinates.

34. (a) Use rotation of axes to show that the following equation represents a parabola.

$$2\sqrt{2}(x + y)^2 = 7x + 9y$$

   (b) Find the XY- and xy-coordinates of the vertex and focus.
   (c) Find the equation of the directrix in XY- and xy-coordinates.

35. Solve the equations

$$x = X \cos \phi - Y \sin \phi$$
$$y = X \sin \phi + Y \cos \phi$$

for X and Y in terms of x and y. [*Hint:* To begin, multiply the first equation by $\cos \phi$ and the second by $\sin \phi$, and then add the two equations to solve for X.]

36. Show that the graph of the equation

$$\sqrt{x} + \sqrt{y} = 1$$

is part of a parabola by rotating the axes through an angle of 45°. [*Hint:* First convert the equation to one that does not involve radicals.]

DISCOVERY ■ DISCUSSION ■ WRITING

37. Matrix Form of Rotation of Axes Formulas

Let Z, Z', and R be the matrices

$$Z = \begin{bmatrix} x \\ y \end{bmatrix} \qquad Z' = \begin{bmatrix} X \\ Y \end{bmatrix}$$

$$R = \begin{bmatrix} \cos \phi & -\sin \phi \\ \sin \phi & \cos \phi \end{bmatrix}$$

Show that the Rotation of Axes Formulas can be written as

$$Z = RZ' \qquad \text{and} \qquad Z' = R^{-1}Z$$

38. Algebraic Invariants A quantity is invariant under rotation if it does not change when the axes are rotated. It was stated in the text that for the general equation of a conic the quantity $B^2 - 4AC$ is invariant under rotation.
   (a) Use the formulas for A', B', and C' on page 760 to prove that the quantity $B^2 - 4AC$ is invariant under rotation; that is, show that

$$B^2 - 4AC = B'^2 - 4A'C'$$

   (b) Prove that $A + C$ is invariant under rotation.
   (c) Is the quantity F invariant under rotation?

39. Geometric Invariants Do you expect that the distance between two points is invariant under rotation? Prove your answer by comparing the distance $d(P, Q)$ and $d(P', Q')$ where P' and Q' are the images of P and Q under a rotation of axes.

 DISCOVERY PROJECT   **Computer Graphics II**

In this project we investigate how matrices are used to rotate images on a computer screen. You can find the project at the book companion website: **www.stewartmath.com**

11.6 POLAR EQUATIONS OF CONICS

| A Unified Geometric Description of Conics ▶ Polar Equations of Conics

▼ A Unified Geometric Description of Conics

Earlier in this chapter, we defined a parabola in terms of a focus and directrix, but we defined the ellipse and hyperbola in terms of two foci. In this section we give a more unified treatment of all three types of conics in terms of a focus and directrix. If we place the focus at the origin, then a conic section has a simple polar equation. Moreover, in polar form, rotation of conics becomes a simple matter. Polar equations of ellipses are crucial in the derivation of Kepler's Laws (see page 754).

SUGGESTED TIME AND EMPHASIS

1 class, optional material

TEXT QUESTION

State a reason that we would want to express a conic in polar form.

Answer

Answers will vary. One reason is that they are easier to rotate when expressed in polar form.

EQUIVALENT DESCRIPTION OF CONICS

Let F be a fixed point (the **focus**), ℓ a fixed line (the **directrix**), and let e be a fixed positive number (the **eccentricity**). The set of all points P such that the ratio of the distance from P to F to the distance from P to ℓ is the constant e is a conic. That is, the set of all points P such that

$$\frac{d(P, F)}{d(P, \ell)} = e$$

is a conic. The conic is a parabola if $e = 1$, an ellipse if $e < 1$, or a hyperbola if $e > 1$.

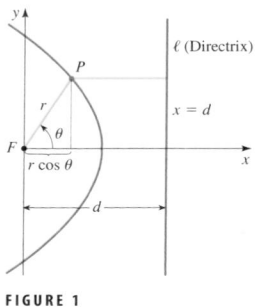

FIGURE 1

PROOF If $e = 1$, then $d(P, F) = d(P, \ell)$, and so the given condition becomes the definition of a parabola as given in Section 11.1.

Now, suppose $e \neq 1$. Let's place the focus F at the origin and the directrix parallel to the y-axis and d units to the right. In this case the directrix has equation $x = d$ and is perpendicular to the polar axis. If the point P has polar coordinates (r, θ), we see from Figure 1 that $d(P, F) = r$ and $d(P, \ell) = d - r \cos \theta$. Thus the condition $d(P, F)/d(P, \ell) = e$, or $d(P, F) = e \cdot d(P, \ell)$, becomes

$$r = e(d - r \cos \theta)$$

If we square both sides of this polar equation and convert to rectangular coordinates, we get

$$x^2 + y^2 = e^2(d - x)^2$$

$$(1 - e^2)x^2 + 2de^2x + y^2 = e^2d^2 \qquad \text{Expand and simplify}$$

$$\left(x + \frac{e^2d}{1 - e^2}\right)^2 + \frac{y^2}{1 - e^2} = \frac{e^2d^2}{(1 - e^2)^2} \qquad \begin{array}{l}\text{Divide by } 1 - e^2 \text{ and complete} \\ \text{the square}\end{array}$$

If $e < 1$, then dividing both sides of this equation by $e^2d^2/(1 - e^2)^2$ gives an equation of the form

$$\frac{(x - h)^2}{a^2} + \frac{y^2}{b^2} = 1$$

where

$$h = \frac{-e^2d}{1 - e^2} \qquad a^2 = \frac{e^2d^2}{(1 - e^2)^2} \qquad b^2 = \frac{e^2d^2}{1 - e^2}$$

This is the equation of an ellipse with center $(h, 0)$. In Section 11.2 we found that the foci of an ellipse are a distance c from the center, where $c^2 = a^2 - b^2$. In our case

$$c^2 = a^2 - b^2 = \frac{e^4d^2}{(1 - e^2)^2}$$

Thus $c = e^2d/(1 - e^2) = -h$, which confirms that the focus defined in the theorem (namely the origin) is the same as the focus defined in Section 11.2. It also follows that

$$e = \frac{c}{a}$$

If $e > 1$, a similar proof shows that the conic is a hyperbola with $e = c/a$, where $c^2 = a^2 + b^2$. ∎

IN-CLASS MATERIALS

Notice the advantages of working with conics in polar form. They are easier to rotate, for example. It is also easier to identify a conic as an ellipse, parabola, or hyperbola by inspection. After some practice, we can even look at such an equation and have a good idea of what the graph will look like, again by inspection.

▼ Polar Equations of Conics

In the proof we saw that the polar equation of the conic in Figure 1 is $r = e(d - r \cos \theta)$. Solving for r, we get

$$r = \frac{ed}{1 + e \cos \theta}$$

If the directrix is chosen to be to the *left* of the focus $(x = -d)$, then we get the equation $r = ed/(1 - e \cos \theta)$. If the directrix is *parallel* to the polar axis $(y = d$ or $y = -d)$, then we get $\sin \theta$ instead of $\cos \theta$ in the equation. These observations are summarized in the following box and in Figure 2.

POLAR EQUATIONS OF CONICS

A polar equation of the form

$$r = \frac{ed}{1 \pm e \cos \theta} \qquad \text{or} \qquad r = \frac{ed}{1 \pm e \sin \theta}$$

represents a conic with one focus at the origin and with eccentricity e. The conic is

1. a parabola if $e = 1$
2. an ellipse if $0 < e < 1$
3. a hyperbola if $e > 1$

   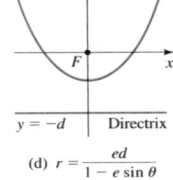

(a) $r = \dfrac{ed}{1 + e \cos \theta}$ (b) $r = \dfrac{ed}{1 - e \cos \theta}$ (c) $r = \dfrac{ed}{1 + e \sin \theta}$ (d) $r = \dfrac{ed}{1 - e \sin \theta}$

FIGURE 2 The form of the polar equation of a conic indicates the location of the directrix.

To graph the polar equation of a conic, we first determine the location of the directrix from the form of the equation. The four cases that arise are shown in Figure 2. (The figure shows only the parts of the graphs that are close to the focus at the origin. The shape of the rest of the graph depends on whether the equation represents a parabola, an ellipse, or a hyperbola.) The axis of a conic is perpendicular to the directrix—specifically we have the following:

1. For a parabola the axis of symmetry is perpendicular to the directrix.
2. For an ellipse the major axis is perpendicular to the directrix.
3. For a hyperbola the transverse axis is perpendicular to the directrix.

EXAMPLE 1 | Finding a Polar Equation for a Conic

Find a polar equation for the parabola that has its focus at the origin and whose directrix is the line $y = -6$.

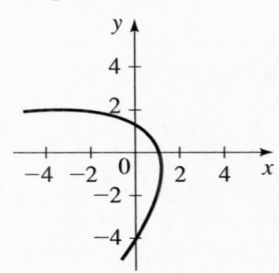
IN-CLASS MATERIALS

It is good to go through an example like Figure 6 with the class, having them use their calculators to vary the eccentricity e of a given conic section and see how it affects the graph. Most graphic calculators have a mode for graphing polar functions as well.

SOLUTION Using $e = 1$ and $d = 6$ and using part (d) of Figure 2, we see that the polar equation of the parabola is

$$r = \frac{6}{1 - \sin\theta}$$

✎ NOW TRY EXERCISE **3**　■

To graph a polar conic, it is helpful to plot the points for which $\theta = 0$, $\pi/2$, π, and $3\pi/2$. Using these points and a knowledge of the type of conic (which we obtain from the eccentricity), we can easily get a rough idea of the shape and location of the graph.

EXAMPLE 2 | Identifying and Sketching a Conic

A conic is given by the polar equation

$$r = \frac{10}{3 - 2\cos\theta}$$

(a) Show that the conic is an ellipse, and sketch the graph.

(b) Find the center of the ellipse and the lengths of the major and minor axes.

SOLUTION

(a) Dividing the numerator and denominator by 3, we have

$$r = \frac{\frac{10}{3}}{1 - \frac{2}{3}\cos\theta}$$

Since $e = \frac{2}{3} < 1$, the equation represents an ellipse. For a rough graph we plot the points for which $\theta = 0$, $\pi/2$, π, $3\pi/2$ (see Figure 3).

θ	r
0	10
$\frac{\pi}{2}$	$\frac{10}{3}$
π	2
$\frac{3\pi}{2}$	$\frac{10}{3}$

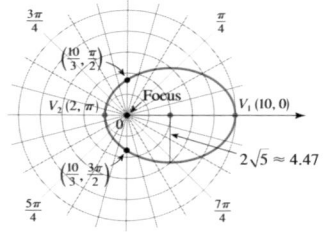

FIGURE 3 $r = \dfrac{10}{3 - 2\cos\theta}$

(b) Comparing the equation to those in Figure 2, we see that the major axis is horizontal. Thus the endpoints of the major axis are $V_1(10, 0)$ and $V_2(2, \pi)$. So the center of the ellipse is at $C(4, 0)$, the midpoint of V_1V_2.

The distance between the vertices V_1 and V_2 is 12; thus the length of the major axis is $2a = 12$, so $a = 6$. To determine the length of the minor axis, we need to find b. From page 766 we have $c = ae = 6\left(\frac{2}{3}\right) = 4$, so

$$b^2 = a^2 - c^2 = 6^2 - 4^2 = 20$$

Thus $b = \sqrt{20} = 2\sqrt{5} \approx 4.47$, and the length of the minor axis is $2b = 4\sqrt{5} \approx 8.94$.

✎ NOW TRY EXERCISES **17** AND **21**　■

ALTERNATE EXAMPLE 2

A conic is given by the polar equation:

$$r = \frac{25}{3 - 2\cos\theta}$$

Identify the conic. If the conic is an ellipse or a hyperbola, find the distances a and b. If the conic is a parabola, find the focus and the equation of the directrix.

ANSWER

Ellipse, 15, 11.18

EXAMPLE

Identifying and graphing a conic section from its polar equation:

$$r = \frac{6}{1 + 3\cos\left(\theta - \dfrac{\pi}{6}\right)}$$

is a hyperbola, rotated 30° from standard position, with eccentricity 3.

IN-CLASS MATERIALS

We have called a circle a degenerate ellipse. The text notes that when e is close to zero, the resultant ellipse is close to circular. Examine the equation of a conic when $e = 0$ to see how it is undefined for that value of e.

EXAMPLE 3 | Identifying and Sketching a Conic

A conic is given by the polar equation

$$r = \frac{12}{2 + 4 \sin \theta}$$

(a) Show that the conic is a hyperbola and sketch the graph.

(b) Find the center of the hyperbola and sketch the asymptotes.

SOLUTION

(a) Dividing the numerator and denominator by 2, we have

$$r = \frac{6}{1 + 2 \sin \theta}$$

Since $e = 2 > 1$, the equation represents a hyperbola. For a rough graph we plot the points for which $\theta = 0, \pi/2, \pi, 3\pi/2$ (see Figure 4).

(b) Comparing the equation to those in Figure 2, we see that the transverse axis is vertical. Thus the endpoints of the transverse axis (the vertices of the hyperbola) are $V_1(2, \pi/2)$ and $V_2(-6, 3\pi/2) = V_2(6, \pi/2)$. So the center of the hyperbola is $C(4, \pi/2)$, the midpoint of V_1V_2.

To sketch the asymptotes, we need to find a and b. The distance between V_1 and V_2 is 4; thus the length of the transverse axis is $2a = 4$, so $a = 2$. To find b, we first find c. From page 766 we have $c = ae = 2 \cdot 2 = 4$, so

$$b^2 = c^2 - a^2 = 4^2 - 2^2 = 12$$

Thus $b = \sqrt{12} = 2\sqrt{3} \approx 3.46$. Knowing a and b allows us to sketch the central box, from which we obtain the asymptotes shown in Figure 4.

θ	r
0	6
$\frac{\pi}{2}$	2
π	6
$\frac{3\pi}{2}$	-6

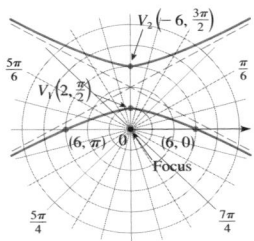

FIGURE 4 $r = \dfrac{12}{2 + 4 \sin \theta}$

 NOW TRY EXERCISE **25**

When we rotate conic sections, it is much more convenient to use polar equations than Cartesian equations. We use the fact that the graph of $r = f(\theta - \alpha)$ is the graph of $r = f(\theta)$ rotated counterclockwise about the origin through an angle α (see Exercise 61 in Section 8.2).

EXAMPLE 4 | Rotating an Ellipse

Suppose the ellipse of Example 2 is rotated through an angle $\pi/4$ about the origin. Find a polar equation for the resulting ellipse, and draw its graph.

ALTERNATE EXAMPLE 3
A conic is given by the polar equation:
$$r = \frac{36}{4 + 8 \sin \theta}$$
Identify the conic. If the conic is an ellipse or a hyperbola, find the distances a and b. If the conic is a parabola, find the focus and the equation of the directrix.

ANSWER
Hyperbola, 3, 5.20

EXAMPLE
Identifying and graphing a conic section from its polar equation:
$$r = \frac{6}{6 + 3 \cos\left(\theta - \dfrac{\pi}{6}\right)}$$
$$= \frac{1}{1 + \dfrac{1}{2}\cos\left(\theta - \dfrac{\pi}{6}\right)}$$
is an ellipse.

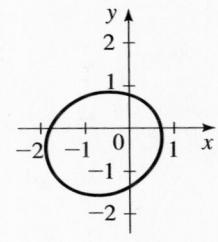

ALTERNATE EXAMPLE 4
Suppose the ellipse
$$r = \frac{8}{4 - 3 \cos \theta}$$ is rotated
through the angle $\dfrac{\pi}{4}$ about the origin. Find a polar equation for the resulting ellipse.

ANSWER
$$r = \frac{8}{4 - 3 \cos\left(\theta - \dfrac{\pi}{4}\right)}$$

DRILL QUESTION

Identify the conic:

$$r = \frac{6}{1 \pm 3 \cos \theta}$$

Answer

It is a hyperbola.

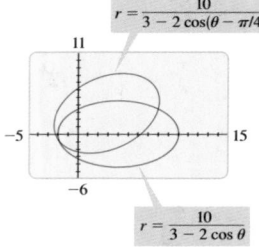

$$r = \frac{10}{3 - 2\cos(\theta - \pi/4)}$$

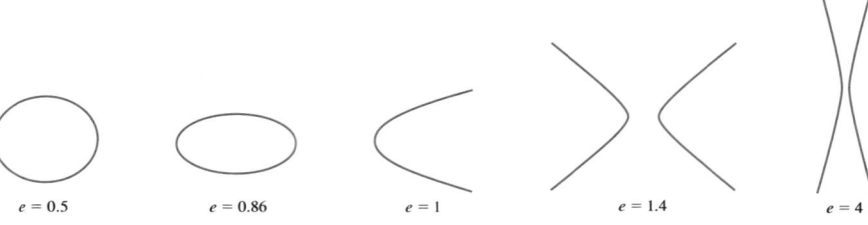

$$r = \frac{10}{3 - 2\cos\theta}$$

FIGURE 5

SOLUTION We get the equation of the rotated ellipse by replacing θ with $\theta - \pi/4$ in the equation given in Example 2. So the new equation is

$$r = \frac{10}{3 - 2\cos(\theta - \pi/4)}$$

We use this equation to graph the rotated ellipse in Figure 5. Notice that the ellipse has been rotated about the focus at the origin.

✎ NOW TRY EXERCISE **37**

In Figure 6 we use a computer to sketch a number of conics to demonstrate the effect of varying the eccentricity e. Notice that when e is close to 0, the ellipse is nearly circular, and it becomes more elongated as e increases. When $e = 1$, of course, the conic is a parabola. As e increases beyond 1, the conic is an ever steeper hyperbola.

$e = 0.5$ $e = 0.86$ $e = 1$ $e = 1.4$ $e = 4$

FIGURE 6

11.6 EXERCISES

CONCEPTS

1. All conics can be described geometrically using a fixed point F called the _____ and a fixed line ℓ called the _____. For a fixed positive number e the set of all points P satisfying

$$\boxed{} = e$$

is a _____. If $e = 1$, the conic is a _____; if $e < 1$, the conic is a _____; and if $e > 1$, the conic is a _____. The number e is called the _____ of the conic.

2. The polar equation of a conic with eccentricity e has one of the following forms:

$$r = \text{_____} \qquad \text{or} \qquad r = \text{_____}$$

SKILLS

3–10 ■ Write a polar equation of a conic that has its focus at the origin and satisfies the given conditions.

3. Ellipse, eccentricity $\frac{2}{3}$, directrix $x = 3$

4. Hyperbola, eccentricity $\frac{4}{3}$, directrix $x = -3$

5. Parabola, directrix $y = 2$

6. Ellipse, eccentricity $\frac{1}{2}$, directrix $y = -4$

7. Hyperbola, eccentricity 4, directrix $r = 5 \sec \theta$

8. Ellipse, eccentricity 0.6, directrix $r = 2 \csc \theta$

9. Parabola, vertex at $(5, \pi/2)$

10. Ellipse, eccentricity 0.4, vertex at $(2, 0)$

11–16 ■ Match the polar equations with the graphs labeled I–VI. Give reasons for your answer.

11. $r = \dfrac{6}{1 + \cos \theta}$

12. $r = \dfrac{2}{2 - \cos \theta}$

13. $r = \dfrac{3}{1 - 2 \sin \theta}$

14. $r = \dfrac{5}{3 - 3 \sin \theta}$

15. $r = \dfrac{12}{3 + 2 \sin \theta}$

16. $r = \dfrac{12}{2 + 3 \cos \theta}$

I

II

III

IV

V

VI
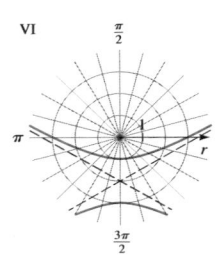

17–20 ■ A polar equation of a conic is given. **(a)** Show that the conic is a parabola and sketch its graph. **(b)** Find the vertex and directrix and indicate them on the graph.

17. $r = \dfrac{4}{1 - \sin \theta}$

18. $r = \dfrac{3}{2 + 2 \sin \theta}$

19. $r = \dfrac{5}{3 + 3 \cos \theta}$

20. $r = \dfrac{2}{5 - 5 \cos \theta}$

21–24 ■ A polar equation of a conic is given. **(a)** Show that the conic is an ellipse, and sketch its graph. **(b)** Find the vertices and directrix, and indicate them on the graph. **(c)** Find the center of the ellipse and the lengths of the major and minor axes.

21. $r = \dfrac{4}{2 - \cos \theta}$

22. $r = \dfrac{6}{3 - 2 \sin \theta}$

23. $r = \dfrac{12}{4 + 3 \sin \theta}$

24. $r = \dfrac{18}{4 + 3 \cos \theta}$

25–28 ■ A polar equation of a conic is given. **(a)** Show that the conic is a hyperbola, and sketch its graph. **(b)** Find the vertices and directrix, and indicate them on the graph. **(c)** Find the center of the hyperbola, and sketch the asymptotes.

25. $r = \dfrac{8}{1 + 2 \cos \theta}$

26. $r = \dfrac{10}{1 - 4 \sin \theta}$

27. $r = \dfrac{20}{2 - 3 \sin \theta}$

28. $r = \dfrac{6}{2 + 7 \cos \theta}$

29–36 ■ **(a)** Find the eccentricity and identify the conic. **(b)** Sketch the conic and label the vertices.

29. $r = \dfrac{4}{1 + 3 \cos \theta}$

30. $r = \dfrac{8}{3 + 3 \cos \theta}$

31. $r = \dfrac{2}{1 - \cos \theta}$

32. $r = \dfrac{10}{3 - 2 \sin \theta}$

33. $r = \dfrac{6}{2 + \sin \theta}$

34. $r = \dfrac{5}{2 - 3 \sin \theta}$

35. $r = \dfrac{7}{2 - 5 \sin \theta}$

36. $r = \dfrac{8}{3 + \cos \theta}$

37–40 ■ A polar equation of a conic is given. (a) Find the eccentricity and the directrix of the conic. (b) If this conic is rotated about the origin through the given angle θ, write the resulting equation. (c) Draw graphs of the original conic and the rotated conic on the same screen.

37. $r = \dfrac{1}{4 - 3\cos\theta}$; $\theta = \dfrac{\pi}{3}$

38. $r = \dfrac{2}{5 - 3\sin\theta}$; $\theta = \dfrac{2\pi}{3}$

39. $r = \dfrac{2}{1 + \sin\theta}$; $\theta = -\dfrac{\pi}{4}$

40. $r = \dfrac{9}{2 + 2\cos\theta}$; $\theta = -\dfrac{5\pi}{6}$

41. Graph the conics $r = e/(1 - e\cos\theta)$ with $e = 0.4, 0.6, 0.8$, and 1.0 on a common screen. How does the value of e affect the shape of the curve?

42. (a) Graph the conics

$$r = \frac{ed}{(1 + e\sin\theta)}$$

for $e = 1$ and various values of d. How does the value of d affect the shape of the conic?

(b) Graph these conics for $d = 1$ and various values of e. How does the value of e affect the shape of the conic?

APPLICATIONS

43. Orbit of the Earth   The polar equation of an ellipse can be expressed in terms of its eccentricity e and the length a of its major axis.

(a) Show that the polar equation of an ellipse with directrix $x = -d$ can be written in the form

$$r = \frac{a(1 - e^2)}{1 - e\cos\theta}$$

[*Hint:* Use the relation $a^2 = e^2 d^2/(1 - e^2)^2$ given in the proof on page 766.]

(b) Find an approximate polar equation for the elliptical orbit of the earth around the sun (at one focus) given that the eccentricity is about 0.017 and the length of the major axis is about 2.99×10^8 km.

44. Perihelion and Aphelion   The planets move around the sun in elliptical orbits with the sun at one focus. The positions of a planet that are closest to, and farthest from, the sun are called its **perihelion** and **aphelion**, respectively.

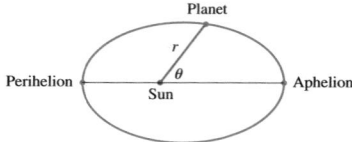

(a) Use Exercise 43(a) to show that the perihelion distance from a planet to the sun is $a(1 - e)$ and the aphelion distance is $a(1 + e)$.

(b) Use the data of Exercise 43(b) to find the distances from the earth to the sun at perihelion and at aphelion.

45. Orbit of Pluto   The distance from Pluto to the sun is 4.43×10^9 km at perihelion and 7.37×10^9 km at aphelion. Use Exercise 44 to find the eccentricity of Pluto's orbit.

DISCOVERY ■ DISCUSSION ■ WRITING

46. Distance to a Focus   When we found polar equations for the conics, we placed one focus at the pole. It's easy to find the distance from that focus to any point on the conic. Explain how the polar equation gives us this distance.

47. Polar Equations of Orbits   When a satellite orbits the earth, its path is an ellipse with one focus at the center of the earth. Why do scientists use polar (rather than rectangular) coordinates to track the position of satellites?   [*Hint:* Your answer to Exercise 46 is relevant here.]

CHAPTER 11 | REVIEW

■ CONCEPT CHECK

1. (a) Give the geometric definition of a parabola. What are the focus and directrix of the parabola?

(b) Sketch the parabola $x^2 = 4py$ for the case $p > 0$. Identify on your diagram the vertex, focus, and directrix. What happens if $p < 0$?

(c) Sketch the parabola $y^2 = 4px$, together with its vertex, focus, and directrix, for the case $p > 0$. What happens if $p < 0$?

2. (a) Give the geometric definition of an ellipse. What are the foci of the ellipse?

(b) For the ellipse with equation

$$\frac{x^2}{a^2} + \frac{y^2}{b^2} = 1$$

where $a > b > 0$, what are the coordinates of the vertices and the foci? What are the major and minor axes? Illustrate with a graph.

(c) Give an expression for the eccentricity of the ellipse in part (b).

(d) State the equation of an ellipse with foci on the y-axis.

3. (a) Give the geometric definition of a hyperbola. What are the foci of the hyperbola?
   (b) For the hyperbola with equation

   $$\frac{x^2}{a^2} - \frac{y^2}{b^2} = 1$$

   what are the coordinates of the vertices and foci? What are the equations of the asymptotes? What is the transverse axis? Illustrate with a graph.
   (c) State the equation of a hyperbola with foci on the y-axis.
   (d) What steps would you take to sketch a hyperbola with a given equation?

4. Suppose h and k are positive numbers. What is the effect on the graph of an equation in x and y if
   (a) x is replaced by $x - h$? By $x + h$?
   (b) y is replaced by $y - k$? By $y + k$?

5. How can you tell whether the following nondegenerate conic is a parabola, an ellipse, or a hyperbola?

   $$Ax^2 + Cy^2 + Dx + Ey + F = 0$$

6. Suppose the x- and y-axes are rotated through an acute angle ϕ to produce the X- and Y-axes. Write equations that relate the coordinates (x, y) and (X, Y) of a point in the xy-plane and XY-plane, respectively.

7. (a) How do you eliminate the xy-term in this equation?

   $$Ax^2 + Bxy + Cy^2 + Dx + Ey + F = 0$$

   (b) What is the discriminant of the conic in part (a)? How can you use the discriminant to determine whether the conic is a parabola, an ellipse, or a hyperbola?

8. (a) Write polar equations that represent a conic with eccentricity e.
   (b) For what values of e is the conic an ellipse? A hyperbola? A parabola?

■ EXERCISES

1–8 ■ Find the vertex, focus, and directrix of the parabola, and sketch the graph.

1. $y^2 = 4x$
2. $x = \frac{1}{12}y^2$
3. $x^2 + 8y = 0$
4. $2x - y^2 = 0$
5. $x - y^2 + 4y - 2 = 0$
6. $2x^2 + 6x + 5y + 10 = 0$
7. $\frac{1}{2}x^2 + 2x = 2y + 4$
8. $x^2 = 3(x + y)$

9–16 ■ Find the center, vertices, foci, and the lengths of the major and minor axes of the ellipse, and sketch the graph.

9. $\dfrac{x^2}{9} + \dfrac{y^2}{25} = 1$
10. $\dfrac{x^2}{49} + \dfrac{y^2}{9} = 1$
11. $x^2 + 4y^2 = 16$
12. $9x^2 + 4y^2 = 1$
13. $\dfrac{(x-3)^2}{9} + \dfrac{y^2}{16} = 1$
14. $\dfrac{(x-2)^2}{25} + \dfrac{(y+3)^2}{16} = 1$
15. $4x^2 + 9y^2 = 36y$
16. $2x^2 + y^2 = 2 + 4(x - y)$

17–24 ■ Find the center, vertices, foci, and asymptotes of the hyperbola, and sketch the graph.

17. $-\dfrac{x^2}{9} + \dfrac{y^2}{16} = 1$
18. $\dfrac{x^2}{49} - \dfrac{y^2}{32} = 1$
19. $x^2 - 2y^2 = 16$
20. $x^2 - 4y^2 + 16 = 0$
21. $\dfrac{(x+4)^2}{16} - \dfrac{y^2}{16} = 1$
22. $\dfrac{(x-2)^2}{8} - \dfrac{(y+2)^2}{8} = 1$
23. $9y^2 + 18y = x^2 + 6x + 18$
24. $y^2 = x^2 + 6y$

25–30 ■ Find an equation for the conic whose graph is shown.

25.

26.

27.

28.

29.

30.
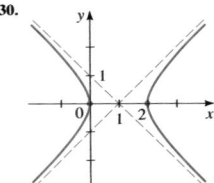

31–42 ■ Determine the type of curve represented by the equation. Find the foci and vertices (if any), and sketch the graph.

31. $\dfrac{x^2}{12} + y = 1$

32. $\dfrac{x^2}{12} + \dfrac{y^2}{144} = \dfrac{y}{12}$

33. $x^2 - y^2 + 144 = 0$

34. $x^2 + 6x = 9y^2$

35. $4x^2 + y^2 = 8(x + y)$

36. $3x^2 - 6(x + y) = 10$

37. $x = y^2 - 16y$

38. $2x^2 + 4 = 4x + y^2$

39. $2x^2 - 12x + y^2 + 6y + 26 = 0$

40. $36x^2 - 4y^2 - 36x - 8y = 31$

41. $9x^2 + 8y^2 - 15x + 8y + 27 = 0$

42. $x^2 + 4y^2 = 4x + 8$

43–50 ■ Find an equation for the conic section with the given properties.

43. The parabola with focus $F(0, 1)$ and directrix $y = -1$

44. The ellipse with center $C(0, 4)$, foci $F_1(0, 0)$ and $F_2(0, 8)$, and major axis of length 10

45. The hyperbola with vertices $V(0, \pm 2)$ and asymptotes $y = \pm\frac{1}{2}x$

46. The hyperbola with center $C(2, 4)$, foci $F_1(2, 1)$ and $F_2(2, 7)$, and vertices $V_1(2, 6)$ and $V_2(2, 2)$

47. The ellipse with foci $F_1(1, 1)$ and $F_2(1, 3)$, and with one vertex on the x-axis

48. The parabola with vertex $V(5, 5)$ and directrix the y-axis

49. The ellipse with vertices $V_1(7, 12)$ and $V_2(7, -8)$, and passing through the point $P(1, 8)$

50. The parabola with vertex $V(-1, 0)$ and horizontal axis of symmetry, and crossing the y-axis at $y = 2$

51. The path of the earth around the sun is an ellipse with the sun at one focus. The ellipse has major axis 186,000,000 mi and eccentricity 0.017. Find the distance between the earth and the sun when the earth is **(a)** closest to the sun and **(b)** farthest from the sun.

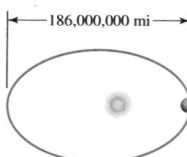

52. A ship is located 40 mi from a straight shoreline. LORAN stations A and B are located on the shoreline, 300 mi apart. From the LORAN signals, the captain determines that his ship is

80 mi closer to A than to B. Find the location of the ship. (Place A and B on the y-axis with the x-axis halfway between them. Find the x- and y-coordinates of the ship.)

53. (a) Draw graphs of the following family of ellipses for $k = 1, 2, 4,$ and 8.

$$\frac{x^2}{16 + k^2} + \frac{y^2}{k^2} = 1$$

(b) Prove that all the ellipses in part (a) have the same foci.

54. (a) Draw graphs of the following family of parabolas for $k = \frac{1}{2}, 1, 2,$ and 4.

$$y = kx^2$$

(b) Find the foci of the parabolas in part (a).

(c) How does the location of the focus change as k increases?

55–58 ■ An equation of a conic is given. **(a)** Use the discriminant to determine whether the graph of the equation is a parabola, an ellipse, or a hyperbola. **(b)** Use a rotation of axes to eliminate the xy-term. **(c)** Sketch the graph.

55. $x^2 + 4xy + y^2 = 1$

56. $5x^2 - 6xy + 5y^2 - 8x + 8y - 8 = 0$

57. $7x^2 - 6\sqrt{3}xy + 13y^2 - 4\sqrt{3}x - 4y = 0$

58. $9x^2 + 24xy + 16y^2 = 25$

59–62 ■ Use a graphing device to graph the conic. Identify the type of conic from the graph.

59. $5x^2 + 3y^2 = 60$ **60.** $9x^2 - 12y^2 + 36 = 0$

61. $6x + y^2 - 12y = 30$ **62.** $52x^2 - 72xy + 73y^2 = 100$

63–66 ■ A polar equation of a conic is given. **(a)** Find the eccentricity and identify the conic. **(b)** Sketch the conic and label the vertices.

63. $r = \dfrac{1}{1 - \cos\theta}$ **64.** $r = \dfrac{2}{3 + 2\sin\theta}$

65. $r = \dfrac{4}{1 + 2\sin\theta}$ **66.** $r = \dfrac{12}{1 - 4\cos\theta}$

1. Find the focus and directrix of the parabola $x^2 = -12y$, and sketch its graph.

2. Find the vertices, foci, and the lengths of the major and minor axes for the ellipse $\dfrac{x^2}{16} + \dfrac{y^2}{4} = 1$. Then sketch its graph.

3. Find the vertices, foci, and asymptotes of the hyperbola $\dfrac{y^2}{9} - \dfrac{x^2}{16} = 1$. Then sketch its graph.

4–6 ■ Find an equation for the conic whose graph is shown.

4.

5.

6.

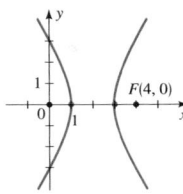

7–9 ■ Sketch the graph of the equation.

7. $16x^2 + 36y^2 - 96x + 36y + 9 = 0$

8. $9x^2 - 8y^2 + 36x + 64y = 164$

9. $2x + y^2 + 8y + 8 = 0$

10. Find an equation for the hyperbola with foci $(0, \pm 5)$ and with asymptotes $y = \pm\frac{3}{4}x$.

11. Find an equation for the parabola with focus $(2, 4)$ and directrix the x-axis.

12. A parabolic reflector for a car headlight forms a bowl shape that is 6 in. wide at its opening and 3 in. deep, as shown in the figure at the left. How far from the vertex should the filament of the bulb be placed if it is to be located at the focus?

13. **(a)** Use the discriminant to determine whether the graph of this equation is a parabola, an ellipse, or a hyperbola:

$$5x^2 + 4xy + 2y^2 = 18$$

   (b) Use rotation of axes to eliminate the xy-term in the equation.

   (c) Sketch the graph of the equation.

   (d) Find the coordinates of the vertices of this conic (in the xy-coordinate system).

14. **(a)** Find the polar equation of the conic that has a focus at the origin, eccentricity $e = \frac{1}{2}$, and directrix $x = 2$. Sketch the graph.

   (b) What type of conic is represented by the following equation? Sketch its graph.

$$r = \frac{3}{2 - \sin\theta}$$

775

Many buildings employ conic sections in their design. Architects have various reasons for using these curves, ranging from structural stability to simple beauty. But how can a huge parabola, ellipse, or hyperbola be accurately constructed in concrete and steel? In this *Focus on Modeling,* we will see how the geometric properties of the conics can be used to construct these shapes.

▼ Conics in Buildings

In ancient times architecture was part of mathematics, so architects had to be mathematicians. Many of the structures they built—pyramids, temples, amphitheaters, and irrigation projects—still stand. In modern times architects employ even more sophisticated mathematical principles. The photographs below show some structures that employ conic sections in their design.

Roman Amphitheater in Alexandria, Egypt (circle)
© Nick Wheeler/CORBIS

Ceiling of Statuary Hall in the U.S. Capitol (ellipse)
Architect of the Capitol

Roof of the Skydome in Toronto, Canada (parabola)
Walter Schmid/© Stone/Getty Images

Roof of Washington Dulles Airport (hyperbola and parabola)
© Richard T. Nowitz/CORBIS

McDonnell Planetarium, St. Louis, MO (hyperbola)
VisionsofAmerica/Joe Sohm

Attic in La Pedrera, Barcelona, Spain (parabola)
© O. Alamany & E. Vincens/CORBIS

Architects have different reasons for using conics in their designs. For example, the Spanish architect Antoni Gaudí used parabolas in the attic of La Pedrera (see photo above). He reasoned that since a rope suspended between two points with an equally distributed load (as in a suspension bridge) has the shape of a parabola, an inverted parabola would provide the best support for a flat roof.

▼ Constructing Conics

The equations of the conics are helpful in manufacturing small objects, because a computer-controlled cutting tool can accurately trace a curve given by an equation. But in a building project, how can we construct a portion of a parabola, ellipse, or hyperbola that spans the ceiling or walls of a building? The geometric properties of the conics provide practical ways of constructing them. For example, if you were building a circular tower, you would choose a center point, then make sure that the walls of the tower were a fixed

776

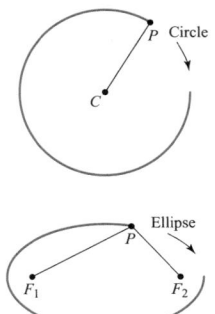

FIGURE 1   Constructing a circle and an ellipse

distance from that point. Elliptical walls can be constructed using a string anchored at two points, as shown in Figure 1.

To construct a parabola, we can use the apparatus shown in Figure 2. A piece of string of length a is anchored at F and A. The T-square, also of length a, slides along the straight bar L. A pencil at P holds the string taut against the T-square. As the T-square slides to the right the pencil traces out a curve.

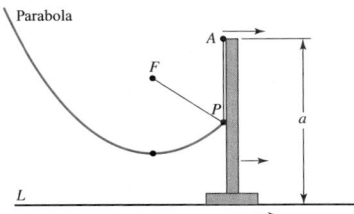

FIGURE 2   Constructing a parabola

From the figure we see that

$$d(F, P) + d(P, A) = a \qquad \text{The string is of length } a$$

$$d(L, P) + d(P, A) = a \qquad \text{The T-square is of length } a$$

It follows that $d(F, P) + d(P, A) = d(L, P) + d(P, A)$. Subtracting $d(P, A)$ from each side, we get

$$d(F, P) = d(L, P)$$

The last equation says that the distance from F to P is equal to the distance from P to the line L. Thus, the curve is a parabola with focus F and directrix L.

In building projects it is easier to construct a straight line than a curve. So in some buildings, such as in the Kobe Tower (see Problem 4), a curved surface is produced by using many straight lines. We can also produce a curve using straight lines, such as the parabola shown in Figure 3.

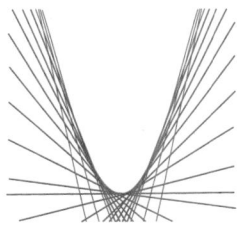

FIGURE 3   Tangent lines to a parabola

Each line is **tangent** to the parabola; that is, the line meets the parabola at exactly one point and does not cross the parabola. The line tangent to the parabola $y = x^2$ at the point (a, a^2) is

$$y = 2ax - a^2$$

You are asked to show this in Problem 6. The parabola is called the **envelope** of all such lines.

PROBLEMS

1. Conics in Architecture   The photographs on page 776 show six examples of buildings that contain conic sections. Search the Internet to find other examples of structures that employ parabolas, ellipses, or hyperbolas in their design. Find at least one example for each type of conic.

2. Constructing a Hyperbola   In this problem we construct a hyperbola. The wooden bar in the figure can pivot at F_1. A string that is shorter than the bar is anchored at F_2 and at A, the other end of the bar. A pencil at P holds the string taut against the bar as it moves counterclockwise around F_1.

(a) Show that the curve traced out by the pencil is one branch of a hyperbola with foci at F_1 and F_2.

(b) How should the apparatus be reconfigured to draw the other branch of the hyperbola?

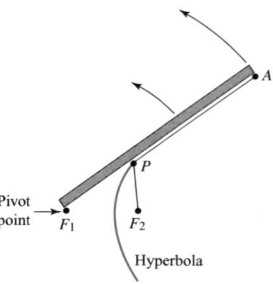

3. A Parabola in a Rectangle   The following method can be used to construct a parabola that fits in a given rectangle. The parabola will be approximated by many short line segments.

First, draw a rectangle. Divide the rectangle in half by a vertical line segment, and label the top endpoint V. Next, divide the length and width of each half rectangle into an equal number of parts to form grid lines, as shown in the figure below. Draw lines from V to the endpoints of horizontal grid line 1, and mark the points where these lines cross the vertical grid lines labeled 1. Next, draw lines from V to the endpoints of horizontal grid line 2, and mark the points where these lines cross the vertical grid lines labeled 2. Continue in this way until you have used all the horizontal grid lines. Now use line segments to connect the points you have marked to obtain an approximation to the desired parabola. Apply this procedure to draw a parabola that fits into a 6 ft by 10 ft rectangle on a lawn.

  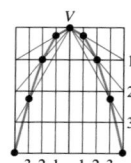

4. Hyperbolas from Straight Lines   In this problem we construct hyperbolic shapes using straight lines. Punch equally spaced holes into the edges of two large plastic lids. Connect corresponding holes with strings of equal lengths as shown in the figure on the next page. Holding the strings taut, twist one lid against the other. An imaginary surface passing through the strings has hyperbolic cross sections. (An architectural example of this is the

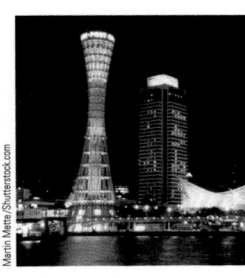

Kobe Tower in Japan, shown in the photograph.) What happens to the vertices of the hyperbolic cross sections as the lids are twisted more?

5. Tangent Lines to a Parabola In this problem we show that the line tangent to the parabola $y = x^2$ at the point (a, a^2) has the equation $y = 2ax - a^2$.

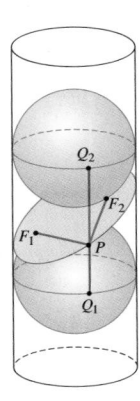

$y = x^2$

a^2

Tangent line

0   a x

(a) Let m be the slope of the tangent line at (a, a^2). Show that the equation of the tangent line is $y - a^2 = m(x - a)$.

(b) Use the fact that the tangent line intersects the parabola at only one point to show that (a, a^2) is the only solution of the system.

$$\begin{cases} y - a^2 = m(x - a) \\ y = x^2 \end{cases}$$

(c) Eliminate y from the system in part (b) to get a quadratic equation in x. Show that the discriminant of this quadratic is $(m - 2a)^2$. Since the system in part (b) has exactly one solution, the discriminant must equal 0. Find m.

(d) Substitute the value for m you found in part (c) into the equation in part (a), and simpify to get the equation of the tangent line.

6. A Cut Cylinder In this problem we prove that when a cylinder is cut by a plane, an ellipse is formed. An architectural example of this is the Tycho Brahe Planetarium in Copenhagen (see the photograph). In the figure, a cylinder is cut by a plane, resulting in the red curve. Two spheres with the same radius as the cylinder slide inside the cylinder so that they just touch the plane at F_1 and F_2. Choose an arbitrary point P on the curve, and let Q_1 and Q_2 be the two points on the cylinder where a vertical line through P touches the "equator" of each sphere.

Q_2

F_2

F_1 P

Q_1

(a) Show that $PF_1 = PQ_1$ and $PF_2 = PQ_2$. [*Hint:* Use the fact that all tangents to a sphere from a given point outside the sphere are of the same length.]

(b) Explain why $PQ_1 + PQ_2$ is the same for all points P on the curve.

(c) Show that $PF_1 + PF_2$ is the same for all points P on the curve.

(d) Conclude that the curve is an ellipse with foci F_1 and F_2.

1. Consider the following system of equations.

$$\begin{cases} x^2 + y^2 = 4y \\ x^2 - 2y = 0 \end{cases}$$

(a) Is the system linear or nonlinear? Explain.
(b) Find all solutions of the system.
(c) The graph of each equation is a conic section. Name the type of conic section in each case.
(d) Graph both equations on the same set of axes.
(e) On your graph, shade the region that corresponds to the solution of the system of inequalities.

$$\begin{cases} x^2 + y^2 \le 4y \\ x^2 - 2y \le 0 \end{cases}$$

2. Find the complete solution of each linear system, or show that no solution exists.

(a) $\begin{cases} x + y - z = 2 \\ 2x + 3y - z = 5 \\ 3x + 5y + 2z = 11 \end{cases}$ (b) $\begin{cases} y - z = 2 \\ x + 2y - 3z = 3 \\ 3x + 5y - 8z = 7 \end{cases}$

3. Xavier, Yolanda, and Zacharay go fishing. Yolanda catches as many fish as Xavier and Zachary put together. Zachary catches 2 more fish than Xavier. The total catch for all three people is 20 fish. How many did each person catch?

4. Let $A = \begin{bmatrix} 1 & 5 \\ 2 & 0 \end{bmatrix}$, $B = \begin{bmatrix} -2 & 1 & 0 \\ -\frac{1}{2} & 0 & 1 \end{bmatrix}$, $C = \begin{bmatrix} 1 & 0 & 1 \\ 0 & 2 & 1 \\ -1 & 0 & 0 \end{bmatrix}$, and $D = \begin{bmatrix} 1 & 4 & 3 \\ 1 & 6 & 5 \\ 0 & 1 & 1 \end{bmatrix}$.

(a) Calculate each of the following, or explain why the calculation can't be done.

$$A + B, \quad C - D, \quad AB, \quad CB, \quad BD, \quad \det(B), \quad \det(C), \quad \det(D)$$

(b) Based on the values you calculated for $\det(C)$ and $\det(D)$, which matrix, C or D, has an inverse? Find the inverse of the invertible one.

5. Consider the following system of equations.

$$\begin{cases} 5x - 3y = 5 \\ 6x - 4y = 0 \end{cases}$$

(a) Write a matrix equation of the form $AX = B$ that is equivalent to this system.
(b) Find A^{-1}, the inverse of the coefficient matrix.
(c) Solve the matrix equation by multiplying each side by A^{-1}.
(d) Now solve the system using the Cramer's Rule. Did you get the same solution as in part (b)?

6. Find the partial fraction decomposition of the rational function $r(x) = \dfrac{4x + 8}{x^4 + 4x^2}$.

7. Find an equation for the parabola with vertex at the origin and focus $F(0, 3)$.

8. Sketch the graph of each conic section, and find the coordinates of its foci. What type of conic section does each equation represent?

(a) $9x^2 + 4y^2 = 24y$ (b) $r = \dfrac{6}{1 - 2\cos\theta}$

780

9. Find an equation for the conic whose graph is shown.

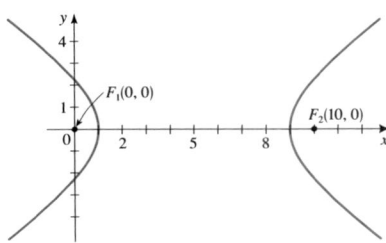

10. Use rotation of axes to graph the equation $7x^2 - 6\sqrt{3}xy + 13y^2 = 16$.

SEQUENCES AND SERIES

A sequence is a list of numbers written in a specific order. For example, the height that a bouncing ball reaches after each bounce is a sequence. This sequence has a definite pattern; describing the pattern allows us to predict the height that the ball reaches after any number of bounces.

The amount in a bank account at the end of each month, mortgage payments, and the amount of an annuity are also sequences. The formulas that generate these sequences drive our economy—they allow us to borrow money to buy our dream home closer to graduation than to retirement. In this chapter we study these and other applications of sequences.

783

**SUGGESTED TIME
AND EMPHASIS**

1 class, optional material

12.1 SEQUENCES AND SUMMATION NOTATION

Sequences ▶ Recursively Defined Sequences ▶ The Partial Sums of a Sequence ▶ Sigma Notation

Roughly speaking, a sequence is an infinite list of numbers. The numbers in the sequence are often written as $a_1, a_2, a_3, \ldots$. The dots mean that the list continues forever. A simple example is the sequence

$$5, \quad 10, \quad 15, \quad 20, \quad 25, \ldots$$
$$\uparrow \quad \uparrow \quad \uparrow \quad \uparrow \quad \uparrow$$
$$a_1 \quad a_2 \quad a_3 \quad a_4 \quad a_5 \ldots$$

We can describe the pattern of the sequence displayed above by the following *formula*:

$$a_n = 5n$$

You may have already thought of a different way to describe the pattern—namely, "you go from one number to the next by adding 5." This natural way of describing the sequence is expressed by the *recursive formula*:

$$a_n = a_{n-1} + 5$$

starting with $a_1 = 5$. Try substituting $n = 1, 2, 3, \ldots$ in each of these formulas to see how they produce the numbers in the sequence. In this section we see how these different ways are used to describe specific sequences.

▼ Sequences

Any ordered list of numbers can be viewed as a function whose input values are 1, 2, 3, . . . and whose output values are the numbers in the list. So we define a sequence as follows:

DEFINITION OF A SEQUENCE

A **sequence** is a function f whose domain is the set of natural numbers. The **terms of the sequence** are the function values

$$f(1), f(2), f(3), \ldots, f(n), \ldots$$

We usually write a_n instead of the function notation $f(n)$. So the terms of the sequence are written as

$$a_1, a_2, a_3, \ldots, a_n, \ldots$$

The number a_1 is called the **first term**, a_2 is called the **second term**, and in general, a_n is called the **nth term**.

Here is a simple example of a sequence:

$$2, 4, 6, 8, 10, \ldots$$

Another way to write this sequence is to use function notation:

$$a(n) = 2n$$

so $a(1) = 2, a(2) = 4, a(3) = 6, \ldots$

We can write a sequence in this way when it's clear what the subsequent terms of the sequence are. This sequence consists of even numbers. To be more accurate, however, we need to specify a procedure for finding *all* the terms of the sequence. This can be done by giving a formula for the nth term a_n of the sequence. In this case,

$$a_n = 2n$$

TEXT QUESTION

Compute $\displaystyle\sum_{k=1}^{5} k$.

Answer

15

and the sequence can be written as

$$2, \quad 4, \quad 6, \quad 8, \quad \ldots, \quad 2n, \quad \ldots$$

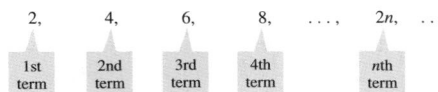

Notice how the formula $a_n = 2n$ gives all the terms of the sequence. For instance, substituting 1, 2, 3, and 4 for n gives the first four terms:

$$a_1 = 2 \cdot 1 = 2 \qquad a_2 = 2 \cdot 2 = 4$$
$$a_3 = 2 \cdot 3 = 6 \qquad a_4 = 2 \cdot 4 = 8$$

To find the 103rd term of this sequence, we use $n = 103$ to get

$$a_{103} = 2 \cdot 103 = 206$$

EXAMPLE 1 | Finding the Terms of a Sequence

Find the first five terms and the 100th term of the sequence defined by each formula.

(a) $a_n = 2n - 1$ \qquad (b) $c_n = n^2 - 1$

(c) $t_n = \dfrac{n}{n+1}$ \qquad (d) $r_n = \dfrac{(-1)^n}{2^n}$

SOLUTION   To find the first five terms, we substitute $n = 1, 2, 3, 4,$ and 5 in the formula for the nth term. To find the 100th term, we substitute $n = 100$. This gives the following.

nth term	First five terms	100th term
(a) $2n - 1$	$1, 3, 5, 7, 9$	199
(b) $n^2 - 1$	$0, 3, 8, 15, 24$	9999
(c) $\dfrac{n}{n+1}$	$\dfrac{1}{2}, \dfrac{2}{3}, \dfrac{3}{4}, \dfrac{4}{5}, \dfrac{5}{6}$	$\dfrac{100}{101}$
(d) $\dfrac{(-1)^n}{2^n}$	$-\dfrac{1}{2}, \dfrac{1}{4}, -\dfrac{1}{8}, \dfrac{1}{16}, -\dfrac{1}{32}$	$\dfrac{1}{2^{100}}$

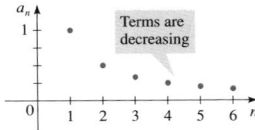

FIGURE 1

✎ **NOW TRY EXERCISES 3, 5, 7, AND 9**

In Example 1(d) the presence of $(-1)^n$ in the sequence has the effect of making successive terms alternately negative and positive.

It is often useful to picture a sequence by sketching its graph. Since a sequence is a function whose domain is the natural numbers, we can draw its graph in the Cartesian plane. For instance, the graph of the sequence

$$1, \frac{1}{2}, \frac{1}{3}, \frac{1}{4}, \frac{1}{5}, \frac{1}{6}, \ldots, \frac{1}{n}, \ldots$$

is shown in Figure 1.

Compare the graph of the sequence shown in Figure 1 to the graph of

$$1, -\frac{1}{2}, \frac{1}{3}, -\frac{1}{4}, \frac{1}{5}, -\frac{1}{6}, \ldots, \frac{(-1)^{n+1}}{n}, \ldots$$

shown in Figure 2. The graph of every sequence consists of isolated points that are *not* connected.

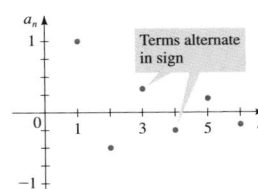

FIGURE 2

ALTERNATE EXAMPLE 1

(a) Find the first five terms and the 150th term of the sequence defined by the following formula: $a_n = 8n - 2$

(b) Find the first five terms and the 100th term of the sequence defined by the following formula: $c_n = n^2 - 4$

ANSWERS

(a) $a_1 = 6, a_2 = 14, a_3 = 22,$ $a_4 = 30, a_5 = 38, a_{150} = 1198$

(b) $c_1 = 3, c_2 = 0, c_3 = 5,$ $c_4 = 12, c_5 = 21, c_{100} = 9996$

IN-CLASS MATERIALS

Have the students try to figure out the pattern of this sequence: $3, 3, 5, 4, 4, 3, 5, 5, 4, 3, \ldots$

Answer

It counts the number of letters in the words *one, two, three, ...*

IN-CLASS MATERIALS

Students often confuse the idea of a function with a sequence. Have the students graph the function $f(n) = \sin(2\pi n)$ $(n \in \mathbb{R})$, and then the sequence $a_n = \sin(2\pi n)$ to make sure they understand the difference.

EXAMPLE

A nonobvious telescoping series:

Consider the sequence $\dfrac{1}{2}, \dfrac{1}{6}, \dfrac{1}{12},$

$\dfrac{1}{20}, \ldots, a_n = \dfrac{1}{n(n+1)}.$ This can

be rewritten as $a_n = \dfrac{1}{n} - \dfrac{1}{n+1}.$

Thus $\displaystyle\sum_{n=1}^{k} a_n = 1 - \dfrac{1}{k+1}$

(as shown in the text).

Graphing calculators are useful in analyzing sequences. To work with sequences on a TI-83, we put the calculator in Seq mode ("sequence" mode) as in Figure 3(a). If we enter the sequence $u(n) = n/(n+1)$ of Example 1(c), we can display the terms using the TABLE command as shown in Figure 3(b). We can also graph the sequence as shown in Figure 3(c).

FIGURE 3
$u(n) = n/(n+1)$

(a)   (b)   (c)

Finding patterns is an important part of mathematics. Consider a sequence that begins

$$1, 4, 9, 16, \ldots$$

Can you detect a pattern in these numbers? In other words, can you define a sequence whose first four terms are these numbers? The answer to this question seems easy; these numbers are the squares of the numbers 1, 2, 3, 4. Thus, the sequence we are looking for is defined by $a_n = n^2$. However, this is not the *only* sequence whose first four terms are 1, 4, 9, 16. In other words, the answer to our problem is not unique (see Exercise 80). In the next example we are interested in finding an *obvious* sequence whose first few terms agree with the given ones.

Not all sequences can be defined by a formula. For example, there is no known formula for the sequence of prime numbers:*

$$2, 3, 5, 7, 11, 13, 17, 19, 23, \ldots$$

EXAMPLE 2 | Finding the nth Term of a Sequence

Find the nth term of a sequence whose first several terms are given.

(a) $\dfrac{1}{2}, \dfrac{3}{4}, \dfrac{5}{6}, \dfrac{7}{8}, \ldots$ (b) $-2, 4, -8, 16, -32, \ldots$

SOLUTION

(a) We notice that the numerators of these fractions are the odd numbers and the denominators are the even numbers. Even numbers are of the form $2n$, and odd numbers are of the form $2n - 1$ (an odd number differs from an even number by 1). So a sequence that has these numbers for its first four terms is given by

$$a_n = \frac{2n-1}{2n}$$

(b) These numbers are powers of 2, and they alternate in sign, so a sequence that agrees with these terms is given by

$$a_n = (-1)^n 2^n$$

You should check that these formulas do indeed generate the given terms.

✎. NOW TRY EXERCISES **25, 27,** AND **29**   ■

Large Prime Numbers
The search for large primes fascinates many people. As of this writing, the largest known prime number is

$$2^{43,112,609} - 1$$

It was discovered by Edson Smith of the Department of Mathematics at UCLA. In decimal notation this number contains 12,978,189 digits. If it were written in full, it would occupy more than three times as many pages as this book contains. Smith was working with a large Internet group known as GIMPS (the Great Internet Mersenne Prime Search). Numbers of the form $2^p - 1$, where p is prime, are called Mersenne numbers and are more easily checked for primality than others. That is why the largest known primes are of this form.

▼ Recursively Defined Sequences

Some sequences do not have simple defining formulas like those of the preceding example. The nth term of a sequence may depend on some or all of the terms preceding it. A sequence defined in this way is called **recursive**. Here are two examples.

---

* A *prime number* is a whole number p whose only divisors are p and 1. (By convention, the number 1 is not considered prime.)

ALTERNATE EXAMPLE 2

Find the nth term of a sequence whose first few terms are

$$\frac{3}{2}, \frac{4}{4}, \frac{5}{8}, \frac{6}{16}, \frac{7}{32}, \frac{8}{64}, \ldots$$

ANSWER

$$\frac{n+2}{2^n}$$

IN-CLASS MATERIALS

Craig High School teacher Melissa Pfohl's favorite sequence is $a_n = n^2 + (-1)^n n$. Starting with $n = 0$, the sequence goes as follows: 0, 0, 6, 6, 20, 20, 42, 42, ... Notice that the formula is far from obvious, and the tantalizing "doubling property" can be proved using elementary methods.

ERATOSTHENES (circa 276–195 B.C.) was a renowned Greek geographer, mathematician, and astronomer. He accurately calculated the circumference of the earth by an ingenious method. He is most famous, however, for his method for finding primes, now called the *sieve of Eratosthenes*. The method consists of listing the integers, beginning with 2 (the first prime), and then crossing out all the multiples of 2, which are not prime. The next number remaining on the list is 3 (the second prime), so we again cross out all multiples of it. The next remaining number is 5 (the third prime number), and we cross out all multiples of it, and so on. In this way all numbers that are not prime are crossed out, and the remaining numbers are the primes.

EXAMPLE 3 | Finding the Terms of a Recursively Defined Sequence

Find the first five terms of the sequence defined recursively by $a_1 = 1$ and

$$a_n = 3(a_{n-1} + 2)$$

SOLUTION The defining formula for this sequence is recursive. It allows us to find the nth term a_n if we know the preceding term a_{n-1}. Thus, we can find the second term from the first term, the third term from the second term, the fourth term from the third term, and so on. Since we are given the first term $a_1 = 1$, we can proceed as follows.

$$a_2 = 3(a_1 + 2) = 3(1 + 2) = 9$$

$$a_3 = 3(a_2 + 2) = 3(9 + 2) = 33$$

$$a_4 = 3(a_3 + 2) = 3(33 + 2) = 105$$

$$a_5 = 3(a_4 + 2) = 3(105 + 2) = 321$$

Thus the first five terms of this sequence are

$$1, 9, 33, 105, 321, \ldots$$

✎. **NOW TRY EXERCISE 13**

Note that to find the 20th term of the sequence in Example 3, we must first find all 19 preceding terms. This is most easily done by using a graphing calculator. Figure 4(a) shows how to enter this sequence on the TI-83 calculator. From Figure 4(b) we see that the 20th term of the sequence is $a_{20} = 4{,}649{,}045{,}865$.

(a)

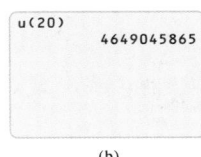

(b)

FIGURE 4 $u(n) = 3(u(n-1) + 2)$, $u(1) = 1$

EXAMPLE 4 | The Fibonacci Sequence

Find the first 11 terms of the sequence defined recursively by $F_1 = 1$, $F_2 = 1$ and

$$F_n = F_{n-1} + F_{n-2}$$

FIBONACCI (1175–1250) was born in Pisa, Italy, and was educated in North Africa. He traveled widely in the Mediterranean area and learned the various methods then in use for writing numbers. On returning to Pisa in 1202, Fibonacci advocated the use of the Hindu-Arabic decimal system, the one we use today, over the Roman numeral system that was used in Europe in his time. His most famous book, *Liber Abaci*, expounds on the advantages of the Hindu-Arabic numerals. In fact, multiplication and division were so complicated using Roman numerals that a college degree was necessary to master these skills. Interestingly, in 1299 the city of Florence outlawed the use of the decimal system for merchants and businesses, requiring numbers to be written in Roman numerals or words. One can only speculate about the reasons for this law.

ALTERNATE EXAMPLE 3
Find the first five terms of the sequence defined recursively by $a_1 = 4$ and $a_n = 2(a_{n-1} + 5)$.

ANSWER
$a_1 = 4$, $a_2 = 18$, $a_3 = 46$, $a_4 = 102$, $a_5 = 214$

EXAMPLE
A sequence whose values look random: $a_n = \sin(n^2)$

ALTERNATE EXAMPLE 4
Find the first 11 terms of the sequence defined recursively by $F_1 = 3$, $F_2 = 8$, and $F_n = F_{n-1} + F_{n-2}$.

ANSWER
$F_1 = 3$, $F_2 = 8$, $F_3 = 11$, $F_4 = 19$, $F_5 = 30$, $F_6 = 49$, $F_7 = 79$, $F_8 = 128$, $F_9 = 207$, $F_{10} = 335$, $F_{11} = 542$

IN-CLASS MATERIALS

There are several ways of making the terms of a sequence alternate. The text gives the term $(-1)^n$. Another alternating sequence is $\cos \pi n$. Ask the students to come up with a formula for the following sequence: 0, 1, 0, −1, 0, 1, 0, −1, ... There are several ways to do this, but the cleanest is $\sin\left(\dfrac{\pi}{2}n\right)$.

SOLUTION To find F_n, we need to find the two preceding terms, F_{n-1} and F_{n-2}. Since we are given F_1 and F_2, we proceed as follows.

$$F_3 = F_2 + F_1 = 1 + 1 = 2$$
$$F_4 = F_3 + F_2 = 2 + 1 = 3$$
$$F_5 = F_4 + F_3 = 3 + 2 = 5$$

It's clear what is happening here. Each term is simply the sum of the two terms that precede it, so we can easily write down as many terms as we please. Here are the first 11 terms:

$$1, 1, 2, 3, 5, 8, 13, 21, 34, 55, 89, \ldots$$

✎. NOW TRY EXERCISE **17** ■

The sequence in Example 4 is called the **Fibonacci sequence**, named after the 13th century Italian mathematician who used it to solve a problem about the breeding of rabbits (see Exercise 79). The sequence also occurs in numerous other applications in nature. (See Figures 5 and 6.) In fact, so many phenomena behave like the Fibonacci sequence that one mathematical journal, the *Fibonacci Quarterly*, is devoted entirely to its properties.

FIGURE 5 The Fibonacci sequence in the branching of a tree

FIGURE 6   Fibonacci spiral   Nautilus shell

IN-CLASS MATERIALS

Note that there are many sequences that have no pattern: $1, \pi, 3, e, -27, \ldots$. Also point out that not every sequence with a pattern has a rule that is easily written as a formula, for example,

$$3, 1, 4, 1, 5, 9, 2, 6, 5, 3, \ldots$$
$$3, 3.1, 3.14, 3.141, 3.1415, \ldots$$
$$0, 0.1, 0.12, 0.123, \ldots, 0.123456789, 0.12345678910, 0.1234567891011, \ldots$$

(The limit of this last sequence is called the Champernowe constant.)

▼ The Partial Sums of a Sequence

In calculus we are often interested in adding the terms of a sequence. This leads to the following definition.

THE PARTIAL SUMS OF A SEQUENCE

For the sequence

$$a_1, a_2, a_3, a_4, \ldots, a_n, \ldots$$

the **partial sums** are

$$S_1 = a_1$$
$$S_2 = a_1 + a_2$$
$$S_3 = a_1 + a_2 + a_3$$
$$S_4 = a_1 + a_2 + a_3 + a_4$$
$$\vdots$$
$$S_n = a_1 + a_2 + a_3 + \cdots + a_n$$
$$\vdots$$

S_1 is called the **first partial sum**, S_2 is the **second partial sum**, and so on. S_n is called the **nth partial sum**. The sequence $S_1, S_2, S_3, \ldots, S_n, \ldots$ is called the **sequence of partial sums**.

EXAMPLE 5 | Finding the Partial Sums of a Sequence

Find the first four partial sums and the nth partial sum of the sequence given by $a_n = 1/2^n$.

SOLUTION The terms of the sequence are

$$\frac{1}{2}, \frac{1}{4}, \frac{1}{8}, \cdots$$

The first four partial sums are

$$S_1 = \frac{1}{2} \qquad\qquad = \frac{1}{2}$$
$$S_2 = \frac{1}{2} + \frac{1}{4} \qquad\qquad = \frac{3}{4}$$
$$S_3 = \frac{1}{2} + \frac{1}{4} + \frac{1}{8} \qquad = \frac{7}{8}$$
$$S_4 = \frac{1}{2} + \frac{1}{4} + \frac{1}{8} + \frac{1}{16} = \frac{15}{16}$$

Notice that in the value of each partial sum, the denominator is a power of 2 and the numerator is one less than the denominator. In general, the nth partial sum is

$$S_n = \frac{2^n - 1}{2^n} = 1 - \frac{1}{2^n}$$

The first five terms of a_n and S_n are graphed in Figure 7.

✎ NOW TRY EXERCISE **37** ◼

FIGURE 7 Graph of the sequence a_n and the sequence of partial sums S_n

ALTERNATE EXAMPLE 5
Find the first four partial sums and the nth partial sum of the sequence given by $a_n = 2n - 1$.

ANSWER
$S_1 = 1$, $S_2 = 4$, $S_3 = 9$, $S_4 = 16$, $S_n = n^2$

IN-CLASS MATERIALS

Have students compute some partial sums that converge quickly to a recognizable number, such as the one associated with $a_n = \dfrac{1}{(n-1)!}$ (with $a_1 = 1$), which converges to e, and $a_n = \left(\dfrac{3}{4}\right)^n$, which converges to 4. Then have them look at some partial sums that go off to infinity, such as the ones associated with $a_n = 10^n$ and $a_n = n$. Then have them conjecture about the fate of $a_n = \dfrac{1}{n}$.

ALTERNATE EXAMPLE 6

Find the first four partial sums and the nth partial sum of the sequence given by

$$a_n = \frac{1}{n+1} - \frac{1}{n+2}.$$

ANSWER

$$S_1 = \frac{1}{2} - \frac{1}{3}, \; S_2 = \frac{1}{2} - \frac{1}{4},$$

$$S_3 = \frac{1}{2} - \frac{1}{5}, \; S_4 = \frac{1}{2} - \frac{1}{6},$$

$$S_n = \frac{1}{2} - \frac{1}{n+2}$$

EXAMPLE 6 | Finding the Partial Sums of a Sequence

Find the first four partial sums and the nth partial sum of the sequence given by

$$a_n = \frac{1}{n} - \frac{1}{n+1}$$

SOLUTION   The first four partial sums are

$$S_1 = \left(1 - \frac{1}{2}\right) \qquad\qquad\qquad\qquad\qquad\qquad = 1 - \frac{1}{2}$$

$$S_2 = \left(1 - \frac{1}{2}\right) + \left(\frac{1}{2} - \frac{1}{3}\right) \qquad\qquad\qquad = 1 - \frac{1}{3}$$

$$S_3 = \left(1 - \frac{1}{2}\right) + \left(\frac{1}{2} - \frac{1}{3}\right) + \left(\frac{1}{3} - \frac{1}{4}\right) \qquad = 1 - \frac{1}{4}$$

$$S_4 = \left(1 - \frac{1}{2}\right) + \left(\frac{1}{2} - \frac{1}{3}\right) + \left(\frac{1}{3} - \frac{1}{4}\right) + \left(\frac{1}{4} - \frac{1}{5}\right) = 1 - \frac{1}{5}$$

Do you detect a pattern here? Of course. The nth partial sum is

$$S_n = 1 - \frac{1}{n+1}$$

✎. **NOW TRY EXERCISE 39**   ■

▼ Sigma Notation

Given a sequence

$$a_1, a_2, a_3, a_4, \dots$$

we can write the sum of the first n terms using **summation notation**, or **sigma notation**. This notation derives its name from the Greek letter Σ (capital sigma, corresponding to our S for "sum"). Sigma notation is used as follows:

This tells us to end with $k = n$

This tells us to add $\displaystyle\sum_{k=1}^{n} a_k$

This tells us to start with $k = 1$

$$\sum_{k=1}^{n} a_k = a_1 + a_2 + a_3 + a_4 + \cdots + a_n$$

The left side of this expression is read, "The sum of a_k from $k = 1$ to $k = n$." The letter k is called the **index of summation**, or the **summation variable**, and the idea is to replace k in the expression after the sigma by the integers $1, 2, 3, \dots, n$, and add the resulting expressions, arriving at the right side of the equation.

EXAMPLE 7 | Sigma Notation

Find each sum.

(a) $\displaystyle\sum_{k=1}^{5} k^2$ (b) $\displaystyle\sum_{j=3}^{5} \frac{1}{j}$ (c) $\displaystyle\sum_{i=5}^{10} i$ (d) $\displaystyle\sum_{i=1}^{6} 2$

SOLUTION

(a) $\displaystyle\sum_{k=1}^{5} k^2 = 1^2 + 2^2 + 3^2 + 4^2 + 5^2 = 55$

(b) $\displaystyle\sum_{j=3}^{5} \frac{1}{j} = \frac{1}{3} + \frac{1}{4} + \frac{1}{5} = \frac{47}{60}$

ALTERNATE EXAMPLE 7

Find the sum.

(a) $\displaystyle\sum_{k=5}^{9} k$

(c) Find the sum.

$$\sum_{i=2}^{9} i$$

(d) Find the sum.

$$\sum_{i=2}^{7} 2$$

ANSWERS

(a) 1925

(c) 44

(d) 12

```
sum(seq(K²,K,1,5,1))
                    55
sum(seq(1/J,J,3,5,
1))▶Frac
                 47/60
```

FIGURE 8

(c) $\displaystyle\sum_{i=5}^{10} i = 5 + 6 + 7 + 8 + 9 + 10 = 45$

(d) $\displaystyle\sum_{i=1}^{6} 2 = 2 + 2 + 2 + 2 + 2 + 2 = 12$

We can use a graphing calculator to evaluate sums. For instance, Figure 8 shows how the TI-83 can be used to evaluate the sums in parts (a) and (b) of Example 7.

✏. NOW TRY EXERCISES **41** AND **43**   ■

EXAMPLE 8 | Writing Sums in Sigma Notation

Write each sum using sigma notation.

(a) $1^3 + 2^3 + 3^3 + 4^3 + 5^3 + 6^3 + 7^3$

(b) $\sqrt{3} + \sqrt{4} + \sqrt{5} + \cdots + \sqrt{77}$

SOLUTION

(a) We can write

$$1^3 + 2^3 + 3^3 + 4^3 + 5^3 + 6^3 + 7^3 = \sum_{k=1}^{7} k^3$$

(b) A natural way to write this sum is

$$\sqrt{3} + \sqrt{4} + \sqrt{5} + \cdots + \sqrt{77} = \sum_{k=3}^{77} \sqrt{k}$$

However, there is no unique way of writing a sum in sigma notation. We could also write this sum as

$$\sqrt{3} + \sqrt{4} + \sqrt{5} + \cdots + \sqrt{77} = \sum_{k=0}^{74} \sqrt{k + 3}$$

or $$\sqrt{3} + \sqrt{4} + \sqrt{5} + \cdots + \sqrt{77} = \sum_{k=1}^{75} \sqrt{k + 2}$$

✏. NOW TRY EXERCISES **61** AND **63**   ■

ALTERNATE EXAMPLE 8
Write the sum using sigma notation, where the index of summation k runs from 1 to 7.
$3^4 + 4^4 + 5^4 + 6^4 + 7^4 + 8^4 + 9^4$

ANSWER
$\displaystyle\sum_{i=2}^{7} (k + 2)^4$

The Golden Ratio

The ancient Greeks considered a line segment to be divided into the **golden ratio** if the ratio of the shorter part to the longer part is the same as the ratio of the longer part to the whole segment.

Thus the segment shown is divided into the golden ratio if

$$\frac{1}{x} = \frac{x}{1 + x}$$

This leads to a quadratic equation whose positive solution is

$$x = \frac{1 + \sqrt{5}}{2} \approx 1.618$$

This ratio occurs naturally in many places. For instance, psychological experiments show that the most pleasing shape of rectangle is one whose sides are in golden ratio. The ancient Greeks agreed with this and built their temples in this ratio.

The golden ratio is related to the Fibonacci sequence. In fact, it can be shown by using calculus* that the ratio of two successive Fibonacci numbers

$$\frac{F_{n+1}}{F_n}$$

gets closer to the golden ratio the larger the value of n. Try finding this ratio for $n = 10$.

*See *Principles of Problem Solving* 13 at the book companion website: **www.stewartmath.com**

DRILL QUESTION

If we have a sequence defined by $a_1 = 4$, $a_2 = -3$, and $a_n = a_{n-2} + a_{n-1}$, what is a_4?

Answer

-2

The following properties of sums are natural consequences of properties of the real numbers.

PROPERTIES OF SUMS

Let $a_1, a_2, a_3, a_4, \ldots$ and $b_1, b_2, b_3, b_4, \ldots$ be sequences. Then for every positive integer n and any real number c, the following properties hold.

1. $\displaystyle\sum_{k=1}^{n} (a_k + b_k) = \sum_{k=1}^{n} a_k + \sum_{k=1}^{n} b_k$

2. $\displaystyle\sum_{k=1}^{n} (a_k - b_k) = \sum_{k=1}^{n} a_k - \sum_{k=1}^{n} b_k$

3. $\displaystyle\sum_{k=1}^{n} c a_k = c \left(\sum_{k=1}^{n} a_k \right)$

PROOF   To prove Property 1, we write out the left side of the equation to get

$$\sum_{k=1}^{n} (a_k + b_k) = (a_1 + b_1) + (a_2 + b_2) + (a_3 + b_3) + \cdots + (a_n + b_n)$$

Because addition is commutative and associative, we can rearrange the terms on the right side to read

$$\sum_{k=1}^{n} (a_k + b_k) = (a_1 + a_2 + a_3 + \cdots + a_n) + (b_1 + b_2 + b_3 + \cdots + b_n)$$

Rewriting the right side using sigma notation gives Property 1. Property 2 is proved in a similar manner. To prove Property 3, we use the Distributive Property:

$$\sum_{k=1}^{n} c a_k = c a_1 + c a_2 + c a_3 + \cdots + c a_n$$

$$= c(a_1 + a_2 + a_3 + \cdots + a_n) = c \left(\sum_{k=1}^{n} a_k \right)$$

12.1 EXERCISES

CONCEPTS

1. A sequence is a function whose domain is _____.

2. The nth partial sum of a sequence is the sum of the first _____ terms of the sequence. So for the sequence $a_n = n^2$ the fourth partial sum is $S_4 =$ ____ + ____ + ____ + ____ = ____.

SKILLS

3–12 ■ Find the first four terms and the 100th term of the sequence.

3. $a_n = n + 1$

4. $a_n = 2n + 3$

5. $a_n = \dfrac{1}{n + 1}$

6. $a_n = n^2 + 1$

7. $a_n = \dfrac{(-1)^n}{n^2}$

8. $a_n = \dfrac{1}{n^2}$

9. $a_n = 1 + (-1)^n$

10. $a_n = (-1)^{n+1} \dfrac{n}{n + 1}$

11. $a_n = n^n$

12. $a_n = 3$

13–18 ■ Find the first five terms of the given recursively defined sequence.

13. $a_n = 2(a_{n-1} - 2)$ and $a_1 = 3$

14. $a_n = \dfrac{a_{n-1}}{2}$ and $a_1 = -8$

15. $a_n = 2a_{n-1} + 1$ and $a_1 = 1$

16. $a_n = \dfrac{1}{1 + a_{n-1}}$ and $a_1 = 1$

17. $a_n = a_{n-1} + a_{n-2}$ and $a_1 = 1, a_2 = 2$

18. $a_n = a_{n-1} + a_{n-2} + a_{n-3}$ and $a_1 = a_2 = a_3 = 1$

19–24 ■ Use a graphing calculator to do the following. **(a)** Find the first 10 terms of the sequence. **(b)** Graph the first 10 terms of the sequence.

19. $a_n = 4n + 3$

20. $a_n = n^2 + n$

21. $a_n = \dfrac{12}{n}$

22. $a_n = 4 - 2(-1)^n$

23. $a_n = \dfrac{1}{a_{n-1}}$ and $a_1 = 2$

24. $a_n = a_{n-1} - a_{n-2}$ and $a_1 = 1, a_2 = 3$

25–32 ■ Find the nth term of a sequence whose first several terms are given.

25. $2, 4, 8, 16, \ldots$

26. $-\frac{1}{3}, \frac{1}{9}, -\frac{1}{27}, \frac{1}{81}, \ldots$

27. $1, 4, 7, 10, \ldots$

28. $5, -25, 125, -625, \ldots$

29. $1, \frac{3}{4}, \frac{5}{9}, \frac{7}{16}, \frac{9}{25}, \ldots$

30. $\frac{3}{4}, \frac{4}{5}, \frac{5}{6}, \frac{6}{7}, \ldots$

31. $0, 2, 0, 2, 0, 2, \ldots$

32. $1, \frac{1}{2}, 3, \frac{1}{4}, 5, \frac{1}{6}, \ldots$

33–36 ■ Find the first six partial sums $S_1, S_2, S_3, S_4, S_5, S_6$ of the sequence.

33. $1, 3, 5, 7, \ldots$

34. $1^2, 2^2, 3^2, 4^2, \ldots$

35. $\dfrac{1}{3}, \dfrac{1}{3^2}, \dfrac{1}{3^3}, \dfrac{1}{3^4}, \ldots$

36. $-1, 1, -1, 1, \ldots$

37–40 ■ Find the first four partial sums and the nth partial sum of the sequence a_n.

37. $a_n = \dfrac{2}{3^n}$

38. $a_n = \dfrac{1}{n+1} - \dfrac{1}{n+2}$

39. $a_n = \sqrt{n} - \sqrt{n+1}$

40. $a_n = \log\left(\dfrac{n}{n+1}\right)$ [*Hint:* Use a property of logarithms to write the nth term as a difference.]

41–48 ■ Find the sum.

41. $\displaystyle\sum_{k=1}^{4} k$

42. $\displaystyle\sum_{k=1}^{4} k^2$

43. $\displaystyle\sum_{k=1}^{3} \dfrac{1}{k}$

44. $\displaystyle\sum_{j=1}^{100} (-1)^j$

45. $\displaystyle\sum_{i=1}^{8} [1 + (-1)^i]$

46. $\displaystyle\sum_{i=4}^{12} 10$

47. $\displaystyle\sum_{k=1}^{5} 2^{k-1}$

48. $\displaystyle\sum_{i=1}^{3} i2^i$

 49–54 ■ Use a graphing calculator to evaluate the sum.

49. $\displaystyle\sum_{k=1}^{10} k^2$

50. $\displaystyle\sum_{k=1}^{100} (3k + 4)$

51. $\displaystyle\sum_{j=7}^{20} j^2(1 + j)$

52. $\displaystyle\sum_{j=5}^{15} \dfrac{1}{j^2 + 1}$

53. $\displaystyle\sum_{n=0}^{22} (-1)^n 2n$

54. $\displaystyle\sum_{n=1}^{100} \dfrac{(-1)^n}{n}$

55–60 ■ Write the sum without using sigma notation.

55. $\displaystyle\sum_{k=1}^{5} \sqrt{k}$

56. $\displaystyle\sum_{i=0}^{4} \dfrac{2i - 1}{2i + 1}$

57. $\displaystyle\sum_{k=0}^{6} \sqrt{k + 4}$

58. $\displaystyle\sum_{k=6}^{9} k(k + 3)$

59. $\displaystyle\sum_{k=3}^{100} x^k$

60. $\displaystyle\sum_{j=1}^{n} (-1)^{j+1} x^j$

61–68 ■ Write the sum using sigma notation.

61. $1 + 2 + 3 + 4 + \cdots + 100$

62. $2 + 4 + 6 + \cdots + 20$

63. $1^2 + 2^2 + 3^2 + \cdots + 10^2$

64. $\dfrac{1}{2 \ln 2} - \dfrac{1}{3 \ln 3} + \dfrac{1}{4 \ln 4} - \dfrac{1}{5 \ln 5} + \cdots + \dfrac{1}{100 \ln 100}$

65. $\dfrac{1}{1 \cdot 2} + \dfrac{1}{2 \cdot 3} + \dfrac{1}{3 \cdot 4} + \cdots + \dfrac{1}{999 \cdot 1000}$

66. $\dfrac{\sqrt{1}}{1^2} + \dfrac{\sqrt{2}}{2^2} + \dfrac{\sqrt{3}}{3^2} + \cdots + \dfrac{\sqrt{n}}{n^2}$

67. $1 + x + x^2 + x^3 + \cdots + x^{100}$

68. $1 - 2x + 3x^2 - 4x^3 + 5x^4 + \cdots - 100x^{99}$

69. Find a formula for the nth term of the sequence

$$\sqrt{2}, \quad \sqrt{2\sqrt{2}}, \quad \sqrt{2\sqrt{2\sqrt{2}}}, \quad \sqrt{2\sqrt{2\sqrt{2\sqrt{2}}}}, \ldots$$

[*Hint:* Write each term as a power of 2.]

 70. Define the sequence

$$G_n = \dfrac{1}{\sqrt{5}}\left(\dfrac{(1 + \sqrt{5})^n - (1 - \sqrt{5})^n}{2^n}\right)$$

Use the ⎡TABLE⎤ command on a graphing calculator to find the first 10 terms of this sequence. Compare to the Fibonacci sequence F_n.

APPLICATIONS

71. Compound Interest   Julio deposits $2000 in a savings account that pays 2.4% interest per year compounded monthly. The amount in the account after n months is given by the sequence

$$A_n = 2000\left(1 + \dfrac{0.024}{12}\right)^n$$

(a) Find the first six terms of the sequence.
(b) Find the amount in the account after 3 years.

72. Compound Interest   Helen deposits $100 at the end of each month into an account that pays 6% interest per year compounded monthly. The amount of interest she has accumulated after n months is given by the sequence

$$I_n = 100\left(\dfrac{1.005^n - 1}{0.005} - n\right)$$

(a) Find the first six terms of the sequence.
(b) Find the interest she has accumulated after 5 years.

73. Population of a City A city was incorporated in 2004 with a population of 35,000. It is expected that the population will increase at a rate of 2% per year. The population n years after 2004 is given by the sequence

$$P_n = 35{,}000(1.02)^n$$

(a) Find the first five terms of the sequence.

(b) Find the population in 2014.

74. Paying off a Debt Margarita borrows $10,000 from her uncle and agrees to repay it in monthly installments of $200. Her uncle charges 0.5% interest per month on the balance.

(a) Show that her balance A_n in the nth month is given recursively by $A_0 = 10{,}000$ and

$$A_n = 1.005A_{n-1} - 200$$

(b) Find her balance after six months.

75. Fish Farming A fish farmer has 5000 catfish in his pond. The number of catfish increases by 8% per month, and the farmer harvests 300 catfish per month.

(a) Show that the catfish population P_n after n months is given recursively by $P_0 = 5000$ and

$$P_n = 1.08P_{n-1} - 300$$

(b) How many fish are in the pond after 12 months?

76. Price of a House The median price of a house in Orange County increases by about 6% per year. In 2002 the median price was $240,000. Let P_n be the median price n years after 2002.

(a) Find a formula for the sequence P_n.

(b) Find the expected median price in 2010.

77. Salary Increases A newly hired salesman is promised a beginning salary of $30,000 a year with a $2000 raise every year. Let S_n be his salary in his nth year of employment.

(a) Find a recursive definition of S_n.

(b) Find his salary in his fifth year of employment.

78. Concentration of a Solution A biologist is trying to find the optimal salt concentration for the growth of a certain species of mollusk. She begins with a brine solution that has 4 g/L of salt and increases the concentration by 10% every day. Let C_0 denote the initial concentration and C_n the concentration after n days.

(a) Find a recursive definition of C_n.

(b) Find the salt concentration after 8 days.

79. Fibonacci's Rabbits Fibonacci posed the following problem: Suppose that rabbits live forever and that every month each pair produces a new pair that becomes productive at age 2 months. If we start with one newborn pair, how many pairs of rabbits will we have in the nth month? Show that the answer is F_n, where F_n is the nth term of the Fibonacci sequence.

DISCOVERY ■ DISCUSSION ■ WRITING

80. Different Sequences That Start the Same

(a) Show that the first four terms of the sequence $a_n = n^2$ are

$$1, 4, 9, 16, \ldots$$

(b) Show that the first four terms of the sequence $a_n = n^2 + (n-1)(n-2)(n-3)(n-4)$ are also

$$1, 4, 9, 16, \ldots$$

(c) Find a sequence whose first six terms are the same as those of $a_n = n^2$ but whose succeeding terms differ from this sequence.

(d) Find two different sequences that begin

$$2, 4, 8, 16, \ldots$$

81. A Recursively Defined Sequence Find the first 40 terms of the sequence defined by

$$a_{n+1} = \begin{cases} \dfrac{a_n}{2} & \text{if } a_n \text{ is an even number} \\ 3a_n + 1 & \text{if } a_n \text{ is an odd number} \end{cases}$$

and $a_1 = 11$. Do the same if $a_1 = 25$. Make a conjecture about this type of sequence. Try several other values for a_1, to test your conjecture.

82. A Different Type of Recursion Find the first 10 terms of the sequence defined by

$$a_n = a_{n-a_{n-1}} + a_{n-a_{n-2}}$$

with

$$a_1 = 1 \quad \text{and} \quad a_2 = 1$$

How is this recursive sequence different from the others in this section?

12.2 ARITHMETIC SEQUENCES

| Arithmetic Sequences ▶ Partial Sums of Arithmetic Sequences

In this section we study a special type of sequence, called an arithmetic sequence.

▼ Arithmetic Sequences

Perhaps the simplest way to generate a sequence is to start with a number a and add to it a fixed constant d, over and over again.

SUGGESTED TIME AND EMPHASIS

$\frac{1}{2}$–1 class, optional material

TEXT QUESTION

What distinguishes an "arithmetic sequence" from an arbitrary "sequence"?

Answer

Successive terms in an arithmetic sequence have a common difference.

DEFINITION OF AN ARITHMETIC SEQUENCE

An **arithmetic sequence** is a sequence of the form

$$a, a + d, a + 2d, a + 3d, a + 4d, \ldots$$

The number a is the **first term**, and d is the **common difference** of the sequence. The nth **term** of an arithmetic sequence is given by

$$a_n = a + (n - 1)d$$

The number d is called the common difference because any two consecutive terms of an arithmetic sequence differ by d.

EXAMPLE 1 | Arithmetic Sequences

(a) If $a = 2$ and $d = 3$, then we have the arithmetic sequence

$$2, 2 + 3, 2 + 6, 2 + 9, \ldots$$

or

$$2, 5, 8, 11, \ldots$$

Any two consecutive terms of this sequence differ by $d = 3$. The nth term is $a_n = 2 + 3(n - 1)$.

(b) Consider the arithmetic sequence

$$9, 4, -1, -6, -11, \ldots$$

Here the common difference is $d = -5$. The terms of an arithmetic sequence decrease if the common difference is negative. The nth term is $a_n = 9 - 5(n - 1)$.

(c) The graph of the arithmetic sequence $a_n = 1 + 2(n - 1)$ is shown in Figure 1. Notice that the points in the graph lie on the straight line $y = 2x - 1$, which has slope $d = 2$.

✎ NOW TRY EXERCISES **5, 9,** AND **13**   ■

FIGURE 1

An arithmetic sequence is determined completely by the first term a and the common difference d. Thus, if we know the first two terms of an arithmetic sequence, then we can find a formula for the nth term, as the next example shows.

EXAMPLE 2 | Finding Terms of an Arithmetic Sequence

Find the first six terms and the 300th term of the arithmetic sequence

$$13, 7, \ldots$$

SOLUTION Since the first term is 13, we have $a = 13$. The common difference is $d = 7 - 13 = -6$. Thus the nth term of this sequence is

$$a_n = 13 - 6(n - 1)$$

From this we find the first six terms:

$$13, 7, 1, -5, -11, -17, \ldots$$

The 300th term is $a_{300} = 13 - 6(299) = -1781$.

✎ NOW TRY EXERCISE **27**   ■

The next example shows that an arithmetic sequence is determined completely by *any* two of its terms.

ALTERNATE EXAMPLE 1

Find the nth term of the arithmetic sequence $9, 4, -1, -6, -11, \ldots$.

ANSWER

$a_n = 9 - 5(n - 1)$

ALTERNATE EXAMPLE 2

Find the 200th term of the arithmetic sequence $14, 8, \ldots$.

ANSWER

$a_{200} = -1180$

IN-CLASS MATERIALS

Have the students try to define an arithmetic sequence recursively. It can be done relatively simply as $a_n = a_{n-1} + d$, but obtaining this formula requires an understanding of arithmetic sequences and recursively defined sequences.

ALTERNATE EXAMPLE 3

The 11th term of an arithmetic sequence is 63, and the 15th term is 87. Find the 800th term.

ANSWER

$a_{800} = 4797$

IN-CLASS MATERIALS

The perfect squares 1, 4, 9, 16, . . . can be represented as a square array of dots.

16

IN-CLASS MATERIALS

The triangular numbers are those that can be represented by a triangular array of dots: 1, 3, 6, 10, 15, ...

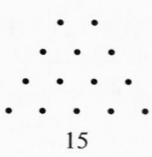

15

Notice that the triangular numbers are precisely the partial sums of the sequence 1, 2, 3, 4, ...

MATHEMATICS IN THE MODERN WORLD

Fair Division of Assets

Dividing an asset fairly among a number of people is of great interest to mathematicians. Problems of this nature include dividing the national budget, disputed land, or assets in divorce cases. In 1994 Brams and Taylor found a mathematical way of dividing things fairly. Their solution has been applied to division problems in political science, legal proceedings, and other areas. To understand the problem, consider the following example. Suppose persons *A* and *B* want to divide a property fairly between them. To divide it *fairly* means that both *A* and *B* must be satisfied with the outcome of the division. Solution: *A* gets to divide the property into two pieces, then *B* gets to choose the piece he or she wants. Since both *A* and *B* had a part in the division process, each should be satisfied. The situation becomes much more complicated if three or more people are involved (and that's where mathematics comes in). Dividing things fairly involves much more than simply cutting things in half; it must take into account the *relative worth* each person attaches to the thing being divided. A story from the Bible illustrates this clearly. Two women appear before King Solomon, each claiming to be the mother of the same newborn baby. King Solomon's solution is to divide the baby in half! The real mother, who attaches far more worth to the baby than anyone else does, immediately gives up her claim to the baby to save the baby's life.

Mathematical solutions to fair-division problems have recently been applied in an international treaty, the Convention on the Law of the Sea. If a country wants to develop a portion of the sea floor, it is required to divide the portion into two parts, one part to be used by itself and the other by a consortium that will preserve it for later use by a less developed country. The consortium gets first pick.

EXAMPLE 3 | Finding Terms of an Arithmetic Sequence

The 11th term of an arithmetic sequence is 52, and the 19th term is 92. Find the 1000th term.

SOLUTION To find the *n*th term of this sequence, we need to find *a* and *d* in the formula

$$a_n = a + (n - 1)d$$

From this formula we get

$$a_{11} = a + (11 - 1)d = a + 10d$$
$$a_{19} = a + (19 - 1)d = a + 18d$$

Since $a_{11} = 52$ and $a_{19} = 92$, we get the two equations:

$$\begin{cases} 52 = a + 10d \\ 92 = a + 18d \end{cases}$$

Solving this system for *a* and *d*, we get $a = 2$ and $d = 5$. (Verify this.) Thus the *n*th term of this sequence is

$$a_n = 2 + 5(n - 1)$$

The 1000th term is $a_{1000} = 2 + 5(1000 - 1) = 4997$.

✎. NOW TRY EXERCISE **37**

▼ Partial Sums of Arithmetic Sequences

Suppose we want to find the sum of the numbers 1, 2, 3, 4, . . . , 100, that is,

$$\sum_{k=1}^{100} k$$

When the famous mathematician C. F. Gauss was a schoolboy, his teacher posed this problem to the class and expected that it would keep the students busy for a long time. But Gauss answered the question almost immediately. His idea was this: Since we are adding numbers produced according to a fixed pattern, there must also be a pattern (or formula) for finding the sum. He started by writing the numbers from 1 to 100 and then below them wrote the same numbers in reverse order. Writing *S* for the sum and adding corresponding terms give

$$\begin{aligned} S &= \quad 1 + \quad 2 + \quad 3 + \cdots + \ 98 + \ 99 + 100 \\ S &= 100 + \ 99 + \ 98 + \cdots + \quad 3 + \quad 2 + \quad 1 \\ \hline 2S &= 101 + 101 + 101 + \cdots + 101 + 101 + 101 \end{aligned}$$

It follows that $2S = 100(101) = 10{,}100$ and so $S = 5050$.

Of course, the sequence of natural numbers 1, 2, 3, . . . is an arithmetic sequence (with $a = 1$ and $d = 1$), and the method for summing the first 100 terms of this sequence can be used to find a formula for the *n*th partial sum of any arithmetic sequence. We want to find the sum of the first *n* terms of the arithmetic sequence whose terms are $a_k = a + (k - 1)d$; that is, we want to find

$$S_n = \sum_{k=1}^{n} [a + (k - 1)d]$$

$$= a + (a + d) + (a + 2d) + (a + 3d) + \cdots + [a + (n - 1)d]$$

Using Gauss's method, we write

$$\begin{aligned} S_n &= \quad\quad a \quad\quad + \quad (a + d) \quad + \cdots + \ [a + (n - 2)d] + [a + (n - 1)d] \\ S_n &= [a + (n - 1)d] + [a + (n - 2)d] + \cdots + \quad (a + d) \quad + \quad\quad a \\ \hline 2S_n &= [2a + (n - 1)d] + [2a + (n - 1)d] + \cdots + [2a + (n - 1)d] + [2a + (n - 1)d] \end{aligned}$$

Show the students that a constant sequence such as 5, 5, 5, 5, . . . is trivially an arithmetic sequence. Notice that the formula for the partial sum is consistent with what we know about basic arithmetic.

There are n identical terms on the right side of this equation, so

$$2S_n = n[2a + (n - 1)d]$$

$$S_n = \frac{n}{2}[2a + (n - 1)d]$$

Notice that $a_n = a + (n - 1)d$ is the nth term of this sequence. So we can write

$$S_n = \frac{n}{2}[a + a + (n - 1)d] = n\left(\frac{a + a_n}{2}\right)$$

This last formula says that the sum of the first n terms of an arithmetic sequence is the average of the first and nth terms multiplied by n, the number of terms in the sum. We now summarize this result.

PARTIAL SUMS OF AN ARITHMETIC SEQUENCE

For the arithmetic sequence $a_n = a + (n - 1)d$ the **nth partial sum**

$$S_n = a + (a + d) + (a + 2d) + (a + 3d) + \cdots + [a + (n - 1)d]$$

is given by either of the following formulas.

1. $S_n = \dfrac{n}{2}[2a + (n - 1)d]$ **2.** $S_n = n\left(\dfrac{a + a_n}{2}\right)$

EXAMPLE 4 | Finding a Partial Sum of an Arithmetic Sequence

Find the sum of the first 40 terms of the arithmetic sequence

$$3, 7, 11, 15, \ldots$$

SOLUTION   For this arithmetic sequence, $a = 3$ and $d = 4$. Using Formula 1 for the partial sum of an arithmetic sequence, we get

$$S_{40} = \tfrac{40}{2}[2(3) + (40 - 1)4] = 20(6 + 156) = 3240$$

✎. NOW TRY EXERCISE **43**   ∎

EXAMPLE 5 | Finding a Partial Sum of an Arithmetic Sequence

Find the sum of the first 50 odd numbers.

SOLUTION   The odd numbers form an arithmetic sequence with $a = 1$ and $d = 2$. The nth term is $a_n = 1 + 2(n - 1) = 2n - 1$, so the 50th odd number is $a_{50} = 2(50) - 1 = 99$. Substituting in Formula 2 for the partial sum of an arithmetic sequence, we get

$$S_{50} = 50\left(\frac{a + a_{50}}{2}\right) = 50\left(\frac{1 + 99}{2}\right) = 50 \cdot 50 = 2500$$

✎. NOW TRY EXERCISE **49**   ∎

EXAMPLE 6 | Finding the Seating Capacity of an Amphitheater

An amphitheater has 50 rows of seats with 30 seats in the first row, 32 in the second, 34 in the third, and so on. Find the total number of seats.

IN-CLASS MATERIALS

Examine this broad triangular array:

16

Notice we run into perfect squares! This can be demonstrated by looking at the partial sums of the arithmetic sequence $1 + 2(n - 1)$ or by rearranging the dots of the broader triangle to make a square.

ALTERNATE EXAMPLE 4

Find the sum of the first 40 terms of the arithmetic sequence 3, 10, 17, 24, ...

ANSWER

5580

ALTERNATE EXAMPLE 5

Find the sum of the first 40 odd numbers.

ANSWER

1600

ALTERNATE EXAMPLE 6

An amphitheater has 40 rows of seats with 30 seats in the first row, 32 in the second, 34 in the third, and so on. Find the total number of seats.

ANSWER

2760

IN-CLASS MATERIALS

Many phenomena are either linear or locally linear (they look linear when viewing them over a narrow range). For example, assume that a company earns about $120,000 in 2011, $140,000 in 2012, $160,000 in 2013, etc. If it is linear growth over 10 years, the total 10-year earnings can be found from adding up the terms of an arithmetic sequence.

SOLUTION

SOLUTION The numbers of seats in the rows form an arithmetic sequence with $a = 30$ and $d = 2$. Since there are 50 rows, the total number of seats is the sum

$$S_{50} = \frac{50}{2}[2(30) + 49(2)] \qquad S_n = \frac{n}{2}[2a + (n-1)d]$$
$$= 3950$$

Thus the amphitheater has 3950 seats.

✎. **NOW TRY EXERCISE 65** ◼

EXAMPLE 7 | Finding the Number of Terms in a Partial Sum

How many terms of the arithmetic sequence 5, 7, 9, . . . must be added to get 572?

SOLUTION We are asked to find n when $S_n = 572$. Substituting $a = 5$, $d = 2$, and $S_n = 572$ in Formula 1 for the partial sum of an arithmetic sequence, we get

$$572 = \frac{n}{2}[2 \cdot 5 + (n-1)2] \qquad S_n = \frac{n}{2}[2a + (n-1)d]$$

$$572 = 5n + n(n-1) \qquad \text{Distributive Property}$$

$$0 = n^2 + 4n - 572 \qquad \text{Expand}$$

$$0 = (n - 22)(n + 26) \qquad \text{Factor}$$

This gives $n = 22$ or $n = -26$. But since n is the *number* of terms in this partial sum, we must have $n = 22$.

✎. **NOW TRY EXERCISE 59** ◼

12.2 EXERCISES

CONCEPTS

1. An arithmetic sequence is a sequence in which the _____ between successive terms is constant.

2. The sequence $a_n = a + (n-1)d$ is an arithmetic sequence in which a is the first term and d is the _____ _____. So for the arithmetic sequence $a_n = 2 + 5(n-1)$ the first term is _____, and the common difference is _____.

3. *True or false?* The nth partial sum of an arithmetic sequence is the average of the first and last terms times n.

4. *True or false?* If we know the first and second terms of an arithmetic sequence, then we can find any other term.

SKILLS

5–8 ■ A sequence is given. **(a)** Find the first five terms of the sequence. **(b)** What is the common difference d? **(c)** Graph the terms you found in (a).

5. $a_n = 5 + 2(n-1)$ **6.** $a_n = 3 - 4(n-1)$

7. $a_n = \frac{5}{2} - (n-1)$ **8.** $a_n = \frac{1}{2}(n-1)$

9–12 ■ Find the nth term of the arithmetic sequence with given first term a and common difference d. What is the 10th term?

9. $a = 3, d = 5$ **10.** $a = -6, d = 3$

11. $a = \frac{5}{2}, d = -\frac{1}{2}$ **12.** $a = \sqrt{3}, d = \sqrt{3}$

13–20 ■ Determine whether the sequence is arithmetic. If it is arithmetic, find the common difference.

13. 5, 8, 11, 14, . . .   **14.** 3, 6, 9, 13, . . .

15. 2, 4, 8, 16, . . .   **16.** 2, 4, 6, 8, . . .

17. $3, \frac{3}{2}, 0, -\frac{3}{2}, \ldots$ **18.** ln 2, ln 4, ln 8, ln 16, . . .

19. 2.6, 4.3, 6.0, 7.7, . . .   **20.** $\frac{1}{2}, \frac{1}{3}, \frac{1}{4}, \frac{1}{5}, \ldots$

21–26 ■ Find the first five terms of the sequence, and determine whether it is arithmetic. If it is arithmetic, find the common difference, and express the nth term of the sequence in the standard form $a_n = a + (n-1)d$.

21. $a_n = 4 + 7n$ **22.** $a_n = 4 + 2^n$

23. $a_n = \dfrac{1}{1 + 2n}$ **24.** $a_n = 1 + \dfrac{n}{2}$

25. $a_n = 6n - 10$ **26.** $a_n = 3 + (-1)^n n$

ALTERNATE EXAMPLE 7
How many terms of the arithmetic sequence 3, 5, 7, . . . must be added to get 624?

ANSWER
24

DRILL QUESTION
Consider the sequence 3, 8, 13, 18, 23, 28, 33, 38, ... Find the 100th partial sum.

Answer
25,050

IN-CLASS MATERIALS

Consider the classic "handshaking problem." If n people are in a room and shake hands, we can ask the question: How many handshakes took place? If, for example, four people (Alfred, Brendel, Claude, and Debussy) all shake hands, a total of six shakes take place:

A & B	B & C	C & D
A & C	B & D	A & D

Allow the students to try to figure out how many handshakes take place if 12, or if n people shake hands. It turns out that the answer is $1 + 2 + \cdots + (n-1)$ (as illustrated), the partial sum of an arithmetic sequence.

27–36 ■ Determine the common difference, the fifth term, the nth term, and the 100th term of the arithmetic sequence.

27. $2, 5, 8, 11, \ldots$ **28.** $1, 5, 9, 13, \ldots$

29. $4, 9, 14, 19, \ldots$ **30.** $11, 8, 5, 2, \ldots$

31. $-12, -8, -4, 0, \ldots$ **32.** $\frac{7}{6}, \frac{5}{3}, \frac{13}{6}, \frac{8}{3}, \ldots$

33. $25, 26.5, 28, 29.5, \ldots$ **34.** $15, 12.3, 9.6, 6.9, \ldots$

35. $2, 2 + s, 2 + 2s, 2 + 3s, \ldots$

36. $-t, -t + 3, -t + 6, -t + 9, \ldots$

37. The tenth term of an arithmetic sequence is $\frac{55}{2}$, and the second term is $\frac{7}{2}$. Find the first term.

38. The 12th term of an arithmetic sequence is 32, and the fifth term is 18. Find the 20th term.

39. The 100th term of an arithmetic sequence is 98, and the common difference is 2. Find the first three terms.

40. The 20th term of an arithmetic sequence is 101, and the common difference is 3. Find a formula for the nth term.

41. Which term of the arithmetic sequence $1, 4, 7, \ldots$ is 88?

42. The first term of an arithmetic sequence is 1, and the common difference is 4. Is 11,937 a term of this sequence? If so, which term is it?

43–48 ■ Find the partial sum S_n of the arithmetic sequence that satisfies the given conditions.

43. $a = 1, d = 2, n = 10$ **44.** $a = 3, d = 2, n = 12$

45. $a = 4, d = 2, n = 20$ **46.** $a = 100, d = -5, n = 8$

47. $a_1 = 55, d = 12, n = 10$ **48.** $a_2 = 8, a_5 = 9.5, n = 15$

49–54 ■ A partial sum of an arithmetic sequence is given. Find the sum.

49. $1 + 5 + 9 + \cdots + 401$

50. $-3 + \left(-\frac{3}{2}\right) + 0 + \frac{3}{2} + 3 + \cdots + 30$

51. $0.7 + 2.7 + 4.7 + \cdots + 56.7$

52. $-10 - 9.9 - 9.8 - \cdots - 0.1$

53. $\displaystyle\sum_{k=0}^{10}(3 + 0.25k)$ **54.** $\displaystyle\sum_{n=0}^{20}(1 - 2n)$

55. Show that a right triangle whose sides are in arithmetic progression is similar to a 3–4–5 triangle.

56. Find the product of the numbers
$$10^{1/10}, 10^{2/10}, 10^{3/10}, 10^{4/10}, \ldots, 10^{19/10}$$

57. A sequence is **harmonic** if the reciprocals of the terms of the sequence form an arithmetic sequence. Determine whether the following sequence is harmonic:
$$1, \frac{3}{5}, \frac{3}{7}, \frac{1}{3}, \ldots$$

58. The **harmonic mean** of two numbers is the reciprocal of the average of the reciprocals of the two numbers. Find the harmonic mean of 3 and 5.

59. An arithmetic sequence has first term $a = 5$ and common difference $d = 2$. How many terms of this sequence must be added to get 2700?

60. An arithmetic sequence has first term $a_1 = 1$ and fourth term $a_4 = 16$. How many terms of this sequence must be added to get 2356?

APPLICATIONS

61. Depreciation The purchase value of an office computer is $12,500. Its annual depreciation is $1875. Find the value of the computer after 6 years.

62. Poles in a Pile Telephone poles are being stored in a pile with 25 poles in the first layer, 24 in the second, and so on. If there are 12 layers, how many telephone poles does the pile contain?

63. Salary Increases A man gets a job with a salary of $30,000 a year. He is promised a $2300 raise each subsequent year. Find his total earnings for a 10-year period.

64. Drive-In Theater A drive-in theater has spaces for 20 cars in the first parking row, 22 in the second, 24 in the third, and so on. If there are 21 rows in the theater, find the number of cars that can be parked.

65. Theater Seating An architect designs a theater with 15 seats in the first row, 18 in the second, 21 in the third, and so on. If the theater is to have a seating capacity of 870, how many rows must the architect use in his design?

66. Falling Ball When an object is allowed to fall freely near the surface of the earth, the gravitational pull is such that the object falls 16 ft in the first second, 48 ft in the next second, 80 ft in the next second, and so on.
(a) Find the total distance a ball falls in 6 s.
(b) Find a formula for the total distance a ball falls in n seconds.

67. The Twelve Days of Christmas In the well-known song "The Twelve Days of Christmas," a person gives his sweetheart k gifts on the kth day for each of the 12 days of Christmas. The person also repeats each gift identically on each subsequent day. Thus, on the 12th day the sweetheart receives a gift for the first day, 2 gifts for the second, 3 gifts for the third, and so on. Show that the number of gifts received on the 12th day is a partial sum of an arithmetic sequence. Find this sum.

DISCOVERY ■ DISCUSSION ■ WRITING

68. Arithmetic Means The **arithmetic mean** (or average) of two numbers a and b is
$$m = \frac{a + b}{2}$$

EXAMPLES

Finding details of an arithmetic sequence given two terms: If an arithmetic sequence has $a_3 = 39$ and $a_{10} = 25$, then we can calculate $a = 43, d = -2$. $a_n = 43 - 2(n - 1)$, so $a_{100} = -155$ and $\displaystyle\sum_{n=1}^{100} 43 - 2(n - 1) = -5600$.

Make sure to point out that this trick works only if we know ahead of time that this is an arithmetic sequence.

Note that m is the same distance from a as from b, so a, m, b is an arithmetic sequence. In general, if $m_1, m_2, \ldots, m_k$ are equally spaced between a and b so that

$$a, m_1, m_2, \ldots, m_k, b$$

is an arithmetic sequence, then $m_1, m_2, \ldots, m_k$ are called k arithmetic means between a and b.

(a) Insert two arithmetic means between 10 and 18.
(b) Insert three arithmetic means between 10 and 18.
(c) Suppose a doctor needs to increase a patient's dosage of a certain medicine from 100 mg to 300 mg per day in five equal steps. How many arithmetic means must be inserted between 100 and 300 to give the progression of daily doses, and what are these means?

12.3 GEOMETRIC SEQUENCES

| Geometric Sequences ▶ Partial Sums of Geometric Sequences ▶ What Is an Infinite Series? ▶ Infinite Geometric Series

In this section we study geometric sequences. This type of sequence occurs frequently in applications to finance, population growth, and other fields.

▼ Geometric Sequences

Recall that an arithmetic sequence is generated when we repeatedly add a number d to an initial term a. A *geometric* sequence is generated when we start with a number a and repeatedly *multiply* by a fixed nonzero constant r.

DEFINITION OF A GEOMETRIC SEQUENCE

A **geometric sequence** is a sequence of the form

$$a, ar, ar^2, ar^3, ar^4, \ldots$$

The number a is the **first term**, and r is the **common ratio** of the sequence. The **nth term** of a geometric sequence is given by

$$a_n = ar^{n-1}$$

The number r is called the common ratio because the ratio of any two consecutive terms of the sequence is r.

EXAMPLE 1 | Geometric Sequences

(a) If $a = 3$ and $r = 2$, then we have the geometric sequence

$$3, \quad 3 \cdot 2, \quad 3 \cdot 2^2, \quad 3 \cdot 2^3, \quad 3 \cdot 2^4, \quad \ldots$$

or $\qquad\qquad 3, 6, 12, 24, 48, \ldots$

Notice that the ratio of any two consecutive terms is $r = 2$. The nth term is $a_n = 3(2)^{n-1}$.

(b) The sequence

$$2, -10, 50, -250, 1250, \ldots$$

is a geometric sequence with $a = 2$ and $r = -5$. When r is negative, the terms of the sequence alternate in sign. The nth term is $a_n = 2(-5)^{n-1}$.

(c) The sequence

$$1, \frac{1}{3}, \frac{1}{9}, \frac{1}{27}, \frac{1}{81}, \ldots$$

is a geometric sequence with $a = 1$ and $r = \frac{1}{3}$. The nth term is $a_n = 1\left(\frac{1}{3}\right)^{n-1}$.

ALTERNATE EXAMPLE 1

(a) Find the first four terms and the nth term of the geometric sequence with $a = 2$ and $r = 3$.
(c) Find the nth term of the geometric sequence 2, 8, 32, 128, ...

ANSWERS

(a) 2, 6, 18, 54, $a_n = 2(3)^{n-1}$
(c) $a_n = 2(4)^{n-1}$

TEXT QUESTION
What distinguishes a "geometric sequence" from an arbitrary "sequence"?

Answer
Successive terms in a geometric sequence have a common ratio.

FIGURE 1

FIGURE 2

(d) The graph of the geometric sequence $a_n = \frac{1}{5} \cdot 2^{n-1}$ is shown in Figure 1. Notice that the points in the graph lie on the graph of the exponential function $y = \frac{1}{5} \cdot 2^{x-1}$.

If $0 < r < 1$, then the terms of the geometric sequence ar^{n-1} decrease, but if $r > 1$, then the terms increase. (What happens if $r = 1$?)

✎ NOW TRY EXERCISES **5**, **9**, AND **13**   ■

Geometric sequences occur naturally. Here is a simple example. Suppose a ball has elasticity such that when it is dropped, it bounces up one-third of the distance it has fallen. If this ball is dropped from a height of 2 m, then it bounces up to a height of $2(\frac{1}{3}) = \frac{2}{3}$ m. On its second bounce, it returns to a height of $(\frac{2}{3})(\frac{1}{3}) = \frac{2}{9}$ m, and so on (see Figure 2). Thus, the height h_n that the ball reaches on its nth bounce is given by the geometric sequence

$$h_n = \tfrac{2}{3}(\tfrac{1}{3})^{n-1} = 2(\tfrac{1}{3})^n$$

We can find the nth term of a geometric sequence if we know any two terms, as the following examples show.

EXAMPLE 2 | Finding Terms of a Geometric Sequence

Find the eighth term of the geometric sequence 5, 15, 45, ...

SOLUTION   To find a formula for the nth term of this sequence, we need to find a and r. Clearly, $a = 5$. To find r, we find the ratio of any two consecutive terms. For instance, $r = \frac{45}{15} = 3$. Thus

$$a_n = 5(3)^{n-1}$$

The eighth term is $a_8 = 5(3)^{8-1} = 5(3)^7 = 10{,}935$.

✎ NOW TRY EXERCISE **27**   ■

EXAMPLE 3 | Finding Terms of a Geometric Sequence

The third term of a geometric sequence is $\frac{63}{4}$, and the sixth term is $\frac{1701}{32}$. Find the fifth term.

SOLUTION   Since this sequence is geometric, its nth term is given by the formula $a_n = ar^{n-1}$. Thus

$$a_3 = ar^{3-1} = ar^2$$
$$a_6 = ar^{6-1} = ar^5$$

From the values we are given for these two terms, we get the following system of equations:

$$\begin{cases} \frac{63}{4} = ar^2 \\ \frac{1701}{32} = ar^5 \end{cases}$$

We solve this system by dividing.

$$\frac{ar^5}{ar^2} = \frac{\frac{1701}{32}}{\frac{63}{4}}$$
$$r^3 = \tfrac{27}{8} \qquad \text{Simplify}$$
$$r = \tfrac{3}{2} \qquad \text{Take cube root of each side}$$

Substituting for r in the first equation, $\frac{63}{4} = ar^2$, gives

$$\tfrac{63}{4} = a(\tfrac{3}{2})^2$$
$$a = 7 \qquad \text{Solve for } a$$

ALTERNATE EXAMPLE 2
Find the eighth term of the geometric sequence 7, 42, 252, ...

ANSWER
1,959,552

ALTERNATE EXAMPLE 3
The third term of a geometric sequence is $\dfrac{75}{16}$, and the sixth term is $\dfrac{9375}{1024}$. Find the fifth term.

ANSWER
$\dfrac{1875}{256}$

IN-CLASS MATERIALS

Represent a geometric series visually. For example, a geometric view of the equation $\displaystyle\sum_{n=1}^{\infty} 1/2^n = 1$ is given here.

It follows that the nth term of this sequence is

$$a_n = 7\left(\tfrac{3}{2}\right)^{n-1}$$

Thus the fifth term is

$$a_5 = 7\left(\tfrac{3}{2}\right)^{5-1} = 7\left(\tfrac{3}{2}\right)^4 = \tfrac{567}{16}$$

✎. NOW TRY EXERCISE **37**   ∎

SRINIVASA RAMANUJAN
(1887–1920) was born into a poor family in the small town of Kumbakonam
in India. Self-taught in mathematics, he
worked in virtual isolation from other
mathematicians. At the age of 25 he
wrote a letter to G. H. Hardy, the leading
British mathematician at the time, listing some of his discoveries. Hardy immediately recognized Ramanujan's genius, and for the next six years the two
worked together in London until
Ramanujan fell ill and returned to his
hometown in India, where he died a
year later. Ramanujan was a genius
with phenomenal ability to see hidden
patterns in the properties of numbers.
Most of his discoveries were written as
complicated infinite series, the importance of which was not recognized until many years after his death. In the last
year of his life he wrote 130 pages of
mysterious formulas, many of which
still defy proof. Hardy tells the story
that when he visited Ramanujan in a
hospital and arrived in a taxi, he re-
marked to Ramanujan that the cab's
number, 1729, was uninteresting.
Ramanujan replied "No, it is a very interesting number. It is the smallest
number expressible as the sum of two
cubes in two different ways."

▼ Partial Sums of Geometric Sequences

For the geometric sequence $a, ar, ar^2, ar^3, ar^4, \ldots, ar^{n-1}, \ldots$, the nth partial sum is

$$S_n = \sum_{k=1}^{n} ar^{k-1} = a + ar + ar^2 + ar^3 + ar^4 + \cdots + ar^{n-1}$$

To find a formula for S_n, we multiply S_n by r and subtract from S_n.

$$S_n = a + ar + ar^2 + ar^3 + ar^4 + \cdots + ar^{n-1}$$

$$\underline{rS_n = \quad\quad ar + ar^2 + ar^3 + ar^4 + \cdots + ar^{n-1} + ar^n}$$

$$S_n - rS_n = a - ar^n$$

So

$$S_n(1 - r) = a(1 - r^n)$$

$$S_n = \frac{a(1 - r^n)}{1 - r} \quad (r \neq 1)$$

We summarize this result.

PARTIAL SUMS OF A GEOMETRIC SEQUENCE

For the geometric sequence $a_n = ar^{n-1}$, the **nth partial sum**

$$S_n = a + ar + ar^2 + ar^3 + ar^4 + \cdots + ar^{n-1} \quad (r \neq 1)$$

is given by

$$S_n = a\frac{1 - r^n}{1 - r}$$

EXAMPLE 4 | Finding a Partial Sum of a Geometric Sequence

Find the sum of the first five terms of the geometric sequence

$$1, 0.7, 0.49, 0.343, \ldots$$

SOLUTION   The required sum is the sum of the first five terms of a geometric sequence
with $a = 1$ and $r = 0.7$. Using the formula for S_n with $n = 5$, we get

$$S_5 = 1 \cdot \frac{1 - (0.7)^5}{1 - 0.7} = 2.7731$$

Thus the sum of the first five terms of this sequence is 2.7731.

✎. NOW TRY EXERCISES **43** AND **47**   ∎

EXAMPLE 5 | Finding a Partial Sum of a Geometric Sequence

Find the sum $\sum_{k=1}^{5} 7\left(-\tfrac{2}{3}\right)^k$.

ALTERNATE EXAMPLE 4
Find the sum of the first 6 terms
of the geometric sequence
$1, 0.6, 0.36, 0.216, \ldots$.

ANSWER
2.38336

ALTERNATE EXAMPLE 5
Find the sum.

$$\sum_{k=1}^{4} 7\left(-\frac{2}{3}\right)^k$$

ANSWER
$-\dfrac{182}{81}$

IN-CLASS MATERIALS

One of the consequences of parenthood is that it often causes otherwise rational adults to say things like,
"If I told you once, I've told you one *hundred* times!" Assume that this was true, and a child was told
something on a Friday. The parental rule means that the child was previously told a fact 100 times, say on
Thursday. Thus, on Wednesday, the child must have been told the information 100 times for every time on
Thursday, or 10,000 times. Use the methods of this section to determine how many times the child has
been told since Monday.

SOLUTION The given sum is the fifth partial sum of a geometric sequence with first term $a = 7\left(-\frac{2}{3}\right)^1 = -\frac{14}{3}$ and common ratio $r = -\frac{2}{3}$. Thus, by the formula for S_n we have

$$S_5 = -\frac{14}{3} \cdot \frac{1 - \left(-\frac{2}{3}\right)^5}{1 - \left(-\frac{2}{3}\right)} = -\frac{14}{3} \cdot \frac{1 + \frac{32}{243}}{\frac{5}{3}} = -\frac{770}{243}$$

✎ NOW TRY EXERCISE **49**　　　　　　　　　　　　　　　　　　　　■

▼ What Is an Infinite Series?

An expression of the form

$$\sum_{k=1}^{\infty} a_k = a_1 + a_2 + a_3 + a_4 + \cdots$$

is called an **infinite series**. The dots mean that we are to continue the addition indefinitely. What meaning can we attach to the sum of infinitely many numbers? It seems at first that it is not possible to add infinitely many numbers and arrive at a finite number. But consider the following problem. You have a cake, and you want to eat it by first eating half the cake, then eating half of what remains, then again eating half of what remains. This process can continue indefinitely because at each stage, some of the cake remains. (See Figure 3.)

    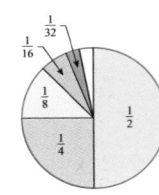

FIGURE 3

Does this mean that it's impossible to eat all of the cake? Of course not. Let's write down what you have eaten from this cake:

$$\sum_{k=1}^{\infty} \frac{1}{2^k} = \frac{1}{2} + \frac{1}{4} + \frac{1}{8} + \frac{1}{16} + \cdots$$

This is an infinite series, and we note two things about it: First, from Figure 3 it's clear that no matter how many terms of this series we add, the total will never exceed 1. Second, the more terms of this series we add, the closer the sum is to 1 (see Figure 3). This suggests that the number 1 can be written as the sum of infinitely many smaller numbers:

$$1 = \frac{1}{2} + \frac{1}{4} + \frac{1}{8} + \frac{1}{16} + \cdots + \frac{1}{2^n} + \cdots$$

To make this more precise, let's look at the partial sums of this series:

$$S_1 = \frac{1}{2} \qquad\qquad\qquad = \frac{1}{2}$$
$$S_2 = \frac{1}{2} + \frac{1}{4} \qquad\qquad = \frac{3}{4}$$
$$S_3 = \frac{1}{2} + \frac{1}{4} + \frac{1}{8} \qquad = \frac{7}{8}$$
$$S_4 = \frac{1}{2} + \frac{1}{4} + \frac{1}{8} + \frac{1}{16} = \frac{15}{16}$$

and, in general (see Example 5 of Section 12.1),

$$S_n = 1 - \frac{1}{2^n}$$

IN-CLASS MATERIALS

Introduce the idea that for any two real numbers A and B, the statement $A = B$ is the same as saying that for any integer N, $|A - B| < 1/N$. Now use this idea to show that $0.9999 \ldots = 0.\overline{9} = 1$, since $|1 - 0.\overline{9}| < |1 - \underbrace{0.99999\ldots99}_{N \text{ nines}}| = \underbrace{\frac{0.00000\ldots0001}{N-1 \text{ zero}}}_{} = 10^{-N} = \frac{1}{10^N}$. Then use the usual approach to define $0.\overline{9}$ as $\sum_{n=1}^{\infty} 9/10^n$ and show directly that $0.\overline{9} = 1$. Generalize this result by pointing out that *any* repeating decimal $(0.\overline{3}, 0.\overline{412}, 0.24\overline{621})$ can be written as a geometric series and can thus be written as a fraction using the formula for a geometric series. Demonstrate with $0.\overline{412} = \left(\dfrac{1}{1 - 1/1000}\right) = \dfrac{412}{999}$.

EXAMPLE

Zeno's paradox: To walk to a wall across the room, you must first walk halfway to the wall, and to do that, you must walk halfway to the halfway point, etc. This process can be viewed as finding the sum of

$$\frac{1}{2} + \frac{1}{4} + \frac{1}{8} + \cdots = 1.$$ The sum of this infinite series is 1.

As n gets larger and larger, we are adding more and more of the terms of this series. Intuitively, as n gets larger, S_n gets closer to the sum of the series. Now notice that as n gets large, $1/2^n$ gets closer and closer to 0. Thus S_n gets close to $1 - 0 = 1$. Using the notation of Section 3.7, we can write

$$S_n \to 1 \quad \text{as} \quad n \to \infty$$

In general, if S_n gets close to a finite number S as n gets large, we say that the infinite series **converges** (or is **convergent**). The number S is called the **sum of the infinite series**. If an infinite series does not converge, we say that the series **diverges** (or is **divergent**).

▼ Infinite Geometric Series

Here is another way to arrive at the formula for the sum of an infinite geometric series:

$$S = a + ar + ar^2 + ar^3 + \cdots$$
$$= a + r(a + ar + ar^2 + \cdots)$$
$$= a + rS$$

Solve the equation $S = a + rS$ for S to get

$$S - rS = a$$
$$(1 - r)S = a$$
$$S = \frac{a}{1 - r}$$

An **infinite geometric series** is a series of the form

$$a + ar + ar^2 + ar^3 + ar^4 + \cdots + ar^{n-1} + \cdots$$

We can apply the reasoning used earlier to find the sum of an infinite geometric series. The nth partial sum of such a series is given by the formula

$$S_n = a\frac{1 - r^n}{1 - r} \qquad (r \neq 1)$$

It can be shown that if $|r| < 1$, then r^n gets close to 0 as n gets large (you can easily convince yourself of this using a calculator). It follows that S_n gets close to $a/(1 - r)$ as n gets large, or

$$S_n \to \frac{a}{1 - r} \quad \text{as} \quad n \to \infty$$

Thus the sum of this infinite geometric series is $a/(1 - r)$.

SUM OF AN INFINITE GEOMETRIC SERIES

If $|r| < 1$, then the infinite geometric series

$$\sum_{k=1}^{\infty} ar^{k-1} = a + ar + ar^2 + ar^3 + \cdots$$

converges and has the sum

$$S = \frac{a}{1 - r}$$

If $|r| \geq 1$, the series diverges.

MATHEMATICS IN THE MODERN WORLD

Fractals

Many of the things we model in this book have regular predictable shapes. But recent advances in mathematics have made it possible to model such seemingly random or even chaotic shapes as those of a cloud, a flickering flame, a mountain, or a jagged coastline. The basic tools in this type of modeling are the fractals invented by the mathematician Benoit Mandelbrot. A *fractal* is a geometric shape built up from a simple basic shape by scaling and repeating the shape indefinitely according to a given rule. Fractals have infinite detail; this means the closer you look, the more you see. They are also *self-similar*; that is, zooming in on a portion of the fractal yields the same detail as the original shape. Because of their beautiful shapes, fractals are used by movie makers to create fictional landscapes and exotic backgrounds.

Although a fractal is a complex shape, it is produced according to very simple rules. This property of fractals is exploited in a process of storing pictures on a computer called *fractal image compression*. In this process a picture is stored as a simple basic shape and a rule; repeating the shape according to the rule produces the original picture. This is an extremely efficient method of storage; that's how thousands of color pictures can be put on a single compact disc.

IN-CLASS MATERIALS

Do Exercise 79 (the "St. Ives" problem) with the students. After obtaining the partial sum solution, point out that traditionally people give the answer 1. The problem says, "As I was going to St. Ives. . . ." So presumably all the other people were going the other way, away from St. Ives!

EXAMPLE 6 | Infinite Series

Determine whether the infinite geometric series is convergent or divergent. If it is convergent, find its sum.

(a) $2 + \frac{2}{5} + \frac{2}{25} + \frac{2}{125} + \cdots$ (b) $1 + \frac{7}{5} + \left(\frac{7}{5}\right)^2 + \left(\frac{7}{5}\right)^3 + \cdots$

SOLUTION

(a) This is an infinite geometric series with $a = 2$ and $r = \frac{1}{5}$. Since $|r| = \left|\frac{1}{5}\right| < 1$, the series converges. By the formula for the sum of an infinite geometric series we have

$$S = \frac{2}{1 - \frac{1}{5}} = \frac{5}{2}$$

(b) This is an infinite geometric series with $a = 1$ and $r = \frac{7}{5}$. Since $|r| = \left|\frac{7}{5}\right| > 1$, the series diverges.

✎. NOW TRY EXERCISES **51** AND **55** ■

EXAMPLE 7 | Writing a Repeated Decimal as a Fraction

Find the fraction that represents the rational number $2.3\overline{51}$.

SOLUTION This repeating decimal can be written as a series:

$$\frac{23}{10} + \frac{51}{1000} + \frac{51}{100,000} + \frac{51}{10,000,000} + \frac{51}{1,000,000,000} + \cdots$$

After the first term, the terms of this series form an infinite geometric series with

$$a = \frac{51}{1000} \quad \text{and} \quad r = \frac{1}{100}$$

Thus the sum of this part of the series is

$$S = \frac{\frac{51}{1000}}{1 - \frac{1}{100}} = \frac{\frac{51}{1000}}{\frac{99}{100}} = \frac{51}{1000} \cdot \frac{100}{99} = \frac{51}{990}$$

So

$$2.3\overline{51} = \frac{23}{10} + \frac{51}{990} = \frac{2328}{990} = \frac{388}{165}$$

✎. NOW TRY EXERCISE **63** ■

12.3 EXERCISES

CONCEPTS

1. A geometric sequence is a sequence in which the _____ of successive terms is constant.

2. The sequence $a_n = ar^{n-1}$ is a geometric sequence in which a is the first term and r is the _____ _____. So for the geometric sequence $a_n = 2(5)^{n-1}$ the first term is _____, and the common ratio is _____.

3. *True or false?* If we know the first and second terms of a geometric sequence, then we can find any other term.

4. (a) The nth partial sum of a geometric sequence $a_n = ar^{n-1}$ is given by $S_n = $ _____.

(b) The series
$$\sum_{k=1}^{\infty} ar^{k-1} = a + ar + ar^2 + ar^3 + \cdots$$
is an infinite _____ series. If $|r| < 1$, then this series _____, and its sum is $S = $ _____. If $|r| \geq 1$, the series _____.

ALTERNATE EXAMPLE 6
Determine whether the following infinite geometric series is convergent or divergent. If it is convergent, find its sum.

$3 + 1 + \frac{1}{3} + \frac{1}{9} + \frac{1}{27} + \ldots$

ANSWER

It is convergent, with $a = 3$ and $r = \frac{1}{3}$. The sum is $\frac{9}{2}$.

ALTERNATE EXAMPLE 7
Find the fraction that represents the rational number $1.8\overline{73}$.

ANSWER
$\frac{371}{198}$

DRILL QUESTION
Find the 100th partial sum of the sequence 2, 6, 18, 54, 162, ...

Answer
$\frac{2(1 - 3^{100})}{1 - 3} \approx 5.154 \times 10^{47}$

IN-CLASS MATERIALS
Explore the "middle third" Cantor set with the class: This set is defined as the set of points obtained by taking the interval $[0, 1]$, throwing out the middle third to obtain $\left[0, \frac{1}{3}\right] \cup \left[\frac{2}{3}, 1\right]$, throwing out the middle third of each remaining interval to obtain $\left[0, \frac{1}{9}\right] \cup \left[\frac{2}{9}, \frac{1}{3}\right] \cup \left[\frac{2}{3}, \frac{7}{9}\right] \cup \left[\frac{8}{9}, 1\right]$, and repeating this process ad infinitum. Point out that there are infinitely many points left after this process. (If a point winds up as the endpoint of an interval, it never gets removed, and new intervals are created with every step.) Now calculate the total length of the sections that were thrown away: $\frac{1}{3} + 2 \cdot \frac{1}{9} + 4 \cdot \frac{1}{27} + \cdots = \sum_{k=0}^{\infty} \frac{2k}{3k + 1} = 1$.

Notice the apparent paradox: We've thrown away a total interval of length 1, but still infinitely many points remain. (See also Exercise 81.)

SKILLS

5–8 ■ The nth term of a sequence is given. **(a)** Find the first five terms of the sequence. **(b)** What is the common ratio r? **(c)** Graph the terms you found in (a).

5. $a_n = 5(2)^{n-1}$ **6.** $a_n = 3(-4)^{n-1}$

7. $a_n = \frac{5}{2}\left(-\frac{1}{2}\right)^{n-1}$ **8.** $a_n = 3^{n-1}$

9–12 ■ Find the nth term of the geometric sequence with given first term a and common ratio r. What is the fourth term?

9. $a = 3$, $r = 5$ **10.** $a = -6$, $r = 3$

11. $a = \frac{5}{2}$, $r = -\frac{1}{2}$ **12.** $a = \sqrt{3}$, $r = \sqrt{3}$

13–20 ■ Determine whether the sequence is geometric. If it is geometric, find the common ratio.

13. $2, 4, 8, 16, \ldots$ **14.** $2, 6, 18, 36, \ldots$

15. $3, \frac{3}{2}, \frac{3}{4}, \frac{3}{8}, \ldots$ **16.** $27, -9, 3, -1, \ldots$

17. $\frac{1}{2}, \frac{1}{3}, \frac{1}{4}, \frac{1}{5}, \ldots$ **18.** $e^2, e^4, e^6, e^8, \ldots$

19. $1.0, 1.1, 1.21, 1.331, \ldots$ **20.** $\frac{1}{2}, \frac{1}{4}, \frac{1}{6}, \frac{1}{8}, \ldots$

21–26 ■ Find the first five terms of the sequence, and determine whether it is geometric. If it is geometric, find the common ratio, and express the nth term of the sequence in the standard form $a_n = ar^{n-1}$.

21. $a_n = 2(3)^n$ **22.** $a_n = 4 + 3^n$

23. $a_n = \dfrac{1}{4^n}$ **24.** $a_n = (-1)^n 2^n$

25. $a_n = \ln(5^{n-1})$ **26.** $a_n = n^n$

27–36 ■ Determine the common ratio, the fifth term, and the nth term of the geometric sequence.

27. $2, 6, 18, 54, \ldots$ **28.** $7, \frac{14}{3}, \frac{28}{9}, \frac{56}{27}, \ldots$

29. $0.3, -0.09, 0.027, -0.0081, \ldots$

30. $1, \sqrt{2}, 2, 2\sqrt{2}, \ldots$

31. $144, -12, 1, -\frac{1}{12}, \ldots$ **32.** $-8, -2, -\frac{1}{2}, -\frac{1}{8}, \ldots$

33. $3, 3^{5/3}, 3^{7/3}, 27, \ldots$ **34.** $t, \dfrac{t^2}{2}, \dfrac{t^3}{4}, \dfrac{t^4}{8}, \ldots$

35. $1, s^{2/7}, s^{4/7}, s^{6/7}, \ldots$ **36.** $5, 5^{c+1}, 5^{2c+1}, 5^{3c+1}, \ldots$

37. The first term of a geometric sequence is 8, and the second term is 4. Find the fifth term.

38. The first term of a geometric sequence is 3, and the third term is $\frac{4}{3}$. Find the fifth term.

39. The common ratio in a geometric sequence is $\frac{2}{5}$, and the fourth term is $\frac{5}{2}$. Find the third term.

40. The common ratio in a geometric sequence is $\frac{3}{2}$, and the fifth term is 1. Find the first three terms.

41. Which term of the geometric sequence $2, 6, 18, \ldots$ is 118,098?

42. The second and fifth terms of a geometric sequence are 10 and 1250, respectively. Is 31,250 a term of this sequence? If so, which term is it?

43–46 ■ Find the partial sum S_n of the geometric sequence that satisfies the given conditions.

43. $a = 5$, $r = 2$, $n = 6$ **44.** $a = \frac{2}{3}$, $r = \frac{1}{3}$, $n = 4$

45. $a_3 = 28$, $a_6 = 224$, $n = 6$

46. $a_2 = 0.12$, $a_5 = 0.00096$, $n = 4$

47–50 ■ Find the sum.

47. $1 + 3 + 9 + \cdots + 2187$

48. $1 - \frac{1}{2} + \frac{1}{4} - \frac{1}{8} + \cdots - \frac{1}{512}$

49. $\displaystyle\sum_{k=0}^{10} 3\left(\frac{1}{2}\right)^k$ **50.** $\displaystyle\sum_{j=0}^{5} 7\left(\frac{3}{2}\right)^j$

51–62 ■ Determine whether the infinite geometric series is convergent or divergent. If it is convergent, find its sum.

51. $1 + \frac{1}{3} + \frac{1}{9} + \frac{1}{27} + \cdots$ **52.** $1 - \frac{1}{2} + \frac{1}{4} - \frac{1}{8} + \cdots$

53. $1 - \frac{1}{3} + \frac{1}{9} - \frac{1}{27} + \cdots$ **54.** $\frac{2}{5} + \frac{4}{25} + \frac{8}{125} + \cdots$

55. $1 + \frac{3}{2} + \left(\frac{3}{2}\right)^2 + \left(\frac{3}{2}\right)^3 + \cdots$

56. $\frac{1}{3^6} + \frac{1}{3^8} + \frac{1}{3^{10}} + \frac{1}{3^{12}} + \cdots$

57. $3 - \frac{3}{2} + \frac{3}{4} - \frac{3}{8} + \cdots$

58. $1 - 1 + 1 - 1 + \cdots$

59. $3 - 3(1.1) + 3(1.1)^2 - 3(1.1)^3 + \cdots$

60. $-\frac{100}{9} + \frac{10}{3} - 1 + \frac{3}{10} - \cdots$

61. $\frac{1}{\sqrt{2}} + \frac{1}{2} + \frac{1}{2\sqrt{2}} + \frac{1}{4} + \cdots$

62. $1 - \sqrt{2} + 2 - 2\sqrt{2} + 4 - \cdots$

63–68 ■ Express the repeating decimal as a fraction.

63. $0.777\ldots$ **64.** $0.2\overline{53}$ **65.** $0.030303\ldots$

66. $2.11\overline{25}$ **67.** $0.\overline{112}$ **68.** $0.123123123\ldots$

69. If the numbers $a_1, a_2, \ldots, a_n$ form a geometric sequence, then $a_2, a_3, \ldots, a_{n-1}$ are **geometric means** between a_1 and a_n. Insert three geometric means between 5 and 80.

70. Find the sum of the first ten terms of the sequence
$$a + b, \; a^2 + 2b, \; a^3 + 3b, \; a^4 + 4b, \ldots$$

APPLICATIONS

71. Depreciation A construction company purchases a bulldozer for $160,000. Each year the value of the bulldozer depreciates by 20% of its value in the preceding year. Let V_n be the value of the bulldozer in the nth year. (Let $n = 1$ be the year the bulldozer is purchased.)
(a) Find a formula for V_n.
(b) In what year will the value of the bulldozer be less than $100,000?

72. Family Tree A person has two parents, four grandparents, eight great-grandparents, and so on. How many ancestors does a person have 15 generations back?

73. Bouncing Ball A ball is dropped from a height of 80 ft. The elasticity of this ball is such that it rebounds three-fourths of the distance it has fallen. How high does the ball rebound on the fifth bounce? Find a formula for how high the ball rebounds on the nth bounce.

74. Bacteria Culture A culture initially has 5000 bacteria, and its size increases by 8% every hour. How many bacteria are present at the end of 5 hours? Find a formula for the number of bacteria present after n hours.

75. Mixing Coolant A truck radiator holds 5 gal and is filled with water. A gallon of water is removed from the radiator and replaced with a gallon of antifreeze; then a gallon of the mixture is removed from the radiator and again replaced by a gallon of antifreeze. This process is repeated indefinitely. How much water remains in the tank after this process is repeated 3 times? 5 times? n times?

76. Musical Frequencies The frequencies of musical notes (measured in cycles per second) form a geometric sequence. Middle C has a frequency of 256, and the C that is an octave higher has a frequency of 512. Find the frequency of C two octaves below middle C.

77. Bouncing Ball A ball is dropped from a height of 9 ft. The elasticity of the ball is such that it always bounces up one-third the distance it has fallen.
(a) Find the total distance the ball has traveled at the instant it hits the ground the fifth time.
(b) Find a formula for the total distance the ball has traveled at the instant it hits the ground the nth time.

78. Geometric Savings Plan A very patient woman wishes to become a billionaire. She decides to follow a simple scheme: She puts aside 1 cent the first day, 2 cents the second day, 4 cents the third day, and so on, doubling the number of cents each day. How much money will she have at the end of 30 days? How many days will it take this woman to realize her wish?

79. St. Ives The following is a well-known children's rhyme:

As I was going to St. Ives,
I met a man with seven wives;
Every wife had seven sacks;
Every sack had seven cats;
Every cat had seven kits;
Kits, cats, sacks, and wives,
How many were going to St. Ives?

Assuming that the entire group is actually going to St. Ives, show that the answer to the question in the rhyme is a partial sum of a geometric sequence, and find the sum.

80. Drug Concentration A certain drug is administered once a day. The concentration of the drug in the patient's bloodstream increases rapidly at first, but each successive dose has less effect than the preceding one. The total amount of the drug (in mg) in the bloodstream after the nth dose is given by

$$\sum_{k=1}^{n} 50\left(\tfrac{1}{2}\right)^{k-1}$$

(a) Find the amount of the drug in the bloodstream after $n = 10$ days.
(b) If the drug is taken on a long-term basis, the amount in the bloodstream is approximated by the infinite series
$$\sum_{k=1}^{\infty} 50\left(\tfrac{1}{2}\right)^{k-1}.$$ Find the sum of this series.

81. Bouncing Ball A certain ball rebounds to half the height from which it is dropped. Use an infinite geometric series to approximate the total distance the ball travels after being dropped from 1 m above the ground until it comes to rest.

82. Bouncing Ball If the ball in Exercise 81 is dropped from a height of 8 ft, then 1 s is required for its first complete bounce—from the instant it first touches the ground until it next touches the ground. Each subsequent complete bounce requires $1/\sqrt{2}$ as long as the preceding complete bounce. Use an infinite geometric series to estimate the time interval from the instant the ball first touches the ground until it stops bouncing.

83. Geometry The midpoints of the sides of a square of side 1 are joined to form a new square. This procedure is repeated for each new square. (See the figure.)
(a) Find the sum of the areas of all the squares.
(b) Find the sum of the perimeters of all the squares.

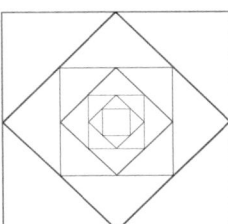

84. Geometry A circular disk of radius R is cut out of paper, as shown in figure (a). Two disks of radius $\frac{1}{2}R$ are cut out of paper and placed on top of the first disk, as in figure (b), and then four disks of radius $\frac{1}{4}R$ are placed on these two disks, as in figure (c). Assuming that this process can be repeated indefinitely, find the total area of all the disks.

(a)   (b)   (c)

85. **Geometry**   A yellow square of side 1 is divided into nine smaller squares, and the middle square is colored blue as shown in the figure. Each of the smaller yellow squares is in turn divided into nine squares, and each middle square is colored blue. If this process is continued indefinitely, what is the total area that is colored blue?

DISCOVERY ▪ DISCUSSION ▪ WRITING

86. **Arithmetic or Geometric?**   The first four terms of a sequence are given. Determine whether these terms can be the terms of an arithmetic sequence, a geometric sequence, or neither. Find the next term if the sequence is arithmetic or geometric.
   (a) $5, -3, 5, -3, \ldots$
   (b) $\frac{1}{3}, 1, \frac{5}{3}, \frac{7}{3}, \ldots$
   (c) $\sqrt{3}, 3, 3\sqrt{3}, 9, \ldots$
   (d) $1, -1, 1, -1, \ldots$
   (e) $2, -1, \frac{1}{2}, 2, \ldots$
   (f) $x - 1, x, x + 1, x + 2, \ldots$
   (g) $-3, -\frac{3}{2}, 0, \frac{3}{2}, \ldots$
   (h) $\sqrt{5}, \sqrt[3]{5}, \sqrt[6]{5}, 1, \ldots$

87. **Reciprocals of a Geometric Sequence**   If $a_1, a_2, a_3, \ldots$ is a geometric sequence with common ratio r, show that the sequence

$$\frac{1}{a_1}, \frac{1}{a_2}, \frac{1}{a_3}, \ldots$$

is also a geometric sequence, and find the common ratio.

88. **Logarithms of a Geometric Sequence**   If $a_1, a_2, a_3, \ldots$ is a geometric sequence with a common ratio $r > 0$ and $a_1 > 0$, show that the sequence

$$\log a_1, \log a_2, \log a_3, \ldots$$

is an arithmetic sequence, and find the common difference.

89. **Exponentials of an Arithmetic Sequence**   If $a_1, a_2, a_3, \ldots$ is an arithmetic sequence with common difference d, show that the sequence

$$10^{a_1}, 10^{a_2}, 10^{a_3}, \ldots$$

is a geometric sequence, and find the common ratio.

 Finding Patterns

In this project we investigate the process of finding patterns in sequences by using "difference sequences." You can find the project at the book companion website: **www.stewartmath.com**

12.4 MATHEMATICS OF FINANCE

| The Amount of an Annuity ▶ The Present Value of an Annuity
| ▶ Installment Buying

Many financial transactions involve payments that are made at regular intervals. For example, if you deposit $100 each month in an interest-bearing account, what will the value of your account be at the end of 5 years? If you borrow $100,000 to buy a house, how much must your monthly payments be in order to pay off the loan in 30 years? Each of these questions involves the sum of a sequence of numbers; we use the results of the preceding section to answer them here.

▼ The Amount of an Annuity

An **annuity** is a sum of money that is paid in regular equal payments. Although the word *annuity* suggests annual (or yearly) payments, they can be made semiannually, quarterly, monthly, or at some other regular interval. Payments are usually made at the end of the payment interval. The **amount of an annuity** is the sum of all the individual payments from the time of the first payment until the last payment is made, together with all the interest. We denote this sum by A_f (the subscript f here is used to denote *final* amount).

EXAMPLE 1 | Calculating the Amount of an Annuity

An investor deposits $400 every December 15 and June 15 for 10 years in an account that earns interest at the rate of 8% per year, compounded semiannually. How much will be in the account immediately after the last payment?

TEXT QUESTION

What is an annuity?

Answer

An annuity is a sum of money paid in regular, equal payments.

SOLUTION We need to find the amount of an annuity consisting of 20 semiannual payments of $400 each. Since the interest rate is 8% per year, compounded semiannually, the interest rate per time period is $i = 0.08/2 = 0.04$. The first payment is in the account for 19 time periods, the second for 18 time periods, and so on.

The last payment receives no interest. The situation can be illustrated by the time line in Figure 1.

When using interest rates in calculators, remember to convert percentages to decimals. For example, 8% is 0.08.

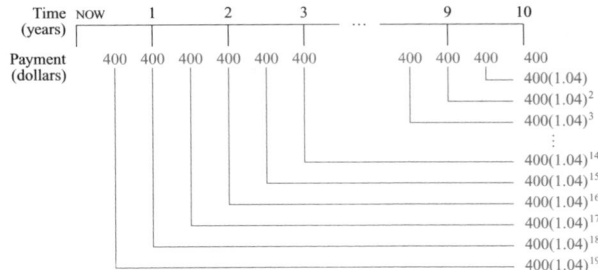

FIGURE 1

The amount A_f of the annuity is the sum of these 20 amounts. Thus

$$A_f = 400 + 400(1.04) + 400(1.04)^2 + \cdots + 400(1.04)^{19}$$

But this is a geometric series with $a = 400$, $r = 1.04$, and $n = 20$, so

$$A_f = 400\frac{1 - (1.04)^{20}}{1 - 1.04} \approx 11{,}911.23$$

Thus the amount in the account after the last payment is $11,911.23.

◤ NOW TRY EXERCISE **3** ∎

In general, the regular annuity payment is called the **periodic rent** and is denoted by R. We also let i denote the interest rate per time period and let n denote the number of payments. *We always assume that the time period in which interest is compounded is equal to the time between payments.* By the same reasoning as in Example 1, we see that the amount A_f of an annuity is

$$A_f = R + R(1 + i) + R(1 + i)^2 + \cdots + R(1 + i)^{n-1}$$

Since this is the nth partial sum of a geometric sequence with $a = R$ and $r = 1 + i$, the formula for the partial sum gives

$$A_f = R\frac{1 - (1 + i)^n}{1 - (1 + i)} = R\frac{1 - (1 + i)^n}{-i} = R\frac{(1 + i)^n - 1}{i}$$

AMOUNT OF AN ANNUITY

The amount A_f of an annuity consisting of n regular equal payments of size R with interest rate i per time period is given by

$$A_f = R\frac{(1 + i)^n - 1}{i}$$

IN-CLASS MATERIALS

The key idea here is that there are many practical examples available to use as illustrations.

MATHEMATICS IN THE MODERN WORLD

Mathematical Economics
The health of the global economy is determined by such interrelated factors as supply, demand, production, consumption, pricing, distribution, and thousands of other factors. These factors are in turn determined by economic decisions (for example, whether or not you buy a certain brand of toothpaste) made by billions of different individuals each day. How will today's creation and distribution of goods affect tomorrow's economy? Such questions are tackled by mathematicians who work on mathematical models of the economy. In the 1940s Wassily Leontief, a pioneer in this area, created a model consisting of thousands of equations that describe how different sectors of the economy, such as the oil industry, transportation, and communication, interact with each other. A different approach to economic models, one dealing with individuals in the economy as opposed to large sectors, was pioneered by John Nash in the 1950s. In his model, which uses *game theory*, the economy is a game where individual players make decisions that often lead to mutual gain. Leontief and Nash were awarded the Nobel Prize in Economics in 1973 and 1994, respectively. Economic theory continues to be a major area of mathematical research.

EXAMPLE 2 | Calculating the Amount of an Annuity

How much money should be invested every month at 12% per year, compounded monthly, in order to have $4000 in 18 months?

SOLUTION   In this problem $i = 0.12/12 = 0.01$, $A_f = 4000$, and $n = 18$. We need to find the amount R of each payment. By the formula for the amount of an annuity,

$$4000 = R\frac{(1 + 0.01)^{18} - 1}{0.01}$$

Solving for R, we get

$$R = \frac{4000(0.01)}{(1 + 0.01)^{18} - 1} \approx 203.928$$

Thus the monthly investment should be $203.93.

✎. NOW TRY EXERCISE **9**   ■

▼ The Present Value of an Annuity

If you were to receive $10,000 five years from now, it would be worth much less than if you got $10,000 right now. This is because of the interest you could accumulate during the next five years if you invested the money now. What smaller amount would you be willing to accept *now* instead of receiving $10,000 in five years? This is the amount of money that, together with interest, would be worth $10,000 in five years. The amount that we are looking for here is called the *discounted value* or *present value*. If the interest rate is 8% per year, compounded quarterly, then the interest per time period is $i = 0.08/4 = 0.02$, and there are $4 \times 5 = 20$ time periods. If we let PV denote the present value, then by the formula for compound interest (Section 4.1), we have

$$10,000 = PV(1 + i)^n = PV(1 + 0.02)^{20}$$

so

$$PV = 10,000(1 + 0.02)^{-20} \approx 6729.713$$

Thus in this situation the present value of $10,000 is $6729.71. This reasoning leads to a general formula for present value. If an amount A_f is to be paid in a lump sum n time periods from now and the interest rate per time period is i, then its **present value** A_p is given by

$$A_p = A_f(1 + i)^{-n}$$

Similarly, the **present value of an annuity** is the amount A_p that must be invested now at the interest rate i per time period to provide n payments, each of amount R. Clearly, A_p is the sum of the present values of each individual payment (see Exercise 29). Another way of finding A_p is to note that A_p is the present value of A_f:

$$A_p = A_f(1 + i)^{-n} = R\,\frac{(1 + i)^n - 1}{i}(1 + i)^{-n} = R\,\frac{1 - (1 + i)^{-n}}{i}$$

THE PRESENT VALUE OF AN ANNUITY

The **present value** A_p of an annuity consisting of n regular equal payments of size R and interest rate i per time period is given by

$$A_p = R\,\frac{1 - (1 + i)^{-n}}{i}$$

EXAMPLE 3 | Calculating the Present Value of an Annuity

A person wins $10,000,000 in the California lottery, and the amount is paid in yearly installments of half a million dollars each for 20 years. What is the present value of his winnings? Assume that he can earn 10% interest, compounded annually.

SOLUTION Since the amount won is paid as an annuity, we need to find its present value. Here, $i = 0.1$, $R = \$500,000$, and $n = 20$. Thus

$$A_p = 500,000\,\frac{1 - (1 + 0.1)^{-20}}{0.1} \approx 4,256,781.859$$

This means that the winner really won only $4,256,781.86 if it were paid immediately.

✎. NOW TRY EXERCISE **11** ∎

▼ Installment Buying

When you buy a house or a car by installment, the payments that you make are an annuity whose present value is the amount of the loan.

EXAMPLE 4 | The Amount of a Loan

A student wishes to buy a car. She can afford to pay $200 per month but has no money for a down payment. If she can make these payments for four years and the interest rate is 12%, what purchase price can she afford?

SOLUTION The payments that the student makes constitute an annuity whose present value is the price of the car (which is also the amount of the loan, in this case). Here, we have $i = 0.12/12 = 0.01$, $R = 200$, and $n = 12 \times 4 = 48$, so

$$A_p = R\,\frac{1 - (1 + i)^{-n}}{i} = 200\,\frac{1 - (1 + 0.01)^{-48}}{0.01} \approx 7594.792$$

Thus the student can buy a car priced at $7594.79.

✎. NOW TRY EXERCISE **19** ∎

When a bank makes a loan that is to be repaid with regular equal payments R, then the payments form an annuity whose present value A_p is the amount of the loan. So to find the size of the payments, we solve for R in the formula for the amount of an annuity. This gives the following formula for R.

INSTALLMENT BUYING

If a loan A_p is to be repaid in n regular equal payments with interest rate i per time period, then the size R of each payment is given by

$$R = \frac{iA_p}{1 - (1 + i)^{-n}}$$

EXAMPLE 5 | Calculating Monthly Mortgage Payments

A couple borrows $100,000 at 9% interest as a mortage loan on a house. They expect to make monthly payments for 30 years to repay the loan. What is the size of each payment?

ALTERNATE EXAMPLE 3

A person wins $3,000,000 in the California lottery, and the amount is paid in yearly installments of half a million dollars for 6 years. What is the present value of his winnings? Assume that he can earn 5% interest, compounded annually. Round your answer (expressed in dollars) to the nearest cent.

ANSWER
$2,537,846.03

ALTERNATE EXAMPLE 4

A student wishes to buy a car. He can afford to pay $400 per month but has no money for a down payment. If he can make these payments for 5 years and the interest rate is 3%, what purchase price can he afford? Round your answer (expressed in dollars) to the nearest cent.

ANSWER
$22,260.94

ALTERNATE EXAMPLE 5

A couple borrows $100,000 at 3% interest as a mortgage loan on a house. They expect to make monthly payments for 34 years to repay the loan. What is the size of each payment? Round your answer (expressed in dollars) to the nearest cent.

ANSWER
$391.27

SOLUTION   The mortgage payments form an annuity whose present value is $A_p = \$100{,}000$. Also, $i = 0.09/12 = 0.0075$, and $n = 12 \times 30 = 360$. We are looking for the amount R of each payment.

From the formula for installment buying, we get

$$R = \frac{iA_p}{1 - (1 + i)^{-n}} = \frac{(0.0075)(100{,}000)}{1 - (1 + 0.0075)^{-360}} \approx 804.623$$

Thus the monthly payments are $804.62.

✎ NOW TRY EXERCISE **15**   ◼

We now illustrate the use of graphing devices in solving problems related to installment buying.

EXAMPLE 6 | Calculating the Interest Rate from the Size of Monthly Payments

A car dealer sells a new car for $18,000. He offers the buyer payments of $405 per month for 5 years. What interest rate is this car dealer charging?

SOLUTION   The payments form an annuity with present value $A_p = \$18{,}000$, $R = 405$, and $n = 12 \times 5 = 60$. To find the interest rate, we must solve for i in the equation

$$R = \frac{iA_p}{1 - (1 + i)^{-n}}$$

A little experimentation will convince you that it is not possible to solve this equation for i algebraically. So to find i, we use a graphing device to graph R as a function of the interest rate x, and we then use the graph to find the interest rate corresponding to the value of R we want ($405 in this case). Since $i = x/12$, we graph the function

$$R(x) = \frac{\frac{x}{12}(18{,}000)}{1 - \left(1 + \frac{x}{12}\right)^{-60}}$$

in the viewing rectangle $[0.06, 0.16] \times [350, 450]$, as shown in Figure 2. We also graph the horizontal line $R(x) = 405$ in the same viewing rectangle. Then, by moving the cursor to the point of intersection of the two graphs, we find that the corresponding x-value is approximately 0.125. Thus the interest rate is about $12\frac{1}{2}\%$.

✎ NOW TRY EXERCISE **25**   ◼

FIGURE 2

12.4 EXERCISES

CONCEPTS

1. An annuity is a sum of money that is paid in regular equal payments. The _____ of an annuity is the sum of all the individual payments together with all the interest.

2. The _____ _____ of an annuity is the amount that must be invested now at interest rate i per time period to provide n payments each of amount R.

APPLICATIONS

✎ **3. Annuity**   Find the amount of an annuity that consists of 10 annual payments of $1000 each into an account that pays 6% interest per year.

4. Annuity   Find the amount of an annuity that consists of 24 monthly payments of $500 each into an account that pays 8% interest per year, compounded monthly.

ALTERNATE EXAMPLE 6

A car dealer sells a new car for $19,000. She offers the buyer payments of $367 per month for 5 years. What interest rate is this car dealer charging? Round your answer to the nearest percent.

ANSWER

6%

DRILL QUESTION

Every year, an investor deposits $2000 in an IRA that earns an interest rate of 6% per year. How much is in the IRA after 10 years?

Answer

$$2000\frac{(1 + 0.06)^{10} - 1}{0.06}$$
$$= 26{,}361.59$$

IN-CLASS MATERIALS

Students can be assigned to contact mortgage brokers to find the size of payments (and current interest rate) on an average 30-year mortgage on a house near their home or school. They then can explore the effects of making a larger or smaller down payment on the house.

5. Annuity Find the amount of an annuity that consists of 20 annual payments of $5000 each into an account that pays interest of 12% per year.

6. Annuity Find the amount of an annuity that consists of 20 semiannual payments of $500 each into an account that pays 6% interest per year, compounded semiannually.

7. Annuity Find the amount of an annuity that consists of 16 quarterly payments of $300 each into an account that pays 8% interest per year, compounded quarterly.

8. Annuity Find the amount of an annuity that consists of 40 annual payments of $2000 each into an account that pays interest of 5% per year.

9. Saving How much money should be invested every quarter at 10% per year, compounded quarterly, to have $5000 in 2 years?

10. Saving How much money should be invested monthly at 6% per year, compounded monthly, to have $2000 in 8 months?

11. Annuity What is the present value of an annuity that consists of 20 semiannual payments of $1000 at an interest rate of 9% per year, compounded semiannually?

12. Annuity What is the present value of an annuity that consists of 30 monthly payments of $300 at an interest rate of 8% per year, compounded monthly.

13. Funding an Annuity How much money must be invested now at 9% per year, compounded semiannually, to fund an annuity of 20 payments of $200 each, paid every 6 months, the first payment being 6 months from now?

14. Funding an Annuity A 55-year-old man deposits $50,000 to fund an annuity with an insurance company. The money will be invested at 8% per year, compounded semiannually. He is to draw semiannual payments until he reaches age 65. What is the amount of each payment?

15. Financing a Car A woman wants to borrow $12,000 to buy a car. She wants to repay the loan by monthly installments for 4 years. If the interest rate on this loan is $10\frac{1}{2}\%$ per year, compounded monthly, what is the amount of each payment?

16. Mortgage What is the monthly payment on a 30-year mortgage of $80,000 at 9% interest? What is the monthly payment on this same mortgage if it is to be repaid over a 15-year period?

17. Mortgage What is the monthly payment on a 30-year mortgage of $100,000 at 8% interest per year, compounded monthly? What is the total amount paid on this loan over the 30-year period?

18. Mortgage What is the monthly payment on a 15-year mortgage of $200,000 at 6% interest? What is the total amount paid on this loan over the 15-year period?

19. Mortgage Dr. Gupta is considering a 30-year mortgage at 6% interest. She can make payments of $3500 a month. What size loan can she afford?

20. Mortgage A couple can afford to make a monthly mortgage payment of $650. If the mortgage rate is 9% and the cou-

ple intends to secure a 30-year mortgage, how much can they borrow?

21. Financing a Car Jane agrees to buy a car for a down payment of $2000 and payments of $220 per month for 3 years. If the interest rate is 8% per year, compounded monthly, what is the actual purchase price of her car?

22. Financing a Ring Mike buys a ring for his fiancee by paying $30 a month for one year. If the interest rate is 10% per year, compounded monthly, what is the price of the ring?

23. Mortgage A couple secures a 30-year loan of $100,000 at $9\frac{3}{4}\%$ per year, compounded monthly, to buy a house.
(a) What is the amount of their monthly payment?
(b) What total amount will they pay over the 30-year period?
(c) If, instead of taking the loan, the couple deposits the monthly payments in an account that pays $9\frac{3}{4}\%$ interest per year, compounded monthly, how much will be in the account at the end of the 30-year period?

24. Mortgage A couple needs a mortgage of $300,000. Their mortgage broker presents them with two options: a 30-year mortgage at $6\frac{1}{2}\%$ interest or a 15-year mortgage at $5\frac{3}{4}\%$ interest.
(a) Find the monthly payment on the 30-year mortgage and on the 15-year mortgage. Which mortgage has the larger monthly payment?
(b) Find the total amount to be paid over the life of each loan. Which mortgage has the lower total payment over its lifetime?

25. Interest Rate John buys a stereo system for $640. He agrees to pay $32 a month for 2 years. Assuming that interest is compounded monthly, what interest rate is he paying?

26. Interest Rate Janet's payments on her $12,500 car are $420 a month for 3 years. Assuming that interest is compounded monthly, what interest rate is she paying on the car loan?

27. Interest Rate An item at a department store is priced at $189.99 and can be bought by making 20 payments of $10.50. Find the interest rate, assuming that interest is compounded monthly.

28. Interest Rate A man purchases a $2000 diamond ring for a down payment of $200 and monthly installments of $88 for 2 years. Assuming that interest is compounded monthly, what interest rate is he paying?

DISCOVERY ▪ DISCUSSION ▪ WRITING

29. Present Value of an Annuity
(a) Draw a time line as in Example 1 to show that the present value of an annuity is the sum of the present values of each payment, that is,

$$A_p = \frac{R}{1+i} + \frac{R}{(1+i)^2} + \frac{R}{(1+i)^3} + \cdots + \frac{R}{(1+i)^n}$$

(b) Use part (a) to derive the formula for A_p given in the text.

30. An Annuity That Lasts Forever An **annuity in perpetuity** is one that continues forever. Such annuities are useful in setting up scholarship funds to ensure that the award continues.

EXAMPLE
A person borrows $20,000 to buy a car and wants to pay it off in 4 years. If the interest rate is 8% per year, compounded monthly, what is the amount of each monthly payment?

ANSWER
$488.26

(a) Draw a time line (as in Example 1) to show that to set up an annuity in perpetuity of amount R per time period, the amount that must be invested now is

$$A_p = \frac{R}{1+i} + \frac{R}{(1+i)^2} + \frac{R}{(1+i)^3} + \cdots + \frac{R}{(1+i)^n} + \cdots$$

where i is the interest rate per time period.

(b) Find the sum of the infinite series in part (a) to show that

$$A_p = \frac{R}{i}$$

(c) How much money must be invested now at 10% per year, compounded annually, to provide an annuity in perpetuity of $5000 per year? The first payment is due in one year.

(d) How much money must be invested now at 8% per year, compounded quarterly, to provide an annuity in perpetuity of $3000 per year? The first payment is due in one year.

31. Amortizing a Mortgage When they bought their house, John and Mary took out a $90,000 mortgage at 9% interest, repayable monthly over 30 years. Their payment is $724.17 per month (check this, using the formula in the text). The bank gave them an **amortization schedule**, which is a table showing how much of each payment is interest, how much goes to-

ward the principal, and the remaining principal after each payment. The table below shows the first few entries in the amortization schedule.

Payment number	Total payment	Interest payment	Principal payment	Remaining principal
1	724.17	675.00	49.17	89,950.83
2	724.17	674.63	49.54	89,901.29
3	724.17	674.26	49.91	89,851.38
4	724.17	673.89	50.28	89,801.10

After 10 years they have made 120 payments and are wondering how much they still owe, but they have lost the amortization schedule.

(a) How much do John and Mary still owe on their mortgage? [*Hint:* The remaining balance is the present value of the 240 remaining payments.]

(b) How much of their next payment is interest, and how much goes toward the principal? [*Hint:* Since $9\% \div 12 = 0.75\%$, they must pay 0.75% of the remaining principal in interest each month.]

SUGGESTED TIME AND EMPHASIS

1–2 classes, optional material

12.5 MATHEMATICAL INDUCTION

| Conjecture and Proof ▶ Mathematical Induction

There are two aspects to mathematics—discovery and proof—and they are of equal importance. We must discover something before we can attempt to prove it, and we cannot be certain of its truth until it has been proved. In this section we examine the relationship between these two key components of mathematics more closely.

▼ Conjecture and Proof

Let's try a simple experiment. We add more and more of the odd numbers as follows:

$$1 = 1$$
$$1 + 3 = 4$$
$$1 + 3 + 5 = 9$$
$$1 + 3 + 5 + 7 = 16$$
$$1 + 3 + 5 + 7 + 9 = 25$$

What do you notice about the numbers on the right side of these equations? They are, in fact, all perfect squares. These equations say the following:

The sum of the first 1 odd number is 1^2.

The sum of the first 2 odd numbers is 2^2.

The sum of the first 3 odd numbers is 3^2.

The sum of the first 4 odd numbers is 4^2.

The sum of the first 5 odd numbers is 5^2.

TEXT QUESTION

There are two main steps to a proof by mathematical induction. What is the first one?

Answer

Any answer getting at the idea of a base case or a "proof for $n = 1$" should be accepted, even if the latter isn't technically true.

Consider the polynomial

$$p(n) = n^2 - n + 41$$

Here are some values of $p(n)$:

$$p(1) = 41 \quad p(2) = 43$$
$$p(3) = 47 \quad p(4) = 53$$
$$p(5) = 61 \quad p(6) = 71$$
$$p(7) = 83 \quad p(8) = 97$$

All the values so far are prime numbers. In fact, if you keep going, you will find that $p(n)$ is prime for all natural numbers up to $n = 40$. It might seem reasonable at this point to conjecture that $p(n)$ is prime for *every* natural number n. But that conjecture would be too hasty, because it is easily seen that $p(41)$ is *not* prime. This illustrates that we cannot be certain of the truth of a statement no matter how many special cases we check. We need a convincing argument—a *proof*—to determine the truth of a statement.

This leads naturally to the following question: Is it true that for every natural number n, the sum of the first n odd numbers is n^2? Could this remarkable property be true? We could try a few more numbers and find that the pattern persists for the first 6, 7, 8, 9, and 10 odd numbers. At this point we feel quite sure that this is always true, so we make a *conjecture*:

The sum of the first n odd numbers is n^2.

Since we know that the nth odd number is $2n - 1$, we can write this statement more precisely as

$$1 + 3 + 5 + \cdots + (2n - 1) = n^2$$

It is important to realize that this is still a conjecture. We cannot conclude by checking a finite number of cases that a property is true for all numbers (there are infinitely many). To see this more clearly, suppose someone tells us that he has added up the first trillion odd numbers and found that they do *not* add up to 1 trillion squared. What would you tell this person? It would be silly to say that you're sure it's true because you have already checked the first five cases. You could, however, take out paper and pencil and start checking it yourself, but this task would probably take the rest of your life. The tragedy would be that after completing this task, you would still not be sure of the truth of the conjecture! Do you see why?

Herein lies the power of mathematical proof. A **proof** is a clear argument that demonstrates the truth of a statement beyond doubt.

▼ Mathematical Induction

Let's consider a special kind of proof called **mathematical induction**. Here is how it works: Suppose we have a statement that says something about all natural numbers n. For example, for any natural number n, let $P(n)$ be the following statement:

$P(n)$:   The sum of the first n odd numbers is n^2

Since this statement is about all natural numbers, it contains infinitely many statements; we will call them $P(1), P(2), \dots$.

$P(1)$:   The sum of the first 1 odd number is 1^2.

$P(2)$:   The sum of the first 2 odd numbers is 2^2.

$P(3)$:   The sum of the first 3 odd numbers is 3^2.

$$\vdots \qquad\qquad \vdots$$

How can we prove all of these statements at once? Mathematical induction is a clever way of doing just that.

The crux of the idea is this: Suppose we can prove that whenever one of these statements is true, then the one following it in the list is also true. In other words,

For every k, if $P(k)$ is true, then $P(k + 1)$ is true.

This is called the **induction step** because it leads us from the truth of one statement to the truth of the next. Now suppose that we can also prove that

$P(1)$ is true.

The induction step now leads us through the following chain of statements:

$P(1)$ is true, so $P(2)$ is true.
$P(2)$ is true, so $P(3)$ is true.
$P(3)$ is true, so $P(4)$ is true.

$$\vdots \qquad\qquad \vdots$$

IN-CLASS MATERIALS

The main thing for induction is to give the students plenty of examples to work from and plenty of practice.

1. We can use induction to show that $\dfrac{(2n)!}{2^n n!}$ is an integer for all positive n. The base case is trivial. The key step is in the inductive case:

$$\frac{(2n + 2)!}{2^{n+1}(n + 1)!} = \frac{(2n)!}{2^n n!} \cdot \frac{(2n + 1)(2n + 2)}{2(n + 1)}$$

and now cancellation occurs.

2. We can use induction to show that the sum of the cubes of three consecutive integers is divisible by 9. The base case is trivial. The key inductive step is:

$$(n + 1)^3 + (n + 2)^3 + (n + 3)^3 = n^3 + (n + 1)^3 + (n + 2)^3 + 9n^2 + 27n + 27$$

3. We can use induction to show:

$$\frac{n^3 - n}{3} = (1 \cdot 2) + (2 \cdot 3) + \cdots + (n - 1) n$$

The base step should be $n = 2$, and the inductive step uses the fact that

$$\frac{(n + 1)^3 - (n + 1)}{3} = \frac{n^3 - n}{3} \frac{3n^2 + 3n}{3}$$

So we see that if both the induction step and $P(1)$ are proved, then statement $P(n)$ is proved for all n. Here is a summary of this important method of proof.

PRINCIPLE OF MATHEMATICAL INDUCTION

For each natural number n, let $P(n)$ be a statement depending on n. Suppose that the following two conditions are satisfied.

1. $P(1)$ is true.

2. For every natural number k, if $P(k)$ is true then $P(k + 1)$ is true.

Then $P(n)$ is true for all natural numbers n.

To apply this principle, there are two steps:

Step 1 Prove that $P(1)$ is true.

Step 2 Assume that $P(k)$ is true, and use this assumption to prove that $P(k + 1)$ is true.

Notice that in Step 2 we do not prove that $P(k)$ is true. We only show that *if* $P(k)$ is true, *then* $P(k + 1)$ is also true. The assumption that $P(k)$ is true is called the **induction hypothesis**.

We now use mathematical induction to prove that the conjecture that we made at the beginning of this section is true.

EXAMPLE 1 | A Proof by Mathematical Induction

Prove that for all natural numbers n,

$$1 + 3 + 5 + \cdots + (2n - 1) = n^2$$

SOLUTION Let $P(n)$ denote the statement $1 + 3 + 5 + \cdots + (2n - 1) = n^2$.

Step 1 We need to show that $P(1)$ is true. But $P(1)$ is simply the statement that $1 = 1^2$, which is of course true.

Step 2 We assume that $P(k)$ is true. Thus our induction hypothesis is

$$1 + 3 + 5 + \cdots + (2k - 1) = k^2$$

We want to use this to show that $P(k + 1)$ is true, that is,

$$1 + 3 + 5 + \cdots + (2k - 1) + [2(k + 1) - 1] = (k + 1)^2$$

[Note that we get $P(k + 1)$ by substituting $k + 1$ for each n in the statement $P(n)$.] We start with the left side and use the induction hypothesis to obtain the right side of the equation:

ALTERNATE EXAMPLE 1

Prove that for all natural numbers n, $2 + 6 + 10 + \cdots + (4n - 2) = 2n^2$.

ANSWER

Let $P(n)$ denote the statement $2 + 6 + 10 + \cdots + (4n - 2) = 2n^2$.

Step 1: $P(1)$ reduces to the statement $2 = 2(1)^2$, which is true.

Step 2: We assume that $P(k)$ is true. Our induction hypothesis is $2 + 6 + 10 + \cdots + (4k - 2) = 2k^2$. We now prove $P(k + 1)$ is true.

$$2 + 6 + 10 + \cdots + (4k - 2) + [4(k + 1) - 2] =$$
$$2k^2 + [4(k + 1) - 2] =$$
$$2k^2 + 4k + 2 =$$
$$2(k + 1)^2$$

SECTION 12.5 | Mathematical Induction　817

$$1 + 3 + 5 + \cdots + (2k - 1) + [2(k + 1) - 1]$$

$$= [1 + 3 + 5 + \cdots + (2k - 1)] + [2(k + 1) - 1] \qquad \text{Group the first } k \text{ terms}$$

$$= k^2 + [2(k + 1) - 1] \qquad \text{Induction hypothesis}$$

$$= k^2 + [2k + 2 - 1] \qquad \text{Distributive Property}$$

$$= k^2 + 2k + 1 \qquad \text{Simplify}$$

$$= (k + 1)^2 \qquad \text{Factor}$$

This equals k^2 by the induction hypothesis

Thus $P(k + 1)$ follows from $P(k)$, and this completes the induction step.

Having proved Steps 1 and 2, we conclude by the Principle of Mathematical Induction that $P(n)$ is true for all natural numbers n.

✎. NOW TRY EXERCISE 3 ■

EXAMPLE 2 | A Proof by Mathematical Induction

Prove that for every natural number n,

$$1 + 2 + 3 + \cdots + n = \frac{n(n + 1)}{2}$$

SOLUTION Let $P(n)$ be the statement $1 + 2 + 3 + \cdots + n = n(n + 1)/2$. We want to show that $P(n)$ is true for all natural numbers n.

Step 1 We need to show that $P(1)$ is true. But $P(1)$ says that

$$1 = \frac{1(1 + 1)}{2}$$

and this statement is clearly true.

Step 2 Assume that $P(k)$ is true. Thus our induction hypothesis is

$$1 + 2 + 3 + \cdots + k = \frac{k(k + 1)}{2}$$

We want to use this to show that $P(k + 1)$ is true, that is,

$$1 + 2 + 3 + \cdots + k + (k + 1) = \frac{(k + 1)[(k + 1) + 1]}{2}$$

So we start with the left side and use the induction hypothesis to obtain the right side:

$$1 + 2 + 3 + \cdots + k + (k + 1)$$

$$= [1 + 2 + 3 + \cdots + k] + (k + 1) \qquad \text{Group the first } k \text{ terms}$$

$$= \frac{k(k + 1)}{2} + (k + 1) \qquad \text{Induction hypothesis}$$

$$= (k + 1)\left(\frac{k}{2} + 1\right) \qquad \text{Factor } k + 1$$

$$= (k + 1)\left(\frac{k + 2}{2}\right) \qquad \text{Common denominator}$$

$$= \frac{(k + 1)[(k + 1) + 1]}{2} \qquad \text{Write } k + 2 \text{ as } k + 1 + 1$$

This equals $\frac{k(k + 1)}{2}$ by the induction hypothesis

Thus $P(k + 1)$ follows from $P(k)$, and this completes the induction step.

ALTERNATE EXAMPLE 2

Prove that for all natural numbers n, $3 + 6 + 9 + 12 + \cdots + 3n = \frac{3n(n + 1)}{2}$.

ANSWER

Let $P(n)$ denote the statement $3 + 6 + 9 + 12 + \cdots + 3n = \frac{3n(n + 1)}{2}$. Step 1: $P(1)$ reduces to the statement $3 = \frac{3(1)(2)}{2}$, which is true.

Step 2: We assume that $P(k)$ is true. Our induction hypothesis is $3 + 6 + 9 + 12 + \cdots + 3k = \frac{3k(k + 1)}{2}$. We now prove $P(k + 1)$ is true.

$$3 + 6 + 9 + 12 + \cdots + 3k + 3(k + 1) =$$

$$\frac{3k(k + 1)}{2} + 3(k + 1) =$$

$$\frac{3k(k + 1)}{2} + \frac{6(k + 1)}{2} =$$

$$\frac{3k^2 + 9k + 6}{2} = \frac{3(k + 1)(k + 2)}{2}$$

CHAPTER 12 Sequences and Series　817

Having proved Steps 1 and 2, we conclude by the Principle of Mathematical Induction that $P(n)$ is true for all natural numbers n.

✎. NOW TRY EXERCISE 5   ■

The following box gives formulas for the sums of powers of the first n natural numbers. These formulas are important in calculus. Formula 1 is proved in Example 2. The other formulas are also proved by using mathematical induction (see Exercises 6 and 9).

SUMS OF POWERS

0. $\displaystyle\sum_{k=1}^{n} 1 = n$ **2.** $\displaystyle\sum_{k=1}^{n} k^2 = \frac{n(n+1)(2n+1)}{6}$

1. $\displaystyle\sum_{k=1}^{n} k = \frac{n(n+1)}{2}$ **3.** $\displaystyle\sum_{k=1}^{n} k^3 = \frac{n^2(n+1)^2}{4}$

It might happen that a statement $P(n)$ is false for the first few natural numbers but true from some number on. For example, we might want to prove that $P(n)$ is true for $n \geq 5$. Notice that if we prove that $P(5)$ is true, then this fact, together with the induction step, would imply the truth of $P(5)$, $P(6)$, $P(7)$, ... The next example illustrates this point.

EXAMPLE 3 | Proving an Inequality by Mathematical Induction

Prove that $4n < 2^n$ for all $n \geq 5$.

SOLUTION Let $P(n)$ denote the statement $4n < 2^n$.

Step 1 $P(5)$ is the statement that $4 \cdot 5 < 2^5$, or $20 < 32$, which is true.

Step 2 Assume that $P(k)$ is true. Thus our induction hypothesis is

$$4k < 2^k$$

We get $P(k + 1)$ by replacing n by $k + 1$ in the statement $P(n)$.

We want to use this to show that $P(k + 1)$ is true, that is,

$$4(k + 1) < 2^{k+1}$$

BLAISE PASCAL (1623–1662) is considered one of the most versatile minds in modern history. He was a writer and philosopher as well as a gifted mathematician and physicist. Among his contributions that appear in this book are Pascal's triangle and the Principle of Mathematical Induction.

Pascal's father, himself a mathematician, believed that his son should not study mathematics until he was 15 or 16. But at age 12, Blaise insisted on learning geometry and proved most of its elementary theorems himself. At 19 he invented the first mechanical adding machine. In 1647, after writing a major treatise on the conic sections, he abruptly abandoned mathematics because he felt that his intense studies were contributing to his ill health. He devoted himself instead to frivolous recreations such as gambling, but this only served to pique his interest in probability. In 1654 he miraculously survived a carriage accident in which his horses ran off a bridge. Taking this to be a sign from God, Pascal entered a monastery, where he pursued theology and philosophy, writing his famous *Pensées*. He also continued his mathematical research. He valued faith and intuition more than reason as the source of truth, declaring that "the heart has its own reasons, which reason cannot know."

ALTERNATE EXAMPLE 3
Use induction to prove that for $n \geq 3$, $2n < 2^n$.

ANSWER
Let $P(n)$ denote the statement $2n < 2^n$.
Step 1: $P(3)$ reduces to the statement $2(3) < 2^3$, which is true.
Step 2: We assume that $P(k)$ is true. Our induction hypothesis is $2k < 2^k$. We now prove $P(k + 1)$ is true:
$2(k + 1) = 2k + 2 < 2^k + 2 = 2^k + 2^k = 2(2^k) = 2^{k+1}$

So we start with the left-hand side of the inequality and use the induction hypothesis to show that it is less than the right-hand side. For $k \geq 5$ we have

$$4(k + 1) = 4k + 4 \qquad \text{Distributive Property}$$
$$< 2^k + 4 \qquad \text{Induction hypothesis}$$
$$< 2^k + 4k \qquad \text{Because } 4 < 4k$$
$$< 2^k + 2^k \qquad \text{Induction hypothesis}$$
$$= 2 \cdot 2^k$$
$$= 2^{k+1} \qquad \text{Property of exponents}$$

Thus $P(k + 1)$ follows from $P(k)$, and this completes the induction step.

Having proved Steps 1 and 2, we conclude by the Principle of Mathematical Induction that $P(n)$ is true for all natural numbers $n \geq 5$.

✎. NOW TRY EXERCISE **21**   ■

DRILL QUESTION
Use mathematical induction to prove that $1 + 2 + \cdots + n$
$$= \frac{n(n + 1)}{2}.$$

Answer
This is Example 2 from the text.

12.5 EXERCISES

CONCEPTS

1. Mathematical induction is a method of proving that a statement $P(n)$ is true for all _____ numbers n. In Step 1 we prove that _____ is true.

2. Which of the following is true about Step 2 in a proof by mathematical induction?
   (i) We prove "$P(k + 1)$ is true."
   (ii) We prove "If $P(k)$ is true, then $P(k + 1)$ is true."

SKILLS

3–14 ■ Use mathematical induction to prove that the formula is true for all natural numbers n.

✎. **3.** $2 + 4 + 6 + \cdots + 2n = n(n + 1)$

4. $1 + 4 + 7 + \cdots + (3n - 2) = \dfrac{n(3n - 1)}{2}$

✎. **5.** $5 + 8 + 11 + \cdots + (3n + 2) = \dfrac{n(3n + 7)}{2}$

6. $1^2 + 2^2 + 3^2 + \cdots + n^2 = \dfrac{n(n + 1)(2n + 1)}{6}$

7. $1 \cdot 2 + 2 \cdot 3 + 3 \cdot 4 + \cdots + n(n + 1) = \dfrac{n(n + 1)(n + 2)}{3}$

8. $1 \cdot 3 + 2 \cdot 4 + 3 \cdot 5 + \cdots + n(n + 2) = \dfrac{n(n + 1)(2n + 7)}{6}$

9. $1^3 + 2^3 + 3^3 + \cdots + n^3 = \dfrac{n^2(n + 1)^2}{4}$

10. $1^3 + 3^3 + 5^3 + \cdots + (2n - 1)^3 = n^2(2n^2 - 1)$

11. $2^3 + 4^3 + 6^3 + \cdots + (2n)^3 = 2n^2(n + 1)^2$

12. $\dfrac{1}{1 \cdot 2} + \dfrac{1}{2 \cdot 3} + \dfrac{1}{3 \cdot 4} + \cdots + \dfrac{1}{n(n + 1)} = \dfrac{n}{(n + 1)}$

13. $1 \cdot 2 + 2 \cdot 2^2 + 3 \cdot 2^3 + 4 \cdot 2^4 + \cdots + n \cdot 2^n$
$$= 2[1 + (n - 1)2^n]$$

14. $1 + 2 + 2^2 + \cdots + 2^{n-1} = 2^n - 1$

15. Show that $n^2 + n$ is divisible by 2 for all natural numbers n.

16. Show that $5^n - 1$ is divisible by 4 for all natural numbers n.

17. Show that $n^2 - n + 41$ is odd for all natural numbers n.

18. Show that $n^3 - n + 3$ is divisible by 3 for all natural numbers n.

19. Show that $8^n - 3^n$ is divisible by 5 for all natural numbers n.

20. Show that $3^{2n} - 1$ is divisible by 8 for all natural numbers n.

✎. **21.** Prove that $n < 2^n$ for all natural numbers n.

22. Prove that $(n + 1)^2 < 2n^2$ for all natural numbers $n \geq 3$.

23. Prove that if $x > -1$, then $(1 + x)^n \geq 1 + nx$ for all natural numbers n.

24. Show that $100n \leq n^2$ for all $n \geq 100$.

25. Let $a_{n+1} = 3a_n$ and $a_1 = 5$. Show that $a_n = 5 \cdot 3^{n-1}$ for all natural numbers n.

26. A sequence is defined recursively by $a_{n+1} = 3a_n - 8$ and $a_1 = 4$. Find an explicit formula for a_n, and then use mathematical induction to prove that the formula you found is true.

27. Show that $x - y$ is a factor of $x^n - y^n$ for all natural numbers n. [*Hint:* $x^{k+1} - y^{k+1} = x^k(x - y) + (x^k - y^k)y$.]

28. Show that $x + y$ is a factor of $x^{2n-1} + y^{2n-1}$ for all natural numbers n.

29–33 ■ F_n denotes the nth term of the Fibonacci sequence discussed in Section 12.1. Use mathematical induction to prove the statement.

29. F_{3n} is even for all natural numbers n.

30. $F_1 + F_2 + F_3 + \cdots + F_n = F_{n+2} - 1$

31. $F_1^2 + F_2^2 + F_3^2 + \cdots + F_n^2 = F_n F_{n+1}$

32. $F_1 + F_3 + \cdots + F_{2n-1} = F_{2n}$

33. For all $n \geq 2$,
$$\begin{bmatrix} 1 & 1 \\ 1 & 0 \end{bmatrix}^n = \begin{bmatrix} F_{n+1} & F_n \\ F_n & F_{n-1} \end{bmatrix}$$

34. Let a_n be the nth term of the sequence defined recursively by
$$a_{n+1} = \frac{1}{1 + a_n}$$
and let $a_1 = 1$. Find a formula for a_n in terms of the Fibonacci numbers F_n. Prove that the formula you found is valid for all natural numbers n.

35. Let F_n be the nth term of the Fibonacci sequence. Find and prove an inequality relating n and F_n for natural numbers n.

36. Find and prove an inequality relating $100n$ and n^3.

DISCOVERY ■ DISCUSSION ■ WRITING

37. True or False? Determine whether each statement is true or false. If you think the statement is true, prove it. If you

think it is false, give an example in which it fails.
(a) $p(n) = n^2 - n + 11$ is prime for all n.
(b) $n^2 > n$ for all $n \geq 2$.
(c) $2^{2n+1} + 1$ is divisible by 3 for all $n \geq 1$.
(d) $n^3 \geq (n + 1)^2$ for all $n \geq 2$.
(e) $n^3 - n$ is divisible by 3 for all $n \geq 2$.
(f) $n^3 - 6n^2 + 11n$ is divisible by 6 for all $n \geq 1$.

38. All Cats Are Black? What is wrong with the following "proof" by mathematical induction that all cats are black? Let $P(n)$ denote the statement "In any group of n cats, if one cat is black, then they are all black."

Step 1 The statement is clearly true for $n = 1$.

Step 2 Suppose that $P(k)$ is true. We show that $P(k + 1)$ is true.

Suppose we have a group of $k + 1$ cats, one of whom is black; call this cat "Tadpole." Remove some other cat (call it "Sparky") from the group. We are left with k cats, one of whom (Tadpole) is black, so by the induction hypothesis, all k of these are black. Now put Sparky back in the group and take out Tadpole. We again have a group of k cats, all of whom— except possibly Sparky—are black. Then by the induction hypothesis, Sparky must be black too. So all $k + 1$ cats in the original group are black.

Thus by induction $P(n)$ is true for all n. Since everyone has seen at least one black cat, it follows that all cats are black.

Tadpole   Sparky

12.6 THE BINOMIAL THEOREM

> Expanding $(a + b)^n$ ▶ The Binomial Coefficients ▶ The Binomial Theorem ▶ Proof of the Binomial Theorem

An expression of the form $a + b$ is called a **binomial**. Although in principle it's easy to raise $a + b$ to any power, raising it to a very high power would be tedious. In this section we find a formula that gives the expansion of $(a + b)^n$ for any natural number n and then prove it using mathematical induction.

TEXT QUESTION

Compute $\binom{5}{4}$.

Answer

5

▼ Expanding $(a + b)^n$

To find a pattern in the expansion of $(a + b)^n$, we first look at some special cases.

$$(a + b)^1 = a + b$$
$$(a + b)^2 = a^2 + 2ab + b^2$$
$$(a + b)^3 = a^3 + 3a^2b + 3ab^2 + b^3$$
$$(a + b)^4 = a^4 + 4a^3b + 6a^2b^2 + 4ab^3 + b^4$$
$$(a + b)^5 = a^5 + 5a^4b + 10a^3b^2 + 10a^2b^3 + 5ab^4 + b^5$$
$$\vdots$$

The following simple patterns emerge for the expansion of $(a + b)^n$.

1. There are $n + 1$ terms, the first being a^n and the last being b^n.
2. The exponents of a decrease by 1 from term to term, while the exponents of b increase by 1.
3. The sum of the exponents of a and b in each term is n.

For instance, notice how the exponents of a and b behave in the expansion of $(a + b)^5$.

The exponents of a decrease:

$$(a + b)^5 = a^{\textcircled{5}} + 5a^{\textcircled{4}}b^1 + 10a^{\textcircled{3}}b^2 + 10a^{\textcircled{2}}b^3 + 5a^{\textcircled{1}} b^4 + b^5$$

The exponents of b increase:

$$(a + b)^5 = a^5 + 5a^4b^{\textcircled{1}} + 10a^3b^{\textcircled{2}} + 10a^2b^{\textcircled{3}} + 5a^1b^{\textcircled{4}} + b^{\textcircled{5}}$$

With these observations we can write the form of the expansion of $(a + b)^n$ for any natural number n. For example, writing a question mark for the missing coefficients, we have

$$(a + b)^8 = a^8 + ?a^7b + ?a^6b^2 + ?a^5b^3 + ?a^4b^4 + ?a^3b^5 + ?a^2b^6 + ?ab^7 + b^8$$

To complete the expansion, we need to determine these coefficients. To find a pattern, let's write the coefficients in the expansion of $(a + b)^n$ for the first few values of n in a triangular array as shown in the following array, which is called **Pascal's triangle**.

$(a + b)^0$						1					
$(a + b)^1$					1		1				
$(a + b)^2$				1		2		1			
$(a + b)^3$			①		③		3		1		
$(a + b)^4$		1		④		⑥		④		1	
$(a + b)^5$	1		5		10		⑩		5		1

The row corresponding to $(a + b)^0$ is called the zeroth row and is included to show the symmetry of the array. The key observation about Pascal's triangle is the following property.

KEY PROPERTY OF PASCAL'S TRIANGLE

Every entry (other than a 1) is the sum of the two entries diagonally above it.

IN-CLASS MATERIALS

Pascal's triangle is actually full of patterns. Have the students see how many they can find. They can look along the diagonals, look down "columns," find the sum of each row, etc. Some instructors spend an entire class on patterns visible in Pascal's triangle. As of this writing, the website http://ptri1.tripod.com has a good discussion of patterns to be found in Pascal's triangle.

What we now call **Pascal's triangle** appears in this Chinese document by Chu Shikie, dated 1303. The title reads "The Old Method Chart of the Seven Multiplying Squares." The triangle was rediscovered by Pascal (see page 818).

From this property it is easy to find any row of Pascal's triangle from the row above it. For instance, we find the sixth and seventh rows, starting with the fifth row:

$$(a + b)^5 \qquad\qquad 1 \quad 5 \quad 10 \quad 10 \quad 5 \quad 1$$
$$(a + b)^6 \qquad 1 \quad 6 \quad 15 \quad 20 \quad 15 \quad 6 \quad 1$$
$$(a + b)^7 \quad 1 \quad 7 \quad 21 \quad 35 \quad 35 \quad 21 \quad 7 \quad 1$$

To see why this property holds, let's consider the following expansions:

$$(a + b)^5 = a^5 + 5a^4b + 10a^3b^2 + 10a^2b^3 + 5ab^4 + b^5$$
$$(a + b)^6 = a^6 + 6a^5b + 15a^4b^2 + 20a^3b^3 + 15a^2b^4 + 6ab^5 + b^6$$

We arrive at the expansion of $(a + b)^6$ by multiplying $(a + b)^5$ by $(a + b)$. Notice, for instance, that the circled term in the expansion of $(a + b)^6$ is obtained via this multiplication from the two circled terms above it. We get this term when the two terms above it are multiplied by b and a, respectively. Thus its coefficient is the sum of the coefficients of these two terms. We will use this observation at the end of this section when we prove the Binomial Theorem.

Having found these patterns, we can now easily obtain the expansion of any binomial, at least to relatively small powers.

EXAMPLE 1 | Expanding a Binomial Using Pascal's Triangle

Find the expansion of $(a + b)^7$ using Pascal's triangle.

SOLUTION The first term in the expansion is a^7, and the last term is b^7. Using the fact that the exponent of a decreases by 1 from term to term and that of b increases by 1 from term to term, we have

$$(a + b)^7 = a^7 + \square a^6b + \square a^5b^2 + \square a^4b^3 + \square a^3b^4 + \square a^2b^5 + \square ab^6 + b^7$$

The appropriate coefficients appear in the seventh row of Pascal's triangle. Thus

$$(a + b)^7 = a^7 + 7a^6b + 21a^5b^2 + 35a^4b^3 + 35a^3b^4 + 21a^2b^5 + 7ab^6 + b^7$$

✎. NOW TRY EXERCISE **5** ∎

EXAMPLE 2 | Expanding a Binomial Using Pascal's Triangle

Use Pascal's triangle to expand $(2 - 3x)^5$.

SOLUTION We find the expansion of $(a + b)^5$ and then substitute 2 for a and $-3x$ for b. Using Pascal's triangle for the coefficients, we get

$$(a + b)^5 = a^5 + 5a^4b + 10a^3b^2 + 10a^2b^3 + 5ab^4 + b^5$$

Substituting $a = 2$ and $b = -3x$ gives

$$(2 - 3x)^5 = (2)^5 + 5(2)^4(-3x) + 10(2)^3(-3x)^2 + 10(2)^2(-3x)^3 + 5(2)(-3x)^4 + (-3x)^5$$

$$= 32 - 240x + 720x^2 - 1080x^3 + 810x^4 - 243x^5$$

✎. NOW TRY EXERCISE **13** ∎

▼ The Binomial Coefficients

Although Pascal's triangle is useful in finding the binomial expansion for reasonably small values of n, it isn't practical for finding $(a + b)^n$ for large values of n. The reason is that the method we use for finding the successive rows of Pascal's triangle is recursive. Thus, to find the 100th row of this triangle, we must first find the preceding 99 rows.

IN-CLASS MATERIALS

If every odd number in Pascal's triangle is colored black and every even number colored white, a figure like Sierpinski's triangle is revealed. Students need complete only a few rows before the recursive structure is visible.

We need to examine the pattern in the coefficients more carefully to develop a formula that allows us to calculate directly any coefficient in the binomial expansion. Such a formula exists, and the rest of this section is devoted to finding and proving it. However, to state this formula, we need some notation.

The product of the first n natural numbers is denoted by $n!$ and is called n **factorial**.

$4! = 1 \cdot 2 \cdot 3 \cdot 4 = 24$
$7! = 1 \cdot 2 \cdot 3 \cdot 4 \cdot 5 \cdot 6 \cdot 7 = 5040$
$10! = 1 \cdot 2 \cdot 3 \cdot 4 \cdot 5 \cdot 6 \cdot 7 \cdot 8 \cdot 9 \cdot 10$
$= 3{,}628{,}800$

$$n! = 1 \cdot 2 \cdot 3 \cdot \cdots \cdot (n-1) \cdot n$$

We also define 0! as follows:

$$0! = 1$$

This definition of 0! makes many formulas involving factorials shorter and easier to write.

THE BINOMIAL COEFFICIENT

Let n and r be nonnegative integers with $r \le n$. The **binomial coefficient** is denoted by $\binom{n}{r}$ and is defined by

$$\binom{n}{r} = \frac{n!}{r!(n-r)!}$$

EXAMPLE 3 | Calculating Binomial Coefficients

(a) $\binom{9}{4} = \frac{9!}{4!(9-4)!} = \frac{9!}{4! \, 5!} = \frac{1 \cdot 2 \cdot 3 \cdot 4 \cdot 5 \cdot 6 \cdot 7 \cdot 8 \cdot 9}{(1 \cdot 2 \cdot 3 \cdot 4)(1 \cdot 2 \cdot 3 \cdot 4 \cdot 5)}$

$= \frac{6 \cdot 7 \cdot 8 \cdot 9}{1 \cdot 2 \cdot 3 \cdot 4} = 126$

(b) $\binom{100}{3} = \frac{100!}{3!(100-3)!} = \frac{1 \cdot 2 \cdot 3 \cdots 97 \cdot 98 \cdot 99 \cdot 100}{(1 \cdot 2 \cdot 3)(1 \cdot 2 \cdot 3 \cdots 97)}$

$= \frac{98 \cdot 99 \cdot 100}{1 \cdot 2 \cdot 3} = 161{,}700$

(c) $\binom{100}{97} = \frac{100!}{97!(100-97)!} = \frac{1 \cdot 2 \cdot 3 \cdots 97 \cdot 98 \cdot 99 \cdot 100}{(1 \cdot 2 \cdot 3 \cdots 97)(1 \cdot 2 \cdot 3)}$

$= \frac{98 \cdot 99 \cdot 100}{1 \cdot 2 \cdot 3} = 161{,}700$

✎ NOW TRY EXERCISES **17** AND **19**

Although the binomial coefficient $\binom{n}{r}$ is defined in terms of a fraction, all the results of Example 3 are natural numbers. In fact, $\binom{n}{r}$ is always a natural number (see Exercise 54). Notice that the binomial coefficients in parts (b) and (c) of Example 3 are equal. This is a special case of the following relation, which you are asked to prove in Exercise 52.

$$\binom{n}{r} = \binom{n}{n-r}$$

Notice again that if n is a positive integer, then we are back to the standard Binomial Theorem, since $\binom{n}{r}$ is 0 for $r > n$. But now we can let $n = -1$ to obtain

$$\frac{1}{x+1} = 1 - x + x^2 - x^3 + x^4 - x^5 + \cdots$$

Similarly, we can let $n = \frac{1}{2}$ to obtain

$$x^5 + 5x^4 \cdot y + 10x\sqrt{x+1} = 1 + \frac{1}{2}x - \frac{1}{8}x^2 + \frac{1}{16}x^3 - \frac{5}{128}x^4 + \cdots$$

with the general term being $(-1)^{n-1} \dfrac{1 \cdot 3 \cdot 5 \cdot 7 \cdot \cdots \cdot (2n-3)}{2^n n!} x^n$.

To see the connection between the binomial coefficients and the binomial expansion of $(a + b)^n$, let's calculate the following binomial coefficients:

$$\binom{5}{2} = \frac{5!}{2!(5-2)!} = 10$$

$$\binom{5}{0} = 1 \qquad \binom{5}{1} = 5 \qquad \binom{5}{2} = 10 \qquad \binom{5}{3} = 10 \qquad \binom{5}{4} = 5 \qquad \binom{5}{5} = 1$$

These are precisely the entries in the fifth row of Pascal's triangle. In fact, we can write Pascal's triangle as follows.

$$\binom{0}{0}$$

$$\binom{1}{0} \quad \binom{1}{1}$$

$$\binom{2}{0} \quad \binom{2}{1} \quad \binom{2}{2}$$

$$\binom{3}{0} \quad \binom{3}{1} \quad \binom{3}{2} \quad \binom{3}{3}$$

$$\binom{4}{0} \quad \binom{4}{1} \quad \binom{4}{2} \quad \binom{4}{3} \quad \binom{4}{4}$$

$$\binom{5}{0} \quad \binom{5}{1} \quad \binom{5}{2} \quad \binom{5}{3} \quad \binom{5}{4} \quad \binom{5}{5}$$

$$\cdot \quad \cdot \quad \cdot \quad \cdot \quad \cdot \quad \cdot \quad \cdot \quad \cdot$$

$$\binom{n}{0} \quad \binom{n}{1} \quad \binom{n}{2} \quad \cdots \quad \binom{n}{n-1} \quad \binom{n}{n}$$

To demonstrate that this pattern holds, we need to show that any entry in this version of Pascal's triangle is the sum of the two entries diagonally above it. In other words, we must show that each entry satisfies the key property of Pascal's triangle. We now state this property in terms of the binomial coefficients.

KEY PROPERTY OF THE BINOMIAL COEFFICIENTS

For any nonnegative integers r and k with $r \le k$,

$$\binom{k}{r-1} + \binom{k}{r} = \binom{k+1}{r}$$

Notice that the two terms on the left-hand side of this equation are adjacent entries in the kth row of Pascal's triangle and the term on the right-hand side is the entry diagonally below them, in the $(k+1)$st row. Thus this equation is a restatement of the key property of Pascal's triangle in terms of the binomial coefficients. A proof of this formula is outlined in Exercise 53.

▼ The Binomial Theorem

We are now ready to state the Binomial Theorem.

THE BINOMIAL THEOREM

$$(a + b)^n = \binom{n}{0}a^n + \binom{n}{1}a^{n-1}b + \binom{n}{2}a^{n-2}b^2 + \cdots + \binom{n}{n-1}ab^{n-1} + \binom{n}{n}b^n$$

EXAMPLE

$(4 - \sqrt{x})^5 = 1024 - 1280\sqrt{x}$
$+ 640x - 160(\sqrt{x})^3 + 20x^2$
$- (\sqrt{x})^5$

EXAMPLE

$\left(x + \dfrac{1}{x}\right)^8 = x^8 + 8x^6 + 28x^4$

$+ 56x^2 + 70 + \dfrac{56}{x^2} + \dfrac{28}{x^4}$

$+ \dfrac{8}{x^6} + \dfrac{1}{x^8}$

IN-CLASS MATERIALS

Point out that some of the formulas previously covered are just special cases of the Binomial Theorem, for example, the formulas for $(x + y)^2$, $(x - y)^2$, $(x + y)^3$, and $(x - y)^3$.

We prove this theorem at the end of this section. First, let's look at some of its applications.

EXAMPLE 4 | Expanding a Binomial Using the Binomial Theorem

Use the Binomial Theorem to expand $(x + y)^4$.

SOLUTION   By the Binomial Theorem,

$$(x + y)^4 = \binom{4}{0}x^4 + \binom{4}{1}x^3y + \binom{4}{2}x^2y^2 + \binom{4}{3}xy^3 + \binom{4}{4}y^4$$

Verify that

$$\binom{4}{0} = 1 \qquad \binom{4}{1} = 4 \qquad \binom{4}{2} = 6 \qquad \binom{4}{3} = 4 \qquad \binom{4}{4} = 1$$

It follows that

$$(x + y)^4 = x^4 + 4x^3y + 6x^2y^2 + 4xy^3 + y^4$$

✎. **NOW TRY EXERCISE 25**   ■

EXAMPLE 5 | Expanding a Binomial Using the Binomial Theorem

Use the Binomial Theorem to expand $\left(\sqrt{x} - 1\right)^8$.

SOLUTION   We first find the expansion of $(a + b)^8$ and then substitute $\sqrt{x}$ for a and -1 for b. Using the Binomial Theorem, we have

$$(a + b)^8 = \binom{8}{0}a^8 + \binom{8}{1}a^7b + \binom{8}{2}a^6b^2 + \binom{8}{3}a^5b^3 + \binom{8}{4}a^4b^4$$

$$+ \binom{8}{5}a^3b^5 + \binom{8}{6}a^2b^6 + \binom{8}{7}ab^7 + \binom{8}{8}b^8$$

Verify that

$$\binom{8}{0} = 1 \qquad \binom{8}{1} = 8 \qquad \binom{8}{2} = 28 \qquad \binom{8}{3} = 56 \qquad \binom{8}{4} = 70$$

$$\binom{8}{5} = 56 \qquad \binom{8}{6} = 28 \qquad \binom{8}{7} = 8 \qquad \binom{8}{8} = 1$$

So

$$(a + b)^8 = a^8 + 8a^7b + 28a^6b^2 + 56a^5b^3 + 70a^4b^4 + 56a^3b^5$$

$$+ 28a^2b^6 + 8ab^7 + b^8$$

Performing the substitutions $a = x^{1/2}$ and $b = -1$ gives

$$\left(\sqrt{x} - 1\right)^8 = (x^{1/2})^8 + 8(x^{1/2})^7(-1) + 28(x^{1/2})^6(-1)^2 + 56(x^{1/2})^5(-1)^3$$

$$+ 70(x^{1/2})^4(-1)^4 + 56(x^{1/2})^3(-1)^5 + 28(x^{1/2})^2(-1)^6$$

$$+ 8(x^{1/2})(-1)^7 + (-1)^8$$

This simplifies to

$$\left(\sqrt{x} - 1\right)^8 = x^4 - 8x^{7/2} + 28x^3 - 56x^{5/2} + 70x^2 - 56x^{3/2} + 28x - 8x^{1/2} + 1$$

✎. **NOW TRY EXERCISE 27**   ■

The Binomial Theorem can be used to find a particular term of a binomial expansion without having to find the entire expansion.

ALTERNATE EXAMPLE 4
Use the Binomial Theorem
to expand $(x + y)^5$.

ANSWER
$x^5 + 5x^4y + 10x^3y^2 + 10x^2y^3$
$+ 5xy^4 + y^5$

ALTERNATE EXAMPLE 5
Use the Binomial Theorem
to expand $\left(\sqrt{x} - 2\right)^6$.

ANSWER
$x^3 - 12x^{5/2} + 60x^2 - 160x^{3/2}$
$+ 240x - 192x^{1/2} + 64$

ALTERNATE EXAMPLE 6

Find the term that contains x^4 in the expansion of $(3x + y)^{15}$.

ANSWER

$110{,}565x^4y^{11}$

ALTERNATE EXAMPLE 7

Find the coefficient of x^6 in the expansion of $\left(x^2 + \dfrac{1}{x} \right)^9$.

ANSWER

126

> **GENERAL TERM OF THE BINOMIAL EXPANSION**
>
> The term that contains a^r in the expansion of $(a + b)^n$ is
>
> $$\binom{n}{n-r}a^r b^{n-r}$$

EXAMPLE 6 | Finding a Particular Term in a Binomial Expansion

Find the term that contains x^5 in the expansion of $(2x + y)^{20}$.

SOLUTION The term that contains x^5 is given by the formula for the general term with $a = 2x$, $b = y$, $n = 20$, and $r = 5$. So this term is

$$\binom{20}{15}a^5b^{15} = \frac{20!}{15!(20-15)!}(2x)^5 y^{15} = \frac{20!}{15!\,5!}32x^5 y^{15} = 496{,}128x^5 y^{15}$$

✎ NOW TRY EXERCISE **39** ■

EXAMPLE 7 | Finding a Particular Term in a Binomial Expansion

Find the coefficient of x^8 in the expansion of $\left(x^2 + \dfrac{1}{x} \right)^{10}$.

SOLUTION Both x^2 and $1/x$ are powers of x, so the power of x in each term of the expansion is determined by both terms of the binomial. To find the required coefficient, we first find the general term in the expansion. By the formula we have $a = x^2$, $b = 1/x$, and $n = 10$, so the general term is

$$\binom{10}{10-r}(x^2)^r\left(\frac{1}{x}\right)^{10-r} = \binom{10}{10-r}x^{2r}(x^{-1})^{10-r} = \binom{10}{10-r}x^{3r-10}$$

Thus the term that contains x^8 is the term in which

$$3r - 10 = 8$$
$$r = 6$$

So the required coefficient is

$$\binom{10}{10-6} = \binom{10}{4} = 210$$

✎ NOW TRY EXERCISE **41** ■

▼ Proof of the Binomial Theorem

We now give a proof of the Binomial Theorem using mathematical induction.

PROOF Let $P(n)$ denote the statement

$$(a+b)^n = \binom{n}{0}a^n + \binom{n}{1}a^{n-1}b + \binom{n}{2}a^{n-2}b^2 + \cdots + \binom{n}{n-1}ab^{n-1} + \binom{n}{n}b^n$$

Step 1 We show that $P(1)$ is true. But $P(1)$ is just the statement

$$(a+b)^1 = \binom{1}{0}a^1 + \binom{1}{1}b^1 = 1a + 1b = a + b$$

which is certainly true.

Step 2 We assume that $P(k)$ is true. Thus our induction hypothesis is

$$(a + b)^k = \binom{k}{0}a^k + \binom{k}{1}a^{k-1}b + \binom{k}{2}a^{k-2}b^2 + \cdots + \binom{k}{k-1}ab^{k-1} + \binom{k}{k}b^k$$

We use this to show that $P(k + 1)$ is true.

$$(a + b)^{k+1} = (a + b)[(a + b)^k]$$

$$= (a + b)\left[\binom{k}{0}a^k + \binom{k}{1}a^{k-1}b + \binom{k}{2}a^{k-2}b^2 + \cdots + \binom{k}{k-1}ab^{k-1} + \binom{k}{k}b^k\right] \quad \text{Induction hypothesis}$$

$$= a\left[\binom{k}{0}a^k + \binom{k}{1}a^{k-1}b + \binom{k}{2}a^{k-2}b^2 + \cdots + \binom{k}{k-1}ab^{k-1} + \binom{k}{k}b^k\right]$$

$$+ b\left[\binom{k}{0}a^k + \binom{k}{1}a^{k-1}b + \binom{k}{2}a^{k-2}b^2 + \cdots + \binom{k}{k-1}ab^{k-1} + \binom{k}{k}b^k\right] \quad \text{Distributive Property}$$

$$= \binom{k}{0}a^{k+1} + \binom{k}{1}a^k b + \binom{k}{2}a^{k-1}b^2 + \cdots + \binom{k}{k-1}a^2 b^{k-1} + \binom{k}{k}ab^k$$

$$+ \binom{k}{0}a^k b + \binom{k}{1}a^{k-1}b^2 + \binom{k}{2}a^{k-2}b^3 + \cdots + \binom{k}{k-1}ab^k + \binom{k}{k}b^{k+1} \quad \text{Distributive Property}$$

$$= \binom{k}{0}a^{k+1} + \left[\binom{k}{0} + \binom{k}{1}\right]a^k b + \left[\binom{k}{1} + \binom{k}{2}\right]a^{k-1}b^2$$

$$+ \cdots + \left[\binom{k}{k-1} + \binom{k}{k}\right]ab^k + \binom{k}{k}b^{k+1} \quad \text{Group like terms}$$

Using the key property of the binomial coefficients, we can write each of the expressions in square brackets as a single binomial coefficient. Also, writing the first and last coefficients as $\binom{k+1}{0}$ and $\binom{k+1}{k+1}$ (these are equal to 1 by Exercise 50) gives

$$(a + b)^{k+1} = \binom{k+1}{0}a^{k+1} + \binom{k+1}{1}a^k b + \binom{k+1}{2}a^{k-1}b^2 + \cdots + \binom{k+1}{k}ab^k + \binom{k+1}{k+1}b^{k+1}$$

But this last equation is precisely $P(k + 1)$, and this completes the induction step.

Having proved Steps 1 and 2, we conclude by the Principle of Mathematical Induction that the theorem is true for all natural numbers n. ■

12.6 EXERCISES

CONCEPTS

1. An algebraic expression of the form $a + b$, which consists of a sum of two terms, is called a _____ .

2. We can find the coefficients in the expansion of $(a + b)^n$ from the nth row of _____ triangle. So

$$(a + b)^4 = \blacksquare a^4 + \blacksquare a^3 b + \blacksquare a^2 b^2 + \blacksquare ab^3 + \blacksquare b^4$$

3. The binomial coefficients can be calculated directly by using

the formula $\binom{n}{k} = $ _____ . So $\binom{4}{3} = $ _____ .

4. To expand $(a + b)^n$, we can use the _____ Theorem. Using this theorem, we find

$$(a + b)^4 =$$
$$\binom{\blacksquare}{\blacksquare}a^4 + \binom{\blacksquare}{\blacksquare}a^3 b + \binom{\blacksquare}{\blacksquare}a^2 b^2 + \binom{\blacksquare}{\blacksquare}ab^3 + \binom{\blacksquare}{\blacksquare}b^4$$

DRILL QUESTION

Expand $(x + 2y)^6$.

Answer

$(x + 2y)^6 = x^6 + 12x^5 y + 60x^4 y^2$
$+ 160x^3 y^3 + 240x^2 y^4 + 192xy^5$
$+ 64y^6$

SKILLS

5–16 ■ Use Pascal's triangle to expand the expression.

5. $(x + y)^6$ **6.** $(2x + 1)^4$ **7.** $\left(x + \dfrac{1}{x}\right)^4$

8. $(x - y)^5$ **9.** $(x - 1)^5$ **10.** $(\sqrt{a} + \sqrt{b})^6$

11. $(x^2 y - 1)^5$ **12.** $(1 + \sqrt{2})^6$ **13.** $(2x - 3y)^3$

14. $(1 + x^3)^3$ **15.** $\left(\dfrac{1}{x} - \sqrt{x}\right)^5$ **16.** $\left(2 + \dfrac{x}{2}\right)^5$

17–24 ■ Evaluate the expression.

17. $\dbinom{6}{4}$ **18.** $\dbinom{8}{3}$ **19.** $\dbinom{100}{98}$

20. $\dbinom{10}{5}$ **21.** $\dbinom{3}{1}\dbinom{4}{2}$ **22.** $\dbinom{5}{2}\dbinom{5}{3}$

23. $\dbinom{5}{0} + \dbinom{5}{1} + \dbinom{5}{2} + \dbinom{5}{3} + \dbinom{5}{4} + \dbinom{5}{5}$

24. $\dbinom{5}{0} - \dbinom{5}{1} + \dbinom{5}{2} - \dbinom{5}{3} + \dbinom{5}{4} - \dbinom{5}{5}$

25–28 ■ Use the Binomial Theorem to expand the expression.

25. $(x + 2y)^4$ **26.** $(1 - x)^5$

27. $\left(1 + \dfrac{1}{x}\right)^6$ **28.** $(2A + B^2)^4$

29. Find the first three terms in the expansion of $(x + 2y)^{20}$.

30. Find the first four terms in the expansion of $(x^{1/2} + 1)^{30}$.

31. Find the last two terms in the expansion of $(a^{2/3} + a^{1/3})^{25}$.

32. Find the first three terms in the expansion of
$$\left(x + \dfrac{1}{x}\right)^{40}$$

33. Find the middle term in the expansion of $(x^2 + 1)^{18}$.

34. Find the fifth term in the expansion of $(ab - 1)^{20}$.

35. Find the 24th term in the expansion of $(a + b)^{25}$.

36. Find the 28th term in the expansion of $(A - B)^{30}$.

37. Find the 100th term in the expansion of $(1 + y)^{100}$.

38. Find the second term in the expansion of
$$\left(x^2 - \dfrac{1}{x}\right)^{25}$$

39. Find the term containing x^4 in the expansion of $(x + 2y)^{10}$.

40. Find the term containing y^3 in the expansion of $(\sqrt{2} + y)^{12}$.

41. Find the term containing b^8 in the expansion of $(a + b^2)^{12}$.

42. Find the term that does not contain x in the expansion of
$$\left(8x + \dfrac{1}{2x}\right)^8$$

43–46 ■ Factor using the Binomial Theorem.

43. $x^4 + 4x^3 y + 6x^2 y^2 + 4xy^3 + y^4$

44. $(x - 1)^5 + 5(x - 1)^4 + 10(x - 1)^3$
$\qquad + 10(x - 1)^2 + 5(x - 1) + 1$

45. $8a^3 + 12a^2 b + 6ab^2 + b^3$

46. $x^8 + 4x^6 y + 6x^4 y^2 + 4x^2 y^3 + y^4$

47–52 ■ Simplify using the Binomial Theorem.

47. $\dfrac{(x + h)^3 - x^3}{h}$ **48.** $\dfrac{(x + h)^4 - x^4}{h}$

49. Show that $(1.01)^{100} > 2$.   [*Hint:* Note that $(1.01)^{100} = (1 + 0.01)^{100}$, and use the Binomial Theorem to show that the sum of the first two terms of the expansion is greater than 2.]

50. Show that $\dbinom{n}{0} = 1$ and $\dbinom{n}{n} = 1$.

51. Show that $\dbinom{n}{1} = \dbinom{n}{n-1} = n$.

52. Show that $\dbinom{n}{r} = \dbinom{n}{n-r}$ for $0 \le r \le n$.

53. In this exercise we prove the identity
$$\binom{n}{r-1} + \binom{n}{r} = \binom{n+1}{r}$$

  (a) Write the left-hand side of this equation as the sum of two fractions.

  (b) Show that a common denominator of the expression that you found in part (a) is $r!(n - r + 1)!$.

  (c) Add the two fractions using the common denominator in part (b), simplify the numerator, and note that the resulting expression is equal to the right-hand side of the equation.

54. Prove that $\binom{n}{r}$ is an integer for all n and for $0 \le r \le n$. [*Suggestion:* Use induction to show that the statement is true for all n, and use Exercise 53 for the induction step.]

APPLICATIONS

55. Difference in Volumes of Cubes   The volume of a cube of side x inches is given by $V(x) = x^3$, so the volume of a cube of side $x + 2$ inches is given by $V(x + 2) = (x + 2)^3$. Use the Binomial Theorem to show that the difference in volume between the larger and smaller cubes is $6x^2 + 12x + 8$ cubic inches.

56. Probability of Hitting a Target   The probability that an archer hits the target is $p = 0.9$, so the probability that he misses the target is $q = 0.1$. It is known that in this situation the probability that the archer hits the target exactly r times in n attempts is given by the term containing p^r in the binomial expansion of $(p + q)^n$. Find the probability that the archer hits the target exactly three times in five attempts.

DISCOVERY ■ DISCUSSION ■ WRITING

57. Powers of Factorials   Which is larger, $(100!)^{101}$ or $(101!)^{100}$?   [*Hint:* Try factoring the expressions. Do they have any common factors?]

58. Sums of Binomial Coefficients Add each of the first five rows of Pascal's triangle, as indicated. Do you see a pattern?

$$1 + 1 = \boxed{?}$$
$$1 + 2 + 1 = \boxed{?}$$
$$1 + 3 + 3 + 1 = \boxed{?}$$
$$1 + 4 + 6 + 4 + 1 = \boxed{?}$$
$$1 + 5 + 10 + 10 + 5 + 1 = \boxed{?}$$

On the basis of the pattern you have found, find the sum of the nth row:

$$\binom{n}{0} + \binom{n}{1} + \binom{n}{2} + \cdots + \binom{n}{n}$$

Prove your result by expanding $(1 + 1)^n$ using the Binomial Theorem.

59. Alternating Sums of Binomial Coefficients Find the sum

$$\binom{n}{0} - \binom{n}{1} + \binom{n}{2} - \cdots + (-1)^n\binom{n}{n}$$

by finding a pattern as in Exercise 58. Prove your result by expanding $(1 - 1)^n$ using the Binomial Theorem.

CHAPTER 12 | REVIEW

■ CONCEPT CHECK

1. (a) What is a sequence?
  (b) What is an arithmetic sequence? Write an expression for the nth term of an arithmetic sequence.
  (c) What is a geometric sequence? Write an expression for the nth term of a geometric sequence.

2. (a) What is a recursively defined sequence?
  (b) What is the Fibonacci sequence?

3. (a) What is meant by the partial sums of a sequence?
  (b) If an arithmetic sequence has first term a and common difference d, write an expression for the sum of its first n terms.
  (c) If a geometric sequence has first term a and common ratio r, write an expression for the sum of its first n terms.
  (d) Write an expression for the sum of an infinite geometric series with first term a and common ratio r. For what values of r is your formula valid?

4. (a) Write the sum $\sum_{k=1}^{n} a_k$ without using sigma notation.
  (b) Write $b_1 + b_2 + b_3 + \cdots + b_n$ using sigma notation.

5. Write an expression for the amount A_f of an annuity consisting of n regular equal payments of size R with interest rate i per time period.

6. State the Principle of Mathematical Induction.

7. Write the first five rows of Pascal's triangle. How are the entries related to each other?

8. (a) What does the symbol $n!$ mean?
  (b) Write an expression for the binomial coefficient $\binom{n}{r}$.
  (c) State the Binomial Theorem.
  (d) Write the term that contains a^r in the expansion of $(a + b)^n$.

■ EXERCISES

1–6 ■ Find the first four terms as well as the tenth term of the sequence with the given nth term.

1. $a_n = \dfrac{n^2}{n + 1}$

2. $a_n = (-1)^n\dfrac{2^n}{n}$

3. $a_n = \dfrac{(-1)^n + 1}{n^3}$

4. $a_n = \dfrac{n(n + 1)}{2}$

5. $a_n = \dfrac{(2n)!}{2^n n!}$

6. $a_n = \binom{n + 1}{2}$

7–10 ■ A sequence is defined recursively. Find the first seven terms of the sequence.

7. $a_n = a_{n-1} + 2n - 1, \quad a_1 = 1$

8. $a_n = \dfrac{a_{n-1}}{n}, \quad a_1 = 1$

9. $a_n = a_{n-1} + 2a_{n-2}, \quad a_1 = 1, a_2 = 3$

10. $a_n = \sqrt{3a_{n-1}}, \quad a_1 = \sqrt{3}$

11–14 ■ The nth term of a sequence is given.
    (a) Find the first five terms of the sequence.
    (b) Graph the terms you found in part (a).
    (c) Find the fifth partial sum of the sequence.
    (d) Determine whether the series is arithmetic or geometric. Find the common difference or the common ratio.

11. $a_n = 2n + 5$ **12.** $a_n = \dfrac{5}{2^n}$

13. $a_n = \dfrac{3^n}{2^{n+1}}$ **14.** $a_n = 4 - \dfrac{n}{2}$

15–22 ■ The first four terms of a sequence are given. Determine whether they can be the terms of an arithmetic sequence, a geometric sequence, or neither. If the sequence is arithmetic or geometric, find the fifth term.

15. $5, 5.5, 6, 6.5, \ldots$ **16.** $\sqrt{2}, 2\sqrt{2}, 3\sqrt{2}, 4\sqrt{2}, \ldots$

17. $t - 3, t - 2, t - 1, t, \ldots$ **18.** $\sqrt{2}, 2, 2\sqrt{2}, 4, \ldots$

19. $t^3, t^2, t, 1, \ldots$ **20.** $1, -\frac{3}{2}, 2, -\frac{5}{2}, \ldots$

21. $\dfrac{3}{4}, \dfrac{1}{2}, \dfrac{1}{3}, \dfrac{2}{9}, \ldots$ **22.** $a, 1, \dfrac{1}{a}, \dfrac{1}{a^2}, \ldots$

23. Show that $3, 6i, -12, -24i, \ldots$ is a geometric sequence, and find the common ratio. (Here $i = \sqrt{-1}$.)

24. Find the nth term of the geometric sequence $2, 2 + 2i, 4i,$ $-4 + 4i, -8, \ldots$ (Here $i = \sqrt{-1}$.)

25. The sixth term of an arithmetic sequence is 17, and the fourth term is 11. Find the second term.

26. The 20th term of an arithmetic sequence is 96, and the common difference is 5. Find the nth term.

27. The third term of a geometric sequence is 9, and the common ratio is $\frac{3}{2}$. Find the fifth term.

28. The second term of a geometric sequence is 10, and the fifth term is $\frac{1250}{27}$. Find the nth term.

29. A teacher makes \$32,000 in his first year at Lakeside School and gets a 5% raise each year.
    (a) Find a formula for his salary A_n in his nth year at this school.
    (b) List his salaries for his first 8 years at this school.

30. A colleague of the teacher in Exercise 29, hired at the same time, makes \$35,000 in her first year, and gets a \$1200 raise each year.
    (a) What is her salary A_n in her nth year at this school?
    (b) Find her salary in her eighth year at this school, and compare it to the salary of the teacher in Exercise 29 in his eighth year.

31. A certain type of bacteria divides every 5 s. If three of these bacteria are put into a petri dish, how many bacteria are in the dish at the end of 1 min?

32. If $a_1, a_2, a_3, \ldots$ and $b_1, b_2, b_3, \ldots$ are arithmetic sequences, show that $a_1 + b_1, a_2 + b_2, a_3 + b_3, \ldots$ is also an arithmetic sequence.

33. If $a_1, a_2, a_3, \ldots$ and $b_1, b_2, b_3, \ldots$ are geometric sequences, show that $a_1 b_1, a_2 b_2, a_3 b_3, \ldots$ is also a geometric sequence.

34. (a) If $a_1, a_2, a_3, \ldots$ is an arithmetic sequence, is the sequence $a_1 + 2, a_2 + 2, a_3 + 2, \ldots$ arithmetic?
    (b) If $a_1, a_2, a_3, \ldots$ is a geometric sequence, is the sequence $5a_1, 5a_2, 5a_3, \ldots$ geometric?

35. Find the values of x for which the sequence $6, x, 12, \ldots$ is
    (a) arithmetic   **(b)** geometric

36. Find the values of x and y for which the sequence $2, x, y,$ $17, \ldots$ is
    (a) arithmetic   **(b)** geometric

37–40 ■ Find the sum.

37. $\displaystyle\sum_{k=3}^{6} (k + 1)^2$ **38.** $\displaystyle\sum_{i=1}^{4} \dfrac{2i}{2i - 1}$

39. $\displaystyle\sum_{k=1}^{6} (k + 1)2^{k-1}$ **40.** $\displaystyle\sum_{m=1}^{5} 3^{m-2}$

41–44 ■ Write the sum without using sigma notation. Do not evaluate.

41. $\displaystyle\sum_{k=1}^{10} (k - 1)^2$ **42.** $\displaystyle\sum_{j=2}^{100} \dfrac{1}{j - 1}$

43. $\displaystyle\sum_{k=1}^{50} \dfrac{3^k}{2^{k+1}}$ **44.** $\displaystyle\sum_{n=1}^{10} n^2 2^n$

45–48 ■ Write the sum using sigma notation. Do not evaluate.

45. $3 + 6 + 9 + 12 + \cdots + 99$

46. $1^2 + 2^2 + 3^2 + \cdots + 100^2$

47. $1 \cdot 2^3 + 2 \cdot 2^4 + 3 \cdot 2^5 + 4 \cdot 2^6 + \cdots + 100 \cdot 2^{102}$

48. $\dfrac{1}{1 \cdot 2} + \dfrac{1}{2 \cdot 3} + \dfrac{1}{3 \cdot 4} + \cdots + \dfrac{1}{999 \cdot 1000}$

49–54 ■ Determine whether the expression is a partial sum of an arithmetic or geometric sequence. Then find the sum.

49. $1 + 0.9 + (0.9)^2 + \cdots + (0.9)^5$

50. $3 + 3.7 + 4.4 + \cdots + 10$

51. $\sqrt{5} + 2\sqrt{5} + 3\sqrt{5} + \cdots + 100\sqrt{5}$

52. $\frac{1}{3} + \frac{2}{3} + 1 + \frac{4}{3} + \cdots + 33$

53. $\displaystyle\sum_{n=0}^{6} 3(-4)^n$ **54.** $\displaystyle\sum_{k=0}^{8} 7(5)^{k/2}$

55–60 ■ Determine whether the infinite geometric series is convergent or divergent. If it is convergent, find its sum.

55. $1 - \frac{2}{5} + \frac{4}{25} - \frac{8}{125} + \cdots$

56. $0.1 + 0.01 + 0.001 + 0.0001 + \cdots$

57. $5 - 5(1.01) + 5(1.01)^2 - 5(1.01)^3 + \cdots$

58. $1 + \dfrac{1}{3^{1/2}} + \dfrac{1}{3} + \dfrac{1}{3^{3/2}} + \cdots$

59. $-1 + \dfrac{9}{8} - \left(\dfrac{9}{8}\right)^2 + \left(\dfrac{9}{8}\right)^3 - \cdots$

60. $a + ab^2 + ab^4 + ab^6 + \cdots, \quad |b| < 1$

61. The first term of an arithmetic sequence is $a = 7$, and the common difference is $d = 3$. How many terms of this sequence must be added to obtain 325?

62. The sum of the first three terms of a geometric series is 52, and the common ratio is $r = 3$. Find the first term.

63. A person has two parents, four grandparents, eight great-grandparents, and so on. What is the total number of a person's ancestors in 15 generations?

64. Find the amount of an annuity consisting of 16 annual payments of $1000 each into an account that pays 8% interest per year, compounded annually.

65. How much money should be invested every quarter at 12% per year, compounded quarterly, in order to have $10,000 in one year?

66. What are the monthly payments on a mortgage of $60,000 at 9% interest if the loan is to be repaid in
   (a) 30 years?   **(b)** 15 years?

67–69 ■ Use mathematical induction to prove that the formula is true for all natural numbers n.

67. $1 + 4 + 7 + \cdots + (3n - 2) = \dfrac{n(3n - 1)}{2}$

68. $\dfrac{1}{1 \cdot 3} + \dfrac{1}{3 \cdot 5} + \dfrac{1}{5 \cdot 7} + \cdots + \dfrac{1}{(2n - 1)(2n + 1)} = \dfrac{n}{2n + 1}$

69. $\left(1 + \dfrac{1}{1}\right)\left(1 + \dfrac{1}{2}\right)\left(1 + \dfrac{1}{3}\right) \cdots \left(1 + \dfrac{1}{n}\right) = n + 1$

70. Show that $7^n - 1$ is divisible by 6 for all natural numbers n.

71. Let $a_{n+1} = 3a_n + 4$ and $a_1 = 4$. Show that $a_n = 2 \cdot 3^n - 2$ for all natural numbers n.

72. Prove that the Fibonacci number F_{4n} is divisible by 3 for all natural numbers n.

73–76 ■ Evaluate the expression.

73. $\dbinom{5}{2}\dbinom{5}{3}$

74. $\dbinom{10}{2} + \dbinom{10}{6}$

75. $\displaystyle\sum_{k=0}^{5} \dbinom{5}{k}$

76. $\displaystyle\sum_{k=0}^{8} \dbinom{8}{k}\dbinom{8}{8 - k}$

77–80 ■ Expand the expression.

77. $(A - B)^3$

78. $(x + 2)^5$

79. $(1 - x^2)^6$

80. $(2x + y)^4$

81. Find the 20th term in the expansion of $(a + b)^{22}$.

82. Find the first three terms in the expansion of $(b^{-2/3} + b^{1/3})^{20}$.

83. Find the term containing A^6 in the expansion of $(A + 3B)^{10}$.

1. Find the first six terms and the sixth partial sum of the sequence whose nth term is $a_n = 2n^2 - n$.

2. A sequence is defined recursively by $a_{n+1} = 3a_n - n$, $a_1 = 2$. Find the first six terms of the sequence.

3. An arithmetic sequence begins $2, 5, 8, 11, 14, \ldots$.
   (a) Find the common difference d for this sequence.
   (b) Find a formula for the nth term a_n of the sequence.
   (c) Find the 35th term of the sequence.

4. A geometric sequence begins $12, 3, 3/4, 3/16, 3/64, \ldots$.
   (a) Find the common ratio r for this sequence.
   (b) Find a formula for the nth term a_n of the sequence.
   (c) Find the tenth term of the sequence.

5. The first term of a geometric sequence is 25, and the fourth term is $\frac{1}{5}$.
   (a) Find the common ratio r and the fifth term.
   (b) Find the partial sum of the first eight terms.

6. The first term of an arithmetic sequence is 10, and the tenth term is 2.
   (a) Find the common difference and the 100th term of the sequence.
   (b) Find the partial sum of the first ten terms.

7. Let $a_1, a_2, a_3, \ldots$ be a geometric sequence with initial term a and common ratio r. Show that $a_1^2, a_2^2, a_3^2, \ldots$ is also a geometric sequence by finding its common ratio.

8. Write the expression without using sigma notation, and then find the sum.
   (a) $\displaystyle\sum_{n=1}^{5} (1 - n^2)$
   (b) $\displaystyle\sum_{n=3}^{6} (-1)^n 2^{n-2}$

9. Find the sum.
   (a) $\dfrac{1}{3} + \dfrac{2}{3^2} + \dfrac{2^2}{3^3} + \dfrac{2^3}{3^4} + \cdots + \dfrac{2^9}{3^{10}}$
   (b) $1 + \dfrac{1}{2^{1/2}} + \dfrac{1}{2} + \dfrac{1}{2^{3/2}} + \cdots$

10. Use mathematical induction to prove that for all natural numbers n,

$$1^2 + 2^2 + 3^2 + \cdots + n^2 = \frac{n(n+1)(2n+1)}{6}$$

11. Expand $(2x + y^2)^5$.

12. Find the term containing x^3 in the binomial expansion of $(3x - 2)^{10}$.

13. A puppy weighs 0.85 lb at birth, and each week he gains 24% in weight. Let a_n be his weight in pounds at the end of his nth week of life.
   (a) Find a formula for a_n.
   (b) How much does the puppy weigh when he is six weeks old?
   (c) Is the sequence $a_1, a_2, a_3, \ldots$ arithmetic, geometric, or neither?

Modeling with Recursive Sequences

Many real-world processes occur in stages. Population growth can be viewed in stages—each new generation represents a stage in population growth. Compound interest is paid in stages—each interest payment creates a new account balance. Many things that change continuously are more easily measured in discrete stages. For example, we can measure the temperature of a continuously cooling object in one-hour intervals. In this *Focus* we learn how recursive sequences are used to model such situations. In some cases we can get an explicit formula for a sequence from the recursion relation that defines it by finding a pattern in the terms of the sequence.

▼ Recursive Sequences as Models

Suppose you deposit some money in an account that pays 6% interest compounded monthly. The bank has a definite rule for paying interest: At the end of each month the bank adds to your account $\frac{1}{2}$% (or 0.005) of the amount in your account at that time. Let's express this rule as follows:

$$\boxed{\text{amount at the end of this month}} = \boxed{\text{amount at the end of last month}} + 0.005 \times \boxed{\text{amount at the end of last month}}$$

Using the Distributive Property, we can write this as

$$\boxed{\text{amount at the end of this month}} = 1.005 \times \boxed{\text{amount at the end of last month}}$$

To model this statement using algebra, let A_0 be the amount of the original deposit, let A_1 be the amount at the end of the first month, let A_2 be the amount at the end of the second month, and so on. So A_n is the amount at the end of the nth month. Thus

$$A_n = 1.005 A_{n-1}$$

We recognize this as a recursively defined sequence—it gives us the amount at each stage in terms of the amount at the preceding stage.

$A_0 \qquad A_1 \qquad A_2 \qquad A_{n-1}$

To find a formula for A_n, let's find the first few terms of the sequence and look for a pattern.

$$A_1 = 1.005 A_0$$
$$A_2 = 1.005 A_1 = (1.005)^2 A_0$$
$$A_3 = 1.005 A_2 = (1.005)^3 A_0$$
$$A_4 = 1.005 A_3 = (1.005)^4 A_0$$

We see that in general, $A_n = (1.005)^n A_0$.

833

EXAMPLE 1 | Population Growth

A certain animal population grows by 2% each year. The initial population is 5000.

(a) Find a recursive sequence that models the population P_n at the end of the nth year.

(b) Find the first five terms of the sequence P_n.

(c) Find a formula for P_n.

SOLUTION

(a) We can model the population using the following rule:

> population at the end of this year $= 1.02 \times$ population at the end of last year

Algebraically, we can write this as the recursion relation

$$P_n = 1.02P_{n-1}$$

(b) Since the initial population is 5000, we have

$$P_0 = 5000$$
$$P_1 = 1.02P_0 = (1.02)5000$$
$$P_2 = 1.02P_1 = (1.02)^2 5000$$
$$P_3 = 1.02P_2 = (1.02)^3 5000$$
$$P_4 = 1.02P_3 = (1.02)^4 5000$$

(c) We see from the pattern exhibited in part (b) that $P_n = (1.02)^n 5000$. (Note that P_n is a geometric sequence, with common ratio $r = 1.02$.)   ∎

EXAMPLE 2 | Daily Drug Dose

A patient is to take a 50-mg pill of a certain drug every morning. It is known that the body eliminates 40% of the drug every 24 hours.

(a) Find a recursive sequence that models the amount A_n of the drug in the patient's body after each pill is taken.

(b) Find the first four terms of the sequence A_n.

(c) Find a formula for A_n.

(d) How much of the drug remains in the patient's body after 5 days? How much will accumulate in his system after prolonged use?

SOLUTION

(a) Each morning, 60% of the drug remains in his system, plus he takes an additional 50 mg (his daily dose).

> amount of drug this morning $= 0.6 \times$ amount of drug yesterday morning $+ 50$ mg

We can express this as a recursion relation

$$A_n = 0.6A_{n-1} + 50$$

(b) Since the initial dose is 50 mg, we have

$$A_0 = 50$$

$$A_1 = 0.6A_0 + 50 = 0.6(50) + 50$$

$$A_2 = 0.6A_1 + 50 = 0.6[0.6(50) + 50] + 50$$

$$= 0.6^2(50) + 0.6(50) + 50$$

$$= 50(0.6^2 + 0.6 + 1)$$

$$A_3 = 0.6A_2 + 50 = 0.6[0.6^2(50) + 0.6(50) + 50] + 50$$

$$= 0.6^3(50) + 0.6^2(50) + 0.6(50) + 50$$

$$= 50(0.6^3 + 0.6^2 + 0.6 + 1)$$

(c) From the pattern in part (b) we see that

$$A_n = 50(1 + 0.6 + 0.6^2 + \cdots + 0.6^n)$$

$$= 50\left(\frac{1 - 0.6^{n+1}}{1 - 0.6}\right) \qquad \text{Partial sum of a geometric sequence (page 802)}$$

$$= 125(1 - 0.6^{n+1}) \qquad \text{Simplify}$$

(d) To find the amount remaining after 5 days, we substitute $n = 5$ and get $A_5 = 125(1 - 0.6^{5+1}) \approx 119$ mg.

To find the amount remaining after prolonged use, we let n become large. As n gets large, 0.6^n approaches 0. That is, $0.6^n \to 0$ as $n \to \infty$ (see Section 4.1). So as $n \to \infty$,

$$A_n = 125(1 - 0.6^{n+1}) \to 125(1 - 0) = 125$$

Thus after prolonged use the amount of drug in the patient's system approaches 125 mg (see Figure 1, where we have used a graphing calculator to graph the sequence).

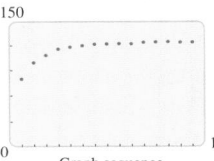

Enter sequence   Graph sequence

FIGURE 1

PROBLEMS

1. Retirement Accounts   Many college professors keep retirement savings with TIAA, the largest annuity program in the world. Interest on these accounts is compounded and credited *daily*. Professor Brown has $275,000 on deposit with TIAA at the start of 2011 and receives 3.65% interest per year on his account.

(a) Find a recursive sequence that models the amount A_n in his account at the end of the nth day of 2011.

(b) Find the first eight terms of the sequence A_n, rounded to the nearest cent.

(c) Find a formula for A_n.

2. Fitness Program   Sheila decides to embark on a swimming program as the best way to maintain cardiovascular health. She begins by swimming 5 min on the first day, then adds $1\frac{1}{2}$ min every day after that.

(a) Find a recursive formula for the number of minutes T_n that she swims on the nth day of her program.

(b) Find the first 6 terms of the sequence T_n.

(c) Find a formula for T_n. What kind of sequence is this?

(d) On what day does Sheila attain her goal of swimming at least 65 min a day?

(e) What is the total amount of time she will have swum after 30 days?

3. Monthly Savings Program   Alice opens a savings account that pays 3% interest per year, compounded monthly. She begins by depositing $100 at the start of the first month and adds $100 at the end of each month, when the interest is credited.

(a) Find a recursive formula for the amount A_n in her account at the end of the nth month. (Include the interest credited for that month and her monthly deposit.)

(b) Find the first five terms of the sequence A_n.

(c) Use the pattern you observed in (b) to find a formula for A_n.   [*Hint:* To find the pattern most easily, it's best *not* to simplify the terms *too* much.]

(d) How much has she saved after 5 years?

4. Stocking a Fish Pond   A pond is stocked with 4000 trout, and through reproduction the population increases by 20% per year. Find a recursive sequence that models the trout population P_n at the end of the nth year under each of the following circumstances. Find the trout population at the end of the fifth year in each case.

(a) The trout population changes only because of reproduction.

(b) Each year 600 trout are harvested.

(c) Each year 250 additional trout are introduced into the pond.

(d) Each year 10% of the trout are harvested, and 300 additional trout are introduced into the pond.

5. Pollution   A chemical plant discharges 2400 tons of pollutants every year into an adjacent lake. Through natural runoff, 70% of the pollutants contained in the lake at the beginning of the year are expelled by the end of the year.

(a) Explain why the following sequence models the amount A_n of the pollutant in the lake at the end of the nth year that the plant is operating.

$$A_n = 0.30A_{n-1} + 2400$$

(b) Find the first five terms of the sequence A_n.

(c) Find a formula for A_n.

(d) How much of the pollutant remains in the lake after 6 years? How much will remain after the plant has been operating a long time?

(e) Verify your answer to part (d) by graphing A_n with a graphing calculator for $n = 1$ to $n = 20$.

6. Annual Savings Program Ursula opens a one-year CD that yields 5% interest per year. She begins with a deposit of $5000. At the end of each year when the CD matures, she reinvests at the same 5% interest rate, also adding 10% to the value of the CD from her other savings. (So for example, after the first year her CD has earned 5% of $5000 in interest, for a value of $5250 at maturity. She then adds 10%, or $525, bringing the total value of her renewed CD to $5775.)

(a) Find a recursive formula for the amount U_n in Ursula's CD when she reinvests at the end of the nth year.

(b) Find the first five terms of the sequence U_n. Does this appear to be a geometric sequence?

(c) Use the pattern you observed in (b) to find a formula for U_n.

(d) How much has she saved after 10 years?

7. Annual Savings Program Victoria opens a one-year CD with a 5% annual interest yield at the same time as her friend Ursula in Problem 6. She also starts with an initial deposit of $5000. However, Victoria decides to add $500 to her CD when she reinvests at the end of the first year, $1000 at the end of the second, $1500 at the end of the third, and so on.

(a) Explain why the recursive formula displayed below gives the amount V_n in Victoria's CD when she reinvests at the end of the nth year.

$$V_n = 1.05V_{n-1} + 500n$$

(b) Using the $\texttt{Seq}$ ("sequence") mode on your graphing calculator, enter the sequences U_n and V_n as shown in the figure. Then use the $\boxed{\texttt{TABLE}}$ command to compare the two sequences. For the first few years, Victoria seems to be accumulating more savings than Ursula. Scroll down in the table to verify that Ursula eventually pulls ahead of Victoria in the savings race. In what year does this occur?

n	$u(n)$	$v(n)$
0	5000	5000
1	5750	5750
2	6612.5	7037.5
3	7604.4	8889.4
4	8745	11334
5	10057	14401
6	11565	18121
$n=0$		

Entering the sequences   Table of values of the sequences

8. Newton's Law of Cooling A tureen of soup at a temperature of 170°F is placed on a table in a dining room in which the thermostat is set at 70°F. The soup cools according to the following rule, a special case of Newton's Law of Cooling: Each minute, the temperature of the soup declines by 3% of the difference between the soup temperature and the room temperature.

(a) Find a recursive sequence that models the soup temperature T_n at the nth minute.

(b) Enter the sequence T_n in your graphing calculator, and use the $\boxed{\texttt{TABLE}}$ command to find the temperature at 10-min increments from $n = 0$ to $n = 60$. (See Problem 7(b).)

(c) Graph the sequence T_n. What temperature will the soup be after a long time?

9. Logistic Population Growth Simple exponential models for population growth do not take into account the fact that when the population increases, survival becomes harder for each individual because of greater competition for food and other resources. We can get a more accurate model by assuming that the birth rate is proportional to the size of the population, but the death rate is proportional to the square of the population. Using this idea, researchers find that the number of raccoons R_n on a certain island is modeled by the following recursive sequence:

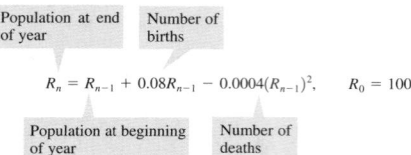

$$R_n = R_{n-1} + 0.08R_{n-1} - 0.0004(R_{n-1})^2, \qquad R_0 = 100$$

Here, n represents the number of years since observations began, R_0 is the initial population, 0.08 is the annual birth rate, and 0.0004 is a constant related to the death rate.

(a) Use the ⎡TABLE⎤ command on a graphing calculator to find the raccoon population for each year from $n = 1$ to $n = 7$.

(b) Graph the sequence R_n. What happens to the raccoon population as n becomes large?

LIMITS: A PREVIEW OF CALCULUS

In this chapter we study the central idea underlying calculus: the concept of a *limit*. Calculus is used in modeling numerous real-life phenomena, particularly situations that involve change or motion. Limits are used in finding the instantaneous rate of change of a function as well as the area of a region with curved boundary. You will learn in calculus that these two apparently different problems are closely related. In this chapter we see how limits allow us to solve both problems.

In Chapter 2 we learned how to find the average rate of change of a function. For example, to find the average speed, we divide the total distance traveled by the total time. But how can we find *instantaneous* speed—that is, the speed at a given instant? We can't divide the total distance by the total time because in an instant the total distance traveled is zero and the total time spent traveling is zero! But we can find the average rate of change on smaller and smaller intervals, zooming in on the instant we want. In other words, the instantaneous speed is a *limit* of the average speeds.

To find the area of region with curved sides, we approximate the area by inscribing polygons in the region. The figure illustrates how this is done for a circle. If we let A_n be the area of the inscribed polygon with n sides, then we see that as n increases, A_n gets closer and closer to the area A of the circle. In other words, the area A is the *limit* of the areas A_n.

SUGGESTED TIME AND EMPHASIS

1–2 classes, optional material

13.1 FINDING LIMITS NUMERICALLY AND GRAPHICALLY

│ Definition of Limit ▶ Estimating Limits Numerically and Graphically ▶
│ Limits That Fail to Exist ▶ One-Sided Limits

In this section we use tables of values and graphs of functions to answer the question, What happens to the values $f(x)$ of a function f as the variable x approaches the number a?

▼ Definition of Limit

We begin by investigating the behavior of the function f defined by

$$f(x) = x^2 - x + 2$$

for values of x near 2. The following tables give values of $f(x)$ for values of x close to 2 but not equal to 2.

x	$f(x)$	x	$f(x)$
1.0	2.000000	3.0	8.000000
1.5	2.750000	2.5	5.750000
1.8	3.440000	2.2	4.640000
1.9	3.710000	2.1	4.310000
1.95	3.852500	2.05	4.152500
1.99	3.970100	2.01	4.030100
1.995	3.985025	2.005	4.015025
1.999	3.997001	2.001	4.003001

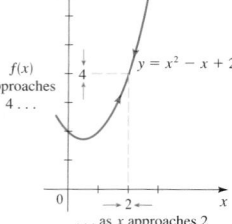

FIGURE 1

From the table and the graph of f (a parabola) shown in Figure 1 we see that when x is close to 2 (on either side of 2), $f(x)$ is close to 4. In fact, it appears that we can make the values of $f(x)$ as close as we like to 4 by taking x sufficiently close to 2. We express this by saying "the limit of the function $f(x) = x^2 - x + 2$ as x approaches 2 is equal to 4." The notation for this is

$$\lim_{x \to 2} (x^2 - x + 2) = 4$$

In general, we use the following notation.

DEFINITION OF THE LIMIT OF A FUNCTION

We write

$$\lim_{x \to a} f(x) = L$$

and say

"the limit of $f(x)$, as x approaches a, equals L"

if we can make the values of $f(x)$ arbitrarily close to L (as close to L as we like) by taking x to be sufficiently close to a, but not equal to a.

Roughly speaking, this says that the values of $f(x)$ get closer and closer to the number L as x gets closer and closer to the number a (from either side of a) but $x \neq a$.

TEXT QUESTION

What is the difference between the statements "$f(a) = L$" and "$\lim_{x \to a} f(x) = L$"?

Answer

The first is a statement about the value of f at the point $x = a$; the second is a statement about the values of f at points near, but not equal to, $x = a$.

An alternative notation for $\lim_{x \to a} f(x) = L$ is

$$f(x) \to L \quad \text{as} \quad x \to a$$

which is usually read "$f(x)$ approaches L as x approaches a." This is the notation we used in Section 3.7 when discussing asymptotes of rational functions.

Notice the phrase "but $x \neq a$" in the definition of limit. This means that in finding the limit of $f(x)$ as x approaches a, we never consider $x = a$. In fact, $f(x)$ need not even be defined when $x = a$. The only thing that matters is how f is defined *near a*.

Figure 2 shows the graphs of three functions. Note that in part (c), $f(a)$ is not defined, and in part (b), $f(a) \neq L$. But in each case, regardless of what happens at a, $\lim_{x \to a} f(x) = L$.

(a)

(b)

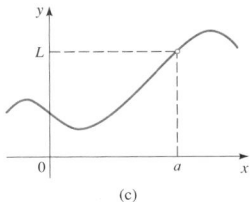
(c)

FIGURE 2 $\lim_{x \to a} f(x) = L$ in all three cases

▼ Estimating Limits Numerically and Graphically

In Section 13.2 we will develop techniques for finding exact values of limits. For now, we use tables and graphs to estimate limits of functions.

EXAMPLE 1 | Estimating a Limit Numerically and Graphically

Estimate the value of the following limit by making a table of values. Check your work with a graph.

$$\lim_{x \to 1} \frac{x - 1}{x^2 - 1}$$

SOLUTION   Notice that the function $f(x) = (x - 1)/(x^2 - 1)$ is not defined when $x = 1$, but this doesn't matter because the definition of $\lim_{x \to a} f(x)$ says that we consider values of x that are close to a but not equal to a. The following tables give values of $f(x)$ (rounded to six decimal places) for values of x that approach 1 (but are not equal to 1).

$x < 1$	$f(x)$	$x < 1$	$f(x)$
0.5	0.666667	1.5	0.400000
0.9	0.526316	1.1	0.476190
0.99	0.502513	1.01	0.497512
0.999	0.500250	1.001	0.499750
0.9999	0.500025	1.0001	0.499975

On the basis of the values in the two tables, we make the guess that

$$\lim_{x \to 1} \frac{x - 1}{x^2 - 1} = 0.5$$

IN-CLASS MATERIALS

Perhaps present the "graphing calculator" definition of limit: We say that $\lim_{x \to a} f(x) = L$ if for any y-range centered at L, there is an x-range centered at a such that the graph is contained in the window. This is a little closer to the formal definition of limit that will be presented in calculus, using a metaphor with which students are familiar.

As a graphical verification we use a graphing device to produce Figure 3. We see that when x is close to 1, y is close to 0.5. If we use the ZOOM and TRACE features to get a closer look, as in Figure 4, we notice that as x gets closer and closer to 1, y becomes closer and closer to 0.5. This reinforces our conclusion.

FIGURE 3   **FIGURE 4**

✎. NOW TRY EXERCISE **3**

ALTERNATE EXAMPLE 2

Find $\lim\limits_{x \to 0} \dfrac{\tan 3x}{x}$.

ANSWER

The table lists the values for various values of x near zero. As x approaches zero, the function values approach 3.

x	$\dfrac{\tan 3x}{x}$
0.1	3.093362496
0.01	3.000900324
0.001	3.000009000
0.0001	3.000000090
−0.0001	−3.000000090
−0.001	−3.000009000
−0.01	−3.000900324
−0.1	−3.093362496

t	$\dfrac{\sqrt{t^2 + 9} - 3}{t^2}$
±1.0	0.16228
±0.5	0.16553
±0.1	0.16662
±0.05	0.16666
±0.01	0.16667

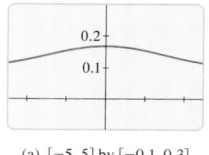

t	$\dfrac{\sqrt{t^2 + 9} - 3}{t^2}$
±0.0005	0.16800
±0.0001	0.20000
±0.00005	0.00000
±0.00001	0.00000

EXAMPLE 2 | Finding a Limit from a Table

Find $\lim\limits_{t \to 0} \dfrac{\sqrt{t^2 + 9} - 3}{t^2}$.

SOLUTION The table in the margin lists values of the function for several values of t near 0. As t approaches 0, the values of the function seem to approach $0.1666666 \ldots$, so we guess that

$$\lim_{t \to 0} \frac{\sqrt{t^2 + 9} - 3}{t^2} = \frac{1}{6}$$

✎. NOW TRY EXERCISE **5**

What would have happened in Example 2 if we had taken even smaller values of t? The table in the margin shows the results from one calculator; you can see that something strange seems to be happening.

If you try these calculations on your own calculator, you might get different values, but eventually, you will get the value 0 if you make t sufficiently small. Does this mean that the answer is really 0 instead of $\frac{1}{6}$? No, the value of the limit is $\frac{1}{6}$, as we will show in the next section. The problem is that the calculator gave false values because $\sqrt{t^2 + 9}$ is very close to 3 when t is small. (In fact, when t is sufficiently small, a calculator's value for $\sqrt{t^2 + 9}$ is 3.000 . . . to as many digits as the calculator is capable of carrying.)

Something similar happens when we try to graph the function of Example 2 on a graphing device. Parts (a) and (b) of Figure 5 show quite accurate graphs of this function, and when we use the TRACE feature, we can easily estimate that the limit is about $\frac{1}{6}$. But if we zoom in too far, as in parts (c) and (d), then we get inaccurate graphs, again because of problems with subtraction.

 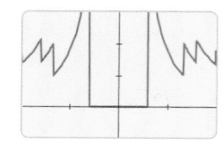

(a) $[-5, 5]$ by $[-0.1, 0.3]$ (b) $[-0.1, 0.1]$ by $[-0.1, 0.3]$ (c) $[-10^{-6}, 10^{-6}]$ by $[-0.1, 0.3]$ (d) $[-10^{-7}, 10^{-7}]$ by $[-0.1, 0.3]$

FIGURE 5

IN-CLASS MATERIALS

Explore $\lim_{x \to 0} (2 - 2^{1/x})$, looking carefully at $2^{1/x}$ from both sides for small x. After numerical and graphical explorations, you can also discuss this from a common-sense perspective. When x is small and positive, what do we know about $1/x$? And then what do we know about $2^{1/x}$? How about $(2 - 2^{1/x})$? Ask these questions again for small, negative values of x.

▼ Limits That Fail to Exist

Functions do not necessarily approach a finite value at every point. In other words, it's possible for a limit not to exist. The next three examples illustrate ways in which this can happen.

EXAMPLE 3 | A Limit That Fails to Exist (A Function with a Jump)

The Heaviside function H is defined by

$$H(t) = \begin{cases} 0 & \text{if } t < 0 \\ 1 & \text{if } t \geq 0 \end{cases}$$

[This function, named after the electrical engineer Oliver Heaviside (1850–1925), can be used to describe an electric current that is switched on at time $t = 0$.] Its graph is shown in Figure 6. Notice the "jump" in the graph at $x = 0$.

As t approaches 0 from the left, $H(t)$ approaches 0. As t approaches 0 from the right, $H(t)$ approaches 1. There is no single number that $H(t)$ approaches as t approaches 0. Therefore, $\lim_{t \to 0} H(t)$ does not exist.

✎. NOW TRY EXERCISE **27**   ■

FIGURE 6

EXAMPLE 4 | A Limit That Fails to Exist (A Function That Oscillates)

Find $\lim_{x \to 0} \sin \dfrac{\pi}{x}$.

SOLUTION   The function $f(x) = \sin(\pi/x)$ is undefined at 0. Evaluating the function for some small values of x, we get

$$f(1) = \sin \pi = 0 \qquad\qquad f\left(\tfrac{1}{2}\right) = \sin 2\pi = 0$$

$$f\left(\tfrac{1}{3}\right) = \sin 3\pi = 0 \qquad\qquad f\left(\tfrac{1}{4}\right) = \sin 4\pi = 0$$

$$f(0.1) = \sin 10\pi = 0 \qquad\quad f(0.01) = \sin 100\pi = 0$$

Similarly, $f(0.001) = f(0.0001) = 0$. On the basis of this information we might be tempted to guess that

$$\lim_{x \to 0} \sin \frac{\pi}{x} \overset{?}{=} 0$$

but this time our guess is wrong. Note that although $f(1/n) = \sin n\pi = 0$ for any integer n, it is also true that $f(x) = 1$ for infinitely many values of x that approach 0. (See the graph in Figure 7.)

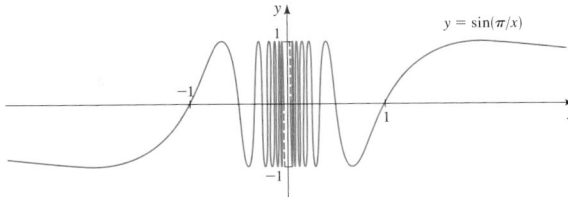

$y = \sin(\pi/x)$

FIGURE 7

The dashed lines indicate that the values of $\sin(\pi/x)$ oscillate between 1 and -1 infinitely often as x approaches 0. Since the values of $f(x)$ do not approach a fixed number as x approaches 0,

$$\lim_{x \to 0} \sin \frac{\pi}{x} \quad \text{does not exist}$$

✎. NOW TRY EXERCISE **25**   ■

ALTERNATE EXAMPLE 4

Find $\displaystyle\lim_{x \to 0} \frac{|x|}{x}$.

ANSWER
It does not exist.

IN-CLASS MATERIALS

After discussing vertical asymptotes (graphical and numerical definitions, followed by the limit definition), ask students to describe horizontal asymptotes from the same perspective. They may come up with the concept of $\lim_{x \to \infty}$ on their own!

Example 4 illustrates some of the pitfalls in guessing the value of a limit. It is easy to guess the wrong value if we use inappropriate values of x, but it is difficult to know when to stop calculating values. And as the discussion after Example 2 shows, sometimes calculators and computers give incorrect values. In the next two sections, however, we will develop foolproof methods for calculating limits.

ALTERNATE EXAMPLE 5

Find $\lim\limits_{x \to 2} \dfrac{1 - x}{(x - 2)^2}$.

ANSWER

It does not exist.

$$\lim_{x \to 2} \frac{1 - x}{(x - 2)^2} = -\infty$$

EXAMPLE 5 | A Limit That Fails to Exist (A Function with a Vertical Asymptote)

Find $\lim\limits_{x \to 0} \dfrac{1}{x^2}$ if it exists.

SOLUTION As x becomes close to 0, x^2 also becomes close to 0, and $1/x^2$ becomes very large. (See the table in the margin.) In fact, it appears from the graph of the function $f(x) = 1/x^2$ shown in Figure 8 that the values of $f(x)$ can be made arbitrarily large by taking x close enough to 0. Thus the values of $f(x)$ do not approach a number, so $\lim_{x \to 0}(1/x^2)$ does not exist.

x	$\dfrac{1}{x^2}$
± 1	1
± 0.5	4
± 0.2	25
± 0.1	100
± 0.05	400
± 0.01	10,000
± 0.001	1,000,000

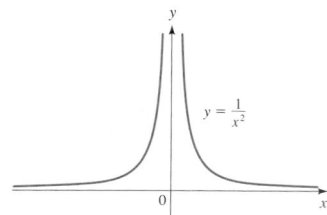

$y = \dfrac{1}{x^2}$

FIGURE 8

✎ NOW TRY EXERCISE **23**

To indicate the kind of behavior exhibited in Example 5, we use the notation

$$\lim_{x \to 0} \frac{1}{x^2} = \infty$$

 This does not mean that we are regarding ∞ as a number. Nor does it mean that the limit exists. It simply expresses the particular way in which the limit does not exist: $1/x^2$ can be made as large as we like by taking x close enough to 0. Notice that the line $x = 0$ (the y-axis) is a vertical asymptote in the sense that we described in Section 3.6.

▼ One-Sided Limits

We noticed in Example 3 that $H(t)$ approaches 0 as t approaches 0 from the left and $H(t)$ approaches 1 as t approaches 0 from the right. We indicate this situation symbolically by writing

$$\lim_{t \to 0^-} H(t) = 0 \qquad \text{and} \qquad \lim_{t \to 0^+} H(t) = 1$$

The symbol "$t \to 0^-$" indicates that we consider only values of t that are less than 0. Likewise, "$t \to 0^+$" indicates that we consider only values of t that are greater than 0.

IN-CLASS MATERIALS

Examine $\lim\limits_{x \to 0} \dfrac{\sin x}{x}$. This limit comes up in calculus and can be explored numerically and graphically.

Once it is established that $\lim\limits_{x \to 0} \dfrac{\sin x}{x} = 1$, you can show students that in the study of optics (or any other application where x is very small), scientists often make the approximation $\sin x \approx x$. Emphasize that they can get away with this only for $x \approx 0$.

> **DEFINITION OF A ONE-SIDED LIMIT**
>
> We write
>
> $$\lim_{x \to a^-} f(x) = L$$
>
> and say the "left-hand limit of $f(x)$ as x approaches a" [or the "limit of $f(x)$ as x approaches a from the left"] is equal to L if we can make the values of $f(x)$ arbitrarily close to L by taking x to be sufficiently close to a and x less than a.

Notice that this definition differs from the definition of a two-sided limit only in that we require x to be less than a. Similarly, if we require that x be greater than a, we get "the **right-hand limit of $f(x)$ as x approaches a** is equal to L," and we write

$$\lim_{x \to a^+} f(x) = L$$

Thus the symbol "$x \to a^+$" means that we consider only $x > a$. These definitions are illustrated in Figure 9.

FIGURE 9

(a) $\lim_{x \to a^-} f(x) = L$

(b) $\lim_{x \to a^+} f(x) = L$

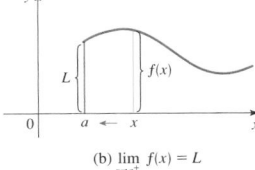

By comparing the definitions of two-sided and one-sided limits, we see that the following is true.

> $$\lim_{x \to a} f(x) = L \quad \text{if and only if} \quad \lim_{x \to a^-} f(x) = L \quad \text{and} \quad \lim_{x \to a^+} f(x) = L$$

Thus if the left-hand and right-hand limits are different, the (two-sided) limit does not exist. We use this fact in the next two examples.

EXAMPLE 6 | Limits from a Graph

The graph of a function g is shown in Figure 10. Use it to state the values (if they exist) of the following:

(a) $\lim_{x \to 2^-} g(x), \quad \lim_{x \to 2^+} g(x), \quad \lim_{x \to 2} g(x)$

(b) $\lim_{x \to 5^-} g(x), \quad \lim_{x \to 5^+} g(x), \quad \lim_{x \to 5} g(x)$

SOLUTION

(a) From the graph we see that the values of $g(x)$ approach 3 as x approaches 2 from the left, but they approach 1 as x approaches 2 from the right. Therefore

$$\lim_{x \to 2^-} g(x) = 3 \quad \text{and} \quad \lim_{x \to 2^+} g(x) = 1$$

Since the left- and right-hand limits are different, we conclude that $\lim_{x \to 2} g(x)$ does not exist.

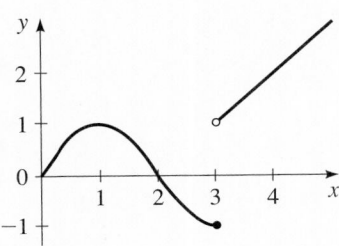

FIGURE 10

ALTERNATE EXAMPLE 6

(a) The graph of a function g is shown here. Use it to state the values (if they exist) of the one-sided limits $\lim_{x \to 1^-} g(x)$ and $\lim_{x \to 1^+} g(x)$ and evaluate the two-sided limit $\lim_{x \to 1} g(x)$.

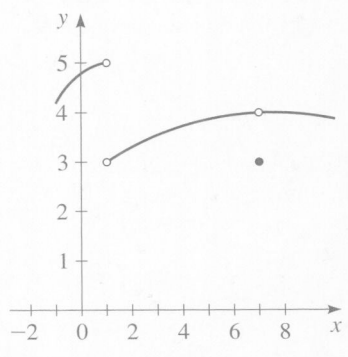

(b) State the values (if they exist) of the one-sided limits $\lim_{x \to 7^-} g(x)$ and $\lim_{x \to 7^+} g(x)$ and evaluate the two-sided limit $\lim_{x \to 7} g(x)$.

ANSWERS

(a) Left-hand limit: 5. Right-hand limit: 3. Two-sided limit: Does not exist.

(b) Left-hand limit: 4. Right-hand limit: 4. Two-sided limit: 4.

EXAMPLE

Graphical: Consider the function f with the following graph:

We have $f(x) = -1$, $\lim_{x \to 3^-} f(x) = -1$, $\lim_{x \to 3^+} f(x) = 1$. Also, $f(4) = 2$ and $\lim_{x \to 4} f(x) = 2$.

(b) The graph also shows that

$$\lim_{x \to 5^-} g(x) = 2 \quad \text{and} \quad \lim_{x \to 5^+} g(x) = 2$$

This time the left- and right-hand limits are the same, so we have

$$\lim_{x \to 5} g(x) = 2$$

Despite this fact, notice that $g(5) \neq 2$.

⬥. NOW TRY EXERCISE **19**

ALTERNATE EXAMPLE 7

Let f be the function defined by

$$f(x) = \begin{cases} x + 8 & \text{if } x < 3 \\ 2x^2 & \text{if } x \geq 3 \end{cases}$$

Use the graph of the function to find $\lim_{x \to 3} f(x)$.

ANSWER
The limit does not exist.

DRILL QUESTIONS

The graph of a function f is shown. Are the following statements about f true or false? Why?

(a) $x = a$ is in the domain of f.
(b) $\lim_{x \to a} f(x)$ exists.
(c) $\lim_{x \to a^+} f(x)$ is equal to $\lim_{x \to a^-} f(x)$.

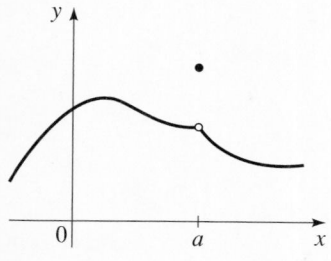

Answers
(a) True, because f is defined at $x = a$.
(b) True, because as x gets close to a, $f(x)$ approaches a value.
(c) True, because the same value is approached from both directions.

EXAMPLE 7 | A Piecewise-Defined Function

Let f be the function defined by

$$f(x) = \begin{cases} 2x^2 & \text{if } x < 1 \\ 4 - x & \text{if } x \geq 1 \end{cases}$$

Graph f, and use the graph to find the following:

(a) $\lim_{x \to 1^-} f(x)$ **(b)** $\lim_{x \to 1^+} f(x)$ **(c)** $\lim_{x \to 1} f(x)$

SOLUTION The graph of f is shown in Figure 11. From the graph we see that the values of $f(x)$ approach 2 as x approaches 1 from the left, but they approach 3 as x approaches 1 from the right. Thus, the left- and right-hand limits are not equal. So we have

(a) $\lim_{x \to 1^-} f(x) = 2$ **(b)** $\lim_{x \to 1^+} f(x) = 3$ **(c)** $\lim_{x \to 1} f(x)$ does not exist.

⬥. NOW TRY EXERCISE **29**

FIGURE 11

13.1 EXERCISES

CONCEPTS

1. When we write $\lim_{x \to a} f(x) = L$ then, roughly speaking, the values of $f(x)$ get closer and closer to the number _____ as the values of x get closer and closer to _____. To determine $\lim_{x \to 5} \dfrac{x - 5}{x - 5}$, we try values for x closer and closer to _____ and find that the limit is _____.

2. We write $\lim_{x \to a} f(x) = L$ and say that the _____ of $f(x)$ as x approaches a from the _____ (left/right) is equal to _____. To find the left-hand limit, we try values for x that are _____ (less/greater) than a. A limit exists if and only if both the _____-hand and _____-hand limits exist and are _____.

SKILLS

3–4 ■ Estimate the value of the limit by making a table of values. Check your work with a graph.

⬥. **3.** $\lim_{x \to 5} \dfrac{x^2 - 25}{x - 5}$ **4.** $\lim_{x \to 3} \dfrac{x^2 - x - 6}{x - 3}$

5–10 ■ Complete the table of values (to five decimal places), and use the table to estimate the value of the limit.

⬥. **5.** $\lim_{x \to 4} \dfrac{\sqrt{x} - 2}{x - 4}$

x	3.9	3.99	3.999	4.001	4.01	4.1
$f(x)$						

6. $\lim_{x \to 2} \dfrac{x - 2}{x^2 + x - 6}$

x	1.9	1.99	1.999	2.001	2.01	2.1
$f(x)$						

7. $\lim_{x \to 1} \dfrac{x - 1}{x^3 - 1}$

x	0.9	0.99	0.999	1.001	1.01	1.1
$f(x)$						

8. $\lim\limits_{x\to 0}\dfrac{e^x - 1}{x}$

x	−0.1	−0.01	−0.001	0.001	0.01	0.1
f(x)						

9. $\lim\limits_{x\to 0}\dfrac{\sin x}{x}$

x	±1	±0.5	±0.1	±0.05	±0.01
f(x)					

10. $\lim\limits_{x\to 0^+} x\ln x$

x	0.1	0.01	0.001	0.0001	0.00001
f(x)					

 11–16 ■ Use a table of values to estimate the value of the limit. Then use a graphing device to confirm your result graphically.

11. $\lim\limits_{x\to -4}\dfrac{x + 4}{x^2 + 7x + 12}$ **12.** $\lim\limits_{x\to 1}\dfrac{x^3 - 1}{x^2 - 1}$

13. $\lim\limits_{x\to 0}\dfrac{5^x - 3^x}{x}$ **14.** $\lim\limits_{x\to 0}\dfrac{\sqrt{x + 9} - 3}{x}$

15. $\lim\limits_{x\to 1}\left(\dfrac{1}{\ln x} - \dfrac{1}{x - 1}\right)$ **16.** $\lim\limits_{x\to 0}\dfrac{\tan 2x}{\tan 3x}$

17. For the function f whose graph is given, state the value of the given quantity if it exists. If it does not exist, explain why.

    (a) $\lim\limits_{x\to 1^-} f(x)$ (b) $\lim\limits_{x\to 1^+} f(x)$ (c) $\lim\limits_{x\to 1} f(x)$

    (d) $\lim\limits_{x\to 5} f(x)$ (e) $f(5)$

18. For the function f whose graph is given, state the value of the given quantity if it exists. If it does not exist, explain why.

    (a) $\lim\limits_{x\to 0} f(x)$ (b) $\lim\limits_{x\to 3^-} f(x)$ (c) $\lim\limits_{x\to 3^+} f(x)$

    (d) $\lim\limits_{x\to 3} f(x)$ (e) $f(3)$

19. For the function g whose graph is given, state the value of the given quantity if it exists. If it does not exist, explain why.

    (a) $\lim\limits_{t\to 0^-} g(t)$ (b) $\lim\limits_{t\to 0^+} g(t)$ (c) $\lim\limits_{t\to 0} g(t)$

    (d) $\lim\limits_{t\to 2^-} g(t)$ (e) $\lim\limits_{t\to 2^+} g(t)$ (f) $\lim\limits_{t\to 2} g(t)$

    (g) $g(2)$ (h) $\lim\limits_{t\to 4} g(t)$

20. State the value of the limit, if it exists, from the given graph of f. If it does not exist, explain why.

    (a) $\lim\limits_{x\to 3} f(x)$ (b) $\lim\limits_{x\to 1} f(x)$ (c) $\lim\limits_{x\to -3} f(x)$

    (d) $\lim\limits_{x\to 2^-} f(x)$ (e) $\lim\limits_{x\to 2^+} f(x)$ (f) $\lim\limits_{x\to 2} f(x)$

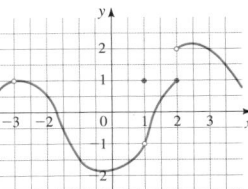

21–28 ■ Use a graphing device to determine whether the limit exists. If the limit exists, estimate its value to two decimal places.

21. $\lim\limits_{x\to 1}\dfrac{x^3 + x^2 + 3x - 5}{2x^2 - 5x + 3}$ **22.** $\lim\limits_{x\to 0}\dfrac{x^2}{\cos 5x - \cos 4x}$

23. $\lim\limits_{x\to 0}\ln(\sin^2 x)$ **24.** $\lim\limits_{x\to 2}\dfrac{x^3 + 6x^2 - 5x + 1}{x^3 - x^2 - 8x + 12}$

25. $\lim\limits_{x\to 0}\cos\dfrac{1}{x}$ **26.** $\lim\limits_{x\to 0}\sin\dfrac{2}{x}$

27. $\lim\limits_{x\to 3}\dfrac{|x - 3|}{x - 3}$ **28.** $\lim\limits_{x\to 0}\dfrac{1}{1 + e^{1/x}}$

29–32 ■ Graph the piecewise-defined function and use your graph to find the values of the limits, if they exist.

29. $f(x) = \begin{cases} x^2 & \text{if } x \le 2 \\ 6 - x & \text{if } x > 2 \end{cases}$

    (a) $\lim\limits_{x\to 2^-} f(x)$ (b) $\lim\limits_{x\to 2^+} f(x)$ (c) $\lim\limits_{x\to 2} f(x)$

30. $f(x) = \begin{cases} 2 & \text{if } x < 0 \\ x + 1 & \text{if } x \ge 0 \end{cases}$

    (a) $\lim\limits_{x\to 0^-} f(x)$ (b) $\lim\limits_{x\to 0^+} f(x)$ (c) $\lim\limits_{x\to 0} f(x)$

31. $f(x) = \begin{cases} -x + 3 & \text{if } x < -1 \\ 3 & \text{if } x \geq -1 \end{cases}$

   (a) $\displaystyle\lim_{x \to -1^-} f(x)$ (b) $\displaystyle\lim_{x \to -1^+} f(x)$ (c) $\displaystyle\lim_{x \to -1} f(x)$

32. $f(x) = \begin{cases} 2x + 10 & \text{if } x \leq -2 \\ -x + 4 & \text{if } x > -2 \end{cases}$

   (a) $\displaystyle\lim_{x \to -2^-} f(x)$ (b) $\displaystyle\lim_{x \to -2^+} f(x)$ (c) $\displaystyle\lim_{x \to -2} f(x)$

DISCOVERY ▪ DISCUSSION ▪ WRITING

33. A Function with Specified Limits   Sketch the graph of an example of a function f that satisfies all of the following conditions.

$$\lim_{x \to 0^-} f(x) = 2 \qquad \lim_{x \to 0^+} f(x) = 0$$
$$\lim_{x \to 2} f(x) = 1 \qquad f(0) = 2 \qquad f(2) = 3$$

How many such functions are there?

34. Graphing Calculator Pitfalls

   (a) Evaluate

$$h(x) = \frac{\tan x - x}{x^3}$$

      for $x = 1, 0.5, 0.1, 0.05, 0.01,$ and 0.005.

   (b) Guess the value of $\displaystyle\lim_{x \to 0} \frac{\tan x - x}{x^3}$.

   (c) Evaluate $h(x)$ for successively smaller values of x until you finally reach 0 values for $h(x)$. Are you still confident that your guess in part (b) is correct? Explain why you eventually obtained 0 values.

   (d) Graph the function h in the viewing rectangle $[-1, 1]$ by $[0, 1]$. Then zoom in toward the point where the graph crosses the y-axis to estimate the limit of $h(x)$ as x approaches 0. Continue to zoom in until you observe distortions in the graph of h. Compare with your results in part (c).

SUGGESTED TIME AND EMPHASIS

1 class, optional material

13.2 FINDING LIMITS ALGEBRAICALLY

| Limit Laws ▶ Applying the Limit Laws ▶ Finding Limits Using Algebra and the Limit Laws ▶ Using Left- and Right-Hand Limits

In Section 13.1 we used calculators and graphs to guess the values of limits, but we saw that such methods don't always lead to the correct answer. In this section we use algebraic methods to find limits exactly.

▼ Limit Laws

We use the following properties of limits, called the *Limit Laws*, to calculate limits.

LIMIT LAWS

Suppose that c is a constant and that the following limits exist:

$$\lim_{x \to a} f(x) \qquad \text{and} \qquad \lim_{x \to a} g(x)$$

Then

1. $\displaystyle\lim_{x \to a} [f(x) + g(x)] = \lim_{x \to a} f(x) + \lim_{x \to a} g(x)$ Limit of a Sum

2. $\displaystyle\lim_{x \to a} [f(x) - g(x)] = \lim_{x \to a} f(x) - \lim_{x \to a} g(x)$ Limit of a Difference

3. $\displaystyle\lim_{x \to a} [cf(x)] = c \lim_{x \to a} f(x)$ Limit of a Constant Multiple

4. $\displaystyle\lim_{x \to a} [f(x)g(x)] = \lim_{x \to a} f(x) \cdot \lim_{x \to a} g(x)$ Limit of a Product

5. $\displaystyle\lim_{x \to a} \frac{f(x)}{g(x)} = \frac{\displaystyle\lim_{x \to a} f(x)}{\displaystyle\lim_{x \to a} g(x)}$ if $\displaystyle\lim_{x \to a} g(x) \neq 0$ Limit of a Quotient

---

These five laws can be stated verbally as follows:

Limit of a Sum   1. The limit of a sum is the sum of the limits.

Limit of a Difference 2. The limit of a difference is the difference of the limits.

Limit of a Constant Multiple 3. The limit of a constant times a function is the constant times the limit of the function.

Limit of a Product   4. The limit of a product is the product of the limits.

Limit of a Quotient   5. The limit of a quotient is the quotient of the limits (provided that the limit of the denominator is not 0).

It's easy to believe that these properties are true. For instance, if $f(x)$ is close to L and $g(x)$ is close to M, it is reasonable to conclude that $f(x) + g(x)$ is close to $L + M$. This gives us an intuitive basis for believing that Law 1 is true.

If we use Law 4 (Limit of a Product) repeatedly with $g(x) = f(x)$, we obtain the following Law 6 for the limit of a power. A similar law holds for roots.

LIMIT LAWS

6. $\lim_{x \to a} [f(x)]^n = [\lim_{x \to a} f(x)]^n$ where n is a positive integer   Limit of a Power

7. $\lim_{x \to a} \sqrt[n]{f(x)} = \sqrt[n]{\lim_{x \to a} f(x)}$ where n is a positive integer   Limit of a Root

[If n is even, we assume that $\lim_{x \to a} f(x) > 0$.]

In words, these laws say the following:

Limit of a Power   **6.** The limit of a power is the power of the limit.

Limit of a Root   **7.** The limit of a root is the root of the limit.

EXAMPLE 1 | Using the Limit Laws

Use the Limit Laws and the graphs of f and g in Figure 1 to evaluate the following limits if they exist.

(a) $\lim_{x \to -2} [f(x) + 5g(x)]$ **(b)** $\lim_{x \to 1} [f(x)g(x)]$

(c) $\lim_{x \to 2} \dfrac{f(x)}{g(x)}$ **(d)** $\lim_{x \to 1} [f(x)]^3$

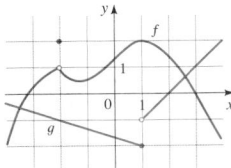

FIGURE 1

SOLUTION

(a) From the graphs of f and g we see that

$$\lim_{x \to -2} f(x) = 1 \quad \text{and} \quad \lim_{x \to -2} g(x) = -1$$

TEXT QUESTION

In Example 1, why isn't $\lim_{x \to -2} f(x) = 2$?

Answer

The limit has nothing to do with the function's value at $x = -2$. It depends only on the values of the function for x close to -2.

Therefore we have

$$\lim_{x\to-2}[f(x) + 5g(x)] = \lim_{x\to-2} f(x) + \lim_{x\to-2}[5g(x)] \qquad \text{Limit of a Sum}$$

$$= \lim_{x\to-2} f(x) + 5\lim_{x\to-2} g(x) \qquad \text{Limit of a Constant Multiple}$$

$$= 1 + 5(-1) = -4$$

(b) We see that $\lim_{x\to1} f(x) = 2$. But $\lim_{x\to1} g(x)$ does not exist because the left- and right-hand limits are different:

$$\lim_{x\to1^-} g(x) = -2 \qquad \lim_{x\to1^+} g(x) = -1$$

So we can't use Law 4 (Limit of a Product). The given limit does not exist, since the left-hand limit is not equal to the right-hand limit.

(c) The graphs show that

$$\lim_{x\to2} f(x) \approx 1.4 \qquad \text{and} \qquad \lim_{x\to2} g(x) = 0$$

Because the limit of the denominator is 0, we can't use Law 5 (Limit of a Quotient). The given limit does not exist because the denominator approaches 0 while the numerator approaches a nonzero number.

(d) Since $\lim_{x\to1} f(x) = 2$, we use Law 6 to get

$$\lim_{x\to1}[f(x)]^3 = [\lim_{x\to1} f(x)]^3 \qquad \text{Limit of a Power}$$

$$= 2^3 = 8$$

✎. NOW TRY EXERCISE **3**

▼ Applying the Limit Laws

In applying the Limit Laws, we need to use four special limits.

SOME SPECIAL LIMITS

1. $\lim_{x\to a} c = c$

2. $\lim_{x\to a} x = a$

3. $\lim_{x\to a} x^n = a^n$ where n is a positive integer

4. $\lim_{x\to a} \sqrt[n]{x} = \sqrt[n]{a}$ where n is a positive integer and $a > 0$

Special Limits 1 and 2 are intuitively obvious—looking at the graphs of $y = c$ and $y = x$ will convince you of their validity. Limits 3 and 4 are special cases of Limit Laws 6 and 7 (Limits of a Power and of a Root).

EXAMPLE 2 | Using the Limit Laws

Evaluate the following limits, and justify each step.

(a) $\lim_{x\to5}(2x^2 - 3x + 4)$

(b) $\lim_{x\to-2}\dfrac{x^3 + 2x^2 - 1}{5 - 3x}$

ALTERNATE EXAMPLE 2

Evaluate the limit:

$$\lim_{x\to-2}(6x^2 - 3x + 1)$$

ANSWER

31

IN-CLASS MATERIALS

Compute some limits of quotients, such as $\lim_{x\to2}\dfrac{x^2 - 4}{x - 2}$, $\lim_{x\to0}\dfrac{x^3 - 8}{x - 2}$, $\lim_{x\to3}\dfrac{x^3 - 8}{x - 2}$, and $\lim_{x\to2}\dfrac{x^3 - 8}{x - 2}$, always attempting to plug in values first.

SOLUTION

(a) $\lim\limits_{x\to5}(2x^2 - 3x + 4) = \lim\limits_{x\to5}(2x^2) - \lim\limits_{x\to5}(3x) + \lim\limits_{x\to5}4$ Limits of a Difference and Sum

$\qquad\qquad\qquad\qquad = 2\lim\limits_{x\to5}x^2 - 3\lim\limits_{x\to5}x + \lim\limits_{x\to5}4$ Limit of a Constant Multiple

$\qquad\qquad\qquad\qquad = 2(5^2) - 3(5) + 4$ Special Limits 3, 2, and 1

$\qquad\qquad\qquad\qquad = 39$

(b) We start by using Law 5, but its use is fully justified only at the final stage when we see that the limits of the numerator and denominator exist and the limit of the denominator is not 0.

$$\lim_{x\to-2}\frac{x^3 + 2x^2 - 1}{5 - 3x} = \frac{\lim\limits_{x\to-2}(x^3 + 2x^2 - 1)}{\lim\limits_{x\to-2}(5 - 3x)}$$ Limit of a Quotient

$$= \frac{\lim\limits_{x\to-2}x^3 + 2\lim\limits_{x\to-2}x^2 - \lim\limits_{x\to-2}1}{\lim\limits_{x\to-2}5 - 3\lim\limits_{x\to-2}x}$$ Limits of Sums, Differences, and Constant Multiples

$$= \frac{(-2)^3 + 2(-2)^2 - 1}{5 - 3(-2)}$$ Special Limits 3, 2, and 1

$$= -\frac{1}{11}$$

✎ NOW TRY EXERCISES **5** AND **7**   ∎

If we let $f(x) = 2x^2 - 3x + 4$, then $f(5) = 39$. In Example 2(a) we found that $\lim_{x\to5}f(x) = 39$. In other words, we would have gotten the correct answer by substituting 5 for x. Similarly, direct substitution provides the correct answer in part (b). The functions in Example 2 are a polynomial and a rational function, respectively, and similar use of the Limit Laws proves that direct substitution always works for such functions. We state this fact as follows.

LIMITS BY DIRECT SUBSTITUTION

If f is a polynomial or a rational function and a is in the domain of f, then

$$\lim_{x\to a}f(x) = f(a)$$

Functions with this direct substitution property are called **continuous at** a. You will learn more about continuous functions when you study calculus.

EXAMPLE 3 | Finding Limits by Direct Substitution

Evaluate the following limits.

(a) $\lim\limits_{x\to3}(2x^3 - 10x - 8)$ **(b)** $\lim\limits_{x\to-1}\dfrac{x^2 + 5x}{x^4 + 2}$

SOLUTION

(a) The function $f(x) = 2x^3 - 10x - 12$ is a polynomial, so we can find the limit by direct substitution:

$$\lim_{x\to3}(2x^3 - 10x - 12) = 2(3)^3 - 10(3) - 8 = 16$$

IN-CLASS MATERIALS

Have students determine the existence of $\lim\limits_{x\to0^+}\sqrt{x}$ and determine why we cannot compute $\lim\limits_{x\to0}\sqrt{x}$.

(b) The function $f(x) = (x^2 + 5x)/(x^4 + 2)$ is a rational function, and $x = -1$ is in its domain (because the denominator is not zero for $x = -1$). Thus, we can find the limit by direct substitution:

$$\lim_{x \to -1} \frac{x^2 + 5x}{x^4 + 2} = \frac{(-1)^2 + 5(-1)}{(-1)^4 + 2} = -\frac{4}{3}$$

➤. NOW TRY EXERCISE **13**   ■

▼ Finding Limits Using Algebra and the Limit Laws

As we saw in Example 3, evaluating limits by direct substitution is easy. But not all limits can be evaluated this way. In fact, most of the situations in which limits are useful require us to work harder to evaluate the limit. The next three examples illustrate how we can use algebra to find limits.

EXAMPLE 4 │ Finding a Limit by Canceling a Common Factor

Find $\lim_{x \to 1} \dfrac{x - 1}{x^2 - 1}$.

SOLUTION   Let $f(x) = (x - 1)/(x^2 - 1)$. We can't find the limit by substituting $x = 1$ because $f(1)$ isn't defined. Nor can we apply Law 5 (Limit of a Quotient) because the limit of the denominator is 0. Instead, we need to do some preliminary algebra. We factor the denominator as a difference of squares:

$$\frac{x - 1}{x^2 - 1} = \frac{x - 1}{(x - 1)(x + 1)}$$

The numerator and denominator have a common factor of $x - 1$. When we take the limit as x approaches 1, we have $x \neq 1$ and so $x - 1 \neq 0$. Therefore we can cancel the common factor and compute the limit as follows:

$$\lim_{x \to 1} \frac{x - 1}{x^2 - 1} = \lim_{x \to 1} \frac{x - 1}{(x - 1)(x + 1)} \qquad \text{Factor}$$

$$= \lim_{x \to 1} \frac{1}{x + 1} \qquad \text{Cancel}$$

$$= \frac{1}{1 + 1} = \frac{1}{2} \qquad \text{Let } x \to 1$$

This calculation confirms algebraically the answer we got numerically and graphically in Example 1 in Section 13.1.

➤. NOW TRY EXERCISE **11**   ■

SIR ISAAC NEWTON (1642–1727) is universally regarded as one of the giants of physics and mathematics. He is well known for discovering the laws of motion and gravity and for inventing calculus, but he also proved the Binomial Theorem and the laws of optics, and he developed methods for solving polynomial equations to any desired accuracy. He was born on Christmas Day, a few months after the death of his father. After an unhappy childhood, he entered Cambridge University, where he learned mathematics by studying the writings of Euclid and Descartes.

During the plague years of 1665 and 1666, when the university was closed, Newton thought and wrote about ideas that, once published, instantly revolutionized the sciences. Imbued with a pathological fear of criticism, he published these writings only after many years of encouragement from Edmund Halley (who discovered the now-famous comet) and other colleagues.

Newton's works brought him enormous fame and prestige. Even poets were moved to praise; Alexander Pope wrote:

Nature and Nature's Laws
lay hid in Night.
God said, "Let Newton be"
and all was Light.

Newton was far more modest about his accomplishments. He said, "I seem to have been only like a boy playing on the seashore … while the great ocean of truth lay all undiscovered before me." Newton was knighted by Queen Anne in 1705 and was buried with great honor in Westminster Abbey.

ALTERNATE EXAMPLE 4

Find $\lim_{x \to 4} \dfrac{x - 4}{x^2 - 16}$.

ANSWER

$\dfrac{1}{8}$

IN-CLASS MATERIALS

Have students check whether $\lim_{x \to -5} \dfrac{x + 5}{|x + 5|}$ exists, and then compute left- and right-hand limits. Then check $\lim_{x \to -5} \dfrac{(x + 5)^2}{|x + 5|}$.

EXAMPLE 5 | Finding a Limit by Simplifying

Evaluate $\lim_{h \to 0} \dfrac{(3 + h)^2 - 9}{h}$.

SOLUTION We can't use direct substitution to evaluate this limit, because the limit of the denominator is 0. So we first simplify the limit algebraically.

$$\lim_{h \to 0} \frac{(3 + h)^2 - 9}{h} = \lim_{h \to 0} \frac{(9 + 6h + h^2) - 9}{h} \qquad \text{Expand}$$

$$= \lim_{h \to 0} \frac{6h + h^2}{h} \qquad \text{Simplify}$$

$$= \lim_{h \to 0} (6 + h) \qquad \text{Cancel } h$$

$$= 6 \qquad \text{Let } h \to 0$$

✎. NOW TRY EXERCISE **17** ◼

EXAMPLE 6 | Finding a Limit by Rationalizing

Find $\lim_{t \to 0} \dfrac{\sqrt{t^2 + 9} - 3}{t^2}$.

SOLUTION We can't apply Law 5 (Limit of a Quotient) immediately, since the limit of the denominator is 0. Here, the preliminary algebra consists of rationalizing the numerator:

$$\lim_{t \to 0} \frac{\sqrt{t^2 + 9} - 3}{t^2} = \lim_{t \to 0} \frac{\sqrt{t^2 + 9} - 3}{t^2} \cdot \frac{\sqrt{t^2 + 9} + 3}{\sqrt{t^2 + 9} + 3} \qquad \text{Rationalize numerator}$$

$$= \lim_{t \to 0} \frac{(t^2 + 9) - 9}{t^2(\sqrt{t^2 + 9} + 3)} = \lim_{t \to 0} \frac{t^2}{t^2(\sqrt{t^2 + 9} + 3)}$$

$$= \lim_{t \to 0} \frac{1}{\sqrt{t^2 + 9} + 3} = \frac{1}{\sqrt{\lim_{t \to 0}(t^2 + 9)} + 3} = \frac{1}{3 + 3} = \frac{1}{6}$$

This calculation confirms the guess that we made in Example 2 in Section 13.1.

✎. NOW TRY EXERCISE **19** ◼

▼ Using Left- and Right-Hand Limits

Some limits are best calculated by first finding the left- and right-hand limits. The following theorem is a reminder of what we discovered in Section 13.1. It says that *a two-sided limit exists if and only if both of the one-sided limits exist and are equal.*

$$\lim_{x \to a} f(x) = L \qquad \text{if and only if} \qquad \lim_{x \to a^-} f(x) = L = \lim_{x \to a^+} f(x)$$

When computing one-sided limits, we use the fact that the Limit Laws also hold for one-sided limits.

EXAMPLE 7 | Comparing Right and Left Limits

Show that $\lim_{x \to 0} |x| = 0$.

ALTERNATE EXAMPLE 5

Evaluate $\lim_{h \to 0} \dfrac{(4 + h)^2 - 16}{h}$.

ANSWER

8

ALTERNATE EXAMPLE 6

Find $\lim_{x \to 1} \dfrac{\sqrt{x} - 1}{x - 1}$.

ANSWER

$\dfrac{1}{2}$

ALTERNATE EXAMPLE 7

Find $\lim_{t \to 0} |t|$.

ANSWER

0

EXAMPLES

Algebraic simplification:

- $\lim_{x \to 2} \dfrac{x - 2}{x^2 + x - 6} = \dfrac{1}{5}$

- $\lim_{x \to 3} \dfrac{x - 2}{x^2 + x - 6}$ does not exist

- $\lim_{x \to 0} \dfrac{x - 2}{x^2 + x - 6} = \dfrac{1}{3}$ by direct substitution

SOLUTION   Recall that

$$|x| = \begin{cases} x & \text{if } x \geq 0 \\ -x & \text{if } x < 0 \end{cases}$$

The result of Example 7 looks plausible from Figure 2.

Since $|x| = x$ for $x > 0$, we have

$$\lim_{x \to 0^+} |x| = \lim_{x \to 0^+} x = 0$$

For $x < 0$, we have $|x| = -x$, so

$$\lim_{x \to 0^-} |x| = \lim_{x \to 0^-} (-x) = 0$$

Therefore

$$\lim_{x \to 0} |x| = 0$$

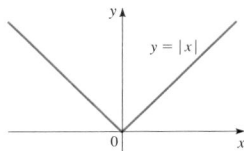

FIGURE 2

✎. **NOW TRY EXERCISE 29** ■

ALTERNATE EXAMPLE 8

Find $\lim_{z \to 0} \dfrac{|2z|}{2z}$.

ANSWER

The limit does not exist.

EXAMPLE 8 | Comparing Right and Left Limits

Prove that $\lim_{x \to 0} \dfrac{|x|}{x}$ does not exist.

SOLUTION   Since $|x| = x$ for $x > 0$ and $|x| = -x$ for $x < 0$, we have

$$\lim_{x \to 0^+} \frac{|x|}{x} = \lim_{x \to 0^+} \frac{x}{x} = \lim_{x \to 0^+} 1 = 1$$

$$\lim_{x \to 0^-} \frac{|x|}{x} = \lim_{x \to 0^-} \frac{-x}{x} = \lim_{x \to 0^-} (-1) = -1$$

Since the right-hand and left-hand limits exist and are different, it follows that $\lim_{x \to 0} |x|/x$ does not exist. The graph of the function $f(x) = |x|/x$ is shown in Figure 3 and supports the limits that we found.

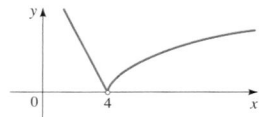

FIGURE 3

✎. **NOW TRY EXERCISE 31** ■

ALTERNATE EXAMPLE 9

Find $\lim_{x \to 7} f(x)$ if:

$$f(x) = \begin{cases} \sqrt{x - 7} & \text{if } x > 7 \\ 28 - 4x & \text{if } x < 7 \end{cases}$$

ANSWER

0

EXAMPLE 9 | The Limit of a Piecewise Defined Function

Let

$$f(x) = \begin{cases} \sqrt{x - 4} & \text{if } x > 4 \\ 8 - 2x & \text{if } x < 4 \end{cases}$$

Determine whether $\lim_{x \to 4} f(x)$ exists.

SOLUTION   Since $f(x) = \sqrt{x - 4}$ for $x > 4$, we have

$$\lim_{x \to 4^+} f(x) = \lim_{x \to 4^+} \sqrt{x - 4} = \sqrt{4 - 4} = 0$$

Since $f(x) = 8 - 2x$ for $x < 4$, we have

$$\lim_{x \to 4^-} f(x) = \lim_{x \to 4^-} (8 - 2x) = 8 - 2 \cdot 4 = 0$$

The right- and left-hand limits are equal. Thus the limit exists, and

$$\lim_{x \to 4} f(x) = 0$$

The graph of f is shown in Figure 4.

FIGURE 4

✎. **NOW TRY EXERCISE 35** ■

EXAMPLE

Algebraic simplification, with variables:

This limit will be seen again in calculus and provides a good review of the algebra involved in working with fractions.

$$\lim_{h \to 0} \frac{\dfrac{1}{x + h} - \dfrac{1}{x}}{h} = \lim_{h \to 0} \frac{\dfrac{x - (x + h)}{x(x + h)}}{h} = \lim_{h \to 0} \frac{x - (x + h)}{hx(x + h)} 1 = \lim_{h \to 0} -\frac{1}{x(x + h)} = -\frac{1}{x^2}$$

13.2 EXERCISES

CONCEPTS

1. Suppose the following limits exist:

$$\lim_{x \to a} f(x) \text{ and } \lim_{x \to a} g(x)$$

Then $\lim_{x \to a} [f(x) + g(x)] = $ _____ + _____ , and

$\lim_{x \to a} [f(x)g(x)] = $ _____ · _____ .

These formulas can be stated verbally as follows: The limit of

a sum is the _____ of the limits, and the limit of a product

is the _____ of the limits.

2. If f is a polynomial or a rational function and a is in the

domain of f, then $\lim_{x \to a} f(x) = $ _____ .

SKILLS

3. Suppose that

$$\lim_{x \to a} f(x) = -3 \qquad \lim_{x \to a} g(x) = 0 \qquad \lim_{x \to a} h(x) = 8$$

Find the value of the given limit. If the limit does not exist, explain why.

(a) $\lim_{x \to a} [f(x) + h(x)]$ **(b)** $\lim_{x \to a} [f(x)]^2$

(c) $\lim_{x \to a} \sqrt[3]{h(x)}$ **(d)** $\lim_{x \to a} \dfrac{1}{f(x)}$

(e) $\lim_{x \to a} \dfrac{f(x)}{h(x)}$ **(f)** $\lim_{x \to a} \dfrac{g(x)}{f(x)}$

(g) $\lim_{x \to a} \dfrac{f(x)}{g(x)}$ **(h)** $\lim_{x \to a} \dfrac{2f(x)}{h(x) - f(x)}$

4. The graphs of f and g are given. Use them to evaluate each limit if it exists. If the limit does not exist, explain why.

(a) $\lim_{x \to 2} [f(x) + g(x)]$ **(b)** $\lim_{x \to 1} [f(x) + g(x)]$

(c) $\lim_{x \to 0} [f(x)g(x)]$ **(d)** $\lim_{x \to -1} \dfrac{f(x)}{g(x)}$

(e) $\lim_{x \to 2} x^3 f(x)$ **(f)** $\lim_{x \to 1} \sqrt{3 + f(x)}$

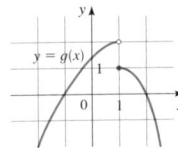

$y = f(x)$

$y = g(x)$

5–10 ■ Evaluate the limit and justify each step by indicating the appropriate Limit Law(s).

5. $\lim_{x \to 4} (5x^2 - 2x + 3)$ **6.** $\lim_{x \to 3} (x^3 + 2)(x^2 - 5x)$

7. $\lim_{x \to -1} \dfrac{x - 2}{x^2 + 4x - 3}$ **8.** $\lim_{x \to 1} \left(\dfrac{x^4 + x^2 - 6}{x^4 + 2x + 3} \right)^2$

9. $\lim_{t \to -2} (t + 1)^9 (t^2 - 1)$ **10.** $\lim_{u \to -2} \sqrt{u^4 + 3u + 6}$

11–22 ■ Evaluate the limit if it exists.

11. $\lim_{x \to 2} \dfrac{x^2 + x - 6}{x - 2}$ **12.** $\lim_{x \to -4} \dfrac{x^2 + 5x + 4}{x^2 + 3x - 4}$

13. $\lim_{x \to 2} \dfrac{x^2 - x + 6}{x + 2}$ **14.** $\lim_{x \to 1} \dfrac{x^3 - 1}{x^2 - 1}$

15. $\lim_{t \to -3} \dfrac{t^2 - 9}{2t^2 + 7t + 3}$ **16.** $\lim_{h \to 0} \dfrac{\sqrt{1 + h} - 1}{h}$

17. $\lim_{h \to 0} \dfrac{(2 + h)^3 - 8}{h}$ **18.** $\lim_{x \to 2} \dfrac{x^4 - 16}{x - 2}$

19. $\lim_{x \to 7} \dfrac{\sqrt{x + 2} - 3}{x - 7}$ **20.** $\lim_{h \to 0} \dfrac{(3 + h)^{-1} - 3^{-1}}{h}$

21. $\lim_{x \to -4} \dfrac{\frac{1}{4} + \frac{1}{x}}{4 + x}$ **22.** $\lim_{t \to 0} \left(\dfrac{1}{t} - \dfrac{1}{t^2 + t} \right)$

23–26 ■ Find the limit and use a graphing device to confirm your result graphically.

23. $\lim_{x \to 1} \dfrac{x^2 - 1}{\sqrt{x} - 1}$ **24.** $\lim_{x \to 0} \dfrac{(4 + x)^3 - 64}{x}$

25. $\lim_{x \to -1} \dfrac{x^2 - x - 2}{x^3 - x}$ **26.** $\lim_{x \to 1} \dfrac{x^8 - 1}{x^5 - x}$

27. (a) Estimate the value of

$$\lim_{x \to 0} \dfrac{x}{\sqrt{1 + 3x} - 1}$$

by graphing the function $f(x) = x/(\sqrt{1 + 3x} - 1)$.

(b) Make a table of values of $f(x)$ for x close to 0, and guess the value of the limit.

(c) Use the Limit Laws to prove that your guess is correct.

28. (a) Use a graph of

$$f(x) = \dfrac{\sqrt{3 + x} - \sqrt{3}}{x}$$

to estimate the value of $\lim_{x \to 0} f(x)$ to two decimal places.

(b) Use a table of values of $f(x)$ to estimate the limit to four decimal places.

(c) Use the Limit Laws to find the exact value of the limit.

29–34 ■ Find the limit, if it exists. If the limit does not exist, explain why.

29. $\lim_{x \to -4} |x + 4|$ **30.** $\lim_{x \to -4} \dfrac{|x + 4|}{x + 4}$

31. $\lim_{x \to 2} \dfrac{|x - 2|}{x - 2}$ **32.** $\lim_{x \to 1.5} \dfrac{2x^2 - 3x}{|2x - 3|}$

33. $\lim_{x \to 0} \left(\dfrac{1}{x} - \dfrac{1}{|x|} \right)$ **34.** $\lim_{x \to 0^-} \left(\dfrac{1}{x} - \dfrac{1}{|x|} \right)$

35. Let

$$f(x) = \begin{cases} x - 1 & \text{if } x < 2 \\ x^2 - 4x + 6 & \text{if } x \geq 2 \end{cases}$$

(a) Find $\lim_{x \to 2^-} f(x)$ and $\lim_{x \to 2^+} f(x)$.
(b) Does $\lim_{x \to 2} f(x)$ exist?
(c) Sketch the graph of f.

36. Let

$$h(x) = \begin{cases} x & \text{if } x < 0 \\ x^2 & \text{if } 0 < x \leq 2 \\ 8 - x & \text{if } x > 2 \end{cases}$$

(a) Evaluate each limit if it exists.

(i) $\lim_{x \to 0^+} h(x)$ (iv) $\lim_{x \to 2^-} h(x)$
(ii) $\lim_{x \to 0} h(x)$ (v) $\lim_{x \to 2^+} h(x)$
(iii) $\lim_{x \to 1} h(x)$ (vi) $\lim_{x \to 2} h(x)$

(b) Sketch the graph of h.

DISCOVERY ▪ DISCUSSION ▪ WRITING

37. Cancellation and Limits

(a) What is wrong with the following equation?

$$\frac{x^2 + x - 6}{x - 2} = x + 3$$

(b) In view of part (a), explain why the equation

$$\lim_{x \to 2} \frac{x^2 + x - 6}{x - 2} = \lim_{x \to 2} (x + 3)$$

is correct.

38. The Lorentz Contraction   In the theory of relativity the Lorentz contraction formula

$$L = L_0 \sqrt{1 - v^2/c^2}$$

expresses the length L of an object as a function of its velocity v with respect to an observer, where L_0 is the length of the object at rest and c is the speed of light. Find $\lim_{v \to c^-} L$, and interpret the result. Why is a left-hand limit necessary?

39. Limits of Sums and Products

(a) Show by means of an example that $\lim_{x \to a} [f(x) + g(x)]$ may exist even though neither $\lim_{x \to a} f(x)$ nor $\lim_{x \to a} g(x)$ exists.

(b) Show by means of an example that $\lim_{x \to a} [f(x)g(x)]$ may exist even though neither $\lim_{x \to a} f(x)$ nor $\lim_{x \to a} g(x)$ exists.

SUGGESTED TIME AND EMPHASIS

1–2 classes, optional material

13.3 TANGENT LINES AND DERIVATIVES

| The Tangent Lines ▶ Derivatives ▶ Instantaneous Rates of Change

In this section we see how limits arise when we attempt to find the tangent line to a curve or the instantaneous rate of change of a function.

▼ The Tangent Problem

A *tangent line* is a line that *just* touches a curve. For instance, Figure 1 shows the parabola $y = x^2$ and the tangent line t that touches the parabola at the point $P(1, 1)$. We will be able to find an equation of the tangent line t as soon as we know its slope m. The difficulty is that we know only one point, P, on t, whereas we need two points to compute the slope. But observe that we can compute an approximation to m by choosing a nearby point $Q(x, x^2)$ on the parabola (as in Figure 2) and computing the slope m_{PQ} of the secant line PQ.

FIGURE 1

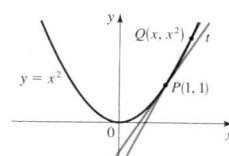

FIGURE 2

TEXT QUESTION

Geometrically, what is "the line tangent to a curve" at a particular point?

Answer

There are different correct answers. Examples include the best linear approximation to a curve at a point and the result of repeated "zooming in" on a curve.

We choose $x \neq 1$ so that $Q \neq P$. Then

$$m_{PQ} = \frac{x^2 - 1}{x - 1}$$

Now we let x approach 1, so Q approaches P along the parabola. Figure 3 shows how the corresponding secant lines rotate about P and approach the tangent line t.

  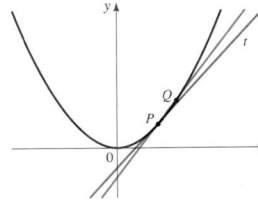

Q approaches P from the right

  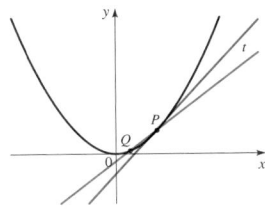

Q approaches P from the left

FIGURE 3

The slope of the tangent line is the limit of the slopes of the secant lines:

$$m = \lim_{Q \to P} m_{PQ}$$

So using the method of Section 13.2, we have

$$m = \lim_{x \to 1} \frac{x^2 - 1}{x - 1} = \lim_{x \to 1} \frac{(x - 1)(x + 1)}{x - 1}$$

$$= \lim_{x \to 1} (x + 1) = 1 + 1 = 2$$

The point-slope form for the equation of a line through the point (x_1, y_1) with slope m is

$$y - y_1 = m(x - x_1)$$

(See Section 1.10.)

Now that we know the slope of the tangent line is $m = 2$, we can use the point-slope form of the equation of a line to find its equation.

$$y - 1 = 2(x - 1) \qquad \text{or} \qquad y = 2x - 1$$

We sometimes refer to the slope of the tangent line to a curve at a point as the **slope of the curve** at the point. The idea is that if we zoom in far enough toward the point, the curve looks almost like a straight line. Figure 4 illustrates this procedure for the curve $y = x^2$. The more we zoom in, the more the parabola looks like a line. In other words, the curve becomes almost indistinguishable from its tangent line.

FIGURE 4 Zooming in toward the point $(1, 1)$ on the parabola $y = x^2$

IN-CLASS MATERIALS

Point out that if a car is driving along a curve, the headlights will point along the direction of the tangent line.

If we have a general curve C with equation $y = f(x)$ and we want to find the tangent line to C at the point $P(a, f(a))$, then we consider a nearby point $Q(x, f(x))$, where $x \neq a$, and compute the slope of the secant line PQ.

$$m_{PQ} = \frac{f(x) - f(a)}{x - a}$$

Then we let Q approach P along the curve C by letting x approach a. If m_{PQ} approaches a number m, then we define the *tangent* t to be the line through P with slope m. (This amounts to saying that the tangent line is the limiting position of the secant line PQ as Q approaches P. See Figure 5.)

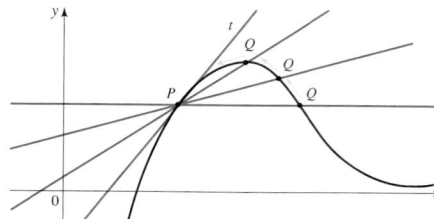

FIGURE 5

DEFINITION OF A TANGENT LINE

The **tangent line** to the curve $y = f(x)$ at the point $P(a, f(a))$ is the line through P with slope

$$m = \lim_{x \to a} \frac{f(x) - f(a)}{x - a}$$

provided that this limit exists.

ALTERNATE EXAMPLE 1

Find an equation of the tangent line to the hyperbola $y = \dfrac{4}{x}$ at the point $(4, 1)$.

ANSWER
$x + 4y - 8 = 0$

EXAMPLE 1 │ Finding a Tangent Line to a Hyperbola

Find an equation of the tangent line to the hyperbola $y = 3/x$ at the point $(3, 1)$.

SOLUTION   Let $f(x) = 3/x$. Then the slope of the tangent line at $(3, 1)$ is

$$m = \lim_{x \to 3} \frac{f(x) - f(3)}{x - 3} \qquad \text{Definition of } m$$

$$= \lim_{x \to 3} \frac{\dfrac{3}{x} - 1}{x - 3} \qquad f(x) = \frac{3}{x}$$

$$= \lim_{x \to 3} \frac{3 - x}{x(x - 3)} \qquad \begin{array}{l}\text{Multiply numerator} \\ \text{and denominator by } x\end{array}$$

$$= \lim_{x \to 3} \left(-\frac{1}{x}\right) \qquad \text{Cancel } x - 3$$

$$= -\frac{1}{3} \qquad \text{Let } x \to 3$$

Therefore an equation of the tangent at the point $(3, 1)$ is

$$y - 1 = -\tfrac{1}{3}(x - 3)$$

IN-CLASS MATERIALS

Illustrate that many functions, such as x^2 and $x - 2 \sin x$, look locally linear, and discuss the relationship of this property to the concept of the tangent line. Then pose the question, "What does a secant line to a linear function look like?"

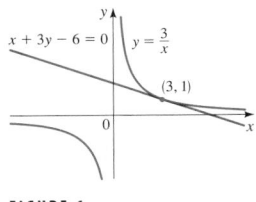

$x + 3y - 6 = 0$ $y = \dfrac{3}{x}$

(3, 1)

FIGURE 6

which simplifies to

$$x + 3y - 6 = 0$$

The hyperbola and its tangent are shown in Figure 6.

✎. NOW TRY EXERCISE **11**

There is another expression for the slope of a tangent line that is sometimes easier to use. Let $h = x - a$. Then $x = a + h$, so the slope of the secant line PQ is

$$m_{PQ} = \frac{f(a + h) - f(a)}{h}$$

See Figure 7, in which the case $h > 0$ is illustrated and Q is to the right of P. If it happened that $h < 0$, however, Q would be to the left of P.

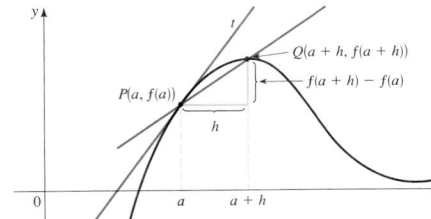

$Q(a + h, f(a + h))$

$f(a + h) - f(a)$

$P(a, f(a))$

t

h

a $a + h$

FIGURE 7

Notice that as x approaches a, h approaches 0 (because $h = x - a$), so the expression for the slope of the tangent line becomes

$$m = \lim_{h \to 0} \frac{f(a + h) - f(a)}{h}$$

Newton and Limits

In 1687 Isaac Newton (see page 852) published his masterpiece *Principia Mathematica*. In this work, the greatest scientific treatise ever written, Newton set forth his version of calculus and used it to investigate mechanics, fluid dynamics, and wave motion and to explain the motion of planets and comets.

The beginnings of calculus are found in the calculations of areas and volumes by ancient Greek scholars such as Eudoxus and Archimedes. Although aspects of the idea of a limit are implicit in their "method of exhaustion," Eudoxus and Archimedes never explicitly formulated the concept of a limit. Likewise, mathematicians such as Cavalieri, Fermat, and Barrow, the immediate precursors of Newton in the development of calculus, did not actually use limits. It was Isaac Newton who first talked explicitly about limits. He explained that the main idea behind limits is that quantities "approach nearer than by any given difference." Newton stated that the limit was the basic concept in calculus, but it was left to later mathematicians like Cauchy and Weierstrass to clarify these ideas.

EXAMPLE 2 | Finding a Tangent Line

Find an equation of the tangent line to the curve $y = x^3 - 2x + 3$ at the point $(1, 2)$.

SOLUTION   If $f(x) = x^3 - 2x + 3$, then the slope of the tangent line where $a = 1$ is

$$m = \lim_{h \to 0} \frac{f(1 + h) - f(1)}{h}$$ Definition of m

$$= \lim_{h \to 0} \frac{[(1 + h)^3 - 2(1 + h) + 3] - [1^3 - 2(1) + 3]}{h}$$ $f(x) = x^3 - 2x + 3$

$$= \lim_{h \to 0} \frac{1 + 3h + 3h^2 + h^3 - 2 - 2h + 3 - 2}{h}$$ Expand numerator

$$= \lim_{h \to 0} \frac{h + 3h^2 + h^3}{h}$$ Simplify

$$= \lim_{h \to 0} (1 + 3h + h^2)$$ Cancel h

$$= 1$$ Let $h \to 0$

So an equation of the tangent line at $(1, 2)$ is

$$y - 2 = 1(x - 1)   \text{or}   y = x + 1$$

✎. NOW TRY EXERCISE **9**

ALTERNATE EXAMPLE 2

Find an equation of the tangent line to the curve $y = x^3 - 2x + 5$ at the point $(1, 5)$.

ANSWER

$y = x + 4$

IN-CLASS MATERIALS

Show that the slope of the tangent line does not exist at $x = 0$ for either of $f(x) = \sqrt[3]{x}$ or $g(x) = |x|$. Note that f has a tangent line (which is vertical), but g does not (it has a cusp).

▼ Derivatives

We have seen that the slope of the tangent line to the curve $y = f(x)$ at the point $(a, f(a))$ can be written as

$$\lim_{h \to 0} \frac{f(a + h) - f(a)}{h}$$

It turns out that this expression arises in many other contexts as well, such as finding velocities and other rates of change. Because this type of limit occurs so widely, it is given a special name and notation.

DEFINITION OF A DERIVATIVE

The **derivative of a function f at a number** a, denoted by $f'(a)$, is

$$f'(a) = \lim_{h \to 0} \frac{f(a + h) - f(a)}{h}$$

if this limit exists.

EXAMPLE 3 | Finding a Derivative at a Point

Find the derivative of the function $f(x) = 5x^2 + 3x - 1$ at the number 2.

SOLUTION   According to the definition of a derivative, with $a = 2$, we have

$$f'(2) = \lim_{h \to 0} \frac{f(2 + h) - f(2)}{h} \qquad \text{Definition of } f'(2)$$

$$= \lim_{h \to 0} \frac{[5(2 + h)^2 + 3(2 + h) - 1] - [5(2)^2 + 3(2) - 1]}{h} \qquad f(x) = 5x^2 + 3x - 1$$

$$= \lim_{h \to 0} \frac{20 + 20h + 5h^2 + 6 + 3h - 1 - 25}{h} \qquad \text{Expand}$$

$$= \lim_{h \to 0} \frac{23h + 5h^2}{h} \qquad \text{Simplify}$$

$$= \lim_{h \to 0}(23 + 5h) \qquad \text{Cancel } h$$

$$= 23 \qquad \text{Let } h \to 0$$

✎. NOW TRY EXERCISE **15**   ■

We see from the definition of a derivative that the number $f'(a)$ is the same as the slope of the tangent line to the curve $y = f(x)$ at the point $(a, f(a))$. So the result of Example 3 shows that the slope of the tangent line to the parabola $y = 5x^2 + 3x - 1$ at the point $(2, 25)$ is $f'(2) = 23$.

EXAMPLE 4 | Finding a Derivative

Let $f(x) = \sqrt{x}$.
(a) Find $f'(a)$.
(b) Find $f'(1)$, $f'(4)$, and $f'(9)$.

ALTERNATE EXAMPLE 3

Find the derivative of the function $f(x) = 8x^2 + 2x - 4$ at the number 2.

ANSWER

34

ALTERNATE EXAMPLE 4

(a) Let $f(x) = \sqrt{7x}$. Find $f'(a)$.
(b) Let $f(x) = \sqrt{x}$. Find $f'(16)$.

ANSWERS

(a) $\dfrac{7}{2\sqrt{7a}}$

(b) $\dfrac{1}{8}$

IN-CLASS MATERIALS

Discuss how physical situations can be translated into statements about derivatives. For example, the budget deficit can be viewed as the derivative of the national debt. Describe the units of derivatives in real-world situations. The budget deficit, for example, is measured in trillions of dollars per year. Another example: If $s(d)$ represents the sales figures for a magazine given d dollars of advertising, where s is the number of magazines sold, then $s'(d)$ is in magazines per dollar spent. Describe enough examples to make the pattern evident.

SOLUTION

(a) We use the definition of the derivative at a:

$$f'(a) = \lim_{h \to 0} \frac{f(a+h) - f(a)}{h} \qquad \text{Definition of derivative}$$

$$= \lim_{h \to 0} \frac{\sqrt{a+h} - \sqrt{a}}{h} \qquad f(x) = \sqrt{x}$$

$$= \lim_{h \to 0} \frac{\sqrt{a+h} - \sqrt{a}}{h} \cdot \frac{\sqrt{a+h} + \sqrt{a}}{\sqrt{a+h} + \sqrt{a}} \qquad \text{Rationalize numerator}$$

$$= \lim_{h \to 0} \frac{(a+h) - a}{h(\sqrt{a+h} + \sqrt{a})} \qquad \text{Difference of squares}$$

$$= \lim_{h \to 0} \frac{h}{h(\sqrt{a+h} + \sqrt{a})} \qquad \text{Simplify numerator}$$

$$= \lim_{h \to 0} \frac{1}{\sqrt{a+h} + \sqrt{a}} \qquad \text{Cancel } h$$

$$= \frac{1}{\sqrt{a} + \sqrt{a}} = \frac{1}{2\sqrt{a}} \qquad \text{Let } h \to 0$$

(b) Substituting $a = 1$, $a = 4$, and $a = 9$ into the result of part (a), we get

$$f'(1) = \frac{1}{2\sqrt{1}} = \frac{1}{2} \qquad f'(4) = \frac{1}{2\sqrt{4}} = \frac{1}{4} \qquad f'(9) = \frac{1}{2\sqrt{9}} = \frac{1}{6}$$

These values of the derivative are the slopes of the tangent lines shown in Figure 8.

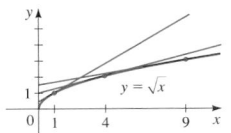

FIGURE 8

$y = \sqrt{x}$

✎ **NOW TRY EXERCISE 21** ∎

▼ Instantaneous Rates of Change

In Section 2.3 we defined the average rate of change of a function f between the numbers a and x as

$$\text{average rate of change} = \frac{\text{change in } y}{\text{change in } x} = \frac{f(x) - f(a)}{x - a}$$

Suppose we consider the average rate of change over smaller and smaller intervals by letting x approach a. The limit of these average rates of change is called the instantaneous rate of change.

INSTANTANEOUS RATE OF CHANGE

If $y = f(x)$, the **instantaneous rate of change of y with respect to x at $x = a$** is the limit of the average rates of change as x approaches a:

$$\text{instantaneous rate of change} = \lim_{x \to a} \frac{f(x) - f(a)}{x - a} = f'(a)$$

Notice that we now have two ways of interpreting the derivative:

- $f'(a)$ is the slope of the tangent line to $y = f(x)$ at $x = a$
- $f'(a)$ is the instantaneous rate of change of y with respect to x at $x = a$

IN-CLASS MATERIALS

Show students how to estimate derivatives from tables of numbers. For example, one can estimate that if the following are position measurements versus time, the maximum velocity is achieved somewhere between $t = 2.9$ and $t = 3$.

t	2.8	2.9	3.0	3.1	3.2	3.3
$P(t)$	1.2	2.4	3.9	5.1	6.1	6.9

In the special case in which $x = t =$ time and $s = f(t) =$ displacement (directed distance) at time t of an object traveling in a straight line, the instantaneous rate of change is called the **instantaneous velocity**.

ALTERNATE EXAMPLE 5

If an object is dropped from a height of 3000 ft, its distance above the ground (in feet) after t seconds is given by $h(t) = 3000 - 18t^2$. Find the object's instantaneous velocity after 3 seconds.

ANSWER

-108 ft/s

EXAMPLE 5 | Instantaneous Velocity of a Falling Object

If an object is dropped from a height of 3000 ft, its distance above the ground (in feet) after t seconds is given by $h(t) = 3000 - 16t^2$. Find the object's instantaneous velocity after 4 seconds.

SOLUTION   After 4 s have elapsed, the height is $h(4) = 2744$ ft. The instantaneous velocity is

$$h'(4) = \lim_{t \to 4} \frac{h(t) - h(4)}{t - 4} \qquad \text{Definition of } h'(4)$$

$$= \lim_{t \to 4} \frac{3000 - 16t^2 - 2744}{t - 4} \qquad h(t) = 3000 - 16t^2$$

$$= \lim_{t \to 4} \frac{256 - 16t^2}{t - 4} \qquad \text{Simplify}$$

$$= \lim_{t \to 4} \frac{16(4 - t)(4 + t)}{t - 4} \qquad \text{Factor numerator}$$

$$= \lim_{t \to 4} -16(4 + t) \qquad \text{Cancel } t - 4$$

$$= -16(4 + 4) = -128 \text{ ft/s} \qquad \text{Let } t \to 4$$

The negative sign indicates that the height is *decreasing* at a rate of 128 ft/s.

✎. NOW TRY EXERCISE **27**   ∎

ALTERNATE EXAMPLE 6

Let $P(t)$ be the population of the United States at time t. The following table gives approximate values of this function by providing midyear population estimates from 1992 to 2000. Estimate the value of $P'(1996)$.

t	$P(t)$
1992	254,999,000
1994	260,295,000
1996	265,254,000
1998	270,004,000
2000	274,634,000

ANSWER

2.4 million people/year

t	$P(t)$
1996	269,667,000
1998	276,115,000
2000	282,192,000
2002	287,941,000
2004	293,655,000

t	$\dfrac{P(t) - P(2000)}{t - 2000}$
1996	3,131,250
1998	3,038,500
2002	2,874,500
2004	2,865,750

Here, we have estimated the derivative by averaging the slopes of two secant lines. Another method is to plot the population function and estimate the slope of the tangent line when $t = 2000$.

EXAMPLE 6 | Estimating an Instantaneous Rate of Change

Let $P(t)$ be the population of the United States at time t. The table in the margin gives approximate values of this function by providing midyear population estimates from 1996 to 2004. Interpret and estimate the value of $P'(2000)$.

SOLUTION   The derivative $P'(2000)$ means the rate of change of P with respect to t when $t = 2000$, that is, the rate of increase of the population in 2000.

According to the definition of a derivative, we have

$$P'(2000) = \lim_{t \to 2000} \frac{P(t) - P(2000)}{t - 2000}$$

So we compute and tabulate values of the difference quotient (the average rates of change) as shown in the table in the margin. We see that $P'(2000)$ lies somewhere between 3,038,500 and 2,874,500. (Here we are making the reasonable assumption that the population didn't fluctuate wildly between 1996 and 2004.) We estimate that the rate of increase of the U.S. population in 2000 was the average of these two numbers, namely,

$$P'(2000) \approx 2.96 \text{ million people/year}$$

✎. NOW TRY EXERCISE **33**   ∎

EXAMPLE

If $f(x) = 3x + 4$, then $f'(2) = 3$. In fact, $f(k) = 3$ for all k.

13.3 EXERCISES

CONCEPTS

1. The derivative of a function f at a number a is

$$f'(a) = \lim_{h \to 0} \frac{\boxed{} - \boxed{}}{\boxed{}}$$

if the limit exists. The derivative $f'(a)$ is the _____ of the tangent line to the curve $y = f(x)$ at the point ($\boxed{}$, $\boxed{}$).

2. If $y = f(x)$, the average rate of change of f between the numbers x and a is $\frac{\boxed{} - \boxed{}}{\boxed{} - \boxed{}}$. The limit of the average rates of change as x approaches a is the _____ rate of change of y with respect to x at $x = a$; this is also the derivative $f'(\boxed{})$.

SKILLS

3–8 ■ Find the slope of the tangent line to the graph of f at the given point.

3. $f(x) = 3x + 4$ at $(1, 7)$

4. $f(x) = 5 - 2x$ at $(-3, 11)$

5. $f(x) = 4x^2 - 3x$ at $(-1, 7)$

6. $f(x) = 1 + 2x - 3x^2$ at $(1, 0)$

7. $f(x) = 2x^3$ at $(2, 16)$

8. $f(x) = \dfrac{6}{x + 1}$ at $(2, 2)$

9–14 ■ Find an equation of the tangent line to the curve at the given point. Graph the curve and the tangent line.

9. $y = x + x^2$ at $(-1, 0)$

10. $y = 2x - x^3$ at $(1, 1)$

11. $y = \dfrac{x}{x - 1}$ at $(2, 2)$

12. $y = \dfrac{1}{x^2}$ at $(-1, 1)$

13. $y = \sqrt{x + 3}$ at $(1, 2)$

14. $y = \sqrt{1 + 2x}$ at $(4, 3)$

15–20 ■ Find the derivative of the function at the given number.

15. $f(x) = 1 - 3x^2$ at 2

16. $f(x) = 2 - 3x + x^2$ at -1

17. $g(x) = x^4$ at 1

18. $g(x) = 2x^2 + x^3$ at 1

19. $F(x) = \dfrac{1}{\sqrt{x}}$ at 4

20. $G(x) = 1 + 2\sqrt{x}$ at 4

21–24 ■ Find $f'(a)$, where a is in the domain of f.

21. $f(x) = x^2 + 2x$

22. $f(x) = -\dfrac{1}{x^2}$

23. $f(x) = \dfrac{x}{x + 1}$

24. $f(x) = \sqrt{x - 2}$

25. (a) If $f(x) = x^3 - 2x + 4$, find $f'(a)$.
(b) Find equations of the tangent lines to the graph of f at the points whose x-coordinates are 0, 1, and 2.
(c) Graph f and the three tangent lines.

26. (a) If $g(x) = 1/(2x - 1)$, find $g'(a)$.
(b) Find equations of the tangent lines to the graph of g at the points whose x-coordinates are -1, 0, and 1.
(c) Graph g and the three tangent lines.

APPLICATIONS

27. Velocity of a Ball If a ball is thrown straight up with a velocity of 40 ft/s, its height (in feet) after t seconds is given by $y = 40t - 16t^2$. Find the instantaneous velocity when $t = 2$.

28. Velocity on the Moon If an arrow is shot upward on the moon with a velocity of 58 m/s, its height (in meters) after t seconds is given by $H = 58t - 0.83t^2$.
(a) Find the instantaneous velocity of the arrow after one second.
(b) Find the instantaneous velocity of the arrow when $t = a$.
(c) At what time t will the arrow hit the moon?
(d) With what velocity will the arrow hit the moon?

29. Velocity of a Particle The displacement s (in meters) of a particle moving in a straight line is given by the equation of motion $s = 4t^3 + 6t + 2$, where t is measured in seconds. Find the instantaneous velocity of the particle s at times $t = a$, $t = 1$, $t = 2$, $t = 3$.

30. Inflating a Balloon A spherical balloon is being inflated. Find the rate of change of the surface area $(S = 4\pi r^2)$ with respect to the radius r when $r = 2$ ft.

31. Temperature Change A roast turkey is taken from an oven when its temperature has reached 185°F and is placed on a table in a room where the temperature is 75°F. The graph shows how the temperature of the turkey decreases and even-

DRILL QUESTION

Draw the line tangent to the following curve at each of the indicated points:

Answer

EXAMPLE

Let $f(x) = x^3$. Then an equation of the line tangent to this curve at $x = \dfrac{1}{2}$ is $y = \dfrac{3}{4}x - \dfrac{1}{4}$.

tually approaches room temperature. By measuring the slope of the tangent, estimate the rate of change of the temperature after an hour.

32. Heart Rate   A cardiac monitor is used to measure the heart rate of a patient after surgery. It compiles the number of heart-beats after t minutes. When the data in the table are graphed, the slope of the tangent line represents the heart rate in beats per minute.

t (min)	Heartbeats
36	2530
38	2661
40	2806
42	2948
44	3080

(a) Find the average heart rates (slopes of the secant lines) over the time intervals $[40, 42]$ and $[42, 44]$.
(b) Estimate the patient's heart rate after 42 minutes by averaging the slopes of these two secant lines.

33. Water Flow   A tank holds 1000 gallons of water, which drains from the bottom of the tank in half an hour. The values in the table show the volume V of water remaining in the tank (in gallons) after t minutes.

t (min)	V (gal)
5	694
10	444
15	250
20	111
25	28
30	0

(a) Find the average rates at which water flows from the tank (slopes of secant lines) for the time intervals $[10, 15]$ and $[15, 20]$.
(b) The slope of the tangent line at the point $(15, 250)$ represents the rate at which water is flowing from the tank after 15 minutes. Estimate this rate by averaging the slopes of the secant lines in part (a).

34. World Population Growth   The table gives the world's population in the 20th century.

Year	Population (millions)	Year	Population (millions)
1900	1650	1960	3040
1910	1750	1970	3710
1920	1860	1980	4450
1930	2070	1990	5280
1940	2300	2000	6080
1950	2560		

Estimate the rate of population growth in 1920 and in 1980 by averaging the slopes of two secant lines.

DISCOVERY ▪ DISCUSSION ▪ WRITING

35. Estimating Derivatives from a Graph   For the function g whose graph is given, arrange the following numbers in increasing order, and explain your reasoning.

$$0 \qquad g'(-2) \qquad g'(0) \qquad g'(2) \qquad g'(4)$$

36. Estimating Velocities from a Graph   The graph shows the position function of a car. Use the shape of the graph to explain your answers to the following questions.
(a) What was the initial velocity of the car?
(b) Was the car going faster at B or at C?
(c) Was the car slowing down or speeding up at A, B, and C?
(d) What happened between D and E?

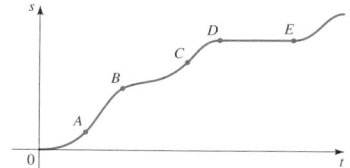

⬤ **DISCOVERY PROJECT**   **Designing a Roller Coaster**

In this project we use derivatives to determine how to connect different parts of a roller coaster in such a way that you get a smooth ride. You can find the project at the book companion website: **www.stewartmath.com**

13.4 LIMITS AT INFINITY; LIMITS OF SEQUENCES

SUGGESTED TIME AND EMPHASIS
1 class, optional material

| Limits at Infinity ▶ Limits of Sequences

In this section we study a special kind of limit called a *limit at infinity*. We examine the limit of a function $f(x)$ as x becomes large. We also examine the limit of a sequence a_n as n becomes large. Limits of sequences will be used in Section 13.5 to help us find the area under the graph of a function.

▼ Limits at Infinity

Let's investigate the behavior of the function f defined by

$$f(x) = \frac{x^2 - 1}{x^2 + 1}$$

as x becomes large. The table in the margin gives values of this function rounded to six decimal places, and the graph of f has been drawn by a computer in Figure 1.

x	$f(x)$
0	-1.000000
± 1	0.000000
± 2	0.600000
± 3	0.800000
± 4	0.882353
± 5	0.923077
± 10	0.980198
± 50	0.999200
± 100	0.999800
± 1000	0.999998

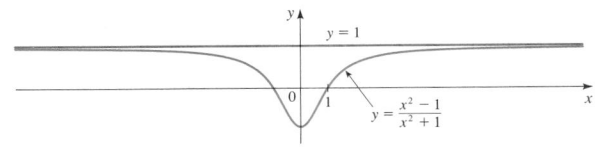

FIGURE 1

As x grows larger and larger, you can see that the values of $f(x)$ get closer and closer to 1. In fact, it seems that we can make the values of $f(x)$ as close as we like to 1 by taking x sufficiently large. This situation is expressed symbolically by writing

$$\lim_{x \to \infty} \frac{x^2 - 1}{x^2 + 1} = 1$$

In general, we use the notation

$$\lim_{x \to \infty} f(x) = L$$

to indicate that the values of $f(x)$ become closer and closer to L as x becomes larger and larger.

LIMIT AT INFINITY

Let f be a function defined on some interval (a, ∞). Then

$$\lim_{x \to \infty} f(x) = L$$

means that the values of $f(x)$ can be made arbitrarily close to L by taking x sufficiently large.

Limits at infinity are also discussed in Section 3.7.

Another notation for $\lim_{x \to \infty} f(x) = L$ is

$$f(x) \to L \qquad \text{as} \qquad x \to \infty$$

TEXT QUESTION

Compute $\lim\limits_{x \to \infty} \dfrac{1}{x^2 + 2}$.

Answer

0

The symbol ∞ does not represent a number. Nevertheless, we often read the expression $\lim_{x \to \infty} f(x) = L$ as

"the limit of $f(x)$, as x approaches infinity, is L"

or   "the limit of $f(x)$, as x becomes infinite, is L"

or   "the limit of $f(x)$, as x increases without bound, is L"

Geometric illustrations are shown in Figure 2. Notice that there are many ways for the graph of f to approach the line $y = L$ (which is called a *horizontal asymptote*) as we look to the far right.

FIGURE 2   Examples illustrating $\lim_{x \to \infty} f(x) = L$

Referring back to Figure 1, we see that for numerically large negative values of x, the values of $f(x)$ are close to 1. By letting x decrease through negative values without bound, we can make $f(x)$ as close as we like to 1. This is expressed by writing

$$\lim_{x \to -\infty} \frac{x^2 - 1}{x^2 + 1} = 1$$

The general definition is as follows.

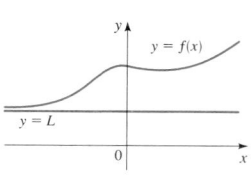

LIMIT AT NEGATIVE INFINITY

Let f be a function defined on some interval $(-\infty, a)$. Then

$$\lim_{x \to -\infty} f(x) = L$$

means that the values of $f(x)$ can be made arbitrarily close to L by taking x sufficiently large negative.

Again, the symbol $-\infty$ does not represent a number, but the expression $\lim_{x \to -\infty} f(x) = L$ is often read as

"the limit of $f(x)$, as x approaches negative infinity, is L"

The definition is illustrated in Figure 3. Notice that the graph approaches the line $y = L$ as we look to the far left.

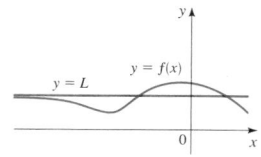

FIGURE 3   Examples illustrating $\lim_{x \to -\infty} f(x) = L$

HORIZONTAL ASYMPTOTE

The line $y = L$ is called a **horizontal asymptote** of the curve $y = f(x)$ if either

$$\lim_{x \to \infty} f(x) = L \qquad \text{or} \qquad \lim_{x \to -\infty} f(x) = L$$

IN-CLASS MATERIALS

Consider the motion of an object on a spring. In a frictionless world, it would oscillate forever. In the real world, the oscillations die out. We can model the height of the object versus time this way:

$$f(x) = e^{-x} \sin kx + H$$

where H is the height of the object at rest.

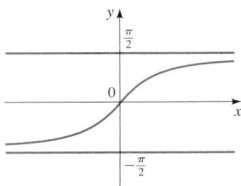

FIGURE 4 $y = \tan^{-1} x$

For instance, the curve illustrated in Figure 1 has the line $y = 1$ as a horizontal asymptote because

$$\lim_{x \to \infty} \frac{x^2 - 1}{x^2 + 1} = 1$$

As we discovered in Section 5.5, an example of a curve with two horizontal asymptotes is $y = \tan^{-1} x$ (see Figure 4). In fact,

$$\lim_{x \to -\infty} \tan^{-1} x = -\frac{\pi}{2} \qquad \text{and} \qquad \lim_{x \to \infty} \tan^{-1} x = \frac{\pi}{2}$$

so both of the lines $y = -\pi/2$ and $y = \pi/2$ are horizontal asymptotes. (This follows from the fact that the lines $x = \pm\pi/2$ are vertical asymptotes of the graph of tan.)

EXAMPLE 1 | Limits at Infinity

Find $\lim\limits_{x \to \infty} \dfrac{1}{x}$ and $\lim\limits_{x \to -\infty} \dfrac{1}{x}$.

We first investigated horizontal asymptotes and limits at infinity for rational functions in Section 3.7.

SOLUTION Observe that when x is large, $1/x$ is small. For instance,

$$\frac{1}{100} = 0.01 \qquad \frac{1}{10,000} = 0.0001 \qquad \frac{1}{1,000,000} = 0.000001$$

In fact, by taking x large enough, we can make $1/x$ as close to 0 as we please. Therefore

$$\lim_{x \to \infty} \frac{1}{x} = 0$$

Similar reasoning shows that when x is large negative, $1/x$ is small negative, so we also have

$$\lim_{x \to -\infty} \frac{1}{x} = 0$$

It follows that the line $y = 0$ (the x-axis) is a horizontal asymptote of the curve $y = 1/x$. (This is a hyperbola; see Figure 5.)

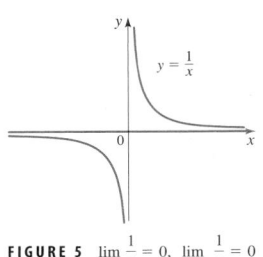

FIGURE 5 $\lim\limits_{x \to \infty} \dfrac{1}{x} = 0$, $\lim\limits_{x \to -\infty} \dfrac{1}{x} = 0$

✎. NOW TRY EXERCISE **5**

The Limit Laws that we studied in Section 13.2 also hold for limits at infinity. In particular, if we combine Law 6 (Limit of a Power) with the results of Example 1, we obtain the following important rule for calculating limits.

> If k is any positive integer, then
>
> $$\lim_{x \to \infty} \frac{1}{x^k} = 0 \qquad \text{and} \qquad \lim_{x \to -\infty} \frac{1}{x^k} = 0$$

EXAMPLE 2 | Finding a Limit at Infinity

Evaluate $\lim\limits_{x \to \infty} \dfrac{3x^2 - x - 2}{5x^2 + 4x + 1}$.

SOLUTION To evaluate the limit at infinity of a rational function, we first divide both the numerator and denominator by the highest power of x that occurs in the

IN-CLASS MATERIALS

Note that sometimes we can approximate an infinite limit by using a calculator to plug large numbers into a function. For example, let $f(x) = \dfrac{2x^2 + \sin x}{x^2 - 30x - 200}$. We can show that $\lim\limits_{x \to \infty} f(x) = 2$, and it is a fact that $f(10)^6 \approx 2.00006$. This method doesn't always work, though. If $g(x) = \ln(\ln x)$, then $\lim\limits_{x \to \infty} g(x) = \infty$; that is, the limit does not exist. Yet $g(10^{99}) \approx 5.4291523$.

denominator. (We may assume that $x \neq 0$, since we are interested only in large values of x.) In this case, the highest power of x in the denominator is x^2, so we have

$$\lim_{x \to \infty} \frac{3x^2 - x - 2}{5x^2 + 4x + 1} = \lim_{x \to \infty} \frac{3 - \dfrac{1}{x} - \dfrac{2}{x^2}}{5 + \dfrac{4}{x} + \dfrac{1}{x^2}}$$ Divide numerator and denominator by x^2

$$= \frac{\displaystyle\lim_{x \to \infty} \left(3 - \dfrac{1}{x} - \dfrac{2}{x^2} \right)}{\displaystyle\lim_{x \to \infty} \left(5 + \dfrac{4}{x} + \dfrac{1}{x^2} \right)}$$ Limit of a Quotient

$$= \frac{\displaystyle\lim_{x \to \infty} 3 - \lim_{x \to \infty} \dfrac{1}{x} - 2 \lim_{x \to \infty} \dfrac{1}{x^2}}{\displaystyle\lim_{x \to \infty} 5 + 4 \lim_{x \to \infty} \dfrac{1}{x} + \lim_{x \to \infty} \dfrac{1}{x^2}}$$ Limits of Sums and Differences

$$= \frac{3 - 0 - 0}{5 + 0 + 0} = \frac{3}{5}$$ Let $x \to \infty$

A similar calculation shows that the limit as $x \to -\infty$ is also $\frac{3}{5}$. Figure 6 illustrates the results of these calculations by showing how the graph of the given rational function approaches the horizontal asymptote $y = \frac{3}{5}$.

✎. **NOW TRY EXERCISE 9**   ■

FIGURE 6

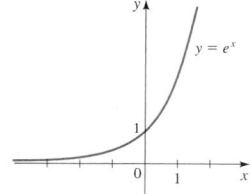

$y = 0.6$

EXAMPLE 3 │ **A Limit at Negative Infinity**

Use numerical and graphical methods to find $\displaystyle\lim_{x \to -\infty} e^x$.

SOLUTION   From the graph of the natural exponential function $y = e^x$ in Figure 7 and the corresponding table of values, we see that

$$\lim_{x \to -\infty} e^x = 0$$

It follows that the line $y = 0$ (the x-axis) is a horizontal asymptote.

$y = e^x$

x	e^x
0	1.00000
-1	0.36788
-2	0.13534
-3	0.04979
-5	0.00674
-8	0.00034
-10	0.00005

FIGURE 7

✎. **NOW TRY EXERCISE 19**   ■

EXAMPLE 4 │ **A Function with No Limit at Infinity**

Evaluate $\displaystyle\lim_{x \to \infty} \sin x$.

IN-CLASS MATERIALS

Have the class come up with functions for which both $\displaystyle\lim_{x \to \infty} f(x)$ and $\displaystyle\lim_{x \to \infty} a_n$ exist, where $a_n = f(n)$. Then have them come up with functions for which they both do not exist. Then have them find one where $\displaystyle\lim_{x \to \infty} f(x)$ does not exist and $\displaystyle\lim_{x \to \infty} a_n$ does. One such case is $f(x) = \sin(2\pi x)$. Finally, have them try to find an example where $\displaystyle\lim_{x \to \infty} a_n$ does not exist and $\displaystyle\lim_{x \to \infty} f(x)$ does. They will fail. The text shows that this is impossible.

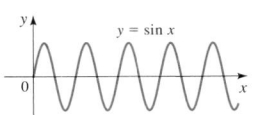

FIGURE 8

SOLUTION From the graph in Figure 8 and the periodic nature of the sine function we see that as x increases, the values of $\sin x$ oscillate between 1 and -1 infinitely often, so they don't approach any definite number. Therefore $\lim_{x \to \infty} \sin x$ does not exist.

✎ NOW TRY EXERCISE **17**

▼ **Limits of Sequences**

In Section 12.1 we introduced the idea of a sequence of numbers $a_1, a_2, a_3, \ldots$. Here we are interested in their behavior as n becomes large. For instance, the sequence defined by

$$a_n = \frac{n}{n+1}$$

FIGURE 9

is pictured in Figure 9 by plotting its terms on a number line and in Figure 10 by plotting its graph. From Figure 9 or 10 it appears that the terms of the sequence $a_n = n/(n+1)$ are approaching 1 as n becomes large. We indicate this by writing

$$\lim_{n \to \infty} \frac{n}{n+1} = 1$$

FIGURE 10

> **DEFINITION OF THE LIMIT OF A SEQUENCE**
>
> A sequence $a_1, a_2, a_3, \ldots$ has the **limit** L and we write
>
> $$\lim_{n \to \infty} a_n = L \qquad \text{or} \qquad a_n \to L \text{ as } n \to \infty$$
>
> if the nth term a_n of the sequence can be made arbitrarily close to L by taking n sufficiently large. If $\lim_{n \to \infty} a_n$ exists, we say the sequence **converges** (or is **convergent**). Otherwise, we say the sequence **diverges** (or is **divergent**).

This definition is illustrated by Figure 11.

FIGURE 11 Graphs of two sequences with $\lim_{n \to \infty} a_n = L$

If we compare the definitions of $\lim_{n \to \infty} a_n = L$ and $\lim_{x \to \infty} f(x) = L$, we see that the only difference is that n is required to be an integer. Thus, the following is true.

> If $\lim_{x \to \infty} f(x) = L$ and $f(n) = a_n$ when n is an integer, then $\lim_{n \to \infty} a_n = L$.

In particular, since we know that $\lim_{x \to \infty} (1/x^k) = 0$ when k is a positive integer, we have

$$\lim_{n \to \infty} \frac{1}{n^k} = 0 \qquad \text{if } k \text{ is a positive integer}$$

Note that the Limit Laws given in Section 13.2 also hold for limits of sequences.

EXAMPLE

If $a_n = \dfrac{n(n+1)(n+2)}{n^4}$, then

$$\lim_{x \to \infty} a_n = 0.$$

EXAMPLES

- $\lim\limits_{x \to \infty} \dfrac{1}{1 - 2^{1/x}} = -\infty$

- $\lim\limits_{x \to -\infty} \dfrac{1}{1 - 2^{1/x}} = \infty$

- $\lim\limits_{x \to \infty} \dfrac{x^2 - 6x}{2x^2 + 2x} = \dfrac{1}{2}$

ALTERNATE EXAMPLE 5

(a) Find $\lim\limits_{n\to\infty} \dfrac{n}{n+4}$.

(b) Find $\lim\limits_{n\to\infty} \dfrac{2n}{n+4}$.

ANSWERS

(a) 1

(b) 2

ALTERNATE EXAMPLE 6

Determine whether the sequence $a_n = 5(-1)^n$ is convergent or divergent.

ANSWER

Divergent

ALTERNATE EXAMPLE 7

Find the limit of the sequence given by

$$a_n = \frac{28}{n^3}\left[\frac{n(n+4)(2n+1)}{8}\right].$$

ANSWER

7

This result shows that the guess we made earlier from Figures 9 and 10 was correct.

FIGURE 12

EXAMPLE 5 | Finding the Limit of a Sequence

Find $\lim\limits_{n\to\infty} \dfrac{n}{n+1}$.

SOLUTION The method is similar to the one we used in Example 2: Divide the numerator and denominator by the highest power of n, and then use the Limit Laws.

$$\lim_{n\to\infty}\frac{n}{n+1} = \lim_{n\to\infty}\frac{1}{1+\dfrac{1}{n}} \qquad \text{Divide numerator and denominator by } n$$

$$= \frac{\lim\limits_{n\to\infty} 1}{\lim\limits_{n\to\infty} 1 + \lim\limits_{n\to\infty}\dfrac{1}{n}} \qquad \text{Limits of a Quotient and a Sum}$$

$$= \frac{1}{1+0} = 1 \qquad \text{Let } n\to\infty$$

Therefore the sequence $a_n = n/(n+1)$ is convergent.

✎. NOW TRY EXERCISE **23** ∎

EXAMPLE 6 | A Sequence That Diverges

Determine whether the sequence $a_n = (-1)^n$ is convergent or divergent.

SOLUTION If we write out the terms of the sequence, we obtain

$$-1, 1, -1, 1, -1, 1, -1, \ldots$$

The graph of this sequence is shown in Figure 12. Since the terms oscillate between 1 and -1 infinitely often, a_n does not approach any number. Thus $\lim_{n\to\infty}(-1)^n$ does not exist; that is, the sequence $a_n = (-1)^n$ is divergent.

✎. NOW TRY EXERCISE **29** ∎

EXAMPLE 7 | Finding the Limit of a Sequence

Find the limit of the sequence given by

$$a_n = \frac{15}{n^3}\left[\frac{n(n+1)(2n+1)}{6}\right]$$

SOLUTION Before calculating the limit, let's first simplify the expression for a_n. Because $n^3 = n\cdot n\cdot n$, we place a factor of n beneath each factor in the numerator that contains an n:

$$a_n = \frac{15}{6}\cdot\frac{n}{n}\cdot\frac{n+1}{n}\cdot\frac{2n+1}{n} = \frac{5}{2}\cdot 1\cdot\left(1+\frac{1}{n}\right)\left(2+\frac{1}{n}\right)$$

Now we can compute the limit:

$$\lim_{n\to\infty} a_n = \lim_{n\to\infty}\frac{5}{2}\left(1+\frac{1}{n}\right)\left(2+\frac{1}{n}\right) \qquad \text{Definition of } a_n$$

$$= \frac{5}{2}\lim_{n\to\infty}\left(1+\frac{1}{n}\right)\lim_{n\to\infty}\left(2+\frac{1}{n}\right) \qquad \text{Limit of a Product}$$

$$= \frac{5}{2}(1)(2) = 5 \qquad \text{Let } n\to\infty$$

✎. NOW TRY EXERCISE **31** ∎

13.4 EXERCISES

CONCEPTS

1. Let f be a function defined on some interval (a, ∞). Then

$$\lim_{x \to \infty} f(x) = L$$

means that the values of $f(x)$ can be made arbitrarily close to

_____ by taking _____ sufficiently large. In this case

the line $y = L$ is called a _____ _____ of the curve

$y = f(x)$. For example, $\lim_{x \to \infty} \dfrac{1}{x} = $ _____ , and the line

$y = $ _____ is a horizontal asymptote.

2. A sequence $a_1, a_2, a_3, \ldots$ has the limit L if the nth term a_n of

the sequence can be made arbitrarily close to _____ by

taking n to be sufficiently _____. If the limit exists, we say

that the sequence _____ ; otherwise, the

sequence _____ .

SKILLS

3–4 ■ **(a)** Use the graph of f to find the following limits.
  (i) $\lim_{x \to \infty} f(x)$
  (ii) $\lim_{x \to \infty} f(x)$

(b) State the equations of the horizontal asymptotes.

 3.

4.

5–18 ■ Find the limit.

5. $\lim_{x \to \infty} \dfrac{6}{x}$

6. $\lim_{x \to \infty} \dfrac{3}{x^4}$

7. $\lim_{x \to \infty} \dfrac{2x + 1}{5x - 1}$

8. $\lim_{x \to \infty} \dfrac{2 - 3x}{4x + 5}$

9. $\lim_{x \to -\infty} \dfrac{4x^2 + 1}{2 + 3x^2}$

10. $\lim_{x \to -\infty} \dfrac{x^2 + 2}{x^3 + x + 1}$

11. $\lim_{t \to \infty} \dfrac{8t^3 + t}{(2t - 1)(2t^2 + 1)}$

12. $\lim_{r \to \infty} \dfrac{4r^3 - r^2}{(r + 1)^3}$

13. $\lim_{x \to \infty} \dfrac{x^4}{1 - x^2 + x^3}$

14. $\lim_{t \to \infty} \left(\dfrac{1}{t} - \dfrac{2t}{t - 1} \right)$

15. $\lim_{x \to -\infty} \left(\dfrac{x - 1}{x + 1} + 6 \right)$

16. $\lim_{x \to -\infty} \left(\dfrac{3 - x}{3 + x} - 2 \right)$

17. $\lim_{x \to \infty} \cos x$

18. $\lim_{x \to \infty} \sin^2 x$

19–22 ■ Use a table of values to estimate the limit. Then use a graphing device to confirm your result graphically.

19. $\lim_{x \to -\infty} \dfrac{\sqrt{x^2 + 4x}}{4x + 1}$

20. $\lim_{x \to \infty} \left(\sqrt{9x^2 + x} - 3x \right)$

21. $\lim_{x \to \infty} \dfrac{x^5}{e^x}$

22. $\lim_{x \to \infty} \left(1 + \dfrac{2}{x} \right)^{3x}$

23–34 ■ If the sequence is convergent, find its limit. If it is divergent, explain why.

23. $a_n = \dfrac{1 + n}{n + n^2}$

24. $a_n = \dfrac{5n}{n + 5}$

25. $a_n = \dfrac{n^2}{n + 1}$

26. $a_n = \dfrac{n - 1}{n^3 + 1}$

27. $a_n = \dfrac{1}{3^n}$

28. $a_n = \dfrac{(-1)^n}{n}$

29. $a_n = \sin(n\pi/2)$

30. $a_n = \cos n\pi$

31. $a_n = \dfrac{3}{n^2} \left[\dfrac{n(n + 1)}{2} \right]$

32. $a_n = \dfrac{5}{n} \left(n + \dfrac{4}{n} \left[\dfrac{n(n + 1)}{2} \right] \right)$

33. $a_n = \dfrac{24}{n^3} \left[\dfrac{n(n + 1)(2n + 1)}{6} \right]$

34. $a_n = \dfrac{12}{n^4} \left[\dfrac{n(n + 1)}{2} \right]^2$

APPLICATIONS

35. Salt Concentration
  (a) A tank contains 5000 L of pure water. Brine that contains 30 g of salt per liter of water is pumped into the tank at a rate of 25 L/min. Show that the concentration of salt after t minutes (in grams per liter) is

$$C(t) = \dfrac{30t}{200 + t}$$

  (b) What happens to the concentration as $t \to \infty$?

36. Velocity of a Raindrop The downward velocity of a falling raindrop at time t is modeled by the function

$$v(t) = 1.2(1 - e^{-8.2t})$$

  (a) Find the terminal velocity of the raindrop by evaluating $\lim_{t \to \infty} v(t)$. (Use the result of Example 3.)

DRILL QUESTIONS

(a) Give an example of a divergent sequence.

(b) Give an example of a sequence whose limit is 2.

Answers

Answers will vary.

(b) Graph $v(t)$, and use the graph to estimate how long it takes for the velocity of the raindrop to reach 99% of its terminal velocity.

$v(t) = 1.2(1 - e^{-8.2t})$

DISCOVERY ▪ DISCUSSION ▪ WRITING

37. The Limit of a Recursive Sequence

(a) A sequence is defined recursively by $a_1 = 0$ and

$$a_{n+1} = \sqrt{2 + a_n}$$

Find the first ten terms of this sequence rounded to eight decimal places. Does this sequence appear to be convergent? If so, guess the value of the limit.

(b) Assuming that the sequence in part (a) is convergent, let $\lim_{n \to \infty} a_n = L$. Explain why $\lim_{n \to \infty} a_{n+1} = L$ also, and therefore

$$L = \sqrt{2 + L}$$

Solve this equation to find the exact value of L.

SUGGESTED TIME AND EMPHASIS

1 class, optional material

13.5 AREAS

| The Area Problem ▶ Definition of Area

We have seen that limits are needed to compute the slope of a tangent line or an instantaneous rate of change. Here we will see that they are also needed to find the area of a region with a curved boundary. The problem of finding such areas has consequences far beyond simply finding area. (See *Focus on Modeling*, page 884.)

▼ The Area Problem

One of the central problems in calculus is the *area problem*: Find the area of the region S that lies under the curve $y = f(x)$ from a to b. This means that S, illustrated in Figure 1, is bounded by the graph of a function f (where $f(x) \geq 0$), the vertical lines $x = a$ and $x = b$, and the x-axis.

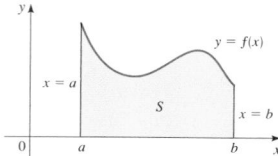

FIGURE 1

In trying to solve the area problem, we have to ask ourselves: What is the meaning of the word *area*? This question is easy to answer for regions with straight sides. For a rectangle, the area is defined as the product of the length and the width. The area of a triangle is half the base times the height. The area of a polygon is found by dividing it into triangles (as in Figure 2) and adding the areas of the triangles.

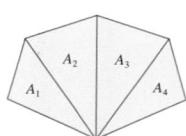

FIGURE 2

$A = lw$ $A = \frac{1}{2}bh$ $A = A_1 + A_2 + A_3 + A_4$

TEXT QUESTION

In the formula $A = \lim_{x \to \infty} \sum_{k=1}^{n} f(x_k)\Delta x$, where does the Δx come from?

Answer

It represents the width of each rectangle.

However, it is not so easy to find the area of a region with curved sides. We all have an intuitive idea of what the area of a region is. But part of the area problem is to make this intuitive idea precise by giving an exact definition of area.

Recall that in defining a tangent, we first approximated the slope of the tangent line by slopes of secant lines, and then we took the limit of these approximations. We pursue a similar idea for areas. We first approximate the region S by rectangles, and then we take the limit of the areas of these rectangles as we increase the number of rectangles. The following example illustrates the procedure.

EXAMPLE 1 | Estimating an Area Using Rectangles

Use rectangles to estimate the area under the parabola $y = x^2$ from 0 to 1 (the parabolic region S illustrated in Figure 3).

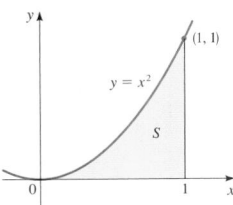

FIGURE 3

SOLUTION We first notice that the area of S must be somewhere between 0 and 1 because S is contained in a square with side length 1, but we can certainly do better than that. Suppose we divide S into four strips S_1, S_2, S_3, and S_4 by drawing the vertical lines $x = \frac{1}{4}$, $x = \frac{1}{2}$, and $x = \frac{3}{4}$ as in Figure 4(a). We can approximate each strip by a rectangle whose base is the same as the strip and whose height is the same as the right edge of the strip (see Figure 4(b)). In other words, the heights of these rectangles are the values of the function $f(x) = x^2$ at the right endpoints of the subintervals $[0, \frac{1}{4}]$, $[\frac{1}{4}, \frac{1}{2}]$, $[\frac{1}{2}, \frac{3}{4}]$, and $[\frac{3}{4}, 1]$.

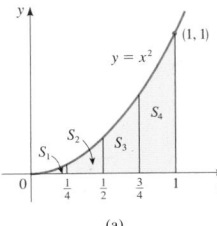

FIGURE 4

(a)　　　(b)

Each rectangle has width $\frac{1}{4}$, and the heights are $\left(\frac{1}{4}\right)^2$, $\left(\frac{1}{2}\right)^2$, $\left(\frac{3}{4}\right)^2$, and 1^2. If we let R_4 be the sum of the areas of these approximating rectangles, we get

$$R_4 = \frac{1}{4} \cdot \left(\frac{1}{4}\right)^2 + \frac{1}{4} \cdot \left(\frac{1}{2}\right)^2 + \frac{1}{4} \cdot \left(\frac{3}{4}\right)^2 + \frac{1}{4} \cdot 1^2 = \frac{15}{32} = 0.46875$$

From Figure 4(b) we see that the area A of S is less than R_4, so

$$A < 0.46875$$

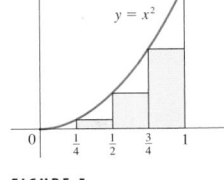

FIGURE 5

Instead of using the rectangles in Figure 4(b), we could use the smaller rectangles in Figure 5 whose heights are the values of f at the left endpoints of the subintervals. (The leftmost rectangle has collapsed because its height is 0.) The sum of the areas of these approximating rectangles is

$$L_4 = \frac{1}{4} \cdot 0^2 + \frac{1}{4} \cdot \left(\frac{1}{4}\right)^2 + \frac{1}{4} \cdot \left(\frac{1}{2}\right)^2 + \frac{1}{4} \cdot \left(\frac{3}{4}\right)^2 = \frac{7}{32} = 0.21875$$

IN-CLASS MATERIALS
Start by showing how the familiar equation $d = rt$ can be illustrated by a statement about the area of a rectangle (below left). Then assert that we can generalize this idea by finding the area under a velocity curve to get net distance traveled (below right).

Rate constant;
distance = shaded area

Rate varies;
distance = shaded area (still)

We see that the area of S is larger than L_4, so we have lower and upper estimates for A:

$$0.21875 < A < 0.46875$$

We can repeat this procedure with a larger number of strips. Figure 6 shows what happens when we divide the region S into eight strips of equal width. By computing the sum of the areas of the smaller rectangles (L_8) and the sum of the areas of the larger rectangles (R_8), we obtain better lower and upper estimates for A:

$$0.2734375 < A < 0.3984375$$

So one possible answer to the question is to say that the true area of S lies somewhere between 0.2734375 and 0.3984375.

(a) Using left endpoints

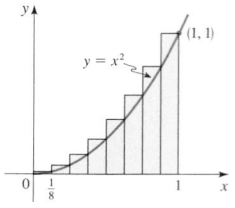

(b) Using right endpoints

FIGURE 6   Approximating S with eight rectangles

n	L_n	R_n
10	0.2850000	0.3850000
20	0.3087500	0.3587500
30	0.3168519	0.3501852
50	0.3234000	0.3434000
100	0.3283500	0.3383500
1000	0.3328335	0.3338335

We could obtain better estimates by increasing the number of strips. The table in the margin shows the results of similar calculations (with a computer) using n rectangles whose heights are found with left endpoints (L_n) or right endpoints (R_n). In particular, we see by using 50 strips that the area lies between 0.3234 and 0.3434. With 1000 strips we narrow it down even more: A lies between 0.3328335 and 0.3338335. A good estimate is obtained by averaging these numbers: $A \approx 0.3333335$.

⬥. NOW TRY EXERCISE **3**   ◼

From the values in the table it looks as if R_n is approaching $\frac{1}{3}$ as n increases. We confirm this in the next example.

EXAMPLE 2 | The Limit of Approximating Sums

For the region S in Example 1, show that the sum of the areas of the upper approximating rectangles approaches $\frac{1}{3}$, that is,

$$\lim_{n \to \infty} R_n = \frac{1}{3}$$

SOLUTION   Let R_n be the sum of the areas of the n rectangles shown in Figure 7. Each rectangle has width $1/n$, and the heights are the values of the function $f(x) = x^2$ at the points $1/n, 2/n, 3/n, \ldots, n/n$. That is, the heights are $(1/n)^2, (2/n)^2, (3/n)^2, \ldots, (n/n)^2$. Thus

$$R_n = \frac{1}{n}\left(\frac{1}{n}\right)^2 + \frac{1}{n}\left(\frac{2}{n}\right)^2 + \frac{1}{n}\left(\frac{3}{n}\right)^2 + \cdots + \frac{1}{n}\left(\frac{n}{n}\right)^2$$

$$= \frac{1}{n} \cdot \frac{1}{n^2}(1^2 + 2^2 + 3^2 + \cdots + n^2)$$

$$= \frac{1}{n^3}(1^2 + 2^2 + 3^2 + \cdots + n^2)$$

FIGURE 7

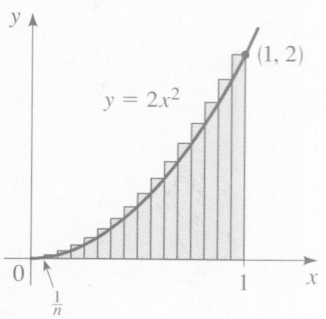
IN-CLASS MATERIALS

Lead students to discover that choosing left endpoints for a decreasing function always leads to an overestimate, whereas choosing right endpoints leads to an underestimate. They should check that the opposite trends hold for increasing functions. Challenge them to find a link between the midpoint estimate and the concavity of a graph.

Here we need the formula for the sum of the squares of the first n positive integers:

This formula was discussed in Section 12.5.

$$1^2 + 2^2 + 3^2 + \cdots + n^2 = \frac{n(n+1)(2n+1)}{6}$$

Putting the preceding formula into our expression for R_n, we get

$$R_n = \frac{1}{n^3} \cdot \frac{n(n+1)(2n+1)}{6} = \frac{(n+1)(2n+1)}{6n^2}$$

Thus we have

$$\lim_{n \to \infty} R_n = \lim_{n \to \infty} \frac{(n+1)(2n+1)}{6n^2}$$

$$= \lim_{n \to \infty} \frac{1}{6}\left(\frac{n+1}{n}\right)\left(\frac{2n+1}{n}\right)$$

$$= \lim_{n \to \infty} \frac{1}{6}\left(1 + \frac{1}{n}\right)\left(2 + \frac{1}{n}\right)$$

$$= \frac{1}{6} \cdot 1 \cdot 2 = \frac{1}{3}$$

✎ **NOW TRY EXERCISE 13**

It can be shown that the lower approximating sums also approach $\frac{1}{3}$, that is,

$$\lim_{n \to \infty} L_n = \frac{1}{3}$$

From Figures 8 and 9 it appears that as n increases, both R_n and L_n become better and better approximations to the area of S. Therefore we *define* the area A to be the limit of the sums of the areas of the approximating rectangles, that is,

$$A = \lim_{n \to \infty} R_n = \lim_{n \to \infty} L_n = \frac{1}{3}$$

FIGURE 8

FIGURE 9

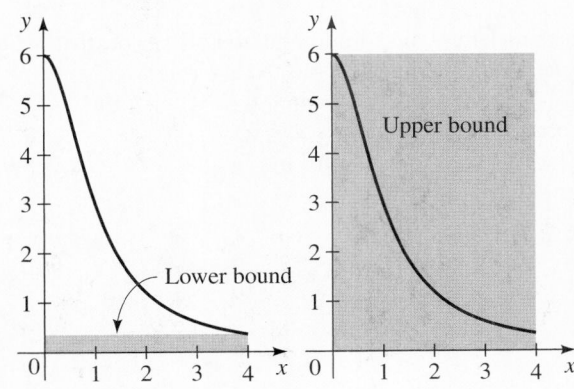

▼ Definition of Area

Let's apply the idea of Examples 1 and 2 to the more general region S of Figure 1. We start by subdividing S into n strips $S_1, S_2, \ldots, S_n$ of equal width as in Figure 10.

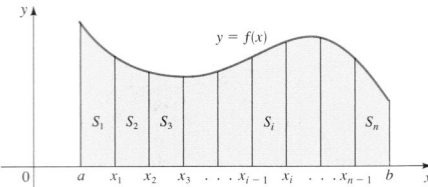

FIGURE 10

The width of the interval $[a, b]$ is $b - a$, so the width of each of the n strips is

$$\Delta x = \frac{b - a}{n}$$

These strips divide the interval $[a, b]$ into n subintervals

$$[x_0, x_1], \quad [x_1, x_2], \quad [x_2, x_3], \quad \ldots, \quad [x_{n-1}, x_n]$$

where $x_0 = a$ and $x_n = b$. The right endpoints of the subintervals are

$$x_1 = a + \Delta x, \quad x_2 = a + 2 \Delta x, \quad x_3 = a + 3 \Delta x, \quad \ldots, \quad x_k = a + k \Delta x, \quad \ldots$$

Let's approximate the kth strip S_k by a rectangle with width Δx and height $f(x_k)$, which is the value of f at the right endpoint (see Figure 11). Then the area of the kth rectangle is $f(x_k)\Delta x$. What we think of intuitively as the area of S is approximated by the sum of the areas of these rectangles, which is

$$R_n = f(x_1)\Delta x + f(x_2)\Delta x + \cdots + f(x_n)\Delta x$$

Figure 12 shows this approximation for $n = 2, 4, 8,$ and 12.

FIGURE 11

 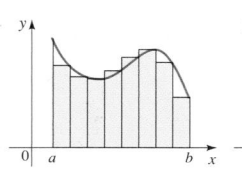

| (a) $n = 2$ | (b) $n = 4$ | (c) $n = 8$ | (d) $n = 12$ |

FIGURE 12

EXAMPLES

Finding the area under $y = \sin x$ from $x = 0$ to $x = \pi$. Note that we get the same results using left endpoints as we do using right endpoints.

With $n = 2$ rectangles, our estimate is $A \approx \dfrac{\pi}{2} \approx 1.5708$

With $n = 4$: $A \approx \dfrac{\pi}{4}(1 + \sqrt{2}) = 1.8961$

With $n = 10$: $A \approx 1.9835$

With $n = 50$: $A \approx 1.9993$

Notice that this approximation appears to become better and better as the number of strips increases, that is, as $n \to \infty$. Therefore, we define the area A of the region S in the following way.

DEFINITION OF AREA

The **area** A of the region S that lies under the graph of the continuous function f is the limit of the sum of the areas of approximating rectangles:

$$A = \lim_{n \to \infty} R_n = \lim_{n \to \infty} [f(x_1)\Delta x + f(x_2)\Delta x + \cdots + f(x_n)\Delta x]$$

Using sigma notation, we write this as follows:

$$A = \lim_{n \to \infty} \sum_{k=1}^{n} f(x_k)\Delta x$$

In using this formula for area, remember that Δx is the width of an approximating rectangle, x_k is the right endpoint of the kth rectangle, and $f(x_k)$ is its height. So

Width: $\qquad \Delta x = \dfrac{b - a}{n}$

Right endpoint: $\qquad x_k = a + k\,\Delta x$

Height: $\qquad f(x_k) = f(a + k\,\Delta x)$

When working with sums, we will need the following properties from Section 12.1:

$$\sum_{k=1}^{n} (a_k \pm b_k) = \sum_{k=1}^{n} a_k \pm \sum_{k=1}^{n} b_k \qquad \sum_{k=1}^{n} ca_k = c \sum_{k=1}^{n} a_k$$

We will also need the following formulas for the sums of the powers of the first n natural numbers from Section 12.5.

$$\sum_{k=1}^{n} c = nc \qquad\qquad \sum_{k=1}^{n} k = \frac{n(n+1)}{2}$$

$$\sum_{k=1}^{n} k^2 = \frac{n(n+1)(2n+1)}{6} \qquad \sum_{k=1}^{n} k^3 = \frac{n^2(n+1)^2}{4}$$

EXAMPLE 3 | Finding the Area Under a Curve

Find the area of the region that lies under the parabola $y = x^2$, $0 \le x \le 5$.

SOLUTION The region is graphed in Figure 13. To find the area, we first find the dimensions of the approximating rectangles at the nth stage.

Width: $\qquad \Delta x = \dfrac{b-a}{n} = \dfrac{5-0}{n} = \dfrac{5}{n}$

Right endpoint: $\qquad x_k = a + k\,\Delta x = 0 + k\left(\dfrac{5}{n}\right) = \dfrac{5k}{n}$

Height: $\qquad f(x_k) = f\left(\dfrac{5k}{n}\right) = \left(\dfrac{5k}{n}\right)^2 = \dfrac{25k^2}{n^2}$

FIGURE 13

ALTERNATE EXAMPLE 3
Find the area of the region that lies under the parabola
$y = x^2$, $0 \le x \le 8$.

ANSWER

$\dfrac{512}{3}$

EXAMPLE
Finding the area under $y = e^x$ from $x = 0$ to $x = 2$:

n	Estimate using left endpoints	Estimate using right endpoints
2	3.7182	10.1073
4	4.9243	8.1189
10	5.7714	7.0492
50	6.2621	6.5177
1000	6.3827	6.3954

Now we substitute these values into the definition of area:

$$A = \lim_{n\to\infty} \sum_{k=1}^{n} f(x_k)\,\Delta x \qquad \text{Definition of area}$$

$$= \lim_{n\to\infty} \sum_{k=1}^{n} \frac{25k^2}{n^2}\cdot\frac{5}{n} \qquad f(x_k)=\frac{25k^2}{n^2},\ \Delta x=\frac{5}{n}$$

$$= \lim_{n\to\infty} \sum_{k=1}^{n} \frac{125k^2}{n^3} \qquad \text{Simplify}$$

$$= \lim_{n\to\infty} \frac{125}{n^3}\sum_{k=1}^{n} k^2 \qquad \text{Factor } \frac{125}{n^3}$$

$$= \lim_{n\to\infty} \frac{125}{n^3}\cdot\frac{n(n+1)(2n+1)}{6} \qquad \text{Sum of Squares Formula}$$

$$= \lim_{n\to\infty} \frac{125(2n^2+3n+1)}{6n^2} \qquad \text{Cancel } n, \text{ and expand the numerator}$$

$$= \lim_{n\to\infty} \frac{125}{6}\left(2+\frac{3}{n}+\frac{1}{n^2}\right) \qquad \text{Divide the numerator and denominator by } n^2$$

$$= \frac{125}{6}(2+0+0) = \frac{125}{3} \qquad \text{Let } n\to\infty$$

We can also calculate the limit by writing

$$\frac{125}{n^3}\cdot\frac{n(n+1)(2n+1)}{6}$$

$$= \frac{125}{6}\left(\frac{n}{n}\right)\left(\frac{n+1}{n}\right)\left(\frac{2n+1}{n}\right)$$

as in Example 2.

Thus, the area of the region is $\frac{125}{3} \approx 41.7$.

✎ NOW TRY EXERCISE **15**

EXAMPLE 4 | Finding the Area Under a Curve

Find the area of the region that lies under the parabola $y = 4x - x^2,\ 1 \le x \le 3$.

SOLUTION We start by finding the dimensions of the approximating rectangles at the nth stage.

Width: $\quad \Delta x = \dfrac{b-a}{n} = \dfrac{3-1}{n} = \dfrac{2}{n}$

Right endpoint: $\quad x_k = a + k\,\Delta x = 1 + k\left(\dfrac{2}{n}\right) = 1 + \dfrac{2k}{n}$

Height: $\quad f(x_k) = f\left(1+\dfrac{2k}{n}\right) = 4\left(1+\dfrac{2k}{n}\right) - \left(1+\dfrac{2k}{n}\right)^2$

$$= 4 + \frac{8k}{n} - 1 - \frac{4k}{n} - \frac{4k^2}{n^2}$$

$$= 3 + \frac{4k}{n} - \frac{4k^2}{n^2}$$

Figure 14 shows the region whose area is computed in Example 4.

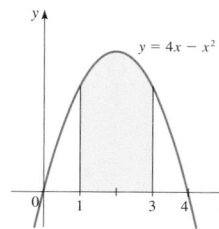

$y = 4x - x^2$

FIGURE 14

Thus according to the definition of area, we get

$$A = \lim_{n \to \infty} \sum_{k=1}^{n} f(x_k)\Delta x = \lim_{n \to \infty} \sum_{k=1}^{n} \left(3 + \frac{4k}{n} - \frac{4k^2}{n^2}\right)\left(\frac{2}{n}\right)$$

$$= \lim_{n \to \infty} \left(\sum_{k=1}^{n} 3 + \frac{4}{n}\sum_{k=1}^{n} k - \frac{4}{n^2}\sum_{k=1}^{n} k^2\right)\left(\frac{2}{n}\right)$$

$$= \lim_{n \to \infty} \left(\frac{2}{n}\sum_{k=1}^{n} 3 + \frac{8}{n^2}\sum_{k=1}^{n} k - \frac{8}{n^3}\sum_{k=1}^{n} k^2\right)$$

$$= \lim_{n \to \infty} \left(\frac{2}{n}(3n) + \frac{8}{n^2}\left[\frac{n(n+1)}{2}\right] - \frac{8}{n^3}\left[\frac{n(n+1)(2n+1)}{6}\right]\right)$$

$$= \lim_{n \to \infty} \left(6 + 4 \cdot \frac{n}{n} \cdot \frac{n+1}{n} - \frac{4}{3} \cdot \frac{n}{n} \cdot \frac{n+1}{n} \cdot \frac{2n+1}{n}\right)$$

$$= \lim_{n \to \infty} \left[6 + 4\left(1 + \frac{1}{n}\right) - \frac{4}{3}\left(1 + \frac{1}{n}\right)\left(2 + \frac{1}{n}\right)\right]$$

$$= 6 + 4 \cdot 1 - \frac{4}{3} \cdot 1 \cdot 2 = \frac{22}{3}$$

✎. NOW TRY EXERCISE **17**

13.5 EXERCISES

CONCEPTS

1–2 ■ The graph of a function f is shown below.

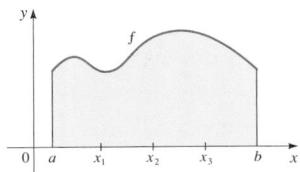

1. To find the area under the graph of f, we first approximate the area by _____. Approximate the area by drawing four rectangles. The area R_4 of this approximation is

$R_4 = $ ▭ $+$ ▭ $+$ ▭ $+$ ▭

2. Let R_n be the approximation obtained by using n rectangles of equal width. The exact area under the graph of f is

$$A = \lim_{n \to \infty} \underline{}$$

SKILLS

✎. **3. (a)** By reading values from the given graph of f, use five rectangles to find a lower estimate and an upper estimate for the area under the given graph of f from $x = 0$ to $x = 10$. In each case, sketch the rectangles that you use.

(b) Find new estimates using ten rectangles in each case.

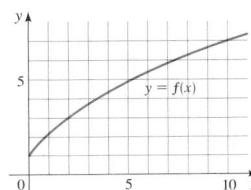

4. (a) Use six rectangles to find estimates of each type for the area under the given graph of f from $x = 0$ to $x = 12$.
   (i) L_6 (using left endpoints)
   (ii) R_6 (using right endpoints)
(b) Is L_6 an underestimate or an overestimate of the true area?
(c) Is R_6 an underestimate or an overestimate of the true area?

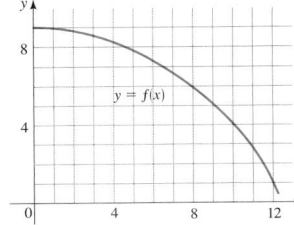

5–8 ■ Approximate the area of the shaded region under the graph of the given function by using the indicated rectangles. (The rectangles have equal width.)

5. $f(x) = \frac{1}{2}x + 2$

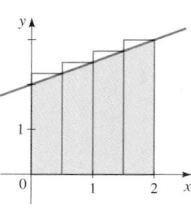

6. $f(x) = 4 - x^2$

7. $f(x) = \frac{4}{x}$

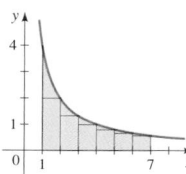

8. $f(x) = 9x - x^3$

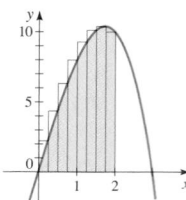

9. (a) Estimate the area under the graph of $f(x) = 1/x$ from $x = 1$ to $x = 5$ using four approximating rectangles and right endpoints. Sketch the graph and the rectangles. Is your estimate an underestimate or an overestimate?
   (b) Repeat part (a), using left endpoints.

10. (a) Estimate the area under the graph of $f(x) = 25 - x^2$ from $x = 0$ to $x = 5$ using five approximating rectangles and right endpoints. Sketch the graph and the rectangles. Is your estimate an underestimate or an overestimate?
   (b) Repeat part (a) using left endpoints.

11. (a) Estimate the area under the graph of $f(x) = 1 + x^2$ from $x = -1$ to $x = 2$ using three rectangles and right endpoints. Then improve your estimate by using six rectangles. Sketch the curve and the approximating rectangles.
   (b) Repeat part (a) using left endpoints.

12. (a) Estimate the area under the graph of $f(x) = e^{-x}$, $0 \le x \le 4$, using four approximating rectangles and taking the sample points to be
   (i) right endpoints
   (ii) left endpoints
   In each case, sketch the curve and the rectangles.
   (b) Improve your estimates in part (a) by using eight rectangles.

13–14 ■ Use the definition of area as a limit to find the area of the region that lies under the curve. Check your answer by sketching the region and using geometry.

13. $y = 3x$, $0 \le x \le 5$ **14.** $y = 2x + 1$, $1 \le x \le 3$

15–20 ■ Find the area of the region that lies under the graph of f over the given interval.

15. $f(x) = 3x^2$, $0 \le x \le 2$

16. $f(x) = x + x^2$, $0 \le x \le 1$

17. $f(x) = x^3 + 2$, $0 \le x \le 5$

18. $f(x) = 4x^3$, $2 \le x \le 5$

19. $f(x) = x + 6x^2$, $1 \le x \le 4$

20. $f(x) = 20 - 2x^2$, $2 \le x \le 3$

DISCOVERY ■ DISCUSSION ■ WRITING

21. Approximating Area with a Calculator When we approximate areas using rectangles as in Example 1, then the more rectangles we use, the more accurate the answer. The following TI-83 program finds the approximate area under the graph of f on the interval $[a, b]$ using n rectangles. To use the program, first store the function f in Y_1. The program prompts you to enter N, the number of rectangles, and A and B, the endpoints of the interval.
   (a) Approximate the area under the graph of $f(x) = x^5 + 2x + 3$ on $[1, 3]$, using 10, 20, and 100 rectangles.
   (b) Approximate the area under the graph of f on the given interval, using 100 rectangles.
      (i) $f(x) = \sin x$, on $[0, \pi]$
      (ii) $f(x) = e^{-x^2}$, on $[-1, 1]$

```
PROGRAM:AREA
:Prompt N
:Prompt A
:Prompt B
:(B-A)/N→D
:0→S
:A→X
:For (K,1,N)
:X+D→X
:S+Y₁→S
:End
:D*S→S
:Disp "AREA IS"
:Disp S
```

22. Regions with Straight Versus Curved Boundaries Write a short essay that explains how you would find the area of a polygon, that is, a region bounded by straight line segments. Then explain how you would find the area of a region whose boundary is curved, as we did in this section. What is the fundamental difference between these two processes?

CHAPTER 13 | REVIEW

■ CONCEPT CHECK

1. Explain in your own words what is meant by the equation

$$\lim_{x \to 2} f(x) = 5$$

   Is it possible for this statement to be true and yet $f(2) = 3$? Explain.

2. Explain what it means to say that

$$\lim_{x \to 1^-} f(x) = 3 \quad \text{and} \quad \lim_{x \to 1^+} f(x) = 7$$

   In this situation is it possible that $\lim_{x \to 1} f(x)$ exists? Explain.

3. Describe several ways in which a limit can fail to exist. Illustrate with sketches.

4. State the following Limit Laws.
   (a) Sum Law
   (b) Difference Law
   (c) Constant Multiple Law
   (d) Product Law
   (e) Quotient Law
   (f) Power Law
   (g) Root Law

5. Write an expression for the slope of the tangent line to the curve $y = f(x)$ at the point $(a, f(a))$.

6. Define the derivative $f'(a)$. Discuss two ways of interpreting this number.

7. If $y = f(x)$, write expressions for the following.
   (a) The average rate of change of y with respect to x between the numbers a and x.
   (b) The instantaneous rate of change of y with respect to x at $x = a$.

8. Explain the meaning of the equation

$$\lim_{x \to \infty} f(x) = 2$$

   Draw sketches to illustrate the various possibilities.

9. (a) What does it mean to say that the line $y = L$ is a horizontal asymptote of the curve $y = f(x)$? Draw curves to illustrate the various possibilities.
   (b) Which of the following curves have horizontal asymptotes?
   (i) $y = x^2$ (iv) $y = \tan^{-1} x$
   (ii) $y = 1/x$ (v) $y = e^x$
   (iii) $y = \sin x$ (vi) $y = \ln x$

10. (a) What is a convergent sequence?
    (b) What does $\lim_{n \to \infty} a_n = 3$ mean?

11. Suppose S is the region that lies under the graph of $y = f(x)$, $a \le x \le b$.
    (a) Explain how this area is approximated using rectangles.
    (b) Write an expression for the area of S as a limit of sums.

■ EXERCISES

 1–6 ■ Use a table of values to estimate the value of the limit. Then use a graphing device to confirm your result graphically.

1. $\displaystyle \lim_{x \to 2} \frac{x - 2}{x^2 - 3x + 2}$

2. $\displaystyle \lim_{t \to -1} \frac{t + 1}{t^3 - t}$

3. $\displaystyle \lim_{x \to 0} \frac{2^x - 1}{x}$

4. $\displaystyle \lim_{x \to 0} \frac{\sin 2x}{x}$

5. $\displaystyle \lim_{x \to 1^+} \ln \sqrt{x - 1}$

6. $\displaystyle \lim_{x \to 0^-} \frac{\tan x}{|x|}$

7. The graph of f is shown in the figure. Find each limit or explain why it does not exist.
   (a) $\displaystyle \lim_{x \to 2^+} f(x)$ (b) $\displaystyle \lim_{x \to -3^+} f(x)$
   (c) $\displaystyle \lim_{x \to -3^-} f(x)$ (d) $\displaystyle \lim_{x \to -3} f(x)$
   (e) $\displaystyle \lim_{x \to 4} f(x)$ (f) $\displaystyle \lim_{x \to \infty} f(x)$

(g) $\displaystyle \lim_{x \to -\infty} f(x)$ (h) $\displaystyle \lim_{x \to 0} f(x)$

8. Let

$$f(x) = \begin{cases} 2 & \text{if } x < -1 \\ x^2 & \text{if } -1 \le x \le 2 \\ x + 2 & \text{if } x > 2 \end{cases}$$

   Find each limit or explain why it does not exist.
   (a) $\displaystyle \lim_{x \to -1^-} f(x)$ (b) $\displaystyle \lim_{x \to -1^+} f(x)$
   (c) $\displaystyle \lim_{x \to -1} f(x)$ (d) $\displaystyle \lim_{x \to 2^-} f(x)$
   (e) $\displaystyle \lim_{x \to 2^+} f(x)$ (f) $\displaystyle \lim_{x \to 2} f(x)$
   (g) $\displaystyle \lim_{x \to 0} f(x)$ (h) $\displaystyle \lim_{x \to 3} (f(x))^2$

9–20 ■ Use the Limit Laws to evaluate the limit, if it exists.

9. $\lim_{x \to 2} \dfrac{x+1}{x-3}$

10. $\lim_{t \to 1} (t^3 - 3t + 6)$

11. $\lim_{x \to 3} \dfrac{x^2 + x - 12}{x-3}$

12. $\lim_{x \to -2} \dfrac{x^2 - 4}{x^2 + x - 2}$

13. $\lim_{u \to 0} \dfrac{(u+1)^2 - 1}{u}$

14. $\lim_{z \to 9} \dfrac{\sqrt{z} - 3}{z - 9}$

15. $\lim_{x \to 3^-} \dfrac{x-3}{|x-3|}$

16. $\lim_{x \to 0} \left(\dfrac{1}{x} + \dfrac{2}{x^2 - 2x} \right)$

17. $\lim_{x \to \infty} \dfrac{2x}{x-4}$

18. $\lim_{x \to \infty} \dfrac{x^2 + 1}{x^4 - 3x + 6}$

19. $\lim_{x \to \infty} \cos^2 x$

20. $\lim_{t \to -\infty} \dfrac{t^4}{t^3 - 1}$

21–24 ■ Find the derivative of the function at the given number.

21. $f(x) = 3x - 5$, at 4

22. $g(x) = 2x^2 - 1$, at -1

23. $f(x) = \sqrt{x}$, at 16

24. $f(x) = \dfrac{x}{x+1}$, at 1

25–28 ■ (a) Find $f'(a)$. (b) Find $f'(2)$ and $f'(-2)$.

25. $f(x) = 6 - 2x$

26. $f(x) = x^2 - 3x$

27. $f(x) = \sqrt{x+6}$

28. $f(x) = \dfrac{4}{x}$

29–30 ■ Find an equation of the tangent line shown in the figure.

29.

30.

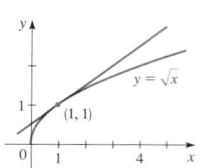

31–34 ■ Find an equation of the line tangent to the graph of f at the given point.

31. $f(x) = 2x$, at $(3, 6)$

32. $f(x) = x^2 - 3$, at $(2, 1)$

33. $f(x) = \dfrac{1}{x}$, at $\left(2, \dfrac{1}{2} \right)$

34. $f(x) = \sqrt{x+1}$, at $(3, 2)$

35. A stone is dropped from the roof of a building 640 ft above the ground. Its height (in feet) after t seconds is given by $h(t) = 640 - 16t^2$.

(a) Find the velocity of the stone when $t = 2$.
(b) Find the velocity of the stone when $t = a$.
(c) At what time t will the stone hit the ground?
(d) With what velocity will the stone hit the ground?

36. If a gas is confined in a fixed volume, then according to Boyle's Law the product of the pressure P and the temperature T is a constant. For a certain gas, $PT = 100$, where P is measured in lb/in² and T is measured in kelvins (K).

(a) Express P as a function of T.
(b) Find the instantaneous rate of change of P with respect to T when $T = 300$ K.

37–42 ■ If the sequence is convergent, find its limit. If it is divergent, explain why.

37. $a_n = \dfrac{n}{5n+1}$

38. $a_n = \dfrac{n^3}{n^3 + 1}$

39. $a_n = \dfrac{n(n+1)}{2n^2}$

40. $a_n = \dfrac{n^3}{2n+6}$

41. $a_n = \cos\left(\dfrac{n\pi}{2} \right)$

42. $a_n = \dfrac{10}{3^n}$

43–44 ■ Approximate the area of the shaded region under the graph of the given function by using the indicated rectangles. (The rectangles have equal width.)

43. $f(x) = \sqrt{x}$

44. $f(x) = 4x - x^2$

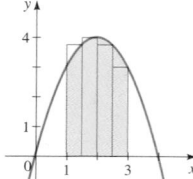

45–48 ■ Use the limit definition of area to find the area of the region that lies under the graph of f over the given interval.

45. $f(x) = 2x + 3$, $0 \le x \le 2$

46. $f(x) = x^2 + 1$, $0 \le x \le 3$

47. $f(x) = x^2 - x$, $1 \le x \le 2$

48. $f(x) = x^3$, $1 \le x \le 2$

1. (a) Use a table of values to estimate the limit

$$\lim_{x \to 0} \frac{x}{\sin 2x}$$

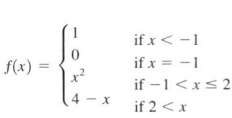 **(b)** Use a graphing calculator to confirm your answer graphically.

2. For the piecewise-defined function f whose graph is shown, find:

(a) $\lim_{x \to -1^-} f(x)$ **(b)** $\lim_{x \to -1^+} f(x)$ **(c)** $\lim_{x \to -1} f(x)$

(d) $\lim_{x \to 0^-} f(x)$ **(e)** $\lim_{x \to 0^+} f(x)$ **(f)** $\lim_{x \to 0} f(x)$

(g) $\lim_{x \to 2^-} f(x)$ **(h)** $\lim_{x \to 2^+} f(x)$ **(i)** $\lim_{x \to 2} f(x)$

$$f(x) = \begin{cases} 1 & \text{if } x < -1 \\ 0 & \text{if } x = -1 \\ x^2 & \text{if } -1 < x \le 2 \\ 4 - x & \text{if } 2 < x \end{cases}$$

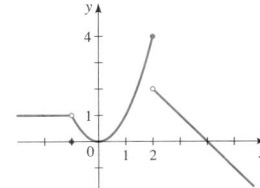

3. Evaluate the limit if it exists.

(a) $\lim_{x \to 2} \dfrac{x^2 + 2x - 8}{x - 2}$ **(b)** $\lim_{x \to 2} \dfrac{x^2 - 2x - 8}{x + 2}$ **(c)** $\lim_{x \to 2} \dfrac{1}{x - 2}$

(d) $\lim_{x \to 2} \dfrac{x - 2}{|x - 2|}$ **(e)** $\lim_{x \to 4} \dfrac{\sqrt{x} - 2}{x - 4}$ **(f)** $\lim_{x \to \infty} \dfrac{2x^2 - 4}{x^2 + x}$

4. Let $f(x) = x^2 - 2x$. Find:

(a) $f'(x)$ **(b)** $f'(-1), f'(1), f'(2)$

5. Find the equation of the line tangent to the graph of $f(x) = \sqrt{x}$ at the point where $x = 9$.

6. Find the limit of the sequence.

(a) $a_n = \dfrac{n}{n^2 + 4}$ **(b)** $a_n = \sec n\pi$

7. The region sketched in the figure in the margin lies under the graph of $f(x) = 4 - x^2$, above the interval $0 \le x \le 1$.

(a) Approximate the area of the region with five rectangles, equally spaced along the x-axis, using right endpoints to determine the heights of the rectangles.

(b) Use the limit definition of area to find the exact value of the area of the region.

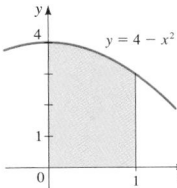
$y = 4 - x^2$

The area under the graph of a function is used to model many quantities in physics, economics, engineering, and other fields. That is why the area problem is so important. Here, we will show how the concept of work (Section 9.2) is modeled by area. Several other applications are explored in the problems.

Recall that the work W done in moving an object is the product of the force F applied to the object and the distance d that the object moves:

$$W = Fd \qquad \text{work} = \text{force} \times \text{distance}$$

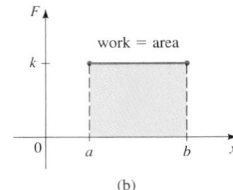

This formula is used if the force is *constant*. For example, suppose you are pushing a crate across a floor, moving along the positive x-axis from $x = a$ to $x = b$, and you apply a constant force $F = k$. The graph of F as a function of the distance x is shown in Figure 1(a). Notice that the work done is $W = Fd = k(b - a)$, which is the area under the graph of F (see Figure 1(b)).

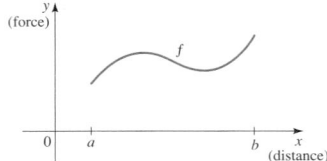

FIGURE 1 A constant force F

(a)   (b)

But what if the force is *not* constant? For example, suppose the force you apply to the crate varies with distance (you push harder at certain places than you do at others). More precisely, suppose that you push the crate along the x-axis in the positive direction, from $x = a$ to $x = b$, and at each point x between a and b you apply a force $f(x)$ to the crate. Figure 2 shows a graph of the force f as a function of the distance x.

FIGURE 2 A variable force

How much work was done? We can't apply the formula for work directly because the force is not constant. So let's divide the interval $[a, b]$ into n subintervals with endpoints $x_0, x_1, \ldots, x_n$ and equal width Δx, as shown in Figure 3(a) on the next page. The force at the right endpoint of the interval $[x_{k-1}, x_k]$ is $f(x_k)$. If n is large, then Δx is small, so the values of f don't change very much over the interval $[x_{k-1}, x_k]$. In other words f is almost constant on the interval, so the work W_k that is done in moving the crate from x_{k-1} to x_k is approximately

$$W_k \approx f(x_k)\,\Delta x$$

Thus we can approximate the work done in moving the crate from $x = a$ to $x = b$ by

$$W \approx \sum_{k=1}^{n} f(x_k)\,\Delta x$$

884

It seems that this approximation becomes better as we make n larger (and so make the interval $[x_{k-1}, x_k]$ smaller). Therefore we define the work done in moving an object from a to b as the limit of this quantity as $n \to \infty$:

$$W = \lim_{n \to \infty} \sum_{k=1}^{n} f(x_k) \Delta x$$

Notice that this is precisely the area under the graph of f between $x = a$ and $x = b$ as defined in Section 13.5. See Figure 3(b).

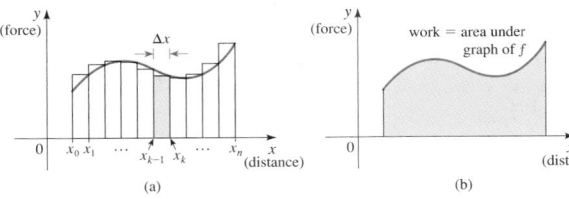

FIGURE 3 Approximating work

(a)   (b)

EXAMPLE | The Work Done by a Variable Force

A man pushes a crate along a straight path a distance of 18 ft. At a distance x from his starting point, he applies a force given by $f(x) = 340 - x^2$. Find the work done by the man.

SOLUTION The graph of f between $x = 0$ and $x = 18$ is shown in Figure 4. Notice how the force the man applies varies: He starts by pushing with a force of 340 lb but steadily applies less force.

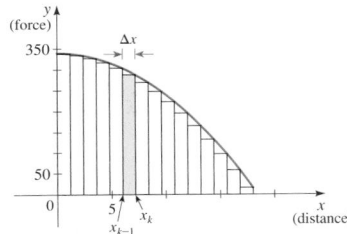

FIGURE 4

The work done is the area under the graph of f on the interval $[0, 18]$. To find this area, we start by finding the dimensions of the approximating rectangles at the nth stage.

Width:
$$\Delta x = \frac{b - a}{n} = \frac{18 - 0}{n} = \frac{18}{n}$$

Right endpoint:
$$x_k = a + k\,\Delta x = 0 + k\left(\frac{18}{n}\right) = \frac{18k}{n}$$

Height:
$$f(x_k) = f\left(\frac{18k}{n}\right) = 340 - \left(\frac{18k}{n}\right)^2$$
$$= 340 - \frac{324k^2}{n^2}$$

Thus according to the definition of work, we get

$$W = \lim_{n \to \infty} \sum_{k=1}^{n} f(x_k) \Delta x = \lim_{n \to \infty} \sum_{k=1}^{n} \left(340 - \frac{324k^2}{n^2} \right)\left(\frac{18}{n} \right)$$

$$= \lim_{n \to \infty} \left(\frac{18}{n} \sum_{k=1}^{n} 340 - \frac{(18)(324)}{n^3} \sum_{k=1}^{n} k^2 \right)$$

$$= \lim_{n \to \infty} \left(\frac{18}{n} \cdot 340n - \frac{5832}{n^3} \left[\frac{n(n+1)(2n+1)}{6} \right] \right)$$

$$= \lim_{n \to \infty} \left(6120 - 972 \cdot \frac{n}{n} \cdot \frac{n+1}{n} \cdot \frac{2n+1}{n} \right)$$

$$= 6120 - 972 \cdot 1 \cdot 1 \cdot 2 = 4176$$

So the work done by the man in moving the crate is 4176 ft-lb.

PROBLEMS

1. **Work Done by a Winch**   A motorized winch is being used to pull a felled tree to a log-ging truck. The motor exerts a force of $f(x) = 1500 + 10x - \frac{1}{2}x^2$ lb on the tree at the instant when the tree has moved x ft. The tree must be moved a distance of 40 ft, from $x = 0$ to $x = 40$. How much work is done by the winch in moving the tree?

2. **Work Done by a Spring**   Hooke's law states that when a spring is stretched, it pulls back with a force proportional to the amount of the stretch. The constant of proportionality is a characteristic of the spring known as the **spring constant**. Thus a spring with spring con-stant k exerts a force $f(x) = kx$ when it is stretched a distance x.

$f(x) = kx$

A certain spring has spring constant $k = 20$ lb/ft. Find the work done when the spring is pulled so that the amount by which it is stretched increases from $x = 0$ to $x = 2$ ft.

3. **Force of Water**   As any diver knows, an object submerged in water experiences pressure, and as depth increases, so does the water pressure. At a depth of x ft, the water pressure is $p(x) = 62.5x$ lb/ft^2. To find the force exerted by the water on a surface, we multiply the pres-sure by the area of the surface:

$$\text{force} = \text{pressure} \times \text{area}$$

Suppose an aquarium that is 3 ft wide, 6 ft long, and 4 ft high is full of water. The bottom of the aquarium has area $3 \times 6 = 18$ ft^2, and it experiences water pressure of $p(4) = 62.5 \times 4 = 250$ lb/ft^2. Thus the total force exerted by the water on the bottom is $250 \times 18 = 4500$ lb.

The water also exerts a force on the sides of the aquarium, but this is not as easy to cal-culate because the pressure increases from top to bottom. To calculate the force on one of the 4 ft by 6 ft sides, we divide its area into n thin horizontal strips of width Δx, as shown in the figure. The area of each strip is

$$\text{length} \times \text{width} = 6 \, \Delta x$$

If the bottom of the kth strip is at the depth x_k, then it experiences water pressure of approximately $p(x_k) = 62.5x_k$ lb/ft^2—the thinner the strip, the more accurate the approximation. Thus on each strip the water exerts a force of

$$\text{pressure} \times \text{area} = 62.5x_k \times 6 \, \Delta x = 375x_k \, \Delta x \text{ lb}$$

(a) Explain why the total force exerted by the water on the 4 ft by 6 ft sides of the aquarium is

$$\lim_{n \to \infty} \sum_{k=1}^{n} 375x_k \, \Delta x$$

where $\Delta x = 4/n$ and $x_k = 4k/n$.

(b) What area does the limit in part (a) represent?

(c) Evaluate the limit in part (a) to find the force exerted by the water on one of the 4 ft by 6 ft sides of the aquarium.

(d) Use the same technique to find the force exerted by the water on one of the 4 ft by 3 ft sides of the aquarium.

Note: Engineers use the technique outlined in this problem to find the total force exerted on a dam by the water in the reservoir behind the dam.

4. Distance Traveled by a Car   Since distance $=$ speed $\times$ time, it is easy to see that a car moving, say, at 70 mi/h for 5 h will travel a distance of 350 mi. But what if the speed varies, as it usually does in practice?

(a) Suppose the speed of a moving object at time t is $v(t)$. Explain why the distance traveled by the object between times $t = a$ and $t = b$ is the area under the graph of v between $t = a$ and $t = b$.

(b) The speed of a car t seconds after it starts moving is given by the function $v(t) = 6t + 0.1t^3$ ft/s. Find the distance traveled by the car from $t = 0$ to $t = 5$ s.

5. Heating Capacity   If the outdoor temperature reaches a maximum of 90°F one day and only 80°F the next, then we would probably say that the first day was hotter than the second. Suppose, however, that on the first day the temperature was below 60°F for most of the day, reaching the high only briefly, whereas on the second day the temperature stayed above 75°F all the time. Now which day is the hotter one? To better measure how hot a particular day is, scientists use the concept of **heating degree-hour**. If the temperature is a constant D degrees for t hours, then the "heating capacity" generated over this period is Dt heating degree-hours.

$$\text{heating degree-hours} = \text{temperature} \times \text{time}$$

If the temperature is not constant, then the number of heating degree-hours equals the area under the graph of the temperature function over the time period in question.

(a) On a particular day the temperature (in °F) was modeled by the function $D(t) = 61 + \frac{6}{5}t - \frac{1}{25}t^2$, where t was measured in hours since midnight. How many heating degree-hours were experienced on this day, from $t = 0$ to $t = 24$?

(b) What was the maximum temperature on the day described in part (a)?

(c) On another day the temperature (in °F) was modeled by the function $E(t) = 50 + 5t - \frac{1}{4}t^2$. How many heating degree-hours were experienced on this day?

(d) What was the maximum temperature on the day described in part (c)?

(e) Which day was "hotter"?

1. For each sequence, find the 7th term, the 20th term, and the limit of the sequence (if it exists).

   (a) $\frac{1}{3}, \frac{2}{5}, \frac{3}{7}, \frac{4}{9}, \frac{5}{11}, \ldots$

   (b) $a_n = \dfrac{2n^2 + 1}{n^3 - n + 4}$

   (c) The arithmetic sequence with initial term $a = \frac{1}{2}$ and common difference $d = 3$.

   (d) The geometric sequence with initial term $a = 12$ and common ratio $r = \frac{5}{6}$.

   (e) The sequence defined recursively by $a_1 = 0.01$ and $a_n = -2a_{n-1}$.

2. Calculate the sum.

   (a) $\frac{3}{5} + \frac{4}{5} + 1 + \frac{6}{5} + \frac{7}{5} + \frac{8}{5} + \cdots + \frac{19}{5} + 4$

   (b) $3 + 9 + 27 + 81 + \cdots + 3^{10}$

   (c) $\displaystyle\sum_{n=0}^{9} \frac{5}{2^n}$

   (d) $6 + 2 + \frac{2}{3} + \frac{2}{9} + \frac{2}{27} + \frac{2}{81} + \cdots$

3. Mary and Kevin buy a vacation home for \$350,000. They pay \$35,000 down and take out a 15-year mortgage for the remainder. If their annual interest rate is 6%, how much will their monthly mortgage payment be?

4. A sequence is defined inductively by $a_1 = 1$ and $a_n = a_{n-1} + 2n - 1$. Use mathematical induction to prove that $a_n = n^2$.

5. (a) Use the Binomial Theorem to expand the expression $\left(2x - \frac{1}{2}\right)^5$.

   (b) Find the term containing x^4 in the binomial expansion of $\left(2x - \frac{1}{2}\right)^{12}$.

6. Let $f(x) = \begin{cases} 3 & \text{if } x < 0 \\ 2 & \text{if } x = 0 \\ 3 - x & \text{if } 0 < x < 2 \\ x & \text{if } x \geq 2 \end{cases}$

   (a) Sketch a graph of f.

   (b) Evaluate: (i) $f(0)$ (ii) $\displaystyle\lim_{x \to 0} f(x)$ (iii) $\displaystyle\lim_{x \to 1} f(x)$ (iv) $\displaystyle\lim_{x \to 2^-} f(x)$ (v) $\displaystyle\lim_{x \to 2^+} f(x)$

7. Use a table of values to estimate the limit $\displaystyle\lim_{x \to 0} \frac{1 - \cos x}{x^2}$.

8. Evaluate the limit, if it exists.

   (a) $\displaystyle\lim_{x \to 3} \frac{x^2 + 4x - 21}{x - 3}$ (b) $\displaystyle\lim_{x \to -3} \frac{x^2 + 4x - 21}{x - 3}$ (c) $\displaystyle\lim_{x \to 2} \frac{x^2 + 4}{x - 2}$

9. Let $g(x) = x^3$. Find:

   (a) The derivative of g

   (b) $g'(-3)$, $g'(0)$, and $g'(a)$

   (c) The equation of the line tangent to the graph of g at the point $(2, 8)$

10. (a) Sketch the graph of the region in the coordinate plane that lies under the graph of $f(x) = 1 + x^2$ and above the x-axis, between $x = 0$ and $x = 1$.

    (b) If A is the area of this region, explain why $1 < A < 1.5$.

    (c) Approximate the area of the region with four rectangles, equally spaced on the x-axis, using left-hand endpoints to determine the heights of the rectangles.

    (d) Use the limit definition of area to find the exact area of the region.

Volodymyr Goinyk/Shutterstock.com

PROBABILITY AND STATISTICS

In the preceding chapters we modeled real-world situations using precise rules, such as equations and functions. But many of our everyday activities are not governed by precise rules, but rather involve randomness. It is remarkable that there are also rules that govern randomness. For example, if we toss a balanced coin many times, we can be pretty sure that "heads" will show up about half of the time. Such patterns in apparently haphazard events allow us to use mathematics to model randomness.

Probability is the mathematical study of chance. Knowing the chance, or probability, of an event happening can be very useful. For example, insurance companies estimate the probability of an automobile accident happening. This allows the company to calculate a reasonable price to charge their customers.

Statistics is the art of collecting and organizing data and then getting information from the data. We usually collect data from a sample of a population. We can then use probability to obtain information about the entire population from properties of the sample. For example, to test the effectiveness of an allergy medication, we try the medication on a sample of the population. The data on the effectiveness of the medication for the individuals in the sample allow us to estimate the probability that the medication is effective for the population in general.

889

SUGGESTED TIME AND EMPHASIS
1–2 classes, optional material

14.1 COUNTING

The Fundamental Counting Principle ▶ Counting Permutations ▶ Counting Combinations ▶ Problem Solving with Permutations and Combinations

Counting the number of apples in a bag or the number of students in an algebra class is easy. But counting all the different ways in which these students can stand in a row is more difficult. It is this latter kind of counting that we'll study in this section.

▼ The Fundamental Counting Principle

Suppose that three towns—Ashbury, Brampton, and Carmichael—are located in such a way that two roads connect Ashbury to Brampton and three roads connect Brampton to Carmichael.

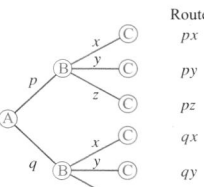

	Route
	px
	py
	pz
	qx
	qy
	qz

FIGURE 1 Tree diagram

How many different routes can one take to travel from Ashbury to Carmichael via Brampton? The key to answering this question is to consider the problem in stages. At the first stage—from Ashbury to Brampton—there are two choices. For each of these choices there are three choices at the second stage—from Brampton to Carmichael. Thus the number of different routes is $2 \times 3 = 6$. These routes are conveniently enumerated by a *tree diagram* as in Figure 1. The method that we used to solve this problem leads to the following principle.

THE FUNDAMENTAL COUNTING PRINCIPLE

Suppose that two events occur in order. If the first event can occur in m ways and the second can occur in n ways (after the first has occurred), then the two events can occur *in order* in $m \times n$ ways.

There is an immediate consequence of this principle for any number of events: If $E_1, E_2, \ldots, E_k$ are events that occur in order and if E_1 can occur in n_1 ways, E_2 in n_2 ways, and so on, then the events can occur in order in $n_1 \times n_2 \times \cdots \times n_k$ ways.

EXAMPLE 1 | Using the Fundamental Counting Principle

An ice-cream store offers three types of cones and 31 flavors. How many different single-scoop ice-cream cones is it possible to buy at this store?

SOLUTION There are two stages for selecting an ice-cream cone. At the first stage we choose a type of cone, and at the second stage we choose a flavor. We can think of the different stages as boxes:

Stage 1: Type of Cone	Stage 2: Flavor

ALTERNATE EXAMPLE 1
A restaurant offers five kinds of beverage, six kinds of main course, and three kinds of dessert. How many possible meals can one get at this restaurant?

ANSWER
$5 \times 6 \times 3 = 90$ meals

TEXT QUESTION
How do we know when to use permutations and when to use combinations?

Answer
We use permutations when order matters, and we use combinations when it does not.

The first box can be filled in three ways, and the second can be filled in 31 ways:

By the Fundamental Counting Principle there are $3 \times 31 = 93$ ways of choosing a single-scoop ice-cream cone at this store.

✎. NOW TRY EXERCISE **17**   ◼

EXAMPLE 2 | Using the Fundamental Counting Principle

In a certain state, automobile license plates display three letters followed by three digits. How many such plates are possible if repetition of the letters

(a) is allowed?   **(b)** is not allowed?

SOLUTION

(a) There are six selection stages, one for each letter or digit on the license plate. As in the preceding example, we sketch a box for each stage:

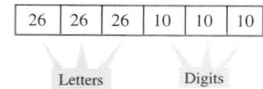

At the first stage we choose a letter (from 26 possible choices); at the second stage we choose another letter (again from 26 choices); at the third stage we choose another letter (26 choices); at the fourth stage we choose a digit (from 10 possible choices); at the fifth stage we choose a digit (again from 10 choices); and at the sixth stage, we choose another digit (10 choices). By the Fundamental Counting Principle the number of possible license plates is

$$26 \times 26 \times 26 \times 10 \times 10 \times 10 = 17,576,000$$

(b) If repetition of letters is not allowed, then we arrange the choices as follows:

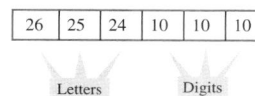

At the first stage we have 26 letters to choose from, but once the first letter has been chosen, there are only 25 letters to choose from at the second stage. Once the first two letters have been chosen, 24 letters are left to choose from for the third stage. The digits are chosen as before. Thus the number of possible license plates in this case is

$$26 \times 25 \times 24 \times 10 \times 10 \times 10 = 15,600,000$$

✎. NOW TRY EXERCISE **29**   ◼

Let S be a set with n elements. A subset of S can be chosen by making one of two choices for each element: We can choose the element to be *in* or *out* of A. Since S has n elements and we have two choices for each element, by the Fundamental Counting Prin-

ALTERNATE EXAMPLE 2
A website requires that a user generate a password to obtain access. A password is 10 characters, where uppercase and lowercase letters are counted as different. One can use letters or the symbols \$, %, !, and @, but the first and last characters must be letters. How many possible passwords are there?

ANSWER
$52 \times 56 \times 56 \times 56 \times 56 \times 56 \times 56 \times 56 \times 56 \times 52 = 261,523,610,496,139,264 \approx 2.61 \times 10^{17}$

IN-CLASS MATERIALS

Note that when the fundamental counting principle is being used, we are assuming that the events are independent and that your first choice does not affect your second choice. For example, if you have 10 shirts and 8 pairs of pants, the principle says you have 80 possible outcomes. But that is assuming that your choice of shirts has no bearing on your choice of pants. For some people, that is true. But for other people, certain shirts will restrict their choice of pants.

ciple the total number of different subsets is $2 \times 2 \times \cdots \times 2$, where there are n factors. This gives the following formula.

THE NUMBER OF SUBSETS OF A SET

A set with n elements has 2^n different subsets.

EXAMPLE 3 | Finding the Number of Subsets

A pizza parlor offers a basic cheese pizza and a choice of 16 toppings. How many different kinds of pizza can be ordered at this pizza parlor?

SOLUTION We need the number of possible subsets of the 16 toppings (including the empty set, which corresponds to a plain cheese pizza). Thus

$$2^{16} = 65,536$$

different pizzas can be ordered.

✎ NOW TRY EXERCISE **37** ◼

▼ Counting Permutations

A **permutation** of a set of distinct objects is an ordering of these objects. For example, some permutations of the letters *ABCD* are

$$ABDC \qquad BACD \qquad DCBA \qquad DABC$$

How many such permutations are possible? There are four choices for the first position, three for the second (after the first has been chosen), two for the third (after the first two have been chosen), and only one choice for the fourth letter (the letter that has not yet been chosen). By the Fundamental Counting Principle the number of possible permutations is

$$4 \times 3 \times 2 \times 1 = 4! = 24$$

The same reasoning with 4 replaced by n leads to the following.

The number of permutations of n objects is $n!$

How many permutations consisting of two letters can be made from these same four letters? Some of these permutations are *AB, AC, BD, DB,* . . . . There are 4 choices of the first letter and 3 for the second letter. By the Fundamental Counting Principle there are $4 \times 3 = 12$ such permutations. In general, if a set has n elements, then the number of ways of ordering r elements from the set is denoted by $P(n, r)$ and is called **the number of permutations of n objects taken r at a time**.

PERMUTATIONS OF n OBJECTS TAKEN r AT A TIME

The number of permutations of n objects taken r at a time is

$$P(n, r) = \frac{n!}{(n-r)!}$$

Permutations of
three colored squares

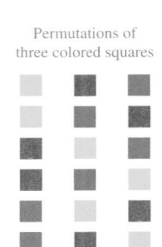

IN-CLASS MATERIALS

When doing counting problems, have students try to guess the order of the answer before doing computations. Is the answer on the order of 100? 1000? 1×10^8? 1×10^{20}? Human beings are not inherently good at estimating very large numbers, so this is a good opportunity to practice.

PROOF There are n objects and r positions to place them in. Thus there are n choices for the first position, $n - 1$ choices for the second, $n - 2$ choices for the third, and so on. The last position can be filled in $n - r + 1$ ways. By the Fundamental Counting Principle we conclude that

$$P(n, r) = n(n - 1)(n - 2) \cdots (n - r + 1)$$

We can express this formula using factorial notation by multiplying numerator and denominator by $(n - r) \cdots 3 \cdot 2 \cdot 1$:

$$P(n, r) = \frac{n(n - 1)(n - 2) \cdots (n - r + 1)(n - r) \cdots 3 \cdot 2 \cdot 1}{(n - r) \cdots 3 \cdot 2 \cdot 1} = \frac{n!}{(n - r)!} \quad ■$$

EXAMPLE 4 | Finding the Number of Permutations

There are six runners in a race that is completed with no tie.

(a) In how many different ways can the race be completed?

(b) In how many different ways can first, second, and third place be decided?

SOLUTION

(a) The number of ways to complete the race is the number of permutations of the six runners: $6! = 720$.

(b) The number of ways in which the first three positions can be decided is:

$$P(6, 3) = \frac{6!}{(6 - 3)!} = \frac{6 \times 5 \times 4 \times \cancel{3 \times 2 \times 1}}{\cancel{3 \times 2 \times 1}} = 120$$

✎ NOW TRY EXERCISE **41** ■

EXAMPLE 5 | Finding the Number of Permutations

A club has nine members. In how many ways can a president, vice president, and secretary be chosen from the members of this club?

SOLUTION We need the number of ways of selecting three members, in order, for the positions of president, vice president, and secretary from the nine club members. This number is

$$P(9, 3) = \frac{9!}{(9 - 3)!} = \frac{9 \times 8 \times 7 \times \cancel{6 \times 5 \times 4 \times 3 \times 2 \times 1}}{\cancel{6 \times 5 \times 4 \times 3 \times 2 \times 1}} = 504$$

✎ NOW TRY EXERCISE **43** ■

RONALD GRAHAM, born in Taft, California, in 1935, is considered the world's leading mathematician in the field of combinatorics, the branch of mathematics that deals with counting. For many years Graham headed the Mathematical Studies Center at Bell Laboratories in Murray Hill, New Jersey, where he solved key problems for the telephone industry. During the *Apollo* program, NASA needed to evaluate mission schedules so that the three astronauts aboard the spacecraft could find the time to perform all the necessary tasks. The number of ways to allot these tasks was astronomical—too vast for even a computer to sort out. Graham, using his knowledge of combinatorics, was able to reassure NASA that there were easy ways of solving their problem that were not too far from the theoretically best possible solution. Besides being a prolific mathematician, Graham is an accomplished juggler (he has been on stage with the Cirque du Soleil and is a past president of the International Jugglers Association). Several of his research papers address the mathematical aspects of juggling. He is also fluent in Mandarin Chinese and Japanese and once spoke with former President Jiang of China in his native language.

Ken Regan /Camera 5

IN-CLASS MATERIALS

If doing an example of counting by enumeration, make sure to stress that when listing a large number of objects, students should strive to do so in an organized way. This will reduce the chance of missing items.

EXAMPLE 6 | Finding the Number of Permutations

From 20 raffle tickets in a hat, 4 tickets are to be selected in order. The holder of the first ticket wins a car, the second a motorcycle, the third a bicycle, and the fourth a skateboard. In how many different ways can these prizes be awarded?

SOLUTION The order in which the tickets are chosen determines who wins each prize. So we need to find the number of ways of selecting 4 objects, in order, from 20 objects (the tickets). This number is

$$P(20, 4) = \frac{20!}{(20-4)!} = \frac{20 \times 19 \times 18 \times 17 \times \cancel{16 \times 15 \times 14 \times \cdots \times 3 \times 2 \times 1}}{\cancel{16 \times 15 \times 14 \times \cdots \times 3 \times 2 \times 1}} = 116{,}280$$

NOW TRY EXERCISE 45

▼ Counting Combinations

When counting permutations, we are interested in the number of ways of ordering the elements of a set. In many counting problems, however, order is not important. For example, a poker hand is the same hand regardless of how it is ordered. A poker player who is interested in the number of possible hands wants to know the number of ways of drawing five cards from 52 cards, without regard to the order in which the cards are dealt. We now develop a formula for counting in situations in which order doesn't matter.

A **combination** of r elements of a set is any subset of r elements from the set (without regard to order). If the set has n elements, then the number of combinations of r elements is denoted by $C(n, r)$ and is called the **number of combinations of n elements taken r at a time.** For example, consider a set with the four elements $A, B, C,$ and D. The combinations of these four elements taken three at a time are listed below. Compare this with the permutations of these elements listed in the margin.

$$ABC \qquad ABD \qquad ACD \qquad BCD$$

We notice that the number of combinations is a lot fewer than the number of permutations. In fact, each combination of three elements generates 3! permutations. So $C(4, 3) = P(4, 3)/3! = 4$. In general, each combination of r objects gives rise to $r!$ permutations of these objects, so we get the following formula.

ABC	ABD	ACD	BCD
ACB	ADB	ADC	BDC
BAC	BAD	CAD	CBD
BCA	BDA	CDA	CDB
CAB	DAB	DAC	DBC
CBA	DBA	DCA	DCB

COMBINATIONS OF n OBJECTS TAKEN r AT A TIME

The number of combinations of n objects taken r at a time is

$$C(n, r) = \frac{n!}{r!\,(n-r)!}$$

The key difference between permutations and combinations is order. If we are interested in ordered arrangements, then we are counting permutations, but if we are concerned with subsets without regard to order, then we are counting combinations. Compare Examples 7 and 8 below (where order doesn't matter) to Examples 5 and 6 (where order does matter).

EXAMPLE 7 | Finding the Number of Combinations

A club has nine members. In how many ways can a committee of three be chosen from the members of this club?

EXAMPLE

A problem for which the fundamental counting principle cannot be used:

How many three-digit numbers are there such that no digit is larger than the first? In this case, there are 10 ways to pick the first digit, but the number of ways to pick the second digit depends on that first digit. So the fundamental counting principle can't be used.

SOLUTION   We need the number of ways of choosing three of the nine members. Order is not important here, because the committee is the same no matter how its members are ordered. So we want the number of combinations of nine objects (the club members) taken three at a time. This number is

$$C(9, 3) = \frac{9!}{3!(9 - 3)!} = \frac{9 \times 8 \times 7 \times 6 \times 5 \times 4 \times 3 \times 2 \times 1}{(3 \times 2 \times 1) \times (6 \times 5 \times 4 \times 3 \times 2 \times 1)} = 84$$

↘ NOW TRY EXERCISE **53**   ∎

EXAMPLE 8 | Finding the Number of Combinations

From 20 raffle tickets in a hat, four tickets are to be chosen at random. The holders of the winning tickets get free trips to the Bahamas. In how many ways can the four winners be chosen?

SOLUTION   We need to find the number of ways of choosing four winners from 20 entries. The order in which the tickets are chosen doesn't matter, because the same prize is awarded to each of the four winners. So we want the number of combinations of 20 objects (the tickets) taken four at a time. This number is

$$C(20, 4) = \frac{20!}{4!(20 - 4)!} = \frac{20 \times 19 \times 18 \times 17 \times 16 \times 15 \times 14 \times \cdots \times 3 \times 2 \times 1}{(4 \times 3 \times 2 \times 1) \times (16 \times 15 \times 14 \times \cdots \times 3 \times 2 \times 1)} = 4845$$

↘ NOW TRY EXERCISE **55**   ∎

▼ Problem Solving with Permutations and Combinations

The crucial step in solving counting problems is deciding whether to use permutations, combinations, or the Fundamental Counting Principle. In some cases the solution of a problem may require using more than one of these principles. Here are some general guidelines to help us decide how to apply these principles.

GUIDELINES FOR SOLVING COUNTING PROBLEMS

1. **Fundamental Counting Principle.**   When consecutive choices are being made, use the Fundamental Counting Principle.

2. **Does Order Matter?**   When we want to find the number of ways of picking r objects from n objects, we need to ask ourselves, "Does the order in which we pick the objects matter?"

   If the order matters, we use permutations.

   If the order doesn't matter, we use combinations.

EXAMPLE 9 | Using Combinations

A group of 25 campers consists of 15 women and 10 men. In how many ways can a scouting party of 6 be chosen if it must consist of 3 women and 2 men?

SOLUTION   Three women can be chosen from the 15 women in $C(15, 3)$ ways, and two men can be chosen from the 10 men in $C(10, 2)$ ways. It follows by the Fundamental Counting Principle that the number of ways of choosing the scouting party is

$$C(15, 3) \times C(10, 2) = 455 \times 45 = 20{,}475$$

↘ NOW TRY EXERCISE **67**   ∎

EXAMPLE 10 | Using Permutations and Combinations

A committee of seven—consisting of a chairman, a vice chairman, a secretary, and four other members—is to be chosen from a class of 20 students. In how many ways can the committee be chosen?

SOLUTION In choosing the three officers, order is important. So the number of ways of choosing them is

$$P(20, 3) = 6840$$

Next, we need to choose four other students from the 17 remaining. Since order doesn't matter in choosing these four members, the number of ways of doing this is

$$C(17, 4) = 2380$$

By the Fundamental Counting Principle the number of ways of choosing this committee is

$$P(20, 3) \times C(17, 4) = 6840 \times 2380 = 16,279,200$$

✎. NOW TRY EXERCISE **69** ■

EXAMPLE 11 | Using Permutations and Combinations

Twelve employees at a company picnic are to stand in a row for a group photograph. In how many ways can this be done if

(a) Jane and John insist on standing next to each other?

(b) Jane and John refuse to stand next to each other?

SOLUTION Since the order in which the people stand is important, we use permutations. But we can't use permutations directly.

(a) Since Jane and John insist on standing together, let's think of them as one object. So we have 11 objects to arrange in a row, and there are $P(11, 11)$ ways of doing this. For each of these arrangements there are two ways of having Jane and John stand together: Jane-John or John-Jane. By the Fundamental Counting Principle the total number of arrangements is

$$2 \times P(11, 11) = 2 \times 11! = 79,833,600$$

(b) There are $P(12, 12)$ ways of arranging the 12 people. Of these, $2 \times P(11, 11)$ have Jane and John standing together (by part (a)). All the rest have Jane and John standing apart. So the number of arrangements with Jane and John standing apart is

$$P(12, 12) - 2 \times P(11, 11) = 12! - 2 \times 11! = 399,168,000$$

✎. NOW TRY EXERCISE **77** ■

14.1 EXERCISES

DRILL QUESTION

How many subsets are there of a set with six elements?

Answer

64

CONCEPTS

1. The Fundamental Counting Principle says that if one event can occur in m ways and a second event can occur in n ways, then the two events can occur in order in _____ × _____ ways. So if you have two choices for shoes and three choices for hats, then the number of different shoe-hat combinations you can wear is _____ × _____ = _____.

2. The number of ways of arranging r objects from n objects in order is called the number of _____ of n objects taken r at a time and is given by the formula $P(n, r) = $ _____.

3. The number of ways of choosing r objects from n objects is called the number of _____ of n objects taken r at a time and is given by the formula $C(n, r) = $ _____.

4. *True or false?*

(a) In counting combinations, order matters.

(b) In counting permutations, order matters.

(c) For a set of n distinct objects, the number of different combinations of these objects is more than the number of different permutations.

(d) If we have a set with five distinct objects, then the number of different ways of choosing two members of this set is the same as the number of ways of choosing three members.

SKILLS

5–16 ■ Evaluate the expression.

5. $P(8, 3)$ **6.** $P(9, 2)$ **7.** $P(11, 4)$

8. $P(10, 5)$ **9.** $P(100, 1)$ **10.** $P(99, 3)$

11. $C(8, 3)$ **12.** $C(9, 2)$ **13.** $C(11, 4)$

14. $C(10, 5)$ **15.** $C(100, 1)$ **16.** $C(99, 3)$

APPLICATIONS

Exercises 17–36 involve the Fundamental Counting Principle.

17. Ice-Cream Cones A vendor sells ice cream from a cart on the boardwalk. He offers vanilla, chocolate, strawberry, and pistachio ice cream, served in either a waffle, sugar, or plain cone. How many different single-scoop ice-cream cones can you buy from this vendor?

18. Three-Letter Words How many three-letter "words" (strings of letters) can be formed by using the 26 letters of the alphabet if repetition of letters

(a) is allowed? (b) is not allowed?

19. Horse Race Eight horses compete in a race. (Assume the race does not end in a tie.)

(a) How many different orders are possible for completing the race?

(b) In how many different ways can first, second, and third places be decided?

20. Multiple-Choice Test A multiple-choice test has five questions with four choices for each question. In how many different ways can the test be completed?

21. Phone Numbers Telephone numbers consist of seven digits; the first digit cannot be 0 or 1. How many telephone numbers are possible?

22. Running a Race In how many different ways can a race with five runners be completed? (Assume that there is no tie.)

23. Restaurant Meals A restaurant offers the items listed in the table. How many different meals consisting of a main course, a drink, and a dessert can be selected at this restaurant?

Main courses	Drinks	Desserts
Chicken	Iced tea	Ice cream
Beef	Apple juice	Layer cake
Lasagna	Cola	Blueberry pie
Quiche	Ginger ale	
	Coffee	

24. Multiple Routes Towns A, B, C, and D are located in such a way that there are four roads from A to B, five roads from B to C, and six roads from C to D. How many routes are there from town A to town D via towns B and C?

25. Flipping a Coin A coin is flipped five times, and the resulting sequence of heads and tails is recorded. How many such sequences are possible?

26. Rolling a Pair of Dice A red die and a white die are rolled, and the numbers that show are recorded. How many different outcomes are possible? (The singular form of the word *dice* is *die*.)

27. Rolling Three Dice A red die, a blue die, and a white die are rolled, and the numbers that show are recorded. How many different outcomes are possible?

28. Choosing Outfits A girl has five skirts, eight blouses, and 12 pairs of shoes. How many different skirt-blouse-shoe outfits can she wear? (Assume that each item matches all the others, so she is willing to wear any combination.)

29. License Plates Standard automobile license plates in California display a nonzero digit, followed by three letters, followed by three digits. How many different standard plates are possible in this system?

30. ID Numbers A company's employee ID number system consists of one letter followed by three digits. How many different ID numbers are possible with this system?

31. Combination Lock A combination lock has 60 different positions. To open the lock, the dial is turned to a certain number in the clockwise direction, then to a number in the counterclockwise direction, and finally to a third number in the clockwise direction. If successive numbers in the combination cannot be the same, how many different combinations are possible?

32. License Plates   A state has registered 8 million automobiles. To simplify the license plate system, a state employee suggests that each plate display only two letters followed by three digits. Will this system create enough different license plates for all the vehicles that are registered?

33. Class Executive   In how many ways can a president, vice president, and secretary be chosen from a class of 30 students?

34. Committee Officers   A senate subcommittee consists of ten Democrats and seven Republicans. In how many ways can a chairman, vice chairman, and secretary be chosen if the chairman must be a Democrat and the vice chairman must be a Republican?

35. Social Security Numbers   Social Security numbers consist of nine digits, with the first digit between 0 and 6, inclusive. How many Social Security numbers are possible?

36. Holiday Photos   A couple have seven children: three girls and four boys. In how many ways can the children be arranged for a holiday photo if the girls sit in a row in the front and the boys stand in a row behind the girls?

Exercises 37–40 involve counting subsets.

37. Subsets   A set has eight elements.
  (a) How many subsets containing five elements does this set have?
  (b) How many subsets does this set have?

38. Travel Brochures   A travel agency has limited numbers of eight different free brochures about Australia. The agent tells you to take any that you like but no more than one of any kind. In how many different ways can you choose brochures (including not choosing any)?

39. Hamburgers   A hamburger chain gives their customers a choice of ten different hamburger toppings. In how many different ways can a customer order a hamburger?

40. To Shop or Not to Shop   Each of 20 shoppers in a shopping mall chooses to enter or not to enter the Dressfastic clothing store. How many different outcomes of their decisions are possible?

Exercises 41–52 involve counting permutations.

41. Seating Arrangements   Ten people are at a party.
  (a) In how many different ways can they be seated in a row of ten chairs?
  (b) In how many different ways can six of these people be selected and then seated in a row of six chairs?

42. Three-Letter Words   How many three-letter "words" can be made from the letters FGHIJK? (Letters may not be repeated.)

43. Class Officers   In how many different ways can a president, vice president, and secretary be chosen from a class of 15 students?

44. Three-Digit Numbers   How many different three-digit whole numbers can be formed by using the digits 1, 3, 5, and 7 if no repetition of digits is allowed?

45. Contest Prizes   In how many different ways can first, second, and third prizes be awarded in a game with eight contestants?

46. Piano Recital   A pianist plans to play eight pieces at a recital. In how many ways can she arrange these pieces in the program?

47. Running a Race   In how many different ways can a race with nine runners be completed, assuming that there is no tie?

48. Signal Flags   A ship carries five signal flags of different colors. How many different signals can be sent by hoisting exactly three of the five flags on the ship's flagpole in different orders?

49. Contest Prizes   In how many ways can first, second, and third prizes be awarded in a contest with 1000 contestants?

50. Class Officers   In how many ways can a president, vice president, secretary, and treasurer be chosen from a class of 30 students?

51. Seating Arrangements   In how many ways can five students be seated in a row of five chairs if Jack insists on sitting in the first chair?

Jack

52. Seating Arrangements   In how many ways can the students in Exercise 51 be seated if Jack insists on sitting in the middle chair?

Exercises 53–66 involve counting combinations.

53. Committee   In how many ways can a committee of three members be chosen from a club of 25 members?

54. Choosing Books   In how many ways can three books be chosen from a group of six different books?

55. Raffle   In a raffle with 12 entries, in how many ways can three winners be selected?

56. Choosing a Group   In how many ways can six people be chosen from a group of ten?

57. Draw Poker Hands   How many different five-card hands can be dealt from a deck of 52 cards?

58. Stud Poker Hands   How many different seven-card hands can be picked from a deck of 52 cards?

59. Choosing Exam Questions   A student must answer seven of the ten questions on an exam. In how many ways can she choose the seven questions?

60. Three-Topping Pizzas A pizza parlor offers a choice of 16 different toppings. How many three-topping pizzas are possible?

61. Violin Recital A violinist has practiced 12 pieces. In how many ways can he choose eight of these pieces for a recital?

62. Choosing Clothing If a woman has eight skirts, in how many ways can she choose five of these to take on a weekend trip?

63. Choosing Clothing If a man has ten pairs of pants, in how many ways can he choose three of these to take on a business trip?

64. Field Trip From a class with 30 students, seven are to be chosen to go on a field trip. Find the number of different ways that the seven students can be chosen under the given condition.
(a) Jack must go on the field trip.
(b) Jack is not allowed to go on the field trip.
(c) There are no restrictions on who can go on the field trip.

65. Lottery In the 6/49 lottery game, a player picks six numbers from 1 to 49. How many different choices does the player have?

66. Jogging Routes A jogger jogs every morning to his health club, which is eight blocks east and five blocks north of his home. He always takes a route that is as short as possible, but he likes to vary it (see the figure). How many different routes can he take? [*Hint:* The route shown can be thought of as *ENNEEENENEENE*, where *E* is East and *N* is North.]

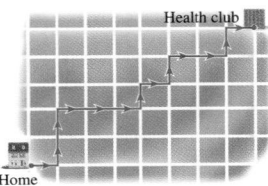

Solve Exercises 67–82 by using the appropriate counting principle(s).

67. Choosing a Committee A class has 20 students, of whom 12 are females and 8 are males. In how many ways can a committee of five students be picked from this class under each condition?
(a) No restriction is placed on the number of males or females on the committee.
(b) No males are to be included on the committee.
(c) The committee must have three females and two males.

68. Doubles Tennis From a group of ten male and ten female tennis players, two men and two women are to face each other in a men-versus-women doubles match. In how many different ways can this match be arranged?

69. Choosing a Committee A committee of six is to be chosen from a class of 20 students. The committee is to consist of a chair, a secretary and four other members. In how many different ways can the committee be picked?

70. Choosing a Group Sixteen boys and nine girls go on a camping trip. In how many ways can a group of six be selected to gather firewood, given the following conditions?
(a) The group consists of two girls and four boys.
(b) The group contains at least two girls.

71. Dance Committee A school dance committee is to consist of two freshmen, three sophomores, four juniors, and five seniors. If six freshmen, eight sophomores, twelve juniors, and ten seniors are eligible to be on the committee, in how many ways can the committee be chosen?

72. Casting a Play A group of 22 aspiring thespians contains 10 men and 12 women. For the next play, the director wants to choose a leading man, a leading lady, a supporting male role, a supporting female role, and eight extras—three women and five men. In how many ways can the cast be chosen?

73. Hockey Lineup A hockey team has 20 players, of whom 12 play forward, six play defense, and two are goalies. In how many ways can the coach pick a starting lineup consisting of three forwards, two defense players, and one goalie?

74. Choosing a Pizza A pizza parlor offers four sizes of pizza (small, medium, large, and colossus), two types of crust (thick and thin), and 14 different toppings. How many different pizzas can be made with these choices?

75. Choosing a Committee In how many ways can a committee of four be chosen from a group of ten if Barry and Harry refuse to serve together on the same committee?

76. Parking Committee A five-person committee consisting of students and teachers is being formed to study the issue of student parking privileges. Of those who have expressed an interest in serving on the committee, 12 are teachers and 14 are students. In how many ways can the committee be formed if at least one student and one teacher must be included?

77. Arranging Books In how many ways can five different mathematics books be placed on a shelf if the two algebra books are to be placed next to each other?

78. Arranging a Class Picture In how many ways can ten students be arranged in a row for a class picture if John and Jane want to stand next to each other and Mike and Molly also insist on standing next to each other?

79. Seating Arrangements In how many ways can four men and four women be seated in a row of eight seats for each of the following arrangements?
(a) The first seat is to be occupied by a man.
(b) The first and last seats are to be occupied by women.

80. Seating Arrangements In how many ways can four men and four women be seated in a row of eight seats for each of the following arrangements?
(a) The women are to be seated together.
(b) The men and women are to be seated alternately by gender.

81. Selecting Prizewinners From a group of 30 contestants, six are to be chosen as semifinalists, then two of those are chosen as finalists, and then the top prize is awarded to one of the finalists. In how many ways can these choices be made in sequence?

82. Choosing a Delegation Three delegates are to be chosen from a group of four lawyers, a priest, and three professors. In how many ways can the delegation be chosen if it must include at least one professor?

DISCOVERY ■ DISCUSSION ■ WRITING

83. Pairs of Initials Explain why in any group of 677 people, at least two people must have the same pair of initials.

84. Complementary Combinations Without performing any calculations, explain in words why the number of ways of choosing two objects from ten objects is the same as the number of ways of choosing eight objects from ten objects. In general, explain why

$$C(n, r) = C(n, n - r)$$

85. An Identity Involving Combinations Kevin has ten different marbles, and he wants to give three of them to Luke and two to Mark. In how many ways can he choose to do this?

There are two ways of analyzing this problem: He could first pick three for Luke and then two for Mark, or he could first pick two for Mark and then three for Luke. Explain how these two viewpoints show that

$$C(10, 3) \cdot C(7, 2) = C(10, 2) \cdot C(8, 3)$$

In general, explain why

$$C(n, r) \cdot C(n - r, k) = C(n, k) \cdot C(n - k, r)$$

86. Why Is $\binom{n}{r}$ the Same as $C(n, r)$? This exercise explains why the binomial coefficients $\binom{n}{r}$ that appear in the expansion of $(x + y)^n$ are the same as $C(n, r)$, the number of ways of choosing r objects from n objects. First, note that expanding a binomial using only the Distributive Property gives

$$(x + y)^2 = (x + y)(x + y)$$
$$= (x + y)x + (x + y)y$$
$$= xx + xy + yx + yy$$
$$(x + y)^3 = (x + y)(xx + xy + yx + yy)$$
$$= xxx + xxy + xyx + xyy + yxx$$
$$+ yxy + yyx + yyy$$

(a) Expand $(x + y)^5$ using only the Distributive Property.
(b) Write all the terms that represent x^2y^3. These are all the terms that contain two x's and three y's.
(c) Note that the two x's appear in all possible positions. Conclude that the number of terms that represent x^2y^3 is $C(5, 2)$.
(d) In general, explain why $\binom{n}{r}$ in the Binomial Theorem is the same as $C(n, r)$.

SUGGESTED TIME AND EMPHASIS
1–2 classes, optional material

14.2 PROBABILITY

> What Is Probability? ▶ Calculating Probability by Counting ▶ The Complement of an Event ▶ The Union of Events ▶ Conditional Probability and the Intersection of Events

In this section we study probability, which is the mathematical study of "chance."

▼ What Is Probability?

The mathematical theory of probability was first discussed in 1654 in a series of letters between Pascal (see page 818) and Fermat (see page 99). Their correspondence was prompted by a question raised by the experienced gambler the Chevalier de Méré. The Chevalier was interested in the equitable distribution of the stakes of an interrupted gambling game (see Problem 3, page 968).

Suppose we roll a die, and we're hoping to get a "two." Of course, it's impossible to predict what number will show up. But here's the key idea: If we roll the die many many times, a "two" will show up about one-sixth of the time. If you try this experiment you'll see that it actually works! We say that the *probability* (or chance) of getting a "two" is $\frac{1}{6}$.

TEXT QUESTION
(a) Give an example of two mutually exclusive events.
(b) Give an example of two independent events.

Answer
Answers will vary.

To discuss probability, let's begin by defining some terms. An **experiment** is a process, such as tossing a coin, that gives definite results, called the **outcomes** of the experiment. The **sample space** of an experiment is the set of all possible outcomes. If we let H stand for heads and T for tails, then the sample space of the coin-tossing experiment is $S = \{H, T\}$. The table gives some experiments and their sample spaces.

Experiment	Sample space
Tossing a coin	$\{H, T\}$
Rolling a die	$\{1, 2, 3, 4, 5, 6\}$
Tossing a coin twice and observing the sequence of heads and tails	$\{HH, HT, TH, TT\}$
Picking a card from a deck and observing the suit	$\{\spadesuit, \heartsuit, \diamondsuit, \clubsuit\}$
Administering a drug to three patients and observing whether they recover (R) or not (N)	$\{RRR, RRN, RNR, RNN,$ $NRR, NRN, NNR, NNN\}$

We will be concerned only with experiments for which all the outcomes are **equally likely**. For example, when we toss a perfectly balanced coin, heads and tails are equally likely outcomes in the sense that if this experiment is repeated many times, we expect that about as many heads as tails will show up.

In any given experiment we are often concerned with a particular set of outcomes. We might be interested in a die showing an even number or in picking an ace from a deck of cards. Any particular set of outcomes is a subset of the sample space. This leads to the following definition.

DEFINITION OF AN EVENT

If S is the sample space of an experiment, then an **event** E is any subset of the sample space.

EXAMPLE 1 | Events in a Sample Space

An experiment consists of tossing a coin three times and recording the results in order. List the outcomes in the sample space, then list the outcome in each event.

(a) The event E of getting "exactly two heads."

(b) The event F of getting "at least two heads."

(c) The event G of getting "no heads."

SOLUTION We write H for heads and T for tails. So the outcome HTH means that the three tosses resulted in Heads, Tails, Heads, in that order. The sample space is

$$S = \{HHH, HHT, HTH, THH, TTH, THT, HTT, TTT\}$$

(a) The event E is the subset of the sample space S that consists of all outcomes with exactly two heads. Thus

$$E = \{HHT, HTH, THH\}$$

(b) The event F is the subset of the sample space S that consists of all outcomes with at least two heads. Thus

$$F = \{HHH, HHT, HTH, THH\}$$

ALTERNATE EXAMPLE 1

An experiment consists of rolling two dice, a red one and a blue one, and recording the results. List the outcomes in the sample space, and then list the outcome in each event.

(a) The event E of getting "a total of six"

(b) The event F of getting "two even numbers"

(c) The event G of getting "a total greater than 10"

ANSWERS

$$S = \begin{Bmatrix} 1,1 & 1,2 & 1,3 & 1,4 & 1,5 & 1,6 \\ 2,1 & 2,2 & 2,3 & 2,4 & 2,5 & 2,6 \\ 3,1 & 3,2 & 3,3 & 3,4 & 3,5 & 3,6 \\ 4,1 & 4,2 & 4,3 & 4,4 & 4,5 & 4,6 \\ 5,1 & 5,2 & 5,3 & 5,4 & 5,5 & 5,6 \\ 6,1 & 6,2 & 6,3 & 6,4 & 6,5 & 6,6 \end{Bmatrix}$$ where we write an outcome in the form *red die, green die.*

(a) $E = \{1,5 \quad 2,4 \quad 3,3 \quad 4,2 \quad 5,1\}$

(b) $F = \begin{Bmatrix} 2,2 & 2,4 & 2,6 \\ 4,2 & 4,4 & 4,6 \\ 6,2 & 6,4 & 6,6 \end{Bmatrix}$

(c) $G = \{6,5 \quad 5,6 \quad 6,6\}$

(c) The event G is the subset of the sample space S that consists of all outcomes with no heads. Thus

$$G = \{TTT\}$$

↖ NOW TRY EXERCISE **5** ∎

We are now ready to define the notion of probability. Intuitively, we know that rolling a die may result in any of six equally likely outcomes, so the chance of any particular outcome occurring is $\frac{1}{6}$. What is the chance of showing an even number? Of the six equally likely outcomes possible, three are even numbers. So it is reasonable to say that the chance of showing an even number is $\frac{3}{6} = \frac{1}{2}$. This reasoning is the intuitive basis for the following definition of probability.

DEFINITION OF PROBABILITY

Let S be the sample space of an experiment in which all outcomes are equally likely, and let E be an event. Then the **probability** of E, written $P(E)$, is

$$P(E) = \frac{n(E)}{n(S)} = \frac{\text{number of elements in } E}{\text{number of elements in } S}$$

Notice that $0 \leq n(E) \leq n(S)$, so the probability $P(E)$ of an event is a number between 0 and 1, that is,

$$0 \leq P(E) \leq 1$$

The closer the probability of an event is to 1, the more likely the event is to happen; the closer to 0, the less likely. If $P(E) = 1$, then E is called a **certain event**; if $P(E) = 0$, then E is called an **impossible event**.

EXAMPLE 2 | Finding the Probability of an Event

A coin is tossed three times, and the results are recorded in order. Find the probability of the following.

(a) The event E of getting "exactly two heads."

(b) The event F of getting "at least two heads."

(c) The event G of getting "no heads."

SOLUTION By the results of Example 1 the sample space S of this experiment contains 8 outcomes.

(a) The event E of getting "exactly two heads" contains 3 outcomes, so by the definition of probability,

$$P(E) = \frac{n(E)}{n(S)} = \frac{3}{8}$$

(b) The event F of getting "at least two heads" has 4 outcomes, so

$$P(F) = \frac{n(F)}{n(S)} = \frac{4}{8} = \frac{1}{2}$$

(c) The event G of getting "no heads" has one outcome, so

$$P(G) = \frac{n(G)}{n(S)} = \frac{1}{8}$$

↖ NOW TRY EXERCISE **7** ∎

ALTERNATE EXAMPLE 2:

An experiment consists of rolling two dice, a red one and a blue one. Find the probability of the following.

(a) The event E of getting "a total of six"

(b) The event F of getting "two even numbers"

(c) The event G of getting "a total greater than 10"

ANSWERS

(a) $\dfrac{5}{36}$

(b) $\dfrac{9}{36} = \dfrac{1}{4}$

(c) $\dfrac{3}{36} = \dfrac{1}{12}$

IN-CLASS MATERIALS

An excellent example of a surprising probability result is Buffon's needle problem, named after the mathematician Georges-Louis Leclerc, Comte de Buffon (1707–1788). Take a needle and a large piece of paper with parallel lines on it. The distance between the parallel lines should be equal to the length of the needle. Ask the class what they think the probability is that, if you drop the needle, it will touch one of the lines. Perhaps do the experiment. The probability turns out to be approximately 0.64. The interesting thing is that the exact answer is $\dfrac{2}{\pi}$. So one can determine π by doing the experiment many times, dividing the answer by 2, and taking the reciprocal.

▼ Calculating Probability by Counting

To find the probability of an event, we do not need to list all the elements in the sample space and the event. We need only the *number* of elements in these sets. The counting techniques that we learned in the preceding sections will be very useful here.

EXAMPLE 3 | Finding the Probability of an Event

A five-card poker hand is drawn from a standard deck of 52 cards. What is the probability that all five cards are spades?

SOLUTION   The experiment here consists of choosing five cards from the deck, and the sample space S consists of all possible five-card hands. Thus the number of elements in the sample space is

$$n(S) = C(52, 5) = \frac{52!}{5!(52 - 5)!} = 2{,}598{,}960$$

The event E that we are interested in consists of choosing five spades. Since the deck contains only 13 spades, the number of ways of choosing five spades is

$$n(E) = C(13, 5) = \frac{13!}{5!(13 - 5)!} = 1287$$

Thus the probability of drawing five spades is

$$P(E) = \frac{n(E)}{n(S)} = \frac{1287}{2{,}598{,}960} \approx 0.0005$$

✎ NOW TRY EXERCISE **15**   ∎

What does the answer to Example 3 tell us? Because $0.0005 = \frac{1}{2000}$, we conclude that if you play poker many, many times, on average you will be dealt a hand consisting of only spades about once in every 2000 hands.

EXAMPLE 4 | Finding the Probability of an Event

A bag contains 20 tennis balls, of which four are defective. If two balls are selected at random from the bag, what is the probability that both are defective?

SOLUTION   The experiment consists of choosing two balls from 20, so the number of elements in the sample space S is $C(20, 2)$. Since there are four defective balls, the number of ways of picking two defective balls is $C(4, 2)$. Thus the probability of the event E of picking two defective balls is

$$P(E) = \frac{n(E)}{n(S)} = \frac{C(4, 2)}{C(20, 2)} = \frac{6}{190} \approx 0.032$$

✎ NOW TRY EXERCISE **17**   ∎

▼ The Complement of an Event

The **complement** of an event E is the set of outcomes in the sample space that is not in E. We denote the complement of E by E'.

By solving this equation for $P(E)$, we also have

$$P(E) = 1 - P(E')$$

PROBABILITY OF THE COMPLEMENT OF AN EVENT

Let S be the sample space of an experiment, and let E be an event. Then the probability of E', the complement of E, is

$$P(E') = 1 - P(E)$$

IN-CLASS MATERIALS

In the media, probabilities are often given in the form of "odds." This is a good bit of vocabulary to share with your students:

Probability	Odds For	Odds Against
$\dfrac{\text{Good outcomes}}{\text{Total possible outcomes}}$	Good outcomes : Bad outcomes	Bad outcomes : Good outcomes

So if, for example, you were playing a game that involved drawing a card and trying to get an ace, we could express the chances in the following ways:

Probability	Odds For	Odds Against
$\dfrac{4}{52} = \dfrac{1}{13}$	1 : 12 for	12 : 1 against

PROOF   We calculate the probability of E' using the definition of probability and the fact that $n(E') = n(S) - n(E)$.

$$P(E') = \frac{n(E')}{n(S)} = \frac{n(S) - n(E)}{n(S)} = \frac{n(S)}{n(S)} - \frac{n(E)}{n(S)} = 1 - P(E) \quad \blacksquare$$

This is a very useful result, since it is often difficult to calculate the probability of an event E but easy to find the probability of E'.

EXAMPLE 5 | Finding a Probability Using the Complement of an Event

An urn contains 10 red balls and 15 blue balls. Six balls are drawn at random from the urn. What is the probability that at least one ball is red?

SOLUTION   Let E be the event that at least one red ball is drawn. It is tedious to count all the possible ways in which one or more of the balls drawn are red. So let's consider E', the complement of this event—namely, that none of the balls that are chosen is red. The number of ways of choosing 6 blue balls from the 15 blue balls is $C(15, 6)$; the number of ways of choosing 6 balls from the 25 balls is $C(25, 6)$. Thus

$$P(E') = \frac{n(E')}{n(S)} = \frac{C(15, 6)}{C(25, 6)} = \frac{5005}{177,100} = \frac{13}{460}$$

By the formula for the complement of an event we have

$$P(E) = 1 - P(E') = 1 - \frac{13}{460} \approx 0.97$$

✎ NOW TRY EXERCISE **19**   ■

▼ The Union of Events

If E and F are events, what is the probability that E or F occurs? The word *or* indicates that we want the probability of the union of these events, that is, $E \cup F$.

PROBABILITY OF THE UNION OF EVENTS

If E and F are events in a sample space S, then the probability of E *or* F is

$$P(E \cup F) = P(E) + P(F) - P(E \cap F)$$

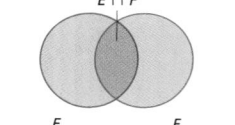

FIGURE 1

PROOF   We need to find the number of elements in $E \cup F$. If we simply added the number of elements in E to the number of elements in F, we would be counting the elements in the overlap twice—once in E and once in F (see Figure 1). To get the correct total, we must subtract the number of elements in $E \cap F$. So $n(E \cup F) = n(E) + n(F) - n(E \cap F)$. Using the definition of probability we get

$$P(E \cup F) = \frac{n(E \cup F)}{n(S)} = \frac{n(E) + n(F) - n(E \cap F)}{n(S)} = P(E) + P(F) - P(E \cap F)$$

$\blacksquare$

EXAMPLE 6 | Finding the Probability of the Union of Events

What is the probability that a card drawn at random from a standard 52-card deck is either a face card or a spade?

ALTERNATE EXAMPLE 5

Some secret codes require a code "key," which is a word with no repeated letters. (A "word" is a list of seven letters—they don't have to be English words. PLATYPUS, MXYZPTLK, ABBBBBAA, and AAABBBBB are all different, valid, eight-letter words, but only the second one can be used as a key.) Assume we choose an eight-letter word at random. What is the probability that it would *not* be a valid key?

ANSWER

$$P(E) = 1 - \frac{P(26, 8)}{26^8} = 0.6984$$

ALTERNATE EXAMPLE 6

What is the probability that a randomly chosen six-letter word begins or ends with "CAT."

ANSWER

$$\frac{26^3}{26^6} + \frac{26^3}{26^6} - \frac{1}{26^6}$$

EXAMPLE

Kate's dorm floor had three positions to fill: president, vice president, and sergeant at arms. Assume 60 people resided on the floor. If the offices were filled randomly, what is the probability Kate would end up an officer?

Answer

$$\frac{C(59, 2)}{C(60, 3)} = \frac{1}{20} \approx 5\%$$

SOLUTION Let E denote the event "the card is a face card," and let F denote the event "the card is a spade." We want to find the probability of E or F, that is, $P(E \cup F)$.

There are 12 face cards and 13 spades in a 52-card deck, so

$$P(E) = \frac{12}{52} \quad \text{and} \quad P(F) = \frac{13}{52}$$

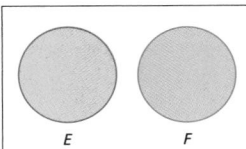

Face cards   Spades

Since 3 cards are simultaneously face cards and spades, we have

$$P(E \cap F) = \frac{3}{52}$$

Now, by the formula for the probability of the union of two events we have

$$P(E \cup F) = P(E) + P(F) - P(E \cap F)$$
$$= \frac{12}{52} + \frac{13}{52} - \frac{3}{52} = \frac{11}{26}$$

✎ NOW TRY EXERCISE **21** ■

Two events that have no outcome in common are said to be **mutually exclusive** (see Figure 2). In other words, the events E and F are mutually exclusive if $E \cap F = \varnothing$. So if the events E and F are mutually exclusive, then $P(E \cap F) = 0$. The following result now follows from the formula for the union of two events.

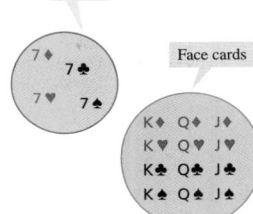

E F

FIGURE 2

PROBABILITY OF THE UNION OF MUTUALLY EXCLUSIVE EVENTS

If E and F are mutually exclusive events, then

$$P(E \cup F) = P(E) + P(F)$$

EXAMPLE 7 | Finding the Probability of the Union of Mutually Exclusive Events

What is the probability that a card drawn at random from a standard 52-card deck is either a seven or a face card?

Sevens

7♦   7♣

7♥   7♠

Face cards

K♦ Q♦ J♦
K♥ Q♥ J♥
K♣ Q♣ J♣
K♠ Q♠ J♠

SOLUTION Let E denote the event "the card is a seven," and let F denote the event "the card is a face card." These events are mutually exclusive because a card cannot be at the same time a seven and a face card. By the above formula we have

$$P(E \cup F) = P(E) + P(F) = \frac{4}{52} + \frac{12}{52} = \frac{4}{13}$$

✎ NOW TRY EXERCISES **23** AND **25** ■

▼ Conditional Probability and the Intersection of Events

When we calculate probabilities, there sometimes is additional information that may alter the probability of an event. For example, suppose a person is chosen at random. What is the probability that the person has long hair? How does the probability change if we are given the additional information that the person chosen is a woman? In general, the probability of an event E given that another event F has occurred is expressed by writing

$$P(E \mid F) = \text{The probability of } E \text{ given } F$$

For example, suppose a die is rolled. Let E be the event of "getting a two" and let F be the event of "getting an even number." Then

$$P(E \mid F) = P(\text{The number is two given that the number is even})$$

ALTERNATE EXAMPLE 7
What is the probability that a randomly chosen six-letter word begins or ends with "FISH."

ANSWER
$$\frac{26^2}{26^6} + \frac{26^2}{26^6}$$

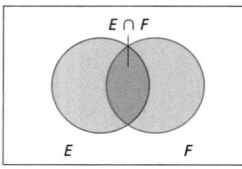

FIGURE 3

Since we know that the number is even, the possible outcomes are the three numbers 2, 4, and 6. So in this case the probability of a "two" is $P(E \mid F) = \frac{1}{3}$.

In general, if we know that F has occurred, then F serves as the sample space (see Figure 3). So $P(E \mid F)$ is determined by the number of outcomes in E that are also in F, that is, the number of outcomes in $E \cap F$.

> **CONDITIONAL PROBABILITY**
>
> Let E and F be events in a sample space S. The **conditional probability of E given that F occurs** is
>
> $$P(E \mid F) = \frac{n(E \cap F)}{n(F)}$$

EXAMPLE 8 | Finding Conditional Probability

A mathematics class consists of 30 students; 12 of them study French, 8 study German, 3 study both of these languages, and the rest do not study a foreign language. If a student is chosen at random from this class, find the probability of each of the following events.

(a) The student studies French.

(b) The student studies French, given that he or she studies German.

(c) The student studies French, given that he or she studies a foreign language.

SOLUTION Let F denote the event "the student studies French," let G be the event "the student studies German," and let L be the event "the student studies a foreign language." It is helpful to organize the information in a Venn diagram, as in Figure 4.

(a) There are 30 students in the class, 12 of whom study French, so

$$P(F) = \frac{12}{30} = \frac{2}{5}$$

(b) We are asked to find $P(F \mid G)$, the probability that a student studies French given that the student studies German. Since eight students study German and three of these study French, it is clear that the required conditional probability is $\frac{3}{8}$. The formula for conditional probability confirms this:

$$P(F \mid G) = \frac{n(F \cap G)}{n(G)} = \frac{3}{8}$$

(c) From the Venn diagram in Figure 4 we see that the number of students who study a foreign language is $9 + 3 + 5 = 17$. Since 12 of these study French, we have

$$P(F \mid L) = \frac{n(F \cap L)}{n(L)} = \frac{12}{17}$$

✎. NOW TRY EXERCISES **27** AND **29** ■

If we start with the expression for conditional probability and then divide numerator and denominator by $n(S)$, we get

$$P(E \mid F) = \frac{n(E \cap F)}{n(F)} = \frac{\dfrac{n(E \cap F)}{n(S)}}{\dfrac{n(F)}{n(S)}} = \frac{P(E \cap F)}{P(F)}$$

FIGURE 4

ALTERNATE EXAMPLE 8

I have 10 friends. Four wear glasses. Three are left-handed. (Two of them wear glasses and are left-handed.)

(a) What is the probability that a randomly chosen friend is left-handed?

(b) What is the probability that a randomly chosen friend is left-handed, given that he or she wears glasses?

(c) What is the probability that a randomly chosen friend wears glasses, given that he or she is left-handed?

ANSWERS

(a) $\dfrac{3 \text{ left-handed friends}}{10 \text{ friends}} = 0.3$

(b) $\dfrac{2 \text{ left-handed glasses wearers}}{4 \text{ glasses wearers}} = 0.5$

(c) $\dfrac{2 \text{ left-handed glasses wearers}}{3 \text{ left-handed friends}} = 0.6\overline{6}$

Multiplying both sides by $P(F)$ gives the following formula.

PROBABILITY OF THE INTERSECTION OF EVENTS

If E and F are events in a sample space S, then the probability of E *and* F is

$$P(E \cap F) = P(E)P(F \mid E)$$

EXAMPLE 9 | Finding the Probability of the Intersection of Events

Two cards are drawn, without replacement, from a 52-card deck. Find the probability of the following events.

(a) The first card drawn is an ace and the second is a king.

(b) The first card drawn is an ace and the second is also an ace.

SOLUTION Let E be the event "the first card is an ace," and let F be the event "the second card is a king."

(a) We are asked to find the probability of E *and* F, that is, $P(E \cap F)$. Now, $P(E) = \frac{4}{52}$. After an ace is drawn, 51 cards remain in the deck; of these, 4 are kings, so $P(F \mid E) = \frac{4}{51}$. By the above formula we have

$$P(E \cap F) = P(E)P(F \mid E) = \frac{4}{52} \times \frac{4}{51} \approx 0.0060$$

(b) Let E be the event "the first card is an ace," and let H be the event "the second card is an ace." The probability that the first card drawn is an ace is $P(E) = \frac{4}{52}$. After an ace is drawn, 51 cards remain; of these, 3 are aces, so $P(H \mid E) = \frac{3}{51}$. By the above formula we have

$$P(E \cap H) = P(E)P(H \mid E) = \frac{4}{52} \times \frac{3}{51} \approx 0.0045$$

✎ NOW TRY EXERCISE **33** ∎

When the occurrence of one event does not affect the probability of the occurrence of another event, we say that the events are **independent**. This means that the events E and F are independent if $P(E \mid F) = P(E)$ and $P(F \mid E) = P(F)$. For instance, if a fair coin is tossed, the probability of showing heads on the second toss is $\frac{1}{2}$, regardless of what was obtained on the first toss. So any two tosses of a coin are independent.

PROBABILITY OF THE INTERSECTION OF INDEPENDENT EVENTS

If E and F are independent events in a sample space S, then the probability of E *and* F is

$$P(E \cap F) = P(E)P(F)$$

EXAMPLE 10 | Finding the Probability of Independent Events

A jar contains five red balls and four black balls. A ball is drawn at random from the jar and then replaced; then another ball is picked. What is the probability that both balls are red?

ALTERNATE EXAMPLE 9

I have 10 friends. Four wear glasses. Three are left-handed. (Two of them wear glasses and are left-handed.) What is the probability that a randomly chosen friend is both left-handed and wears glasses?

ANSWER

$P(\text{glasses}) = \dfrac{4}{10}$,

$P(\text{left-handed}|\text{glasses}) = \dfrac{5}{10}$,

$P(E) = \left(\dfrac{4}{10}\right)\left(\dfrac{5}{10}\right) = 0.2$

Notice that this also can be computed directly:

$$\frac{2 \text{ friends that are left-handed glasses wearers}}{10 \text{ friends}} = 0.2$$

ALTERNATE EXAMPLE 10

The booster seats at a restaurant are colored red, yellow, blue, orange, and purple. When a child is seated with her parents, she gets one at random. What is the probability that the seat she selects during the first family visit is a primary color and the seat she selects during the second visit is a secondary color?

ANSWER

The two events are independent.

$$\left(\frac{3}{5}\right)\left(\frac{2}{5}\right) = \frac{6}{25} = 0.24$$

SOLUTION Let E be the event "the first ball drawn is red," and let F be the event "the second ball drawn is red." Since we replace the first ball before drawing the second, the events E and F are independent. Now, the probability that the first ball is red is $\frac{5}{9}$. The probability that the second is red is also $\frac{5}{9}$. Thus the probability that both balls are red is

$$P(E \cap F) = P(E)P(F) = \frac{5}{9} \times \frac{5}{9} \approx 0.31$$

✎ NOW TRY EXERCISE **37**

CONCEPTS

1. The set of all possible outcomes of an experiment is called the

_____ _____. A subset of the sample space is

called an _____. The sample space for the experiment

of tossing two coins is $S = \{HH, \_\_\_, \_\_\_, \_\_\_\}$. The

event "getting at least one head" is $E = \{HH, \_\_\_, \_\_\_\}$.
The probability of getting at least one head is

$$P(E) = \frac{n(\_\_\_)}{n(\_\_\_)} = \_\_\_\_.$$

2. Let E and F be events in a sample space S.
   (a) The probability of E or F occurring is

   $$P(E \cup F) = _____.$$
   (b) If the events E and F have no outcome in common (that is, the intersection of E and F is empty), then the events are

   called _____ _____. So in drawing a card
   from a deck, the event E, "getting a heart," and the event

   F, "getting a spade," are _____ _____.
   (c) If E and F are mutually exclusive, then the probability of

   E or F is $P(E \cup F) = _____.$

3. The conditional probability of E given that F occurs is

   $P(E \mid F) = $ _____. So in tossing a die the conditional
   probability of the event E, "getting a six," given that the event
   F, "getting an even number," has occurred is

   $P(E \mid F) = $ _____.

4. Let E and F be events in a sample space S.
   (a) The probability of E *and* F occurring is

   $$P(E \cap F) = _____.$$
   (b) If the occurrence of E does not affect the probability of

   the occurrence F, then the events are called _____.
   So in tossing a coin twice, the event E, "getting heads on
   the first toss," and the event F, "getting heads on the

   second toss," are _____.

(c) If E and F are independent events, then the probability of

   E *and* F is $P(E \cap F) = $ _____.

SKILLS

✎ **5.** An experiment consists of rolling a die. List the elements in the following sets.
   (a) The sample space
   (b) The event "getting an even number"
   (c) The event "getting a number greater than 4"

6. An experiment consists of tossing a coin and drawing a card from a deck.
   (a) How many elements does the sample space have?
   (b) List the elements in the event "getting heads and an ace."
   (c) List the elements in the event "getting tails and a face card."
   (d) List the elements in the event "getting heads and a spade."

Exercises 7–20 are about finding probability by counting.

✎ **7.** An experiment consists of tossing a coin twice.
   (a) Find the sample space.
   (b) Find the probability of getting heads exactly two times.
   (c) Find the probability of getting heads at least one time.
   (d) Find the probability of getting heads exactly one time.

8. An experiment consists of tossing a coin and rolling a die.
   (a) Find the sample space.
   (b) Find the probability of getting heads and an even number.
   (c) Find the probability of getting heads and a number greater than 4.
   (d) Find the probability of getting tails and an odd number.

9–10 ■ A die is rolled. Find the probability of the given event.

9. (a) The number showing is a six.
   (b) The number showing is an even number.
   (c) The number showing is greater than five.

10. (a) The number showing is a two or a three.
   (b) The number showing is an odd number.
   (c) The number showing is a number divisible by 3.

DRILL QUESTION

Assume a bag has 3 black balls, 5 green balls, and 20 white balls. If you draw one ball from the bag, what is the probability that it is green?

Answer

$\dfrac{5}{28} \approx 18\%$

11–12 ■ A card is drawn randomly from a standard 52-card deck. Find the probability of the given event.

11. (a) The card drawn is a king.
   (b) The card drawn is a face card.
   (c) The card drawn is not a face card.

12. (a) The card drawn is a heart.
   (b) The card drawn is either a heart or a spade.
   (c) The card drawn is a heart, a diamond, or a spade.

13–14 ■ A ball is drawn randomly from a jar that contains five red balls, two white balls, and one yellow ball. Find the probability of the given event.

13. (a) A red ball is drawn.
   (b) The ball drawn is not yellow.
   (c) A black ball is drawn.

14. (a) Neither a white nor yellow ball is drawn.
   (b) A red, white, or yellow ball is drawn.
   (c) The ball that is drawn is not white.

15. A poker hand, consisting of five cards, is dealt from a standard deck of 52 cards. Find the probability that the hand contains the cards described.
   (a) Five hearts
   (b) Five cards of the same suit
   (c) Five face cards
   (d) An ace, king, queen, jack, and a ten, all of the same suit (royal flush)

16. Three CDs are picked at random from a collection of 12 CDs of which four are defective. Find the probability of the following.
   (a) All three CDs are defective.
   (b) All three CDs are functioning properly.

17. Two balls are picked at random from a jar that contains three red and five white balls. Find the probability of the following events.
   (a) Both balls are red.
   (b) Both balls are white.

18. A letter is chosen at random from the word *EXTRATERRESTRIAL.* Find the probability of the given event.
   (a) The letter *T* is chosen.
   (b) The letter chosen is a vowel.
   (c) The letter chosen is a consonant.

19. A five-card poker hand is drawn from a standard 52-card deck. Find the probability of the following events.
   (a) At least one card is a spade.
   (b) At least one card is a face card.

20. A pair of dice is rolled, and the numbers showing are observed.
   (a) List the sample space of this experiment.
   (b) Find the probability of getting a sum of 7.
   (c) Find the probability of getting a sum of 9.
   (d) Find the probability that the two dice show doubles (the same number).
   (e) Find the probability that the two dice show different numbers.
   (f) Find the probability of getting a sum of 9 or higher.

Exercises 21–26 are about the probability of the union of events.

21–22 ■ Refer to the spinner shown in the figure. Find the probability of the given event.

21. (a) The spinner stops on red.
   (b) The spinner stops on an even number.
   (c) The spinner stops on red or an even number.

22. (a) The spinner stops on blue.
   (b) The spinner stops on an odd number.
   (c) The spinner stops on blue or an odd number.

23–24 ■ A die is rolled, and the number showing is observed. Determine whether the events *E* and *F* are mutually exclusive. Then find the probability of the event $E \cup F$.

23. (a) *E:* The number is even.
        F: The number is odd.

   (b) *E:* The number is even.
        F: The number is greater than 4.

24. (a) *E:* The number is greater than 3.
        F: The number is less than 5.

   (b) *E:* The number is divisible by 3.
        F: The number is less than 3.

25–26 ■ A card is drawn at random from a standard 52-card deck. Determine whether the events *E* and *F* are mutually exclusive. Then find the probability of the event $E \cup F$.

25. (a) *E:* The card is a face card.
        F: The card is a spade.

   (b) *E:* The card is a heart.
        F: The card is a spade.

26. (a) *E:* The card is a club.
        F: The card is a king.

   (b) *E:* The card is an ace.
        F: The card is a spade.

Exercises 27–32 are about conditional probability.

27. A die is rolled. Find the given conditional probability.
   (a) A "five" shows, given that the number showing is greater than 3.
   (b) A "three" shows, given that the number showing is odd.

28. A card is drawn from a deck. Find the following conditional probability.
   (a) The card is a queen, given that it is a face card.
   (b) The card is a king, given that it is a spade.
   (c) The card is a spade, given that it is a king.

29–30 ■ Refer to the spinner in Exercises 21–22.

29. Find the probability that the spinner has stopped on an even number, given that it has stopped on red.

30. Find the probability that the spinner has stopped on a number divisible by 3, given that it has stopped on blue.

31–32 ■ A jar contains five red balls numbered 1 to 5, and seven green balls numbered 1 to 7.

31. A ball is drawn at random from the jar. Find the following conditional probabilities.
 (a) The ball is red, given that it is numbered 3.
 (b) The ball is green, given that it is numbered 7.
 (c) The ball is red, given that it has an even number.
 (d) The ball has an even number, given that it is red.

32. Two balls are drawn at random from the jar. Find the following conditional probabilities.
 (a) The second ball drawn is red, given that the first is red.
 (b) The second ball drawn is red, given that the first is green.
 (c) The second ball drawn is even-numbered, given that the first is odd-numbered.
 (d) The second ball drawn is even-numbered, given that the first is even-numbered.

Exercises 33–40 are about the probability of the intersection of events.

33. A jar contains seven black balls and three white balls. Two balls are drawn, without replacement, from the jar. Find the probability of the following events.
 (a) The first ball drawn is black, and the second is white.
 (b) The first ball drawn is black, and the second is black.

34. A drawer contains an unorganized collection of 18 socks. Three pairs are red, two pairs are white, and four pairs are black.
 (a) If one sock is drawn at random from the drawer, what is the probability that it is red?
 (b) Once a sock is drawn and discovered to be red, what is the probability of drawing another red sock to make a matching pair?
 (c) If two socks are drawn from the drawer at the same time, what is the probability that both are red?

35. Two cards are drawn from a deck without replacement. Find the probability of the following events.
 (a) The first is an ace and the second a king?
 (b) Both cards are aces?

36. A die is rolled twice. Let E and F be the following events:

 E: The first roll shows a "six."
 F: The second roll shows a "six."

 (a) Are the events E and F independent?
 (b) Find the probability of showing a "six" on both rolls.

37. A die is rolled twice. What is the probability of getting a "one" on the first roll and an even number on the second roll?

38. A coin is tossed and a die is rolled.
 (a) Are the events "tails" and "even number" independent?
 (b) Find the probability of getting a tail and an even number.

39–40 ■ Spinners A and B shown in the figure are spun at the same time.

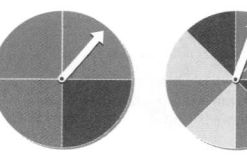

Spinner A   Spinner B

39. (a) Are the events "spinner A stops on red" and "spinner B stops on yellow" independent?
 (b) Find the probability that spinner A stops on red and spinner B stops on yellow

40. (a) Find the probability that both spinners stop on purple.
 (b) Find the probability that both spinners stop on blue.

APPLICATIONS

41. Four Siblings A couple intends to have four children. Assume that having a boy and having a girl are equally likely events.
 (a) List the sample space of this experiment.
 (b) Find the probability that the couple will have only boys.
 (c) Find the probability that the couple will have two boys and two girls.
 (d) Find the probability that the couple will have four children of the same gender.
 (e) Find the probability that the couple will have at least two girls.

42. Bridge Hands What is the probability that a 13-card bridge hand consists of all cards from the same suit?

43. Roulette An American roulette wheel has 38 slots; two slots are numbered 0 and 00, and the remaining slots are numbered from 1 to 36. Find the probability that the ball lands in an odd-numbered slot.

44. Making Words A toddler has wooden blocks showing the letters C, E, F, H, N, and R. Find the probability that the child arranges the letters in the indicated order.
 (a) In the order *FRENCH*
 (b) In alphabetical order

45. Lottery In the 6/49 lottery game, a player selects six numbers from 1 to 49. What is the probability of picking the six winning numbers?

46. An Unlikely Event The president of a large company selects six employees to receive a special bonus. He claims that the six employees are chosen randomly from among the 30 employees, of whom 19 are women and 11 are men. What is the probability that no woman is chosen?

47. Guessing on a Test An exam has ten true-false questions. A student who has not studied answers all ten questions by just guessing. Find the probability that the student correctly answers the given number of questions.
 (a) All ten questions
 (b) Exactly seven questions

48. Quality Control To control the quality of their product, the Bright-Light Company inspects three light bulbs out of each batch of ten bulbs manufactured. If a defective bulb is found, the batch is discarded. Suppose a batch contains two defective bulbs. What is the probability that the batch will be discarded?

49. Monkeys Typing Shakespeare An often-quoted example of an event of extremely low probability is that a monkey types Shakespeare's entire play *Hamlet* by randomly striking keys on a typewriter. Assume that the typewriter has 48 keys (including the space bar) and that the monkey is equally likely to hit any key.
   (a) Find the probability that such a monkey will actually correctly type just the title of the play as his first word.
   (b) What is the probability that the monkey will type the phrase "To be or not to be" as his first words?

50. Making Words A monkey is trained to arrange wooden blocks in a straight line. He is then given six blocks showing the letters *A, E, H, L, M, T*.
   (a) What is the probability that he will arrange them to spell the word *HAMLET*?
   (b) What is the probability that he will arrange them to spell the word *HAMLET* three consecutive times?

51. Making Words A toddler has eight wooden blocks showing the letters *A, E, I, G, L, N, T,* and *R*. What is the probability that the child will arrange the letters to spell one of the words *TRIANGLE* or *INTEGRAL*?

52. Horse Race Eight horses are entered in a race. You randomly predict a particular order for the horses to complete the race. What is the probability that your prediction is correct?

53. Genetics Many genetic traits are controlled by two genes, one dominant and one recessive. In Gregor Mendel's original experiments with peas, the genes controlling the height of the plant are denoted by T (tall) and t (short). The gene T is dominant, so a plant with the genotype (genetic makeup) TT or Tt is tall, whereas one with genotype tt is short. By a statistical analysis of the offspring in his experiments, Mendel concluded that offspring inherit one gene from each parent and that each possible combination of the two genes is equally likely. If each parent has the genotype Tt, then the following chart gives the possible genotypes of the offspring:

		Parent 2	
		T	**t**
Parent 1	**T**	TT	Tt
	t	Tt	tt

Find the probability that a given offspring of these parents will be
   (a) tall   (b) short

54. Genetics Refer to Exercise 53. Make a chart of the possible genotypes of the offspring if one parent has genotype Tt and the other has tt. Find the probability that a given offspring will be
   (a) tall   (b) short

55. Roulette An American roulette wheel has 38 slots. Two of the slots are numbered 0 and 00, and the rest are numbered from 1 to 36. A player places a bet on a number between 1 and 36 and wins if a ball thrown into the spinning roulette wheel lands in the slot with the same number. Find the probability of winning on two consecutive spins of the roulette wheel.

56. Choosing a Committee A committee of five is chosen randomly from a group of six males and eight females. What is the probability that the committee includes either all males or all females?

57. Snake Eyes What is the probability of rolling snake eyes ("double ones") three times in a row?

58. Lottery In the 6/49 lottery game a player selects six numbers from 1 to 49. What is the probability of selecting at least five of the six winning numbers?

59. Marbles in a Jar A jar contains six red marbles numbered 1 to 6 and ten blue marbles numbered 1 to 10. A marble is drawn at random from the jar. Find the probability that the given event occurs.
   (a) The marble is red.
   (b) The marble is odd-numbered.
   (c) The marble is red or odd-numbered.
   (d) The marble is blue or even-numbered.

60. Lottery In the 6/49 lottery game, a player selects six numbers from 1 to 49 and wins if he or she selects the winning six numbers. What is the probability of winning the lottery two times in a row?

61. Balls in a Jar Jar A contains three red balls and four white balls. Jar B contains five red balls and two white balls. Which one of the following ways of randomly selecting balls gives the greatest probability of drawing two red balls?
   (i)   Draw two balls from jar B.
   (ii) Draw one ball from each jar.
   (iii) Put all the balls in one jar, and then draw two balls.

62. Slot Machine A slot machine has three wheels. Each wheel has 11 positions: a bar and the digits 0, 1, 2, . . . , 9. When the handle is pulled, the three wheels spin independently before coming to rest. Find the probability that the wheels stop on the following positions.
   (a) Three bars

(b) The same number on each wheel
(c) At least one bar.

63. **Combination Lock**   A student has locked her locker with a combination lock, showing numbers from 1 to 40, but she has forgotten the three-number combination that opens the lock. She remembers that all three numbers in the combination are different. To open the lock, she decides to try all possible combinations. If she can try ten different combinations every minute, what is the probability that she will open the lock within one hour?

64. **Committee Membership**   A mathematics department consists of ten men and eight women. Six mathematics faculty members are to be selected at random for the curriculum committee.
(a) What is the probability that two women and four men are selected?

(b) What is the probability that two or fewer women are selected?
(c) What is the probability that more than two women are selected?

65. **Class Photo**   Twenty students are arranged randomly in a row for a class picture. Paul wants to stand next to Phyllis. Find the probability that he gets his wish.

DISCOVERY ▪ DISCUSSION ▪ WRITING

66. **Oldest Son**   A family with two children is randomly selected. Assume that the events of having a boy or a girl are equally likely. Find the following probabilities.
(a) The family has two boys given that the oldest child is a boy.
(b) The family has two boys given that one of the children is a boy.

DISCOVERY PROJECT   Small Samples, Big Results

In this project we perform several experiments that show how we can obtain information about a big population from a small sample. You can find the project at the book companion website: **www.stewartmath.com**

SUGGESTED TIME AND EMPHASIS

1 class, optional material

14.3 BINOMIAL PROBABILITY

| Binomial Probability ▶ The Binomial Distribution

In this section we study a special kind of probability that plays a crucial role in modeling many real-world situations.

▼ Binomial Probability

Calculating the probability of independent events is studied on page 907.

A coin is weighted so that the probability of heads is 0.6. What is the probability of getting exactly two heads in five tosses of this coin? Since the tosses are independent, the probability of getting two heads followed by three tails is

$$0.6 \times 0.6 \times 0.4 \times 0.4 \times 0.4 = (0.6)^2(0.4)^3$$

But this is not the only way we can get exactly two heads. The two heads can occur, for example, on the second toss and the last toss. In this case the probability is

$$0.4 \times 0.6 \times 0.4 \times 0.4 \times 0.6 = (0.6)^2(0.4)^3$$

TEXT QUESTION

In the context of this section, if the probability of a "success" is p, is it possible to determine the probability of a failure? If so, what is it?

Answer

Yes, $1 - p$

In fact, the two heads could occur on any two of the five tosses. Thus there are $C(5, 2)$ ways in which this can happen, each with probability $(0.6)^2(0.4)^3$. It follows that

$$P(\text{exactly 2 heads in 5 tosses}) = C(5, 2)(0.6)^2(0.4)^3 \approx 0.023$$

The probability that we have just calculated is an example of a binomial probability. In general, a **binomial experiment** is one in which there are two outcomes, which are called "success" and "failure." In the coin-tossing experiment described above, "success" is getting "heads," and "failure" is getting "tails." The following box tells us how to calculate the probabilities associated with binomial experiments when we perform them many times.

BINOMIAL PROBABILITY

The name "binomial probability" is appropriate because $C(n, r)$ is the same as the binomial coefficient $\binom{n}{r}$ (see Exercise 86, page 900).

An experiment has two possible outcomes called "success" and "failure," with $P(\text{success}) = p$ and $P(\text{failure}) = 1 - p$. The probability of getting exactly r successes in n independent trials of the experiment is

$$P(r \text{ successes in } n \text{ trials}) = C(n, r)p^r(1 - p)^{n-r}$$

EXAMPLE 1 | Binomial Probability

A fair die is rolled 10 times. Find the probability of each event.

(a) Exactly 2 sixes.

(b) At most 1 six.

(c) At least 2 sixes.

SOLUTION Let's call "getting a six" success and "not getting a six" failure. So $P(\text{success}) = \frac{1}{6}$ and $P(\text{failure}) = \frac{5}{6}$. Since each roll of the die is independent of the other rolls, we can use the formula for binomial probability with $n = 10$ and $p = \frac{1}{6}$.

(a) $P(\text{exactly 2 sixes}) = C(10, 2)(\frac{1}{6})^2(\frac{5}{6})^8 \approx 0.29$

(b) The statement "at most 1 six" means 0 sixes or 1 six. So

$P(\text{at most one six})$

$= P(0 \text{ sixes or } 1 \text{ six})$ Meaning of "at most"

$= P(0 \text{ sixes}) + P(1 \text{ six})$ $P(A \text{ or } B) = P(A) + P(B)$

$= C(10, 0)\left(\dfrac{1}{6}\right)^0\left(\dfrac{5}{6}\right)^{10} + C(10, 1)\left(\dfrac{1}{6}\right)^1\left(\dfrac{5}{6}\right)^9$ Binomial probability

$\approx 0.1615 + 0.3230$ Calculator

≈ 0.4845 Calculator

(c) The statement "at least two sixes" means two or more sixes. Instead of adding the probabilities of getting 2, 3, 4, 5, 6, 7, 8, 9, or 10 sixes (which is a lot of work), it's easier to find the probability of the complement of this event. The complement of the event "two or more sixes" is "0 or 1 six." So

$P(\text{two or more sixes}) = 1 - P(0 \text{ or } 1 \text{ six})$ $P(E) = 1 - P(E')$

$= 1 - 0.4845$ From part (b)

$= 0.5155$ Calculator

✎ NOW TRY EXERCISES 3 AND 21 ∎

ALTERNATE EXAMPLE 1

When Liza plays Scrabble with her mother, the probability of her winning a game is 48%. When Liza visits her, they usually play five games during the course of the weekend.

(a) What is the probability that Liza will win exactly two games?

(b) What is the probability that Liza will win at most two games?

(c) What is the probability that Liza will win at least three games?

ANSWERS

(a) $C(5, 2)(0.48)^2(1 - 0.48)^{5-2}$ $= 32.4\%$

(b) $C(5, 0)(0.48)^0(1 - 0.48)^{5-0} +$ $C(5, 1)(0.48)^1(1 - 0.48)^{5-1} +$ $C(5, 2)(0.48)^2(1 - 0.48)^{5-2}$ $= 53.7\%$

(c) $100\% - 53.7\% = 46.3\%$

IN-CLASS MATERIALS

The derivation of the binomial probability formula is straightforward and should not be skipped. The text has a nice, quick explanation that can be discussed, perhaps using a die instead of a coin for variety.

ALTERNATE EXAMPLE 2

ALTERNATE EXAMPLE 2

The probability of getting a red gumball out of the gumball machine is 0.23. If you buy one a day for a week, what is the probability of getting at least two red gumballs?

ANSWER

$1 - C(7, 0)(0.23)^0(0.77)^7 - C(7, 1)(0.23)^1(0.77)^6 \approx 0.5040$

ALTERNATE EXAMPLE 3

A sibling throws rock, paper, and scissors with equal frequency when choosing who has to do the dishes. Make a table of the probability distribution and draw a histogram.

ANSWER

Item thrown	Probability
Rock	1/3
Paper	1/3
Scissors	1/3

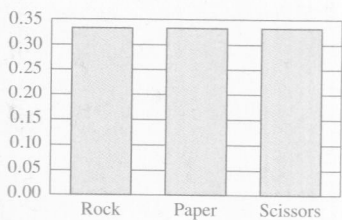

EXAMPLE 2 | Binomial Probability

Patients infected with a certain virus have a 40% chance of surviving. There are 10 patients in a hospital who have acquired this virus. Find the probability that 7 or more of the patients survive.

SOLUTION   Let's call the event "patient survives" success and the event "patient dies" failure. We are given that the probability of success is $p = 0.4$, so the probability of failure is $1 - p = 1 - 0.4 = 0.6$. We need to calculate the probability of 7, 8, 9, or 10 successes in 10 trials.

$$P(7 \text{ out of } 10 \text{ recover}) = C(10, 7)(0.4)^7(0.6)^3 \approx 0.04247$$
$$P(8 \text{ out of } 10 \text{ recover}) = C(10, 8)(0.4)^8(0.6)^2 \approx 0.01062$$
$$P(9 \text{ out of } 10 \text{ recover}) = C(10, 9)(0.4)^9(0.6)^1 \approx 0.00157$$
$$P(10 \text{ out of } 10 \text{ recover}) = C(10, 10)(0.4)^{10}(0.6)^0 \approx 0.00010$$

Adding the probabilities, we find that

$$P(7 \text{ or more recover}) \approx 0.05476$$

There is about a 1 in 20 chance that 7 or more patients recover.

✎. NOW TRY EXERCISE **35** ■

▼ The Binomial Distribution

We can describe how the probabilities of an experiment are "distributed" among all the outcomes of an experiment by making a table of values. The function that assigns to each outcome its corresponding probability is called a **probability distribution**. A bar graph of a probability distribution in which the width of each bar is 1 is called a **probability histogram**. The next example illustrates these concepts.

EXAMPLE 3 | Probability Distributions

Make a table of the probability distribution for the experiment of rolling a fair die and observing the number of dots. Draw a histogram of the distribution.

SOLUTION   When rolling a fair die each face has probability 1/6 of showing. The probability distribution is shown in the following table. To draw a histogram, we draw bars of width 1 and height $\frac{1}{6}$ corresponding to each outcome.

Probability Distribution

Outcome (dots)	Probability
1	$\frac{1}{6}$
2	$\frac{1}{6}$
3	$\frac{1}{6}$
4	$\frac{1}{6}$
5	$\frac{1}{6}$
6	$\frac{1}{6}$

Probability Histogram

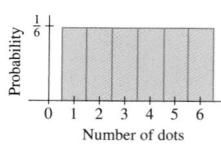

✎. NOW TRY EXERCISE **15** ■

IN-CLASS MATERIALS

Many people misunderstand the role of skill in games where skill and chance combine. For example, consider the game of cribbage. Assume that Tracy is so much better than Paul at cribbage that she wins three times as often as he does. (Given that cribbage is played with cards and has some degree of luck to it, she must be significantly better to overcome the vagaries of chance.) Assume they play once a day for a week. Have the students guess the chance that she will win every game. Repeat for two weeks. Then compute the chance that Paul wins two or fewer games.

A probability distribution in which all outcomes have the same probability is called a **uniform distribution**. The rolling-a-die experiment in Example 3 is a uniform distribution. The probability distribution of a binomial experiment is called a **binomial distribution**.

EXAMPLE 4 | A Binomial Distribution

A fair coin is tossed eight times, and the number of heads is observed. Make a table of the probability distribution, and draw a histogram. What is the number of heads that is most likely to show up?

SOLUTION   This is a binomial experiment with $n = 8$ and $p = \frac{1}{2}$, so $1 - p = \frac{1}{2}$ as well. We need to calculate the probability of getting 0 heads, 1 head, 2 heads, 3 heads, and so on. For example, to calculate the probability of 3 heads we have

$$P(3 \text{ heads}) = C(8, 3)\left(\frac{1}{2}\right)^3\left(\frac{1}{2}\right)^5 = \frac{28}{256}$$

The other entries in the following table are calculated similarly. We draw the histogram by making a bar for each outcome with width 1 and height equal to the corresponding probability.

Probability Distribution

Outcome (heads)	Probability
0	$\frac{1}{256}$
1	$\frac{8}{256}$
2	$\frac{28}{256}$
3	$\frac{56}{256}$
4	$\frac{70}{256}$
5	$\frac{56}{256}$
6	$\frac{28}{256}$
7	$\frac{8}{256}$
8	$\frac{1}{256}$

Probability Histogram

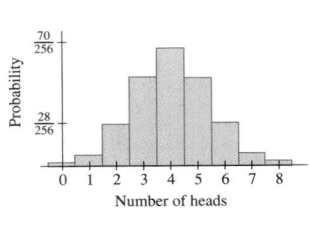

■ NOW TRY EXERCISE **17**

Notice that the sum of the probabilities in a probability distribution is 1, because the sum is the probability of the occurrence of *any* outcome in the sample space (this is the certain event).

14.3 EXERCISES

CONCEPTS

1. A binomial experiment is one in which there are exactly

_____ outcomes. One outcome is called _____,

and the other is called _____.

2. If a binomial experiment has probability p of success, then the

probability of failure is _____. The probability of getting exactly r successes in n trials of this experiment is

$C(\underline{\quad}, \underline{\quad})p^{\square}(1 - p)^{\square}$.

SKILLS

3–14 ■ Five independent trials of a binomial experiment with probability of success $p = 0.7$ are performed. Find the probability of each event.

3. Exactly two successes   **4.** Exactly three successes

5. No successes   **6.** All successes

7. Exactly one success   **8.** Exactly one failure

9. At least four successes   **10.** At least three successes

---

IN-CLASS MATERIALS

Problems such as "What is the probability that if five coins are tossed, there will be exactly n heads?" aren't that hard to verify experimentally, particularly if a computer or programmable calculator is used. A probability distribution or histogram can be drawn, and then experimental results can be compared with the theoretical results.

11. At most one failure   **12.** At most two failures

13. At least two successes   **14.** At most three failures

15–16 ■ An experiment is described. **(a)** Complete the table of the probability distribution. **(b)** Draw a probability histogram.

15. A jar contains five balls numbered 1 to 5. A ball is drawn at random, and the number of the ball is observed.

Outcome	Probability
1	0.2
2	
3	
4	
5	

16. A jar contains five balls numbered 1, three balls numbered 2, one ball numbered 3, and one ball numbered 4. A ball is drawn at random and the number of the ball is observed.

Outcome	Probability
1	0.5
2	
3	
4	
5	

17–20 ■ A binomial experiment with probability of success p is performed n times. **(a)** Make a table of the probability distribution. **(b)** Draw a probability histogram.

17. $n = 4$, $p = 0.5$ **18.** $n = 5$, $p = 0.4$

19. $n = 7$, $p = 0.2$ **20.** $n = 6$, $p = 0.9$

APPLICATIONS

21. Rolling Dice   Six dice are rolled. Find the probability that two of them show a four.

22. Archery   An archer hits his target 80% of the time. If he shoots seven arrows, what is the probability of each event?
(a) He never hits the target.
(b) He hits the target each time.
(c) He hits the target more than once.
(d) He hits the target at least five times.

23. Television Ratings   According to a ratings survey, 40% of the households in a certain city tune in to the local evening TV news. If ten households are visited at random, what is the probability that four of them will have their television tuned to the local news?

24. Spread of Disease   Health authorities estimate that 10% of the raccoons in a certain rural county are carriers of rabies. A dog is bitten by four different raccoons in this county. What is the probability that he was bitten by at least one rabies carrier?

25. Blood Type   About 45% of the populations of the United States and Canada have Type O blood.
(a) If a random sample of ten people is selected, what is the probability that exactly five have Type O blood?
(b) What is the probability that at least three of the random sample of ten have Type O blood?

26. Handedness   A psychologist needs 12 left-handed subjects for an experiment, and she interviews 15 potential subjects. About 10% of the population is left-handed.
(a) What is the probability that exactly 12 of the potential subjects are left-handed?
(b) What is the probability that 12 or more are left-handed?

27. Germination Rates   A certain brand of tomato seeds has a 0.75 probability of germinating. To increase the chance that at least one tomato plant per seed hill germinates, a gardener plants four seeds in each hill.
(a) What is the probability that at least one seed germinates in a given hill?
(b) What is the probability that two or more seeds will germinate in a given hill?
(c) What is the probability that all four seeds germinate in a given hill?

28. Genders of Children   Assume that for any given live human birth, the chances that the child is a boy or a girl are equally likely.
(a) What is the probability that in a family of five children a majority are boys?
(b) What is the probability that in a family of seven children a majority are girls?

29. Genders of Children   The ratio of male to female births is in fact not exactly one to one. The probability that a newborn turns out to be a male is about 0.52. A family has ten children.
(a) What is the probability that all ten children are boys?
(b) What is the probability all are girls?
(c) What is the probability that five are girls and five are boys?

30. Education Level   In a certain county 20% of the population has a college degree. A jury consisting of 12 people is selected at random from this county.
(a) What is the probability that exactly two of the jurors have a college degree?
(b) What is the probability that three or more of the jurors have a college degree?

31. Defective Light Bulbs   The DimBulb Lighting Company manufactures light bulbs for appliances such as ovens and refrigerators. Typically, 0.5% of their bulbs are defective.

EXAMPLES

When I play the "throw a dart" game at the carnival, I have a 5% chance of winning a doll.
(a) What is the probability I will win a least one doll if I play 10 times?
(b) I have two children. What is the probability I will win at least two dolls if I play 20 times?
(c) How many times do I have to play to have a 75% chance of winning at least two dolls?

Answers

(a) $1 - C(10, 0)\left(\dfrac{1}{20}\right)^0 \left(\dfrac{19}{20}\right)^{10} \approx 40\%$

(b) $1 - C(10, 0)\left(\dfrac{1}{20}\right)^0 \left(\dfrac{19}{20}\right)^{10} - C(10, 1)\left(\dfrac{1}{20}\right)^1 \left(\dfrac{19}{20}\right)^9 \approx 8.6\%$

(c) 36 times

From a crate with 100 bulbs, three are tested. Find the probability that the given event occurs.
(a) All three bulbs are defective.
(b) One or more bulbs is defective.

32. Quality Control An assembly line that manufactures fuses for automotive use is checked every hour to ensure the quality of the finished product. Ten fuses are selected randomly, and if any one of the ten is found to be defective, the process is halted and the machines are recalibrated. Suppose that at a certain time 5% of the fuses being produced are actually defective. What is the probability that the assembly line is halted at that hour's quality check?

33. Sick Leave The probability that a given worker at Dyno Nutrition will call in sick on a Monday is 0.04. The packaging department has eight workers. What is the probability that two or more packaging workers will call in sick next Monday?

34. Political Surveys In a certain county, 60% of the voters are in favor of an upcoming school bond initiative. If five voters are interviewed at random, what is the probability that exactly three of them will favor the initiative?

35. Pharmaceuticals A drug that is used to prevent motion sickness is found to be effective about 75% of the time. Six friends, all prone to seasickness, go on a sailing cruise, and all take the drug. Find the probability of each event.
(a) None of the friends gets seasick.
(b) All of the friends get seasick.
(c) Exactly three get seasick.
(d) At least two get seasick.

36. Reliability of a Machine A machine that is used in a manufacturing process has four separate components, each of which has a 0.01 probability of failing on any given day. If any component fails, the entire machine breaks down. Find the probability that on a given day the indicated event occurs.
(a) The machine breaks down.
(b) The machine does not break down.
(c) Only one component does not fail.

37. Genetics Huntington's disease is a hereditary ailment caused by a recessive gene. If both parents carry the gene but do not have the disease, there is a 0.25 probability that an offspring will fall victim to the condition. A newlywed couple find through genetic testing that they both carry the gene (but do not have the disease). If they intend to have four children, find the probability of each event.
(a) At least one child gets the disease.
(b) At least three of the children get the disease.

38. Selecting Cards Three cards are randomly selected from a standard 52-card deck, one at a time, with each card replaced in the deck before the next one is picked. Find the probability of each event.
(a) All three cards are hearts.
(b) Exactly two of the cards are spades.
(c) None of the cards is a diamond.
(d) At least one of the cards is a club.

39. Smokers and Nonsmokers The participants at a mathematics conference are housed dormitory-style, five to a room. Because of an oversight, conference organizers forget to ask whether the participants are smokers. In fact, it turns out that 30% are smokers. Find the probability that Fred, a nonsmoking conference participant, will be housed with:
(a) Exactly one smoker.
(b) One or more smokers.

40. Telephone Marketing A mortgage company advertises its rates by making unsolicited telephone calls to random numbers. About 2% of the calls reach consumers who are interested in the company's services. A telephone consultant can make 100 calls per evening shift.
(a) What is the probability that two or more calls will reach an interested party in one shift?
(b) How many calls does a consultant need to make to ensure at least a 0.5 probability of reaching one or more interested parties? [*Hint:* Use trial and error.]

41. Effectiveness of a Drug A certain disease has a mortality rate of 60%. A new drug is tested for its effectiveness against this disease. Ten patients are given the drug, and eight of them recover.
(a) Find the probability that eight or more of the patients would have recovered without the drug.
(b) Does the drug appear to be effective? (Consider the drug effective if the probability in part (a) is 0.05 or less.)

42. Hitting a Target An archer normally hits the target with probability of 0.6. She hires a new coach for a series of special lessons. After the lessons she hits the target in five out of eight attempts.
(a) Find the probability that she would have hit five or more out of the eight attempts before her lessons with the new coach.
(b) Did the new coaching appear to make a difference? (Consider the coaching effective if the probability in part (a) is 0.05 or less.)

DISCOVERY ▪ DISCUSSION ▪ WRITING

43. Most Likely Outcome for *n* Tosses of a Coin A balanced coin is tossed *n* times. In this exercise we investigate the following question: What is the number of heads that has the greatest probability of occurring? Note that for a balanced coin the probability of heads is $p = 0.5$.

(a) Suppose $n = 8$. Draw a probability histogram for the resulting binomial distribution. What number of heads has the greatest probability of occurring? If $n = 100$, what number of heads has the greatest probability of occurring?

(b) Suppose $n = 9$. Draw a probability histogram for the resulting binomial distribution. What number of heads has the greatest probability of occurring? If $n = 101$, what number of heads has the greatest probability of occurring?

14.4 EXPECTED VALUE

| Expected Value ▶ What Is a Fair Game?

In this section we study an important application of probability called *expected value*.

▼ Expected Value

Suppose that a coin has probability 0.8 of showing heads. If the coin is tossed many times, we would *expect* to get heads about 80% of the time. Now, suppose that you get a payout of one dollar for each head. If you play this game many times, you would expect *on average* to gain $0.80 per game:

$$\begin{pmatrix} \text{Expected payout} \\ \text{per game} \end{pmatrix} = \begin{pmatrix} \text{Amount of payout} \\ \text{per game} \end{pmatrix} \times \begin{pmatrix} \text{Probability of payout} \\ \text{per game} \end{pmatrix}$$

$$= \$1.00 \times 0.80 = \$0.80$$

The reasoning in this example motivates the following definition.

DEFINITION OF EXPECTED VALUE

A game gives payouts $a_1, a_2, \ldots, a_n$ with probabilities $p_1, p_2, \ldots, p_n$. The **expected value** (or **expectation**) E of this game is

$$E = a_1p_1 + a_2p_2 + \cdots + a_np_n$$

EXAMPLE 1 | Finding Expected Value

A die is rolled, and you receive $1 for each point that shows. What is your expectation?

SOLUTION Each face of the die has probability $\frac{1}{6}$ of showing. So you get $1 with probability $\frac{1}{6}$, $2 with probability $\frac{1}{6}$, $3 with probability $\frac{1}{6}$, and so on. Thus the expected value is

$$E = 1\left(\frac{1}{6}\right) + 2\left(\frac{1}{6}\right) + 3\left(\frac{1}{6}\right) + 4\left(\frac{1}{6}\right) + 5\left(\frac{1}{6}\right) + 6\left(\frac{1}{6}\right) = 3.5$$

So if you play this game many times, you will make, on average, $3.50 per game.

◥. NOW TRY EXERCISE **3** ■

EXAMPLE 2 | Finding Expected Value

In Monte Carlo the game of roulette is played on a wheel with slots numbered 0, 1, 2, . . . , 36. The wheel is spun, and a ball dropped in the wheel is equally likely to end up in any

---

ALTERNATE EXAMPLE 1

A sales clerk works for commission only. If 20% of the customers purchase an item for which the clerk gets a $3 commission, 10% purchase an item for which the clerk gets a $5 commission, and 5% purchase an item for which the clerk gets an $8 commission, what is the expected value per customer who enters the store?

ANSWER

$1.50

ALTERNATE EXAMPLE 2

A game consists of rolling a die. You receive the face value in dollars if an odd number is rolled. If the game costs $1.50 to play, what is the expected value to you?

ANSWER

The expected value is 0.

TEXT QUESTION

I'm going to roll a die. I'll pay you $1 if I roll a 1, and $3 if I roll an even number. What is the expected value of this game?

Answer:

$\frac{5}{3} \approx \$1.67$

one of the slots. To play the game, you bet $1 on any number. (For example, you may bet $1 on number 23.) If the ball stops in your slot, you get $36 (the $1 you bet plus $35). Find the expected value of this game.

SOLUTION   The gambler can gain $35 with probability $\frac{1}{37}$ and can lose $1 with probability $\frac{36}{37}$. So the gambler's expected value is

$$E = (35)\frac{1}{37} + (-1)\frac{36}{37} \approx -0.027$$

In other words, if you play this game many times, you would expect to lose 2.7 cents on every dollar you bet (on average). Consequently, the house expects to gain 2.7 cents on every dollar that is bet.

✎ NOW TRY EXERCISE **13**   ■

EXAMPLE 3 | Expected Number

At any given time, the express checkout lane at a small supermarket has three shoppers in line with probability 0.2, two shoppers with probability 0.5, one shopper with probability 0.2, and no shoppers with probability 0.1. If you go to this market, how many shoppers would you expect to find waiting in the express checkout lane?

SOLUTION   The "payouts" here are the number of shoppers waiting in line. To find the expected number of shoppers waiting in line, we multiply each "payout" by its probability and add the results.

$$E = 3(0.2) + 2(0.5) + 1(0.2) + 0(0.1) = 1.8$$

So on average, you would expect 1.8 shoppers waiting in the express lane.

✎ NOW TRY EXERCISE **21**   ■

▼ What Is a Fair Game?

A **fair game** is game with expected value zero. So if you play a fair game many times, you would expect, on average, to break even.

EXAMPLE 4 | A Fair Game?

Suppose that you play the following game. A card is drawn from a deck. If the card is an ace, you get a payout of $10. If the card is not an ace, you have to pay $1.

(a) Is this a fair game?

(b) If the game is not fair, find the payout amount that would make this game a fair game.

MATHEMATICS IN THE MODERN WORLD

Fair Voting Methods
The methods of mathematics have recently been applied to problems in the social sciences. For example, how do we find fair voting methods? You may ask, "What is the problem with how we vote in elections?" Well, suppose candidates A, B, and C are running for president. The final vote tally is as follows: A gets 40%, B gets 39%, and C gets 21%. So candidate A wins. But 60% of the voters *didn't* want A. Moreover, suppose you voted for C, but you dislike A so much that you would have been willing to change your vote to B to avoid having A win. Suppose most of the voters who voted for C feel the same way you do. Then we have a situation in which most of the voters prefer B over A, but A wins. Is that fair?
    In the 1950s Kenneth Arrow showed mathematically that no democratic method of voting can be completely fair; he later won a Nobel

Prize for his work. Mathematicians continue to work on finding fairer voting systems. The system that is most often used in federal, state, and local elections is called *plurality voting* (the candidate with the most votes wins). Other systems include *majority voting* (if no candidate gets a majority, a runoff is held between the top two vote-getters), *approval voting* (each voter can vote for as many candidates as he or she approves of), *preference voting* (each voter orders the candidates according to his or her preference), and *cumulative voting* (each voter gets as many votes as there are candidates and can give all of his or her votes to one candidate or distribute them among the candidates as he or she sees fit). This last system is often used to select corporate boards of directors. Each system of voting has both advantages and disadvantages.

IN-CLASS MATERIALS

- Describe the law of large numbers. If you play a game long enough, your average winnings will approach your expectation. But there are no guarantees for the short term. If you have a 99.9% chance of losing $1 and a 0.1% chance of winning $10,000, the game has a highly positive expected value, but it would be a bad idea to play without a dollar in your pocket.

- The concept of expected value can be used to foreshadow the idea of standard deviation. Consider these two deals:

Game 1: You pay $100 to play. There is a 1 in 1000 chance of winning $101,000.
Game 2: I give you a dollar, no questions asked.
Ask your students which game they would rather play. Let them discuss and debate (fostering debate if necessary). Point out that both games have the same expected value, but they are qualitatively different. The fact that people have preferences one way or another shows that they are different. Now you can discuss the idea of standard deviation.

SOLUTION

(a) In this game you get a payout of $10 if an ace is drawn (probability $\frac{4}{52}$), and you lose $1 if any other card is drawn (probability $\frac{48}{52}$). So the expected value is

$$E = 10\left(\frac{4}{52}\right) - 1\left(\frac{48}{52}\right) = -\frac{8}{52}$$

Since the expected value is not zero, the game is not fair. If you play this game many times, you would expect to lose, on average, $\frac{8}{52} \approx \$0.15$ per game.

(b) We want to find the payout x that makes the expected value 0.

$$E = x\left(\frac{4}{52}\right) - 1\left(\frac{48}{52}\right) = 0$$

Solving this equation we get $x = 12$. So a payout of $12 for an ace would make this a fair game.

✎. NOW TRY EXERCISE **25**

Games of chance in casinos are never fair; the gambler always has a negative expected value (as in Examples 2 and 4(a)). This makes gambling profitable for the casino and unprofitable for the gambler.

14.4 EXERCISES

CONCEPTS

1. If a game gives payoffs of $10 and $100 with probabilities 0.9 and 0.1, respectively, then the expected value of this game is

   $E = $ _____ $\times 0.9 + $ _____ $\times 0.1 = $ _____

2. If you played the game in Exercise 1 many times, then you would expect your average payoff per game to be about

   $ _____ .

SKILLS

3–12 ■ Find the expected value (or expectation) of the games described.

✎. 3. Mike wins $2 if a coin toss shows heads and $1 if it shows tails.

4. Jane wins $10 if a die roll shows a six, and she loses $1 otherwise.

5. The game consists of drawing a card from a deck. You win $100 if you draw the ace of spades or lose $1 if you draw any other card.

6. Tim wins $3 if a coin toss shows heads or $2 if it shows tails.

7. Carol wins $3 if a die roll shows a six, and she wins $0.50 otherwise.

8. A coin is tossed twice. Albert wins $2 for each heads and must pay $1 for each tails.

9. A die is rolled. Tom wins $2 if the die shows an even number, and he pays $2 otherwise.

10. A card is drawn from a deck. You win $104 if the card is an ace, $26 if it is a face card, and $13 if it is the 8 of clubs.

11. A bag contains two silver dollars and eight slugs. You pay 50 cents to reach into the bag and take a coin, which you get to keep.

12. A bag contains eight white balls and two black balls. John picks two balls at random from the bag, and he wins $5 if he does not pick a black ball.

APPLICATIONS

✎. 13. **Roulette** In the game of roulette as played in Las Vegas, the wheel has 38 slots. Two slots are numbered 0 and 00, and the rest are numbered 1 to 36. A $1 bet on any number wins $36 ($35 plus the $1 bet). Find the expected value of this game.

14. **Sweepstakes** A sweepstakes offers a first prize of $1,000,000, second prize of $100,000, and third prize of $10,000. Suppose that two million people enter the contest and three names are drawn randomly for the three prizes.
    (a) Find the expected winnings for a person participating in this contest.
    (b) Is it worth paying a dollar to enter this sweepstakes?

15. **A Game of Chance** A box contains 100 envelopes. Ten envelopes contain $10 each, ten contain $5 each, two are "unlucky," and the rest are empty. A player draws an envelope from the box and keeps whatever is in it. If a person draws an unlucky envelope, however, he must pay $100. What is the expectation of a person playing this game?

DRILL QUESTION

Is it possible for the expected value of a game to be $3.50 if you can win only a whole number of dollars at the game? Why or why not?

Answer

Sure. If you flip a coin and get $4 for heads and $3 for tails, the expected value is $3.50.

EXAMPLES

(a) Frances had a garage sale. A total of 50% of the people didn't buy anything, 30% of the people spent $5, and 20% spent $10. What is the expected value of a sale?

(b) A random number between 1 and 333 is picked. If the number is divisible by 3, I give you $10. If not, you give me $10. What is the expected value of this game for you?

Answers

(a) $3.50

(b) $-10/3$

16. Combination Lock A safe containing $1,000,000 is locked with a combination lock. You pay $1 for one guess at the six-digit combination. If you open the lock, you get to keep the million dollars. What is your expectation?

17. Gambling on Stocks An investor buys 1000 shares of a risky stock for $5 a share. She estimates that the probability that the stock will rise in value to $20 a share is 0.1 and the probability that it will fall to $1 a share is 0.9. If the only criterion for her decision to buy this stock was the expected value of her profit, did she make a wise investment?

18. Slot Machine A slot machine has three wheels, and each wheel has 11 positions: the digits 0, 1, 2, . . . , 9 and the picture of a watermelon. When a quarter is placed in the machine and the handle is pulled, the three wheels spin independently and come to rest. When three watermelons show, the machine pays the player $5; otherwise, nothing is paid. What is the expected value of this game?

19. Lottery In a 6/49 lottery game, a player pays $1 and selects six numbers from 1 to 49. Any player who has chosen the six winning numbers wins $1,000,000. Assuming that this is the only way to win, what is the expected value of this game?

20. Lightning Insurance An insurance company has determined that in a certain region the probability of lightning striking a house in a given year is about 0.0003, and the average cost of repairs of lightning damage is $7500 per incident. The company charges $25 per year for lightning insurance.
   (a) Find the company's expected value for each lightning insurance policy.
   (b) If the company has 450,000 lightning damage policies, what is the company's expected yearly income from lightning insurance?

21. Expected Number During the school year, a college student watches TV for two hours a week with probability 0.15, three hours with probability 0.45, four hours with probability 0.30, and five hours with probability 0.10. Find the expected number of hours of TV that he watches per week.

22. Expected Number In a large liberal arts college 5% of the students are studying three foreign languages, 15% are studying two foreign languages, 45% are studying one foreign language, and 35% are not studying a foreign language. If a student is selected at random, find the expected number of foreign languages that he or she is studying.

23. Expected Number A student goes to swim practice several times a week. In any given week the probability that he swims three times is 0.30, two times is 0.45, one time is 0.15, and no times is 0.10. Find the expected number of times the student goes to practice in any given week.

24. Expected Number Consider families with three children, and assume that the probability of having a girl is $\frac{1}{2}$.
   (a) Complete the table for the probabilities of having 0, 1, 2, or 3 girls in a family of three children.
   (b) Find the expected number of girls in a family of three children.

Number of girls	Probability
0	$\frac{1}{8}$
1	
2	
3	

25–30 ■ A game of chance is described. (a) Is the game fair? (b) If the game is not fair, find the payout amount that would make the game fair.

25. A Fair Game? A card is drawn from a deck. If the card is the ace of spades you get a payout of $12. If the card is not an ace you have to pay $0.50.

26. A Fair Game? A die is rolled. You get $20 if a one or a six shows; otherwise, you pay $10.

27. A Fair Game? A pair of dice is rolled. You get $30 if two ones show; otherwise, you pay $2.

28. A Fair Game? A die is rolled and a coin is tossed. If the result is a "six" and "heads," you get $10. For any other result you pay $1.

29. A Fair Game? A card is drawn from a deck, a die is rolled, and a coin is tossed. If the result is the "ace of spades," a "six," and "heads," you get $600. For any other result you pay $1.

30. A Fair Game? A bag contains two silver dollars and six slugs. A game consists of reaching into the bag and drawing a coin, which you get to keep. If you draw a slug, you pay $0.50.

DISCOVERY ■ DISCUSSION ■ WRITING

31. The Expected Value of a Sweepstakes Contest
A magazine clearinghouse holds a sweepstakes contest to sell subscriptions. If you return the winning number, you win $1,000,000. You have a 1-in-20-million chance of winning, but your only cost to enter the contest is a first-class stamp to mail the entry. Use the current price of a first-class stamp to calculate your expected net winnings if you enter this contest. Is it worth entering the contest?

SUGGESTED TIME AND EMPHASIS

1–3 classes, depending on coverage, optional material

14.5 DESCRIPTIVE STATISTICS (NUMERICAL)

Measures of Central Tendency: Mean, Median, Mode ▶ Organizing Data: Frequency Tables and Stemplots ▶ Measures of Spread: Variance and Standard Deviation ▶ The Five-Number Summary: Box Plots

In *Focus on Modeling* on pages 130–139 we studied **two-variable data**. For example, the data on page 133 measure *two* quantities: asbestos level *and* number of cancer tumors for each individual rat.

Our world is filled with data: weather data, economic data, health data, medical data, political data, census data, and many more. The things that a data set describes are called **individuals**. So individuals could be people, trees, buildings, etc. The property of the individuals that is described by the data is called a **variable**. In this chapter we study **one-variable data**, in which only one property of each individual is measured. For example, the individuals of a data set could be cows, and the variable could be milk production in gallons for each cow.

Data usually consist of thousands or even millions of numbers. The first goal of statistics is to describe such huge sets of data in simpler terms. A **summary statistic** is a single number that summarizes some property of the data. For example, the *average* of a data set is a single number that tells us where the "center" of the data lies. In this section we study several summary statistics.

▼ Measures of Central Tendency: Mean, Median, Mode

One way to make sense of data is to find a "typical" number or the "center" of the data. Any such number is called a **measure of central tendency**. One measure of central tendency is the average (or the mean).

The mean is a summary statistic.

THE MEAN

Let $x_1, x_2, \ldots, x_n$ be n data points. The **mean** (or **average**), denoted by $\bar{x}$, is the sum divided by n:

$$\bar{x} = \frac{x_1 + x_2 + \cdots + x_n}{n}$$

ALTERNATE EXAMPLE 1

The ages (in years) of a certain group of college students are given in the table. Find the average age of someone in the group:

17	18	18	18	18	19	19	19	19	41

ANSWER

20.6

EXAMPLE 1 | The Mean Age of Preschoolers

The ages (in years) of the students in a certain class of preschoolers are listed below. Find the average age of a preschooler in this class.

2 2 2 3 3 3 4 4 4 4 4 5

SOLUTION Since the number of children in the class is 12, we find the average by adding up the ages of the children and dividing by 12:

$$\bar{x} = \frac{2 + 2 + 2 + 3 + 3 + 3 + 4 + 4 + 4 + 4 + 4 + 5}{12} = \frac{40}{12} \approx 3.3$$

So the average age of a preschooler in this class is about 3.3 years.

✎ NOW TRY EXERCISES **5** AND **25**

Another measure of central tendency is the *median,* which is the middle number of an ordered list of numbers—there are as many data points above the median as there are below it.

TEXT QUESTION

What advantage does a stem plot have over a histogram of the same data?

Answer

A stem plot allows one to recover the actual data from the picture.

> **THE MEDIAN**
>
> Let $x_1, x_2, \ldots, x_n$ be n data points, written in increasing order.
> - If n is odd, the **median** is the middle number.
> - If n is even, the **median** is the average of the two middle numbers.

The median is a summary statistic.

EXAMPLE 2 | Mean and Median Income

The yearly incomes (in thousands of dollars) of five college graduates are listed below.

$$280 \quad 56 \quad 59 \quad 62 \quad 51$$

(a) Find the mean income.

(b) Find the median income.

(c) Which do you think is a better indicator of central tendency in this case: the mean or the median?

SOLUTION

(a) We add the incomes and divide by 5:

$$\bar{x} = \frac{280 + 56 + 59 + 62 + 51}{5} \approx 102$$

So the average income of the five graduates is about $102,000.

(b) To find the median income, we first put the list of incomes in increasing order:

$$51 \quad 56 \quad 59 \quad 62 \quad 280$$

Since there are five numbers in this list and 5 is odd, the median is the middle number, 59. So the median income of the five graduates is $59,000.

(c) We see from parts (a) and (b) that the mean and the median are different. The average income of the five graduates is $102,000, but this is not the typical income. In fact, not one of the graduates had an income even close to $102,000. However, the median income of $59,000 is a more typical income for these five graduates. So in this case the median income is a better description of the central tendency than the mean is.

Graphing Calculator Note   To obtain summary statistics on the TI-83 graphing calculator, follow the steps on page 929. The calculator output for the data in this example is shown in Figure 1.

```
1-Var Stats
  x̄=102
   ⋮
  Med=59
   ⋮
```

FIGURE 1

✎. NOW TRY EXERCISES **9** AND **27** ∎

If a data set includes a number that is "far out" or far away from the rest of the data, that data point is called an **outlier**. In Example 2, $280,000 is an outlier. In general, when a data set has outliers, the median is a better indicator of central tendency than the mean.

EXAMPLE 3 | Effect of Outliers on the Mean and Median

The table in the margin gives the selling prices of houses sold in 2007 in a small coastal California town.

Address	Selling price ($)
First Street	210,000
Elm Street	260,000
Ocean Avenue	1,800,000
Desert Lane	245,000
Cactus Lane	230,000
Jacaranda Avenue	255,000

(a) Find the mean house price.

(b) Find the median house price.

(c) The house on Ocean Avenue is resold the same year for $2,400,000. Find the mean and median house price for the adjusted data.

(d) Comment on the effects of outliers on the mean and median.

The National Association of Realtors publishes yearly data on the *median* price of a house, not the average price. This is because the few houses that cost tens of millions of dollars are outliers. These outliers have a large effect on the average price but not on the median price, as we see from Example 3.

SOLUTION

(a) Writing the prices in thousands of dollars, we have

$$\bar{x} = \frac{210 + 260 + 1{,}800 + 245 + 230 + 255}{6} = 500$$

So the average house price is $500,000.

(b) To find the median, we first arrange the prices in order.

$$210 \quad 230 \quad \underbrace{245 \quad 255}_{\text{Middle two numbers}} \quad 260 \quad 1800$$

Since there is an even number of prices, the median is the average of the middle two numbers:

$$\text{median} = \frac{245 + 255}{2} = 250$$

So the median house price is $250,000.

(c) For the revised data

$$\bar{x} = \frac{210 + 260 + 2{,}400 + 245 + 230 + 255}{6} = 600$$

So the mean price for the revised data is $600,000. But the median price is unchanged at $250,000.

(d) The $1,800,000 price is an outlier. Because of this outlier the average price of $500,000 is not a typical price (the majority of houses sold for prices in the 200,000s). The median of $250,000 is a more typical price. We observe that changing the value of an outlier affects the average but not the median (as long as the change in the outlier keeps the outlier on the same side of the median).

NOW TRY EXERCISE 31 ∎

The *mode* of a data set is a summary statistic that is usually less informative than the mean or median, but has the advantage of not being limited to numerical data.

The mode is a summary statistic.

> **THE MODE**
>
> The **mode** of a data set is the element that appears most often in the data.

For example, the mode of the (non-numerical) data consisting of Korean last names is Kim. The mode of the data set 1, 1, 2, 2, 2, 3, 5, 8 is the number 2. The data set 1, 2, 2, 3, 5, 5, 8 has two modes: 2 and 5. Data sets with two modes are called **bimodal**. The data set 1, 2, 4, 5, 7, 8 has **no mode**.

▼ Organizing Data: Frequency Tables and Stemplots

Sometimes listing the data in a special way can help us get useful information about the data. Two such methods are *frequency tables* and *stemplots*.

A **frequency table** for a set of data is a table that includes each different data point and the number of times that point occurs in the data. The mode is most easily determined from a frequency table.

EXAMPLE

The mean, median, mode, and standard deviation for a data set:
12, 6, 6, 7, 9, 5, 3, 7, 9, 9, 6, 3, 5, 3, 4, 4, 7, 9, 9, 9, 10, 8, 11, 3, 8, 5, 4, 6, 6, 5
Mean: 6.6; median: 6; mode: 9; standard deviation: 2.471

Frequency Table

Score	Frequency
5	16
4	8
3	5
2	5
1	3
0	3

In Example 5 the mean, median, and mode are different from each other, and each gives us different information about the central tendency of the data.

EXAMPLE 4 | Using a Frequency Table

The scores obtained by the students in an algebra class on a five-question quiz are given in the frequency table in the margin. Find the mean, median, and mode of the scores.

SOLUTION The mode is 5, because more students got this score than any other score.

The total number of quizzes is $16 + 8 + 5 + 5 + 3 + 3 = 40$. To find the mean, we add all the scores and divide by 40. Note that the score 5 occurs 16 times, the score 4 occurs 8 times, and so on. So the mean score is

$$\frac{5(16) + 4(8) + 3(5) + 2(5) + 1(3) + 0(3)}{40} = 3.5$$

There are 40 students in this class. If we rank the scores from highest to lowest, the median score is the average of the 20th and 21st scores. Looking down the frequency column in the table, we see that these scores are each 4. So the median score is 4.

Graphing Calculator Note To obtain the mean and median on the TI-83, follow the instructions on page 929 for calculating with data given by a frequency table.

✎. NOW TRY EXERCISES **15** AND **35** ∎

A **stemplot** (or a **stem-and-leaf plot**) organizes the data by using the digits of the numbers in the data. Each number in the data is written as a **stem** consisting of the leftmost digits and a **leaf** consisting of the rightmost digit. Numbers with the same stem are grouped together in a row, with the stem written only once. The next example illustrates the method.

EXAMPLE 5 | Making a Stem-and-Leaf Plot

Swim Times (s)

42.8	41.5	42.7	46.2
41.1	42.9	40.2	43.6
42.7	39.5	43.1	40.5
43.3	41.1	46.7	42.7

A county swim club records the times (in seconds) shown in the margin for the 50-yard freestyle swim event.

(a) Make a stem-and-leaf plot of the data.

(b) Find the median and mode using the stemplot from part (a).

SOLUTION

(a) We use the first two digits for the stems and the digit after the decimal point for the leaves. For example, 39.5 has stem 39 and leaf 5.

We include the stems that have no leaves, because they provide information about the data. In this case no swimmer had a time in the 44- or 45-second range.

```
Stem | Leaves
  39 | 5
  40 | 2 5
  41 | 1 1 5
  42 | 7 7 7 8 9
  43 | 1 3 6
  44 |
  45 |
  46 | 2 7
```
39 | 5 means 39.5

(b) There are 16 data points. The stem-and-leaf plot displays the data in increasing order. So to find the median, we count the leaves starting at the smallest data point until we reach the middle two numbers (the eighth and ninth leaves). The corresponding data points are 42.7 and 42.8, so the median is

$$\text{median} = \frac{42.7 + 42.8}{2} = 42.75$$

The mode is the number that appears most often in the data. We can see from the stem-and-leaf plot that this number is 42.7.

✎. NOW TRY EXERCISES **17** AND **37** ∎

ALTERNATE EXAMPLE 6

A stem plot of the scores of a group of bowlers is shown:

```
11 | 1
12 |
13 | 0 0 3 9 9
14 | 1 3 3 4 4 6 6 7 7 7 8 9
15 | 0 1 1 2 3 4 7
16 | 3 3 6 8
17 | 3 6 7
18 | 2
19 | 7
20 |
21 | 2
```

(a) How many bowlers scored 147?

(b) How many bowlers scored in the 150s?

(c) What was the total number of bowlers?

(d) What are the best and worst scores?

(e) Find the mean, median, and mode.

ANSWERS

(a) 3

(b) 7

(c) 35

(d) 111, 212

(e) Mean: 153.49; median: 149; mode: 147

Stem	Leaves
0	5
1	7
2	9 9
3	
4	
5	5 6 6
6	2 8 9 9 9 9
7	3 4
8	3
9	8

2 | 8 means 28

EXAMPLE 6 | Reading a Stem-and-Leaf Plot

A stemplot of the ages of patients in a hospital ward is shown in the margin.

(a) How many patients are 56 years old?

(b) How many patients are in their 50s? In their 40s?

(c) What is the total number of patients in the ward?

(d) What age group had the most patients?

(e) What are the ages of the youngest and oldest patients?

(f) Find the mean, median, and mode.

SOLUTION From the statement "2 | 8 means 28" we see that the stem represents the tens digit and the leaves represent the units digit. Reading the stemplot starting at the lowest age, we get 5, 17, 29, 29, 55, 56, 56, and so on until we reach 98.

(a) Two patients are 56 years old.

(b) Counting the leaves that correspond to the stem 5, we see that there are three patients in their 50s. There are no patients in their 40s.

(c) Counting all the leaves, we see that there are 17 patients.

(d) The stem with the most leaves is 6, so the patients in their 60s are the largest group.

(e) The youngest patient is 5, and the oldest is 98.

(f) The mode is 69. There are 17 patients, so the median is the middle age (the ninth age), which is 68. To find the mean, we add all the ages and divide by 17:

$$\bar{x} = \frac{5 + 17 + 2(29) + 55 + 2(56) + 62 + 68 + 4(69) + 73 + 74 + 83 + 98}{17} \approx 57.7$$

So the mean age is approximately 57.7 years.

◥ NOW TRY EXERCISES **19** AND **39**   ∎

▼ Measures of Spread: Variance and Standard Deviation

Measures of central tendency identify the "center" or "typical value" of the data. **Measures of spread** (also called **measures of dispersion**) describe the spread or variability of the data around a central value. For example, each of the following data sets has mean 72, but it is clear that the first set of data has more variability than the second.

$$50, 58, 78, 81, 93 \qquad 72, 71, 72, 72, 73$$

The most important measures of variability in statistics are the *variance* and *standard deviation*.

The standard deviation and variance are summary statistics.

The symbol σ is the lower case Greek letter "sigma."

THE VARIANCE AND STANDARD DEVIATION

Let $x_1, x_2, \ldots, x_N$ be N data points, and let $\bar{x}$ be their mean. The **standard deviation** of the data is

$$\sigma = \sqrt{\frac{1}{N}\sum_{k=1}^{N}(x_k - \bar{x})^2}$$

The **variance** is σ^2, the square of the standard deviation.

EXAMPLE 7 | Calculating Standard Deviation

Two machines are used in filling 16-ounce soda bottles. To test how consistently each machine fills the bottles, a sample of 20 bottles from the output of each machine is selected. Find the standard deviation for each machine. Which machine is more consistent in filling the bottles?

Soda Machine I (x)				Soda Machine II (y)			
16.2	16.1	15.9	16.0	16.1	16.2	16.4	.15.8
16.4	16.1	16.1	16.1	16.2	15.6	16.3	16.3
15.8	15.9	16.1	15.8	16.8	15.4	16.0	15.6
16.0	16.0	16.2	15.9	15.8	16.2	16.2	16.1
16.3	16.1	16.0	16.0	16.3	15.8	16.0	15.9

SOLUTION   The first step is to find the mean for each soda machine:

$$\bar{x} = \frac{16.2 + 16.1 + \cdots + 16.0}{20} = 16.05$$

$$\bar{y} = \frac{16.1 + 16.2 + \cdots + 15.9}{20} = 16.05$$

The standard deviations σ_x and σ_y for Soda Machines I and II, respectively, are

$$\sigma_x = \sqrt{\frac{(16.2 - 16.05)^2 + (16.1 - 16.05)^2 + \cdots + (16.0 - 16.05)^2}{20}} \approx 0.15$$

$$\sigma_y = \sqrt{\frac{(16.1 - 16.05)^2 + (16.2 - 16.05)^2 + \cdots + (15.9 - 16.05)^2}{20}} \approx 0.32$$

Soda Machine I is more consistent in filling the bottles because the standard deviation of the data from Machine I is much smaller than that of the data from Machine II.

Graphing Calculator Note   Follow the steps on page 929 to obtain summary statistics on the TI-83 graphing calculator. The calculator output for Machine I is shown in Figure 2.

```
1-Var Stats
x̄=16.05
  ⋮
σx=.15
  ⋮
```

FIGURE 2

◄. NOW TRY EXERCISES **21** AND **41**   ■

▼ The Five-Number Summary: Box Plots

A simple indicator of the spread of data is the location of the **minimum** and **maximum** values. Other indicators of spread are the *quartiles*. Recall that the median divides a data set in half. The median of the lower half of the data is called the **first quartile**, Q_1. The median of the upper half of the data is called the **third quartile**, Q_3. The minimum, maximum, median, and first and third quartiles together give a good picture of the spread *and* center of the data.

THE FIVE-NUMBER SUMMARY

The **five-number summary** for a data set are the five numbers below, written in the indicated order.

minimum, Q_1, median, Q_3, maximum

ALTERNATE EXAMPLE 7
A machine is used for filling 16-oz soda bottles. Find the standard deviation for the following machine, given the list of samples below:

16.0	16.1	15.9	15.9
16.3	16.0	16.2	16.2
15.8	15.7	16.3	16.0
16.0	16.4	16.1	15.7
16.3	16.2	16.0	15.9

ANSWER
Mean: 16.05; standard deviation: 0.196

Figure 3 shows how these five numbers are related for a data set listed in order. For the data in the figure, $Q_1 = (2 + 4)/2 = 3$ and $Q_3 = (16 + 20)/2 = 18$.

1   2   2   4   8   9   10   12   14   16   20   21   31
Min Q_1 Med Q_3 Max

FIGURE 3 The five-number summary

The five-number summary allows us to quickly calculate the following two different indicators of spread. A simple indicator of spread is the **range**, which is the difference between the maximum and minimum values:

$$\text{Range} = \text{Maximum} - \text{Minimum}$$

This can be compared to the spread of the middle of the data as measured by the **interquartile range (IQR)**, which is the difference between the third and first quartiles:

$$\text{IQR} = Q_3 - Q_1$$

For the data in Figure 3 the range is $41 - 1 = 40$, and the interquartile range is $\text{IQR} = 18 - 3 = 15$.

EXAMPLE 8 | Using a Five-Number Summary

The lists in the margin give HDL cholesterol levels ("good cholesterol") for 17 male and 13 females who participated in a health survey. Find the five-number summary for each group. Compare the center and the spread in cholesterol levels for the two groups.

SOLUTION   For each group we first arrange the data in ascending order and then find the median. Next we find Q_1, the median of the lower half of the data, and Q_3, the median of the upper half of the data. You can check that the five-number summaries are as follows:

Males: 29, 30.5, 41, 48, 55
Females: 46, 49.5, 53, 55.5, 60

The range and interquartile range are calculated as follows:

Males: Range $= 55 - 29 = 26$ IQR $= 48 - 30.5 = 17.5$
Females: Range $= 60 - 46 = 14$ IQR $= 55.5 - 49.5 = 6.0$

We first observe that the median HDL level for females, 53, is significantly higher than that of the males, 41. Moreover, female HDL levels show considerably less variability than the males, as measured by the IQR.

Graphing Calculator Note   To obtain the five-number summary on the TI-83 calculator, follow the instructions on page 929. The calculator output for the male HDL data is shown in Figure 4.

✎ NOW TRY EXERCISES **23(a)** AND **43**   ■

A **box plot** (also called a **box-and-whisker plot**) is a method for graphically displaying a five-number summary. The plot consists of a rectangle whose left- and right-hand sides correspond to Q_1 and Q_3, respectively. The box is divided by a line segment at the location of the *median*. The **whiskers** are line segments that extend from both sides of the box to the location of the *maximum* and *minimum* values. Figure 5 shows a box plot for the data in Figure 3.

(*Text continues on page 930.*)

### Margin content

Males

32	52	30	42	44
52	55	29	29	31
42	46	41	34	50
36	30			

Females

58	60	48	55	56
46	54	50	49	51
53	54	53		

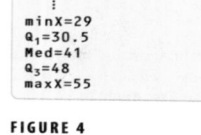

```
1-Var Stats
  ⋮
minX=29
Q₁=30.5
Med=41
Q₃=48
maxX=55
```

FIGURE 4

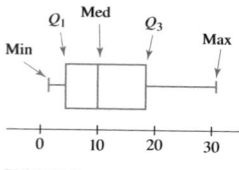

FIGURE 5

### Left margin

ALTERNATE EXAMPLE 8
The following table gives high-density lipoprotein (HDL) cholesterol levels for 21 people. Find the 5-number summary for this group. Find the range and the interquartile range (IQR).

32	29	30	58	49	52	31
46	53	48	42	42	29	36
36	24	36	40	29	31	31

ANSWER
5-number summary: 24, 30, 36, 42, 58; range: 34; IQR: 12

SUMMARY STATISTICS
On a Graphing Calculator

The following steps show how to obtain summary statistics on the TI-83 or TI-84 calculators.

Step 1   Enter the Data

Press the STAT key. Choose E D I T, then 1 : E d i t, then press ENTER. Now enter the data in one of the columns labeled L1, L2, L3, …. Enter different data sets in separate columns as shown below. If the data are given in a frequency table, enter the data in L1 and the corresponding frequencies in L2.

   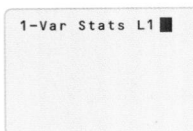

Step 2   Select Summary Statistics

Press the STAT key, choose CALC and 1 : 1 - V a r   S t a t s, then press ENTER. Next, choose the column in which the data have been entered. To select L1, press 2nd 1; the result is shown below. If the data are entered in L1 and the corresponding frequencies are entered in L2, select L1, L2 (separated by a comma).

   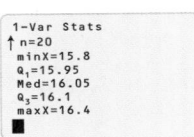

Step 3   Obtain Results

Press ENTER to obtain the summary statistics for the data, as shown below. Scroll down to see more of the statistics.

ALTERNATE EXAMPLE 9

Draw a box plot for the data set in Alternate Example 8.

ANSWER

DRILL QUESTION

Find the mean, median, and mode of the following data, and draw a stem plot:

22, 45, 11, 11, 25, 19, 26, 45, 26, 23, 11, 33, 30, 23, 50

Answer

Mean: 26.66̄; median: 25;
mode: 11

1	1 1 1 9
2	2 3 3 5 6 6
3	0 3
4	5 5
5	0

FIGURE 6

EXAMPLE 9 | Box Plots

Draw box plots for the two data sets in Example 8. Use the box plots to compare the central tendency and the spread of the two data sets.

SOLUTION The box plots are drawn by using a graphing calculator in Figure 6. From the box plots we can visually compare the relative locations of the five number summaries for each data set.

The median for females is considerably to the right of the median for males, so the median HDL is higher for females. The horizontal length of the box is the interquartile range. From Figure 6 we see that the IQR is quite a bit wider for males, indicating more variability in the male data. The ends of the whiskers indicate the minimum and maximum values. Again, we see that the male data have a much larger range and that the female data are toward the top end of the male data.

Graphing Calculator Note To obtain box plots on the TI-83, follow the instructions on page 939 in Section 14.6.

✎. NOW TRY EXERCISES **23(b)** AND **43** ∎

When we are working with quartiles, the median of the data is also called the **second quartile**, Q_2. So the three quartiles Q_1, Q_2, and Q_3 separate the data into four parts. Statisticians also use *quintiles, deciles,* and *percentiles.* The familiar **percentiles** are numbers that divide the data into 100 parts, each with the same number of data points. Standardized test scores are often reported as percentiles. So a score in the 99th percentile is a score in the top one-hundredth part of the scores on that test.

14.5 EXERCISES

CONCEPTS

1. If we measure one property of the individuals in a group

(height, for example) we obtain _____-variable data. What is meant by a measure of *central tendency* for one-variable data? Measures of central tendency for one-variable data include the

_____, the _____, and the _____.

2. (a) To find the average of a list of n numbers, we first _____

all the numbers and then divide by _____.

(b) The mode of a data set is the data point that appears

_____ often.

3. To find the median of a list of n numbers, we first put the

numbers in _____.

(a) If n is odd, the median is the _____ number in the list.

(b) If n is even, the median is the average of the two

_____ numbers in the list.

4. (a) What is meant by a *measure of spread* for a data set? Measures of spread for a data set include the standard

_____.

(b) The numbers in the *five-number summary* of a data set are

the _____, the _____,

the _____, the _____, and

the _____.

SKILLS

5–10 ■ A data set is given. **(a)** Find the median of the data.
(b) Find the average of the data. How many data points are greater than the average?

5. 113   21   16   18   19   29   22

6. 130   510   116   132   140   132   121

7. 69   71   74   73   72   73   69   69

8. 91   87   84   82   87   84   93   82

9. 39   28   57   11   45   72   38
    28   41   43   60   59   24   17

10. 109   110   97   130   112   102   95
    81   14   200   117   110   119

11–12 ■ A frequency table for a data set is given. Find the mean, median, and mode.

11.   Frequency Table

x	Frequency
16	13
17	5
18	12
19	0
20	2

12.   Frequency Table

x	Frequency
4	1
5	0
6	2
7	10
8	12
9	8
10	5

13–16 ■ A data set is given. (a) Organize the data into a frequency table. (b) Find the mean, median, and mode of the data.

13. 11 9 6 8 11 9 8 11

14. 20 21 17 21 20 20 19 20

15. 52 49 47 38 52 49
52 52 47 52 49 52
38 41 41 49 52 52

16. 17 19 20 13 21 15 15 17
17 15 19 19 15 14 20 14
14 17 17 13 17 15 20 19

17–18 ■ A stem-and-leaf plot of a data set is given. (a) What is the total number of data points? (b) Find the median and mode of the data.

17.
```
Stem | Leaves
0    | 3 4
1    | 0 1 1 5
2    | 3
3    | 4 4
4    |
5    | 5 6 6 6 9
6    | 2 3 7 7 8 8
7    | 4 5
8    | 2 3 3
9    | 1 4 5 5

1 | 2 means 12
```

18.
```
Stem | Leaves
3.1  | 4 4 5 6 9
3.2  | 0 0 3 5 5 7
3.3  | 9
3.4  | 2 3 3 5 8 8
3.5  | 1 1 1 3

3.1 | 2 means 3.12
```

19–20 ■ A data set is given. (a) Make a stem-and-leaf plot of the data. (b) Find the median and mode of the data using the stemplot of part (a).

19. 13 21 41 42 41
40 32 33 35 33
41 41 35 22 29

20. 1.10 1.17 1.22 1.31 1.18 1.17 1.35
1.24 1.26 1.23 1.17 1.46 1.47 1.40
1.16 1.47 1.31 1.36 1.34 1.22 1.25

21–22 ■ A data set is given. (a) Find the mean. (b) Find the standard deviation.

21. 28.6 30.2 29.5 30.9 31.2
29.5 30.2 30.8 28.2 29.6
32.1 31.6 30.2 28.4 29.0

22. 8 8 11 6 5
6 8 9 6 10
9 9 6 8 4
3 7 8 10 9

23–24 ■ A data set is given. (a) Find the five-number summary for the data set. (b) Draw a box plot for the data.

23. 13 15 17 18 16
15 13 12 17 21
29 28 19 26 25
22 25

24. 62 70 95 61 72 73 89
82 85 68 99 93 64 71
79 78 65 85 86 72 92
94 97 83 85 70

APPLICATIONS

25. Basketball Stats The data set below shows the number of points scored by Kobe Bryant of the Los Angeles Lakers in each basketball game in which he played in February 2007. What is the average number of points per game that Kobe Bryant scored in that month?

46 30 6 11 36
33 31 29 23 41
17 21 30 21 33

26. Lion Prides A wildlife biologist in the southern Sahara Desert of Africa records the number of lions in the different prides in her area. What is the average number of lions in a pride?

18 8 14 15 16 12 17

27. Apgar Score Doctors use the Apgar score to assess the health of a newborn baby immediately after the child is born. The data set below shows the Apgar scores of babies born in Memorial Hospital on March 11, 2007. Find the average and the median Apgar scores for these babies.

9 8 10 3 5 8 10

28. Weights of Sextuplets The Hanselman sextuplets were born three months premature on February 26, 2004, in Akron, Ohio, and they have all survived to this date. The data set below shows the birth weights of each child in kilograms. What are the average and the median birth weights of these sextuplets?

2.6 1.6 2.4 2.5 2.5 2.1

29. Quiz Average The data set below shows Jordan's scores on her first five algebra quizzes.
(a) What is her average quiz score?
(b) Jordan receives a score of 10 on her sixth quiz, so now what is her average quiz score?

9 9 6 7 7

30. **Quiz Average**   The data set below shows Chad's scores on his first four geography quizzes.
   (a) What is his average quiz score?
   (b) Chad receives a score of 5 on his fifth quiz, so now what is his average quiz score?

$$7 \quad 9 \quad 8 \quad 9$$

31. **Investment Seminar**   The organizer of an investment seminar surveys the participants on their yearly income. The data set below shows the yearly income (in dollars) of the participants.
   (a) Find the average and median income of the participants.
   (b) How many participants have an income above the average?
   (c) A new participant joins the seminar, and her yearly income is $500,000. Now what are the average and median incomes? In this case, do you think that the average or the median is the better indicator of central tendency?
   (d) Comment on the effects of outliers on the mean and median.

$$56,000 \quad 58,000 \quad 48,000 \quad 45,000$$
$$59,000 \quad 72,000 \quad 63,000$$

32. **Dairy Farming**   A dairy farmer in Illinois records the weights (in pounds) of all his cows. The table below shows his data.
   (a) Find the average and median weight of the cows on the farm.
   (b) How many cows have a weight above the average?
   (c) The farmer purchases a calf that weighs only 420 pounds. Now what are the average and median weights of the cows on the farm? In this case, do you think that the average or the median is the better indicator of central tendency?
   (d) Comment on the effects of outliers on the mean and median.

$$880 \quad 970 \quad 930 \quad 890 \quad 980 \quad 920 \quad 900$$

33. **Home Sales**   A realty agency in Albuquerque, New Mexico, records the prices (in dollars) of homes sold in one neighborhood.
   (a) What are the average and median home prices in this neighborhood? Which do you think is the better indicator of central tendency?
   (b) Is the house that sold for $329,000 above or below the average price? The median price?
   (c) After these data were gathered, another home in the neighborhood sold for $2,860,000. Now what are the average and median home prices? In this case, do you think that the average or the median is the better indicator of central tendency?

$$299,000 \quad 329,000 \quad 355,000$$
$$316,000 \quad 330,000$$

34. **Home Sales**   A realty agency in Napa Valley, California records the prices (in dollars) of homes sold in one neighborhood.
   (a) What are the average and median home prices in this neighborhood? Which is the better indicator of central tendency?

   (b) Is the house that sold for $2,319,000 above or below the average price? The median price?
   (c) After these data were gathered, another home in the neighborhood sold for $300,000. Now what are the average and median home prices? Which do you think is the better indicator of central tendency in this case?

$$2,278,000 \quad 2,231,000 \quad 2,319,000 \quad 2,279,000$$
$$2,365,000 \quad 2,279,000 \quad 2,319,000$$

35. **Mice**   The weights of newborn mice are given in the following frequency table. Find the mean, median, and mode of the weights.

Frequency Table

Weight (gm)	Frequency
0.6	2
0.7	5
0.8	9
0.9	10
1.0	16
1.1	15
1.2	18
1.3	8
1.4	6

36. **Goals**   A statistician records the total number of goals in the last game of the season for each soccer team in a local club. Find the mean, median, and mode of the number of goals.

Frequency Table

Number	Frequency
0	4
1	5
2	3
3	2
4	3
5	2
6	1
7	2
8	1

37. **Basketball Team**   The stemplot below shows the total number of points scored in the first game of the season for each player on a local basketball team.
   (a) How many players scored 12 points?
   (b) How many players scored more than ten points?
   (c) What is the total number of players on the team?
   (d) What is the total number of points scored?
   (e) Find the mean, median, and mode.

Stem	Leaves
0	1 2 2 3 3 5 8
1	2 2 2 5
2	1
3	0

2 | 1 means 21

38. Weddell Seals   The stemplot below shows weights (in pounds) of a sample of adult Weddell seals recorded in an area of Antarctica.
(a) How many seals weigh 962 pounds?
(b) How many seals weigh between 940 and 960 pounds?
(c) How many seals were weighed?
(d) Find the mean, median, and mode.

Stem	Leaves
90	2 7
91	
92	0 1 4 8
93	2 4 7 9 9
94	3 5 8 8 8 8 8 9
95	1 4 4 7 8
96	1 1 2 2 2 4 5 5 7 8 8 9 9
97	0 1 4 5 5 9
98	1 2 2 4 6 7 7
99	1 6

91 | 5 means 915

39. Blood-Clotting Test   A sample of patients on the antico-agualant Warfarin is tested for their blood coagulation (clotting) rate with the INR test. The results of the test are listed below.
(a) Make a stem-and-leaf plot of the data.
(b) Find the median and mode using the stemplot from part (a).

INR

1.8	3.2	2.4	3.1
3.4	2.4	2.6	4.0
2.6	2.9	3.0	4.1
2.6	2.3	2.8	2.2

40. Gasoline Prices   Listed below are the gasoline prices for regular unleaded gas in a one-month period at a local station.
(a) Make a stem-and-leaf plot of the data.
(b) Find the median and mode using the stemplot from part (a).

Gasoline Price ($)

3.01	3.03	3.10	3.05	3.02
3.02	3.25	3.09	3.10	3.09
3.08	3.02	3.41	3.43	3.05
3.22	3.26	3.04	3.23	3.07
3.09	3.10	3.09	3.24	3.12
3.31	3.35	3.36	3.19	3.17

41. Incomes and Gender   Listed below are the yearly incomes of a sample of men and women in the state of New York. Find the mean and standard deviation for the two data sets. Does there appear to be a difference in variation between the two data sets?

Yearly Income of Men ($)

46,000	49,000	54,000	35,000
72,000	57,000	56,000	51,000
48,000	53,000	61,000	59,000

Yearly Income of Women ($)

48,000	46,000	32,000	58,000
33,000	59,000	61,000	45,000
39,000	65,000	62,000	41,000

42. Crop Rotation   Crop rotation is the practice of planting dissimilar crops sequentially in one location to avoid the buildup of pathogens and pests and the depletion of nutrients in the soil. A researcher conducts an experiment on crop rotation of strawberries. He uses crop rotation on 12 garden plots and does not use crop rotation on 12 other garden plots. Listed below are the numbers of pounds of strawberries harvested from each plot in the final growing season. Find the mean and standard deviation for each data set. Does there appear to be a difference in variation between the two data sets?

Crop Rotation (lb)				No Crop Rotation (lb)			
37	42	44	46	29	35	34	27
41	39	29	31	31	36	41	40
37	41	42	45	37	29	31	36

43. Carbohydrates   The daily carbohydrate intake (in grams) of 18 Asians and 20 Hispanics who participated in a health survey are listed below. Find the five-number summary, and draw a box plot for each group. Compare the center and the spread in carbohydrate intake levels for the two groups.

Asian				Hispanic			
344	285	244	382	310	330	289	287
310	265	272	310	370	305	314	267
291	286	288	305	273	325	347	364
410	350	230	273	268	272	329	340
286	291			289	295	349	278

44. Test Scores   The standardized test scores for seventh graders from two different schools in the same neighborhood are listed below. One sample is taken from a school with less than 100 students, and the other sample is taken from a school with more than 400 students. Find the five-number summary, and draw a box plot for each group. Compare the center and the spread in test scores for the two groups.

Small School Test Scores				Large School Test Scores			
1429	1172	1396	1550	1509	1572	1190	950
1245	1162	1051	1276	1143	1432	1198	1171
1367	1301	1265	1156	1039	967	1013	1025
1274	1105	1050	1040	1127	1041	1053	1429
1187				1592	1450	1590	1229

DISCOVERY ■ DISCUSSION ■ WRITING

45. Measures of Central Tendency   For each of the following situations, determine whether the mean, median, or mode gives the most appropriate measure of central tendency. Explain your answer.
(a) A botanist counts the number of buds on each rose bush in his collection of 50 floribunda rose bushes. Most bushes have about 30 buds, but a few are sickly and have very few buds.
(b) The heights of 30 kindergarten students in an elementary school are measured.
(c) A researcher records the blood type of each individual in a sample of 60 middle-aged males.

46. Measures of Central Tendency A researcher computes the mean, median, and mode for the weights of milking cows on a small dairy farm. Determine which of the following statements *cannot* be true, and explain your answer.

(a) More than half of the cows have weights below the mode.
(b) More than half the cows have weights below the median.
(c) More than half the cows have weights below the mean.

(d) None of the cows have a weight exactly equal to the mean.
(e) None of the cows have a weight exactly equal to the mode.
(f) None of the cows have a weight exactly equal to the median.

14.6 DESCRIPTIVE STATISTICS (GRAPHICAL)

Data in Categories ▶ Histograms and the Distribution of Data ▶ The Normal Distribution

In the preceding section we described data using summary statistics for central tendency and spread. In this section we describe data using graphs called histograms. Histograms allow us to see how the *entire* data set is *distributed* among its different values.

▼ Data in Categories

In Section 14.5 we studied **numerical data**—that is, data whose values are real numbers. For example, age, height, and cholesterol level are real numbers. But in many situations we obtain **categorical data**—that is, the data tell us only whether an individual does or does not belong to a particular category. For example, a survey of your class could include categorical data such as hair color (black, brown, blond, red), political affiliation (Democrat, Republican, Independent), and so on. In this case the data indicate the *number* of individuals in each category. Categorical data can be represented by *bar graphs* or *pie charts*.

A **bar graph** consists of vertical bars, one bar for each category. The height of each bar is proportional to the number of individuals in that category. So the *y*-axis has a numerical scale corresponding to the number (or the proportion) of the individuals in each category. The labels on the *x*-axis describe the different categories. See Figure 1(a).

A **pie chart** consists of a circle divided into sectors, one sector for each category. The central angle of each sector is proportional to the number of individuals in that category. Each sector is labeled with the name of the corresponding category. See Figure 1(b).

FIGURE 1 U.S. energy sources

(a) Bar graph   (b) Pie chart

▼ Histograms and the Distribution of Data

For categorical data, bar graphs are an excellent method of visualizing how the data are distributed among the different categories. To visualize the distribution of one-variable

---

SUGGESTED TIME AND EMPHASIS

1 class, optional material

TEXT QUESTION

Is the following a normal distribution? How do you know?

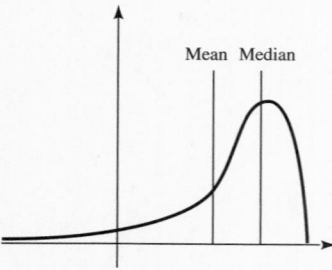

Answer

It is not, because it does not have the symmetrical bell shape that characterizes a normal distribution.

IN-CLASS MATERIALS

- Poll results on television often boast of accuracies of 95%. This is a direct result of their applying the Empirical Rule to their data.

- A surprising amount of data are normally distributed. The exact weights of "1-pound" loaves of bread at a store, the life spans of lightbulbs, and the *x*-coordinate of a dart thrown at a target (where the bull's-eye is the origin) are all usually normally distributed.

numerical data, we first convert the data into categorical data. For example, "Age" is a numerical variable, but we can convert it into a categorical variable by placing individuals in age categories (for example, 0–10 years, 11–20 years, and so on) and recording the number of individuals in each category.

In general, to put numerical data into categories, we divide the range of the data into nonoverlapping contiguous intervals of equal lengths, called **bins**. To draw a **histogram** of the data, we first label the bins on the x-axis and then erect a rectangle on each bin; the height (and hence also the area) of each rectangle is proportional to the number of data points in that bin.

EXAMPLE 1 | Drawing a Histogram

52	68	69	70	78
78	79	81	83	88
88	88	88	89	89
89	92	92	95	95
95	98	98	98	99
99	101	101	103	106
108	108	109	109	113
115	115	119	128	139

Hospitals routinely measure patients' heart rates. The list in the margin gives the heart rate (in beats per minute) of 40 patients admitted to the ICU unit at a city hospital. Draw a histogram of the heart rate data. Use bins of size 10 starting at 50 beats per minute.

SOLUTION We first organize the data into bins of size 10, as in the frequency distribution table below. Next, we graph a bar over each interval; the height of each bar is the number of data points in that interval. For example, the height of the bar over the interval $60 \leq x < 70$ is 2. The histogram is shown in Figure 2.

Frequency Distribution

Interval	Frequency
$50 \leq x < 60$	1
$60 \leq x < 70$	2
$70 \leq x < 80$	4
$80 \leq x < 90$	9
$90 \leq x < 100$	10
$100 \leq x < 110$	8
$110 \leq x < 120$	4
$120 \leq x < 130$	1
$130 \leq x < 140$	1

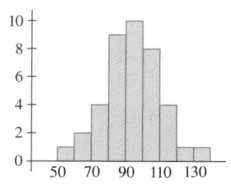

FIGURE 2 Histogram of heart rate data

Graphing Calculator Note   To graph a histogram on a TI-83 calculator, follow the instructions on page 939.

✎. **NOW TRY EXERCISE 3**   ■

A histogram gives a visual representation of how the data are **distributed** in the different bins. The histogram allows us to determine whether the data are **symmetric** about the mean, as in Figure 3. The heart rate data in Figure 2 are approximately symmetric. If the histogram has a long "tail" on the right, we say that the data are **skewed to the right**. Similarly, if there is a long tail on the left, the data are **skewed to the left**. Since the area of each bar in the histogram is proportional to the number of data points in that category, it follows that the **median** of the data is located at the x-value that divides the area of the histogram in half. Recall that extreme values have a large effect on the mean but not on the median (see Example 3 on page 923). So if the data are skewed to the right, the mean is to the right of the median; if the data are skewed to the left, the mean is to the left of the median.

FIGURE 3 Symmetric and skew distributions

Skew left

Symmetric

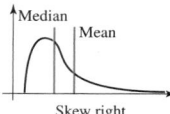
Skew right

CHAPTER 14 Probability and Statistics   935

ALTERNATE EXAMPLE 1

Thirty college students have their average response times tested, and these are the results, in seconds:

2.41	3.37	2.62	3.22	2.67
2.66	3.88	2.96	2.87	2.88
2.50	2.43	3.15	3.05	2.36
2.83	3.57	2.32	3.09	2.83
3.29	2.66	3.19	3.27	2.91
3.36	3.42	2.74	3.14	3.34

Draw a histogram of this data set.

ANSWER

Using bins of width 1/3 obtains:

EXAMPLE

The normal distribution with $\sigma = 1, 2, 3$.

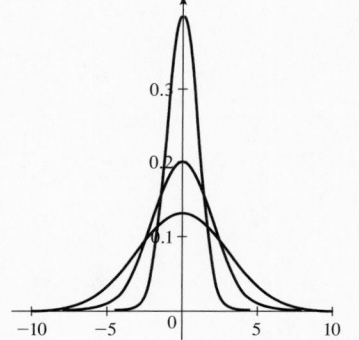

ALTERNATE EXAMPLE 2

The following histogram shows the wait time in minutes for a technical support line over a sample of 21 calls. Estimate the median wait time. Is the average wait time above or below the median?

ANSWER

The median is between 3 and 4; we can approximate it by 3.5. The mean will lie to the right of the median.

EXAMPLE 2 | Getting Information from a Histogram

Graduates of Universities I, II, III, and IV are surveyed about their yearly salaries. Histograms of the data are shown below, with the x-axis representing salaries in thousands of dollars. Are the data symmetric, skew, or neither? Determine the approximate location of the median, and determine the relative location of the mean.

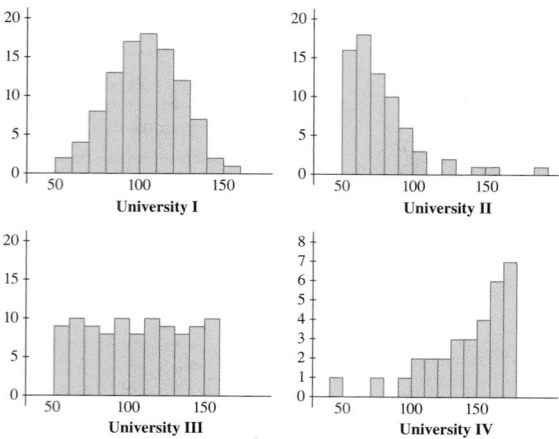

SOLUTION

University I: The histogram shows that the data are more or less symmetric. The mean and median salaries are about $100,000. Most of the salaries are close to the mean, with fewer salaries at the extremes.

University II: The histogram shows that the data are skewed to the right. The median is about $70,000, because half the area of the histogram is below this salary and half is above. Since the data are skewed to the right, the mean is higher than $70,000.

University III: The histogram shows that the data are more or less symmetric. The mean and median salaries are about $100,000. But unlike University I, the salaries are more or less *uniformly* distributed, with approximately the same number of graduates in each salary category.

University IV: The histogram shows that the data are skewed to the left. The median is about $150,000, because half the area of the histogram is below this salary and half is above. Since the data are skewed to the left, the mean is less than $150,000.

✎ NOW TRY EXERCISE 5 ∎

▼ The Normal Distribution

The binomial distribution we studied in Section 14.3 is also approximately normal.

Most real-world data are distributed in a special way called a *normal distribution*. For example, the heart rate data in Example 1 are approximately normally distributed. Figure 4 shows how a histogram of heart rate data with more data and smaller interval sizes fits a curve. The curve can be modeled by a function that we now define.

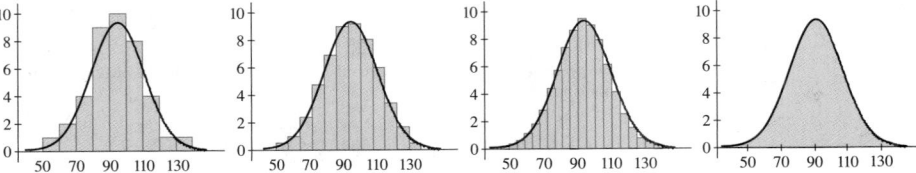

FIGURE 4 Histogram approximates normal curve

The **standard normal distribution** (or **standard normal curve**) is modeled by the function

$$f(z) = \frac{1}{\sqrt{2\pi}} \, e^{-z^2/2}$$

This distribution has mean 0 and standard deviation 1. **Normal distributions** with different means and standard deviations are modeled by transformations (shifting and stretching) of the above function. Specifically, the normal distribution with mean μ and standard deviation σ is modeled by the function

$$f(z) = \frac{1}{\sqrt{2\pi}\,\sigma} \, e^{-\frac{1}{2}\left(\frac{z-\mu}{\sigma}\right)^2}$$

All normal distributions have the same general shape, called a **bell curve**. Graphs of several normal distributions are shown in Figure 5.

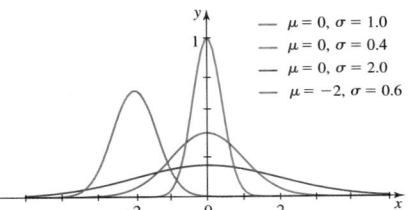

— $\mu = 0$, $\sigma = 1.0$
— $\mu = 0$, $\sigma = 0.4$
— $\mu = 0$, $\sigma = 2.0$
— $\mu = -2$, $\sigma = 0.6$

FIGURE 5   Normal curves

It can be shown by using calculus that for *any* data that are normally distributed about 68% of the data are within one standard deviation of the mean, about 95% are within two standard deviations of the mean, and about 99.7% are within three standard deviations of the mean. In fact, for normally distributed data the proportion of the data between any two values is completely determined by the mean and standard deviation of the data. This information is programmed into most graphing calculators.

NORMALLY DISTRIBUTED DATA

For normally distributed data with mean μ and standard deviation σ we have the following facts, called the **Empirical Rule**.

- Approximately 68% of the data are between $\mu - \sigma$ and $\mu + \sigma$.
- Approximately 95% of the data are between $\mu - 2\sigma$ and $\mu + 2\sigma$.
- Approximately 99.7% of the data are between $\mu - 3\sigma$ and $\mu + 3\sigma$.

The percentage of the data between other values can be obtained by using a graphing calculator.

ALTERNATE EXAMPLE 3

The weights of jars at a craft fair are normally distributed with a mean of 5 pounds and a standard deviation of 1.5 points. Find the probability that a randomly selected individual has an IQ score in the given interval:

(a) 3.5 to 6.5 pounds
(b) More than 2 pounds
(c) Less than 2 pounds

ANSWERS

(a) 0.68
(b) 0.975
(c) 0.025

EXAMPLE 3 | Using the Normal Distribution (Empirical Rule)

IQ scores are normally distributed with mean 100 and standard deviation 15. Find the proportion of the population with IQ scores in the given interval. Also find the probability that a randomly selected individual has an IQ score in the given interval.

(a) Between 85 and 115   (b) At least 130   (c) At most 130

SOLUTION

(a) IQ scores between 85 and 115 are within one standard deviation of the mean:

$$100 - 15 = 85 \qquad \text{and} \qquad 100 + 15 = 115$$

By the Empirical Rule, about 68% of the population have IQ scores between 85 and 115. So the probability that a randomly selected individual has an IQ between 85 and 115 is 0.68.

(b) IQ scores between 70 and 130 are within two standard deviations of the mean:

$$100 - 2(15) = 70 \qquad \text{and} \qquad 100 + 2(15) = 130$$

By the Empirical Rule, about 95% of the population have IQ scores between 70 and 130. The remaining 5% of the population have IQ scores above 130 or below 70. Since normally distributed data are symmetric about the mean, it follows that 2.5% have IQ scores above 130 (and 2.5% below 70). So the probability that a randomly selected individual has an IQ of at least 130 is 0.025.

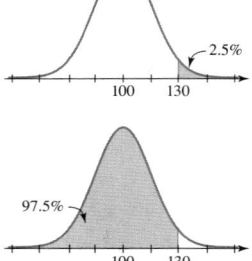

(c) By part (b), 2.5% of the population have IQ scores above 130. It follows that the rest of the population have IQ scores below 130. Thus 97.5% of the population have IQ scores of 130 or below. So the probability that a randomly selected individual has an IQ of 130 at most is 0.975.

✎. NOW TRY EXERCISE **13**   ∎

STATISTICAL GRAPHS
On a Graphing Calculator

The following steps show how to obtain histograms and box plots on the TI-83 or TI-84 calculators.

Step 1   Enter the Data

Press the $\boxed{\text{STAT}}$ key. Choose **EDIT**, then **1:EDIT**, then press $\boxed{\text{ENTER}}$. Now enter the data in one of the columns lableded **L1, L2, L3,** …. If the data are from a frequency table, enter the frequencies in another column.

Step 2   Choose the Type of Graph

Press $\boxed{\text{2nd}}$ $\boxed{\text{STAT PLOT}}$. To draw a histogram or box plot, choose **1:Plot1** and press $\boxed{\text{ENTER}}$. Select **ON**, the type of plot, and the location of the data (if the data are in **L1**, press $\boxed{\text{2nd}}$ $\boxed{1}$). Set **Freq** to 1 (or choose the column where you have entered the frequencies of the data).

Step 3   Obtain the Graph(s)

To obtain the graph, press $\boxed{\text{GRAPH}}$, but first set the $\boxed{\text{WINDOW}}$. For a *histogram*, set **Xscale** to correspond to the desired width of each interval. For a ***box plot***, choose **Xmin** and **Xmax** so that they encompass the range of the data.

Histogram

25   65
Box plot

For normally distributed data, the Empirical Rule gives the proportions of the data within one, two, or three standard deviations from the mean. To find the proportion in other intervals, we use a graphing calculator.

On the TI-83, go to the distribution menu [DISTR] by selecting [2nd] [VARS], then choose 2:normalcdf(and press [ENTER]. To find the proportion of the population between x_1 and x_2 we enter

$$\texttt{normalcdf(x}_1\texttt{, x}_2\texttt{, } \mu \texttt{, } \sigma \texttt{)}$$

where μ and σ are the mean and standard deviation of the population.

EXAMPLE 4 | Using the Normal Distribution (Calculator)

The heights of adult males in the United States are normally distributed with mean 69 inches and standard deviation 2.8 inches. Find the proportion of the adult male population with height in the given interval. Also find the probability that a randomly selected individual has height in the given interval.

(a) Between 67 in. and 70 in.　　**(b)** At least 75 in.

SOLUTION The Empirical Rule does not apply to the required intervals, so we use a graphing calculator as described above.

(a) To find the proportion between 67 and 70 on the TI-83, we use the command

$$\texttt{normalcdf(67, 70, 69, 2.8)}$$

The result is 0.4019823224. We conclude that about 40% of the population is in the given range. The probability that a randomly selected adult male has height between 67 and 70 inches is 0.40.

(b) In this case the lower bound is $x_1 = 75$ inches, and there is no upper bound. So we enter a very large number for the upper bound, say, $x_2 = 1000$.

$$\texttt{normalcdf(75, 1000, 69, 2.8)}$$

The result is 0.0160622279. We conclude that about 1.6% of the population is in the given range. The probability that a randomly selected adult male has height 75 inches or more is 0.016.

NOW TRY EXERCISE 17 ■

The heights of adult males in the United States are normally distributed with a mean of 69 inches and a standard deviation of 2.8 inches. Find the proportion of the adult male population with height in the given interval.

(a) Greater than 6 feet tall

(b) Between 5 feet tall and 5.5 feet tall

ANSWERS

(a) 14.2%

(b) 14.1%

DRILL QUESTION

The average income of a graduate from the University of Eastern West Virginia is $50,000 per year, with a standard deviation of $2500 per year. Approximate the probability that a graduate will have an income between $45,000 and $55,000 per year.

Answer

∼ 95%

14.6 EXERCISES

CONCEPTS

1. When we construct a *histogram* of data, the data must be divided into _____. To draw the histogram, we label the categories on the ____-axis and erect a rectangle on each category that has height proportional to the number of _____ in that category. A histogram gives a visual representation of how the data are _____.

2. Many real-world data are _____ distributed. For normally distributed data with mean μ and standard deviation σ, approximately _____ % of the data are between $\mu - \sigma$ and $\mu + \sigma$, and approximately _____ % of the data are between $\mu - 2\sigma$ and $\mu + 2\sigma$.

SKILLS

3–4 ■ A data set is given. Draw a histogram of the data, using bins (or intervals) of the given size.

3. Bin length is 10, starting at 0

23	17	40	32	24	5	35	18	36	37
31	42	28	50	22	47	61	31	13	27
26	46	48	44	15	28	38	8	52	29

4. Bin length is 1, starting at 0

1.2	3.4	5.8	3.2	4.0	1.7	2.3	3.6
3.2	4.7	4.9	6.1	2.3	1.5	3.9	3.8
4.2	5.7	6.1	2.6	3.2	2.1	4.1	5.2
1.1	0.9	2.5	3.3	2.7	5.6	6.2	6.9

5–8 ■ A histogram of data is shown. **(a)** Are the data approximately symmetric, skew right, or skew left? **(b)** Determine the approximate location of the median and the relative location of the mean.

5.

6.

7.

8.

9–12 ■ A data set is given. **(a)** Draw a histogram of the data, using bins (or intervals) of the given size. **(b)** Are the data symmetric, skew, or neither? **(c)** Calculate the median and the mean.

9. Bin length is 50, starting at 0

690	554	571	524	312	91	440
457	568	669	653	591	378	637
622	582	512	201	557	661	613
482	173	597	658	651	517	588
542	632	30	431	656	663	412
673	655	539	602	609	625	663

10. Bin length is 3, starting at 30

36	39	46	44	38	73	37	38
82	54	37	43	39	49	41	42
36	53	40	39	38	51	42	37
41	45	47	42	37	39	40	61

11. Bin length is 5, starting at 30

61	83	72	48	60	66	82	76	46	62
51	72	63	67	88	41	56	66	58	37
64	47	71	69	51	72	52	56	63	54
73	56	68	49	70	55	63	51	76	57
60	63	58	69	78	63	68	56	65	69

12. Bin length is 25, starting at 50

189	346	245	338	298	159	349	127
305	220	229	235	247	162	107	358
182	217	193	244	258	290	202	129
270	184	180	270	284	115	131	320
152	213	112	373	219	257	248	133
348	374	321	296	157	283	310	259

13–16 ■ A data set is normally distributed with mean 35 and standard deviation 9. Use the Empirical Rule to find the proportion of data points that lie in the given interval.

13. Between 26 and 44   **14.** Between 17 and 53

15. At most 17   **16.** At least 53

17–20 ■ A data set is normally distributed with mean 35 and standard deviation 9. Use a graphing calculator to find the proportion of data points that lie in the given interval.

17. Between 29 and 38   **18.** Between 15 and 40

19. At least 32   **20.** At most 21

APPLICATIONS

21. Multiple Sclerosis Multiple sclerosis (MS) is one of the most common neurological disorders causing disability in young adults. The list gives the age of onset for a sample of MS patients. Draw a histogram of the data, using bins of size 2 starting at 0.

23	52	32	27	28	30	13	37
33	29	25	31	26	30	5	29
41	27	30	34	28	19	31	29
32	28	33	28	31	29	29	30

22. Monarch Butterfly Monarch butterflies migrate thousands of miles each year to overwinter in a small mountainous area of Mexico. The list shows the wingspans (in centimeters) of a sample of monarch butterflies captured in their wintering grounds. Draw a histogram of the data, using bins of size 0.5 starting at 8.0.

8.6	10.9	9.8	12.4	10.6	10.7	10.9
10.0	10.2	10.3	9.4	9.1	11.2	9.7
11.6	12.0	10.4	9.5	10.9	10.5	9.9
11.1	10.5	11.3	11.7	11.3	10.3	11.5

23. Los Angeles Lakers Salaries Kobe Bryant of the Los Angeles Lakers basketball team earned a salary of 24.8 million dollars for the 2010–2011 season. The list gives the salaries (in millions of dollars) of each team member of the Los Angeles Lakers for the 2010–2011 season.
(a) Draw a histogram of the data, using bins (or intervals) of size 2 starting at 0.
(b) Are the data symmetric, skew, or neither?

(c) Calculate the median and the mean.

5.26	24.8	6.3	5.5	0.854	1.8	4.0
0.474	17.8	2.2	13.7	3.7	0.474	8.2

24. Hotel Room Rates The list gives the average daily room rate for various hotels in the San Francisco area.

(a) Draw a histogram of the data, using bins (or intervals) of size 25, starting at 0.

(b) Are the data symmetric, skew, or neither?

(c) Calculate the median and the mean.

129	192	105	89	152	159	227	111
159	185	179	90	109	59	169	109
215	87	119	69	94	109	118	355
127	59	160	67	149	188	269	75
99	94	242	129	159	215	155	475

25. Starting Salaries Graduates earning bachelor's degrees in engineering are surveyed about their starting salary. A histogram of the data is shown below, with the *x*-axis representing salaries in thousands of dollars. Are the data symmetric, skew, or neither? Determine the approximate location of the median and determine the relative location of the mean.

26. Savings A recent survey was taken to estimate the amount of savings for employees in a large advertising firm. A histogram of the data is shown below, with the *x*-axis representing savings in thousands of dollars. Are the data symmetric, skew, or neither? Determine the approximate location of the median and determine the relative location of the mean.

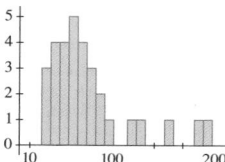

27. Cap Size A men's baseball cap is designed to fit heads with a circumference measuring from 21.25 in. to 24.25 in. The head circumferences of men are normally distributed with mean 22.75 in. and standard deviation 0.75 in. Use the Empirical Rule to find the proportion of men who will be able to wear this design of baseball cap.

28. Airline Seatbelts The seatbelts on a particular airplane are designed to fit people with waist sizes measuring up to 50 in. The waist size of the adult male population is normally distributed with mean 40.5 in. and standard deviation 4.75 in. Use the Empirical Rule to find the proportion of the adult male population who do not fit the airline's seatbelts.

29. Fashion Model The heights of adult females in the United States are normally distributed with mean 63.5 in. and standard deviation 2.5 in. Most fashion models have a height of 69 in. or more. Use a graphing calculator to find the proportion of women in the United States who are 69 in. or taller.

30. Rabbit Gestation The length of pregnancy (gestational period) of rabbits is normally distributed with mean 31.7 days and standard deviation 1.1 days. Use a graphing calculator to find the proportion of rabbit gestations that lie in the given interval.

(a) Between 30 and 33 days

(b) At most 34 days

31. Birth Weight Birth weight is a major determinant of infant mortality in the first year of life. The World Health Organization defines a low birth weight to be less than 2500 grams.

(a) The birth weights of infants born in the United States are normally distributed with mean 3250 grams and standard deviation 450 grams. Use a graphing calculator to find the probability that a randomly selected infant in the United States has a low birth weight.

(b) The birth weights of infants born in a particular country are normally distributed with mean 3000 grams and standard deviation 580 grams. Use a graphing calculator to find the probability that a randomly selected infant in this country has a low birth weight.

32. SAT Scores The SAT math scores of college applicants are normally distributed with mean 515 and standard deviation 100.

(a) A requirement for admission into a particular Ivy League university is an SAT math score of at least 690. What is the probability that a randomly selected college applicant has an SAT math score that meets the requirements for admission into that university?

(b) A requirement for admission into a particular state university is an SAT math score of at least 550. What is the probability that a randomly selected college applicant has an SAT math score that meets the requirements for admission into that university?

⬤ **DISCOVERY PROJECT** | **Bias in Presenting Data**

In this project we learn to avoid misleading ways of presenting and interpreting data. You can find the project at the book companion website: **www.stewartmath.com**

14.7 INTRODUCTION TO STATISTICAL THINKING

| The Key Role of Randomness ▶ Design of Experiments ▶ Sample Size and Margin of Error ▶ Two-Variable Data and Correlation

Statistical thinking:
A chef tastes a small sample of a stew to determine the quality of the entire stew.

Statistical pitfall:
A student decides that all cars of a certain model are defective on the basis of the problems he's having with his own car.

In **statistical thinking** we make judgments about an entire population based on a sample. A **population** consists of *all* the individuals in a group. A **sample** is any subset of the population. Everyone uses statistical thinking in everyday life but sometimes incorrectly. In this section we investigate key features of statistical thinking as well as some common **statistical pitfalls**.

Why do we use samples? It may appear that a **census** (that is, data obtained from the *entire* population) is a better guarantee of correct results. But a census is not necessarily more accurate. Imagine attempting to survey each of the over 300 million individuals in the United States. This would be an enormously costly and time-consuming task, and numerous data errors would inevitably occur. A carefully selected sample would most likely give more accurate results.

Data are collected in many contexts. In **survey sampling**, data are collected through responses to questionnaires. In **observational studies**, data are collected by observation (such as when bird-watchers make their traditional Christmas bird count). In **experimental studies**, data are collected by performing experiments.

▼ The Key Role of Randomness

A **random sample** is one that is selected arbitrarily and without bias. In selecting a sample, the importance of randomness cannot be overemphasized. In statistical thinking *we expect a random sample to share approximately the same properties as the population.* Also, the larger the sample size, the more closely the sample properties approximate those of the population.

For example, to estimate the average height of adult males, it would be highly biased to select a sample from among NBA players. In general, **non-random samples** are generated when there is bias in the selection process. Such samples are **useless** for statistical purposes, because the sample is not representative of the population.

A **simple random sample** is one in which every individual in the population has the same probability of being selected. To satisfy this requirement, the sampling method that is used must be free of bias with respect to the property being measured. The "lottery method" of selection appears to produce a simple random sample (see the margin). **Computer-generated random numbers** (also called **pseudo-random numbers**) can be used in selecting random samples: We first assign a number to each individual in the population and then use a computer random number generator to select from the assigned numbers. The following are common types of sampling bias.

The lottery method:
Balls are labeled with the lottery numbers. The balls are placed in a sphere and subjected to forced air. Any ball that is expelled from the sphere is considered randomly selected.

1. **Undercoverage bias** (or **exclusion bias**), in which part of the population is excluded from the sampling process.

2. **Response bias**, in which the wording of a questionnaire is not neutral but rather suggests or provokes a particular response.

3. **Nonresponse bias**, in which individuals with a common characteristic are unwilling (or neglect) to respond to a questionnaire. (Notice that this is not the opposite of response bias.)

4. **Self-selection bias** (or **voluntary response bias**), in which individuals select themselves (or volunteer) for the sample.

Many of these biases are a result of **convenience sampling**, in which individuals are sampled only because they are nearby or easily accessible.

TEXT QUESTION

You are surveying students to see if they want the principal to be replaced. Give an example of a question that suffers from response bias.

Answer

Answers will vary.

ALTERNATE EXAMPLE 1

A sample is selected as described. Is the sample a random sample? If not, identify the type of sampling bias.

(a) A student organization distributes a poll on Friday night as students enter the dorm cafeteria.

(b) A group of students in a sociology course are asked if they have ever smoked marijuana; they are to indicate their answers by raising their hands if they have.

ANSWERS

(a) This sample has undercoverage bias; students who eat out or leave town on the weekends will never get a copy of the poll.

(b) This sample has nonresponse bias; individuals who have smoked marijuana are not likely to raise their hands to confess to a federal crime.

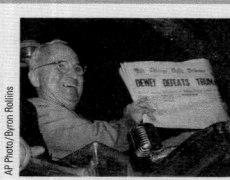

AP Photo/Byron Rollins

"DEWEY DEFEATS TRUMAN"
This banner headline appeared in the *Chicago Tribune* on November 3, 1948, the morning after Election Day. The headline was wrong. In fact, Truman defeated Dewey by more than two million votes in the popular count. The conclusion of the *Chicago Tribune* was partly based on a telephone poll (a convenience sample). In 1948 few people had telephones; only the relatively wealthy could afford them. So the telephone poll suffered from undercoverage bias. A lot was learned from this embarrassing gaffe. Today, polling companies spend millions of dollars researching methods of selecting random samples. The methods they use are often kept as trade secrets.

EXAMPLE 1 | Bias in Sampling

A sample is selected as described. Is the sample a random sample? If not, identify the type of sampling bias.

(a) A political blog conducts an online poll to gauge the approval rating of a candidate for political office.

(b) To investigate people's preference for different brands of toothpaste, a polling firm selects a random sample of telephone numbers from the telephone directories of several large cities.

(c) To investigate the amount of energy drinks consumed by college freshmen, a student stands on a campus sidewalk and interviews willing participants.

(d) A mail survey asks people's opinion on the preservation of wilderness areas. Only a small percentage of the surveys were completed and returned, and those mostly favored an increase in wilderness areas.

(e) A survey designed by residents opposed to building a new mall in their neighborhood asks: "Do you support the building of the mall which will increase traffic and lower property values?"

SOLUTION

(a) The respondents select themselves to participate in the survey. So the sample suffers from a self-selection bias. The sample also suffers from undercoverage bias, since only visitors to the blog can participate.

(b) Many teenagers and an increasing number of adults rely solely on cell phones, which are not listed in telephone directories. So this sampling technique suffers from undercoverage bias, since teenagers would probably be underrepresented in the sample.

(c) This is a convenience sample. The student is surveying freshmen who are easily accessible. The sampling technique suffers from undercoverage bias (since not all freshmen are equally likely to pass by that particular sidewalk) as well as self-selection bias (since the surveyor depends on participants who stop by for the interview).

(d) It's possible that there is nonresponse bias. People who are not interested in the wilderness issue simply did not respond to the survey.

(e) This survey question is clearly designed to obtain a No response, so this sampling technique suffers from response bias.

✎. NOW TRY EXERCISE **7** ■

In practice, it is difficult to ensure the selection of a random sample. Several methods have been developed for sampling in particular situations. Some of the most common are as follows.

1. **Systematic Sampling:** In systematic sampling, a sample is chosen systematically from a list. For example, we may pick every 100th name in a telephone book.

2. **Stratified Sampling:** In stratified sampling, the population is first divided into nonoverlapping groups (or strata), and then the sample is chosen proportionally from each group. For example, to pick a sample of registered voters, we may want to stratify the population into groups—white, African American, Hispanic, and other—and then randomly pick registered voters, choosing from each group a number proportional to the size of the group in the population.

3. **Cluster Sampling:** In cluster sampling, the population is divided into groups (or clusters) and then a random sample of *clusters* is selected. For example, to survey apartment dwellers in Los Angeles, we would first randomly select a collection of apartment *buildings* (the clusters) and then interview every resident in the selected buildings. This type of sampling reduces the enormous time and cost for the pollster in traveling from apartment to apartment.

IN-CLASS MATERIALS

■ This section is directly related to terms being used in the media all the time. Students can be asked to bring in newspaper clippings involving margins of error and to explain what they mean. If local newspapers conduct their own polls, students can call the paper and ask for details about sample size and verify the stated margins of error.

■ A quite surprising result is hidden in the margin of error formula. The statistical margin of error is independent of the size of the underlying population. In other words, a random sample of 500 people out of 1000 gives the same margin of error as a random sample of 500 people out of 1,000,000! It is, of course, harder to get a truly random sample from such a large population.

EXAMPLE 2 | Sampling Methods

A sampling scenario is given. Classify the sampling method as systematic sampling, stratified sampling, or cluster sampling.

(a) To investigate student attitudes about the Big Bang Theory, a researcher first partitions students into class categories—freshmen, sophomores, juniors, and seniors—and then selects the random sample proportionally from each group.

(b) To gauge voter attitudes on an upcoming ballot measure, a pollster selects a sample by starting at an arbitrary name in a list of registered voters and then selecting every fiftieth voter on the list.

(c) To investigate college administrators' attitudes on grading practices, a researcher randomly selects a sample of universities, then interviews all top-level administrators at the selected universities.

SOLUTION

(a) This is stratified sampling. The strata from which the sample is selected are the class categories.

(b) This is systematic sampling since a sample is selected systematically (every fiftieth voter) from the voter list.

(c) This is cluster sampling. The clusters are the universities.

✎ **NOW TRY EXERCISE 13** ■

▼ Design of Experiments

In observational studies, the researcher has no control over the factors affecting the property being studied—the researcher is merely an observer. Extraneous or unintended variables that systematically affect the property being studied are called **confounding variables** (or **confounding factors** or **lurking variables**). Such variables are said to **confound** (or mix up) the results of the study. The following examples show how this can happen.

EXAMPLE 3 | Confounding Variables

Describe some possible confounding variables in each situation.

(a) To discover any relationship between heavy drinking and lung cancer, a researcher selects a random sample of heavy drinkers.

(b) To test a gasoline additive that claims to increase gas mileage, a researcher solicits volunteers to test the product in their cars.

(c) A new method of teaching mathematics is advertised to increase student scores on standardized tests. To test this claim, a researcher selects the mathematics classes at a local private school.

SOLUTION

(a) A possible confounding variable here is smoking. Many people who drink excessively also smoke. So the study may inadvertently measure the effects of smoking, not drinking.

(b) A possible confounding variable is the mechanical condition of the cars in the sample. The volunteers may own older or defective cars in which the additive is not effective.

(c) The students' mathematical aptitude (before the experiment) may be a confounding variable. If the students in the study normally score high on standardized tests, they probably would score high on the next standardized test with or without the new teaching method. The instructor's teaching skill may also be a confounding variable.

✎ **NOW TRY EXERCISE 17(a)** ■

ALTERNATE EXAMPLE 2
A university mails a survey to the group of students whose student numbers end with a "3." Is this sampling method systematic sampling, stratified sampling, or cluster sampling?

ANSWER
Systematic sampling

ALTERNATE EXAMPLE 3
To determine whether violent video games cause violent behavior in children, sociologists interview a random sample of eight-year-old children who play more than 3 hours of violent video games per day. What are some confounding variables in this situation?

ANSWER
Answers may vary. One possible answer is that eight-year-old children who are allowed to play more than 3 hours of violent video games per day have parents who are atypical and that any violent behavior exhibited by the children may be due to other factors in their environment.

Testing the Salk Vaccine
From 1916 to the 1950s a polio epidemic was sweeping the United States. The crippling disease affected millions of Americans. In the 1950s Jonas Salk developed a polio vaccine. The vaccine had to be tested before it could be approved for general use. Several experimental designs involving first, second, and third graders were suggested. To test the vaccine on children, parental approval had to be obtained. One of the suggested experimental designs was to use the children with parental approval as the treatment group and the others as the control group. But it was observed that this would confound the study because parents who gave approval tended to be more educated (and possibly more hygienic). The actual design involved treatment and control groups randomly selected from the children with parental approval. The study was double-blinded, and placebos were given to the control group. The experimental study involved many thousands of children. Statistical analysis of the results showed that the vaccine was highly effective. Subsequently, the general use of the Salk vaccine practically wiped out the disease in the United States.

To eliminate or vastly reduce the effects of confounding variables, researchers often conduct *experiments* so that such variables can be *controlled*. In an **experimental study,** two groups are selected: a **treatment group** (in which individuals are given a treatment) and a **control group** (in which individuals are not given the treatment). The individuals in the experiment are called **subjects** (or **experimental units**). The goal is to measure the **response** of the subjects to the treatment—that is, whether or not the treatment has an effect. The next step is to make sure that the two groups are as similar as possible except for the treatment. If the two groups are alike except for the treatment, then any statistical difference in response between the groups can be confidently attributed to the treatment. Here are some typical experimental designs.

1. **Completely Randomized Design:** The effects of unknown variables that may confound the experiment can be reduced or eliminated by randomization, that is, by assigning individuals randomly to the treatment or control groups. Randomization ensures that the effects of any confounding variables are equally likely to occur in either group. So any difference between the two groups in the response to the treatment can be attributed to the treatment.

2. **Randomized Block Design:** Variables that are known (prior to the experiment) to affect the response can be controlled by **blocking**. The participants are arranged into **blocks** (or groups) consisting of subjects with similar characteristics, and then treatment and control groups are randomly selected within each block. For example, if sex is a known source of variability in response, then a male block and a female block are formed. Treatment and control subjects are then randomly selected from the male block and from the female block. This design specifically "controls" for a known confounding factor by ensuring equal participation of individuals from each block in the treatment and control groups.

3. **Matched Pair Design:** In this design, the subjects are matched in pairs based on variables that may affect the response to the treatment. For example, the subjects of the study may be matched in pairs based on age and sex (a young male with a young male, a senior female with a senior female, and so on). Then an individual from each pair is randomly assigned to the treatment group, and the other is assigned to the control group. In this example, the treatment and control groups have equal participation with respect to two possible confounding variables (age and sex).

A common confounding factor is the **placebo effect**, in which patients who *think* they are receiving a medication report an improvement (perceived or actual), even though the "treatment" they received was a **placebo**—a simulated or false treatment (sometimes called a "sugar pill"). To control the placebo effect, a researcher may use **single-blinding**, a method in which subjects don't know whether they are in the treatment or control group, or **double-blinding**, in which the researchers are also not privy to this information during the course of the experiment. **Replication**, the repetition of the experiment, can also reinforce the reliability of the results.

EXAMPLE 4 | Designing an Experiment

To test the effectiveness of a new flu vaccine a researcher conducts a study with 800 individuals: 500 women and 300 men. The subjects are to be assigned to treatment and control groups. Suggest different experimental designs for this study.

SOLUTION   We suggest three possible designs. In each design, the subjects in the treatment group are given the vaccine, and those in the control group are given a placebo. To further unbias the procedures in the experiment, we suggest double-blinding.

Completely Randomized Design: We randomly assign 400 patients to the treatment group and 400 to the control group. (It is convenient but not necessary to have the same number of subjects in each group.) We can assign an ID number to each participant and then use a computer random-number generator to select the two groups.

Randomized Block Design: It is known that the sex of an individual frequently affects the response to medication (men and women often have different physiological responses to medication). To control for this factor, we use blocking: We put men and women in separate blocks. Subjects from each block are randomly assigned to the treatment or control group. So each group would contain 250 women and 150 men.

Matched Pair Design: It is also known that the age of an individual may affect the response to medication. So in this design, we place participants in *pairs* matched by age and sex. To do this, we may want to decide on age categories. Then each pair would consist of individuals of the same sex and the same age category. From each pair we pick one for the treatment group and one for the control group. (We can do this by flipping a coin.)

✎. NOW TRY EXERCISE **17(b)**   ∎

▼ Sample Size and Margin of Error

One of the most important features of statistical thinking is the realization that statistics does not provide exact answers. Statisticians *estimate* properties of a population by examining a random sample from that population. Statistical conclusions are based on probability and are always accompanied by a confidence level. The 95% **confidence level** means that there is less than a 5% chance (or 0.05 probability) that the result obtained from the sample could be obtained by chance alone. In the popular press, poll results are accompanied by a *margin of error.* For example, a magazine article states:

> "A recent poll shows that Candidate X has 57% of the vote. The poll was conducted among a random sample of 600 registered voters. The margin of error of the poll is ±3%."

This means that 57% of the voters in the *sample* prefer Candidate X. But how does this compare with the true proportion that prefer Candidate X in the entire *population*? Traditionally, poll results are stated at the 95% confidence level. So the statement in the magazine means that there is a 95% chance (or 0.95 probability) that the true proportion is between $57 - 3 = 54\%$ and $57 + 3 = 60\%$. That is, if we conduct this poll many times, we would expect the true proportion to be contained in the intervals we get about 95% of the time.

Each time the poll is conducted, a new value for p_0 and a new interval $(p_0 - d, p_0 + d)$ are obtained. At the 95% confidence level we would expect 95% of the intervals so constructed to contain the true proportion p. (Stated another way, we would expect only 5% of the intervals constructed in this way to fail to contain p.)

In general, the proportion p_0 of individuals with a particular characteristic in a sample is an *estimate* of the true proportion p of such individuals in the population. It is clear that the larger the sample size, the more accurate the estimate is likely to be. The **margin of error** of the estimate associated with the sample is a number d satisfying the following:

> There is a 95% probability that the interval $(p_0 - d, p_0 + d)$ contains the true proportion p.

Notice that the true proportion p is a fixed number that we do not know. The random sample allows us to construct an interval that is very likely (probability 0.95) to contain p. The interval $(p_0 - d, p_0 + d)$ is called the 95% **confidence interval**. The following formula allows us to find the margin of error associated with a given sample size.

MARGIN OF ERROR AND SAMPLE SIZE

At the 95% confidence level, the margin of error d and the sample size n are related by the formula*

$$d = \frac{1.96}{2\sqrt{n}}$$

---

*The formula is derived by using calculus and relies on properties of the binomial and normal distributions. The number 1.96 in the formula is a slightly more precise form of the second statement in the Empirical Rule (page 938): For a normal distribution 95% of the data is between $\mu - 1.96\sigma$ and $\mu + 1.96\sigma$.

A poll is conducted to gauge audience reaction to a movie. A random sample of 300 filmgoers is polled. The poll indicates that 175 of those surveyed enjoyed the movie.

(a) Estimate the percentage of the filmgoers who enjoyed the movie.

(b) Find the margin of error of the poll (at the 95% confidence level).

(c) State the 95% confidence interval for the percentage of the filmgoers who enjoyed the movie.

ANSWERS

(a) 58.3%

(b) ±5.7%

(c) (0.526, 0.64)

A poll is conducted to gauge audience reaction to a movie. How many people need to be polled to ensure that the margin of error is ±2%?

ANSWER

2401 people

EXAMPLE 5 | Margin of Error and Sample Size

A political poll is conducted to gauge the approval rating of Candidate X. A random sample of 600 voters is polled. The poll indicates that 324 of those surveyed approve of the candidate.

(a) Estimate the percentage of the voters in the population who prefer Candidate X.

(b) Find the margin of error of the poll (at the 95% confidence level).

(c) State the 95% confidence interval for the percentage of the population who prefer Candidate X.

SOLUTION

(a) The proportion of the sample who prefer Candidate X is

$$\frac{324}{600} = 0.54$$

So we estimate that 54% of the voter population prefer Candidate X.

(b) Since $n = 600$, we have

$$d = \frac{1.96}{2\sqrt{n}} = \frac{1.96}{2\sqrt{600}} \approx 0.04$$

So the margin of error of the poll is ±4%.

(c) The 95% confidence interval for the proportion who prefer Candidate X is

$$(0.54 - 0.04, 0.54 + 0.04) = (0.50, 0.58)$$

So we can say with 95% confidence that between 50% and 58% of voters prefer Candidate X.

✎ NOW TRY EXERCISE **21** ∎

EXAMPLE 6 | Margin of Error and Sample Size

A political polling firm is hired to conduct a poll for Candidate X. Determine the required sample size if the candidate would like the poll to have the following margin of error.

(a) ±3%   (b) ±1%

SOLUTION

(a) We set $d = 0.03$ in the formula for margin of error and solve for n:

$$0.03 = \frac{1.96}{2\sqrt{n}} \qquad \text{Set } d = 0.03 \text{ in formula}$$

$$n \approx 1067.1 \qquad \text{Solve for } n$$

So a random sample of 1067 or greater would provide a margin of error of ±3% or better.

(b) We set $d = 0.01$ in the formula for margin of error and solve for n:

From Example 6 we see that a very small margin of error requires a very large sample.

$$0.01 = \frac{1.96}{2\sqrt{n}} \qquad \text{Set } d = 0.03 \text{ in formula}$$

$$n \approx 9604 \qquad \text{Solve for } n$$

So a random sample of 9604 or greater would provide a margin of error of ±1% or better.

✎ NOW TRY EXERCISE **25** ∎

▼ Two-Variable Data and Correlation

So far in our study of statistics we've learned about **one-variable** data, in which only one property of each individual is measured. For example, we can measure the height of individuals. We now consider **two-variable** data, in which two properties of each individual are measured. For example, we can record the height *and* salary of each individual. In studying two-variable data, our goal is to discover whether there is a linear relationship between the two variables.

Two-variable data can be graphed in a coordinate plane, resulting in a **scatter plot**. In *Focus on Modeling*, page 130, we analyzed such data mathematically by finding the line that best fits the data, called the **regression line**. Associated with the regression line is a **correlation coefficient**, which is a mathematical measure of how well the data fit along the regression line, or how well the two variables are **correlated**. The correlation coefficient r satisfies

$$-1 \le r \le 1$$

If r is close to zero, the variables have little correlation. The closer r is to 1 or -1, the closer the data points are to the regression line. (The slope of the regression line determines the sign of the correlation coefficient.)

Now let's think about these issues statistically. In statistics the data are a *sample* from a *population*. Our goal is to discover the relationship between the two variables in the population by examining the sample. So if we find that the sample shows a strong correlation between the two variables, we would intuitively assume that the same is true in the population. But there is another variable that is always involved in statistical conclusions: sample size. In statistics we think as follows. We first skeptically assume that these two variables are not correlated at all in the population and then ask:

What is the probability that the correlation in the sample is due to chance alone?

If this probability is small (less than 0.05), then we say that the correlation is **statistically significant** (at the 95% **confidence level**). (Assuming that the data are normally distributed, the value of this probability can be calculated precisely by using calculus.) For example, if the sample consists of only three individuals, even a strong correlation coefficient may not be significant. On the other hand, for a large sample, a small correlation coefficient may be significant. This is because if there is no correlation at all in the population, it's very unlikely that a large random sample would produce data that have a linear trend, whereas a small sample is more likely to produce correlated data by chance alone.

Table 1 relates the sample size with critical values of the correlation coefficient, at the 95% confidence level. For example, for a sample of size 10 we need a correlation coefficient greater than 0.632 to conclude that there is a statistically significant linear relationship between the two variables at the 95% confidence level. This means that if there is actually no correlation at all between the variables in the population, there is only a 0.05 probability of obtaining a sample of 10 with a correlation coefficient greater than 0.632.

A positive correlation between height and salary means that taller people tend to have bigger salaries. A negative correlation would indicate that taller people tend to have smaller salaries.

TABLE 1

Critical values of the correlation coefficient r for sample size n (at the 95% confidence level)

n	r	n	r	n	r
3	0.997	11	0.602	35	0.334
4	0.950	12	0.576	40	0.312
5	0.878	13	0.553	50	0.279
6	0.811	14	0.532	60	0.254
7	0.754	15	0.514	70	0.235
8	0.707	20	0.444	80	0.220
9	0.666	25	0.396	90	0.207
10	0.632	30	0.361	100	0.197

ALTERNATE EXAMPLE 7

A student observes that she seems to read slower the longer she's been reading. She decides to conduct an experiment. She takes a book she enjoys and reads it for 6 hours; she then notes how many pages she's read:

Hour	Pages read
1	150
2	140
3	135
4	130
5	120
6	122

(a) Find the correlation coefficient.

(b) Are the results of the study statistically significant? Explain how your conclusion is supported by the information in Table 1 from the text.

ANSWERS

(a) -0.968

(b) Yes

DRILL QUESTION

A survey is given with a sample size of 1000 people. At the 95% confidence interval, what is the margin of error?

Answer

0.031

TABLE 2

Study hours	Blood pressure
0	129
1	120
3	130
4	128
6	132

Finding the regression line on a graphing calculator is explained on pages 130–135.

TABLE 3

Asbestos exposure (fibers/mL)	Percent that develop tumors
50	2
400	6
500	5
900	10
1100	26
1600	42
1800	37
2000	28
3000	50

EXAMPLE 7 | Is the Correlation Statistically Significant?

A student wants to test the relationship between study time and blood pressure. Table 2 gives the data the student obtained.

(a) Find the correlation coefficient.

(b) Are the results of the study statistically significant? Explain how your conclusion is supported by the information in Table 1.

SOLUTION

(a) We use a graphing calculator to find the regression line. The calculator also gives the correlation coefficient $r = 0.564$.

(b) The sample contains only five data points. According to Table 1 the correlation coefficient is not statistically significant (it is less than 0.878). This means that there is a greater than 0.05 probability that the observed correlation is due to chance alone.

✎ NOW TRY EXERCISE 33   ■

EXAMPLE 8 | Is the Correlation Statistically Significant?

When laboratory rats are exposed to asbestos fibers, some of them develop lung tumors. Table 3 gives the data from several different experiments. (See Example 3, page 133.)

(a) Find the correlation coefficient.

(b) Are the results of the study statistically significant? Explain how your conclusion is supported by the information in Table 1.

SOLUTION

(a) On page 134 we found the regression line for these data. The calculator also gives the correlation coefficient $r = 0.924$.

(b) The sample contains nine data points. According to Table 1 this correlation coefficient is statistically significant (because it is greater than 0.666). This means that there is less than a 0.05 probability that the observed correlation is due to chance alone.

✎ NOW TRY EXERCISE 35   ■

Is Correlation the Same as Causation? The answer is no. For example, there is a very strong correlation between the number of grocery stores in a city and the number of robberies in that city. Can we conclude from this that grocery stores cause robberies? Of course not—population is a lurking variable in this situation. Larger cities have more of everything, including grocery stores and robberies. Nevertheless, correlation is an excellent statistical tool for discovering hidden relationships. For example, the discovery of a statistically significant correlation between smoking and lung cancer led scientists to search for the causal relationship between these variables. You can learn much more about this topic in the *Discovery Project* referenced on page 953.

14.7 EXERCISES

CONCEPTS

1. When we analyze a population statistically by performing a survey or making an observational study, it is important that

we select a _____ sample, to avoid bias.

2. In selecting a sample for a statistical study, a researcher must be careful to avoid the following types of bias.

(a) If part of the population is excluded from the sampling

process, the sample will suffer from _____ bias.

(b) If the wording of the questions in a survey are intended to elicit a specific response, the sample will suffer from

_____ bias.

(c) If some members of the sample are inclined not to answer some of the questions in a survey, the sample will suffer

from _____ bias.

(d) If the sample consists of individuals who have volunteered to take part in the survey, or study because of their per-

sonal interest, the sample will suffer from _____ bias.

3. Since a simple random sample is often difficult or costly to select, statisticians have developed other sampling methods.
   (a) If we obtain a sample systematically from a list, we are

   conducting _____ sampling.
   (b) If we first divide the population into groups and then randomly select a sample proportionally from each group, we

   are conducting _____ sampling.
   (c) If we first divide the population into groups and then select a random sample of groups, we are conducting

   _____ sampling.

4. In an observational study (such as one that tests the effectiveness of an experimental drug), a researcher will usually divide the sample into two groups: One group receives the treatment

being tested and is called the _____ group; the other group does not receive the treatment and is called the

_____ group. This is done to ensure that the treatment is the actual cause of any positive results obtained and to

eliminate the effect of unintended _____ variables.

5. When a poll is conducted, then at the 95% confidence level the margin of error d and the sample size n are related by the

formula $d =$ _____ .

6. When we analyze two-variable data by finding a regression

line, then both the _____ coefficient r and the

_____ size n are important in determining whether the

correlation is statistically _____ .

APPLICATIONS

7–12 ■ A sample is selected as described. Is the sample a random sample? If it isn't, identify the type of sampling bias.

7. Athletic Program A middle school wishes to determine how important an athletic program is to the parents of its students. It mails a survey to all 230 parents whose children are enrolled at the school and asks them whether they consider the program "important," "somewhat important," or "not important." They receive 37 responses, of which most consider the athletic program "important."

8. Cosmetic Product The Exfolique Cosmetics Company wishes to demonstrate how effective its products are in improving women's skin health. The company places surveyors at its cosmetics counters in department stores who question the first

ten clients who show up at each counter about how satisfied they are with the effect of Exfolique products on their skin.

9. Call-In Poll A news-talk radio station for a certain large city conducts a call-in poll on the popularity of a mayoral candidate. The sample selected consists of listeners who call in to the radio station.

10. Study Hours To estimate the average number of hours freshmen study each week, a sample of freshmen from the university is selected as follows. The ID numbers of all freshmen are entered into a computer, and a random-number generator is used to randomly select 50 of those ID numbers. Students with the selected ID numbers are interviewed about their study habits.

11. Impaired Driving Survey A Pennsylvania county offers first-time drunk driving offenders the option of completing a six-week educational program in lieu of jail time after conviction. To measure the effectiveness of the program, they interview 200 graduates of the program and ask them about their impaired driving behavior (or lack of it) after completion of the program.

12. Food Waste Nanaimo Regional District officials have decided to add food waste to the materials that residents must recycle as part of their waste management program. The new system is criticized in the local press, so the district management mails surveys to all homeowners on its tax rolls explaining the many advantages of the program and asking whether the program should be continued. The responses to the survey are overwhelmingly supportive of the program.

13–16 ■ A sampling technique is described. Identify the type of sampling used.

13. Gypsy Moths After gypsy moths infest the trees in a large suburban park, officials decide to measure the degree of the infestation. Using a topographical map, park rangers divide the park into a grid of 1000 equally sized blocks. They then select 20 blocks at random; from each of these blocks they randomly select 15 trees and observe the degree of gypsy moth infestation in each of the selected trees.

14. Congressional Candidates An election in a swing congressional district pits two highly respected candidates against each other. A pollster obtains the list of registered voters for the district and interviews every 500th person on the list as to the person's preference to determine who is ahead in the election.

15. Customer Satisfaction A financial services company wishes to study customer satisfaction. To select a sample for the study, the market research branch of the company first classifies the customers into four groups: small, medium, large, and preferred investors. A random sample of customers is selected by randomly selecting from each group a number of customers that is proportional to the size of the class group.

16. Clean-Up Crew On a camping trip with 200 campers, some are selected for clean-up as follows. For each camper a die is rolled. The campers who get the numbers 1 and 2 are selected for the clean-up crew.

17–20 ■ An experiment is described. **(a)** Describe some possible confounding variable(s) in the experiment. **(b)** Suggest an experimental design that would eliminate the confounding variable(s). Identify the type of design you are suggesting.

17. Synthetic Oil Versus Conventional Oil   A petrochemical researcher wants to compare the effectiveness of synthetic oil and conventional oil on the durability of automobile engines. His firm purchases ten Acura TLs and ten Skoda Octavias, all of them new 2011 models, for his experiment. The Acuras are lubricated with synthetic oil, and the Skodas are lubricated with conventional oil. After 100,000 km of travel with regular oil changes, the engines are dismantled, and their wear is compared.

18. Exercise and Cancer   To determine whether exercise helps to prevent cancer, a medical professor selects 60 sedentary students from his classes and 35 people who exercise regularly at the gym in his uncle's retirement home. He then tracks their medical history for a five-year period, recording the number of cancer cases that arise.

19. Bottled Water and Health   The Zxyzx bottled water company conducts a study on the health benefits of drinking their very expensive bottled water. The company selects 50 households that regularly use Zxyzx and 50 households that drink tap water. The study finds that the children in the Zxyzx households have fewer health problems.

20. Restless Arm Syndrome   A new medication for restless arm syndrome is to be tested among 400 patients suffering with the ailment. The subjects of the study consist of 300 women and 100 men, ranging in age from 20 to 40 years of age. The medication is administered to the women, whereas the men get a placebo. Their responses are recorded and analyzed.

21–24 ■ To determine the approval rating of a candidate for governor, a random sample of registered voters is selected. The sample size n and the number x who plan to vote for the candidate are given.
(a) Estimate the percentage of the voters in the population of registered voters that prefer the candidate.
(b) Find the margin of error of the poll (at the 95% confidence level).
(c) State the 95% confidence interval for the percentage of the population who prefer the candidate.

21. $n = 400$, $x = 180$ **22.** $n = 200$, $x = 80$

23. $n = 1000$, $x = 600$ **24.** $n = 10$, $x = 4$

25–28 ■ A polling firm is hired to conduct a poll for Candidate X. The candidate wants the poll to have margin of error d. Find the required sample size n.

25. $d = 0.015$ **26.** $d = 0.025$

27. $d = 0.05$ **28.** $d = 0.005$

29. Tasting Phenylthiocarbamide (PTC)   The ability to taste the chemical PTC is genetically determined. For those who can taste it, PTC has a bitter taste; for others it is tasteless. To estimate the proportion of people in a certain Scandinavian country who can taste PTC, a researcher selects a random sample of 1500 individuals. The researcher finds that 1230 of these can taste PTC. Estimate the percentage of people in that country who can taste PTC, and state the margin of error of your estimate.

30. Methylmercury in Fish   Fish concentrate mercury in their bodies in the form of methylmercury, a biological form of mercury, which is highly toxic to humans. To estimate the proportion of fish in a particular lake that are contaminated with methylmercury, a researcher obtains a random sample of 600 fish from the lake. The researcher finds that 153 of these are contaminated. Estimate the percentage of fish in the entire lake that are contaminated, and state the margin of error of your estimate.

31. Car Accidents near Home   To estimate the number of car accidents that occur "near home" (within 5 miles of home), a researcher obtains a random sample of 8000 accident reports. It is found that 4220 accidents occurred near home. Use these data to estimate the percentage of all accidents that occur near home and state the margin of error.

32. Tomato Seeds   A seed company wishes to estimate the proportion of its hybridized tomato seeds that germinate. A random sample of 2200 of the tomato seeds is selected and planted; 2035 of them germinate. Estimate the percentage of the company's tomato seeds that will germinate, and state the margin of error of your estimate.

33–34 ■ Two-variable data are given. **(a)** Use a graphing calculator to find the correlation coefficient r. **(b)** Determine whether the correlation between the variables is statistically significant at the 95% significance level.

33. Video Games   A student obtains the following two-variable data from three of his friends. The data give the number of hours per day that each student plays video games and their grade on the last precalculus test. The student claims that playing video games is strongly positively correlated to mathematics test scores.

Hours	Score
1	72
2	70
3	80

34. Too Much Studying   A student claims that studying too much lowers your grade in calculus. The student offers the following data for his claim.

Hours of study	Test score
1	80
2	78
3	77
4	88

35–40 ■ Refer to the two-variable data in the indicated exercises on pages 135–139. **(a)** Use a graphing calculator to find the correlation coefficient r. **(b)** Determine whether the correlation between the variables is statistically significant at the 95% significance level.

35. Exercise 1   **36.** Exercise 4

37. Exercise 5   **38.** Exercise 6

39. Exercise 7   **40.** Exercise 8

DISCOVERY PROJECT | **Correlation and Causation**

In this project we explore the relationship between correlation and causation. You can find the project at the book companion website: **www.stewartmath.com**

14.8 INTRODUCTION TO INFERENTIAL STATISTICS

Testing a Claim About a Population Proportion Intuitively ▶ Testing a Claim About a Population Proportion Using Probability: The *P*-Value ▶ Inference About Two Proportions

The goal of **inferential statistics** is to get (or infer) information about an entire population by examining a random sample from that population. We can use a sample to test the validity of a hypothesis (or a claim) about the population mean, variance, standard deviation, and other properties of a population. In this introduction to statistical inference we use a random sample from a population to test a claim about a **population proportion**.

▼ Testing a Claim About a Population Proportion Intuitively

In statistics a **hypothesis** is a statement (or a claim) about a property of an entire population. In this section we study hypotheses about the true proportion p of individuals in the population with a particular characteristic: for example, the true proportion of registered voters who will vote Yes in an upcoming ballot or the true proportion of patients who react well to a new medication.

Suppose that individuals having a particular property are *assumed* to form a proportion p_0 of a population. How does this assumption compare to the *true* proportion p of these individuals? To answer this question, we begin by stating two opposing hypotheses.

The **null hypothesis**, denoted by H_0, states the "assumed state of affairs" and is expressed as an equality: $p = p_0$. The **alternative hypothesis** (also called the **research hypothesis**), denoted by H_1, is the proposed substitute to the null hypothesis and is expressed as an inequality: $p > p_0$, or $p < p_0$, or $p \neq p_0$.

To test a hypothesis, we examine a random sample from the population. The claim is either supported or refuted by data from that random sample.

If, under the assumption that the null hypothesis is true, the observed sample proportion (or a more extreme proportion, depending on H_1) is *very unlikely* to have occurred by chance alone, we **reject the null hypothesis**. Otherwise, the data does not provide us with enough evidence to reject the null hypothesis, so we **fail to reject the null hypothesis**. The next example illustrates how these ideas are used.

EXAMPLE 1 | Testing a Hypothesis Intuitively

It is assumed that voter sentiment on a California ballot measure is equally divided between Yes and No. An advocate for the measure claims that more than half of the voters support the measure. To test this claim, a *random* sample of 1000 voters is selected.

(a) Formulate a hypothesis test.

(b) What should we conclude about the claim if the sample has 820 Yes votes? 508 Yes votes? 535 Yes votes?

SUGGESTED TIME AND EMPHASIS
1–2 classes, optional material

ALTERNATE EXAMPLE 1
A person claims that 75% of Americans are not eating enough vegetables. A total of 1000 people are polled, and 200 of them are not eating enough vegetables. Formulate a hypothesis test. What should we conclude about the claim?

ANSWER
The null hypothesis is that the proportion of Americans not eating enough vegetables is 0.75. The alternative hypothesis is that it is less than 0.75. If the null hypothesis is true, then it is very unlikely that the number of them is 200. So we reject the null hypothesis.

TEXT QUESTION
We can "reject the null hypothesis" or "fail to reject the null hypothesis." Why do we never "accept the null hypothesis"?

Answer
Because there is always a chance, however slight, that the hypothesis is false and all the positive results are random chance.

FLORENCE NIGHTINGALE
(1820–1919) was a British nurse who tended to wounded soldiers during the Crimean war. She laid the foundation for the modern science of nursing by using data analysis to investigate the conditions of medical care in Britain. After the war she established the first professional school of nursing.

Florence exhibited a strong interest in mathematics at an early age. As a nurse she used her knowledge of mathematics to collect and exhibit data on sanitary conditions in hospitals. She was a pioneer in the use of graphical representations of data. She was one of the first to use pie charts and invented another method of presenting data graphically now known as Rose Diagrams.

Florence Nightingale was enamored by the powerful uses of statistics. She wrote: "Statistics is the most important science in the whole world, for upon it depends the practical application of every other science and of every art, the one science essential to all political and social administration, all education, all organization based on experience, for it only gives results of our experience."

SOLUTION

(a) The null hypothesis is that the proportion of Yes is half: $p = 0.5$. The alternative hypothesis is that the proportion is greater than half: $p > 0.5$. We state these hypotheses as follows:

$$H_0: p = 0.5$$
$$H_1: p > 0.5$$

(b) If the null hypothesis is true, we would expect our random sample of 1000 voters to have about 500 Yes votes.

If the null hypothesis is true, it would be *very unlikely* to have 820 or more Yes votes in a random sample of 1000 voters. This sample provides overwhelming evidence against the null hypothesis. So in this case we reject the null hypothesis.

If the null hypothesis is true, it is *not unlikely* that we would have 508 Yes votes in our sample. So the sample does not provide enough evidence to reject the null hypothesis. So we fail to reject the null hypothesis.

If the null hypothesis is true, the 535 Yes votes in the sample is higher than expected. But it is difficult to decide on the basis of intuition alone whether this sample provides enough evidence to reject the null hypothesis. (We'll see how to answer this question in the next example.)

✎ **NOW TRY EXERCISE 3**　　　　　　　　　　　　　　　　　　　　　　　■

▼ Testing a Claim About a Population Proportion Using Probability: The *P*-Value

Example 1 contains the main concept of testing a hypothesis. The only missing ingredient is the calculation of probabilities. In the solution to Example 1 we used the phrases "very unlikely" and "not unlikely." We need to replace these phrases with probabilities.

The **P-value** associated with the observed sample is the probability of obtaining a random sample with a proportion at least as extreme (depending on H_1) as the proportion in our random sample, given that H_0 is true. So a "very small" *P*-value tells us that it is "very unlikely" that the sample we got was obtained by chance alone, so we should reject the null hypothesis. The *P*-value at which we decide to reject the null hypothesis is called the **significance level** of the test and is denoted by α. Experience among statisticians indicates that the significance level $\alpha = 0.05$ (or 5%) is adequate for most purposes. In critical studies, such as the testing for the effectiveness of drugs, a much more stringent level of significance is used (usually $\alpha = 0.01$).

TESTING A HYPOTHESIS

To test a hypothesis, we use the following steps.

1. **Formulate the Hypotheses.**　First state a null hypothesis and an alternative hypothesis.

2. **Obtain a Random Sample.**　Obtain a sample that is selected arbitrarily and without bias.

3. **Calculate the P-Value.**　Use a calculator to find the *P*-value associated with the sample obtained.

4. **Make a Conclusion.**　A *P*-value smaller than the significance level of the test indicates that we should reject the null hypothesis. Otherwise, we fail to reject the null hypothesis.

IN-CLASS MATERIALS

■ Ask your students this question: "If I flip a coin and it comes up heads twice in a row, do you believe the coin is weighted?" And then ask, "If I flip a coin and it comes up heads 300 times in a row, do you believe the coin is weighted?" Try to establish the idea that as the number of heads gets larger, the likelihood that the run is due to random chance decreases, but it never goes away entirely. Perhaps vary the question: "What if I don't get 300 heads in a row, but I flip it 300 times and get 260 heads?" Explain that part of the point to this section is to give a bit of precision to this idea.

■ Some students find the *P*-value counterintuitive. If people believe that two variables are correlated, they want to show the correlation coefficient is far from zero. If people use the *P*-value to test a hypothesis, they want to show the correlation is close to zero.

The logic of hypothesis testing outlined here is the same as the logic used in legal proceedings. In court, the defendant is presumed to be innocent (this is the null hypothesis). Next, the facts of the case (the data) are presented in court. The jury must decide the case on reasonable doubt (corresponding to the P-value). Suppose the defendant is found fleeing the scene in the victim's car with the murder weapon by his side and the victim in the back seat. The jury will conclude that there is only a small chance (small P-value) of this happening if the hypothesis of innocence (the null hypothesis) is true, so the jury decides on guilt (rejects the null hypothesis). On the other hand, if the facts of the case show that the defendant was most likely in another town when the crime occurred and no facts were presented that he ever had access to the murder weapon, the jury may find reasonable doubt (large P-value) and fail to convict the defendant (fail to reject the null hypothesis).

The calculation of P-values is very difficult and requires advanced calculus. Fortunately, the formulas needed to calculate P-values are programmed into most graphing calculators. We now test the hypotheses in Example 1 by calculating P-values.

EXAMPLE 2 | Testing a Hypothesis Using the P-Value

It is assumed that voter sentiment on a California ballot measure is equally divided between Yes and No. An advocate for the measure claims that Yes voters are more than half of all voters. To test this claim, a *random* sample of 1000 voters is selected. The sample has 535 Yes voters.

(a) Formulate a hypothesis test.

(b) Calculate the P-value.

(c) Make a conclusion using the $\alpha = 0.05$ significance level.

(d) Explain how the P-value supports your conclusion.

SOLUTION

(a) Let p be the true proportion of Yes voters in the population. As in Example 1, the hypothesis test is formulated as follows:

$$H_0: p = 0.5$$
$$H_1: p > 0.5$$

(b) To find the P-value on a TI-83 calculator, follow the instructions on page 957. On the 1-PropZTest menu, use $p_0 = 0.5$, $x = 535$, $n = 1000$, and Prop > p_0, and then calculate. The calculator output is shown on page 957. We see that, rounded to three decimals, the P-value is 0.013.

If the true proportion of Yes voters is 0.5, then in a random sample of 1000 voters we would expect *about* 500 Yes votes. But we should *not* expect exactly 500 votes. The question is "Is the deviation from 500 (or from what we expect) statistically significant?"

(c) Since the P-value is less than 0.05, we reject the null hypothesis. We conclude that on the basis of this sample, it is very likely that the proportion of Yes voters is greater than one half.

(d) The P-value tells us that there is only a very small chance (probability 0.013) that we would obtain 535 Yes votes in a random sample of 1000 voters, given that the null hypothesis is true (i.e., given that the true proportion of Yes voters is 0.5). That's why we reject the null hypothesis.

✎ NOW TRY EXERCISE 5   ◼

How is the P-value calculated?   In Example 2 the P-value is the probability that a random sample of 1000 voters would contain 535 or more Yes voters, given that the null hypothesis is true. Since the null hypothesis states that $p = 0.5$, the P-value is the binomial probability of 535 or more "successes" (Yes votes).

$$P = C(1000, 535)(0.5)^{535}(0.5)^{465} + C(1000, 536)(0.5)^{536}(0.5)^{464} + \cdots + C(1000, 1000)(0.5)^{1000}(0.5)^0$$

ALTERNATE EXAMPLE 2
A person claims that 75% of Americans are not eating enough vegetables. A total of 1000 people are polled, and 700 of them are not eating enough vegetables. What should we conclude about the claim?

ANSWER
$p_0 = .75$, $x = 700$, $n = 1000$. P: 0.013 Since the P-value is less than 0.05, we reject the null hypothesis. We believe that it is reasonable to believe that 75% of Americans are not eating enough vegetables.

This calculation involves huge numbers. Graphing calculators are programmed with advanced methods to approximate such probabilities. That's why we need the capability of a graphing calculator in Example 2(b).

ALTERNATE EXAMPLE 3

A person claims that 75% of Americans are not eating enough vegetables. A total of 1000 people are polled, and 500 of them are not eating enough vegetables. What should we conclude about the claim?

ANSWER

$p_0 = .75, x = 500, n = 1000.$ P: 1 Since the P-value is greater than 0.05, we cannot accept the null hypothesis. It is possible that fewer than 75% of Americans are not eating enough vegetables.

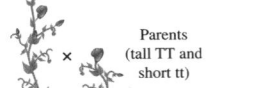

Parents
(tall TT and
short tt)

Generation 1
(all tall Tt)

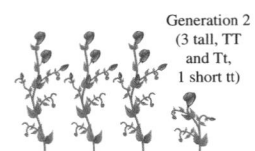

Generation 2
(3 tall, TT
and Tt,
1 short tt)

Is 23.3% the same as 25%?
In Example 3 the proportion of tall peas in the student's sample is 23.3%, but we did not reject the hypothesis that the true proportion is 25%. So is 23.3% the same as 25%? In mathematics the answer is a simple No. But in statistics the situation is quite different. In this example our answer is that we cannot say No on the basis of this sample at the 0.05 significance level. In other words, if the true proportion is 25%, we would expect to obtain the results of this sample more than 5% of the time (in fact, about 39.4% of the time).

EXAMPLE 3 | Hypothesis Test (Proportion)

In his pioneering genetic studies, Gregor Mendel experimented with hybridized (tall and short) pea plants. Mendel claimed that the cross of such hybridized plants results in tall plants 25% of the time. A biology student theorizes that the proportion of tall plants should be less than 25%. The student replicates Mendel's experiment and obtains 360 offspring of hybridized pea plants, of which 84 are tall. (See Exercise 53, page 911.)

(a) Formulate a hypothesis test.

(b) Calculate the P-value.

(c) Make a conclusion using the $\alpha = 0.05$ significance level.

(d) Explain how the P-value supports your conclusion.

SOLUTION

(a) The generally accepted claim is that the true proportion p of tall offspring is 25%, so the null hypothesis is $p = 0.25$. The student theorizes that $p < 0.25$.

$$H_0: p = 0.25$$
$$H_1: p < 0.25$$

(b) To find the P-value on a TI-83 calculator, follow the instructions on page 957. On the 1-PropZTest menu, use $p_0 = 0.25$, $x = 84$, $n = 360$, and Prop $< p_0$, and then calculate. We find that the P-value is 0.394.

(c) The P-value is greater than 0.05, so we fail to reject the null hypothesis. We conclude that on the basis of this experiment, it is entirely possible that the true proportion is 0.25.

(d) The P-value tells us that there is a high probability (greater than 0.05) that the results of this experiment are due to chance alone, given that the null hypothesis is true. This means that the experiment does not provide enough evidence to refute Mendel's claim (the null hypothesis).

✎ NOW TRY EXERCISE 7 ■

It is important to understand that hypothesis tests do not determine truth; they determine only the probability of truth. For example, in the courtroom analogy described earlier, there may be another explanation for the defendant's predicament, and he may actually be innocent. The jury determines only that it is *unlikely* (small P-value) that the defendant is innocent given the facts of the case. For this reason we can have only a certain level of confidence in the jury decision. For any hypothesis test, the 5% significance level can also be expressed as a 95% **confidence level** in the conclusion of the test. This indicates that there is only a 1 in 20 chance (5% chance) that we falsely rejected the null hypothesis.

▼ Inference About Two Proportions

Most statistical studies involve a comparison of two groups, usually called the **treatment group** and the **control group**. For example, when researchers are testing the effectiveness of an investigational medication, two groups of patients are selected. The individuals in the treatment group are given the medication; the individuals in the control group are not. The proportions of patients who recover in each group is compared. The goal of the study

STATISTICAL TESTS
On a Graphing Calculator

Graphing calculators are capable of calculating the *P*-values we use in this section. The following steps show how to obtain *P*-values on the TI-83 or TI-84 calculators.

Step 1   Choose the Test

Press the [STAT] key, choose TESTS, then select the appropriate test and press [ENTER].

   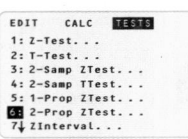

Step 2   Enter the Required Information

Enter the information required for the test. The screens for the test of a proportion `1-propZTest` and `2-propZTest` are shown.

   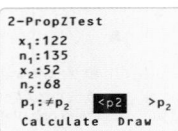

Step 3   Obtain Results

Choose `Calculate`, and press [ENTER]. The screen shows several results. We are interested in the *P*-value.

is to determine whether the difference in the proportion that recovers is *statistically significant* (and not just the result of chance alone).

Let p_1 and p_2 be the true proportions of patients who recover in the control and treatment groups, respectively. The null hypothesis is that the medication (the treatment) has no effect: $p_1 = p_2$. The alternative hypothesis is that the treatment does have an effect: $p_1 < p_2$. The *P*-value is the probability that the difference between the proportions in the two samples is due to chance alone. So if the *P*-value is small (less than the significance level of the test), we reject the null hypothesis.

EXAMPLE 4 | Two-Sample Hypothesis Test

In a study of an investigational medication the researcher selects a treatment group and a control group. Of the 68 patients in the control group, 52 recover; and of the 135 patients in the treatment group, 122 recover.

(a) Formulate a hypothesis test.

(b) Calculate the *P*-value.

(c) Make a conclusion using the $\alpha = 0.01$ significance level.

(d) Explain how the *P*-value supports your conclusion.

SOLUTION

(a) Let p_1 be the true proportion of patients who recover without the medication, and let p_2 be the true proportions of patients who recover with the medication. The null hypothesis is that the medication has no effect, that is, $p_1 = p_2$. The alternative hypothesis is that the medication is effective, that is, $p_1 < p_2$.

$$H_0: p_1 = p_2$$
$$H_1: p_1 < p_2$$

(b) To find the *P*-value on a TI-83 calculator, follow the instructions on page 957. On the 2-PropZTest menu, use $x_1 = 52$, $n_1 = 68$, $x_2 = 122$, $n_2 = 135$, and $p_1 < p_2$, and then calculate. The calculator output is shown on page 957. We see that, rounded to four decimals, the *P*-value is 0.0038.

(c) Since the *P*-value is less than 0.01, we reject the null hypothesis. We conclude that on the basis of this study, the medication is very likely to be effective.

(d) The *P*-value tells us that it is very unlikely (probability 0.0038) that the results obtained were due to chance alone, given that the null hypothesis is true. That's why we reject the null hypothesis.

✎. NOW TRY EXERCISE **9**

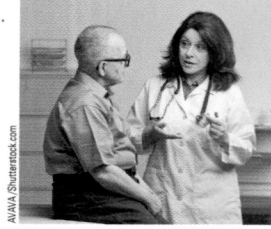

AVAVA/Shutterstock.com

ALTERNATE EXAMPLE 4

Two classes are taught by the same teacher. In the first class, the teacher wears a suit and tie. There are 58 students in this class, and 40 students pass. In the second class, the teacher wears blue jeans and a T-shirt. There are 54 students in this class, and 33 students pass. Can we conclude that the way the professor dresses affects the performance of the students?

ANSWER

The *P*-value is 0.19. We can reject the null hypothesis; there is not enough evidence to conclude that there was an effect.

DRILL QUESTION

Someone develops a drug that is supposed to cure leprosy. They wish to test the drug to see if it works. What is the null hypothesis?

Answer

The null hypothesis is that the drug has no effect on leprosy.

14.8 EXERCISES

CONCEPTS

1. A hypothesis is a statement or a claim about a _____ (population / sample).

2. To test a claim about a population proportion, we first state two hypotheses. The _____ hypothesis, denoted by H_0, is the assumed value of the proportion. The _____ hypothesis, denoted by H_1, is also called the research hypothesis.

✎. **3.** A very large glass jar is filled with black and white beans. Your friend claims that the proportion of black beans is 0.3.

By looking at the jar, you believe that the proportion of black beans is greater than 0.3. To test the claim that the proportion p of black beans is greater than 0.3, we mix the beans thoroughly and use a large cup to scoop out a random sample.

(a) State the null and alternative hypotheses.

$$H_0: \underline{\qquad}$$
$$H_1: \underline{\qquad}$$

(b) Suppose that the random sample we obtained consists of 200 beans, of which 180 are black. On the basis of intuition alone, which of the following conclusions would we make: reject H_0 or fail to reject H_0.

4. The students in Exercise 3 find that the proportion of black beans in the sample is 0.36. They use a calculator to find the P-value associated with this sample. This P-value is the

_____ of getting a random sample with the proportion

of black beans greater than or equal to _____ , assuming

that the _____ hypothesis is true. Use the $\alpha = 0.05$ significance level to answer the following.
   (a) If the students obtain a P-value 0.01, they should

   _____ the null hypothesis.
   (b) If the students obtain a P-value of 0.2, they should

   _____ the null hypothesis.

SKILLS

5–8 ■ Perform a hypothesis test for the proportion of "successes" in a population as follows. Use the 0.05 significance level.
(a) State the null and alternative hypotheses.
(b) Calculate the P-value.
(c) Make a conclusion.
(d) Explain how the P-value supports your conclusion.

5. Test whether the proportion of "successes" in a population is greater than 0.5. A random sample of 100 has 59 successes.

6. Test whether the proportion of "successes" in a population is greater than 0.7. A random sample of 1000 has 716 successes.

7. Test whether the proportion of "successes" in a population is less than 0.6. A random sample of 200 has 114 successes.

8. Test whether the proportion of "successes" in a population is less than 0.6. A random sample of 200 has 107 successes.

9–12 ■ An experiment is performed to test the effectiveness of a medication. The treatment group has n_1 subjects, and x_1 of them recover; the control group has n_2 subjects, and x_2 recover. Let p_1 and p_2 be the true proportions of those who recover with and without the medication, respectively. Perform a two-sample hypothesis test as follows.
(a) State the null and alternative hypotheses.
(b) Calculate the P-value.
(c) Make a conclusion (use the $\alpha = 0.01$ significance level).
(d) Explain how the P-value supports your conclusion.

9. $n_1 = 60$, $n_2 = 70$, $x_1 = 20$, $x_2 = 29$

10. $n_1 = 100$, $n_2 = 100$, $x_1 = 58$, $x_2 = 49$

11. $n_1 = 1000$, $n_2 = 800$, $x_1 = 312$, $x_2 = 207$

12. $n_1 = 500$, $n_2 = 350$, $x_1 = 220$, $x_2 = 142$

APPLICATIONS

13–24 ■ For each situation perform a hypothesis as follows.
(a) State the null and alternative hypotheses.
(b) Calculate the P-value.
(c) Make a conclusion.

13. Political Poll   In a poll of 1000 registered voters 548 indicate that they would vote for the Republican candidate for governor. Does this poll provide sufficient evidence that the Republican candidate is likely to win the election (i.e., get more than 50% of the vote)? Use the 0.05 significance level.

14. Political Poll   In a poll of 1100 registered voters 560 indicate that they would vote for the Democratic candidate for the Senate. Does this poll provide sufficient evidence that the Democratic candidate is likely to win election to the Senate (i.e., get more than 50% of the vote)? Use the 0.05 significance level.

15. Choosing the Gender of a Baby   A herbalist claims that his herbal drinks increase the proportion of male births to greater than 0.5. In a sample of 100 couples using the herbalist's system 62 have a male birth. Is the herbalist's claim supported by this sample? Use the 0.01 significance level.

16. Choosing the Gender of a Baby   A herbalist claims that his herbal pills increase the proportion of female births to greater than 0.5. In a sample of 100 couples using the herbalist's system 55 have a female birth. Is the herbalist's claim supported by this sample? Use the 0.01 significance level.

17. Tasting Phenylthiocarbamide (PTC)   The ability to taste the chemical PTC is genetically determined. For those who can taste it, PTC has a bitter taste; for others it is tasteless. It is known that 70% of the U.S. population can taste PTC. In a sample of 200 Native Americans it is found that 162 can taste this chemical. Test the hypothesis that the proportion of Native Americans who can taste PTC is greater than 0.70. Use the 0.01 significance level.

18. Cell Phones and Brain Cancer   In a landmark 2006 study in Denmark on the health effects of prolonged exposure to cell phone radiation, a cohort of 400,095 cell phone users were considered. The proportion of the population who acquire brain cancer is 0.0015; the number of subjects in the study who acquired brain cancer is 580. Test the hypothesis that there is a higher incidence of brain cancer among cell phone users. Use the 0.01 significance level.

19. New Teaching Method   A new method of teaching school mathematics claims to increase the proportion of students passing the entry-level mathematics (ELM) test. In a group of 416 students being taught with the new method, 280 pass the ELM test. Test the hypothesis that the proportion passing the exam is greater than the usual 0.70. Use the 0.05 significance level.

20. Methylmercury in Fish   Fish concentrate mercury in their bodies in the form of methylmercury, a biological form of mercury, which is highly toxic to humans. Approximately 25% of the fish in lakes and streams in the United States have mercury levels above the safety levels determined by the U.S. Environmental Protection Agency. After a clean-up program to reduce the presence of mercury in the water, a random sample of 1500 fish was tested, and 343 of these had high mercury levels. Test the hypothesis that the clean-up program reduced the proportion of contaminated fish to less than 0.25. Use the 0.05 significance level.

21. Mission to Mars   Polls are periodically conducted to gauge the public's support for funding space missions. In a poll of 600 Americans 316 say that it is important for the United States to be first to put a person on Mars. Test the claim that a majority (more than 50%) of Americans feel that it is important for the United States to be first to put a person on Mars. Use the 0.05 significance level.

22. **Car Accidents near Home** It is commonly assumed that 50% of car accidents occur "near home" (within 5 miles of home). In a randomly selected sample of 8000 accident reports, it is found that 4220 accidents occurred near home. Test the hypothesis that the proportion of accidents occurring within 5 miles of home is greater than 0.50. Use the 0.05 significance level.

23. **Tomato Seeds** A seed company claims that more than 95% of their hybridized tomato seeds germinate. To test the company's claim, a random sample of 2200 of the company's tomato seeds is selected and planted; 2080 of them germinate. Test the company's claim. Use the 0.05 significance level.

24. **Dutch Elm Disease** Dutch elm disease has been a persistent tree infestation across the northern United States. In a randomly selected sample of 2000 elm trees in a certain forest it was found that 650 have the disease. Test the hypothesis that more than 30% of the elm trees in the forest have the disease. Use the 0.05 significance level.

25–28 ■ Perform a two sample hypothesis test for each experiment as follows.
(a) Identify the two proportions, p_1 and p_2, that are to be compared.
(b) State the null and alternative hypotheses.
(c) Calculate the P-value
(d) Make a conclusion.

25. **Vaccine Effectiveness** To test the effectiveness of a flu vaccine, researchers set up an experiment. The vaccine is administered to the 150 subjects in the treatment group, and a placebo is given to the 70 subjects in the control group. In the treatment group 12 subjects get the flu, and in the control group 10 get the flu. Do the results indicate that the vaccine is effective in preventing the flu? Use the 0.01 significance level.

26. **Helsinki Heart Study** In a 1982–1987 study on the relationship between cholesterol levels and heart attacks, 4081 middle-aged men from Helsinki, Finland were the subjects.

The 2051 men in the treatment group were given gemfibrozil, a cholesterol-lowering drug. The 2030 men in the control group were given a placebo. In the five-year period of the study, the incidence of heart attacks comprised 56 men in the treatment group and 84 men in the control group. Do the results indicate that gemfibrozil is effective in preventing heart attacks? Use the 0.01 significance level.

27. **Gender and Nightmares** In a 2009 study at the University of West England, 100 female students and 93 male students were interviewed about their dreams. When asked to describe their most recent dream, 34 of the women and 18 of the men reported having a nightmare. Is there a statistically significant difference in the proportion of men and women having nightmares? Use the 0.05 significance level.

28. **Teaching Methods** A study seeks to compare two mathematics teaching methods designed to prepare students for the college entry level mathematics exam (ELM). In the study, 380 students are taught by using method A, and 410 students are taught by using Method B. From the Method A group, 270 pass the ELM; from the Method B group, 290 pass. Is there a statistically significant difference in the proportion of students who pass the ELM in the two groups? Use the 0.05 significance level.

DISCOVERY ■ DISCUSSION ■ WRITING

29. **The Significance Level** Suppose you perform a hypothesis test at the 0.01 significance level and you *reject* the null hypothesis. What would your conclusion be if you used the 0.05 significance level?

30. **The Significance Level** Suppose you perform a hypothesis test at the 0.05 significance level and you *fail to reject* the null hypothesis. If you use the 0.01 significance level, would you still fail to reject the null hypothesis?

CHAPTER 14 | REVIEW

■ CONCEPT CHECK

1. What does the Fundamental Counting Principle say?

2. (a) What is a permutation of a set of distinct objects?
   (b) How many permutations are there of n objects?
   (c) How many permutations are there of n objects taken r at a time?

3. (a) What is a combination of r elements of a set?
   (b) How many combinations are there of n elements taken r at a time?
   (c) How many subsets does a set with n elements have?

4. In solving a problem involving picking r objects from n objects, how do you know whether to use permutations or combinations?

5. (a) What is meant by the sample space of an experiment?
   (b) What is an event?

   (c) Define the probability of an event E in a sample space S.
   (d) What is the probability of the complement of E?

6. (a) What are mutually exclusive events?
   (b) If E and F are mutually exclusive events, what is the probability of E or F occurring? What if E and F are not mutually exclusive?

7. (a) What is meant by the conditional probability of E given F? How is this probability calculated?
   (b) What are independent events?
   (c) If E and F are independent events, what is the probability of E and F occurring? What if E and F are not independent?

8. An experiment has two outcomes, S and F, where the probability of S is p. The experiment is performed n times.
   (a) What type of probability is associated with this experiment?
   (b) What is the probability that S occurs exactly r times?

9. Suppose that a game gives payouts $a_1, a_2, \ldots, a_n$ with probabilities $p_1, p_2, \ldots, p_n$.
- **(a)** What is the expected value of this game?
- **(b)** What is the significance of the expected value?
- **(c)** What is meant by a fair game? How do we determine whether the game is fair?

10. Suppose we have a set of one-variable data.
- **(a)** What are "numerical data" and "categorical data"? Give examples of each type.
- **(b)** What is meant by a 'measure of central tendency'? Describe three different measures of central tendency.
- **(c)** What is meant by a "measure of spread"? Describe one such measure.
- **(d)** What is a frequency table of data?
- **(e)** What is a stemplot of data?
- **(f)** What is a "five-number summary" of data?

11. Suppose we have a set of one-variable data.
- **(a)** What is a histogram of the data? What information about the data does a histogram give us?
- **(b)** What is a normal distribution?
- **(c)** State the Empirical Rule for normally distributed data.

12. (a) Define "sample" and "population."
- **(b)** To get information about a population from a sample, why is it important that the sample be randomly selected?
- **(c)** Describe some of the methods of obtaining a random sample.
- **(d)** Describe some types of sampling bias.
- **(e)** What is a statistical experiment? Describe some possible experimental designs.

13. When using a sample to estimate a population proportion, what is "the margin of error"? How are sample size and margin of error related?

14. Suppose we have a set of two-variable data.
- **(a)** Give some examples of two-variable data and possible relationships between the variables.
- **(b)** How are the regression line, the correlation coefficient, the sample size, and the statistical significance of the correlation coefficient related?

15. (a) What is a hypothesis?
- **(b)** In testing a hypothesis, what is the null hypothesis and what is the alternative hypothesis?
- **(c)** What are the possible conclusions of a hypothesis test?

■ EXERCISES

1. A coin is tossed, a die is rolled, and a card is drawn from a deck. How many possible outcomes does this experiment have?

2. How many three-digit numbers can be formed by using the digits 1, 2, 3, 4, 5, and 6 if repetition of digits
- **(a)** is allowed?
- **(b)** is not allowed?

3. (a) How many different two-element subsets does the set {A, E, I, O, U} have?
- **(b)** How many different two-letter "words" can be made by using the letters from the set in part (a)?

4. An airline company has overbooked a particular flight, and seven passengers must be "bumped" from the flight. If 120 passengers are booked on this flight, in how many ways can the airline choose the seven passengers to be bumped?

5. A quiz has ten true-false questions. In how many different ways can a student earn a score of exactly 70% on this quiz?

6. A test has ten true-false questions and five multiple-choice questions with four choices for each. In how many ways can this test be completed?

7. If you must answer only eight of ten questions on a test, how many ways do you have of choosing the questions you will omit?

8. An ice-cream store offers 15 flavors of ice cream. The specialty is a banana split with four scoops of ice cream. If each scoop must be a different flavor, how many different banana splits may be ordered?

9. A company uses a different three-letter security code for each of its employees. What is the maximum number of codes this security system can generate?

10. A group of students determines that they can stand in a row for their class picture in 120 different ways. How many students are in this class?

11. A coin is tossed ten times. In how many different ways can the result be three heads and seven tails?

12. The Yukon Territory in Canada uses a license-plate system for automobiles that consists of two letters followed by three numbers. Explain how we can know that fewer than 700,000 autos are licensed in the Yukon.

13. A group of friends have reserved a tennis court. They find that there are ten different ways in which two of them can play a singles game on this court. How many friends are in this group?

14. A pizza parlor advertises that they prepare 2048 different types of pizza. How many toppings does this parlor offer?

15. In Morse code, each letter is represented by a sequence of dots and dashes, with repetition allowed. How many letters can be represented by using Morse code if three or fewer symbols are used?

16. The genetic code is based on the four nucleotides adenine (A), cytosine (C), guanine (G), and thymine (T). These are connected in long strings to form DNA molecules. For example, a sequence in the DNA may look like CAGTGGTACC . . . . The code uses "words," all the same length, that are composed of the nucleotides A, C, G, and T. It is known that at least 20 different words exist. What is the minimum word length necessary to generate 20 words?

17. Given 16 subjects from which to choose, in how many ways can a student select fields of study as follows?
- **(a)** A major and a minor
- **(b)** A major, a first minor, and a second minor
- **(c)** A major and two minors

18. (a) How many three-digit numbers can be formed by using the digits 0, 1, . . . , 9? (Remember, a three-digit number cannot have 0 as the leftmost digit.)
    (b) If a number is chosen randomly from the set {0, 1, 2, . . . , 1000}, what is the probability that the number chosen is a three-digit number?

19–20 ■ An **anagram** of a word is a permutation of the letters of that word. For example, anagrams of the word *triangle* include *griantle*, *integral*, and *tenalgir*.

19. How many anagrams of the word *TRIANGLE* are possible?

20. How many anagrams are possible from the word *RANDOM* ?

21. A committee of seven is to be chosen from a group of ten men and eight women. In how many ways can the committee be chosen using each of the following selection requirements?
    (a) No restriction is placed on the number of men and women on the committee.
    (b) The committee must have exactly four men and three women.
    (c) Susie refuses to serve on the committee.
    (d) At least five women must serve on the committee.
    (e) At most two men can serve on the committee.
    (f) The committee is to have a chairman, a vice chairman, a secretary, and four other members.

22. The U.S. Senate has two senators from each of the 50 states. In how many ways can a committee of five senators be chosen if no state is to have two members on the committee?

23. A jar contains ten red balls labeled 0, 1, 2, . . . , 9 and five white balls labeled 0, 1, 2, 3, 4. If a ball is drawn from the jar, find the probability of the given event.
    (a) The ball is red.
    (b) The ball is even-numbered.
    (c) The ball is white and odd-numbered.
    (d) The ball is red or odd-numbered.

24. If two balls are drawn from the jar in Exercise 23, find the probability of the given event.
    (a) Both balls are red.
    (b) One ball is white, and the other is red.
    (c) At least one ball is red.
    (d) Both balls are red and even-numbered.
    (e) Both balls are white and odd-numbered.

25. A coin is tossed three times in a row, and the outcomes of each toss are observed.
    (a) Find the sample space for this experiment.
    (b) Find the probability of getting three heads.
    (c) Find the probability of getting two or more heads.
    (d) Find the probability of getting tails on the first toss.

26. A shelf has ten books: two mysteries, four romance novels, and four mathematics textbooks. If you select a book at random to take to the beach, what is the probability that it turns out to be a mathematics text?

27. A die is rolled, and a card is selected from a standard 52-card deck. What is the probability that both the die and the card show a six?

28. Find the probability that the indicated card is drawn at random from a 52-card deck.
    (a) An ace
    (b) An ace or a jack

(c) An ace or a spade
(d) A red ace

29. A card is drawn from a 52-card deck, a die is rolled, and a coin is tossed. Find the probability of each outcome.
    (a) The ace of spades, a six, and heads
    (b) A spade, a six, and heads
    (c) A face card, a number greater than 3, and heads

30. Two dice are rolled. Find the probability of each outcome.
    (a) The dice show the same number.
    (b) The dice show different numbers.

31. Four cards are dealt from a standard 52-card deck. Find the probability that the cards are
    (a) all kings
    (b) all spades
    (c) all the same color

32. In the "numbers game" lottery a player picks a three-digit number (from 000 to 999), and if the number is selected in the drawing, the player wins $500. If another number with the same digits (in any order) is drawn, the player wins $50. John plays the number 159.
    (a) What is the probability that he will win $500?
    (b) What is the probability that he will win $50?

33. In a TV game show, a contestant is given five cards with a different digit on each and is asked to arrange them to match the price of a brand-new car. If she gets the price right, she wins the car. What is the probability that she wins, assuming that she knows the first digit but must guess the remaining four?

34. A pizza parlor offers 12 different toppings, one of which is anchovies. If a pizza is ordered at random (that is, any number of the toppings from 0 to all 12 may be ordered), what is the probability that anchovies is one of the toppings selected?

35. A drawer contains an unorganized collection of 50 socks; 20 are red and 30 are blue. Suppose the lights go out, so Kathy can't distinguish the color of the socks.
    (a) What is the minimum number of socks Kathy must take out of the drawer to be sure of getting a matching pair?
    (b) If two socks are taken at random from the drawer, what is the probability that they make a matching pair?

36. A volleyball team has nine players. In how many ways can a starting lineup be chosen if it consists of two forward players and three defense players?

37. Zip codes consist of five digits.
    (a) How many different zip codes are possible?
    (b) How many different zip codes can be read when the envelope is turned upside down? (An upside-down 9 is a 6; and 0, 1, and 8 are the same when read upside down.)
    (c) What is the probability that a randomly chosen zip code can be read upside down?
    (d) How many zip codes read the same upside down as right side up?

38. In the Zip+4 postal code system, zip codes consist of nine digits.
    (a) How many different Zip+4 codes are possible?
    (b) How many different Zip+4 codes are palindromes? (A palindrome is a number that reads the same from left to right as right to left.)
    (c) What is the probability that a randomly chosen Zip+4 code is a palindrome?

39. Let $N = 3,600,000$. (Note that $N = 2^7 3^2 5^5$.)
   (a) How many divisors does N have?
   (b) How many even divisors does N have?
   (c) How many divisors of N are multiples of 6?
   (d) What is the probability that a randomly chosen divisor of N is even?

40. A fair die is rolled eight times. Find the probability of each event.
   (a) A six occurs four times.
   (b) An even number occurs two or more times.

41. Pacific Chinook salmon occur in two varieties: white-fleshed and red-fleshed. It is impossible to tell without cutting the fish open whether it is the white or red variety. About 30% of Chinooks have white flesh. An angler catches five Chinooks. Find the probability of each event.
   (a) All are white.
   (b) All are red.
   (c) Exactly two are white.
   (d) Three or more are red.

42. Two dice are rolled. John gets $5 if they show the same number; he pays $1 if they show different numbers. What is the expected value of this game?

43. Three dice are rolled. John gets $5 if they all show the same number; he pays $1 otherwise. What is the expected value of this game?

44. Mary will win $1,000,000 if she can name the 13 original states in the order in which they ratified the U.S. Constitution. Mary has no knowledge of this order, so she makes a guess. What is her expectation?

45–46 ■ A list of one-variable data is given. **(a)** Find the mean and median of the data. **(b)** Find the standard deviation.

45. 13   4   10   5   4   0

46. 10.3   6.5   7.2   4.6   9.1   8.4   5.0

47–48 ■ A list of one-variable data is given. **(a)** Find the five-number summary for the data set. **(b)** Draw a box plot for the data.

47. 9   7   6   8   7   6   2
   5   6   4   9   8   6   7
   6   7   9   9   10   8   7

48. 37   81   79   65   78   62
   73   90   92   68   76   73
   69   77   78   85   84   79

49–50 ■ A frequency table for a set of one-variable data is given. **(a)** Find the mean, median, and mode of the data. **(b)** Draw a histogram of the data, with bins of length 2 starting at 18.

49. Frequency Table

x	Frequency
20	1
21	3
22	6
23	8
24	7
25	3

50. Frequency Table

x	Frequency
20	1
21	0
22	4
23	5
24	6
25	7
26	8
27	10

51–52 ■ A stem-and-leaf plot of data is given. **(a)** Find the mean, median, and mode of the data. **(b)** Find the five-number summary for the data. **(c)** Draw a box plot for the data.

51.

Stem	Leaves
0	1 5
1	1 3 7
2	3 4 4 4 5 9
3	0 5 8 8
4	
5	4

1 | 3 means 13

52.

Stem	Leaves
2.0	0 1
2.1	
2.2	2 3 6
2.3	1 2 2 3 5 7
2.4	0 2

2.3 | 2 means 2.32

53–54 ■ A data set is approximately normally distributed with mean 41 and standard deviation 3.5. Use the Empirical Rule to find the proportion of data points that lie in the given interval.

53. Between 34 and 48

54. At most 44.5

55–56 ■ A data set is approximately normally distributed with mean 105 and standard deviation 22. Use a graphing calculator to find the proportion of data points that lie in the given interval.

55. Between 99 and 121

56. At least 79

57. Test Scores The stem-and-leaf plot shows the scores on a U.S. history exam.
   (a) Find the mean and median score on the exam.
   (b) Find the standard deviation for the scores.
   (c) Find the five-number summary and draw a box plot for the scores.
   (d) Draw a histogram of the data, with bins of length 5 starting at 40.
   (e) A student in the class takes the exam late and receives a score of 83. Find the new mean and median score.

Stem	Leaves
4	5
5	
6	5 9
7	1 2 3 5 8
8	2 4 5 7 8 9
9	0 3 4 9

8 | 2 means 82

58. Gasoline Prices The lists on the following page show the price per gallon (in dollars) for gasoline at gas stations in East Springfield and West Springfield.
   (a) Make a stem-and-leaf plot of the data. (3.1|2 means 3.12.)
   (b) Find the mean and standard deviation for each gas station.
   (c) Find the five-number summary and draw a box plot for each gas station. Compare the center and the spread in prices for the two stations.

(d) Draw histograms of the data, with bins of length 0.05, starting at 3.00.

East Springfield				West Springfield			
3.19	3.18	3.12	3.10	3.25	3.29	3.37	3.21
3.08	3.02	3.05	3.10	3.19	3.11	3.14	3.22
3.15	3.18	3.20	3.22	3.29	3.35	3.39	3.43
3.25	3.33			3.45	3.49		

59. Birch Heights The heights of birch trees in a Finnish national forest are approximately normally distributed with mean 11.3 meters and standard deviation 4.4 meters.
   (a) Use the Empirical Rule to find the proportion of birch trees that have height between 6.9 and 15.7 meters and the proportion of birch trees that have height more than 20.1 meters.
   (b) Use a graphing calculator to find the proportion of birch trees that have height less than 17 meters.

60. Body-Mass Index The body-mass index (BMI) is a measure for obesity. A person who has a BMI that is above 25 is considered overweight. The BMI for U.S. citizens is normally distributed with a mean of 22.2 and standard deviation of 3.9.
   (a) Use the Empirical Rule to find the proportion of U.S. citizens who have a BMI less than18.3 and the proportion of U.S. citizens who have a BMI more than 26.1.
   (b) Use a graphing calculator to find the proportion of U.S. citizens who have a BMI more than 25.

61–64 ■ A sample is selected as described. Is the sample a random sample? If it isn't, identify the type of sampling bias.

61. Satisfaction Survey To gauge customer satisfaction with their services, a car tire company places questionnaires in the waiting room. The completed questionnaires are collected and analyzed.

62. Department Store A group that opposes the building of a new department store in their neighborhood conducts a survey. The survey question states: "A large department store in our neighborhood will destroy local businesses, increase traffic congestion, and pollute the environment. Do you support the building of this store?"

63. Light Pollution Astronomy enthusiasts use the term *light pollution* to describe city lights that make it difficult to see stars at night. An astronomy club mails a survey to a sample of home owners of a community asking their opinion on removing all street lights. Very few surveys are returned, and most of these support the elimination of all street lights.

64. Texting and Driving To gauge drivers' attitudes toward texting while driving, a survey asking about the advantages of texting and driving is distributed to residents of a local retirement community.

65–66 ■ A study is described. State some possible confounding or lurking variable(s).

65. Caviar and the Common Cold To test the effect of eating caviar in preventing the common cold, a researcher selects a random sample of 50 individuals who regularly eat caviar and a random sample of 100 individuals who do not eat caviar. The researcher records the number of colds acquired in each group in a two-year period.

66. Religion and City Size A radio talk show host claims that people living in large cities are more religious than those who live in smaller towns. To test the claim, a random sample of 100 large cities (population over one million) and a random sample of 100 small towns (population under 100,000) are selected. The number of churches in each group is recorded.

67. Experimental Design To test the effectiveness of an investigational treatment for ADHD, a researcher selects a sample of 700 individuals (400 males and 300 females) diagnosed with the condition. Describe how treatment and control groups should be selected from the sample for the given experimental design. Sex (male or female) and BMI ("Normal" BMI $\leq$ 25 and "overweight" BMI $>$ 25) may be factors affecting the results of the treatment.
   (a) Completely randomized design.
   (b) Block design (controlling for sex).
   (c) Matched pair design (controlling for sex and BMI).

68. Pooraholics Anonymous Individuals with "pooraholic syndrome" tend to take jobs that are far below their potential or educational level. A psychologist forms a support group for such individuals. To test the effectiveness of her Pooraholics Anonymous support therapy, a sample of 200 individuals with the syndrome is selected (100 men and 100 women). It is thought that sex (male or female) and general happiness (happy or unhappy) are factors affecting the success of the therapy. Describe how treatment and control groups should be selected from the sample for the given experimental design.
   (a) Completely randomized design.
   (b) Block design (controlling for sex).
   (c) Matched pair design (controlling for sex and happiness).

69. Popping Popcorn A popcorn company wants to estimate the proportion of the kernels of their brand ZIP popcorn that pop when heated. The company tests 500 randomly selected kernels and finds that 480 pop. Estimate the proportion of the kernels of brand ZIP popcorn that pop, and find the margin or error.

70. Popping Popcorn The popcorn company in Exercise 69 wants to estimate the proportion of brand POP popcorn that pops with a margin of error of 1%. What sample size should the company use?

71–72 ■ A claim is made. Use the appropriate hypothesis testing methods as follows: **(a)** State the null and alternative hypotheses. **(b)** Calculate the *P*-value. **(c)** Make a conclusion.

71. Dentists Recommend Toothpaste A toothpaste company advertises that nine out of ten dentists recommend their Brand X toothpaste. A consumer group claims that fewer than 90% of dentists recommend Brand X. To test their claim, a random sample of 500 dentists is selected. Of these, 405 recommend Brand X. Is the consumer group's claim supported by these data? Use the $\alpha = 0.05$ significance level.

72. Brand Loyalty for Toothpaste A customer is considered "loyal'" to a particular brand of toothpaste if the customer purchases the brand, then purchases the same brand again within three months. The makers of Toothpaste Y claim that its customers are more loyal than those who use Toothpaste X. To test this claim, two random samples of shoppers are selected: 60 who purchased Toothpaste X and 80 who purchased Toothpaste Y. Of the Toothpaste X group, 50 purchase the same brand again within three months, and of the Toothpaste Y group, 72 purchase the same brand again within three months. Is the loyalty claim of Toothpaste Y supported by these data? Use the $\alpha = 0.05$ significance level.

1. Alice and Bill have four grandchildren, and they have three framed pictures of each grandchild. They wish to choose one picture of each grandchild to display on the piano in their living room, arranged from oldest to youngest. In how many ways can they do this?

2. A hospital cafeteria offers a fixed-price lunch consisting of a main course, a dessert, and a drink. If there are four main courses, three desserts, and six drinks to pick from, in how many ways can a customer select a meal consisting of one choice from each category?

3. An Internet service provider requires its customers to select a password consisting of four letters followed by three digits. Find how many such passwords are possible in each of the following cases:

    (a) Repetition of letters and digits is allowed.

    (b) Repetition of letters and digits is not allowed.

4. Over the past year, John has purchased 30 books.

    (a) In how many ways can he pick four of these books and arrange them, in order, on his nightstand bookshelf?

    (b) In how many ways can he choose four of these books to take with him on his vacation at the shore?

5. A commuter must travel from Ajax to Barrie and back every day. Four roads join the two cities. The commuter likes to vary the trip as much as possible, so she always leaves and returns by different roads. In how many different ways can she make the round-trip?

6. A pizza parlor offers four sizes of pizza and 14 different toppings. A customer may choose any number of toppings (or no topping at all). How many different pizzas does this parlor offer?

7. An *anagram* of a word is a rearrangement of the letters of the word.

    (a) How many anagrams of the word *LOVE* are possible?

    (b) How many different anagrams of the word *KISSES* are possible?

8. A board of directors consisting of eight members is to be chosen from a pool of 30 candidates. The board is to have a chairman, a treasurer, a secretary, and five other members. In how many ways can the board of directors be chosen?

9. One card is drawn from a deck. Find the probability of each event.

    (a) The card is red.

    (b) The card is a king.

    (c) The card is a red king.

10. A jar contains five red balls, numbered 1 to 5, and eight white balls, numbered 1 to 8. A ball is chosen at random from the jar. Find the probability of each event.

    (a) The ball is red.

    (b) The ball is even-numbered.

    (c) The ball is red or even-numbered.

11. Three people are chosen at random from a group of five men and ten women. What is the probability that all three are men?

12. Two dice are rolled. What is the probability of getting doubles?

13. In a group of four students, what is the probability that at least two have the same astrological sign?

14. An unbalanced coin is weighted so that the probability of heads is 0.55. The coin is tossed ten times.

    (a) What is the probability of getting exactly 6 heads?

    (b) What is the probability of getting less than 3 heads?

15. You are to draw one card from a deck. If it is an ace, you win $10; if it is a face card, you win $1; otherwise, you lose $0.50. What is the expected value of this game?

965

16. A data set is given.

  (a) Make a frequency table for the data.

  (b) Find the mean, median, mode, and standard deviation of the data.

  (c) Find the five-number summary of the data, and draw a box plot.

  (d) Draw a histogram of the data, with bins of length 2 starting at 30.

$$
\begin{array}{ccccccc}
38 & 36 & 37 & 35 & 39 & 38 & 31 \\
34 & 34 & 37 & 39 & 37 & 38 & 38
\end{array}
$$

17. The birth weights of infants born in India are normally distributed with a mean of 2900 grams and standard deviation of 450 grams.

  (a) Use the Empirical Rule to find the probability that a randomly selected infant in India has a birth weight of at most 3350 grams.

  (b) Use a graphing calculator to find the probability that a randomly selected infant in India has a birth weight of at least 2500 grams.

18. In a poll of 500 randomly selected residents of a small town, 340 support the building of a new community center. Estimate the proportion of residents who support the building project, and determine the margin of error.

19. The National Institute of Mental Health reports that 10% of people suffer from some form of depression. A coastal New Hampshire town claims that its residents are very happy, and consequently, fewer than 10% suffer from depression. In a random sample of 300 people from the town 21 suffer from depression. Test the town's claim as follows.

  (a) State the null and alternative hypotheses.

  (b) Calculate the P-value.

  (c) Make a conclusion. (Use the $\alpha = 0.05$ significance level.)

20. In 2009 Bayer conducted a randomized double-blind clinical trial with 170 subjects of the drug moxifloxacin for the treatment of tuberculosis. Of the trial subjects, 85 were assigned to the treatment group and 85 to the control group. The drug moxifloxacin was administered to the treatment group, and ethambutol (another drug) was administered to the control group.

  (a) From the description of this trial as "randomized," how were subjects assigned to the treatment and control groups?

  (b) At the end of the trial 68 subjects in the treatment group and 54 in the control group tested negative for the presence of the tuberculosis bacterium. Use these data to test the hypothesis that moxifloxacin is more effective than ethambutol for the treatment of tuberculosis, and state the P-value. (Use the $\alpha = 0.01$ significance level.)

The Monte Carlo Method

A good way to familiarize ourselves with a fact is to experiment with it. For instance, to convince ourselves that the earth is a sphere (which was considered a major paradox at one time), we could go up in a space shuttle to see that it is so; to see whether a given equation is an identity, we might try some special cases to make sure there are no obvious counterexamples. In problems involving probability, we can perform an experiment many times and use the results to estimate the probability in question. In fact, we often model the experiment on a computer, thereby making it feasible to perform the experiment a large number of times. This technique is called the **Monte Carlo method**, named after the famous gambling casino in Monaco.

EXAMPLE 1 | The Contestant's Dilemma

In a TV game show, a contestant chooses one of three doors. Behind one of them is a valuable prize; the other two doors have nothing behind them. After the contestant has made her choice, the host opens one of the other two doors—one that he knows does not conceal a prize—and then gives her the opportunity to change her choice.

Should the contestant switch or stay, or does it matter? In other words, by switching doors, does she increase, decrease, or leave unchanged her probability of winning? At first, it may seem that switching doors doesn't make any difference. After all, two doors are left—one with the prize and one without—so it seems reasonable that the contestant has an equal chance of winning or losing. But if you play this game many times, you will find that by switching doors, you actually win about $\frac{2}{3}$ of the time.

The authors modeled this game on a computer and found that in one million games the simulated contestant (who always switches) won 667,049 times—very close to $\frac{2}{3}$ of the time. Thus it seems that switching doors does make a difference: Switching increases the contestant's chances of winning. This experiment forces us to reexamine our reasoning. Here is why switching doors is the correct strategy:

Contestant: "I choose door number 2."

1. When the contestant first made her choice, she had a $\frac{1}{3}$ chance of winning. If she doesn't switch, no matter what the host does, her probability of winning remains $\frac{1}{3}$.

Contestant: "Oh no, what should I do?"

2. If the contestant decides to switch, she will switch to the winning door if she had initially chosen a losing one or to a losing door if she had initially chosen the winning one. Since the probability of having initially selected a losing door is $\frac{2}{3}$, by switching the probability of winning then becomes $\frac{2}{3}$.

We conclude that the contestant should switch, because her probability of winning is $\frac{2}{3}$ if she switches and $\frac{1}{3}$ if she doesn't. Put simply, there is a much greater chance that she initially chose a losing door (since there are more of these), so she should switch. ■

An experiment can be modeled by using any computer language or programmable calculator that has a random-number generator. This is a command or function (usually called Rnd or Rand) that returns a randomly chosen number x with $0 \le x < 1$. In the next example we see how to use this to model a simple experiment.

EXAMPLE 2 | Monte Carlo Model of a Coin Toss

When a balanced coin is tossed, each outcome—"heads" or "tails"—has probability $\frac{1}{2}$. This doesn't mean that if we toss a coin several times, we will necessarily get exactly half heads and half tails. We would expect, however, the proportion of heads and of tails to get closer and closer to $\frac{1}{2}$ as the number of tosses increases. To test this hypothesis, we could toss a coin a very large number of times and keep track of the results. But this is a very tedious process, so we will use the Monte Carlo method to model this process.

To model a coin toss with a calculator or computer, we use the random-number generator to get a random number x such that $0 \le x < 1$. Because the number is chosen randomly, the probability that it lies in the first half of this interval $\left(0 \le x < \frac{1}{2}\right)$ is the same

967

```
PROGRAM:HEADTAIL
:0→J:0→K
:For(N,1,100)
:rand→X
:int(2X)→Y
:J+(1-Y)→J
:K+Y→K
:END
:Disp"HEADS=",J
:Disp"TAILS=",K
```

as the probability that it lies in the second half $\left(\frac{1}{2} \le x < 1\right)$. Thus we could model the outcome "heads" by the event that $0 \le x < \frac{1}{2}$ and the outcome "tails" by the event that $\frac{1}{2} \le x < 1$.

An easier way to keep track of heads and tails is to note that if $0 \le x < 1$, then $0 \le 2x < 2$, and so $[\![2x]\!]$, the integer part of $2x$, is either 0 or 1, each with probability $\frac{1}{2}$. (On most programmable calculators, the function $\texttt{Int}$ gives the integer part of a number.) Thus we could model "heads" with the outcome "0" and "tails" with the outcome "1" when we take the integer part of $2x$. The program in the margin models 100 tosses of a coin on the TI-83 calculator. The graph in Figure 1 shows what proportion p of the tosses have come up "heads" after n tosses. As you can see, this proportion settles down near 0.5 as the number n of tosses increases—just as we hypothesized.

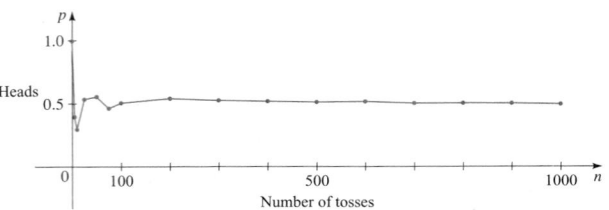

FIGURE 1 Relative frequency of "heads"

In general, if a process has n equally likely outcomes, then we can model the process using a random-number generator as follows: If our program or calculator produces the random number x, with $0 \le x < 1$, then the integer part of nx will be a random choice from the n integers $0, 1, 2, \ldots, n-1$. Thus we can use the outcomes $0, 1, 2, \ldots, n-1$ as models for the outcomes of the actual experiment.

PROBLEMS

1. **Winning Strategy**   In a game show like the one described in Example 1, a prize is concealed behind one of ten doors. After the contestant chooses a door, the host opens eight losing doors and then gives the contestant the opportunity to switch to the other unopened door.

   (a) Play this game with a friend 30 or more times, using the strategy of switching doors each time. Count the number of times you win, and estimate the probability of winning with this strategy.

   (b) Calculate the probability of winning with the "switching" strategy using reasoning similar to that in Example 1. Compare with your result from part (a).

2. **Family Planning**   A couple intend to have two children. What is the probability that they will have one child of each sex? The French mathematician D'Alembert analyzed this problem (incorrectly) by reasoning that three outcomes are possible: two boys, or two girls, or one child of each sex. He concluded that the probability of having one of each sex is $\frac{1}{3}$, mistakenly assuming that the three outcomes are equally likely.

   (a) Model this problem with a pair of coins (using "heads" for boys and "tails" for girls), or write a program to model the problem. Perform the experiment 40 or more times, counting the number of boy-girl combinations. Estimate the probability of having one child of each sex.

   (b) Calculate the correct probability of having one child of each sex, and compare this with your result from part (a).

3. **Dividing a Jackpot**   A game between two players consists of tossing a coin. Player A gets a point if the coin shows heads, and player B gets a point if it shows tails. The first player to get six points wins an $8000 jackpot. As it happens, the police raid the place when player A has five points and B has three points. After everyone has calmed down, how

should the jackpot be divided between the two players? In other words, what is the probability of A winning (and that of B winning) if the game were to continue?

The French mathematicians Pascal and Fermat corresponded about this problem, and both came to the same correct conclusion (though by very different reasonings). Their friend Roberval disagreed with both of them. He argued that player A has probability $\frac{3}{4}$ of winning, because the game can end in the four ways H, TH, TTH, TTT, and in three of these, A wins. Roberval's reasoning was wrong.

   (a) Continue the game from the point at which it was interrupted, using either a coin or a modeling program. Perform this experiment 80 or more times, and estimate the probability that player A wins.

   (b) Calculate the probability that player A wins. Compare with your estimate from part (a).

4. Long or Short World Series? In the World Series the top teams in the National League and the American League play a best-of-seven series; that is, they play until one team has won four games. (No tie is allowed, so this results in a maximum of seven games.) Suppose the teams are evenly matched, so the probability that either team wins a given game is $\frac{1}{2}$.

   (a) Use a coin or a modeling program to model a World Series, in which "heads" represents a win by Team A and "tails" represents a win by Team B. Perform this experiment at least 80 times, keeping track of how many games are needed to decide each series. Estimate the probability that an evenly matched series will end in four games. Do the same for five, six, and seven games.

   (b) What is the probability that the series will end in four games? Five games? Six games? Seven games? Compare with your estimates from part (a).

   (c) Find the expected value for the number of games until the series ends.   [*Hint:* This will be $P(\text{four games}) \times 4 + P(\text{five}) \times 5 + P(\text{six}) \times 6 + P(\text{seven}) \times 7$.]

5. Estimating π In this problem we use the Monte Carlo method to estimate the value of π. The circle in the figure has radius 1, so its area is π, and the square has area 4. If we choose a point at random from the square, the probability that it lies inside the circle will be

$$\frac{\text{area of circle}}{\text{area of square}} = \frac{\pi}{4}$$

The Monte Carlo method involves choosing many points inside the square. Then we have

$$\frac{\text{number of hits inside circle}}{\text{number of hits inside square}} \approx \frac{\pi}{4}$$

```
PROGRAM:PI
:0→P
:For(N,1,1000)
:rand→X:rand→Y
:P+((X²+Y²)<1)→P
:End
:Disp "PI IS
APPROX",4*P/N
```

Thus 4 times this ratio will give us an approximation for π.

To implement this method, we use a random-number generator to obtain the coordinates (x, y) of a random point in the square and then check to see whether it lies inside the circle (that is, we check if $x^2 + y^2 < 1$). Note that we need to use only points in the first quadrant, since the ratio of areas is the same in each quadrant. The program in the margin shows a way of doing this on the TI-83 calculator for 1000 randomly selected points.

Carry out this Monte Carlo simulation for as many points as you can. How do your results compare with the actual value of π? Do you think this is a reasonable way to get a good approximation for π?

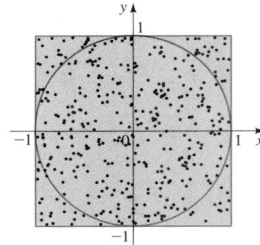

The "contestant's dilemma" problem discussed on page 967 is an example of how subtle probability can be. This problem was posed in a nationally syndicated column in *Parade* magazine in 1990. The correct solution was presented in the column, but it generated considerable controversy, with thousands of letters arguing that the solution was wrong. This shows how problems in probability can be quite tricky. Without a lot of experience in probabilistic thinking, it's easy to make a mistake. Even great mathematicians such as D'Alembert and Roberval (see Problems 2 and 3) made mistakes in probability. Professor David Burton writes in his book *The History of Mathematics*, "Probability theory abounds in paradoxes that wrench the common sense and trip the unwary."

6. **Areas of Curved Regions**   The Monte Carlo method can be used to estimate the area under the graph of a function. The figure below shows the region under the graph of $f(x) = x^2$, above the x-axis, between $x = 0$ and $x = 1$. If we choose a point in the square at random, the probability that it lies under the graph of $f(x) = x^2$ is the area under the graph divided by the area of the square. So if we randomly select a large number of points in the square, we have

$$\frac{\text{number of hits under graph}}{\text{number of hits in square}} \approx \frac{\text{area under graph}}{\text{area of square}}$$

Modify the program from Problem 5 to carry out this Monte Carlo simulation and approximate the required area.

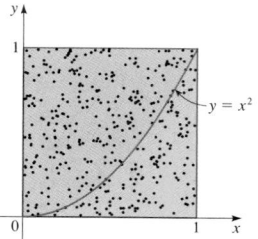

7. **Random Numbers**   Choose two numbers at random from the interval $[0, 1)$. What is the probability that the sum of the two numbers is less than 1?

   (a) Use a Monte Carlo model to estimate the probability.

   (b) Calculate the exact value of the probability.   [*Hint:* Call the numbers x and y. Choosing these numbers is the same as choosing an ordered pair (x, y) in the unit square $\{(x, y) \mid 0 \le x < 1, 0 \le y < 1\}$. What proportion of the points in this square corresponds to $x + y$ being less than 1?]

Most of the applied examples and exercises in this book involve approximate values. For example, one exercise states that the moon has a radius of 1074 miles. This does not mean that the moon's radius is exactly 1074 miles but simply that this is the radius rounded to the nearest mile.

One simple method for specifying the accuracy of a number is to state how many **significant digits** it has. The significant digits in a number are the ones from the first nonzero digit to the last nonzero digit (reading from left to right). Thus, 1074 has four significant digits, 1070 has three, 1100 has two, and 1000 has one significant digit. This rule may sometimes lead to ambiguities. For example, if a distance is 200 km to the nearest kilometer, then the number 200 really has three significant digits, not just one. This ambiguity is avoided if we use scientific notation—that is, if we express the number as a multiple of a power of 10:

$$2.00 \times 10^2$$

When working with approximate values, students often make the mistake of giving a final answer with *more* significant digits than the original data. This is incorrect because you cannot "create" precision by using a calculator. The final result can be no more accurate than the measurements given in the problem. For example, suppose we are told that the two shorter sides of a right triangle are measured to be 1.25 and 2.33 inches long. By the Pythagorean Theorem, we find, using a calculator, that the hypotenuse has length

$$\sqrt{1.25^2 + 2.33^2} \approx 2.644125564 \text{ in.}$$

But since the given lengths were expressed to three significant digits, the answer cannot be any more accurate. We can therefore say only that the hypotenuse is 2.64 in. long, rounding to the nearest hundredth.

In general, the final answer should be expressed with the same accuracy as the *least-accurate* measurement given in the statement of the problem. The following rules make this principle more precise.

RULES FOR WORKING WITH APPROXIMATE DATA

1. When multiplying or dividing, round off the final result so that it has as many *significant digits* as the given value with the fewest number of significant digits.

2. When adding or subtracting, round off the final result so that it has its last significant digit in the *decimal place* in which the least-accurate given value has its last significant digit.

3. When taking powers or roots, round off the final result so that it has the same number of *significant digits* as the given value.

As an example, suppose that a rectangular table top is measured to be 122.64 in. by 37.3 in. We express its area and perimeter as follows:

Area = length × width = 122.64 × 37.3 ≈ 4570 in²   Three significant digits

Perimeter = 2(length + width) = 2(122.64 + 37.3) ≈ 319.9 in.   Tenths digit

 Note that in the formula for the perimeter, the value 2 is an exact value, not an approximate measurement. It therefore does not affect the accuracy of the final result. In general, if a problem involves only exact values, we may express the final answer with as many significant digits as we wish.

Note also that to make the final result as accurate as possible, *you should wait until the last step to round off your answer.* If necessary, use the memory feature of your calculator to retain the results of intermediate calculations.

PROLOGUE ▪ **PAGE P4**

1. It can't go fast enough. **2.** 40% discount **3.** 427, $3n + 1$
4. 57 min **5.** No, not necessarily **6.** The same amount **7.** 2π
8. The North Pole is one such point; there are infinitely many
others near the South Pole.

CHAPTER 1

SECTION 1.1 ▪ **PAGE 10**

1. Answers may vary. Examples: **(a)** 2 **(b)** -3 **(c)** $\frac{3}{2}$ **(d)** $\sqrt{2}$
2. (a) ba; Commutative **(b)** $(a + b) + c$; Associative
(c) $ab + ac$; Distributive **3.** $\{x \mid 2 < x < 7\}$; $(2, 7)$
4. absolute value; positive **5. (a)** 50 **(b)** $0, -10, 50$
(c) $0, -10, 50, \frac{22}{7}, 0.538, 1.2\overline{3}, -\frac{1}{3}$ **(d)** $\sqrt{7}, \sqrt[3]{2}$
6. (a) $11, \sqrt{16}$ **(b)** $-11, 11, \sqrt{16}$ **(c)** $1.001, 0.3\overline{3}, -11, 11,$
$\frac{13}{15}, \sqrt{16}, 3.14, \frac{15}{3}$ **(d)** $-\pi$ **7.** Commutative Property for addition
8. Commutative Property for multiplication
9. Associative Property for addition **10.** Distributive Property
11. Distributive Property **12.** Distributive Property
13. Commutative Property for multiplication
14. Distributive Property **15.** $3 + x$ **16.** $(7 \cdot 3)x$ **17.** $4A + 4B$
18. $5(x + y)$ **19.** $3x + 3y$ **20.** $8a - 8b$ **21.** $8m$ **22.** $-8y$
23. $-5x + 10y$ **24.** $3ab + 3ac - 6ad$ **25. (a)** $\frac{17}{30}$ **(b)** $\frac{9}{20}$
26. (a) $\frac{1}{15}$ **(b)** $\frac{35}{24}$ **27. (a)** 3 **(b)** $\frac{25}{72}$ **28. (a)** $\frac{13}{20}$ **(b)** $\frac{5}{36}$
29. (a) $\frac{8}{3}$ **(b)** 6 **30. (a)** $\frac{15}{2}$ **(b)** 3 **31. (a)** $<$ **(b)** $>$
(c) $=$ **32. (a)** $<$ **(b)** $>$ **(c)** $=$ **33. (a)** False **(b)** True
34. (a) True **(b)** False **35. (a)** False **(b)** True
36. (a) False **(b)** True **37. (a)** $x > 0$ **(b)** $t < 4$ **(c)** $a \geq \pi$
(d) $-5 < x < \frac{1}{3}$ **(e)** $|p - 3| \leq 5$ **38. (a)** $y < 0$ **(b)** $z > 1$
(c) $b \leq 8$ **(d)** $0 < w \leq 17$ **(e)** $|y - \pi| \geq 2$
39. (a) $\{1, 2, 3, 4, 5, 6, 7, 8\}$ **(b)** $\{2, 4, 6\}$
40. (a) $\{2, 4, 6, 7, 8, 9, 10\}$ **(b)** $\{8\}$
41. (a) $\{1, 2, 3, 4, 5, 6, 7, 8, 9, 10\}$ **(b)** $\{7\}$
42. (a) $\{1, 2, 3, 4, 5, 6, 7, 8, 9, 10\}$ **(b)** $\varnothing$
43. (a) $\{x \mid x \leq 5\}$ **(b)** $\{x \mid -1 < x < 4\}$
44. (a) $\{x \mid -1 < x \leq 5\}$ **(b)** $\{x \mid -2 \leq x < 4\}$
45. $-3 < x < 0$ **46.** $2 < x \leq 8$

47. $2 \leq x < 8$ **48.** $-6 \leq x \leq -\frac{1}{2}$

49. $x \geq 2$ **50.** $x < 1$

51. $(-\infty, 1]$

52. $[1, 2]$

53. $(-2, 1]$

54. $[-5, \infty)$

55. $(-1, \infty)$

56. $(-5, 2)$

57. (a) $[-3, 5]$ **(b)** $(-3, 5]$ **58. (a)** $[0, 2)$ **(b)** $(-2, 0]$
59.   **60.**
61.   **62.**
63.   **64.**

65. (a) 100 **(b)** 73 **66. (a)** $5 - \sqrt{5}$ **(b)** $10 - \pi$
67. (a) 2 **(b)** -1 **68. (a)** 10 **(b)** -1 **69. (a)** 12
(b) 5 **70. (a)** $\frac{1}{4}$ **(b)** 1 **71.** 5 **72.** 4 **73. (a)** 15 **(b)** 24
(c) $\frac{67}{40}$ **74. (a)** $\frac{18}{35}$ **(b)** 19 **(c)** 0.8 **75. (a)** $\frac{7}{9}$ **(b)** $\frac{13}{45}$
(c) $\frac{19}{33}$ **76. (a)** $\frac{518}{99}$ **(b)** $\frac{62}{45}$ **(c)** $\frac{1057}{495}$ **77.** Distributive Property
78. $T_O - T_G$: $-9, -3, 0, 5, 8, 1, -1$
$|T_O - T_G|$: $9, 3, 0, 5, 8, 1, 1$
$T_O - T_G$ gives more information because it tells us which city
had the higher (or lower) temperature.
79. (a) Yes, no **(b)** 6 ft

SECTION 1.2 ▪ **PAGE 21**

1. (a) 5^6 **(b)** base, exponent **2. (a)** add, 3^9 **(b)** subtract, 3^3
3. (a) $5^{1/3}$ **(b)** $\sqrt{5}$ **(c)** No **4.** $(4^{1/2})^3 = 8, (4^3)^{1/2} = 8$
5. $\frac{1}{\sqrt{3}} = \frac{1}{\sqrt{3}} \cdot \frac{\sqrt{3}}{\sqrt{3}} = \frac{\sqrt{3}}{3}$ **6.** $\frac{2}{3}$ **7.** $5^{-1/2}$ **8.** $7^{2/3}$ **9.** $\sqrt[3]{4^2}$
10. $\frac{1}{\sqrt{11^3}}$ **11.** $5^{3/5}$ **12.** $\frac{1}{\sqrt{8}}$ **13.** $\sqrt[5]{a^2}$ **14.** $x^{-5/2}$
15. (a) -9 **(b)** 9 **(c)** $\frac{1}{9}$ **16. (a)** 25 **(b)** 1,000 **(c)** 27
17. (a) $\frac{1}{2}$ **(b)** $\frac{1}{8}$ **(c)** 16 **18. (a)** $-\frac{27}{8}$ **(b)** $\frac{1}{4}$ **(c)** $\frac{1}{100}$
19. (a) 4 **(b)** 2 **(c)** $\frac{1}{2}$ **20. (a)** 8 **(b)** -4 **(c)** -2
21. (a) $\frac{2}{3}$ **(b)** 4 **(c)** $\frac{1}{2}$ **22. (a)** 14 **(b)** 4 **(c)** 6 **23. (a)** $\frac{3}{2}$
(b) 4 **(c)** -4 **24. (a)** $\frac{1}{2}$ **(b)** $\frac{9}{4}$ **(c)** $\frac{512}{125}$ **25.** 5 **26.** 3
27. 14 **28.** $\frac{1}{144}$ **29.** $7\sqrt{2}$ **30.** $9\sqrt{3}$ **31.** $3\sqrt[5]{3}$ **32.** $\sqrt[4]{3}$
33. $(x^2 + 4)\sqrt{x}$ **34.** $(\sqrt[3]{2}y - 1)\sqrt[3]{y}$ **35. (a)** x^{10} **(b)** $12y^7$
(c) $\frac{1}{x^4}$ **36. (a)** $\frac{1}{x^2}$ **(b)** 1 **(c)** $\frac{1}{z^2}$ **37. (a)** y^3 **(b)** $\frac{1}{x^4}$ **(c)** a^6

38. (a) z^4 (b) $8y^6$ (c) $64x^2$ **39.** (a) a^{18} (b) $\dfrac{a^6}{64}$ (c) $\dfrac{1}{24z^4}$

40. (a) $\frac{1}{32}$ (b) $16a^{20}$ (c) $\dfrac{9x^4}{16}$ **41.** (a) $8x^7y^5$ (b) $4a^5z^5$

42. (a) $6a^3b^2$ (b) $8s^{10}t^3$ **43.** (a) $405x^{10}y^{23}$ (b) $500a^{12}b^{19}$

44. (a) s^2t^7 (b) $72v^{11}$ **45.** (a) $\dfrac{3y^2}{z}$ (b) $\dfrac{y^2z^9}{x^2}$ **46.** (a) $\dfrac{2y}{x^2}$

(b) $4v^3$ **47.** (a) $\dfrac{a^{19}b}{c^9}$ (b) $\dfrac{v^{10}}{u^{11}}$ **48.** (a) $\dfrac{x^{10}}{yz^4}$ (b) r^9s^2

49. (a) $\dfrac{4a^8}{b^9}$ (b) $\dfrac{125}{x^6y^3}$ **50.** (a) $5x^2y$ (b) $\dfrac{a^9}{8b^{12}}$ **51.** (a) $\dfrac{b^3}{3a}$

(b) $\dfrac{s^3}{q^7r^4}$ **52.** (a) $\dfrac{25t^{10}}{s^6}$ (b) $\dfrac{x^3y^{15}}{z^3}$ **53.** $|x|$ **54.** x^2

55. $2x^2$ **56.** xy^2 **57.** $2ab\sqrt[6]{b}$ **58.** $4a^2\sqrt[3]{b^2}$ **59.** $2|x|$

60. $|x|\sqrt{|yz|}$ **61.** (a) x^2 (b) y^2 **62.** (a) $16b^{3/4}$ (b) $45a^2$

63. (a) $w^{5/3}$ (b) $4s^{9/2}$ **64.** (a) $\dfrac{1}{4y^2}$ (b) $\dfrac{1}{u^{4/3}v^2}$

65. (a) $4a^4b$ (b) $8a^9b^{12}$ **66.** (a) $\dfrac{x^3}{y^{1/5}}$ (b) $2x^6$

67. (a) $4st^4$ (b) 4 **68.** (a) $\dfrac{2y^{4/3}}{x^2}$ (b) $-\dfrac{y^{3/4}z^2}{2}$ **69.** (a) $\dfrac{1}{x}$

(b) $\dfrac{8y^8}{x^2}$ **70.** (a) $\dfrac{x}{ab^{10}y^{10/3}}$ (b) $4s^{3/2}t^{9/2}$ **71.** (a) $y^{3/2}$ (b) $10x^{7/12}$

72. (a) $b^{5/4}$ (b) $2a^{7/6}$ **73.** (a) $2st^{11/6}$ (b) x **74.** (a) xy^2

(b) $2x^{1/6}$ **75.** (a) $y^{1/2}$ (b) $\dfrac{4u}{v^2}$ **76.** (a) $s^{5/4}$ (b) $\dfrac{3y}{x}$

77. (a) 6.93×10^7 (b) 7.2×10^{12} (c) 2.8536×10^{-5}
(d) 1.213×10^{-4} **78.** (a) 1.2954×10^8 (b) 7.259×10^9
(c) 1.4×10^{-9} (d) 7.029×10^{-4} **79.** (a) $319{,}000$
(b) $272{,}100{,}000$ (c) 0.00000002670 (d) 0.000000009999
80. (a) $710{,}000{,}000{,}000{,}000$ (b) $6{,}000{,}000{,}000{,}000$
(c) 0.00855 (d) 0.0000000006257 **81.** (a) 5.9×10^{12} mi
(b) 4×10^{-13} cm (c) 3.3×10^{19} molecules
82. (a) 9.3×10^7 mi (b) 5.3×10^{-23} g (c) 5.97×10^{24} kg
83. 1.3×10^{-20} **84.** 9.14×10^{43} **85.** 1.429×10^{19}
86. 6.3×10^{38} **87.** 7.4×10^{-14} **88.** 3.19×10^{-106}

89. (a) $\dfrac{\sqrt{10}}{10}$ (b) $\dfrac{\sqrt{2x}}{x}$ (c) $\dfrac{\sqrt{3x}}{3}$

90. (a) $\dfrac{\sqrt{15}}{6}$ (b) $\dfrac{\sqrt{6x}}{6}$ (c) $\dfrac{\sqrt{2yz}}{2z}$

91. (a) $\dfrac{2\sqrt[3]{x^2}}{x}$ (b) $\dfrac{\sqrt[4]{y}}{y}$ (c) $\dfrac{xy^{3/5}}{y}$

92. (a) $\dfrac{\sqrt[4]{a^3}}{a}$ (b) $\dfrac{a\sqrt[3]{b}}{b}$ (c) $\dfrac{c^{4/7}}{c}$

93. (a) Negative (b) Positive (c) Negative (d) Negative
(e) Positive (f) Negative **95.** 2.5×10^{13} mi **96.** $8\frac{1}{3}$ min
97. 1.3×10^{21} L **98.** $\$43{,}000$ **99.** 4.03×10^{27} molecules
100. 41.3 mi **101.** (a) 28 mi/h (b) 167 ft **102.** 1.5×10^{11} m

SECTION 1.3 ■ PAGE 32

1. 3; $2x^5$, $6x^4$, $4x^3$; $2x^3$, $2x^3(x^2 + 3x + 2)$
2. $10, 7$; $2, 5$; $(x + 2)(x + 5)$
3. $A^2 + 2AB + B^2$; $4x^2 + 12x + 9$ **4.** $A^2 - B^2$; $25 - x^2$
5. $(A + B)(A - B)$; $(2x - 5)(2x + 5)$ **6.** $(A + B)^2$; $(x + 5)^2$

7. Trinomial; x^2, $-3x$, 7; 2 **8.** Binomial; $2x^5$, $4x^2$; 5
9. Monomial; -8; 0 **10.** Monomial; $\frac{1}{2}x^7$; 7 **11.** Four terms;
$-x^4$, x^3, $-x^2$, x; 4 **12.** Binomial; $\sqrt{2}x$, $-\sqrt{3}$; 1 **13.** $7x + 5$
14. $-3 - x$ **15.** $5x^2 - 2x - 4$ **16.** $x^2 + 4x + 6$
17. $x^3 + 3x^2 - 6x + 11$ **18.** $7x + 5$ **19.** $9x + 103$
20. $x^2 - 6x + 17$ **21.** $-t^4 + t^3 - t^2 - 10t + 5$
22. $-3t^2 + 21t - 22$ **23.** $21t^2 - 26t + 8$ **24.** $8s^2 + 18s - 5$
25. $6x^2 + 7x - 5$ **26.** $14y^2 - 13y + 3$ **27.** $2x^2 + 5xy - 3y^2$
28. $12x^2 - 19xy + 5y^2$ **29.** $9x^2 + 24x + 16$
30. $4y^2 - 4y + 1$ **31.** $4u^2 + 4uv + v^2$ **32.** $x^2 - 6xy + 9y^2$
33. $4x^2 + 12xy + 9y^2$ **34.** $r^2 - 4rs + 4s^2$ **35.** $x^2 - 25$
36. $y^2 - 9$ **37.** $9x^2 - 16$ **38.** $4y^2 - 25$ **39.** $x - 4$
40. $y - 2$ **41.** $y^3 + 6y^2 + 12y + 8$ **42.** $x^3 - 9x^2 + 27x - 27$
43. $-8r^3 + 12r^2 - 6r + 1$ **44.** $8y^3 + 36y^2 + 54y + 27$
45. $x^3 + 4x^2 + 7x + 6$ **46.** $2x^3 + x^2 + 1$
47. $2x^3 - 7x^2 + 7x - 5$ **48.** $2x^3 - 5x^2 - x + 1$
49. $x\sqrt{x} - x$ **50.** $x^2 - x$ **51.** $y^2 + y$ **52.** $2x - \sqrt{x}$
53. $x^4 - a^4$ **54.** $x - y$ **55.** $a - b^2$ **56.** h^2
57. $-x^4 + x^2 - 2x + 1$ **58.** $-x^4 - 3x^2 - 4$
59. $4x^2 + 4xy + y^2 - 9$ **60.** $x^2 - y^2 - z^2 - 2yz$
61. $2x(-x^2 + 8)$ **62.** $2x^2(x^2 + 2x - 7)$
63. $(y - 6)(y + 9)$ **64.** $(z + 2)(z - 3)$
65. $xy(2x - 6y + 3)$ **66.** $7xy^2(-x^3 + 2y + 3y^2)$
67. $(x - 1)(x + 3)$ **68.** $(x - 1)(x - 5)$
69. $(2x - 5)(4x + 3)$ **70.** $(y + 3)(6y - 7)$
71. $(3x - 1)(x - 5)$ **72.** $(5x + 3)(x - 2)$
73. $(3x + 4)(3x + 8)$ **74.** $(2a + 2b - 1)(a + b + 3)$
75. $(3a - 4)(3a + 4)$ **76.** $(x + 1)(x + 5)$
77. $(3x + y)(9x^2 - 3xy + y^2)$ **78.** $(a - b^2)(a^2 + ab^2 + b^4)$
79. $(2s - 5t)(4s^2 + 10st + 25t^2)$
80. $(1 + 10y)(1 - 10y + 100y^2)$ **81.** $(x + 6)^2$ **82.** $(4z - 3)^2$
83. $(x + 4)(x^2 + 1)$ **84.** $(3x - 1)(x^2 + 2)$
85. $(2x + 1)(x^2 - 3)$ **86.** $(3x + 1)(1 - 3x^2)$
87. $(x + 1)(x^2 + 1)$ **88.** $(x + 1)(x^4 + 1)$

89. $\sqrt{x}(x - 1)(x + 1)$ **90.** $\dfrac{(3 + x)(1 + x)}{\sqrt{x}}$

91. $x^{-3/2}(1 + x)^2$ **92.** $x(x - 2)(x - 1)^{3/2}$
93. $(x^2 + 1)^{-1/2}(x^2 + 3)$ **94.** $x^{-1/2}(x + 1)^{-1/2}(2x + 1)$
95. $6x(2x^2 + 3)$ **96.** $15x^3(2 + x)$ **97.** $(x - 4)(x + 2)$
98. $(x - 8)(x - 6)$ **99.** $(2x + 3)(x + 1)$
100. $(2x - 1)(x + 4)$ **101.** $9(x - 5)(x + 1)$
102. $(4x + 3)(2x + 1)$ **103.** $(7 - 2y)(7 + 2y)$
104. $(2t - 3s)(2t + 3s)$ **105.** $(t - 3)^2$ **106.** $(x + 5)^2$

107. $(2x + y)^2$ **108.** $(r - 3s)^2$ **109.** $4ab$ **110.** $\dfrac{4}{x}$

111. $(x - 1)(x + 1)(x - 3)(x + 3)$
112. $(a - 1)(a + 1)(b - 2)(b + 2)$
113. $(2x - 5)(4x^2 + 10x + 25)$ **114.** $(x^2 + 4)(x^4 - 4x^2 + 16)$
115. $x(x + 1)^2$ **116.** $3x(x - 3)(x + 3)$
117. $x^2y^3(x + y)(x - y)$ **118.** $2xy^3(9x - y)$
119. $(x + 2)(2x^2 + 1)$
120. $(x^2 - 2)(3x + 5)$ **121.** $3(x - 1)(x + 2)$
122. $y^4(y + 2)^3(y + 1)^2$ **123.** $(a - 1)(a + 1)(a - 2)(a + 2)$
124. $(a - 1)(a + 3)(a + 1)^2$
125. $2(x^2 + 4)^4(x - 2)^3(7x^2 - 10x + 8)$
126. $(2x - 1)^2(x + 3)^{-1/2}(7x + \frac{35}{2})$
127. $(x^2 + 3)^{-4/3}(\frac{1}{3}x^2 + 3)$ **128.** $2x^{-1/2}(3x + 4)^{-1/2}$
129. (d) $(a + b + c)(a + b - c)(a - b + c)(b - a + c)$

SECTION 1.4 ■ PAGE 41

1. (a), (c)   **2.** numerator; denominator; $\dfrac{x+1}{x+3}$

3. numerators; denominators; $\dfrac{2x}{x^2+4x+3}$

4. (a) 3   (b) $x(x+1)^2$ (c) $\dfrac{-2x^2+1}{x(x+1)^2}$

5. $\mathbb{R}$ **6.** $\mathbb{R}$ **7.** $x \neq 4$ **8.** $t \neq -2$ **9.** $x \geq -3$
10. $x > 1$ **11.** $\{x \mid x \neq -1, 2\}$ **12.** $\{x \mid x \geq 0\}$

13. $\dfrac{x+2}{2(x-1)}$ **14.** $\dfrac{x+1}{3(x+2)}$ **15.** $\dfrac{1}{x+2}$ **16.** $\dfrac{x-2}{x-1}$

17. $\dfrac{x+2}{x+1}$ **18.** $\dfrac{x-4}{x+2}$ **19.** $\dfrac{y}{y-1}$ **20.** $\dfrac{(y-6)(y+3)}{(2y+3)(y+1)}$

21. $\dfrac{x(2x+3)}{2x-3}$ **22.** $\dfrac{-(x+1)}{x^2+x+1}$ **23.** $\dfrac{1}{4(x-2)}$ **24.** $\dfrac{x-5}{x-4}$

25. $\dfrac{x+3}{x-3}$ **26.** $\dfrac{1-x}{x+1}$ **27.** $\dfrac{1}{t^2+9}$ **28.** x **29.** $\dfrac{x+4}{x+1}$

30. $\dfrac{2x+y}{x-2y}$ **31.** $\dfrac{x+5}{(2x+3)(x+4)}$ **32.** $\dfrac{1}{(2x-5)(3x-2)}$

33. $\dfrac{(2x+1)(2x-1)}{(x+5)^2}$ **34.** 1   **35.** $x^2(x+1)$ **36.** $\dfrac{x-2}{x+1}$

37. $\dfrac{x}{yz}$ **38.** $\dfrac{xz}{y}$ **39.** $\dfrac{3(x+2)}{x+3}$ **40.** $\dfrac{x-5}{x+4}$

41. $\dfrac{3x+7}{(x-3)(x+5)}$ **42.** $\dfrac{2x}{(x+1)(x-1)}$

43. $\dfrac{1}{(x+1)(x+2)}$ **44.** $\dfrac{x^2+3x+12}{(x-4)(x+6)}$ **45.** $\dfrac{3x+2}{(x+1)^2}$

46. $\dfrac{2(5x-9)}{(2x-3)^2}$ **47.** $\dfrac{u^2+3u+1}{u+1}$ **48.** $\dfrac{2b^2-3ab+4a^2}{a^2b^2}$

49. $\dfrac{2x+1}{x^2(x+1)}$ **50.** $\dfrac{x^2+x+1}{x^3}$ **51.** $\dfrac{2x+7}{(x+3)(x+4)}$

52. $\dfrac{2(x+1)}{(x-2)(x+2)}$ **53.** $\dfrac{x-2}{(x+3)(x-3)}$

54. $\dfrac{x^2-6x-4}{(x-1)(x+2)(x-4)}$ **55.** $\dfrac{5x-6}{x(x-1)}$

56. $\dfrac{-2x-1}{(x-3)(x+2)}$ **57.** $\dfrac{-5}{(x+1)(x+2)(x-3)}$

58. $\dfrac{x^2+x+4}{(x-1)(x+1)^2}$ **59.** $\dfrac{(x+1)^2}{x^2+2x-1}$ **60.** $\dfrac{c}{c-2}$

61. $\dfrac{4x-7}{(x-2)(x-1)(x+2)}$ **62.** $\dfrac{5}{(x-4)(x+3)(x+1)}$

63. $-xy$ **64.** $\dfrac{x^3}{x^2+y^2}$ **65.** $\dfrac{y-x}{xy}$ **66.** $\dfrac{(x+y)^2}{xy}$ **67.** $\dfrac{1}{1-x}$

68. $\dfrac{2x+3}{x+2}$ **69.** $-\dfrac{1}{(1+x)(1+x+h)}$

70. $-\dfrac{1}{\sqrt{x}\sqrt{x+h}\,(\sqrt{x}+\sqrt{x+h})}$ **71.** $-\dfrac{2x+h}{x^2(x+h)^2}$

72. $3x^2+3xh+h^2-7$ **73.** $\dfrac{1}{\sqrt{1-x^2}}$ **74.** $\left|x^3+\dfrac{1}{4x^3}\right|$

75. $\dfrac{(x+2)^2(x-13)}{(x-3)^3}$ **76.** $\dfrac{2x(6-x)}{(x+6)^5}$ **77.** $\dfrac{x+2}{(x+1)^{3/2}}$

78. $\dfrac{1}{(1-x^2)^{3/2}}$ **79.** $\dfrac{2x+3}{(x+1)^{4/3}}$ **80.** $\dfrac{7-\frac{3}{2}x}{(7-3x)^{3/2}}$

81. $2+\sqrt{3}$ **82.** $\dfrac{3+\sqrt{5}}{2}$ **83.** $\dfrac{2(\sqrt{7}-\sqrt{2})}{5}$

84. $\dfrac{\sqrt{x}-1}{x-1}$ **85.** $\dfrac{y\sqrt{3}-y\sqrt{y}}{3-y}$ **86.** $2(\sqrt{x}+\sqrt{y})$

87. $\dfrac{-4}{3(1+\sqrt{5})}$ **88.** $\dfrac{-1}{\sqrt{3}-\sqrt{5}}$ **89.** $\dfrac{r-2}{5(\sqrt{r}-\sqrt{2})}$

90. $\dfrac{-1}{\sqrt{x}\sqrt{x+h}(\sqrt{x}+\sqrt{x+h})}$ **91.** $\dfrac{1}{\sqrt{x^2+1}+x}$

92. $\dfrac{1}{\sqrt{x+1}+\sqrt{x}}$ **93.** True   **94.** False   **95.** False

96. False   **97.** False   **98.** False   **99.** True   **100.** True

101. (a) $\dfrac{R_1 R_2}{R_1+R_2}$ (b) $\frac{20}{3} \approx 6.7$ ohms   **102.** \$56.10, \$31.20,
\$16.50, \$12.00, \$10.50, \$12.00, \$16.50

SECTION 1.5 ■ PAGE 54

1. (a) True   (b) False (because quantity could be 0)   (c) False
2. (a) Factor into $(x+1)(x-5)$, and use the Zero-Product
Property.   (b) Add 5 to each side, then complete the square by
adding 4 to both sides.   (c) Insert coefficients into the Quadratic
Formula.   **3.** (a) 0, 4   (b) factor   **4.** (a) $\sqrt{2x}=-x$
(b) $2x=x^2$ (c) 0, 2   (d) 0
5. quadratic; $x+1$; $W^2-5W+6=0$
6. quadratic; x^3; $W^2+7W-8=0$ **7.** (a) No   (b) Yes
8. (a) Yes   (b) No   **9.** (a) Yes   (b) No   **10.** (a) Yes
(b) No   **11.** 12   **12.** $\frac{7}{5}$ **13.** 18   **14.** 6   **15.** -3 **16.** $\frac{5}{2}$
17. 12   **18.** -70 **19.** $-\frac{3}{4}$ **20.** $\frac{21}{11}$ **21.** 30   **22.** $\frac{1}{17}$ **23.** $-\frac{1}{3}$
24. $\frac{13}{6}$ **25.** $\frac{13}{3}$ **26.** $\frac{11}{2}$ **27.** -2 **28.** $-\frac{1}{2}$
29. $R=\dfrac{PV}{nT}$ **30.** $m=\dfrac{Fr^2}{GM}$ **31.** $w=\dfrac{P-2l}{2}$

32. $R_1=\dfrac{RR_2}{R_2-R}$ **33.** $x=\dfrac{2d-b}{a-2c}$

34. $x=\dfrac{-6+a-2b+6c}{6}$ **35.** $x=\dfrac{1-a}{a^2-a-1}$

36. $a=\frac{1}{2}(b^2+b)$ **37.** $r=\pm\sqrt{\dfrac{3V}{\pi h}}$

38. $r=\pm\sqrt{G\dfrac{mM}{F}}$ **39.** $b=\pm\sqrt{c^2-a^2}$

40. $i=-100\pm100\sqrt{A/P}$ **41.** $t=\dfrac{-v_0\pm\sqrt{v_0^2+2gh}}{g}$

42. $n=\dfrac{-1\pm\sqrt{1+8S}}{2}$ **43.** $-4, 3$ **44.** $-4, 1$

45. 3, 4   **46.** $-6, -2$ **47.** $-\frac{3}{2}, \frac{5}{2}$ **48.** $-3, -\frac{1}{2}$ **49.** $-2, \frac{1}{3}$

50. $-\frac{3}{2}, \frac{7}{3}$ **51.** ±2 **52.** ±3 **53.** $-\dfrac{2\pm\sqrt{10}}{3}$ **54.** $\frac{1}{2}\pm\sqrt{2}$

55. $-1\pm\sqrt{6}$ **56.** $2\pm\sqrt{2}$ **57.** $3\pm2\sqrt{5}$ **58.** $\frac{1}{2}, -\frac{7}{2}$

59. $-2\pm\frac{\sqrt{14}}{2}$ **60.** $1\pm\frac{2\sqrt{3}}{3}$ **61.** $0, \frac{1}{4}$ **62.** $\frac{1}{4}, \frac{1}{2}$ **63.** $-3, 5$

64. $-6, 1$ **65.** 2, 5   **66.** $-20, -10$ **67.** $-\frac{3}{2}, 1$ **68.** $-\frac{4}{3}, -1$

69. $-1\pm\frac{2\sqrt{6}}{3}$ **70.** $3\pm2\sqrt{2}$ **71.** $\frac{3}{4}$ **72.** $\dfrac{1\pm\sqrt{5}}{4}$ **73.** $-\frac{9}{2}, \frac{1}{2}$

74. $2 \pm \sqrt{3}$ **75.** No real solution   **76.** $\dfrac{-5 \pm \sqrt{13}}{2}$

77. $\dfrac{-8 \pm \sqrt{14}}{10}$ **78.** $-\frac{7}{5}$ **79.** 2   **80.** No real solution   **81.** 1

82. 2   **83.** No real solution   **84.** 2   **85.** $-\frac{7}{5}, 2$ **86.** $-\frac{3}{2}, 5$

87. $-50, 100$ **88.** No real solution   **89.** -4 **90.** $-4, -\frac{7}{3}$

91. 4   **92.** 4   **93.** 3   **94.** 21   **95.** $\pm 2\sqrt{2}, \pm\sqrt{5}$

96. $-2, -1, 1, 2$ **97.** No real solution   **98.** $-1, \sqrt[3]{3}$

99. $\pm 3\sqrt{3}, \pm 2\sqrt{2}$ **100.** 256   **101.** $-1, 0, 3$ **102.** 2

103. 27, 729   **104.** 4, 9   **105.** $-2, -\frac{4}{3}$ **106.** $-\frac{3}{2}, \frac{3}{2}$

107. 3.99, 4.01   **108.** No real solution   **109.** 4.24 s

110. (a) 1.732 s   **(b)** 2.449 s   **111. (a)** After 1 s and $1\frac{1}{2}$ s

(b) Never   **(c)** 25 ft   **(d)** After $1\frac{1}{4}$ s   **(e)** After $2\frac{1}{2}$ s

112. 80 ft/s   **113. (a)** 0.00055, 12.018 m   **(b)** 234.375 kg/m³

114. 12 cm   **115. (a)** After 17 yr, on Jan. 1, 2019

(b) After 18.612 yr, on Aug. 12, 2020   **116.** 89 days

117. 50   **118.** 215,000 mi   **119.** 132.6 ft

SECTION 1.6 ■ PAGE 67

2. principal; interest rate; time in years   **3. (a)** x^2 **(b)** lw

(c) πr^2 **4.** 1.6   **5.** $\dfrac{1}{x}$ **6.** $r = \dfrac{d}{t}, t = \dfrac{d}{r}$ **7.** $3n + 3$ **8.** $3n$

9. $\dfrac{160 + s}{3}$ **10.** $\dfrac{24 + q}{4}$ **11.** $0.025x$ **12.** $795n$ **13.** $3w^2$

14. $4w + 10$ **15.** $\frac{3}{4}s$ **16.** $\dfrac{d}{55}$ **17.** $\dfrac{25}{3 + x}$ **18.** $131p + 140$

19. 400 mi   **20.** 1285 messages   **21.** $9000 at $4\frac{1}{2}$% and

$3000 at 4%   **22.** $2000   **23.** 7.5%   **24.** 6%   **25.** $7400

26. $32,500   **27.** $45,000   **28.** 8 h   **29.** Plumber, 70 h;

assistant, 35 h   **30.** 12   **31.** 40 years old   **32.** 714

33. 9 pennies, 9 nickels, 9 dimes   **34.** 5 quarters, 10 dimes,

15 nickels   **35.** 45 ft   **36.** 240 ft   **37.** 120 ft by 120 ft

38. 66 ft by 330 ft   **39.** 25 ft by 35 ft   **40.** 12 ft   **41.** 60 ft by

40 ft   **42.** 120 ft by 126 ft   **43.** 120 ft   **44.** 35 yd

45. (a) 9 cm   **(b)** 5 in.   **46. (a)** 8.94 in.   **(b)** 48 cm

47. 4 in.   **48.** 30 cm   **49.** 18 ft   **50.** 32 ft 4 in.   **51.** 5 m

52. 95 ft   **53.** 200 mL   **54.** 75 mL   **55.** 18 g   **56.** 2.4 L

57. 0.6 L   **58.** 3.06 gal   **59.** 35%   **60.** 48 lb of $3.00/lb tea

and 32 lb of $2.75/lb tea   **61.** 37 min 20 s   **62.** 120 min

63. 3 h   **64.** 40.5 h for Jim's hose, 32.4 h for Bob's hose

65. Irene 3 h, Henry $4\frac{1}{2}$ h   **66.** 3 h   **67.** 4 h

68. 15 mi/h; 30 mi/h   **69.** 500 mi/h   **70.** 55 mi/h

71. 50 mi/h (or 240 mi/h)   **72.** 50 mi/h   **73.** 6 km/h

74. 9 mi/h   **75.** 6.4 ft from the fulcrum   **76.** 1200 lb

77. 2 ft by 6 ft by 15 ft   **78.** 4.63 mm   **79.** 13 in. by 13 in.

80. 4 cm   **81.** 2.88 ft   **82.** 49 ft, 168 ft, and 175 ft

83. 16 mi; no   **84.** 440 ft or 720 ft   **85.** 7.52 ft   **86.** 27.4 in.

87. 18 ft   **88.** 169.1 in., 190.9 in.   **89.** 4.55 ft

SECTION 1.7 ■ PAGE 80

1. (a) $<$ **(b)** $\le$ **(c)** $\le$ **(d)** $>$ **2. (a)** True   **(b)** False

3. (a) $[-3, 3]$ **(b)** $(-\infty, -3], [3, \infty)$ **4. (a)** < 3 **(b)** > 3

5. $\{\sqrt{2}, 2, 4\}$ **6.** $\{1, \sqrt{2}, 2, 4\}$ **7.** $\{4\}$ **8.** $\{\sqrt{2}, 2, 4\}$

9. $\{-2, -1, 2, 4\}$ **10.** $\{-1, 0, \frac{1}{2}, 1\}$

11. $\left(-\infty, \frac{7}{2}\right]$

12. $\left(-\infty, -\frac{5}{2}\right]$

13. $(4, \infty)$

14. $(-\infty, -2)$

15. $(-\infty, 2]$

16. $[7, \infty)$

17. $\left(-\infty, -\frac{1}{2}\right)$

18. $\left(-\infty, \frac{5}{2}\right)$

19. $[1, \infty)$

20. $(-\infty, -1]$

21. $\left(\frac{16}{3}, \infty\right)$

22. $\left(-\infty, -\frac{1}{3}\right)$

23. $(-\infty, -18)$

24. $\left(-\infty, \frac{1}{3}\right]$

25. $(-\infty, -1]$

26. $(-\infty, 11]$

27. $[-3, -1)$

28. $[3, 6]$

29. $(2, 6)$

30. $(-1, 4]$

31. $\left[\frac{9}{2}, 5\right)$

32. $\left[-\frac{10}{3}, -\frac{13}{6}\right]$

33. $\left(\frac{15}{2}, \frac{21}{2}\right]$

34. $\left[\frac{11}{12}, \frac{13}{6}\right]$

35. $(-2, 3)$

36. $(-\infty, -4] \cup [5, \infty)$

37. $\left(-\infty, -\frac{7}{2}\right] \cup [0, \infty)$

38. $(-\infty, 0] \cup \left[\frac{2}{3}, \infty\right)$

39. $[-3, 6]$

40. $(-\infty, -3) \cup (-2, \infty)$

41. $\left(-\infty, -1\right] \cup \left[\frac{1}{2}, \infty\right)$

42. $(-1, 2)$

43. $(-1, 4)$

44. $(-\infty, -2] \cup \left[\frac{1}{2}, \infty\right)$

45. $(-\infty, -3) \cup (6, \infty)$

46. $(-\infty, -3) \cup (1, \infty)$

47. $(-2, 2)$

48. $(-\infty, -3] \cup [3, \infty)$

49. $(-\infty, -2] \cup [1, 3]$

50. $(-1, 2) \cup (5, \infty)$

51. $(-\infty, -2] \cup (-2, 4)$ **52.** $(-1, \infty)$

53. $[-1, 3]$ **54.** $(-\infty, -1] \cup \{0\} \cup [1, \infty)$

55. $(-2, 0) \cup (2, \infty)$ **56.** $[-4, 0] \cup [4, \infty)$

57. $(-\infty, -1) \cup [3, \infty)$ **58.** $(-3, 2)$

59. $\left(-\infty, -\frac{3}{2}\right)$ **60.** $\left(-\infty, \frac{5}{3}\right) \cup (3, \infty)$

61. $(-\infty, 5) \cup [16, \infty)$ **62.** $[0, 3)$

63. $(-2, 0) \cup (2, \infty)$ **64.** $(-\infty, -1) \cup \left(-\frac{2}{3}, 0\right)$

65. $[-2, -1) \cup (0, 1]$ **66.** $[-2, 0) \cup (1, 2]$

67. $[-2, 0) \cup (1, 3]$ **68.** $[-2, -1) \cup [9, \infty)$

69. $\left(-3, -\frac{1}{2}\right) \cup (2, \infty)$ **70.** $(-\infty, -2) \cup \left[-\frac{3}{2}, -1\right)$

71. $(-\infty, -1) \cup (1, \infty)$ **72.** $(1, \infty)$

73. $[-4, 4]$ **74.** $(-5, 5)$

75. $\left(-\infty, -\frac{7}{2}\right) \cup \left(\frac{7}{2}, \infty\right)$ **76.** $(-\infty, -2] \cup [2, \infty)$

77. $[2, 8]$ **78.** $(-\infty, -2] \cup [0, \infty)$

79. $[1.3, 1.7]$ **80.** $\left(-\frac{4}{5}, \frac{8}{5}\right)$

81. $(-\infty, -1] \cup \left[\frac{7}{3}, \infty\right)$ **82.** $\left(-\infty, -\frac{15}{8}\right) \cup \left(\frac{9}{8}, \infty\right)$

83. $(-4, 8)$ **84.** $(-\infty, -9] \cup [7, \infty)$

85. $(-6.001, -5.999)$ **86.** $(-\infty, -3] \cup [-1, \infty)$

87. $\left[-\frac{1}{2}, \frac{3}{2}\right]$ **88.** $(-\infty, \infty)$

89. $|x| < 3$ **90.** $|x| > 2$ **91.** $|x - 7| \geq 5$

92. $|x - 2| \leq 4$ **93.** $|x| \leq 2$ **94.** $|x| \geq 1$ **95.** $|x| > 3$
96. $|x| < 4$ **97.** $|x - 1| \leq 3$ **98.** $|x + 2| > 1$
99. $-\frac{4}{3} \leq x \leq \frac{4}{3}$ **100.** $x \leq \frac{2}{3}$ or $x \geq 1$ **101.** $x < -2$ or $x > 7$
102. $-2 < x \leq 1$ **103.** **(a)** $x \geq \frac{c}{a} + \frac{c}{b}$

(b) $\frac{a - c}{b} \leq x < \frac{2a - c}{b}$
105. $68 \leq F \leq 86$ **106.** $10 \leq C \leq 35$ **107.** More than 200 mi
108. Less than 286 min **109.** Between 12,000 mi and 14,000 mi
110. **(a)** $T = 20 - \frac{h}{100}$ **(b)** From 20°C down to -30°C
111. **(a)** $-\frac{1}{3}P + \frac{560}{3}$ **(b)** From \$215 to \$290
112. ± 0.195 dollars **113.** Distances between 20,000 km and
100,000 km **114.** Distances greater than 30 m
115. From 0 s to 3 s **116.** Between 40 and 50 mi/h
117. Between 0 and 60 mi/h **118.** Between 400 and 4400 units
119. Between 20 and 40 ft
120. **(a)** $|x - 0.020| \leq 0.003$ **(b)** $0.017 \leq x \leq 0.023$
121. Between 62.4 and 74.0 in.

SECTION 1.8 ■ PAGE 92

1. $(3, -5)$ **2.** $\sqrt{(c - a)^2 + (d - b)^2}$; 10

3. $\left(\frac{a + c}{2}, \frac{b + d}{2}\right)$; $(4, 6)$ **4.** 2; 3; No **5.** **(a)** y; x; -1

(b) x; y; $\frac{1}{2}$ **6.** $(1, 2)$; 3

7.

8. $A(5, 1)$, $B(1, 2)$, $C(-2, 6)$, $D(-6, 2)$, $E(-4, -1)$, $F(-2, 0)$,
$G(-1, -3)$, $H(2, -2)$ **9.** **(a)** $\sqrt{13}$ **(b)** $\left(\frac{3}{2}, 1\right)$ **10.** **(a)** 5
(b) $\left(0, \frac{1}{2}\right)$ **11.** **(a)** 10 **(b)** $(1, 0)$ **12.** **(a)** $2\sqrt{10}$ **(b)** $(1, -2)$
13. **(a)** **14.** **(a)**

(b) 10 **(c)** $(3, 12)$ **(b)** 13 **(c)** $\left(4, \frac{5}{2}\right)$
15. **(a)** **16.** **(a)**

(b) 25 **(c)** $\left(\frac{1}{2}, 6\right)$ **(b)** $10\sqrt{2}$ **(c)** $(4, 4)$

17. (a)

18. (a)

29.

30.

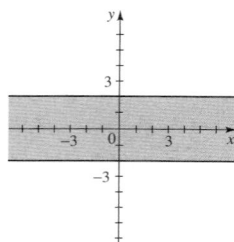

(b) $4\sqrt{10}$ **(c)** $(0,0)$
19. 24

(b) $\sqrt{61}$ **(c)** $\left(\frac{5}{2}, -3\right)$
20. 16

31.

32.

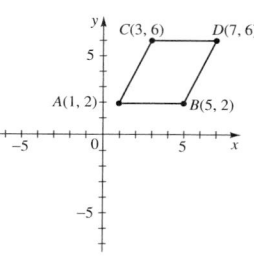

33. $A(6,7)$ **34.** $C(-6,3)$
35. $Q(-1,3)$ **38.** 9
39. (b) 10   **43.** $(0,-4)$
44. $\sqrt{37}, \dfrac{\sqrt{109}}{2}, \dfrac{\sqrt{145}}{2}$
45. $(2,-3)$

21. Trapezoid, area $= 9$ **22.** 50

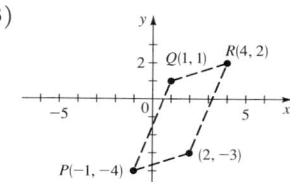

46. $(10, 13)$
47. (a)

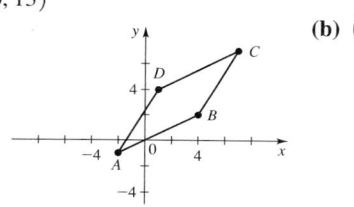

(b) $\left(\frac{5}{2}, 3\right), \left(\frac{5}{2}, 3\right)$

23.

24.

25.

26.

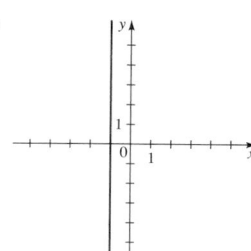

49. No, yes, yes   **50.** No, yes, yes
51. Yes, no, yes
52. Yes, yes, yes
53. x-intercepts 0, 4; y-intercept 0
54. x-intercepts -3, 3; y-intercepts -2, 2
55. x-intercepts -2, 2; y-intercepts -4, 4
56. x-intercepts -8, 8; y-intercept 4
57. x-intercept 4,
y-intercept 4,
no symmetry
58. x-intercept -1,
y-intercept 3,
no symmetry

27.

28.

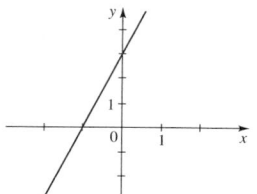

59. *x*-intercept 3,
    y-intercept −6,
    no symmetry

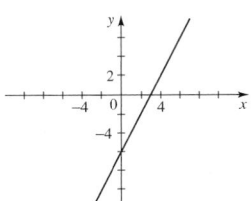

60. *x*-intercept 3,
    y-intercept 3,
    no symmetry

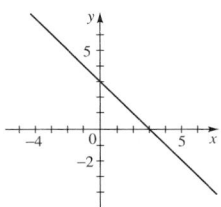

61. *x*-intercepts ±1,
    y-intercept 1,
    symmetry about *y*-axis

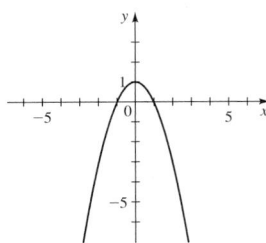

62. No *x*-intercepts,
    y-intercept 2,
    symmetry about *y*-axis

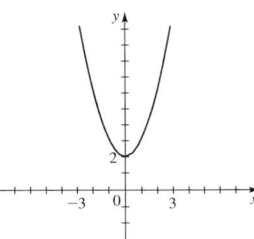

63. *x*-intercept 0,
    y-intercept 0,
    symmetry about *y*-axis

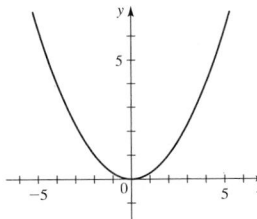

64. *x*-intercept 0,
    y-intercept 0,
    symmetry about origin

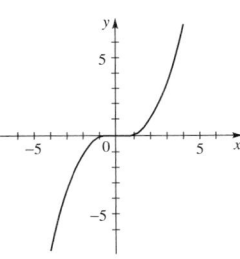

65. *x*-intercepts ±3,
    y-intercept −9,
    symmetry about *y*-axis

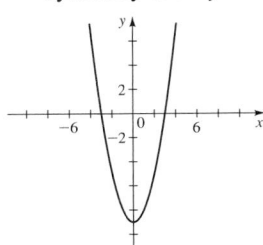

66. *x*-intercepts −3, 3,
    y-intercept 9,
    symmetry about *y*-axis

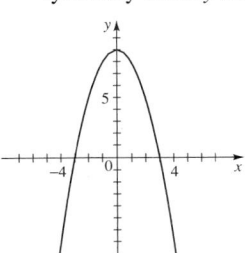

67. No intercepts,
    symmetry about origin

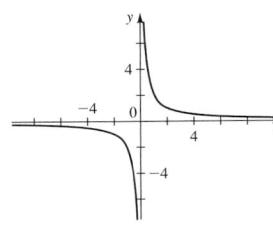

68. *x*-intercept −4,
    y-intercept 2,
    no symmetry

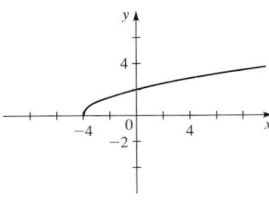

69. *x*-intercepts ±2,
    y-intercept 2,
    symmetry about *y*-axis

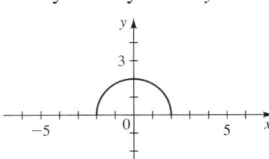

70. *x*-intercepts −2, 2,
    y-intercept −2,
    symmetry about *y*-axis

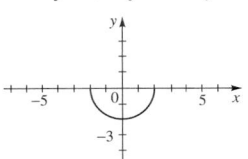

71. *x*-intercept 4,
    y-intercepts −2, 2,
    symmetry about *x*-axis

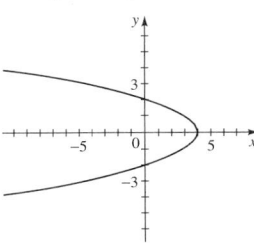

72. *x*-intercept 0,
    y-intercept 0,
    symmetry about origin

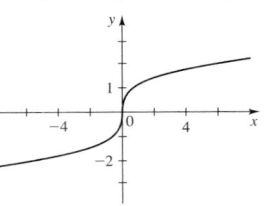

73. *x*-intercepts ±2,
    y-intercept 16,
    symmetry about *y*-axis

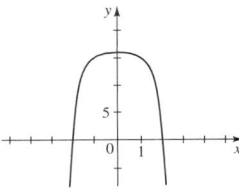

74. *x*-intercept 0,
    y-intercept 0,
    symmetry about *x*-axis

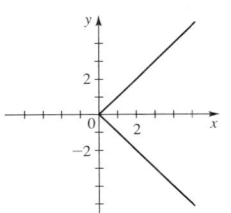

75. *x*-intercepts ±4,
    y-intercept 4,
    symmetry about *y*-axis

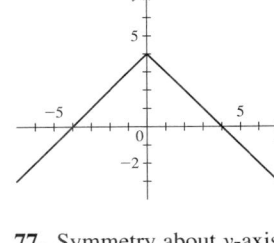

76. *x*-intercept 4,
    y-intercept 4,
    no symmetry

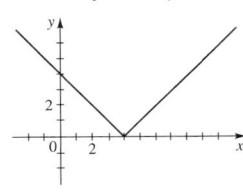

77. Symmetry about *y*-axis   **78.** Symmetry about *x*-axis
79. Symmetry about origin   **80.** Symmetry about *x*-axis, *y*-axis,
and origin   **81.** Symmetry about origin   **82.** Symmetry about
y-axis

83.

84.

85.

86.

87. $(0, 0)$, 3

88. $(0, 0)$, $\sqrt{5}$

89. $(3, 0)$, 4

90. $(0, 2)$, 2

91. $(-3, 4)$, 5

92. $(-1, -2)$, 6

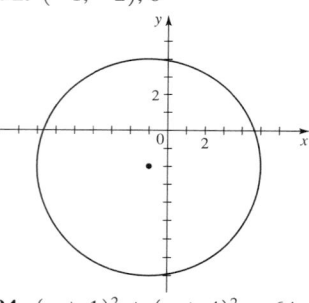

93. $(x - 2)^2 + (y + 1)^2 = 9$ **94.** $(x + 1)^2 + (y + 4)^2 = 64$
95. $x^2 + y^2 = 65$ **96.** $(x + 1)^2 + (y - 5)^2 = 130$
97. $(x - 2)^2 + (y - 5)^2 = 25$ **98.** $(x - 3)^2 + (y + 1)^2 = 32$
99. $(x - 7)^2 + (y + 3)^2 = 9$ **100.** $(x - 5)^2 + (y - 5)^2 = 25$
101. $(x + 2)^2 + (y - 2)^2 = 4$ **102.** $(x + 1)^2 + (y - 1)^2 = 10$
103. $(2, -5), 4$ **104.** $(0, -3), \sqrt{7}$ **105.** $\left(\frac{1}{4}, -\frac{1}{4}\right), \frac{1}{2}$
106. $\left(-\frac{1}{4}, -1\right), 1$ **107.** $\left(\frac{3}{4}, 0\right), \frac{3}{4}$ **108.** $\left(-1, \frac{1}{6}\right), \sqrt{37}/6$
109.

110.

111. 12π

112. $\dfrac{9\pi}{4}$

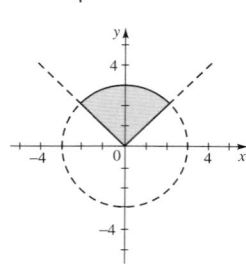

113. **(a)** 5   **(b)** 31; 25   **(c)** Points P and Q must either be on the same street or the same avenue.   **114.** **(a)** 15th Street and 12th Avenue   **(b)** 17 blocks   **115.** **(a)** 2 Mm, 8 Mm
(b) -1.33, 7.33; 2.40 Mm, 7.60 Mm

SECTION 1.9 ■ PAGE 104

1. x **2.** above   **3.** **(a)** $x = -1, 0, 1, 3$ **(b)** $[-1, 0] \cup [1, 3]$
4. **(a)** $x = 1, 4$ **(b)** $(1, 4)$ **5.** (c)   **6.** (c)   **7.** (c)   **8.** (d)
9. (c)   **10.** (d)
11.

12.

13.

14.

15.

16.

17.

18.

19.

20.

21.

22.
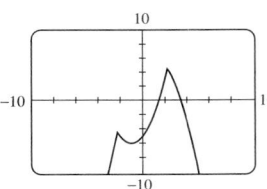

23. No   **24.** No   **25.** Yes, 2   **26.** Yes, 1

27.

28.

29.

30.
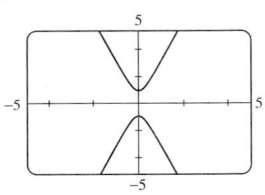

31. -4 **32.** -6 **33.** $\frac{5}{14}$ **34.** -4 **35.** $\pm 4\sqrt{2} \approx \pm 5.7$
36. $-2\sqrt[3]{2} \approx -2.52$ **37.** No solution   **38.** No solution
39. $2.5, -2.5$ **40.** $\frac{3}{2}\sqrt[5]{16} \approx 2.61$
41. $5 + 2\sqrt[4]{5} \approx 7.99, 5 - 2\sqrt[4]{5} \approx 2.01$
42. $-2 + \frac{2}{3}\sqrt[5]{81} \approx -0.39$ **43.** $3.00, 4.00$ **44.** $0.25, 0.50$
45. $1.00, 2.00, 3.00$ **46.** $-1.00, -0.25, 0.25$ **47.** 1.62
48. $0.00, 2.31$ **49.** $-1.00, 0.00, 1.00$ **50.** $0.00, 3.31$ **51.** 4
52. 4 **53.** No solution   **54.** $-1, 1.44$ **55.** 2.55 **56.** -2.78,
$-0.51, 0.51, 2.78$ **57.** $-2.05, 0, 1.05$ **58.** $-2.31, 1.79$
59. $[-2.00, 5.00]$ **60.** $[-2, 0.25]$
61. $(-\infty, 1.00] \cup [2.00, 3.00]$
62. $(-1, -0.25) \cup (-0.25, \infty)$ **63.** $(-1.00, 0) \cup (1.00, \infty)$
64. $(-\infty, -0.535] \cup [0.535, \infty)$ **65.** $(-\infty, 0)$
66. $[2.148, \infty)$ **67.** $(-1, 4)$ **68.** $(-\infty, -2] \cup [0.5, \infty)$
69. $[-1, 3]$ **70.** $(-\infty, -1] \cup \{0\} \cup [1, \infty)$ **71.** $0, 0.01$
72. (a)
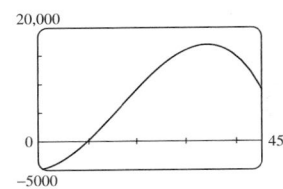

(b) 101 cooktops
(c) $279 < x < 400$

73. (a)
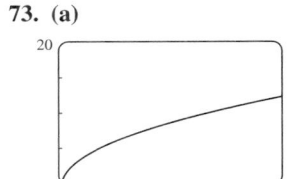

(b) 67 mi

SECTION 1.10 ▪ PAGE 115

1. $y; x; 2$ **2. (a)** 3 **(b)** 3 **(c)** $-\frac{1}{3}$ **3.** $y - 2 = 3(x - 1)$
4. (a) $0; y = 3$ **(b)** Undefined; $x = 2$ **5.** $\frac{1}{2}$ **6.** -3 **7.** $\frac{1}{6}$
8. $\frac{1}{2}$ **9.** $-\frac{1}{2}$ **10.** $-\frac{4}{3}$ **11.** $-\frac{9}{2}$ **12.** $\frac{4}{7}$ **13.** $-2, \frac{1}{2}, 3, -\frac{1}{4}$
14. (a)   **(b)**

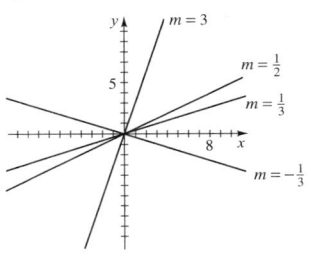

15. $x + y - 4 = 0$ **16.** $2x - y + 4 = 0$ **17.** $3x - 2y - 6 = 0$
18. $4x + 3y + 12 = 0$ **19.** $5x - y - 7 = 0$ **20.** $x + y - 2 = 0$
21. $2x - 3y + 19 = 0$ **22.** $7x + 2y + 31 = 0$
23. $5x + y - 11 = 0$ **24.** $x - y - 1 = 0$ **25.** $3x - y - 2 = 0$
26. $2x - 5y + 20 = 0$ **27.** $3x - y - 3 = 0$
28. $3x - 4y + 24 = 0$ **29.** $y = 5$ **30.** $x = 4$
31. $x + 2y + 11 = 0$ **32.** $2x + 3y - 18 = 0$ **33.** $x = -1$
34. $x = 2$ **35.** $5x - 2y + 1 = 0$ **36.** $6x + 3y - 1 = 0$
37. $x - y + 6 = 0$ **38.** $2x - y - 7 = 0$
39. (a)   **40. (a)**

(b) $3x - 2y + 8 = 0$ **(b)** $2x + y - 7 = 0$
41. They all have the   **42.** They all have the
same slope.   same y-intercept.

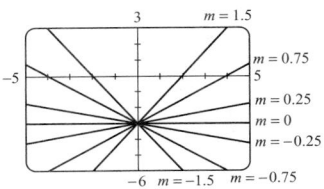

43. They all have the same *x*-intercept.

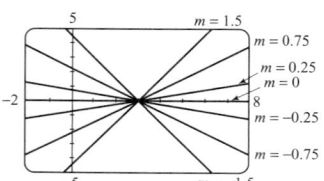

44. They all pass through the point $(-3, 2)$.

55. $-\frac{3}{4}, \frac{1}{4}$

56. $-\frac{4}{5}, 2$

45. $-1, 3$

46. $\frac{3}{2}, -6$

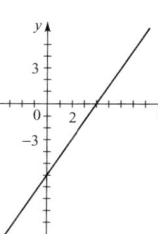

60. (a) Yes **(b)** No **61.** $x - y - 3 = 0$ **62.** 3
63. (b) $4x - 3y - 24 = 0$ **64. (a)** $3x - 4y - 25 = 0$
(b) $(-3, 4)$ **65.** 16,667 ft **66. (a)** The slope is the rate of increase in average surface temperature, and the *T*-intercept is the average surface temperature in 1950. **(b)** 17.0°C **67. (a)** 8.34; the slope represents the increase in dosage for a one-year increase in age. **(b)** 8.34 mg

68. (a)

47. $-\frac{1}{3}, 0$

48. $\frac{2}{5}, 0$

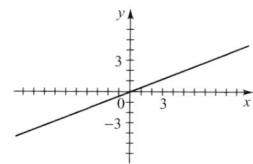

(b) The slope is the rate of decline in number of spaces sold, the *y*-intercept is the number of spaces, and the *x*-intercept is the cost per space when the manager rents no spaces.

69. (a)

(b) The slope represents production cost per toaster; the *y*-intercept represents monthly fixed cost.

49. $\frac{3}{2}, 3$

50. $-\frac{3}{5}, 6$

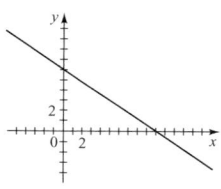

70. (a)

C	$-30°$	$-20°$	$-10°$	$0°$	$10°$	$20°$	$30°$
F	$-22°$	$-4°$	$14°$	$32°$	$50°$	$68°$	$86°$

51. $0, 4$

52. Undefined, none

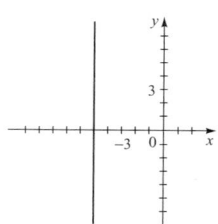

(b) $-40°$
71. (a) $t = \frac{5}{24}n + 45$ **(b)** 76°F
72. (a) $V = -950t + 4000$
(b)

53. $\frac{3}{4}, -3$

54. $0, -2$

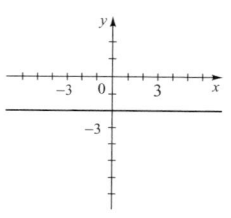

(c) The slope is the rate of decrease in value of the computer, and the *V*-intercept is the price of the computer. **(d)** $1150
73. (a) $P = 0.434d + 15$, where P is pressure in lb/in² and d is depth in feet

(b)

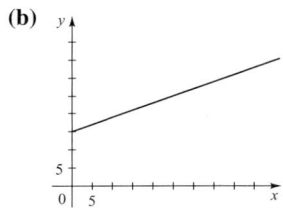

(c) The slope is the rate of increase in water pressure, and the y-intercept is the air pressure at the surface.   **(d)** 196 ft
74. (a) $d = 48t$
(b)

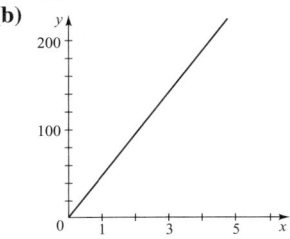

(c) 48, speed
75. (a) $C = \frac{1}{4}d + 260$
(b) $635
(c) The slope represents cost per mile.
(d) The y-intercept represents monthly fixed cost.

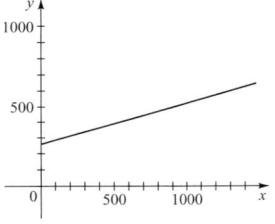

76. (a) $y = 13x + 900$
(b) 13; slope is cost of producing each additional chair
(c) 900; y-intercept is fixed daily cost

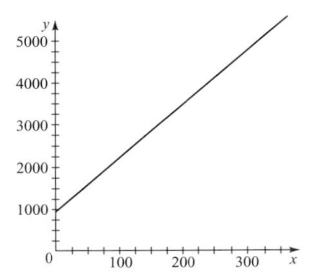

SECTION 1.11 ■ PAGE 121

1. directly proportional; proportionality   **2.** inversely proportional; proportionality   **3.** directly proportional; inversely proportional
4. $\frac{1}{2}xy$ **5.** $T = kx$ **6.** $P = kw$ **7.** $v = k/z$ **8.** $w = kmn$
9. $y = ks/t$ **10.** $P = k/T$ **11.** $z = k\sqrt{y}$ **12.** $A = k\dfrac{t^2}{x^3}$
13. $V = klwh$ **14.** $S = kr^2\theta^2$ **15.** $R = k\dfrac{i}{Pt}$ **16.** $A = k\sqrt{xy}$
17. $y = 7x$ **18.** $z = 15/t$ **19.** $R = 12/s$ **20.** $P = \frac{1}{15}T$
21. $M = 15x/y$ **22.** $S = 9pq$ **23.** $W = 360/r^2$ **24.** $t = 50\dfrac{xy}{r}$
25. $C = 16lwh$ **26.** $H = 81l^2w^2$ **27.** $s = 500/\sqrt{t}$
28. $M = 32\dfrac{abc}{d}$ **29. (a)** $F = kx$ **(b)** 8   **(c)** 32 N
30. (a) $T = k\sqrt{l}$ **(b)** quadruple the length l **31. (a)** $C = kpm$

(b) 0.125   **(c)** $57,500   **32. (a)** $P = kT/V$ **(b)** 8.3
(c) 51.9 kPa   **33. (a)** $P = ks^3$ **(b)** 0.012   **(c)** 324
34. 270 hp   **35.** 0.7 dB   **36.** 40 mi/h (for safety round down, not up)   **37.** 4   **38.** 1305.6 lb   **39.** 5.3 mi/h
40. (a) $F = kws^2/r$ **(b)** 48 mi/h
41. (a) $R = kL/d^2$ **(b)** $0.00291\overline{6}$ **(c)** $R \approx 137\ \Omega$
42. (a) $T^2 = kd^3$ **(b)** 1.66×10^{-19} **(c)** 164 yr
43. (a) 160,000   **(b)** 1,930,670,340   **44.** $51,200   **45.** 36 lb
46. 25.2 ft   **47. (a)** $f = \dfrac{k}{L}$ **(b)** Halves it
48. (a) $r = kx(P - x)$ **(b)** Infection rate when 1000 people are infected is about 80 times larger   **(c)** 0, since no more people can be infected

CHAPTER 1 REVIEW ■ PAGE 125

1. Commutative Property for addition
2. Commutative Property for multiplication
3. Distributive Property   **4.** Distributive Property
5. $-2 \leq x < 6$
6. $x \leq 4$
7. $[5, \infty)$
8. $(-1, 5]$
9. 6   **10.** 1   **11.** $\frac{1}{72}$ **12.** -5 **13.** $\frac{1}{6}$ **14.** 16   **15.** 11
16. 6   **17.** 4   **18.** 10   **19.** $16x^3$ **20.** b^{14} **21.** $12xy^8$
22. $r^{10}s^2$ **23.** x^2y^2 **24.** $|x|y^2$ **25.** $3x^{3/2}y^2$
26. x^8 **27.** $\dfrac{4r^{5/2}}{s^7}$ **28.** $\dfrac{4a^4c^6}{b^{12}}$ **29.** 7.825×10^{10}
30. 0.0000000208   **31.** 1.65×10^{-32} **32.** 3.8×10^9 times
33. $3xy^2(4xy^2 - y^3 + 3x^2)$ **34.** $(x - 6)(x - 3)$
35. $(x - 2)(x + 5)$ **36.** $(3x - 4)(2x + 3)$
37. $(4t + 3)(t - 4)$ **38.** $(x - 1)^2(x + 1)^2$
39. $(5 - 4t)(5 + 4t)$ **40.** $2y^2(y^2 + 4)(y + 2)(y - 2)$
41. $(x - 1)(x^2 + x + 1)(x + 1)(x^2 - x + 1)$
42. $(y - 2)(y - 1)(y + 1)$ **43.** $x^{-1/2}(x - 1)^2$
44. $ab^2(a + b)(a^2 - ab + b^2)$ **45.** $(x - 2)(4x^2 + 3)$
46. $(2x + y^2)(4x^2 - 2xy^2 + y^4)$ **47.** $\sqrt{x^2 + 2}(x^2 + x + 2)^2$
48. $(3x - 2)(x^2 + 6)$ **49.** $6x^2 - 21x + 3$ **50.** $4y^2 - 49$
51. $-7 + x$ **52.** $2x^{3/2} + x - x^{1/2}$ **53.** $2x^3 - 6x^2 + 4x$
54. $\dfrac{x - 3}{2x + 3}$ **55.** $\dfrac{3(x + 3)}{x + 4}$ **56.** $\dfrac{t^2 + t + 1}{t + 1}$ **57.** $\dfrac{x + 1}{x - 4}$
58. $\dfrac{3x^2 - 7x + 8}{x(x - 2)^2}$ **59.** $\dfrac{1}{x + 1}$ **60.** $\dfrac{x^2 - 2x - 5}{(x - 2)(x + 1)(x + 2)}$
61. $-\dfrac{1}{2x}$ **62.** $\dfrac{1}{2x + 1}$ **63.** $3\sqrt{2} - 2\sqrt{3}$
64. $\dfrac{1}{\sqrt{x + h} + \sqrt{x}}$ **65.** 5   **66.** -2 **67.** No solution
68. 1   **69.** 2, 7   **70.** -12 **71.** $-1, \frac{1}{2}$ **72.** $-2, \frac{1}{3}$
73. $0, \pm\frac{5}{2}$ **74.** $2, \pm\sqrt{5}$ **75.** $\dfrac{-2 \pm \sqrt{7}}{3}$ **76.** $\dfrac{3 \pm \sqrt{6}}{3}$
77. -5 **78.** ± 3 **79.** 3, 11   **80.** $-2, 7$ **81.** 20 lb raisins, 30 lb nuts   **82.** 4:00 P.M.   **83.** $\frac{1}{4}(\sqrt{329} - 3) \approx 3.78$ mi/h
84. 12 cm, 16 cm   **85.** 1 h 50 min
86. 10 ft by 8 ft or 12 ft by 6.67 ft
87. $(-3, \infty)$
88. $(-3, -1]$

89. $(-\infty, -6) \cup (2, \infty)$

90. $[-1, 1]$

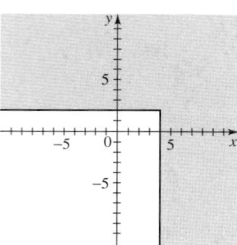

91. $(-\infty, -2) \cup (2, 4]$

92. $(-\infty, -2) \cup (1, 2)$

93. $[2, 8]$

94. $(3.98, 4.02)$

95. $-1, 7$ **96.** $-2.50, 2.76$
97. $[1, 3]$ **98.** $(5.07, \infty)$

99. (a)

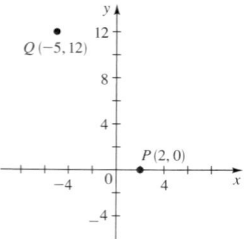

(b) $\sqrt{193}$
(d) $y = -\frac{12}{7}x + \frac{24}{7}$

(c) $\left(-\frac{3}{2}, 6\right)$
(e) $(x - 2)^2 + y^2 = 193$

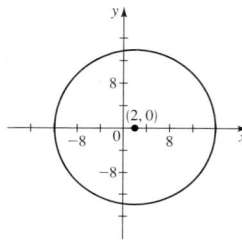

100. (a)

(b) $5\sqrt{5}$ **(c)** $\left(\frac{9}{2}, -6\right)$

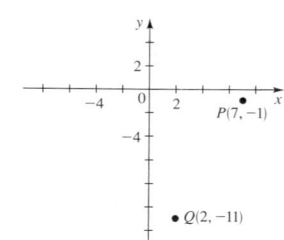

(d) $y = 2x - 15$

(e) $(x - 7)^2 + (y + 1)^2 = 125$

101.

102.

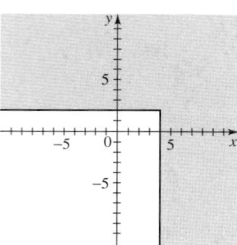

103. B **104.** $(x - 2)^2 + (y + 5)^2 = 2$
105. $(x + 5)^2 + (y + 1)^2 = 26$
106. $\left(x - \frac{1}{2}\right)^2 + \left(y - \frac{11}{2}\right)^2 = \frac{17}{2}$
107. Circle, center $(-1, 3)$, radius 1
108. Circle; $\left(\frac{1}{2}, -2\right)$, $3/\sqrt{2}$
109. No graph   **110.** Point
111. No symmetry   **112.** No symmetry

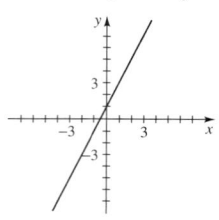

113. No symmetry   **114.** No symmetry

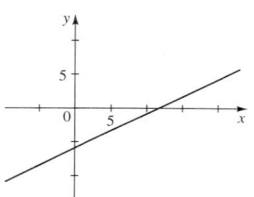

115. Symmetry about y-axis   **116.** Symmetry about x-axis

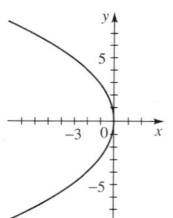

117. No symmetry   **118.** Symmetry about y-axis

119.

120.

121.

122.

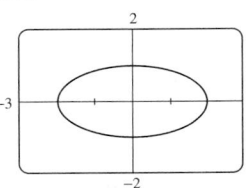

123. $2x - 3y - 16 = 0$ **124.** $2y + x = 0$
125. $3x + y - 12 = 0$ **126.** $3x + y - 10 = 0$
127. $x + 5y = 0$ **128.** $5x - 4y - 17 = 0$
129. $x^2 + y^2 = 169$, $5x - 12y + 169 = 0$
130. $(x - 5)^2 + (y - 5)^2 = 25$, $4x + 3y - 35 = 0$
131. (a) The slope represents the amount the spring
lengthens for a one-pound increase in weight. The S-intercept
represents the unstretched length of the spring.   **(b)** 4 in.
132. (a) $S = 3{,}500t + 60{,}000$ **(b)** The slope is her annual increase in salary and the S-intercept is her initial salary.
(c) \$102,000   **133.** $M = 8z$ **134.** $z = 192/y$
135. (a) $I = k/d^2$ **(b)** 64,000   **(c)** 160 candles   **136.** 8 in.
137. 11.0 mi/h   **138.** 329.4 ft

CHAPTER 1 TEST ■ PAGE 128

1. (a)

(b) $(-\infty, 3], [-1, 4)$ **(c)** 16
2. (a) 81   **(b)** -81 **(c)** $\frac{1}{81}$ **(d)** 25   **(e)** $\frac{9}{4}$ **(f)** $\frac{1}{8}$
3. (a) 1.86×10^{11} **(b)** 3.965×10^{-7}
4. (a) $6\sqrt{2}$ **(b)** $48a^5b^7$ **(c)** $\dfrac{x}{9y^7}$ **(d)** $\dfrac{x + 2}{x - 2}$ **(e)** $\dfrac{1}{x - 2}$

(f) $-(x + y)$ **5.** $5\sqrt{2} + 2\sqrt{10}$
6. (a) $11x - 2$ **(b)** $4x^2 + 7x - 15$ **(c)** $a - b$
(d) $4x^2 + 12x + 9$ **(e)** $x^3 + 6x^2 + 12x + 8$
7. (a) $(2x - 5)(2x + 5)$ **(b)** $(2x - 3)(x + 4)$
(c) $(x - 3)(x - 2)(x + 2)$
(d) $x(x + 3)(x^2 - 3x + 9)$
(e) $3x^{-1/2}(x - 1)(x - 2)$ **(f)** $xy(x - 2)(x + 2)$

8. (a) 6   **(b)** 1   **(c)** $-3, 4$ **(d)** $-1 \pm \dfrac{\sqrt{2}}{2}$

(e) No real solution   **(f)** $\pm 1, \pm\sqrt{2}$ **(g)** $\frac{2}{3}, \frac{22}{3}$ **9.** 120 mi
10. 50 ft by 120 ft
11. (a) $[-4, 3)$

(b) $(-2, 0) \cup (1, \infty)$

(c) $(1, 7)$

(d) $(-1, 4]$

12. Between $41°F$ and $50°F$ **13.** $0 \le x \le 6$
14. (a) $-2.94, -0.11, 3.05$ **(b)** $[-1, 2]$
15. (a) $S(3, 6)$ **(b)** 18

16. (a)

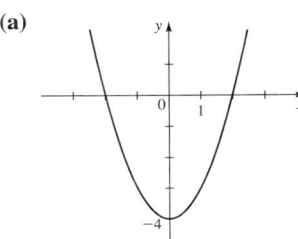

(b) x-intercepts $-2, 2$
y-intercept -4
(c) Symmetric about
y-axis

17. (a)

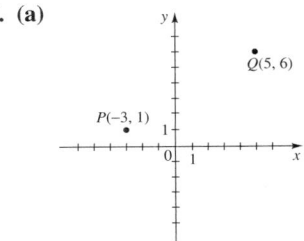

(b) $\sqrt{89}$ **(c)** $\left(1, \frac{7}{2}\right)$ **(d)** $\frac{5}{8}$ **(e)** $y = -\frac{8}{5}x + \frac{51}{10}$
(f) $(x - 1)^2 + \left(y - \frac{7}{2}\right)^2 = \frac{89}{4}$

18. (a) $(0, 0), 5$ **(b)** $(2, -1), 3$

(c) $(-3, 1), 2$

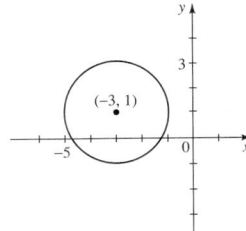

19. $y = \frac{2}{3}x - 5$

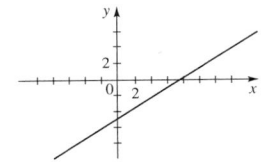

slope $\frac{2}{3}$; y-intercept -5

20. (a) $3x + y - 3 = 0$ **(b)** $2x + 3y - 12 = 0$
21. (a) $4°C$ **(b)**

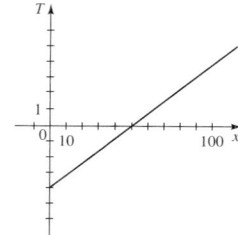

(c) The slope is the rate of change in temperature, the x-intercept is the depth at which the temperature is $0°C$, and the T-intercept is the temperature at ground level.
22. (a) $M = kwh^2/L$ **(b)** 400 **(c)** $12,000$ lb

FOCUS ON MODELING ▪ PAGE 135

1. (a)

(b) $y = 1.8807x + 82.65$ **(c)** 191.7 cm
2. (a)

(b) $y = 16.4163x - 621.83$ **(c)** 938 cans
3. (a)

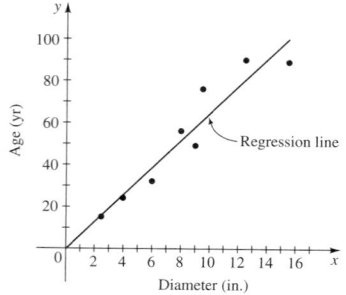

(b) $y = 6.451x - 0.1523$ **(c)** 116 years

4. (a)

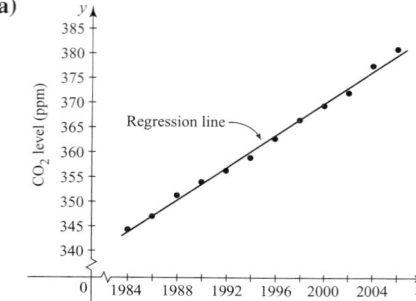

(b) $y = 1.6318x - 2893.7$ **(c)** 378.1 ppm
5. (a)

(b) $y = 4.857x - 220.97$ **(c)** 265 chirps/min
6. (a)

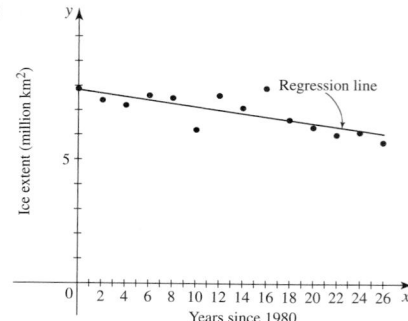

(b) $y = -0.0689x + 7.831$ **(c)** 5.8 million km^2
7. (a)

(b) $y = -0.168x + 19.89$ **(c)** 8.13%

8. (a)

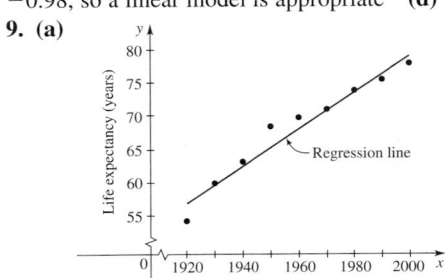

(b) $y = -3.9018x + 419.7$ **(c)** The correlation coefficient is -0.98, so a linear model is appropriate   **(d)** 53%

9. (a)

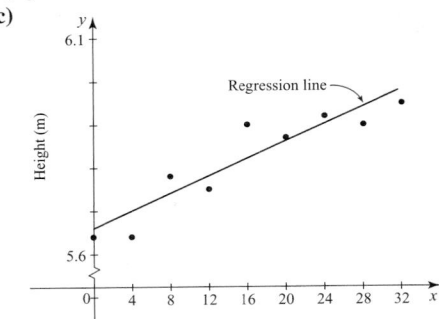

(b) $y = 0.2708x - 462.9$ **(c)** 80.3 years

10. (a)

Year	x	Height (m)
1972	0	5.64
1976	4	5.64
1980	8	5.78
1984	12	5.75
1988	16	5.90
1992	20	5.87
1996	24	5.92
2000	28	5.90
2004	32	5.95

(b) $y = 0.0101x + 5.66$
(c)

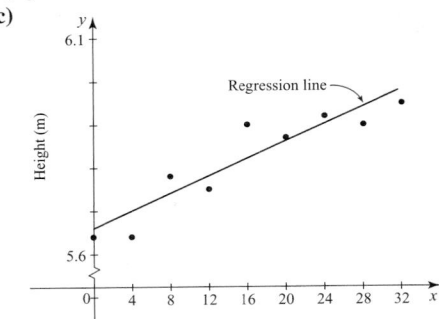

(d) 6.02 m

11. (a) Men: $y = -0.1703x + 64.61$, women $y = -0.2603x + 78.27$; x represents years since 1900
                                          (b) 2052

Chapter 2

SECTION 2.1 ■ PAGE 149

1. value   **2.** domain, range   **3. (a)** f and g
(b) $f(5) = 10, g(5) = 0$ **4. (a)** square, add 3

(b)

x	0	2	4	6
$f(x)$	19	7	3	7

5. $f(x) = 2(x + 3)$ **6.** $f(x) = \frac{x}{7} - 4$ **7.** $f(x) = (x - 5)^2$
8. $f(x) = \frac{1}{3}(\sqrt{x} + 8)$ **9.** Square, then add 2   **10.** Add 2, then take the square root   **11.** Subtract 4, then divide by 3
12. Divide by 3, then subtract 4

13.   **14.**

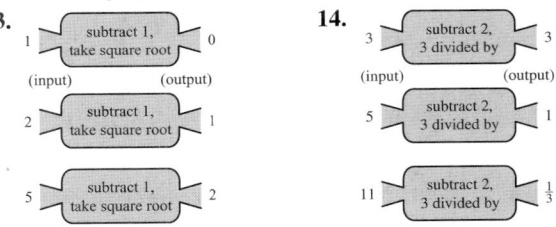

15.

x	$f(x)$
-1	8
0	2
1	0
2	2
3	8

16.

x	$g(x)$
-3	3
-2	1
0	3
1	5
3	9

17. $3, 3, -6, -\frac{23}{4}, 94$ **18.** $-12, 3, 0, \frac{19}{27}, 0.408$
19. $3, -3, 2, 2a + 1, -2a + 1, 2a + 2b + 1$

20. $0, 15, 3, a^2 + 2a, x^2 - 2x, \dfrac{1}{a^2} + \dfrac{2}{a}$

21. $-\dfrac{1}{3}, -3, \dfrac{1}{3}, \dfrac{1-a}{1+a}, \dfrac{2-a}{a}$, undefined

22. $2, -2, \dfrac{5}{2}, \dfrac{5}{2}, x + \dfrac{1}{x}, \dfrac{1}{x} + x$

23. $-4, 10, -2, 3\sqrt{2}, 2x^2 + 7x + 1, 2x^2 - 3x - 4$

24. $0, -3, -5, -\dfrac{45}{8}, \dfrac{x^3}{8} - x^2, x^6 - 4x^4$

25. 6, 2, 1, 2, $2|x|$, $2(x^2 + 1)$

26. -1, -1, not defined, 1, 1, $x/|x|$ **27.** 4, 1, 1, 2, 3

28. 5, 5, 5, 3, 7   **29.** 8, $-\frac{3}{4}$, -1, 0, -1 **30.** -15, 1, 2, 3, 9

31. $x^2 + 4x + 5$, $x^2 + 6$ **32.** $6x - 1$, $6x - 2$

33. $x^2 + 4$, $x^2 + 8x + 16$ **34.** $2x - 18$, $2x - 6$

35. $3a + 2$, $3(a + h) + 2$, 3

36. $a^2 + 1$, $a^2 + 2ah + h^2 + 1$, $2a + h$

37. 5, 5, 0   **38.** $\dfrac{1}{a + 1}$, $\dfrac{1}{a + h + 1}$, $\dfrac{-1}{(a + 1)(a + h + 1)}$

39. $\dfrac{a}{a + 1}$, $\dfrac{a + h}{a + h + 1}$, $\dfrac{1}{(a + h + 1)(a + 1)}$

40. $\dfrac{2a}{a - 1}$, $\dfrac{2(a + h)}{a + h - 1}$, $\dfrac{-2}{(a + h - 1)(a - 1)}$

41. $3 - 5a + 4a^2$, $3 - 5a - 5h + 4a^2 + 8ah + 4h^2$, $-5 + 8a + 4h$ **42.** a^3, $a^3 + 3a^2h + 3ah^2 + h^3$, $3a^2 + 3ah + h^2$

43. $(-\infty, \infty)$ **44.** $(-\infty, \infty)$ **45.** $[-1, 5]$ **46.** $[0, 5]$

47. $\{x \mid x \neq 3\}$ **48.** $\{x \mid x \neq 2\}$ **49.** $\{x \mid x \neq \pm 1\}$

50. $\{x \mid x \neq -3, x \neq 2\}$ **51.** $[5, \infty)$ **52.** $[-9, \infty)$

53. $(-\infty, \infty)$ **54.** $(-\infty, \frac{7}{3}]$ **55.** $[\frac{5}{2}, \infty)$

56. $(-\infty, -3] \cup [3, \infty)$ **57.** $[-2, 3) \cup (3, \infty)$

58. $[0, \frac{1}{2}) \cup (\frac{1}{2}, \infty)$ **59.** $(-\infty, 0] \cup [6, \infty)$

60. $(-\infty, -2] \cup [4, \infty)$ **61.** $(4, \infty)$ **62.** $(-\infty, 6)$

63. $(\frac{1}{2}, \infty)$ **64.** $(-3, 3)$ **65.** (a) $f(x) = \dfrac{x}{3} + \dfrac{2}{3}$

(b)

x	$f(x)$
2	$\frac{4}{3}$
4	2
6	$\frac{8}{3}$
8	$\frac{10}{3}$

(c)

66. (a) $g(x) = \frac{3}{4}(x - 4)$

(b)

x	$g(x)$
2	$-\frac{3}{2}$
4	0
6	$\frac{3}{2}$
8	3

(c)

67. (a) $T(x) = 0.08x$

(b)

x	$T(x)$
2	0.16
4	0.32
6	0.48
8	0.64

(c)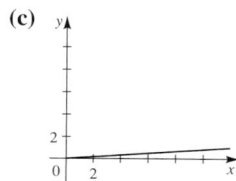

68. (a) $V(d) = \dfrac{\pi d^3}{6}$

(b)

d	$V(d)$
2	$\frac{4\pi}{3}$
4	$\frac{32\pi}{3}$
6	36π
8	$\frac{256\pi}{3}$

(c)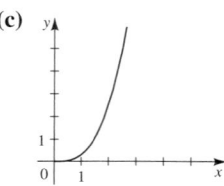

69. (a) $C(10) = 1532.1$, $C(100) = 2100$ (b) The cost of producing 10 yd and 100 yd   (c) $C(0) = 1500$ **70.** (a) 50.27, 113.10   (b) $S(2)$ is the surface area of a sphere of radius 2, and $S(3)$ is the surface area of a sphere of radius 3.   **71.** (a) 50, 0   (b) $V(0)$ is the volume of the full tank, and $V(20)$ is the volume of the empty tank, 20 minutes later.

(c)

x	$V(x)$
0	50
5	28.125
10	12.5
15	3.125
20	0

72. (a) $D(0.1) = 28.1$, $D(0.2) = 39.8$ (b) 41.3 mi   (c) 235.6 mi   **73.** (a) $v(0.1) = 4440$, $v(0.4) = 1665$ (b) Flow is faster near central axis.

(c)

r	$v(r)$
0	4625
0.1	4440
0.2	3885
0.3	2960
0.4	1665
0.5	0

74. (a) 2, 1.66, 1.48

(b)

x	$R(x)$
1	2
10	1.66
100	1.48
200	1.44
500	1.41
1000	1.39

75. (a) 8.66 m, 6.61 m, 4.36 m   (b) It will appear to get shorter.
76. (a) $T(5000) = 0$, $T(12,000) = 960$, $T(25,000) = 5350$
(b) The amount of tax paid on incomes of 5000, 12,000, and 25,000
77. (a) $90, $105, $100, $105
(b) Total cost of an order, including shipping

78. (a) $T(x) = \begin{cases} 75x & \text{if } 0 \le x \le 2 \\ 150 + 50(x - 2) & \text{if } x > 2 \end{cases}$

(b) $150, $200, $300   (c) Total cost of staying at the hotel

79. (a) $F(x) = \begin{cases} 15(40 - x) & \text{if } 0 < x < 40 \\ 0 & \text{if } 40 \le x \le 65 \\ 15(x - 65) & \text{if } x > 65 \end{cases}$

(b) \$150, \$0, \$150   **(c)** Fines for violating the speed limits

80.

81.

82.

83.

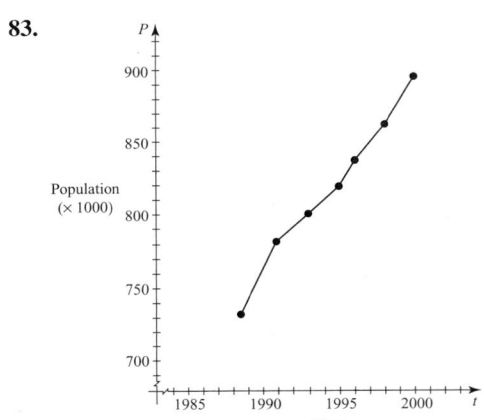

SECTION 2.2 ■ PAGE 159

1. $f(x)$, $x^3 + 2$, 10, 10   **2.** 3   **3.** 3   **4. (a)** IV   **(b)** II
(c) I   **(d)** III

5.

6.

7.

8.

9.

10.

11.

12.

13.

14.

15.

16.

17.

18.

19.

20.

21.

22.

23.

24.

25.

26.

27.

28.

29. (a)

(b)

(c)

(d)

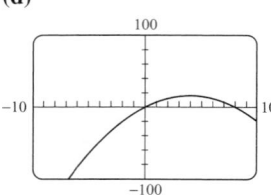

Graph (c) is the most appropriate.

30. (a)

(b)

(c)

(d)

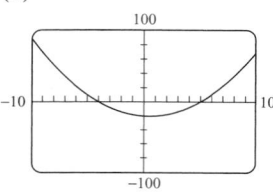

Graph (c) is the most appropriate.

31. (a)

(b)

(c)

(d)

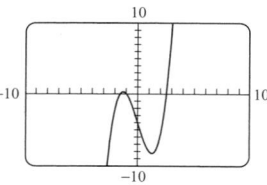

Graph (c) is the most appropriate.

32. (a)

(b)

(c)

(d)

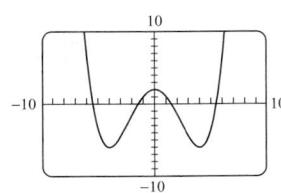

Graph (d) is the most appropriate.

33.

34.

35.

36.

37.

38.

39.

40.

41.

42.

43.

44.

45.

46.

47.

48.

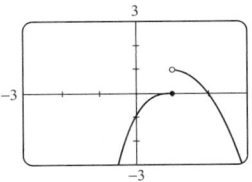

49. $f(x) = \begin{cases} -2 & \text{if } x < -2 \\ x & \text{if } -2 \le x \le 2 \\ 2 & \text{if } x > 2 \end{cases}$

50. $f(x) = \begin{cases} 1 & \text{if } x \le -1 \\ 1 - x & \text{if } -1 < x \le 2 \\ -2 & \text{if } x > 2 \end{cases}$

51. (a) Yes   **(b)** No   **(c)** Yes   **(d)** No   **52. (a)** No   **(b)** Yes
(c) Yes   **(d)** No   **53.** Function, domain $[-3, 2]$, range $[-2, 2]$
54. Not a function   **55.** Not a function   **56.** Function,
domain $[-3, 2]$, range $\{-2\} \cup (0, 3]$ **57.** Yes   **58.** Yes   **59.** No
60. No   **61.** No   **62.** Yes   **63.** Yes   **64.** Yes   **65.** Yes
66. No   **67.** Yes   **68.** No
69. (a)

(b)

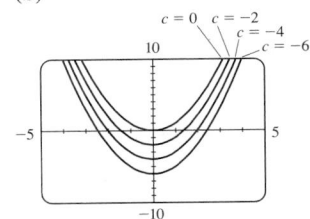

(c) If $c > 0$, then the graph of $f(x) = x^2 + c$ is the same as the
graph of $y = x^2$ shifted upward c units. If $c < 0$, then the graph of
$f(x) = x^2 + c$ is the same as the graph of $y = x^2$ shifted downward c units.

70. (a) **(b)**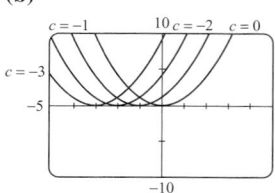

(c) The graphs in part (a) are obtained by shifting the graph of $y = x^2$ to the right 1, 2, and 3 units, while the graphs in part (b) are obtained by shifting the graph of $y = x^2$ to the left, 1, 2, and 3 units.

71. (a) **(b)**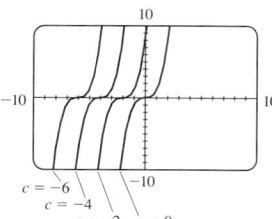

(c) If $c > 0$, then the graph of $f(x) = (x - c)^3$ is the same as the graph of $y = x^3$ shifted to the right c units. If $c < 0$, then the graph of $f(x) = (x - c)^3$ is the same as the graph of $y = x^3$ shifted to the left c units.

72. (a) **(b)**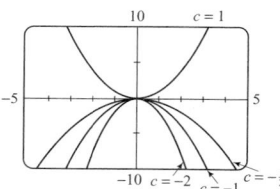

(c) As $|c|$ increases, the graph of $f(x) = cx^2$ is stretched vertically. As $|c|$ decreases, the graph of f is flattened. When $c < 0$, the graph is reflected about the x-axis.

73. (a) **(b)**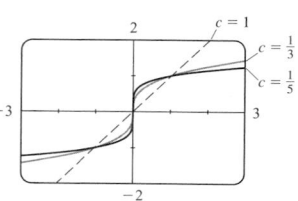

(c) Graphs of even roots are similar to $\sqrt{x}$; graphs of odd roots are similar to $\sqrt[3]{x}$. As c increases, the graph of $y = \sqrt[c]{x}$ becomes steeper near 0 and flatter when $x > 1$.

74. (a) **(b)**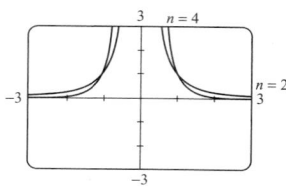

(c) As n increases, the graphs of $y = 1/x^n$ go to zero faster for x large. Also, as n increases and x goes to 0, the graphs of $y = 1/x^n$ go to infinity faster. The graphs of $y = 1/x^n$ for n odd are similar to each other. Likewise, the graphs for n even are similar to each other.

75. $f(x) = -\frac{7}{6}x - \frac{4}{3}, -2 \le x \le 4$

76. $f(x) = \frac{5}{9}x - \frac{1}{3}, -3 \le x \le 6$ **77.** $f(x) = \sqrt{9 - x^2}$, $-3 \le x \le 3$ **78.** $f(x) = -\sqrt{9 - x^2}, -3 \le x \le 3$

79. **80.**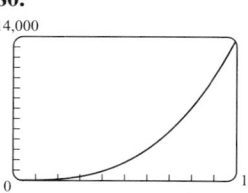

81. (a) $E(x) = \begin{cases} 6 + 0.10x & 0 \le x \le 300 \\ 36 + 0.06(x - 300), & x > 300 \end{cases}$

(b)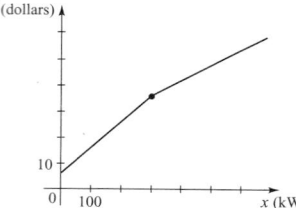

82. $C(x) = \begin{cases} 2 & 0 < x \le 1 \\ 2.2 & 1 < x \le 1.1 \\ 2.4 & 1.1 < x \le 1.2 \\ \vdots \\ 4.0 & 1.9 < x < 2.0 \end{cases}$

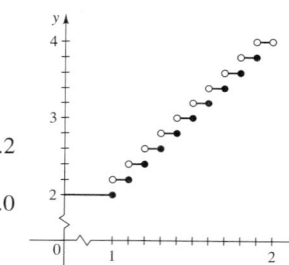

83. $P(x) = \begin{cases} 0.44 & \text{if } 0 < x \le 1 \\ 0.61 & \text{if } 1 < x \le 2 \\ 0.78 & \text{if } 2 < x \le 3 \\ 0.95 & \text{if } 3 < x \le 3.5 \end{cases}$

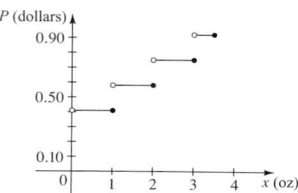

SECTION 2.3 ▪ PAGE 168

1. a, 4 **2.** x, y, $[1, 6]$, $[1, 7]$ **3. (a)** increase, $[1, 2]$, $[4, 5]$ **(b)** decrease, $[2, 4]$, $[5, 6]$ **4. (a)** largest, 7, 2 **(b)** smallest, 2, 4 **5. (a)** 1, -1, 3, 4 **(b)** Domain $[-3, 4]$, range $[-1, 4]$ **(c)** $-3, 2, 4$ **(d)** $-3 \le x \le 2$ and $x = 4$ **6. (a)** 4, 7, 4 **(b)** $[-2, 8]$, $[2, 7]$ **(c)** $-2, 2, 7$ **(d)** $-2 < x < 2$ and $7 < x \le 8$ **7. (a)** 3, 2, -2, 1, 0 **(b)** Domain $[-4, 4]$, range $[-2, 3]$ **8. (a)** $f(0)$ **(b)** $g(-3)$ **(c)** $-2, 2$

9. (a)

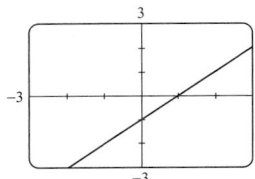

(b) Domain $(-\infty, \infty)$, range $(-\infty, \infty)$

11. (a)

(b) Domain $[1, 3]$, range $\{4\}$

13. (a)

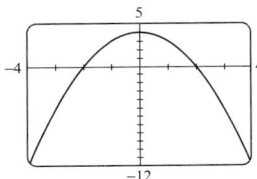

(b) Domain $(-\infty, \infty)$, range $(-\infty, 4]$

15. (a)

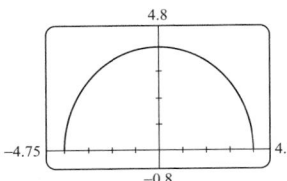

(b) Domain $[-4, 4]$, range $[0, 4]$

17. (a)

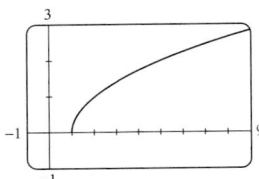

(b) Domain $[1, \infty)$, range $[0, \infty)$

19. (a) $[-1, 1], [2, 4]$ **(b)** $[1, 2]$
20. (a) $[0, 1]$ **(b)** $[-2, 0], [1, 3]$
21. (a) $[-2, -1], [1, 2]$ **(b)** $[-3, -2], [-1, 1], [2, 3]$
22. (a) $[-1, 1]$ **(b)** $[-2, -1], [1, 2]$

10. (a)

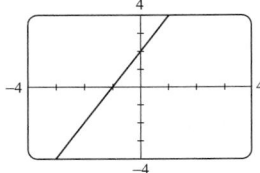

(b) Domain $(-\infty, \infty)$, range $(-\infty, \infty)$

12. (a)

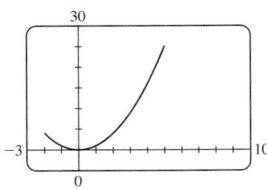

(b) Domain $[-2, 5]$, range $[0, 25]$

14. (a)

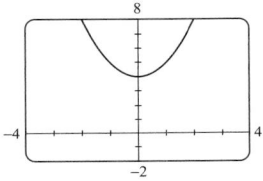

(b) Domain $(-\infty, \infty)$, range $[4, \infty)$

16. (a)

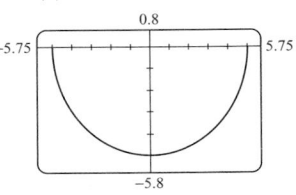

(b) Domain $[-5, 5]$, range $[-5, 0]$

18. (a)

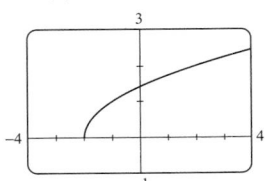

(b) Domain $[-2, \infty)$, range $[0, \infty)$

23. (a)

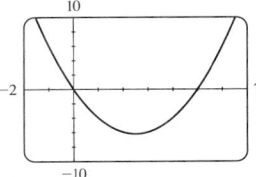

(b) Increasing on $[2.5, \infty)$; decreasing on $(-\infty, 2.5]$

25. (a)

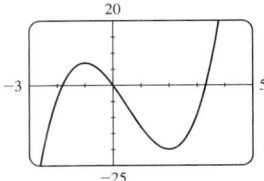

(b) Increasing on $(-\infty, -1]$, $[2, \infty)$; decreasing on $[-1, 2]$

27. (a)

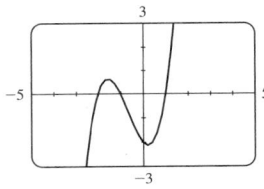

(b) Increasing on $(-\infty, -1.55], [0.22, \infty)$; decreasing on $[-1.55, 0.22]$

29. (a)

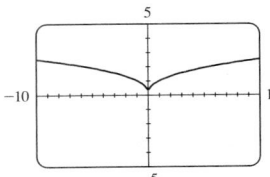

(b) Increasing on $[0, \infty)$; decreasing on $(-\infty, 0]$

24. (a)

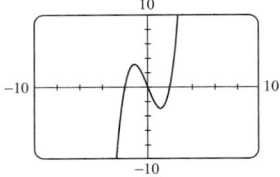

(b) Increasing on $(\infty, -1.15]$, $[1.15, \infty)$; decreasing on $[-1.15, 1.15]$

26. (a)

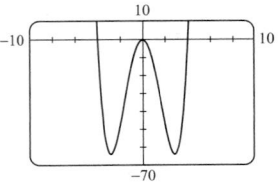

(b) Increasing on $[-2.83, 0]$, $[2.83, \infty)$; decreasing on $[-\infty, -2.83], [0, 2.83]$

28. (a)

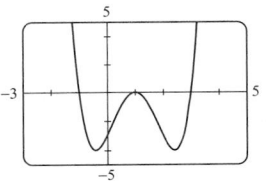

(b) Increasing on $[-0.4, 1]$, $[2.4, \infty)$; decreasing on $(-\infty, -0.4], [1, 2.4]$

30. (a)

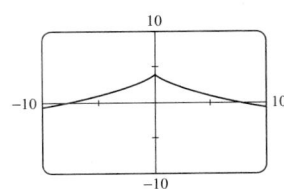

(b) Increasing on $(-\infty, 0]$; decreasing on $[0, \infty)$

31. (a) Local maximum 2 when $x = 0$; local minimum -1 when $x = -2$, local minimum 0 when $x = 2$ **(b)** Increasing on $[-2, 0] \cup [2, \infty)$; decreasing on $(-\infty, -2] \cup [0, 2]$
32. (a) Local maximum 1 when $x = 2$, local maximum 2 when $x = -2$; local minimum -1 when $x = 0$ **(b)** Increasing on $(-\infty, -2] \cup [0, 2]$; decreasing on $[-2, 0] \cup [2, \infty)$
33. (a) Local maximum 0 when $x = 0$; local maximum 1 when $x = 3$, local minimum -2 when $x = -2$, local minimum -1 when $x = 1$ **(b)** Increasing on $[-2, 0] \cup [1, 3]$; decreasing on $(-\infty, -2] \cup [0, 1] \cup [3, \infty)$ **34. (a)** Local maximum 2 when $x = 1$, local maximum 3 when $x = -2$; local minimum -1 when $x = 2$, local minimum 0 when $x = -1$ **(b)** Increasing on $(-\infty, -2] \cup [-1, 1] \cup [2, \infty)$; decreasing on $[-2, -1] \cup [1, 2]$

35. (a) Local maximum ≈ 0.38 when $x \approx -0.58$; local minimum ≈ -0.38 when $x \approx 0.58$ **(b)** Increasing on $(-\infty, -0.58] \cup [0.58, \infty)$; decreasing on $[-0.58, 0.58]$
36. (a) Local maximum ≈ 4.00 when $x \approx 1.00$; local minimum ≈ 2.81 when $x \approx -0.33$ **(b)** Increasing on $[-0.33, 1.00]$; decreasing on $(-\infty, -0.33] \cup [1.00, \infty]$ **37. (a)** Local maximum ≈ 0 when $x = 0$; local minimum ≈ -13.61 when $x \approx -1.71$, local minimum ≈ -73.32 when $x \approx 3.21$
(b) Increasing on $[-1.71, 0] \cup [3.21, \infty)$; decreasing on $(-\infty, -1.71] \cup [0, 3.21]$ **38. (a)** Local maximum ≈ 13.02 when $x \approx 1.04$, local maximum ≈ -7.87 when $x \approx -1.93$; local minimum ≈ -13.02 when $x \approx -1.04$, local minimum ≈ 7.87 when $x \approx 1.93$ **(b)** Increasing on $(-\infty, -1.93] \cup [-1.04, 1.04] \cup [1.93, \infty)$; decreasing on $[-1.93, -1.04] \cup [1.04, 1.93]$
39. (a) Local maximum ≈ 5.66 when $x \approx 4.00$ **(b)** Increasing on $(-\infty, 4.00]$; decreasing on $[4.00, 6.00]$ **40. (a)** Local maximum ≈ 0.32 when $x \approx 0.75$ **(b)** Increasing on $[0, 0.75]$; decreasing on $[0.75, 1.00]$ **41. (a)** Local maximum ≈ 0.38 when $x \approx -1.73$; local minimum ≈ -0.38 when $x \approx 1.73$ **(b)** Increasing on $(-\infty, -1.73] \cup [1.73, \infty]$; decreasing on $[-1.73, 0) \cup (0, 1.73]$
42. (a) Local maximum ≈ 1.33 when $x \approx -0.50$ **(b)** Increasing on $(-\infty, -0.50]$; decreasing on $[-0.50, \infty)$ **43. (a)** 500 MW, 725 MW   **(b)** Between 3:00 A.M. and 4:00 A.M.   **(c)** Just before noon   **44. (a)** 5 s   **(b)** 30 s   **(c)** 17 s   **45. (a)** Increasing on $[0, 30] \cup [32, 68]$; decreasing on $[30, 32]$ **(b)** He went on a crash diet and lost weight, only to regain it again later.   **46. (a)** Increasing on the intervals 8:00 A.M. to 9:00 A.M., 10:00 A.M. to noon, and 3:00 P.M. to 5:00 P.M.; decreasing on the intervals 1:00 P.M. to 3:00 P.M. and 6:00 P.M. to 7:00 P.M.   **(b)** The sales representative travels away from home and stops to make a sales call between 9:00 A.M. and 10:00 A.M.; he then travels farther from home for a sales call between 12:00 noon and 1:00 P.M. Next he travels along a route that takes him closer to home before taking him farther away from home. He makes a final sales call between 5:00 P.M. and 6:00 P.M. and then returns home.   **47. (a)** Increasing on $[0, 150] \cup [300, \infty)$; decreasing on $[150, 300]$ **(b)** Local maximum when $x = 150$; local minimum when $x = 300$
48. (a) Increasing on $[0, 25]$; decreasing on $[25, 50]$ **(b)** 50,000 in the year 1975   **49.** Runner A won the race. All runners finished. Runner B fell but got up again to finish second.
50. (a)

51. (a)

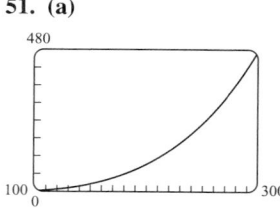

(b) Decreases   **(b)** Increases
52. 7.5 mi/h   **53.** 20 mi/h   **54.** 3.96°C   **55.** $r \approx 0.67$ cm

SECTION 2.4 ■ PAGE 177

1. $\dfrac{100 \text{ miles}}{2 \text{ hours}} = 50$ mi/h   **2.** $\dfrac{f(b) - f(a)}{b - a}$ **3.** $\dfrac{25 - 1}{5 - 1} = 6$
4. (a) secant   **(b)** 3   **5.** $\frac{2}{3}$ **6.** $-\frac{1}{2}$ **7.** $-\frac{4}{5}$ **8.** $\frac{2}{3}$ **9.** 3   **10.** $\frac{1}{2}$
11. 5   **12.** 6   **13.** 60   **14.** 21   **15.** $12 + 3h$ **16.** $-2 - h$
17. $-\dfrac{1}{a}$ **18.** $-\dfrac{2}{h + 1}$ **19.** $\dfrac{-2}{a(a + h)}$ **20.** $\dfrac{1}{\sqrt{a + h} + \sqrt{a}}$

21. (a) $\frac{1}{2}$ **22. (a)** -4 **23.** -0.25 ft/day   **24. (a)** 0   **(b)** In this period the population increased the same amount as it decreased.   **25. (a)** 245 persons/yr   **(b)** -328.5 persons/yr   **(c)** 1997–2001   **(d)** 2001–2006   **26. (a)** 4.76 m/s   **(b)** 2.68 m/s   **(c)** 6.25 m/s, 5.56 m/s, 5.00 m/s, 4.55 m/s, 3.92 m/s, 3.33 m/s, 2.78 m/s, 2.60 m/s; he is slowing down.   **27. (a)** 7.2 units/yr   **(b)** 8 units/yr   **(c)** -55 units/yr   **(d)** 2000–2001, 2001–2002

28.

Year	Number of books
1980	420
1981	460
1982	500
1985	620
1990	820
1992	900
1995	1020
1997	1100
1998	1140
1999	1180
2000	1220

29. First 20 minutes: 4.05°F/min, next 20 minutes: 1.5°F/min; first interval   **30. (a) (i)** 84 farms/yr   **(ii)** -130 farms/yr   **(b)** 1950–1960

SECTION 2.5 ■ PAGE 187

1. (a) up   **(b)** left   **2. (a)** down   **(b)** right   **3. (a)** x-axis **(b)** y-axis   **4. (a)** II   **(b)** IV   **(c)** I   **(d)** III   **5. (a)** Shift downward 5 units   **(b)** Shift to the right 5 units   **6. (a)** Shift to the left 7 units   **(b)** Shift upward 7 units   **7. (a)** Reflect in the x-axis **(b)** Reflect in the y-axis   **8. (a)** Reflect in the x-axis, then stretch vertically by a factor of 2   **(b)** Reflect in the x-axis, then shrink vertically by a factor of $\frac{1}{2}$ **9. (a)** Reflect in the x-axis, then shift upward 5 units   **(b)** Stretch vertically by a factor of 3, then shift downward 5 units   **10. (a)** Shift to the right 4 units, then upward $\frac{3}{4}$ unit   **(b)** Shift to the left 4 units, then downward $\frac{3}{4}$ unit
11. (a) Shift to the left 1 unit, stretch vertically by a factor of 2, then shift downward 3 units   **(b)** Shift to the right 1 unit, stretch vertically by a factor of 2, then shift upward 3 units   **12. (a)** Reflect in the x-axis, stretch vertically by a factor of 2, then shift upward 3 units   **(b)** Reflect in the x- and y-axes, then shift upward 2 units   **13. (a)** Shrink horizontally by a factor of $\frac{1}{4}$ **(b)** Stretch horizontally by a factor of 4   **14. (a)** Shrink horizontally by a factor of $\frac{1}{2}$, then shift downward 1 unit   **(b)** Stretch horizontally by a factor of 2, then stretch vertically by a factor of 2   **15. (a)** Shift to the left 2 units   **(b)** Shift upward 2 units   **16. (a)** Shift to the right 4 units   **(b)** Shift downward 4 units   **17. (a)** Shift to the left 2 units, then shift downward 2 units   **(b)** Shift to the right 2 units, then shift upward 2 units   **18. (a)** Reflect in the x-axis, then shift upward 1 unit   **(b)** Reflect in the y-axis, then shift upward 1 unit
19. (a)   **(b)**

(c)

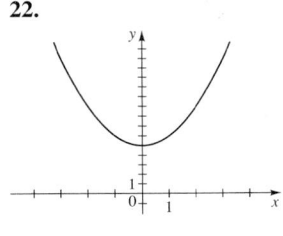

(d)

20. (a)

(b)

(c)

(d)

21.

22.

23.

24.

25.

26.

27.

28.

29.

30.

31.

32.

33.

34.

35.

36.

37.

38.

39.

40.

(e)

(f)

41.

42.

64. (a)

(b)

43.

44.

(c)

(d)

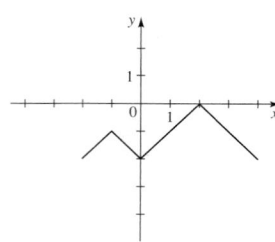

45. $f(x) = x^2 + 3$ **46.** $f(x) = x^3 - 1$ **47.** $f(x) = \sqrt{x + 2}$
48. $f(x) = \sqrt[3]{x - 1}$ **49.** $f(x) = |x - 3| + 1$
50. $f(x) = |x + 4| - 2$ **51.** $f(x) = \sqrt[4]{-x} + 1$
52. $f(x) = -(x + 2)^2$ **53.** $f(x) = 2(x - 3)^2 - 2$
54. $f(x) = \frac{1}{2}|x + 1| + 3$ **55.** $g(x) = (x - 2)^2$
56. $g(x) = x^3 + 3$ **57.** $g(x) = |x + 1| + 2$ **58.** $g(x) = 2|x|$
59. $g(x) = -\sqrt{x + 2}$ **60.** $g(x) = -(x - 2)^2 + 1$ **61. (a)** 3
(b) 1   **(c)** 2   **(d)** 4   **62. (a)** 2   **(b)** 3   **(c)** 1   **(d)** 4
63. (a)

(e)

(f)

(b)

65. (a)

(b)

(c)

(d)

66. (a)

(b)

67.

68.

69.

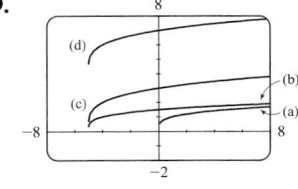

For part (b) shift the graph in (a) to the left 5 units; for part (c) shift the graph in (a) to the left 5 units and stretch vertically by a factor of 2; for part (d) shift the graph in (a) to the left 5 units, stretch vertically by a factor of 2, and then shift upward 4 units.

70.

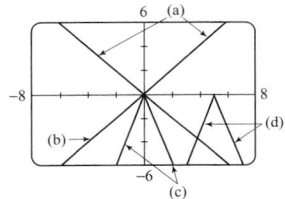

For part (b) reflect in the x-axis; for part (c) stretch vertically by a factor of 3 and reflect in the x-axis; for part (d) shift to the right 5 units, stretch vertically by a factor of 3, and reflect in the x-axis.

71.

For part (b) shrink the graph in (a) vertically by a factor of $\frac{1}{3}$; for part (c) shrink the graph in (a) vertically by a factor of $\frac{1}{3}$ and reflect in the x-axis; for part (d) shift the graph in (a) to the right 4 units, shrink vertically by a factor of $\frac{1}{3}$, and then reflect in the x-axis.

72.

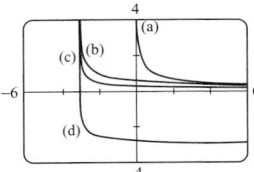

For part (b) shift to the left 3 units; for part (c) shift to the left 3 units and shrink vertically by a factor of $\frac{1}{2}$; for part (d) shift to the left 3 units, shrink vertically by a factor of $\frac{1}{2}$, and then shift downward 3 units.

73.

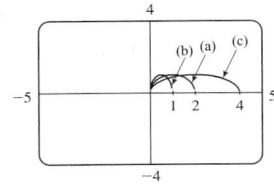

The graph in part (b) is shrunk horizontally by a factor of $\frac{1}{2}$ and the graph in part (c) is stretched by a factor of 2.

74. (a)

(b) Reflect in y-axis

(c) Reflect in origin

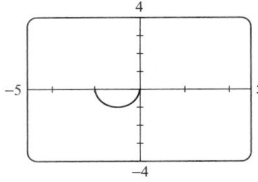

(d) Reflect in y-axis, then horizontally shrink by a factor of $\frac{1}{2}$

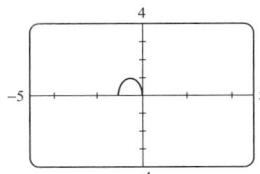

(e) Reflect in y-axis, then horizontally stretch by a factor of 2

75. Even

76. Odd

77. Neither
78. Even

79. Odd

80. Neither
82. Odd

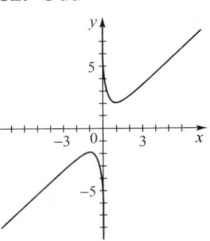

81. Neither

83. (a)   **(b)**

84. (a)   **(b)**

    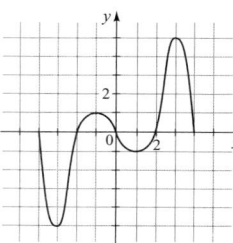

85. To obtain the graph of g, reflect in the x-axis the part of the graph of f that is below the x-axis.

86.

87. (a)   **(b)**

88. (a)   **(b)**

    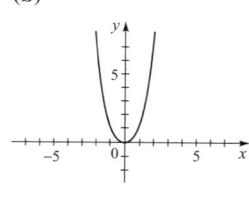

89. (a) Shift upward 4 units, shrink vertically by a factor of 0.01
(b) Shift to the right 10 units; $g(t) = 4 + 0.01(t - 10)^2$
90. (a) Shrink vertically by a factor of $\frac{1}{2}$, then shift upward 2 units
(b) Stretch vertically by a factor of $\frac{9}{5}$, then shift upward 32 units;
$F(t) = \frac{9}{10}t^2 + \frac{178}{5}$

SECTION 2.6 ■ PAGE 196

1. $8, -2, 15, \dfrac{3}{5}$ **2.** $f(g(x)), 12$ **3.** Multiply by 2, then add 1;
Add 1, then multiply by 2   **4.** $x + 1, 2x, 2x + 1, 2(x + 1)$

5. $(f + g)(x) = x^2 + x - 3, (-\infty, \infty)$;
$(f - g)(x) = -x^2 + x - 3, (-\infty, \infty)$;
$(fg)(x) = x^3 - 3x^2, (-\infty, \infty)$;
$\left(\dfrac{f}{g}\right)(x) = \dfrac{x - 3}{x^2}, (-\infty, 0) \cup (0, \infty)$

6. $(f + g)(x) = 4x^2 + 2x - 1, (-\infty, \infty)$;
$(f - g)(x) = -2x^2 + 2x + 1, (-\infty, \infty)$;
$(fg)(x) = 3x^4 + 6x^3 - x^2 - 2x, (-\infty, \infty)$;
$\left(\dfrac{f}{g}\right)(x) = \dfrac{x^2 + 2x}{3x^2 - 1}, x \neq \pm\dfrac{1}{\sqrt{3}}$

7. $(f + g)(x) = \sqrt{4 - x^2} + \sqrt{1 + x}, [-1, 2]$;
$(f - g)(x) = \sqrt{4 - x^2} - \sqrt{1 + x}, [-1, 2]$;
$(fg)(x) = \sqrt{-x^3 - x^2 + 4x + 4}, [-1, 2]$;
$\left(\dfrac{f}{g}\right)(x) = \sqrt{\dfrac{4 - x^2}{1 + x}}, (-1, 2]$

8. $(f + g)(x) = \sqrt{9 - x^2} + \sqrt{x^2 - 4}, [-3, -2] \cup [2, 3]$;
$(f - g)(x) = \sqrt{9 - x^2} - \sqrt{x^2 - 4}, [-3, -2] \cup [2, 3]$;
$(fg)(x) = \sqrt{-x^4 + 13x^2 - 36}, [-3, -2] \cup [2, 3]$;
$\left(\dfrac{f}{g}\right)(x) = \sqrt{\dfrac{9 - x^2}{x^2 - 4}}, [-3, -2) \cup (2, 3]$

9. $(f + g)(x) = \dfrac{6x + 8}{x^2 + 4x}, x \neq -4, x \neq 0$;

$(f - g)(x) = \dfrac{-2x + 8}{x^2 + 4x}, x \neq -4, x \neq 0$;

$(fg)(x) = \dfrac{8}{x^2 + 4x}, x \neq -4, x \neq 0$;

$\left(\dfrac{f}{g}\right)(x) = \dfrac{x + 4}{2x}, x \neq -4, x \neq 0$

10. $(f + g)(x) = \dfrac{2 + x}{x + 1}, x \neq -1; (f - g)(x) = \dfrac{2 - x}{x + 1}, x \neq -1$;

$(fg)(x) = \dfrac{2x}{(x + 1)^2}, x \neq -1; \left(\dfrac{f}{g}\right)(x) = \dfrac{2}{x}, x \neq -1, x \neq 0$

11. $[0, 1]$ **12.** $[-1, 0) \cup (0, \infty)$ **13.** $(3, \infty)$
14. $[-3, 1) \cup (1, \infty)$
15.   **16.**

17.

18.

19.

20.

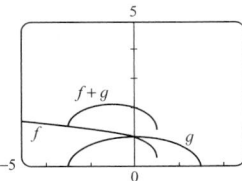

21. (a) 1 (b) -23 **22.** (a) 16 (b) -47 **23.** (a) -11
(b) -119 **24.** (a) -29 (b) -2 **25.** (a) $-3x^2 + 1$
(b) $-9x^2 + 30x - 23$ **26.** (a) $9x - 20$ (b) $-x^4 + 4x^2 - 2$
27. 4 **28.** 3 **29.** 5 **30.** 0 **31.** 4 **32.** -2
33. $(f \circ g)(x) = 8x + 1, (-\infty, \infty)$;
$(g \circ f)(x) = 8x + 11, (-\infty, \infty)$; $(f \circ f)(x) = 4x + 9, (-\infty, \infty)$;
$(g \circ g)(x) = 16x - 5, (-\infty, \infty)$
34. $(f \circ g)(x) = 3x - 5, (-\infty, \infty)$;
$(g \circ f)(x) = 3x - \frac{5}{2}, (-\infty, \infty)$;
$(f \circ f)(x) = 36x - 35, (-\infty, \infty)$; $(g \circ g)(x) = \frac{x}{4}, (-\infty, \infty)$
35. $(f \circ g)(x) = (x + 1)^2, (-\infty, \infty)$;
$(g \circ f)(x) = x^2 + 1, (-\infty, \infty)$; $(f \circ f)(x) = x^4, (-\infty, \infty)$;
$(g \circ g)(x) = x + 2, (-\infty, \infty)$ **36.** $(f \circ g)(x) = x + 2, (-\infty, \infty)$;
$(g \circ f)(x) = \sqrt[3]{x^3 + 2}, (-\infty, \infty)$;
$(f \circ f)(x) = x^9 + 6x^6 + 12x^3 + 10, (-\infty, \infty)$;
$(g \circ g)(x) = x^{1/9}, (-\infty, \infty)$
37. $(f \circ g)(x) = \dfrac{1}{2x + 4}, x \neq -2$; $(g \circ f)(x) = \dfrac{2}{x} + 4, x \neq 0$;
$(f \circ f)(x) = x, x \neq 0, (g \circ g)(x) = 4x + 12, (-\infty, \infty)$
38. $(f \circ g)(x) = x - 3, [3, \infty)$;
$(g \circ f)(x) = \sqrt{x^2 - 3}, (-\infty, -\sqrt{3}] \cup [\sqrt{3}, \infty)$;
$(f \circ f)(x) = x^4, (-\infty, \infty)$; $(g \circ g)(x) = \sqrt{\sqrt{x - 3} - 3}, [12, \infty)$
39. $(f \circ g)(x) = |2x + 3|, (-\infty, \infty)$;
$(g \circ f)(x) = 2|x| + 3, (-\infty, \infty)$; $(f \circ f)(x) = |x|, (-\infty, \infty)$;
$(g \circ g)(x) = 4x + 9, (-\infty, \infty)$
40. $(f \circ g)(x) = |x + 4| - 4, (-\infty, \infty)$;
$(g \circ f)(x) = |x|, (-\infty, \infty)$; $(f \circ f)(x) = x - 8, (-\infty, \infty)$;
$(g \circ g)(x) = |x + 4| + 4, (-\infty, \infty)$
41. $(f \circ g)(x) = \dfrac{2x - 1}{2x}, x \neq 0$; $(g \circ f)(x) = \dfrac{2x}{x + 1} - 1, x \neq -1$;
$(f \circ f)(x) = \dfrac{x}{2x + 1}, x \neq -1, x \neq -\frac{1}{2}$;
$(g \circ g)(x) = 4x - 3, (-\infty, \infty)$

42. $(f \circ g)(x) = \dfrac{1}{\sqrt{x^2 - 4x}}, (-\infty, 0) \cup (4, \infty)$;
$(g \circ f)(x) = \dfrac{1}{x} - \dfrac{4}{\sqrt{x}}, (0, \infty)$; $(f \circ f)(x) = x^{1/4}, (0, \infty)$;
$(g \circ g)(x) = x^4 - 8x^3 + 12x^2 + 16x, (-\infty, \infty)$
43. $(f \circ g)(x) = \dfrac{1}{x + 1}, x \neq -1, x \neq 0$; $(g \circ f)(x) = \dfrac{x + 1}{x}$,
$x \neq -1, x \neq 0$; $(f \circ f)(x) = \dfrac{x}{2x + 1}, x \neq -1, x \neq -\frac{1}{2}$;
$(g \circ g)(x) = x, x \neq 0$
44. $(f \circ g)(x) = \dfrac{2x + 4}{x}, x \neq -2, x \neq 0$;
$(g \circ f)(x) = \dfrac{1}{1 + x}, x \neq -1, x \neq 0$; $(f \circ f)(x) = x, x \neq 0$;
$(g \circ g)(x) = \dfrac{x}{3x + 4}, x \neq -2, x \neq -\frac{4}{3}$
45. $(f \circ g \circ h)(x) = \sqrt{x - 1} - 1$
46. $(f \circ g \circ h)(x) = \dfrac{1}{x^6 + 6x^4 + 12x^2 + 8}$
47. $(f \circ g \circ h)(x) = (\sqrt{x} - 5)^4 + 1$
48. $(f \circ g \circ h)(x) = \sqrt{\dfrac{\sqrt[3]{x}}{\sqrt[3]{x} - 1}}$ **49.** $g(x) = x - 9, f(x) = x^5$
50. $g(x) = \sqrt{x}, f(x) = x + 1$ **51.** $g(x) = x^2, f(x) = x/(x + 4)$
52. $g(x) = x + 3, f(x) = 1/x$ **53.** $g(x) = 1 - x^3, f(x) = |x|$
54. $g(x) = \sqrt{x}, f(x) = \sqrt{1 + x}$
55. $h(x) = x^2, g(x) = x + 1, f(x) = 1/x$
56. $h(x) = \sqrt{x}, g(x) = x - 1, f(x) = \sqrt[3]{x}$
57. $h(x) = \sqrt[3]{x}, g(x) = 4 + x, f(x) = x^9$
58. $h(x) = \sqrt{x}, g(x) = 3 + x, f(x) = 2/x^2$
59. $R(x) = 0.15x - 0.000002x^2$
60. $P(x) = 0.055x - 0.0000015x^2$ **61.** (a) $g(t) = 60t$
(b) $f(r) = \pi r^2$ (c) $(f \circ g)(t) = 3600\pi t^2$ **62.** (a) $f(t) = t$
(b) $g(r) = \frac{4}{3}\pi r^3$ (c) $(g \circ f)(t) = \frac{4}{3}\pi t^3$; the volume as a
function of time **63.** $A(t) = 16\pi t^2$ **64.** (a) $f(x) = 0.80x$
(b) $g(x) = x - 50$ (c) $(f \circ g)(x) = 0.80x - 40$;
$(g \circ f)(x) = 0.80x - 50$; applying the 20% discount, then \$50
coupon $(g \circ f)$ gives the lower price **65.** (a) $f(x) = 0.9x$
(b) $g(x) = x - 100$ (c) $(f \circ g)(x) = 0.9x - 90$,
$(g \circ f)(x) = 0.9x - 100, f \circ g$: first rebate, then discount,
$g \circ f$: first discount, then rebate, $g \circ f$ is the better deal
66. (a) $s = \sqrt{1 + d^2}$ (b) $d = 350t$
(c) $s(t) = \sqrt{1 + 122{,}500t^2}$

SECTION 2.7 ■ PAGE 204

1. different, Horizontal Line **2.** (a) one-to-one, $g(x) = x^3$
(b) $g^{-1}(x) = x^{1/3}$ **3.** (a) Take the cube root, subtract 5, then
divide the result by 3. (b) $f(x) = (3x + 5)^3, f^{-1}(x) = \dfrac{x^{1/3} - 5}{3}$
4. (a) False (b) True **5.** No **6.** Yes **7.** Yes **8.** No **9.** No
10. Yes **11.** Yes **12.** Yes **13.** Yes **14.** No **15.** No

16. Yes **17.** No **18.** Yes **19.** No **20.** Yes **21.** (a) 2
(b) 3 **22.** (a) 5 (b) 4 **23.** 1 **24.** 1 **37.** $f^{-1}(x) = \frac{1}{2}(x-1)$

38. $f^{-1}(x) = 6 - x$ **39.** $f^{-1}(x) = \frac{1}{4}(x-7)$

40. $f^{-1}(x) = \frac{1}{5}(3-x)$ **41.** $f^{-1}(x) = \sqrt[3]{\frac{1}{4}(5-x)}$

42. $f^{-1}(x) = 1/\sqrt{x}, x > 0$ **43.** $f^{-1}(x) = (1/x) - 2$

44. $f^{-1}(x) = \dfrac{-2(x+1)}{x-1}$ **45.** $f^{-1}(x) = \dfrac{4x}{1-x}$

46. $f^{-1}(x) = \dfrac{2x}{x-3}$ **47.** $f^{-1}(x) = \dfrac{7x+5}{x-2}$

48. $f^{-1}(x) = \dfrac{x+2}{4-3x}$ **49.** $f^{-1}(x) = (5x-1)/(2x+3)$

50. $f^{-1}(x) = (3x-1)/(x-2)$ **51.** $f^{-1}(x) = \frac{1}{5}(x^2 - 2), x \geq 0$

52. $f^{-1}(x) = \sqrt{x + \frac{1}{4}} - \frac{1}{2}, x \geq -\frac{1}{4}$

53. $f^{-1}(x) = \sqrt{4-x}, x \leq 4$

54. $f^{-1}(x) = \frac{1}{2}(x^2 + 1), x \geq 0$ **55.** $f^{-1}(x) = (x-4)^3$

56. $f^{-1}(x) = \sqrt[3]{2} - \sqrt[5]{x}$ **57.** $f^{-1}(x) = x^2 - 2x, x \geq 1$

58. $f^{-1}(x) = \sqrt{9 - x^2}, 0 \leq x \leq 3$ **59.** $f^{-1}(x) = \sqrt[4]{x}$

60. $f^{-1}(x) = \sqrt[3]{1-x}$

61. (a)

(b)

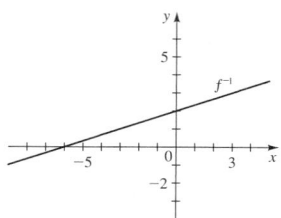

(c) $f^{-1}(x) = \frac{1}{3}(x+6)$

62. (a)

(b)

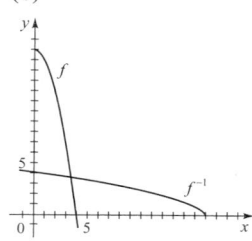

(c) $f^{-1}(x) = \sqrt{16-x}, x \leq 16$

63. (a)

(b)

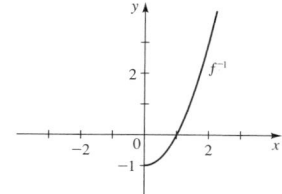

(c) $f^{-1}(x) = x^2 - 1, x \geq 0$

64. (a)

(b)

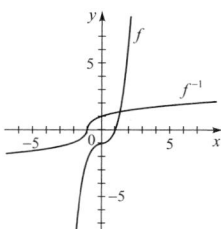

(c) $f^{-1}(x) = \sqrt[3]{x+1}$

65. Not one-to-one

66. One-to-one

67. One-to-one

68. Not one-to-one

69. Not one-to-one

70. One-to-one

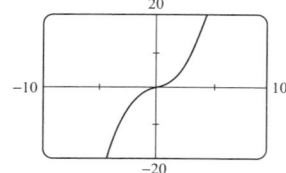

71. (a) $f^{-1}(x) = x - 2$

(b)

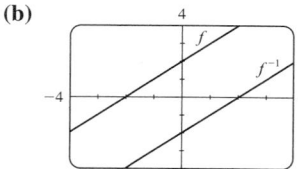

72. (a) $f^{-1}(x) = 4 - 2x$

(b)

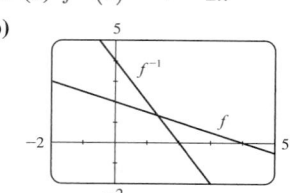

73. (a) $g^{-1}(x) = x^2 - 3, x \geq 0$

(b)

74. (a) $g^{-1}(x) = \sqrt{x-1}$

(b)

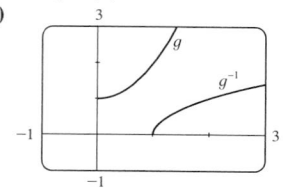

75. $x \geq 0, f^{-1}(x) = \sqrt{4 - x}$ **76.** $x \geq 1, g^{-1}(x) = 1 + \sqrt{x}$

77. $x \geq -2, h^{-1}(x) = \sqrt{x} - 2$ **78.** $x \geq 3, k^{-1}(x) = 3 + x$

79.

80.

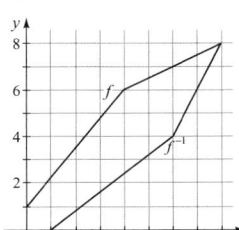

81. (a) $f(x) = 500 + 80x$ **(b)** $f^{-1}(x) = \frac{1}{80}(x - 500)$, the number of hours worked as a function of the fee   **(c)** 9; if he charges $1220, he worked 9 h   **82. (a)** $V^{-1}(t) = 40 - 4\sqrt{t}$, time elapsed since the tank started to leak   **(b)** 24.5 min; in 24.5 min the tank drained 15 gal of water   **83. (a)** $v^{-1}(t) = \sqrt{0.25 - \dfrac{t}{18,500}}$

(b) 0.498; at a distance 0.498 from the central axis the velocity is 30
84. (a) $D^{-1}(p) = 50 - \frac{1}{3}p$, the price associated with the demand D **(b)** 40; when the demand is 30 units, the price is $40
85. (a) $F^{-1}(x) = \frac{5}{9}(x - 32)$; the Celsius temperature when the Fahrenheit temperature is x **(b)** $F^{-1}(86) = 30$; when the temperature is 86°F, it is 30°C   **86. (a)** $f(x) = 1.0573x$
(b) $f^{-1}(x) = 0.9458x$, the exchange rate from U.S. dollars to Canadian dollars   **(c)** $11,586.05 in Canadian currency

87. (a) $f(x) = \begin{cases} 0.1x & \text{if } 0 \leq x \leq 20{,}000 \\ 2000 + 0.2(x - 20{,}000) & \text{if } x > 20{,}000 \end{cases}$

(b) $f^{-1}(x) = \begin{cases} 10x & \text{if } 0 \leq x \leq 2000 \\ 10{,}000 + 5x & \text{if } x > 2000 \end{cases}$

If you pay x euros (€) in taxes, your income is $f^{-1}(x)$.
(c) $f^{-1}(10{,}000) = $ € 60,000   **88. (a)** $f(x) = 0.85x$
(b) $g(x) = x - 1000$ **(c)** $H = 0.85x - 850$
(d) $H^{-1}(x) = 1.176x + 1000$, the original sticker price for a given discounted price   **(e)** $16,288, the original price of the car when the discounted price ($1000 rebate, then 15% off) is $13,000
89. $f^{-1}(x) = \frac{1}{2}(x - 7)$. A pizza costing x dollars has $f^{-1}(x)$ toppings.

CHAPTER 2 REVIEW ■ PAGE 208

1. $f(x) = x^2 - 5$ **2.** $f(x) = \dfrac{x}{2} + 9$ **3.** Add 10, then multiply the result by 3.   **4.** Multiply by 6, subtract 10, then take the square root of the result.

5.

x	$g(x)$
-1	5
0	0
1	-3
2	-4
3	-3

6.

x	$h(x)$
-2	3
-1	-4
0	-5
1	0
2	11

7. (a) $C(1000) = 34{,}000, C(10{,}000) = 205{,}000$ **(b)** The costs of printing 1000 and 10,000 copies of the book   **(c)** $C(0) = 5000$; fixed costs   **8. (a)** $E(2000) = 460, E(15{,}000) = 850$
(b) Earnings for $2000 and $15,000 of goods sold
(c) $E(0) = 400$; base salary   **(d)** 3%   **9.** 6, 2, 18, $a^2 - 4a + 6$, $a^2 + 4a + 6, x^2 - 2x + 3, 4x^2 - 8x + 6, 2x^2 - 8x + 10$

10. $1, 4 - \sqrt{21}, 4 - \sqrt{3a}, 4 - \sqrt{-3x - 6}, 4 - \sqrt{3x^2 - 6}$, $3x - 8\sqrt{3x - 6} + 10$ **11. (a)** Not a function   **(b)** Function
(c) Function, one-to-one   **(d)** Not a function   **12. (a)** $-1, 2$
(b) $[-4, 5]$ **(c)** $[-4, 4]$ **(d)** Increasing on $[-4, -2]$ and $[-1, 4]$; decreasing on $[-2, -1]$ and $[4, 5]$ **(e)** $-1, 4$ **(f)** No
13. Domain $[-3, \infty)$, range $[0, \infty)$ **14.** Domain $(-\infty, \infty)$, range $[4, \infty)$ **15.** $(-\infty, \infty)$ **16.** $x \neq \frac{1}{2}$ **17.** $[-4, \infty)$
18. $(-1, \infty)$ **19.** $\{x \mid x \neq -2, -1, 0\}$ **20.** $x \neq -\frac{1}{2}, x \neq 3$
21. $(-\infty, -1] \cup [1, 4]$ **22.** $x \neq -4$
23.

24.

25.

26.

27.

28.

29.

30.

31.

32.

33.

34.

35.

36.

37.

38.

39.

40.

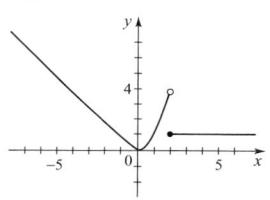

41. No   **42.** Yes   **43.** Yes   **44.** No   **45.** (iii)   **46.** (iii)

47.

48.

49.

50.

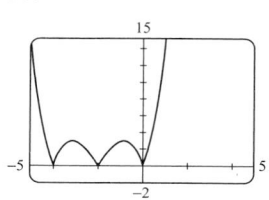

51. $[-2.1, 0.2] \cup [1.9, \infty)$ **52.** $[-7.10, \infty)$

53.

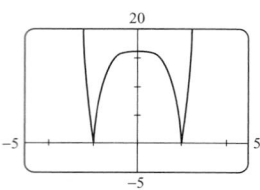

Increasing on $(-\infty, 0]$, $[2.67, \infty)$; decreasing on $[0, 2.67]$

54.

Increasing on $[-2, 0]$, $[2, \infty)$; decreasing on $(-\infty, -2]$, $[0, 2]$

55. 5   **56.** $-\frac{1}{12}$ **57.** $\dfrac{-1}{3(3 + h)}$ **58.** $2a + h + 2$

59. (a) $P(10) = 5010$, $P(20) = 7040$; the populations in 1995 and 2005   (b) 203 people/yr; average annual population increase   **60.** (a) $D(0) = 3500$, $D(15) = 6875$; initial deposit, amount deposited in 2010   (b) 2025   (c) $225/yr; average annual deposit increase from 1995 to 2010   **61.** (a) $\frac{1}{2}, \frac{1}{2}$ (b) Yes, because it is a linear function   **62.** (a) $-3, -3$ (b) Yes, because it is a linear function   **63.** (a) Shift upward 8 units   (b) Shift to the left 8 units   (c) Stretch vertically by a factor of 2, then shift upward 1 unit   (d) Shift to the right 2 units and downward 2 units   (e) Reflect in y-axis   (f) Reflect in y-axis, then in x-axis   (g) Reflect in x-axis   (h) Reflect in line $y = x$

64. (a)

(b)

(c)

(d)

(e)

(f)

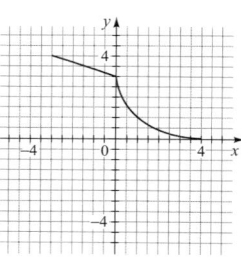

65. (a) Neither **(b)** Odd **(c)** Even **(d)** Neither **66. (a)** Odd **(b)** Neither **(c)** Even **(d)** Neither **67.** $g(-1) = -7$ **68.** $\frac{5}{4}$ **69.** 68 ft **70.** \$88,500, 15,000 units **71.** Local maximum $\approx$ 3.79 when $x \approx 0.46$; local minimum ≈ 2.81 when $x \approx -0.46$ **72.** Local maximum ≈ 3.175 when $x \approx 4.00$; local minimum $= 0$ when $x = 0$

73.

74.

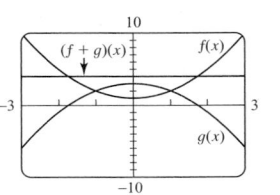

75. (a) $(f + g)(x) = x^2 - 6x + 6$ **(b)** $(f - g)(x) = x^2 - 2$ **(c)** $(fg)(x) = -3x^3 + 13x^2 - 18x + 8$ **(d)** $(f/g)(x) = (x^2 - 3x + 2)/(4 - 3x)$ **(e)** $(f \circ g)(x) = 9x^2 - 15x + 6$ **(f)** $(g \circ f)(x) = -3x^2 + 9x - 2$ **76. (a)** $(f \circ g)(x) = x$ **(b)** $(g \circ f)(x) = |x|$ **(c)** 2 **(d)** 26 **(e)** $(f \circ g \circ f)(x) = 1 + x^2$ **(f)** $(g \circ f \circ g)(x) = \sqrt{x-1}$ **77.** $(f \circ g)(x) = -3x^2 + 6x - 1, (-\infty, \infty)$; $(g \circ f)(x) = -9x^2 + 12x - 3, (-\infty, \infty); (f \circ f)(x) = 9x - 4,$ $(-\infty, \infty); (g \circ g)(x) = -x^4 + 4x^3 - 6x^2 + 4x, (-\infty, \infty)$ **78.** $(f \circ g)(x) = \sqrt{\dfrac{2}{x-4}}, (4, \infty); (g \circ f)(x) = \dfrac{2}{\sqrt{x} - 4},$ $[0, 16) \cup (16, \infty); (f \circ f)(x) = x^{1/4}, [0, \infty); (g \circ g)(x) = \dfrac{x-4}{9 - 2x},$ $x \neq 4, x \neq \frac{9}{2}$ **79.** $(f \circ g \circ h)(x) = 1 + \sqrt{x}$ **80.** $h(x) = \sqrt{x},$ $g(x) = 1 + x, f(x) = 1/\sqrt{x}$ **81.** Yes **82.** No **83.** No **84.** Yes **85.** No **86.** Yes **87.** $f^{-1}(x) = \dfrac{x + 2}{3}$ **88.** $f^{-1}(x) = \frac{1}{2}(3x - 1)$ **89.** $f^{-1}(x) = \sqrt[3]{x} - 1$ **90.** $f^{-1}(x) = 2 + (x - 1)^5$ **91. (a), (b)**

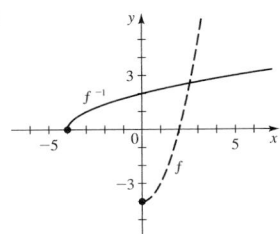

(c) $f^{-1}(x) = \sqrt{x + 4}$
92. (b)

(c)

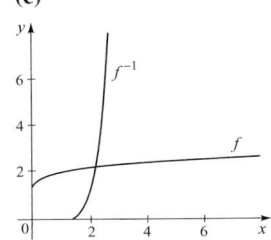

(d) $f^{-1}(x) = (x - 1)^4, x \geq 1$

CHAPTER 2 TEST ▪ PAGE 211

1. (a) and **(b)** are graphs of functions, **(a)** is one-to-one
2. (a) $2/3$, $\sqrt{6}/5$, $\sqrt{a}/(a - 1)$ **(b)** $[-1, 0) \cup (0, \infty)$
3. (a) $f(x) = (x - 2)^3$

(b)

x	$f(x)$
-1	-27
0	-8
1	-1
2	0
3	1
4	8

(c)

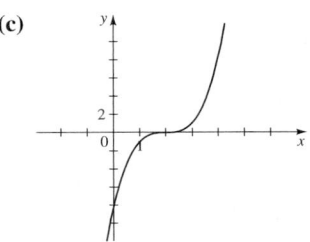

(d) By the Horizontal Line Test; take the cube root, then add 2 **(e)** $f^{-1}(x) = x^{1/3} + 2$ **4. (a)** $R(2) = 4000, R(4) = 4000$; total sales revenue with prices of \$2 and \$4

(b)

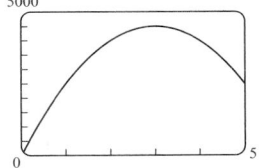

Revenue increases until price reaches \$3, then decreases

(c) \$4500; \$3 **5.** 5
6. (a)

(b)

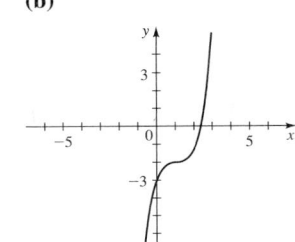

7. (a) Shift to the right 3 units, then shift upward 2 units **(b)** Reflect in y-axis **8. (a)** 3, 0
(b)

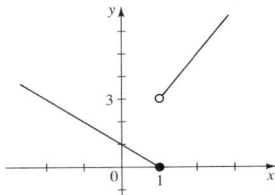

9. (a) $(f \circ g)(x) = (x - 3)^2 + 1$ **(b)** $(g \circ f)(x) = x^2 - 2$ **(c)** 2 **(d)** 2 **(e)** $(g \circ g \circ g)(x) = x - 9$ **10. (a)** $f^{-1}(x) = 3 - x^2, x \geq 0$
(b)

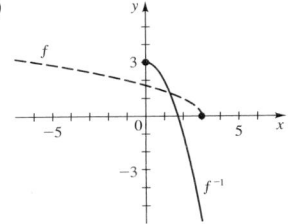

11. (a) Domain $[0, 6]$, range $[1, 7]$
(b)

(c) $\frac{5}{4}$

12. (a)
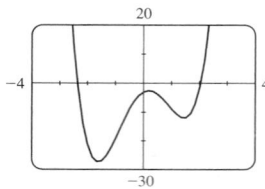
(b) No

(c) Local minimum ≈ -27.18 when $x \approx -1.61$;
local maximum ≈ -2.55 when $x \approx 0.18$;
local minimum ≈ -11.93 when $x \approx 1.43$
(d) $[-27.18, \infty)$ **(e)** Increasing on $[-1.61, 0.18] \cup [1.43, \infty)$;
decreasing on $(-\infty, -1.61] \cup [0.18, 1.43]$

FOCUS ON MODELING ■ PAGE 218

1. $A(w) = 3w^2, w > 0$ **2.** $A(w) = w^2 + 10w$

3. $V(w) = \frac{1}{2}w^3, w > 0$ **4.** $V(r) = 4\pi r^3$

5. $A(x) = 10x - x^2, 0 < x < 10$ **6.** $P(x) = 2x + \dfrac{32}{x}, x > 0$

7. $A(x) = (\sqrt{3}/4)x^2, x > 0$ **8.** $S(V) = 6V^{2/3}, V > 0$

9. $r(A) = \sqrt{A/\pi}, A > 0$ **10.** $A(C) = \dfrac{C^2}{4\pi}, C > 0$

11. $S(x) = 2x^2 + 240/x, x > 0$ **12.** $L(d) = \frac{5}{7}d$

13. $D(t) = 25t, t \geq 0$ **14.** $P(x) = 60x - x^2$

15. $A(b) = b\sqrt{4 - b}, 0 < b < 4$ **16.** $P(x) = (3 + \sqrt{5})x$

17. $A(h) = 2h\sqrt{100 - h^2}, 0 < h < 10$ **18.** $h(r) = \dfrac{300}{\pi r^2}$

19. (b) $p(x) = x(19 - x)$ **(c)** 9.5, 9.5   **20.** 50, 50
21. (b) $A(x) = x(2400 - 2x)$ **(c)** 600 ft by 1200 ft
22. (a) $A(w) = -\frac{5}{2}(w^2 - 150w)$ **(b)** 14,062.5 ft²
23. (a) $f(w) = 8w + 7200/w$ **(b)** Width along road is 30 ft,
length is 40 ft   **(c)** 15 ft to 60 ft   **24. (a)** $A(x) = \frac{1}{8}x^2 - \frac{5}{4}x + \frac{25}{4}$

(b) 5 cm   **25. (a)** $A(x) = 15x - \left(\dfrac{\pi + 4}{8}\right)x^2$

(b) Width ≈ 8.40 ft, height of rectangular part ≈ 4.20 ft
26. (a) $V(x) = 4x^3 - 64x^2 + 240x, 0 < x < 6$
(b) $1.174 \leq x \leq 3.898$ **(c)** 262.682 in³
27. (a) $A(x) = x^2 + 48/x$ **(b)** Height ≈ 1.44 ft, width ≈ 2.88 ft

28. 3.27 by 5.33   **29. (a)** $A(x) = 2x + \dfrac{200}{x}$ **(b)** 10 m by 10 m

30. (a) $T(x) = \dfrac{1}{2}\sqrt{x^2 - 14x + 53} + \dfrac{1}{5}x$ **(b)** 6.13 mi from B

31. (b) To point C, 5.1 mi from B **32. (b)** 9.23 by 13.00

CHAPTER 3

SECTION 3.1 ■ PAGE 229

1. square   **2. (a)** (h, k) **(b)** upward, minimum   **(c)** downward,
maximum   **3.** upward, $(3, 5)$, 5, minimum   **4.** downward, $(3, 5)$,
5, maximum   **5. (a)** $(3, 4)$ **(b)** 4   **(c)** $\mathbb{R}, (-\infty, 4]$
6. (a) $(-2, 8)$ **(b)** 8   **(c)** $\mathbb{R}, (-\infty, 8]$
7. (a) $(1, -3)$ **(b)** -3 **(c)** $\mathbb{R}, [-3, \infty)$
8. (a) $(-1, -4)$ **(b)** -4 **(c)** $\mathbb{R}, [-4, \infty)$
9. (a) $f(x) = (x - 3)^2 - 9$ **10. (a)** $f(x) = (x + 4)^2 - 16$
(b) Vertex $(3, -9)$ **(b)** Vertex $(-4, -16)$
x-intercepts 0, 6 x-intercepts 0, -8
y-intercept 0 y-intercept 0
(c)   **(c)**
   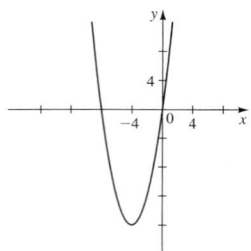

11. (a) $f(x) = 2\left(x + \frac{3}{2}\right)^2 - \frac{9}{2}$ **12. (a)** $f(x) = -(x - 5)^2 + 25$
(b) Vertex $\left(-\frac{3}{2}, -\frac{9}{2}\right)$ **(b)** Vertex $(5, 25)$
x-intercepts 0, -3, x-intercepts 0, 10
y-intercept 0 y-intercept 0
(c)   **(c)**
   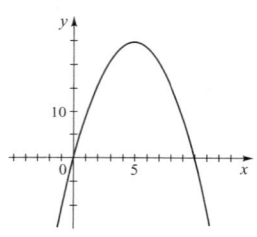

13. (a) $f(x) = (x + 2)^2 - 1$ **14. (a)** $f(x) = (x - 1)^2 + 1$
(b) Vertex $(-2, -1)$ **(b)** Vertex $(1, 1)$
x-intercepts $-1, -3$ no x-intercepts
y-intercept 3 y-intercept 2
(c)   **(c)**
   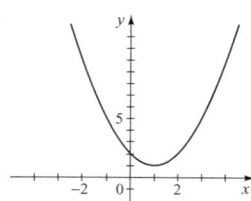

15. (a) $f(x) = -(x - 3)^2 + 13$
(b) Vertex $(3, 13)$; x-intercepts $3 \pm \sqrt{13}$; y-intercept 4
(c)
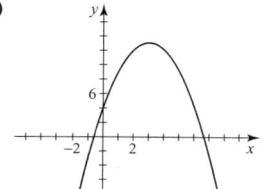

16. **(a)** $f(x) = -(x + 2)^2 + 8$
(b) Vertex $(-2, 8)$; x-intercepts $-2 \pm 2\sqrt{2}$; y-intercept 4
(c)

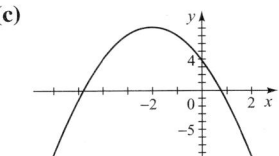

17. **(a)** $f(x) = 2(x + 1)^2 + 1$
(b) Vertex $(-1, 1)$; no x-intercept; y-intercept 3
(c)

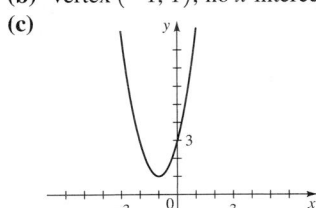

18. **(a)** $f(x) = -3(x - 1)^2 + 1$
(b) Vertex $(1, 1)$; x-intercepts $1 \pm \sqrt{\frac{1}{3}}$; y-intercept -2
(c)

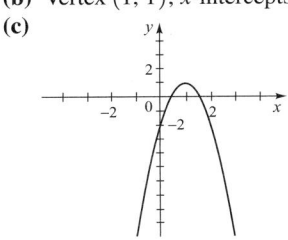

19. **(a)** $f(x) = 2(x - 5)^2 + 7$
(b) Vertex $(5, 7)$; no x-intercept; y-intercept 57
(c)

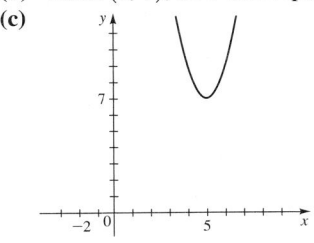

20. **(a)** $f(x) = 2\left(x + \frac{1}{4}\right)^2 - \frac{49}{8}$
(b) Vertex $\left(-\frac{1}{4}, -\frac{49}{8}\right)$; x-intercepts $-2, \frac{3}{2}$; y-intercept -6
(c)

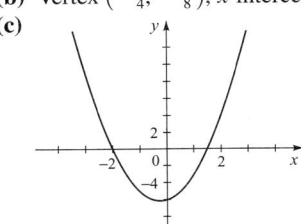

21. **(a)** $f(x) = -4(x + 2)^2 + 19$

(b) Vertex $(-2, 19)$; x-intercepts $-2 \pm \frac{1}{2}\sqrt{19}$; y-intercept 3
(c)

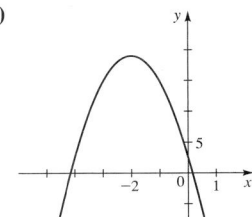

22. **(a)** $f(x) = 6(x + 1)^2 - 11$

(b) Vertex $(-1, -11)$; x-intercepts $\dfrac{-6 \pm \sqrt{66}}{6}$; y-intercept -5

(c)

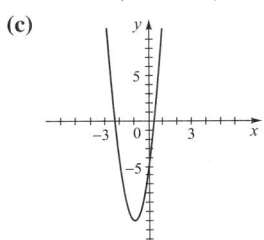

23. **(a)** $f(x) = (x + 1)^2 - 2$
(b)

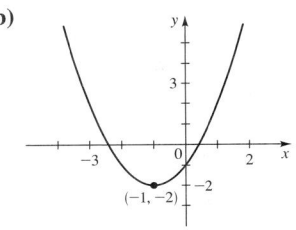

24. **(a)** $f(x) = (x - 4)^2 - 8$
(b)

(c) Minimum $f(-1) = -2$
(c) Minimum $f(4) = -8$

25. **(a)** $f(x) = 3(x - 1)^2 - 2$
(b)

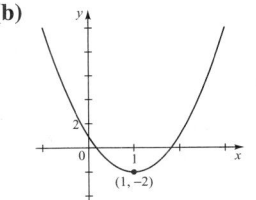

26. **(a)** $f(x) = 5(x + 3)^2 - 41$
(b)

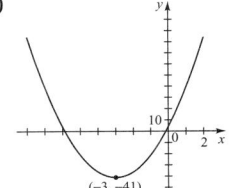

(c) Minimum $f(1) = -2$
(c) Minimum $f(-3) = -41$

27. **(a)** $f(x) = -\left(x + \frac{3}{2}\right)^2 + \frac{21}{4}$
(b)

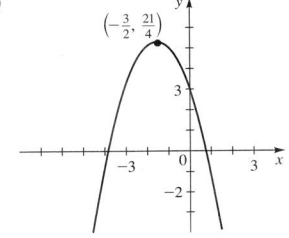

28. **(a)** $f(x) = -(x + 3)^2 + 10$
(b)

(c) Maximum $f\left(-\frac{3}{2}\right) = \frac{21}{4}$
(c) Maximum $f(-3) = 10$

29. (a) $g(x) = 3(x - 2)^2 + 1$
(b)

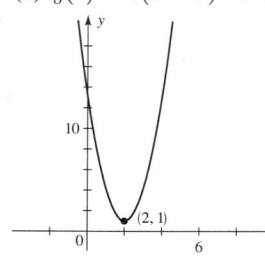

30. (a) $g(x) = 2(x + 2)^2 + 3$
(b)

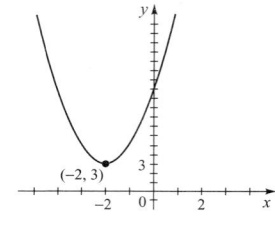

(c) Minimum $g(2) = 1$

(c) Minimum $g(-2) = 3$

31. (a) $h(x) = -\left(x + \frac{1}{2}\right)^2 + \frac{5}{4}$
(b)

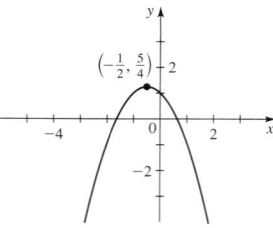

32. (a) $h(x) = -4\left(x + \frac{1}{2}\right)^2 + 4$
(b)

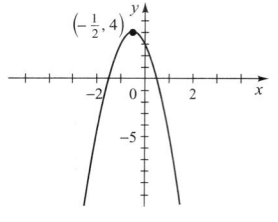

(c) Maximum $h\left(-\frac{1}{2}\right) = \frac{5}{4}$

(c) Maximum $h\left(-\frac{1}{2}\right) = 4$

33. Minimum $f\left(-\frac{1}{2}\right) = \frac{3}{4}$ **34.** Maximum $f\left(\frac{3}{2}\right) = \frac{13}{4}$
35. Maximum $f(-3.5) = 185.75$ **36.** Minimum $f(-2) = 73$
37. Minimum $f(0.6) = 15.64$ **38.** Minimum $g\left(\frac{15}{2}\right) = -5625$
39. Minimum $h(-2) = -8$ **40.** Maximum $f(3) = 10$
41. Maximum $f(-1) = \frac{7}{2}$ **42.** Minimum $g(2) = -1$
43. $f(x) = 2x^2 - 4x$ **44.** $f(x) = -3(x - 3)^2 + 4$
45. $(-\infty, \infty), (-\infty, 1]$ **46.** $(-\infty, \infty), [-4, \infty)$
47. $(-\infty, \infty), \left[-\frac{23}{2}, \infty\right)$ **48.** $(-\infty, \infty), (-\infty, 7]$
49. (a) -4.01 **(b)** -4.011025 **50. (a)** 1.18
(b) $\dfrac{8 + \sqrt{2}}{8} \approx 1.176777$ **51.** Local maximum 2; local minima
$-1, 0$ **52.** Local maxima 1, 2; local minimum -1 **53.** Local
maxima 0, 1; local minima $-2, -1$ **54.** Local maxima 2, 3;
local minima 0, -1 **55.** Local maximum ≈ 0.38 when
$x \approx -0.58$; local minimum ≈ -0.38 when $x \approx 0.58$ **56.** Local
maximum ≈ 4.00 when $x \approx 1.00$; local minimum ≈ 2.81 when
$x \approx -0.33$ **57.** Local maximum ≈ 0 when $x = 0$; local minimum
≈ -13.61 when $x \approx -1.71$; local minimum ≈ -73.32 when
$x \approx 3.21$ **58.** Local maximum ≈ 13.02 when $x \approx 1.04$; local
maximum ≈ -7.87 when $x \approx -1.93$; local minimum ≈ -13.02
when $x \approx -1.04$; local minimum ≈ 7.87 when $x \approx 1.93$
59. Local maximum ≈ 5.66 when $x \approx 4.00$ **60.** Local maximum
≈ 0.32 when $x \approx 0.75$ **61.** Local maximum ≈ 0.38 when
$x \approx -1.73$; local minimum ≈ -0.38 when $x \approx 1.73$ **62.** Local
maximum ≈ 1.33 when $x \approx -0.50$ **63.** 25 ft   **64. (a)** 8.125 ft
(b) 16.3 ft   **65.** \$4000, 100 units   **66.** \$450, 1500 cans
67. 30 times   **68.** 150 min, 4.5 mg/L   **69.** 50 trees per acre
70. 850 vines   **71.** 600 ft by 1200 ft   **72.** 14,062.5 ft^2
73. Width 8.40 ft, height of rectangular part 4.20 ft   **74.** 5 cm
75. (a) $f(x) = x(1200 - x)$ **(b)** 600 ft by 600 ft
76. (a) $f(x) = x(30 - 2x)$ **(b)** 7.5 in.   **(c)** 112.5 in^2
77. (a) $R(x) = x(57,000 - 3000x)$ **(b)** \$9.50   **(c)** \$19.00
78. (a) $P(x) = -2x^2 + 52x - 240$ **(b)** \$13.00, \$98.00

SECTION 3.2 ■ PAGE 243

1. II   **2. (a)** (ii)   **(b)** (iv)   **3. (a), (c)**   **4. (a)**
5. (a)

(b)

(c)

(d)

6. (a)

(b)

(c)

(d)

7. (a)

(b)

(c)

(d)

8. (a)

(b)

(c)

(d)

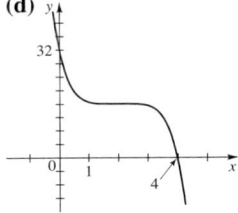

9. III **10.** I **11.** V **12.** II **13.** VI **14.** IV

15.

16.

17.

18.

19.

20.

21.

22.

23.

24.

25.

26.

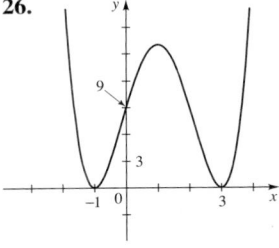

27. $P(x) = x(x + 2)(x - 3)$

28. $P(x) = x(x - 2)(x + 4)$

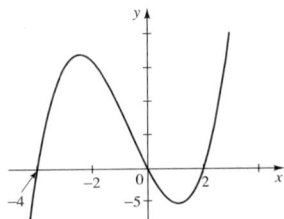

29. $P(x) = -x(x + 3)(x - 4)$

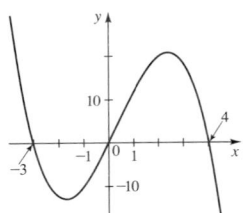

30. $P(x) = -x(2x - 1)(x + 1)$

31. $P(x) = x^2(x - 1)(x - 2)$

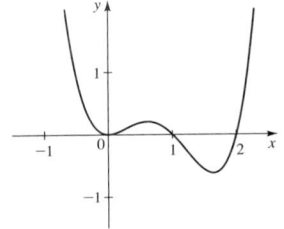

32. $P(x) = x^3(x + 3)(x - 3)$ **33.** $P(x) = (x + 1)^2(x - 1)$ **38.** $P(x) = (x + 2)(x - 2)(x^2 - 2x + 4)$

    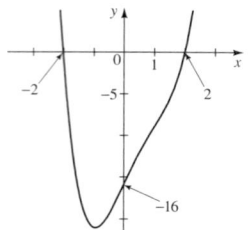

34. $P(x) = (x + 3)(x - 2)(x + 2)$ **39.** $P(x) = (x^2 + 1)(x + 2)(x - 2)$

  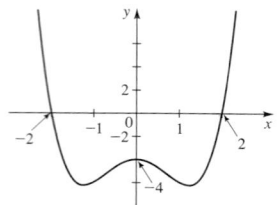

35. $P(x) = (2x - 1)(x + 3)(x - 3)$ **40.** $P(x) = (x - 1)^2(x^2 + x + 1)^2$

  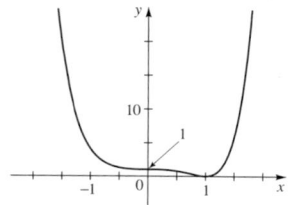

41. $y \to \infty$ as $x \to \infty$, $y \to -\infty$ as $x \to -\infty$ **42.** $y \to -\infty$ as $x \to \infty$, $y \to \infty$ as $x \to -\infty$ **43.** $y \to \infty$ as $x \to \pm\infty$

36. $P(x) = \frac{1}{8}(x - 2)^2(2x + 3)^2(x^2 + 2x + 4)^2$

44. $y \to -\infty$ as $x \to \infty$, $y \to \infty$ as $x \to -\infty$ **45.** $y \to \infty$ as $x \to \infty$, $y \to -\infty$ as $x \to -\infty$

46. $y \to -\infty$ as $x \to \pm\infty$ **47.** (a) x-intercepts 0, 4; y-intercept 0   (b) $(2, 4)$ **48.** (a) x-intercepts 0, 4.5; y-intercept 0 (b) $(0, 0), (3, -3)$ **49.** (a) x-intercepts -2, 1; y-intercept -1 (b) $(-1, -2), (1, 0)$ **50.** (a) x-intercepts 0, 4; y-intercept 0 (b) $(3, -3)$

51.

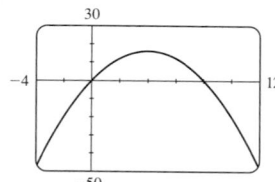

local maximum $(4, 16)$

37. $P(x) = (x - 2)^2(x^2 + 2x + 4)$

52.

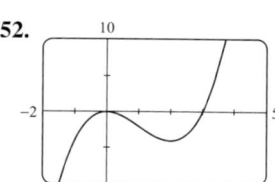

local minimum $(2, -4)$,
local maximum $(0, 0)$

53.

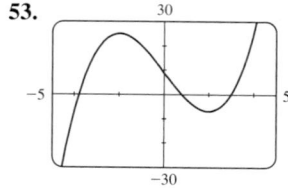

local maximum $(-2, 25)$,
local minimum $(2, -7)$

54.

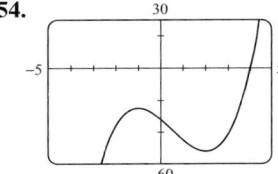

local minimum $(2, -52)$,
local maximum $(-1, -25)$

55.

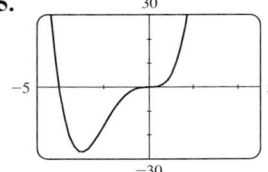

local minimum $(-3, -27)$

56.

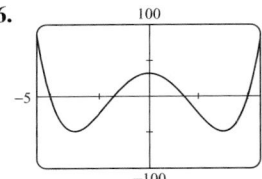

local minima $(-3, -49)$
and $(3, -49)$,
local maximum $(0, 32)$

57.

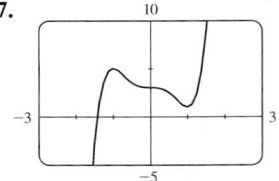

local maximum $(-1, 5)$,
local minimum $(1, 1)$

local maximum $(0, 6)$,
local minimum $(1.26, 1.24)$

58.

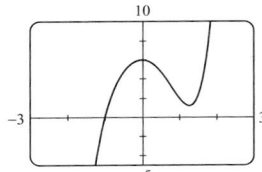

59. One local maximum, no local minimum
60. No local extremum
61. One local maximum, one local minimum
62. No local extremum
63. One local maximum, two local minima
64. Two local maxima, two local minima
65. No local extrema   **66.** One local minimum
67. One local maximum, two local minima
68. One local maximum, one local minimum
69.

Increasing the value of c
stretches the graph vertically.

70.

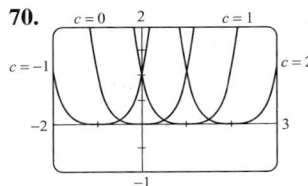

Increasing the value of c shifts
the graph to the right.

71.

Increasing the value of c
moves the graph up.

72.

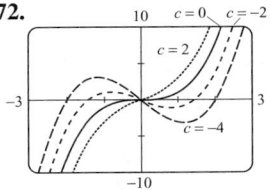

Increasing the value of c makes
the "bumps" in the graph flatter.

73.

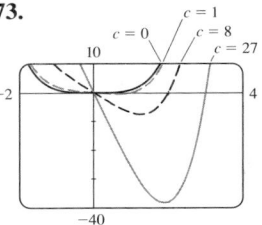

Increasing the value of c
causes a deeper dip in the
graph in the fourth quadrant
and moves the positive
x-intercept to the right.

74.

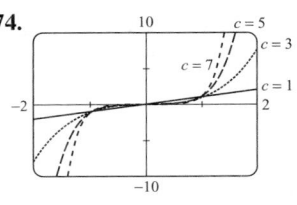

The larger c gets, the flatter
the graph is near the origin,
and the steeper it is away
from the origin.

75. (a)

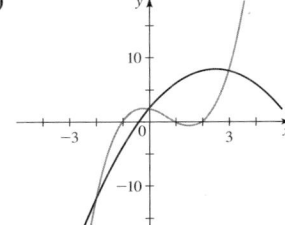

(b) Three   **(c)** $(0, 2), (3, 8), (-2, -12)$
76. ① is $y = x^4$;   ② is $y = x^2$;   ③ is $y = x^6$;   ④ is $y = x^3$;
⑤ is $y = x^5$ **77. (d)** $P(x) = P_O(x) + P_E(x)$, where
$P_O(x) = x^5 + 6x^3 - 2x$ and $P_E(x) = -x^2 + 5$
78. (a)

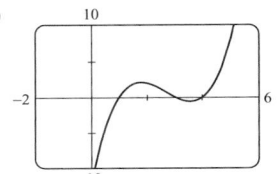

local maximum $(1.8, 2.1)$
local minimum $(3.6, -0.6)$

(b)

local maximum $(1.8, 7.1)$
local minimum
$(3.5, 4.4)$

79. (a) Two local extrema

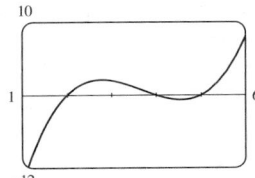

80. (a) Three x-intercepts, two local extrema   **(b)** One x-intercept,
no local extrema   **(c)** Three x-intercepts, two local extrema; one
x-intercept, no local extrema   **81. (a)** 26 blenders   **(b)** No;
$3276.22   **82. (a)** 1380 rabbits, after 4.2 months   **(b)** After 8.4
months   **83. (a)** $V(x) = 4x^3 - 120x^2 + 800x$ **(b)** $0 < x < 10$

(c) Maximum volume ≈ 1539.6 cm^3

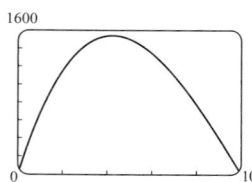

84. (b) Domain $\{x \mid 0 < x < 18\}$ **(c)** 1728 in^3

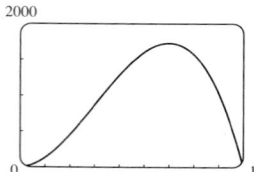

SECTION 3.3 ■ PAGE 251

1. quotient, remainder **2. (a)** factor **(b)** k
3. $(x + 3)(3x - 4) + 8$ **4.** $(x - 1)(x^2 + 5x - 1)$
5. $(2x - 3)(x^2 - 1) - 3$ **6.** $(2x + 1)(2x^2 - x + 4) + 5$
7. $(x^2 + 3)(x^2 - x - 3) + (7x + 11)$
8. $(x^2 - 2)(2x^3 + 4x^2 + 8) + (-x + 13)$
9. $x + 1 + \dfrac{-11}{x + 3}$ **10.** $x^2 + 4x + 22 + \dfrac{93}{x - 4}$
11. $2x - \dfrac{1}{2} + \dfrac{-\frac{15}{2}}{2x - 1}$ **12.** $2x^2 + 3x + \dfrac{5}{3x - 4}$
13. $2x^2 - x + 1 + \dfrac{4x - 4}{x^2 + 4}$ **14.** $x^3 - x + 1 + \dfrac{-x + 2}{x^2 + x - 1}$

In answers 15–38 the first polynomial given is the quotient, and the second is the remainder.
15. $x - 2, -16$ **16.** $x^2 + x, 6$ **17.** $2x^2 - 1, -2$
18. $\frac{1}{3}x^2 + \frac{1}{3}x + \frac{2}{3}, -1$ **19.** $x + 2, 8x - 1$
20. $3x^2 - 8x - 1, 5x - 2$ **21.** $3x + 1, 7x - 5$ **22.** $3, 20x + 5$
23. $x^4 + 1, 0$ **24.** $\frac{1}{2}x^3 - x^2 - \frac{5}{2}x - \frac{7}{4}, \frac{19}{2}x + 1$ **25.** $x - 2, -2$
26. $x - 4, 0$ **27.** $3x + 23, 138$ **28.** $4x - 20, 97$
29. $x^2 + 2, -3$ **30.** $3x^2 + 3x + 6, 31$ **31.** $x^2 - 3x + 1, -1$
32. $x^3 + x^2 + 3x + 5, 12$ **33.** $x^4 + x^3 + 4x^2 + 4x + 4, -2$
34. $x^2 - 6x + 9, 0$ **35.** $2x^2 + 4x, 1$ **36.** $6x^3 + 6x^2 + x + \frac{1}{3}, \frac{7}{9}$
37. $x^2 + 3x + 9, 0$ **38.** $x^3 - 2x^2 + 4x - 8, 0$ **39.** -3 **40.** 6
41. 12 **42.** 2 **43.** -7 **44.** 20 **45.** -483 **46.** -273
47. 2159 **48.** 100 **49.** $\frac{7}{3}$ **50.** $\frac{49}{64}$ **51.** -8.279 **52. (a)** 1
(b) 1 **57.** $-1 \pm \sqrt{6}$ **58.** $-1, 3$ **59.** $x^3 - 3x^2 - x + 3$
60. $x^4 - 4x^3 - 4x^2 + 16x$ **61.** $x^4 - 8x^3 + 14x^2 + 8x - 15$
62. $x^5 - 5x^3 + 4x$ **63.** $-\frac{3}{2}x^3 + 3x^2 + \frac{15}{2}x - 9$
64. $2x^4 - 5x^3 + 5x - 2$ **65.** $(x + 1)(x - 1)(x - 2)$
66. $(x + 1)(x - 2)^2$ **67.** $(x + 2)^2(x - 1)^2$
68. $(x + 2)(x + 1)(x - 1)^2$

SECTION 3.4 ■ PAGE 260

1. $a_0, a_n; \pm 1, \pm\frac{1}{2}, \pm\frac{1}{3}, \pm\frac{1}{6}, \pm 2, \pm\frac{2}{3}, \pm 5, \pm\frac{5}{2}, \pm\frac{5}{3}, \pm\frac{5}{6}, \pm 10, \pm\frac{10}{3}$
2. 1, 3, 5; 0 **3.** True **4.** False **5.** $\pm 1, \pm 3$ **6.** $\pm 1, \pm 2,$
$\pm 4, \pm 8$ **7.** $\pm 1, \pm 2, \pm 4, \pm 8, \pm\frac{1}{2}$ **8.** $\pm 1, \pm 2, \pm 3, \pm 4, \pm 6,$
$\pm 12, \pm\frac{1}{2}, \pm\frac{3}{2}, \pm\frac{1}{3}, \pm\frac{2}{3}, \pm\frac{4}{3}, \pm\frac{1}{6}$ **9.** $\pm 1, \pm 7, \pm\frac{1}{2}, \pm\frac{7}{2}, \pm\frac{1}{4}, \pm\frac{7}{4}$
10. $\pm 1, \pm 2, \pm 4, \pm 8, \pm\frac{1}{2}, \pm\frac{1}{3}, \pm\frac{2}{3}, \pm\frac{4}{3}, \pm\frac{8}{3}, \pm\frac{1}{4}, \pm\frac{1}{6}, \pm\frac{1}{12}$

11. (a) $\pm 1, \pm\frac{1}{5}$ **(b)** $-1, 1, \frac{1}{5}$ **12. (a)** $\pm 1, \pm 2, \pm\frac{1}{3}, \pm\frac{2}{3}$
(b) $-1, \frac{2}{3}$ **13. (a)** $\pm 1, \pm 3, \pm\frac{1}{2}, \pm\frac{3}{2}$ **(b)** $-\frac{1}{2}, 1, 3$ **14. (a)** $\pm 1,$
$\pm\frac{1}{2}, \pm\frac{1}{4}$ **(b)** $\frac{1}{4}, 1$ **15.** $-2, 1; P(x) = (x + 2)^2(x - 1)$
16. $1, 2, 4; P(x) = (x - 1)(x - 2)(x - 4)$
17. $-1, 2; P(x) = (x + 1)^2(x - 2)$
18. $-3, 2; P(x) = (x + 3)^2(x - 2)$ **19.** $2; P(x) = (x - 2)^3$
20. $-3, 2; P(x) = (x + 3)(x - 2)^2$
21. $-1, 2, 3; P(x) = (x + 1)(x - 2)(x - 3)$
22. $-2, 1, 5; P(x) = (x + 2)(x - 1)(x - 5)$
23. $-3, -1, 1; P(x) = (x + 3)(x + 1)(x - 1)$
24. $-3, 2, 5; P(x) = (x + 3)(x - 2)(x - 5)$
25. $\pm 1, \pm 2; P(x) = (x - 2)(x + 2)(x - 1)(x + 1)$
26. $-2, 1, 2; P(x) = (x - 1)^2(x - 2)(x + 2)$
27. $-4, -2, -1, 1; P(x) = (x + 4)(x + 2)(x - 1)(x + 1)$
28. $-3, 2, 5; P(x) = (x + 3)^2(x - 2)(x - 5)$
29. $\pm 2, \pm\frac{3}{2}; P(x) = (x - 2)(x + 2)(2x - 3)(2x + 3)$
30. $\pm 3, -\frac{1}{2}, 1; P(x) = (x - 1)(x - 3)(x + 3)(2x + 1)$
31. $\pm 2, \frac{1}{3}, 3; P(x) = (x - 2)(x + 2)(x - 3)(3x - 1)$
32. $-2, \frac{1}{2}; P(x) = (x + 2)^2(2x - 1)$
33. $-1, \pm\frac{1}{2}; P(x) = (x + 1)(2x - 1)(2x + 1)$
34. $\pm 1, \frac{3}{2}; P(x) = (x - 1)(x + 1)(2x - 3)$
35. $-\frac{3}{2}, \frac{1}{2}, 1; P(x) = (x - 1)(2x + 3)(2x - 1)$
36. $-1, -\frac{3}{4}, \frac{1}{2}; P(x) = (x + 1)(4x + 3)(2x - 1)$
37. $-\frac{5}{2}, -1, \frac{3}{2}; P(x) = (x + 1)(2x + 5)(2x - 3)$
38. $-2, -\frac{1}{3}, \frac{1}{2}; P(x) = (x + 2)(3x + 1)(2x - 1)$
39. $-\frac{1}{2}, \frac{2}{5}, \frac{1}{2}; P(x) = (2x - 1)(5x - 2)(2x + 1)$
40. $-\frac{1}{3}, \frac{1}{2}, \frac{3}{2}; P(x) = (2x - 1)(2x - 3)(3x + 1)$
41. $-1, \frac{1}{2}, 2; P(x) = (x + 1)(x - 2)^2(2x - 1)$
42. $-1, -\frac{1}{3}, \frac{1}{2}, 2; P(x) = (x + 1)(x - 2)(3x + 1)(2x - 1)$
43. $-3, -2, 1, 3; P(x) = (x + 3)(x + 2)^2(x - 1)(x - 3)$
44. $-2, -1, 2, 3; P(x) = (x + 2)(x + 1)(x - 2)^2(x - 3)$
45. $-1, -\frac{1}{3}, 2, 5; P(x) = (x + 1)^2(x - 2)(x - 5)(3x + 1)$
46. $-3, 2, \frac{1}{2}; P(x) = (x + 3)(2x - 1)(x^2 + 1)(x - 2)^2$
47. $-2, -1 \pm \sqrt{2}$ **48.** $3, 1 \pm \sqrt{5}$ **49.** $-1, 4, \dfrac{3 \pm \sqrt{13}}{2}$
50. $-2, 1, \dfrac{-1 \pm \sqrt{5}}{2}$ **51.** $3, \dfrac{1 \pm \sqrt{5}}{2}$ **52.** $-1, 2, 2 \pm \sqrt{2}$
53. $\frac{1}{2}, \dfrac{1 \pm \sqrt{3}}{2}$ **54.** $-\frac{1}{3}, 1 \pm \sqrt{3}$ **55.** $-1, -\frac{1}{2}, -3 \pm \sqrt{10}$
56. $\frac{1}{2}, 3, \dfrac{-2 \pm \sqrt{6}}{2}$
57. (a) $-2, 2, 3$ **(b)**

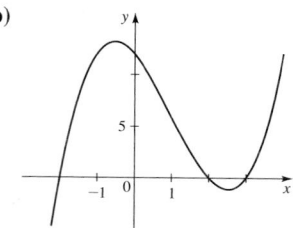

58. (a) $2, -1, -3$ **(b)**

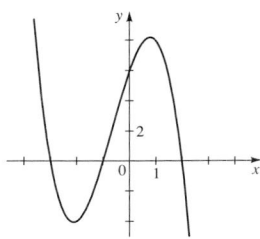

59. (a) $-\frac{1}{2}, 2$ **(b)**

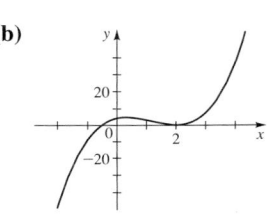

60. (a) $-3, \frac{1}{3}$ **(b)**

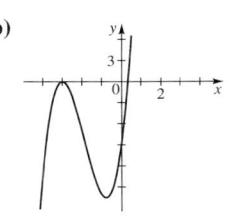

61. (a) $-1, 2$ **(b)**

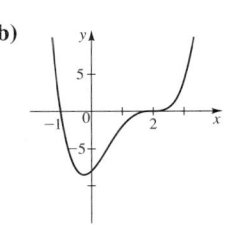

62. (a) $-2, 2 \pm \sqrt{2}$ **(b)**

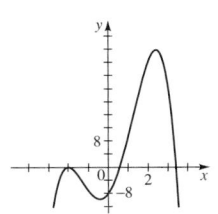

63. (a) $-1, 2$ **(b)**

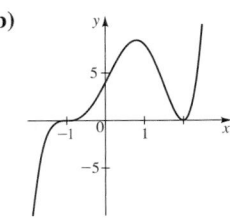

64. (a) $-3, 1$ **(b)**

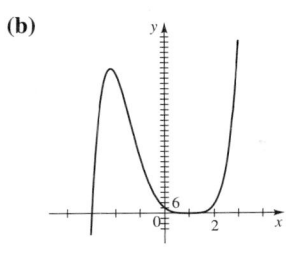

65. 1 positive, 2 or 0 negative; 3 or 1 real   **66.** 3 or 1 positive, no negative; 1 or 3 real   **67.** 1 positive, 1 negative; 2 real
68. No positive, 4, 2, or 0 negative; 0, 2, or 4 real   **69.** 2 or 0 positive, 0 negative; 3 or 1 real (since 0 is a zero but is neither positive nor negative)   **70.** 6, 4, 2, or 0 positive, no negative; 6, 4, 2, or 0 real   **75.** $3, -2$ **76.** $3, -2$ **77.** $3, -1$ **78.** $1, -1$ **79.** -2,

$\frac{1}{2}, \pm 1$ **80.** $-2, -\frac{1}{2}, \dfrac{-5 \pm \sqrt{17}}{2}$ **81.** $\pm \frac{1}{2}, \pm \sqrt{5}$ **82.** $-1, 0, \frac{1}{2}, \frac{5}{3}$

83. $-2, 1, 3, 4$ **84.** $-2, \frac{3}{4}, 1, \dfrac{2 \pm \sqrt{2}}{2}$ **89.** $-2, 2, 3$

90. $-2, -1, 1, 2$ **91.** $-\frac{3}{2}, -1, 1, 4$ **92.** -2 **93.** $-1.28, 1.53$
94. 3   **95.** -1.50 **96.** $-1.71, -1.20, -0.80$ **99.** 11.3 ft
100. 47 ft by 106 ft   **101. (a)** It began to snow again.   **(b)** No
(c) Just before midnight on Saturday night   **102.** 5 cm by 10 cm by 30 cm or 3.49 cm by 13.03 cm by 33.03 cm   **103.** 2.76 m
104. (b) 1.45 ft by 1.34 ft or 2.31 ft by 0.53 ft   **105.** 88 in. (or 3.21 in.)

SECTION 3.5 ■ PAGE 268

1. -1 **2.** 3, 4   **3. (a)** $3 - 4i$ **(b)** $9 + 16 = 25$ **4.** $3 - 4i$
5. Real part 5, imaginary part -7 **6.** Real part -6, imaginary part 4   **7.** Real part $-\frac{2}{3}$, imaginary part $-\frac{5}{3}$ **8.** Real part 2, imaginary part $\frac{7}{2}$ **9.** Real part 3, imaginary part 0   **10.** Real part $-\frac{1}{2}$, imaginary part 0   **11.** Real part 0, imaginary part $-\frac{2}{3}$
12. Real part 0, imaginary part $\sqrt{3}$ **13.** Real part $\sqrt{3}$, imaginary part 2   **14.** Real part 2, imaginary part $-\sqrt{5}$ **15.** $5 - i$
16. $6 - i$ **17.** $3 + 5i$ **18.** $-2 - \frac{7}{3}i$ **19.** $2 - 2i$
20. $-6 + 6i$ **21.** $-19 + 4i$ **22.** $-4 + 7i$ **23.** $-4 + 8i$
24. $2 + i$ **25.** $30 + 10i$ **26.** $8 + 2i$ **27.** $-33 - 56i$
28. $-\frac{2591}{9} + 18i$ **29.** $27 - 8i$ **30.** $1 + 17i$ **31.** $-i$ **32.** 16
33. 1   **34.** -1 **35.** $-i$ **36.** $\frac{1}{2} - \frac{1}{2}i$ **37.** $\frac{8}{5} + \frac{1}{5}i$ **38.** $\frac{11}{25} - \frac{23}{25}i$
39. $-5 + 12i$ **40.** $4 + 3i$ **41.** $-4 + 2i$ **42.** $\frac{2}{13} + \frac{3}{13}i$
43. $2 - \frac{4}{3}i$ **44.** $\frac{1}{5} + \frac{1}{5}i$ **45.** $-i$ **46.** $3 + i$ **47.** $5i$ **48.** $\frac{3}{2}i$
49. -6 **50.** $3i$ **51.** $(3 + \sqrt{5}) + (3 - \sqrt{5})i$
52. $-\sqrt{2} - 4\sqrt{6}i$ **53.** 2   **54.** $-i$ **55.** $-i\sqrt{2}$ **56.** $-\frac{7}{2}$
57. $\pm 7i$ **58.** $\pm \frac{2}{3}i$ **59.** $2 \pm i$ **60.** $-1 \pm i$ **61.** $-1 \pm 2i$

62. $3 \pm i$ **63.** $-\frac{1}{2} \pm \dfrac{\sqrt{3}}{2}i$ **64.** $\frac{3}{2} \pm \dfrac{\sqrt{3}}{2}i$ **65.** $\frac{1}{2} \pm \frac{1}{2}i$

66. $\frac{1}{2} \pm \dfrac{\sqrt{5}}{2}i$ **67.** $-\frac{3}{2} \pm \dfrac{\sqrt{3}}{2}i$ **68.** $-2 \pm 2\sqrt{2}i$

69. $\dfrac{-6 \pm \sqrt{6}i}{6}$ **70.** $2 \pm \dfrac{\sqrt{3}}{2}i$ **71.** $1 \pm 3i$ **72.** $-\frac{1}{4} \pm \dfrac{\sqrt{15}}{4}i$

SECTION 3.6 ■ PAGE 276

1. $5, -2, 3, 1$ **2. (a)** $x - a$ **(b)** $(x - a)^m$ **3.** n **4.** $a - bi$
5. (a) $0, \pm 2i$ **(b)** $x^2(x - 2i)(x + 2i)$
6. (a) $0, \pm 3i$ **(b)** $x^3(x - 3i)(x + 3i)$
7. (a) $0, 1 \pm i$ **(b)** $x(x - 1 - i)(x - 1 + i)$
8. (a) $0, -\frac{1}{2} \pm \frac{1}{2}i\sqrt{3}$ **(b)** $x\left(x + \frac{1}{2} - \frac{1}{2}i\sqrt{3}\right)\left(x + \frac{1}{2} + \frac{1}{2}i\sqrt{3}\right)$
9. (a) $\pm i$ **(b)** $(x - i)^2(x + i)^2$
10. (a) $\pm \sqrt{2}, \pm i$ **(b)** $(x - \sqrt{2})(x + \sqrt{2})(x - i)(x + i)$
11. (a) $\pm 2, \pm 2i$ **(b)** $(x - 2)(x + 2)(x - 2i)(x + 2i)$
12. (a) $\pm i\sqrt{3}$ **(b)** $(x - i\sqrt{3})^2(x + i\sqrt{3})^2$
13. (a) $-2, 1 \pm i\sqrt{3}$
(b) $(x + 2)(x - 1 - i\sqrt{3})(x - 1 + i\sqrt{3})$

14. (a) $2, -1 \pm i\sqrt{3}$

(b) $(x - 2)(x + 1 - i\sqrt{3})(x + 1 + i\sqrt{3})$

15. (a) $\pm 1, \frac{1}{2} \pm \frac{1}{2}i\sqrt{3}, -\frac{1}{2} \pm \frac{1}{2}i\sqrt{3}$

(b) $(x - 1)(x + 1)(x - \frac{1}{2} - \frac{1}{2}i\sqrt{3})(x - \frac{1}{2} + \frac{1}{2}i\sqrt{3}) \times$
$(x + \frac{1}{2} - \frac{1}{2}i\sqrt{3})(x + \frac{1}{2} + \frac{1}{2}i\sqrt{3})$

16. (a) $-1, 2, -1 \pm i\sqrt{3}, \frac{1}{2} \pm \frac{1}{2}i\sqrt{3}$

(b) $(x + 1)(x - 2)(x + 1 - i\sqrt{3})(x + 1 + i\sqrt{3}) \times$
$(x - \frac{1}{2} - \frac{1}{2}i\sqrt{3})(x - \frac{1}{2} + \frac{1}{2}i\sqrt{3})$

In answers 17–34 the factored form is given first, then the zeros are listed with the multiplicity of each in parentheses.

17. $(x - 5i)(x + 5i); \pm 5i\ (1)$ **18.** $(2x - 3i)(2x + 3i); \pm \frac{3}{2}i\ (1)$

19. $[x - (-1 + i)][x - (-1 - i)]; -1 + i\ (1), -1 - i\ (1)$

20. $(x - 4 - i)(x - 4 + i); 4 + i\ (1), 4 - i\ (1)$

21. $x(x - 2i)(x + 2i); 0\ (1), 2i\ (1), -2i\ (1)$

22. $x(x - \frac{1}{2} - \frac{1}{2}i\sqrt{3})(x - \frac{1}{2} + \frac{1}{2}i\sqrt{3}); 0\ (1), \frac{1}{2} \pm \frac{1}{2}i\sqrt{3}\ (1)$

23. $(x - 1)(x + 1)(x - i)(x + i); 1\ (1), -1\ (1), i\ (1), -i\ (1)$

24. $(x - 5)(x + 5)(x - 5i)(x + 5i); \pm 5\ (1), \pm 5i\ (1)$

25. $16(x - \frac{3}{2})(x + \frac{3}{2})(x - \frac{3}{2}i)(x + \frac{3}{2}i); \frac{3}{2}\ (1), -\frac{3}{2}\ (1), \frac{3}{2}i\ (1), -\frac{3}{2}i\ (1)$

26. $(x - 4)(x + 2 - 2i\sqrt{3})(x + 2 + 2i\sqrt{3});$
$4\ (1), -2 \pm 2i\sqrt{3}\ (1)$

27. $(x + 1)(x - 3i)(x + 3i); -1\ (1), 3i\ (1), -3i\ (1)$

28. $(x - 3)(x + 3)(x - \frac{3}{2} - \frac{3}{2}i\sqrt{3})(x - \frac{3}{2} + \frac{3}{2}i\sqrt{3}) \times$
$(x + \frac{3}{2} - \frac{3}{2}i\sqrt{3})(x + \frac{3}{2} + \frac{3}{2}i\sqrt{3}); \pm 3\ (1),$
$\frac{3}{2} \pm \frac{3}{2}i\sqrt{3}\ (1), -\frac{3}{2} \pm \frac{3}{2}i\sqrt{3}\ (1)$

29. $(x - i)^2(x + i)^2; i\ (2), -i\ (2)$

30. $(x - i\sqrt{5})^2(x + i\sqrt{5})^2; \pm i\sqrt{5}\ (2)$

31. $(x - 1)(x + 1)(x - 2i)(x + 2i); 1\ (1), -1\ (1), 2i\ (1), -2i\ (1)$

32. $x^3(x - i\sqrt{7})(x + i\sqrt{7}); 0\ (3), \pm i\sqrt{7}\ (1)$

33. $x(x - i\sqrt{3})^2(x + i\sqrt{3})^2; 0\ (1), i\sqrt{3}\ (2), -i\sqrt{3}\ (2)$

34. $(x + 2)^2(x - 1 - i\sqrt{3})^2(x - 1 + i\sqrt{3})^2; -2\ (2),$
$1 \pm i\sqrt{3}\ (2)$ **35.** $P(x) = x^2 - 2x + 2$ **36.** $P(x) = x^2 - 2x + 3$

37. $Q(x) = x^3 - 3x^2 + 4x - 12$ **38.** $Q(x) = x^3 + x$

39. $P(x) = x^3 - 2x^2 + x - 2$ **40.** $Q(x) = x^3 + x^2 - 4x + 6$

41. $R(x) = x^4 - 4x^3 + 10x^2 - 12x + 5$

42. $S(x) = x^4 + 13x^2 + 36$

43. $T(x) = 6x^4 - 12x^3 + 18x^2 - 12x + 12$

44. $U(x) = 4x^5 + 6x^4 + 4x^3 + 4x^2 - 2$ **45.** $-2, \pm 2i$

46. $3, 2 \pm i$ **47.** $1, \dfrac{1 \pm i\sqrt{3}}{2}$ **48.** $-3, -2 \pm i\sqrt{2}$

49. $2, \dfrac{1 \pm i\sqrt{3}}{2}$ **50.** $2, -1 \pm i\sqrt{2}$ **51.** $-\frac{3}{2}, -1 \pm i\sqrt{2}$

52. $3, \frac{1}{2} \pm \frac{1}{2}i\sqrt{5}$ **53.** $-2, 1, \pm 3i$ **54.** $3, -1, \pm i$

55. $1, \pm 2i, \pm i\sqrt{3}$ **56.** $-2, \pm i, 1 \pm i\sqrt{3}$

57. 3 (multiplicity 2), $\pm 2i$ **58.** $-1, 1 \pm i$

59. $-\frac{1}{2}$ (multiplicity 2), $\pm i$ **60.** $-\frac{1}{2}, 1, -\frac{1}{2} \pm \frac{1}{2}i$

61. 1 (multiplicity 3), $\pm 3i$ **62.** $2, \pm i$

63. (a) $(x - 5)(x^2 + 4)$

(b) $(x - 5)(x - 2i)(x + 2i)$

64. (a) $(x - 2)(x^2 + 2x + 2)$

(b) $(x - 2)(x + 1 - i)(x + 1 + i)$

65. (a) $(x - 1)(x + 1)(x^2 + 9)$

(b) $(x - 1)(x + 1)(x - 3i)(x + 3i)$

66. (a) $(x^2 + 4)^2$ **(b)** $(x - 2i)^2(x + 2i)^2$

67. (a) $(x - 2)(x + 2)(x^2 - 2x + 4)(x^2 + 2x + 4)$

(b) $(x - 2)(x + 2)[x - (1 + i\sqrt{3})][x - (1 - i\sqrt{3})] \times$
$[x + (1 + i\sqrt{3})][x + (1 - i\sqrt{3})]$

68. (a) $x(x - 2)(x + 2)(x^2 + 4)$

(b) $x(x - 2)(x + 2)(x - 2i)(x + 2i)$ **69. (a)** 4 real

(b) 2 real, 2 imaginary   **(c)** 4 imaginary   **70. (a)** $\frac{1}{2} - 2i$ **(b)** $0, i$

(c) $-i$ **(d)** $-1 \pm i\sqrt{2}$ **72. (a)** $x^4 - 2x^3 + 3x^2 - 2x + 2$

(b) $x^2 - (1 + 2i)x - 1 + i$

SECTION 3.7 ■ PAGE 289

1. $-\infty, \infty$ **2.** 2   **3.** $-1, 2$ **4.** $\frac{1}{3}$ **5.** $-2, 3$ **6.** 1

7. (a) $-3, -19, -199, -1999; 5, 21, 201, 2001;$
$1.2500, 1.0417, 1.0204, 1.0020; 0.8333, 0.9615, 0.9804, 0.9980$

(b) $r(x) \to -\infty$ as $x \to 2^-$; $r(x) \to \infty$ as $x \to 2^+$

(c) Horizontal asymptote $y = 1$ **8. (a)** $-14, -86, -896,$
$-8996; 22, 94, 904, 9004; 5.1250, 4.1875, 4.0918, 4.0090;$
$3.2500, 3.8269, 3.9118, 3.9910$

(b) $r(x) \to -\infty$ as $x \to 2^-$; $r(x) \to \infty$ as $x \to 2^+$

(c) Horizontal asymptote $y = 4$

9. (a) $-22, -430, -40,300, -4,003,000;$
$-10, -370, -39,700, -3,997,000;$
$0.3125, 0.0608, 0.0302, 0.0030;$
$-0.2778, -0.0592, -0.0298, -0.0030$

(b) $r(x) \to -\infty$ as $x \to 2^-$; $r(x) \to -\infty$ as $x \to 2^+$

(c) Horizontal asymptote $y = 0$

10. (a) $31, 1183, 128,803, 12,988,003;$
$79, 1423, 131,203, 13,012,003;$
$4.7031, 3.2556, 3.1238, 3.0120;$
$2.0903, 2.7740, 2.8836, 2.9880$

(b) $r(x) \to \infty$ as $x \to 2^-$; $r(x) \to \infty$ as $x \to 2^+$

(c) Horizontal asymptote $y = 3$ **11.** x-intercept 1, y-intercept $-\frac{1}{4}$

12. x-intercept 0, y-intercept 0   **13.** x-intercepts $-1, 2$;
y-intercept $\frac{1}{3}$ **14.** no x-intercept, y-intercept $-\frac{1}{2}$

15. x-intercepts $-3, 3$; no y-intercept   **16.** x-intercept -2,
y-intercept 2   **17.** x-intercept 3, y-intercept 3, vertical $x = 2$;
horizontal $y = 2$ **18.** x-intercept 0, y-intercept 0, vertical $x = -1$,
$x = 2$; horizontal $y = 0$ **19.** x-intercepts $-1, 1$; y-intercept $\frac{1}{4}$;
vertical $x = -2, x = 2$; horizontal $y = 1$ **20.** x-intercepts $-2, 2$;
y-intercept -6; horizontal $y = 2$

21. Vertical $x = 2$; horizontal $y = 0$

22. Vertical $x = -1, x = 1$; horizontal $y = 0$

23. Horizontal $y = 0$ **24.** Horizontal $y = 0$

25. Vertical $x = \frac{1}{2}, x = -1$; horizontal $y = 3$

26. Vertical $x = -\frac{3}{2}, x = 1$; horizontal $y = 2$

27. Vertical $x = \frac{1}{3}, x = -2$; horizontal $y = \frac{5}{3}$

28. Vertical $x = \frac{1}{3}, x = 4$; horizontal $y = \frac{2}{3}$

29. Vertical $x = 0$; horizontal $y = 3$

30. Vertical $x = 0$; horizontal $y = 5$

31. Vertical $x = 1$ **32.** Vertical $x = 2, x = -2$

33.

34.

35.

36.

37.

38.

39.

40.

41.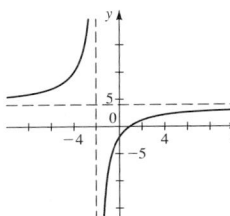

x-intercept 1
y-intercept −2
vertical $x = -2$
horizontal $y = 4$
domain $\{x \mid x \neq -2\}$
range $\{y \mid y \neq 4\}$

42.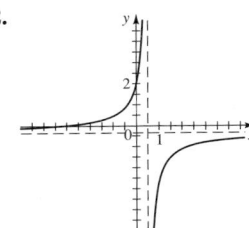

x-intercept −3
y-intercept 2
vertical $x = \frac{1}{2}$
horizontal $y = -\frac{1}{3}$
domain $\{x \mid x \neq \frac{1}{2}\}$
range $\{y \mid y \neq -\frac{1}{3}\}$

43.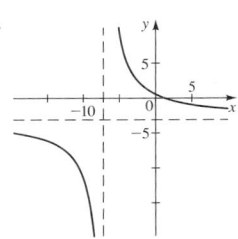

x-intercept $\frac{4}{3}$
y-intercept $\frac{4}{7}$
vertical $x = -7$
horizontal $y = -3$
domain $\{x \mid x \neq -7\}$
range $\{y \mid y \neq -3\}$

44.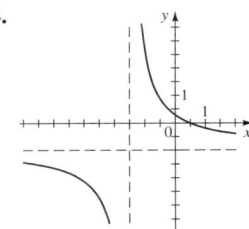

x-intercept $\frac{1}{2}$
y-intercept $\frac{1}{3}$
vertical $x = -\frac{3}{2}$
horizontal $y = -1$
domain $\{x \mid x \neq -\frac{3}{2}\}$
range $\{y \mid y \neq -1\}$

45.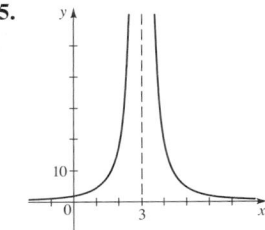

y-intercept 2
vertical $x = 3$
horizontal $y = 0$
domain $\{x \mid x \neq 3\}$
range $\{y \mid y > 0\}$

46.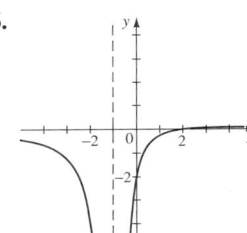

x-intercept 2
y-intercept −2
vertical $x = -1$
horizontal $y = 0$
domain $\{x \mid x \neq -1\}$
range $\{y \mid y \leq 0.1\}$

47.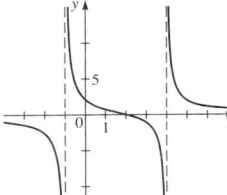

x-intercept 2
y-intercept 2
vertical $x = -1, x = 4$
horizontal $y = 0$
domain $\{x \mid x \neq -1, 4\}$
range $\mathbb{R}$

48.

x-intercept −2
y-intercept $-\frac{2}{3}$
vertical $x = -3, x = 1$
horizontal $y = 0$
domain $\{x \mid x \neq -3, 1\}$
range $\mathbb{R}$

49.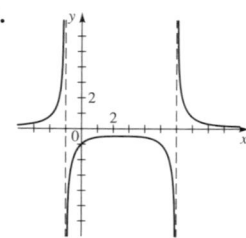
y-intercept -1
vertical $x = -1$, $x = 6$
horizontal $y = 0$
domain $\{x \mid x \neq -1, 6\}$
range $\{y \mid y \leq -0.5 \text{ or } y > 0\}$

55.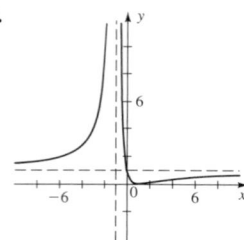
x-intercept 1
y-intercept 1
vertical $x = -1$
horizontal $y = 1$
domain $\{x \mid x \neq -1\}$
range $\{y \mid y \geq 0\}$

50.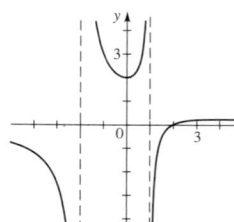
x-intercept 2
y-intercept 2
vertical $x = -2$, $x = 1$
horizontal $y = 0$
domain $\{x \mid x \neq -2, 1\}$
range $\{y \mid y \leq 0.2 \text{ or } y \geq 2\}$

56.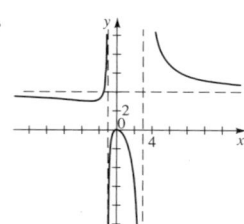
x-intercept 0
y-intercept 0
vertical $x = -1$, $x = 3$
horizontal $y = 4$
domain $\{x \mid x \neq -1, 3\}$
range $\{y \mid y \leq 0 \text{ or } y \geq 2.9\}$

51.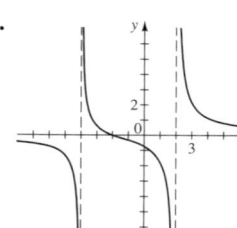
x-intercept -2
y-intercept $-\frac{3}{4}$
vertical $x = -4$, $x = 2$
horizontal $y = 0$
domain $\{x \mid x \neq -4, 2\}$
range $\mathbb{R}$

57.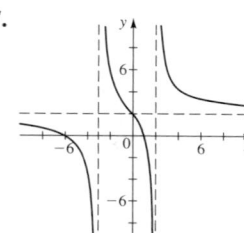
x-intercepts -6, 1
y-intercept 2
vertical $x = -3$, $x = 2$
horizontal $y = 2$
domain $\{x \mid x \neq -3, 2\}$
range $\mathbb{R}$

52.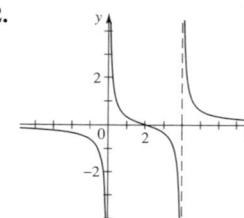
x-intercept 2
vertical $x = 0$, $x = 4$
horizontal $y = 0$
domain $\{x \mid x \neq 0, 4\}$
range $\mathbb{R}$

58.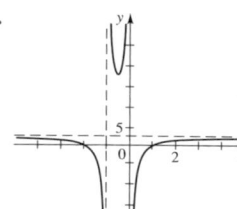
x-intercepts 1, -2
vertical $x = -1$, $x = 0$
horizontal $y = 2$
domain $\{x \mid x \neq -1, 0\}$
range $\{y \mid y < 2 \text{ or } y \geq 18.4\}$

53.
x-intercepts -2, 1
y-intercept $\frac{2}{3}$
vertical $x = -1$, $x = 3$
horizontal $y = 1$
domain $\{x \mid x \neq -1, 3\}$
range $\mathbb{R}$

59.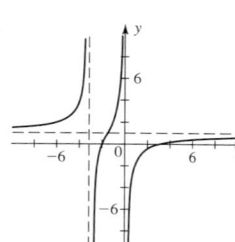
x-intercepts -2, 3
vertical $x = -3$, $x = 0$
horizontal $y = 1$
domain $\{x \mid x \neq -3, 0\}$
range $\mathbb{R}$

60.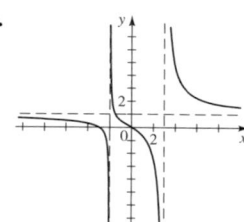
x-intercepts 0, -3
y-intercept 0
vertical $x = -2$, $x = 3$,
horizontal $y = 1$
domain $\{x \mid x \neq -2, 3\}$
range $\mathbb{R}$

54.
x-intercepts 0, -2
y-intercept 0
vertical $x = 1$, $x = 4$
horizontal $y = 2$
domain $\{x \mid x \neq 1, 4\}$
range
$\{y \mid y \leq -7.8 \text{ or } y \geq -0.04\}$

61.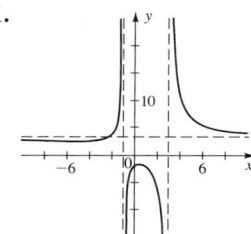

y-intercept -2
vertical $x = -1, x = 3$
horizontal $y = 3$
domain $\{x \mid x \neq -1, 3\}$
range $\{y \mid y \leq -1.5 \text{ or } y \geq 2.4\}$

67.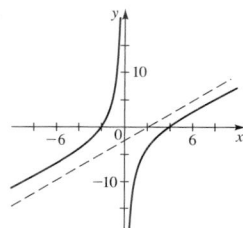

slant $y = x - 2$
vertical $x = 0$

62.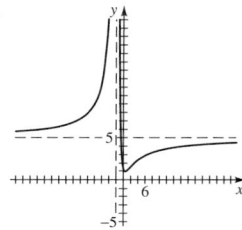

y-intercept $\frac{5}{4}$
vertical $x = -2$
horizontal $y = 5$
domain $\{x \mid x \neq -2\}$
range $\{y \mid y \geq 1.0\}$

68.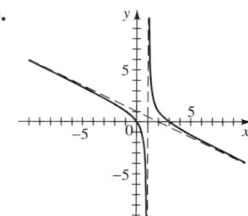

slant $y = -\frac{1}{2}x + 1$
vertical $x = 1$

63.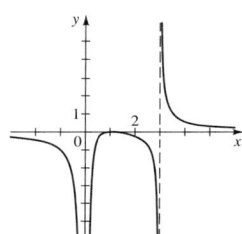

x-intercept 1
vertical $x = 0, x = 3$
horizontal $y = 0$
domain $\{x \mid x \neq 0, 3\}$
range $\mathbb{R}$

69.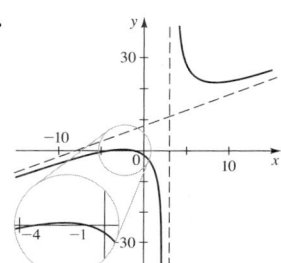

slant $y = x + 8$
vertical $x = 3$

64.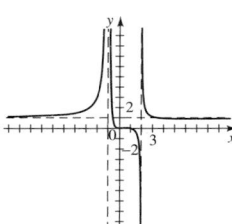

x-intercepts 0, 1
y-intercept 0
vertical $x = -1, x = 2$
horizontal $y = 1$
domain $\{x \mid x \neq -1, 2\}$
range $\mathbb{R}$

70.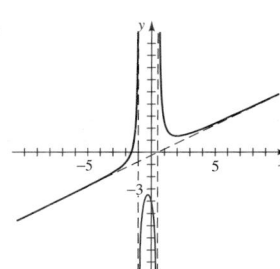

slant $y = \frac{1}{2}x - \frac{1}{4}$
vertical $x = -1, x = \frac{1}{2}$

65.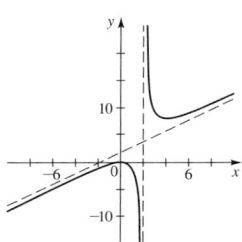

slant $y = x + 2$
vertical $x = 2$

71.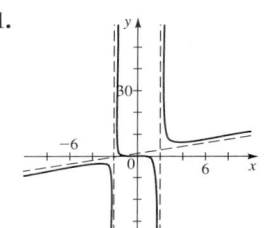

slant $y = x + 1$
vertical $x = 2, x = -2$

66.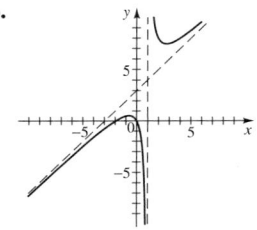

slant $y = x + 3$
vertical $x = 1$

72.

slant $y = 2x$
vertical $x = -1, x = 1$

73. 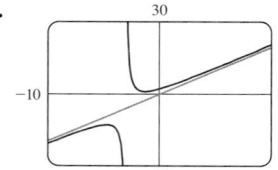 vertical $x = -3$

74. vertical $x = 0$, $x = 2$

75. 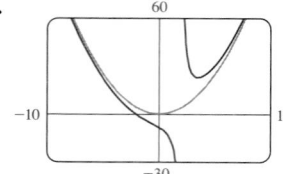 vertical $x = 2$

76. 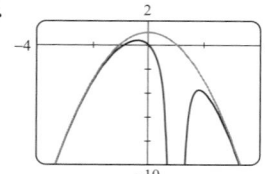 vertical $x = 1$

77. 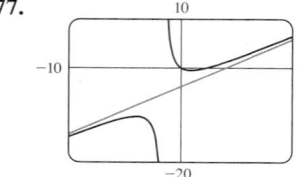 vertical $x = -1.5$
x-intercepts 0, 2.5
y-intercept 0, local
maximum $(-3.9, -10.4)$
local minimum $(0.9, -0.6)$
end behavior: $y = x - 4$

78. 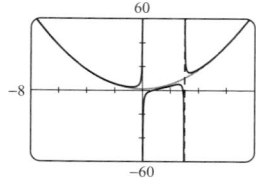 vertical $x = 0$, $x = 3$
x-intercept 0.82, local
maximum $(2.56, 4.88)$
local minima $(-0.80, 2.63)$,
$(3.38, 14.76)$
end behavior $y = x^2 + 1$

79. 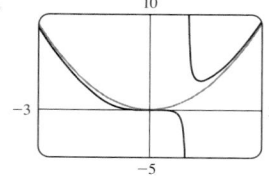 vertical $x = 1$
x-intercept 0
y-intercept 0
local minimum $(1.4, 3.1)$
end behavior: $y = x^2$

80. 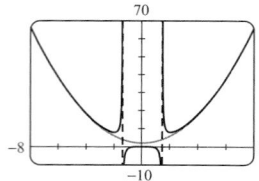 vertical $x = -1.41$, $x = 1.41$
x-intercept 0
y-intercept 0
local maximum $(0, 0)$
local minima $(-2, 8)$, $(2, 8)$
end behavior $y = x^2 + 2$

81. 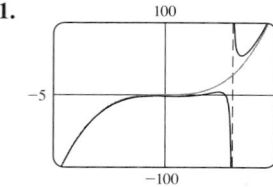 vertical $x = 3$
x-intercepts 1.6, 2.7
y-intercept -2
local maxima $(-0.4, -1.8)$,
$(2.4, 3.8)$,
local minima $(0.6, -2.3)$,
$(3.4, 54.3)$
end behavior $y = x^3$

82. 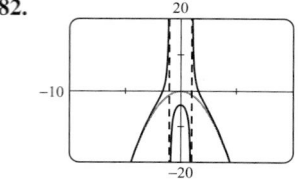 vertical $x = -1$, $x = 1$
x-intercepts -1.6, 1.6
y-intercept -4
local maximum $(0, -4)$
end behavior $y = -x^2$

83. (a) 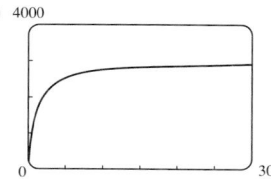 **(b)** It levels off at 3000.

84. (a) 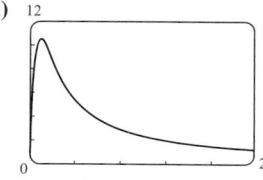 **(b)** It decreases to 0.

85. (a) 2.50 mg/L **(b)** It decreases to 0. **(c)** 16.61 h

86. 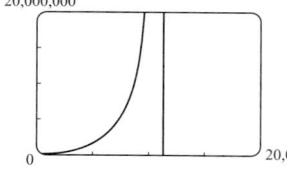 The vertical asymptote represents the escape velocity from the earth's gravitational pull.

87. 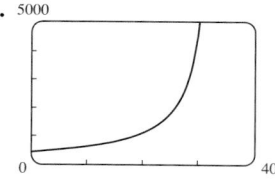 If the speed of the train approaches the speed of sound, then the pitch increases indefinitely (a sonic boom).

88. (a) $y = \dfrac{55x}{x - 55}$

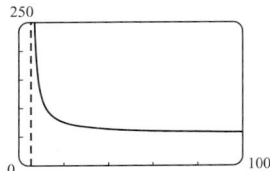

(b) y approaches 55 mm   **(c)** y approaches ∞

CHAPTER 3 REVIEW ■ PAGE 292

1. (a) $f(x) = (x + 2)^2 - 3$ **2. (a)** $f(x) = -2(x - 3)^2 + 30$

(b)

(b)

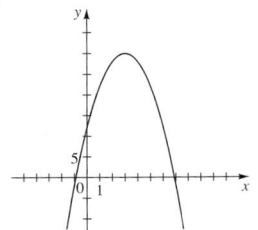

3. (a) $g(x) = -(x - 4)^2 + 17$ **4. (a)** $h(x) = -3(x - 1)^2 + 3$

(b)

(b)

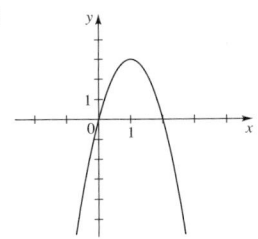

5. Minimum $f(-1) = -7$
6. Maximum $g\left(-\tfrac{1}{2}\right) = \tfrac{5}{4}$
7. 68 feet   **8.** \$7500, 1500 units

9.

10.

11.

12.

13.

14.

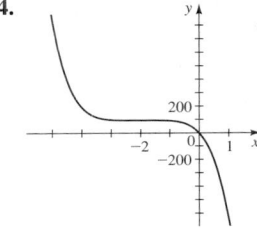

15. (a) 0 (multiplicity 3),
  2 (multiplicity 2)

(b)

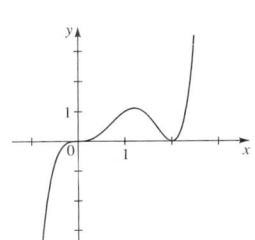

16. (a) 0 (multiplicity 1),
  -1 (multiplicity 3),
  1 (multiplicity 2)

(b)

17.

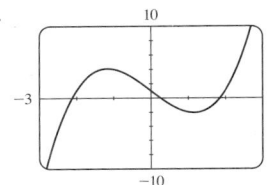

x-intercepts $-2.1, 0.3, 1.9$
y-intercept 1
local maximum $(-1.2, 4.1)$
local minimum $(1.2, -2.1)$
$y \to \infty$ as $x \to \infty$
$y \to -\infty$ as $x \to -\infty$

18.

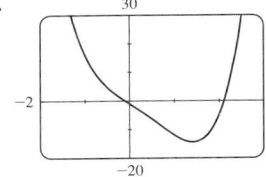

x-intercepts $-0.5, 0.7,$ and 2.9
y-intercept -2
local maximum $(2, 6)$
local minimum $(0, -2)$
$y \to \infty$ as $x \to -\infty$ and
$y \to -\infty$ as $x \to \infty$

19.

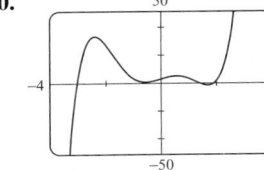

x-intercepts $-0.1, 2.1$
y-intercept -1
local minimum $(1.4, -14.5)$
$y \to \infty$ as $x \to \infty$
$y \to \infty$ as $x \to -\infty$

20.

x-intercepts $-3.0, 1.3,$ and 1.9
y-intercept 3
local maxima $(-2.4, 33.2)$ and
$(0.5, 5.0)$
local minima $(-0.6, 0.6)$ and
$(1.6, -1.6)$
$y \to -\infty$ as $x \to -\infty$ and
$y \to \infty$ as $x \to \infty$

21. (a) $S = 13.8x(100 - x^2)$ **(b)** $0 \le x \le 10$
(c) 6000

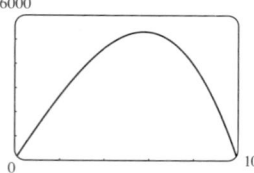

(d) 5.8 in.

22. (a) $V(x) = 600x - x^3$

(b) 6000

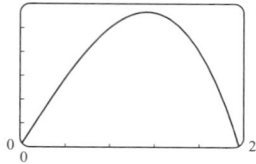

(c) 14.14 in. by 28.28 in.

In answers 23–30 the first polynomial given is the quotient, and the second is the remainder.
23. $x - 1, 3$ **24.** $x + 4, 0$ **25.** $x^2 + 3x + 23, 94$
26. $x^2 - x + 3, -19$ **27.** $x^3 - 5x^2 + 17x - 83, 422$
28. $2x^3 - 5x^2 + 20x - 80, 308$ **29.** $2x - 3, 12$
30. $x^2 + x - 4, 12$ **31.** 3   **32.** 21   **35.** 8   **36.** 0
37. (a) $\pm 1, \pm 2, \pm 3, \pm 6, \pm 9, \pm 18$ **(b)** 2 or 0 positive, 3 or 1
negative   **38. (a)** $\pm 1, \pm 2, \pm 4, \pm \frac{1}{2}, \pm \frac{1}{3}, \pm \frac{2}{3}, \pm \frac{4}{3}, \pm \frac{1}{6}$
(b) 0 positive, 0, 2, or 4 negative

39. (a) $-4, 0, 4$ **40. (a)** $-1, 0, 4$
(b)   **(b)**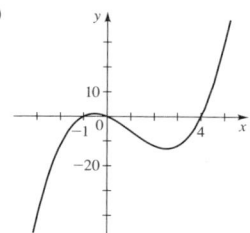

41. (a) $-2, 0$ (multiplicity 2), 1   **42. (a)** $-2, -1, 1, 2$
(b)   **(b)**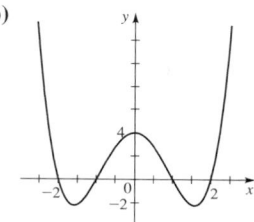

43. (a) $-2, -1, 2, 3$ **44. (a)** $-2, 2$
(b)   **(b)**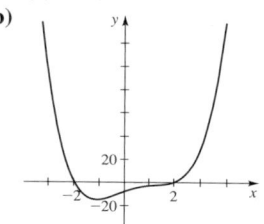

45. (a) $-\frac{1}{2}, 1$

(b)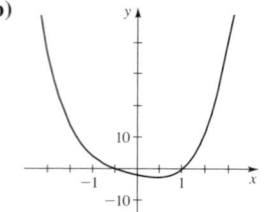

46. (a) $-\frac{1}{3}$ (multiplicity 2),
1 (multiplicity 3)

(b)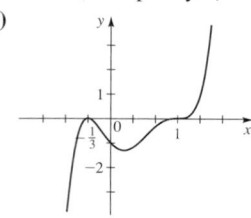

47. $3 + i$ **48.** $-3 - 2i$ **49.** $8 - i$ **50.** $2 + 8i$ **51.** $\frac{6}{5} + \frac{8}{5}i$
52. $\frac{41}{25} - \frac{12}{25}i$ **53.** i **54.** $-2 + 2i$ **55.** 2   **56.** -20
57. $4x^3 - 18x^2 + 14x + 12$ **58.** $x^4 - 8x^3 + 25x^2 - 72x + 144$
59. No; since the complex conjugates of imaginary zeros will also
be zeros, the polynomial would have 8 zeros, contradicting the
requirement that it have degree 4.   **61.** $-3, 1, 5$ **62.** $-3, -1, \frac{3}{2}$
63. $-1 \pm 2i, -2$ (multiplicity 2)   **64.** $-4, -1, -1 \pm \sqrt{6}$
65. $\pm 2, 1$ (multiplicity 3)   **66.** $-3, 3, \pm 3i$ **67.** $\pm 2, \pm 1 \pm i\sqrt{3}$
68. $\frac{1}{2}, -\frac{1}{3}$ (multiplicity 2)   **69.** $1, 3, \dfrac{-1 \pm i\sqrt{7}}{2}$ **70.** $\pm 3i, \pm i\sqrt{6}$
71. $x = -0.5, 3$ **72.** $x = -3, -2, 4$ **73.** $x \approx -0.24, 4.24$
74. $x \approx 1.34$ **75.** 2, $P(x) = (x - 2)(x^2 + 2x + 2)$
76. $\pm 1, P(x) = (x - 1)(x + 1)(x^2 + 4)$

77.

78.

79.

80.

81.

82.

83.

x-intercept 3
y-intercept -0.5
vertical $x = -3$
horizontal $y = 0.5$
no local extrema

84.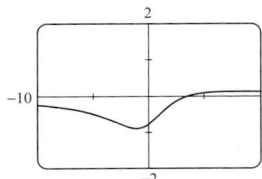

x-intercept 3.5
y-intercept -0.78
horizontal $y = 0$
local minimum $(-1.11, -0.90)$
local maximum $(8.11, 0.12)$

85.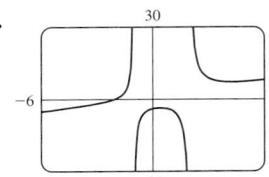

x-intercept -2
y-intercept -4
vertical $x = -1, x = 2$
slant $y = x + 1$
local maximum
$(0.425, -3.599)$
local minimum $(4.216, 7.175)$

86.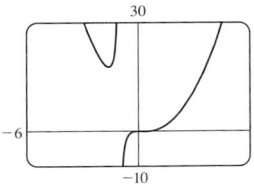

x-intercepts $0, \frac{1}{2}$
y-intercept 0; vertical $x = -1$
local maximum $(0, 0)$
local minimums $(-1.57, 17.90)$,
$(0.32, -0.03)$
end behavior
$y = 2x^2 - 3x + 3$

87. $(-2, -28), (1, 26), (2, 68), (5, 770)$

CHAPTER 3 TEST ▪ PAGE 295

1. $f(x) = \left(x - \frac{1}{2}\right)^2 - \frac{25}{4}$

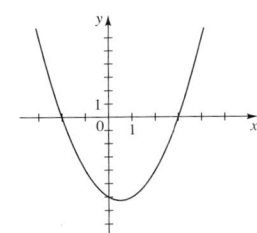

2. Minimum $f\left(-\frac{3}{2}\right) = -\frac{3}{2}$ **3. (a)** 2500 ft   **(b)** 1000 ft

4.

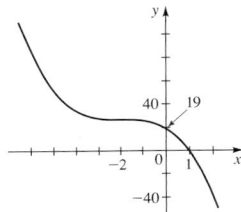

5. (a) $x^3 + 2x^2 + 2, 9$ **(b)** $x^3 + 2x^2 + \frac{1}{2}, \frac{15}{2}$
6. (a) $\pm 1, \pm 3, \pm\frac{1}{2}, \pm\frac{3}{2}$ **(b)** $2(x - 3)\left(x - \frac{1}{2}\right)(x + 1)$

(c) $-1, \frac{1}{2}, 3$ **(d)**

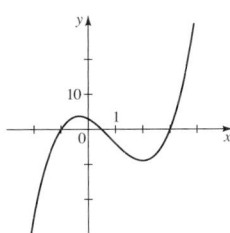

7. (a) $7 + i$ **(b)** $-1 - 5i$ **(c)** $18 + i$ **(d)** $\frac{6}{25} - \frac{17}{25}i$
(e) 1   **(f)** $6 - 2i$ **8.** $3, -1 \pm i$ **9.** $(x - 1)^2(x - 2i)(x + 2i)$
10. $x^4 + 2x^3 + 10x^2 + 18x + 9$
11. (a) 4, 2, or 0 positive; 0 negative
(c) 0.17, 3.93

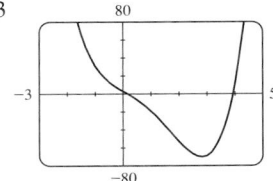

(d) Local minimum $(2.8, -70.3)$
12. (a) r, u **(b)** s **(c)** s **(d)**

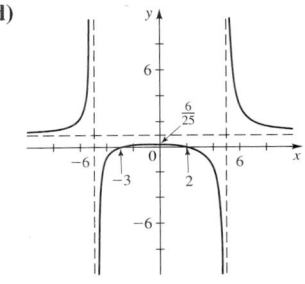

(e) $x^2 - 2x - 5$

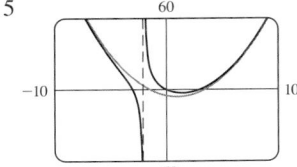

FOCUS ON MODELING ▪ PAGE 298

1. (a) $y = -0.275428x^2 + 19.7485x - 273.5523$
(b)

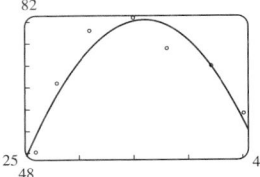

(c) 35.85 lb/in^2
2. (a) $y = -0.0000002783333x^2 + 0.0184655x - 166.732$
(b)   **(c)** ≈ 135 bushels/acre

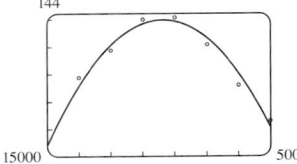

3. (a) $y = 0.00203708x^3 - 0.104521x^2 + 1.966206x + 1.45576$
(b) 22

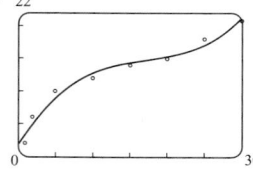

(c) 43 vegetables   **(d)** 2.0 s
4. (a) $y = -55.908x^4 + 1414.88x^3 - 12199.1x^2 + 42577.2x - 25714.6$
(b) 44000

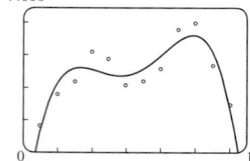

(c) Yes, since there are two peaks in sales.
5. (a) Degree 2
(b) $y = -16.0x^2 + 51.8429x + 4.20714$

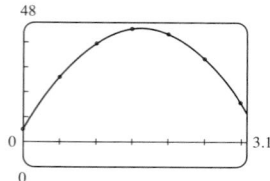

(c) 0.3 s and 2.9 s   **(d)** 46.2 ft
6. (a) $y = 0.0120536x^2 - 0.490357x + 4.96571$
(b) 5.1   **(c)** 19.0 min

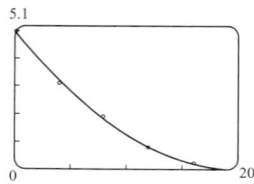

CHAPTER 4

SECTION 4.1 ▪ PAGE 307

1. $5; \frac{1}{25}, 1, 25, 15{,}625$ **2. (a)** III   **(b)** I   **(c)** II   **(d)** IV
3. (a) downward   **(b)** right   **4.** principal, interest rate per year, number of times interest is compounded per year, number of years, amount after t years; $112.65   **5.** 2.000, 7.103, 77.880, 1.587
6. 0.577, 20.115, 0.095, 0.760   **7.** 0.885, 0.606, 0.117, 1.837
8. 0.668, 0.467, 0.833, 0.681
9.

10.

11.

12.

13.

14.

15.

16.

17.

18.

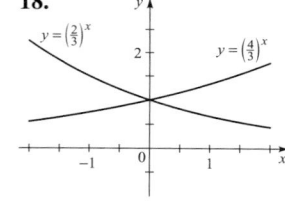

19. $f(x) = 3^x$ **20.** $f(x) = 5^x$
21. $f(x) = \left(\frac{1}{4}\right)^x$
22. $f(x) = \left(\frac{1}{2}\right)^x$ **23.** II   **24.** I
25. $\mathbb{R}, (-\infty, 0), y = 0$ **26.** $\mathbb{R}, (0, \infty), y = 0$

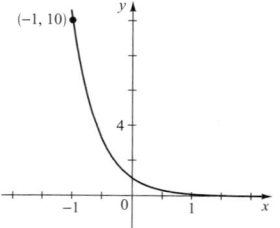

27. $\mathbb{R}, (-3, \infty), y = -3$

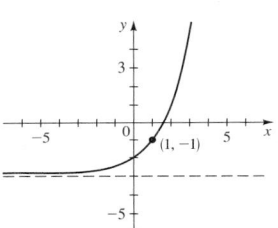

28. $\mathbb{R}, (0, \infty), y = 0$

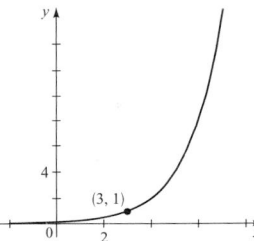

29. $\mathbb{R}, (4, \infty), y = 4$

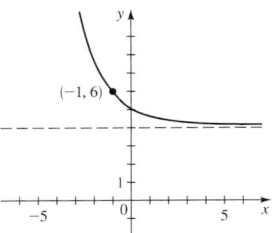

30. $\mathbb{R}, (-\infty, 6), y = 6$

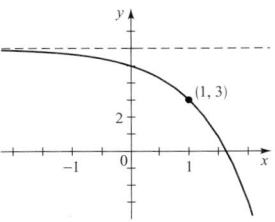

31. $\mathbb{R}, (0, \infty), y = 0$

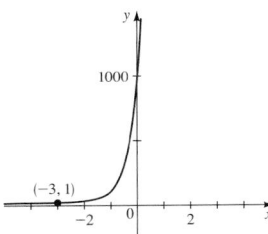

32. $\mathbb{R}, (-\infty, 0), y = 0$

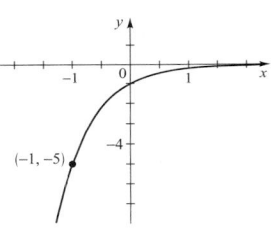

33. $\mathbb{R}, (1, \infty), y = 1$

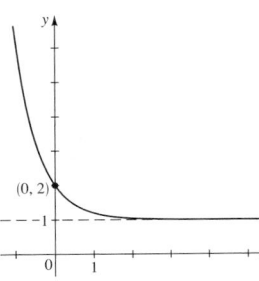

34. $\mathbb{R}, (-\infty, 1), y = 1$

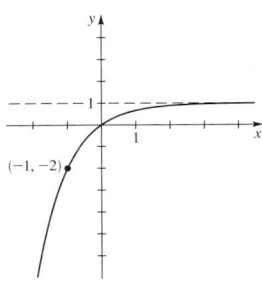

35. $\mathbb{R}, (-\infty, 3), y = 3$

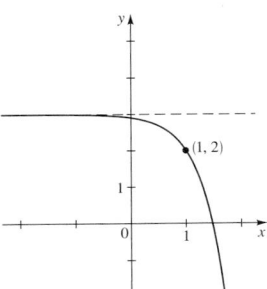

36. $\mathbb{R}, (1, \infty), y = 1$

37. (a)

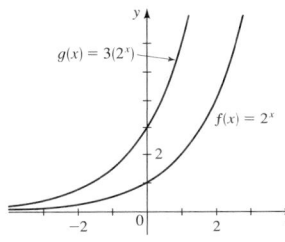

(b) The graph of g is steeper than that of f.

38. (a)

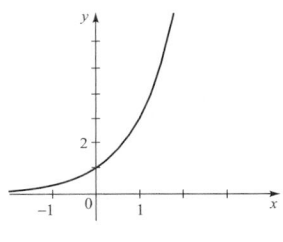

(b) The graphs of $f(x)$ and $g(x)$ are the same.

39.

41. (a)

(i)

(ii)

(iii)

The graph of f ultimately increases much more quickly than that of g.

(b) 1.2, 22.4

42. (a)

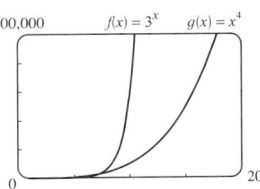

(b) $-0.80, 1.52, 7.17$

43.

44.

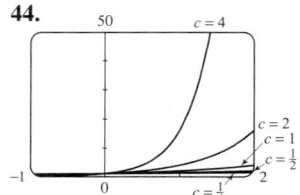

The larger the value of c, the more rapidly the graph increases.

The larger the value of c, the more rapidly the graph increases.

45. (a) Increasing on $(-\infty, 0.50]$; decreasing on $[0.50, \infty)$
(b) $(0, 1.78]$ **46. (a)** Increasing on $(-1.44, \infty)$, decreasing on
$(-\infty, -1.44)$ **(b)** $(-0.53, \infty)$ **47. (a)** $1500 \cdot 2^t$
(b) $25,165,824,000$ **48. (a)** $320 \cdot 2^t$ **(b)** $81,920$
49. $5203.71, $5415.71, $5636.36, $5865.99, $6104.98, $6353.71
50. $5256.25, $5525.39, $5808.08, $6104.98, $6416.79, $6744.25
51. (a) $11,605.41   **(b)** $13,468.55   **(c)** $15,630.80
52. (a) $2628.17   **(b)** $2694.70   **(c)** $2904.57
53. (a) $519.02   **(b)** $538.75   **(c)** $726.23   **54. (a)** $5026.16
(b) $5634.10   **(c)** $6315.58   **55.** $7678.96   **56.** $67,121.04
57. 8.30% **58.** 5.61%

SECTION 4.2 ▪ PAGE 312

1. natural; 2.71828   **2.** principal, interest rate per year, number of
years; amount after t years; $112.75   **3.** 20.085, 1.259, 2.718, 0.135
4. 0.135, 0.059, 403.429, 0.368

5.

x	y
-2	0.41
-1	1.10
-0.5	1.82
0	3
0.5	4.95
1	8.15
2	22.17

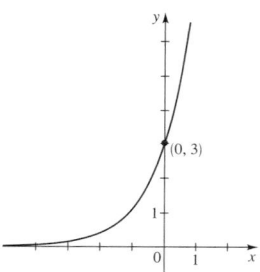

6.

x	y
-3	8.96
-2	5.44
-1	3.30
0	2
1	1.21
2	0.74
3	0.45

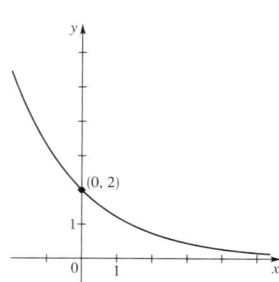

7. $\mathbb{R}, (-\infty, 0), y = 0$

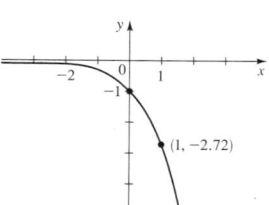

8. $\mathbb{R}, (-\infty, 1), y = 1$

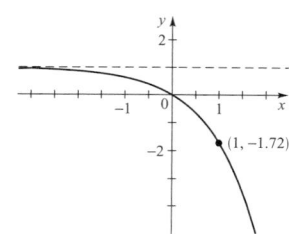

9. $\mathbb{R}, (-1, \infty), y = -1$

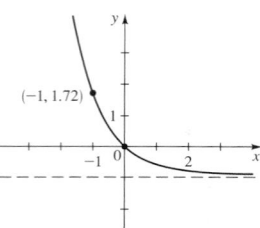

10. $\mathbb{R}, (-\infty, 0), y = 0$

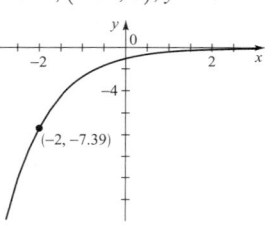

11. $\mathbb{R}, (0, \infty), y = 0$

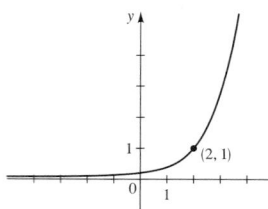

12. $\mathbb{R}, (4, \infty), y = 4$

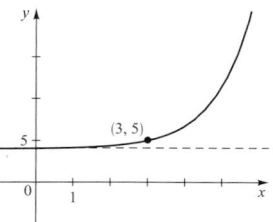

13. $\mathbb{R}, (-3, \infty), y = -3$

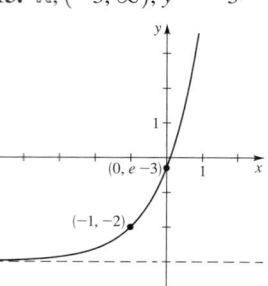

14. $\mathbb{R}, (-\infty, -2), y = -2$

15. (a)

16. (a)

17. (a)

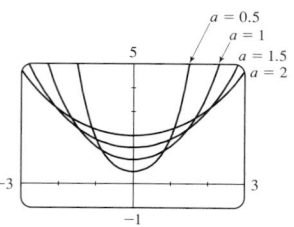

(b) The larger the value of a, the wider the graph.
18. Local minimum $(0.37, 0.69)$
19. Local minimum $\approx (0.27, 1.75)$
20. 27.4 mg   **21. (a)** 13 kg   **(b)** 6.6 kg
22. (a) 6 g   **(b)** 1 g

23. (a) 0
(b) 50.6 ft/s, 69.2 ft/s
(c)

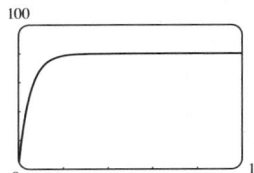

24. (a) 2.7 lb
(b) 4.9 lb
(c)

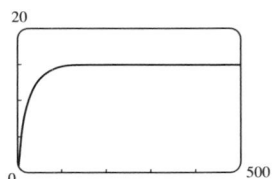

5.

Logarithmic form	Exponential form
$\log_8 8 = 1$	$8^1 = 8$
$\log_8 64 = 2$	$8^2 = 64$
$\log_8 4 = \frac{2}{3}$	$8^{2/3} = 4$
$\log_8 512 = 3$	$8^3 = 512$
$\log_8 \frac{1}{8} = -1$	$8^{-1} = \frac{1}{8}$
$\log_8 \frac{1}{64} = -2$	$8^{-2} = \frac{1}{64}$

(d) 80 ft/s
25. (a) 100   **(b)** 482, 999, 1168   **(c)** 1200
26. (a) 200
(b)

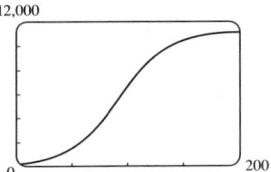

(d) 15 lb; yes

(c) 11,200

6.

Logarithmic form	Exponential form
$\log_4 64 = 3$	$4^3 = 64$
$\log_4 2 = \frac{1}{2}$	$4^{1/2} = 2$
$\log_4 8 = \frac{3}{2}$	$4^{3/2} = 8$
$\log_4 \frac{1}{16} = -2$	$4^{-2} = \frac{1}{16}$
$\log_4 \frac{1}{2} = -\frac{1}{2}$	$4^{-1/2} = \frac{1}{2}$
$\log_4 \frac{1}{32} = -\frac{5}{2}$	$4^{-5/2} = \frac{1}{32}$

27. (a) 11.79 billion, 11.97 billion
(b)

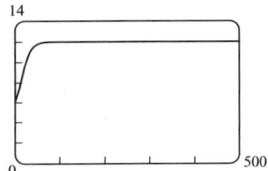

(c) 12 billion

28. 1.6 ft   **29.** $7213.18, $7432.86, $7659.22, $7892.48,
$8132.84, $8380.52   **30.** $7736.20, $8549.82, $9449.01,
$10442.77, $11541.05, $12754.83   **31. (a)** $2145.02
(b) $2300.55   **(c)** $3043.92   **32. (a)** $4221.81
(b) $5092.47   **(c)** $6142.69   **33. (a)** $768.05   **(b)** $769.22
(c) $769.82   **(d)** $770.42   **34. (a)** $10,169.99   **(b)** $11,466.64
(c) $13,728.05   **(d)** $18,530.94   **35.** (a) is best.   **36.** (a) is best.
37. (a) $A(t) = 5000e^{0.09t}$ **(b)**

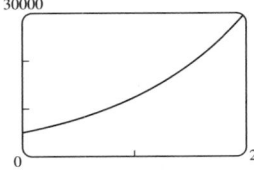

(c) After 17.88 yr

SECTION 4.3 ■ PAGE 322

1. 10^x

x	10^3	10^2	10^1	10^0	10^{-1}	10^{-2}	10^{-3}	$10^{1/2}$
$\log x$	3	2	1	0	-1	-2	-3	$\frac{1}{2}$

2. $9; 1, 0, -1, 2, \frac{1}{2}$
3. (a) $\log_5 125 = 3$ **(b)** $5^2 = 25$ **4. (a)** III   **(b)** II   **(c)** I
(d) IV

7. (a) $5^2 = 25$ **(b)** $5^0 = 1$ **8. (a)** $10^{-1} = 0.1$ **(b)** $8^3 = 512$
9. (a) $8^{1/3} = 2$ **(b)** $2^{-3} = \frac{1}{8}$ **10. (a)** $3^4 = 81$ **(b)** $8^{2/3} = 4$
11. (a) $e^x = 5$ **(b)** $e^5 = y$ **12. (a)** $e^2 = x + 1$ **(b)** $e^4 = x - 1$
13. (a) $\log_5 125 = 3$ **(b)** $\log_{10} 0.0001 = -4$
14. (a) $\log_{10} 1000 = 3$ **(b)** $\log_{81} 9 = \frac{1}{2}$ **15. (a)** $\log_8 \frac{1}{8} = -1$
(b) $\log_2 \frac{1}{8} = -3$ **16. (a)** $\log_4 0.125 = -\frac{3}{2}$ **(b)** $\log_7 343 = 3$
17. (a) $\ln 2 = x$ **(b)** $\ln y = 3$ **18. (a)** $\ln 0.5 = x + 1$
(b) $\ln t = 0.5x$ **19. (a)** 1   **(b)** 0   **(c)** 2   **20. (a)** 4   **(b)** 3
(c) 1   **21. (a)** 2   **(b)** 2   **(c)** 10   **22. (a)** 5   **(b)** 17   **(c)** 0
23. (a) -3 **(b)** $\frac{1}{2}$ **(c)** -1 **24. (a)** 3   **(b)** $\frac{1}{2}$ **(c)** $\frac{1}{4}$
25. (a) 37   **(b)** 8   **(c)** $\sqrt{5}$ **26. (a)** π **(b)** 5   **(c)** 87
27. (a) $-\frac{2}{3}$ **(b)** 4   **(c)** -1 **28. (a)** $\frac{1}{4}$ **(b)** $-\frac{1}{2}$ **(c)** $\frac{3}{2}$
29. (a) 32   **(b)** 4   **30. (a)** 625   **(b)** -1 **31. (a)** 5   **(b)** 27
32. (a) $\frac{1}{2}$ **(b)** 16   **33. (a)** 100   **(b)** 25   **34. (a)** 10   **(b)** 5
35. (a) 2   **(b)** 4   **36. (a)** 36   **(b)** 27   **37. (a)** 0.3010
(b) 1.5465   **(c)** -0.1761 **38. (a)** 1.6990   **(b)** 0.1505
(c) 0.6276   **39. (a)** 1.6094   **(b)** 3.2308   **(c)** 1.0051
40. (a) 3.2958   **(b)** 2.0001   **(c)** 4.0000

41.

42.

43.

44.

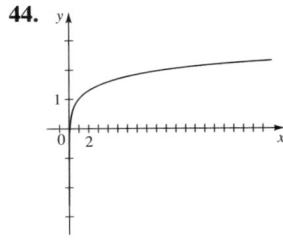

45. $y = \log_5 x$ **46.** $y = \log_2 x$ **47.** $y = \log_9 x$
48. $y = \log_3 x$ **49.** I   **50.** II
51.

52.

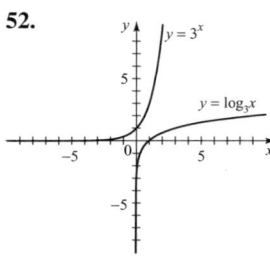

53. $(4, \infty), \mathbb{R}, x = 4$

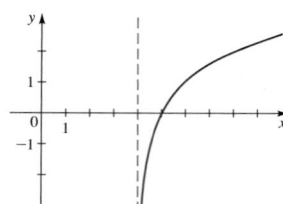

54. $(0, \infty), \mathbb{R}, x = 0$

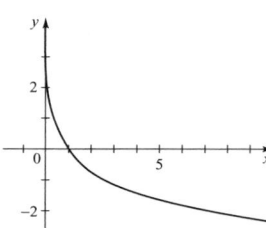

55. $(-\infty, 0), \mathbb{R}, x = 0$

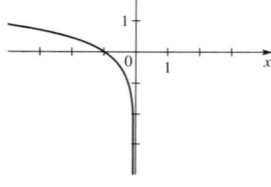

56. $(-2, \infty), \mathbb{R}, x = -2$

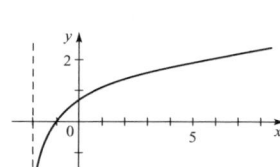

57. $(0, \infty), \mathbb{R}, x = 0$

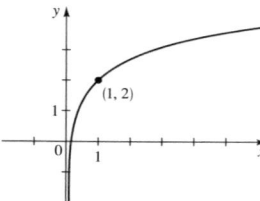

58. $(1, \infty), \mathbb{R}, x = 1$

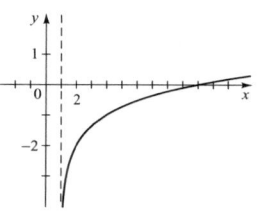

59. $(0, \infty), \mathbb{R}, x = 0$

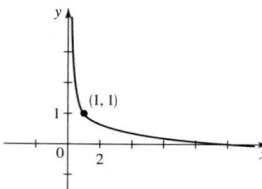

60. $(-\infty, 0), \mathbb{R}, x = 0$

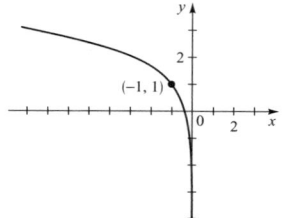

61. $(0, \infty), [0, \infty), x = 0$ **62.** $(-\infty, 0) \cup (0, \infty), \mathbb{R}, x = 0$

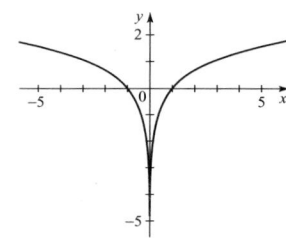

63. $(-3, \infty)$ **64.** $(-\infty, 4)$ **65.** $(-\infty, -1) \cup (1, \infty)$
66. $(0, 1)$ **67.** $(0, 2)$ **68.** $[2, 10)$

69.

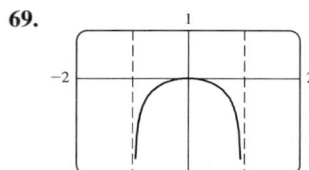

domain $(-1, 1)$
vertical asymptotes $x = 1$,
$x = -1$
local maximum $(0, 0)$

70.

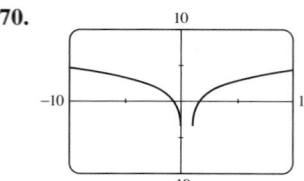

domain $(-\infty, 0) \cup (1, \infty)$
vertical asymptotes $x = 0$
and $x = 1$
no local extrema

71.

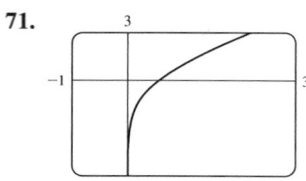

domain $(0, \infty)$
vertical asymptote $x = 0$
no maximum or minimum

72.

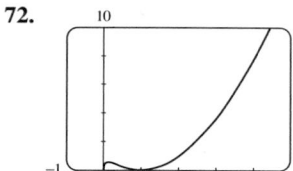

domain $(0, \infty)$
vertical asymptote none
local minimum $(1, 0)$
local maximum $(0.14, 0.54)$

73.

domain $(0, \infty)$
vertical asymptote $x = 0$
horizontal asymptote $y = 0$
local maximum
$\approx (2.72, 0.37)$

74.

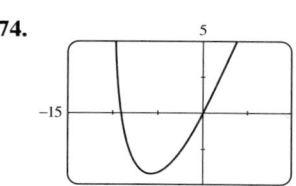

domain $(-10, \infty)$
vertical asymptote $x = -10$
local minimum
$\approx (-5.87, -3.62)$

75. $(f \circ g)(x) = 2^{x+1}, (-\infty, \infty); (g \circ f)(x) = 2^x + 1, (-\infty, \infty)$
76. $(f \circ g)(x) = 3^{x^2+1}, (-\infty, \infty); (g \circ f)(x) = 3^{2x} + 1, (-\infty, \infty)$
77. $(f \circ g)(x) = \log_2(x - 2), (2, \infty);$
$(g \circ f)(x) = \log_2 x - 2, (0, \infty);$
78. $(f \circ g)(x) = 2 \log x, (0, \infty); (g \circ f)(x) = (\log x)^2, (0, \infty)$
79. The graph of f grows more slowly than g.
80. (b) 13.50
81. (a)

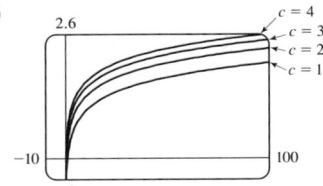

(b) The graph of $f(x) = \log(cx)$ is the graph of $f(x) = \log(x)$ shifted upward $\log c$ units.

82. (a)

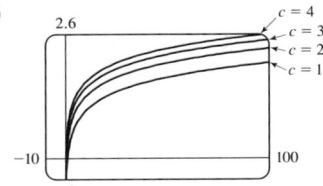

(b) As c increases, the graph of $f(x) = c \log(x)$ stretches vertically by a factor of c.

83. (a) $(1, \infty)$ **(b)** $f^{-1}(x) = 10^{2^x}$ **84. (a)** (e, ∞)

(b) $f^{-1}(x) = e^{e^x}$ **85. (a)** $f^{-1}(x) = \log_2\left(\dfrac{x}{1 - x}\right)$

(b) $(0, 1)$ **86.** 891.69 M **87.** 2602 yr **88.** 42.86 h
89. 11.5 yr, 9.9 yr, 8.7 yr **90.** 0.58 h **91.** 5.32, 4.32

SECTION 4.4 ■ PAGE 329

1. sum; $\log_5 25 + \log_5 125 = 2 + 3$
2. difference; $\log_5 25 - \log_5 125 = 2 - 3$
3. times; $10 \cdot \log_5 25$ **4. (a)** $2 \log x + \log y - \log z$
(b) $\log\left(\dfrac{x^2 y}{z}\right)$ **5.** $10, e$; Change of Base; $\log_7 12 = \dfrac{\log 12}{\log 7} = 1.277$
6. True **7.** $\frac{3}{2}$ **8.** 5 **9.** 2 **10.** $-\frac{3}{2}$ **11.** 3 **12.** 2 **13.** 3
14. -2 **15.** 200 **16.** 99 **17.** 4 **18.** 200 **19.** $1 + \log_2 x$
20. $\log_3 5 + \log_3 y$ **21.** $\log_2 x + \log_2(x - 1)$
22. $\log_5 x - \log_5 2$ **23.** $10 \log 6$ **24.** $\frac{1}{2} \ln z$
25. $\log_2 A + 2 \log_2 B$ **26.** $\frac{1}{4} \log_6 17$ **27.** $\log_3 x + \frac{1}{2} \log_3 y$
28. $10(\log_2 x + \log_2 y)$ **29.** $\frac{1}{3} \log_5(x^2 + 1)$
30. $2 \log_a x - (\log_a y + 3 \log_a z)$ **31.** $\frac{1}{2}(\ln a + \ln b)$
32. $\frac{1}{3}(\ln 3 + 2 \ln r + \ln s)$ **33.** $3 \log x + 4 \log y - 6 \log z$
34. $2 \log a - (4 \log b + \frac{1}{2} \log c)$
35. $\log_2 x + \log_2(x^2 + 1) - \frac{1}{2} \log_2(x^2 - 1)$
36. $\frac{1}{2}[\log_5(x - 1) - \log_5(x + 1)]$ **37.** $\ln x + \frac{1}{2}(\ln y - \ln z)$
38. $\ln 3 + 2 \ln x - 10 \ln(x + 1)$ **39.** $\frac{1}{4} \log(x^2 + y^2)$
40. $\log x - \frac{1}{3} \log(1 - x)$
41. $\frac{1}{2}[\log(x^2 + 4) - \log(x^2 + 1) - 2 \log(x^3 - 7)]$
42. $\frac{1}{2} \log x + \frac{1}{4} \log y + \frac{1}{8} \log z$
43. $3 \ln x + \frac{1}{2} \ln(x - 1) - \ln(3x + 4)$
44. $x - [\log x + \log(x^2 + 1) + \log(x^4 + 2)]$
45. $\log_3 160$ **46.** $\log(6\sqrt{7})$ **47.** $\log_2(AB/C^2)$ **48.** $\log_5(x + 1)$

49. $\log\left(\dfrac{x^4(x - 1)^2}{\sqrt[3]{x^2 + 1}}\right)$ **50.** $\ln\dfrac{a^2 - b^2}{c^2}$ **51.** $\ln(5x^2(x^2 + 5)^3)$

52. $\log_5 \dfrac{x^2 y^4}{z^6}$ **53.** $\log\left(\dfrac{x^2}{x - 3}\right)$ **54.** $\log_a \dfrac{bd^c}{s^r}$ **55.** 2.321928

56. 0.430677 **57.** 2.523719 **58.** 2.523658 **59.** 0.493008
60. 3.503061 **61.** 3.482892 **62.** 0.368743
63.   **64.**

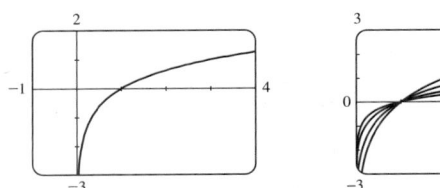

The graph of $y = \log_c x$ is obtained from the graph of $y = \ln x$ by either shrinking or stretching vertically by a factor of $1/(\ln c)$ depending on whether $\ln c > 1$ or $\ln c < 1$ (respectively).

66. $\log_2 7$ **68.** 30 **69. (a)** $P = c/W^k$ **(b)** 1866, 64
70. (a) $S = cA^k$ **71. (a)** $M = -2.5 \log B + 2.5 \log B_0$

SECTION 4.5 ■ PAGE 338

1. (a) $e^x = 25$ **(b)** $x = \ln 25$ **(c)** 3.219
2. (a) $\log 3(x - 2) = \log x$ **(b)** $3(x - 2) = x$ **(c)** 3 **3.** 1.3979
4. -0.6021 **5.** -0.9730 **6.** 0.8283 **7.** -0.5850 **8.** 1.2325
9. 1.2040 **10.** 0.1783 **11.** 0.0767 **12.** 0.0194 **13.** 0.2524
14. 1.6958 **15.** 1.9349 **16.** -29.3426 **17.** -43.0677
18. 0.0455 **19.** 2.1492 **20.** -3.1144 **21.** 6.2126 **22.** 0.5624
23. -2.9469 **24.** 0.6232 **25.** -2.4423 **26.** -1.3863
27. 14.0055 **28.** 9.2708 **29.** $\ln 2 \approx 0.6931, 0$ **30.** 1.0986
31. $\frac{1}{2} \ln 3 \approx 0.5493$ **32.** 1.3863 **33.** ± 1 **34.** $2, -1$ **35.** $0, \frac{4}{3}$

36. $\dfrac{-1 \pm \sqrt{5}}{2}$ **37.** $e^{10} \approx 22026$ **38.** 0.7183 **39.** 0.01

40. 1004 **41.** $\frac{95}{3}$ **42.** -25 **43.** -7 **44.** $-2, 3$ **45.** 5
46. 2, 4 **47.** 5 **48.** 4 **49.** $\frac{13}{12}$ **50.** 3 **51.** 4 **52.** 5 **53.** 6
54. 1.7290 **55.** $\frac{3}{2}$ **56.** $1, 0.0185, 53.9574$ **57.** $1/\sqrt{5} \approx 0.4472$
58. 43,046,721 **59.** 2.21 **60.** 0.01, 1.47 **61.** 0.00, 1.14
62. $-1.96, 1.06$ **63.** -0.57 **64.** 1.38 **65.** 0.36
66. $-0.89, 0.71$ **67.** $2 < x < 4$ or $7 < x < 9$ **68.** $8 \leq x \leq 16$
69. $\log 2 < x < \log 5$ **70.** $-\sqrt{2} < x < \sqrt{2}$

71. $f^{-1}(x) = \dfrac{\ln x}{2 \ln 2}$ **72.** $f^{-1}(x) = \dfrac{\ln x}{\ln 3} - 1$

73. $f^{-1}(x) = 2^x + 1$ **74.** $f^{-1}(x) = \dfrac{10^x}{3}$

75. (a) \$6435.09 **(b)** 8.24 yr **76. (a)** \$7328.73 **(b)** 3.46 yr
77. 6.33 yr **78.** 2.34 yr **79.** 8.15 yr **80.** 9.25% **81.** 13 days
82. 10 s **83. (a)** 7337 **(b)** 1.73 yr **84. (a)** 7.87 lumens
(b) 86.6 ft **85. (a)** $P = P_0 e^{-h/k}$ **(b)** 56.47 kPa
86. (a) $T = 200e^{-0.11t} + 20$ **(b)** 42.2°F
87. (a) $t = -\frac{5}{13} \ln(1 - \frac{13}{60} I)$ **(b)** 0.218 s

88. (a) $t = -\dfrac{1}{k} \ln\left(\dfrac{M - P}{C}\right)$ **(b)** 23 months

(c)

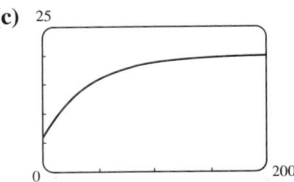

SECTION 4.6 ■ PAGE 350

1. (a) $n(t) = 10 \cdot 2^{2t/3}$ **(b)** 1.05×10^8 **(c)** After 14.9 h
2. (a) $n(t) = 25.2^{t/5}$ **(b)** 303 **(c)** After 76.4 h
3. (a) 3125 **(b)** 317,480 **(c)** *n* (millions)

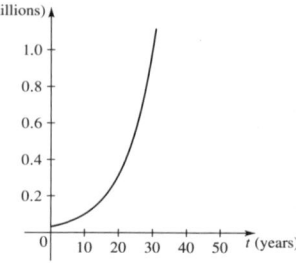

4. (a) 2298 **(b)** 18,385 **(c)** *n* (thousands)

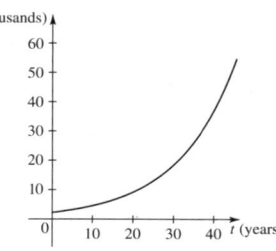

5. (a) $n(t) = 18,000e^{0.08t}$ **(b)** 34,137
(c) *n(t)*

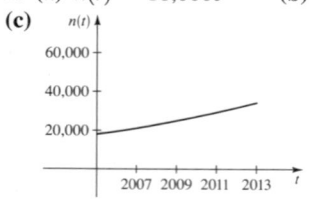

6. (a) $n(t) = 12e^{0.012t}$ **(b)** 12,742,000
(c) *n* (millions)

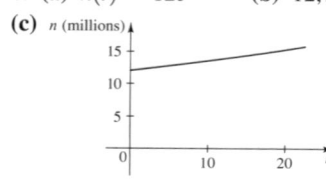

7. (a) 233 million **(b)** 181 million **8. (a)** 392 **(b)** 73
9. (a) $n(t) = 112,000 \cdot 2^{t/18}$ **(b)** $n(t) = 112,000e^{0.0385t}$
(c) *n* (millions) **(d)** In the year 2045

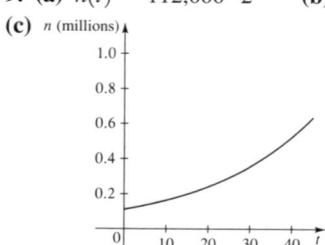

10. (a) $n(t) = 350,000 \cdot 2^{t/25}$ **(b)** $n(t) = 350,000e^{0.0277t}$
(c) *n* (millions) **(d)** In the year 2072

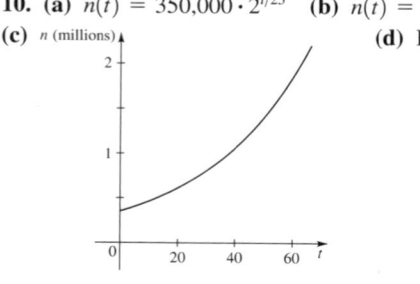

11. (a) 20,000 **(b)** $n(t) = 20,000e^{0.1096t}$ **(c)** About 48,000
(d) 2017 **12. (a)** 100 **(b)** $n(t) = 100e^{0.4055t}$ **(c)** 43,812
(d) 16.3 yr **13. (a)** $n(t) = 8600e^{0.1508t}$ **(b)** About 11,600
(c) 4.6 h **14. (a)** 104% **(b)** 50 **(c)** $n(t) = 50e^{1.04t}$
(d) 5400 **(e)** 6.64 h **15. (a)** $n(t) = 29.76e^{0.012936t}$ million
(b) 53.5 yr **(c)** 38.55 million **16. (a)** 2029 **(b)** 2049
17. (a) $m(t) = 22 \cdot 2^{-t/1600}$ **(b)** $m(t) = 22e^{-0.000433t}$ **(c)** 3.9 mg
(d) 463.4 yr **18. (a)** $m(t) = 10 \cdot 2^{-t/30}$ **(b)** $n(t) = 10e^{-0.0231t}$
(c) 1.6 g **(d)** 70 yr **19.** 18 yr **20.** 130 s **21.** 149 h
22. (a) 3.82 days **(b)** 9 days **23.** 3560 yr **24.** 4360 yr
25. (a) 210°F **(b)** 153°F **(c)** 28 min
26. (a) $T(t) = 60 + 38.6e^{-0.1947t}$ **(b)** 6 h **27. (a)** 137°F
(b) 116 min **28.** 63°C

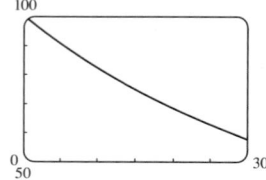

29. (a) 2.3 **(b)** 3.5 **(c)** 8.3 **30.** 7.5, basic **31. (a)** 10^{-3} M
(b) 3.2×10^{-7} M **32. (a)** 2.5×10^{-5} M **(b)** 5.0×10^{-8} M
33. $4.8 \le \text{pH} \le 6.4$ **34.** 1.58×10^{-4} to 1.58×10^{-3}
35. $\log 20 \approx 1.3$ **36.** 2500 times **37.** Twice as intense
38. 2.5 times **39.** 8.2 **40.** 6.3×10^{-3} W/m² **41.** 73 dB
42. 25 **43. (b)** 106 dB

CHAPTER 4 REVIEW ■ PAGE 353

1. 0.089, 9.739, 55.902 **2.** 0.653, 18.775, 135.765
3. 11.954, 2.989, 2.518 **4.** 0.644, 26.888, 174.098
5. $\mathbb{R}, (0, \infty), y = 0$ **6.** $\mathbb{R}, (0, \infty), y = 0$

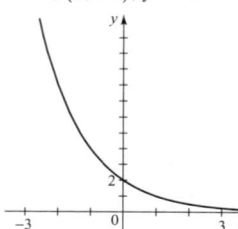

7. $\mathbb{R}, (3, \infty), y = 3$ **8.** $\mathbb{R}, (-5, \infty), y = -5$

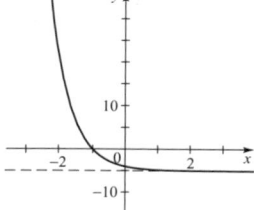

9. $(1, \infty), \mathbb{R}, x = 1$ **10.** $(-\infty, 0), \mathbb{R}, x = 0$

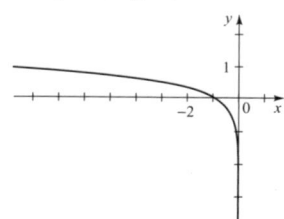

11. $(0, \infty)$, $\mathbb{R}$, $x = 0$

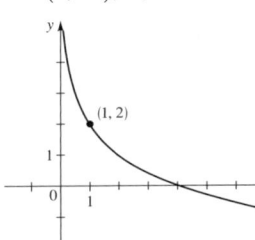

12. $(-4, \infty)$, $\mathbb{R}$, $x = -4$

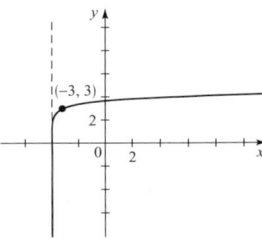

13. $\mathbb{R}$, $(-1, \infty)$, $y = -1$ **14.** $\mathbb{R}$, $(0, \infty)$, $y = 0$

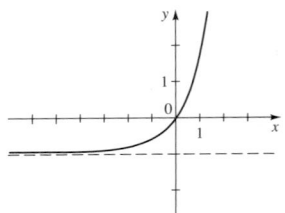

15. $(0, \infty)$, $\mathbb{R}$, $x = 0$

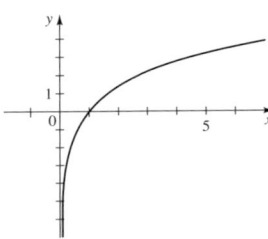

16. $(-\infty, 0) \cup (0, \infty)$, $\mathbb{R}$, $x = 0$

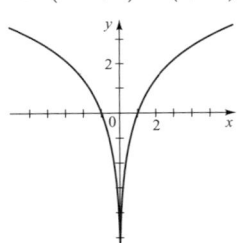

17. $\left(-\infty, \frac{1}{2}\right)$ **18.** $(-1, 2)$ **19.** $(-\infty, -2) \cup (2, \infty)$
20. $(-\infty, 0) \cup (0, \infty)$ **21.** $2^{10} = 1024$ **22.** $6^x = 37$
23. $10^y = x$ **24.** $e^{17} = c$ **25.** $\log_2 64 = 6$ **26.** $\log_{49} \frac{1}{7} = -\frac{1}{2}$
27. $\log 74 = x$ **28.** $\ln m = k$ **29.** 7 **30.** 0 **31.** 45
32. -6 **33.** 6 **34.** $\frac{3}{2}$ **35.** -3 **36.** 13 **37.** $\frac{1}{2}$ **38.** 49
39. 2 **40.** $\frac{5}{2}$ **41.** 92 **42.** 3 **43.** $\frac{2}{3}$ **44.** 2
45. $\log A + 2 \log B + 3 \log C$ **46.** $\log_2 x + \frac{1}{2} \log_2(x^2 + 1)$
47. $\frac{1}{2}[\ln(x^2 - 1) - \ln(x^2 + 1)]$
48. $\log 4 + 3 \log x - [2 \log y + 5 \log(x - 1)]$
49. $2 \log_5 x + \frac{3}{2} \log_5(1 - 5x) - \frac{1}{2} \log_5(x^3 - x)$
50. $\frac{1}{3} \ln(x^4 + 12) - [\ln(x + 16) + \frac{1}{2} \ln(x - 3)]$ **51.** $\log 96$
52. $\log(x^3 y^4)$ **53.** $\log_2\left(\dfrac{(x - y)^{3/2}}{(x^2 + y^2)^2}\right)$ **54.** $\log_5\left(\dfrac{2(x + 1)}{\sqrt[3]{3x + 7}}\right)$

55. $\log\left(\dfrac{x^2 - 4}{\sqrt{x^2 + 4}}\right)$ **56.** $\ln \sqrt{(x - 4)(x^2 + 4x)^5}$ **57.** 5 **58.** 7
59. 2.60 **60.** 1.58 **61.** -1.15 **62.** 3.07 **63.** $-4, 2$ **64.** 1
65. -15 **66.** 3 **67.** 3 **68.** 1.68 **69.** 0.430618 **70.** 2.602452
71. 2.303600 **72.** -0.614023
73.

vertical asymptote
$x = -2$
horizontal asymptote
$y = 2.72$
no maximum or minimum

74.

horizontal asymptote $y = 0$
one local minimum
$\approx (-0.5, -0.13)$

75.

vertical asymptotes
$x = -1$, $x = 0$, $x = 1$
local maximum
$\approx (-0.58, -0.41)$

76.

vertical asymptote $x = 0$
one local minimum
$\approx (0.5, 1.19)$

77. 2.42 **78.** $-0.64, 2$ **79.** $0.16 < x < 3.15$
80. $(-\infty, -0.41) \cup (0.71, 4.31)$
81. Increasing on $(-\infty, 0]$ and $[1.10, \infty)$, decreasing on $[0, 1.10]$
82. $y = \dfrac{a}{e^a - 1}(x - 1)$

83. 1.953445 **84.** -0.147839 **85.** -0.579352 **86.** 1.198970
87. $\log_4 258$ **88.** $f^{-1}(x) = \log_3(\log_2 x)$; domain $(1, \infty)$,
range $(-\infty, \infty)$ **89.** (a) \$16,081.15 (b) \$16,178.18
(c) \$16,197.64 (d) \$16,198.31 **90.** (a) \$5,664.98 (b) 4.04 yr
(c) 3.96 yr **91.** 1.83 yr **92.** 15.4 yr **93.** 4.341% **94.** 3.247%
95. (a) $n(t) = 30e^{0.15t}$ (b) 55 (c) 19 yr **96.** (a) 45 min
(b) 156,250 **97.** (a) 9.97 mg (b) 1.39×10^5 yr
98. (a) 5 days (b) 19% **99.** (a) $n(t) = 150e^{-0.0004359t}$
(b) 97.0 mg (c) 2520 yr **100.** (a) 12 g
(b) $m(t) = 12e^{-0.173t}$ (c) 7.1 g (d) 25 days
101. (a) $n(t) = 1500e^{0.1515t}$ (b) 7940 **102.** 43 min
103. 7.9, basic **104.** 1.26×10^{-2} M **105.** 8.0
106. 2.51×10^{10}

CHAPTER 4 TEST ■ PAGE 356

1. (a) $\mathbb{R}$, $(4, \infty)$, $y = 4$ **(b)** $(-3, \infty)$, $\mathbb{R}$, $x = -3$

   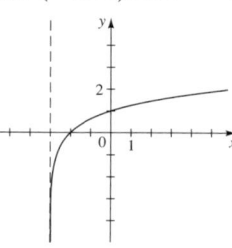

2. (a) $\log_6 25 = 2x$ **(b)** $e^3 = A$

3. (a) 36   **(b)** 3   **(c)** $\frac{3}{2}$ **(d)** 3   **(e)** $\frac{2}{3}$ **(f)** 2

4. $\frac{1}{3}[\log(x + 2) - 4 \log x - \log(x^2 + 4)]$

5. $\ln\left(\dfrac{x\sqrt{3 - x^4}}{(x^2 + 1)^2}\right)$ **6. (a)** 4.32   **(b)** 0.77   **(c)** 5.39   **(d)** 2

7. (a) $n(t) = 1000e^{2.07944t}$ **(b)** 22,627   **(c)** 1.3 h

(d)

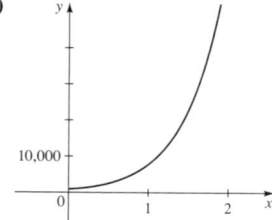

8. (a) $A(t) = 12{,}000\left(1 + \dfrac{0.056}{12}\right)^{12t}$ **(b)** \$14,195.06

(c) 9.249 yr   **9. (a)** $A(t) = 3e^{-0.069t}$ **(b)** 0.048 g
(c) after 3.6 min   **10.** 1995 times more intense

FOCUS ON MODELING ■ PAGE 363

1. (a)

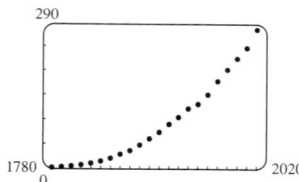

(b) $y = ab^t$, where $a = 1.180609 \times 10^{-15}$, $b = 1.0204139$, and y is the population in millions in the year t **(c)** 515.9 million
(d) 207.8 million   **(e)** No

2. (a)

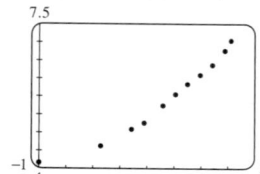

(b) $y = at^b$, where $a = 4.9622$ and $b = 2.0027$ **(c)** 44.792 m

3. (a) Yes   **(b)** Yes, the scatter plot appears linear.

(c) $\ln E = 4.551436 + 0.092383t$, where t is years since 1970 and E is expenditure in billions of dollars
(d) $E = 94.76838139e^{at}$, where $a = 0.0923827621$
(e) 3478.5 billion dollars

4. (a)

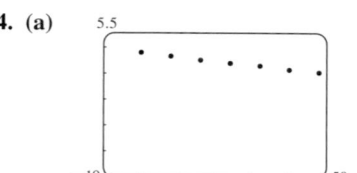

(b) $y = ab^t$, where $a = 4.79246$ and $b = 0.99642$
(c) 192.8 h
5. (a) $I_0 = 22.7586444$, $k = 0.1062398$
(b)

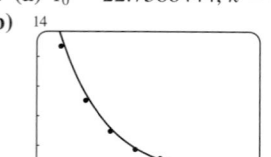

(c) 47.3 ft
6. (a) $y = at^b$, where $a = 49.70030$ and $b = -0.15437$;
$y = ab^t$, where $a = 44.82418$ and $b = 0.99317$
(b)

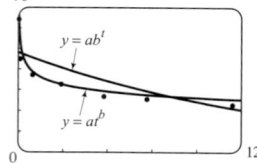

(c) The power function
7. (a) $S = 0.14A^{0.64}$

(b)

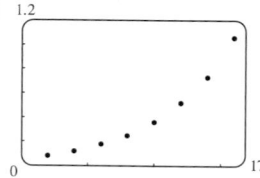

(c) 4 species
8. $y = ab^x$, where $a = 2.414$ and $b = 1.05452$
9. (a)

(b)

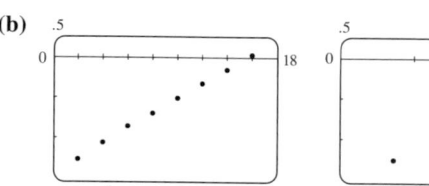

(c) Exponential function
(d) $y = ab^x$ where $a = 0.057697$ and $b = 1.200236$

10. (a)

(b)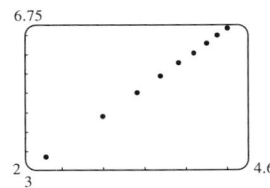

(c) The power function
(d) $y = ax^b$, where $a = 0.893421326$ and $b = 1.50983$

11. (a) $y = \dfrac{c}{1 + ae^{-bx}}$, where $a = 49.10976596$,

$b = 0.4981144989$, and $c = 500.855793$ **(b)** 10.58 days
12. (a) $y = a + b \ln t$ where $a = -7154.888$, $b = 1061.007$, and y
is metric tons of coal produced in the year t **(b)** 915 metric tons

CUMULATIVE REVIEW TEST FOR
CHAPTERS 2, 3, AND 4 ▪ PAGE 367

1. (a) $(-\infty, \infty)$ **(b)** $[-4, \infty)$ **(c)** $12, 0, 0, 2, 2\sqrt{3}$, undefined
(d) $x^2 - 4$, $\sqrt{x + 6}$, $-4 + h^2$ **(e)** $\frac{1}{8}$
(f) $f \circ g = x + 4 - \sqrt{x + 4}$, $g \circ f = |x - 2|$, $f(g(12)) = 0$,
$g(f(12)) = 10$ **(g)** $g^{-1}(x) = x^2 - 4$, $x \ge 0$
2. (a) $4, 4, 4, 0, 1$ **(b)**

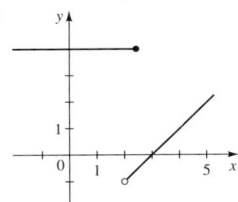

3. (a) $f(x) = -2(x - 2)^2 + 13$ **(b)** Maximum 13
(c)

(d) Increasing on $(-\infty, 2]$;
decreasing on $[2, \infty)$
(e) Shift upward 5 units
(f) Shift to the left 3 units

4. f, D; g, C; r, A; s, F; h, B; k, E
5. (a) $\pm 1, \pm 2, \pm 4, \pm 8, \pm\frac{1}{2}$ **(b)** $2, 4, -\frac{1}{2}$
(c) $P(x) = 2(x - 2)(x - 4)\left(x + \frac{1}{2}\right)$ **(d)**

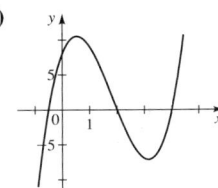

6. (a) 1 (multiplicity 2); $-1, 1 + i, 1 - i$ (multiplicity 1)
(b) $Q(x) = (x - 1)^2(x + 1)(x - 1 - i)(x - 1 + i)$
(c) $Q(x) = (x - 1)^2(x + 1)(x^2 - 2x + 2)$

7. x-intercepts $0, -2$; y-intercept 0; horizontal
asymptote $y = 3$; vertical asymptotes $x = 2$
and $x = -1$

8.

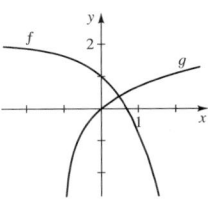

9. (a) -4 **(b)** $5 \log x + \frac{1}{2} \log(x - 1) - \log(2x - 3)$
10. (a) 4 **(b)** $\ln 2, \ln 4$ **11. (a)** $\$29{,}396.15$
(b) After 6.23 years   **(c)** 12.837 years
12. (a) $P(t) = 120e^{0.0565t}$ **(b)** 917 **(c)** After 49.8 months

CHAPTER 5

SECTION 5.1 ▪ PAGE 375

1. (a) $(0, 0), 1$ **(b)** $x^2 + y^2 = 1$ **(c) (i)** 0 **(ii)** 0 **(iii)** 0
(iv) 0 **2. (a)** terminal   **(b)** $(0, 1), (-1, 0), (0, -1), (1, 0)$
9. $-\frac{4}{5}$ **10.** $\frac{24}{25}$ **11.** $-2\sqrt{2}/3$ **12.** $\sqrt{21}/5$ **13.** $3\sqrt{5}/7$
14. $\sqrt{5}/3$ **15.** $P\left(\frac{4}{5}, \frac{3}{5}\right)$ **16.** $P\left(2\sqrt{2}/3, -\frac{1}{3}\right)$
17. $P\left(-\sqrt{5}/3, \frac{2}{3}\right)$ **18.** $P\left(2\sqrt{5}/5, -\sqrt{5}/5\right)$
19. $P\left(-\sqrt{2}/3, -\sqrt{7}/3\right)$ **20.** $P\left(-\frac{2}{5}, \sqrt{21}/5\right)$
21. $t = \pi/4, \left(\sqrt{2}/2, \sqrt{2}/2\right); t = \pi/2, (0, 1);$
$t = 3\pi/4, \left(-\sqrt{2}/2, \sqrt{2}/2\right); t = \pi, (-1, 0);$
$t = 5\pi/4, \left(-\sqrt{2}/2, -\sqrt{2}/2\right); t = 3\pi/2, (0, -1);$
$t = 7\pi/4, \left(\sqrt{2}/2, -\sqrt{2}/2\right); t = 2\pi, (1, 0)$
22. $t = \pi/6, \left(\sqrt{3}/2, \frac{1}{2}\right); t = \pi/3, \left(\frac{1}{2}, \sqrt{3}/2\right); t = \pi/2, (0, 1);$
$t = 2\pi/3, \left(-\frac{1}{2}, \sqrt{3}/2\right); t = 5\pi/6, \left(-\sqrt{3}/2, \frac{1}{2}\right); t = \pi, (-1, 0);$
$t = 7\pi/6, \left(-\sqrt{3}/2, -\frac{1}{2}\right); t = 4\pi/3, \left(-\frac{1}{2}, -\sqrt{3}/2\right);$
$t = 3\pi/2, (0, -1); t = 5\pi/3, \left(\frac{1}{2}, -\sqrt{3}/2\right);$
$t = 11\pi/6, \left(\sqrt{3}/2, -\frac{1}{2}\right); t = 2\pi, (1, 0)$
23. $(0, 1)$ **24.** $(0, -1)$ **25.** $\left(-\sqrt{3}/2, \frac{1}{2}\right)$ **26.** $\left(-\sqrt{3}/2, -\frac{1}{2}\right)$
27. $\left(\frac{1}{2}, -\sqrt{3}/2\right)$ **28.** $\left(\frac{1}{2}, -\sqrt{3}/2\right)$ **29.** $\left(-\frac{1}{2}, \sqrt{3}/2\right)$
30. $(0, -1)$ **31.** $\left(-\sqrt{2}/2, -\sqrt{2}/2\right)$ **32.** $\left(\sqrt{3}/2, -\frac{1}{2}\right)$
33. (a) $\left(-\frac{3}{5}, \frac{4}{5}\right)$ **(b)** $\left(\frac{3}{5}, -\frac{4}{5}\right)$ **(c)** $\left(-\frac{3}{5}, -\frac{4}{5}\right)$ **(d)** $\left(\frac{3}{5}, \frac{4}{5}\right)$
34. (a) $\left(\frac{3}{4}, -\sqrt{7}/4\right)$ **(b)** $\left(\frac{3}{4}, \sqrt{7}/4\right)$ **(c)** $\left(-\frac{3}{4}, \sqrt{7}/4\right)$
(d) $\left(-\frac{3}{4}, -\sqrt{7}/4\right)$
35. (a) $\pi/4$ **(b)** $\pi/3$ **(c)** $\pi/3$ **(d)** $\pi/6$
36. (a) $\pi/6$ **(b)** $\pi/6$ **(c)** $\pi/3$ **(d)** $\pi/4$
37. (a) $2\pi/7$ **(b)** $2\pi/9$ **(c)** $\pi - 3 \approx 0.14$
(d) $2\pi - 5 \approx 1.28$
38. (a) $\pi/5$ **(b)** $2\pi/7$ **(c)** $2\pi - 6 \approx 0.28$
(d) $7 - 2\pi \approx 0.72$
39. (a) $\pi/3$ **(b)** $\left(-\frac{1}{2}, \sqrt{3}/2\right)$
40. (a) $\pi/3$ **(b)** $\left(-\frac{1}{2}, -\sqrt{3}/2\right)$
41. (a) $\pi/4$ **(b)** $\left(-\sqrt{2}/2, \sqrt{2}/2\right)$
42. (a) $\pi/3$ **(b)** $\left(\frac{1}{2}, \sqrt{3}/2\right)$
43. (a) $\pi/3$ **(b)** $\left(-\frac{1}{2}, -\sqrt{3}/2\right)$
44. (a) $\pi/6$ **(b)** $\left(-\sqrt{3}/2, \frac{1}{2}\right)$
45. (a) $\pi/4$ **(b)** $\left(-\sqrt{2}/2, -\sqrt{2}/2\right)$
46. (a) $\pi/6$ **(b)** $\left(\sqrt{3}/2, \frac{1}{2}\right)$
47. (a) $\pi/6$ **(b)** $\left(-\sqrt{3}/2, -\frac{1}{2}\right)$
48. (a) $\pi/4$ **(b)** $\left(\sqrt{2}/2, \sqrt{2}/2\right)$
49. (a) $\pi/3$ **(b)** $\left(\frac{1}{2}, \sqrt{3}/2\right)$

50. (a) $\pi/6$ **(b)** $\left(-\sqrt{3}/2, -\frac{1}{2}\right)$
51. (a) $\pi/3$ **(b)** $\left(-\frac{1}{2}, -\sqrt{3}/2\right)$
52. (a) $\pi/4$ **(b)** $\left(\sqrt{2}/2, -\sqrt{2}/2\right)$ **53.** $(0.5, 0.8)$
54. $(-0.8, 0.6)$ **55.** $(0.5, -0.9)$ **56.** $(-0.6, -0.9)$

SECTION 5.2 ■ PAGE 384

1. $y, x, y/x$ **2.** $1, 1$ **3.** $t = \pi/4$, $\sin t = \sqrt{2}/2$, $\cos t = \sqrt{2}/2$;
$t = \pi/2$, $\sin t = 1$, $\cos t = 0$; $t = 3\pi/4$,
$\sin t = \sqrt{2}/2$, $\cos t = -\sqrt{2}/2$;
$t = \pi$, $\sin t = 0$, $\cos t = -1$; $t = 5\pi/4$,
$\sin t = -\sqrt{2}/2$, $\cos t = -\sqrt{2}/2$; $t = 3\pi/2$, $\sin t = -1$,
$\cos t = 0$; $t = 7\pi/4$, $\sin t = -\sqrt{2}/2$, $\cos t = \sqrt{2}/2$;
$t = 2\pi$, $\sin t = 0$, $\cos t = 1$
4. $t = \pi/6$, $\sin t = \frac{1}{2}$, $\cos t = \sqrt{3}/2$;
$t = \pi/3$, $\sin t = \sqrt{3}/2$, $\cos t = \frac{1}{2}$;
$t = \pi/2$, $\sin t = 1$, $\cos t = 0$;
$t = 2\pi/3$, $\sin t = \sqrt{3}/2$, $\cos t = -\frac{1}{2}$;
$t = 5\pi/6$, $\sin t = \frac{1}{2}$, $\cos t = -\sqrt{3}/2$;
$t = \pi$, $\sin t = 0$, $\cos t = -1$;
$t = 7\pi/6$, $\sin t = -\frac{1}{2}$, $\cos t = -\sqrt{3}/2$;
$t = 4\pi/3$, $\sin t = -\sqrt{3}/2$, $\cos t = -\frac{1}{2}$;
$t = 3\pi/2$, $\sin t = -1$, $\cos t = 0$;
$t = 5\pi/3$, $\sin t = -\sqrt{3}/2$, $\cos t = \frac{1}{2}$;
$t = 11\pi/6$, $\sin t = -\frac{1}{2}$, $\cos t = \sqrt{3}/2$;
$t = 2\pi$, $\sin t = 0$, $\cos t = 1$
5. (a) $\sqrt{3}/2$ **(b)** $-1/2$ **(c)** $-\sqrt{3}$
6. (a) $1/2$ **(b)** $-\sqrt{3}/2$ **(c)** $-\sqrt{3}/3$
7. (a) $-1/2$ **(b)** $-1/2$ **(c)** $-1/2$
8. (a) $1/2$ **(b)** $1/2$ **(c)** $1/2$
9. (a) $-\sqrt{2}/2$ **(b)** $-\sqrt{2}/2$ **(c)** $\sqrt{2}/2$
10. (a) $\sqrt{2}/2$ **(b)** $-\sqrt{2}/2$ **(c)** $-\sqrt{2}/2$
11. (a) $\sqrt{3}/2$ **(b)** $2\sqrt{3}/3$ **(c)** $\sqrt{3}/3$
12. (a) $1/2$ **(b)** 2 **(c)** $-\sqrt{3}$ **13. (a)** -1 **(b)** 0 **(c)** 0
14. (a) 1 **(b)** 0 **(c)** 0 **15. (a)** 2 **(b)** $-2\sqrt{3}/3$ **(c)** 2
16. (a) $-\sqrt{3}/2$ **(b)** $-2\sqrt{3}/3$ **(c)** -2
17. (a) $-\sqrt{3}/3$ **(b)** $\sqrt{3}/3$ **(c)** $-\sqrt{3}/3$
18. (a) $-\sqrt{3}/3$ **(b)** $-\sqrt{3}/3$ **(c)** $-\sqrt{3}/3$
19. (a) $\sqrt{2}/2$ **(b)** $-\sqrt{2}$ **(c)** -1
20. (a) $-\sqrt{2}/2$ **(b)** $-\sqrt{2}$ **(c)** 1
21. (a) -1 **(b)** 1 **(c)** -1 **22. (a)** -1 **(b)** -1 **(c)** 1
23. (a) 0 **(b)** 1 **(c)** 0 **24. (a)** 1 **(b)** 0 **(c)** 0
25. $\sin 0 = 0$, $\cos 0 = 1$, $\tan 0 = 0$, $\sec 0 = 1$,
others undefined
26. $\sin \pi/2 = 1$, $\cos \pi/2 = 0$, $\cot \pi/2 = 0$, $\csc \pi/2 = 1$,
others undefined
27. $\sin \pi = 0$, $\cos \pi = -1$, $\tan \pi = 0$, $\sec \pi = -1$,
others undefined
28. $\sin 3\pi/2 = -1$, $\cos 3\pi/2 = 0$, $\cot 3\pi/2 = 0$,
$\csc 3\pi/2 = -1$, others undefined
29. $\frac{4}{5}, \frac{3}{5}, \frac{4}{3}$ **30.** $\frac{4}{5}, -\frac{3}{5}, -\frac{4}{3}$ **31.** $-\sqrt{11}/4, \sqrt{5}/4, -\sqrt{55}/5$
32. $-2\sqrt{2}/3, -1/3, 2\sqrt{2}$ **33.** $\sqrt{13}/7, -6/7, -\sqrt{13}/6$
34. $\frac{9}{41}, \frac{40}{41}, \frac{9}{40}$ **35.** $-\frac{12}{13}, -\frac{5}{13}, \frac{12}{5}$ **36.** $2\sqrt{5}/5, \sqrt{5}/5, 2$
37. $\frac{21}{29}, -\frac{20}{29}, -\frac{21}{20}$ **38.** $-\frac{7}{25}, \frac{24}{25}, -\frac{7}{24}$ **39. (a)** 0.8 **(b)** 0.84147
40. (a) 0.7 **(b)** 0.69671 **41. (a)** 0.9 **(b)** 0.93204
42. (a) 0.3 **(b)** 0.28366 **43. (a)** 1 **(b)** 1.02964
44. (a) -3.6 **(b)** -3.60210 **45. (a)** -0.6 **(b)** -0.57482
46. (a) 0.9 **(b)** 0.88345 **47.** Negative **48.** Negative
49. Negative **50.** Positive **51.** II **52.** III **53.** II **54.** II
55. $\sin t = \sqrt{1 - \cos^2 t}$ **56.** $\cos t = \sqrt{1 - \sin^2 t}$

57. $\tan t = (\sin t)/\sqrt{1 - \sin^2 t}$ **58.** $\tan t = -\dfrac{\sqrt{1 - \cos^2 t}}{\cos t}$
59. $\sec t = -\sqrt{1 + \tan^2 t}$ **60.** $\csc t = -\sqrt{1 + \cot^2 t}$
61. $\tan t = \sqrt{\sec^2 t - 1}$ **62.** $\sin t = -\dfrac{\sqrt{\sec^2 t - 1}}{\sec t}$
63. $\tan^2 t = (\sin^2 t)/(1 - \sin^2 t)$ **64.** $\sec^2 t \sin^2 t = \dfrac{1 - \cos^2 t}{\cos^2 t}$
65. $\cos t = -\frac{4}{5}$, $\tan t = -\frac{3}{4}$, $\csc t = \frac{5}{3}$, $\sec t = -\frac{5}{4}$, $\cot t = -\frac{4}{3}$
66. $\sin t = -\frac{3}{5}$, $\tan t = \frac{3}{4}$, $\csc t = -\frac{5}{3}$, $\sec t = -\frac{5}{4}$, $\cot t = \frac{4}{3}$
67. $\sin t = -2\sqrt{2}/3$, $\cos t = \frac{1}{3}$, $\tan t = -2\sqrt{2}$,
$\csc t = -\frac{3}{4}\sqrt{2}$, $\cot t = -\sqrt{2}/4$
68. $\sin t = -\sqrt{17}/17$, $\cos t = -4\sqrt{17}/17$,
$\csc t = -\sqrt{17}$, $\sec t = -\sqrt{17}/4$, $\cot t = 4$
69. $\sin t = -\frac{3}{5}$, $\cos t = \frac{4}{5}$, $\csc t = -\frac{5}{3}$, $\sec t = \frac{5}{4}$, $\cot t = -\frac{4}{3}$
70. $\sin t = -\sqrt{3}/2$, $\cos t = \frac{1}{2}$, $\tan t = -\sqrt{3}$,
$\csc t = -2\sqrt{3}/3$, $\cot t = -\sqrt{3}/3$
71. $\cos t = -\sqrt{15}/4$, $\tan t = \sqrt{15}/15$, $\csc t = -4$,
$\sec t = -4\sqrt{15}/15$, $\cot t = \sqrt{15}$
72. $\sin t = 4\sqrt{17}/17$, $\cos t = -\sqrt{17}/17$,
$\csc t = \sqrt{17}/4$, $\sec t = -\sqrt{17}$, $\cot t = -\frac{1}{4}$
73. Odd **74.** Even **75.** Odd **76.** Neither **77.** Even
78. Even **79.** Neither **80.** Even
81. $y(0) = 4$, $y(0.25) = -2.828$, $y(0.50) = 0$,
$y(0.75) = 2.828$, $y(1.00) = -4$, $y(1.25) = 2.828$
82. (a) 87 mmHg **(b)** 82.7 mmHg **(c)** 80 mmHg
(d) 73.9 mmHg **83. (a)** 0.49870 amp **(b)** -0.17117 amp
84. $H(0) = 175$ m, $H(1) = 150.4$ m, $H(2) = 100$ m,
$H(4) = 38.6$ m, $H(6) = 100$ m, $H(8) = 150.3$ m,
$H(12) = 58.8$ m

SECTION 5.3 ■ PAGE 396

1. $1, 2\pi$

2. $3, \pi$

3.

4.

5.

6.

7.

8.

9.

10.

11.

12.

13.

14.

15.

16.

17. $1, \pi$

18. $1, \pi$

19. $3, 2\pi/3$

20. $\frac{1}{2}, \pi/2$

21. $10, 4\pi$

22. $5, 8\pi$

23. $\frac{1}{3}, 6\pi$

24. $4, \pi$

25. $2, 1$

26. $3, 2$

27. $\frac{1}{2}, 2$

28. $1, \frac{1}{2}$

29. $1, 2\pi, \pi/2$

30. $2, 2\pi, \pi/3$

31. $2, 2\pi, \pi/6$

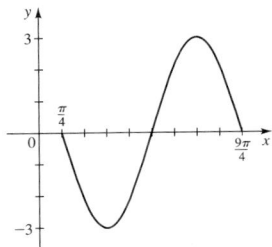

32. $3, 2\pi, -\pi/4$

33. $4, \pi, -\pi/2$

34. $1, 4\pi, -\pi/4$

35. $5, 2\pi/3, \pi/12$

36. $2, 3\pi, \pi/4$

37. $\frac{1}{2}, \pi, \pi/6$

38. $1, 2\pi/3, -\pi/6$

39. $3, 2, -\frac{1}{2}$

40. $2, 2\pi/3, -1$

41. $1, 2\pi/3, -\pi/3$

42. $1, 2\pi, \pi/2$

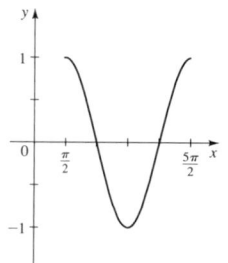

43. (a) $4, 2\pi, 0$ (b) $y = 4\sin x$
44. (a) $2, \pi, 0$ (b) $y = 2\cos 2x$
45. (a) $\frac{3}{2}, \frac{2\pi}{3}, 0$ (b) $y = \frac{3}{2}\cos 3x$
46. (a) $3, 4\pi, 0$ (b) $y = 3\sin\frac{1}{2}x$
47. (a) $\frac{1}{2}, \pi, -\frac{\pi}{3}$ (b) $y = -\frac{1}{2}\cos 2(x + \pi/3)$

48. (a) $\frac{1}{10}, \pi, -\frac{3\pi}{4}$ (b) $y = -\frac{1}{10}\cos 2(x + 3\pi/4)$
49. (a) $4, \frac{3}{2}, -\frac{1}{2}$ (b) $y = 4\sin\frac{4\pi}{3}\left(x + \frac{1}{2}\right)$
50. (a) $5, 1, -\frac{1}{4}$ (b) $y = 5\sin 2\pi\left(x + \frac{1}{4}\right)$

51.

52.

53.

54.

55.

56.

57.

58.

59.

60.

61.

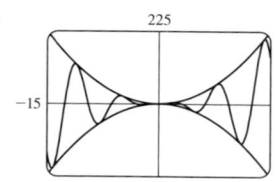

$y = x^2\sin x$ is a sine curve that lies between the graphs of $y = x^2$ and $y = -x^2$

62.

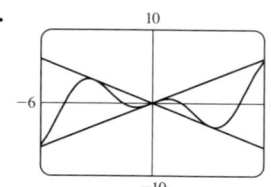

$y = x\cos x$ is a cosine curve that lies between the graphs of $y = x$ and $y = -x$

63. 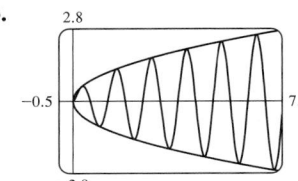 $y = \sqrt{x} \sin 5\pi x$ is a sine curve that lies between the graphs of $y = \sqrt{x}$ and $y = -\sqrt{x}$

64. 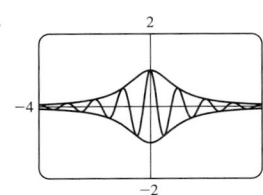 $y = \dfrac{\cos 2\pi x}{1 + x^2}$ is a cosine curve that lies between the graphs of $y = \dfrac{1}{1 + x^2}$ and $y = -\dfrac{1}{1 + x^2}$

65. 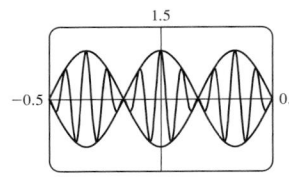 $y = \cos 3\pi x \cos 21\pi x$ is a co-sine curve that lies between the graphs of $y = \cos 3\pi x$ and $y = -\cos 3\pi x$

66. 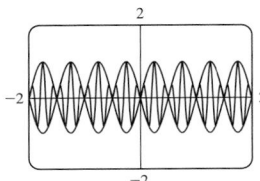 $y = \sin 2\pi x \sin 10\pi x$ is a sine curve that lies between the graphs of $y = \sin 2\pi x$ and $y = -\sin 2\pi x$

67. Maximum value 1.76 when $x \approx 0.94$, minimum value -1.76 when $x \approx -0.94$ (The same maximum and minimum values occur at infinitely many other values of x.)

68. Maximum value 6.97 when $x \approx 5.24$, minimum value -0.68 when $x \approx 1.05$ (The same maximum and minimum values occur at infinitely many other values of x.)

69. Maximum value 3.00 when $x \approx 1.57$, minimum value -1.00 when $x \approx -1.57$ (The same maximum and minimum values occur at infinitely many other values of x.)

70. Maximum value 0.58 when $x \approx 5.76$ (exact value is $x = 11\pi/6$; Minimum value -0.58 when $x \approx 3.67$ (exact value is $x = 7\pi/6$) (The same maximum and minimum values occur at infinitely many other values of x.)

71. 1.16   **72.** 1.11   **73.** 0.34, 2.80   **74.** 0.74

75. (a) Odd   **(b)** $0, \pm2\pi, \pm4\pi, \pm6\pi, \ldots$
(c) 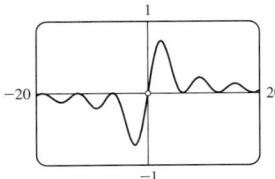   **(d)** $f(x)$ approaches 0
   (e) $f(x)$ approaches 0

76. (a) Even
(b) $0, \pm\pi/4, \pm2\pi/4, \pm3\pi/4, \ldots$

(c) 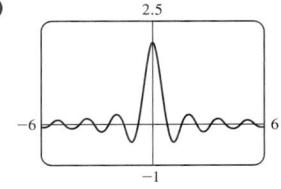   **(d)** $f(x)$ approaches 0
   (e) $f(x)$ approaches 2

77. (a) 20 s   **(b)** 6 ft
78. (a) $\frac{1}{440}$ s   **(b)** 440   **(c)**
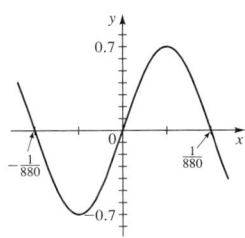

79. (a) $\frac{1}{80}$ min   **(b)** 80
(c) 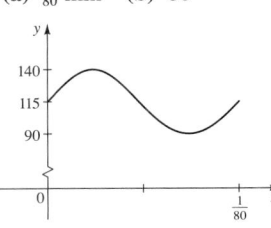   **(d)** $\frac{140}{90}$; it is higher than normal

80. (a) 312 days   **(b)** 10, 5.8   **(c)**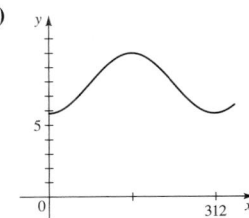

SECTION 5.4 ■ PAGE 405

1. π; $\frac{\pi}{2} + n\pi$, n an integer   **2.** 2π; $n\pi$, n an integer
 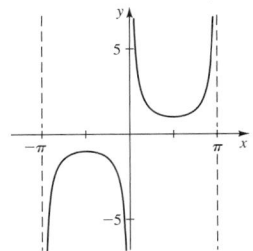

3. II   **4.** III   **5.** VI   **6.** I   **7.** IV   **8.** V
9. π **10.** π

11. π

12. π

21. 2π

22. 2π

13. π

14. π

23. π

24. 2π

15. 2π

16. 2π

25. 2π

26. 2π

17. 2π

18. 2π

27. $\pi/4$

28. 2π

19. π

20. π

29. 4

30. 2

31. π

32. $2\pi/3$

41. $\pi/2$

42. π

33. $\pi/2$

34. 4π

43. $\pi/2$

44. 1

35. $\frac{1}{3}$

36. 2

45. 2

46. 4π

37. $\frac{4}{3}$

38. 1

47. $2\pi/3$

48. 1

39. $\pi/2$

40. π

49. $3\pi/2$

50. 2π

51. 2

52. $2\pi/3$

53. $\pi/2$

54. $2\pi/3$

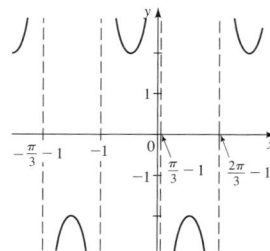

57. (a) 1.53 mi, 3.00 mi, 18.94 mi
(b)

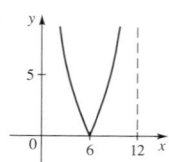

(c) $d(t)$ approaches ∞
58. (a) $S(2) = 10.39$ ft, $S(8) = 3.46$ ft, $S\left(11\frac{3}{4}\right) = 91.54$ ft, $S(12)$ is undefined
(b)

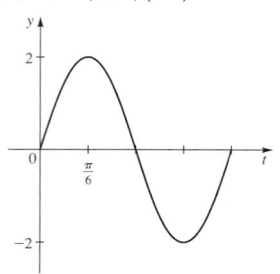

(c) 3, 9; 9:00 A.M., 3:00 P.M.
(d) The shadow gets increasingly longer.

SECTION 5.5 ■ PAGE 411

1. (a) $\left[-\pi/2, \pi/2\right]$, y, x, $\pi/6$, $\pi/6$, $\frac{1}{2}$
(b) $\left[0, \pi\right]$; y, x, $\pi/3$, $\pi/3$, $\frac{1}{2}$ **2.** $[-1, 1]$; (b)
3. (a) $\pi/2$ **(b)** $\pi/3$ **(c)** Undefined **4. (a)** $-\pi/2$ **(b)** $\pi/4$
(c) Undefined **5. (a)** π **(b)** $\pi/3$ **(c)** $5\pi/6$ **6. (a)** $\pi/4$
(b) 0 **(c)** $3\pi/4$ **7. (a)** $-\pi/4$ **(b)** $\pi/3$ **(c)** $\pi/6$ **8. (a)** 0
(b) $-\pi/3$ **(c)** $-\pi/6$ **9. (a)** $2\pi/3$ **(b)** $-\pi/4$ **(c)** $\pi/4$
10. (a) $\pi/2$ **(b)** 0 **(c)** $-\pi/6$ **11.** 0.72973 **12.** -1.09491
13. 2.01371 **14.** 1.11024 **15.** 2.75876 **16.** 0.13889
17. 1.47113 **18.** -1.53235 **19.** 0.88998 **20.** Undefined
21. -0.26005 **22.** -0.25168 **23.** $\frac{1}{4}$ **24.** $\frac{2}{3}$ **25.** 5
26. Undefined **27.** Undefined **28.** $\frac{3}{2}$ **29.** $5\pi/6$ **30.** $\pi/4$
31. $-\pi/6$ **32.** $-\pi/4$ **33.** $\pi/6$ **34.** $\pi/6$ **35.** $\pi/6$ **36.** $\pi/3$
37. $-\pi/3$ **38.** $\pi/4$ **39.** $\sqrt{3}/3$ **40.** 1 **41.** $\frac{1}{2}$ **42.** 1
43. $-\sqrt{2}/2$ **44.** $-\sqrt{3}/2$

SECTION 5.6 ■ PAGE 420

1. (a) $a \sin \omega t$ **(b)** $a \cos \omega t$
2. (a) $ke^{-ct} \sin \omega t$ **(b)** $ke^{-ct} \cos \omega t$
3. (a) $2, 2\pi/3, 3/(2\pi)$ **4. (a)** $3, 4\pi, 1/(4\pi)$
(b)

(b)

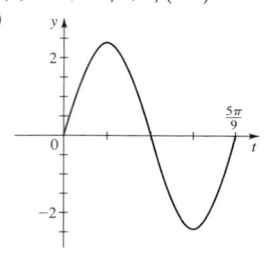

5. (a) $1, 20\pi/3, 3/(20\pi)$ **6. (a)** $2.4, 5\pi/9, 9/(5\pi)$
(b)

(b)

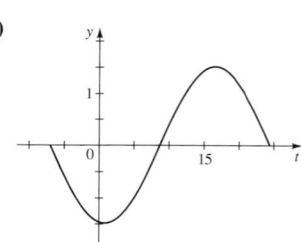

7. (a) $\frac{1}{4}, 4\pi/3, 3/(4\pi)$ **(b)**

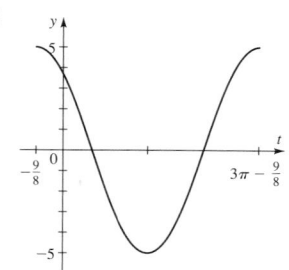

8. (a) $\frac{3}{2}, 10\pi, 1/(10\pi)$ **(b)**

9. (a) $5, 3\pi, 1/(3\pi)$ **(b)**

10. (a) $1.6, 2\pi, 1/(2\pi)$ **(b)**

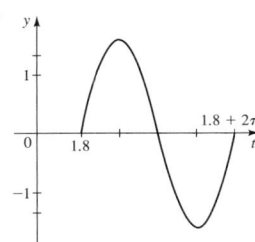

11. $y = 10 \sin\left(\dfrac{2\pi}{3}t\right)$ **12.** $y = 24 \sin(\pi t)$

13. $y = 6 \sin(10t)$ **14.** $y = 1.2 \sin(\pi t)$

15. $y = 60 \cos(4\pi t)$ **16.** $y = 35 \cos(\frac{1}{4}\pi t)$

17. $y = 2.4 \cos(1500\pi t)$ **18.** $y = 6.25 \cos(120\pi t)$

19. (a) $y = 2e^{-1.5t} \cos 6\pi t$ **(b)**

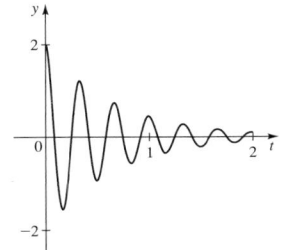

20. (a) $y = 15e^{-0.25t} \cos(1.2\pi t)$
(b)

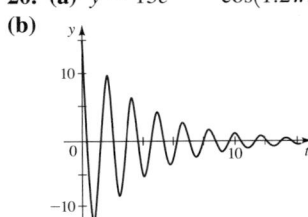

21. (a) $y = 100e^{-0.05t} \cos \dfrac{\pi}{2}t$

(b)

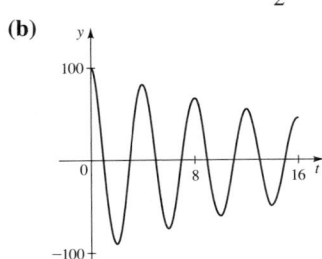

22. (a) $y = 0.75e^{-3t} \cos\left(\frac{2}{3}t\right)$
(b)

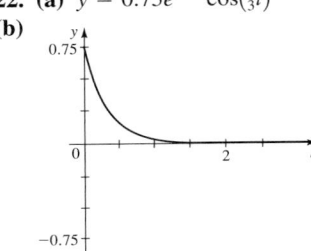

23. (a) $y = 7e^{-10t} \sin 12t$ **(b)**

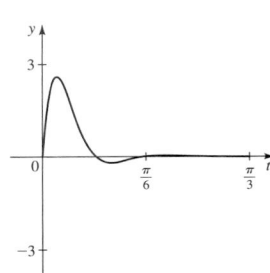

24. (a) $y = e^{-t} \sin(2\pi t)$ **(b)**

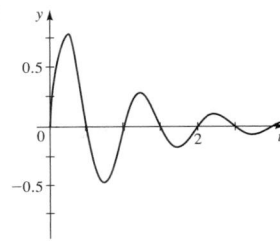

25. (a) $y = 0.3e^{-0.2t} \sin(40\pi t)$
(b)

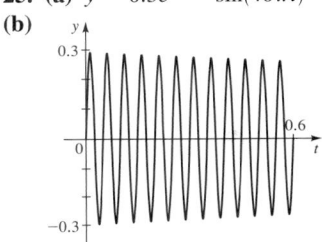

26. (a) $y = 12e^{-0.01t} \sin(16\pi t)$
(b)

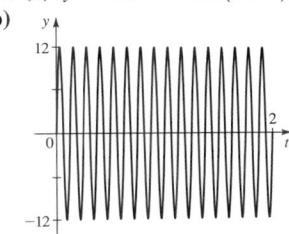

27. (a) 10 cycles per minute
(b)   **(c)** 0.4 m

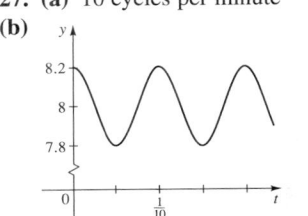

28. $1.09 \times 10^{-8}, 9.15 \times 10^{7}$
29. (a) $25, 0.0125, 80$ **(b)**

(c) The period decreases and the frequency increases.

30. (a) 8900 **(b)** about 3.14 yr

31. $d(t) = 5 \sin(5\pi t)$ **32.** $y = -6 \sin\left(\dfrac{\pi}{6}t\right)$

33. $y = 21 \sin\left(\dfrac{\pi}{6}t\right)$

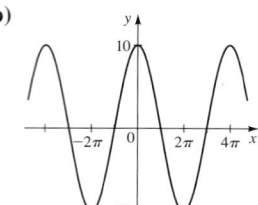

34. $y = -2 \cos 2\pi t$ **35.** $y = 5 \cos(2\pi t)$

36. (a) $f(t) = 5 \cos\left(\sqrt{\dfrac{3}{10}}t\right)$ **(b)** $\dfrac{1}{2\pi}\sqrt{\dfrac{k}{m}}$

(c) The frequency decreases; slower
(d) The frequency increases; faster

37. $y = 11 + 10 \sin\left(\dfrac{\pi t}{10}\right)$ **38.** $f(t) = 10 \sin \pi t$

39. $y = 3.8 + 0.2 \sin\left(\dfrac{\pi}{5}t\right)$

40. $R(t) = 20 + 1.5 \sin\left(\dfrac{2\pi}{5.4}t\right)$, where R is measured in

millions of miles and t is measured in days

41. $f(t) = 10 \sin\left(\dfrac{\pi}{12}(t - 8)\right) + 90$

42. $E(t) = 310 \cos(200\pi t)$, 219.2 V
43. (a) 45 V **(b)** 40 **(c)** 40 **(d)** $E(t) = 45 \cos(80\pi t)$
44. (a) 553.9 Hz; 455.6 Hz **(b)** $y = A \sin(1107.8\pi t)$,
$y = A \sin(911.2\pi t)$
45. $f(t) = e^{-0.9t} \sin \pi t$ **46. (a)** $f(t) = 6e^{-2.8t} \cos 4\pi t$

(b) $\dfrac{\ln 12}{2.8} \approx 0.88$ s **47.** $e = \dfrac{1}{3} \ln 4 \approx 0.46$

48. (a) $c = \dfrac{1}{2} \ln 5 \approx 0.80$ **(b)** $f(t) = 3e^{-0.8t} \cos 330\pi t$

CHAPTER 5 REVIEW ■ PAGE 424

1. (b) $\frac{1}{2}, -\sqrt{3}/2, -\sqrt{3}/3$ **2. (b)** $-\frac{4}{5}, \frac{3}{5}, -\frac{4}{3}$
3. (a) $\pi/3$ **(b)** $\left(-\frac{1}{2}, \sqrt{3}/2\right)$
(c) $\sin t = \sqrt{3}/2, \cos t = -\frac{1}{2}, \tan t = -\sqrt{3}, \csc t = 2\sqrt{3}/3$,
$\sec t = -2, \cot t = -\sqrt{3}/3$
4. (a) $\pi/3$ **(b)** $\left(\frac{1}{2}, -\sqrt{3}/2\right)$ **(c)** $\sin t = -\sqrt{3}/2, \cos t = \frac{1}{2}$,
$\tan t = -\sqrt{3}, \csc t = -2\sqrt{3}/3, \sec t = 2, \cot t = -\sqrt{3}/3$
5. (a) $\pi/4$ **(b)** $\left(-\sqrt{2}/2, -\sqrt{2}/2\right)$
(c) $\sin t = -\sqrt{2}/2, \cos t = -\sqrt{2}/2$,
$\tan t = 1, \csc t = -\sqrt{2}, \sec t = -\sqrt{2}, \cot t = 1$
6. (a) $\pi/6$ **(b)** $\left(-\sqrt{3}/2, \frac{1}{2}\right)$
(c) $\sin t = \frac{1}{2}, \cos t = -\sqrt{3}/2, \tan t = -\sqrt{3}/3$,
$\csc t = 2, \sec t = -2\sqrt{3}/3, \cot t = -\sqrt{3}$
7. (a) $\sqrt{2}/2$ **(b)** $-\sqrt{2}/2$ **8. (a)** $\sqrt{3}$ **(b)** $-\sqrt{3}$
9. (a) 0.89121 **(b)** 0.45360 **10. (a)** 0.80902 **(b)** 0.80902
11. (a) 0 **(b)** Undefined **12. (a)** 0.43388 **(b)** 2.30476
13. (a) Undefined **(b)** 0 **14. (a)** 0 **(b)** Undefined
15. (a) $-\sqrt{3}/3$ **(b)** $-\sqrt{3}$ **16. (a)** $\frac{1}{2}$ **(b)** $\frac{1}{2}$

17. $(\sin t)/(1 - \sin^2 t)$ **18.** $\dfrac{1 - \cos^2 t}{\cos^3 t}$

19. $(\sin t)/\sqrt{1 - \sin^2 t}$ **20.** $\dfrac{1}{-\sqrt{1 - \sin^2 t}}$

21. $\tan t = -\frac{5}{12}, \csc t = \frac{13}{5}, \sec t = -\frac{13}{12}, \cot t = -\frac{12}{5}$
22. $\cos t = \sqrt{3}/2, \tan t = -\sqrt{3}/3$,
$\csc t = -2, \sec t = 2\sqrt{3}/3, \cot t = -\sqrt{3}$
23. $\sin t = 2\sqrt{5}/5, \cos t = -\sqrt{5}/5$,
$\tan t = -2, \sec t = -\sqrt{5}$
24. $\sin t = \frac{4}{5}, \tan t = -\frac{4}{3}, \csc t = \frac{5}{4}, \sec t = -\frac{5}{3}, \cot t = -\frac{3}{4}$
25. $(16 - \sqrt{17})/4$ **26.** $-\frac{119}{120}$ **27.** 3 **28.** 1

29. (a) $10, 4\pi, 0$
(b)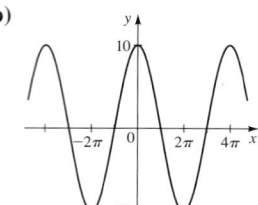

30. (a) $4, 1, 0$
(b)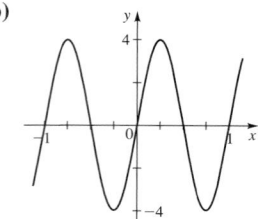

31. (a) $1, 4\pi, 0$
(b)

32. (a) $2, 2\pi, \pi/4$
(b)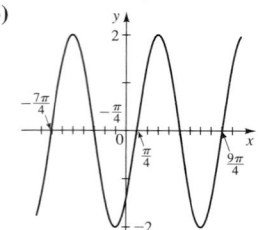

33. (a) $3, \pi, 1$
(b)

34. (a) $1, \pi, \pi/2$
(b)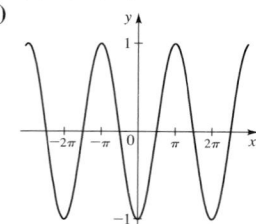

35. (a) $1, 4, -\frac{1}{3}$
(b)

36. (a) $10, \pi, \pi/4$
(b)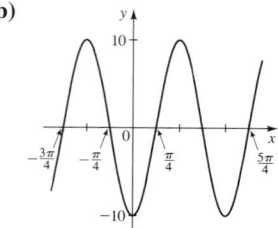

37. $y = 5 \sin 4x$ **38.** $y = 2 \sin\left(\frac{\pi}{2}x\right)$
39. $y = \frac{1}{2} \sin 2\pi\left(x + \frac{1}{3}\right)$ **40.** $y = 4 \sin\frac{3}{2}(x + \pi/3)$
41. π **42.** 1

43. π

44. 4π

45. π

46. π

47. 2π

48. $\frac{1}{2}$

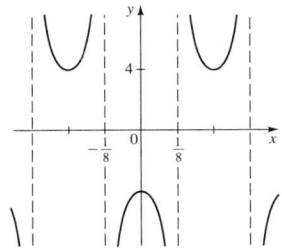

49. $\frac{\pi}{2}$ **50.** $\frac{2\pi}{3}$ **51.** $\frac{\pi}{6}$ **52.** $\sqrt{3}$

53. (a)

54. (a)

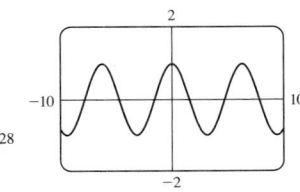

(b) Period π
(c) Even

(b) Period 2π
(c) Even

55. (a)

56. (a)

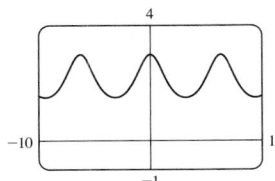

(b) Not periodic
(c) Neither

(b) Period 2π
(c) Even

57. (a)

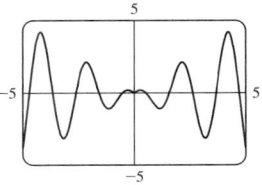

(b) Not periodic
(c) Even

58. (a)

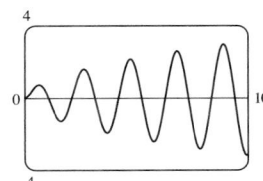

(b) Not periodic
(c) Neither

59.

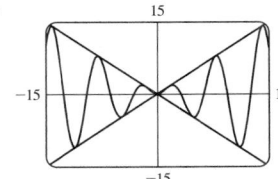

$y = x \sin x$ is a sine function whose graph lies between those of $y = x$ and $y = -x$

60.

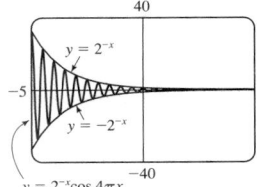

$y = 2^{-x} \cos 4\pi x$ is a cosine function whose graph lies between the graphs of $y = 2^{-x}$ and $y = -2^{-x}$

61.

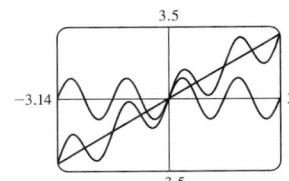

The graphs are related by graphical addition.

62.

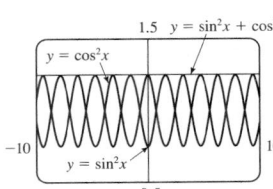

The graphs are related by graphical addition.

63. $1.76, -1.76$ **64.** $1.25, -1$ **65.** $0.30, 2.84$ **66.** 0.390
67. (a) Odd   **(b)** $0, \pm\pi, \pm 2\pi, \ldots$
(c)

(d) $f(x)$ approaches 0
(e) $f(x)$ approaches 0

68. (a)

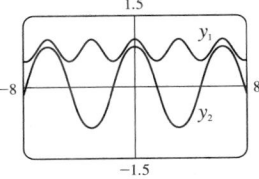

(b) y_1 has period π, y_2 has period 2π
(c) $\sin(\cos x) < \cos(\sin x)$, for all x

69. $y = 50 \cos(16\pi t)$
70. $y = -50 \cos(9\pi t)$ **71.** $y = 4 \cos\left(\frac{\pi}{6} t\right)$
72. (a) $y = 16e^{-0.72t} \cos 2.8\pi t$
(b)   **(c)** 0.012 cm

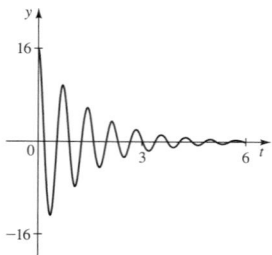

CHAPTER 5 TEST ▪ PAGE 426

1. $y = -\frac{5}{6}$ **2. (a)** $\frac{4}{5}$ **(b)** $-\frac{3}{5}$ **(c)** $-\frac{4}{3}$ **(d)** $-\frac{5}{3}$
3. (a) $-\frac{1}{2}$ **(b)** $-\sqrt{2}/2$ **(c)** $\sqrt{3}$ **(d)** -1
4. $\tan t = -(\sin t)/\sqrt{1 - \sin^2 t}$ **5.** $-\frac{2}{15}$
6. (a) $5, \pi/2, 0$ **7. (a)** $2, 4\pi, \pi/3$
(b)   **(b)**

8. π **9.** $\pi/2$

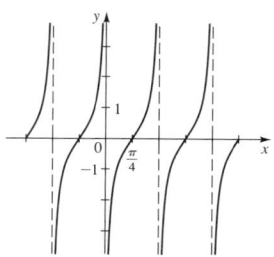

10. (a) $\pi/4$ **(b)** $5\pi/6$ **(c)** 0   **(d)** 1/2
11. $y = 2 \sin 2(x + \pi/3)$
12. (a)   **(b)** Even
                                       (c) Minimum value -0.11
                                       when $x \approx \pm 2.54$, maximum
                                       value 1 when $x = 0$

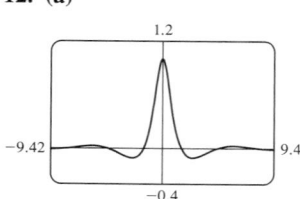

13. $y = 5 \sin(4\pi t)$
14. $y = 16e^{-0.1t} \cos 24\pi t$

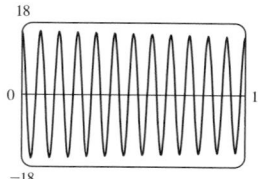

FOCUS ON MODELING ▪ PAGE 430

1. (a) and (c)

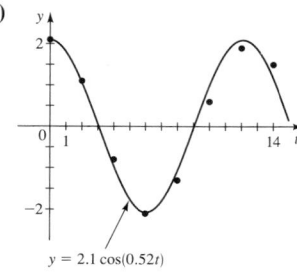

$y = 2.1 \cos(0.52t)$

(b) $y = 2.1 \cos(0.52t)$
(d) $y = 2.05 \sin(0.50t + 1.55) - 0.01$ **(e)** The formula of (d)
reduces to $y = 2.05 \cos(0.50t - 0.02) - 0.01$. Same as (b),
rounded to one decimal.
2. (a) and (c)

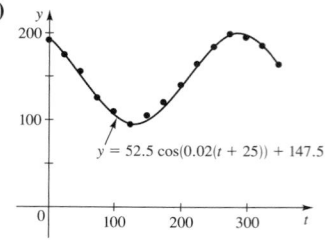

$y = 52.5 \cos(0.02(t + 25)) + 147.5$

(b) $y = 52.5 \cos(0.02(t + 25)) + 147.5$
(d) $y = 49.70 \sin(0.02t + 2.09) + 149.13$ **(e)** The formula of
(d) reduces to $y = 49.70 \cos(0.02t + 0.52) + 149.13$. Close, but
not identical, to (b).
3. (a) and (c)

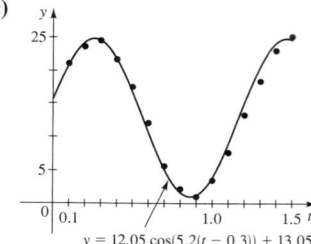

$y = 12.05 \cos(5.2(t - 0.3)) + 13.05$

(b) $y = 12.05 \cos(5.2(t - 0.3)) + 13.05$
(d) $y = 11.72 \sin(5.05t + 0.24) + 12.96$ **(e)** The formula of
(d) reduces to $y = 11.72 \cos(5.05(t - 0.26)) + 12.96$. Close, but
not identical, to (b).
4. (a) and (c)

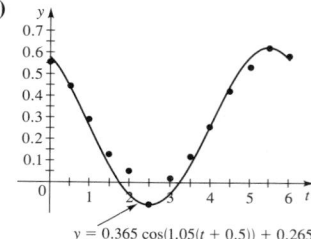

$y = 0.365 \cos(1.05(t + 0.5)) + 0.265$

(b) $y = 0.365 \cos(1.05(t + 0.5)) + 0.265$
(d) $y = 0.33 \sin(1.02t + 2.12) + 0.29$ **(e)** The formula of (d)
reduces to $y = 0.33 \cos(1.02(t + 0.52)) + 0.29$. Same as (b),
rounded to one decimal.

5. (a) and **(c)**

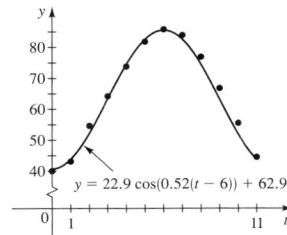

(b) $y = 22.9 \cos(0.52(t - 6)) + 62.9$, where y is temperature (°F) and t is months (January = 0)
(d) $y = 23.4 \sin(0.48t - 1.36) + 62.2$

6. (a) and **(c)**

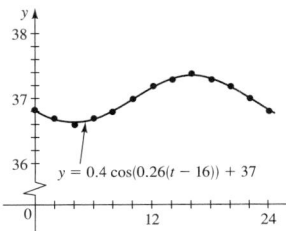

(b) $y = 0.4 \cos(0.26(t - 16)) + 37$, where y is the body temperature (°C) and t is hours since midnight
(d) $y = 0.37 \sin(0.26t - 2.62) + 37.0$

7. (a) and **(c)**

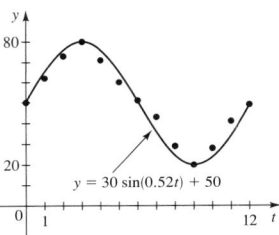

(b) $y = 30 \sin(0.52t) + 50$ where y is the owl population in year t
(d) $y = 25.8 \sin(0.52t - 0.02) + 50.6$

8. (a) and **(c)**

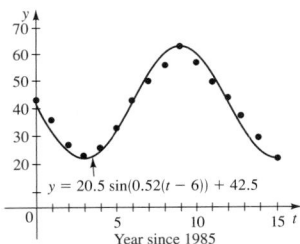

(b) $y = 20.5 \sin(0.52(t - 6)) + 42.5$, where y is the salmon population ($\times$ 1000), and t is years since 1985
(d) $y = 17.8 \sin(0.52t + 3.11) + 42.4$

9. (a) and **(c)**

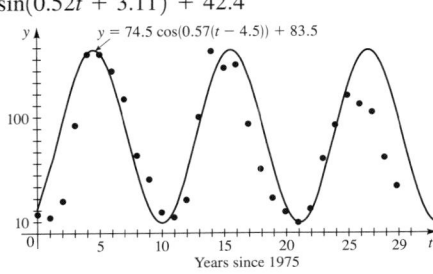

(b) $y = 74.5 \cos(0.57(t - 4.5)) + 83.5$, where y is the average daily sunspot count, and t is the years since 1975
(d) $y = 67.65 \sin(0.62t - 1.65) + 74.5$

CHAPTER 6

SECTION 6.1 ■ PAGE 440

1. (a) arc, 1 **(b)** $\pi/180$ **(c)** $180/\pi$ **2. (a)** $r\theta$ **(b)** $\frac{1}{2}r^2\theta$
3. $2\pi/5 \approx 1.257$ rad **4.** $3\pi/10 \approx 0.942$ rad
5. $-\pi/4 \approx -0.785$ rad **6.** $-\pi/3 \approx -1.047$ rad
7. $-5\pi/12 \approx -1.309$ rad **8.** $-5\pi/3 \approx -5.236$ rad
9. $6\pi \approx 18.850$ rad **10.** $22\pi \approx 69.115$ rad
11. $8\pi/15 \approx 1.676$ rad **12.** $\pi/12 \approx 0.262$ rad
13. $\pi/24 \approx 0.131$ rad **14.** $9\pi/8 \approx 3.534$ rad
15. $210°$ **16.** $660°$ **17.** $-225°$ **18.** $-270°$
19. $540/\pi \approx 171.9°$ **20.** $-360/\pi \approx 114.6°$
21. $-216/\pi \approx -68.8°$ **22.** $612/\pi \approx 194.8°$
23. $18°$ **24.** $50°$ **25.** $-24°$ **26.** $-195°$
27. $410°, 770°, -310°, -670°$
28. $495°, 855°, -225°, -585°$
29. $11\pi/4, 19\pi/4, -5\pi/4, -13\pi/4$
30. $23\pi/6, 35\pi/6, -\pi/6, -13\pi/6$
31. $7\pi/4, 15\pi/4, -9\pi/4, -17\pi/4$
32. $315°, 675°, -405°, -765°$ **33.** Yes
34. Yes **35.** Yes **36.** No **37.** Yes
38. No **39.** $13°$ **40.** $1°$ **41.** $30°$
42. $260°$ **43.** $280°$ **44.** $190°$ **45.** $5\pi/6$
46. $5\pi/3$ **47.** π **48.** $10 - 2\pi \approx 3.717$ rad
49. $\pi/4$ **50.** $3\pi/2$ **51.** $55\pi/9 \approx 19.2$
52. $360/\pi \approx 114.6°$ **53.** 4 **54.** $5\pi/2 \approx 7.85$ m
55. 4 mi **56.** $216/\pi \approx 68.8°$, 1.2 rad
57. 2 rad $\approx 114.6°$ **58.** 6.88 ft **59.** $36/\pi \approx 11.459$ m
60. $16/(3\pi) \approx 1.698$ ft **61. (a)** 35.45 **(b)** 25
62. (a) 5.855 **(b)** 3.028 **63.** 50 m^2
64. 4.7 mi^2 **65.** 4 m **66.** $57.3°$ **67.** 6 cm^2
68. $\pi/4$ ft^2 **69.** 13.9 mi **70.** 672 **71.** 330π mi ≈ 1037 mi
72. 110π mi ≈ 346 mi **73.** 1.6 million mi
74. 3979 mi, 25,000 mi **75.** 1.15 mi
76. $70{,}000\pi \approx 219{,}911$ ft^2 **77.** 360π in$^2 \approx 1130.97$ in^2
78. 3750π ft$^2 \approx 11{,}781$ ft^2 **79. (a)** 90π rad/min
(b) 1440π in./min ≈ 4523.9 in./min
80. (a) 2000π rad/min **(b)** $50\pi/3$ ft/s ≈ 52.4 ft/s
81. $32\pi/15$ ft/s ≈ 6.7 ft/s **82.** 39.3 mi/h **83.** 1039.6 mi/h
84. (a) 1100 rad/min **(b)** 175 **85.** 2.1 m/s
86. (a) 160 rad/min **(b)** 2080π ft/min ≈ 74.26 mi/h
87. (a) 10π cm ≈ 31.4 cm **(b)** 5 cm **(c)** 3.32 cm
(d) 86.8 cm^3
88. (b) **(c)** 5.13 rad

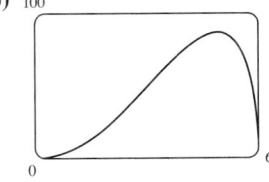

SECTION 6.2 ■ PAGE 448

1. (a)

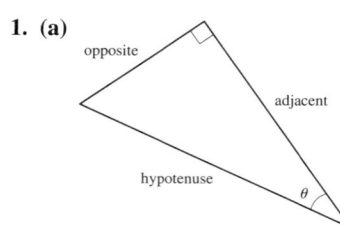

opposite

adjacent

hypotenuse

θ

(b) $\dfrac{\text{opposite}}{\text{hypotenuse}}, \dfrac{\text{adjacent}}{\text{hypotenuse}}, \dfrac{\text{opposite}}{\text{adjacent}}$ **(c)** similar

2. $\sin \theta, \cos \theta, \tan \theta$

3. $\sin \theta = \frac{4}{5}, \cos \theta = \frac{3}{5}, \tan \theta = \frac{4}{3}, \csc \theta = \frac{5}{4}, \sec \theta = \frac{5}{3}, \cot \theta = \frac{3}{4}$

4. $\sin \theta = \frac{7}{25}, \cos \theta = \frac{24}{25}, \tan \theta = \frac{7}{24}, \csc \theta = \frac{25}{7}, \sec \theta = \frac{25}{24},$ $\cot \theta = \frac{24}{7}$ **5.** $\sin \theta = \frac{40}{41}, \cos \theta = \frac{9}{41}, \tan \theta = \frac{40}{9}, \csc \theta = \frac{41}{40},$ $\sec \theta = \frac{41}{9}, \cot \theta = \frac{9}{40}$ **6.** $\sin \theta = \frac{15}{17}, \cos \theta = \frac{8}{17}, \tan \theta = \frac{15}{8},$ $\csc \theta = \frac{17}{15}, \sec \theta = \frac{17}{8}, \cot \theta = \frac{8}{15}$

7. $\sin \theta = 2\sqrt{13}/13, \cos \theta = 3\sqrt{13}/13, \tan \theta = \frac{2}{3},$ $\csc \theta = \sqrt{13}/2, \sec \theta = \sqrt{13}/3, \cot \theta = \frac{3}{2}$

8. $\sin \theta = \frac{7}{8}, \cos \theta = \sqrt{15}/8, \tan \theta = 7\sqrt{15}/15,$ $\csc \theta = \frac{8}{7}, \sec \theta = 8\sqrt{15}/15, \cot \theta = \sqrt{15}/7$

9. (a) $3\sqrt{34}/34, 3\sqrt{34}/34$ **(b)** $\frac{3}{5}, \frac{3}{5}$ **(c)** $\sqrt{34}/5, \sqrt{34}/5$

10. (a) $\frac{4}{7}, \frac{4}{7}$ **(b)** $4\sqrt{33}/33, 4\sqrt{33}/33$ **(c)** $7\sqrt{33}/33, 7\sqrt{33}/33$

11. $\frac{25}{2}$ **12.** $12\sqrt{2}$ **13.** $13\sqrt{3}/2$ **14.** $4\sqrt{3}$ **15.** 16.51658

16. 31.30339   **17.** $x = 28 \cos \theta, y = 28 \sin \theta$

18. $x = 4 \tan \theta, y = 4 \sec \theta$

19. $\cos \theta = \frac{4}{5}, \tan \theta = \frac{3}{4}, \csc \theta = \frac{5}{3}, \sec \theta = \frac{5}{4}, \cot \theta = \frac{4}{3}$

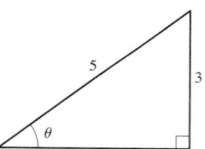

5

3

θ

20. $\sin \theta = 7\sqrt{31}/40, \tan \theta = 7\sqrt{31}/9, \csc \theta = 40\sqrt{31}/217,$ $\sec \theta = \frac{40}{9}, \cot \theta = 9\sqrt{31}/217$

40

θ 9

21. $\sin \theta = \sqrt{2}/2, \cos \theta = \sqrt{2}/2, \tan \theta = 1,$ $\csc \theta = \sqrt{2}, \sec \theta = \sqrt{2}$

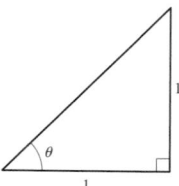

1

θ

1

22. $\sin \theta = \sqrt{3}/2, \cos \theta = \frac{1}{2}, \csc \theta = 2\sqrt{3}/3,$ $\sec \theta = 2, \cot \theta = \sqrt{3}/3$

2

$\sqrt{3}$

θ

1

23. $\sin \theta = 3\sqrt{5}/7, \cos \theta = \frac{2}{7}, \tan \theta = 3\sqrt{5}/2,$ $\csc \theta = 7\sqrt{5}/15, \cot \theta = 2\sqrt{5}/15$

7

θ

2

24. $\sin \theta = \frac{12}{13}, \cos \theta = \frac{5}{13}, \tan \theta = \frac{12}{5}, \sec \theta = \frac{13}{5}, \cot \theta = \frac{5}{12}$

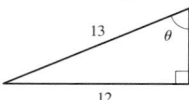

13

θ

12

25. $(1 + \sqrt{3})/2$ **26.** 1   **27.** 1   **28.** 1   **29.** $\frac{1}{2}$

30. $\frac{1}{4}(2 - \sqrt{3})$

31.

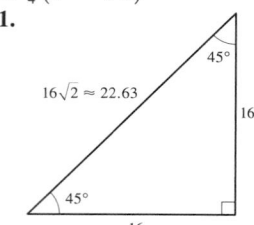

$45°$

$16\sqrt{2} \approx 22.63$

16

$45°$

16

32.

103.52 /15° 100

$75°$

26.79

33.

$38°$

44.79

56.85

$52°$

35

34.

22°

1000   927.18

68°

374.61

35.

$\frac{\pi}{8}$

30.95   33.5

$\frac{3\pi}{8}$

12.82

36.

$\frac{\pi}{6}$

83.48   72.3

$\frac{\pi}{3}$

41.74

37.

$\frac{3\pi}{10}$

106   180.34

$\frac{\pi}{5}$

145.90

38.

425

$\frac{3\pi}{8}$ 162.64

$\frac{\pi}{8}$

392.65

39. $\sin \theta \approx 0.45, \cos \theta \approx 0.89, \tan \theta = 0.50, \csc \theta \approx 2.24,$ $\sec \theta \approx 1.12, \cot \theta = 2.00$

40. $\sin 40° \approx 0.64, \cos 40° \approx 0.77, \tan 40° \approx 0.83, \csc 40° \approx 1.56,$ $\sec 40° \approx 1.39, \cot 40° \approx 1.20$ **41.** 230.9   **42.** 98.1   **43.** 63.7

44. 5.8   **45.** $x = 10 \tan \theta \sin \theta$

46. $a = \sin \theta, b = \tan \theta, c = \sec \theta, d = \cos \theta$ **47.** 1026 ft

48. (a) 93,431 ft   **(b)** 86,628 ft   **49. (a)** 2100 mi   **(b)** No

50. 471 ft   **51.** 19 ft   **52.** 544 ft   **53.** 345 ft   **54.** 104.5 ft

55. 415 ft, 152 ft   **56.** 11,379 ft   **57.** 2570 ft   **58.** 3.7 mi

59. 5808 ft   **60.** 473 m   **61.** 91.7 million mi   **62. (a)** 89.05°

(b) 236,000 mi   **63.** 3960 mi   **64.** 2.53×10^{13} mi

65. 0.723 AU

SECTION 6.3 ■ PAGE 459

1. y/r, x/r, y/x **2.** quadrant, positive, negative, negative
3. (a) 30° (b) 30° (c) 30°   **4.** (a) 60° (b) 30° (c) 60°
5. (a) 45° (b) 90° (c) 75°   **6.** (a) 81° (b) 19° (c) 1°
7. (a) $\pi/4$ (b) $\pi/6$ (c) $\pi/3$ **8.** (a) $\pi/3$ (b) $\pi/4$
(c) $\pi/6$ **9.** (a) $2\pi/7$ (b) 0.4π (c) 1.4   **10.** (a) 0.3π
(b) 0.84 (c) 0   **11.** $\frac{1}{2}$ **12.** $-\sqrt{2}/2$ **13.** $-\sqrt{3}/2$
14. $\frac{1}{2}$ **15.** $-\sqrt{3}$ **16.** 2   **17.** 1   **18.** $\sqrt{3}$ **19.** $-\sqrt{3}/2$
20. -2 **21.** $\sqrt{3}/3$ **22.** $\frac{1}{2}$ **23.** $\sqrt{3}/2$ **24.** $-\sqrt{3}/2$
25. -1 **26.** $\frac{1}{2}$ **27.** $\frac{1}{2}$ **28.** $-\sqrt{3}/3$ **29.** 2   **30.** $-\sqrt{2}$
31. -1 **32.** $\sqrt{2}/2$ **33.** Undefined   **34.** $-\frac{1}{2}$
35. III   **36.** IV   **37.** IV   **38.** II
39. $\tan\theta = -\sqrt{1-\cos^2\theta}/\cos\theta$
40. $\cot\theta = -\sqrt{1-\sin^2\theta}/\sin\theta$
41. $\cos\theta = \sqrt{1-\sin^2\theta}$ **42.** $\sec\theta = \dfrac{1}{\sqrt{1-\sin^2\theta}}$
43. $\sec\theta = -\sqrt{1+\tan^2\theta}$ **44.** $\csc\theta = -\sqrt{1+\cot^2\theta}$
45. $\cos\theta = -\frac{4}{5}$, $\tan\theta = -\frac{3}{4}$, $\csc\theta = \frac{5}{3}$, $\sec\theta = -\frac{5}{4}$, $\cot\theta = -\frac{4}{3}$
46. $\sin\theta = -\sqrt{95}/12$, $\tan\theta = \sqrt{95}/7$, $\csc\theta = -12\sqrt{95}/95$,
$\sec\theta = -12/7$, $\cot\theta = 7\sqrt{95}/95$
47. $\sin\theta = -\frac{3}{5}$, $\cos\theta = \frac{4}{5}$, $\csc\theta = -\frac{5}{3}$, $\sec\theta = \frac{5}{4}$, $\cot\theta = -\frac{4}{3}$
48. $\sin\theta = -2\sqrt{6}/5$, $\cos\theta = \frac{1}{5}$, $\tan\theta = -2\sqrt{6}$,
$\csc\theta = -5\sqrt{6}/12$, $\cot\theta = -\sqrt{6}/12$
49. $\sin\theta = \frac{1}{2}$, $\cos\theta = \sqrt{3}/2$, $\tan\theta = \sqrt{3}/3$,
$\sec\theta = 2\sqrt{3}/3$, $\cot\theta = \sqrt{3}$
50. $\sin\theta = -4\sqrt{17}/17$, $\cos\theta = -\sqrt{17}/17$, $\tan\theta = 4$,
$\csc\theta = -\sqrt{17}/4$, $\sec\theta = -\sqrt{17}$
51. $\sin\theta = 3\sqrt{5}/7$, $\tan\theta = -3\sqrt{5}/2$, $\csc\theta = 7\sqrt{5}/15$,
$\sec\theta = -\frac{7}{2}$, $\cot\theta = -2\sqrt{5}/15$
52. $\sin\theta = 4\sqrt{17}/17$, $\cos\theta = -\sqrt{17}/17$, $\csc\theta = \sqrt{17}/4$,
$\sec\theta = -\sqrt{17}$, $\cot\theta = -\frac{1}{4}$ **53.** (a) $\sqrt{3}/2$, $\sqrt{3}$
(b) $\frac{1}{2}$, $\sqrt{3}/4$ (c) $\frac{3}{4}$, 0.88967   **54.** 30.0   **55.** 19.1   **56.** 43.3
57. 66.1°   **58.** $\sqrt{96}$ cm $\approx$ 9.8 cm   **59.** $(4\pi/3) - \sqrt{3} \approx 2.46$
60. $120\pi + 36\sqrt{3} \approx 439.3$
63. (b)

θ	20°	60°	80°	85°
h	1922	9145	29,944	60,351

64. (b) 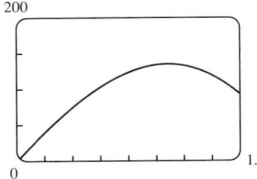   (c) 60°

65. (a) $A(\theta) = 400 \sin\theta\cos\theta$
(b)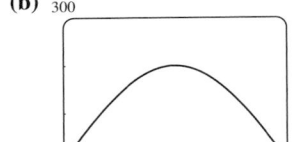

(c) width = depth $\approx$ 14.14 in.
66. $S(\theta) = 8000\,k\cos\theta\sin^2\theta$
67. (a) $9\sqrt{3}/4$ ft $\approx$ 3.897 ft, $\frac{9}{16}$ ft = 0.5625 ft
(b) 23.982 ft, 3.462 ft   **68.** 15.8 s

69. (a) 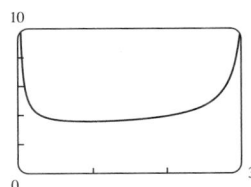   (b) 0.946 rad or 54°

70. (b)   (c) 21.07   **71.** 42°
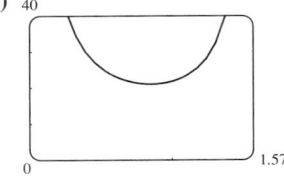

SECTION 6.4 ■ PAGE 467

1. (a) $[-1, 1]$, $[-\pi/2, \pi/2]$ (b) $[-1, 1]$, $[0, \pi]$
(c) $\mathbb{R}$, $(-\pi/2, \pi/2)$ **2.** (a) $\frac{8}{10}$ (b) $\frac{6}{10}$ (c) $\frac{8}{6}$ **3.** (a) $\pi/6$
(b) $5\pi/6$ (c) $-\pi/4$ **4.** (a) $-\pi/3$ (b) $3\pi/4$ (c) $-\pi/3$
5. (a) $-\pi/6$ (b) $\pi/3$ (c) $\pi/6$ **6.** (a) $-\pi/2$ (b) 0 (c) 0
7. 0.46677   **8.** 2.41886   **9.** 1.82348   **10.** 0.33984
11. 1.24905   **12.** -1.32582 **13.** Undefined   **14.** Undefined
15. 36.9°   **16.** 21.3°   **17.** 34.7°   **18.** 25.4°   **19.** 34.9°
20. 27.3°   **21.** 30°, 150°   **22.** 60°, 120°   **23.** 44.4°, 135.6°
24. 14.5°, 165.5°   **25.** 45.6°   **26.** 83.6°   **27.** $\frac{4}{5}$ **28.** $\frac{4}{3}$ **29.** $\frac{13}{5}$
30. $\frac{25}{24}$ **31.** $\frac{12}{5}$ **32.** $\sqrt{5}/2$ **33.** $\sqrt{1-x^2}$ **34.** $x/\sqrt{x^2+1}$
35. $x/\sqrt{1-x^2}$ **36.** $1/\sqrt{x^2+1}$ **37.** 72.5°, 19 ft   **38.** 38.7°
39. (a) $h = 2\tan\theta$ (b) $\theta = \tan^{-1}(h/2)$
40. (a) $\theta = \tan^{-1}(50/s)$ (b) $\theta = 68.2°$
41. (a) $\theta = \sin^{-1}(h/680)$ (b) $\theta = 0.826$ rad
42. (a) $\theta = \cos^{-1}\left(\dfrac{3960}{h+3960}\right)$ (b) $s = 7920\theta$

(c) $s = 7920\cos^{-1}\left(\dfrac{3960}{h+3960}\right)$ (d) 1761.5 mi   (e) 197.3 mi

43. (a) 54.1°   (b) 48.3°, 32.2°, 24.5°. The function $\sin^{-1}$ is
undefined for values outside the interval $[-1, 1]$.

SECTION 6.5 ■ PAGE 473

1. $\dfrac{\sin A}{a} = \dfrac{\sin B}{b} = \dfrac{\sin C}{c}$ **2.** ASA, SSA   **3.** 318.8   **4.** 25.4
5. 24.8   **6.** 40.3°   **7.** 44°   **8.** 144.9   **9.** $\angle C = 114°$, $a \approx 51$,
$b \approx 24$ **10.** $\angle B = 50°$, $a \approx 1.31$, $c \approx 2.57$
11. $\angle A = 44°$, $\angle B = 68°$, $a \approx 8.99$
12. $\angle B \approx 31.0°$, $\angle C \approx 69°$, $c \approx 6.2$
13. $\angle C = 62°$, $a \approx 200$, $b \approx 242$

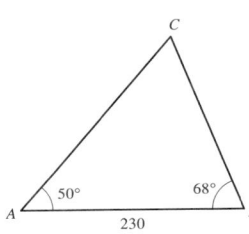

14. $\angle C = 47°$, $a \approx 26.7$, $b \approx 64.2$

15. $\angle B = 85°$, $a \approx 5$, $c \approx 9$

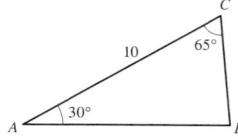

16. $\angle C = 63°$, $b \approx 1116.9$, $c \approx 999.0$

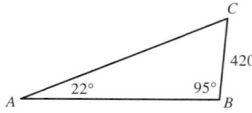

17. $\angle A = 100°$, $a \approx 89$, $c \approx 71$

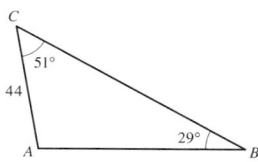

18. $\angle A = 70°$, $a \approx 109.7$, $b \approx 20.3$

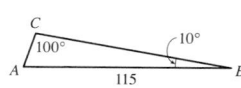

19. $\angle B \approx 30°$, $\angle C \approx 40°$, $c \approx 19$
20. $\angle B_1 \approx 89.6°$, $\angle C_1 \approx 53.4°$, $b_1 \approx 49.8$;
$\angle B_2 \approx 16.4°$, $\angle C_2 \approx 126.6°$, $b_2 \approx 14.1$ **21.** No solution
22. $\angle A_1 \approx 100.7°$, $\angle B_1 \approx 41.3°$, $a_1 \approx 67.0$;
$\angle A_2 \approx 3.3°$, $\angle B_2 \approx 138.7°$, $a_2 \approx 3.9$
23. $\angle A_1 \approx 125°$, $\angle C_1 \approx 30°$, $a_1 \approx 49$;
$\angle A_2 \approx 5°$, $\angle C_2 \approx 150°$, $a_2 \approx 5.6$
24. $\angle B_1 \approx 41.8°$, $\angle C_1 \approx 108.2°$, $c_1 \approx 142.5$;
$\angle B_2 \approx 138.2°$, $\angle C_2 \approx 11.8°$, $c_2 \approx 30.7$ **25.** No solution
26. $\angle B \approx 34.4°$, $\angle C \approx 10.6°$, $c \approx 25.9$
27. $\angle A_1 \approx 57.2°$, $\angle B_1 \approx 93.8°$, $b_1 \approx 30.9$;
$\angle A_2 \approx 122.8°$, $\angle B_2 \approx 28.2°$, $b_2 \approx 14.6$
28. $\angle A_1 \approx 49.7°$, $\angle C_1 \approx 72.3°$, $a_1 \approx 65.7$;
$\angle A_2 \approx 14.3°$, $\angle C_2 \approx 107.7°$, $a_2 \approx 21.3$
29. (a) $91.146°$ **(b)** $14.427°$ **30.** 5.25 **33. (a)** 1018 mi
(b) 1017 mi   **34. (a)** 3.77 mi   **(b)** 2.00 mi   **35.** 219 ft
36. 678.5 ft   **37.** 55.9 m   **38.** 161.1 ft   **39.** 175 ft
40. 155 m   **41.** 192 m   **42.** $48.2°$ **43.** 0.427 AU, 1.119 AU
44. (b) 12 cm   **(c)** A plane

SECTION 6.6 ■ PAGE 480

1. $a^2 + b^2 - 2ab\cos C$ **2.** SSS, SAS   **3.** 28.9   **4.** 26.8
5. 47   **6.** 8.2   **7.** 29.89°   **8.** 111°   **9.** 15   **10.** 130.54°
11. $\angle A \approx 39.4°$, $\angle B \approx 20.6°$, $c \approx 24.6$
12. $\angle A \approx 63.0°$, $\angle B \approx 15.5°$, $\angle C \approx 101.5°$
13. $\angle A \approx 48°$, $\angle B \approx 79°$, $c \approx 3.2$
14. $\angle B \approx 80.5°$, $\angle C \approx 29.5°$, $a \approx 57.2$
15. $\angle A \approx 50°$, $\angle B \approx 73°$, $\angle C \approx 57°$
16. $\angle A \approx 38.6°$, $\angle B \approx 48.5°$, $\angle C \approx 92.9°$
17. $\angle A_1 \approx 83.6°$, $\angle C_1 \approx 56.4°$, $a_1 \approx 193$;
$\angle A_2 \approx 16.4°$, $\angle C_2 \approx 123.6$, $a_2 \approx 54.9$ **18.** No such triangle
19. No such triangle   **20.** $\angle A = 36°$, $b \approx 109.4$, $c \approx 124.1$
21. 2   **22.** 12.2   **23.** 25.4   **24.** 21.3°   **25.** 89.2°
26. 126.5°   **27.** 24.3   **28.** 1180.8   **29.** 54   **30.** 0.97
31. 26.83   **32.** 549.6   **33.** 5.33   **34.** 9.798   **35.** 40.77
36. 2.46   **37.** 3.85 cm²   **39.** 2.30 mi   **40.** 7.3, 3.8
41. 23.1 mi   **42.** 56.0 mi   **43.** 2179 mi   **44.** 28 mi

45. (a) 62.6 mi   **(b)** S 18.2° E   **46. (a)** 232.5 mi
(b) N 50° E   **47.** 96°   **48.** 31°   **49.** 211 ft   **50.** 161 ft
51. 3835 ft   **52.** 1679 ft   **53.** $165,554

CHAPTER 6 REVIEW ■ PAGE 483

1. (a) $\pi/3$ **(b)** $11\pi/6$ **(c)** $-3\pi/4$ **(d)** $-\pi/2$
2. (a) $2\pi/15$ **(b)** $-11\pi/6$ **(c)** $25\pi/6$ **(d)** $\pi/36$
3. (a) 450°   **(b)** $-30°$ **(c)** 405°   **(d)** $(558/\pi)° \approx 177.6°$
4. (a) $(1440/\pi)° \approx 458.37°$ **(b)** $(450/\pi)° \approx 143.24°$
(c) 330°   **(d)** 108°   **5.** 8 m   **6.** 1.4 rad $\approx 80.2°$
7. 82 ft   **8.** 21,609   **9.** 0.619 rad $\approx 35.4°$ **10.** 25 m²
11. 18,151 ft²   **12.** 0.4 rad $\approx 22.9°$
13. 300π rad/min ≈ 942.5 rad/min,
7539.8 in./min = 628.3 ft/min
14. (a) 7000π rad/min $\approx 21{,}991$ rad/min
(b) 7777.8π rad/min $\approx 24{,}434.6$ rad/min
(c) 268,780 in./min ≈ 255 mi/h
15. $\sin\theta = 5/\sqrt{74}$, $\cos\theta = 7/\sqrt{74}$, $\tan\theta = \frac{5}{7}$,
$\csc\theta = \sqrt{74}/5$, $\sec\theta = \sqrt{74}/7$, $\cot\theta = \frac{7}{5}$
16. $\sin\theta = \frac{3}{10}$, $\cos\theta = \sqrt{91}/10$, $\tan\theta = 3\sqrt{91}/91$,
$\csc\theta = \frac{10}{3}$, $\sec\theta = 10\sqrt{91}/91$, $\cot\theta = \sqrt{91}/3$
17. $x \approx 3.83$, $y \approx 3.21$ **18.** $x \approx 2.44$, $y \approx 1.40$
19. $x \approx 2.92$, $y \approx 3.11$ **20.** $x \approx 3.46$, $y \approx 1.73$
21. $A = 70°$, $a \approx 2.819$, $b \approx 1.026$
22. $C = 30°$, $a = 40$, $b \approx 34.64$
23. $A \approx 16.3°$, $C \approx 73.7°$, $c = 24$
24. $A \approx 22.6°$, $C \approx 67.4°$, $b = 13$
25. $a = \cot\theta$, $b = \csc\theta$ **26.** 550 m   **27.** 48 m
28. $h = \sqrt{64 - 4\cos^2\theta} + 2\sin\theta$
29. 1076 mi   **30.** 14,400 ft   **31.** $-\sqrt{2}/2$ **32.** $\sqrt{2}$
33. 1   **34.** $-\sqrt{3}/2$ **35.** $-\sqrt{3}/3$ **36.** $\sqrt{2}/2$ **37.** $-\sqrt{2}/2$
38. -2 **39.** $2\sqrt{3}/3$ **40.** $2\sqrt{3}/3$ **41.** $-\sqrt{3}$ **42.** -1
43. $\sin\theta = \frac{12}{13}$, $\cos\theta = -\frac{5}{13}$, $\tan\theta = -\frac{12}{5}$,
$\csc\theta = \frac{13}{12}$, $\sec\theta = -\frac{13}{5}$, $\cot\theta = -\frac{5}{12}$ **44.** $\frac{1}{2}$ **45.** 60°
46. $\sin\theta = -\sqrt{5}/5$, $\cos\theta = -2\sqrt{5}/5$, $\tan\theta = \frac{1}{2}$,
$\csc\theta = -\sqrt{5}$, $\sec\theta = -\sqrt{5}/2$, $\cot\theta = 2$
47. $\tan\theta = -\sqrt{1 - \cos^2\theta}/\cos\theta$
48. $\sec\theta = -1/\sqrt{1 - \sin^2\theta}$ **49.** $\tan^2\theta = \sin^2\theta/(1 - \sin^2\theta)$
50. $\csc^2\theta\cos^2\theta = \dfrac{1}{\sin^2\theta} - 1$
51. $\sin\theta = \sqrt{7}/4$, $\cos\theta = \frac{3}{4}$, $\csc\theta = 4\sqrt{7}/7$, $\cot\theta = 3\sqrt{7}/7$
52. $\sin\theta = -\frac{9}{41}$, $\cos\theta = \frac{40}{41}$, $\tan\theta = -\frac{9}{40}$, $\cot\theta = -\frac{40}{9}$
53. $\cos\theta = -\frac{4}{5}$, $\tan\theta = -\frac{3}{4}$, $\csc\theta = \frac{5}{3}$, $\sec\theta = -\frac{5}{4}$, $\cot\theta = -\frac{4}{3}$
54. $\sin\theta = -\frac{12}{13}$, $\cos\theta = -\frac{5}{13}$, $\tan\theta = \frac{12}{5}$, $\csc\theta = -\frac{13}{12}$, $\cot\theta = \frac{5}{12}$
55. $-\sqrt{5}/5$ **56.** $\sqrt{3}$ **57.** 1   **58.** $-\sqrt{3}/2$
59. $\pi/3$ **60.** $\pi/6$ **61.** $2/\sqrt{21}$ **62.** $\sqrt{55}/8$ **63.** $x/\sqrt{1 + x^2}$
64. $1/\sqrt{1 - x^2}$ **65.** $\theta = \cos^{-1}(x/3)$ **66.** $\theta = \tan^{-1}(x/2)$
67. 5.32   **68.** 1.46   **69.** 148.07   **70.** 77.82   **71.** 9.17   **72.** 3.3
73. 54.1° or 125.9°   **74.** 52.0°   **75.** 80.4°   **76.** 153.2°
77. 77.3 mi   **78.** 1160 ft   **79.** 3.9 mi   **80.** 80.8 mi
81. 32.12   **82.** 14.98

CHAPTER 6 TEST ■ PAGE 487

1. $11\pi/6$, $-3\pi/4$ **2.** 240°, $-74.5°$
3. (a) 240π rad/min ≈ 753.98 rad/min
(b) 12,063.7 ft/min = 137 mi/h   **4. (a)** $\sqrt{2}/2$
(b) $\sqrt{3}/3$ **(c)** 2   **(d)** 1   **5.** $(26 + 6\sqrt{13})/39$
6. $a = 24\sin\theta$, $b = 24\cos\theta$ **7.** $(4 - 3\sqrt{2})/4$

8. $-\frac{13}{12}$ **9.** $\tan\theta = -\sqrt{\sec^2\theta - 1}$ **10.** 19.6 ft
11. (a) $\theta = \tan^{-1}(x/4)$ **(b)** $\theta = \cos^{-1}(3/x)$ **12.** $\frac{40}{41}$
13. 9.1   **14.** 250.5   **15.** 8.4   **16.** 19.5   **17.** 78.6°   **18.** 40.2°
19. (a) 15.3 m^2 **(b)** 24.3 m   **20. (a)** 129.9°   **(b)** 44.9
21. 554 ft

FOCUS ON MODELING ▪ PAGE 490

1. 1.41 mi   **2.** 1.31 mi
3. 14.3 m   **4.** 119.2 m
5. (c) 2349.8 ft   **6.** 4194 ft
7.

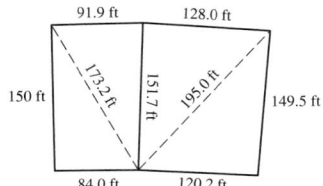

91.9 ft   128.0 ft
173.2 ft   151.7 ft   195.0 ft
150 ft   149.5 ft
84.0 ft   120.2 ft

CHAPTER 7

SECTION 7.1 ▪ PAGE 498

1. all; 1   **2.** $\cos(-x) = \cos x$ **3.** $\sin t$ **4.** $\cot t$ **5.** $\tan\theta$
6. $\sec\theta$ **7.** -1 **8.** $\tan x$ **9.** $\csc u$ **10.** 1   **11.** $\tan\theta$
12. $\sec\theta$ **13.** 1   **14.** $\cos x$ **15.** $\cos y$ **16.** $\sin x$ **17.** $\sin^2 x$
18. $\sin x$ **19.** $\sec x$ **20.** 1   **21.** $2\sec u$ **22.** 1   **23.** $\cos^2 x$
24. $\sin A + \cos A$ **25.** $\cos\theta$ **26.** $1 - \sin x$

27. (a) LHS $= \dfrac{1 - \sin^2 x}{\sin x} = $ RHS

28. (a) LHS $= \dfrac{1 - \cos^2 y}{\cos y} = $ RHS

29. LHS $= \sin\theta \dfrac{\cos\theta}{\sin\theta} = $ RHS

30. LHS $= \dfrac{\sin x}{\cos x}\cdot\cos x = $ RHS

31. LHS $= \cos u\dfrac{1}{\cos u}\cot u = $ RHS

32. LHS $= \dfrac{\cos x}{\sin x}\cdot\dfrac{1}{\cos x}\cdot\sin x = $ RHS

33. LHS $= \sin B + \cos B\dfrac{\cos B}{\sin B}$
$= \dfrac{\sin^2 B + \cos^2 B}{\sin B} = \dfrac{1}{\sin B} = $ RHS

34. LHS $= \cos x - (-\sin x) = $ RHS

35. LHS $= -\dfrac{\cos\alpha}{\sin\alpha}\cos\alpha - \sin\alpha = \dfrac{-\cos^2\alpha - \sin^2\alpha}{\sin\alpha}$
$= \dfrac{-1}{\sin\alpha} = $ RHS

36. LHS $= \csc^2 x - \sin x\csc x = \csc^2 x - 1 = $ RHS

37. LHS $= \dfrac{\sin\theta}{\cos\theta} + \dfrac{\cos\theta}{\sin\theta} = \dfrac{\sin^2\theta + \cos^2\theta}{\cos\theta\sin\theta}$
$= \dfrac{1}{\cos\theta\sin\theta} = $ RHS

38. LHS $= \sin^2 x + 2\sin x\cos x + \cos^2 x = $ RHS
39. LHS $= 1 - \cos^2\beta = \sin^2\beta = $ RHS
40. LHS $= \cos^2 x + \sin^2 x = $ RHS

41. LHS $= \dfrac{(\sin x + \cos x)^2}{(\sin x + \cos x)(\sin x - \cos x)} = \dfrac{\sin x + \cos x}{\sin x - \cos x}$
$= \dfrac{(\sin x + \cos x)(\sin x - \cos x)}{(\sin x - \cos x)(\sin x - \cos x)} = $ RHS

42. LHS $= \left[(\sin x + \cos x)^2\right]^2$
$= (\sin^2 x + 2\sin x\cos x + \cos^2 x)^2 = $ RHS

43. LHS $= \dfrac{\frac{1}{\cos t} - \cos t}{\frac{1}{\cos t}}\cdot\dfrac{\cos t}{\cos t} = \dfrac{1 - \cos^2 t}{1} = $ RHS

44. LHS $= \dfrac{1 - \sin x}{1 + \sin x}\cdot\dfrac{1 - \sin x}{1 - \sin x} = \dfrac{1 - 2\sin x + \sin^2 x}{1 - \sin^2 x}$
$= \dfrac{1}{\cos^2 x} - \dfrac{2\sin x}{\cos^2 x} + \dfrac{\sin^2 x}{\cos^2 x}$
$= \sec^2 x - 2\sec x\tan x + \tan^2 x$
$= (\sec x - \tan x)^2 = $ RHS

45. LHS $= \dfrac{1}{\cos^2 y} = \sec^2 y = $ RHS

46. LHS $= \dfrac{1}{\sin x} - \sin x = \dfrac{1 - \sin^2 x}{\sin x} = \dfrac{\cos^2 x}{\sin x} = $ RHS

47. LHS $= \cot x\cos x + \cot x - \csc x\cos x - \csc x$
$= \dfrac{\cos^2 x}{\sin x} + \dfrac{\cos x}{\sin x} - \dfrac{\cos x}{\sin x} - \dfrac{1}{\sin x} = \dfrac{\cos^2 x - 1}{\sin x}$
$= \dfrac{-\sin^2 x}{\sin x} = $ RHS

48. LHS $= (\sin^2\theta)^2 - (\cos^2\theta)^2$
$= (\sin^2\theta - \cos^2\theta)(\sin^2\theta + \cos^2\theta) = $ RHS

49. LHS $= \sin^2 x\left(1 + \dfrac{\cos^2 x}{\sin^2 x}\right) = \sin^2 x + \cos^2 x = $ RHS
50. LHS $= \cos^2 x - (1 - \cos^2 x) = 2\cos^2 x - 1 = $ RHS
51. LHS $= 2(1 - \sin^2 x) - 1 = 2 - 2\sin^2 x - 1 = $ RHS

52. LHS $= \left(\dfrac{\sin y}{\cos y} + \dfrac{\cos y}{\sin y}\right)\sin y\cos y$
$= \sin^2 y + \cos^2 y = $ RHS

53. LHS $= \dfrac{1 - \cos\alpha}{\sin\alpha}\cdot\dfrac{1 + \cos\alpha}{1 + \cos\alpha}$
$= \dfrac{1 - \cos^2\alpha}{\sin\alpha(1 + \cos\alpha)} = \dfrac{\sin^2\alpha}{\sin\alpha(1 + \cos\alpha)} = $ RHS

54. LHS $= 1 + \tan^2\alpha = \sec^2\alpha = $ RHS

55. LHS $= \dfrac{\sin^2\theta}{\cos^2\theta} - \dfrac{\sin^2\theta\cos^2\theta}{\cos^2\theta}$
$= \dfrac{\sin^2\theta(1 - \cos^2\theta)}{\cos^2\theta} = \dfrac{\sin^2\theta\sin^2\theta}{\cos^2\theta} = $ RHS

56. LHS $= \dfrac{\cos^2\theta}{\sin^2\theta}\cos^2\theta = \dfrac{\cos^2\theta(1 - \sin^2\theta)}{\sin^2\theta}$
$= \dfrac{\cos^2\theta}{\sin^2\theta} - \dfrac{\cos^2\theta\sin^2\theta}{\sin^2\theta} = $ RHS

57. LHS $= \dfrac{\sin x - 1}{\sin x + 1}\cdot\dfrac{\sin x + 1}{\sin x + 1} = \dfrac{\sin^2 x - 1}{(\sin x + 1)^2} = $ RHS

58. LHS $= \dfrac{\sin w}{\sin w + \cos w}\cdot\dfrac{\frac{1}{\cos w}}{\frac{1}{\cos w}} = \dfrac{\frac{\sin w}{\cos w}}{\frac{\sin w}{\cos w} + \frac{\cos w}{\cos w}} = $ RHS

59. LHS $= \dfrac{\sin^2 t + 2\sin t\cos t + \cos^2 t}{\sin t\cos t}$
$= \dfrac{\sin^2 t + \cos^2 t}{\sin t\cos t} + \dfrac{2\sin t\cos t}{\sin t\cos t} = \dfrac{1}{\sin t\cos t} + 2$
$= $ RHS

60. LHS $= \dfrac{1}{\cos t} \cdot \dfrac{1}{\sin t} \cdot \left(\dfrac{\sin t}{\cos t} + \dfrac{\cos t}{\sin t} \right)$

$= \dfrac{1}{\cos^2 t} + \dfrac{1}{\sin^2 t} = $ RHS

61. LHS $= \dfrac{1 + \frac{\sin^2 u}{\cos^2 u}}{1 - \frac{\sin^2 u}{\cos^2 u}} \cdot \dfrac{\cos^2 u}{\cos^2 u} = \dfrac{\cos^2 u + \sin^2 u}{\cos^2 u - \sin^2 u} = $ RHS

62. LHS $= \dfrac{1 + \sec^2 x}{\sec^2 x} = \dfrac{1}{\sec^2 x} + 1 = \cos^2 x + 1 = $ RHS

63. LHS $= \dfrac{\sec x}{\sec x - \tan x} \cdot \dfrac{\sec x + \tan x}{\sec x + \tan x}$

$= \dfrac{\sec x (\sec x + \tan x)}{\sec^2 x - \tan^2 x} = $ RHS

64. LHS $= \dfrac{\frac{1}{\cos x} + \frac{1}{\sin x}}{\frac{\sin x}{\cos x} + \frac{\cos x}{\sin x}} \cdot \dfrac{\sin x \cos x}{\sin x \cos x} = \dfrac{\sin x + \cos x}{\sin^2 x + \cos^2 x} = $ RHS

65. LHS $= (\sec v - \tan v) \cdot \dfrac{\sec v + \tan v}{\sec v + \tan v}$

$= \dfrac{\sec^2 v - \tan^2 v}{\sec v + \tan v} = $ RHS

66. LHS $= \dfrac{\sin A}{1 - \cos A} \cdot \dfrac{1 + \cos A}{1 + \cos A} - \cot A$

$= \dfrac{\sin A(1 + \cos A)}{1 - \cos^2 A} - \cot A$

$= \dfrac{\sin A(1 + \cos A)}{\sin^2 A} - \dfrac{\cos A}{\sin A}$

$= \dfrac{1}{\sin A} + \dfrac{\cos A}{\sin A} - \dfrac{\cos A}{\sin A} = $ RHS

67. LHS $= \dfrac{\sin x + \cos x}{\frac{1}{\cos x} + \frac{1}{\sin x}} = \dfrac{\sin x + \cos x}{\frac{\sin x + \cos x}{\cos x \sin x}}$

$= (\sin x + \cos x) \dfrac{\cos x \sin x}{\sin x + \cos x} = $ RHS

68. LHS $= \dfrac{1 - \cos x}{\sin x} \cdot \dfrac{1 - \cos x}{1 - \cos x} + \dfrac{\sin x}{1 - \cos x} \cdot \dfrac{\sin x}{\sin x}$

$= \dfrac{1 - 2 \cos x + \cos^2 x + \sin^2 x}{\sin x(1 - \cos x)} = \dfrac{2 - 2 \cos x}{\sin x(1 - \cos x)}$

$= \dfrac{2(1 - \cos x)}{\sin x(1 - \cos x)} = $ RHS

69. LHS $= \dfrac{\frac{1}{\sin x} - \frac{\cos x}{\sin x}}{\frac{1}{\cos x} - 1} \cdot \dfrac{\sin x \cos x}{\sin x \cos x} = \dfrac{\cos x(1 - \cos x)}{\sin x(1 - \cos x)}$

$= \dfrac{\cos x}{\sin x} = $ RHS

70. LHS $= \dfrac{1}{\sec^2 x} = \cos^2 x = $ RHS

71. LHS $= \dfrac{\sin^2 u}{\cos^2 u} - \dfrac{\sin^2 u \cos^2 u}{\cos^2 u} = \dfrac{\sin^2 u}{\cos^2 u}(1 - \cos^2 u) = $ RHS

72. LHS $= \dfrac{\tan v \sin v}{\tan v + \sin v} \cdot \dfrac{\tan v - \sin v}{\tan v - \sin v}$

$= \dfrac{\tan v \sin v (\tan v - \sin v)}{\tan^2 v - \sin^2 v}$

$= \dfrac{\tan v \sin v (\tan v - \sin v)}{\sin^2 v (\sec^2 v - 1)}$

$= \dfrac{\tan v \sin v (\tan v - \sin v)}{\sin^2 v \tan^2 v} = $ RHS

73. LHS $= (\sec^2 x - \tan^2 x)(\sec^2 x + \tan^2 x) = $ RHS

74. LHS $= \dfrac{\cos \theta}{1 - \sin \theta} \cdot \dfrac{1 + \sin \theta}{1 + \sin \theta} = \dfrac{\cos \theta(1 + \sin \theta)}{1 - \sin^2 \theta}$

$= \dfrac{\cos \theta(1 + \sin \theta)}{\cos^2 \theta} = $ RHS

75. RHS $= \dfrac{\sin \theta - \frac{1}{\sin \theta}}{\cos \theta - \frac{\cos \theta}{\sin \theta}} = \dfrac{\frac{\sin^2 \theta - 1}{\sin \theta}}{\frac{\cos \theta \sin \theta - \cos \theta}{\sin \theta}}$

$= \dfrac{\cos^2 \theta}{\cos \theta(\sin \theta - 1)} = $ LHS

76. LHS $= \dfrac{1 + \frac{\sin x}{\cos x}}{1 - \frac{\sin x}{\cos x}} \cdot \dfrac{\cos x}{\cos x} = \dfrac{\cos x + \sin x}{\cos x - \sin x} = $ RHS

77. LHS $= \dfrac{-\sin^2 t + \tan^2 t}{\sin^2 t} = -1 + \dfrac{\sin^2 t}{\cos^2 t} \cdot \dfrac{1}{\sin^2 t}$

$= -1 + \sec^2 t = $ RHS

78. LHS $= \dfrac{(1 + \sin x) - (1 - \sin x)}{(1 - \sin x)(1 + \sin x)} = \dfrac{2 \sin x}{1 - \sin^2 x} = \dfrac{2 \sin x}{\cos^2 x}$

$= 2 \dfrac{1}{\cos x} \cdot \dfrac{\sin x}{\cos x} = $ RHS

79. LHS $= \dfrac{\sec x - \tan x + \sec x + \tan x}{(\sec x + \tan x)(\sec x - \tan x)}$

$= \dfrac{2 \sec x}{\sec^2 x - \tan^2 x} = $ RHS

80. LHS $= \dfrac{(1 + \sin x)^2 - (1 - \sin x)^2}{(1 - \sin x)(1 + \sin x)}$

$= \dfrac{1 + 2 \sin x + \sin^2 x - 1 + 2 \sin x - \sin^2 x}{1 - \sin^2 x}$

$= \dfrac{4 \sin x}{\cos^2 x} = 4 \dfrac{\sin x}{\cos x} \cdot \dfrac{1}{\cos x} = $ RHS

81. LHS $= \tan^2 x + 2 \tan x \cot x + \cot^2 x = \tan^2 x + 2 + \cot^2 x$

$= (\tan^2 x + 1) + (\cot^2 x + 1) = $ RHS

82. LHS $= (\sec^2 x - 1) - (\csc^2 x - 1)$

$= \sec^2 x - \csc^2 x = $ RHS

83. LHS $= \dfrac{\frac{1}{\cos u} - 1}{\frac{1}{\cos u} + 1} \cdot \dfrac{\cos u}{\cos u} = $ RHS

84. LHS $= \dfrac{\cot x + 1}{\cot x - 1} \cdot \dfrac{\tan x}{\tan x} = \dfrac{\tan x \cot x + \tan x}{\tan x \cot x - \tan x}$

$= \dfrac{1 + \tan x}{1 - \tan x} = $ RHS

85. LHS $= \dfrac{(\sin x + \cos x)(\sin^2 x - \sin x \cos x + \cos^2 x)}{\sin x + \cos x}$

$= \sin^2 x - \sin x \cos x + \cos^2 x = $ RHS

86. LHS $= \dfrac{\tan v - \cot v}{(\tan v - \cot v)(\tan v + \cot v)}$

$= \dfrac{1}{\tan v + \cot v} = \dfrac{1}{\frac{\sin v}{\cos v} + \frac{\cos v}{\sin v}} \cdot \dfrac{\sin v \cos v}{\sin v \cos v}$

$= \dfrac{\sin v \cos v}{\sin^2 v + \cos^2 v} = $ RHS

87. LHS $= \dfrac{1 + \sin x}{1 - \sin x} \cdot \dfrac{1 + \sin x}{1 + \sin x} = \dfrac{(1 + \sin x)^2}{1 - \sin^2 x}$

$= \dfrac{(1 + \sin x)^2}{\cos^2 x} = \left(\dfrac{1 + \sin x}{\cos x} \right)^2 = $ RHS

88. LHS $= \dfrac{\frac{\sin x}{\cos x} + \frac{\sin y}{\cos y}}{\frac{\cos x}{\sin x} + \frac{\cos y}{\sin y}} = \left(\dfrac{\sin x \cos y + \cos x \sin y}{\cos x \cos y} \right)$

$\times \left(\dfrac{\sin x \sin y}{\cos x \sin y + \sin x \cos y} \right)$

$= \dfrac{\sin x \sin y}{\cos x \cos y} = \tan x \tan y = $ RHS

89. LHS $= \left(\dfrac{\sin x}{\cos x} + \dfrac{\cos x}{\sin x} \right)^4 = \left(\dfrac{\sin^2 x + \cos^2 x}{\sin x \cos x} \right)^4$

$= \left(\dfrac{1}{\sin x \cos x} \right)^4 = $ RHS

90. LHS $= \left(\sin \alpha - \dfrac{\sin \alpha}{\cos \alpha} \right)\left(\cos \alpha - \dfrac{\cos \alpha}{\sin \alpha} \right)$

$= \sin \alpha \left(1 - \dfrac{1}{\cos \alpha} \right) \cdot \cos \alpha \left(1 - \dfrac{1}{\sin \alpha} \right)$

$= \cos \alpha \left(1 - \dfrac{1}{\cos \alpha} \right) \sin \alpha \left(1 - \dfrac{1}{\sin \alpha} \right)$

$= (\cos \alpha - 1)(\sin \alpha - 1) = $ RHS

91. $\tan \theta$ **92.** $\sec \theta$ **93.** $\tan \theta$ **94.** $\frac{1}{8} \cot^2 \theta \cos \theta$
95. $3 \cos \theta$ **96.** $\sin \theta$

97.

Yes

98.

No

99.

No

100.

Yes

SECTION 7.2 ■ PAGE 505

1. addition; $\sin x \cos y + \cos x \sin y$
2. subtraction; $\cos x \cos y + \sin x \sin y$

3. $\dfrac{\sqrt{6} + \sqrt{2}}{4}$ **4.** $\dfrac{\sqrt{6} - \sqrt{2}}{4}$ **5.** $\dfrac{\sqrt{2} - \sqrt{6}}{4}$

6. $-\dfrac{\sqrt{2} + \sqrt{6}}{4}$ **7.** $2 - \sqrt{3}$ **8.** $\sqrt{3} - 2$

9. $-\dfrac{\sqrt{6} + \sqrt{2}}{4}$ **10.** $\dfrac{\sqrt{2} - \sqrt{6}}{4}$ **11.** $\sqrt{3} - 2$

12. $-\dfrac{\sqrt{6} + \sqrt{2}}{4}$ **13.** $-\dfrac{\sqrt{6} + \sqrt{2}}{4}$ **14.** $-(2 + \sqrt{3})$

15. $\sqrt{2}/2$ **16.** 0 **17.** $\frac{1}{2}$ **18.** $\sqrt{3}/3$ **19.** $\sqrt{3}$ **20.** $-\frac{1}{2}$

21. LHS $= \dfrac{\sin\left(\frac{\pi}{2} - u\right)}{\cos\left(\frac{\pi}{2} - u\right)} = \dfrac{\sin \frac{\pi}{2} \cos u - \cos \frac{\pi}{2} \sin u}{\cos \frac{\pi}{2} \cos u + \sin \frac{\pi}{2} \sin u}$

$= \dfrac{\cos u}{\sin u} = $ RHS

22. LHS $= \dfrac{\cos\left(\frac{\pi}{2} - u\right)}{\sin\left(\frac{\pi}{2} - u\right)} = \dfrac{\cos \frac{\pi}{2} \cos u + \sin \frac{\pi}{2} \sin u}{\sin \frac{\pi}{2} \cos u - \cos \frac{\pi}{2} \sin u}$

$= \dfrac{\sin u}{\cos u} = $ RHS

23. LHS $= \dfrac{1}{\cos\left(\frac{\pi}{2} - u\right)} = \dfrac{1}{\cos \frac{\pi}{2} \cos u + \sin \frac{\pi}{2} \sin u}$

$= \dfrac{1}{\sin u} = $ RHS

24. LHS $= \dfrac{1}{\sin\left(\frac{\pi}{2} - u\right)} = \dfrac{1}{\sin \frac{\pi}{2} \cos u - \cos \frac{\pi}{2} \sin u}$

$= \dfrac{1}{\cos u} = $ RHS

25. LHS $= \sin x \cos \frac{\pi}{2} - \cos x \sin \frac{\pi}{2} = $ RHS
26. LHS $= \cos x \cos \frac{\pi}{2} + \sin x \sin \frac{\pi}{2} = $ RHS
27. LHS $= \sin x \cos \pi - \cos x \sin \pi = $ RHS
28. LHS $= \cos x \cos \pi + \sin x \sin \pi = $ RHS

29. LHS $= \dfrac{\tan x - \tan \pi}{1 + \tan x \tan \pi} = $ RHS

30. LHS $= \sin\left(\dfrac{\pi}{2} - x\right) = \sin \dfrac{\pi}{2} \cos x - \cos \dfrac{\pi}{2} \sin x = \cos x$

RHS $= \sin\left(\dfrac{\pi}{2} + x\right) = \sin \dfrac{\pi}{2} \cos x + \cos \dfrac{\pi}{2} \sin x = \cos x$

31. LHS $= \cos x \cos \frac{\pi}{6} - \sin x \sin \frac{\pi}{6} + \sin x \cos \frac{\pi}{3} - \cos x \sin \frac{\pi}{3}$

$= \frac{\sqrt{3}}{2} \cos x - \frac{1}{2} \sin x + \frac{1}{2} \sin x - \frac{\sqrt{3}}{2} \cos x = $ RHS

32. LHS $= \dfrac{\tan x - \tan \frac{\pi}{4}}{1 + \tan x \tan \frac{\pi}{4}} = $ RHS

33. LHS $= \sin x \cos y + \cos x \sin y$
$- (\sin x \cos y - \cos x \sin y) = $ RHS

34. LHS $= \cos x \cos y - \sin x \sin y + \cos x \cos y$
$+ \sin x \sin y = $ RHS

35. LHS $= \dfrac{1}{\tan(x - y)} = \dfrac{1 + \tan x \tan y}{\tan x - \tan y}$

$= \dfrac{1 + \frac{1}{\cot x} \frac{1}{\cot y}}{\frac{1}{\cot x} - \frac{1}{\cot y}} \cdot \dfrac{\cot x \cot y}{\cot x \cot y} = $ RHS

36. LHS $= \dfrac{1}{\tan(x + y)} = \dfrac{1 - \tan x \tan y}{\tan x + \tan y}$

$= \dfrac{1 - \frac{1}{\cot x} \frac{1}{\cot y}}{\frac{1}{\cot x} + \frac{1}{\cot y}} \cdot \dfrac{\cot x \cot y}{\cot x \cot y}$

$= \dfrac{\cot x \cot y - 1}{\cot x + \cot y} = $ RHS

37. LHS $= \dfrac{\sin x}{\cos x} - \dfrac{\sin y}{\cos y} = \dfrac{\sin x \cos y - \cos x \sin y}{\cos x \cos y} = $ RHS

38. LHS $= 1 - \dfrac{\sin x \sin y}{\cos x \cos y} = \dfrac{\cos x \cos y - \sin x \sin y}{\cos x \cos y} = $ RHS

39. LHS $= \dfrac{\sin x \cos y + \cos x \sin y - (\sin x \cos y - \cos x \sin y)}{\cos x \cos y - \sin x \sin y + \cos x \cos y + \sin x \sin y}$

$= \dfrac{2 \cos x \sin y}{2 \cos x \cos y} = $ RHS

40. LHS $= (\cos x \cos y - \sin x \sin y)(\cos x \cos y + \sin x \sin y)$

$= \cos^2 x \cos^2 y - \sin^2 x \sin^2 y$

$= \cos^2 x (1 - \sin^2 y) - (1 - \cos^2 x) \sin^2 y$

$= \cos^2 x - \sin^2 y \cos^2 x + \sin^2 y \cos^2 x - \sin^2 y = $ RHS

41. LHS $= \sin((x + y) + z)$

$= \sin(x + y) \cos z + \cos(x + y) \sin z$

$= \cos z [\sin x \cos y + \cos x \sin y]$

$\quad + \sin z [\cos x \cos y - \sin x \sin y] = $ RHS

42. LHS $= \tan(x - y + y - z)[1 - \tan(x - y) \tan(y - z)]$

$\quad + \tan(z - x)$

$= \tan(x - z)[1 - \tan(x - y) \tan(y - z)]$

$\quad + \tan(z - x)$

$= \tan(x - z) + \tan(z - x) - \tan(x - y)$

$\quad \times \tan(y - z) \tan(x - z)$

$= \tan(x - z) - \tan(x - z) - \tan(x - y)$

$\quad \times \tan(y - z) \tan(x - z)$

$= 0 - \tan(x - y) \tan(y - z) \tan(x - z) = $ RHS

43. $\dfrac{\sqrt{1 - x^2} + xy}{\sqrt{1 + y^2}}$ **44.** $\dfrac{xy + \sqrt{1 - x^2}\,\sqrt{1 - y^2}}{y\sqrt{1 - x^2} - x\sqrt{1 - y^2}}$

45. $\dfrac{x - y}{\sqrt{1 + x^2}\,\sqrt{1 + y^2}}$ **46.** $xy + \sqrt{1 - x^2} \cdot \sqrt{1 - y^2}$

47. $\frac{1}{4}(\sqrt{6} + \sqrt{2})$ **48.** 0 **49.** $\dfrac{3 - 2\sqrt{14}}{\sqrt{7} + 6\sqrt{2}}$

50. $\frac{1}{15}(10 - 2\sqrt{5})$ **51.** $-\frac{1}{10}(3 + 4\sqrt{3})$ **52.** $-3\sqrt{10}/10$

53. $2\sqrt{5}/65$ **54.** $\dfrac{2\sqrt{30} - 1}{\sqrt{15} + 2\sqrt{2}}$ **55.** $2 \sin\left(x + \dfrac{5\pi}{6}\right)$

56. $\sqrt{2} \sin\left(x + \dfrac{\pi}{4}\right)$ **57.** $5\sqrt{2} \sin\left(2x + \dfrac{7\pi}{4}\right)$

58. $6 \sin \pi\left(x + \frac{1}{3}\right)$

59. (a) $g(x) = 2 \sin 2\left(x + \dfrac{\pi}{12}\right)$

(b)

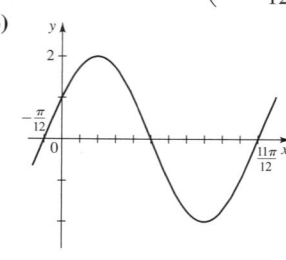

60. (a) $f(x) = \sqrt{2} \sin\left(x + \dfrac{\pi}{4}\right)$

(b)

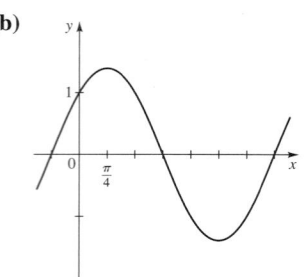

63. $\tan \gamma = \frac{17}{6}$ **64. (c)** $3\pi/4$

65. (a)

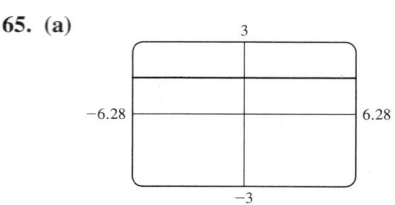

$\sin^2\left(x + \dfrac{\pi}{4}\right) + \sin^2\left(x - \dfrac{\pi}{4}\right) = 1$

66. (a)

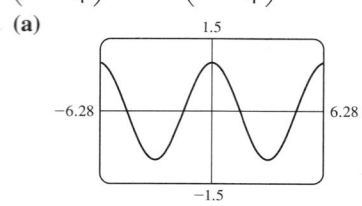

$-\frac{1}{2}[\cos(x + \pi) + \cos(x - \pi)] = \cos x$

67. $\pi/2$

68. (a)

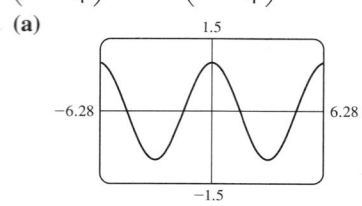

(b) $k = 5\sqrt{2}$, $\phi = \pi/4$

69. (b) $k = 10\sqrt{3}$, $\phi = \pi/6$

SECTION 7.3 ■ PAGE 514

1. Double-Angle; $2 \sin x \cos x$

2. Half-Angle; $\pm\sqrt{(1 - \cos x)/2}$

3. $\frac{120}{169}, \frac{119}{169}, \frac{120}{119}$ **4.** $-\frac{24}{25}, -\frac{7}{25}, \frac{24}{7}$ **5.** $-\frac{24}{25}, \frac{7}{25}, -\frac{24}{7}$

6. $-\sqrt{15}/8, \frac{7}{8}, -\sqrt{15}/7$ **7.** $\frac{24}{25}, \frac{7}{25}, \frac{24}{7}$ **8.** $-\sqrt{3}/2, -\frac{1}{2}, \sqrt{3}$

9. $-\frac{3}{5}, \frac{4}{5}, -\frac{3}{4}$ **10.** $\frac{12}{13}, -\frac{5}{13}, -\frac{12}{5}$ **11.** $\frac{1}{2}(\frac{3}{4} - \cos 2x + \frac{1}{4}\cos 4x)$

12. $\frac{1}{2}(\frac{3}{4} + \cos 2x + \frac{1}{4}\cos 4x)$

13. $\frac{1}{16}(1 - \cos 2x - \cos 4x + \cos 2x \cos 4x)$

14. $\frac{1}{16}(1 - \cos 4x + \cos 2x - \cos 2x \cos 4x)$

15. $\frac{1}{32}(\frac{3}{4} - \cos 4x + \frac{1}{4}\cos 8x)$

16. $\frac{1}{16}(3 + 7 \cos 2x + \cos 4x + \cos 2x \cos 4x)$

17. $\frac{1}{2}\sqrt{2 - \sqrt{3}}$ **18.** $2 - \sqrt{3}$ **19.** $\sqrt{2} - 1$

20. $\frac{1}{2}\sqrt{2+\sqrt{3}}$ **21.** $-\frac{1}{2}\sqrt{2+\sqrt{3}}$ **22.** $-\frac{1}{2}\sqrt{2-\sqrt{2}}$

23. $\sqrt{2}-1$ **24.** $\frac{1}{2}\sqrt{2-\sqrt{2}}$ **25.** $\frac{1}{2}\sqrt{2+\sqrt{3}}$

26. $2+\sqrt{3}$ **27.** $-\frac{1}{2}\sqrt{2-\sqrt{2}}$ **28.** $\frac{1}{2}\sqrt{2-\sqrt{3}}$

29. (a) $\sin 36°$ (b) $\sin 6\theta$

30. (a) $\tan 14°$ (b) $\tan 14\theta$

31. (a) $\cos 68°$ (b) $\cos 10\theta$

32. (a) $\cos\theta$ (b) $\sin\theta$

33. (a) $\tan 4°$ (b) $\tan 2\theta$

34. (a) $\sin 15°$ (b) $\sin 4\theta$

37. $\sqrt{10}/10,\ 3\sqrt{10}/10,\ \frac{1}{3}$ **38.** $3\sqrt{10}/10,\ -\sqrt{10}/10,\ -3$

39. $\sqrt{(3+2\sqrt{2})}/6,\ \sqrt{(3-2\sqrt{2})}/6,\ 3+2\sqrt{2}$

40. $\frac{1}{2}\sqrt{2-\sqrt{2}},\ \frac{1}{2}\sqrt{2+\sqrt{2}},\ \sqrt{2}-1$

41. $\sqrt{6}/6,\ -\sqrt{30}/6,\ -\sqrt{5}/5$

42. $\frac{1}{2}\sqrt{(26+5\sqrt{26})}/13,$
$-\frac{1}{2}\sqrt{(26-5\sqrt{26})}/13,\ -5-\sqrt{26}$

43. $\dfrac{2x}{1+x^2}$ **44.** $\dfrac{2x\sqrt{1-x^2}}{2x^2-1}$ **45.** $\sqrt{\dfrac{1-x}{2}}$ **46.** $1-2x^2$

47. $\frac{336}{625}$ **48.** $-\frac{119}{169}$ **49.** $\frac{8}{7}$ **50.** $\sqrt{5}/5$ **51.** $\frac{7}{25}$ **52.** $\sqrt{26}/26$

53. $-8\sqrt{3}/49$ **54.** $-\frac{24}{7}$ **55.** $\frac{1}{2}(\sin 5x - \sin x)$

56. $\frac{1}{2}(\cos 4x - \cos 6x)$ **57.** $\frac{1}{2}(\sin 5x + \sin 3x)$

58. $\frac{1}{2}(\cos 8x + \cos 2x)$ **59.** $\frac{3}{2}(\cos 11x + \cos 3x)$

60. $\frac{11}{2}\left(\sin\dfrac{3x}{4} + \sin\dfrac{x}{4}\right)$ **61.** $2\sin 4x\cos x$

62. $-2\cos\dfrac{5x}{2}\sin\dfrac{3x}{2}$ **63.** $2\sin 5x\sin x$ **64.** $2\cos\dfrac{11x}{2}\cos\dfrac{7x}{2}$

65. $-2\cos\frac{9}{2}x\sin\frac{5}{2}x$ **66.** $2\sin\dfrac{7x}{2}\cos\dfrac{x}{2}$

67. $(\sqrt{2}+\sqrt{3})/2$ **68.** $\frac{3}{4}(\sqrt{2}+\sqrt{3})$ **69.** $\frac{1}{4}(\sqrt{2}-1)$

70. $\sqrt{6}/2$ **71.** $\sqrt{2}/2$ **72.** $\sqrt{6}/2$

73. LHS $= \cos(2\cdot 5x) =$ RHS

74. LHS $= \sin(2\cdot 4x) =$ RHS

75. LHS $= \sin^2 x + 2\sin x\cos x + \cos^2 x$
$= 1 + 2\sin x\cos x =$ RHS

76. LHS $= \dfrac{2\tan x}{\sec^2 x} = 2\cdot\dfrac{\sin x}{\cos x}\cos^2 x = 2\sin x\cos x =$ RHS

77. LHS $= \dfrac{2\sin 2x\cos 2x}{\sin x} = \dfrac{2(2\sin x\cos x)(\cos 2x)}{\sin x} =$ RHS

78. LHS $= \dfrac{1+2\sin x\cos x}{2\sin x\cos x} = 1 + \dfrac{1}{2\sin x\cos x} =$ RHS

79. LHS $= \dfrac{2(\tan x - \cot x)}{(\tan x + \cot x)(\tan x - \cot x)} = \dfrac{2}{\tan x + \cot x}$
$= \dfrac{2}{\frac{\sin x}{\cos x} + \frac{\cos x}{\sin x}}\cdot\dfrac{\sin x\cos x}{\sin x\cos x} = \dfrac{2\sin x\cos x}{\sin^2 x + \cos^2 x}$
$= 2\sin x\cos x =$ RHS

80. LHS $= \dfrac{1}{\tan 2x} = \dfrac{1}{\frac{2\tan x}{1-\tan^2 x}} =$ RHS

81. LHS $= \tan(2x+x) = \dfrac{\tan 2x + \tan x}{1 - \tan 2x\tan x}$
$= \dfrac{\frac{2\tan x}{1-\tan^2 x} + \tan x}{1 - \frac{2\tan x}{1-\tan^2 x}\tan x}$
$= \dfrac{2\tan x + \tan x(1-\tan^2 x)}{1-\tan^2 x - 2\tan x\tan x} =$ RHS

82. LHS $= 4[(\sin^2 x + \cos^2 x)^3 - 3(\sin^4 x\cos^2 x + \sin^2 x\cos^4 x)]$
$= 4[1 - 3\sin^2 x\cos^2 x(\sin^2 x + \cos^2 x)]$
$= 4 - 12\sin^2 x\cos^2 x = 4 - 3(2\sin x\cos x)^2 =$ RHS

83. LHS $= (\cos^2 x + \sin^2 x)(\cos^2 x - \sin^2 x)$
$= \cos^2 x - \sin^2 x =$ RHS

84. LHS $= \dfrac{1 - \cos 2\left(\frac{x}{2}+\frac{\pi}{4}\right)}{1 + \cos 2\left(\frac{x}{2}+\frac{\pi}{4}\right)} = \dfrac{1 - \cos\left(x+\frac{\pi}{2}\right)}{1 + \cos\left(x+\frac{\pi}{2}\right)}$
$= \dfrac{1 - (-\sin x)}{1 + (-\sin x)} =$ RHS

85. LHS $= \dfrac{2\sin 3x\cos 2x}{2\cos 3x\cos 2x} = \dfrac{\sin 3x}{\cos 3x} =$ RHS

86. LHS $= \dfrac{2\sin 5x\cos 2x}{-2\sin 5x\sin(-2x)} = \dfrac{\cos 2x}{\sin 2x} =$ RHS

87. LHS $= \dfrac{2\sin 5x\cos 5x}{2\sin 5x\cos 4x} =$ RHS

88. $\dfrac{\sin x + \sin 3x + \sin 5x}{\cos x + \cos 3x + \cos 5x} = \dfrac{\sin x + \sin 5x + \sin 3x}{\cos x + \cos 5x + \cos 3x}$
$= \dfrac{2\sin 3x\cos 2x + \sin 3x}{2\cos 3x\cos 2x + \cos 3x} = \dfrac{\sin 3x(2\cos 2x + 1)}{\cos 3x(2\cos 2x + 1)}$
$= \tan 3x$

89. LHS $= \dfrac{2\sin\left(\frac{x+y}{2}\right)\cos\left(\frac{x-y}{2}\right)}{2\cos\left(\frac{x+y}{2}\right)\cos\left(\frac{x-y}{2}\right)}$
$= \dfrac{\sin\left(\frac{x+y}{2}\right)}{\cos\left(\frac{x+y}{2}\right)} =$ RHS

90. $\dfrac{\sin(x+y) - \sin(x-y)}{\cos(x+y) + \cos(x-y)}$
$= \dfrac{2\sin\left(\frac{x+y+x-y}{2}\right)\cos\left(\frac{x+y-x+y}{2}\right)}{2\cos\left(\frac{x+y+x-y}{2}\right)\cos\left(\frac{x+y-x+y}{2}\right)} = \dfrac{\sin x}{\cos x} = \tan x$

95. LHS $= \dfrac{(\sin x + \sin 5x) + (\sin 2x + \sin 4x) + \sin 3x}{(\cos x + \cos 5x) + (\cos 2x + \cos 4x) + \cos 3x}$
$= \dfrac{2\sin 3x\cos 2x + 2\sin 3x\cos x + \sin 3x}{2\cos 3x\cos 2x + 2\cos 3x\cos x + \cos 3x}$
$= \dfrac{\sin 3x(2\cos 2x + 2\cos x + 1)}{\cos 3x(2\cos 2x + 2\cos x + 1)} =$ RHS

97. (a)

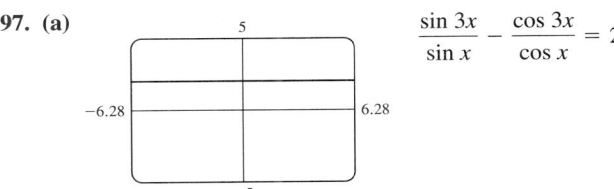

$\dfrac{\sin 3x}{\sin x} - \dfrac{\cos 3x}{\cos x} = 2$

98. (a)

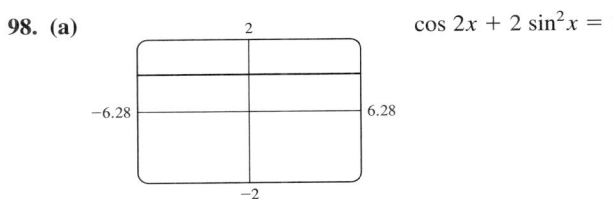

$\cos 2x + 2\sin^2 x = 1$

99. (a)

(c)

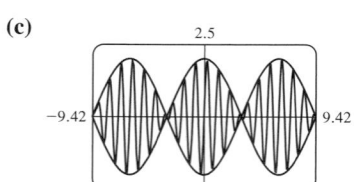

The graph of $y = f(x)$ lies between the two other graphs.

101. (a) $P(t) = 8t^4 - 8t^2 + 1$ **(b)** $Q(t) = 16t^5 - 20t^3 + 5t$
104. (b) 25 cm² **(c)** 7.07 cm × 3.54 cm
107. (a) and **(c)**

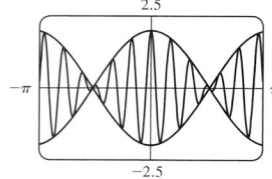

The graph of f lies between the graphs of $y = 2 \cos t$ and $y = -2 \cos t$. Thus, the loudness of the sound varies between $y = \pm 2 \cos t$.
108. (a) $y = \sin 1540\pi t + \sin 2418\pi t$
(b) $y = 2 \sin 1979\pi t \cos 439\pi t$
(c)

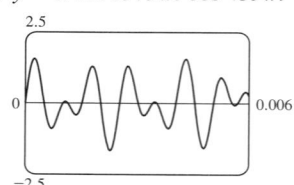

SECTION 7.4 ■ PAGE 522

1. infinitely many **2.** no, infinitely many
3. 0.3; $x \approx -9.7, -6.0, -3.4, 0.3, 2.8, 6.6, 9.1$ **4. (a)** 0.30, 2.84
(b) $2\pi, 0.30 + 2k\pi, 2.84 + 2k\pi$ **5.** $\dfrac{\pi}{3} + 2k\pi, \dfrac{2\pi}{3} + 2k\pi$

6. $-\dfrac{\pi}{4} + 2k\pi, \dfrac{5\pi}{4} + 2k\pi$ **7.** $(2k + 1)\pi$

8. $\dfrac{\pi}{6} + 2k\pi, \dfrac{11\pi}{6} + 2k\pi$ **9.** $1.32 + 2k\pi, 4.97 + 2k\pi$
10. $-0.30 + 2k\pi, 3.45 + 2k\pi$ **11.** $-0.47 + 2k\pi, 3.61 + 2k\pi$
12. $1.25 + 2k\pi, 5.04 + 2k\pi$ **13.** $-\dfrac{\pi}{3} + k\pi$ **14.** $\dfrac{\pi}{4} + k\pi$
15. $1.37 + k\pi$ **16.** $-0.32 + k\pi$ **17.** $\dfrac{5\pi}{6} + 2k\pi, \dfrac{7\pi}{6} + 2k\pi;$
$-7\pi/6, -5\pi/6, 5\pi/6, 7\pi/6, 17\pi/6, 19\pi/6$
18. $-\dfrac{\pi}{3} + 2k\pi, \dfrac{\pi}{3} + 2k\pi; -5\pi/3, -\pi/3, \pi/3, 5\pi/3, 7\pi/3, 11\pi/3$
19. $\dfrac{\pi}{4} + 2k\pi, \dfrac{3\pi}{4} + 2k\pi; -7\pi/4, -5\pi/4, \pi/4, 3\pi/4, 9\pi/4, 11\pi/4$
20. $-\dfrac{\pi}{3} + 2k\pi, \dfrac{4\pi}{3} + 2k\pi;$
$-2\pi/3, -\pi/3, 4\pi/3, 5\pi/3, 10\pi/3, 11\pi/3$

21. $1.29 + 2k\pi, 5.00 + 2k\pi; -5.00, -1.29, 1.29, 5.00, 7.57, 11.28$
22. $1.19 + k\pi; -5.09, -1.95, 1.19, 4.33, 7.47, 10.61$
23. $-1.47 + k\pi; -7.75, -4.61, -1.47, 1.67, 4.81, 7.95$
24. $-1.12 + 2k\pi, 4.26 + 2k\pi; -2.02, -1.12, 4.26, 5.16, 10.54,$
11.44 **25.** $(2k + 1)\pi$ **26.** $\dfrac{3\pi}{2} + 2k\pi$
27. $-\dfrac{\pi}{4} + 2k\pi, \dfrac{5\pi}{4} + 2k\pi$ **28.** $-\dfrac{\pi}{4} + 2k\pi, \dfrac{\pi}{4} + 2k\pi$
29. $0.20 + 2k\pi, 2.94 + 2k\pi$ **30.** $1.82 + 2k\pi, 4.46 + 2k\pi$
31. $-\dfrac{\pi}{6} + k\pi, \dfrac{\pi}{6} + k\pi$ **32.** $\dfrac{3\pi}{4} + k\pi$ **33.** $\dfrac{\pi}{4} + k\pi, \dfrac{3\pi}{4} + k\pi$
34. $\dfrac{\pi}{3} + k\pi, \dfrac{2\pi}{3} + k\pi$ **35.** $-1.11 + k\pi, 1.11 + k\pi$
36. $-0.34 + k\pi, 0.34 + k\pi$ **37.** $\dfrac{\pi}{4} + k\pi, \dfrac{3\pi}{4} + k\pi$
38. $\dfrac{\pi}{6} + k\pi, \dfrac{5\pi}{6} + k\pi$
39. $-1.11 + k\pi, 1.11 + k\pi, \dfrac{2\pi}{3} + 2k\pi, \dfrac{4\pi}{3} + 2k\pi$
40. $-0.25 + k\pi, 1.11 + k\pi, 0.25 + k\pi$
41. $\dfrac{\pi}{3} + 2k\pi, \dfrac{5\pi}{3} + 2k\pi$ **42.** $\dfrac{7\pi}{6} + 2k\pi, \dfrac{11\pi}{6} + 2k\pi, \dfrac{\pi}{2} + 2k\pi$
43. $0.34 + 2k\pi, 2.80 + 2k\pi$ **44.** $\pm 1.25 + k\pi, \pm 1.11 + k\pi$
45. $\dfrac{\pi}{3} + 2k\pi, \dfrac{5\pi}{3} + 2k\pi$ **46.** $\dfrac{3\pi}{2} + 2k\pi$ **47.** No solution
48. No solution **49.** $\dfrac{3\pi}{2} + 2k\pi$ **50.** $k\pi, \dfrac{\pi}{6} + k\pi, \dfrac{5\pi}{6} + k\pi$
51. $\dfrac{\pi}{2} + k\pi, \dfrac{7\pi}{6} + 2k\pi, \dfrac{11\pi}{6} + 2k\pi$
52. $\dfrac{\pi}{4} + 2k\pi, \dfrac{7\pi}{4} + 2k\pi$
53. $\dfrac{\pi}{2} + k\pi$ **54.** $k\pi, \dfrac{3\pi}{4} + k\pi$
55. $k\pi, 0.73 + 2k\pi, 2.41 + 2k\pi$
56. $\dfrac{\pi}{2} + k\pi, -0.85 + 2k\pi, 3.99 + 2k\pi$
57. 44.95° **58.** 41.1°
59. (a) 0° **(b)** 60°, 120° **(c)** 90°, 270° **(d)** 180°

SECTION 7.5 ■ PAGE 528

1. $\sin x = 0, k\pi$ **2.** $\sin x + 2 \sin x \cos x = 0,$
$\sin x = 0, 1 + 2 \cos x = 0$ **3.** $-\dfrac{\pi}{6} + 2k\pi, \dfrac{7\pi}{6} + 2k\pi, \dfrac{\pi}{2} + 2k\pi$
4. No solution **5.** $(2k + 1)\pi, 1.23 + 2k\pi, 5.05 + 2k\pi$
6. $-\dfrac{\pi}{4} + k\pi, 0.46 + k\pi$ **7.** $k\pi, 0.72 + 2k\pi, 5.56 + 2k\pi$
8. $k\pi, 1.23 + 2k\pi, 5.05 + 2k\pi$ **9.** $\dfrac{\pi}{6} + 2k\pi, \dfrac{5\pi}{6} + 2k\pi$
10. $\dfrac{\pi}{4} + k\pi, \dfrac{3\pi}{4} + k\pi$ **11.** $\dfrac{\pi}{3} + 2k\pi, \dfrac{5\pi}{3} + 2k\pi, (2k + 1)\pi$
12. $\dfrac{\pi}{3} + k\pi, \dfrac{2\pi}{3} + k\pi$ **13.** $(2k + 1)\pi, \dfrac{\pi}{2} + 2k\pi$
14. $2k\pi, \dfrac{3\pi}{2} + 2k\pi$ **15.** $2k\pi$ **16.** $-1.24 + k\pi, \dfrac{\pi}{4} + k\pi$

17. (a) $\dfrac{\pi}{9} + \dfrac{2k\pi}{3}, \dfrac{5\pi}{9} + \dfrac{2k\pi}{3}$ **(b)** $\pi/9, 5\pi/9, 7\pi/9, 11\pi/9,$

$13\pi/9, 17\pi/9$ **18. (a)** $\dfrac{\pi}{3} + k\pi, \dfrac{2\pi}{3} + k\pi$

(b) $\pi/3, 2\pi/3, 4\pi/3, 5\pi/3$ **19. (a)** $\dfrac{\pi}{3} + k\pi, \dfrac{2\pi}{3} + k\pi$

(b) $\pi/3, 2\pi/3, 4\pi/3, 5\pi/3$ **20. (a)** $\dfrac{7\pi}{18} + \dfrac{2k\pi}{3}, \dfrac{11\pi}{18} + \dfrac{2k\pi}{3}$

(b) $7\pi/18, 11\pi/18, 19\pi/18, 23\pi/18, 31\pi/18, 35\pi/18$

21. (a) $\dfrac{5\pi}{18} + \dfrac{k\pi}{3}$ **(b)** $5\pi/18, 11\pi/18, 17\pi/18, 23\pi/18,$

$29\pi/18, 35\pi/18$ **22. (a)** $\dfrac{\pi}{12} + \dfrac{k\pi}{2}, \dfrac{5\pi}{12} + \dfrac{k\pi}{2}$

(b) $\pi/12, 5\pi/12, 7\pi/12, 11\pi/12, 13\pi/12, 17\pi/12, 19\pi/12, 23\pi/12$

23. (a) $4k\pi$ **(b)** 0 **24. (a)** $\dfrac{8\pi}{3} + 4k\pi$ **(b)** None

25. (a) $4\pi + 6k\pi, 5\pi + 6k\pi$ **(b)** None **26. (a)** $2k\pi$ **(b)** 0

27. (a) $0.62 + \dfrac{k\pi}{2}$ **(b)** $0.62, 2.19, 3.76, 5.33$

28. (a) $0.15 + \dfrac{k\pi}{3}, 0.89 + \dfrac{k\pi}{3}$ **(b)** $0.15, 0.89, 1.20, 1.94, 2.24,$

$2.98, 3.29, 4.03, 4.34, 5.08, 5.39, 6.13$ **29. (a)** $k\pi$ **(b)** $0, \pi$

30. (a) $2k\pi/3$ **(b)** $0, 2\pi/3, 4\pi/3$

31. (a) $\dfrac{\pi}{6} + k\pi, \dfrac{\pi}{4} + k\pi, \dfrac{5\pi}{6} + k\pi$

(b) $\pi/6, \pi/4, 5\pi/6, 7\pi/6, 5\pi/4, 11\pi/6$

32. (a) $\dfrac{\pi}{6} + 2k\pi, \dfrac{2\pi}{3} + 2k\pi, \dfrac{5\pi}{6} + 2k\pi, \dfrac{4\pi}{3} + 2k\pi$

(b) $\pi/6, 2\pi/3, 5\pi/6, 4\pi/3$

33. (a) $\dfrac{\pi}{6} + 2k\pi, \dfrac{5\pi}{6} + 2k\pi, \dfrac{3\pi}{4} + k\pi$

(b) $\pi/6, 3\pi/4, 5\pi/6, 7\pi/4$

34. (a) $\dfrac{\pi}{4} + k\pi, \dfrac{3\pi}{4} + k\pi$ **(b)** $\pi/4, 3\pi/4, 5\pi/4, 7\pi/4$

35. (a)

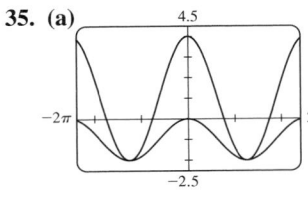

$(\pm 3.14, -2)$

(b) $((2k + 1)\pi, -2)$

36. (a)

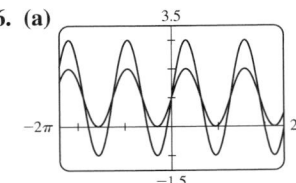

$(\pm 6.28, 1), (\pm 4.71, 1),$
$(\pm 3.14, 1), (\pm 1.57, 1), (0, 1)$

(b) $(\frac{1}{2}k\pi, 1)$

37. (a)

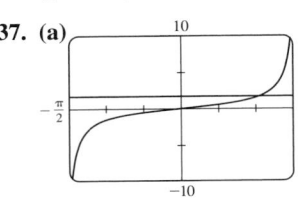

$(1.04, 1.73)$

(b) $\left(\dfrac{\pi}{3} + k\pi, \sqrt{3}\right)$

38. (a)

$(-4.71, 0), (-3.14, 1),$
$(1.57, 0), (3.14, -1)$

(b) $(\pi + 2k\pi, -1), \left(\dfrac{\pi}{2} + 2k\pi, 0\right)$

39. $\pi/8, 3\pi/8, 5\pi/8, 7\pi/8, 9\pi/8, 11\pi/8, 13\pi/8, 15\pi/8$
40. $\pi/3, 5\pi/3$ **41.** $\pi/3, 2\pi/3$ **42.** $0, \pi/2, \pi, 3\pi/2$
43. $\pi/2, 7\pi/6, 3\pi/2, 11\pi/6$ **44.** $0, \pi/2, 3\pi/2$ **45.** 0
46. $\pi/8, 3\pi/8, 5\pi/8, 7\pi/8, 9\pi/8, 11\pi/8, 13\pi/8, 15\pi/8$
47. $0, \pi$ **48.** $\pi/3, 2\pi/3, 4\pi/3, 5\pi/3$
49. $0, \pi/3, 2\pi/3, \pi, 4\pi/3, 5\pi/3$ **50.** $0, \pi/9, \pi/3, 5\pi/9, 2\pi/3,$
$7\pi/9, \pi, 11\pi/9, 4\pi/3, 13\pi/9, 5\pi/3, 17\pi/9$ **51.** $\pi/6, 3\pi/2$
52. $1.15, 3.57$ **53.** $k\pi/2$ **54.** $k\pi/6$
55. $\dfrac{\pi}{2} + k\pi, \dfrac{\pi}{9} + \dfrac{2k\pi}{3}, \dfrac{5\pi}{9} + \dfrac{2k\pi}{3}$
56. $\dfrac{\pi}{8} + \dfrac{k\pi}{4}, \dfrac{\pi}{6} + 2k\pi, \dfrac{5\pi}{6} + 2k\pi$ **57.** $0, \pm 0.95$
58. $1.17, -2.66, -2.94$ **59.** 1.92 **60.** $0, \pm 0.93$ **61.** ± 0.71
62. 0 **63.** $0.94721°$ or $89.05279°$ **64.** $0, \frac{1}{2}, 1, \frac{3}{2}, \ldots$
65. (a) 34th day (February 3), 308th day (November 4)
(b) 275 days **66. (b)** 1.047 rad $\approx 60°$

CHAPTER 7 REVIEW ■ PAGE 530

1. LHS $= \sin\theta\left(\dfrac{\cos\theta}{\sin\theta} + \dfrac{\sin\theta}{\cos\theta}\right) = \cos\theta + \dfrac{\sin^2\theta}{\cos\theta}$

$\quad = \dfrac{\cos^2\theta + \sin^2\theta}{\cos\theta} =$ RHS

2. LHS $= \sec^2\theta - 1 =$ RHS

3. LHS $= (1 - \sin^2 x)\csc x - \csc x$

$\quad = \csc x - \sin^2 x \csc x - \csc x$

$\quad = -\sin^2 x \dfrac{1}{\sin x} =$ RHS

4. LHS $= \dfrac{1}{\cos^2 x} = \sec^2 x =$ RHS

5. LHS $= \dfrac{\cos^2 x}{\sin^2 x} - \dfrac{\tan^2 x}{\sin^2 x} = \cot^2 x - \dfrac{1}{\cos^2 x} =$ RHS

6. LHS $= \dfrac{1}{\sec x} + 1 = 1 + \cos x = (1 + \cos x) \cdot \dfrac{1 - \cos x}{1 - \cos x}$

$\quad = \dfrac{1 - \cos^2 x}{1 - \cos x} =$ RHS

7. LHS $= \dfrac{\cos x}{\frac{1}{\cos x}(1 - \sin x)} = \dfrac{\cos x}{\frac{1}{\cos x} - \frac{\sin x}{\cos x}} =$ RHS

8. LHS $= 1 - \cot x - \tan x + \tan x \cot x$

$\quad = 2 - (\cot x + \tan x)$

$\quad = 2 - \left(\dfrac{\cos x}{\sin x} + \dfrac{\sin x}{\cos x}\right) = 2 - \dfrac{\cos^2 x + \sin^2 x}{\cos x \sin x}$

$\quad = 2 - \dfrac{1}{\cos x \sin x} =$ RHS

9. LHS $= \sin^2 x \dfrac{\cos^2 x}{\sin^2 x} + \cos^2 x \dfrac{\sin^2 x}{\cos^2 x} = \cos^2 x + \sin^2 x =$ RHS

10. LHS $= \left(\dfrac{\sin x}{\cos x} + \dfrac{\cos x}{\sin x}\right)^2 = \left(\dfrac{\sin^2 x + \cos^2 x}{\cos x \sin x}\right)^2$

$\quad = \left(\dfrac{1}{\cos x \sin x}\right)^2 =$ RHS

11. LHS $= \dfrac{2\sin x \cos x}{1 + 2\cos^2 x - 1} = \dfrac{2\sin x \cos x}{2\cos^2 x} = \dfrac{2\sin x}{2\cos x} =$ RHS

12. LHS $= \dfrac{\cos x \cos y - \sin x \sin y}{\cos x \sin y}$

$\quad = \dfrac{\cos x \cos y}{\cos x \sin y} - \dfrac{\sin x \sin y}{\cos x \sin y} = \dfrac{\cos y}{\sin y} - \dfrac{\sin x}{\cos x} =$ RHS

13. LHS $= \dfrac{1 - \cos x}{\sin x} = \dfrac{1}{\sin x} - \dfrac{\cos x}{\sin x} =$ RHS

14. LHS $= \dfrac{2 \sin\left(\frac{(x+y)\,+\,(x-y)}{2}\right) \cos\left(\frac{(x+y)\,-\,(x-y)}{2}\right)}{2 \cos\left(\frac{(x+y)\,+\,(x-y)}{2}\right) \cos\left(\frac{(x+y)\,-\,(x-y)}{2}\right)}$

$= \dfrac{2 \sin x \cos y}{2 \cos x \cos y} =$ RHS

15. LHS $= \frac{1}{2}[\cos((x + y) - (x - y))$
$\quad - \cos((x + y) + (x - y))]$
$= \frac{1}{2}(\cos 2y - \cos 2x)$
$= \frac{1}{2}[1 - 2\sin^2 y - (1 - 2\sin^2 x)]$
$= \frac{1}{2}(2\sin^2 x - 2\sin^2 y) =$ RHS

16. LHS $= \csc x - \dfrac{1 - \cos x}{\sin x}$
$= \csc x - (\csc x - \cot x) =$ RHS

17. LHS $= 1 + \dfrac{\sin x}{\cos x} \cdot \dfrac{1 - \cos x}{\sin x} = 1 + \dfrac{1 - \cos x}{\cos x}$

$= 1 + \dfrac{1}{\cos x} - 1 =$ RHS

18. LHS $= \dfrac{\sin(x + 2x) + \cos(x + 2x)}{\cos x - \sin x}$

$= \dfrac{\sin x \cos 2x + \cos x \sin 2x + \cos x \cos 2x - \sin x \sin 2x}{\cos x - \sin x}$

$= \dfrac{\cos 2x(\sin x + \cos x) + \sin 2x(\cos x - \sin x)}{\cos x - \sin x}$

$= \dfrac{\cos 2x(\sin x + \cos x)}{\cos x - \sin x} + \sin 2x$

$= \dfrac{(\cos^2 x - \sin^2 x)(\sin x + \cos x)}{\cos x - \sin x} + \sin 2x$

$= (\cos x + \sin x)(\sin x + \cos x) + \sin 2x$
$= \sin^2 x + \cos^2 x + 2\sin x \cos x + \sin 2x$
$= 1 + \sin 2x + \sin 2x =$ RHS

19. LHS $= \cos^2 \frac{x}{2} - 2\sin \frac{x}{2} \cos \frac{x}{2} + \sin^2 \frac{x}{2}$
$= 1 - \sin\left(2 \cdot \frac{x}{2}\right) =$ RHS

20. LHS $= \dfrac{-2 \sin\left(\frac{3x+7x}{2}\right) \sin\left(\frac{3x-7x}{2}\right)}{2 \sin\left(\frac{3x+7x}{2}\right) \cos\left(\frac{3x-7x}{2}\right)} = \dfrac{-2 \sin 5x \sin(-2x)}{2 \sin 5x \cos(-2x)}$

$= \dfrac{2 \sin 5x \sin 2x}{2 \sin 5x \cos 2x} =$ RHS

21. LHS $= \dfrac{2 \sin x \cos x}{\sin x} - \dfrac{2\cos^2 x - 1}{\cos x}$

$= 2 \cos x - 2 \cos x + \dfrac{1}{\cos x} =$ RHS

22. LHS $= \cos^2 x + 2 \cos x \cos y + \cos^2 y$
$\quad + \sin^2 x - 2 \sin x \sin y + \sin^2 y$
$= (\cos^2 x + \sin^2 x) + (\sin^2 y + \cos^2 y)$
$\quad + 2(\cos x \cos y - \sin x \sin y) =$ RHS

23. LHS $= \dfrac{\tan x + \tan \frac{\pi}{4}}{1 - \tan x \tan \frac{\pi}{4}} =$ RHS

24. LHS $= \dfrac{\frac{1}{\cos x} - 1}{\sin x \frac{1}{\cos x}} = \left(\dfrac{1}{\cos x} - 1\right) \dfrac{\cos x}{\sin x}$

$= \dfrac{1 - \cos x}{\sin x} =$ RHS

25. (a)   **(b)** Yes

26. (a)   **(b)** No

27. (a)   **(b)** No

28. (a)   **(b)** Yes

29. (a) 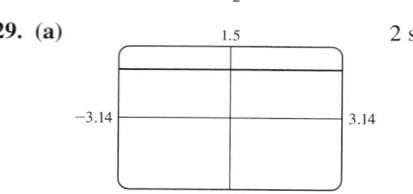 $2 \sin^2 3x + \cos 6x = 1$

30. (a) 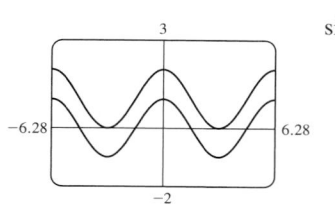 $\sin x \cot \dfrac{x}{2} = \cos x + 1$

31. 0.85, 2.29   **32.** 2.21, 4.07   **33.** 0, π **34.** 0, $\pi/6$, $5\pi/6$, π
35. $\pi/6$, $5\pi/6$ **36.** 0, $\pi/4$, $5\pi/4$ **37.** $\pi/3$, $5\pi/3$
38. $\pi/4$, $3\pi/4$, $5\pi/4$, $7\pi/4$ **39.** $2\pi/3$, $4\pi/3$
40. $\pi/6$, $3\pi/2$, $5\pi/6$ **41.** $\pi/3$, $2\pi/3$, $3\pi/4$, $4\pi/3$, $5\pi/3$, $7\pi/4$
42. $\pi/4$, $3\pi/4$, $5\pi/4$, $7\pi/4$
43. $\pi/6$, $\pi/2$, $5\pi/6$, $7\pi/6$, $3\pi/2$, $11\pi/6$
44. $\pi/4$, $3\pi/4$, $5\pi/4$, $7\pi/4$, $2\pi/3$, $4\pi/3$ **45.** $\pi/6$
46. $\pi/6$, $5\pi/6$ **47.** 1.18   **48.** 2.22   **49. (a)** 63.4°   **(b)** No
(c) 90°   **50.** $t = 0.25k$, $k = 0, 1, 2, \ldots$ **51.** $\frac{1}{2}\sqrt{2 + \sqrt{3}}$
52. $\dfrac{\sqrt{2} + \sqrt{6}}{4}$ **53.** $\sqrt{2} - 1$ **54.** $\frac{1}{2}$ **55.** $\sqrt{2}/2$
56. $\sqrt{3}$ **57.** $\sqrt{2}/2$ **58.** $\sqrt{2}/2$ **59.** $\dfrac{\sqrt{2} + \sqrt{3}}{4}$

60. $\sqrt{\dfrac{2 + \sqrt{2}}{2}}$ **61.** $2\dfrac{\sqrt{10} + 1}{9}$ **62.** $\frac{1}{9}(4\sqrt{2} + \sqrt{5})$

63. $\frac{2}{3}(\sqrt{2} + \sqrt{5})$ **64.** $4\sqrt{5}/9$ **65.** $\sqrt{(3 + 2\sqrt{2})/6}$

66. $3 - 2\sqrt{2}$ **67.** $-\dfrac{12\sqrt{10}}{31}$ **68.** $\frac{63}{65}$ **69.** $\dfrac{2x}{1 - x^2}$

70. $y\sqrt{1 - x^2} - x\sqrt{1 - y^2}$

71. (a) $\theta = \tan^{-1}\left(\dfrac{10}{x}\right)$ **(b)** 286.4 ft

72. (a) $\theta = \tan^{-1}\left(\dfrac{420}{x}\right) - \tan^{-1}\left(\dfrac{380}{x}\right)$ **(b)** 400 ft

CHAPTER 7 TEST ▪ PAGE 532

1. (a) LHS $= \dfrac{\sin \theta}{\cos \theta} \sin \theta + \cos \theta = \dfrac{\sin^2\theta + \cos^2\theta}{\cos \theta} =$ RHS

(b) LHS $= \dfrac{\tan x}{1 - \cos x} \cdot \dfrac{1 + \cos x}{1 + \cos x} = \dfrac{\tan x(1 + \cos x)}{1 - \cos^2 x}$

$= \dfrac{\frac{\sin x}{\cos x}(1 + \cos x)}{\sin^2 x} = \dfrac{1}{\sin x} \cdot \dfrac{1 + \cos x}{\cos x} =$ RHS

(c) LHS $= \dfrac{2 \tan x}{\sec^2 x} = \dfrac{2 \sin x}{\cos x} \cdot \cos^2 x = 2 \sin x \cos x =$ RHS

2. $\tan \theta$ **3. (a)** $\frac{1}{2}$ **(b)** $\dfrac{\sqrt{2} + \sqrt{6}}{4}$ **(c)** $\frac{1}{2}\sqrt{2 - \sqrt{3}}$

4. $(10 - 2\sqrt{5})/15$

5. (a) $\frac{1}{2}(\sin 8x - \sin 2x)$ **(b)** $-2 \cos \frac{7}{2}x \sin \frac{3}{2}x$ **6.** -2

7. (a) 0.34, 2.80 **(b)** $\pi/3, \pi/2, 5\pi/3$ **(c)** $2\pi/3, 4\pi/3$

(d) $\pi/6, \pi/2, 5\pi/6, 3\pi/2$ **8.** 0.58, 2.56, 3.72, 5.70 **9.** $\frac{1519}{1681}$

10. $\dfrac{\sqrt{1 - x^2} - xy}{\sqrt{1 + y^2}}$

FOCUS ON MODELING ▪ PAGE 536

1. (a) $y = -5 \sin\left(\dfrac{\pi}{2}t\right)$ **(b)**

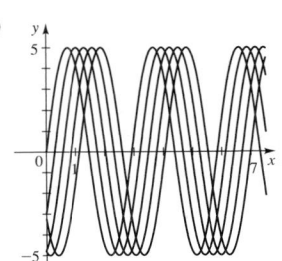

(c) $v = \pi/4$ Yes, it is a traveling wave.

2. (a) $y = 0.4 \sin(1.047x) \cos(0.524t); 3, 6, 9, 12, \dots$

(b)

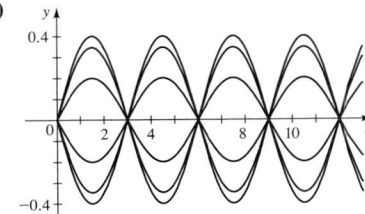

Yes, this is a standing wave.

3. $y(x, t) = 2.7 \sin(0.68x - 4.10t)$

4. (a) $y(x, t) = 5 \sin(3x - 1.5t)$

(b)

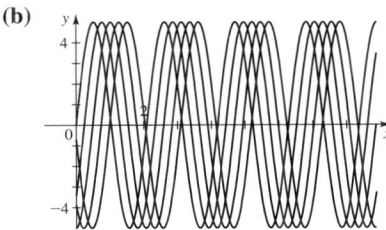

5. $y(x, t) = 0.6 \sin(\pi x) \cos(40\pi t)$

6. $y(x, t) = 7 \sin 2x \cos \frac{1}{2}t$

7. (a) 1, 2, 3, 4

(b) 5:

6:

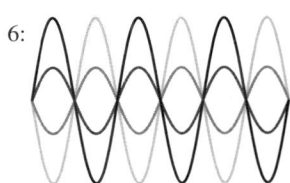

(c) 880π **(d)** $y(x, t) = \sin t \cos(880\pi t);$

$y(x, t) = \sin(2t) \cos(880\pi t); y(x, t) = \sin(3t) \cos(880\pi t);$

$y(x, t) = \sin(4t) \cos(880\pi t)$

8. (a) $\pi, 3\pi, 5\pi, 7\pi, 9\pi, 11\pi;$ no **(b)** 25 Hz

CUMULATIVE REVIEW TEST FOR CHAPTERS 5, 6 AND 7 ▪ PAGE 539

1. (a) $\sqrt{5}/3$ **(b)** $-2/3$ **(c)** $-\sqrt{5}/2$ **(d)** $3\sqrt{3}/5$

2. (a) $2\sqrt{10}/7$ **(b)** $7/3$ **(c)** $3\sqrt{10}/20$

3. (a) $-\sqrt{3}/2$ **(b)** -1 **(c)** $2\sqrt{3}/3$ **(d)** -1

4. $\sin t = -24/25, \tan t = -24/7, \cot t = -7/24, \sec t = 25/7,$

$\csc t = -25/24$ **5. (a)** $2, \pi, \pi/4$ **(b)**

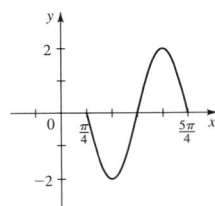

6. $y = 3 \cos \frac{1}{2}(x - \frac{\pi}{3})$ **7. (a)** $h(t) = 45 - 40 \cos 8\pi t$

(b) $2\sqrt{19} \approx 8.7$ cm **8. (a)** 7.2 **(b)** 92.9°

9. (a) LHS $= \dfrac{(\sec \theta - 1)(\sec \theta + 1)}{\tan \theta \,(\sec \theta + 1)}$

$= \dfrac{\sec^2\theta - 1}{\tan \theta \,(\sec \theta + 1)} = \dfrac{\tan^2\theta}{\tan \theta \,(\sec \theta + 1)} =$ RHS

(b) RHS $= 1 - (1 - 2 \sin^2 2\theta) = 2 \sin^2 2\theta = 2(2 \sin \theta \cos \theta)^2$

$=$ LHS

10. $2 \cos \dfrac{7x}{2} \cos \dfrac{x}{2}$ **11. (a)** Domain $[-1, 1]$, range $[0, \pi]$

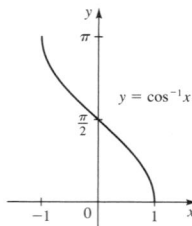

(b) $5\pi/6$ **(c)** $\sqrt{1 - x^2}/x$ **12.** $\pi/6, 5\pi/6, 3\pi/2$

CHAPTER 8

SECTION 8.1 ■ PAGE 546

1. coordinate; $(1, 1), (\sqrt{2}, \pi/4)$ **2. (a)** $r \cos \theta, r \sin \theta$
(b) $x^2 + y^2, y/x$
3.

4.

5.

6.

7.

8.

9.

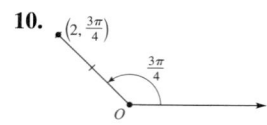

$\left(-3, \dfrac{3\pi}{2}\right), \left(3, \dfrac{5\pi}{2}\right)$

10.

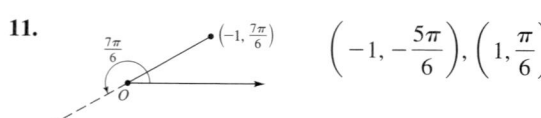

$\left(-2, \dfrac{7\pi}{4}\right), \left(2, \dfrac{11\pi}{4}\right)$

11.

$\left(-1, -\dfrac{5\pi}{6}\right), \left(1, \dfrac{\pi}{6}\right)$

12.

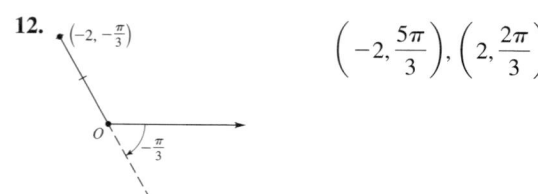

$\left(-2, \dfrac{5\pi}{3}\right), \left(2, \dfrac{2\pi}{3}\right)$

13.

$(-5, 2\pi), (5, \pi)$

14.

$(3, 1 + 2\pi), (-3, 1 + \pi)$

15. Q **16.** R **17.** Q **18.** P **19.** P **20.** Q **21.** P
22. S **23.** $(3\sqrt{2}, 3\pi/4)$ **24.** $(3, 3\pi/2)$
25. $\left(-\dfrac{5}{2}, -\dfrac{5\sqrt{3}}{2}\right)$ **26.** $\left(\dfrac{-3\sqrt{3}}{2}, 1\right)$ **27.** $(2\sqrt{3}, 2)$
28. $(-3, 3\sqrt{3})$ **29.** $(1, -1)$ **30.** $(0, -1)$ **31.** $(-5, 0)$
32. $(0, 0)$ **33.** $(3\sqrt{6}, -3\sqrt{2})$ **34.** $(\sqrt{3}/2, \tfrac{3}{2})$
35. $(\sqrt{2}, 3\pi/4)$ **36.** $(6, 11\pi/6)$ **37.** $(4, \pi/4)$
38. $(2\sqrt{2}, 7\pi/6)$ **39.** $(5, \tan^{-1}\tfrac{4}{3})$
40. $(\sqrt{5}, 2\pi + \tan^{-1}(-2))$ **41.** $(6, \pi)$ **42.** $(\sqrt{3}, 3\pi/2)$
43. $\theta = \pi/4$ **44.** $r = 3$ **45.** $r = \tan \theta \sec \theta$
46. $r = 5 \csc \theta$ **47.** $r = 4 \sec \theta$ **48.** $r^2 = \sec 2\theta$
49. $x^2 + y^2 = 49$ **50.** $x^2 + y^2 = 9$ **51.** $x = 0$ **52.** $y = 0$
53. $x = 6$ **54.** $y = 2$ **55.** $x^2 + (y - 2)^2 = 4$
56. $(x - 3)^2 + y^2 = 9$ **57.** $x^2 + y^2 = (x^2 + y^2 - x)^2$
58. $(x^2 + y^2 + 3y)^2 = 9(x^2 + y^2)$
59. $(x^2 + y^2 - 2y)^2 = x^2 + y^2$
60. $(x^2 + y^2 - x)^2 = 4(x^2 + y^2)$ **61.** $y - x = 1$
62. $x^2 + 2y - 1 = 0$ **63.** $x^2 - 3y^2 + 16y - 16 = 0$
64. $y^2 = 4x + 4$ **65.** $x^2 + y^2 = \dfrac{y}{x}$
66. $x^4 + 2x^2 y^2 + y^4 - 2xy = 0$
67. $y = \pm\sqrt{3}x$ **68.** $y = 0$

SECTION 8.2 ■ PAGE 553

1. circles, rays   **2. (a)** satisfy   **(b)** circle, 3, pole; line, pole, 1
3. VI   **4.** III   **5.** II   **6.** IV   **7.** I   **8.** V
9. Symmetric about $\theta = \pi/2$
10. Symmetric about the polar axis
11. Symmetric about the polar axis
12. Symmetric about the pole
13. Symmetric about $\theta = \pi/2$
14. Symmetric about the polar axis
15. All three types of symmetry
16. Symmetric about the pole and about $\theta = \pi/2$
17.

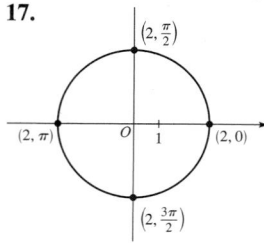

$x^2 + y^2 = 4$

18.

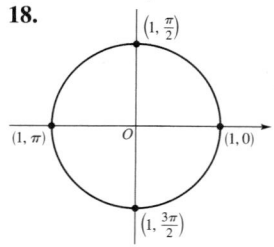

$x^2 + y^2 = 1$

19.

$x = 0$

20.

$y = -\dfrac{\sqrt{3}}{3}x$

21.
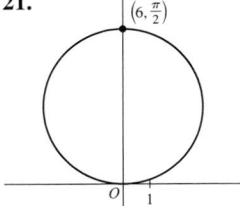
$(6, \frac{\pi}{2})$

$x^2 + (y - 3)^2 = 9$

22.

$(0, \frac{\pi}{2})$ $(1, 0)$

$(x - \frac{1}{2})^2 + y^2 = \frac{1}{4}$

23.

$(-2, 0)$

24.
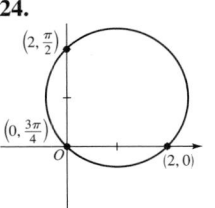
$(2, \frac{\pi}{2})$ $(0, \frac{3\pi}{4})$ $(2, 0)$

25.
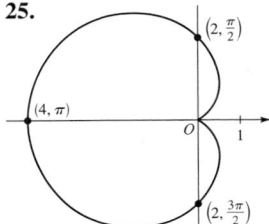
$(2, \frac{\pi}{2})$ $(4, \pi)$ $(2, \frac{3\pi}{2})$

26.
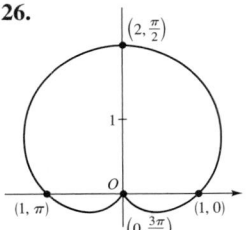
$(2, \frac{\pi}{2})$ $(1, \pi)$ $(1, 0)$ $(0, \frac{3\pi}{2})$

27.
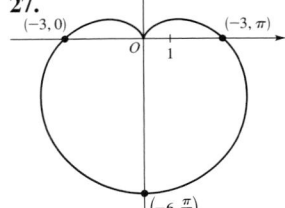
$(-3, 0)$ $(-3, \pi)$ $(-6, \frac{\pi}{2})$

28.
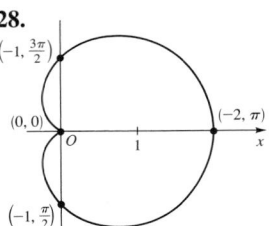
$(-1, \frac{3\pi}{2})$ $(0, 0)$ $(-2, \pi)$ $(-1, \frac{\pi}{2})$

29.

30.

31.

32.

33.
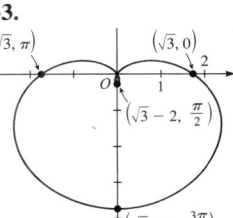
$(\sqrt{3}, \pi)$ $(\sqrt{3}, 0)$ $(\sqrt{3} - 2, \frac{\pi}{2})$ $(\sqrt{3} + 2, \frac{3\pi}{2})$

34.
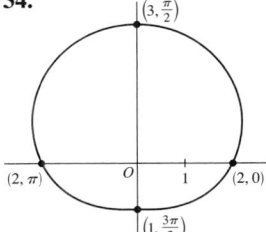
$(3, \frac{\pi}{2})$ $(2, \pi)$ $(2, 0)$ $(1, \frac{3\pi}{2})$

35.
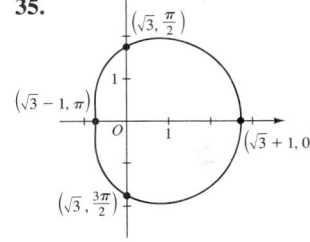
$(\sqrt{3}, \frac{\pi}{2})$ $(\sqrt{3} - 1, \pi)$ $(\sqrt{3} + 1, 0)$ $(\sqrt{3}, \frac{3\pi}{2})$

36.
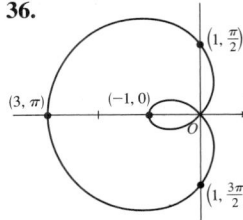
$(1, \frac{\pi}{2})$ $(3, \pi)$ $(-1, 0)$ $(1, \frac{3\pi}{2})$

37.

38.

39.

(π, π)

40.
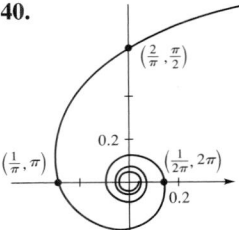
$(\frac{2}{\pi}, \frac{\pi}{2})$ $(\frac{1}{\pi}, \pi)$ $(\frac{1}{2\pi}, 2\pi)$

41.

$(3, 0)$

42.
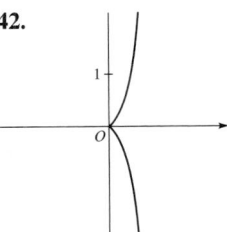

43. $0 \le \theta \le 4\pi$
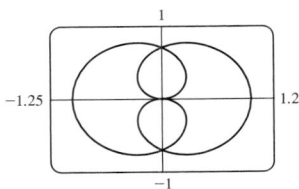

44. $0 \le \theta \le 10\pi$
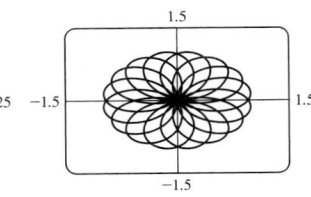

45. $0 \le \theta \le 4\pi$

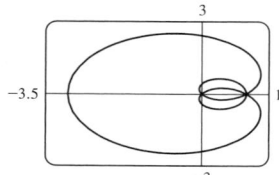

46. $0 \le \theta \le 2\pi$

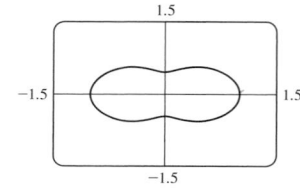

47. The graph of $r = 1 + \sin n\theta$ has n loops.
48. As c increases, the "dimple" of the graph becomes an inner loop.   **49.** IV   **50.** I   **51.** III   **52.** II
53.

54.

55.

56.

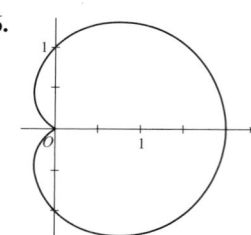

57. $\left(\dfrac{a}{2}, \dfrac{b}{2}\right)$, $\dfrac{\sqrt{a^2 + b^2}}{2}$

58. (a)

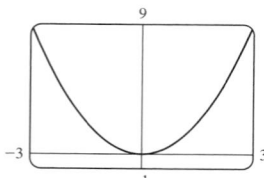

(b) $y = x^2$
59. (a) Elliptical

(b) π; 540 mi
60. (a) Spiral

(b) 2.1 rad

SECTION 8.3 ▪ PAGE 562
1. real, imaginary, (a, b) **2. (a)** $\sqrt{a^2 + b^2}$, b/a
(b) $r(\cos\theta + i\sin\theta)$

3. (a) $\sqrt{2}\left(\cos\dfrac{3\pi}{4} + i\sin\dfrac{3\pi}{4}\right)$; $\sqrt{3} + i$

(b) $1 + i$, $\sqrt{2}\left(\cos\dfrac{\pi}{4} + i\sin\dfrac{\pi}{4}\right)$

4. n; four; 2, $2i$, -2, $-2i$; 2

5. 4

6. 3

7. 2

8. 6

9. $\sqrt{29}$

10. $\sqrt{58}$

11. 2

12. $2\sqrt{3}/3$

13. 1

14. 1

15.

16.

17.

18.

19.

20.

21.

22.

23.

24.

25.

26.

27.

28.

29. $\sqrt{2}\left(\cos\dfrac{\pi}{4} + i\sin\dfrac{\pi}{4}\right)$ **30.** $2\left(\cos\dfrac{\pi}{3} + i\sin\dfrac{\pi}{3}\right)$

31. $2\left(\cos\dfrac{7\pi}{4} + i\sin\dfrac{7\pi}{4}\right)$ **32.** $\sqrt{2}\left(\cos\dfrac{7\pi}{4} + i\sin\dfrac{7\pi}{4}\right)$

33. $4\left(\cos\dfrac{11\pi}{6} + i\sin\dfrac{11\pi}{6}\right)$ **34.** $\sqrt{2}\left(\cos\dfrac{3\pi}{4} + i\sin\dfrac{3\pi}{4}\right)$

35. $3\left(\cos\dfrac{3\pi}{2} + i\sin\dfrac{3\pi}{2}\right)$ **36.** $6\left(\cos\dfrac{4\pi}{3} + i\sin\dfrac{4\pi}{3}\right)$

37. $5\sqrt{2}\left(\cos\dfrac{\pi}{4} + i\sin\dfrac{\pi}{4}\right)$ **38.** $4(\cos 0 + i\sin 0)$

39. $8\left(\cos\dfrac{11\pi}{6} + i\sin\dfrac{11\pi}{6}\right)$ **40.** $8\left(\cos\dfrac{\pi}{2} + i\sin\dfrac{\pi}{2}\right)$

41. $20(\cos\pi + i\sin\pi)$ **42.** $2\left(\cos\dfrac{\pi}{6} + i\sin\dfrac{\pi}{6}\right)$

43. $5\left[\cos\left(\tan^{-1}\tfrac{4}{3}\right) + i\sin\left(\tan^{-1}\tfrac{4}{3}\right)\right]$

44. $2\sqrt{2}\left(\cos\dfrac{\pi}{4} + i\sin\dfrac{\pi}{4}\right)$ **45.** $3\sqrt{2}\left(\cos\dfrac{3\pi}{4} + i\sin\dfrac{3\pi}{4}\right)$

46. $2\sqrt{2}\left(\cos\dfrac{7\pi}{4} + i\sin\dfrac{7\pi}{4}\right)$ **47.** $8\left(\cos\dfrac{\pi}{6} + i\sin\dfrac{\pi}{6}\right)$

48. $3\sqrt{2}\left(\cos\dfrac{5\pi}{4} + i\sin\dfrac{5\pi}{4}\right)$

49. $\sqrt{5}\left[\cos\left(\tan^{-1}\tfrac{1}{2}\right) + i\sin\left(\tan^{-1}\tfrac{1}{2}\right)\right]$

50. $2\sqrt{3}\left(\cos\dfrac{\pi}{6} + i\sin\dfrac{\pi}{6}\right)$ **51.** $2\left(\cos\dfrac{\pi}{4} + i\sin\dfrac{\pi}{4}\right)$

52. $\pi\left(\cos\dfrac{3\pi}{2} + i\sin\dfrac{3\pi}{2}\right)$

53. $z_1 z_2 = \cos\dfrac{4\pi}{3} + i\sin\dfrac{4\pi}{3}, \quad \dfrac{z_1}{z_2} = \cos\dfrac{2\pi}{3} + i\sin\dfrac{2\pi}{3}$

54. $z_1 z_2 = \cos\pi + i\sin\pi, \quad \dfrac{z_1}{z_2} = \cos\dfrac{\pi}{2} - i\sin\dfrac{\pi}{2}$

55. $z_1 z_2 = 15\left(\cos\dfrac{3\pi}{2} + i\sin\dfrac{3\pi}{2}\right)$

$\dfrac{z_1}{z_2} = \dfrac{3}{5}\left(\cos\dfrac{7\pi}{6} - i\sin\dfrac{7\pi}{6}\right)$

56. $z_1 z_2 = 14\left(\cos\dfrac{5\pi}{4} + i\sin\dfrac{5\pi}{4}\right)$

$z_1/z_2 = \tfrac{7}{2}(\cos\pi + i\sin\pi)$

57. $z_1 z_2 = 8(\cos 150° + i\sin 150°)$

$z_1/z_2 = 2(\cos 90° + i\sin 90°)$

58. $z_1 z_2 = 6(\cos 135° + i\sin 135°)$

$z_1/z_2 = \tfrac{1}{3}(\cos 15° + i\sin 15°)$

59. $z_1 z_2 = 100(\cos 350° + i\sin 350°)$

$z_1/z_2 = \tfrac{4}{25}(\cos 50° + i\sin 50°)$

60. $z_1 z_2 = \tfrac{4}{25}(\cos 180° + i\sin 180°)$

$z_1/z_2 = 4(\cos 130° - i\sin 130°)$

61. $z_1 = 2\left(\cos\dfrac{\pi}{6} + i\sin\dfrac{\pi}{6}\right)$

$z_2 = 2\left(\cos\dfrac{\pi}{3} + i\sin\dfrac{\pi}{3}\right)$

$z_1 z_2 = 4\left(\cos\dfrac{\pi}{2} + i\sin\dfrac{\pi}{2}\right)$

$\dfrac{z_1}{z_2} = \cos\dfrac{\pi}{6} - i\sin\dfrac{\pi}{6}$

$\dfrac{1}{z_1} = \dfrac{1}{2}\left(\cos\dfrac{\pi}{6} - i\sin\dfrac{\pi}{6}\right)$

62. $z_1 = 2\left(\cos\dfrac{7\pi}{4} + i\sin\dfrac{7\pi}{4}\right)$

$z_2 = \sqrt{2}\left(\cos\dfrac{7\pi}{4} + i\sin\dfrac{7\pi}{4}\right)$

$z_1z_2 = 2\sqrt{2}\left(\cos\dfrac{\pi}{2} - i\sin\dfrac{\pi}{2}\right)$

$\dfrac{z_1}{z_2} = \sqrt{2}(\cos 0 + i\sin 0)$

$\dfrac{1}{z_1} = \dfrac{1}{2}\left(\cos\dfrac{7\pi}{4} - i\sin\dfrac{7\pi}{4}\right)$

63. $z_1 = 4\left(\cos\dfrac{11\pi}{6} + i\sin\dfrac{11\pi}{6}\right)$

$z_2 = \sqrt{2}\left(\cos\dfrac{3\pi}{4} + i\sin\dfrac{3\pi}{4}\right)$

$z_1z_2 = 4\sqrt{2}\left(\cos\dfrac{7\pi}{12} + i\sin\dfrac{7\pi}{12}\right)$

$\dfrac{z_1}{z_2} = 2\sqrt{2}\left(\cos\dfrac{13\pi}{12} + i\sin\dfrac{13\pi}{12}\right)$

$\dfrac{1}{z_1} = \dfrac{1}{4}\left(\cos\dfrac{11\pi}{6} - i\sin\dfrac{11\pi}{6}\right)$

64. $z_1 = \sqrt{2}\left(\cos\dfrac{3\pi}{2} + i\sin\dfrac{3\pi}{2}\right)$

$z_2 = 6\left(\cos\dfrac{4\pi}{3} + i\sin\dfrac{4\pi}{3}\right)$

$z_1z_2 = 6\sqrt{2}\left(\cos\dfrac{5\pi}{6} + i\sin\dfrac{5\pi}{6}\right)$

$\dfrac{z_1}{z_2} = \dfrac{\sqrt{2}}{6}\left(\cos\dfrac{\pi}{6} + i\sin\dfrac{\pi}{6}\right)$

$\dfrac{1}{z_1} = \dfrac{\sqrt{2}}{2}\left(\cos\dfrac{3\pi}{2} - i\sin\dfrac{3\pi}{2}\right)$

65. $z_1 = 5\sqrt{2}\left(\cos\dfrac{\pi}{4} + i\sin\dfrac{\pi}{4}\right)$

$z_2 = 4(\cos 0 + i\sin 0)$

$z_1z_2 = 20\sqrt{2}\left(\cos\dfrac{\pi}{4} + i\sin\dfrac{\pi}{4}\right)$

$\dfrac{z_1}{z_2} = \dfrac{5\sqrt{2}}{4}\left(\cos\dfrac{\pi}{4} + i\sin\dfrac{\pi}{4}\right)$

$\dfrac{1}{z_1} = \dfrac{\sqrt{2}}{10}\left(\cos\dfrac{\pi}{4} - i\sin\dfrac{\pi}{4}\right)$

66. $z_1 = 8\left(\cos\dfrac{11\pi}{6} + i\sin\dfrac{11\pi}{6}\right)$

$z_2 = 8\left(\cos\dfrac{\pi}{2} + i\sin\dfrac{\pi}{2}\right)$

$z_1z_2 = 64\left(\cos\dfrac{\pi}{3} + i\sin\dfrac{\pi}{3}\right)$

$\dfrac{z_1}{z_2} = \cos\dfrac{4\pi}{3} + i\sin\dfrac{4\pi}{3}$

$\dfrac{1}{z_1} = \dfrac{1}{8}\left(\cos\dfrac{11\pi}{6} - i\sin\dfrac{11\pi}{6}\right)$

67. $z_1 = 20(\cos\pi + i\sin\pi)$

$z_2 = 2\left(\cos\dfrac{\pi}{6} + i\sin\dfrac{\pi}{6}\right)$

$z_1z_2 = 40\left(\cos\dfrac{7\pi}{6} + i\sin\dfrac{7\pi}{6}\right)$

$\dfrac{z_1}{z_2} = 10\left(\cos\dfrac{5\pi}{6} + i\sin\dfrac{5\pi}{6}\right)$

$\dfrac{1}{z_1} = \dfrac{1}{20}(\cos\pi - i\sin\pi)$

68. $z_1 = 5[\cos(0.927) + i\sin(0.927)]$

$z_2 = 2\sqrt{2}\left(\cos\dfrac{7\pi}{4} + i\sin\dfrac{7\pi}{4}\right)$

$z_1z_2 = 10\sqrt{2}[\cos(0.142) + i\sin(0.142)]$

$\dfrac{z_1}{z_2} = \dfrac{5\sqrt{2}}{4}[\cos(4.57) - i\sin(4.57)]$

$\dfrac{1}{z_1} = \dfrac{1}{5}[\cos(0.927) - i\sin(0.927)]$

69. -1024 **70.** $16 + 16\sqrt{3}i$

71. $512(-\sqrt{3} + i)$

72. 16 **73.** -1 **74.** $\dfrac{1}{2048}(-1 + \sqrt{3}i)$ **75.** 4096

76. 1 **77.** $8(-1 + i)$ **78.** $72(-1 + \sqrt{3}i)$

79. $\dfrac{1}{2048}(-\sqrt{3} - i)$ **80.** $\dfrac{1}{16}$

81. $2\sqrt{2}\left(\cos\dfrac{\pi}{12} + i\sin\dfrac{\pi}{12}\right)$,

$2\sqrt{2}\left(\cos\dfrac{13\pi}{12} + i\sin\dfrac{13\pi}{12}\right)$

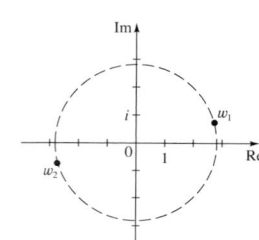

82. $2\left(\cos\dfrac{\pi}{18} + i\sin\dfrac{\pi}{18}\right)$,

$2\left(\cos\dfrac{13\pi}{18} + i\sin\dfrac{13\pi}{18}\right)$,

$2\left(\cos\dfrac{25\pi}{18} + i\sin\dfrac{25\pi}{18}\right)$

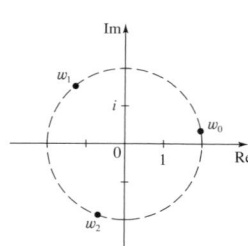

83. $3\left(\cos\dfrac{3\pi}{8} + i\sin\dfrac{3\pi}{8}\right)$,

$3\left(\cos\dfrac{7\pi}{8} + i\sin\dfrac{7\pi}{8}\right)$,

$3\left(\cos\dfrac{11\pi}{8} + i\sin\dfrac{11\pi}{8}\right)$,

$3\left(\cos\dfrac{15\pi}{8} + i\sin\dfrac{15\pi}{8}\right)$

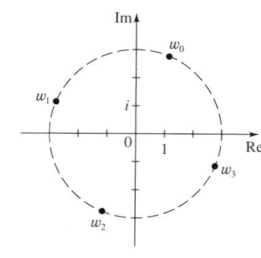

84. $2, 2\left(\cos\dfrac{2\pi}{5} + i\sin\dfrac{2\pi}{5}\right),$

$2\left(\cos\dfrac{4\pi}{5} + i\sin\dfrac{4\pi}{5}\right),$

$2\left(\cos\dfrac{6\pi}{5} + i\sin\dfrac{6\pi}{5}\right),$

$2\left(\cos\dfrac{8\pi}{5} + i\sin\dfrac{8\pi}{5}\right)$

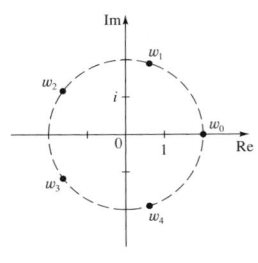

85. $\pm 1, \pm i, \pm\dfrac{\sqrt{2}}{2} \pm \dfrac{\sqrt{2}}{2}i$

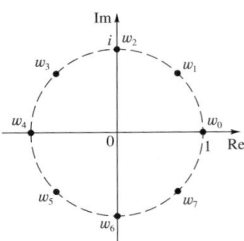

86. $2^{1/6}\left(\cos\dfrac{\pi}{12} + i\sin\dfrac{\pi}{12}\right),$

$2^{1/6}\left(\cos\dfrac{9\pi}{12} + i\sin\dfrac{9\pi}{12}\right),$

$2^{1/6}\left(\cos\dfrac{17\pi}{12} + i\sin\dfrac{17\pi}{12}\right)$

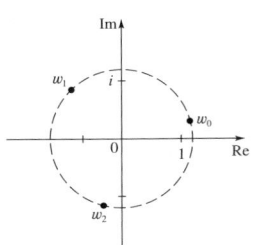

87. $\dfrac{\sqrt{3}}{2} + \dfrac{1}{2}i, -\dfrac{\sqrt{3}}{2} + \dfrac{1}{2}i, -i$

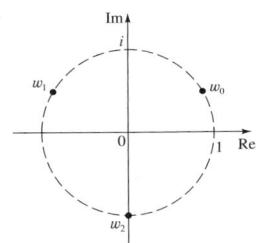

88. $\cos\dfrac{\pi}{10} + i\sin\dfrac{\pi}{10}, \cos\dfrac{\pi}{2} + i\sin\dfrac{\pi}{2}, \cos\dfrac{9\pi}{10} + i\sin\dfrac{9\pi}{10},$

$\cos\dfrac{13\pi}{10} + i\sin\dfrac{13\pi}{10}, \cos\dfrac{17\pi}{10} + i\sin\dfrac{17\pi}{10}$

89. $\pm\dfrac{\sqrt{2}}{2} \pm \dfrac{\sqrt{2}}{2}i$

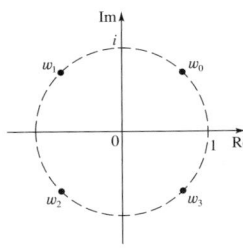

90. $2\left(\cos\dfrac{4\pi}{15} + i\sin\dfrac{4\pi}{15}\right), 2\left(\cos\dfrac{2\pi}{3} + i\sin\dfrac{2\pi}{3}\right),$

$2\left(\cos\dfrac{16\pi}{15} + i\sin\dfrac{16\pi}{15}\right), 2\left(\cos\dfrac{22\pi}{15} + i\sin\dfrac{22\pi}{15}\right),$

$2\left(\cos\dfrac{28\pi}{15} + i\sin\dfrac{28\pi}{15}\right)$

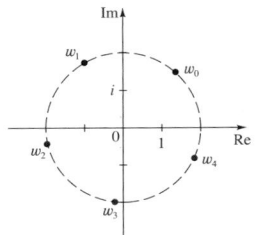

91. $\pm\dfrac{\sqrt{2}}{2} \pm \dfrac{\sqrt{2}}{2}i$

92. $\cos\dfrac{\pi}{16} + i\sin\dfrac{\pi}{16}, \cos\dfrac{5\pi}{16} + i\sin\dfrac{5\pi}{16}, \cos\dfrac{9\pi}{16} + i\sin\dfrac{9\pi}{16},$

$\cos\dfrac{13\pi}{16} + i\sin\dfrac{13\pi}{16}, \cos\dfrac{17\pi}{6} + i\sin\dfrac{17\pi}{16},$

$\cos\dfrac{21\pi}{16} + i\sin\dfrac{21\pi}{16}, \cos\dfrac{25\pi}{16} + i\sin\dfrac{25\pi}{16},$

$\cos\dfrac{29\pi}{16} + i\sin\dfrac{29\pi}{16}$

93. $2\left(\cos\dfrac{\pi}{18} + i\sin\dfrac{\pi}{18}\right), 2\left(\cos\dfrac{13\pi}{18} + i\sin\dfrac{13\pi}{18}\right),$

$2\left(\cos\dfrac{25\pi}{18} + i\sin\dfrac{25\pi}{18}\right)$

94. $\pm 1, \pm\dfrac{1}{2} \pm \dfrac{\sqrt{3}}{2}i$

95. $2^{1/6}\left(\cos\dfrac{5\pi}{12} + i\sin\dfrac{5\pi}{12}\right), 2^{1/6}\left(\cos\dfrac{13\pi}{12} + i\sin\dfrac{13\pi}{12}\right),$

$2^{1/6}\left(\cos\dfrac{21\pi}{12} + i\sin\dfrac{21\pi}{12}\right)$

96. $1, -\dfrac{1}{2} \pm \dfrac{\sqrt{3}}{2}i$

SECTION 8.4 ■ PAGE 569

1. (a) parameter **(b)** $(0, 0), (1, 1)$ **(c)** x^2; parabola
2. (a) True **(b)** $(0, 0), (2, 4)$ **(c)** x^2; path

3. (a)

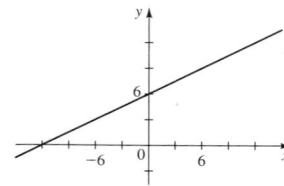

(b) $x - 2y + 12 = 0$

5. (a)

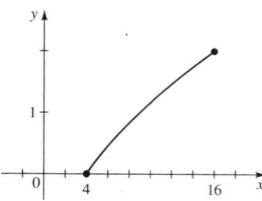

(b) $x = (y + 2)^2$

7. (a)

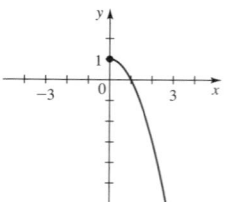

(b) $x = \sqrt{1 - y}$

9. (a)

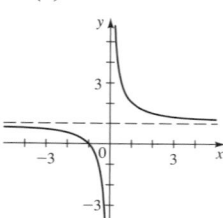

(b) $y = \dfrac{1}{x} + 1$

11. (a)

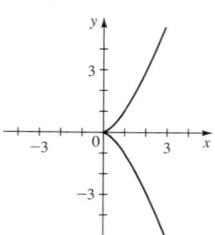

(b) $x^3 = y^2$

4. (a)

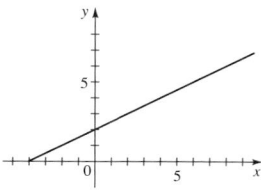

(b) $2y = x + 4, y \geq 0$

6. (a)

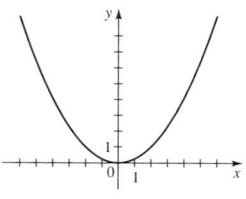

(b) $y = \dfrac{1}{4}x^2$

8. (a)

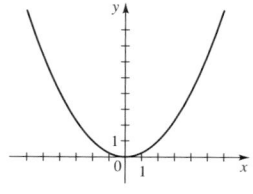

(b) $y = x^2 + 1, x \geq 0$

10. (a)

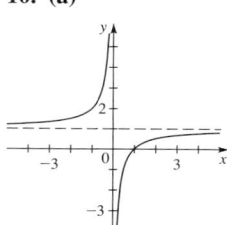

(b) $y = \dfrac{x - 1}{x}$

12. (a)

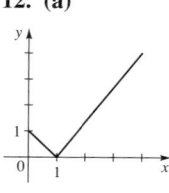

(b) $y = |1 - x|, x \geq 0$

13. (a)

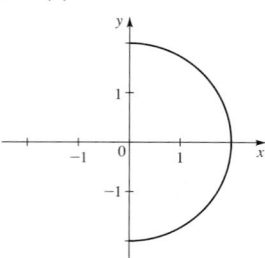

(b) $x^2 + y^2 = 4, x \geq 0$

15. (a)

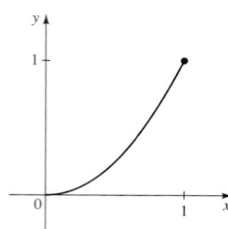

(b) $y = x^2, 0 \leq x \leq 1$

17. (a)

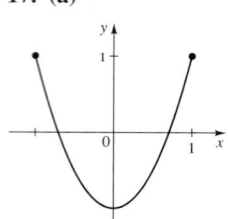

(b) $y = 2x^2 - 1, -1 \leq x \leq 1$

19. (a)

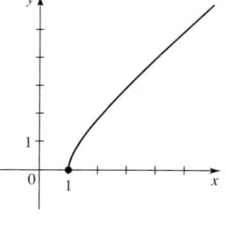

(b) $x^2 - y^2 = 1, x \geq 1, y \geq 0$

21. (a)

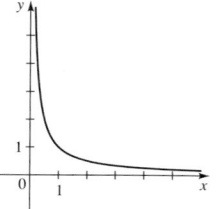

(b) $xy = 1, x \geq 0$

14. (a)

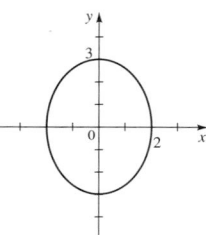

(b) $\dfrac{x^2}{4} + \dfrac{y^2}{9} = 1$

16. (a)

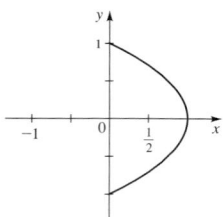

(b) $x = 1 - y^2, -1 \leq y \leq 1$

18. (a)

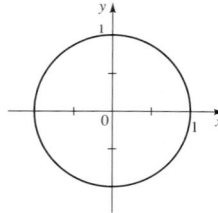

(b) $x^2 + y^2 = 1$

20. (a)

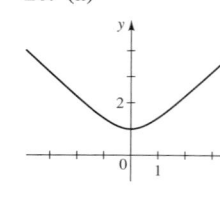

(b) $y^2 - x^2 = 1, y \geq 1$

22. (a)

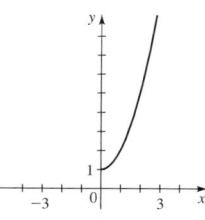

(b) $x = y^2 + 1, y \geq 0$

23. (a)

24. (a)

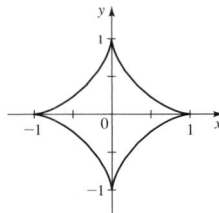

(b) $x + y = 1, 0 \le x \le 1$ **(b)** $x^{2/3} + y^{2/3} = 1$

25. 3, (3, 0), counterclockwise, 2π

26. 2, (0, 2), clockwise, 2π **27.** 1, (0, 1), clockwise, π

28. 2, (4, 0), counterclockwise, $2\pi/3$

29. $x = 4 + t, y = -1 + \frac{1}{2}t$

30. $x = -10 + t, y = -20 - 2t$

31. $x = 6 + t, y = 7 + t$ **32.** $x = t, y = \frac{7}{12}t$

33. $x = a \cos t, y = a \sin t$ **34.** $x = a \cos t, y = b \sin t$

37.

38.

39.

40.

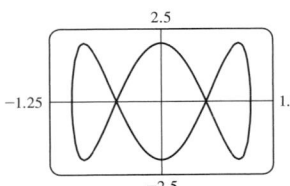

42. (a) 64 s   **(b)** 21.5 mi

(c) 16,384 ft $\approx$ 3.1 mi

43.

44.

45.

46.

47.

48.

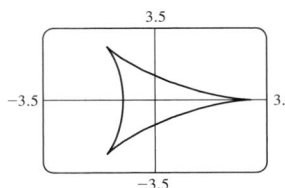

49. (a) $x = 2^{t/12} \cos t, y = 2^{t/12} \sin t$

(b)

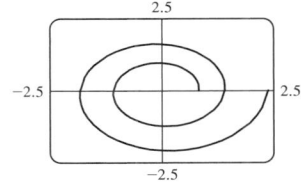

50. (a) $x = (\sin t + 2 \cos t)\cos t, y = (\sin t + 2 \cos t)\sin t$

(b)

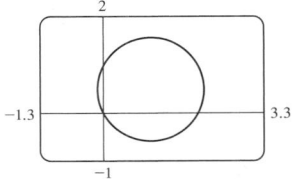

51. (a) $x = \dfrac{4 \cos t}{2 - \cos t}, y = \dfrac{4 \sin t}{2 - \cos t}$

(b)

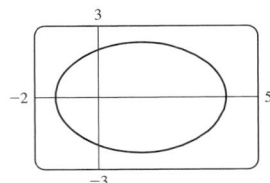

52. (a) $x = 2^{\sin t} \cos t, y = 2^{\sin t} \sin t$

(b)

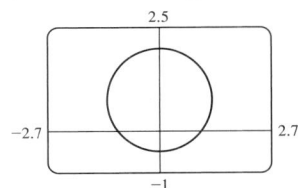

53. III   **54.** IV   **55.** II   **56.** I

57.

58.

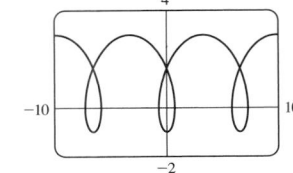

59. (b) $x^{2/3} + y^{2/3} = a^{2/3}$

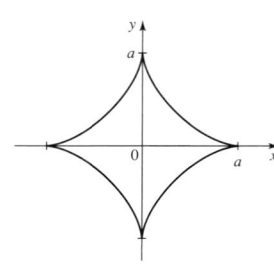

60. $x = (a + b)\cos t - b \cos\left(\dfrac{a + b}{b}\right)t,$

$y = (a + b)\sin t - b \sin\left(\dfrac{a + b}{b}\right)t$

61. $x = a(\sin\theta \cos\theta + \cot\theta), \; y = a(1 + \sin^2\theta)$

62. (a) $x = a \cos\theta, \; y = b \sin\theta$

(b)

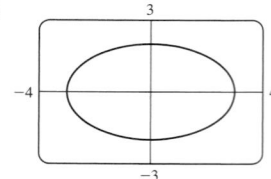

(c) $\dfrac{x^2}{a^2} + \dfrac{y^2}{b^2} = 1$

63. (a) $x = a \sec\theta, \; y = b \sin\theta$

(b)

64. (b)

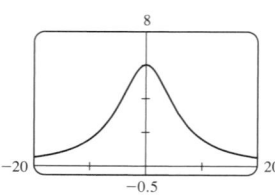

65. $y = a - a \cos\left(\dfrac{x + \sqrt{2ay - y^2}}{a}\right)$

66. (a)

$R = 0.5$

$R = 1$

$R = 3$

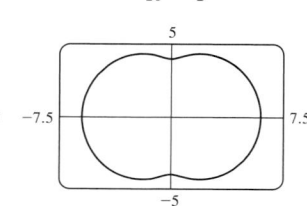

$R = 5$

(b) $R = 5$

67. (b)

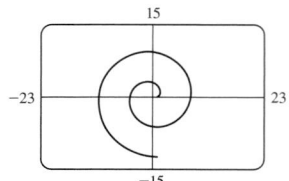

CHAPTER 8 REVIEW ▪ PAGE 572

1. (a)

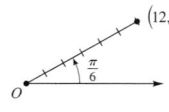

(b) $(6\sqrt{3}, 6)$

2. (a)

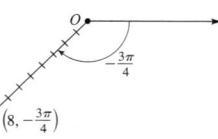

(b) $(-4\sqrt{2}, -4\sqrt{2})$

3. (a)

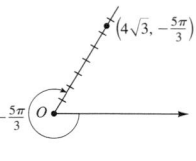

(b) $\left(\dfrac{-3\sqrt{2}}{2}, \dfrac{3\sqrt{2}}{2}\right)$

4. (a)

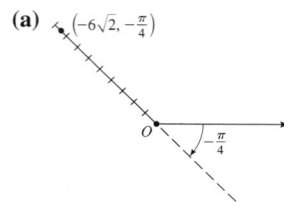

(b) $\left(\dfrac{\sqrt{3}}{2}, -\dfrac{3}{2}\right)$

5. (a)

(b) $(2\sqrt{3}, 6)$

6. (a)

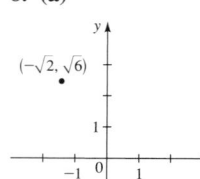

(b) $(-6, 6)$

7. (a)

(b) $\left(8\sqrt{2}, \dfrac{\pi}{4}\right)$

(c) $\left(-8\sqrt{2}, \dfrac{5\pi}{4}\right)$

8. (a)

(b) $\left(2\sqrt{2}, \dfrac{2\pi}{3}\right)$

(c) $\left(-2\sqrt{2}, \dfrac{5\pi}{3}\right)$

9. (a)

10. (a)

17. (a)

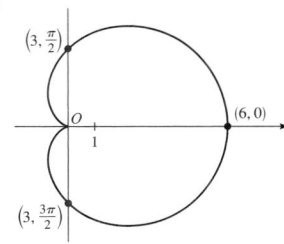

(b) $\left(12, \dfrac{5\pi}{4}\right)$

(b) $\left(6, \dfrac{\pi}{6}\right)$

(c) $\left(-12, \dfrac{\pi}{4}\right)$

(c) $\left(-6, \dfrac{7\pi}{6}\right)$

(b) $(x^2 + y^2 - 3x)^2 = 9(x^2 + y^2)$

11. (a)

(b) $\left(2\sqrt{3}, \dfrac{5\pi}{6}\right)$

(c) $\left(-2\sqrt{3}, -\dfrac{\pi}{6}\right)$

18. (a)

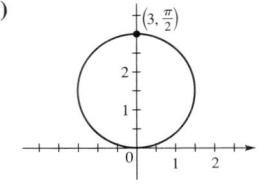

(b) $x^2 + \left(y - \dfrac{3}{2}\right)^2 = \dfrac{9}{4}$

12. (a)

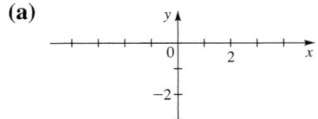

(b) $\left(4\sqrt{2}, \dfrac{7\pi}{4}\right)$

(c) $\left(-4\sqrt{2}, \dfrac{3\pi}{4}\right)$

19. (a)

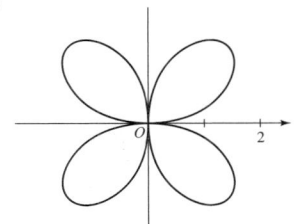

13. (a) $r = \dfrac{4}{\cos\theta + \sin\theta}$

(b)

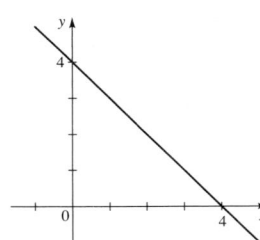

(b) $(x^2 + y^2)^3 = 16x^2y^2$

20. (a)

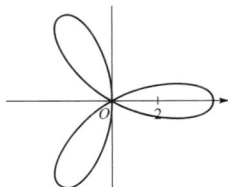

14. (a) $r^2 = 2\csc 2\theta$

(b)

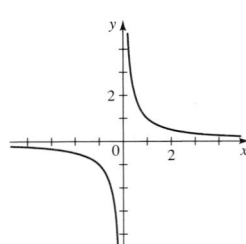

15. (a) $r = 4(\cos\theta + \sin\theta)$

(b)

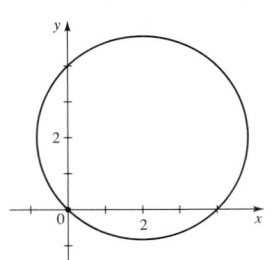

(b) $(x^2 + y^2)^2 = 4x^3 - 12xy^2$

21. (a)

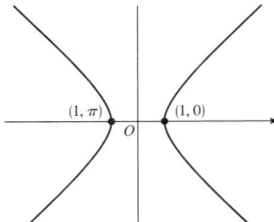

16. (a) $r^2 = \sin 2\theta$

(b)

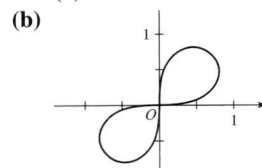

(b) $x^2 - y^2 = 1$

22. (a)

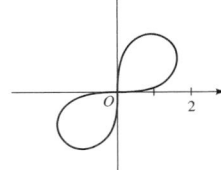

(b) $(x^2 + y^2)^2 = 8xy$

23. (a)

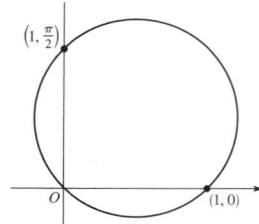

(b) $x^2 + y^2 = x + y$

24. (a)

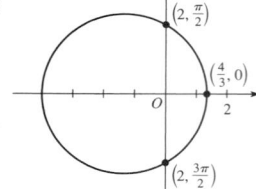

(b) $\dfrac{\left(x + \frac{4}{3}\right)^2}{\frac{64}{9}} + \dfrac{y^2}{\frac{16}{9}} = 1$

25. $0 \le \theta \le 6\pi$

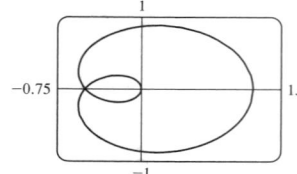

26. $0 \le \theta \le 8\pi$

27. $0 \le \theta \le 6\pi$

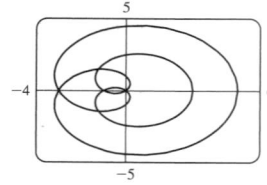

28. $-6\pi \le \theta \le 6\pi$

29. (a)

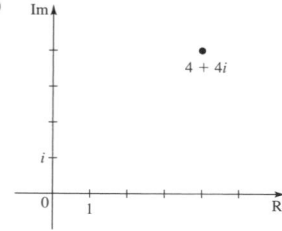

(b) $4\sqrt{2}, \dfrac{\pi}{4}$ **(c)** $4\sqrt{2}\left(\cos\dfrac{\pi}{4} + i\sin\dfrac{\pi}{4}\right)$

30. (a)

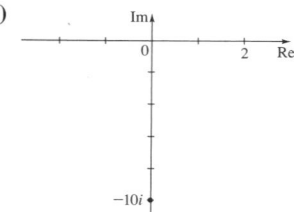

(b) $10, \dfrac{3\pi}{2}$ **(c)** $10\left(\cos\dfrac{3\pi}{2} + i\sin\dfrac{3\pi}{2}\right)$

31. (a)

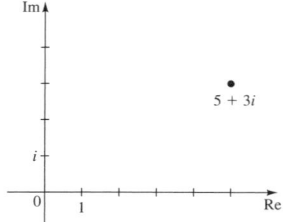

(b) $\sqrt{34}, \tan^{-1}\left(\frac{3}{5}\right)$ **(c)** $\sqrt{34}\left[\cos\left(\tan^{-1}\frac{3}{5}\right) + i\sin\left(\tan^{-1}\frac{3}{5}\right)\right]$

32. (a)

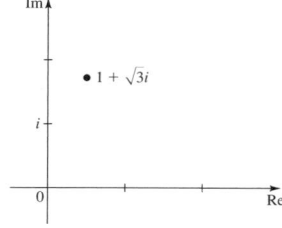

(b) $2, \dfrac{\pi}{3}$ **(c)** $2\left(\cos\dfrac{\pi}{3} + i\sin\dfrac{\pi}{3}\right)$

33. (a)

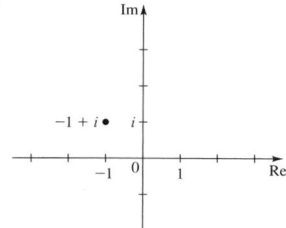

(b) $\sqrt{2}, \dfrac{3\pi}{4}$ **(c)** $\sqrt{2}\left(\cos\dfrac{3\pi}{4} + i\sin\dfrac{3\pi}{4}\right)$

34. (a)

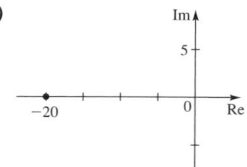

(b) $20, \pi$ **(c)** $20(\cos\pi + i\sin\pi)$

35. $8(-1 + i\sqrt{3})$ **36.** 16 **37.** $-\frac{1}{32}(1 + i\sqrt{3})$

38. $\frac{1}{2}(-1 + i\sqrt{3})$ **39.** $\pm 2\sqrt{2}(1 - i)$

40. $2\left(\cos\dfrac{\pi}{9} + i\sin\dfrac{\pi}{9}\right), 2\left(\cos\dfrac{7\pi}{9} + i\sin\dfrac{7\pi}{9}\right),$
$2\left(\cos\dfrac{13\pi}{9} + i\sin\dfrac{13\pi}{9}\right)$

41. $\pm 1, \pm\dfrac{1}{2} \pm \dfrac{\sqrt{3}}{2}i$

42. $\cos\dfrac{\pi}{16} + i\sin\dfrac{\pi}{16}, \cos\dfrac{5\pi}{16} + i\sin\dfrac{5\pi}{16},$
$\cos\dfrac{9\pi}{16} + i\sin\dfrac{9\pi}{16}, \cos\dfrac{13\pi}{16} + i\sin\dfrac{13\pi}{16},$
$\cos\dfrac{17\pi}{16} + i\sin\dfrac{17\pi}{16}, \cos\dfrac{21\pi}{16} + i\sin\dfrac{21\pi}{16},$
$\cos\dfrac{25\pi}{16} + i\sin\dfrac{25\pi}{16}, \cos\dfrac{29\pi}{16} + i\sin\dfrac{29\pi}{16}$

43. (a)

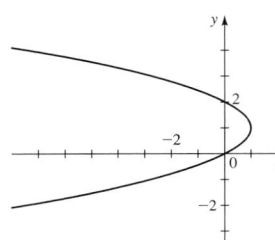

(b) $x = 2y - y^2$

45. (a)

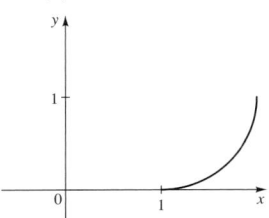

(b) $(x - 1)^2 + (y - 1)^2 = 1$,
$1 \le x \le 2, 0 \le y \le 1$

47.

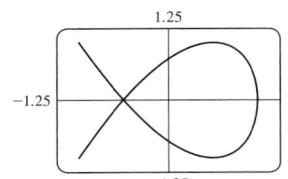

49. $x = \frac{1}{2}(1 + \cos \theta), y = \frac{1}{2}(\sin \theta + \tan \theta)$

CHAPTER 8 TEST ▪ PAGE 574

1. (a) $\left(-4\sqrt{2}, -4\sqrt{2}\right)$ **(b)** $\left(4\sqrt{3}, 5\pi/6\right), \left(-4\sqrt{3}, 11\pi/6\right)$

2. (a)   circle

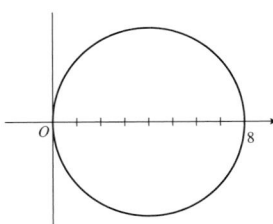

(b) $(x - 4)^2 + y^2 = 16$

3.   limaçon

44. (a)

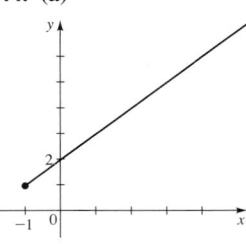

(b) $y = x + 2, x \ge -1$

46. (a)

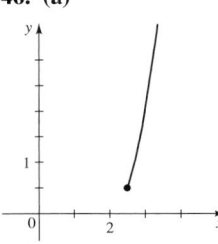

(b) $y = 2(x - 2)^2, x \ge \frac{5}{2}$

48.

4. (a)

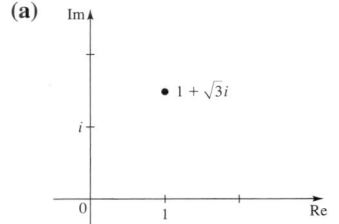

(b) $2\left(\cos \dfrac{\pi}{3} + i \sin \dfrac{\pi}{3}\right)$ **(c)** -512 **5.** $-8, \sqrt{3} + i$

6. $-3i, 3\left(\pm \dfrac{\sqrt{3}}{2} + \dfrac{1}{2}i\right)$

7. (a)

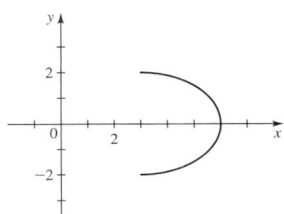

(b) $\dfrac{(x - 3)^2}{9} + \dfrac{y^2}{4} = 1, x \ge 3$

8. $x = 3 + t, y = 5 + 2t$

FOCUS ON MODELING ▪ PAGE 577

1. $y = -\left(\dfrac{g}{2v_0^2 \cos^2\theta}\right)x^2 + (\tan \theta)x$

2. (a) $x = 15t, y = 4 + 15\sqrt{3}t - 16t^2$

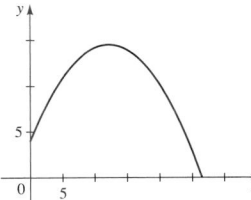

(b) 26.5 ft, 1.77 s

3. (a) 5.45 s **(b)** 118.7 ft **(c)** 5426.5 ft

(d)

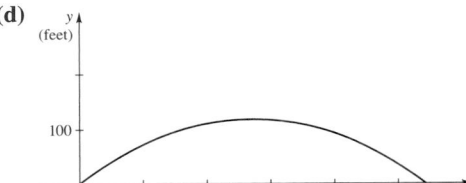

4. (a) 32.08° or 115.85°

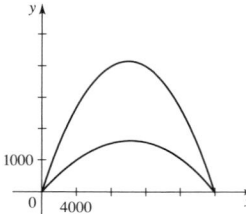

(b) 32.08°

5. $\dfrac{v_0^2 \sin^2\theta}{2g}$ **6.** $x = (v_0 \cos\theta - w)t,\ y = (v_0 \sin\theta)t - \frac{1}{2}gt^2$

7. No, $\theta \approx 23°$ **8. (b)** Same spot; the projectile fired with $\theta = 30°$ lands first. **(c)** Increases the maximum height by a factor of 4.

Chapter 9

SECTION 9.1 ■ PAGE 587

1. (a) A, B

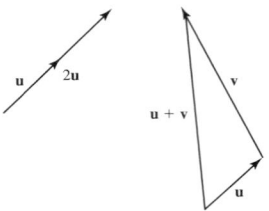

(b) $(2, 1), (4, 3), \langle 2, 2\rangle, \langle -3, 6\rangle, \langle 4, 4\rangle, \langle -1, 8\rangle$

2. (a) $\sqrt{a^2 + b^2}, 2\sqrt{2}$ **(b)** $(|\mathbf{w}| \cos\theta, |\mathbf{w}| \sin\theta)$

3.

4.

5.

6.

7.

8.

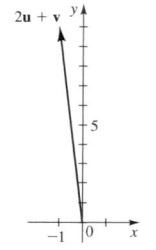

9. $\langle 3, 3\rangle$ **10.** $\langle -5, 3\rangle$ **11.** $\langle 3, -1\rangle$ **12.** $\langle 2, -3\rangle$ **13.** $\langle 5, 7\rangle$
14. $\langle 8, 8\rangle$ **15.** $\langle -4, -3\rangle$ **16.** $\langle -5, -4\rangle$ **17.** $\langle 0, 2\rangle$ **18.** $\langle 7, 5\rangle$

19.

20.

21.

22.

23.

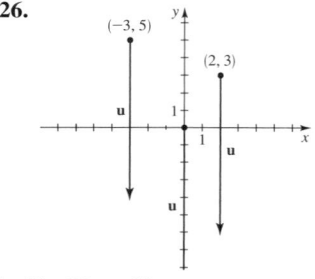

24.

25.

26.

27. $\mathbf{i} + 4\mathbf{j}$ **28.** $-2\mathbf{i} + 10\mathbf{j}$ **29.** $3\mathbf{i}$ **30.** $-5\mathbf{j}$
31. $\langle 4, 14\rangle, \langle -9, -3\rangle, \langle 5, 8\rangle, \langle -6, 17\rangle$
32. $\langle -4, 10\rangle, \langle -6, 24\rangle, \langle 0, -3\rangle, \langle -14, 47\rangle$
33. $\langle 0, -2\rangle, \langle 6, 0\rangle, \langle -2, -1\rangle, \langle 8, -3\rangle$
34. $2\mathbf{i}, 6\mathbf{j}, \mathbf{i} - 2\mathbf{j}, 3\mathbf{i} + 8\mathbf{j}$
35. $4\mathbf{i}, -9\mathbf{i} + 6\mathbf{j}, 5\mathbf{i} - 2\mathbf{j}, -6\mathbf{i} + 8\mathbf{j}$
36. $2\mathbf{i} + 2\mathbf{j}, -3\mathbf{i} + 3\mathbf{j}, 2\mathbf{i}, -\mathbf{i} + 7\mathbf{j}$
37. $\sqrt{5}, \sqrt{13}, 2\sqrt{5}, \frac{1}{2}\sqrt{13}, \sqrt{26}, \sqrt{10}, \sqrt{5} - \sqrt{13}$
38. $\sqrt{13}, \sqrt{5}, 2\sqrt{13}, \sqrt{5}/2, \sqrt{2}, \sqrt{34}, \sqrt{13} - \sqrt{5}$
39. $\sqrt{101}, 2\sqrt{2}, 2\sqrt{101}, \sqrt{2}, \sqrt{73}, \sqrt{145}, \sqrt{101} - 2\sqrt{2}$
40. $6\sqrt{2}, \sqrt{5}, 12\sqrt{2}, \sqrt{5}/2, \sqrt{89}, \sqrt{63}, 6\sqrt{2} - \sqrt{5}$

41. $20\sqrt{3}\,\mathbf{i} + 20\mathbf{j}$ **42.** $-25\mathbf{i} + 25\sqrt{3}\,\mathbf{j}$ **43.** $-\dfrac{\sqrt{2}}{2}\mathbf{i} - \dfrac{\sqrt{2}}{2}\mathbf{j}$

44. $800 \cos 125°\mathbf{i} + 800 \sin 125°\mathbf{j} \approx -458.86\mathbf{i} + 655.32\mathbf{j}$
45. $4 \cos 10°\mathbf{i} + 4 \sin 10°\mathbf{j} \approx 3.94\mathbf{i} + 0.69\mathbf{j}$
46. $\dfrac{\sqrt{3}}{2}\mathbf{i} - \dfrac{3}{2}\mathbf{j}$ **47.** 5, 53.13° **48.** 1, 225° **49.** 13, 157.38°
50. 41, 12.68° **51.** 2, 60° **52.** $\sqrt{2}, 45°$ **53.** $15\sqrt{3}, -15$
54. 469.85 mi/h, 171.01 mi/h **55.** $2\mathbf{i} - 3\mathbf{j}$

56. N 53.1° E　**57.** S 84.26° W

58. $\left(\dfrac{5\sqrt{2}}{2}+3\right)\mathbf{i}+\left(\dfrac{5\sqrt{2}}{2}\right)\mathbf{j}$　**59. (a)** 40$\mathbf{j}$　**(b)** 425$\mathbf{i}$

(c) 425$\mathbf{i}$ + 40$\mathbf{j}$　**(d)** 427 mi/h, N 84.6° E

60. (a) $\left\langle\dfrac{55}{2},\dfrac{55\sqrt{3}}{2}\right\rangle$　**(b)** $\left\langle\dfrac{765\sqrt{2}}{2},\dfrac{765\sqrt{2}}{2}\right\rangle$

(c) $\langle 568.44, 588.57\rangle$　**(d)** 818 mi/h, N 44° E

61. 794 mi/h, N 26.6° W　**62.** N 2.1° W

63. (a) 10$\mathbf{i}$　**(b)** 10$\mathbf{i}$ + 17.32$\mathbf{j}$　**(c)** 20$\mathbf{i}$ + 17.32$\mathbf{j}$

(d) 26.5 mi/h, N 49.1° E　**64.** N 30° W

65. (a) 22.8$\mathbf{i}$ + 7.4$\mathbf{j}$　**(b)** 7.4 mi/h, 22.8 mi/h

66. 25.08 mi/h, N 4.57° W　**67. (a)** $\langle 5, -3\rangle$　**(b)** $\langle -5, 3\rangle$

68. (a) $\langle 0, 0\rangle$　**(b)** None　**69. (a)** $-4\mathbf{j}$　**(b)** 4$\mathbf{j}$

70. (a) $\mathbf{j}$　**(b)** $-\mathbf{j}$　**71. (a)** $\langle -7.57, 10.61\rangle$

(b) $\langle 7.57, -10.61\rangle$　**72. (a)** $\langle 2, -4\rangle$　**(b)** $\langle -2, 4\rangle$

73. $\mathbf{T}_1 \approx -56.5\mathbf{i} + 67.4\mathbf{j}$, $\mathbf{T}_2 \approx 56.5\mathbf{i} + 32.6\mathbf{j}$

74. $\mathbf{T}_1 \approx -14{,}116\mathbf{i} + 5{,}789\mathbf{j}$, $\mathbf{T}_2 \approx 14{,}116\mathbf{i} + 12{,}488\mathbf{j}$

SECTION 9.2 ■ PAGE 595

1. $a_1a_2 + b_1b_2$; real number or scalar　**2.** $\dfrac{\mathbf{a}\cdot\mathbf{b}}{|\mathbf{a}||\mathbf{b}|}$; perpendicular

3. (a) $\dfrac{\mathbf{a}\cdot\mathbf{b}}{|\mathbf{b}|}$　**(b)** $\left(\dfrac{\mathbf{a}\cdot\mathbf{b}}{|\mathbf{b}|^2}\right)\mathbf{b}$

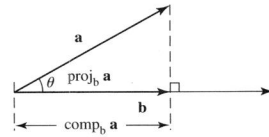

4. $\mathbf{F}\cdot\mathbf{D}$　**5. (a)** 2　**(b)** 45°　**6. (a)** 0　**(b)** 90°

7. (a) 13　**(b)** 56°　**8. (a)** -12　**(b)** 180°

9. (a) -1　**(b)** 97°　**10. (a)** 4　**(b)** 60.3°

11. (a) $5\sqrt{3}$　**(b)** 30°　**12. (a)** 0　**(b)** 90°

13. (a) 1　**(b)** 86°　**14. (a)** -10　**(b)** 153°

15. Yes　**16.** Yes　**17.** No

18. Yes　**19.** Yes　**20.** No　**21.** 9

22. 9　**23.** -5　**24.** -10　**25.** $-\frac{12}{5}$

26. $\sqrt{2}$　**27.** -24　**28.** $\frac{28}{5}$

29. (a) $\langle 1, 1\rangle$　**(b)** $\mathbf{u}_1 = \langle 1, 1\rangle$, $\mathbf{u}_2 = \langle -3, 3\rangle$

30. (a) $\langle 4, 2\rangle$　**(b)** $\mathbf{u}_1 = \langle 4, 2\rangle$, $\mathbf{u}_2 = \langle 3, -6\rangle$

31. (a) $\langle -\frac{1}{2}, \frac{3}{2}\rangle$　**(b)** $\mathbf{u}_1 = \langle -\frac{1}{2}, \frac{3}{2}\rangle$, $\mathbf{u}_2 = \langle \frac{3}{2}, \frac{1}{2}\rangle$

32. (a) $\langle 9, 6\rangle$　**(b)** $\mathbf{u}_1 = \langle 9, 6\rangle$, $\mathbf{u}_2 = \langle 2, -3\rangle$

33. (a) $\langle -\frac{18}{5}, \frac{24}{5}\rangle$　**(b)** $\mathbf{u}_1 = \langle -\frac{18}{5}, \frac{24}{5}\rangle$, $\mathbf{u}_2 = \langle \frac{28}{5}, \frac{21}{5}\rangle$

34. (a) $\langle \frac{2}{5}, -\frac{1}{5}\rangle$　**(b)** $\mathbf{u}_1 = \langle \frac{2}{5}, -\frac{1}{5}\rangle$, $\mathbf{u}_2 = \langle \frac{3}{5}, \frac{6}{5}\rangle$

35. -28　**36.** 80,400　**37.** 25　**38.** 280　**44.** $\mathbf{u}\cdot\mathbf{v}$

45. 16 ft-lb　**46.** 82 ft-lb　**47.** 8660 ft-lb　**48.** 260,000 ft-lb

49. 1164 lb　**50. (a)** 2822 lb　**(b)** 2779 lb　**51.** 23.6°

52. 54.6 lb

SECTION 9.3 ■ PAGE 602

1. x, y, z; $(5, 2, 3)$; $y = 2$

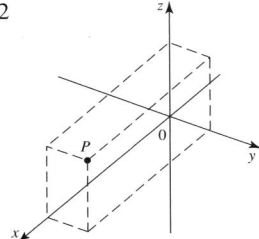

2. $\sqrt{(x_2 - x_1)^2 + (y_2 - y_1)^2 + (z_2 - z_1)^2}$;

$\sqrt{38}$; $(x - 5)^2 + (y - 2)^2 + (z - 3)^2 = 9$

3. (a)

4. (a)

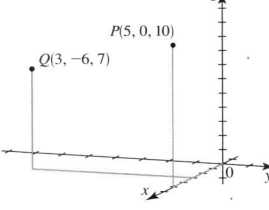

(b) $\sqrt{42}$

(b) 7

5. (a)

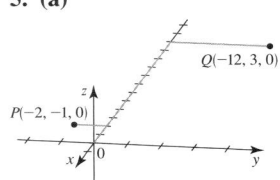

6. (a)

(b) $2\sqrt{29}$

(b) $\sqrt{118}$

7. Plane parallel to the yz-plane

8. Plane parallel to the xz-plane

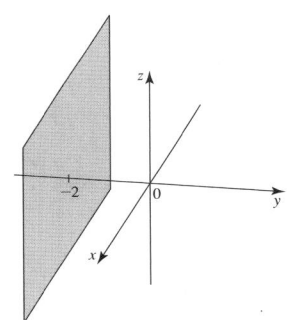

9. Plane parallel to the xy-plane

10. Plane parallel to the xz-plane

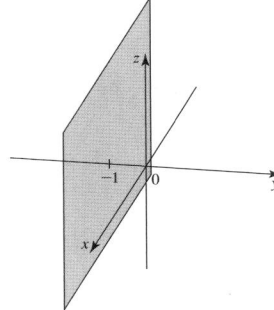

11. $(x - 2)^2 + (y + 5)^2 + (z - 3)^2 = 25$

12. $(x + 1)^2 + (y - 4)^2 + (z + 7)^2 = 9$

13. $(x - 3)^2 + (y + 1)^2 + z^2 = 6$

14. $(x + 10)^2 + y^2 + (z - 1)^2 = 11$

15. Center: $(5, -1, -4)$, radius: $\sqrt{51}$

16. Center: $(-2, 3, -1)$, radius: $2\sqrt{6}$

17. Center: $(6, 1, 0)$, radius: $\sqrt{37}$
18. Center: $(0, 7, -3)$, radius: $\sqrt{58}$
19. (a) Circle, center: $(0, 2, -10)$, radius: $3\sqrt{11}$
(b) Circle, center: $(4, 2, -10)$, radius: $5\sqrt{3}$
20. (a) Circle, center: $(0, 0, 3)$, radius: $8\sqrt{2}$
(b) Circle, center: $(0, 4, -2)$, radius: $\sqrt{119}$
21. (a) 3   **22. (a)** $x^2 + y^2 + z^2 = 4$ **(b)** $x^2 + y^2 = \frac{7}{4}$

SECTION 9.4 ■ PAGE 608

1. unit, $a_1\mathbf{i} + a_2\mathbf{j} + a_3\mathbf{k}$; $\sqrt{a_1^2 + a_2^2 + a_3^2}$; 4, (-2), 4, $\langle 0, 7, -24 \rangle$
2. $\dfrac{\mathbf{u} \cdot \mathbf{v}}{|\mathbf{u}||\mathbf{v}|}$; 0; 0, perpendicular   **3.** $\langle -1, -1, 5 \rangle$ **4.** $\langle 2, -3, 3 \rangle$
5. $\langle -6, -2, 0 \rangle$ **6.** $\langle -1, 1, 0 \rangle$ **7.** $(5, 4, -1)$ **8.** $(0, 1, 0)$
9. $(1, 0, -1)$ **10.** $(17, -1, 14)$ **11.** 3   **12.** 13   **13.** $5\sqrt{2}$
14. $3\sqrt{5}$ **15.** $\langle 2, -3, 2 \rangle, \langle 2, -11, 4 \rangle, \langle 6, -23, \frac{19}{2} \rangle$
16. $\langle 4, 3, -3 \rangle, \langle -4, -1, -3 \rangle, \langle -2, 2, -9 \rangle$
17. $\mathbf{i} - 2\mathbf{k}, \mathbf{i} + 2\mathbf{j} + 2\mathbf{k}, 3\mathbf{i} + \frac{7}{2}\mathbf{j} + \mathbf{k}$
18. $\langle -3a, 3b, c \rangle, \langle 5a, b, 5c \rangle, \langle 5a, \frac{11}{2}b, 10c \rangle$ **19.** $12\mathbf{i} + 2\mathbf{k}$
20. $-3\mathbf{j} + 5\mathbf{k}$ **21.** $3\mathbf{i} - 3\mathbf{j}$ **22.** $-a\mathbf{i} + \frac{1}{3}a\mathbf{j} + 4\mathbf{k}$
23. (a) $\langle 3, 1, -2 \rangle$ **(b)** $3\mathbf{i} + \mathbf{j} - 2\mathbf{k}$ **24. (a)** $\langle 3, -2, -15 \rangle$
(b) $3\mathbf{i} - 2\mathbf{j} - 15\mathbf{k}$ **25.** -4 **26.** -4 **27.** 1   **28.** -5
29. Yes   **30.** No   **31.** No   **32.** Yes   **33.** $116.4°$ **34.** $36.9°$
35. $100.9°$ **36.** $48.2°$ **37.** $\alpha \approx 65°, \beta \approx 56°, \gamma = 45°$
38. $\alpha \approx 66°, \beta \approx 145°, \gamma \approx 114°$ **39.** $\alpha \approx 73°, \beta \approx 65°,$
$\gamma \approx 149°$ **40.** $\alpha \approx 48°, \beta \approx 109°, \gamma \approx 48°$ **41.** $\pi/4$ **42.** $\pi/3$
43. $125°$ **44.** $90°$ **47. (a)** $-7\mathbf{i} - 24\mathbf{j} + 25\mathbf{k}$ **(b)** $25\sqrt{2}$
48. (b) $109.5°$

SECTION 9.5 ■ PAGE 615

1. $\begin{vmatrix} \mathbf{i} & \mathbf{j} & \mathbf{k} \\ a_1 & a_2 & a_3 \\ b_1 & b_2 & b_3 \end{vmatrix} = (a_2b_3 - a_3b_2)\mathbf{i} + (a_3b_1 - a_1b_3)\mathbf{j} + (a_1b_2 - a_2b_1)\mathbf{k}, -3\mathbf{i} + 2\mathbf{j} + 3\mathbf{k}$

2. perpendicular; perpendicular   **3.** $9\mathbf{i} - 6\mathbf{j} + 3\mathbf{k}$
4. $7\mathbf{i} + \mathbf{j} + 4\mathbf{k}$ **5.** 0   **6.** 0   **7.** $-4\mathbf{i} + 7\mathbf{j} - 3\mathbf{k}$

8. $-\mathbf{i} - 3\mathbf{j} - 9\mathbf{k}$ **9. (a)** $\langle 0, 2, 2 \rangle$ **(b)** $\left\langle 0, \dfrac{\sqrt{2}}{2}, \dfrac{\sqrt{2}}{2} \right\rangle$

10. (a) $\langle 1, 11, -19 \rangle$ **(b)** $\left\langle \dfrac{\sqrt{483}}{483}, \dfrac{11\sqrt{483}}{483}, \dfrac{-19\sqrt{483}}{483} \right\rangle$

11. (a) $14\mathbf{i} + 7\mathbf{j}$ **(b)** $\dfrac{2\sqrt{5}}{5}\mathbf{i} + \dfrac{\sqrt{5}}{5}\mathbf{j}$

12. (a) $6\mathbf{i} - 5\mathbf{j} + 3\mathbf{k}$ **(b)** $\dfrac{3\sqrt{70}}{35}\mathbf{i} - \dfrac{\sqrt{70}}{14}\mathbf{j} + \dfrac{3\sqrt{70}}{70}\mathbf{k}$

13. $\dfrac{3\sqrt{3}}{2}$ **14.** 10   **15.** 100   **16.** 0.145   **17.** $\langle 0, 2, 2 \rangle$

18. $\langle 4, 0, -4 \rangle$ **19.** $\langle 10, -10, 0 \rangle$ **20.** $\langle 12, 43, 10 \rangle$ **21.** $4\sqrt{6}$

22. $\sqrt{469}$ **23.** $\dfrac{5\sqrt{14}}{2}$ **24.** $2\sqrt{2}$ **25.** $\sqrt{14}$ **26.** $\dfrac{\sqrt{101}}{2}$

27. $18\sqrt{3}$ **28.** $12\sqrt{10}$ **29. (a)** 0   **(b)** Yes   **30. (a)** 0
(b) Yes   **31. (a)** 55   **(b)** No, 55   **32. (a)** 0   **(b)** Yes
33. (a) -2 **(b)** No, 2   **34. (a)** -6 **(b)** No, 6
35. (a) $2,700,000\sqrt{3}$ **(b)** 4677 liters   **36. (a)** $\frac{1}{3}$

SECTION 9.6 ■ PAGE 619

1. parametric; $x = x_0 + at, y = y_0 + bt, z = z_0 + ct$
2. $a(x - x_0) + b(y - y_0) + c(z - z_0) = 0$
3. $x = 1 + 3t, y = 2t, z = -2 - 3t$
4. $x = 2t, y = -5, z = 3 - 4t$
5. $x = 3, y = 2 - 4t, z = 1 + 2t$
6. $x = -4t, y = 3t, z = 5t$
7. $x = 1 + 2t, y = 0, z = -2 - 5t$
8. $x = 1 + t, y = 1 - t, z = 1 + t$
9. $x = 1 + t, y = -3 + 4t, z = 2 - 3t$
10. $x = 2 - 2t, y = -1 + 2t, z = -2 - t$
11. $x = 1 - t, y = 1 + t, z = 2t$
12. $x = 3 + 4t, y = 3 - 3t, z = 3 - 3t$
13. $x = 3 + 4t, y = 7 - 4t, z = -5$
14. $x = 12, y = 16 - 22t, z = 18 - 18t$
15. (a) $x + y - z = 5$ **(b)** x-intercept 5, y-intercept 5, z-intercept -5

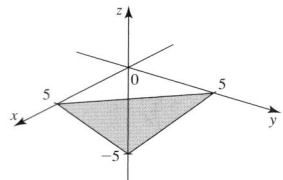

16. (a) $3x + 2y = 7$ **(b)** x-intercept $\frac{7}{3}$, y-intercept $\frac{7}{2}$, no z-intercept

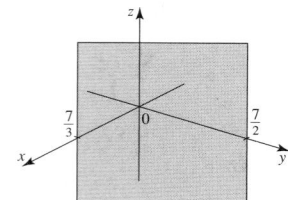

17. (a) $6x - z = 4$ **(b)** x-intercept $\frac{2}{3}$, no y-intercept, z-intercept -4

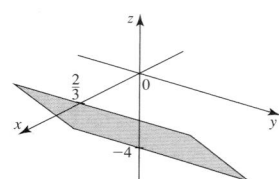

18. (a) $2x + y - 3z = -3$ **(b)** x-intercept $-\frac{3}{2}$, y-intercept -3, z-intercept 1

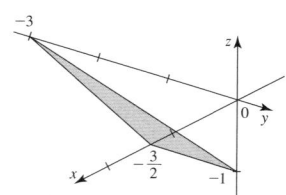

19. (a) $3x - y + 2z = -8$ **(b)** x-intercept $-\frac{8}{3}$, y-intercept 8, z-intercept -4

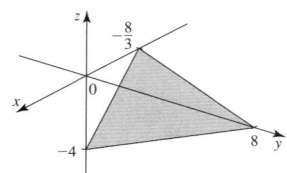

20. (a) $x + 4y = 1$ **(b)** x-intercept 1, y-intercept $\frac{1}{4}$, no z-intercept

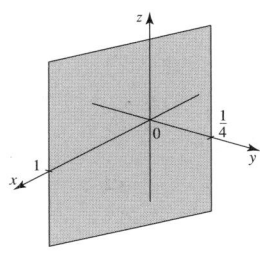

21. $5x - 3y - z = 35$ **22.** $x - z = -2$ **23.** $x - 3y = 2$
24. $y + z = 2$ **25.** $2x - 3y - 9z = 0$ **26.** $2x + 3y + z = 4$
27. $x = 2t, y = 5t, z = 4 - 4t$
28. $x = -2 + 2t, y = 0, z = 10t$ **29.** $x = 2, y = -1 + t, z = 5$
30. $x = -3, y = t, z = 2$ **31.** $12x + 4y + 3z = 12$
32. $3x + 6y - 2z = -6$ **33.** $x - 2y + 4z = 0$
34. $12x + 9y - z = 30$

CHAPTER 9 REVIEW ▪ PAGE 621

1. $\sqrt{13}, \langle 6, 4 \rangle, \langle -10, 2 \rangle, \langle -4, 6 \rangle, \langle -22, 7 \rangle$
2. $\sqrt{29}, \langle 2, -2 \rangle, \langle 8, -2 \rangle, \langle 10, -4 \rangle, \langle 21, -6 \rangle$
3. $\sqrt{5}, 3\mathbf{i} - \mathbf{j}, \mathbf{i} + 3\mathbf{j}, 4\mathbf{i} + 2\mathbf{j}, 4\mathbf{i} + 7\mathbf{j}$
4. $3, -\mathbf{i} + 5\mathbf{j}, \mathbf{i} + \mathbf{j}, 6\mathbf{j}, 2\mathbf{i} + 5\mathbf{j}$ **5.** $\langle 3, -4 \rangle$ **6.** $(10, -2)$
7. $4, 120°$ **8.** $\sqrt{29}, 291.8°$ **9.** $\langle 10, 10\sqrt{3} \rangle$ **10.** $\langle -7.7, 11.1 \rangle$
11. (a) $(4.8\mathbf{i} + 0.4\mathbf{j}) \times 10^4$ **(b)** 4.8×10^4 lb, N 85.2° E
12. (a) $\langle 300\sqrt{3} - 25, 300 + 25\sqrt{3} \rangle$ **(b)** 602 mi/h, N 55.2° E
13. $5, 25, 60$ **14.** $13, 169, 2$ **15.** $2\sqrt{2}, 8, 0$ **16.** $10, 100, -30$
17. Yes **18.** No, 77.5° **19.** No, 45° **20.** Yes

21. (a) $\dfrac{17\sqrt{37}}{37}$ **(b)** $\langle \frac{102}{37}, -\frac{17}{37} \rangle$
(c) $\mathbf{u}_1 = \langle \frac{102}{37}, -\frac{17}{37} \rangle, \mathbf{u}_2 = \langle \frac{9}{37}, \frac{54}{37} \rangle$ **22. (a)** $-\sqrt{2}$
(b) $\langle -1, -1 \rangle$ **(c)** $\mathbf{u}_1 = \langle -1, -1 \rangle, \mathbf{u}_2 = \langle -7, 7 \rangle$

23. (a) $-\dfrac{14\sqrt{97}}{97}$ **(b)** $-\frac{56}{97}\mathbf{i} + \frac{126}{97}\mathbf{j}$
(c) $\mathbf{u}_1 = -\frac{56}{97}\mathbf{i} + \frac{126}{97}\mathbf{j}, \mathbf{u}_2 = \frac{153}{97}\mathbf{i} + \frac{68}{97}\mathbf{j}$ **24. (a)** 4 **(b)** $4\mathbf{j}$
(c) $\mathbf{u}_1 = 4\mathbf{j}, \mathbf{u}_2 = 2\mathbf{i}$
25. 3   **26.** $3\sqrt{2}$

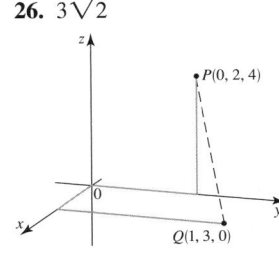

27. $x^2 + y^2 + z^2 = 36$
28. $(x - 1)^2 + (y + 2)^2 + (z - 4)^2 = 4$
29. Center: $(1, 3, -2)$, radius: 4
30. Center: $(0, 2, 2)$, radius: $2\sqrt{2}$
31. $6, \langle 6, 1, 3 \rangle, \langle 2, -5, 5 \rangle, \langle -1, -\frac{15}{2}, 5 \rangle$

32. $10, 7\mathbf{i} - \mathbf{j} - 7\mathbf{k}, 5\mathbf{i} + \mathbf{j} - 9\mathbf{k}, \frac{5}{2}\mathbf{i} + 2\mathbf{j} - 8\mathbf{k}$
33. (a) -1 **(b)** No, 92.8° **34. (a)** 0 **(b)** Yes **35. (a)** 0
(b) Yes **36. (a)** 1 **(b)** No, 60° **37. (a)** $\langle -2, 17, -5 \rangle$
(b) $\left\langle -\dfrac{\sqrt{318}}{159}, \dfrac{17\sqrt{318}}{318}, -\dfrac{5\sqrt{318}}{318} \right\rangle$ **38. (a)** $\langle -3, 2, 8 \rangle$
(b) $\left\langle -\dfrac{3\sqrt{77}}{77}, \dfrac{2\sqrt{77}}{77}, \dfrac{8\sqrt{77}}{77} \right\rangle$ **39. (a)** $\mathbf{i} + \mathbf{j} + 2\mathbf{k}$
(b) $\dfrac{\sqrt{6}}{6}\mathbf{i} + \dfrac{\sqrt{6}}{6}\mathbf{j} + \dfrac{\sqrt{6}}{3}\mathbf{k}$ **40. (a)** $-2\mathbf{j} - 2\mathbf{k}$
(b) $-\dfrac{\sqrt{2}}{2}\mathbf{j} - \dfrac{\sqrt{2}}{2}\mathbf{k}$ **41.** $\frac{15}{2}$ **42.** $9\sqrt{2}$ **43.** 9 **44.** 14
45. $x = 2 + 3t, y = t, z = -6$
46. $x = 5 + 2t, y = 2 - t, z = 8 + 5t$
47. $x = 6 - 2t, y = -2 + 3t, z = -3 + t$
48. $x = 1 + 2t, y = -4t, z = 2t$
49. $2x + 3y - 5z = 2$ **50.** $x + 2y - 7z = -6$
51. $7x + 7y + 6z = 20$ **52.** $15x - 20y - 12z = 60$
53. $x = 2 - 2t, y = 0, z = -4t$ **54.** $4x - 2y - z = 14$

CHAPTER 9 TEST ▪ PAGE 623

1. (a)   **(b)** $-6\mathbf{i} + 10\mathbf{j}$ **(c)** $2\sqrt{34}$

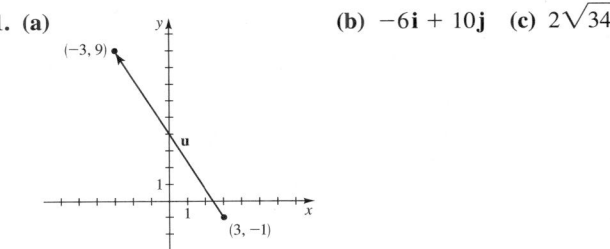

2. (a) $\langle 19, -3 \rangle$ **(b)** $5\sqrt{2}$ **(c)** 0 **(d)** Yes
3. (a)   **(b)** 8, 150°

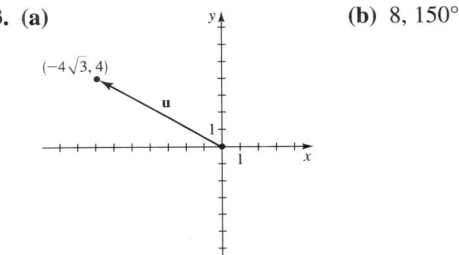

4. (a) $14\mathbf{i} + 6\sqrt{3}\mathbf{j}$ **(b)** 17.4 mi/h, N 53.4° E **5. (a)** 45.0°
(b) $\dfrac{\sqrt{26}}{2}$ **(c)** $\frac{5}{2}\mathbf{i} - \frac{1}{2}\mathbf{j}$ **6.** 90 **7. (a)** 6
(b) $(x - 4)^2 + (y - 3)^2 + (z + 1)^2 = 36$
(c) $\langle 2, -4, 4 \rangle = 2\mathbf{i} - 4\mathbf{j} + 4\mathbf{k}$ **8. (a)** $11\mathbf{i} - 4\mathbf{j} - \mathbf{k}$ **(b)** $\sqrt{6}$
(c) -1 **(d)** $-3\mathbf{i} - 7\mathbf{j} - 5\mathbf{k}$ **(e)** $3\sqrt{35}$ **(f)** 18 **(g)** 96.3°
9. $\left\langle \dfrac{7\sqrt{6}}{18}, \dfrac{\sqrt{6}}{9}, -\dfrac{\sqrt{6}}{18} \right\rangle, \left\langle -\dfrac{7\sqrt{6}}{18}, -\dfrac{\sqrt{6}}{9}, \dfrac{\sqrt{6}}{18} \right\rangle$
10. (a) $\langle 4, -3, 4 \rangle$ **(b)** $4x - 3y + 4z = 4$ **(c)** $\dfrac{\sqrt{41}}{2}$
11. $x = 2 - 2t, y = -4 + t, z = 7 - 2t$

CHAPTER 9 FOCUS ON MODELING ▪ PAGE 626

1.

2.

3.

4.

5.

6.

7.

8.

9. **10.**

11. II   **12.** IV   **13.** I   **14.** III   **15.** IV   **16.** I   **17.** III
18. II

19.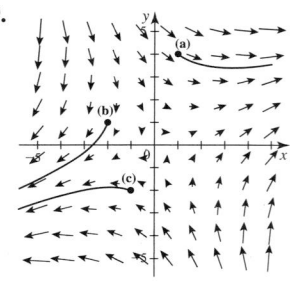

CUMULATIVE REVIEW TEST FOR CHAPTERS 8 AND 9 ▪ PAGE 628

1. $(8\sqrt{2}, 7\pi/4), (-8\sqrt{2}, 3\pi/4)$

2. (a) 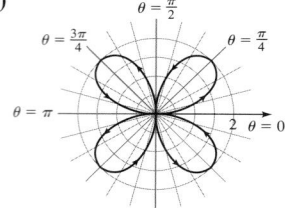   **(b)** $(x^2 + y^2)^{3/2} = 4xy$

3. (a) $z = 2\left(\cos\dfrac{11\pi}{6} + i\sin\dfrac{11\pi}{6}\right)$

(b) $zw = 12\left(\cos\dfrac{\pi}{4} + i\sin\dfrac{\pi}{4}\right) = 6\sqrt{2} + 6\sqrt{2}i$,

$z/w = \dfrac{1}{3}\left(\cos\dfrac{17\pi}{12} + i\sin\dfrac{17\pi}{12}\right)$

(c) $z^{10} = 1024\left(\cos\dfrac{\pi}{3} + i\sin\dfrac{\pi}{3}\right) = 512 + 512\sqrt{3}i$

(d) $\sqrt[3]{2}\left(\cos\dfrac{11\pi}{18} + i\sin\dfrac{11\pi}{18}\right)$, $\sqrt[3]{2}\left(\cos\dfrac{23\pi}{18} + i\sin\dfrac{23\pi}{18}\right)$,

$\sqrt[3]{2}\left(\cos\dfrac{35\pi}{18} + i\sin\dfrac{35\pi}{18}\right)$

4. (a) 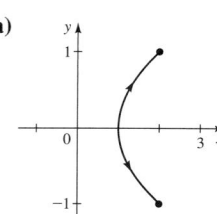   **(b)** $x = y^2 + 1$, parabola

5. (a) 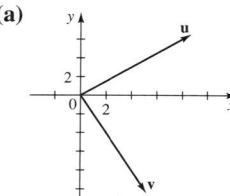   **(b)** $\mathbf{u} + \mathbf{v} = \langle 13, -4 \rangle$,
$2\mathbf{u} - \mathbf{v} = \langle 11, 22 \rangle$,
$\theta \approx 100.3°$, $\text{proj}_{\mathbf{v}}\,\mathbf{u} = \langle -\frac{4}{5}, \frac{8}{5} \rangle$
(c) 82

6. (a) 3   **(b)** $(x - 1)^2 + (y + 1)^2 + (z - 3)^2 = 9$
(c) $x = 1 + 2t,\quad y = -1 - t,\quad z = 3 - 2t$
7. (a) $\mathbf{a} \cdot \mathbf{b} = 0$, $\mathbf{a} \times \mathbf{b} = \langle 2, -13, -3 \rangle$, perpendicular
(b) $2x - 13y - 3z = 21$

CHAPTER 10

SECTION 10.1 ■ PAGE 638

1. x, y; equation; $(2, 1)$ **2.** substitution, elimination, graphical **3.** no, infinitely many **4.** infinitely many; $1 - t$; $(1, 0), (-3, 4), (5, -4)$ **5.** $(3, 2)$ **6.** $(1, -2)$
7. $(3, 1)$ **8.** $(4, -1)$ **9.** $(2, 1)$ **10.** $(5, 1)$ **11.** $(1, 2)$
12. $(2, -1)$ **13.** $(-2, 3)$ **14.** $(3, -1)$
15. $(2, -2)$ **16.** $(2, 0)$

  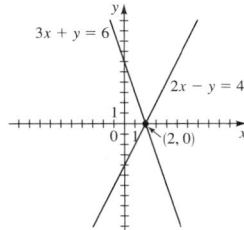

17. No solution **18.** No solution

  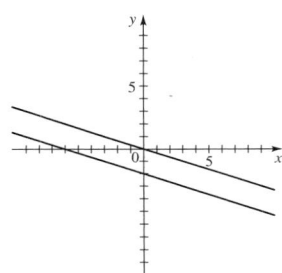

19. Infinitely many solutions **20.** Infinitely many solutions

  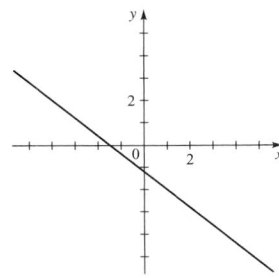

21. $(2, 2)$ **22.** $(4, 1)$ **23.** $(3, -1)$ **24.** $(4, -6)$ **25.** $(2, 1)$
26. $(4, 3)$ **27.** $(3, 5)$ **28.** $(-2, -12)$ **29.** $(1, 3)$ **30.** $(12, 4)$
31. $(10, -9)$ **32.** $(-6, 3)$ **33.** $(2, 1)$ **34.** $(10, -12)$
35. No solution **36.** No solution **37.** $\left(x, \frac{1}{3}x - \frac{5}{3}\right)$
38. No solution **39.** $\left(x, 3 - \frac{3}{2}x\right)$ **40.** $\left(x, \frac{1}{3}x - \frac{4}{3}\right)$
41. $(-3, -7)$ **42.** $(25, 1)$ **43.** $\left(x, 5 - \frac{5}{6}x\right)$ **44.** $(5, 21)$
45. $(5, 10)$ **46.** $(1, 3)$ **47.** No solution **48.** $\left(x, \frac{1}{5}x + 8\right)$
49. $(3.87, 2.74)$ **50.** $(-0.71, -1.72)$ **51.** $(61.00, 20.00)$
52. $(2.85, 1.36)$ **53.** $\left(-\dfrac{1}{a - 1}, \dfrac{1}{a - 1}\right)$ **54.** $\left(\dfrac{b}{b - a}, \dfrac{a}{a - b}\right)$
55. $\left(\dfrac{1}{a + b}, \dfrac{1}{a + b}\right)$ **56.** $\left(\dfrac{1}{a^2 - ab}, \dfrac{1}{b^2 - ab}\right)$ **57.** $22, 12$

58. $6, 18$ **59.** 5 dimes, 9 quarters **60.** 1500 children, 700 adults
61. 200 gallons of regular gas, 80 gallons of premium gas
62. 80 boxes of standard strawberries, 55 boxes of deluxe strawberries **63.** Plane's speed 120 mi/h, wind speed 30 mi/h
64. Boat speed 14 mi/h, current 6 mi/h **65.** 200 g of A, 40 g of B
66. 2.5 lb of Kenyan, 0.5 lb of Sri Lankan **67.** 25%, 10%
68. 400 mL of 5% solution, 600 mL of 20% solution **69.** $14,000 at 5%, $6,000 at 8% **70.** $16,000 at 10%, $32,000 at 6%
71. John $2\frac{1}{4}$ h, Mary $2\frac{1}{2}$ h **72.** Run 5 mi/h, cycle 20 mi/h
73. 25 **74.** 6

SECTION 10.2 ■ PAGE 646

1. $x + 3z = 1$ **2.** $-3; 4y - 5z = -4$ **3.** Linear **4.** Nonlinear
5. Nonlinear **6.** Linear **7.** $(1, 3, 2)$ **8.** $(3, 2, -1)$ **9.** $(4, 0, 3)$
10. $(4, 3, 4)$ **11.** $\left(5, 2, -\frac{1}{2}\right)$ **12.** $\left(-\frac{7}{2}, 1, 8\right)$
13. $\begin{cases} x - 2y - z = 4 \\ -y - 4z = 4 \\ 2x + y + z = 0 \end{cases}$ **14.** $\begin{cases} x + y - 3z = 3 \\ 5y - 5z = 8 \\ x - y + 2z = 0 \end{cases}$
15. $\begin{cases} 2x - y + 3z = 2 \\ x + 2y - z = 4 \\ 3y + 7z = 14 \end{cases}$ **16.** $\begin{cases} x - 4y + z = 3 \\ y - 3z = 10 \\ z = -6 \end{cases}$
17. $(2, 1, -3)$ **18.** $(1, 0, -1)$ **19.** $(1, 2, 1)$ **20.** $(1, -3, 2)$
21. $(5, 0, 1)$ **22.** $(-1, 1, 2)$ **23.** $(0, 1, 2)$ **24.** $(-1, -2, 4)$
25. $(1 - 3t, 2t, t)$ **26.** $(-2, 0, 3)$ **27.** No solution
28. No solution **29.** No solution **30.** No solution
31. $(3 - t, -3 + 2t, t)$ **32.** $(7t + 1, 4t - 1, t)$
33. $\left(2 - 2t, -\frac{2}{3} + \frac{4}{3}t, t\right)$ **34.** $(-2t + 2, t, 1)$ **35.** $(1, -1, 1, 2)$
36. $(-1, 1, -1, 1)$ **37.** $30,000 in short-term bonds, $30,000 in intermediate-term bonds, $40,000 in long-term bonds **38.** $10,000 in short-term, $45,000 in intermediate-term, $45,000 in long-term
39. 250 acres corn, 500 acres wheat, 450 acres soybeans
40. 4500 gallons of Regular, 500 gallons of Performance Plus, 1500 gallons of Premium **41.** Impossible **42.** 1 serving of toast, 2 servings of cottage cheese, 2 servings of fruit **43.** 50 Midnight Mango, 60 Tropical Torrent, 30 Pineapple Power **44.** 6 days for Factory A, 2 days for Factory B, 3 days for Factory C **45.** 1500 shares of A, 1200 shares of B, 1000 shares of C **46.** $I_1 \approx 0.39$, $I_2 \approx 0.29$, $I_3 \approx 0.68$

SECTION 10.3 ■ PAGE 659

1. dependent, inconsistent
2. $\begin{bmatrix} 1 & 1 & -1 & 1 \\ 1 & 0 & 2 & -3 \\ 0 & 2 & -1 & 3 \end{bmatrix}$
3. (a) x and y (b) dependent (c) $x = 3 + t, y = 5 - 2t, z = t$
4. (a) $x = 2, y = 1, z = 3$ (b) $x = 2 - t, y = 1 - t, z = t$
(c) No solution **5.** 3×2 **6.** 2×4 **7.** 2×1 **8.** 3×1
9. 1×3 **10.** 2×2 **11.** (a) Yes (b) Yes (c) $\begin{cases} x = -3 \\ y = 5 \end{cases}$
12. (a) Yes (b) No (c) $\begin{cases} x + 3y = -3 \\ y = 5 \end{cases}$
13. (a) Yes (b) No (c) $\begin{cases} x + 2y + 8z = 0 \\ y + 3z = 2 \\ 0 = 0 \end{cases}$

14. (a) Yes **(b)** Yes **(c)** $\begin{cases} x \quad\quad\ - 7z = 0 \\ \quad\ y + 3z = 0 \\ \quad\quad\quad\quad 0 = 1 \end{cases}$

15. (a) No **(b)** No **(c)** $\begin{cases} x \quad\quad\quad\quad = 0 \\ \quad\quad\quad\quad 0 = 0 \\ \quad\ y + 5z = 1 \end{cases}$

16. (a) Yes **(b)** Yes **(c)** $\begin{cases} x = 1 \\ y = 2 \\ z = 3 \end{cases}$

17. (a) Yes **(b)** Yes **(c)** $\begin{cases} x + 3y - \quad w = 0 \\ \quad\quad\quad z + 2w = 0 \\ \quad\quad\quad\quad\quad 0 = 1 \\ \quad\quad\quad\quad\quad 0 = 0 \end{cases}$

18. (a) No **(b)** No **(c)** $\begin{cases} x + 3y + \quad w \quad\ = 0 \\ \quad\ y + 4w \quad\ = 0 \\ \quad\quad\quad w + u = 2 \\ \quad\quad\quad w \quad\quad = 0 \end{cases}$

19. $(1, 1, 2)$ **20.** $(-1, 4, 0)$ **21.** $(1, 0, 1)$ **22.** $(-2, 3, 3)$
23. $(-1, 0, 1)$ **24.** $(3, 1, 2)$ **25.** $(-1, 5, 0)$ **26.** $(3, 1, 1)$
27. $(10, 3, -2)$ **28.** $(1, 1, -2)$ **29.** No solution
30. No solution **31.** $(2 - 3t, 3 - 5t, t)$ **32.** $\left(-4t + 10, \frac{1}{2}t + \frac{7}{2}, t\right)$
33. No solution **34.** $(3t + 2, t, 4)$ **35.** $(-2t + 5, t - 2, t)$
36. $(t, 5, t)$ **37.** $x = -\frac{1}{2}s + t + 6, y = s, z = t$ **38.** No solution
39. $(-2, 1, 3)$ **40.** $(-1, 3, 5)$ **41.** No solution
42. $x = 7t - 5, y = 8t - 4, z = t$ **43.** $(-9, 2, 0)$
44. No solution **45.** $x = 5 - t, y = -3 + 5t, z = t$
46. $(-2, 1, 3)$ **47.** $(0, -3, 0, -3)$ **48.** $(1, 3, 0, -2)$
49. $(-1, 0, 0, 1)$ **50.** $(-2, 1, 0, 3)$ **51.** $x = \frac{1}{3}s - \frac{2}{3}t,$
$y = \frac{1}{3}s + \frac{1}{3}t, z = s, w = t$ **52.** $(20 - 12t, 31 - 19t, -2 + 2t, t)$
53. $\left(\frac{7}{4} - \frac{7}{4}t, -\frac{7}{4} + \frac{3}{4}t, \frac{9}{4} + \frac{3}{4}t, t\right)$ **54.** $\left(-2t + 6, \frac{5}{2}t - 9, \frac{9}{2}t - 9, t\right)$
55. 2 VitaMax, 1 Vitron, 2 VitaPlus **56.** 40 mL of 10% acid,
50 mL of 20% acid, 10 mL of 40% acid **57.** 5-mile run, 2-mile
swim, 30-mile cycle **58.** 20 in room A, 50 in room B, 30 in
room C **59.** Impossible **60.** $x = t - 50, y = 170 + t,$
$z = 430 - t, w = t,$ where $50 \le t \le 430$

SECTION 10.4 ▪ PAGE 669

1. dimension **2. (a)** columns, rows **(b)** (ii), (iii) **3.** (i), (ii)

4. $\begin{bmatrix} 4 & 9 & -7 \\ 7 & -7 & 0 \\ 4 & -5 & -5 \end{bmatrix}$ **5.** No **6.** Yes **7.** $\begin{bmatrix} 1 & 3 \\ 1 & 5 \end{bmatrix}$

8. $\begin{bmatrix} -2 & 0 & 2 \\ 0 & -2 & 2 \end{bmatrix}$ **9.** $\begin{bmatrix} 3 & 6 \\ 12 & -3 \\ 3 & 0 \end{bmatrix}$ **10.** Impossible

11. Impossible **12.** $\begin{bmatrix} 1 & 2 \\ 7 & 64 \end{bmatrix}$ **13.** $\begin{bmatrix} 5 & 2 & 1 \\ 7 & 10 & -7 \end{bmatrix}$

14. $\begin{bmatrix} 7 \\ 1 \\ 7 \end{bmatrix}$ **15.** $\begin{bmatrix} -1 & -\frac{1}{2} \\ 1 & 2 \end{bmatrix}$ **16.** Impossible **17.** No solution

18. $\begin{bmatrix} 4 & 7 \\ 7 & 4 \\ 2 & 2 \end{bmatrix}$ **19.** $\begin{bmatrix} 0 & -5 \\ -25 & -20 \\ -10 & 10 \end{bmatrix}$ **20.** $\begin{bmatrix} -2 & -\frac{7}{3} \\ \frac{1}{3} & \frac{1}{3} \end{bmatrix}$

21. (a) $\begin{bmatrix} 5 & -2 & 5 \\ 1 & 1 & 0 \end{bmatrix}$ **(b)** Impossible

22. (a) $\begin{bmatrix} -1 & -3 & -5 \\ -1 & 3 & -6 \end{bmatrix}$ **(b)** $\begin{bmatrix} -14 & -8 & -30 \\ -6 & 10 & -24 \end{bmatrix}$

23. (a) $\begin{bmatrix} 10 & -25 \\ 0 & 35 \end{bmatrix}$ **(b)** Impossible **24. (a)** $\begin{bmatrix} 13 & -\frac{7}{2} & 15 \\ 3 & 1 & 3 \end{bmatrix}$

(b) Impossible **25. (a)** Impossible **(b)** $\begin{bmatrix} 14 & -14 \end{bmatrix}$

26. (a) $\begin{bmatrix} 27 & 4 \end{bmatrix}$ **(b)** Impossible **27. (a)** $\begin{bmatrix} -4 & 7 \\ 14 & -7 \end{bmatrix}$

(b) $\begin{bmatrix} 6 & -8 \\ 4 & -17 \end{bmatrix}$ **28. (a)** Impossible **(b)** $\begin{bmatrix} 3 & \frac{1}{2} & 5 \\ 1 & -1 & 3 \end{bmatrix}$

29. (a) $\begin{bmatrix} 5 & -3 & 10 \\ 6 & 1 & 0 \\ -5 & 2 & 2 \end{bmatrix}$ **(b)** $\begin{bmatrix} -1 \\ 8 \\ -1 \end{bmatrix}$ **30. (a)** Impossible

(b) $\begin{bmatrix} 1 & 0 & 0 \\ 0 & 1 & 0 \\ 0 & 0 & 1 \end{bmatrix}$ **31. (a)** $\begin{bmatrix} 4 & -45 \\ 0 & 49 \end{bmatrix}$ **(b)** $\begin{bmatrix} 8 & -335 \\ 0 & 343 \end{bmatrix}$

32. (a) $\begin{bmatrix} 28 & 21 & 28 \end{bmatrix}$ **(b)** $\begin{bmatrix} 28 & 21 & 28 \end{bmatrix}$ **33. (a)** $\begin{bmatrix} 13 \\ -7 \end{bmatrix}$

(b) Impossible **34. (a)** $\begin{bmatrix} 38 & -11 & 35 \end{bmatrix}$ **(b)** Impossible
35. $x = 2, y = -1$ **36.** $x = 2, y = -3$ **37.** $x = 1, y = -2$

38. $x = 5, y = 1$ **39.** $\begin{bmatrix} 2 & -5 \\ 3 & 2 \end{bmatrix}\begin{bmatrix} x \\ y \end{bmatrix} = \begin{bmatrix} 7 \\ 4 \end{bmatrix}$

40. $\begin{bmatrix} 6 & -1 & 1 \\ 2 & 0 & 1 \\ 0 & 1 & -2 \end{bmatrix}\begin{bmatrix} x \\ y \\ z \end{bmatrix} = \begin{bmatrix} 12 \\ 7 \\ 4 \end{bmatrix}$

41. $\begin{bmatrix} 3 & 2 & -1 & 1 \\ 1 & 0 & -1 & 0 \\ 0 & 3 & 1 & -1 \end{bmatrix}\begin{bmatrix} x_1 \\ x_2 \\ x_3 \\ x_4 \end{bmatrix} = \begin{bmatrix} 0 \\ 5 \\ 4 \end{bmatrix}$

42. $\begin{bmatrix} 1 & -1 & 1 \\ 4 & -2 & -1 \\ 1 & 1 & 5 \\ -1 & -1 & -1 \end{bmatrix}\begin{bmatrix} x \\ y \\ z \end{bmatrix} = \begin{bmatrix} 2 \\ 2 \\ 2 \\ 2 \end{bmatrix}$

43. Only ACB is defined. $ACB = \begin{bmatrix} -3 & -21 & 27 & -6 \\ -2 & -14 & 18 & -4 \end{bmatrix}$

44. (b) No **45. (a)** $\begin{bmatrix} 4,690 & 1,690 & 13,210 \end{bmatrix}$
(b) Total revenue in Santa Monica, Long Beach, and Anaheim,
respectively.

46. (a) $\begin{bmatrix} \$32,000 & \$18,000 \\ \$42,000 & \$26,800 \\ \$44,000 & \$26,800 \end{bmatrix}$ **(b)** $42,000 **(c)** $71,600

47. (a) $\begin{bmatrix} 105,000 & 58,000 \end{bmatrix}$ **(b)** The first entry is the total
amount (in ounces) of tomato sauce produced, and the second en-
try is the total amount (in ounces) of tomato paste produced.

48. (a) $\begin{bmatrix} 97.00 \\ 46.50 \\ 41.00 \end{bmatrix}$ Amy's stand sold \$97 of produce on Saturday.
Beth's stand sold \$46.50.
Chad's stand sold \$41.

(b) $\begin{bmatrix} 70.00 \\ 33.50 \\ 48.50 \end{bmatrix}$ Amy's stand sold \$70 of produce on Sunday.
Beth's stand sold \$33.50.
Chad's stand sold \$48.50.

(c) $\begin{bmatrix} 220 & 110 & 90 \\ 75 & 45 & 50 \\ 120 & 55 & 50 \end{bmatrix}$ This represents the melons, squash, and tomatoes they sold during the weekend.

(d) $\begin{bmatrix} 167.00 \\ 80.00 \\ 89.50 \end{bmatrix}$ During the weekend Amy's stand sold \$167, Beth's stand sold \$80, and Chad's stand sold \$89.50 of produce.

49.

(a) $\begin{bmatrix} 1 & 0 & 1 & 0 & 1 & 1 \\ 0 & 3 & 0 & 1 & 2 & 1 \\ 1 & 2 & 0 & 0 & 3 & 0 \\ 1 & 3 & 2 & 3 & 2 & 0 \\ 0 & 3 & 0 & 0 & 2 & 1 \\ 1 & 2 & 0 & 1 & 3 & 1 \end{bmatrix}$ **(b)** $\begin{bmatrix} 2 & 1 & 2 & 1 & 2 & 2 \\ 1 & 3 & 1 & 2 & 3 & 2 \\ 2 & 3 & 1 & 1 & 3 & 1 \\ 2 & 3 & 3 & 3 & 3 & 1 \\ 1 & 3 & 1 & 1 & 3 & 2 \\ 2 & 3 & 1 & 2 & 3 & 2 \end{bmatrix}$

(c) $\begin{bmatrix} 2 & 3 & 2 & 3 & 2 & 2 \\ 3 & 0 & 3 & 2 & 1 & 2 \\ 2 & 1 & 3 & 3 & 0 & 3 \\ 2 & 0 & 1 & 0 & 1 & 3 \\ 3 & 0 & 3 & 3 & 1 & 2 \\ 2 & 1 & 3 & 2 & 0 & 2 \end{bmatrix}$

(d) $\begin{bmatrix} 3 & 3 & 3 & 3 & 3 & 3 \\ 3 & 0 & 3 & 3 & 0 & 3 \\ 3 & 0 & 3 & 3 & 0 & 3 \\ 3 & 0 & 0 & 0 & 0 & 3 \\ 3 & 0 & 3 & 3 & 0 & 3 \\ 3 & 0 & 3 & 3 & 0 & 3 \end{bmatrix}$

(e) The letter E

SECTION 10.5 ■ PAGE 680

1. (a) identity **(b)** A, A **(c)** inverse

2. (a) $\overset{A}{\begin{bmatrix} 5 & 3 \\ 3 & 2 \end{bmatrix}} \overset{X}{\begin{bmatrix} x \\ y \end{bmatrix}} = \overset{B}{\begin{bmatrix} 4 \\ 3 \end{bmatrix}}$ **(b)** $\begin{bmatrix} 2 & -3 \\ -3 & 5 \end{bmatrix}$

(c) $\overset{A^{-1}}{\begin{bmatrix} 2 & -3 \\ -3 & 5 \end{bmatrix}} \overset{B}{\begin{bmatrix} 4 \\ 3 \end{bmatrix}} = \overset{X}{\begin{bmatrix} x \\ y \end{bmatrix}}$ **(d)** $x = -1, y = 3$ **7.** $\begin{bmatrix} 1 & -2 \\ -\frac{3}{2} & \frac{7}{2} \end{bmatrix}$

8. $\begin{bmatrix} -1 & 1 & -1 \\ 2 & -2 & 1 \\ -2 & \frac{5}{2} & -1 \end{bmatrix}$ **9.** $\begin{bmatrix} 3 & 5 \\ -2 & -3 \end{bmatrix}$ **10.** $\begin{bmatrix} -9 & 4 \\ 7 & -3 \end{bmatrix}$

11. $\begin{bmatrix} 13 & 5 \\ -5 & -2 \end{bmatrix}$ **12.** $\begin{bmatrix} -\frac{5}{3} & -\frac{4}{3} \\ -\frac{8}{3} & -\frac{7}{3} \end{bmatrix}$ **13.** No inverse

14. $\begin{bmatrix} 12 & -1 \\ -15 & \frac{3}{2} \end{bmatrix}$ **15.** $\begin{bmatrix} 1 & 2 \\ -\frac{1}{2} & \frac{2}{3} \end{bmatrix}$ **16.** $\begin{bmatrix} 3 & -2 & -5 \\ -1 & 1 & 1 \\ -3 & 2 & 6 \end{bmatrix}$

17. $\begin{bmatrix} -4 & -4 & 5 \\ 1 & 1 & -1 \\ 5 & 4 & -6 \end{bmatrix}$ **18.** $\begin{bmatrix} 26 & 7 & -25 \\ -3 & -1 & 3 \\ -27 & -7 & 26 \end{bmatrix}$

19. No inverse **20.** $\begin{bmatrix} -1 & -1 & 2 \\ 3 & 2 & -4 \\ -\frac{1}{2} & 0 & \frac{1}{2} \end{bmatrix}$ **21.** $\begin{bmatrix} -\frac{9}{2} & -1 & 4 \\ 3 & 1 & -3 \\ \frac{7}{2} & 1 & -3 \end{bmatrix}$

22. $\begin{bmatrix} 1 & 0 & -1 \\ 1 & 0 & -\frac{3}{2} \\ -6 & 1 & \frac{13}{2} \end{bmatrix}$ **23.** $\begin{bmatrix} 0 & 0 & -2 & 1 \\ -1 & 0 & 1 & 1 \\ 0 & 1 & -1 & 0 \\ 1 & 0 & 0 & -1 \end{bmatrix}$ **24.** No inverse

25. $x = 12, y = -8$ **26.** $x = -10, y = 10$
27. $x = 126, y = -50$ **28.** $x = -\frac{400}{3}, y = -\frac{700}{3}$
29. $x = -38, y = 9, z = 47$ **30.** $x = 8, y = -1, z = -8$
31. $x = -20, y = 10, z = 16$ **32.** $x = -1, y = 5, z = -1,$
$w = -3$ **33.** $x = 3, y = 2, z = 1$ **34.** $x = -1, y = 2, z = 3$
35. $x = 3, y = -2, z = 2$ **36.** $x = 6, y = 12, z = 24$
37. $x = 8, y = 1, z = 0, w = 3$ **38.** $x = 8, y = 4, z = 2, w = 1$

39. $\begin{bmatrix} 7 & 2 & 3 \\ 10 & 3 & 5 \end{bmatrix}$ **40.** $\begin{bmatrix} -\frac{39}{2} & -39 \\ 15 & 30 \\ \frac{33}{2} & 33 \end{bmatrix}$

41. $\dfrac{1}{2a}\begin{bmatrix} 1 & 1 \\ -1 & 1 \end{bmatrix}$ **42.** $\begin{bmatrix} \frac{1}{a} & 0 & 0 & 0 \\ 0 & \frac{1}{b} & 0 & 0 \\ 0 & 0 & \frac{1}{c} & 0 \\ 0 & 0 & 0 & \frac{1}{d} \end{bmatrix}$

43. $\begin{bmatrix} 1 & -\frac{1}{x} \\ -\frac{1}{x} & \frac{2}{x^2} \end{bmatrix}$; inverse does not exist for $x = 0$

44. $\dfrac{1}{2}\begin{bmatrix} e^{-x} & e^{-2x} \\ -e^{-2x} & e^{-3x} \end{bmatrix}$; inverse exists for all x

45. $\dfrac{1}{2}\begin{bmatrix} 1 & e^{-x} & 0 \\ e^{-x} & -e^{-2x} & 0 \\ 0 & 0 & 1 \end{bmatrix}$; inverse exists for all x

46. $\begin{bmatrix} \frac{1}{x^2} & -\frac{x-1}{x^2} \\ \frac{x-1}{x} & \frac{x-1}{x} \end{bmatrix}$; inverse does not exist for $x = 0, x = 1$

47. (a) $\begin{bmatrix} 0 & 1 & -1 \\ -2 & \frac{3}{2} & 0 \\ 1 & -\frac{3}{2} & 1 \end{bmatrix}$ **(b)** 1 oz A, 1 oz B, 2 oz C

(c) 2 oz A, 0 oz B, 1 oz C **(d)** No
48. No, since the inverse does not exist in this case

49. (a) $\begin{cases} x + y + 2z = 675 \\ 2x + y + z = 600 \\ x + 2y + z = 625 \end{cases}$

(b) $\begin{bmatrix} 1 & 1 & 2 \\ 2 & 1 & 1 \\ 1 & 2 & 1 \end{bmatrix}\begin{bmatrix} x \\ y \\ z \end{bmatrix} = \begin{bmatrix} 675 \\ 600 \\ 625 \end{bmatrix}$ **(c)** $A^{-1} = \begin{bmatrix} -\frac{1}{4} & \frac{3}{4} & -\frac{1}{4} \\ -\frac{1}{4} & -\frac{1}{4} & \frac{3}{4} \\ \frac{3}{4} & -\frac{1}{4} & -\frac{1}{4} \end{bmatrix}$

She earns \$125 on a standard set, \$150 on a deluxe set, and \$200 on a leather-bound set.

SECTION 10.6 ■ PAGE 690

1. True **2.** True **3.** True **4. (a)** $2 \cdot 4 - (-3) \cdot 1 = 11$
(b)
$$+1(2 \cdot 4 - (-3) \cdot 1) - 0(3 \cdot 4 - 0 \cdot 1) + 2(3 \cdot (-3) - 0 \cdot 2) = -7$$
5. 6 **6.** 2 **7.** -4 **8.** 1 **9.** Does not exist

10. Does not exist   **11.** $\frac{1}{8}$ **12.** 2.9   **13.** 20, 20   **14.** 5, 5
15. $-12, 12$ **16.** 0, 0   **17.** 0, 0   **18.** $\frac{7}{2}, -\frac{7}{2}$ **19.** 4, has an inverse
20. 0, does not have an inverse   **21.** 5000, has an inverse
22. -4, has an inverse   **23.** 0, does not have an inverse
24. 2, has an inverse   **25.** -4, has an inverse   **26.** 92, has an
inverse   **27.** -18 **28.** -1183 **29.** 120   **30.** 32   **31. (a)** -2
(b) -2 **(c)** Yes   **32. (b)** -46 **(c)** No other solutions
(d) Yes, since $|M| \neq 0$ **33.** $(-2, 5)$ **34.** $\left(\frac{3}{2}, 2\right)$ **35.** $(0.6, -0.4)$
36. $(-2, 6)$ **37.** $(4, -1)$ **38.** $\left(\frac{2}{5}, -1\right)$ **39.** $(4, 2, -1)$
40. $(1, -2, -5)$ **41.** $(1, 3, 2)$ **42.** $(-1, 5, 0)$ **43.** $(0, -1, 1)$
44. $(2, -1, 3)$ **45.** $\left(\frac{189}{29}, -\frac{108}{29}, \frac{88}{29}\right)$ **46.** $\left(\frac{22}{5}, \frac{24}{25}, -\frac{66}{25}\right)$
47. $\left(\frac{1}{2}, \frac{1}{4}, \frac{1}{4}, -1\right)$ **48.** $(-1, 2, 0, 3)$ **49.** $abcde$ **50.** a^5
51. 0, 1, 2   **52.** 1   **53.** 1, -1 **54.** a, b **55.** 21
56. $\frac{19}{2}$ **57.** $\frac{63}{2}$ **58.** 33

60. (a)
$$\begin{cases} x + y + z = 18 \\ 75x + 90y + 60z = 1380 \\ -75x + 90y + 60z = 180 \end{cases}$$

(b) 8 apples, 6 peaches, 4 pears

61. (a)
$$\begin{cases} 100a + 10b + c = 25 \\ 225a + 15b + c = 33\frac{3}{4} \\ 1600a + 40b + c = 40 \end{cases}$$

(b) $y = -0.05x^2 + 3x$ **62.** 7 million ft^2

SECTION 10.7 ▪ PAGE 697

1. (iii)   **2.** (ii)   **3.** $\dfrac{A}{x-1} + \dfrac{B}{x+2}$ **4.** $\dfrac{A}{(x-1)} + \dfrac{B}{(x+4)}$

5. $\dfrac{A}{x-2} + \dfrac{B}{(x-2)^2} + \dfrac{C}{x+4}$ **6.** $\dfrac{A}{x} + \dfrac{B}{x^2} + \dfrac{C}{x^3} + \dfrac{D}{x-1}$

7. $\dfrac{A}{x-3} + \dfrac{Bx+C}{x^2+4}$ **8.** $\dfrac{A}{x-1} + \dfrac{B}{x+1} + \dfrac{Cx+D}{x^2+1}$

9. $\dfrac{Ax+B}{x^2+1} + \dfrac{Cx+D}{x^2+2}$ **10.** $\dfrac{A}{x} + \dfrac{B}{x^2} + \dfrac{Cx+D}{x^2+4} + \dfrac{Ex+F}{(x^2+4)^2}$

11. $\dfrac{A}{x} + \dfrac{B}{2x-5} + \dfrac{C}{(2x-5)^2} + \dfrac{D}{(2x-5)^3}$
$+ \dfrac{Ex+F}{x^2+2x+5} + \dfrac{Gx+H}{(x^2+2x+5)^2}$

12. $\dfrac{A}{x-1} + \dfrac{B}{(x-1)^2} + \dfrac{C}{x+1} + \dfrac{Dx+E}{x^2+x+1}$

13. $\dfrac{1}{x-1} - \dfrac{1}{x+1}$ **14.** $\dfrac{1}{x-1} + \dfrac{1}{x+1}$ **15.** $\dfrac{1}{x-1} - \dfrac{1}{x+4}$

16. $\dfrac{2}{x} - \dfrac{1}{x+3}$ **17.** $\dfrac{2}{x-3} - \dfrac{2}{x+3}$ **18.** $\dfrac{3}{x} - \dfrac{2}{x-4}$

19. $\dfrac{1}{x-2} - \dfrac{1}{x+2}$ **20.** $\dfrac{1}{x+2} + \dfrac{1}{x-1}$ **21.** $\dfrac{3}{x-4} - \dfrac{2}{x+2}$

22. $\dfrac{3}{x} + \dfrac{2}{2x-1}$ **23.** $\dfrac{-\frac{1}{2}}{2x-1} + \dfrac{\frac{3}{2}}{4x-3}$

24. $\dfrac{1}{x} - \dfrac{2}{x+3} + \dfrac{1}{x-1}$ **25.** $\dfrac{2}{x-2} + \dfrac{3}{x+2} - \dfrac{1}{2x-1}$

26. $\dfrac{-3}{x+2} + \dfrac{1}{2x-3} + \dfrac{1}{x+3}$ **27.** $\dfrac{2}{x+1} - \dfrac{1}{x} + \dfrac{1}{x^2}$

28. $\dfrac{\frac{-135}{64}}{3x+2} + \dfrac{\frac{109}{64}}{x-2} + \dfrac{\frac{9}{8}}{(x-2)^2}$ **29.** $\dfrac{1}{2x+3} - \dfrac{3}{(2x+3)^2}$

30. $\dfrac{\frac{1}{2}}{2x-5} - \dfrac{\frac{3}{2}}{(2x-5)^2}$ **31.** $\dfrac{2}{x} - \dfrac{1}{x^3} - \dfrac{2}{x+2}$

32. $\dfrac{1}{x} - \dfrac{2}{x^2} - \dfrac{4}{x^3} + \dfrac{3}{x^4}$

33. $\dfrac{4}{x+2} - \dfrac{4}{x-1} + \dfrac{2}{(x-1)^2} + \dfrac{1}{(x-1)^3}$

34. $\dfrac{1}{x+1} - \dfrac{1}{x-1} + \dfrac{1}{(x-1)^3}$

35. $\dfrac{3}{x+2} - \dfrac{1}{(x+2)^2} - \dfrac{1}{(x+3)^2}$

36. $-\dfrac{1}{x+2} - \dfrac{2}{(x+2)^2} + \dfrac{1}{x-2} + \dfrac{1}{(x-2)^2}$

37. $\dfrac{x+1}{x^2+3} - \dfrac{1}{x}$ **38.** $-\dfrac{2}{x^2+2} + \dfrac{3}{x-1}$

39. $\dfrac{2x-5}{x^2+x+2} + \dfrac{5}{x^2+1}$ **40.** $\dfrac{2x+1}{2x^2+1} - \dfrac{x}{x^2+1}$

41. $\dfrac{1}{x^2+1} - \dfrac{x+2}{(x^2+1)^2} + \dfrac{1}{x}$ **42.** $\dfrac{2}{x^2+4} - \dfrac{1}{(x^2+4)^2}$

43. $x^2 + \dfrac{3}{x-2} - \dfrac{x+1}{x^2+1}$ **44.** $x+1 + \dfrac{2}{(x-2)^2} + \dfrac{x}{x^2+2}$

45. $A = \dfrac{a+b}{2}, B = \dfrac{a-b}{2}$

46. $A = a, B = b, C = -a, D = -b$

SECTION 10.8 ▪ PAGE 701

1. $(4, 8), (-2, 2)$ **3.** $(4, 16), (-3, 9)$
4. $(-\sqrt{5}, -2\sqrt{5}), (\sqrt{5}, 2\sqrt{5})$ **5.** $(2, -2), (-2, 2)$
6. $(-3, 0), (2, 5)$ **7.** $(-25, 5), (-25, -5)$ **8.** $(-2, 3), (2, 3)$
9. $(-3, 4) (3, 4)$ **10.** $(-\sqrt{11}, -4) (\sqrt{11}, -4)$
11. $(-2, -1), (-2, 1), (2, -1), (2, 1)$
12. $\left(\dfrac{-5\sqrt{2}}{2}, -3\right), \left(\dfrac{5\sqrt{2}}{2}, -3\right), \left(\dfrac{-3\sqrt{2}}{2}, 1\right), \left(\dfrac{3\sqrt{2}}{2}, 1\right)$
13. $(-1, \sqrt{2}), (-1, -\sqrt{2}), (\frac{1}{2}, \sqrt{\frac{7}{2}}), (\frac{1}{2}, -\sqrt{\frac{7}{2}})$
14. $(-1, 0), (2, -\sqrt{3}), (2, \sqrt{3})$ **15.** $(2, 4), \left(-\frac{5}{2}, \frac{7}{4}\right)$
16. $(0, -2), (5, 3)$ **17.** $(0, 0), (1, -1), (-2, -4)$
18. $(0, 0), (3, \sqrt{3}), (3, -\sqrt{3})$ **19.** $(4, 0)$ **20.** $(0, 0), (1, 1)$
21. $(-2, -2)$ **22.** $(-2, 0), (2, 0)$ **23.** $(6, 2), (-2, -6)$
24. $(4, 6), (-4, -6)$ **25.** No solution   **26.** $(-\sqrt{6}, 6)$
27. $(\sqrt{5}, 2), (\sqrt{5}, -2), (-\sqrt{5}, 2), (-\sqrt{5}, -2)$
28. No solution   **29.** $(3, -\frac{1}{2}), (-3, -\frac{1}{2})$ **30.** $(-2, 1), (2, 1)$
31. $(\frac{1}{5}, \frac{1}{3})$ **32.** $(-\sqrt{2}, -\sqrt{2}), (-\sqrt{2}, \sqrt{2}), (\sqrt{2}, -\sqrt{2}),$
$(\sqrt{2}, \sqrt{2})$ **33.** $(2.00, 20.00), (-8.00, 0)$
34. $(0.35, -1.30), (5.65, 9.30)$ **35.** $(-4.51, 2.17),$
$(4.91, -0.97)$ **36.** $(2, -3.61), (2, 3.61)$ **37.** $(1.23, 3.87),$
$(-0.35, -4.21)$ **38.** $(-2.22, 1.40), (-1.88, -0.72),$
$(3.45, -2.99), (4.65, 4.31)$ **39.** $(-2.30, -0.70), (0.48, -1.19)$

40. $(-1.19, 3.59), (1.19, 3.59)$ **41.** 12 cm by 15 cm

42. 7 ft by 24 ft   **43.** 15, 20   **44.** $4\sqrt{5}$ in. by $8\sqrt{5}$ in.

45. $(400.50, 200.25)$, 447.77 m   **46.** 2π by $\dfrac{600}{\pi}$ **47.** $(12, 8)$

SECTION 10.9 ■ PAGE 708

1. equation; $y = x + 1$; test

2. (a)

(b)

(c)

(d)

3.

4.

5.

6.

7.

8.

9.

10.

11.

12.

13.

14.

15.

16.

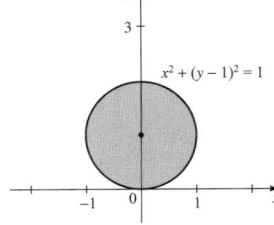

17. $y \leq \frac{1}{2}x - 1$ **18.** $y \leq x^2 + 2$ **19.** $x^2 + y^2 > 4$

20. $y \geq x^3 - 4x$

21.

Not bounded

22.

Not bounded

23.

Not bounded

24.

Not bounded

25.

Bounded

26.

Bounded

27.

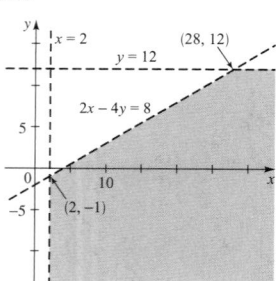

Bounded

28.

Not bounded

29.

Bounded

30.

Bounded

31.

Bounded

32.

Not bounded

33.

Bounded

34.

Bounded

35.

Bounded

36.

Bounded

37.

Not bounded

38.

Not bounded

39.

Bounded

40.

Bounded

41.

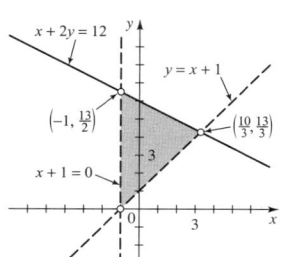

Bounded

42. No solution

51. x = number of fiction books
y = number of nonfiction books

$$\begin{cases} x + y \leq 100 \\ 20 \leq y, \quad x \geq y \\ x \geq 0, \quad y \geq 0 \end{cases}$$

43.

Bounded

44.

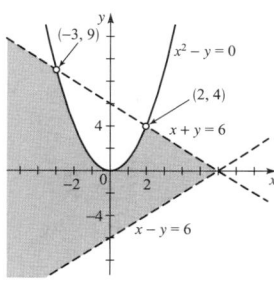

Not bounded

52. x = number of chairs
y = number of tables

$$\begin{cases} 3y + 2x \leq 12 \\ y + 2x \leq 8 \\ x \geq 0, \quad y \geq 0 \end{cases}$$

45.

Bounded

46.

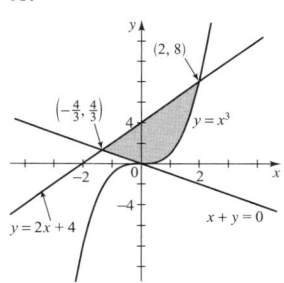

Bounded

53. x = number of standard packages
y = number of deluxe packages

$$\begin{cases} \frac{1}{4}x + \frac{5}{8}y \leq 80 \\ \frac{3}{4}x + \frac{3}{8}y \leq 90 \\ x \geq 0, \quad y \geq 0 \end{cases}$$

47.

48.

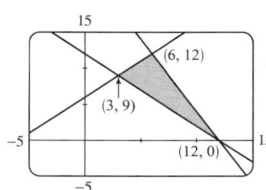

54. x = oz of fish
y = oz of beef

$$\begin{cases} 12x + 6y \geq 60 \\ 3x + 9y \geq 45 \\ x \geq 0, \quad y \geq 0 \end{cases}$$

49.

50.

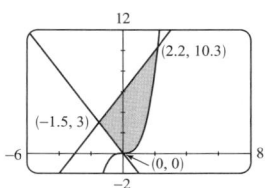

CHAPTER 10 REVIEW ■ PAGE 711

1. $(2, 1)$

2. $(-1, 4)$

3. $x =$ any number
$y = \frac{2}{7}x - 4$

4. No solution

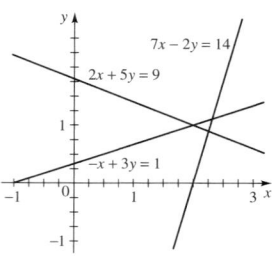

5. No solution

6. No solution

7. $(-3, 3), (2, 8)$
8. $\left(-1 - \sqrt{3}, 1 - \sqrt{3}\right), \left(-1 + \sqrt{3}, 1 + \sqrt{3}\right)$
9. $\left(\frac{16}{7}, -\frac{14}{3}\right)$ **10.** $\left(-\sqrt{6}, 2\right), \left(\sqrt{6}, 2\right)$
11. $(21.41, -15.93)$ **12.** $(61.04, -105.73)$
13. $(11.94, -1.39), (12.07, 1.44)$
14. $(-1.45, -1.35), (1, 6), (1.51, 12.93)$
15. **(a)** 2×3 **(b)** Yes **(c)** No
(d) $\begin{cases} x + 2y = -5 \\ y = 3 \end{cases}$
16. **(a)** 2×3 **(b)** Yes **(c)** Yes
(d) $\begin{cases} x = 6 \\ y = 0 \end{cases}$
17. **(a)** 3×4 **(b)** Yes **(c)** Yes
(d) $\begin{cases} x + 8z = 0 \\ y + 5z = -1 \\ 0 = 0 \end{cases}$
18. **(a)** 3×4 **(b)** No **(c)** No
(d) $\begin{cases} x + 3y + 6z = 2 \\ 2x + y = 5 \\ z = 0 \end{cases}$
19. **(a)** 3×4 **(b)** No **(c)** No
(d) $\begin{cases} y - 3z = 4 \\ x + y = 7 \\ x + 2y + z = 2 \end{cases}$
20. **(a)** 4×4 **(b)** No **(c)** No
(d) $\begin{cases} x + 8y + 6z = -4 \\ y - 3z = 5 \\ 2z = -7 \\ x + y + z = 0 \end{cases}$
21. $(1, 1, 2)$ **22.** $(3, 1, 0)$
23. No solution   **24.** $(1, 0, -1, 2)$
25. $(-8, -7, 10)$ **26.** $(2, 1, 1)$ **27.** No solution
28. $(-2t + 4, -t + 2, t)$ **29.** $(1, 0, 1, -2)$
30. $(2, 1, -1, -1)$
31. $x = -4t + 1, y = -t - 1, z = t$ **32.** No solution
33. $x = 6 - 5t, y = \frac{1}{2}(7 - 3t), z = t$ **34.** $\left(\frac{2}{11}, \frac{48}{11}, -\frac{60}{11}, -\frac{40}{11}\right)$

35. $\left(-\frac{4}{3}t + \frac{4}{3}, \frac{5}{3}t - \frac{2}{3}, t\right)$ **36.** $(2 - t, 1 - t, t)$
37. $(s + 1, 2s - t + 1, s, t)$ **38.** No solution   **39.** No solution
40. No solution   **41.** $(1, t + 1, t, 0)$ **42.** No solution
43. \$3000 at 6%, \$6000 at 7%
44. 12 nickels, 30 dimes, 8 quarters
45. \$11,250 in bank A, \$22,500 in bank B, \$26,250 in bank C
46. 160 haddock, 340 sea bass, 60 red snapper
47. Impossible
48. $\begin{bmatrix} -\frac{1}{2} & -1 \\ 2 & \frac{5}{2} \\ -4 & 1 \end{bmatrix}$ **49.** $\begin{bmatrix} 4 & 18 \\ 4 & 0 \\ 2 & 2 \end{bmatrix}$ **50.** Impossible
51. $\begin{bmatrix} 10 & 0 & -5 \end{bmatrix}$ **52.** Impossible   **53.** $\begin{bmatrix} -\frac{7}{2} & 10 \\ 1 & -\frac{9}{2} \end{bmatrix}$
54. $\begin{bmatrix} -\frac{11}{2} & 4 & 2 \\ -1 & \frac{11}{2} & 8 \\ -4 & -3 & -8 \end{bmatrix}$ **55.** $\begin{bmatrix} 30 & 22 & 2 \\ -9 & 1 & -4 \end{bmatrix}$
56. $\begin{bmatrix} -2 & 14 \\ \frac{3}{2} & -\frac{3}{2} \\ \frac{27}{2} & \frac{57}{2} \end{bmatrix}$ **57.** $\begin{bmatrix} -\frac{1}{2} & \frac{11}{2} \\ \frac{15}{4} & -\frac{3}{2} \\ -\frac{1}{2} & 1 \end{bmatrix}$ **58.** $\begin{bmatrix} -12 & 12 \\ 4 & 2 \\ 20 & 34 \end{bmatrix}$
61. $\frac{1}{3}\begin{bmatrix} -1 & -3 \\ -5 & 2 \end{bmatrix}$ **62.** $\begin{bmatrix} 6 & -2 \\ 2 & 12 \end{bmatrix}$ **63.** $\begin{bmatrix} \frac{7}{2} & -2 \\ 0 & 8 \end{bmatrix}$
64. Impossible   **65.** $\begin{bmatrix} 2 & -2 & 6 \\ -4 & 5 & -9 \end{bmatrix}$ **66.** $\begin{bmatrix} 4 & -8 \\ -7 & 14 \end{bmatrix}$
67. $1, \begin{bmatrix} 9 & -4 \\ -2 & 1 \end{bmatrix}$ **68.** $-8, \begin{bmatrix} \frac{3}{8} & \frac{1}{4} \\ \frac{1}{8} & -\frac{1}{4} \end{bmatrix}$ **69.** 0, no inverse
70. 0, no inverse   **71.** $-1, \begin{bmatrix} 3 & 2 & -3 \\ 2 & 1 & -2 \\ -8 & -6 & 9 \end{bmatrix}$
72. $1, \begin{bmatrix} -1 & 3 & -2 \\ -2 & 0 & 1 \\ 2 & -1 & 0 \end{bmatrix}$ **73.** $24, \begin{bmatrix} 1 & 0 & 0 & -\frac{1}{4} \\ 0 & \frac{1}{2} & 0 & -\frac{1}{4} \\ 0 & 0 & \frac{1}{3} & -\frac{1}{4} \\ 0 & 0 & 0 & \frac{1}{4} \end{bmatrix}$
74. 0, no inverse   **75.** $(65, 154)$ **76.** $(6, 7)$ **77.** $\left(-\frac{1}{12}, \frac{1}{12}, \frac{1}{12}\right)$
78. $(10, 20, -5)$ **79.** $\left(\frac{1}{5}, \frac{9}{5}\right)$ **80.** $(8, -4)$ **81.** $\left(-\frac{87}{26}, \frac{21}{26}, \frac{3}{2}\right)$
82. $\left(\frac{860}{41}, -\frac{540}{41}, \frac{10}{41}\right)$ **83.** 11 **84.** $\frac{51}{2}$
85. $\dfrac{2}{x - 5} + \dfrac{1}{x + 3}$ **86.** $\dfrac{-2}{x} + \dfrac{1}{x - 2} + \dfrac{1}{x + 2}$
87. $\dfrac{-4}{x} + \dfrac{4}{x - 1} + \dfrac{-2}{(x - 1)^2}$ **88.** $\dfrac{x + 1}{x^2 + 4} + \dfrac{1}{x - 2}$
89. $\dfrac{-1}{x} + \dfrac{x + 2}{x^2 + 1}$ **90.** $\dfrac{2}{x - 1} - \dfrac{3}{x + 1} + \dfrac{x}{x^2 + 2}$
91. $(2, 1)$ **92.** $(-2, 14), (4, -4)$ **93.** $\left(-\frac{1}{2}, \frac{7}{4}\right), (2, -2)$
94. $(-2, 0), (2, 4)$ **95.** $x + y^2 \le 4$ **96.** $x^2 + y^2 \ge 8$
97.   **98.**

99.

100.

101.

102.

103.

104.

105.

Bounded

106.

Bounded

107.

Bounded

108.

Not bounded

109. $x = \dfrac{b + c}{2}, y = \dfrac{a + c}{2}, z = \dfrac{a + b}{2}$ **110.** $(1, -1, 1)$
111. 2, 3   **112.** $\frac{1}{5}$

CHAPTER 10 TEST ▪ PAGE 714

1. (a) Linear   **(b)** $(-2, 3)$ **2. (a)** Nonlinear
(b) $(1, -2), \left(\frac{5}{3}, 0\right)$
3. $(-0.55, -0.78), (0.43, -0.29), (2.12, 0.56)$
4. Wind 60 km/h, airplane 300 km/h
5. (a) Row-echelon form   **(b)** Reduced row-echelon form
(c) Neither   **6. (a)** $\left(\frac{5}{2}, \frac{5}{2}, 0\right)$ **(b)** No solution
7. $\left(-\frac{3}{5} + \frac{2}{5}t, \frac{1}{5} + \frac{1}{5}t, t\right)$
8. Coffee $1.50, juice $1.75, donut $0.75
9. (a) Incompatible dimensions
(b) Incompatible dimensions

(c) $\begin{bmatrix} 6 & 10 \\ 3 & -2 \\ -3 & 9 \end{bmatrix}$ **(d)** $\begin{bmatrix} 36 & 58 \\ 0 & -3 \\ 18 & 28 \end{bmatrix}$ **(e)** $\begin{bmatrix} 2 & -\frac{3}{2} \\ -1 & 1 \end{bmatrix}$

(f) B is not square   **(g)** B is not square   **(h)** -3
10. (a) $\begin{bmatrix} 4 & -3 \\ 3 & -2 \end{bmatrix}\begin{bmatrix} x \\ y \end{bmatrix} = \begin{bmatrix} 10 \\ 30 \end{bmatrix}$ **(b)** $(70, 90)$

11. $|A| = 0, |B| = 2, B^{-1} = \begin{bmatrix} 1 & -2 & 0 \\ 0 & \frac{1}{2} & 0 \\ 3 & -6 & 1 \end{bmatrix}$

12. $(5, -5, -4)$
13. (a) $\dfrac{1}{x - 1} + \dfrac{1}{(x - 1)^2} - \dfrac{1}{x + 2}$ **(b)** $-\dfrac{1}{x} + \dfrac{x + 2}{x^2 + 3}$
14. (a)   **(b)**

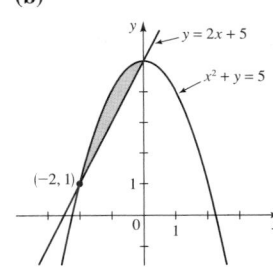

FOCUS ON MODELING ▪ PAGE 720

1. 198, 195   **2.** 42, 40.375
3.

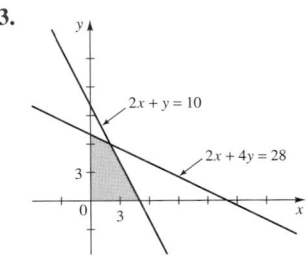

maximum 161
minimum 135

4.

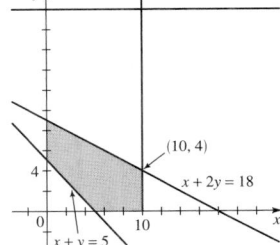

maximum 1028
minimum 350

5. 3 tables, 34 chairs   **6.** 0 colonial, 90 ranch;
10 lots vacant   **7.** 30 grapefruit crates, 30 orange crates
8. (a) 120 standard, 80 scientific   **(b)** 100 standard,
170 scientific   **9.** 15 Pasadena to Santa Monica,
3 Pasadena to El Toro, 0 Long Beach to Santa Monica,
16 Long Beach to El Toro   **10.** 5 sheets from east-side
to customer A, 70 sheets from east-side to customer B,
45 sheets from west-side to customer A, 0 sheets from
west-side to customer B   **11.** 90 standard, 40 deluxe
12. 3 oz type I, 0 type II
13. $7500 in municipal bonds, $2500 in bank certificates,
$2000 in high-risk bonds   **14.** $47.50
15. 4 games, 32 educational, 0 utility
16. (a)   **(b)**

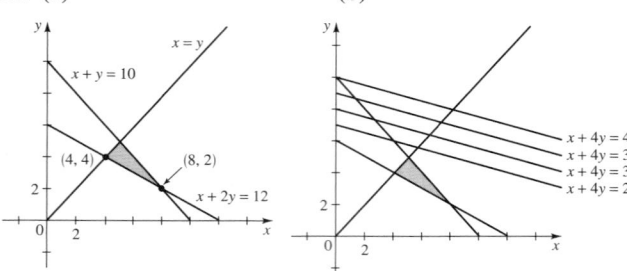

(c) $(4, 4)$

CHAPTER 11

SECTION 11.1 ▪ PAGE 730

1. focus, directrix   **2.** $F(0, p)$, $y = -p$, $F(0, 3)$, $y = -3$
3. $F(p, 0)$, $x = -p$, $F(3, 0)$, $x = -3$
4. (a)   **(b)**

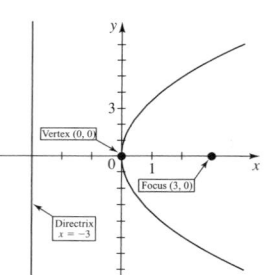

5. III   **6.** V   **7.** II   **8.** I   **9.** VI   **10.** IV

Order of answers: focus; directrix; focal diameter

11. $F\left(0, \frac{9}{4}\right)$; $y = -\frac{9}{4}$; 9   **12.** $F\left(0, \frac{1}{4}\right)$; $y = -\frac{1}{4}$; 1

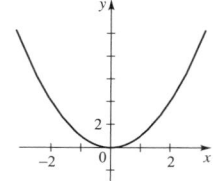

13. $F(1, 0)$; $x = -1$; 4   **14.** $F\left(\frac{3}{4}, 0\right)$; $x = -\frac{3}{4}$; 3

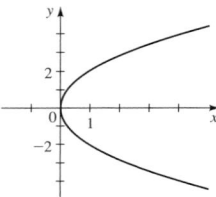

15. $F\left(0, \frac{1}{20}\right)$; $y = -\frac{1}{20}$; $\frac{1}{5}$ **16.** $F\left(0, -\frac{1}{8}\right)$; $y = \frac{1}{8}$; $\frac{1}{2}$

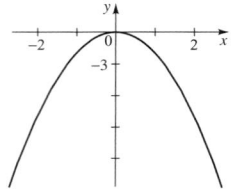

17. $F\left(-\frac{1}{32}, 0\right)$; $x = \frac{1}{32}$; $\frac{1}{8}$ **18.** $F\left(\frac{1}{2}, 0\right)$; $x = -\frac{1}{2}$; 2

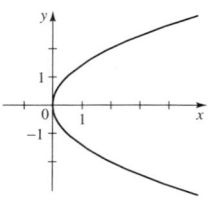

19. $F\left(0, -\frac{3}{2}\right)$; $y = \frac{3}{2}$; 6   **20.** $F\left(\frac{1}{28}, 0\right)$; $x = -\frac{1}{28}$; $\frac{1}{7}$

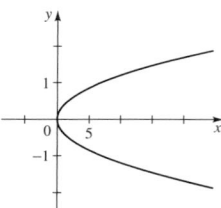

21. $F\left(-\frac{5}{12}, 0\right)$; $x = \frac{5}{12}$; $\frac{5}{3}$ **22.** $F\left(0, -\frac{3}{8}\right)$; $y = \frac{3}{8}$; $\frac{3}{2}$

23.   **24.**

25.   **26.**

27.   **28.**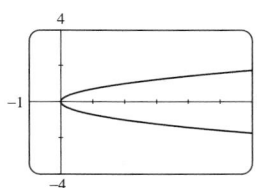

29. $x^2 = 8y$ **30.** $x^2 = -2y$
31. $y^2 = -32x$ **32.** $y^2 = 20x$
33. $y^2 = -8x$ **34.** $x^2 = -24y$
35. $x^2 = 40y$ **36.** $y^2 = \frac{1}{2}x$
37. $y^2 = 4x$ **38.** $x^2 = -24y$
39. $x^2 = 20y$ **40.** $x^2 = -8y$
41. $x^2 = 8y$ **42.** $y^2 = 8x$
43. $y^2 = -16x$ **44.** $x^2 = -12y$
45. $y^2 = -3x$ **46.** $x^2 = 10y$
47. $x = y^2$ **48.** $y^2 = 16x$
49. $x^2 = -4\sqrt{2}y$ **50.** $x^2 = 2(\sqrt{5} - 1)y$
51. (a) $x^2 = -4py$, $p = \frac{1}{2}$, 1, 4, and 8
(b) The closer the directrix to the
vertex, the steeper the parabola.

52. (a)

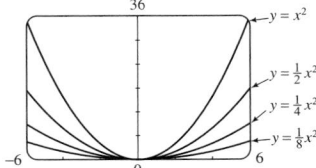

(b) The larger the focal diameter, the wider the parabola.
53. (a) $y^2 = 12x$ **(b)** $8\sqrt{15} \approx 31$ cm   **54.** 25 ft
55. $x^2 = 600y$ **56.** 659.63 in.

SECTION 11.2 ■ PAGE 738

1. sum; foci
2. $(a, 0), (-a, 0); c = \sqrt{a^2 - b^2}; (5, 0), (-5, 0), (3, 0), (-3, 0)$
3. $(0, a), (0, -a); c = \sqrt{a^2 - b^2}; (0, 5), (0, -5), (0, 3), (0, -3)$

4. (a)   **(b)**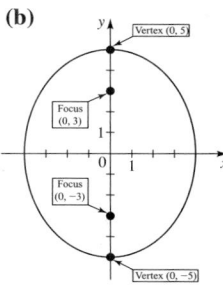

5. II   **6.** IV   **7.** I   **8.** III

Order of answers: vertices; foci; eccentricity; major axis
and minor axis
9. $V(\pm 5, 0); F(\pm 4, 0);$ **10.** $V(0, \pm 5); F(0, \pm 3);$
$\frac{4}{5}$; 10, 6   0.6; 10, 8

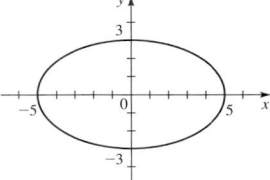

11. $V(0, \pm 3); F(0, \pm\sqrt{5});$ **12.** $V(\pm 5, 0); F(\pm\sqrt{21}, 0);$
$\sqrt{5}/3$; 6, 4 $\sqrt{21}/5$; 10, 4

   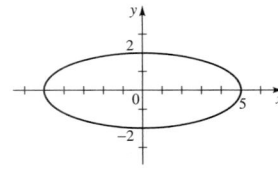

13. $V(\pm 4, 0); F(\pm 2\sqrt{3}, 0);$ **14.** $V(0, \pm 4); F(0, \pm 2\sqrt{3});$
$\sqrt{3}/2$; 8, 4 $\sqrt{3}/2$; 8, 4

   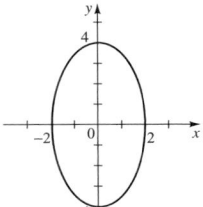

15. $V(0, \pm\sqrt{3}); F(0, \pm\sqrt{3/2});$ **16.** $V(\pm\sqrt{6}, 0); F(\pm 1, 0);$
$1/\sqrt{2}$; $2\sqrt{3}$, $\sqrt{6}$ $\sqrt{6}/6$; $2\sqrt{6}$, $2\sqrt{5}$

   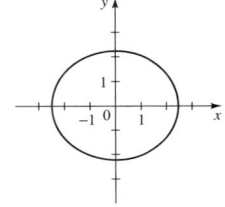

17. $V(\pm 1, 0)$; $F(\pm\sqrt{3}/2, 0)$; $\sqrt{3}/2$; 2, 1

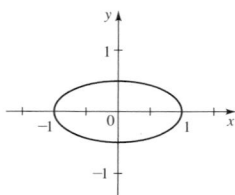

18. $V(0, \pm\frac{1}{2})$; $F(0, \pm\sqrt{5}/6)$; $\sqrt{5}/3$; 1, $\frac{2}{3}$

19. $V(0, \pm\sqrt{2})$; $F(0, \pm\sqrt{3}/2)$; $\sqrt{3}/2$; $2\sqrt{2}$, $\sqrt{2}$

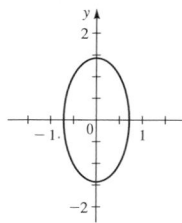

20. $V(\pm 2, 0)$; $F(\pm\sqrt{2}, 0)$; $\sqrt{2}/2$; 4, $2\sqrt{2}$

21. $V(0, \pm 1)$; $F(0, \pm 1/\sqrt{2})$; $1/\sqrt{2}$; 2, $\sqrt{2}$

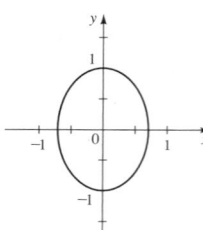

22. $V(0, \pm\sqrt{5}/2)$; $F(0, \pm 1)$; $2\sqrt{5}/5$; $\sqrt{5}$, 1

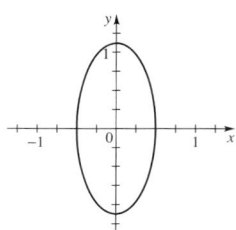

23. $\dfrac{x^2}{25} + \dfrac{y^2}{16} = 1$ **24.** $\dfrac{x^2}{4} + \dfrac{y^2}{25} = 1$ **25.** $\dfrac{x^2}{4} + \dfrac{y^2}{8} = 1$

26. $\dfrac{x^2}{7} + \dfrac{y^2}{16} = 1$ **27.** $\dfrac{x^2}{256} + \dfrac{y^2}{48} = 1$ **28.** $\dfrac{x^2}{4} + \dfrac{3y^2}{16} = 1$

29.

30.

31.

32.

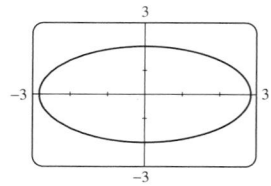

33. $\dfrac{x^2}{25} + \dfrac{y^2}{9} = 1$ **34.** $\dfrac{x^2}{16} + \dfrac{y^2}{25} = 1$

35. $x^2 + \dfrac{y^2}{4} = 1$ **36.** $\dfrac{x^2}{9} + \dfrac{y^2}{4} = 1$

37. $\dfrac{x^2}{9} + \dfrac{y^2}{13} = 1$ **38.** $\dfrac{x^2}{36} + \dfrac{y^2}{11} = 1$

39. $\dfrac{x^2}{100} + \dfrac{y^2}{91} = 1$ **40.** $\dfrac{x^2}{25} + \dfrac{y^2}{9} = 1$

41. $\dfrac{x^2}{25} + \dfrac{y^2}{5} = 1$ **42.** $\dfrac{x^2}{320} + \dfrac{y^2}{324} = 1$

43. $\dfrac{64x^2}{225} + \dfrac{64y^2}{81} = 1$ **44.** $x^2 + \dfrac{y^2}{4} = 1$

45. $(0, \pm 2)$ **46.** $\left(\pm\frac{12}{5}, \pm\frac{12}{5}\right)$

   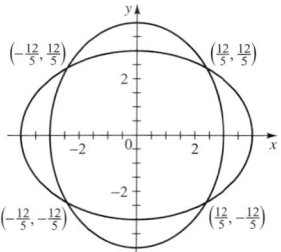

47. $(\pm 1, 0)$ **48.** (a) $x^2 + y^2 = 4$

49. (a)

(b) Common major axes and vertices; eccentricity increases as k increases.

51. $\dfrac{x^2}{2.2500 \times 10^{16}} + \dfrac{y^2}{2.2491 \times 10^{16}} = 1$

52. Perihelion 3.87×10^9 km; aphelion 6.45×10^9 km

53. $\dfrac{x^2}{1,455,642} + \dfrac{y^2}{1,451,610} = 1$

54. 8 ft; 6.92 ft apart

55. $5\sqrt{39}/2 \approx 15.6$ in.

SECTION 11.3 ■ PAGE 747

1. difference; foci

2. $(-a, 0), (a, 0)$; $\sqrt{a^2 + b^2}$; $(-4, 0), (4, 0), (-5, 0), (5, 0)$

3. $(0, -a), (0, a)$; $\sqrt{a^2 + b^2}$; $(0, -4), (0, 4), (0, -5), (0, 5)$

4. (a)   **(b)**

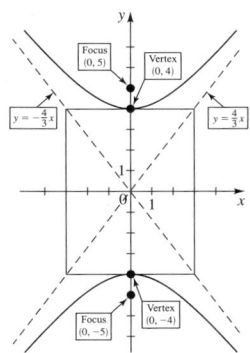

5. III   **6.** IV   **7.** II   **8.** I

Order of answers: vertices; foci; asymptotes

9. $V(\pm 2, 0)$; $F(\pm 2\sqrt{5}, 0)$;   **10.** $V(0, \pm 3)$; $F(0, \pm 5)$;

$y = \pm 2x$ $y = \pm \frac{3}{4}x$

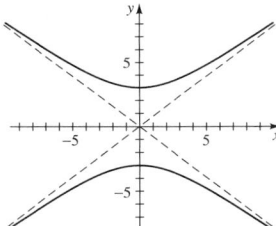

11. $V(0, \pm 1)$; $F(0, \pm\sqrt{26})$;   **12.** $V(\pm\sqrt{2}, 0)$; $F(\pm\sqrt{3}, 0)$;

$y = \pm \frac{1}{5}x$ $y = \pm \dfrac{1}{\sqrt{2}}x$

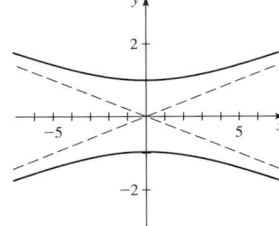

13. $V(\pm 1, 0)$; $F(\pm\sqrt{2}, 0)$;   **14.** $V(\pm 2, 0)$; $F(\pm\sqrt{13}, 0)$;

$y = \pm x$ $y = \pm \frac{3}{2}x$

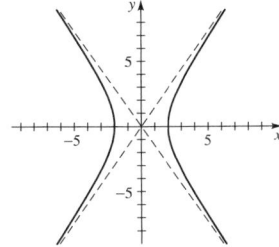

15. $V(0, \pm 3)$; $F(0, \pm\sqrt{34})$;   **16.** $V(0, \pm 2)$; $F(0, \pm 2\sqrt{2})$;

$y = \pm \frac{3}{5}x$ $y = \pm x$

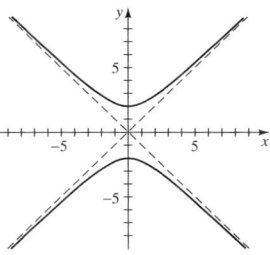

17. $V(\pm 2\sqrt{2}, 0)$; $F(\pm\sqrt{10}, 0)$;   **18.** $V(\pm\sqrt{3}, 0)$; $F(\pm 3/\sqrt{2}, 0)$;

$y = \pm \frac{1}{2}x$ $y = \pm \dfrac{\sqrt{2}}{2}x$

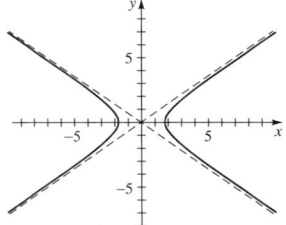

19. $V(0, \pm \frac{1}{2})$; $F(0, \pm\sqrt{5}/2)$;   **20.** $V(\pm \frac{1}{3}, 0)$; $F(\pm \frac{5}{12}, 0)$;

$y = \pm \frac{1}{2}x$ $y = \pm \frac{3}{4}x$

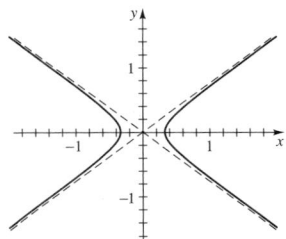

21. $\dfrac{x^2}{4} - \dfrac{y^2}{12} = 1$ **22.** $\dfrac{y^2}{144} - \dfrac{x^2}{25} = 1$ **23.** $\dfrac{y^2}{16} - \dfrac{x^2}{16} = 1$

24. $\dfrac{x^2}{12} - \dfrac{y^2}{48} = 1$ **25.** $\dfrac{x^2}{9} - \dfrac{4y^2}{9} = 1$ **26.** $\dfrac{y^2}{9} - x^2 = 1$

27.   **28.**

29.   **30.**

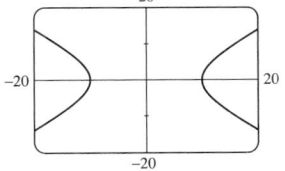

31. $\dfrac{x^2}{9} - \dfrac{y^2}{16} = 1$ **32.** $\dfrac{y^2}{64} - \dfrac{x^2}{36} = 1$ **33.** $y^2 - \dfrac{x^2}{3} = 1$

34. $\dfrac{x^2}{4} - \dfrac{y^2}{32} = 1$ **35.** $x^2 - \dfrac{y^2}{25} = 1$ **36.** $\dfrac{y^2}{36} - \dfrac{x^2}{324} = 1$

37. $\dfrac{5y^2}{64} - \dfrac{5x^2}{256} = 1$ **38.** $\dfrac{y^2}{36} - \dfrac{x^2}{20} = 1$ **39.** $\dfrac{x^2}{16} - \dfrac{y^2}{16} = 1$

40. $\dfrac{x^2}{8} - y^2 = 1$ **41.** $\dfrac{x^2}{9} - \dfrac{y^2}{16} = 1$ **42.** $4y^2 - \dfrac{4x^2}{3} = 1$

43. (b) $x^2 - y^2 = c^2/2$ **44. (b)** They both have asymptotes $y = \pm\frac{1}{2}x$.   **46. (a)** $a = 3, b = 4, c = 5; F_1(5, 0), F_2(-5, 0)$
(c) $d(P, F_1) = \frac{16}{3}, d(P, F_2) = \frac{34}{3}$

47. (b)

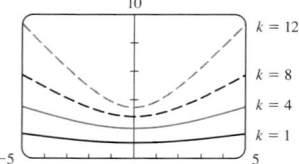

As k increases, the asymptotes get steeper.

48. (a) 490 mi   **(b)** $\dfrac{y^2}{60{,}025} - \dfrac{x^2}{2475} = 1$ **(c)** 10.1 mi

49. $x^2 - y^2 = 2.3 \times 10^{19}$

SECTION 11.4 ■ PAGE 755

1. (a) right; left   **(b)** upward; downward

2.

3.

4.

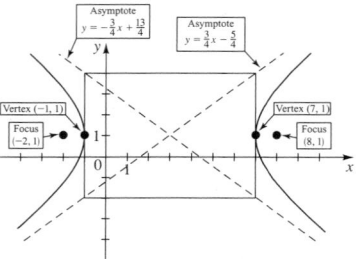

5. Center $C(2, 1)$;
foci $F(2 \pm \sqrt{5}, 1)$;
vertices $V_1(-1, 1), V_2(5, 1)$;
major axis 6, minor axis 4

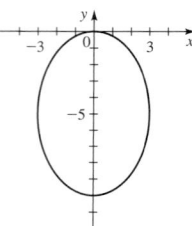

6. Center $C(3, -3)$;
foci $F(3 \pm \sqrt{15}, -3)$;
vertices $V_1(-1, -3), V_2(7, -3)$;
major axis 8, minor axis 2

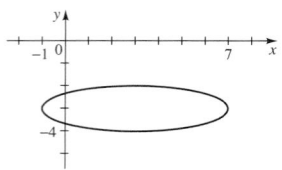

7. Center $C(0, -5)$;
foci $F_1(0, -1), F_2(0, -9)$;
vertices $V_1(0, 0), V_2(0, -10)$;
major axis 10, minor axis 6

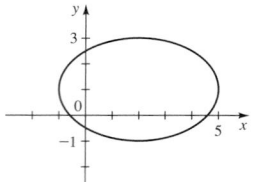

8. Center $C(-2, 0)$;
foci $F(-2 \pm \sqrt{3}, 0)$;
vertices $V_1(-4, 0), V_2(0, 0)$;
major axis 4, minor axis 2

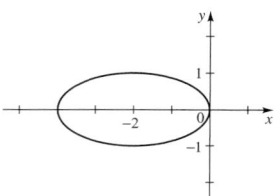

9. Vertex $V(3, -1)$;
focus $F(3, 1)$;
directrix $y = -3$

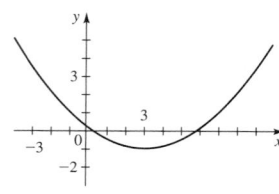

10. Vertex $V(2, -5)$;
focus $F\left(\frac{1}{2}, -5\right)$;
directrix $x = \frac{7}{2}$

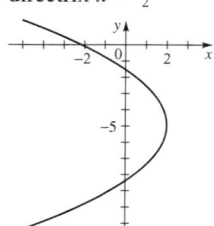

11. Vertex $V\left(-\frac{1}{2}, 0\right)$;
focus $F\left(-\frac{1}{2}, -\frac{1}{16}\right)$;
directrix $y = \frac{1}{16}$

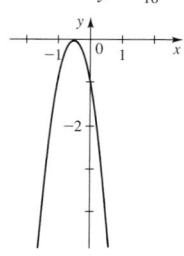

12. Vertex $V\left(\frac{1}{2}, 0\right)$;
focus $F\left(\frac{9}{2}, 0\right)$;
directrix $x = -\frac{7}{2}$

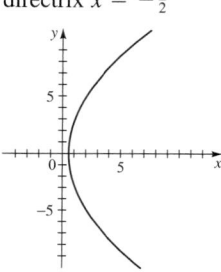

13. Center $C(-1, 3)$;
foci $F_1(-6, 3)$, $F_2(4, 3)$;
vertices $V_1(-4, 3)$, $V_2(2, 3)$;
asymptotes
$y = \pm\frac{4}{3}(x + 1) + 3$

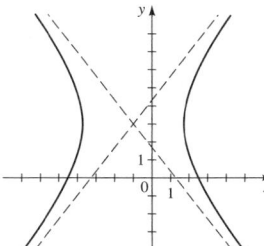

14. Center $C(8, -6)$;
foci $F(8 \pm \sqrt{2}, -6)$;
vertices $V_1(7, -6)$, $V_2(9, -6)$;
asymptotes $y = -x + 2$,
$y = x - 14$

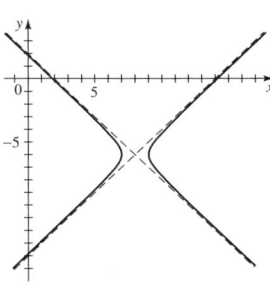

15. Center $C(-1, 0)$;
foci $F(-1, \pm\sqrt{5})$;
vertices $V(-1, \pm 1)$;
asymptotes
$y = \pm\frac{1}{2}(x + 1)$

16. Center $C(-3, 1)$;
foci $F(-3, 1 \pm \sqrt{26})$;
vertices $V_1(-3, -4)$, $V_2(-3, 6)$;
asymptotes $y = -5x - 14$,
$y = 5x + 16$

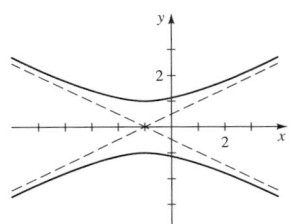

17. $x^2 = -\frac{1}{4}(y - 4)$ **18.** $y^2 = 24(x + 6)$

19. $\dfrac{(x - 5)^2}{25} + \dfrac{y^2}{16} = 1$ **20.** $\dfrac{(x - 2)^2}{4} + \dfrac{(y + 3)^2}{9} = 1$

21. $(y - 1)^2 - x^2 = 1$ **22.** $\dfrac{(x - 4)^2}{4} - \dfrac{3y^2}{16} = 1$

23. Parabola;
$V(-4, 4)$;
$F(-3, 4)$;
$x = -5$

24. Ellipse; $C(2, 0)$;
$F(2, \pm\sqrt{5})$; $V(2, \pm 3)$;
major axis 6,
minor axis 4

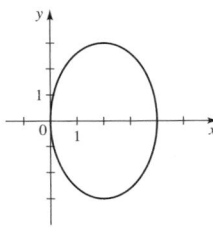

25. Hyperbola;
$C(1, 2)$; $F_1\left(-\frac{3}{2}, 2\right)$, $F_2\left(\frac{7}{2}, 2\right)$;
$V(1 \pm \sqrt{5}, 2)$; asymptotes
$y = \pm\frac{1}{2}(x - 1) + 2$

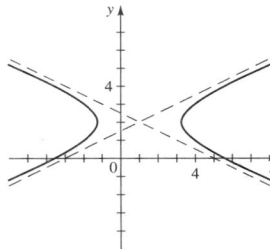

26. Parabola;
$V(-3, 0)$;
$F(-3, -3)$;
$y = 3$

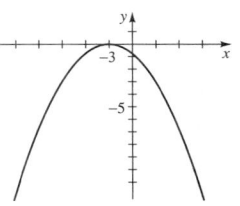

27. Ellipse; $C(3, -5)$;
$F(3 \pm \sqrt{21}, -5)$;
$V_1(-2, -5)$, $V_1(8, -5)$;
major axis 10,
minor axis 4

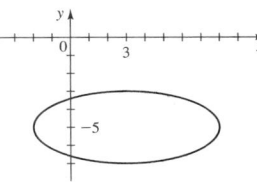

28. Ellipse;
$C(0, 1)$; $F_1(0, 0)$, $F_2(0, 2)$;
$V(0, 1 \pm \sqrt{2})$;
major axis $2\sqrt{2}$,
minor axis 2

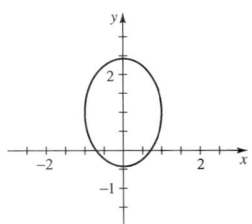

29. Hyperbola; $C(3, 0)$;
$F(3, \pm 5)$; $V(3, \pm 4)$;
asymptotes $y = \pm\frac{4}{3}(x - 3)$

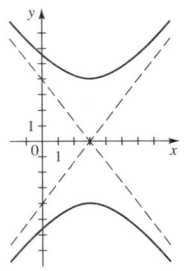

30. Parabola;
$V\left(\frac{1}{2}, 1\right)$; $F\left(\frac{1}{2}, \frac{3}{2}\right)$; $y = \frac{1}{2}$

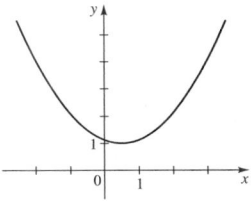

31. Degenerate conic
(pair of lines),
$y = \pm\frac{1}{2}(x - 4)$

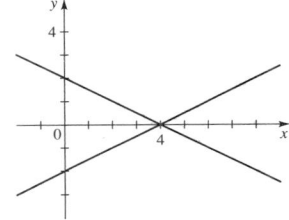

32. Hyperbola;
$C(5, 5)$; $F(5 \pm \sqrt{2}, 5)$;
$V_1(4, 5)$, $V_2(6, 5)$;
asymptotes $y = x$,
$y = -x + 10$

33. Point $(1, 3)$

34. No graph

35.

36.

37.

38.

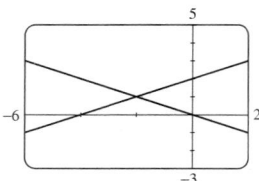

39. **(a)** $F < 17$ **(b)** $F = 17$ **(c)** $F > 17$

40. $\dfrac{x^2}{25} + \dfrac{(8y - 399)^2}{160,801} = 1$

41. **(a)**

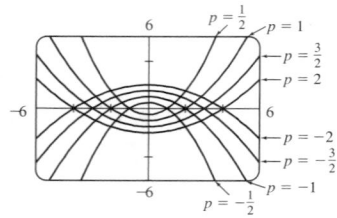

(c) The parabolas become narrower.

42. $(x - 800)^2 = -200(y - 3200)$

43. $\dfrac{(x + 150)^2}{18,062,500} + \dfrac{y^2}{18,040,000} = 1$

SECTION 11.5 ■ PAGE 764

1. $x = X \cos \phi - Y \sin \phi,\ y = X \sin \phi + Y \cos \phi,$
$X = x \cos \phi + y \sin \phi,\ Y = -x \sin \phi + y \cos \phi$
2. **(a)** conic section   **(b)** $(A - C)/B$ **(c)** $B^2 - 4AC$, parabola,

ellipse, hyperbola   **3.** $\left(\sqrt{2}, 0 \right)$ **4.** $\left(1 - \dfrac{\sqrt{3}}{2}, 1 + \dfrac{\sqrt{3}}{2} \right)$

5. $\left(0, -2\sqrt{3} \right)$ **6.** $(1.9319, -0.5176)$ **7.** $(1.6383, 1.1472)$

8. $(5, 3)$ **9.** $X^2 + \sqrt{3}XY + 2 = 0$
10. $X^2 + Y^2 - 2XY - 3\sqrt{2}X + \sqrt{2}Y + 2 = 0$
11. $7Y^2 - 48XY - 7X^2 - 40X - 30Y = 0$
12. $34X^2 + 41Y^2 + 24XY = 400$ **13.** $X^2 - Y^2 = 2$
14. $\dfrac{(X - \sqrt{2})^2}{2} - \dfrac{Y^2}{2} = 1$
15. **(a)** Hyberbola   **(b)** $X^2 - Y^2 = 16$
(c) $\phi = 45°$

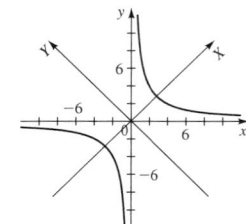

16. **(a)** Hyperbola
(b) $\dfrac{Y^2}{8} - \dfrac{X^2}{8} = 1$
(c) $\phi = 45°$

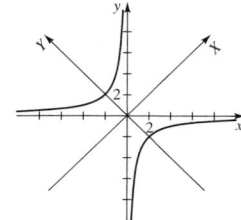

17. **(a)** Hyberbola
(b) $Y^2 - X^2 = 1$
(c) $\phi = 30°$

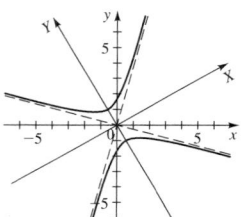

18. **(a)** Ellipse
(b) $X^2 + \dfrac{Y^2}{4} = 1$
(c) $\phi = 30°$

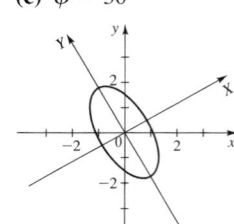

19. **(a)** Hyperbola
(b) $\dfrac{X^2}{4} - Y^2 = 1$
(c) $\phi \approx 53°$

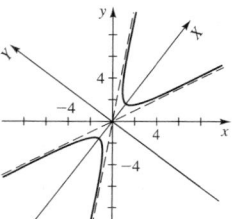

20. **(a)** Ellipse
(b) $\dfrac{X^2}{4} + \dfrac{Y^2}{9} = 1$
(c) $\phi = 60°$

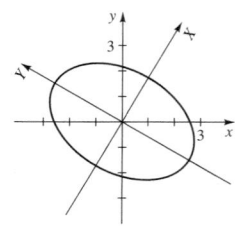

21. (a) Hyberbola
(b) $3X^2 - Y^2 = 2\sqrt{3}$
(c) $\phi = 30°$

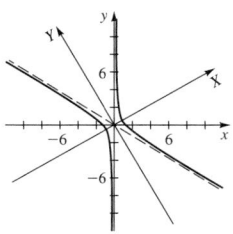

22. (a) Ellipse
(b) $X^2 + \dfrac{Y^2}{9} = 1$
(c) $\phi \approx 37°$

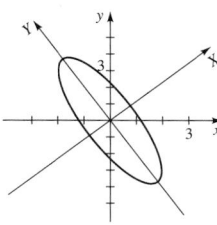

23. (a) Parabola
(b) $Y = \sqrt{2}X^2$
(c) $\phi = 45°$

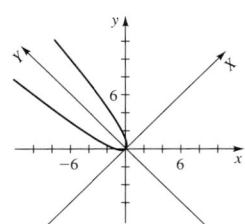

24. (a) Parabola
(b) $X = Y^2$
(c) $\phi \approx 23°$

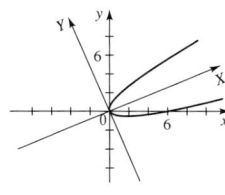

25. (a) Hyberbola
(b) $(X - 1)^2 - 3Y^2 = 1$
(c) $\phi = 60°$

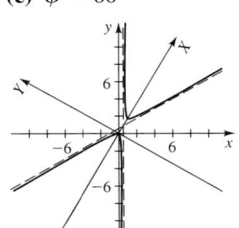

26. (a) Parabola
(b) $\dfrac{4}{5}\left(X + \tfrac{24}{5}\right) = \left(Y + \tfrac{14}{5}\right)^2$
(c) $\phi \approx 37°$

27. (a) Ellipse
(b) $X^2 + \dfrac{(Y + 1)^2}{4} = 1$
(c) $\phi \approx 53°$

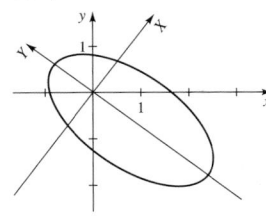

28. (a) Parabola
(b) $X^2 = -\left(Y - \tfrac{1}{25}\right)$
(c) $\phi \approx 74°$

29. (a) Parabola
(b)

30. (a) Ellipse
(b)

31. (a) Hyperbola
(b)

32. (a) Parabola
(b)

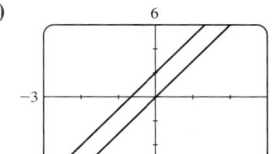

33. (a) $(X - 5)^2 - Y^2 = 1$
(b) XY-coordinates:
$C(5, 0)$; $V_1(6, 0)$, $V_2(4, 0)$; $F(5 \pm \sqrt{2}, 0)$;
xy-coordinates:
$C(4, 3)$; $V_1\left(\tfrac{24}{5}, \tfrac{18}{5}\right)$, $V_2\left(\tfrac{16}{5}, \tfrac{12}{5}\right)$; $F_1\left(4 + \tfrac{4}{5}\sqrt{2}, 3 + \tfrac{3}{5}\sqrt{2}\right)$,
$F_2\left(4 - \tfrac{4}{5}\sqrt{2}, 3 - \tfrac{3}{5}\sqrt{2}\right)$
(c) $Y = \pm(X - 5)$; $7x - y - 25 = 0$, $x + 7y - 25 = 0$
34. (a) $4(X + 1)^2 = Y + 4$
(b) XY-coordinates: $V(-1, -4)$, $F\left(-1, -\tfrac{63}{16}\right)$; xy-coordinates:
$$V\left(\frac{3\sqrt{2}}{2}, -\frac{5\sqrt{2}}{2}\right), F\left(\frac{47\sqrt{2}}{32}, -\frac{79\sqrt{2}}{32}\right)$$
(c) $Y = -\dfrac{65}{16}$; $y = x - \dfrac{65\sqrt{2}}{16}$
35. $X = x \cos\phi + y \sin\phi$; $Y = -x \sin\phi + y \cos\phi$
36. $Y^2 = \sqrt{2}\left(X - \dfrac{\sqrt{2}}{4}\right)$

SECTION 11.6 ■ PAGE 770

1. focus, directrix; $\dfrac{\text{distance from } P \text{ to } F}{\text{distance from } P \text{ to } \ell}$, conic section; parabola,
ellipse, hyperbola, eccentricity　**2.** $\dfrac{ed}{1 \pm e \cos\theta}$, $\dfrac{ed}{1 \pm e \sin\theta}$
3. $r = 6/(3 + 2 \cos\theta)$
4. $r = 12/(3 - 4 \cos\theta)$
5. $r = 2/(1 + \sin\theta)$
6. $r = 4/(2 - \sin\theta)$
7. $r = 20/(1 + 4 \cos\theta)$
8. $r = 1.2/(1 + 0.6 \sin\theta)$
9. $r = 10/(1 + \sin\theta)$
10. $r = 2.8/(1 + 0.4 \cos\theta)$
11. II　**12.** III　**13.** VI　**14.** I　**15.** IV　**16.** V
17.

18.

19.

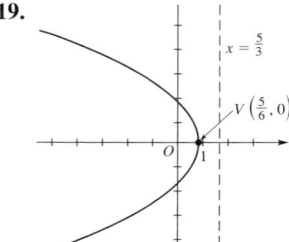

$x = \frac{5}{3}$

$V\left(\frac{5}{6}, 0\right)$

20.

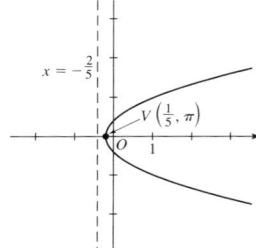

$x = -\frac{2}{5}$

$V\left(\frac{1}{5}, \pi\right)$

21. (a), (b)

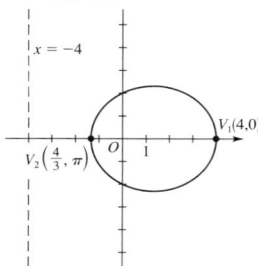

$x = -4$

$V_1(4,0)$

$V_2\left(\frac{4}{3}, \pi\right)$

(c) $C\left(\frac{4}{3}, 0\right)$, major axis: $\frac{16}{3}$, minor axis: $\frac{8\sqrt{3}}{3}$

22. (a), (b)

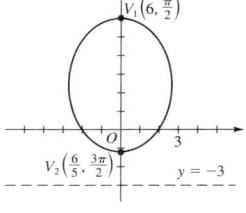

$V_1\left(6, \frac{\pi}{2}\right)$

$V_2\left(\frac{6}{5}, \frac{3\pi}{2}\right)$

$y = -3$

(c) $C\left(\frac{12}{5}, \frac{\pi}{2}\right)$, major axis: $\frac{36}{5}$, minor axis: $\frac{12\sqrt{5}}{5}$

23. (a), (b)

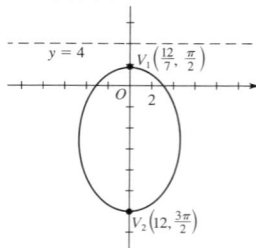

$y = 4$

$V_1\left(\frac{12}{7}, \frac{\pi}{2}\right)$

$V_2\left(12, \frac{3\pi}{2}\right)$

(c) $C\left(\frac{36}{7}, \frac{3\pi}{2}\right)$, major axis: $\frac{96}{7}$, minor axis: $\frac{24\sqrt{7}}{7}$

24. (a), (b)

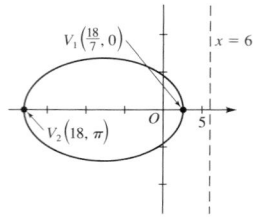

$V_1\left(\frac{18}{7}, 0\right)$

$x = 6$

$V_2(18, \pi)$

(c) $C\left(\frac{54}{7}, \pi\right)$, major axis: $\frac{144}{7}$, minor axis: $\frac{36\sqrt{7}}{7}$

25. (a), (b)

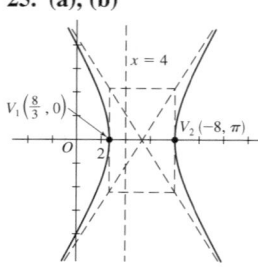

$x = 4$

$V_1\left(\frac{8}{3}, 0\right)$

$V_2(-8, \pi)$

(c) $\left(\frac{16}{3}, 0\right)$

26. (a), (b)

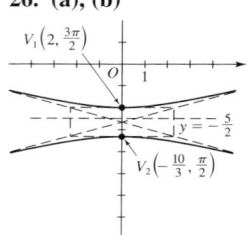

$V_1\left(2, \frac{3\pi}{2}\right)$

$y = -\frac{5}{2}$

$V_2\left(-\frac{10}{3}, \frac{\pi}{2}\right)$

(c) $\left(\frac{8}{3}, \frac{3\pi}{2}\right)$

27. (a), (b)

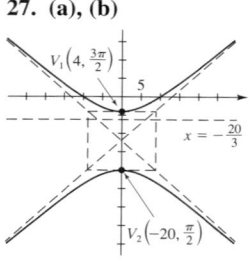

$V_1\left(4, \frac{3\pi}{2}\right)$

$x = -\frac{20}{3}$

$V_2\left(-20, \frac{\pi}{2}\right)$

(c) $\left(12, \frac{3\pi}{2}\right)$

28. (a), (b)

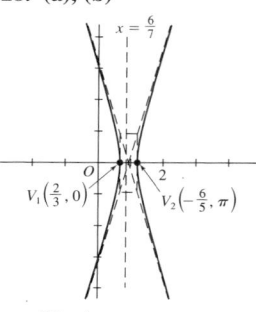

$x = \frac{6}{7}$

$V_1\left(\frac{2}{3}, 0\right)$

$V_2\left(-\frac{6}{5}, \pi\right)$

(c) $\left(\frac{14}{15}, 0\right)$

29. (a) 3, hyperbola

(b)

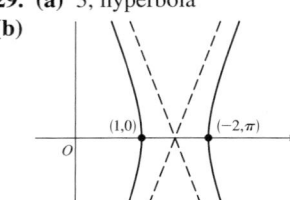

$(1,0)$ $(-2,\pi)$

30. (a) 1, parabola

(b)

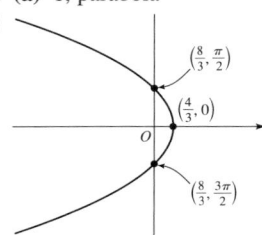

$\left(\frac{8}{3}, \frac{\pi}{2}\right)$

$\left(\frac{4}{3}, 0\right)$

$\left(\frac{8}{3}, \frac{3\pi}{2}\right)$

31. (a) 1, parabola

(b)

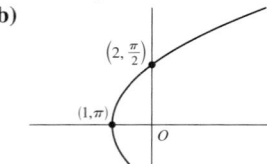

$\left(2, \frac{\pi}{2}\right)$

$(1, \pi)$

$\left(2, \frac{3\pi}{2}\right)$

32. (a) $\frac{2}{3}$, ellipse

(b)

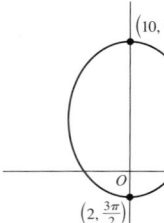

$\left(10, \frac{\pi}{2}\right)$

$\left(\frac{10}{3}, 0\right)$

$\left(2, \frac{3\pi}{2}\right)$

33. (a) $\frac{1}{2}$, ellipse

(b)

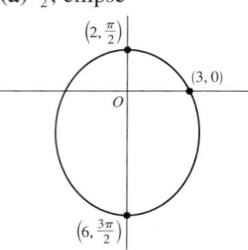

$\left(2, \frac{\pi}{2}\right)$

$(3, 0)$

$\left(6, \frac{3\pi}{2}\right)$

34. (a) $\frac{3}{2}$, hyperbola

(b)

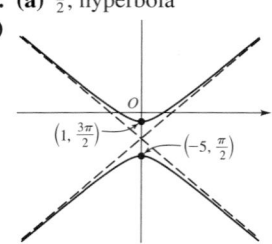

$\left(1, \frac{3\pi}{2}\right)$

$\left(-5, \frac{\pi}{2}\right)$

35. (a) $\frac{5}{2}$, hyperbola

(b)

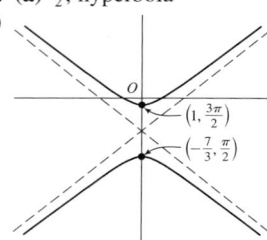

$\left(1, \frac{3\pi}{2}\right)$

$\left(-\frac{7}{3}, \frac{\pi}{2}\right)$

36. (a) $\frac{1}{3}$, ellipse

(b)

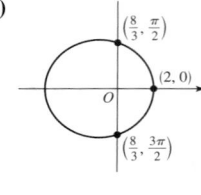

$\left(\frac{8}{3}, \frac{\pi}{2}\right)$

$(2, 0)$

$\left(\frac{8}{3}, \frac{3\pi}{2}\right)$

37. (a) eccentricity $\frac{3}{4}$, directrix $x = -\frac{1}{3}$

(b) $r = \dfrac{1}{4 - 3\cos\left(\theta - \frac{\pi}{3}\right)}$

(c)

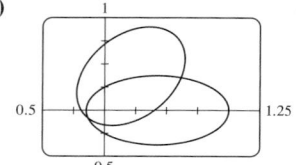

0.5   1.25   0.5

38. (a) eccentricity $\frac{3}{5}$, directrix $y = -\frac{2}{3}$

(b) $r = \dfrac{2}{5 - 3\sin\left(\theta - \frac{2\pi}{3}\right)}$

(c)

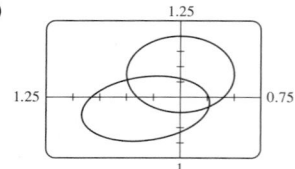

1.25   1.25   0.75   1

39. (a) eccentricity 1, directrix $y = 2$

(b) $r = \dfrac{2}{1 + \sin\left(\theta + \frac{\pi}{4}\right)}$

(c)
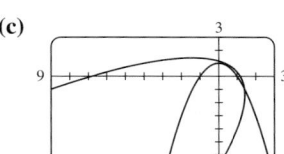

40. (a) eccentricity 1, directrix $x = \frac{9}{2}$

(b) $r = \dfrac{9}{2 + 2\cos\left(\theta + \frac{5\pi}{6}\right)}$

(c)
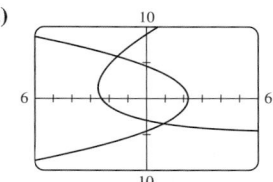

41. The ellipse is nearly circular when e is close to 0 and becomes more elongated as $e \to 1^-$. At $e = 1$, the curve becomes a parabola.
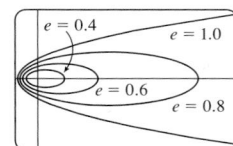

42. (a) As d increases, the parabolas get flatter while the vertex moves farther from the focus at the origin.
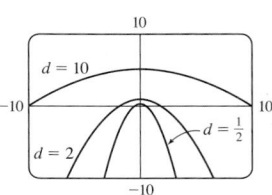

(b) As e increases, the conics change from ellipses to a parabola, and finally to hyperbolas, with the vertices getting closer to the directrix (shown as dashed line).
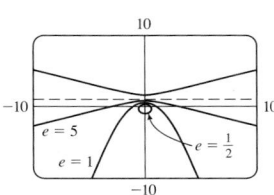

43. (b) $r = (1.49 \times 10^8)/(1 - 0.017 \cos\theta)$
44. (b) 1.468×10^8 km, 1.520×10^8 km   **45.** 0.25

CHAPTER 11 REVIEW ▪ PAGE 773

1. $V(0,0)$; $F(1,0)$; $x = -1$

2. $V(0,0)$; $F(3,0)$; $x = -3$
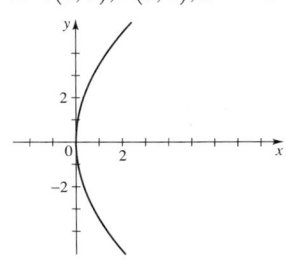

3. $V(0,0)$; $F(0,-2)$; $y = 2$

4. $V(0,0)$; $F\left(\frac{1}{2},0\right)$; $x = -\frac{1}{2}$
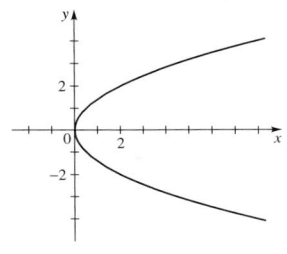

5. $V(-2,2)$; $F\left(-\frac{7}{4},2\right)$; $x = -\frac{9}{4}$
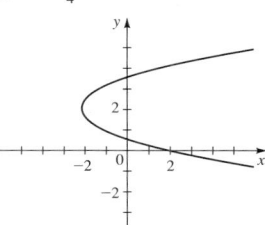

6. $V\left(-\frac{3}{2}, -\frac{11}{10}\right)$; $F\left(-\frac{3}{2}, -\frac{69}{20}\right)$; $y = -\frac{19}{40}$
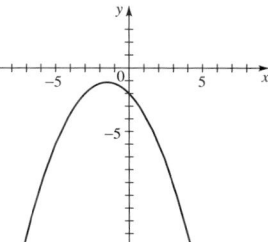

7. $V(-2,-3)$; $F(-2,-2)$; $y = -4$
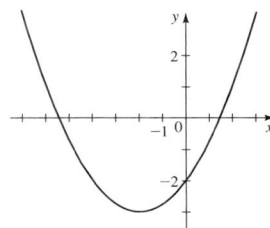

8. $V\left(\frac{3}{2}, -\frac{3}{4}\right)$; $F\left(\frac{3}{2},0\right)$; $y = -\frac{3}{2}$
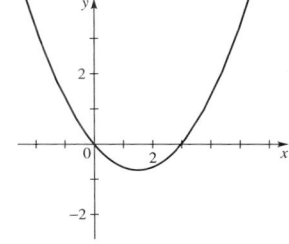

9. $C(0,0)$; $V(0,\pm5)$; $F(0,\pm4)$; axes 10, 6
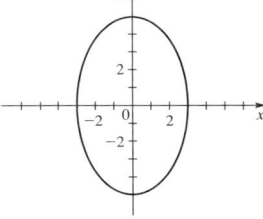

10. $C(0,0)$; $V(\pm7,0)$; $F(\pm2\sqrt{10},0)$; axes 14, 6
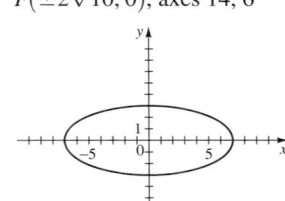

11. $C(0,0)$; $V(\pm4,0)$; $F(\pm2\sqrt{3},0)$; axes 8, 4
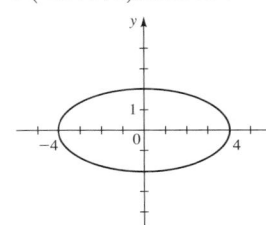

12. $C(0,0)$; $V\left(0,\pm\frac{1}{2}\right)$; $F\left(0,\pm\frac{1}{6}\sqrt{5}\right)$; axes 1, $\frac{2}{3}$

13. $C(3,0)$; $V(3,\pm4)$; $F(3,\pm\sqrt{7})$; axes 8, 6
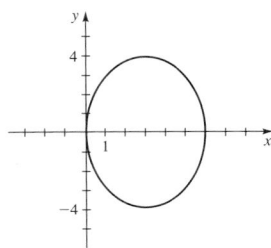

14. $C(2,-3)$; $V_1(-3,-3)$, $V_2(7,-3)$; $F_1(-1,-3)$, $F_2(5,-3)$; axes 10, 8
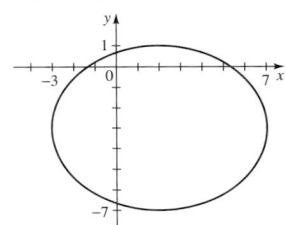

15. $C(0, 2)$; $V(\pm 3, 2)$; $F(\pm\sqrt{5}, 2)$; axes 6, 4

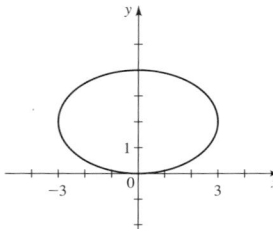

16. $C(1, -2)$; $V(1, -2 \pm 2\sqrt{2})$; $F_1(1, 0)$, $F_2(1, -4)$; axes $4\sqrt{2}$, 4

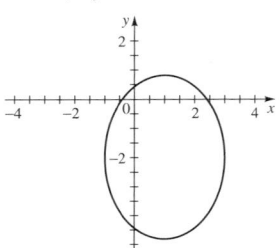

17. $C(0, 0)$; $V(0, \pm 4)$; $F(0, \pm 5)$; asymptotes $y = \pm\frac{4}{3}x$

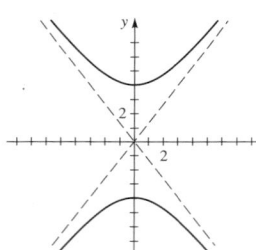

18. $C(0, 0)$; $V(\pm 7, 0)$; $F(\pm 9, 0)$; asymptotes $y = \pm\frac{4\sqrt{2}}{7}x$

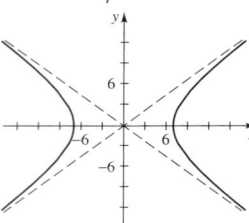

19. $C(0, 0)$; $V(\pm 4, 0)$; $F(\pm 2\sqrt{6}, 0)$; asymptotes $y = \pm\frac{1}{\sqrt{2}}x$

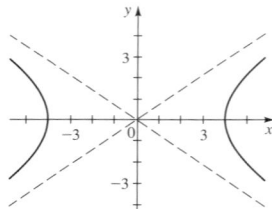

20. $C(0, 0)$; $V(0, \pm 2)$; $F(0, \pm 2\sqrt{5})$; asymptotes $y = \pm\frac{1}{2}x$

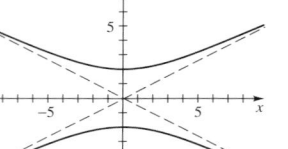

21. $C(-4, 0)$; $V_1(-8, 0)$, $V_2(0, 0)$; $F(-4 \pm 4\sqrt{2}, 0)$; asymptotes $y = \pm(x + 4)$

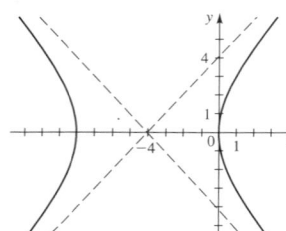

22. $C(2, -2)$; $V(2 \pm 2\sqrt{2}, -2)$; $F_1(-2, -2)$, $F_2(6, -2)$; asymptotes $y = -x$, $y = x - 4$

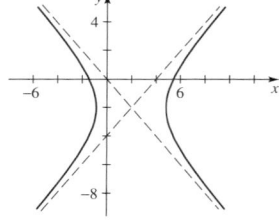

23. $C(-3, -1)$; $V(-3, -1 \pm \sqrt{2})$; $F(-3, -1 \pm 2\sqrt{5})$; asymptotes $y = \frac{1}{3}x$, $y = -\frac{1}{3}x - 2$

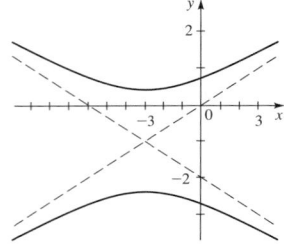

24. $C(0, 3)$; $V_1(0, 0)$, $V_2(0, 6)$; $F(0, 3 \pm 3\sqrt{2})$; asymptotes $y = x + 3$, $y = -x + 3$

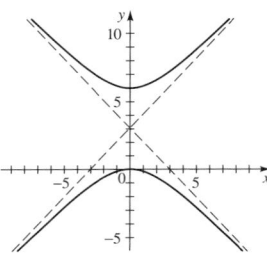

25. $y^2 = 8x$ **26.** $\dfrac{x^2}{144} + \dfrac{y^2}{25} = 1$ **27.** $\dfrac{y^2}{16} - \dfrac{x^2}{9} = 1$

28. $(y - 4)^2 = -4(x - 4)$ **29.** $\dfrac{(x - 4)^2}{16} + \dfrac{(y - 2)^2}{4} = 1$

30. $(x - 1)^2 - y^2 = 1$

31. Parabola; $F(0, -2)$; $V(0, 1)$

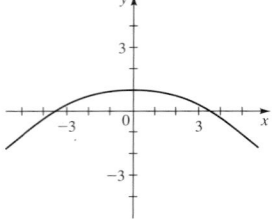

32. Ellipse; $F(0, 6 \pm \sqrt{33})$; $V_1(0, 0)$, $V_2(0, 12)$

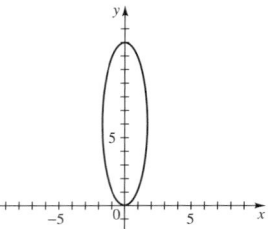

33. Hyperbola; $F(0, \pm 12\sqrt{2})$; $V(0, \pm 12)$

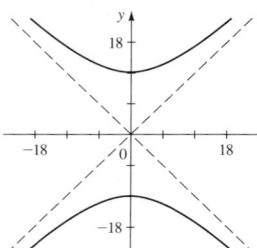

34. Hyperbola; $F(-3 \pm \sqrt{10}, 0)$; $V_1(-6, 0)$, $V_2(0, 0)$

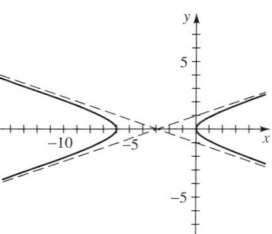

35. Ellipse; $F(1, 4 \pm \sqrt{15})$; $V(1, 4 \pm 2\sqrt{5})$

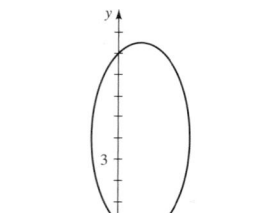

36. Parabola; $F(1, -\frac{5}{3})$; $V(1, -\frac{13}{6})$

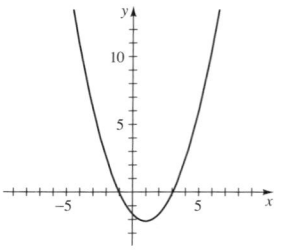

37. Parabola;
$F\left(-\frac{255}{4}, 8\right)$; $V(-64, 8)$

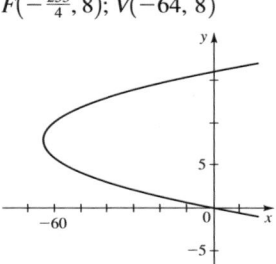

38. Hyperbola;
$F(1, \pm\sqrt{3})$; $V(1, \pm\sqrt{2})$

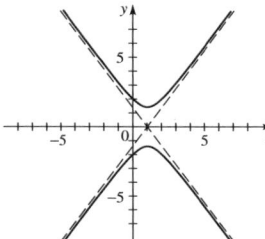

39. Ellipse;
$F(3, -3 \pm 1/\sqrt{2})$;
$V_1(3, -4)$, $V_2(3, -2)$

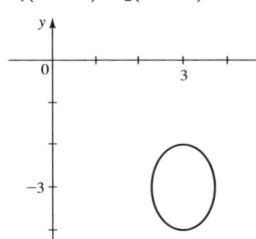

40. Hyperbola;
$F\left(\frac{1}{2} \pm \sqrt{10}, -1\right)$;
$V_1\left(-\frac{1}{2}, -1\right)$, $V_2\left(\frac{3}{2}, -1\right)$

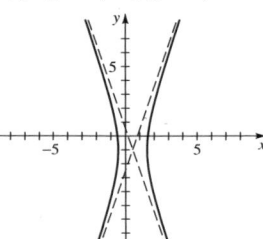

41. Has no graph
42. Ellipse; $F_1(-1, 0)$, $F_2(5, 0)$; $V(2 \pm 2\sqrt{3}, 0)$

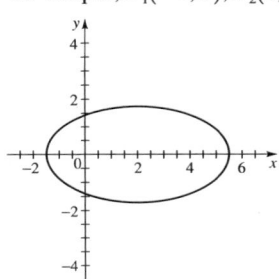

43. $x^2 = 4y$ **44.** $\dfrac{x^2}{9} + \dfrac{(y-4)^2}{25} = 1$ **45.** $\dfrac{y^2}{4} - \dfrac{x^2}{16} = 1$

46. $\dfrac{(y-4)^2}{4} - \dfrac{(x-2)^2}{5} = 1$ **47.** $\dfrac{(x-1)^2}{3} + \dfrac{(y-2)^2}{4} = 1$

48. $(y-5)^2 = 20(x-5)$ **49.** $\dfrac{4(x-7)^2}{225} + \dfrac{(y-2)^2}{100} = 1$

50. $y^2 = 4(x+1)$ **51.** (a) 91,419,000 mi
(b) 94,581,000 mi **52.** (40, 41.5)
53. (a)

54. (a)

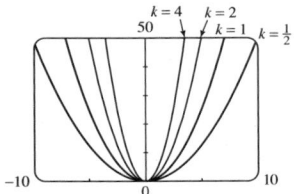

(b) $F\left(0, \frac{1}{4}k\right)$ (c) As k
increases, the focus gets
closer to the vertex.

55. (a) Hyperbola (b) $3X^2 - Y^2 = 1$
(c) $\phi = 45°$

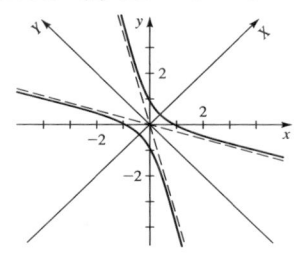

56. (a) Ellipse (b) $\dfrac{X^2}{6} + \dfrac{(Y+1)^2}{\frac{3}{2}} = 1$

(c) $\phi = 45°$

57. (a) Ellipse
(b) $(X-1)^2 + 4Y^2 = 1$
(c) $\phi = 30°$

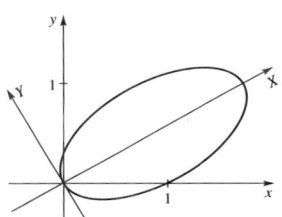

58. (a) Parabola
(b) $X = \pm 1$
(c) $\phi \approx 53°$

59. Ellipse

60. Hyperbola

61. Parabola

62. Ellipse

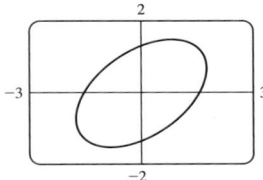

63. (a) $e = 1$, parabola
(b)

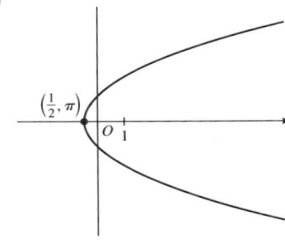

64. (a) $e = \frac{2}{3}$, ellipse
(b)

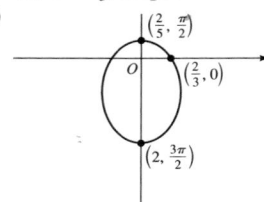

65. (a) $e = 2$, hyperbola
(b)

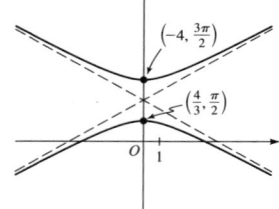

66. (a) $e = 4$, hyperbola
(b)

CHAPTER 11 TEST ▪ **PAGE 775**

1. $F(0, -3)$, $y = 3$

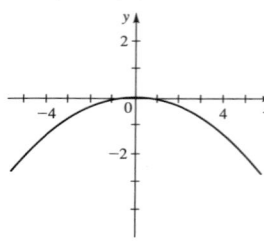

2. $V(\pm 4, 0)$; $F(\pm 2\sqrt{3}, 0)$; 8, 4

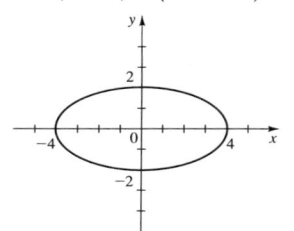

3. $V(0, \pm 3)$; $F(0, \pm 5)$; $y = \pm\frac{3}{4}x$

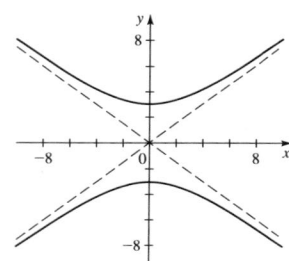

4. $y^2 = -x$ **5.** $\dfrac{x^2}{16} + \dfrac{(y-3)^2}{9} = 1$ **6.** $(x-2)^2 - \dfrac{y^2}{3} = 1$

7. $\dfrac{(x-3)^2}{9} + \dfrac{(y + \frac{1}{2})^2}{4} = 1$ **8.** $\dfrac{(x+2)^2}{8} - \dfrac{(y-4)^2}{9} = 1$

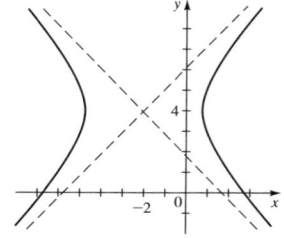

9. $(y + 4)^2 = -2(x - 4)$

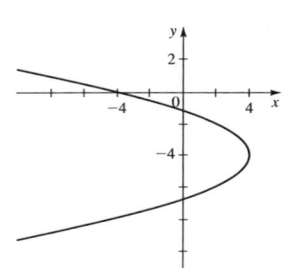

10. $\dfrac{y^2}{9} - \dfrac{x^2}{16} = 1$ **11.** $x^2 - 4x - 8y + 20 = 0$

12. $\frac{3}{4}$ in. **13. (a)** Ellipse **(b)** $\dfrac{X^2}{3} + \dfrac{Y^2}{18} = 1$

(c) $\phi \approx 27°$

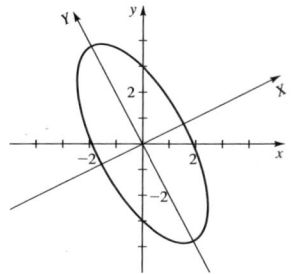

(d) $\left(-3\sqrt{2/5}, 6\sqrt{2/5}\right)$, $\left(3\sqrt{2/5}, -6\sqrt{2/5}\right)$

14. (a) $r = \dfrac{1}{1 + 0.5\cos\theta}$

(b) Ellipse

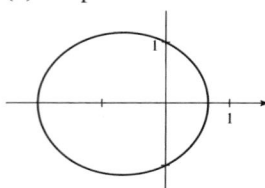

FOCUS ON MODELING ▪ **PAGE 778**

2. (b) Anchor the bar at F_2 and the string at F_1.
4. The vertices get closer together.
5. (c) $x^2 - mx + (ma - a^2) = 0$,
discriminant $m^2 - 4ma + 4a^2 = (m - 2a)^2$, $m = 2a$

CUMULATIVE REVIEW TEST FOR CHAPTERS 10 AND 11
▪ **PAGE 780**

1. (a) Nonlinear **(b)** $(0, 0), (2, 2), (-2, 2)$ **(c)** Circle, parabola **(d), (e)**

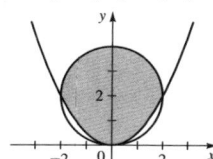

2. (a) $(3, 0, 1)$ **(b)** $x = t - 1$, $y = t + 2$, $z = t$
3. Xavier 4, Yolanda 10, Zachary 6
4. (a) $A + B$ impossible;

$$C - D = \begin{bmatrix} 0 & -4 & -2 \\ -1 & -4 & -4 \\ -1 & -1 & -1 \end{bmatrix}; \quad AB = \begin{bmatrix} -\frac{9}{2} & 1 & 5 \\ -4 & 2 & 0 \end{bmatrix};$$

CB impossible;

$$BD = \begin{bmatrix} -1 & -2 & -1 \\ -\frac{1}{2} & -1 & -\frac{1}{2} \end{bmatrix};$$

$\det(B)$ impossible; $\det(C) = 2$; $\det(D) = 0$

(b) $C^{-1} = \begin{bmatrix} 0 & 0 & -1 \\ -\frac{1}{2} & \frac{1}{2} & -\frac{1}{2} \\ 1 & 0 & 1 \end{bmatrix}$ **5. (a)** $\begin{bmatrix} 5 & -3 \\ 6 & -4 \end{bmatrix}\begin{bmatrix} x \\ y \end{bmatrix} = \begin{bmatrix} 5 \\ 0 \end{bmatrix}$

(b) $\begin{bmatrix} 2 & -\frac{3}{2} \\ 3 & -\frac{5}{2} \end{bmatrix}$ **(c)** $X = \begin{bmatrix} 10 \\ 15 \end{bmatrix}$ **(d)** $x = 10, y = 15$

6. $\dfrac{1}{x} + \dfrac{2}{x^2} - \dfrac{x+2}{x^2+4}$ **7.** $x^2 = 12y$

8. (a)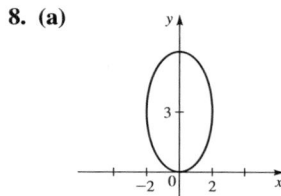

$F_1(0, 3 + \sqrt{5}), F_2(0, 3 - \sqrt{5})$, ellipse

(b)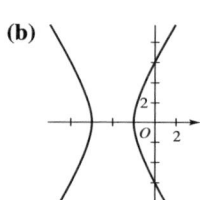

$F_1(0, 0), F_2(8, \pi)$, hyperbola

9. $\dfrac{(x-5)^2}{16} - \dfrac{y^2}{9} = 1$ **10.**

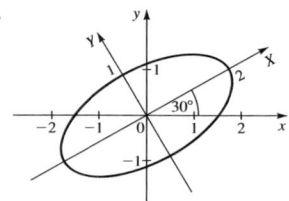

CHAPTER 12

SECTION 12.1 ■ PAGE 792

1. the natural numbers **2.** n; $1^2 + 2^2 + 3^2 + 4^2 = 30$
3. 2, 3, 4, 5; 101 **4.** 5, 7, 9, 11; 203 **5.** $\frac{1}{2}, \frac{1}{3}, \frac{1}{4}, \frac{1}{5}; \frac{1}{101}$
6. 2, 5, 10, 17; 10,001 **7.** $-1, \frac{1}{4}, -\frac{1}{9}, \frac{1}{16}; \frac{1}{10,000}$
8. $1, \frac{1}{4}, \frac{1}{9}, \frac{1}{16}; \frac{1}{10,000}$ **9.** 0, 2, 0, 2; 2 **10.** $\frac{1}{2}, -\frac{2}{3}, \frac{3}{4}, -\frac{4}{5}; -\frac{100}{101}$
11. 1, 4, 27, 256; 100^{100} **12.** 3, 3, 3, 3; 3
13. 3, 2, 0, −4, −12 **14.** −8, −4, −2, −1, $-\frac{1}{2}$
15. 1, 3, 7, 15, 31 **16.** $1, \frac{1}{2}, \frac{2}{3}, \frac{3}{5}, \frac{5}{8}$ **17.** 1, 2, 3, 5, 8
18. 1, 1, 1, 3, 5
19. (a) 7, 11, 15, 19, 23, 27, 31, 35, 39, 43
(b)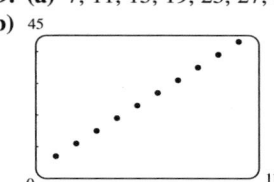

20. (a) 2, 6, 12, 20, 30, 42, 56, 72, 90, 110
(b)

21. (a) 12, 6, 4, 3, $\frac{12}{5}$, 2, $\frac{12}{7}$, $\frac{3}{2}$, $\frac{4}{3}$, $\frac{6}{5}$
(b)

22. (a) 6, 2, 6, 2, 6, 2, 6, 2, 6, 2
(b)

23. (a) 2, $\frac{1}{2}$, 2, $\frac{1}{2}$, 2, $\frac{1}{2}$, 2, $\frac{1}{2}$, 2, $\frac{1}{2}$
(b)

24. (a) 1, 3, 2, −1, −3, −2, 1, 3, 2, −1
(b)

25. 2^n **26.** $a_n = \dfrac{(-1)^n}{3^n}$ **27.** $3n - 2$ **28.** $a_n = (-1)^{n+1}5^n$
29. $(2n-1)/n^2$ **30.** $a_n = \dfrac{n+2}{n+3}$ **31.** $1 + (-1)^n$
32. $a_n = n^{(-1)^{n+1}}$ **33.** 1, 4, 9, 16, 25, 36
34. 1, 5, 14, 30, 55, 91 **35.** $\frac{1}{3}, \frac{4}{9}, \frac{13}{27}, \frac{40}{81}, \frac{121}{243}, \frac{364}{729}$
36. −1, 0, −1, 0, −1, 0 **37.** $\frac{2}{3}, \frac{8}{9}, \frac{26}{27}, \frac{80}{81}; S_n = 1 - \dfrac{1}{3^n}$
38. $\frac{1}{6}, \frac{1}{4}, \frac{3}{10}, \frac{1}{3}; S_n = \dfrac{1}{2} - \dfrac{1}{n+2}$
39. $1 - \sqrt{2}, 1 - \sqrt{3}, -1, 1 - \sqrt{5}; S_n = 1 - \sqrt{n+1}$
40. $-\log 2, -\log 3, -\log 4, -\log 5; S_n = -\log(n+1)$
41. 10 **42.** 30 **43.** $\frac{11}{6}$ **44.** 0 **45.** 8 **46.** 90 **47.** 31
48. 34 **49.** 385 **50.** 15,550 **51.** 46,438 **52.** 0.153146
53. 22 **54.** −0.688172 **55.** $\sqrt{1} + \sqrt{2} + \sqrt{3} + \sqrt{4} + \sqrt{5}$
56. $-1 + \frac{1}{3} + \frac{3}{5} + \frac{5}{7} + \frac{7}{9}$

57. $\sqrt{4} + \sqrt{5} + \sqrt{6} + \sqrt{7} + \sqrt{8} + \sqrt{9} + \sqrt{10}$

58. $6 \cdot 9 + 7 \cdot 10 + 8 \cdot 11 + 9 \cdot 12$

59. $x^3 + x^4 + \cdots + x^{100}$ **60.** $x - x^2 + x^3 - \cdots + (-1)^{n+1}x^n$

61. $\sum_{k=1}^{100} k$ **62.** $\sum_{k=1}^{10} 2k$ **63.** $\sum_{k=1}^{10} k^2$ **64.** $\sum_{k=2}^{100} \dfrac{(-1)^k}{k \ln k}$

65. $\sum_{k=1}^{999} \dfrac{1}{k(k+1)}$ **66.** $\sum_{k=1}^{n} \dfrac{\sqrt{k}}{k^2}$ **67.** $\sum_{k=0}^{100} x^k$

68. $\sum_{k=1}^{100} (-1)^{k+1} kx^{k-1}$ **69.** $2^{(2^n - 1)/2^n}$

70.

n	G_n
1	1
2	1
3	2
4	3
5	5
6	8
7	13
8	21
9	34
10	55

71. (a) 2004.00, 2008.01, 2012.02, 2016.05, 2020.08, 2024.12
(b) \$2149.16   **72. (a)** 0, 0.50, 1.50, 3.01, 5.03, 7.55
(b) \$977.00   **73. (a)** 35,700, 36,414, 37,142, 37,885, 38,643
(b) 42,665   **74. (b)** \$9088.67   **75. (b)** 6898
76. (a) $P_n = 240{,}000(1.06)^n$ **(b)** \$382,524
77. (a) $S_n = S_{n-1} + 2000$ **(b)** \$38,000
78. (a) $C_n = 1.1C_{n-1}, C_0 = 4$ **(b)** 8.6 g/L

SECTION 12.2 ■ PAGE 798

1. difference   **2.** common difference; 2, 5   **3.** True   **4.** True
5. (a) 5, 7, 9, 11, 13   **6. (a)** 3, -1, -5, -9, -13
(b) 2   **(b)** -4
(c)

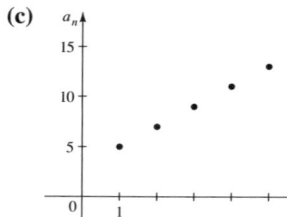

7. (a) $\frac{5}{2}, \frac{3}{2}, \frac{1}{2}, -\frac{1}{2}, -\frac{3}{2}$ **(b)** -1 **8. (a)** $0, \frac{1}{2}, 1, \frac{3}{2}, 2$ **(b)** $\frac{1}{2}$
(c)

9. $a_n = 3 + 5(n-1), a_{10} = 48$
10. $a_n = -6 + 3(n-1), a_{10} = 21$
11. $a_n = \frac{5}{2} - \frac{1}{2}(n-1), a_{10} = -2$
12. $a_n = \sqrt{3} + \sqrt{3}(n-1), a_{10} = 10\sqrt{3}$

13. Arithmetic, 3   **14.** Not arithmetic   **15.** Not arithmetic
16. Arithmetic, 2   **17.** Arithmetic, $-\frac{3}{2}$ **18.** Arithmetic, ln 2
19. Arithmetic, 1.7   **20.** Not arithmetic
21. 11, 18, 25, 32, 39; 7; $a_n = 11 + 7(n-1)$
22. 6, 8, 12, 20, 36; not arithmetic
23. $\frac{1}{3}, \frac{1}{5}, \frac{1}{7}, \frac{1}{9}, \frac{1}{11}$; not arithmetic
24. $\frac{3}{2}, 2, \frac{5}{2}, 3, \frac{7}{2}; \frac{1}{2}; a_n = \frac{3}{2} + \frac{1}{2}(n-1)$
25. $-4, 2, 8, 14, 20; 6; a_n = -4 + 6(n-1)$
26. 2, 5, 0, 7, -2; not arithmetic
27. 3, $a_5 = 14, a_n = 2 + 3(n-1), a_{100} = 299$
28. 4, $a_5 = 17, a_n = 1 + 4(n-1), a_{100} = 397$
29. 5, $a_5 = 24, a_n = 4 + 5(n-1), a_{100} = 499$
30. $-3, a_5 = -1, a_n = 11 - 3(n-1), a_{100} = -286$
31. 4, $a_5 = 4, a_n = -12 + 4(n-1), a_{100} = 384$
32. $\frac{1}{2}, a_5 = \frac{19}{6}, a_n = \frac{7}{6} + \frac{1}{2}(n-1), a_{100} = \frac{152}{3}$
33. 1.5, $a_5 = 31, a_n = 25 + 1.5(n-1), a_{100} = 173.5$
34. $-2.7, a_5 = 4.2, a_n = 15 - 2.7(n-1), a_{100} = -252.3$
35. $s, a_5 = 2 + 4s, a_n = 2 + (n-1)s, a_{100} = 2 + 99s$
36. 3, $a_5 = -t + 12, a_n = -t + 3(n-1), a_{100} = -t + 297$
37. $\frac{1}{2}$ **38.** 48   **39.** $-100, -98, -96$
40. $a_n = 44 + 3(n-1)$ **41.** 30th   **42.** Yes, the 2985th term
43. 100   **44.** 168   **45.** 460   **46.** 660   **47.** 1090   **48.** 165
49. 20,301   **50.** 310.5   **51.** 832.3   **52.** -505 **53.** 46.75
54. -399 **56.** 10^{19} **57.** Yes   **58.** $\frac{15}{4}$ **59.** 50   **60.** 31
61. \$1250   **62.** 234   **63.** \$403,500   **64.** 840   **65.** 20
66. (a) 576 ft   **(b)** $16n^2$ ft   **67.** 78

SECTION 12.3 ■ PAGE 805

1. ratio   **2.** common ratio; 2, 5   **3.** True   **4. (a)** $a\left(\dfrac{1 - r^n}{1 - r}\right)$

(b) geometric; converges, $a/(1 - r)$; diverges
5. (a) 5, 10, 20, 40, 80   **6. (a)** 3, -12, 48, -192, 768
(b) 2   **(b)** -4
(c)

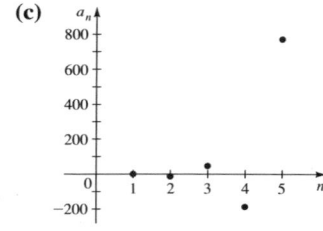

7. (a) $\frac{5}{2}, -\frac{5}{4}, \frac{5}{8}, -\frac{5}{16}, \frac{5}{32}$ **8. (a)** 1, 3, 9, 27, 81
(b) $-\frac{1}{2}$ **(b)** 3
(c)

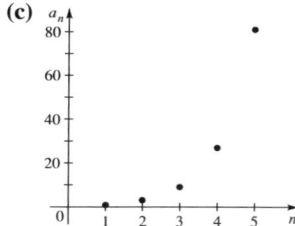

9. $a_n = 3 \cdot 5^{n-1}, a_4 = 375$ **10.** $a_n = -6 \cdot 3^{n-1}, a_4 = -162$
11. $a_n = \frac{5}{2}\left(-\frac{1}{2}\right)^{n-1}, a_4 = -\frac{5}{16}$ **12.** $a_n = \sqrt{3}(\sqrt{3})^{n-1}, a_4 = 9$
13. Geometric, 2   **14.** Not geometric   **15.** Geometric, $\frac{1}{2}$

16. Geometric, $-\frac{1}{3}$　**17.** Not geometric　**18.** Geometric, e^2
19. Geometric, 1.1　**20.** Not geometric　**21.** 6, 18, 54, 162, 486; geometric, common ratio 3; $a_n = 6 \cdot 3^{n-1}$　**22.** 7, 13, 31, 85, 247;
not geometric　**23.** $\frac{1}{4}, \frac{1}{16}, \frac{1}{64}, \frac{1}{256}, \frac{1}{1024}$; geometric, common ratio $\frac{1}{4}$;
$a_n = \frac{1}{4}\left(\frac{1}{4}\right)^{n-1}$　**24.** $-2, 4, -8, 16, -32$; geometric, common ratio
-2, $a_n = -2 \cdot (-2)^{n-1}$　**25.** $0, \ln 5, 2 \ln 5, 3 \ln 5, 4 \ln 5$;
not geometric　**26.** 1, 4, 27, 256, 3125; not geometric
27. $3, a_5 = 162, a_n = 2 \cdot 3^{n-1}$　**28.** $\frac{2}{3}, a_5 = \frac{112}{81}, a_n = 7\left(\frac{2}{3}\right)^{n-1}$
29. $-0.3, a_5 = 0.00243, a_n = (0.3)(-0.3)^{n-1}$
30. $\sqrt{2}, a_5 = 4, a_n = \left(\sqrt{2}\right)^{n-1}$
31. $-\frac{1}{12}, a_5 = \frac{1}{144}, a_n = 144\left(-\frac{1}{12}\right)^{n-1}$
32. $\frac{1}{4}, a_5 = -\frac{1}{32}, a_n = -8\left(\frac{1}{4}\right)^{n-1}$　**33.** $3^{2/3}, a_5 = 3^{11/3}, a_n = 3^{(2n+1)/3}$
34. $t/2, a_5 = t^5/16, a_n = t(t/2)^{n-1}$
35. $s^{2/7}, a_5 = s^{8/7}, a_n = s^{2(n-1)/7}$　**36.** $5^c, a_5 = 5^{4c+1}, a_n = 5 \cdot (5^c)^{n-1}$
37. $\frac{1}{2}$　**38.** $\frac{16}{27}$　**39.** $\frac{25}{4}$　**40.** $\frac{16}{81}, \frac{8}{27}, \frac{4}{9}$　**41.** 11th　**42.** Yes, the
7th term　**43.** 315　**44.** $\frac{80}{81}$　**45.** 441　**46.** 0.7488　**47.** 3280
48. $\frac{341}{512}$　**49.** $\frac{6141}{1024}$　**50.** $\frac{4655}{32}$　**51.** $\frac{3}{2}$　**52.** $\frac{2}{3}$　**53.** $\frac{3}{4}$　**54.** $\frac{2}{3}$
55. divergent　**56.** $\frac{1}{648}$　**57.** 2　**58.** divergent　**59.** divergent
60. $-\frac{1000}{117}$　**61.** $\sqrt{2} + 1$　**62.** divergent　**63.** $\frac{7}{9}$　**64.** $\frac{251}{990}$　**65.** $\frac{1}{33}$
66. $\frac{10,457}{4950}$　**67.** $\frac{112}{999}$　**68.** $\frac{41}{333}$　**69.** 10, 20, 40
70. $a \cdot \dfrac{1 - a^{10}}{1 - a} + 55b$　**71.** (a) $V_n = 160,000(0.80)^{n-1}$
(b) 4th year　**72.** 32,768　**73.** 19 ft, $80\left(\frac{3}{4}\right)^n$
74. 7347, $a_n = 5000 \cdot (1.08)^n$　**75.** $\frac{64}{25}, \frac{1024}{625}, 5\left(\frac{4}{5}\right)^n$　**76.** 64
77. (a) $17\frac{8}{9}$ ft　**(b)** $18 - \left(\frac{1}{3}\right)^{n-3}$　**78.** $\$10,737,418.23$, 37 days
79. 2801　**80.** (a) 99.90 mg　**(b)** 100 mg　**81.** 3 m
82. $2 + \sqrt{2} \approx 3.41$ s　**83.** (a) 2　**(b)** $8 + 4\sqrt{2}$
84. $2\pi R^2$　**85.** 1

SECTION 12.4 ▪ PAGE 812

1. amount　**2.** present value　**3.** $\$13,180.79$　**4.** $\$12,966.59$
5. $\$360,262.21$　**6.** $\$13,435.19$　**7.** $\$5,591.79$　**8.** $\$241,599.55$
9. $\$572.34$　**10.** $\$245.66$　**11.** $\$13,007.94$　**12.** $\$8,132.65$
13. $\$2,601.59$　**14.** $\$3,679.09$　**15.** $\$307.24$　**16.** $\$643.70$,
$\$811.41$　**17.** $\$733.76$, $\$264,153.60$　**18.** Monthly payment:
$\$1,687.71$; total amount paid: $\$303,787.80$　**19.** $\$583,770.65$
20. $\$80,783.21$　**21.** $\$9020.60$　**22.** $\$341.24$　**23.** (a) $\$859.15$
(b) $\$309,294.00$　**(c)** $\$1,841,519.29$　**24.** (a) $\$1896.20$, $\$2491.23$;
15-year　**(b)** $\$682,632.00$, $\$448,421.40$; 15-year　**25.** 18.16%
26. 12.80%　**27.** 11.68%　**28.** 15.84%

SECTION 12.5 ▪ PAGE 819

1. natural; $P(1)$　**2.** (ii)
3. Let $P(n)$ denote the statement $2 + 4 + \cdots + 2n = n(n + 1)$.

Step 1 $P(1)$ is true, since $2 = 1(1 + 1)$.
Step 2 Suppose $P(k)$ is true. Then

$$2 + 4 + \cdots + 2k + 2(k + 1)$$

$$= k(k + 1) + 2(k + 1) \qquad \text{Induction hypothesis}$$

$$= (k + 1)(k + 2)$$

So $P(k + 1)$ follows from $P(k)$. Thus by the Principle of
Mathematical Induction $P(n)$ holds for all n.

4. Let $P(n)$ denote the statement

$$1 + 4 + 7 + \cdots + (3n - 2) = \frac{n(3n - 1)}{2}.$$

Step 1 $P(1)$ is true, since $1 = \dfrac{1(3 \cdot 1 - 1)}{2}$.
Step 2 Suppose $P(k)$ is true. Then

$$1 + 4 + 7 + \cdots + (3k - 2) + [3(k + 1) - 2]$$

$$= \frac{k(3k - 1)}{2} + [3(k + 1) - 2] \qquad \text{Induction hypothesis}$$

$$= \frac{3k^2 + 5k + 2}{2} = \frac{(k + 1)[3(k + 1) - 1]}{2}$$

So $P(k + 1)$ follows from $P(k)$. Thus by the Principle of
Mathematical Induction $P(n)$ holds for all n.

5. Let $P(n)$ denote the statement

$$5 + 8 + \cdots + (3n + 2) = \frac{n(3n + 7)}{2}.$$

Step 1 $P(1)$ is true, since $5 = \dfrac{1(3 \cdot 1 + 7)}{2}$
Step 2 Suppose $P(k)$ is true. Then

$$5 + 8 + \cdots + (3k + 2) + [3(k + 1) + 2]$$

$$= \frac{k(3k + 7)}{2} + (3k + 5) \qquad \text{Induction hypothesis}$$

$$= \frac{3k^2 + 13k + 10}{2}$$

$$= \frac{(k + 1)[3(k + 1) + 7]}{2}$$

So $P(k + 1)$ follows from $P(k)$. Thus by the Principle of
Mathematical Induction $P(n)$ holds for all n.

6. Let $P(n)$ denote the statement

$$1^2 + 2^2 + \cdots + n^2 = \frac{n(n + 1)(2n + 1)}{6}.$$

Step 1 $P(1)$ is true, since $1^2 = \dfrac{1(1 + 1)(2 \cdot 1 + 1)}{6}$.
Step 2 Suppose $P(k)$ is true. Then

$$1^2 + 2^2 + \cdots + k^2 + (k + 1)^2$$

$$= \frac{k(k + 1)(2k + 1)}{6} + (k + 1)^2 \qquad \text{Induction hypothesis}$$

$$= \frac{(k + 1)[2k^2 + 7k + 6]}{6}$$

$$= \frac{(k + 1)[(k + 1) + 1][2(k + 1) + 1]}{6}$$

So $P(k + 1)$ follows from $P(k)$. Thus by the Principle of
Mathematical Induction $P(n)$ holds for all n.

7. Let $P(n)$ denote the statement

$$1 \cdot 2 + 2 \cdot 3 + \cdots + n(n + 1) = \frac{n(n + 1)(n + 2)}{3}.$$

Step 1 $P(1)$ is true, since $1 \cdot 2 = \frac{1 \cdot (1 + 1) \cdot (1 + 2)}{3}$.

Step 2 Suppose $P(k)$ is true. Then

$$1 \cdot 2 + 2 \cdot 3 + \cdots + k(k + 1) + (k + 1)(k + 2)$$

$$= \frac{k(k + 1)(k + 2)}{3} + (k + 1)(k + 2) \qquad \text{Induction hypothesis}$$

$$= \frac{(k + 1)(k + 2)(k + 3)}{3}$$

So $P(k + 1)$ follows from $P(k)$. Thus by the Principle of Mathematical Induction $P(n)$ holds for all n.

8. Let $P(n)$ denote the statement

$$1 \cdot 3 + 2 \cdot 4 + \cdots + n(n + 2) = \frac{n(n + 1)(2n + 7)}{6}.$$

Step 1 $P(1)$ is true, since $1 \cdot 3 = \frac{1(1 + 1)(2 \cdot 1 + 7)}{6}$.

Step 2 Suppose $P(k)$ is true. Then

$$1 \cdot 3 + 2 \cdot 4 + \cdots + k(k + 2) + (k + 1)[(k + 1) + 2]$$

$$= \frac{k(k + 1)(2k + 7)}{6} + (k + 1)[(k + 1) + 2] \qquad \text{Induction hypothesis}$$

$$= \frac{(k + 1)(2k^2 + 13k + 18)}{6}$$

$$= \frac{(k + 1)[(k + 1) + 1][2(k + 1) + 7]}{6}$$

So $P(k + 1)$ follows from $P(k)$. Thus by the Principle of Mathematical Induction $P(n)$ holds for all n.

9. Let $P(n)$ denote the statement

$$1^3 + 2^3 + \cdots + n^3 = \frac{n^2(n + 1)^2}{4}.$$

Step 1 $P(1)$ is true, since $1^3 = \frac{1^2 \cdot (1 + 1)^2}{4}$.

Step 2 Suppose $P(k)$ is true. Then

$$1^3 + 2^3 + \cdots + k^3 + (k + 1)^3$$

$$= \frac{k^2(k + 1)^2}{4} + (k + 1)^3 \qquad \text{Induction hypothesis}$$

$$= \frac{(k + 1)^2[k^2 + 4(k + 1)]}{4}$$

$$= \frac{(k + 1)^2(k + 2)^2}{4}$$

So $P(k + 1)$ follows from $P(k)$. Thus by the Principle of Mathematical Induction $P(n)$ holds for all n.

10. Let $P(n)$ denote the statement

$$1^3 + 3^3 + \cdots + (2n - 1)^3 = n^2(2n^2 - 1).$$

Step 1 $P(1)$ is true, since $1^3 = 1^2(2 \cdot 1^2 - 1)$.

Step 2 Suppose $P(k)$ is true. Then

$$1^3 + 2^3 + \cdots + (2k - 1)^3 + (2k + 1)^3$$

$$= k^2(2k^2 - 1) + (2k + 1)^3 \qquad \text{Induction hypothesis}$$

$$= 2k^4 + 8k^3 + 11k^2 + 6k + 1$$

$$= (k + 1)(k + 1)(2k^2 + 4k + 1) \qquad \text{Factor (see Sec. 3.3)}$$

$$= (k + 1)^2[2(k + 1)^2 - 1]$$

So $P(k + 1)$ follows from $P(k)$. Thus by the Principle of Mathematical Induction $P(n)$ holds for all n.

11. Let $P(n)$ denote the statement

$$2^3 + 4^3 + \cdots + (2n)^3 = 2n^2(n + 1)^2.$$

Step 1 $P(1)$ is true, since $2^3 = 2 \cdot 1^2(1 + 1)^2$.

Step 2 Suppose $P(k)$ is true. Then

$$2^3 + 4^3 + \cdots + (2k)^3 + [2(k + 1)]^3$$

$$= 2k^2(k + 1)^2 + [2(k + 1)]^3 \qquad \text{Induction hypothesis}$$

$$= (k + 1)^2(2k^2 + 8k + 8)$$

$$= 2(k + 1)^2(k + 2)^2$$

So $P(k + 1)$ follows from $P(k)$. Thus by the Principle of Mathematical Induction $P(n)$ holds for all n.

12. Let $P(n)$ denote the statement

$$\frac{1}{1 \cdot 2} + \frac{1}{2 \cdot 3} + \cdots + \frac{1}{n(n + 1)} = \frac{n}{n + 1}.$$

Step 1 $P(1)$ is true, since $\frac{1}{1 \cdot 2} = \frac{1}{1 + 1}$.

Step 2 Suppose $P(k)$ is true. Then

$$\frac{1}{1 \cdot 2} + \frac{1}{2 \cdot 3} + \cdots + \frac{1}{k(k + 1)} + \frac{1}{(k + 1)[(k + 1) + 1]}$$

$$= \frac{k}{k + 1} + \frac{1}{(k + 1)[(k + 1) + 1]} \qquad \text{Induction hypothesis}$$

$$= \frac{k^2 + 2k + 1}{(k + 1)(k + 2)} = \frac{k + 1}{k + 2}$$

So $P(k + 1)$ follows from $P(k)$. Thus by the Principle of Mathematical Induction $P(n)$ holds for all n.

13. Let $P(n)$ denote the statement

$$1 \cdot 2 + 2 \cdot 2^2 + \cdots + n \cdot 2^n = 2[1 + (n - 1)2^n].$$

Step 1 $P(1)$ is true, since $1 \cdot 2 = 2[1 + 0]$.

Step 2 Suppose $P(k)$ is true. Then

$$1 \cdot 2 + 2 \cdot 2^2 + \cdots + k \cdot 2^k + (k + 1) \cdot 2^{k+1}$$

$$= 2[1 + (k - 1)2^k] + (k + 1) \cdot 2^{k+1} \qquad \text{Induction hypothesis}$$

$$= 2 + (k - 1)2^{k+1} + (k + 1) \cdot 2^{k+1}$$

$$= 2 + 2k2^{k+1} = 2(1 + k2^{k+1})$$

So $P(k + 1)$ follows from $P(k)$. Thus by the Principle of Mathematical Induction $P(n)$ holds for all n.

14. Let $P(n)$ denote the statement
$1 + 2 + 2^2 + \cdots + 2^{n-1} = 2^n - 1$.

Step 1 $P(1)$ is true, since $1 = 2^1 - 1$.
Step 2 Suppose $P(k)$ is true. Then

$$1 + 2 + 2^2 + \cdots + 2^{k-1} + 2^k$$

$$= (2^k - 1) + 2^k \qquad \text{Induction hypothesis}$$

$$= 2 \cdot 2^k - 1 = 2^{k+1} - 1$$

So $P(k + 1)$ follows from $P(k)$. Thus by the Principle of Mathematical Induction $P(n)$ holds for all n.

15. Let $P(n)$ denote the statement $n^2 + n$ is divisible by 2.

Step 1 $P(1)$ is true, since $1^2 + 1$ is divisible by 2.
Step 2 Suppose $P(k)$ is true. Now

$$(k + 1)^2 + (k + 1) = k^2 + 2k + 1 + k + 1$$

$$= (k^2 + k) + 2(k + 1)$$

But $k^2 + k$ is divisible by 2 (by the induction hypothesis), and $2(k + 1)$ is clearly divisible by 2, so $(k + 1)^2 + (k + 1)$ is divisible by 2. So $P(k + 1)$ follows from $P(k)$. Thus by the Principle of Mathematical Induction $P(n)$ holds for all n.

16. Let $P(n)$ denote the statement that $5^n - 1$ is divisible by 4.

Step 1 $P(1)$ is true, since $5^1 - 1 = 4$.
Step 2 Suppose $P(k)$ is true. We have

$$5^{k+1} - 1 = 5(5^k - 1) + 4$$

Now $5^k - 1$ is divisible by 4 (induction hypothesis), and so is 4, and hence $5(5^k - 1) + 4$ is also divisible by 4. So $P(k + 1)$ follows from $P(k)$. Thus by the Principle of Mathematical Induction $P(n)$ holds for all n.

17. Let $P(n)$ denote the statement $n^2 - n + 41$ is odd.

Step 1 $P(1)$ is true, since $1^2 - 1 + 41$ is odd.
Step 2 Suppose $P(k)$ is true. Now

$$(k + 1)^2 - (k + 1) + 41 = (k^2 - k + 41) + 2k$$

But $k^2 - k + 41$ is odd (by the induction hypothesis), and $2k$ is clearly even, so their sum is odd. So $P(k + 1)$ follows from $P(k)$. Thus by the Principle of Mathematical Induction $P(n)$ holds for all n.

18. Let $P(n)$ denote the statement that $n^3 - n + 3$ is divisible by 3.

Step 1 $P(1)$ is true, since $1^3 - 1 + 3 = 3$.
Step 2 Suppose $P(k)$ is true. We have

$$(k + 1)^3 - (k + 1) + 3 = k^3 - k + 3 + 3(k^2 + k)$$

Now $k^3 - k + 3$ is divisible by 3 (induction hypothesis), and so is $3(k^2 + k)$. So $P(k + 1)$ follows from $P(k)$. Thus by the Principle of Mathematical Induction $P(n)$ holds for all n.

19. Let $P(n)$ denote the statement $8^n - 3^n$ is divisible by 5.

Step 1 $P(1)$ is true, since $8^1 - 3^1$ is divisible by 5.
Step 2 Suppose $P(k)$ is true. Now

$$8^{k+1} - 3^{k+1} = 8 \cdot 8^k - 3 \cdot 3^k$$

$$= 8 \cdot 8^k - (8 - 5) \cdot 3^k = 8 \cdot (8^k - 3^k) + 5 \cdot 3^k$$

which is divisible by 5 because $8^k - 3^k$ is divisible by 5 (by the induction hypothesis) and $5 \cdot 3^k$ is clearly divisible by 5. So $P(k + 1)$ follows from $P(k)$. Thus by the Principle of Mathematical Induction $P(n)$ holds for all n.

20. Let $P(n)$ denote the statement that $3^{2n} - 1$ is divisible by 8.

Step 1 $P(1)$ is true, since $3^{2 \cdot 1} - 1 = 8$.
Step 2 Suppose $P(k)$ is true. We have

$$3^{2(k+1)} - 1 = 9(3^{2k} - 1) + 8$$

Now $3^{2k} - 1$ is divisible by 8 (induction hypothesis), and so is 8, and hence $9(3^{2k} - 1) + 8$ is also divisible by 8. So $P(k + 1)$ follows from $P(k)$. Thus by the Principle of Mathematical Induction $P(n)$ holds for all n.

21. Let $P(n)$ denote the statement $n < 2^n$.

Step 1 $P(1)$ is true, since $1 < 2^1$.
Step 2 Suppose $P(k)$ is true. Then

$$k + 1 < 2^k + 1 \qquad \text{Induction hypothesis}$$

$$< 2^k + 2^k \qquad \text{Because } 1 < 2^k$$

$$= 2 \cdot 2^k = 2^{k+1}$$

So $P(k + 1)$ follows from $P(k)$. Thus by the Principle of Mathematical Induction $P(n)$ holds for all n.

22. Let $P(n)$ denote the statement that $(n + 1)^2 < 2n^2$ for all $n \geq 3$.

Step 1 $P(3)$ is true, since $(3 + 1)^2 < 2 \cdot 3^2$.
Step 2 Suppose $P(k)$ is true. Then

$$[(k + 1) + 1]^2 = (k + 1)^2 + 2(k + 1) + 1$$

$$< 2k^2 + 2(k + 1) + 1 \qquad \text{Induction hypothesis}$$

$$< 2k^2 + 4k + 2 \qquad \text{Because } 2k - 1 > 0 \text{ for } k \geq 3$$

$$= 2(k + 1)^2$$

So $P(k + 1)$ follows from $P(k)$. Thus by the Principle of Mathematical Induction $P(n)$ holds for all n.

23. Let $P(n)$ denote the statement $(1 + x)^n \geq 1 + nx$ for $x > -1$.

Step 1 $P(1)$ is true, since $(1 + x)^1 \geq 1 + 1 \cdot x$.
Step 2 Suppose $P(k)$ is true. Then

$$(1 + x)^{k+1} = (1 + x)(1 + x)^k$$

$$\geq (1 + x)(1 + kx) \qquad \text{Induction hypothesis}$$

$$= 1 + (k + 1)x + kx^2$$

$$\geq 1 + (k + 1)x$$

So $P(k + 1)$ follows from $P(k)$. Thus by the Principle of Mathematical Induction $P(n)$ holds for all n.

24. Let $P(n)$ denote the statement that $100n \leq n^2$ for all $n \geq 100$.

Step 1 $P(100)$ is true, since $100(100) \leq (100)^2$.
Step 2 Suppose $P(k)$ is true. Then

$$100(k + 1) = 100k + 100$$

$$\leq k^2 + 100 \qquad \text{Induction hypothesis}$$

$$\leq k^2 + 2k + 1 \qquad \text{Because } 100 \leq 2k + 1 \text{ for } k \geq 100$$

$$= (k + 1)^2$$

So $P(k + 1)$ follows from $P(k)$. Thus by the Principle of Mathematical Induction $P(n)$ holds for all n.

25. Let $P(n)$ denote the statement $a_n = 5 \cdot 3^{n-1}$.

Step 1 $P(1)$ is true, since $a_1 = 5 \cdot 3^0 = 5$.
Step 2 Suppose $P(k)$ is true. Then

$$a_{k+1} = 3 \cdot a_k \qquad \text{Definition of } a_{k+1}$$
$$= 3 \cdot 5 \cdot 3^{k-1} \qquad \text{Induction hypothesis}$$
$$= 5 \cdot 3^k$$

So $P(k+1)$ follows from $P(k)$. Thus by the Principle of Mathematical Induction $P(n)$ holds for all n.

26. $a_n = 4$ for all n.
Let $P(n)$ denote the statement $a_n = 4$.

Step 1 $P(1)$ is true, since $a_1 = 4$.
Step 2 Suppose $P(k)$ is true. Then

$$a_{k+1} = 3a_k - 8 \qquad \text{Definition of } a_k$$
$$= 3 \cdot 4 - 8 \qquad \text{Induction hypothesis}$$
$$= 4$$

So $P(k+1)$ follows from $P(k)$. Thus by the Principle of Mathematical Induction $P(n)$ holds for all n.

27. Let $P(n)$ denote the statement $x - y$ is a factor of $x^n - y^n$.

Step 1 $P(1)$ is true, since $x - y$ is a factor of $x^1 - y^1$.
Step 2 Suppose $P(k)$ is true. Now

$$x^{k+1} - y^{k+1} = x^{k+1} - x^k y + x^k y - y^{k+1}$$
$$= x^k(x - y) + (x^k - y^k)y$$

But $x^k(x - y)$ is clearly divisible by $x - y$, and $(x^k - y^k)y$ is divisible by $x - y$ (by the induction hypothesis), so their sum is divisible by $x - y$. So $P(k+1)$ follows from $P(k)$. Thus by the Principle of Mathematical Induction $P(n)$ holds for all n.

28. Let $P(n)$ denote the statement that $x + y$ is a factor of $x^{2n-1} + y^{2n-1}$.

Step 1 $P(1)$ is obviously true.
Step 2 Suppose $P(k)$ is true. Then
$$x^{2(k+1)-1} + y^{2(k+1)-1} = x^{2k-1}(x^2 - y^2) + (x^{2k-1} + y^{2k-1})y^2$$

The first term in this sum is obviously divisible by $x + y$, and the second term is divisible by $x + y$ by the induction hypothesis, so the sum is also divisible by $x + y$. Thus by the Principle of Mathematical Induction $P(n)$ holds for all n.

29. Let $P(n)$ denote the statement F_{3n} is even.

Step 1 $P(1)$ is true, since $F_{3 \cdot 1} = 2$, which is even.
Step 2 Suppose $P(k)$ is true. Now, by the definition of the Fibonacci sequence

$$F_{3(k+1)} = F_{3k+3} = F_{3k+2} + F_{3k+1}$$
$$= F_{3k+1} + F_{3k} + F_{3k+1}$$
$$= F_{3k} + 2 \cdot F_{3k+1}$$

But F_{3k} is even (by the induction hypothesis), and $2 \cdot F_{3k+1}$ is clearly even, so $F_{3(k+1)}$ is even. So $P(k+1)$ follows from $P(k)$. Thus by the Principle of Mathematical Induction $P(n)$ holds for all n.

30. Let $P(n)$ denote the statement
$F_1 + F_2 + \cdots + F_n = F_{n+2} - 1$.

Step 1 $P(1)$ is true, since $F_1 = 1$ and $F_{1+2} = 2$.
Step 2 Suppose $P(k)$ is true. Then

$$F_1 + F_2 + \cdots + F_k + F_{k+1} \qquad \text{Induction hypothesis}$$
$$= (F_{k+2} - 1) + F_{k+1}$$
$$= (F_{k+2} + F_{k+1}) - 1 = F_{k+3} - 1 \qquad \text{Definition of the Fibonacci sequence}$$

So $P(k+1)$ follows from $P(k)$. Thus by the Principle of Mathematical Induction $P(n)$ holds for all n.

31. Let $P(n)$ denote the statement
$F_1^2 + F_2^2 + \cdots + F_n^2 = F_n \cdot F_{n+1}$.

Step 1 $P(1)$ is true, since $F_1^2 = F_1 \cdot F_2$ (because $F_1 = F_2 = 1$).
Step 2 Suppose $P(k)$ is true. Then

$$F_1^2 + F_2^2 + \cdots + F_k^2 + F_{k+1}^2$$
$$= F_k \cdot F_{k+1} + F_{k+1}^2 \qquad \text{Induction hypothesis}$$
$$= F_{k+1}(F_k + F_{k+1}) \qquad \text{Definition of the Fibonacci sequence}$$
$$= F_{k+1} \cdot F_{k+2}$$

So $P(k+1)$ follows from $P(k)$. Thus by the Principle of Mathematical Induction $P(n)$ holds for all n.

32. Let $P(n)$ denote the statement
$F_1 + F_3 + \cdots + F_{2n-1} = F_{2n}$

Step 1 $P(1)$ is true, since $F_1 = F_{2 \cdot 1}$
Step 2 Suppose $P(k)$ is true. Then

$$F_1 + F_3 + \cdots + F_{2k-1} + F_{2k+1} = F_{2k} + F_{2k+1} \qquad \text{Induction hypothesis}$$
$$= F_{2k+2}$$
$$= F_{2(k+1)}$$

So $P(k+1)$ follows from $P(k)$. Thus by the Principle of Mathematical Induction $P(n)$ holds for all n.

33. Let $P(n)$ denote the statement $\begin{bmatrix} 1 & 1 \\ 1 & 0 \end{bmatrix}^n = \begin{bmatrix} F_{n+1} & F_n \\ F_n & F_{n-1} \end{bmatrix}$.

Step 1 $P(2)$ is true, since $\begin{bmatrix} 1 & 1 \\ 1 & 0 \end{bmatrix}^2 = \begin{bmatrix} 2 & 1 \\ 1 & 1 \end{bmatrix} = \begin{bmatrix} F_3 & F_2 \\ F_2 & F_1 \end{bmatrix}$.
Step 2 Suppose $P(k)$ is true. Then

$$\begin{bmatrix} 1 & 1 \\ 1 & 0 \end{bmatrix}^{k+1} = \begin{bmatrix} 1 & 1 \\ 1 & 0 \end{bmatrix}^k \begin{bmatrix} 1 & 1 \\ 1 & 0 \end{bmatrix}$$
$$= \begin{bmatrix} F_{k+1} & F_k \\ F_k & F_{k-1} \end{bmatrix}\begin{bmatrix} 1 & 1 \\ 1 & 0 \end{bmatrix} \qquad \text{Induction hypothesis}$$
$$= \begin{bmatrix} F_{k+1} + F_k & F_{k+1} \\ F_k + F_{k-1} & F_k \end{bmatrix}$$
$$= \begin{bmatrix} F_{k+2} & F_{k+1} \\ F_{k+1} & F_k \end{bmatrix} \qquad \text{Definition of the Fibonacci sequence}$$

So $P(k+1)$ follows from $P(k)$. Thus by the Principle of Mathematical Induction $P(n)$ holds for all $n \geq 2$.

34. $a_n = \dfrac{F_n}{F_{n+1}}$ for all n.

Let $P(n)$ denote the statement $a_n = \dfrac{F_n}{F_{n+1}}$.

Step 1 $P(1)$ is true, since $\dfrac{F_1}{F_{1+1}} = \dfrac{1}{1} = 1 = a_1$.

Step 2 Suppose $P(k)$ is true. Then

$$a_{k+1} = \frac{1}{1 + a_k} \qquad \text{Definition of } a_k$$

$$= \frac{1}{1 + \dfrac{F_k}{F_{k+1}}} \qquad \text{Induction hypothesis}$$

$$= \frac{F_{k+1}}{F_{k+1} + F_k} \qquad \begin{array}{l}\text{Multiply numerator and}\\ \text{denominator by } F_{k+1}\end{array}$$

$$= \frac{F_{k+1}}{F_{k+2}} \qquad \text{Definition of Fibonacci sequence}$$

So $P(k + 1)$ follows from $P(k)$. Thus by the Principle of Mathematical Induction $P(n)$ holds for all n.

35. Let $P(n)$ denote the statement $F_n \geq n$.

Step 1 $P(5)$ is true, since $F_5 \geq 5$ (because $F_5 = 5$).
Step 2 Suppose $P(k)$ is true. Now

$$F_{k+1} = F_k + F_{k-1} \qquad \text{Definition of the Fibonacci sequence}$$

$$\geq k + F_{k-1} \qquad \text{Induction hypothesis}$$

$$\geq k + 1 \qquad \text{Because } F_{k-1} \geq 1$$

So $P(k + 1)$ follows from $P(k)$. Thus by the Principle of Mathematical Induction $P(n)$ holds for all $n \geq 5$.

36. $100n \leq n^3$ for $n \geq 10$.
Let $P(n)$ denote the statement that $100n \leq n^3$.

Step 1 $P(10)$ is true, since $100(10) \leq 10^3$.
Step 2 Suppose $P(k)$ is true. Then

$$100(k + 1) = 100k + 100$$

$$\leq k^3 + 100 \qquad \text{Induction hypothesis}$$

$$\leq k^3 + 3k^2 + 3k + 1 \qquad \begin{array}{l}\text{Because } 100 \leq 3k^2 + 3k + 1\\ \text{for } k \geq 10\end{array}$$

$$= (k + 1)^3$$

So $P(k + 1)$ follows from $P(k)$. Thus by the Principle of Mathematical Induction $P(n)$ holds for all $n \geq 10$.

SECTION 12.6 ■ PAGE 827

1. binomial   **2.** Pascal's; 1, 4, 6, 4, 1

3. $\dfrac{n!}{k!(n - k)!}$; $\dfrac{4!}{3!(4 - 3)!} = 4$

4. Binomial; $\dbinom{4}{0}, \dbinom{4}{1}, \dbinom{4}{2}, \dbinom{4}{3}, \dbinom{4}{4}$

5. $x^6 + 6x^5y + 15x^4y^2 + 20x^3y^3 + 15x^2y^4 + 6xy^5 + y^6$
6. $16x^4 + 32x^3 + 24x^2 + 8x + 1$

7. $x^4 + 4x^2 + 6 + \dfrac{4}{x^2} + \dfrac{1}{x^4}$

8. $x^5 - 5x^4y + 10x^3y^2 - 10x^2y^3 + 5xy^4 - y^5$
9. $x^5 - 5x^4 + 10x^3 - 10x^2 + 5x - 1$

10. $a^3 + 6a^{5/2}b^{1/2} + 15a^2b + 20a^{3/2}b^{3/2} + 15ab^2$
$+ 6a^{1/2}b^{5/2} + b^3$
11. $x^{10}y^5 - 5x^8y^4 + 10x^6y^3 - 10x^4y^2 + 5x^2y - 1$
12. $99 + 70\sqrt{2}$ **13.** $8x^3 - 36x^2y + 54xy^2 - 27y^3$

14. $1 + 3x^3 + 3x^6 + x^9$ **15.** $\dfrac{1}{x^5} - \dfrac{5}{x^{7/2}} + \dfrac{10}{x^2} - \dfrac{10}{x^{1/2}} + 5x - x^{5/2}$

16. $32 + 40x + 20x^2 + 5x^3 + \frac{5}{8}x^4 + \frac{1}{32}x^5$

17. 15   **18.** 56   **19.** 4950   **20.** 252   **21.** 18   **22.** 100
23. 32   **24.** 0   **25.** $x^4 + 8x^3y + 24x^2y^2 + 32xy^3 + 16y^4$
26. $1 - 5x + 10x^2 - 10x^3 + 5x^4 - x^5$

27. $1 + \dfrac{6}{x} + \dfrac{15}{x^2} + \dfrac{20}{x^3} + \dfrac{15}{x^4} + \dfrac{6}{x^5} + \dfrac{1}{x^6}$

28. $16A^4 + 32A^3B^2 + 24A^2B^4 + 8AB^6 + B^8$
29. $x^{20} + 40x^{19}y + 760x^{18}y^2$
30. $x^{15} + 30x^{29/2} + 435x^{14} + 4060x^{27/2}$ **31.** $25a^{26/3} + a^{25/3}$
32. $x^{40} + 40x^{38} + 780x^{36}$ **33.** $48{,}620x^{18}$ **34.** $4845a^{16}b^{16}$
35. $300a^2b^{23}$ **36.** $-4060A^3B^{27}$ **37.** $100y^{99}$ **38.** $-25x^{47}$
39. $13{,}440x^4y^6$ **40.** $3520\sqrt{2}y^3$ **41.** $495a^8b^8$ **42.** 17,920
43. $(x + y)^4$ **44.** $[(x - 1) + 1]^5 = x^5$ **45.** $(2a + b)^3$
46. $(x^2 + y)^4$ **47.** $3x^2 + 3xh + h^2$
48. $4x^3 + 6x^2h + 4xh^2 + h^3$ **56.** 0.0729

CHAPTER 12 REVIEW ■ PAGE 829

1. $\frac{1}{2}, \frac{4}{3}, \frac{9}{4}, \frac{16}{5}, \frac{100}{11}$ **2.** $-2, 2, -\frac{8}{3}, 4; \frac{512}{5}$ **3.** $0, \frac{1}{4}, 0, \frac{1}{32}; \frac{1}{500}$
4. 1, 3, 6, 10; 55   **5.** 1, 3, 15, 105; 654,729,075
6. 1, 3, 6, 10; 55   **7.** 1, 4, 9, 16, 25, 36, 49
8. $1, \frac{1}{2}, \frac{1}{6}, \frac{1}{24}, \frac{1}{120}, \frac{1}{720}, \frac{1}{5040}$ **9.** 1, 3, 5, 11, 21, 43, 85
10. $3^{1/2}, 3^{3/4}, 3^{7/8}, 3^{15/16}, 3^{31/32}, 3^{63/64}, 3^{127/128}$

11. (a) 7, 9, 11, 13, 15   **12. (a)** $\frac{5}{2}, \frac{5}{4}, \frac{5}{8}, \frac{5}{16}, \frac{5}{32}$
(b) a_n **(b)** a_n

          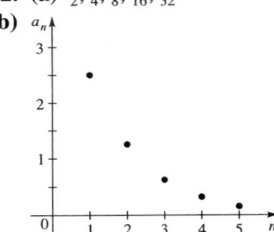

(c) 55   **(c)** $\frac{155}{32}$
(d) Arithmetic, common difference 2   **(d)** Geometric, common ratio $\frac{1}{2}$

13. (a) $\frac{3}{4}, \frac{9}{8}, \frac{27}{16}, \frac{81}{32}, \frac{243}{64}$ **14. (a)** $\frac{7}{2}, 3, \frac{5}{2}, 2, \frac{3}{2}$
(b) a_n **(b)** a_n

          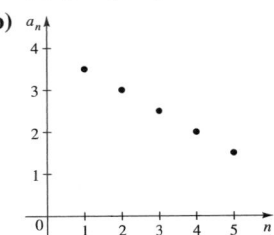

(c) $\frac{633}{64}$ **(c)** $\frac{25}{2}$
(d) Geometric, common ratio $\frac{3}{2}$ **(d)** Arithmetic, common difference $\frac{1}{2}$

15. Arithmetic, 7   **16.** Arithmetic, $5\sqrt{2}$ **17.** Arithmetic, $t + 1$
18. Geometric, $4\sqrt{2}$ **19.** Geometric, $\dfrac{1}{t}$ **20.** Neither

21. Geometric, $\frac{4}{27}$ **22.** Geometric, $\frac{1}{a^3}$ **23.** $2i$

24. $a_n = 2(1 + i)^{n-1}$ **25.** 5 **26.** $a_n = 1 + 5(n - 1)$

27. $\frac{81}{4}$ **28.** $a_n = 6\left(\frac{5}{3}\right)^{n-1}$ **29.** (a) $A_n = 32{,}000(1.05)^{n-1}$

(b) \$32,000, \$33,600, \$35,280, \$37,044, \$38,896.20, \$40,841.01, \$42,883.06, \$45,027.21 **30.** (a) $A_n = 35{,}000 + 1200(n - 1)$

(b) \$43,400 **31.** 12,288 **34.** (a) Yes (b) Yes **35.** (a) 9

(b) $\pm 6\sqrt{2}$ **36.** (a) 7, 12 (b) $2^{2/3}17^{1/3}, 2^{1/3}17^{2/3}$ **37.** 126

38. $\frac{596}{105}$ **39.** 384 **40.** $\frac{121}{3}$ **41.** $0^2 + 1^2 + 2^2 + \cdots + 9^2$

42. $\frac{1}{1} + \frac{1}{2} + \frac{1}{3} + \cdots + \frac{1}{99}$ **43.** $\frac{3}{2^2} + \frac{3^2}{2^3} + \frac{3^3}{2^4} + \cdots + \frac{3^{50}}{2^{51}}$

44. $1^2 \cdot 2^1 + 2^2 \cdot 2^2 + 3^2 \cdot 2^3 + 4^2 \cdot 2^4 + \cdots + 10^2 \cdot 2^{10}$

45. $\displaystyle\sum_{k=1}^{33} 3k$ **46.** $\displaystyle\sum_{k=1}^{100} k^2$ **47.** $\displaystyle\sum_{k=1}^{100} k2^{k+2}$ **48.** $\displaystyle\sum_{k=1}^{999} \frac{1}{k(k+1)}$

49. Geometric; 4.68559 **50.** Arithmetic, 71.5

51. Arithmetic, 5050$\sqrt{5}$ **52.** Arithmetic, 1650

53. Geometric, 9831 **54.** Geometric, $5467 + 1092\sqrt{5} \approx 7908.8$

55. $\frac{5}{7}$ **56.** $\frac{1}{9}$ **57.** Divergent **58.** $\frac{1}{2}(3 + \sqrt{3})$ **59.** Divergent

60. $\dfrac{a}{1 - b^2}$ **61.** 13 **62.** 4 **63.** 65,534 **64.** \$30,324.28

65. \$2390.27 **66.** (a) \$482.77 (b) \$608.56

67. Let $P(n)$ denote the statement

$$1 + 4 + 7 + \cdots + (3n - 2) = \frac{n(3n - 1)}{2}.$$

Step 1 $P(1)$ is true, since $1 = \dfrac{1(3 \cdot 1 - 1)}{2}$.

Step 2 Suppose $P(k)$ is true. Then

$$1 + 4 + 7 + \cdots + (3k - 2) + [3(k + 1) - 2]$$

$$= \frac{k(3k - 1)}{2} + [3k + 1] \qquad \text{Induction hypothesis}$$

$$= \frac{3k^2 - k + 6k + 2}{2}$$

$$= \frac{(k + 1)(3k + 2)}{2}$$

$$= \frac{(k + 1)[3(k + 1) - 1]}{2}$$

So $P(k + 1)$ follows from $P(k)$. Thus by the Principle of Mathematical Induction $P(n)$ holds for all n.

68. Let $P(n)$ denote the statement

$$\frac{1}{1 \cdot 3} + \frac{1}{3 \cdot 5} + \cdots + \frac{1}{(2n - 1)(2n + 1)} = \frac{n}{2n + 1}.$$

Step 1 $P(1)$ is true, since $\dfrac{1}{1 \cdot 3} = \dfrac{1}{2 \cdot 1 + 1}$.

Step 2 Suppose $P(k)$ is true. Then

$$\frac{1}{1 \cdot 3} + \frac{1}{3 \cdot 5} + \cdots + \frac{1}{(2k - 1)(2k + 1)} + \frac{1}{(2k + 1)(2k + 3)}$$

$$= \frac{k}{2k + 1} + \frac{1}{(2k + 1)(2k + 3)} \qquad \text{Induction hypothesis}$$

$$= \frac{2k^2 + 3k + 1}{(2k + 1)(2k + 3)} = \frac{k + 1}{2k + 3}$$

So $P(k + 1)$ follows from $P(k)$. Thus by the Principle of Mathematical Induction $P(n)$ holds for all n.

69. Let $P(n)$ denote the statement
$$\left(1 + \frac{1}{1}\right)\left(1 + \frac{1}{2}\right) \cdots \left(1 + \frac{1}{n}\right) = n + 1.$$

Step 1 $P(1)$ is true, since $\left(1 + \frac{1}{1}\right) = 1 + 1$.
Step 2 Suppose $P(k)$ is true. Then

$$\left(1 + \frac{1}{1}\right)\left(1 + \frac{1}{2}\right) \cdots \left(1 + \frac{1}{k}\right)\left(1 + \frac{1}{k + 1}\right)$$

$$= (k + 1)\left(1 + \frac{1}{k + 1}\right) \qquad \text{Induction hypothesis}$$

$$= (k + 1) + 1$$

So $P(k + 1)$ follows from $P(k)$. Thus by the Principle of Mathematical Induction $P(n)$ holds for all n.

70. Let $P(n)$ denote the statement that $7^n - 1$ is divisible by 6.

Step 1 $P(1)$ is true, since $7^1 - 1 = 6$.
Step 2 Suppose $P(k)$ is true. We have

$$7^{k+1} - 1 = 7(7^k - 1) + 6$$

Now $7^k - 1$ is divisible by 6 (induction hypothesis), and so is 6, and hence $7(7^k - 1) + 6$ is also divisible by 6. So $P(k + 1)$ follows from $P(k)$. Thus by the Principle of Mathematical Induction $P(n)$ holds for all n.

71. Let $P(n)$ denote the statement $a_n = 2 \cdot 3^n - 2$.

Step 1 $P(1)$ is true, since $a_1 = 2 \cdot 3^1 - 2 = 4$.
Step 2 Suppose $P(k)$ is true. Then

$$a_{k+1} = 3a_k + 4$$

$$= 3(2 \cdot 3^k - 2) + 4 \qquad \text{Induction hypothesis}$$

$$= 2 \cdot 3^{k+1} - 2$$

So $P(k + 1)$ follows from $P(k)$. Thus by the Principle of Mathematical Induction $P(n)$ holds for all n.

72. Let $P(n)$ denote the statement that F_{4n} is divisible by 3.

Step 1 $P(1)$ is true, since $F_4 = 3$.
Step 2 Suppose $P(k)$ is true. Then F_{4k} is divisible by 3. Using the definition of the Fibonacci sequence repeatedly, we get

$$F_{4(k+1)} = F_{4k+4} = F_{4k+3} + F_{4k+2}$$

$$= (F_{4k+2} + F_{4k+1}) + (F_{4k+1} + F_{4k})$$

$$= [(F_{4k+1} + F_{4k}) + F_{4k+1}] + (F_{4k+1} + F_{4k})$$

$$= 3F_{4k+1} + 2F_{4k}$$

The first term is clearly divisible by 3, and so is the second by the induction hypothesis. So $P(k + 1)$ follows from $P(k)$. Thus by the Principle of Mathematical Induction $P(n)$ holds for all n.

73. 100 **74.** 255 **75.** 32 **76.** 12,870
77. $A^3 - 3A^2B + 3AB^2 - B^3$
78. $x^5 + 10x^4 + 40x^3 + 80x^2 + 80x + 32$
79. $1 - 6x^2 + 15x^4 - 20x^6 + 15x^8 - 6x^{10} + x^{12}$
80. $16x^4 + 32x^3y + 24x^2y^2 + 8xy^3 + y^4$ **81.** $1540a^3b^{19}$
82. $b^{-40/3} + 20b^{-37/3} + 190b^{-34/3}$ **83.** $17{,}010A^6B^4$

CHAPTER 12 TEST ▪ PAGE 832

1. 1, 6, 15, 28, 45, 66; 161 **2.** 2, 5, 13, 36, 104, 307 **3. (a)** 3
(b) $a_n = 2 + (n - 1)3$ **(c)** 104 **4. (a)** $\frac{1}{4}$ **(b)** $a_n = 12\left(\frac{1}{4}\right)^{n-1}$

(c) $3/4^8$ **5. (a)** $\frac{1}{5}, \frac{1}{25}$ **(b)** $\dfrac{5^8 - 1}{12,500}$ **6. (a)** $-\frac{8}{9}, -78$ **(b)** 60

8. (a) $(1 - 1^2) + (1 - 2^2) + (1 - 3^2) + (1 - 4^2) +$
$(1 - 5^2) = -50$
(b) $(-1)^3 2^1 + (-1)^4 2^2 + (-1)^5 2^3 + (-1)^6 2^4 = 10$
9. (a) $\frac{58,025}{59,049}$ **(b)** $2 + \sqrt{2}$

10. Let $P(n)$ denote the statement

$$1^2 + 2^2 + \cdots + n^2 = \frac{n(n + 1)(2n + 1)}{6}.$$

Step 1 $P(1)$ is true, since $1^2 = \dfrac{1(1 + 1)(2 \cdot 1 + 1)}{6}$.

Step 2 Suppose $P(k)$ is true. Then

$$1^2 + 2^2 + \cdots + k^2 + (k + 1)^2$$

$$= \frac{k(k + 1)(2k + 1)}{6} + (k + 1)^2 \qquad \text{Induction hypothesis}$$

$$= \frac{k(k + 1)(2k + 1) + 6(k + 1)^2}{6}$$

$$= \frac{(k + 1)[k(2k + 1) + 6(k + 1)]}{6}$$

$$= \frac{(k + 1)(2k^2 + 7k + 6)}{6}$$

$$= \frac{(k + 1)[(k + 1) + 1][2(k + 1) + 1]}{6}$$

So $P(k + 1)$ follows from $P(k)$. Thus by the Principle of
Mathematical Induction $P(n)$ holds for all n.

11. $32x^5 + 80x^4 y^2 + 80x^3 y^4 + 40x^2 y^6 + 10xy^8 + y^{10}$

12. $\dbinom{10}{3}(3x)^3(-2)^7 = -414,720x^3$

13. (a) $a_n = (0.85)(1.24)^n$ **(b)** 3.09 lb **(c)** Geometric

FOCUS ON MODELING ▪ PAGE 835

1. (a) $A_n = 1.0001A_{n-1}, A_0 = 275,000$ **(b)** $A_0 = 275,000,$
$A_1 = 275,027.50, A_2 = 275,055.00, A_3 = 275,082.51,$
$A_4 = 275,110.02, A_5 = 275,137.53, A_6 = 275,165.04,$
$A_7 = 275,192.56$ **(c)** $A_n = 1.0001^n(275,000)$
2. (a) $T_n = T_{n-1} + 1.5, T_1 = 5$ **(b)** $T_1 = 5, T_2 = 6.5,$
$T_3 = 8, T_4 = 9.5, T_5 = 11, T_6 = 12.5$ **(c)** $T_n = 5 + 1.5(n - 1),$
arithmetic **(d)** On the 41st day **(e)** 802.5 min = 13 h 22.5 min
3. (a) $A_n = 1.0025A_{n-1} + 100, A_0 = 100$ **(b)** $A_0 = 100,$
$A_1 = 200.25, A_2 = 300.75, A_3 = 401.50, A_4 = 502.51$
(c) $A_n = 100[(1.0025^{n+1} - 1)/0.0025]$ **(d)** \$6580.83
4. In each part $P_0 = 4000$. **(a)** $P_n = 1.2P_{n-1}, P_5 = 9953$
(b) $P_n = 1.2P_{n-1} - 600, P_5 = 5488$ **(c)** $P_n = 1.2P_{n-1} + 250,$
$P_5 = 11,814$ **(d)** $P_n = 1.2P_{n-1} - 0.1P_{n-1} + 300, P_5 = 8274$

5. (b) $A_0 = 2400, A_1 = 3120, A_2 = 3336, A_3 = 3400.8,$
$A_4 = 3420.2$ **(c)** $A_n = 3428.6(1 - 0.3^{n+1})$
(d) 3427.8 tons, 3428.6 tons
(e)

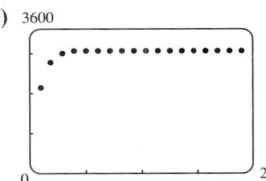

6. (a) $U_n = U_{n-1} + 0.05U_{n-1} + 0.1(U_{n-1} + 0.05U_{n-1}) =$
$1.155U_{n-1}, U_0 = 5000$ **(b)** $U_0 = 5000, U_1 = 5775,$
$U_2 = 6670.13, U_3 = 7703.99, U_4 = 8898.11$
(c) $U_n = 5000(1.155)^n$ **(d)** \$21,124.67
7. (b) In the 35th year
8. (a) $T_n = T_{n-1} - 0.03(T_{n-1} - 70), T_0 = 170$
(b) $T_0 = 170, T_{10} = 143.7, T_{20} = 124.4, T_{30} = 110.1,$
$T_{40} = 99.6, T_{50} = 91.8, T_{60} = 86.1$
(c) It approaches 70°F.

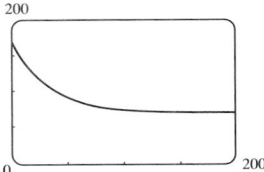

9. (a) $R_1 = 104, R_2 = 108, R_3 = 112, R_4 = 116, R_5 = 120,$
$R_6 = 124, R_7 = 127$ **(b)** It approaches 200.

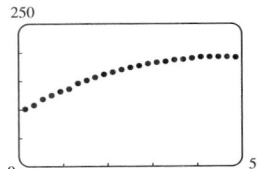

CHAPTER 13

SECTION 13.1 ▪ PAGE 846

1. $L, a; 5, 1$ **2.** limit, left, L; less; left, right, equal **3.** 10 **4.** 5
5. $\frac{1}{4}$ **6.** 0.2 **7.** $\frac{1}{3}$ **8.** 1 **9.** 1 **10.** 0 **11.** -1 **12.** 1.5
13. 0.51 **14.** 0.1667 **15.** $\frac{1}{2}$ **16.** 0.6667 **17. (a)** 2 **(b)** 3
(c) Does not exist **(d)** 4 **(e)** Not defined **18. (a)** 3
(b) 4 **(c)** 2 **(d)** Does not exist **(e)** 3
19. (a) -1 **(b)** -2 **(c)** Does not exist **(d)** 2 **(e)** 0
(f) Does not exist **(g)** 1 **(h)** 3 **20. (a)** 2 **(b)** -1 **(c)** 1
(d) 1 **(e)** 2 **(f)** Does not exist **21.** -8 **22.** -0.22
23. Does not exist **24.** Does not exist **25.** Does not exist
26. Does not exist **27.** Does not exist **28.** Does not exist
29. (a) 4 **(b)** 4 **(c)** 4

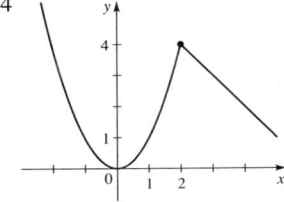

30. (a) 2 **(b)** 1 **(c)** Does not exist

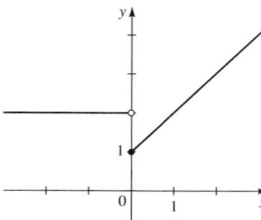

31. (a) 4 **(b)** 3 **(c)** Does not exist

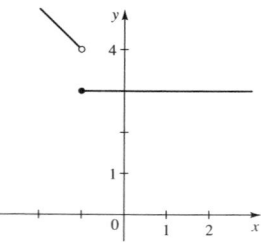

32. (a) 6 **(b)** 6 **(c)** 6

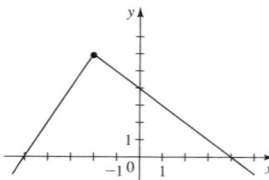

SECTION 13.2 ▪ PAGE 855

1. $\lim_{x \to a} f(x) + \lim_{x \to a} g(x)$, $\lim_{x \to a} f(x) \cdot \lim_{x \to a} g(x)$; sum, product **2.** $f(a)$
3. (a) 5 **(b)** 9 **(c)** 2 **(d)** $-\frac{1}{3}$ **(e)** $-\frac{3}{8}$ **(f)** 0 **(g)** Does not
exist **(h)** $-\frac{6}{11}$ **4. (a)** 2 **(b)** Does not exist **(c)** 0
(d) Does not exist **(e)** 16 **(f)** 2 **5.** 75 **6.** -174 **7.** $\frac{1}{2}$
8. $\frac{4}{9}$ **9.** -3 **10.** 4 **11.** 5 **12.** $\frac{3}{5}$ **13.** 2 **14.** $\frac{3}{2}$ **15.** $\frac{6}{5}$
16. $\frac{1}{2}$ **17.** 12 **18.** 32 **19.** $\frac{1}{6}$ **20.** $\frac{1}{9}$ **21.** $-\frac{1}{16}$ **22.** 1
23. 4 **24.** 48

25. $-\frac{3}{2}$ **26.** $\frac{8}{5}$

27. (a) 0.667

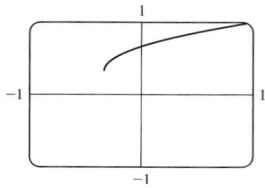

(b) 0.667

x	$f(x)$		x	$f(x)$
0.1	0.71339		-0.1	0.61222
0.01	0.67163		-0.01	0.66163
0.001	0.66717		-0.001	0.66617
0.0001	0.66672		-0.0001	0.66662

(c) $\frac{2}{3}$
28. (a) 0.29

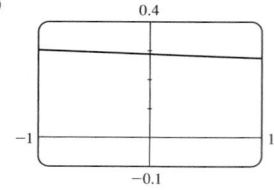

(b) 0.2887

x	$f(x)$		x	$f(x)$
-0.1	0.29112		0.1	0.28631
-0.01	0.28892		0.01	0.28843
-0.001	0.28870		0.001	0.28865
-0.0001	0.28868		0.0001	0.28867

(c) $1/(2\sqrt{3})$
29. 0 **30.** Does not exist **31.** Does not exist
32. Does not exist **33.** Does not exist **34.** 0
35. (a) 1, 2 **(b)** Does not exist
(c)

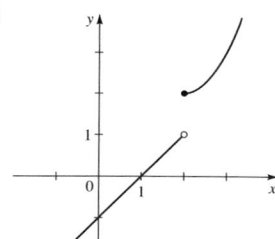

36. (a) 0, 0, 1, 4, 6, does not exist
(b)

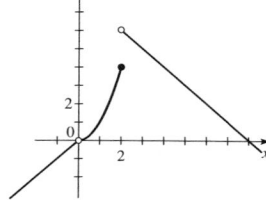

SECTION 13.3 ■ PAGE 863

1. $\dfrac{f(a+h)-f(a)}{h}$; slope, $(a, f(a))$ **2.** $\dfrac{f(x)-f(a)}{x-a}$,
instantaneous, a **3.** 3   **4.** -2 **5.** -11 **6.** -4 **7.** 24   **8.** $-\frac{2}{3}$
9. $y = -x - 1$ **10.** $y = -x + 2$

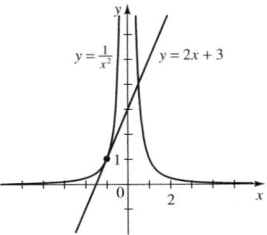

11. $y = -x + 4$ **12.** $y = 2x + 3$

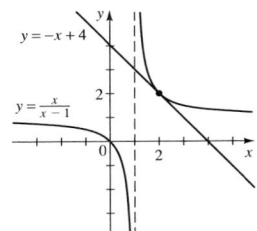

13. $y = \frac{1}{4}x + \frac{7}{4}$ **14.** $y = \frac{1}{3}x + \frac{5}{3}$

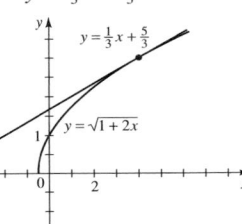

15. $f'(2) = -12$ **16.** $f'(-1) = -5$ **17.** $g'(1) = 4$
18. $g'(1) = 7$ **19.** $F'(4) = -\frac{1}{16}$ **20.** $G'(4) = \frac{1}{2}$
21. $f'(a) = 2a + 2$ **22.** $f'(a) = \frac{2}{a^3}$
23. $f'(a) = \dfrac{1}{(a+1)^2}$ **24.** $f'(a) = 1/(2\sqrt{a-2})$
25. (a) $f'(a) = 3a^2 - 2$
(b) $y = -2x + 4$, $y = x + 2$, $y = 10x - 12$
(c)

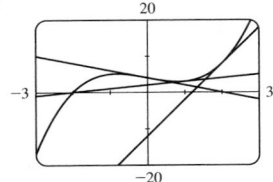

26. (a) $g'(a) = \dfrac{-2}{(2a-1)^2}$ **(b)** $y = -\dfrac{2}{9}x - \dfrac{5}{9}$,
$y = -2x - 1$, $y = -2x + 3$
(c)

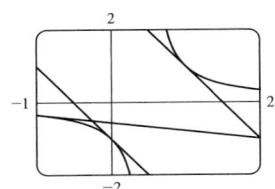

27. -24 ft/s   **28. (a)** 56.34 m/s   **(b)** $58 - 1.66a$ m/s
(c) 69.88 s   **(d)** -58 m/s   **29.** $12a^2 + 6$ m/s, 18 m/s,
54 m/s, 114 m/s   **30.** 16π ft/s   **31.** $0.75°/$min
32. (a) 71 heartbeats/min, 66 heartbeats/min
(b) 68.5 heartbeats/min   **33. (a)** -38.3 gal/min,
-27.8 gal/min   **(b)** -33.3 gal/min   **34.** 16 million/year

SECTION 13.4 ■ PAGE 871

1. L, x; horizontal asymptote; 0, 0   **2.** L, large; converges,
diverges   **3. (a)** $-1, 2$ **(b)** $y = -1$, $y = 2$ **4. (a)** $3, -2$
(b) $y = 3$, $y = -2$ **5.** 0   **6.** 0   **7.** $\frac{2}{5}$ **8.** $-\frac{3}{4}$ **9.** $\frac{4}{3}$ **10.** 0
11. 2   **12.** 4   **13.** Does not exist   **14.** -2 **15.** 7   **16.** -3
17. Does not exist   **18.** Does not exist   **19.** $-\frac{1}{4}$ **20.** 0.1667
21. 0   **22.** 403.4288   **23.** 0   **24.** 5   **25.** Divergent   **26.** 0
27. 0   **28.** 0   **29.** Divergent   **30.** Divergent   **31.** $\frac{3}{2}$ **32.** 15
33. 8   **34.** 3   **35. (b)** 30 g/L
36. (a) 1.2   **(b)** 0.56 s

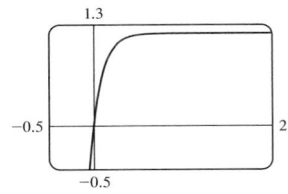

SECTION 13.5 ■ PAGE 879

1. rectangles;
$f(x_1)(x_1 - a) + f(x_2)(x_2 - x_1) + f(x_3)(x_3 - x_2) + f(b)(b - x_3)$
2. $\displaystyle\sum_{k=1}^{n} f(x_k)\Delta x$
3. (a) 40, 52

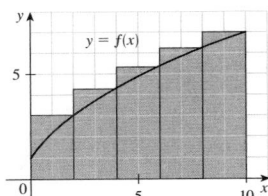

(b) 43.2, 49.2
4. (a) 86.6, 70.6

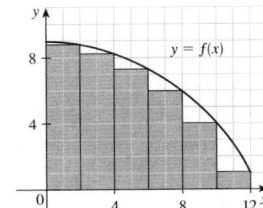

(b) Overestimate   **(c)** Underestimate
5. 5.25   **6.** $\frac{29}{4}$ **7.** $\frac{223}{35}$ **8.** 15.1875
9. (a) $\frac{77}{60}$, underestimate   **(b)** $\frac{25}{12}$, overestimate

10. (a) 70, underestimate   **(b)** 95, overestimate

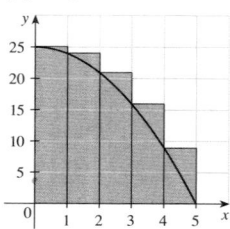

11. (a) 8, 6.875   **(b)** 5, 5.375

12. (a) 0.5712, 1.5529

(b) 0.75655, 1.25655

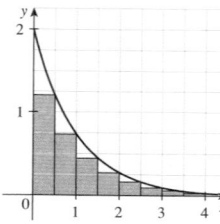

13. 37.5   **14.** 10   **15.** 8   **16.** $\frac{5}{6}$ **17.** 166.25   **18.** 609
19. 133.5   **20.** $\frac{22}{3}$

CHAPTER 13 REVIEW ■ PAGE 881

1. 1   **2.** 0.5   **3.** 0.69   **4.** 2   **5.** Does not exist   **6.** −1
7. (a) Does not exist   **(b)** 2.4   **(c)** 2.4   **(d)** 2.4   **(e)** 0.5
(f) 1   **(g)** 2   **(h)** 0   **8. (a)** 2   **(b)** 1   **(c)** Does not exist
(d) 4   **(e)** 4   **(f)** 4   **(g)** 0   **(h)** 25   **9.** $\div$3   **10.** 4   **11.** 7
12. $\frac{4}{3}$ **13.** 2   **14.** $\frac{1}{6}$ **15.** −1   **16.** −$\frac{1}{2}$ **17.** 2   **18.** 0
19. Does not exist   **20.** Does not exist
21. $f'(4) = 3$ **22.** $g'(-1) = -4$ **23.** $f'(16) = \frac{1}{8}$
24. $f'(1) = \frac{1}{4}$ **25. (a)** $f'(a) = -2$ **(b)** −2, −2
26. (a) $f'(a) = 2a - 3$ **(b)** 1, −7
27. (a) $f'(a) = 1/(2\sqrt{a+6})$ **(b)** $1/(4\sqrt{2})$, 1/4

28. (a) $f'(a) = -\dfrac{4}{a^2}$ **(b)** −1, −1   **29.** $y = 2x + 1$
30. $y = \frac{1}{2}x + \frac{1}{2}$ **31.** $y = 2x$ **32.** $y = 4x - 7$
33. $y = -\frac{1}{4}x + 1$ **34.** $y = \frac{1}{4}x + \frac{5}{4}$ **35. (a)** −64 ft/s
(b) −32a ft/s   **(c)** $\sqrt{40} \approx 6.32$ s   **(d)** −202.4 ft/s
36. (a) $P = 100/T$ **(b)** −$\frac{1}{900}$ **37.** $\frac{1}{5}$ **38.** 1   **39.** $\frac{1}{2}$
40. Divergent   **41.** Divergent   **42.** 0   **43.** 3.83   **44.** 7.25
45. 10   **46.** 12   **47.** $\frac{5}{6}$ **48.** 3.75

CHAPTER 13 TEST ■ PAGE 883

1. (a) $\frac{1}{2}$ **(b)**

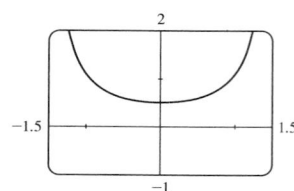

2. (a) 1   **(b)** 1   **(c)** 1   **(d)** 0   **(e)** 0   **(f)** 0   **(g)** 4   **(h)** 2
(i) Does not exist   **3. (a)** 6   **(b)** −2   **(c)** Does not exist
(d) Does not exist   **(e)** $\frac{1}{4}$ **(f)** 2   **4. (a)** $f'(x) = 2x - 2$
(b) −4, 0, 2   **5.** $y = \frac{1}{6}x + \frac{3}{2}$ **6. (a)** 0   **(b)** Does not exist
7. (a) $\frac{89}{25}$ **(b)** $\frac{11}{3}$

FOCUS ON MODELING ■ PAGE 886

1. 57,333$\frac{1}{3}$ ft-lb   **2.** 40 ft-lb   **3. (b)** Area under the graph of
$p(x) = 375x$ between $x = 0$ and $x = 4$ **(c)** 3000 lb
(d) 1500 lb   **4. (b)** 90.625 ft   **5. (a)** 1625.28 heating degree-
hours   **(b)** 70°F   **(c)** 1488 heating degree-hours   **(d)** 75°F
(e) The day in part (a)

CUMULATIVE REVIEW TEST FOR
CHAPTERS 12 AND 13 ■ PAGE 888

1. (a) $\frac{7}{15}, \frac{20}{41}, \frac{1}{2}$ **(b)** $\frac{99}{340}, \frac{801}{7984}, 0$ **(c)** $\frac{37}{2}, \frac{115}{2}$, no limit
(d) $12(\frac{5}{6})^6, 12(\frac{5}{6})^{19}, 0$ **(e)** 0.64, −5242.88, no limit
2. (a) 41.4   **(b)** 88,572   **(c)** 5115/512   **(d)** 9
3. \$2658.15   **4.** Hint: Induction step is
$a_{n+1} = a_n + 2(n+1) - 1 = n^2 + 2n + 1 = (n+1)^2$.
5. (a) $32x^5 - 40x^4 + 20x^3 - 5x^2 + \frac{5}{8}x - \frac{1}{32}$ **(b)** $\frac{495}{16}x^4$
6. (a)

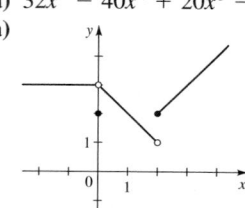

(b) (i) 2   **(ii)** 3   **(iii)** 2
(iv) 1   **(v)** 2
7. $\frac{1}{2}$ **8. (a)** 10   **(b)** 4
(c) Does not exist
9. (a) $3x^2$ **(b)** 27, 0, $3a^2$
(c) $y = 12x - 16$

10. (a)

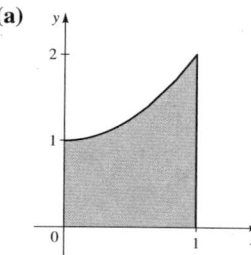

(b) A lies between the 1 × 1
square in the first quadrant, with
corner at the origin, which has
area 1, and the trapezoid with
corners (0, 0), (1, 0), (1, 2), and
(0, 1), which has area $\frac{3}{2}$.
(c) 39/32   **(d)** 4/3

CHAPTER 14

SECTION 14.1 ■ PAGE 896

1. $m \times n$; $2 \times 3 = 6$ **2.** permutations, $n!/(n-r)!$
3. combinations, $n!/[r!(n-r)!]$ **4. (a)** False **(b)** True
(c) False **(d)** True **5.** 336 **6.** 72 **7.** 7920 **8.** 30,240
9. 100 **10.** 941,094 **11.** 56 **12.** 36 **13.** 330 **14.** 252
15. 100 **16.** 156,849 **17.** 12 **18. (a)** 17,576 **(b)** 15,600
19. (a) 40,320 **(b)** 336 **20.** 1024 **21.** 8,000,000 **22.** 120
23. 60 **24.** 120 **25.** 32 **26.** 36 **27.** 216 **28.** 480
29. 158,184,000 **30.** 26,000 **31.** 208,860 **32.** No
33. 24,360 **34.** 1050 **35.** 700,000,000 **36.** 144
37. (a) 56 **(b)** 256 **38.** 256 **39.** 1024 **40.** 1,048,576
41. (a) 3,628,800 **(b)** 151,200 **42.** 120 **43.** 2730 **44.** 24
45. 336 **46.** 40,320 **47.** 362,880 **48.** 60 **49.** 997,002,000
50. 657,720 **51.** 24 **52.** 24 **53.** 2300 **54.** 20 **55.** 220
56. 210 **57.** 2,598,960 **58.** 133,784,560 **59.** 120 **60.** 560
61. 495 **62.** 56 **63.** 120 **64. (a)** 475,020 **(b)** 1,560,780
(c) 2,035,800 **65.** 13,983,816 **66.** 1287 **67. (a)** 15,504
(b) 792 **(c)** 6160 **68.** 2025 **69.** 1,162,800 **70. (a)** 65,520
(b) 129,780 **71.** 104,781,600 **72.** 79,833,600 **73.** 6600
74. 131,072 **75.** 182 **76.** 62,986 **77.** 48 **78.** 161,280
79. (a) 20,160 **(b)** 8640 **80. (a)** 2880 **(b)** 1152
81. 17,813,250 **82.** 46

SECTION 14.2 ■ PAGE 908

1. sample space; event; $S = \{HH, HT, TH, TT\}$; $E = \{HH, HT, TH\}$;
$P(E) = \dfrac{n(E)}{n(S)} = \dfrac{3}{4}$ **2. (a)** $P(E \cup F) = P(E) + P(F) - P(E \cap F)$
(b) mutually exclusive; mutually exclusive
(c) $P(E \cup F) = P(E) + P(F)$ **3.** $P(E \mid F) = \dfrac{n(E \cap F)}{n(F)}$;
$P(E \mid F) = \dfrac{1}{3}$ **4. (a)** $P(E \cap F) = P(E)P(F \mid E)$
(b) independent; independent **(c)** $P(E \cap F) = P(E) \cdot P(F)$
5. (a) $\{1, 2, 3, 4, 5, 6\}$ **(b)** $\{2, 4, 6\}$ **(c)** $\{5, 6\}$
6. (a) 104 **(b)** $E = \{HA\clubsuit, HA\diamondsuit, HA\heartsuit, HA\spadesuit\}$
(c) $E = \{TK\clubsuit, TK\diamondsuit, TK\heartsuit, TK\spadesuit, TQ\clubsuit, TQ\diamondsuit, TQ\heartsuit, TQ\spadesuit, TJ\clubsuit, TJ\diamondsuit,$
$TJ\heartsuit, TJ\spadesuit\}$ **(d)** $E = \{H2\spadesuit, H3\spadesuit, H4\spadesuit, H5\spadesuit, H6\spadesuit, H7\spadesuit, H8\spadesuit, H9\spadesuit,$
$H10\spadesuit, HJ\spadesuit, HQ\spadesuit, HK\spadesuit, HA\spadesuit\}$
7. (a) $S = \{HH, HT, TH, TT\}$ **(b)** $\frac{1}{4}$ **(c)** $\frac{3}{4}$ **(d)** $\frac{1}{2}$
8. (a) $S = \{H1, H2, H3, H4, H5, H6, T1, T2, T3, T4, T5, T6\}$
(b) $\frac{1}{4}$ **(c)** $\frac{1}{6}$ **(d)** $\frac{1}{4}$ **9. (a)** $\frac{1}{6}$ **(b)** $\frac{1}{2}$ **(c)** $\frac{1}{6}$ **10. (a)** $\frac{1}{3}$ **(b)** $\frac{1}{2}$
(c) $\frac{1}{3}$ **11. (a)** $\frac{1}{13}$ **(b)** $\frac{3}{13}$ **(c)** $\frac{10}{13}$ **12. (a)** $\frac{1}{4}$ **(b)** $\frac{1}{2}$ **(c)** $\frac{3}{4}$
13. (a) $\frac{5}{8}$ **(b)** $\frac{7}{8}$ **(c)** 0 **14. (a)** $\frac{5}{8}$ **(b)** 1 **(c)** $\frac{3}{4}$
15. (a) $\dfrac{C(13, 5)}{C(52, 5)} \approx 0.000495$ **(b)** $\dfrac{4 \cdot C(13, 5)}{C(52, 5)} \approx 0.00198$
(c) $\dfrac{C(12, 5)}{C(52, 5)} \approx 0.000305$ **(d)** $\dfrac{4}{C(52, 5)} \approx 0.00000154$
16. (a) $\dfrac{C(4, 3)}{C(12, 3)} \approx 0.018$ **(b)** $\dfrac{C(8, 3)}{C(12, 3)} \approx 0.255$
17. (a) $\dfrac{C(3, 2)}{C(8, 2)} \approx 0.11$ **(b)** $\dfrac{C(5, 2)}{C(8, 2)} \approx 0.36$
18. (a) $\frac{3}{16}$ **(b)** $\frac{3}{8}$ **(c)** $\frac{5}{8}$
19. (a) $1 - \dfrac{C(39, 5)}{C(52, 5)} \approx 0.778$ **(b)** $1 - \dfrac{C(40, 5)}{C(52, 5)} \approx 0.747$

20. (a) $S = \{(1, 1), (1, 2), (1, 3), (1, 4), (1, 5), (1, 6), (2, 1),$
$(2, 2), (2, 3), (2, 4), (2, 5), (2, 6), (3, 1), (3, 2), (3, 3), (3, 4), (3, 5),$
$(3, 6), (4, 1), (4, 2), (4, 3), (4, 4), (4, 5), (4, 6), (5, 1), (5, 2), (5, 3),$
$(5, 4), (5, 5), (5, 6), (6, 1), (6, 2), (6, 3), (6, 4), (6, 5), (6, 6)\}$
(b) $\frac{1}{6}$ **(c)** $\frac{1}{9}$ **(d)** $\frac{1}{6}$ **(e)** $\frac{5}{6}$ **(f)** $\frac{5}{18}$ **21. (a)** $\frac{3}{4}$ **(b)** $\frac{1}{2}$ **(c)** 1
22. (a) $\frac{1}{4}$ **(b)** $\frac{1}{2}$ **(c)** $\frac{3}{4}$ **23. (a)** Mutually exclusive; 1
(b) Not mutually exlusive; $\frac{2}{3}$ **24. (a)** Not mutually exclusive; 1
(b) Mutually exlusive; $\frac{2}{3}$ **25. (a)** Not mutually exclusive; $\frac{11}{26}$
(b) Mutually exclusive; $\frac{1}{2}$ **26. (a)** Not mutually exclusive; $\frac{4}{13}$
(b) Not mutually exclusive; $\frac{4}{13}$ **27. (a)** $\frac{1}{3}$ **(b)** $\frac{1}{3}$ **28. (a)** $\frac{1}{3}$
(b) $\frac{1}{13}$ **(c)** $\frac{1}{4}$ **29.** $\frac{1}{3}$ **30.** $\frac{1}{4}$ **31. (a)** $\frac{1}{2}$ **(b)** 1 **(c)** $\frac{2}{5}$ **(d)** $\frac{2}{5}$
32. (a) $\frac{4}{11}$ **(b)** $\frac{5}{11}$ **(c)** $\frac{5}{11}$ **(d)** $\frac{4}{11}$ **33. (a)** $\frac{7}{30}$ **(b)** $\frac{7}{15}$ **34. (a)** $\frac{1}{3}$
(b) $\frac{5}{17}$ **(c)** $\frac{5}{51}$ **35. (a)** $\frac{4}{663}$ **(b)** $\frac{1}{221}$ **36. (a)** Yes **(b)** $\frac{1}{36}$ **37.** $\frac{1}{12}$
38. (a) Yes **(b)** $\frac{1}{4}$ **39. (a)** Yes **(b)** $\frac{1}{8}$ **40. (a)** $\frac{1}{16}$ **(b)** $\frac{1}{32}$
41. (a) $S = \{GGGG, GGGB, GGBG, GBGG, BGGG, GGBB,$
$GBGB, BGGB, BGBG, BBGG, GBBG, GBBB, BGBB, BBGB,$
$BBBG, BBBB\}$ **(b)** $\frac{1}{16}$ **(c)** $\frac{3}{8}$ **(d)** $\frac{1}{8}$ **(e)** $\frac{11}{16}$
42. $4/C(52, 13) \approx 6.3 \times 10^{-12}$ **43.** $\frac{9}{19}$ **44. (a)** $\frac{1}{720} \approx 0.0014$
(b) $\frac{1}{720} \approx 0.0014$ **45.** $1/C(49, 6) \approx 7.15 \times 10^{-8}$
46. $C(11, 6)/C(30, 6) \approx 0.00078$ **47. (a)** $\frac{1}{1024}$ **(b)** $\frac{15}{128}$
48. $1 - \dfrac{C(8, 3)}{C(10, 3)} \approx 0.5333$ **49. (a)** $1/48^6 \approx 8.18 \times 10^{-11}$
(b) $1/48^{18} \approx 5.47 \times 10^{-31}$ **50. (a)** $1/720 \approx 0.0014$
(b) $1/720^3 \approx 2.68 \times 10^{-9}$ **51.** $\dfrac{1}{P(8, 8)} + \dfrac{1}{P(8, 8)} \approx 0.0000496$
52. $1/P(8, 8) \approx 0.0000248$ **53. (a)** $\frac{3}{4}$ **(b)** $\frac{1}{4}$ **54. (a)** $\frac{1}{2}$ **(b)** $\frac{1}{2}$
55. $\frac{1}{1444}$ **56.** $\frac{31}{1001}$ **57.** $1/36^3 \approx 2.14 \times 10^{-5}$
58. $\dfrac{C(6, 5) \cdot C(43, 1)}{C(49, 6)} + \dfrac{1}{C(49,6)} \approx 0.0000185$ **59. (a)** $\frac{3}{8}$ **(b)** $\frac{1}{2}$
(c) $\frac{11}{16}$ **(d)** $\frac{13}{16}$ **60.** $(1/C(49, 6))^2 \approx 5.11 \times 10^{-15}$ **61. (i)**
62. (a) $\frac{1}{1331}$ **(b)** $\frac{10}{1331}$ **(c)** $\frac{331}{1331}$ **63.** $600/P(40, 3) = 5/494$
64. (a) $\dfrac{C(8, 2) \cdot C(10, 4)}{C(18, 6)} = \dfrac{490}{1547}$
(b) $\dfrac{C(8, 0) \cdot C(10, 6)}{C(18, 6)} + \dfrac{C(8, 1) \cdot C(10, 5)}{C(18, 6)} + \dfrac{C(8, 2) \cdot C(10, 4)}{C(18, 6)} = \dfrac{193}{442}$
(c) $1 - \dfrac{193}{442} = \dfrac{249}{442}$ **65.** $\frac{1}{10}$

SECTION 14.3 ■ PAGE 915

1. two; success, failure **2.** $1 - p$; $C(n, r)p^r(1 - p)^{n-r}$
3. $C(5, 2)(0.7)^2(0.3)^3 = 0.1323$
4. $C(5, 3)(0.7)^3(0.3)^2 = 0.3087$
5. $C(5, 0)(0.7)^0(0.3)^5 = 0.00243$
6. $C(5, 5)(0.7)^5(0.3)^0 = 0.16807$
7. $C(5, 1)(0.7)^1(0.3)^4 = 0.02835$
8. $C(5, 1)(0.7)^4(0.3)^1 = 0.36015$
9. $C(5, 4)(0.7)^4(0.3)^1 + C(5, 5)(0.7)^5(0.3)^0 = 0.52822$
10. $C(5, 3)(0.7)^3(0.3)^2 + C(5, 4)(0.7)^4(0.3)^1 +$
$C(5, 5)(0.7)^5(0.3)^0 = 0.83692$
11. $C(5, 5)(0.7)^5(0.3)^0 + C(5, 4)(0.7)^4(0.3)^1 = 0.52822$
12. $C(5, 0)(0.7)^5(0.3)^0 + C(5, 1)(0.7)^4(0.3)^1 +$
$C(5, 2)(0.7)^3(0.3)^2 = 0.83692$
13. $1 - C(5, 0)(0.7)^0(0.3)^5 - C(5, 1)(0.7)^1(0.3)^4 = 0.96922$
14. $1 - C(5, 4)(0.7)^1(0.3)^4 - C(5, 5)(0.7)^0(0.3)^5 = 0.96922$

15. (a)

Outcome	Probability
1	0.2
2	0.2
3	0.2
4	0.2
5	0.2

(b)

16. (a)

Outcome	Probability
1	0.5
2	0.3
3	0.1
4	0.1

(b)
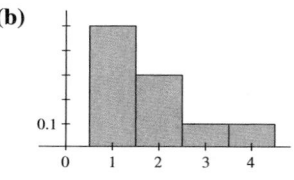

17. (a)

r	Probability
0	$\frac{1}{16}$
1	$\frac{4}{16}$
2	$\frac{6}{16}$
3	$\frac{4}{16}$
4	$\frac{1}{16}$

(b)
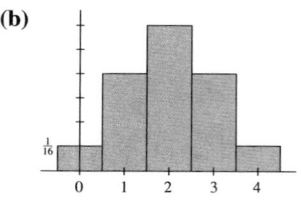

18. (a)

r	Probability
0	0.0776
1	0.2592
2	0.3456
3	0.2304
4	0.0768
5	0.0102

(b)

19. (a)

r	Probability
0	0.2097
1	0.3670
2	0.2753
3	0.1147
4	0.0287
5	0.0043
6	0.00036
7	0.000013

(b)

20. (a)

r	Probability
0	0.000001
1	0.000054
2	0.001215
3	0.014580
4	0.098415
5	0.354294
6	0.531441

(b)

21. $C(6, 2)(1/6)^2(5/6)^4 \approx 0.20094$

22. (a) $C(7, 0)(0.8)^0(0.2)^7 = 1.28 \times 10^{-5}$

(b) $C(7, 7)(0.8)^7(0.2)^0 \approx 0.209715$

(c) $1 - C(7, 0)(0.8)^0(0.2)^7 - C(7, 1)(0.8)^1(0.2)^6 \approx 0.99963$

(d) $C(7, 5)(0.8)^5(0.2)^2 + C(7, 6)(0.8)^6(0.2)^1 + C(7, 7)(0.8)^7(0.2)^0 \approx 0.85197$

23. $C(10, 4)(0.4)^4(0.6)^6 \approx 0.25082$

24. $1 - C(4, 0)(0.1)^0(0.9)^4 = 0.3439$

25. (a) $C(10, 5)(0.45)^5(0.55)^5 \approx 0.23403$

(b) $1 - C(10, 0)(0.45)^0(0.55)^{10} - C(10, 1)(0.45)^1(0.55)^9 - C(10, 2)(0.45)^2(0.55)^8 \approx 0.90044$

26. (a) $C(15, 12)(0.1)^{12}(0.9)^3 = 3.31695 \times 10^{-10}$

(b) $C(15, 12)(0.1)^{12}(0.9)^3 + C(15, 13)(0.1)^{13}(0.9)^2 + C(15, 14)(0.1)^{14}(0.9)^1 + C(15, 15)(0.1)^{15}(0.9)^0 = 3.40336 \times 10^{-10}$

27. (a) $1 - C(4, 0)(0.75)^0(0.25)^4 \approx 0.99609$

(b) $C(4, 2)(0.75)^2(0.25)^2 + C(4, 3)(0.75)^3(0.25)^1 + C(4, 4)(0.75)^4(0.25)^0 \approx 0.94922$

(c) $C(4, 4)(0.75)^4(0.25)^0 \approx 0.31641$

28. (a) $C(5, 3)(0.5)^3(0.5)^2 + C(5, 4)(0.5)^4(0.5)^1 + C(5, 5)(0.5)^5(0.5)^0 = 0.5$

(b) $C(7, 4)(0.5)^4(0.5)^3 + C(7, 5)(0.5)^5(0.5)^2 + C(7, 6)(0.5)^6(0.5)^1 + C(7, 7)(0.5)^7(0.5)^0 = 0.5$

29. (a) $(0.52)^{10} \approx 1.4456 \times 10^{-3}$

(b) $(0.48)^{10} \approx 6.4925 \times 10^{-4}$

(c) $C(10, 5)(0.52)^5(0.48)^5 \approx 0.24413$

30. (a) $C(12, 2)(0.2)^2(0.8)^{10} \approx 0.28347$

(b) $1 - C(12, 0)(0.2)^0(0.8)^{12} - C(12, 1)(0.2)^1(0.8)^{11} - C(12, 2)(0.2)^2(0.8)^{10} \approx 0.44165$

31. (a) $(0.005)^3 = 1.25 \times 10^{-7}$

(b) $1 - (0.995)^3 \approx 0.014925$ **32.** $1 - (0.95)^{10} \approx 0.40126$

33. $1 - C(8, 0)(0.04)^0(0.96)^8 - C(8, 1)(0.04)^1(0.96)^7 \approx 0.038147$

34. $C(5, 3)(0.6)^3(0.4)^2 = 0.3456$

35. (a) $(0.75)^6 \approx 0.17798$ **(b)** $(0.25)^6 \approx 2.4414 \times 10^{-4}$

(c) $C(6, 3)(0.75)^3(0.25)^3 \approx 0.13184$

(d) $1 - C(6, 6)(0.25)^0(0.75)^6 - C(6, 5)(0.25)^1(0.75)^5 \approx 0.46606$

36. (a) $1 - (0.99)^4 = 0.039404$ **(b)** $(0.99)^4 = 0.960596$

(c) $C(4, 1)(0.99)^1(0.01)^3 = 3.96 \times 10^{-6}$

37. (a) $1 - (0.75)^4 \approx 0.68359$

(b) $C(4, 3)(0.25)^3(0.75)^1 + C(4, 4)(0.25)^4(0.75)^0 \approx 0.05078$

38. (a) $(0.25)^3 \approx 0.015625$

(b) $C(3, 2)(0.25)^2(0.75)^1 = 0.140625$

(c) $C(3, 0)(0.25)^0(0.75)^3 = 0.421875$

(d) $1 - C(3, 0)(0.25)^0(0.75)^3 \approx 0.578125$

39. (a) $C(4, 1)(0.3)^1(0.7)^3 = 0.4116$

(b) $1 - (0.7)^4 = 0.7599$

40. (a) $1 - C(100, 0)(0.02)^0(0.98)^{100} - C(100, 1)(0.02)^1(0.98)^{99} \approx 0.59673$ **(b)** 35

41. (a) $C(10, 8)(0.4)^8 (0.6)^2 + C(10, 9)(0.4)^9(0.6)^1 + C(10, 10)(0.4)^{10}(0.6)^0 \approx 0.0123$ **(b)** Yes

42. (a) $C(8, 5)(0.6)^5(0.4)^3 + C(8, 6)(0.6)^6(0.4)^2 + C(8, 7)(0.6)^7(0.4)^1 + C(8, 8)(0.6)^8(0.4)^0 \approx 0.594$ **(b)** No

SECTION 14.4 ■ PAGE 920

1. $E = \$10 \times 0.9 + \$100 \times 0.1 = \$19$ **2.** $19 **3.** $1.50
4. $0.83 **5.** $0.94 **6.** $2.50 **7.** $0.92 **8.** $1.00 **9.** 0
10. $14.25 **11.** $-\$0.30$ **12.** $3.11 **13.** $-\$0.0526$
14. (a) $0.56 (b) No **15.** $-\$0.50$ **16.** 0
17. No, she should expect to lose $2.10 per stock.
18. $-\$0.246$ **19.** $-\$0.93$ **20.** (a) $22.7425
(b) $10,234,125 **21.** 3.35 h **22.** 0.9 language **23.** 1.95

24. (a)

Outcome	Probability
0	$\frac{1}{8}$
1	$\frac{3}{8}$
2	$\frac{3}{8}$
3	$\frac{1}{8}$

(b) 1.5

25. (a) No (b) $25.50 **26.** (a) Yes **27.** (a) No (b) $70
28. (a) No (b) $11 **29.** (a) No (b) $623
30. (a) No (b) $1.50

SECTION 14.5 ■ PAGE 930

1. one; mean; median; mode **2.** (a) add; n (b) most
3. order (a) middle (b) middle **4.** (a) deviation
(b) minimum; first quartile; median; third quartile; maximum
5. (a) 21 (b) 34, 1 **6.** (a) 132 (b) 183; 1
7. (a) 71.5 (b) 71.25; 4 **8.** (a) 85.5 (b) 86.25; 4
9. (a) 40 (b) $\frac{281}{7} \approx 40.14$; 7 **10.** (a) 110 (b) 107.4; 8
11. 17.16; 17; 16 **12.** 8; 8; 8

13. (a)

x	Frequency
6	1
8	2
9	2
11	3

(b) 9.125; 9; 11

14. (a)

x	Frequency
17	1
19	1
20	4
21	2

(b) 19.75; 20; 20

15. (a)

x	Frequency
38	2
41	2
47	2
49	4
52	8

(b) 48; 49; 52

16. (a)

x	Frequency
13	2
14	3
15	5
17	6
19	4
20	3
21	1

(b) 16.75; 17; 17

17. (a) 29 (b) 62; 56 **18.** (a) 22 (b) 3.33; 3.51

19. (a)

Stem	Leaves
1	3
2	1 2 9
3	2 3 3 5 5
4	0 1 1 1 1 2

1 | 2 means 12

(b) 35; 41

20. (a)

Stem	Leaves
1.1	0 6 7 7 7 8
1.2	2 2 3 4 5 6
1.3	1 1 4 5 6
1.4	0 6 7 7

1.1 | 2 means 1.12

(b) 1.25; 1.17

21. (a) 30.0 (b) 1.137 **22.** (a) 7.5 (b) 2.037
23. (a) 12, 15, 18, 25, 29 (b)

24. (a) 61, 70, 80.5, 89, 99 (b)

25. 27.2 **26.** 14.3 **27.** 7.6; 8 **28.** 2.3; 2.45
29. (a) 7.6 (b) 8 **30.** (a) 8.25 (b) 7.6
31. (a) $57,286; $58,000 (b) 4 (c) $112,625; $58,500; median
32. (a) 924 lb; 920 lb (b) 3 (c) 861 lb; 910 lb; median
33. (a) $325,800; $329,000; same (b) Above; same
(c) $748,167; $329,500; median
34. (a) $2,295,714; $2,279,000; same (b) Above; above
(c) $2,046,250; $2,279,000; median **35.** 1.054; 1.1; 1.2
36. 2.9; 2; 1 **37.** (a) 3 (b) 6 (c) 13 (d) 126 (e) 9.7; 8; 12
38. (a) 3 (b) 13 (c) 52 (d) 957.6; 961.5; 948

39. (a)

Stem	Leaves
1	8
2	2 3 4 4 6 6 6 8 9
3	0 1 2 4
4	0 1

1 | 8 means 18

(b) 2.7; 2.6

40. (a)

Stem	Leaves
3.0	1 2 2 2 3 4 5 5 7 8 9 9 9 9
3.1	0 0 0 2 7 9
3.2	2 3 4 5 6
3.3	1 5 6
3.4	1 3

3.1 | 2 means 3.12

(b) 3.10; 3.09
41. Men $53,417; $8674. Women $49,083; $11,124. Yes, the variation for the women's data is greater.
42. Crop rotation 39.5 lb; 5.0 lb. No crop rotation 33.8 lb; 4.3 lb. Yes, the variation for the crop rotation data is greater.

43. Asian 230, 273, 289.5, 310, 410; Hispanic 267, 282.5, 307.5, 335, 370

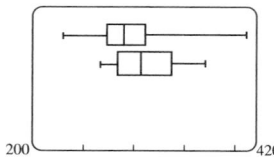

44. Small school 1040, 1130.5, 1245, 1334, 1550; Large school 950, 1040, 1180.5, 1441, 1592

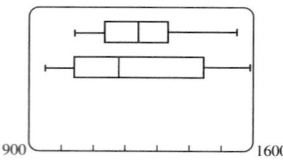

SECTION 14.6 ■ PAGE 940

1. bins (or intervals); x; individuals; distributed
2. normally; 68; 95
3.

4.

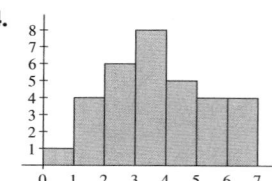

5. (a) approximately normal; approximately symmetric
(b) 600; the mean is about the same as the median
6. (a) approximately uniform; approximately symmetric
(b) 600; the mean is about the same as the median
7. (a) skew left   **(b)** 700; mean is to the left of the median
8. (a) skew right   **(b)** 300; mean is to the right of the median
9. (a)

(b) Skew left
(c) 585; 530.5

10. (a)

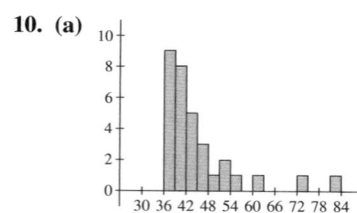

(b) Skew right
(c) 41; 44.6

11. (a)

(b) Symmetric
(c) 63; 62.4

12. (a)

(b) Symmetric
(c) 244.5; 238.3

13. 68%   **14.** 95%   **15.** 2.5%   **16.** 2.5%
17. 38%   **18.** 70%   **19.** 63%   **20.** 6%
21.

22.

23. (a)

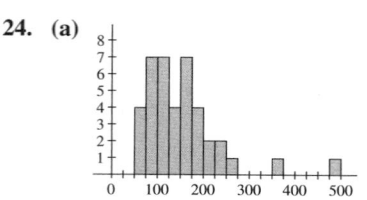

(b) Skew right
(c) $4.63 million;
$6.79 million

24. (a)

(b) Skew right
(c) $129; $151.28

25. approximately symmetric; median and mean about $65,000
26. Skew right; median about $60,000, mean is greater
27. 95%   **28.** 2.5%   **29.** 1.4%   **30. (a)** 82%   **(b)** 98.17%
31. (a) 0.048   **(b)** 0.194   **32. (a)** 0.04   **(b)** 0.36

SECTION 14.7 ■ PAGE 950

1. random   **2. (a)** undercoverage   **(b)** response
(c) nonresponse   **(d)** self-selection   **3. (a)** systematic
(b) stratified   **(c)** cluster   **4.** treatment; control; confounding
5. $1.96/(2\sqrt{n})$ **6.** correlation; sample; significant
7. No; self-selection bias   **8.** No; undercoverage bias
9. No; self-selection bias   **10.** Yes   **11.** No; nonresponse bias
12. No; response bias   **13.** Stratified sampling
14. Systematic sampling   **15.** Cluster sampling
16. True random sampling   **17. (a)** Make of car
(b) Use matched pair design.   **18. (a)** Age of participants
(b) Use randomized block design.   **19. (a)** Household income
(b) Use completely randomized design.
20. (a) Sex of participants   **(b)** Use randomized block design.
21. (a) 45%   **(b)** ±4.9%   **(c)** (0.401, 0.499), that is, between 40.1% and 49.9%   **22. (a)** 40%   **(b)** ±6.9%
(c) (0.331, 0.469), that is, between 33.1% and 46.9%
23. (a) 60%   **(b)** ±3.1%   **(c)** (0.569, 0.631), that is, between 56.9% and 63.1%   **24. (a)** 40%   **(b)** ±31%
(c) (0.09, 0.71), that is, between 9% and 71%   **25.** 4268
26. 1537   **27.** 384   **28.** 38,416   **29.** 82%; 2.53%

30. 25.5%; 4.0%   **31.** 52.75%; 1.10%   **32.** 92.5%; 2.1%

33. (a) $r = 0.756$ **(b)** Not significant

34. (a) $r = 0.595$ **(b)** Not significant

35. (a) $r = 0.96$ **(b)** Statistically significant

36. (a) $r = 0.997$ **(b)** Statistically significant

37. (a) $r = 0.997$ **(b)** Statistically significant

38. (a) $r = -0.757$ **(b)** Statistically significant

39. (a) $r = -0.97$ **(b)** Statistically significant

40. (a) $r = -0.98$ **(b)** Statistically significant

SECTION 14.8 ■ PAGE 958

1. population   **2.** null; alternative

3. (a) $H_0: p = 0.3, H_1: p > 0.3$ **(b)** reject

4. probability; 0.36; null   **(a)** reject   **(b)** fail to reject

5. (a) $H_0: p = 0.5, H_1: p > 0.5$ **(b)** $P = 0.036$
(c) Reject the null hypothesis.   **(d)** There is only a 0.036 probability that the observed number of successes (or more) could have come about by chance.

6. (a) $H_0: p = 0.7, H_1: p > 0.7$ **(b)** $P = 0.135$
(c) Fail to reject the null hypothesis.   **(d)** There is a 0.135 probability that the observed number of successes (or more) could have come about by chance.

7. (a) $H_0: p = 0.6, H_1: p < 0.6$ **(b)** $P = 0.193$
(c) Fail to reject the null hypothesis.   **(d)** There is a 0.193 probability that the observed number of successes (or more) could have come about by chance.

8. (a) $H_0: p = 0.6, H_1: p < 0.6$ **(b)** $P = 0.030$
(c) Reject the null hypothesis.   **(d)** There is only a 0.030 probability that the observed number of successes (or more) could have come about by chance.

9. (a) $H_0: p_1 = p_2, H_1: p_1 > p_2$ **(b)** $P = 0.83$
(c) Fail to reject the null hypothesis; there is not enough evidence to show that the medication is effective.   **(d)** There is a 0.83 probability that the result could have come about by chance.

10. (a) $H_0: p_1 = p_2, H_1: p_1 > p_2$ **(b)** $P = 0.0036$
(c) Reject the null hypothesis; there is a high probability that the medication is effective.   **(d)** There is only a 0.0036 probability that the result could have come about by chance.

11. (a) $H_0: p_1 = p_2, H_1: p_1 > p_2$ **(b)** $P = 0.0066$
(c) Reject the null hypothesis; there is a high probability that the medication is effective.   **(d)** There is only a 0.0066 probability that the result could have come about by chance.

12. (a) $H_0: p_1 = p_2, H_1: p_1 > p_2$ **(b)** $P = 0.16$
(c) Fail to reject the null hypothesis; there is not enough evidence to show that the medication is effective.   **(d)** There is a 0.16 probability that the result could have come about by chance.

13. (a) $H_0: p = 0.5, H_1: p > 0.5$ **(b)** $P = 0.0012$
(c) Reject the null hypothesis; the Republican is likely to win.

14. (a) $H_0: p = 0.5, H_1: p > 0.5$ **(b)** $P = 0.27$
(c) Fail to reject the null hypothesis; there is not enough evidence to show that the Democrat will win.

15. (a) $H_0: p = 0.5, H_1: p > 0.5$ **(b)** $P = 0.0082$
(c) Reject the null hypothesis; there is a high probability that the herbal drinks work.

16. (a) $H_0: p = 0.5, H_1: p > 0.5$ **(b)** $P = 0.16$
(c) Fail to reject the null hypothesis; there is not enough evidence to show that the herbal pills work.

17. (a) $H_0: p = 0.7, H_1: p > 0.7$ **(b)** $P = 0.00034$
(c) Reject the null hypothesis; there is a high probability that more than 70% of Native Americans can taste PTC .

18. (a) $H_0: p = 0.0015, H_1: p > 0.0015$ **(b)** $P = 0.79$
(c) Fail to reject the null hypothesis; there is not enough evidence to show that cell phones cause brain cancer.

19. (a) $H_0: p = 0.7, H_1: p > 0.7$ **(b)** $P = 0.88$
(c) Fail to reject the null hypothesis; there is not enough evidence to show that the new teaching method is effective.

20. (a) $H_0: p = 0.25, H_1: p < 0.25$ **(b)** $P = 0.028$
(c) Reject the null hypothesis; there is a high probability that the clean-up program worked.

21. (a) $H_0: p = 0.5, H_1: p > 0.5$ **(b)** $P = 0.096$
(c) Fail to reject the null hypothesis; the sample does not provide enough evidence that a majority think that it's important for the United States to be first.

22. (a) $H_0: p = 0.5, H_1: p > 0.5$ **(b)** $P = 0.00043$
(c) Reject the null hypothesis; there is a high probability that more than 50% of accidents occur near home.

23. (a) $H_0: p = 0.95, H_1: p > 0.95$ **(b)** $P = 0.84$
(c) Fail to reject the null hypothesis; there is not enough evidence to show that more than 95% of the seeds germinate.

24. (a) $H_0: p = 0.3, H_1: p > 0.3$ **(b)** $P = 0.0073$
(c) Reject the null hypothesis; there is a high probability that more than 30% of the elms in the forest have Dutch elm disease.

25. (a) p_1 is the proportion of the vaccinated population that gets the flu; p_2 is the proportion of the unvaccinated population that gets the flu **(b)** $H_0: p_1 = p_2, H_1: p_1 < p_2$ **(c)** $P = 0.074$
(d) Fail to reject the null hypothesis; there is not enough evidence to show that the flu vaccine is effective.

26. (a) p_1 is the proportion of the population using the drug that has a heart attack; p_2 is the proportion of the population not using the drug that has a heart attack   **(b)** $H_0: p_1 = p_2, H_1: p_1 < p_2$
(c) $P = 0.0068$ **(d)** Reject the null hypothesis; there is a high probability that the drug helps to prevent heart attacks.

27. (a) p_1 is the proportion of women who have nightmares; p_2 is the proportion of men   **(b)** $H_0: p_1 = p_2, H_1: p_1 \neq p_2$
(c) $P = 0.002$ **(d)** Reject the null hypothesis; there is a statistically significant difference in the proportions of men and women having nightmares.

28. (a) p_1 is the proportion of students taught using Method A who pass the ELM; p_2 is the proportion of students taught using Method B who pass the ELM   **(b)** $H_0: p_1 = p_2, H_1: p_1 < p_2$
(c) $P = 0.92$ **(d)** Fail to reject the null hypothesis; there no statistically significant difference in the ELM passing rate for the two groups.

CHAPTER 14 REVIEW ■ PAGE 961

1. 624   **2. (a)** $6^3 = 216$ **(b)** $6 \cdot 5 \cdot 4 = 120$ **3. (a)** 10
(b) 20   **4.** $C(120, 7) \approx 5.9488 \times 10^{10}$ **5.** 120
6. $2^{10} \cdot 4^5 = 1{,}048{,}576$ **7.** 45   **8.** $C(15, 4) = 1365$
9. 17,576   **10.** 5   **11.** 120   **12.** $26^2 \cdot 10^3 < 700{,}000$ **13.** 5
14. 11   **15.** 14   **16.** 3   **17. (a)** 240   **(b)** 3360   **(c)** 1680
18. (a) 900   **(b)** $\frac{900}{1001} \approx 0.899$ **19.** 40,320   **20.** $6! = 720$
21. (a) 31,824   **(b)** 11,760   **(c)** 19,448   **(d)** 2808   **(e)** 2808
(f) 6,683,040   **22.** $C(50, 5) \cdot 2^5 = 67{,}800{,}320$
23. (a) $\frac{2}{3}$ **(b)** $\frac{8}{15}$ **(c)** $\frac{2}{15}$ **(d)** $\frac{4}{5}$
24. (a) $\frac{3}{7}$ **(b)** $\frac{10}{21}$ **(c)** $\frac{19}{21}$ **(d)** $\frac{2}{21}$ **(e)** $\frac{1}{105}$
25. (a) $S = \{HHH, HHT, HTH, HTT, THH, THT, TTH, TTT\}$
(b) $\frac{1}{8}$ **(c)** $\frac{1}{2}$ **(d)** $\frac{1}{2}$ **26.** $\frac{2}{5}$ **27.** $\frac{1}{78}$ **28. (a)** $\frac{1}{13}$ **(b)** $\frac{2}{13}$ **(c)** $\frac{4}{13}$
(d) $\frac{1}{26}$ **29. (a)** $\frac{1}{624}$ **(b)** $\frac{1}{48}$ **(c)** $\frac{3}{52}$ **30. (a)** $\frac{1}{6}$ **(b)** $\frac{5}{6}$

31. (a) $\dfrac{C(4, 4)}{C(52, 4)} \approx 3.69 \times 10^{-6}$ **(b)** $\dfrac{C(13, 4)}{C(52, 4)} \approx 0.00264$

(c) $\dfrac{2 \cdot C(26, 4)}{C(52, 4)} \approx 0.11044$ **32. (a)** $\frac{1}{1000}$ **(b)** $\frac{1}{200}$ **33.** $\frac{1}{24}$ **34.** $\frac{1}{2}$

35. (a) 3 **(b)** 0.51 **36.** $C(9, 2) \cdot C(7, 3) = 1260$ **37. (a)** 10^5

(b) 5^5 **(c)** $\frac{1}{32}$ **(d)** 75 **38. (a)** 10^9 **(b)** 10^5 **(c)** 10^{-4}

39. (a) 144 **(b)** 126 **(c)** 84 **(d)** $\frac{7}{8}$

40. (a) $C(8, 4)\left(\frac{1}{6}\right)^4\left(\frac{5}{6}\right)^4 \approx 0.02605$

(b) $1 - C(8, 0)\left(\frac{1}{2}\right)^0\left(\frac{1}{2}\right)^8 - C(8, 1)\left(\frac{1}{2}\right)^1\left(\frac{1}{2}\right)^7 \approx 0.9648$

41. (a) $(0.3)^5 = 0.00243$ **(b)** $(0.7)^5 = 0.16807$

(c) $C(5, 2)(0.3)^2(0.7)^3 = 0.3087$

(d) $C(5, 3)(0.3)^2(0.7)^3 + C(5, 4)(0.3)^1(0.7)^4 +$
$C(5, 5)(0.3)^0(0.7)^5 = 0.83692$

42. 0 **43.** −$0.83 **44.** $0.00016

45. (a) Mean 6, median 4.5 **(b)** Standard deviation 4.28

46. (a) Mean 7.3, median 7.2 **(b)** Standard deviation 1.95

47. 2, 6, 7, 8.5, 10

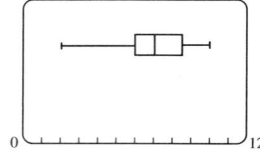

48. 37, 69, 77.5, 81, 92

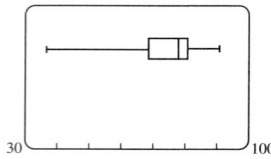

49. (a) 22.9, 23, 23 **(b)**

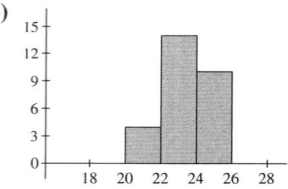

50. (a) 24.9, 25, 27 **(b)**

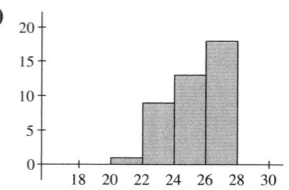

51. (a) 24.4, 24, 24 **(b)** 1, 15, 24, 32.5, 54
(c)

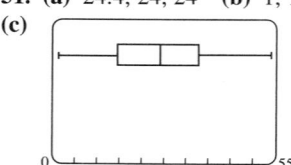

52. (a) 2.272, 2.32, 2.32 **(b)** 2.00, 2.225, 2.32, 2.36, 2.42
(c)

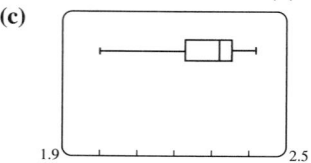

53. 95% **54.** 84% **55.** 37.4% **56.** 88.1%

57. (a) 79.9, 83, no mode **(b)** 12.6

(c) 45, 72, 83, 89, 99

 (d)

(e) 80.1, 83

58. (a)

East Springfield		West Springfield	
Stem	Leaves	Stem	Leaves
3.0	2 5 8	3.0	
3.1	0 0 2 5 8 8 9	3.1	1 4 9
3.2	0 2 5	3.2	1 2 5 9 9
3.3	3	3.3	5 7 9
3.4		3.4	3 5 9

3.1 | 2 means 3.12   3.1 | 2 means 3.12

(b) East Springfield: 3.155, 0.080; West Springfield: 3.30, 0.114
(c) East Springfield: 3.02, 3.10, 3.165, 3.20, 3.33;
West Springfield: 3.11, 3.21, 3.29, 3.39, 3.49; both center and
spread are larger for West Springfield

(d)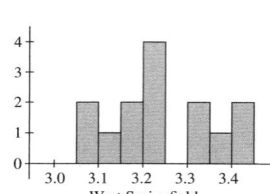

59. (a) 68%; 2.5% **(b)** 90.24%

60. (a) 16%; 16% **(b)** 23.6% **61.** No; self-selection bias

62. No; response bias **63.** No; nonresponse bias

64. No; undercoverage bias **65.** Caviar eaters are likely to be
wealthier and have better health care. **66.** Larger cities will have
more churches simply because of population size.

67. (a) Assign each person randomly to the treatment or the control group. **(b)** Divide the men and the women each into equally
sized treatment and control groups. **(c)** Divide the subjects into
four categories: overweight men, "normal" men, overweight
women, "normal" women. Group the subjects in each category
into pairs, and randomly select one subject in each pair for treatment, the other for control. **68. (a)** Assign each person randomly
to the treatment or the control group. **(b)** Divide the men and the
women each into equally-sized treatment and control groups.
(c) Divide the subjects into four categories: happy men, unhappy
men, happy women, unhappy women. Group the subjects in each
category into pairs, and randomly select one subject in each pair
for treatment, the other for control **69.** 96%, ±4.4%

70. 9604 kernels **71. (a)** $H_0\colon p = 0.9,\ H_1\colon p < 0.9$

(b) $P = 0.018$ **(c)** Reject the null hypothesis; there is a high
probability that less than 90% of dentists recommend Brand X.

72. (a) $H_0: p_1 = p_2, H_1: p_1 < p_2$ **(b)** $P = 0.12$ **(c)** Fail to reject the null hypothesis; there is not enough evidence to show that users of Toothpaste Y are more loyal.

CHAPTER 14 TEST ■ PAGE 965

1. 81   **2.** 72   **3. (a)** 456,976,000   **(b)** 258,336,000
4. (a) $P(30, 4) = 657,720$ **(b)** $C(30, 4) = 27,405$ **5.** 12
6. $4 \cdot 2^{14} = 65,536$ **7. (a)** $4! = 24$ **(b)** $6!/3! = 120$
8. $30 \cdot 29 \cdot 28 \cdot C(27, 5) = 1,966,582,800$ **9. (a)** $\frac{1}{2}$ **(b)** $\frac{1}{13}$
(c) $\frac{1}{26}$ **10. (a)** $\frac{5}{13}$ **(b)** $\frac{6}{13}$ **(c)** $\frac{9}{13}$
11. $C(5, 3)/C(15, 3) \approx 0.022$ **12.** $\frac{1}{6}$
13. $1 - 1 \cdot \frac{11}{12} \cdot \frac{10}{12} \cdot \frac{9}{12} \approx 0.427$
14. (a) $C(10, 6)(0.55)^6(0.45)^4 \approx 0.23837$
(b) $C(10, 0)(0.55)^0(0.45)^{10} + C(10, 1)(0.55)^1(0.45)^9 +$
$C(10, 2)(0.55)^2(0.45)^8 \approx 0.02739$ **15.** $0.65

16. (a)

x	Frequency
31	1
34	2
35	1
36	1
37	3
38	4
39	2

(b) 36.5, 37, 38, 2.2

(c) 31, 35, 37, 38, 39

(d)

17. (a) 0.84   **(b)** 0.813   **18.** 68%; ±4.4%
19. (a) $H_0: p = 0.1, H_1: p < 0.1$ **(b)** $P = 0.042$
(c) Reject the null hypothesis; there is statistically significant evidence that the town's claim is true.
20. (a) Subjects were randomly assigned to the treatment and control groups.   **(b)** $P = 0.0085$; there is statistically significant evidence that moxifloxacin is more effective than ethambutol.

FOCUS ON MODELING ■ PAGE 968

1. (b) $\frac{9}{10}$ **2. (b)** $\frac{1}{2}$ **3. (b)** $\frac{7}{8}$ **4. (b)** $\frac{1}{8}, \frac{1}{4}, \frac{5}{16}, \frac{5}{16}$ **(c)** 5.8
7. (b) $\frac{1}{2}$

SEQUENCES AND SERIES

Arithmetic

$$a, a + d, a + 2d, a + 3d, a + 4d, \ldots$$

$$a_n = a + (n - 1)d$$

$$S_n = \sum_{k=1}^{n} a_k = \frac{n}{2}[2a + (n - 1)d] = n\left(\frac{a + a_n}{2}\right)$$

Geometric

$$a, ar, ar^2, ar^3, ar^4, \ldots$$

$$a_n = ar^{n-1}$$

$$S_n = \sum_{k=1}^{n} a_k = a\frac{1 - r^n}{1 - r}$$

If $|r| < 1$, then the sum of an infinite geometric series is

$$S = \frac{a}{1 - r}$$

THE BINOMIAL THEOREM

$$(a + b)^n = \binom{n}{0}a^n + \binom{n}{1}a^{n-1}b + \cdots + \binom{n}{n-1}ab^{n-1} + \binom{n}{n}b^n$$

FINANCE

Compound interest

$$A = P\left(1 + \frac{r}{n}\right)^{nt}$$

where A is the amount after t years, P is the principal, r is the interest rate, and the interest is compounded n times per year.

Amount of an annuity

$$A_f = R\frac{(1 + i)^n - 1}{i}$$

where A_f is the final amount, i is the interest rate per time period, and there are n payments of size R.

Present value of an annuity

$$A_p = R\frac{1 - (1 + i)^{-n}}{i}$$

where A_p is the present value, i is the interest rate per time period, and there are n payments of size R.

Installment buying

$$R = \frac{iA_p}{1 - (1 + i)^{-n}}$$

where R is the size of each payment, i is the interest rate per time period, A_p is the amount of the loan, and n is the number of payments.

CONIC SECTIONS

Circles

$$(x - h)^2 + (y - k)^2 = r^2$$

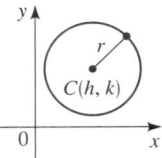

Parabolas

$$x^2 = 4py \qquad\qquad y^2 = 4px$$

 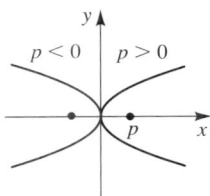

Focus $(0, p)$, directrix $y = -p$ Focus $(p, 0)$, directrix $x = -p$

 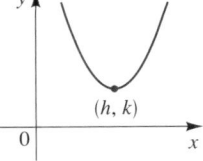

$y = a(x - h)^2 + k,$ $y = a(x - h)^2 + k,$
$a < 0, \quad h > 0, \quad k > 0$ $a > 0, \quad h > 0, \quad k > 0$

Ellipses

$$\frac{x^2}{a^2} + \frac{y^2}{b^2} = 1 \qquad\qquad \frac{x^2}{b^2} + \frac{y^2}{a^2} = 1$$

 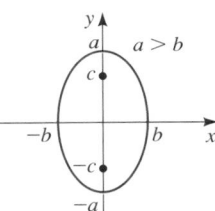

Foci $(\pm c, 0)$, $c^2 = a^2 - b^2$ Foci $(0, \pm c)$, $c^2 = a^2 - b^2$

Hyperbolas

$$\frac{x^2}{a^2} - \frac{y^2}{b^2} = 1 \qquad\qquad -\frac{x^2}{b^2} + \frac{y^2}{a^2} = 1$$

 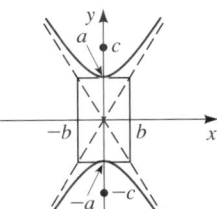

Foci $(\pm c, 0)$, $c^2 = a^2 + b^2$ Foci $(0, \pm c)$, $c^2 = a^2 + b^2$

ANGLE MEASUREMENT

π radians $= 180°$

$1° = \dfrac{\pi}{180}$ rad $\qquad$ 1 rad $= \dfrac{180°}{\pi}$

$s = r\theta \qquad A = \frac{1}{2}r^2\theta \quad (\theta \text{ in radians})$

To convert from degrees to radians, multiply by $\dfrac{\pi}{180}$.

To convert from radians to degrees, multiply by $\dfrac{180}{\pi}$.

TRIGONOMETRIC FUNCTIONS OF REAL NUMBERS

$\sin t = y \qquad\qquad \csc t = \dfrac{1}{y}$

$\cos t = x \qquad\qquad \sec t = \dfrac{1}{x}$

$\tan t = \dfrac{y}{x} \qquad\qquad \cot t = \dfrac{x}{y}$

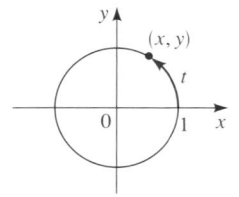

TRIGONOMETRIC FUNCTIONS OF ANGLES

$\sin \theta = \dfrac{y}{r} \qquad\qquad \csc \theta = \dfrac{r}{y}$

$\cos \theta = \dfrac{x}{r} \qquad\qquad \sec \theta = \dfrac{r}{x}$

$\tan \theta = \dfrac{y}{x} \qquad\qquad \cot \theta = \dfrac{x}{y}$

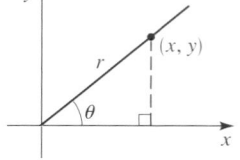

RIGHT ANGLE TRIGONOMETRY

$\sin \theta = \dfrac{\text{opp}}{\text{hyp}} \qquad\qquad \csc \theta = \dfrac{\text{hyp}}{\text{opp}}$

$\cos \theta = \dfrac{\text{adj}}{\text{hyp}} \qquad\qquad \sec \theta = \dfrac{\text{hyp}}{\text{adj}}$

$\tan \theta = \dfrac{\text{opp}}{\text{adj}} \qquad\qquad \cot \theta = \dfrac{\text{adj}}{\text{opp}}$

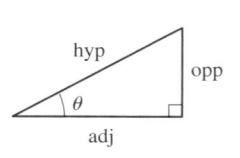

SPECIAL VALUES OF THE TRIGONOMETRIC FUNCTIONS

θ	radians	$\sin \theta$	$\cos \theta$	$\tan \theta$
0°	0	0	1	0
30°	$\pi/6$	1/2	$\sqrt{3}/2$	$\sqrt{3}/3$
45°	$\pi/4$	$\sqrt{2}/2$	$\sqrt{2}/2$	1
60°	$\pi/3$	$\sqrt{3}/2$	1/2	$\sqrt{3}$
90°	$\pi/2$	1	0	—
180°	π	0	−1	0
270°	$3\pi/2$	−1	0	—

SPECIAL TRIANGLES

 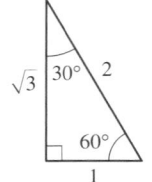

GRAPHS OF THE TRIGONOMETRIC FUNCTIONS

  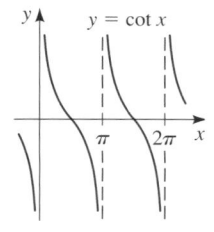

SINE AND COSINE CURVES

$y = a \sin k(x - b) \quad (k > 0) \qquad\qquad y = a \cos k(x - b) \quad (k > 0)$

 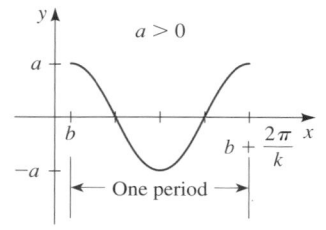

amplitude: $|a|$ $\qquad$ period: $2\pi/k$ $\qquad$ phase shift: b

GRAPHS OF THE INVERSE TRIGONOMETRIC FUNCTIONS

$y = \sin^{-1}x \qquad\qquad y = \cos^{-1}x \qquad\qquad y = \tan^{-1}x$

  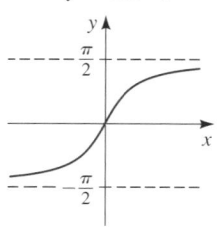